STANDARDIZED PLANT NAMES

SECOND EDITION

A Revised and Enlarged Listing of Approved Scientific and Common Names of Plants and Plant Products in American Commerce or Use

Prepared for the

AMERICAN JOINT COMMITTEE ON HORTICULTURAL NOMENCLATURE

by its Editorial Committee

HARLAN P. KELSEY AND WILLIAM A. DAYTON

HARRISBURG, PA.

J. HORACE McFARLAND COMPANY

FOR AMERICAN JOINT COMMITTEE ON HORTICULTURAL NOMENCLATURE

1942

Organized 1914

J. HORACE McFARLAND, *Chairman*
HARLAN P. KELSEY, *Secretary-Treasurer*

Organization of the American Joint Committee on Horticultural Nomenclature

American Association of Nurserymen
Ornamental Growers' Association
American Society of Landscape Architects
American Pharmaceutical Association
American Institute of Park Executives
Society of American Florists and Ornamental Horticulturists

And in Cooperation with

American Amaryllis Society
American Begonia Society
American Dahlia Society
American Forestry Association
American Gladiolus Society
American Iris Society
American Peony Society
American Pomological Society
American Rose Society
American Seed Trade Association
American Sweet Pea Society
Camellia Society of America
Chrysanthemum Society of America
Northern Nut Growers Association

With the Active Assistance of Many Sections of
The United States Department of Agriculture

Mount Pleasant Press
J. Horace McFarland Company
HARRISBURG, PA.

PREFACE TO THE SECOND EDITION

THE purpose of STANDARDIZED PLANT NAMES is to bring intelligent order out of the chaos in names of plants and plant products existing the world over. Such standardization, supported by adequate authority, will not only promote satisfactory understanding between those who sell and those who buy, but will also improve the multifarious relations, scientific, educational and social, into which the advancing plant consciousness of America has grown.

The preface to the first edition of STANDARDIZED PLANT NAMES, published in 1923, stated the general principles and the historical background guiding its development. The quotations from that edition which follow adequately set forth the basis of this new and greatly enlarged edition.

"The American Joint Committee on Horticultural Nomenclature was formed in 1915 by committees of the American Association of Nurserymen and of the Ornamental Growers' Association.

"*Purposes.* As first constituted, the stated purpose of the Committee was to 'make buying easy' by bringing about so far as practicable, the consistent use of a single standardized 'scientific' name, and a single standardized 'common' name for every tree, shrub, and plant in American commerce. . . .

"To establish . . . A well-organized mechanism for the registration and identification of horticultural varieties, and the adoption of standard rules of nomenclature for the guidance of those naming horticultural varieties."

To further clarify the need for STANDARDIZED PLANT NAMES the *Statement of the Problem*, as first set forth in 1917, was worded as follows:

"*Practical Importance of Stability in Nomenclature.* The confusion of names in the horticultural plant world is at present so great as to clog popular plant knowledge and actually to limit to no small degree the use of certain trees, shrubs, and flowers in our American plantings. The consequent loss to the tradesman and planter is obvious. For example, take the common Virginia Creeper: We find this catalogued in 1916 under no less than six Latin binomials—*Ampelopsis quinquefolia, A. virginica, Parthenocissus quinquefolia, P. virginica, Vitis hederacea*, and *Psedera quinquefolia*, while as common names we have Woodbine, American Woodbine, Virginia Creeper, American Ivy, Common Virginia Creeper, Virginian Creeper, Wild Woodvine, and Five-fingered Ivy. Today both American and foreign nursery catalogues are filled largely with confused and contradictory lists of plant names, while popular books on gardening and horticulture and the horticultural press themselves are at sea, and little if any better off than the tradesman. It is thus often impossible for the buyer to know whether he will get what he has in mind when placing an order, or something entirely different.

"Further, owing to the differing names under which both new and old plants are often catalogued, described, and disseminated, the plantsman and buyer become perplexed and discouraged, and proper interest is not awakened. This often results in the over-use of the commoner and less worthy trees and plants, to the exclusion of many beautiful things.

"*Causes of Confusion.* Even when there is complete and well-established agreement among botanists as to the classification and naming of any given plant, mistakes by nurserymen or dealers in identification and labeling are liable to occur, giving rise to much confusion. When a dealer, either through ignorance or accident, sends out a comparatively unknown plant labeled with the name of some other little-known plant, the misapplied name is likely to follow the first plant and become established in trade.

"A striking case of this sort is that of the tree so widely disseminated for street planting under the common name 'Carolina Poplar.' Experts on the poplar state that this is probably *Populus eugenei*, a hybrid originated in Europe, and that the native Carolina Poplar practically never passes in the trade under that name. In this extreme case the transferred name is so universally accepted by the trade that an attempt to correct the original mistake would be inadvisable at present.

"When, however, a plant has been widely distributed under the name of some other plant, through a mere mistake in identification, and the plant whose name was mistakenly applied to the other is also in cultivation, there is serious confusion, which can usually best be settled by correcting the original mistake, even if it has become widely accepted.

"*Botanists Disagree.* Other causes than mistaken identification of plants have contributed to the existing confusion. These involve differences of opinion and of practice among botanists in regard to plant names when there is no question at all about the identity of the plants. For one thing, in doubtful cases they are not yet wholly agreed upon the rules or 'code' which shall apply, to decide which of two or more names shall stand; but these differences are comparatively few. Much more important are differences of personal judgment among botanists as to what constitutes in any given case a sufficient difference between two groups of related plants to place them in different genera; for example, whether the known difference between apples and pears is enough to separate them into two genera, Malus and Pyrus, or is so slight that they should be consolidated into a single genus. The same sort of difference in judgment arises as to what constitutes a sufficient difference to call for separation into distinct species, and as to what are of varietal rank. These differences are inevitable, and are independent of rules or other arbitrary decisions.

"For example, Azalea is now classed under Rhododendron by some botanists, yet for trade reasons it seems inexpedient to catalogue the Azaleas as Rhododendrons.

"*Why Botanical Names Change.* Probably the most important cause of changes in botanical nomenclature in recent years is the constant collection of new evidence as to the facts. This evidence is of two sorts: evidence found in botanical literature as to the first proper description and naming of each kind of plant, and evidence as to the structure and habits of the plants themselves. When any group of plants is studied more carefully and thoroughly than before, new facts are sure to be discovered which may alter the classification and nomenclature based on previous incomplete knowledge.

"Absolute and permanent fixity of botanical nomenclature, therefore, cannot be insured by an arbitrary agreement."

Since this Committee was first established, the general basis of its work has come to be *to agree arbitrarily upon some one name for each plant, by which name it can be designated for a definite term of years*, with provision for periodic revision for cause.

The fact that the American Joint Committee on Horticultural Nomenclature has in this revision worked in accord with the International Rules of Botanical Nomenclature made imperative the publication of a new edition of STANDARDIZED PLANT NAMES, inasmuch as the 1923 edition had been largely based on the American Code. Two other vital factors cited below also made this new edition imperative.

1. *Rapidly Increasing Variety of Plants.* The 1923 edition attempted to cover only the field of horticulture. While more comprehensive than any other single list previously published, there were still great numbers of additional plants that needed to be listed. Annually, approximately 3000 new plants, including importations, hybrids, strains, etc., are added to American horticulture and agriculture. Since little or no organized attempt is made to insure standard naming, there has naturally arisen further confusion in current plant names.

2. *Plant Field Wider than Horticulture.* It is obvious that horticulture alone does not monopolize the wide fields of economic and social activity covered by plants and plant products. Agronomy, farming, fiber crops, forestry, fruit-growing, gums and latex, pharmacy, spices and condiments, range and wildlife management, and soil conservation, are among the important fields in which plant science and standardized terminology are vital. (See Index of special groups of plants and plant products on page 675.) Despite the broadened outlook of this edition there are still some serious gaps, due to the inability of the Editorial Committee to obtain the necessary cooperation.

PREPARING MATERIAL FOR THE 1942 EDITION

Since the publication of the 1923 edition, the Editorial Committee has continued to collect material and to work on common-name lists and other problems, in active cooperation with the United States Department of Agriculture.

In 1937 preparation of the copy for this new edition began. Dr. Donald Wyman, Horticulturist of the Arnold Arboretum, at that time a member of the Editorial Committee, supervised the listing of all items offered in more than 1500 nursery, seed, and other horticultural trade catalogs, current for 1937–38, including over 300 foreign catalogs. Besides this, practically every species and variety appearing in the 1940 edition of Rehder's "Manual of Cultivated Trees and Shrubs" and in the 1935 edition of Bailey's "Hortus" were added, as well as large numbers of items from other sources.

A list of the more outstanding collaborators follows from page xi; credit also is given in the introduction to important sections, as, for example, Drug Plant Names (page 175). Three of the more noteworthy sources of additional names to the body of the work are here mentioned:

Through the cooperation of the Division of Plant Exploration and Introduction, United States Department of Agriculture, T. B. McClelland, Joseph Z. Fennell, and David A. Bisset supplied nearly 600 names of newly introduced tropical and subtropical plants of all kinds.

Some 2000 names of plants useful to fish, animal, bird, and other wildlife were supplied by the Fish and Wildlife Service, United States Department of Interior. Although entered in regular alphabetical sequence these important items can be readily identified by the accompanying symbol lw.

A notable list of approximately 4800 varieties of plants growing in the San Francisco Parks was supplied by Eric Walther, including 109 introduced Eucalyptus and large numbers of rare and unusual plants, particularly from Australia and Africa.

In this edition there are approximately 90,000 separate entries of plant and plant product names, not including cross-indexing, or more than twice as many as appeared in the first edition. More than 8000 new common names have been introduced by the Editors, and many more thousands were selected from other sources.

Innovations of 1923 Edition Retained. It is pertinent to recall a few of the important innovations introduced into the 1923 edition of STAND-

ARDIZED PLANT NAMES which are continued in this book. The five main innovations are, for convenience and emphasis, here restated:

"1. DISUSE OF CAPITAL INITIALS FOR ALL SPECIES AND BOTANICAL VARIETIES. In regard to two matters of typography and spelling, the Committee has broken with the prevailing practice among botanists, by a large majority vote, but not without a vigorous and well-presented opposition by a minority. One of these decisions was to use no capitals in scientific names except for invariably beginning a genus name with a capital. This is a practice which some botanists and some horticulturists have long followed and which is universally followed by American zoologists. The rule as to capitalizing species names as followed, for example, in Bailey's Cyclopedia and by many botanical authorities seems unnecessarily complicated in its application. The simple rule adopted by the American Joint Committee standardizes horticultural name typography and is unmistakable in meaning and use."

This simplifying practice is being adopted by a rapidly increasing number of botanists and institutions and probably will become universal.

"2. DOUBLE 'II' ENDING OF SPECIES NAMES CHANGED TO SINGLE 'I.'* The other of these decisions was to end all species names having the form of a second declension genitive with a single 'i' instead of with 'ii.' This practice also has been followed for some time by zoologists and by some horticulturists. There is just as good classic Latin authority for the 'i' form as there is for the 'ii' form, and it seems absurd to burden ourselves with trying to follow with precision the choice of each particular original author of a Latin plant name as to whether he would spell his genitive in 'ii' or in the equally proper 'i.'"

This procedure also has proved desirable and is being widely practiced.

"3. SIGN OF THE POSSESSIVE (') OMITTED. In possessive adjectival names the possessive sign has been dropped, and the accompanying letter 's' except where required for euphony or clearness. Example: Browns Lily, not Brown's Lily or Brown Lily."

This has now become a general practice of horticulturists, botanists, and zoologists.

"4. ONE STANDARD COMMON NAME FOR EACH PLANT. The confusion in common names has been, of course, even worse than in scientific names. A single plant is sometimes known by twenty or more different names, some very closely localized, some very widespread. For example, Van Wijk's Dictionary of Plant Names credits the European White Waterlily, *Nymphaea alba,* with 15 English, 44 French, 105 German, and 81 Dutch common names, or a total of 245 vernacular appellations—a ridiculous state of affairs. Many other examples similarly absurd could be cited. More confusing still, the same common name is often applied in different parts of the country to wholly different plants. Some of these contradictory and confusing names are so firmly entrenched in local popular usage that it may be quite impossible to eradicate them. The Committee, in proposing one of a plant's common names as a national standard common name for that plant, does not imply that some of the other common names in use for it are not just as good, or even in some respects better. But if we are ever going to reduce the confusion, some *one* name must be selected more or less arbitrarily."

The obvious value of this practice has been conclusively demonstrated and is now extended to all types of plants and plant products.

"5. CONSOLIDATING COMPOUND NAMES—ELIMINATION OF HYPHENS.† Some difficulty has been experienced in establishing a standard practice in the use or omission of hyphens in compound words. The trend of usage in English is undoubtedly toward the closer consolidation of the parts of a compound as the combination becomes familiar.

"Therefore, for simplicity and convenience, hyphens are avoided where they are not clearly desirable, but a hyphen must be used where the meaning is made clearer, or where the pronunciation of the compound would be seriously difficult to recognize when printed as a single word.

"Examples: Vi-apple, not Viapple for *Spondias cytherea;* but Pineapple, *not* Pine-apple *nor* Pine Apple, for *Ananas sativus,* because this compound has become sufficiently familiar. Bellflower, *not* Bell Flower *nor* Bell-flower; Longleaf, *not* Long-leaf *nor* Long Leaf; Longspur, *not* Long-spur."

This practice was conservatively followed in the 1923 edition of STANDARDIZED PLANT NAMES, particularly as to English or common names of species and natural varieties, and horticultural variety names, but with misgivings by at least an interested few. However, it proved to be a satisfactory way, not only to improve and shorten many common names, but to reduce many trinomials and quadrinomials to standard binomials or even monomials, and it has met with general approval. In this edition, therefore, the Editors have used this means to reduce the number of long common names and common name combinations.

INNOVATIONS OF THIS 1942 EDITION

1. *Pronunciation.* Since the publication of the 1923 edition there has been a growing demand for some aid to the proper pronunciation of scientific

*"It should be noted in regard to such matters as the capitalizing or the decapitalizing of species names, the retention or omission of the second 'i' in second declension genitives (as *Thunbergii* for *thunbergi*), and the insertion or omission of hyphens in compound names (as Horse-chestnut, Horsechestnut), that no serious confusion of meaning is likely to be caused by diversity of usage or lack of standardization in these matters. While the Joint Committee believes the standards adopted in this publication in these matters are convenient, economical, and desirable as trade usages, the one essential purpose of the publication, namely, the *standardization of the names themselves,* will not be affected if some users of the publication choose to adhere to other standards in regard to these less essential details of typography.

"On the other hand, in the case of compound names in which a name properly belonging to one genus is applied in compound to a different genus, like Horsechestnut or Mayapple, failure to write or print them as compound words, either with a hyphen or 'solid,' is in many cases likely to cause serious confusion and should be consistently avoided. The committee prefers and prints Mayapple. It makes no serious objection to May-apple. It objects very positively to May Apple, which is apt to mean, for anyone not familiar with the plant, that it is a species or variety of the genus Malus."

†See footnote in first column referring to the use of hyphens.

or Latin plant names. This need has been met, so far as feasible, by placing an acute accent close to the main syllable stressed. In certain cases classic vowel quantities have been disregarded, either for the sake of euphony or because of general usage.

2. *Clons* (Symbol ₵). The great need of indicating clons by a suitable symbol seems satisfactorily provided for, it is believed, by the Committee's method of using, so far as time and other limitations permitted, the symbol ₵. (See definition of *clon* in Glossary, page 669.) It is desirable that this practice be followed generally in horticultural catalogs, garden books, and plant publications of every kind.

3. *Polybrid* (Symbol ∞)—*A new group-name term.* In preparing this 1942 edition of STANDARDIZED PLANT NAMES the Editorial Committee felt the need of a term, the meaning and significance of which would be clear to all, as indicated by a suitable accompanying symbol, to serve as a sort of red flag of warning as to the genetic inconstancy and unreliability of certain group hybrid names. Therefore, the Committee invented and uses the term *polybrid*, adopting for it the "indefinite" symbol (∞) as defined in the Glossary. About six months after the Editorial Committee initiated this usage, Stout's definition of *heterogen* was published. We believe that the term *polybrid*, as earlier adopted, fills a longfelt need, and more specifically covers the phase of group hybridity we have in mind, with its attendant unreliability from the standpoint of the breeder and grower.

Several authorities were consulted and, with his permission, we quote the following extract from a letter from Robert Cook, Secretary of the American Genetic Association:

"*Washington, D. C., Sept. 19, 1940*

"It seems to me that there are clear and important distinctions between this term (*heterogen*) and the proposed term *polybrid* as defined in your forthcoming Glossary. Heterogen concerns the genetic constitution of a group of (assumedly) closely related plants 'various members of which and among which are at least several phenotypes' (Stout). Furthermore the fundamental concept is of *differences in genetic structure*, regardless of how these arose, rather than of differences in genetic structure due specifically to hybridity. Your term polybrid is certainly distinct from this definition, in that its basic concept is purely *operational:* 'A group name for hybrids from crosses between two particular species, varieties or genera.' This clearly states the relationship of the plants involved, and it limits the concept quite definitely to plants which arise through crossing *taxonomic groups*, and without committing yourself as to the genetic meaning of these taxonomic terms. A term so defined should be very useful in horticultural practice and should help to clarify a confused and perplexing situation.

"ROBERT COOK
"Secretary American Genetic Association."

In this book therefore the Committee has followed, *so far as conditions and limitations have permitted*, the practice of placing the polybrid symbol (∞) before such group names, and recommends its general use.

4. *Glossary.* The carefully prepared Glossary (see page 669) will, it is hoped, be found a valuable reference for users of STANDARDIZED PLANT NAMES.

Plant Identification. It must be continually borne in mind that however good plant naming may be, it does not answer the serious problem of plant identification. A right label on the wrong plant or plant product may cause even more loss or disaster than a wrong label on the right plant or plant product. This subject was discussed in the preface of the 1923 edition, but its important implications lead us again to stress its importance and the urgent need for reform.

Plant Importations. Through the cooperation of the Federal Bureau of Entomology and Plant Quarantine by its late Chief, Lee A. Strong, and Assistant Chief, Avery S. Hoyt, the American Joint Committee was supplied with a list of the 1938 importations of plants into the United States, covering 50,000 separately named varieties. This seemed an incredible number, until examination showed a great majority of the names were synonymous, or otherwise untenable. The Bureau grants importation licenses for plants under the names supplied by applicants, there being no existing provisions to insure correct identification and nomenclature either before or after importation. Many of the plants thus brought in for testing and eventual dissemination are unquestionably advertised and sold under incorrect names, adding materially to the existing plant name confusion.

It is well known that in the importations of lumber, fibers, drugs, cereals, fruits, gums, and many other plant products, a similar condition exists, perhaps to a somewhat less degree, yet of vital concern to the welfare and health of the American people. These and many other compelling reasons indicate why the standardization of names should be not only adequately continued and perfected, but should receive without delay full official sanction and effective administration.

Misuse of Latin Plant Names. The giving of Latin or botanical names instead of suitable English or common names to horticultural varieties, hybrids, clons, or polybrids is one of the chief causes of confusion and error in plant identification, propagation, and dissemination. In our judgment it is a cumbersome, needless, and basically unscientific practice. In the case of clons (whether from hybrid, seed, budsport, or other sources) the mischief is not so pronounced, for the reason that a clon is perpetuated by vegetative reproduction only, while an ordinary hybrid or polybrid may be and usually is, reproduced by seed, and the resulting issues are rarely, if ever, identical with the parent. A typical example of a seed clon being given a useless botanical name is *Tsuga canadensis jenkinsi*, a particular selected variation of *Tsuga canadensis*. A sounder procedure would have been to name this clon Jenkins Canada Hemlock.

A much graver situation exists in the case of polybrid (group hybrid) names such as ∞ *Malus zumi* (*M. baccata mandshurica* × *M. sieboldi*). It is insisted by botanists that the result of any cross at any time or place of the two parents named above shall be called *Malus zumi;* and this regardless of the well-known fact that the progeny may be, and usually will be, entirely different from the botanists' description of *Malus zumi, which has been made from a particular or selected clon*, and which therefore is inaccurate for other clons or progeny of such a cross.

STANDARDIZED PLANT NAMES adopts the rule that species and natural varieties only are entitled to Latin or botanical names, and that all hybrids, clons, polybrids, horticultural varieties, and the like should receive suitable English or common names. (It is pertinent to note that Rule "b," Appendix VII in the International Rules of Botanical Nomenclature, which provides for giving a Latin name to horticultural varieties in certain cases, has since been voted down by the International Committee for Horticultural Nomenclature.) Time and other serious handicaps made it impossible for the Editors to consistently carry out these principles. Yet reasonable progress has been made, and it is hoped a later edition may see all necessary changes made in conformity with this beginning.

International Plant Naming Rules. At various International Congresses attempts have been made to establish and agree upon rules for naming so-called garden plants, but as yet with only meager success. A draft of such rules was presented at the International Conference in London in 1930. Some of these rules are excellent, while others from our standpoint are entirely inadmissible. We quote verbatim a few with which we are in agreement, in the hope that they will serve as a partial standard in plant naming:

"Varietal names must not be translated when transferred from other languages, but must be preserved in the language in which they were originally described. Where desirable a translation may be placed in brackets after the varietal name.

"So far as possible names of horticultural varieties should consist of a single word; the use of not more than three words is permitted as a maximum.

"1. A varietal name in use for one variety of a kind of plant should not be used for another variety of that kind, even though it may be attached to a different species. Thus the use of the name Narcissus pseudonarcissus 'Victoria' should preclude the use of 'Victoria' as a varietal name for any other species of Narcissus, such as Narcissus poeticus 'Victoria.' Similarly there should be but one Iris 'Bridesmaid,' one Plum 'Superb,' and so on.

"2. Varietal names likely to be confused with one another should be avoided. For instance, the use of the name 'Alexander' should preclude the use of 'Alexandra,' 'Alexandria,' and 'Alexandrina' as varietal names for the same kind of plant.

"3. Where personal names are used to designate varieties, the prefix Mr., Mrs., Miss, and their equivalents should be avoided.

"4. Excessively long words and words difficult to pronounce should be avoided.

"5. The articles 'a' and 'the' and their equivalents should be avoided in all languages when they do not form an integral part of the substantive. For instance, 'Colonel,' not 'The Colonel'; 'Giant,' not 'The Giant'; 'Bride,' not 'The Bride.' "

A Standard Code of rules governing the naming of plants and plant products should be made and officially adopted as soon as possible.

Plant Name Registration. As recommended in

the 1923 edition, the American Joint Committee urges that means be provided for registration of new horticultural varieties at an early date, with authority to enforce proper regulations.

In addition to other rules suggested above, the following are most important:

1. Homonyms (*the same name for a different plant or untenable because preoccupied; for example, the generic name Pinus would be a homonym and untenable if applied to any group of plants other than the Pines*), *to be definitely disbarred from use, and listed only as synonyms.*

2. Priority. *The principle of priority should prevail. Until definite and authoritative action for registration is taken, name piracy with its consequent evils will continue. Fortunately, with the universal adoption of International Botanical Rules far fewer genus, species, and natural variety botanical name changes will occur in the future than in the past, and if the English or common name problem is likewise improved, the entire name situation will tend toward stabilization.*

Forest Tree Names. Sudworth's Check List of the Forest Trees of the United States has for years been accepted by the United States Department of Agriculture, the United States Forest Service, and the Government Printing Office as authority for the names of United States forest trees. As Standardized Plant Names also was accepted as authority by these agencies, much confusion arose because of the numerous differences between these two standards. To correct this anomalous situation, the American Joint Committee on Horticultural Nomenclature approached the late Major F. A. Silcox, Chief of the Forest Service, looking toward the revision of this Check List in accordance with Standardized Plant Names principles. With his approval, detailed recommendations were made by a special committee of two representing the Editorial Committee of Standardized Plant Names and the Forest Service Tree Name Committee. These recommendations were carefully considered by the Forest Service Tree Name Committee, which includes Dr. Homer L. Shantz as Chairman, Dr. Warren D. Brush, Perkins Coville, W. A. Dayton, Lawrence S. Gross, and Verne L. Harper. In a published memorandum dated January 23, 1940, referred to in the bibliography for the Lumber Trade Names list in this book (see page 343) the Forest Service Tree Name Committee, with the approval of Acting Chief C. M. Granger of the Forest Service, reported 720 official changes in the names in Sudworth's Check List. These changes are in accord with Standardized Plant Names principles, and compose one of the most significant and important single contributions to this book.

United States Department of Agriculture Committee on Plant Names. In the fall of 1938 the Chairman of the Editorial Committee of Standardized Plant Names informally consulted with a number of officials of the United States Department of Agriculture, including Drs. E. C. Auchter and M. A. McCall, Chief and Assistant Chief of the Bureau of Plant Industry, and the late Major F. A. Silcox, Chief of the Forest Service, and urged the desirability of the Department of Agriculture assuming leadership in this country in the fields of plant name standardization and registration. Attention was called to the fact that the American Joint Committee on Horticultural Nomenclature had produced the first edition of Standardized Plant Names only because it had been unable to get the Department of Agriculture or other adequate authority to take the main responsibility for this increasingly important work. However, the Department at that time was unwilling to assume the burden of plant name registration, an added responsibility which might require special action of Congress. But on March 15, 1939, the Hon. Henry A. Wallace, then Secretary of Agriculture, appointed, for the first time, a standing Department Committee on Plant Names, consisting of Max A. McCall (Chairman), B. Y. Morrison, W. A. Dayton, Neil Hotchkiss, and Dr. William R. Van Dersal, representing the four Bureaus of the Department most directly concerned with plant nomenclature. To this Committee, Dr. Melvin C. Merrill, Chief of Publications in the Department, has recently been added, while Neil Hotchkiss and his proxy Alexander C. Martin now serve in an advisory capacity, since their Bureau (formerly the Biological Survey, and now the Fish and Wildlife Service) has recently been transferred to the Department of the Interior.

In his memorandum announcing the formation of this Committee, Secretary Wallace defined the duties and functions of the Committee as follows:

"It shall be the duty of this committee to consider and to recommend for use by the Department such plant nomenclature, both scientific and common names, as may be desirable. In performing this function the committee will consult with all bureaus of the Department interested in the use of plant names, and with all other Government or private agencies so concerned. The duties of the committee are to be continuous, to provide for revisions and additions as may be needed from time to time."

A mutually agreeable understanding existed between the American Joint Committee on Horticultural Nomenclature and the new Department of Agriculture Committee on Plant Names that, in view of the progress already made in the preparation of the second edition of STANDARDIZED PLANT NAMES, in the arrangements made for its publication, and in time limitations, the Department Committee would cooperate in any way possible. The Editorial Committee gratefully acknowledges its indebtedness to the Department of Agriculture for its interest and support in the preparation of this book, for the advice it has cheerfully given, on request, in connection with plant names and other technical problems, and for its liberal share in providing financial and personnel assistance through the several Bureaus represented.

That it is of paramount importance to carry on the work of standardizing the names of all plants and plant products, no intelligent citizen will deny. The logical responsibility for this activity rests directly with the Department of Agriculture; it should not permanently rest on the shoulders of lay volunteers. A permanent responsible authority must exist, which can actively devote to this subject the necessary time, thought, and ability to conduct it efficiently. It is also obviously necessary to adopt a sound philosophy of name standardization, based on logical, orderly, and scientific principles, such a code to be administered with complete impartiality.

As previously stated, it is significant that the International Rules of Botanical Nomenclature are now recognized almost without exception throughout the world. They have recently been formally adopted by the United States Department of Agriculture, and have governed the scientific nomenclature of this book.

Collaboration

Among more than 200 collaborators in this book, the personnel of the Federal Government occupies a conspicuous place. Two Departments, besides the Smithsonian Institution, 5 Bureaus, and at least 10 Divisions are represented in the work. In the Department of Agriculture, the Bureaus of Entomology and Plant Quarantine, Plant Industry, Forest Service, and Soil Conservation Service are represented. The late Major F. A. Silcox, Chief of the Forest Service, gave the work his enthusiastic support, and he, together with Eugene C. Auchter, Chief of the Bureau of Plant Industry, deserves a large share of the credit for getting Departmental support for the project. Clarence L. Forsling, Assistant Chief of the Forest Service, in charge of Research, and W. R. Chapline, Chief of the Division of Range Research, greatly facilitated the work by arrangements for necessary personnel details, etc. The Forest Service furnished the Department of Agriculture member of the Editorial Committee, making available for over two years the service of William A. Dayton, Chief of the Section of Range Forage Investigations, Division of Range Research, to supervise the assembly, reviewing, and preliminary checking of names for final review and approval by the Editorial Committee, in which work he received assistance at times from two of his colleagues, Doris W. Hayes and Miriam L. Bomhard. In addition, advice and assistance was received from some of the field units of the Forest Service. The Soil Conservation Service assisted with funds and clerical personnel. William R. Van Dersal, Edward H. Graham, and various field men of that Bureau took an active interest in the progress of the work and made many helpful suggestions.

The Bureau of Plant Industry has furnished personnel and the unrivaled facilities of its wide array of technical knowledge.

We are greatly indebted to Max A. McCall, Assistant Chief of the Bureau of Plant Industry and Chairman of the U. S. Department of Agriculture Committee on Plant Names, and to his associate Henry E. Allanson, for facilitating the work of the Committee in many ways, particularly through services rendered by members of the Bureau staff. Our cordial thanks are extended to the following specialists of the Division of Plant Exploration and Introduction: Sidney F. Blake, Latin nomenclature of Compositae, Dipsaceae, Hydnoraceae, Piperaceae, Plumbaginaceae, and Polygalaceae; Carl O. Erlanson, Latin nomenclature of Iridaceae, Liliaceae, and Violaceae; F. R. Fosberg, Latin nomenclature of Aizoaceae, Amaranthaceae, Asclepiadaceae, Basellaceae, Caryophyllaceae, Chenopodiaceae, Halorrhagidaceae, Nyctaginaceae, Passifloraceae, Polemoniaceae, Portulacaceae, (herbaceous) Rubiaceae, and Urticaceae; Oliver M. Freeman, Latin nomenclature of Labiatae, Lentibulariaceae, and Nepenthaceae; Frederick J. Hermann, Latin nomenclature of Amaryllidaceae, Capparidaceae, Cyperaceae, Dioscoreaceae, Hydrocharitaceae, Juncaceae, (herbaceous) Leguminosae, Orchidaceae, and Zingiberaceae; Robert F. Martin, Latin nomenclature of Convolvulaceae, Crassulaceae, Cruciferae, Cucurbitaceae, Gentianaceae, Malvaceae, Martyniaceae, Plantaginaceae, and Ranunculaceae; Rogers McVaugh, Latin nomenclature of Euphorbiaceae, Polygonaceae, (herbaceous) Rosaceae, and Scrophulariaceae; Cornelius H. Muller, Latin nomenclature of Borraginaceae, Loasaceae, Melastomataceae, Pyrolaceae, Solanaceae, and (herbaceous) Verbenaceae; Paul Russell, for the Oriental Flowering Cherries list; Daniel C. Sullivan, for assistance with accents and miscellaneous botanical nomenclatorial problems.

Appreciation is extended to David Fairchild for his valuable advice and suggestions, and to William Montgomery for placing the facilities of his collections of Palms and Cycads at Coconut Grove, Florida, at our disposal.

Among institutions to which our thanks are extended are the Arnold Arboretum, Smithsonian Institution, Brooklyn Botanic Garden, Cornell University Arboretum, Missouri Botanical Garden, Rancho Santa Ana Botanic Garden, California; Hemlock Arboretum, Philadelphia; Arthur Hoyt Scott Horticultural Foundation, Swarthmore, Pa.; Sanford Arboretum, Knoxville, Tenn., and others.

The Editorial Committee extends its warm thanks to Alfred Rehder, distinguished author of the standard work, "Manual of Cultivated Trees and Shrubs," not only for his careful check of the nomenclature of the woody plants in this new edition of Standardized Plant Names, but for his unremitting patience and kindness in answering innumerable questions throughout the progress of the work. Cordial appreciation is also expressed to Elmer D. Merrill, Director of the Arnold Arboretum, Harvard University, for his interest and invaluable advice during the initiation and progress of the work.

The Editorial Committee accepts responsibility for this work, and neither the Arnold Arboretum nor the United States Department of Agriculture should be held responsible for the common names, accents, terminology, or symbols.

Editorial Succession

The late Frederick V. Coville was a member of the committee which prepared the original 1917 "Official Code of Standardized Plant Names" and the major edition of 1923. In the interim between the 1923 and 1942 editions of this book, the editorial activities of the American Joint Committee continued through its Secretary and the two other editorial members, Frederick V. Coville and Frederick Law Olmsted. Dr. Coville died in 1937, and Donald Wyman was appointed a member of the Editorial Committee of Standardized Plant Names, resigning in 1939. In 1938, Mr. Olmsted resigned from the Editorial Committee because of ill health, and William A. Dayton, of the Forest Service, was appointed to the Editorial Committee, succeeding Dr. Coville as representative of the Department of Agriculture. (A special tribute to Dr. Coville will be found on page xvi.)

It is natural that a great number of people have been connected, in one capacity or another, with the preparation of this edition. This situation, moreover, was emphasized by the continuous changes in personnel during the period of preparation, a circumstance over which the Editorial

Committee had no control. It is not feasible to name all these persons, who rendered faithful service and cheerfully worked overtime of their own volition. Special mention should be made of Catherine E. Meikle, of the Mount Pleasant Press (which has carried through the typography of the work), who has most efficiently handled the voluminous cross-indexing of the book, with its inevitable accompaniment of detecting and correcting numerous errors.

Other Collaborators

Space prevents the full enumeration of many hundreds of correspondents whose advice and constructive criticisms have materially aided the Committee in its work. However, special acknowledgment is made under certain important genera, groups, and subjects as below printed.

Allium: C. V. Morton, Smithsonian Inst., Washington, D. C.

Amaryllis Family Genera: Hamilton P. Traub, Beltsville, Md.; Carl O. Erlanson, Bur. of Plant Ind., Washington, D. C.; Wyndham Hayward, Winter Park, Fla.

Aquarium Plants: E. J. Alexander, New York Bot. Gard., New York, N. Y.

Arctostaphylos: Beryl O. Schreiber, Calif. Forest and Range Exp. Sta., Forest Serv., Berkeley, Calif.

Aster: Ray M. Koon, Waltham Field Sta., Waltham, Mass.; S. F. Blake, Bur. of Plant Ind., Washington, D. C.

Bamboo Genera: Floyd A. McClure, Curator of Econ. Botany, Lingnan Nat. Hist. Survey & Mus., Lingnan Univ., Canton, China; Robert A. Young, Bur. of Plant Ind., Washington, D. C.

Barberry: L. M. Ames, Jamaica Plain, Mass.; S. B. Fracker, Bur. of Ent. and Plant Quar., Washington, D. C.

Begonia: Bessie R. Buxton, Peabody, Mass.; Burdell Bulgren, Long Beach, Calif.; William Casely, Long Beach, Calif.

Botanical Names: Alfred Rehder, Arnold Arboretum, Jamaica Plain, Mass. (woody plants). Botanical staff of Bureau of Plant Industry (herbaceous plants)—see page xi. Also various other specialists, as shown in this list.

Cactus Genera: Elzada U. Clover, Univ. of Mich., Ann Arbor, Mich.; W. Taylor Marshall, Los Angeles, Calif.; R. W. Poindexter, Compton, Calif.

California Plants: Maxim Ethan Armbruster, Pittsburgh, Pa.; John A. Armstrong, Ontario, Calif.; Blakesley Bot. Gard., Santa Barbara, Calif.; W. B. Clarke, San Jose, Calif.; H. McFadden, Compton, Calif.; H. E. McMinn, Mills Coll., Oakland, Calif.; Eric Walther, Golden Gate Park, San Francisco, Calif.; Carl B. Wolf, Rancho Santa Ana Bot. Gard., Santa Ana Canyon, Calif.

Calochortus: Marion Ownbey, State Coll. of Wash., Pullman, Wash.

Camellia: H. Harold Hume, Fla. Agr. Exp. Sta., Gainesville, Fla.

Canna: Robert Pyle, West Grove, Pa.

Carnation: A. F. J. Baur, Editor Amer. Carnation Register, New Augusta, Ind.; F. A. Baur, Past-Secretary, The American Carnation Soc., New Augusta, Ind.

Ceanothus: Beryl O. Schreiber, Calif. Forest and Range Exp. Sta., Forest Serv., Berkeley, Calif.; H. E. McMinn, Mills Coll., Oakland, Calif.

Cereals: Burton B. Bayles; J. Allen Clark; Arthur C. Dillman; Jenkin W. Jones; John H. Martin; Max A. McCall; Brittain B. Robinson; T. R. Stanton; John W. Taylor; Gustav A. Wiebe, Bur. of Plant Ind., Washington, D. C.

Cherries, Oriental Flowering: Paul Russell, Bur. of Plant Ind., Washington, D. C.

Chrysanthemum: Alex Cumming, Jr., Vice-Pres. Amer. Chrysanthemum Soc., Bristol, Conn.; Arno Nehrling, Boston, Mass.; G. H. Poesch, Sec., Chrysanthemum Soc. of America, Ohio State Univ., Columbus, Ohio; Elmer D. Smith (deceased), Adrian, Mich.; John C. Wister, Germantown, Philadelphia, Pa.

Citrus: Walter T. Swingle, Bur. of Plant Ind., Washington, D. C.; Herbert J. Webber, Citrus Exp. Sta., Riverside, Calif.

Clematis: J. E. Spingarn (deceased), Rhinebeck, N. Y.

Cryptogams, Economic: John A. Stevenson, Bur. of Plant Ind., Washington, D. C.

Cycad Genera: Charles J. Chamberlain, Univ. of Chicago, Chicago, Ill.; Adriane S. Foster, Univ. of Calif., Berkeley, Calif.; A. W. Haupt, Univ. of Calif. at Los Angeles, Los Angeles, Calif.; William Hertrich, Curator, Huntington Bot. Gard., San Marino, Calif.; H. A. Van Hermann, Servicio de Calles y Parques de O. P., Havana, Cuba.

Dahlia: C. H. Connors, N. J. Agr. Exp. Sta., New Brunswick, N. J.

Delphinium: R. C. Allen, Cornell Univ., Ithaca, N. Y.; L. H. Bailey, Bailey Hortorium, Ithaca, N. Y.; Earle I. Wilde, Pa. State Coll., State College, Pa.

Drug Plant Names: Heber W. Youngken, Mass. Coll. of Pharmacy, Boston, Mass.; Charles W. Ballard, Coll. of Pharmacy, Columbia Univ., New York City; E. N. Gathercoal, Pentwater, Mich.; Ludwig Metzger, Univ. of Wash., Seattle, Wash.

Economic Plants: Albert F. Hill, Harvard Univ., Cambridge, Mass.

Eucalyptus: Eric Walther, Golden Gate Park, San Francisco, Calif.

Euphorbiaceae: Louis C. Wheeler, American Univ., Washington, D. C.

Fern Genera: William R. Maxon, Asst. Curator, and C. V. Morton, U. S. Nat. Mus., Washington, D. C.; Ralph C. Benedict, Brooklyn Bot. Gard., Brooklyn, N. Y.

Fiber Plants: Lyster H. Dewey, Conrad B. Doyle, Harry T. Edwards, Thomas H. Kearney, and Brittain B. Robinson, Bur. of Plant Ind., Washington, D. C.

Forest Tree Names: See page x.

Fruit and Edible Nut Names: W. W. Aldrich, Div. of Subtrop. Hort., Bur. of Plant Ind., Indio, Calif.; J. Harold Clark, N. J. Agr. Exp. Sta., New Brunswick, N. J.; I. J. Condit and Herbert J. Webber, Citrus Exp. Sta., Univ. of Calif., Riverside, Calif.; M. J. Dorsey, Amer. Pomol. Soc., Univ. of Ill., Urbana, Ill.; H. L. Crane, H. P. Gould, Charles F. Kinman, C. S. Pomeroy, C. A. Reed, and Hamilton P. Traub, Div. Fruit and Veg. Crops and Diseases, Bur. of Plant Ind., Beltsville, Md.; Robert W. Hodgson, Calif. Agr. Exp. Sta., Univ. of Calif. at Los Angeles, Los Angeles, Calif.; H. L. Lantz, Walter T. Swingle, and W. E. Whitehouse, Bur. of Plant Ind., Washington, D. C.; J. Russell Smith, Columbia Univ., New York, N. Y.; Warren P. Tufts, Div. Pomology, Univ. of Calif., Davis, Calif.; H. S. Wolfe,

Univ. of Fla., Gainesville, Fla.; G. A. Zimmerman (deceased), Harrisburg, Pa.

Fuchsia: George Budgen, Berkeley, Calif.

Genetics: Robert C. Cook, Amer. Genetic Assoc., Washington, D. C.

Gladiolus: Alfred M. S. Pridham, Cornell Univ., Ithaca, N. Y.; James H. Odell, Wellesley Hills, Mass.; Ronald Bamford, Univ. of Md., College Park, Md.

Grass Genera: Jason R. Swallen, A. S. Hitchcock (deceased), and Agnes Chase, Bur. of Plant Ind., Washington, D. C.; Calif. Forest and Range Exp. Sta., Forest Serv., Berkeley, Calif. For additional list of collaborators, see Grass Genera, page 278.

Hemerocallis: A. B. Stout, N. Y. Bot. Gard., New York, N. Y.

Hemlock: John C. Swartley, Ohio State Univ., Columbus, Ohio; Charles Francis Jenkins, Philadelphia, Pa.

Herbgarden Plants: Helen Noyes Webster, Lexington, Mass.

Iris: Charles E. F. Gersdorff, Washington, D. C.; Ethel Anson S. Peckham, Sterlington, N. Y.; Howard R. Watkins, Bur. of Plant Ind., Washington, D. C.; John C. Wister, Germantown, Philadelphia, Pa.

Lilacs: John C. Wister, Germantown, Philadelphia, Pa.; Donald Wyman, Arnold Arb., Jamaica Plain, Mass.

Liliaceae: Carl O. Erlanson, Bur. of Plant Ind., Washington, D. C.; Hamilton P. Traub, Bur. of Plant Ind., Beltsville, Md.

Lilium: George L. Slate, N. Y. Agr. Exp. Sta., Geneva, N. Y.

Lumber Trade Names: Warren D. Brush, Forest Serv., Washington, D. C. For additional list of collaborators, see Lumber Trade Names, page 342.

Narcissus: Frederick J. Hermann, Bur. of Plant Ind., Washington, D. C.; Ore. Bulb Farm, Sandy, Ore.; William A. Sperling, Amer. Narcissus Growers Assoc., New York, N. Y.

Nasturtium: Elizabeth M. Bodger, El Monte, Calif.

Palm Genera: Miriam L. Bomhard, Forest Serv., Washington, D. C.

Patents, Plant: Lawrence J. Blackmer, Patent Off., Dept. Comm., Washington, D. C.

Pelargonium: Mrs. Roderick H. Vandivert, Colonia, N. J.

Peony: W. F. Christman, Sec., Amer. Peony Soc., Northbrook, Ill.; George W. Peyton, Reg. Vice-Pres., Rapidan, Va.; A. F. Saunders, Amer. Peony Soc., Northbrook, Ill.

Phlox: Alfred M. S. Pridham, Cornell Univ., Ithaca, N. Y.; Edgar T. Wherry, Univ. of Penna., Philadelphia, Pa.

Plant Importations: See page viii.

Poplar: A. B. Stout, N. Y. Bot. Gard., New York, N. Y.

Poppies: John D. Siebenthaler, Dayton, Ohio; J. J. Grullemans, Mentor, Ohio.

Range Plants: William A. Dayton and Doris W. Hayes, Forest Serv., Washington, D. C.; Calif. Forest and Range Exp. Sta., Forest Serv., Berkeley, Calif.

Rhododendron (including Azalea): John C. Wister, Germantown, Philadelphia, Pa.; Donald Wyman, Arnold Arb., Jamaica Plain, Mass.; E. H. M. Cox, Broughty Ferry, Dundee, Scotland; Peter M. Koster, Huntington Sta., L. I., N. Y.

Ribes: S. B. Fracker, Bur. of Ent. and Plant Quar., Washington, D. C.

Rosa: R. Marion Hatton, Harrisburg, Pa.; J. Horace McFarland, Harrisburg, Pa.; C. R. McGinnes, Reading, Pa.; Alfred Rehder, Jamaica Plain, Mass.

Salix: C. R. Ball, Dept. of Agr., Washington, D. C.

Smilax: Ellsworth P. Killip; C. V. Morton, U. S. Nat. Herb., Smithsonian Inst., Washington, D. C.

Soil Conservation Plants: S. B. Detwiler, Soil Cons. Serv., Washington, D. C.

State Flowers and Trees: C. W. Johnson, Springfield, Mass. For full list of collaborators, see State Flowers and Trees, page 596.

Succulents: Robert T. Clausen, Cornell Univ., Ithaca, N. Y.; Carl O. Erlanson, Bur. of Plant Ind., Washington, D. C.; Scott Hazelton, Pasadena, Calif.; William Taylor Marshall, Pasadena, Calif.; R.W. Poindexter, Compton, Calif.

Sweetpea: Elizabeth M. Bodger, El Monte, Calif.

Trifolium: Edward H. Graham, Soil Cons. Serv., Washington, D. C.

Tropical and Subtropical Plants and Fruits: David Fairchild, Coconut Grove, Fla.; I. J. Condit, Citrus Exp. Sta., Univ. of Calif., Riverside, Calif.; Hamilton P. Traub, Bur. of Plant Ind., Beltsville, Md.; Hugh Evans, Los Angeles, Calif.; J. A. McDonald, Miles, Calif.

Vetch: Olaf S. Aamodt, F. J. Hermann, and Roland McKee, Bur. of Plant Ind., Washington, D. C.; Atlee L. Hafenrichter, Pullman, Wash.; Harry A. Schoth, Bur. of Plant Ind. Corvallis, Ore.; and William R. Van Dersal, Soil Cons. Serv., Washington, D. C.

Viola: Maxim Ethan Armbruster, Pittsburgh, Pa.; Carl O. Erlanson, Bur. of Plant Ind., Washington, D. C.

Vitis: L. H. Bailey, Bailey Hortorium, Ithaca, N. Y. Dr. Bailey liberally made available his unmatched facilities for plant name research.

Waterlily Genera: G. H. Pring, Missouri Bot. Gard., St. Louis, Mo.; Henry S. Conard, Grinnell Coll., Grinnell, Iowa.

Weeds: Walter C. Muenscher, N. Y. State Coll. of Agr., Cornell Univ., Ithaca, N. Y.

Wildlife Plants: Neil Hotchkiss and Alexander C. Martin, Fish and Wildlife Serv., Washington, D. C.; William R. Van Dersal, Soil Cons. Serv., Washington, D. C.

Bibliography

The number of publications consulted in the preparation of this edition of Standardized Plant Names runs well into several hundred titles, and space does not permit mentioning all of them. Over a hundred works of reference in fact, are cited in connection with the special lists in this book; see especially Economic Cryptogams; Glossary; Lumber Trade Names; Succulents. Probably the works which were most consulted in the preparation of the book are:

Bailey, L. H. The Standard Cyclopedia of Horticulture. 3 vols. N. Y. 1935.

Bailey, L. H., and Bailey, Ethel Zoe. Hortus. Rev. ed. N. Y. 1935.

Briquet, John, et al. International Rules of Botanical Nomenclature. Jena. 1935.

Forest Service Tree Name Committee. Approved Changes in Sudworth's Check List. Mimeographed. 1940.

Hooker, Joseph D., Jackson, B. Daydon, et al. Index Kewensis Plantarum Phanerogamarum. 4 vols. 9 supplements. Oxford, England. 1893–1938.

Olmsted, Frederick Law, Coville, Frederick V., and Kelsey, Harlan P. Standardized Plant Names. Salem, Mass. 1923.

REHDER, ALFRED. Manual of Cultivated Trees and Shrubs. N. Y. 1940.

SUDWORTH, GEORGE B. Check List of the Forest Trees of the United States. U. S. Dept. Agr. Misc. Circ. 92. 1927.

VAN WIJK, H. L. GERTH. A Dictionary of Plant Names. 2 vols. The Hague. 1911–1916.

Among other books of outstanding assistance should be mentioned:

ABRAMS, LEROY. An Illustrated Flora of the Pacific States. Stanford Univ., Calif. 1923.

BAILEY, L. H. The Cultivated Conifers in North America. N. Y. 1933.

BEAN, W. J. Trees and Shrubs Hardy in the British Isles. 3 vols. 6th ed. London. 1936.

BRITTON, NATHANIEL LORD, and BROWN, ADDISON. An Illustrated Flora of the Northern United States, Canada and the British Possessions. N. Y. 3 vols. 1913.

COOK, O. F., and COLLINS, G. N. Economic Plants of Porto Rico. Contributions U. S. Natl. Herbarium 8: 57–259. 1903.

COVILLE, FREDERICK V. Seed List. U. S. Dept. Agr. Processed. 1935.

DAYTON, WILLIAM A. Important Western Browse Plants. U. S. Dept. Agr. Misc. Pub. 101. 1931.

DAYTON, WILLIAM A., et al. Range Plant Handbook. Forest Serv. U. S. Dept. Agr. 1937.

DEAM, CHARLES C. Flora of Indiana. Indiana Dept. of Conservation. 1940.

FAIRCHILD, DAVID. Exploring for Plants. N. Y. 1931.

FREEMAN, W. G., and WILLIAMS, R. O. The Useful and Ornamental Plants of Trinidad and Tobago. Trinidad and Tobago Dept. Agr. Mem. No. 4. 1927.

GUILFOYLE, W. R. Australian Plants. Melbourne. 2d ed. (1910?)

HEDRICK, U. P. (editor). Sturtevant's Notes on Edible Plants. 27th Annl. Rpt. N. Y. Agr. Expt. Sta. 2 vols. Albany. 1919.

HITCHCOCK, A. S. Manual of the Grasses of the United States. U. S. Dept. Agriculture Misc. Pub. 200. 1935.

JEPSON, WILLIS LINN. A Flora of California. (2 vols. published.) San Francisco. 1909–1936.

JEPSON, WILLIS LINN. A Manual of the Flowering Plants of California. Berkeley. 1923–1925.

MARIE-VICTORIN, FRERE. Flore Laurentienne. Montreal. 1935.

MARTIN, A. C., and UHLER, F. M. Food of Game Ducks in the United States and Canada. U. S. Dept. Agr. Tech. Bull. 634. 1939.

MATTOON, WILBUR R. Forest Trees and Forest Regions of the United States. U. S. Dept. Agr. Misc. Pub. 217. 1936.

MCMINN, HOWARD E. An Illustrated Manual of California Shrubs. San Francisco. 1939.

MOWRY, HAROLD. Ornamental Trees. Fla. Agr. Extens. Bull. 95. 1938.

MUNZ, PHILIP A. A Manual of Southern California Botany. Claremont, Calif. 1935.

PARSONS, MARY ELIZABETH. The Wild Flowers of California. San Francisco, Calif. 1916.

PIPER, C. V. Flora of the State of Washington. Contributions U. S. Natl. Herbarium 11. 1906.

POPENOE, WILSON. Manual of Tropical and Sub-Tropical Fruits. N. Y. 1938.

ROBINSON, BENJAMIN LINCOLN, and FERNALD, MERRITT LYNDON. Gray's New Manual of Botany. 7th ed. N. Y., etc. 1908.

RYDBERG, P. A. Flora of the Rocky Mountains and Adjacent Plains. N. Y. 1917.

RYDBERG, PER AXEL. Flora of the Prairies and Plains of Central North America. N. Y. 1932.

SANFORD, SAMUEL. New England Herbs. New Engl. Mus. of Nat. Hist. Spec. Pub. 2. 1937.

SMALL, JOHN KUNKEL. Manual of the Southeastern Flora. N. Y. 1933.

STANDLEY, PAUL CARPENTER. Trees and Shrubs of Mexico. Contributions U. S. Natl. Herbarium 23. 1920–1926.

STANDLEY, PAUL C. Flora of the Panama Canal Zone. Contributions U. S. Natl. Herbarium 27. 1928.

TIDESTROM, IVAR. Flora of Utah and Nevada. Contributions U. S. Natl. Herbarium 25. 1925.

VAN DERSAL, WILLIAM R. Native Woody Plants of the United States. U. S. Dept. Agr. Misc. Pub. 303. 1938.

WOOTON, E. O., and STANDLEY, PAUL C. Flora of New Mexico. Contributions U. S. Natl. Herbarium 19. 1915.

IMPORTANT NOTICE

IN this 1942 edition of STANDARDIZED PLANT NAMES *the Editors have adopted what seemed the best common names for plants and plant products so far as was feasible at this time. Many thousands of new names were supplied for plants that had no common names, or with common names wholly unsuitable or more properly belonging to other plants.*

In thousands of other cases, especially of plants new or little known, common names are missing, for an appropriate name suggests itself usually only on intimate acquaintance with the particular plant or with its history.

The users of STANDARDIZED PLANT NAMES *will confer a great favor by offering constructive criticism on common names in this book, by suggesting new names where names are now missing and especially by supplying lists of new plant introductions or other plants and plant products brought into use in America, so that future editions of this work or supplements thereof may be made more complete and more valuable. Address*

HARLAN P. KELSEY, *Secretary*
American Joint Committee, East Boxford, Massachusetts

In Memoriam

FREDERICK VERNON COVILLE

MEMBER EDITORIAL COMMITTEE, REPRESENTING THE UNITED STATES DEPARTMENT OF AGRICULTURE, STANDARDIZED PLANT NAMES: SCHOLAR, BOTANIST AND PIONEER IN THE ART AND PRACTICE OF PLANT NAMING: CONGENIAL, CONSIDERATE AND INSPIRING COLLEAGUE.

FROM the publication of the 1923 edition of STANDARDIZED PLANT NAMES to the time of his death, Dr. Coville continued unremittingly at the task of remedying existing plant name chaos.

He enriched plant literature with more than a thousand suitable new common names and name combinations, particularly in the field of Western American plants, including grasses, most of which appear in this new edition, thus greatly facilitating the task of the present Committee.

Dr. Coville had a remarkably discriminating sense and an extraordinary ability to select suitable common names for plants. A list of 1707 plant names at variance with usual dictionary forms, including hundreds of new names of which he was author, were submitted by Dr. Coville and adopted by the Government Printing Office. These now appear in the Government Style Manual and in STANDARDIZED PLANT NAMES.

Dr. Coville was a born leader. He pioneered in the study of desert plants, the administration of public grazing lands, Indian plant lore, botanical bibliography, the nature and use of acid soils, blueberry domestication, and in many other fields, especially of botany, ecology, and horticulture. He was the author of about two hundred publications on these subjects. Many of the plants listed in this book were discovered or first described by Dr. Coville or named in his honor.

The present Editorial Committee here acknowledges its deep sense of obligation for the fruits of Dr. Coville's unceasing labors in his invaluable contributions to this book, which, it is hoped, may not too inadequately help to perpetuate the memory of his great services to the botanical and horticultural world.

His past colleagues, with a feeling of profound and irreparable loss, render homage to the memory of a true gentleman, great plantsman, wise counselor, happy companion, and loyal friend.

HARLAN P. KELSEY
FREDERICK LAW OLMSTED
WILLIAM A. DAYTON

STANDARDIZED PLANT NAMES

BOLD-face, whether capitals or small letters, indicates approved scientific names.

SMALL CAPITALS indicate approved common and horticultural variety names.

ITALIC, whether capitals or *small letters,* indicates synonyms or unapproved names.

Abbreviations: hort. var.; HV. = horticultural variety (or varieties)*; sp. = species (singular); spp. = species (plural).

Symbols: ₵ = clon; × (as a prefix) = hybrid; × (between scientific plant names) = crossed by; ∞ = polybrid; lw = plant useful to wildlife. (See Glossary for definitions of *clon, hybrid,* and *polybrid.*)

Names of authors are omitted after botanical names except in the cases of homonyms; in such cases authors are necessary to distinguish otherwise identical names.

*In tabular lists of hort. var. the symbol HV. appears after the first entry only, and is understood to apply to all immediately following. Examples: See hort. var. of Aster alpinus, p. 25, or Hibiscus syriacus, p. 304.

ABBEVIL'LEA (*CAMPOMANESIA*)
fenzlia'na (*Campomanesia f.*) . . . GUABIROBA

ABE'LIA . . . . ABELIA
biflo'ra . . . . . . TWINFLOWER A.
chinen'sis (*rupestris*) . . CHINESE A.
engleria'na . . . . . ENGLER A.
floribun'da . . . . . . MEXICAN A.
graebneria'na . . . . GRAEBNER A.
—vedrarien'sis
∞ **grandiflo'ra** (*chinensis × uniflora*) . . . ∞ GLOSSY A.
rupes'tris . . . . **A. chinensis**
schu'manni (*longituba* Turrill, *not* Rehd.) . . . . . . SCHUMANN A.
serra'ta . . . . NOTCHLEAF A.
spathula'ta . . . . . . JAPANESE A.
triflo'ra . . . . HIMALAYA A.
umbella'ta . . . . UMBEL A.
uniflo'ra . . . . PINKBELL A.
zan'deri . . . . ZANDER A.
₵GOUCHER (∞*grandiflora* × *schumanni*) HV. Abelia
₵SHERWOOD (*sherwoodi*)

ABELIA . . . . **Abelia**
CHINESE A. . . . . . **A. chinensis**
ENGLER A. . . . . . **A. engleriana**
∞ GLOSSY A. . . . . . ∞ **A. grandiflora**
GRAEBNER A. . . . **A. graebneriana**
HIMALAYA A. . . . . **A. triflora**
JAPANESE A. . . . . . **A. spathulata**
MEXICAN A. . . . . . **A. floribunda**
NOTCHLEAF A. . . . . . . **A. serrata**
PINKBELL A. . . . . . . **A. uniflora**
SCHUMANN A. . . . . **A. schumanni**
TWINFLOWER A. . . . . . **A. biflora**
UMBEL A. . . . . . . **A. umbellata**
ZANDER A. . . . . **A. zanderi**

ABELIALEAF . . . . **Abeliophyllum**
KOREAN A. . . . . . . **A. distichum**

ABELIOPHYL'LUM . . . ABELIALEAF
dis'tichum . . . . KOREAN A.

ABELMOS'CHUS . . . **HIBISCUS**

ABE'RIA . . . . **DOVYALIS**
gard'neri . . . . . . **D. hebecarpa**

A'BIES lw . . . . FIR
al'ba (*nobilis* A. Dietr., *not* Lindl.; *pectinata; picea* Lindl., *not* Mill.) SILVER F.
—columna'ris . . . . COLUMNAR S.F.
—compac'ta . . . . . DWARF S.F.
—equi-tro'jani . . . . TROJAN S.F.
—pen'dula . . . . . WEEPING S.F.
—pyramida'lis . . . . SENTINEL S.F.
—tortuo'sa . . . . . TWISTED S.F.
amab'ilis . . . . . CASCADES F.; PACIFIC SILVER F. (Forestry)

ABIES, continued
apol'linis . . . . . **A. cephalonica a.**
arizo'nica . . . . . **A. lasiocarpa a.**
baboren'sis . . . . **A. numidica**
balsa'mea lw . . . . BALSAM FIR
—hudso'nia (*A. b. hudsonica*) . . . HUDSON B.F.
—macrocar'pa . . . . BIGCONE B.F.
—na'na . . . . DWARF B.F.
—phanero'lepis . . . BRACTED B.F.
beissneria'na Mott. (1902) . . . ×**A. insignis b.**
beissneria'na Rehd. & Wils. (1914) . . . **A. ernesti**
bi'fida . . . . **A. firma**
borisire'gis . . . . KINGBORIS F.
bornmuelleria'na . BORNMUELLER F.
brachyphyl'la . . . . . **A. homolepis**
bractea'ta . . . . **A. venusta**
cephalon'ica . . . . GREEK F.
—apol'linis (*A. apollinis*) . APOLLO F.
chensien'sis . . . . SHENSI F.
cilic'ica . . . . CILICIAN F.
con'color lw . . . . WHITE F.
—au'rea . . . . GOLDEN W.F.
—brevifo'lia . . . . SHORTLEAF W.F.
—can'dicans . . . . . . HOARY W.F.
—co'nica . . . . . . CONICAL W.F.
—globo'sa . . . . GLOBE W.F.
—lowia'na (*A. lowiana*). PACIFIC W.F.
—pen'dula . . . . . WEEPING W.F.
—viola'cea . . . . PURPLECONE W.F.
—watte'zi . . . . WATTEZ W.F.
delavay'i Mast., *not* Franch. . . **A. fabri**
ernest'i (*beissneriana* Rehd. & Wils., *not* Mott.) . . . . ERNEST F.
fa'bri (*delavayi* Mast., *not* Franch.; *faberi*) . . . . FABER F.
far'gesi . . . . FARGES F.
₵WEEPING. HV.
faxonia'na . . . . FAXON F.
firm'a (*bifida; momi*) . . . MOMI F.
for'resti . . . . FORREST F.
fra'seri . . . . . FRASER BALSAM F.
—prostra'ta . . . PROSTRATE F.B.F.
gam'blei . . . . **A. pindrow brevifolia**
george'i . . . . GEORGES F.
gran'dis (*gordoniana*) . . . GRAND F.
holophyl'la . . . . . MANCHURIAN F.
homole'pis (*brachyphylla; tschonoskiana*) . . . . NIKKO F.
—scot'tae . . . . DWARF N.F.
—tomo'mi (*A. tomomi*). TOMOMI N.F.
—umbella'ta (*A. umbilicata*) . . . DIMPLECONE N.F.
×**insig'nis** (*nordmanniana × pinsapo*) . . . NORDISH F.
×**—beissneria'na** (*A. beissneriana* Mott., *not* Rehd. & Wils.) BEISSNER N.F.
₵KENT (*kentiana*) HV. A. insignis

ABIES insignis, continued
₵MASTERS (*mastersiana*)
₵SPECIOSA
kawaka'mi . . . . . KAWAKAMI FIR
korea'na . . . . KOREAN F.
lasiocar'pa (*subalpina*) lw . ALPINE F.
—arizo'nica (*A. arizonica*) CORKBARK F.
—compac'ta . . . . . DWARF A.F.
lowia'na . . . . **A. concolor l.**
magnif'ica lw . . . . RED F.; CALIFORNIA R.F. (Forestry)
—argen'tea . . . . SILVERLEAF R.F.
—glau'ca . . . . AZURE R.F.
—shasten'sis (*A. shastensis*) . . . SHASTA R.F.
maries'i . . . . MARIES F.
mo'mi . . . . **A. firma**
nephro'lepis . . . . . . KHINGAN F.
no'bilis A. Dietr. . . . . . . **A. alba**
no'bilis Lindl. . . . . . . **A. procera**
nordmannia'na . . . . NORDMANN F.
—au'rea . . . . GOLDEN N.F.
—tortifo'lia . . . . TWISTLEAF N.F.
numid'ica (*baborensis*) . . ALGERIAN F.
—glau'ca . . . . BLUE A.F.
pectina'ta . . . . **A. alba**
pi'cea Lindl., *not* Mill. . . . . **A. alba**
pi'cea Mill . . . . **Picea abies**
pind'row . . . . PINDROW F.
—brevifo'lia (*A. gamblei*) . . . SHORTLEAF P.F.
pinsa'po . . . . SPANISH F.
—glau'ca . . . . BLUE S.F.
—pen'dula . . . . . . WEEPING S.F.
pro'cera (*nobilis* Lindl., *not* A. Dietr.) . . . NOBLE F.

Prof. Rehder offers the new name, Abies procera, to replace Lindley's A. nobilis, which he has recently discovered to be a homonym and untenable.

—argen'tea . . . . . . SILVER N.F.
—glau'ca . . . . . . BLUELEAF N.F.
recurva'ta . . . . MIN F.
religio'sa . . . . SACRED F.
sachalinen'sis . . . . . SAKHALIN F.
—nemoren'sis (*A. wilsoni*) . . . WILSON S.F.
shasten'sis . . . . . . **A. magnifica s.**
sibir'ica . . . . SIBERIAN F.
spectab'ilis (*webbiana*) . HIMALAYAN F.
—brevifo'lia . . . SMOOTHBARK H.F.
squama'ta . . . . FLAKY F.
subalpi'na . . . . **A. lasiocarpa**
sutchuenen'sis . . . . SZECHWAN F.
tomo'mi . . . . **A. homolepis t.**
tschonoskia'na . . . . **A. homolepis**
umbella'ta . . . . . **A. homolepis u.**
umbilica'ta . . . . . **A. h. umbellata**
veitch'i . . . . VEITCH F.
—nikkoen'sis . . . LITTLECONE V.F.

ABIES, continued
veitch'i oliva'cea Olivecone Veitch Fir
venus'ta (*bracteata*) . Bristlecone F.
×**vilmori'ni** (*cephalonica* × *pinsapo*) Vilmorin F.
webbia'na . . . . . . **A. spectabilis**
wil'soni . **A. sachalinensis nemorensis**

Abiu . . . . **Pouteria caimito**

ABOB'RA . . . . . Cranberrygourd
tenuifo'lia (*viridiflora*) Cranberrygourd

ABRO'MA . . . . Abroma
angus'ta . . . . Cotton A.

ABRO'NIA |w . . . . . Sandverbena
al'ba . . . . White S.
fra'grans . . . . . . Snowball S.
latifo'lia (*arenaria*) . . . Yellow S.
marit'ima . . . . Seaside S.
pogonan'tha . . . . . . Bearded S.
umbella'ta . . . . Pink S.
—grandiflo'ra Hort. . . Showy P.S.
villo'sa . . . . Desert S.

ABROPHYL'LUM . . . . Richbush
or'nans . . . . Richbush

A'BRUS . . . . Rosarypea
laeviga'tus . . . . . . Licorice R.
praecato'rius . . . . . Jequirity R.
pulchel'lus . . . . Mauve R.

Absinth . . . . Wormwood, Common: **Artemisia absinthium**

ABU'MON . . . . . **AGAPANTHUS**

ABU'TILON |w . . . . . . Abutilon
avicen'nae . . . . . **A. theophrasti**
berlandier'i |w . . . . Berlandier A.
cris'pum |w . . . . Curly A.
dar'wini . . . . Darwin A.
gigan'teum . . . . Velvetleaf A.
hy'bridum
A gardener's name loosely and erroneously used for various hybrids.
inca'num |w . . . Indianmallow A.
in'dicum . . . . India A.
insig'ne . . . . Colombian A.
megapota'micum (*vexillarium*) Brazilian A.
mil'leri . . . . Miller A.
Possibly a hybrid.
mollis'simum . . . . . Softleaf A.
par'vulum |w
pic'tum . . . . Painted A.
A. striatum is often miscalled A. pictum.
×**pleniflo'rum** . . . . Yellowvein A.
sinen'se . . . . Chinese A.
sono'rae |w . . . . Sonora A.
specio'sum
stria'tum . . . . Redvein A.
A. striatum is often miscalled A. pictum.
×**—thomp'soni** . . . Thompson R.A.
theophras'ti (*avicennae*) |w Chingma A. (*Piemarker*)
thur'beri |w . . . . . . Thurber A.
veno'sum . . . . . . Orangebell A.
vexilla'rium . . . **A. megapotamicum**
vitifo'lium . . . . . . Grapeleaf A.
—al'bum . . . . White G.A.
₵Arthur Belsham. hv. Abutilon
₵Boule de Neige
₵California
₵Caprice
₵Coolidge
₵Driven Snow
₵Eclipse

ABUTILON, continued
₵Erectum
₵Fireball
₵Goldball
₵Goldenbell
₵Goldenfleece
₵Royal Scarlet
₵Santana
₵Savitz (*savitzi*)
₵Snowstorm
₵Souvenir de Bonn
₵Splendens
₵Vesuvius

Abutilon . . . . **Abutilon**
Berlandier A. . . . . . **A. berlandieri**
Brazilian A. . . . **A. megapotamicum**
Chinese A. . . . . **A. sinense**
Chingma A. . . . . . **A. theophrasti**
Colombian A. . . . . **A. insigne**
Curly A. . . . . **A. crispum**
Darwin A. . . . . **A. darwini**
Grapeleaf A. . . . . . . **A. vitifolium**
India A. . . . . **A. indicum**
Indianmallow A. . . . . **A. incanum**
Miller A. . . . . **A. milleri**
Orangebell A. . . . . . . **A. venosum**
Painted A. . . . . **A. pictum**
Redvein A. . . . . **A. striatum**
Softleaf A. . . . . . . **A. mollissimum**
Sonora A. . . . . **A. sonorae**
Thompson Redvein A. ×**A. striatum thompsoni**
Thurber A. . . . . **A. thurberi**
Velvetleaf A. . . . . . . **A. giganteum**
White Grapeleaf A. **A. vitifolium album**
Yellowvein A. . . ×**A. pleniflorum**

ACA'CIA |w . . . . Acacia
acanthoc'lada . . . . Windi A.
ac'cola
acina'cea (*latrobei*) . . . Latrobe A.
acumina'ta . . . . Raspberry A.
adanso'ni . . . . Adanson A.
adun'ca . . . . **A. crassiuscula**
aestiva'lis . . . . Summer A.
ala'ta . . . . Winged A.
—platyp'tera (*A. platyptera*) Broadwing A.
al'bicans
aneu'ra . . . . Mulga A.
angustis'sima |w . . . . . . Prairie A.
ara'bica . . . . Babul A.
arma'ta (*paradoxa; tristis; undulata*) Kangaroo-thorn A.
—pen'dula . . . . Weeping K.A.
as'pera . . . . Roughleaf A.
auriculaefor'mis . . . . . . Earleaf A.
baileya'na . Cootamundra-wattle A.
—purpu'rea . . . . . . Purpleleaf C.A.
betch'i . . . . Betch A.
binerva'ta . . . Twinvein-wattle A.
bonarien'sis
brachybot'rya . . . . . . Silverleaf A.
brachystach'ya . . . . Shortstem A.
buxifo'lia . . . . Boxleaf A.
cae'sia
calamifo'lia . . . . Broomwattle A.
ca'techu . . . . Catechu A.
cave'nia . . . . Cavenia A.
choriophyl'la
confu'sa
constric'ta |w . . . . Mescat A.
—paucispi'na
corda'ta
cornig'era . . . . Bullhorn A.
crassius'cula (*adunca*) . . Thicket A.
cultrifor'mis . . . . Knife A.

ACACIA, continued
cunea'ta . . . . Wedgeleaf Acacia
cuspida'ta
cyanophyl'la . . . . . . Blueleaf A.
cy'clops . . . . Cyclops A.
decip'iens . . . . Lagoon A.
deco'ra . . . . Graceful-wattle A.
decur'rens |w . . . . Greenwattle A.
—dealba'ta (*A. dealbata*) Silvergreen-wattle A.
—mol'lis (*A. mollissima*) Blackgreen-wattle A.
—norma'lis . . . . . . Queenwattle A.
₵Nabonnand. hv. A. decurrens
dentif'era . . . . Toothed A.
det'inens . . . . Trap A.
dietrichia'na . . . . Queensland A.
diffu'sa . . . . Pinbush A.
dinkla'gi . . . . Dinklag A.
dis'color . . . . Sunshine-wattle A.
dodonaeifo'lia . . . . . . Hopbush A.
doratox'ylon . . . . . . Currawong A.
drum'mondi . . . . Drummond A.
ebur'nea . . . . Ivory A.
ela'ta . . . . Cedar A.
elonga'ta . . . . Longpod A.
emoria'na . . . . Emory A.
estrophiola'ta
exten'sa . . . . Blackswan A.
falca'ta . . . . Burra A.
farnesia'na . . . . Sweet A.
fasciculif'era . . . . . . Fascicled A.
filicioi'des (*filicina*) . . . Fernleaf A.
floribun'da . . . . **A. longifolia f.**
giraf'fae . . . . Giraffe A.
glauces'cens . . . . Brigalow A.
gran'dis . . . . **A. pulchella g.**
gregg'i |w . . . . Catclaw A.
gummif'era . . . . Mogador A.
harpophyl'la . . . . . . Sickleleaf A.
hastula'ta
hebe'clada
heterophyl'la . . . . . . Mascarene A.
hispidis'sima . . . . . . **A. pulchella h.**
holoseri'cea . . . . Warroon A.
homalophyl'la . . . . Gidgee A.
hor'rida . . . . Allthorn A.
implex'a . . . . Lightwood A.
jones'i . . . . Jones A.
julibris'sin . . . . **Albizzia j.**
juncifo'lia (*pinifolia*) . Rushleaf A.
juniperi'na . . . . Juniper-wattle A.
kettlewell'i . . . . Kettlewell A.
ko'a . . . . Koa A.
lae'ta . . . . Gay A.
latifo'lia . . . . Broadleaf A.
latro'bei . . . . **A. acinacea**
lem'moni . . . . Lemmons A.
lepro'sa . . . . Scurfy A.
leptoc'lada . . . . Slimtwig A.
linea'ris . . . . Needle A.
linea'ta . . . . Lineleaf A.
linifo'lia . . . . Flaxleaf A.
—prom'inens (*A. prominens*) Greater F.A.
litakunen'sis . . . . Moshu A.
longifo'lia . . . . Sydney A.
—floribun'da (*A. floribunda*) Gossamer S.A.
—magnif'ica . . . . Greater S.A.
—mucrona'ta (*A. mucronata*) Narrow S.A.
—sopho'rae (*A. sophorae*)
lophan'tha . . . . **Albizzia l.**
luna'ta . . . . Crescentleaf A.
lute'a . . . . Lemon A.
macracan'tha . . . . . . Longspine A.
macracanthoi'des

ACACIA, continued
macraden'ia . . . . . Toney Acacia
macran'tha . . . . Steel A.
mai'deni . . . . Maidens A.
malifor'mis . . . . Apple A.
meiss'neri . . . . . Meissner A.
melanox'ylon . . . . Blackwood A.
microbo'trya . . . . . . Badjong A.
millifo'lia
mirab'ilis
mollis'sima . . . **A. decurrens mollis**
mucrona'ta . . . . . . **A. longifolia m.**
myrtifo'lia . . . . Myrtle A.
ne'mu . . . . . . **Albizzia julibrissin**
neriifo'lia . . . . Oleander A.
ni'gricans . . . . Sable A.
obli'qua . . . . Finger A.
obtusa'ta . . . . Bluntleaf A.
oswal'di . . . . Umbrella A.
oxyce'drus . . . . Savin A.
paradox'a . . . . **A. armata**
pen'dula . . . . Weeping Boree A.
penniner'vis . . . . Hickory A.
—falcifor'mis . . . Sickleleaf H.A.
pentaden'ia . . . . . . Fivegland A.
pinifo'lia . . . . **A. juncifolia**
platyp'tera . . . . **A. alata p.**
podalyriaefo'lia . . . . . . Pearl A.
pravis'sima . . . . Ovens A.
prom'inens . . . . . . **A. linifolia p.**
pruino'sa . . . . . . Frostystem A.
pubes'cens . . . . Hairywattle A.
pulchel'la . . . . Glory A.
—gran'dis (*A. grandis*) . Great G.A.
—hispidis'sima (*A. hispidissima*)
Prickly G.A.
pycnan'tha . . . . Goldenwattle A.
reticula'ta . . . . Netvein A.
retino'des . . . . Wirilda A.
—floribun'da . . . . . . Showy W.A.
—gracil'lima . . . . Slim W.A.
—triner'vius . . . Threenerve W.A.
ricea'na . . . . Rice A.
rich'i . . . . Rich A.

Possibly a synonym of A. confusa.

roemeria'na lw . . . . . Roemer A.
rus'tica
salici'na . . . . Willow A.
—way'ae . . . . Ways W.A.
salig'na . . . . . . Goldwreath A.
scorpioi'des . . . . . . Fiddleneck A.
sen'egal . . . . Gumarabic A.
sen'tis . . . . Bramble A.
sey'al . . . . Seyal A.
shreve'i . . . . Shreve A.
siculifor'mis . . . . . . Streamlet A.
sopho'rae . . . . . . **A. longifolia s.**
spadicig'era . . . . Oxhorn A.
spectab'ilis . . . . Mudgee A.
stenophyl'la . . . . Dalby A.
stenop'tera . . . . Narrowwing A.
suave'olens . . . . Honey A.
subula'ta . . . . Awlleaf A.
suffrutes'cens
su'ma . . . . . . Suma-catechu A.
tenuifo'lia . . . . Slimleaf A.
tortuo'sa . . . . Twisted A.
tris'tis; undula'ta . . . . . **A. armata**
undulifo'lia . . . . . . Wavyleaf A.
vernico'sa lw
verticilla'ta . . . . Star A.
vesti'ta
viscid'ula . . . . Waxy A.
willardia'na . . . . Willard A.
wright'i . . . . Wright A.
Bermont. hv. Acacia
Bon Accueil

ACACIA, continued
Briarcliff
Gaulois
Joffre
Nabonnand
Tournaire

Acacia . . . . **Acacia**
Adanson A. . . . . **A. adansoni**
Allthorn A. . . . . **A. horrida**
Apple A. . . . . **A. maliformis**
Awlleaf A. . . . . **A. subulata**
Babul A. . . . . **A. arabica**
Badjong A. . . . . **A. microbotrya**
Betch A. . . . . **A. betchi**
Blackgreen-wattle A.
A. decurrens mollis
Blackswan A. . . . . **A. extensa**
Blackwood A. . . . . . **A. melanoxylon**
Blueleaf A. . . . . . . **A. cyanophylla**
Bluntleaf A. . . . . **A. obtusata**
Boxleaf A. . . . . **A. buxifolia**
Bramble A. . . . . **A. sentis**
Brigalow A. . . . . . . **A. glaucescens**
Broadleaf A. . . . . **A. latifolia**
Broadwing A. . . . . **A. alata platyptera**
Broomwattle A. . . . . . . **A. calamifolia**
Bullhorn A. . . . . **A. cornigera**
Burra A. . . . . **A. falcata**
Catclaw A. . . . . **A. greggi**
Catechu A. . . . . **A. catechu**
Cavenia A. . . . . **A. cavenia**
Cedar A. . . . . **A. elata**
Cootamundra-wattle A. **A. baileyana**
Crescentleaf A. . . . . **A. lunata**
Currawong A. . . . . . . **A. doratoxylon**
Cyclops A. . . . . **A. cyclops**
Dalby A. . . . . **A. stenophylla**
Dinklag A. . . . . **A. dinklagi**
Drummond A. . . . . **A. drummondi**
Earleaf A. . . . . . **A. auriculaeformis**
Emory A. . . . . **A. emoriana**
Fascicled A. . . . . . . **A. fasciculifera**
Fernleaf A. . . . . **A. filicioides**
Fiddleneck A. . . . . **A. scorpioides**
Finger A. . . . . **A. obliqua**
Fivegland A. . . . . **A. pentadenia**
Flaxleaf A. . . . . **A. linifolia**
Frostystem A. . . . . **A. pruinosa**
Gay A. . . . . **A. laeta**
Gidgee A. . . . . **A. homalophylla**
Giraffe A. . . . . **A. giraffae**
Glory A. . . . . **A. pulchella**
Goldenwattle A. . . . . . . **A. pycnantha**
Goldwreath A. . . . . **A. saligna**
Gossamer Sydney A.
A. longifolia floribunda
Graceful-wattle A. . . . . . **A. decora**
Greater Flaxleaf A.
A. linifolia prominens
Greater Sydney A.
A. longifolia magnifica
Great Glory A. . **A. pulchella grandis**
Greenwattle A. . . . . **A. decurrens**
Gumarabic A. . . . . **A. senegal**
Hairywattle A. . . . . . . **A. pubescens**
Hickory A. . . . . **A. penninervis**
Honey A. . . . . **A. suaveolens**
Hopbush A. . . . . **A. dodonaeifolia**
Ivory A. . . . . **A. eburnea**
Jones A. . . . . **A. jonesi**
Juniper-wattle A. . . . **A. juniperina**
Kangaroo-thorn A. . . . . . **A. armata**
Kettlewell A. . . . . **A. kettlewelli**
Knife A. . . . . **A. cultriformis**
Koa A. . . . . **A. koa**
Lagoon A. . . . . **A. decipiens**
Latrobe A. . . . . **A. acinacea**

Acacia, continued
Lemmons A. . . . . **Acacia lemmoni**
Lemon A. . . . . **A. lutea**
Lightwood A. . . . . **A. implexa**
Lineleaf A. . . . . **A. lineata**
Longpod A. . . . . **A. elongata**
Longspine A. . . . . . . **A. macracantha**
Maidens A. . . . . **A. maideni**
Mascarene A. . . . . . . **A. heterophylla**
Meissner A. . . . . **A. meissneri**
Mescat A. . . . . **A. constricta**
Mogador A. . . . . **A. gummifera**
Moshu A. . . . . **A. litakunensis**
Mudgee A. . . . . **A. spectabilis**
Mulga A. . . . . **A. aneura**
Myrtle A. . . . . **A. myrtifolia**
Narrow Sydney A.
A. longifolia mucronata
Narrowwing A. . . . . **A. stenoptera**
Needle A. . . . . **A. linearis**
Netvein A. . . . . **A. reticulata**
Oleander A. . . . . **A. neriifolia**
Ovens A. . . . . **A. pravissima**
Oxhorn A. . . . . **A. spadicigera**
Pearl A. . . . . **A. podalyriaefolia**
Pinbush A. . . . . **A. diffusa**
Prairie A. . . . . **A. angustissima**
Prickly Glory A.
A. pulchella hispidissima
Purpleleaf Cootamundra-wattle A.
A. baileyana purpurea
Queensland A. . . . **A. dietrichiana**
Queenwattle A.
A. decurrens normalis
Raspberry A. . . . . **A. acuminata**
Rice A. . . . . **A. riceana**
Rich A. **A. richi**
Roemer A. . . . . **A. roemeriana**
Roughleaf A. . . . . **A. aspera**
Rushleaf A. . . . . **A. juncifolia**
Sable A. . . . . **A. nigricans**
Savin A. . . . . **A. oxycedrus**
Scurfy A. . . . . **A. leprosa**
Seyal A. **A. seyal**
Shortstem A. . . . . . . **A. brachystachya**
Showy Wirilda A.
A. retinodes floribunda
Shreve A. . . . . **A. shrevei**
Sickleleaf A. . . . . **A. harpophylla**
Sickleleaf Hickory A.
A. penninervis falciformis
Silvergreen-wattle A.
A. decurrens dealbata
Silverleaf A. . . . . **A. brachybotrya**
Slimleaf A. . . . . **A. tenuifolia**
Slimtwig A. . . . . **A. leptoclada**
Slim Wirilda A. **A. retinodes gracillima**
Star A. . . . . **A. verticillata**
Steel A. . . . . **A. macrantha**
Streamlet A. . . . . **A. siculiformis**
Suma-catechu A. . . . . **A. suma**
Summer A. . . . . **A. aestivalis**
Sunshine-wattle A. . . . . **A. discolor**
Sweet A. . . . . **A. farnesiana**
Sydney A. . . . . **A. longifolia**
Thicket A. . . . . **A. crassiuscula**
Threenerve Wirilda A.
A. retinodes trinervius
Toney A. . . . . **A. macradenia**
Toothed A. . . . . **A. dentifera**
Trap A. . . . . **A. detinens**
Twinvein-wattle A. . . . . **A. binervata**
Twisted A. . . . . **A. tortuosa**
Umbrella A. . . . . **A. oswaldi**
Warroon A. . . . . **A. holosericea**
Wavyleaf A. . . . . **A. undulifolia**
Waxy A. . . . . **A. viscidula**
Ways Willow A. . . **A. salicina wayae**

ACACIA, continued
WEDGELEAF A. . . . . . **Acacia cuneata**
WEEPING BOREE A. . . . **A. pendula**
WEEPING KANGAROO-THORN A.
A. armata p.
WILLARD A. . . . . . **A. willardiana**
WILLOW A. . . . . . . **A. salicina**
WINDI A. . . . . . **A. acanthoclada**
WINGED A. . . . . **A. alata**
WIRILDA A. . . . . . . **A. retinodes**
WRIGHT A. . . . . **A. wrighti**

ACAE'NA . . . . SHEEPBUR
argen'tea . . . . SILVER S.
buchan'ani . . . . . BUCHANAN S.
cylindrosta'chya . . . . CYLINDER S.
gla'bra . . . . SMOOTH S.
glau'ca Hort. . . . . GRAY S.
microphyl'la . . . . . . REDSPINE S.
—iner'mis . . . . NAKED R.S.
myriophyl'la . . . . . . SILKLEAF S.
novae-zealand'iae . NEWZEALAND S.
ovalifo'lia . . . . CHILEAN S.
ovi'na . . . . AUSTRALIAN S.
pinnatif'ida . . . . FEATHERLEAF S.
sanguisor'bae (*sarmentosa*). BURNET S.
seric'ea . . . . PATAGONIAN S.

ACALY'PHA ⊌ . . . . . COPPERLEAF
bal'fouri . . . . BALFOUR C.
califor'nica . . . . . CALIFORNIA C.
godseffia'na
LANCE (*heterophylla*) HV.
grac'ilens ⊌ . . . . . . SLENDER C.
his'pida (*sanderi*) . . . CHENILLE C.
RAMOSA HV.
WHITE CHENILLE (*alba*)
lindheim'eri . . . . . LINDHEIMER C.
neomexica'na ⊌ . . NEWMEXICO C.
ostryaefo'lia . . . HOPHORNBEAM C.
poiret'i (*indica; macrostachya*)
POIRETS C.
virgin'ica ⊌ . . . . VIRGINIA C.
wilkesia'na (*illustris; tricolor*)
PAINTED C.
₵BANANA (*musaica*) HV.
₵MACAFEE
₵MACROPHYLLA
₵MARGINATA
₵OBOVATA
₵TRIUMPHANS

ACAM'PE
See **ORCHID GENERA.**

ACAMPTOPAP'PUS . . GOLDENHEAD
shock'leyi . . . . . . SHOCKLEY G.
sphaerocep h'alus . . . . RAYLESS G.

ACANTHOCALYC'IUM
See **CACTUS GENERA.**

ACANTHOCE'REUS . ACANTHOCEREUS
See **CACTUS GENERA.**

ACANTHOLI'MON . PRICKLYTHRIFT
androsa'ceum
gluma'ceum . . . . COMB P.
lepturoi'des
venus'tum . . . . . LARGEFLOWER P.

ACANTHOPAN'AX . ACANTHOPANAX
acerifo'lius **Kalopanax pictus magnificus**
aculea'tus . . . . **A. trifoliatus**
divarica'tus
gir'aldi . . . . GIRALD A.
—iner'mis . . . . . THORNLESS G.A.
hen'ryi . . . . HENRY A.
innov'ans
lasiogy'ne
leucorrhi'zus
—fulves'cens

ACANTHOPANAX, continued
leucorrhi'zus scaber'ulus
pentaphyl'lus . . . . **A. sieboldianus**
ricinifo'lius . . . **Kalopanax pictus**
—maximowicz'i . . . . **K. pictus m.**
sciadophylloi'des
sentico'sus
—iner'mis
septemlo'bus . . . **Kalopanax pictus**
—maximowicz'i . . . . . **K. pictus m.**
sessiliflo'rus (*Panax sessiliflorum*)
—par'viceps
setchuenen'sis
sieboldia'nus (*pentaphyllus; Aralia pentaphylla* Sieb. & Zucc., *not* Thunb.)
—variega'tus
si'moni
spino'sus (*Aralia pentaphylla* Thunb.)
Misapplied to A. sieboldianus.
terna'tus
trifolia'tus (*aculeatus*)

ACANTHOPHIP'PIUM
See **ORCHID GENERA.**

ACANTHOPHOE'NIX . . SPINEPALM
See **PALM GENERA.**

ACANTHOPHYL'LUM . . SPINEPINK
pun'gens (*spinosum*). ROCKGARDEN S.
The name Dianthus spinosus is frequently misapplied to this plant.

ACANTHORHIP'SALIS
See **CACTUS GENERA.**

ACANTHORRHI'ZA **CRYOSOPHILA**
See **PALM GENERA.**

ACANTHOSA'BAL . . **PAUROTIS**
See **PALM GENERA.**

ACANTHOSPER'MUM . . . STARBUR
austra'le (*brasilum*) . . PARAGUAY S.

ACAN'THUS . . . . . . ACANTHUS
arbo'reus . . . . TREE A.
mol'lis . . . . SOFT A.
—latifo'lius (*A. latifolius; A. lusitanicus*) . . . . . BROADLEAF S.A.
monta'nus
per'ringi
spino'sus . . . . SPINY A.

ACAPULCOGRASS . . **Opizia stolonifera**

A'CER (*NEGUNDO; RULAC; SACCHARODENDRON*) ⊌ . MAPLE
acumina'tum
argu'tum
arizo'nicum . . . . . . **A. negundo a.**
barbiner've
∞ **bornmuel'leri** (*campestre × monspessulanum*) . . ∞ BORNMUELLER M.
∞ **bosc'i** (*pennsylvanicum × tataricum*)
∞ BOSC M.
brachyp'terum . **A. grandidentatum b.**
buergeria'num (*trifidum*). TRIDENT M.
—triner've
cae'sium
califor'nicum . . . . . **A. negundo c.**
campbell'i . . . . . . CAMPBELL M.
campes'tre . . . . HEDGE M.
—austri'acum . . . . AUSTRIAN H.M.
—hebecar'pum . . . . . WILD H.M.
—leiocar'pum . . SMOOTHKEY H.M.
—taur'icum . . . . . TAURUS H.M.
₵DUSTY (*pulverulentum*) HV. A. campestre
₵POSTEL (*postelense*)
₵SCHWERIN (*schwerini*)
₵WHITESPOT (*albovariegatum*)

ACER, continued
capil'lipes
cappado'cicum (*colchicum; laetum*)
COLISEUM MAPLE
—au'reum . . . . . . GOLDEN C.M.
—ru'brum (*A. colchicum r.; A. laetum horticola*) . . . . RED C.M.
—sin'icum
—tricauda'tum
—tri'color (*A. laetum t.*) TRICOLOR C.M.
carpinifo'lium . . . . HORNBEAM M.
catalpifo'lium . . . . . CATALPA M.
cauda'tum
—multiserra'tum
—ukurunduen'se
cineras'cens
circina'tum ⊌ . . . . VINE M.
cissifo'lium (*Negundo c.*)
col'chicum . . . . . **A. cappadocicum**
—ru'brum . . . . . **A. cappadocicum r.**
∞ **coria'ceum** (*monspessulanum × pseudoplatanus; creticum* Schmidt, *not* L.; *parvifolium; polymorphum*)
∞ THICKLEAF M.
crataegifo'lium . . . HAWTHORN M.
—veitch'i
cre'ticum L. . . . . . . **A. orientale**
cre'ticum Schmidt, *not* L.
∞ **A. coriaceum**
dasycar'pum . . . . **A. saccharinum**
dav'idi . . . . DAVID M.
—for'resti . . . . **A. forresti**
diabol'icum . . . . DEVIL M.
—purpuras'cens . . . . . RED D.M.
∞ **dieck'i** (*lobeli × platanoides; A. platanoides integrilobum*)
dis'tylum
doug'lasi . . . . **A. glabrum d.**
∞ **duret'ti** (*monspessulanum × opalus*)
∞ DURETT M.
This appears to be a clon.
erian'thum
eriocar'pum . . . . **A. saccharinum**
far'gesi . . . . FARGES M.
flabella'tum
florida'num . . . . . . FLORIDA M.
—vil'lipes . . . . HAIRY F.M.
for'resti (*A. davidi f.*) . FORRESTS M.
franchet'i . . . . . . FRANCHET M.
fulves'cens
ginna'la (*A. tataricum aidzuense*)
AMUR M.
—semeno'vi
gla'brum . . . ROCKYMOUNTAIN M.
—doug'lasi (*A. douglasi*)
DOUGLAS R.M.
—rhodocar'pum
—triparti'tum (*A. g. trisectum*)
THREELEAF R.M.
grandidenta'tum . . . BIGTOOTH M
—brachyp'terum (*A. brachypterum*)
SOUTHWESTERN B.M.
gris'eum . . . . . . PAPERBARK M.
gros'seri . . . . GROSSERS M.
—hers'i (*A. hersi*)
heldreich'i . . . . BALKAN M.
—purpura'tum . . . . PURPLE B.M.
hen'ryi . . . . HENRY M.
hook'eri . . . . HOOKER M.
× **hy'bridum** (*?monspessulanum × pseudoplatanus*)
This appears to be a clon. Perhaps synonymous with ∞ A. coriaceum.
hyrca'num (*A. italum h.; A. opulus h.; tauricum*)
insig'ne . . **A. velutinum glabrescens**
This name is also sometimes misapplied to A. trautvetteri.

ACER, continued
insig'ne percken'se **A. velutinum vanvolxemi**
—vanvolx'emi . . . **A. velutinum v.**
—veluti'num . . . . . **A. velutinum**
inte'rius . . . . **A. negundo i.**
japon'icum . . . Fullmoon Maple
₵Bigmoon (*macrophyllum*) hv.
₵Fernleaf (*aconitifolium; filicifolium; parsonsi*)
₵Goldenmoon (*aureum*)
₵Littleleaf (*microphyllum*)
lae'tum . . . . . . **A. cappadocicum**
—hortic'ola . . . . . **A. c. rubrum**
—tri'color . . . . . . **A. c. tricolor**
laeviga'tum
laxiflo'rum
—longilo'bum
leucoder'me . . . . . . Chalk M.
lo'beli . . . . Lobel M.
lon'gipes (*longifolium*)
macrophyl'lum |w . . . . Bigleaf M.
—kim'ballae . . . . . Kimball B.M.
mandshur'icum . . Manchurian M.
maximowicz'i . . . Maximowicz M.
mayr'i . . . . Mayrs M.
micran'thum . . . . . Pagoda M.
microphyl'lum . **A. rubrum trilobum**
miya'bei . . . . Miyabe M.
mo'no (*A. pictum m.; A. p. parviflorum*) Mono M.
—conniv'ens
—dissec'tum . . . . Cutleaf M.M.
—marmora'tum (*A. pictum* Thunb. 1784, *not* 1783) . . . Painted M.M.
—tricus'pis (*A. tenellum*)
monspessula'num . . Montpelier M.
—iber'icum
negun'do(*Negundo aceroides; N. fraxinifolium; Rulac negundo*) |w Boxelder
—arizo'nicum (*A. arizonicum*) Arizona B.
—califor'nicum (*A. californicum*) California B.
—inte'rius (*A. interius*) . . Inland B.
—texa'num . . . . Texas B.
—viola'ceum . . . . Violet B.
₵Curlyleaf (*crispum*) hv. A. negundo
₵Goldedge (*aureomarginatum*)
₵Goldspot (*aureovariegatum*)
₵New California (*pseudo-californicum*)
₵Silverleaf (*variegatum*)
₵Yellowleaf (*auratum; odessanum*)
ni'grum (*A. saccharum n.*). Black M.
—pal'meri . . . . . . Palmer B.M.
nikoen'se . . . . Nikko M.
nippon'icum (*parviflorum*)
oblon'gum
—con'color
oliveria'num . . . . . . Oliver M.
o'palus
—hyrca'num . . . . . **A. hyrcanum**
—obtusa'tum
—tomento'sum
orienta'le (*creticum* L., *not* Schmidt) Oriental M.
palma'tum (*A. polymorphum p.*) Japanese M.
—heptalo'bum (*A. p. septemlobum* in part) . . . . . Sevenlobe J.M.
₵Bloodleaf (*atropurpureum; A. p. nigrum*) hv. A. palmatum
₵Bloodvein (*atrolineare*)
₵Crested (*crispum*)
Fingerlobe (*linearilobum; A. scolopendrifolium*)

ACER palmatum, continued
₵Greennet (*reticulatum*)
₵Pinkedge (*roseomarginatum*)
₵Red (*rubrum*)
₵Scarlet (*sanguineum*)
₵Spiderleaf (*ornatum*)
₵Stalkless (*sessilifolium*)
₵Sunrise (*aureum*)
₵Threadleaf (*dissectum; multifidum; palmatifidum*)
₵Versicolor
parviflo'rum . . . . . **A. nipponicum**
parvifo'lium . . . . . ∞**A. coriaceum**
pensylvan'icum (*striatum*) |w Striped Maple
—erythrocla'dum
pic'tum Thunb. 1874, *not* 1783 **A. mono marmoratum**
—mo'no . . . . **A. mono**
—parviflo'rum . . . . . . **A. mono**
pilo'sum
platanoi'des . . . . . . Norway M.
—integrilo'bum . . . . . ∞**A. diecki**
₵*Bentleaf.* Eagle Claw. hv. A. platanoides
₵Bloodleaf (*reitenbachi; rubrum*)
₵Column (*columnare*)
₵Crimped (*cucullatum*)
₵Cutleaf (*dissectum; palmatifidum*)
₵Dwarf (*nanum*)
₵Eagle Claw (*laciniatum. Bentleaf*)
₵Erect (*erectum*)
₵Geneva
₵Globe (*globosum*)
₵Lorberg (*lorbergi; palmatum*)
₵Schwedler (*schwedleri*)
₵Spaeth Pinkleaf (*spaethi*)
₵Stoll (*stolli*)
₵Variegated (*variegatum*)
₵Yellowrim (*aureomarginatum*)
polymor'phum . . . . ∞**A. coriaceum**
—palma'tum . . . . . **A. palmatum**
pseudoplat'anus . . . Planetree M. (*Sycamore M.*)
—euchlo'rum . . . . Bigkey P.M.
—tomento'sum . . . . Woolly P.M.
₵Brilliant (*brilliantissimum*) hv. A. pseudoplatanus
₵Corstorphin (*corstorphinense*)
₵Goldfleck (*aureovariegatum; flavovariegatum*)
₵Leopold (*leopoldi*)
₵Nizet (*nizeti*)
₵Purpleleaf (*atropurpureum; purpurascens; purpureum*)
₵Scarletfruit (*erythrocarpum*)
₵Tricolor
₵Variegated (*albovariegatum; variegatum*)
₵Veiny (*nervosum*)
₵Yellow (*worleei*)
pseudo-sieboldia'num Purplebloom M.
∞**pu'sillum** (*monspessulanum* × *tataricum*)
×**ramo'sum** (*campestre* × ? *pseudoplatanus*)
This appears to be a clon.
robus'tum
×**rotundilo'bum** (*opalus obtusatum* × *pseudoplatanus*)
This appears to be a clon.
ru'brum |w . . . . Red M.
—drum'mondi . . Drummond R.M.
—pallidiflo'rum . Paleflower R.M.
—trilo'bum (*A. microphyllum; A. r. tridens; A. semiorbiculatum; A. tridens*) . . . . Trident R.M.

ACER rubrum, continued
₵Column (*columnare*) hv. A. rubrum
₵Dwarf (*globosum*)
₵Schlesinger (*schlesingeri*)
Woolly (*fulgens; tomentosum*)
rufiner've . . . . . Redvein Maple
₵Whitedot (*albo-limbatum*) hv.
sacchari'num (*dasycarpum; eriocarpum*) |w . . . . Silver M.
₵Cutleaf (*laciniatum*) hv.
₵Pyramidal (*pyramidale*)
₵Skinners (*skinneri; A. skinneri*)
₵Trefoil (*tripartitum*)
₵Weeping (*pendulum*)
₵Wier (*wieri*)
₵Yellow Bronze (*lutescens*)
sac'charum |w . . . . Sugar M.
—ni'grum . . . . **A. nigrum**
—ru'geli . . . . Rugel S.M.
—schneck'i . . . . . Schneck S.M.
₵Blue (*glaucum*) hv. A. saccharum
₵Conic (*conicum*)
₵Pyramidal (*pyramidale*)
₵Sentry (*monumentale*)
schwer'ini . . . . . . Schwerin M.
semiorbicula'tum . **A. rubrum trilobum**
seric'eum
Possibly a hybrid, with A. pseudoplatanus as one of the parents.
sieboldia'num . . . . . Siebold M.
—microphyl'lum . . Littleleaf S.M.
sikkimen'se . . . . . . Sikkim M.
sinen'se . . . . Chinese M.
—con'color
spica'tum |w . . . . . Mountain M.
stria'tum . . . . **A. pensylvanicum**
syri'acum . . . . Syrian M.
taronen'se . . . . Taron M.
tatar'icum . . . . . . Tatarian M.
—aidzuen'se . . . . **A. ginnala**
taur'icum . . . . **A. hyrcanum**
tegmento'sum . . Manchustripe M.
tenel'lum . . . **A. mono tricuspis**
tetrame'rum
—betulifo'lium
—lobula'tum
—tiliifo'lium
trautvet'teri . . . . . . Redbud M.
tri'dens . . . . . **A. rubrum trilobum**
trif'idum . . . . . . **A. buergerianum**
triflo'rum . . . . Threeflower M.
trunca'tum . . . . Purpleblow M.
tschon'oski . . . . . Tschonoski M.
vanvolx'emi . . . . . **A. velutinum v.**
veitch'i . . . . Veitch M.
veluti'num (*A. insigne v.*). Velvet M.
—glabres'cens (*A. insigne*) Persian V.M.
—vanvolx'emi (*A. insigne perckense; A. insigne v.; A. vanvolxemi*) Vanvolxem V.M.
₵Persian. hv. A. velutinum
₵Wolfs (*insigne wolfi; v. wolfi*)
villo'sum
wil'soni . . . . Wilson M.

ACERAN'THUS . . . . . . Maplewort
di'phyllus (*Epimedium diphyllum*) Doubleleaf M.

ACERA'TES . . . . Acerates
pu'mila
viridiflo'ra . . . . Green A.

ACHA'NIA . . . . . **MALVAVISCUS**

ACHILLE'A |w . . . . Yarrow
abrotanoi'des
aegypti'aca (*tourneforti*) . Egyptian Y.

ACHILLEA, continued
ageratifo'lia . . . . Greek Yarrow
—**ai'zoon** (*Anthemis aizoon*). Aizoon Y.
agera'tum . . . . Sweet Y.
alpic'ola . . . . **A. lanulosa a.**
alpi'na . . . . Alpine Y.
argen'tea . . . . Silver Y.
atra'ta
au'rea . . . . **A. tomentosa a.**
cartilagi'nea
chrysoco'ma
claven'nae . . . . Clavenn Y.
clypeola'ta
filipenduli'na (*eupatorium*) Fernleaf Y.
fraas'i
×**fronmuel'leri** (*abrotanoides* × *moschata*) Fronmueller Y.
Apparently a clon.
herbaro'ta
holoseric'ea
impa'tiens
lanulo'sa (*A. millefolium l.*) |w Western Y.
—**alpic'ola** (*A. alpicola; A. subalpina*) Subalpine Y.
ligus'tica . . . . Lovage Y.
macedo'nica . . . . Macedonian Y.
mag'na . . . . Brownedge Y.
millefo'lium |w . . . . . Common Y.
—*lanulo'sa* . . . . . . **A. lanulosa**
—**purpu'reum** . . . . . Purple C.Y.
—**rose'um** . . . . Pink C.Y.
—**ru'brum** . . . . Red C.Y.
Cerise Queen. hv. A. millefolium
mongo'lica . . . . **A. sibirica**
moscha'ta . . . . Musk Y.
na'na . . . . Dwarf Y.
odora'ta (*nobilis*)
pal'meri . . . . Palmer Y.
ptar'mica . . . . Sneezewort Y.
Boule de Neige (*palmeri*) hv.
Globe (*florepleno*)
Pearl
Perry White
rupes'tris . . . . Italian Y.
santolinoi'des . . . . Santolin Y.
ser'bica . . . . Serbian Y.
seta'cea
sibir'ica (*mongolica*) . . . Siberian Y.
subalpi'na| . . . . **A. lanulosa alpicola**
tomento'sa . . . . . . Woolly Y.
—**au'rea** (*A. aurea*) . Yellow W.Y.
King Edward. hv. A. tomentosa
tournefor'ti . . . . . . **A. aegyptiaca**
umbella'ta . . . . Umbel Y.
wilczekia'na

ACHIM'ENES . . . . . Achimenes
grandiflo'ra . . . . Bigpurple A.
longiflo'ra (*haageana*) . . Trumpet A.
pa'tens . . . . Violet A.
₵Magnificent (*magnifica*) hv. Achimenes
₵Swainson (*swainsoni*)

ACH'LYS . . . . . . Vanillaleaf
triphyl'la . . . . . . Deerfoot V.

ACH'RAS
zapo'ta (*sapota; Sapota achras; S. zapotilla*) . . . . Sapodilla
Unfortunately this name is sometimes confused with Sapote (Calocarpum sapota).

ACHYRACHAE'NA
mol'lis . . . . Blowwives

ACHYRAN'THES
Plants of this genus have been much confused with Alternanthera and Iresine.
abyssin'ica

ACHYRANTHES, continued
acumina'ta . . . . . . **Iresine lindeni**
austra'lis
herbst'i . . . . **Iresine h.**
verschaffelt'i . . . . **Iresine herbsti**

ACHYRO'DES . . . . **LAMARCKIA**
See **GRASS GENERA.**

ACIDAN'THERA . . . . . Gladixia
bi'color . . . . Darkeye G.
muriel'ae Hort. . . **Gladiolus m.** Hort.

ACINE'TA
See **ORCHID GENERA.**

ACIPHYL'LA
colen'soi

ACK'AMA
rosaefo'lia

ACME'NA
smith'i (*Eugenia s.; Syzygium s.*) Lillipillitree

AC'MISPON . . . . **LOTUS**

ACNI'DA |w . . . . Waterhemp
alabamen'sis |w . . . Gulfcoast W.
altis'sima (*tuberculata*) |w . Tall W.
cannabi'na |w . . . . . Tidemarsh W.
cuspida'ta (*australis*) |w
florida'na |w . . . . . . Florida W.
tamarisci'na |w

ACNIS'TUS . . . . . Wildtobacco
arbores'cens . . . . Tree W.
parviflo'rus . . . Littleflower W.

ACOELORRA'PHE
BRAHEA; PAUROTIS; SERENOA
See **PALM GENERA.**

ACOKAN'THERA (*TOXICOPHLOEA*) Bushmanspoison
abyssin'ica . . . . . Abyssinian B.
ouaba'io . . . . Ouabaio B.
spectab'ilis . . . Wintersweet B.
venena'ta . . . . True B.

Acomas'tylis turbina'ta **Geum turbinatum**

ACONI'TUM . . . . . . Monkshood
acu'tum . . . . **A. napellus**
antho'ra (*pyrenaicum*) . Pyrenees M.
autumna'le . . . . . . Autumn M.
ba'keri . . . . Baker M.
bi'color
This name is sometimes used by gardeners erroneously for Bicolor Aconite, hort. var. of A. napellus, and for Azure Monkshood, A. fischeri.

camma'rum (*exaltatum*) Hungarian M.
chinen'se . . . . Chinese M.
columbia'num (*californicum*) Columbia M.
corda'tum
fer'ox
fisch'eri (*sinense*) . . . . Azure M.
—**wil'soni** (*wilsoni*) . . Wilson A.M.
gigan'teum . . . . **A. napellus**
glaber'rimum . . . . . Smooth M.
hel'leri . . . . Heller M.
how'elli . . . . Howell M.
japon'icum . . . . . . Japanese M.
kusnez'offi . . . . . . Kusnezoff M.
leiberg'i . . . . Leiberg M.
lutes'cens . . . . Yellow M.
lycocto'num (*septentrionale; vulparia*) Wolfbane M.
napel'lus (*acutum; giganteum; pyramidale; wildenowi*) . . . Aconite M.

ACONITUM, continued
napel'lus al'bum White Aconite Monkshood
—**prae'cox** . . . . Early A.M.
₵Bicolor. hv. A. napellus
₵Fleshcolor (*carneum*)
₵Sparks
orienta'le . . . . . . Caucasian M.
panicula'tum . . . . . Panicled M.
pulchel'lum
pyramida'le . . . . **A. napellus**
pyrena'icum . . . . **A. anthora**
septentriona'le . . . . **A. lycoctonum**
sinen'se . . . . **A. fischeri**
thyra'icum
uncina'tum . . . . Clambering M.
variega'tum . . . Manchurian M.
₵Arbor (*volubilis latisectum*) hv.
vilmorinia'num . . . . Vilmorin M.
vulpa'ria . . . . **A. lycoctonum**
wildenow'i . . . . **A. napellus**
wil'soni . . . . **A. fischeri w.**

ACONOG'ONUM . . **POLYGONUM**

Acorn
Acorns are the characteristic fruits of Oaks (Quercus spp.). They are important sources of food (mast) for wildlife and swine. Those of a few species are edible nuts for human beings. See **NUT GROUP COMMON NAMES.**

AC'ORUS |w . . . . . Sweetflag
cal'amus |w . . . Drug S. (*Calamus*)
Yellowstripe (*variegatus*) hv.
gramin'eus (*japonicus*) . Japanese S.
—**pusil'lus**
Whitestripe (*variegatus*) hv. A. gramineus

ACRIS'TA . . . . **EUTERPE**
See **PALM GENERA.**

ACROCAR'PUS
fraxinifo'lius

ACROCLIN'IUM . . **HELIPTERUM**

ACROCO'MIA . . . . . Acrocomia
See **PALM GENERA.**

AC'RODON
MESEMBRYANTHEMUM
See **SUCCULENTS.**

ACROLA'SIA . . . . **MENTZELIA**
au'rea . . . . **M. lindleyi**

ACRONY'CHIA . . . . . Acronychia
bau'eri . . . . Bauer A.

ACRO'PERA . . . . . **GONGORA**
See **ORCHID GENERA.**

ACTAE'A . . . . Baneberry
al'ba (*pachypoda; A. spicata a.*) White B.
argu'ta (*A. spicata a.*) . . Western B.
eburne'a . . . . Ivory B.
japon'ica . . . . **Cimicifuga j.**
ru'bra (*A. spicata r.*) . . . . Red B.
spica'ta . . . . Black B.
—*al'ba* . . . . **A. alba**
—*argu'ta* . . . . **A. arguta**
—*ru'bra* . . . . **A. rubra**
viridiflo'ra . . . . Green B.

ACTINE'A (*ACTINELLA* Auth., *not* Pers.; *HYMENOXYS; MACDOUGALIA; PICRADENIA; RYDBERGIA; TETRANEURIS*) |w . . . . . . Actinea
acau'lis (*Actinella a.; Tetraneuris a.*) Stemless A.

ACTINEA, continued
acau'lis arizo'nica (*Tetraneuris arizonica*) ARIZONA STEMLESS ACTINEA
—lanig'era (*Tetraneuris lanata; T. lanigera*) . . . . . . WOOLLY S.A.
—septentriona'lis (*Tetraneuris s.*) NORTHERN S.A.
—sim'plex (*A. simplex; Tetraneuris s.*) SAGEBRUSH S.A.
bigelo'vi (*Macdougalia b.*). BIGELOW A.
brandeg'ei (*Rydbergia b.*) BRANDEGEE A.
fastigia'ta (*Tetraneuris stenophylla*)
grandiflo'ra (*Rydbergia g.*) GRAYLOCKS A.
herba'cea (*Tetraneuris h.*). ONTARIO A.
linearifo'lia (*Tetraneuris l.*) FINELEAF A.
odora'ta (*Hymenoxys cockerelli; H. multiflora; H. odorata*) BITTERWEED A.
richardso'ni (*Hymenoxys floribunda; H. richardsoni; Picradenia f.*) PINGUE A. (*Colorado Rubberweed*)
scapo'sa (*Tetraneuris s.*)
—linea'ris (*Tetraneuris l.*)
sim'plex . . . . **A. acaulis s.**

ACTINEA . . . . **Actinea**
ARIZONA STEMLESS A. **A. acaulis arizonica**
BIGELOW A. . . . . **A. bigelovi**
BITTERWEED A. . . . . . **A. odorata**
BRANDEGEE A. . . . . . **A. brandegei**
FINELEAF A. . . . . . . **A. linearifolia**
GRAYLOCKS A. . . . . . **A. grandiflora**
NORTHERN STEMLESS A. **A. acaulis septentrionalis**
ONTARIO A. . . . . . . **A. herbacea**
PINGUE A. . . . . . . **A. richardsoni**
SAGEBRUSH STEMLESS A. **A. acaulis simplex**
STEMLESS A. . . . . **A. acaulis**
WOOLLY S. A. . . . . . **A. a. lanigera**

ACTINEL'LA } . . . . . **ACTINEA**

ACTINID'IA . . . . ACTINIDIA
argu'ta . . . BOWER A. (*Tara Vine*)
—cordifo'lia
callo'sa
—hen'ryi
chinen'sis . . . . YANGTAO A.
coria'cea
×**fair'childi** . . . . . . FAIRCHILD A.
gir'aldi . . . . GIRALD A.
kolomik'ta . . . . . . KOLOMIKTA A.
lanceola'ta
melanan'dra
poly'gama . . . . . . SILVERVINE A.
purpu'rea . . . . PURPLE A.
rubricau'lis
tetrame'ra
veno'sa

ACTINOLE'PIS . **BAERIA; EATONELLA; ERIOPHYLLUM**
corona'ria . . . . **B. aristata**

ACTINOMER'IS
squarro'sa (*alternifolia*)

ACTINOPHLOE'US (*ROMANOVIA*) CLUSTERPALM
See **PALM GENERA.**

ACTINORHY'TIS
See **PALM GENERA.**

ACTINOSTRO'BUS
pyramida'lis (*Callitris actinostrobus*)

ACTINO'TUS
helian'thi

AC'UAN . . . . . . **DESMANTHUS**
james'i . . . . **D. cooleyi**

A'DA
See **ORCHID GENERA.**

ADANSO'NIA
digita'ta . . . . BAOBAB

ADDERSTONGUE . . . . . **Ophioglossum**
COMMON A. . . . . . . **O. vulgatum**
ENGELMANN A. . . . **O. engelmanni**

Adderstongue . FAWNLILY: **Erythronium**

ADE'LIA . . . . ADELIA
va'seyi (*Euphorbia v.; Ricinella v.*) VASEY A.

ADE'LIA Michx., *not* L.. **FORESTIERA**
parvifo'lia . . . . . **F. neomexicana**

ADELOCA'RYUM
coelesti'num

ADENAN'THERA . . . . . BEADTREE
microsper'ma . . . . . LADYCOOT B.
pavoni'na . . . . SANDAL B.

ADENOCAL'YMNA
allia'ceum (*Bignonia alliacea*)

ADENOCAR'PUS . . . . . FLATPOD
anagy'rus (*frankenioides*)
complica'tus
decor'ticans
foliolo'sus . . . . CANARYISLANDS F.
visco'sus . . . . STICKY F.

ADENOCAU'LON . . . ADENOCAULON
bi'color . . . . AMERICAN A.

ADENOPH'ORA . . . . . . LADYBELL
bulleya'na . . . . BULLEYS L.
denticula'ta
diplodon'ta
latifo'lia . . . . BROADLEAF L.
lilifo'lia . . . . LILYLEAF L.
marsupiiflo'ra
nikoen'sis . . . . NIKKO L.
orna'ta . . . . LOVELY L.
polymor'pha . . . . FICKLE L.
potani'ni . . . . BUSH L.
remotiflo'ra
stric'ta
stylo'sa
takeda'i
verticilla'ta

ADENORO'PIUM . . . . **JATROPHA**

ADENOSTE'GIA. **CORDYLANTHUS**

ADENOS'TOMA . . . . . . CHAMISE
fascicula'tum . . . GREASEWOOD C.
sparsifo'lium . . . . . REDSHANK C.

ADES'MIA . . . . ADESMIA
balsa'mica . . . . BALSAM A.
boronioi'des . . MAGELLANSTRAITS A.
glutino'sa . . . . GUMMY A.

ADHATO'DA
cydoniaefo'lia . BRAZIL BOWERPLANT
va'sica (*Justicia v.*) . . MALABARNUT

ADIAN'TUM . . . . . MAIDENHAIR
See **FERN GENERA.**

ADI'NA . . . . ADINA
cordifo'lia . . . . . . HEARTLEAF A.

Adip'era laeviga'ta . . . . . **Cassia l.**

ADLU'MIA . . . . . MOUNTAINFRINGE
fungo'sa (*cirrhosa*) MOUNTAINFRINGE

Adoden'dron chamaecis'tus **Rhodothamnus c.**

ADOL'PHIA . . . . ADOLPHIA
califor'nica . . . . . CALIFORNIA A.
infes'ta . . . . TEXAS A.

ADONID'IA . . . . ADONIDIA
See **PALM GENERA.**

ADO'NIS . . . . ADONIS
aestiva'lis . . . . SUMMER A.
alep'pica . . . . ALEPPO A.
amuren'sis . . . . AMUR A.
an'nua (*autumnalis*) PHEASANTS-EYE A.
flam'mea . . . . FLAME A.
pyrena'ica . . . . PYRENEES A.
verna'lis . . . . SPRING A.

ADOX'A . . . . MUSKROOT
moschatelli'na . . . . . MUSKROOT

ADROMIS'CHUS . . . ADROMISCHUS
See **SUCCULENTS.**

AECH'MEA
bar'leei
bractea'ta
calycula'ta
coeles'tis
fascia'ta (*Billbergia rhodocyanea*)
ful'gens
—dis'color
magdale'nae (*Ananas m.*) . PITAFLOJA
—dis'color
mariae-regi'nae
mexica'na
minia'ta
nudicau'lis
ort'giesi
polysta'chya
weilbach'ia

AE'GILOPS . . . . GOATGRASS
See **GRASS GENERA.**

AE'GLE . . . . BAELFRUIT
mar'melos . . . . BAELFRUIT

AEGLOP'SIS . . . AEGLOPSIS (*Dwarf Powderflaskfruit*)
chevalier'i . . . . . . IVORYCOAST A.
eggling'i . . . . UGANDA A.

AEGOPO'DIUM . . . . . GOUTWEED
podogra'ria . . . . BISHOPS G.
—variega'tum Hort. SILVEREDGE B.G.

AEGOPO'GON
See **GRASS GENERA.**

AELURO'PUS
See **GRASS GENERA.**

AEO'NIUM . . . . AEONIUM
See **SUCCULENTS.**

AE'RIA . . . . **GAUSSIA**
See **PALM GENERA.**

AERI'DES
See **ORCHID GENERA.**

Hort. var.; HV. = horticultural variety (or varieties); sp. = species (singular); spp. = species (plural).
₵ = clon; × (as a prefix) = hybrid; × (between scientific plant names) = crossed by; ∞ = polybrid; W = plant useful to wildlife.
See Glossary for definitions of clon, hybrid, and polybrid.

AESCHYNAN'THUS (*TRICHOSPORUM*) . . . . . . BASKETVINE

Aeschynanthus is recommended to be conserved by the International Committee on Botanical Nomenclature.

boschia'nus (*Trichosporum boschianum*) SUMATRA B.
grandiflo'rus (*Trichosporum grandiflorum*) . . . . LOBECUP B.
lobbia'nus (*Trichosporum lobbianum*) LOBBS B.
marmora'tus (*zebrinus; Trichosporum marmoratum*) . . . . MARBLED B.
pul'cher (*Trichosporum pulchrum*) SCARLET B.

AESCHYNO'MENE ⌊w . . JOINTVETCH
america'na . . . . . AMERICAN J.
virgin'ica ⌊w . . . . . SENSITIVE J.
viscid'ula . . . . STICKY J.

AES'CULUS (*PAVIA*) BUCKEYE; HORSECHESTNUT
argu'ta (*buckleyi*) . . . . TEXAS B.
∞ **arnoldia'na** (*glabra* × *hybrida*) ∞ ARNOLD B.
∞ **bush'i** (*discolor* × *glabra*) ∞ ARKANSAS B.
califor'nica . . . . . CALIFORNIA B.
∞ **car'nea** (*hippocastanum* × *pavia; rubicunda*) . . . . ∞ RED H.
¢DAMASK (*plantierensis*) HV.
¢RUBY (*brioti*)
¢WEEPING (*pendula*)
chinen'sis . . . . CHINESE H.
dis'color . . . . WOOLLY B.
—**flaves'cens** . . . . YELLOW W.B.
—**koehn'ei** . . . . . SHRUBBY W.B.
—**mol'lis** (*austrina*) . . SCARLET W.B.
∞ **dupont'i** (*neglecta* × *pavia*) ∞ DUPONT B.
¢HESSE (*hessei*) HV.
fla'va . . . . **A. octandra**
gla'bra . . . . OHIO B.
—**leucoder'mis** . . . WHITEBARK O.B.
—**montic'ola** . . . . OKLAHOMA B.
—**pal'lida** . . . . PALE O.B.
—**sar'genti** . . . . . SARGENT O.B.
glauces'cens
harbiso'ni . **A. mutabilis** ¢ HARBISON
hippocasta'num . . . . COMMON H.
¢BAUMANN (*baumanni; flore pleno*) HV.
¢CUTLEAF (*dissecta; incisa; laciniata*)
¢HENKEL (*henkeli*)
¢MEMMINGER (*memmingeri*)
¢PYRAMIDAL (*pyramidalis*)
¢UMBRELLA (*umbraculifera*)
¢WEEPING (*pendula*)
¢WHITESPOT (*albovariegata*)
¢YELLOWSPOT (*luteovariegata*)
∞ **hy'brida** (*octandra* × *pavia*) ∞ HYBRID B.
in'dica . . . . INDIES H.
macrostach'ya . . . . . . **A. parviflora**
∞ **maryland'ica** (*glabra* × *octandra*) ∞ MARYLAND HYBRID B.
∞ **mississippien'sis** (*glabra* × *pavia*) ∞ MISSISSIPPI B.
∞ **mutab'ilis** (*discolor mollis* × *neglecta georgiana*) . . . . ∞ ARBORETUM B.
¢HARBISON (*A. harbisoni; A. m. harbisoni*) HV.
¢NODDING (*penduliflora; lutea* Spaeth, *not* Waugh. × *pavia humilis*)
¢VELVETLEAF (*induta. Hesse*)
neglec'ta (*michauxi*) . . PAINTED B.
—**georgia'na** . . . . GEORGIA P.B.
—**lanceola'ta** . . . . . RABUN P.B.

AESCULUS, continued
neglec'ta pubes'cens ETOWAH PAINTED BUCKEYE
—**tomento'sa** . . . . OCONEE P.B.
octan'dra (*flava; Pavia f.*). YELLOW B.
—**purpuras'cens** . . . PURPLE Y.B.
—**vesti'ta** . . . . . . CAROLINA Y.B.
—**virgin'ica** . . . . . TRICOLOR Y.B.
parviflo'ra (*macrostachya; Pavia m.*) BOTTLEBRUSH B.
—**serot'ina** . . . . LATE B.B.
pa'via (*rubra; Pavia r.*) . . . RED B.
—**sublacinia'ta**
¢DARK RED (*atrosanguinea*) HV. A. pavia
¢GROUND (*humilis*)
splen'dens . . . . FLAME B.
turbina'ta JAPANESE HORSECHESTNUT
wil'soni . . . . WILSON H.
woerlitzen'sis . . . . . WOERLITZ B.
Perhaps a hybrid.
—**ellwan'geri** (*A. pavia whitleyi*) ELLWANGER B.

AETHEOPAP'PUS . **CENTAUREA**

AETHIONE'MA . . . . . STONECRESS
alpi'num . . . . ALPINE S.
amoe'num . . . . SHOWY S.
arme'num . . . . . . ARMENIAN S.
bux'baumi (*cappadocicum*) BUXBAUM S.
cordifo'lium (*jucundum; Iberis jucunda*) LEBANON S.
cre'ticum (*ovalifolium*) . . CRETE S.
diastro'phis
grac'ile . . . . SLENDER S.
grandiflo'rum . . . . . PERSIAN S.
iberid'eum . . . . SPANISH S.
kot'schyi Hort. . . . . . KOTSCHY S.
membrana'ceum
oppositifo'lium . . . . . . GREEK S.
per'sicum Hort.
pulchel'lum
purpu'reum Hort. . . . . . PURPLE S.
pyrena'icum . . . . . . PYRENEES S.
saxat'ile . . . . CLIFF S.
schisto'sum
stylo'sum
triner'vium (*Iberidella trinervia*)
warleyen'se . . . . . . WARLEY S.

AETHU'SA . . . . AETHUSA
cyna'pium . . . . FOOLSPARSLEY A.

AFRAE'GLE . . . AFRAEGLE (*Powderflaskfruit*)
gabonen'sis . . . . GABON A.
panicula'ta . . . . NIGERIA A.

AFRAMO'MUM
grana-paradi'si (*Amomum g.*) PARADISE MELEGUETAPEPPER
melegue'ta (*Amomum m.*) . DRUG M.

Africanmillet . . . . . RAGIMILLET: **Eleusine coracana**
AFRICAN-TEAK . . . **Oldfieldia africana**
AFRICANVALERIAN . . . . **Fedia**
AFRICANVIOLET . . . . . . **Saintpaulia**
COMMON A. . . . . **S. ionantha**
KEW A. . . . . **S. kewensis**

AFROLICA'NIA
eleosper'ma . . . . NIKKONUTTREE

AFZE'LIA . . . . AFZELIA
africa'na . . . . AFRICAN A.
bi'juga . . . . FIJI A.
bipinden'sis . . . . . . ARYIAN A.
bractea'ta . . . . . . GLORYSEED A.
cassioi'des . . . . . . **Seymeria c.**

AGALI'NIS . . . . . . **GERARDIA**
pedicula'ria . . . . . **Aureolaria p.**

AGANOS'MA
acumina'ta

AGAPAN'THUS (*ABUMON*) AGAPANTHUS
africa'nus (*umbellatus*) . AFRICAN A.
¢ARTHINGTON WORSLEY. HV.
¢BLUEBELLS (*campanulatus*)
¢DARKVIOLET (*atrocaeruleus*)
¢DOUBLEWHITE (*florepleno*)
¢GIANT (*giganteus*)
¢GLOBE (*globosus*)
¢GOLDSTRIPE (*aureis vittatis*)
¢KRELAGE (*krelagei*)
¢MAXIMUS
¢MAY (*praecox*)
¢MILKLEAF (*insignis*)
¢MOORE (*mooreanus*)
¢MULTIFLORUS
¢SAINT PAUL (*sanctipauli*)
¢SAUNDERSON (*saundersonianus*)
¢SILVERSTRIPE (*argentis vittatis*)
¢SNOWFLAKE (*albidus*)
¢SPRENGER (*caulescens*)
¢WELLIGH (*wellighi*)
¢WHITE MAXIMUS (*maximus albus*)

AGAR (*Agar-agar*) . . . . . **Gelidium**
COMMON A. . . . . **G. corneum**

AGAR'ICUS . . . . AGARICUS
arven'sis . . . . HORSE A.
campes'tris . COMMON MUSHROOM A.
placomy'ces . . . . FLATCAP A.
rod'mani . . . . RODMANS A.
silvic'ola . . . . FOREST A.
subrufes'cens

AGAS'TACHE ⌊w . . . GIANTHYSSOP
ca'na (*Brittonastrum canum; Cedronella cana*) . . . . . . MOSQUITOPLANT
foenic'ulum (*anethiodora*). FENNEL G.
mexica'na (*Brittonastrum mexicanum; Cedronella mexicana*) . MEXICAN G.
nepetoi'des . . . . CATNIP G.
rugo'sa . . . . WRINKLED G.
urticifo'lia . . . . . NETTLELEAF G.

AGATHAE'A . . . . **FELICIA**
coeles'tis . . . . **F. amelloides**

AG'ATHIS (*DAMMARA*) DAMMARPINE
al'ba (*orientalis; Dammara a.*) WHITE D.
austra'lis (*Dammara a.*) . . KAURI D.
microsta'chys
palmersto'ni . . . . PALMERSTON D.
robus'ta (*Dammara r.*) . . . BIG D.

AGATHOS'MA (*HARTOGIA*) AGATHOSMA
ventenatia'na (*Hartogia v.*)
villo'sa (*Diosma purpurea; Hartogia v.*) HAIRY A.

AGA'TI . . . . **SESBANIA**

AGA'VE . . . . AGAVE
See **SUCCULENTS**.

AGAVE . . . . **Agave**
BERGER A. . . . . **A. bergeri**
BLUE A. . . . . **A. neglecta**
BLUE HEDGEHOG A. . **A. stricta glauca**
CENTURYPLANT A. . . . **A. americana**
CRESTED A. . . . . **A. lophantha**
DWARF A. . . . . . . **A. miradorensis**
HEDGEHOG A. . . . . **A. stricta**
HENEQUEN A. . . . . **A. fourcroydes**
HUACHUCA A. . . . . **A. huachucensis**
JAUMAVE LECHUGUILLA. . **A. funkiana**

Agave, continued
Lechuguilla A. **Agave lophantha poselgeri**
Letona A. . . . . **A. letonae**
Margarita A. . . . . . **A. margaritae**
Mescalfiber A. . . **A. pseudotequilana**
Orcutt A. . . . . **A. orcuttiana**
Palmer A. . . . . **A. palmeri**
Parry A. . . . . **A. parryi**
Pulque A. . . . . **A. atrovirens**
Sisal A. . . . . **A. sisalana**
Tequila A. . . . . **A. tequilana**
Utah A. . . . . **A. utahensis**

Agave-cactus **Leuchtenbergia principis**

Agboin . . . . . Piptadenia, African: **Piptadenia africana**

AGDES'TIS
clema'tidae

AGELAE'A . . . . Agelaea
lamarck'i . . . . Lamarck A.

AGERA'TUM . . . . . . Ageratum

The plants known to gardeners as Ageratum are in a state of great confusion botanically. They apparently include species of the genera Ageratum, Alomia, and Eupatorium.

conspic'uum **Eupatorium glechonophyllum**
conyzoi'des . . . . Tropic A.
houstonia'num (*mexicanum*) Mexican A.
Blue Perfection (*muticescens*) hv.
Dwarf (*nanum*)
lasseaux'i; rose'um . . **Eupatorium l.**

AGLAONE'MA
commuta'tum (*Schismatoglottis marantifolium maculatum*)
costa'tum
marantifo'lium (*Schismatoglottis m.*)
ni'tidum
pic'tum
—tri'color Hort.
siamen'se (*robelini*)
sim'plex . . . . Chinagreen (*Chinese Evergreen*)

AGNIRIC'TUS **MESEMBRYANTHEMUM**
See **SUCCULENTS.**

AGO'NIS
flexuo'sa (*Leptospermum flexuosum*) Peppermինttree
grandiflo'ra
juniperi'na
linearifo'lia
margina'ta
obtusis'sima

AGO'SERIS (*TROXIMON*) |w Agoseris
arizo'nica . . . . Arizona A.
auranti'aca . . . . . . Orange A.
cuspida'ta . . . . Wavyleaf A.
glau'ca . . . . Pale A.
—parviflo'ra . . Littleflower P.A.
grac'ilens . . . . Slender A.
—green'ei . . . . . . Greenes S.A.
grandiflo'ra |w
heterophyl'la (*major*) |w . Annual A.
hirsu'ta
pu'mila . . . . Low A.
purpu'rea (*T. purpureum*) . Purple A.
scorzoneraefo'lia . . Scorzonera A.
taraxacifo'lia . . . . . Dandelion A.

Agoseris . . . . **Agoseris**
Annual A. . . . . . **A. heterophylla**
Arizona A. . . . . **A. arizonica**
Dandelion A. . . . **A. taraxacifolia**

Agoseris, continued
Greenes Slender A. **Agoseris gracilens greenei**
Littleflower Pale A. **A. glauca parviflora**
Low A. . . . . **A. pumila**
Orange A. . . . . **A. aurantiaca**
Pale A. . . . . **A. glauca**
Purple A. . . . . **A. purpurea**
Scorzonera A. . . **A. scorzoneraefolia**
Slender A. . . . . **A. gracilens**
Wavyleaf A. . . . . . . **A. cuspidata**

AGRIMO'NIA |w . . . . . Agrimony
eupato'ria . . . . Common A.
gryposep'ala
mol'lis |w
pilo'sa . . . . Hairvein A.
stria'ta |w . . . . Roadside A.

AGRIOPHYL'LUM
arena'rium

AGROPY'RON . . . . . Wheatgrass
See **GRASS GENERA.**

AGROSTEM'MA |w . . Corncockle
coeliro'sa . . . . **Lychnis c.**
corona'ria . . . . **Lychnis c.**
flosjo'vis . . . . **Lychnis f.**
githa'go (*Lychnis g.*) |w . Common C.

AGROS'TIS . . . . Bentgrass
See **GRASS GENERA.**

AICHRY'SON . . . . . Aichryson
See **SUCCULENTS.**

AILAN'THUS . . . . . Ailanthus
altis'sima (*glandulosa*) Treeofheaven A.
—erythrocar'pa
—sutchuenen'sis . . . Szechwan A.
¢Redfruit (*erythrocarpa; rubra*) hv. A. altissima
¢Weeping (*pendulifolia*)
gir'aldi . . . . Girald A.
¢Ducloux (*duclouxi*) hv.
imberbiflo'ra
vilmorinia'na . . . . . Vilmorin A.

AI'PHANES (*CURIMA; MARARA; MARTINEZIA* Auth., *not* Ruiz & Pav.; *TILMIA*) . . Rufflepalm
See **PALM GENERA.**

AI'RA (*ASPRIS*) . . . . Hairgrass
See **GRASS GENERA.**

AI'RA Auth., *not* L. . **DESCHAMPSIA**
See **GRASS GENERA.**

Airbrom . . . . **Billbergia**
Bluerim A. . . . . **B. nutans**
Bluetip A. . . . . **B. speciosa**
Cappes A. . . . . **B. cappei**
Forget A. . . . . . . **B. forgetiana**
Libon A. . . . . **B. liboniana**
Morel A. . . . . **B. moreli**
Sander A. . . . . . . **B. sanderiana**
Showy A. . . . . **B. amoena**
Violetrim A. . . . . **B. pyramidalis**
Zebra A. . . . . **B. zebrina**

A'JAX . . . . **NARCISSUS**

Ajowan-caraway. **Trachyspermum ammi**

AJU'GA . . . . Bugle
brockbank'i Hort. . . Brockbank B.
chamaepi'tys . . . Groundpine B.
geneven'sis (*alpina; rugosa*) Geneva B.
¢Curly (*crispa*) hv.
¢Metallic (*metallica*)
¢Rose (*rosea*)

AJUGA, continued
pyramida'lis
rep'tans . . . . . . Carpet Bugle
—al'ba . . . . White C.B.
¢Bronzeleaf (*atropurpurea*) hv. A. reptans
¢Harlequin (*multicolor*)
¢Purpleleaf (*rubra*)
¢Variegated (*variegata*)
rugo'sa . . . . **A. genevensis**
tottenham'i . . . . . Tottenham B.

AKE'BIA . . . . Akebia
×**pentaphyl'la**
quina'ta . . . . Fiveleaf A.
trifolia'ta (*lobata*) . . . Threeleaf A.
—austra'lis

Akee . . . . **Blighia; B. sapida**

ALAN'GIUM . . . . Alangium
chinen'se (*begoniifolium*) Chinese A.
platanifo'lium . . . . . Planeleaf A.
salviifo'lium (*lamarcki*) . Angola A.

ALA'RIA . Wingkelp (*Kombu; Murlin*)
esculen'ta . . . . . Badderlocks W.

ALBIZ'ZIA . . . . Albizzia
ac'le . . . . Acle A.
anthelmin'tica . . . . . Musenna A.
fastigia'ta . . . . . . Flatcrown A.
julibris'sin (*Acacia j.; A. nemu*) Silktree A.
—rose'a . . . . Hardy S.A.
kalko'ra (*lebbek* Hemsl., *not* Benth.) Lebbek A.
lebbekoi'des
lophan'tha (*Acacia l.*) . . . Plume A.
molucca'na . . . . Molucca A.
odoratis'sima . . . . Fragrant A.
polyphyl'la
pro'cera . . . . Tall A.
thorel'i . . . . Thorel A.

ALBU'CA
ma'jor
mi'nor

ALCHEMIL'LA . . . . Ladysmantle
alpi'na . . . . Mountain L.
arven'sis (*Aphanes a.*) . . Field L.
chirophyl'la
ma'jor . . . . Large L.
praten'sis
pubes'cens
seric'ea
sylves'tris
vulga'ris . . . . Common L.

ALCHOR'NEA . . . . Christmasbush
corda'ta . . . . Cordate C.
cordifo'lia . . . . . . Heartleaf C.
ilicifo'lia . . . . Hollyleaf C.

ALCICOR'NIUM . . **PLATYCERIUM**
See **FERN GENERA.**

Alcornoco . . . **Bowdichia virgilioides**

Alder . . . . **Alnus**
American Green A. . . . . **A. crispa**
American Speckled A. **A. incana glauca**
Ascherson A. . . ×**A. aschersoniana**
Caucasian A. . . . . **A. subcordata**
Cutleaf Red A. **A. rubra pinnatisecta**
European A. . . . . . . **A. glutinosa**
European Green A. . . . **A. viridis**
European Speckled A. **A. incana vulgaris**
Hairy European A. **A. glutinosa barbata**

ALDER, continued
Hazel A. . . . . **Alnus rugosa**
Italian A. . . . . **A. cordata**
Japanese A. . . . . **A. japonica**
Japanese Green A. . . . . **A. firma**
∞ Koehne A. . . . . . . **∞ A. koehnei**
Manchu A. . . . . **A. fruticosa**
Manchurian A. . . . . . **A. hirsuta**
Matsumura A. . . . **A. matsumurae**
Mediterranean A.
A. glutinosa denticulata
Nepal A. . . . . . . **A. nepalensis**
NewMexican A. . . . **A. oblongifolia**
Nodding A. . . . . . . **A. pendula**
Oregon A. . . . . **A. oregana**
Oriental A. . . . . . . **A. orientalis**
Red A. . . . . **A. rubra**
SantaAna Sierra A.
A. rhombifolia bernardina
Seaside A. . . . . **A. maritima**
Sierra A. . . . . . . **A. rhombifolia**
Silesian A. . . . . . **×A. silesiaca**
Silky Green A. . . **A. crispa mollis**
Sitka A. . . . . **A. sinuata**
Smooth Speckled A. **A. incana glauca**
∞ Spaeth A. . . . . **∞ A. spaethi**
Speckled A. . . . . **A. incana**
Thinleaf A. . . . . . . **A. tenuifolia**
Woollyleaf A. . . . . . . **A. lanata**

ALDROVAN'DA
vesiculo'sa . . . . . Waterbugtrap

ALECTO'RIA . . . . . . Alectoria
juba'ta . . . . Rockhair A.

ALECTOROLO'PHUS . . Rattlepot
mi'nus . . . . Little R.

ALEC'TRYON . . . . . . Alectryon
excel'sum . . . . Titoki A.
subcine'reum

ALE'TRIS . . . . Stargrass
farino'sa . . . . . . Whitetube S.

ALEURI'TES
corda'ta . . . . Japan Woodoiltree
ford'i . . . . Tungoiltree
molucca'na (*triloba*) . Candlenuttree
monta'na . . . . Mu-oiltree
trisper'ma . . . . . . Soft Lumbang

ALEX'A
imperat'ricis

Alexandrialaurel. **Danae; D. racemosa**

Alfalfa . . . . **Medicago sativa**
Sickle A. . . . . **M. s. falcata**

Alfileria . . . . **Erodium cicutarium**

ALFONS'IA . . . . **COROZO**
See **PALM GENERA.**

Algerita . . . . Mahonia, Laredo:
Mahonia trifoliolata

ALHA'GI
pseudalha'gi (*camelorum*) Camelthorn

ALIBER'TIA
ed'ulis

Alicia . . . . **Chapmannia**
Florida A. . . . . **C. floridana**

ALIS'MA |w . . . . . Waterplantain
gey'eri |w . . . . Geyer W.
planta'go (*gramineum*) . . Grass W.
plantago-aquat'ica |w . American W.
subcorda'tum . . . Subcordate W.

Alkaligrass . . . . **Puccinellia**
Arctic A. . . . . **P. pumila**
British A. . . . . . . **P. rupestris**

Alkaligrass, continued
California A. . . **Puccinellia simplex**
Lemmon A. . . . . **P. lemmoni**
Nootka A. . . . . . **P. nutkaensis**
Nuttall A. . . . . . **P. nuttalliana**
Parish A. . . . . **P. parishi**
Seashore A. . . . . . **P. maritima**
Torrey A. . . . . . . **P. fasciculata**
Weeping A. . . . . **P. distans**

ALKAN'NA . . . . Alkanet
tincto'ria . . . . Dyers A. (*Redroot*)

ALLAGOP'TERA (*DIPLOTHEMIUM* in part). See **PALM GENERA.**

ALLAMAN'DA . . . . . . Allamanda
cathar'tica . . . . Common A.
—grandiflo'ra . . . Bigflower C.A.
—henderso'ni (*A. hendersoni*)
Henderson C.A.
—no'bilis (*A. nobilis*)
—schott'i (*A. schotti*) . Schott C.A.
—williams'i Hort. . . Williams A.
neriifo'lia . . . . . . Oleander A.
viola'cea . . . . Violet A.

ALLENROL'FEA |w . . Pickleweed
occidenta'lis |w . . . . Pickleweed

Alligator Apple . . . . . . Pondapple:
Annona glabra

Alligator Pear . . . . Avocado:
Persea americana

ALLIO'NIA (*WEDELIA; WEDELIELLA*) . . . . Allionia
incarna'ta (*Wedeliella i.*). Trailing A.
nyctagin'ea . . . . . . Prairie A.

AL'LIUM |w . . . . Onion
acumina'tum (*cuspidatum*) Tapertip O.
acutan'gulum . . . . . . **A. angulosum**
aflatunen'se
al'bidum
albopilo'sum . . . . . . Persian O.
alleghanien'se . . . . Allegany O.
ammo'philum . . . . . Goldball O.
amplec'tens
angulo'sum (*acutangulum*) . Angle O.
ascalon'icum . . . . Shallot
atropurpu'reum . . Rosepurple O.
atroru'bens
azu'reum . . . . . . **A. caeruleum**
baicalen'se . . **A. montanum glaucum**
beesia'num . . . . Bees O.
biscep'trum
bolan'deri (*stenanthum*) Bolander O.
brandeg'ei . . . . . . Brandegee O.
brevisty'lum . . . . . Shortstyle O.
brew'eri . . . . Brewer O.
caeru'leum (*azureum*) . Blueglobe O.
canaden'se (*mutabile*) Canada Garlic
carina'tum . . . . Keeled O.
ce'pa . . . . Garden O.
—sola'nium (*A. c. multiplicans*)
Multiplier O.
—vivip'arum (*A. c. bulbelliferum*) Top O.
cer'nuum (*neomexicanum; recurvatum*)
Nodding O.
cilia'tum . . . . . **A. subhirsutum**
co'ryi . . . . Cory O.
crenula'tum
cris'pum . . . . . **A. peninsulare c.**
cuspida'tum . . . . . **A. acuminatum**
cya'neum
darwas'icum
delicat'ulum
dichlamy'deum . . . . Twocloak O.
dioscor'idis . . . . . Dioscorides O.
doug'lasi . . . . Douglas O.

ALLIUM, continued
drum'mondi (*mutabile* Auth., *not* Michx.)
falcifo'lium . . . Sickleleaf Onion
fal'lax . . . . **A. montanum petraeum**
far'reri . . . . Farrer O.
fibril'lum . . . BlueMountains O.
fimbria'tum
fistulo'sum . . . . Welsh O.
fla'vum . . . . Yellow O.
—mi'nus
frig'idum
galan'thum . . . . Milk O.
gey'eri . . . . Geyer O.
gigan'teum . . . . Giant O.
glacia'le . . . . Glacier O.
globo'sum . . . . . . Rosestripe O.
haematochi'ton . . . Bloodtunic O.
heldreich'i . . . . Heldreich O.
hel'leri . . . . **A. nuttalli**
hermet'ti . . . . . . **A. neapolitanum**
hyali'num . . . . Eldorado O.
hymenorrhi'zum
japon'icum . . . . Japanese O.
kansuen'se . . . . Kansu O.
karatavien'se . . . . . Turkestan O.
ledebouria'num . . . . . Ledebour O.
lem'moni . . . . Lemmons O.
liban'i . . . . Lebanon O.
linea're
macran'thum . . . . . . Bigbloom O.
margarita'ceum . . . . . . Pearl O.
mo'ly . . . . Lily Leek
monadel'phum
monta'num . . . . Alps O.
—glau'cum (*A. baicalense*)
—petrae'um (*A. fallax*) . Dwarf A.O.
moscha'tum . . . . Musk O.
mutab'ile . . . . **A. canadense**
mutab'ile Auth., *not* Michx.
A. drummondi
nanhoen'se Hort.
narcissiflo'rum (*pedemontanum*)
Narcissus O.
neapolita'num (*hermetti*) . . Naples O.
neomexica'num . . . . . **A. cernuum**
nevaden'se . . . . Nevada O.
nev'i
ni'grum . . . . Black O.
nu'tans . . . . Steppes O.
nutt'alli (*helleri*) . . . . Nuttall O.
obli'quum . . Twistedleaf Garlic
ochroleu'cum
odo'rum . . . . Fragrant O.
olera'ceum . . . . Potherb O.
oreoph'ilum
ostrowskia'num . . . Ostrowsky O.
pal'lens . . . . Pale O.
panicula'tum . . . Mediterranean O.
par'vum
pedemonta'num . . **A. narcissiflorum**
peninsula're . . . . . . Mexicali O.
—cris'pum (*A. crispum*) Curled M.O.
platycau'le
platyspa'thum
polyphyl'lum . . . . Leafy O.
por'rum . . . . Leek
pulchel'lum
pur'domi . . . . Purdom O.
pyrena'icum . . . . . . Pyrenees O.
recurva'tum . . . . **A. cernuum**
reticula'tum . . . . **A. textile**
rosenbachia'num . . . Rosenbach O.
rose'um . . . . Rosy O.
—grandiflo'rum . . Bigflower R.O.
rotun'dum
sati'vum . . . . Garlic
scapo'sum

ALLIUM, continued
schoeno'prasum . . . . . . Chive
—sibir'icum (*A. sibiricum*) Siberian C.
schu'berti . . . . . Schubert Onion
scorodo'prasum . . . Giant Garlic
serra'tum . . . . . . Serrate O.
sibir'icum . . . **A. schoenoprasum s.**
sphaerocеph'alum . . Ballhead O.
stella'tum . . . . Prairie O.
stelleria'num . . . . . . Stellers O.
—al'bum . . . . White S.O.
stenan'thum . . . . . . **A. bolanderi**
stric'tum . . . Streakleaf Garlic
suave'olens
subhirsu'tum (*ciliatum*)
tangu'ticum . . . . Tangut O.
tatar'icum . . . . . . Tartar O.
tex'tile (*reticulatum*) . . Textile O.
tibet'icum . . . . Tibet O.
tol'miei . . . . Tolmie O.
tribractea'tum . . . Threebract O.
tricoc'cum . . . Wild Leek (*Ramps*)
trique'trum . . . . . Triangle O.
unifo'lium . . . . Oneleaf O.
urceola'tum . . . . Urn O.
ursi'num . . . . Ramsons (*Ramps*)
val'idum . . . . Pacific O.
victoria'lis . . . . . . Longroot O.
vinea'le . . Field Garlic (*Crow G.*)
vivip'arum . . . . . . Viviparous O.
winkleria'num . . . . . Winkler O.
yunnanen'se . . . . . . Yunnan O.

ALLOCA'RYA. . **PLAGIOBOTHRYS**
califor'nica . **P. reticulatus rossianorum**

ALLOPHYL'LUS
occidenta'lis

ALLOPHY'TON (*TETRANEMA*)
mexica'num (*Tetranema m.; Penstemon mexicanus*)

ALLOPLEC'TUS
schlim'i

Allthorn . . . . **Koeberlinia**
Spiny A. . . . . **K. spinosa**

Almendro . . . . Tonkabean, Panama: **Dipteryx panamensis**

Almon . . . . Shorea, Almon: **Shorea eximia**

Almond . . . . . . **Prunus amygdalus**
See also Apricot, Birdcherry, Bushcherry, Cherry, Chokecherry, Laurelcherry, Peach, Peachbrush, Plum. For cultivated varieties see **FRUIT AND EDIBLE NUT NAMES.**

∞ Arnold Flowering A. ∞ **P. arnoldiana**
Bitter A. . . . . **P. a. amara**
Fenzl A. . . . . **P. fenzliana**
Roundfruit Russian A. **P. tenella campestris**
Russian A. . . . . **P. tenella**
Sweginzow A. . . . . **P. sweginzowi**
Tangut A. . . . . . . **P. tangutica**
Turkestan A. . . . **P. petunnikowi**
White Russian A. . . **P. tenella alba**

ALNIPHYL'LUM . . . . Chinabells
fortun'ei (*Halesia f.*) . Fortunes C.

AL'NUS |w . . . . Alder
acumina'ta
alnobet'ula . . . . **A. viridis**
×**aschersonia'na** (*incana* × *rugosa*) Ascherson A.

ALNUS, continued
califor'nica . . . . . **A. rhombifolia**
corda'ta . . . . Italian Alder
cremastogy'ne
cris'pa (*mitchelliana; viridis* of Am. Auth.) . . . American Green A.
—mol'lis (*A. mollis*) . . Silky G.A.
fir'ma . . . . . Japanese Green A.
—hirtel'la
—multiner'vis . . . . . **A. pendula**
frutico'sa . . . . Manchu A.
glau'ca . . . . **A. icana g.**
glutino'sa . . . . European A.
—barba'ta . . . . Hairy E.A.
—denticula'ta . Mediterranean E.A.
₵Cutleaf (*laciniata*) hv. A. glutinosa
₵Incised (*incisa*)
₵Laplobe (*sorbifolia*)
₵Oakleaf (*quercifolia*)
₵Pyramidal (*pyramidalis*)
₵Redvein (*rubrinervia*)
₵Royal (*imperialis*)
₵Yellowleaf (*aurea*)
hirsu'ta (*tinctoria*) . Manchurian A.
—sibir'ica
∞ **hy'brida** (*glutinosa* × *incana*)
inca'na |w . . . . Speckled A.
—glau'ca (*A. glauca; A. i. americana*) American S.A.
—vulga'ris . . . . . European S.A.
₵Featherleaf (*pinnatifida; pinnatisecta*) hv. A. incana
₵Flatbranch (*monstrosa*)
₵Halflobe (*acuminata*)
₵Ragleaf (*tomophylla*)
₵Redstem (*coccinea*)
₵Weeping (*pendula*)
₵Yellowleaf (*aurea*)
japon'ica . . . . Japanese A.
∞ **koeh'nei** (*incana* × *subcordata*) ∞ Koehne A.
lana'ta . . . . Woollyleaf A.
latifo'lia . . . . **A. rugosa**
macrophyl'la . . . . . **A. subcordata**
marit'ima . . . . Seaside A.
matsumu'rae . . . . . Matsumura A.
mitchellia'na . . . . **A. crispa**
mol'lis . . . . **A. crispa m.**
nepalen'sis . . . . Nepal A.
ni'tida
oblongifo'lia . . . . NewMexican A.
orega'na . . . . **A. rubra**
This synonymous name is frequently misspelled A. oregona.

orienta'lis . . . . Oriental A.
pen'dula (*A. firma multinervis*) Nodding A.
rhombifo'lia (*californica*) . Sierra A.
—bernardi'na . . . . SantaAna S.A.
ru'bra (*oregana*) |w . . . . Red A.
—pinnatisec'ta . . . . Cutleaf R.A.
rugo'sa (*latifolia; serrulata*) |w Hazel A.
×**silesia'ca** (*glutinosa* × *rugosa*) Silesian A.
sinua'ta (*sitchensis*) . . . . Sitka A.
∞ **spaeth'i** (*japonica* × *subcordata*) ∞ Spaeth A.

The Spaeth Alder of cultivation presumably is a clon of this polybrid.

∞ **spectab'ilis** (*incana* × *japonica*)
subcorda'ta (*macrophylla*) Caucasian A.
tenuifo'lia . . . . . . Thinleaf A.
—occidenta'lis
tincto'ria . . . . **A. hirsuta**

ALNUS, continued
vir'idis (*alnobetula*) European Green Alder
Often confused with American Green Alder. The name Alnus alnobetula has sometimes been used in nurseries for both the European and the American Green Alder.

ALOCA'SIA . . . . Alocasia
argyrae'a
cu'prea
in'dica . . . . . . IndoMalayan A.
—metal'lica (*A. plumbea*) Metallic I.A.
Mottled (*variegata*) hv.
korthal'si (*thibautiana*)
low'i . . . . Lows A.
Veitch (*veitchi; A. veitchi*) hv.
macrorhi'za . . . . Giant A.
Mottled (*variegata*) hv.
∞ **mortenfontanen'sis** (*lowi* × *sanderiana*)
odo'ra
plum'bea . . . . . **A. indica metallica**
porphyroneu'ra (*princeps*)
∞ **rodigasia'na** (*korthalsi* × *regina*)
sanderia'na
∞ **se'deni** (*cuprea* × *lowi*)
thibautia'na . . . . **A. korthalsi**
×**vanhouttea'na**
Parentage uncertain.
watsonia'na
zebri'na

A'LOE . . . . Aloe
See **SUCCULENTS.**

ALON'SOA . . . . . . Maskflower
acutifo'lia (*myrtifolia*) . Lanceleaf M.
—can'dida . . . . White L.M.
cauliala'ta
incisifo'lia
linea'ris (*liniflora*) . . Flaxleaf M.
meridiona'lis (*mutisi*)
warscewicz'i (*grandiflora*) Heartleaf M.

ALOPECU'RUS . . . . . . Foxtail
See **GRASS GENERA.**

ALOY'SIA . . . . **LIPPIA**

Alpenclock . . . . **Soldanella**
∞ Ganders A. . . . . . . ∞ **S. ganderi**
Glacier A. . . . . **S. alpina**
Greater A. . . . . **S. montana**
Least A. . . . . **S. minima**
Little A. . . . . **S. pusilla**

Alpencress . . . . **Hutchinsia alpina**

ALPHITO'NIA . . . . Treebuckthorn
excel'sa . . . . . . Treebuckthorn

Alpineazalea **Loiseleuria; L. procumbens**

Alpineshrub . . . . **Rhodothamnus**
Rosy A. . . . . . . **R. chamaecistus**

ALPIN'IA Roxb., *not* L. (*LANGUAS*) Galangal
Alpinia is conserved under International Rules.
calcara'ta . . . . India G.
formosa'na . . . . Formosa G.
galan'ga (*Languas g.*)
mu'tica . . . . Malay G.
officina'rum (*Languas o.*) . Lesser G.
san'derae (*vittata*) . . . . Banded G.
specio'sa (*nutans; Languas s.*) Shellflower G.
tri'color . . . . Tricolor G.
vitelli'na (*Amomum vitellinum*) Malacca G.

ALPIN'IA L., *not* Roxb. . . **RENEALMIA**

Alplily . . . **Lloydia**
Common A. . . . **L. serotina**

ALSEUOS'MIA . . . Crimsonbead
i'lex . . . Holly C.
macrophyl'la . . . Bigleaf C.
quercifo'lia . . . Oakleaf C.

ALSI'NE . . . **STELLARIA**

ALSO'PHILA . . . Treefern
See **FERN GENERA.**

ALSTO'NIA . . . Alstonia
congen'sis . . . Congo A.
constric'ta . . . Quinine A.
macrophyl'la . . . Deviltree A.
schola'ris . . . Palimara A.
venena'ta . . . India A.

ALSTROEMER'IA . . . Alstroemeria
auranti'aca (*aurea*) . . . Yellow A.
Lutea. hv.
brasilien'sis . . . Brazilian A.
chilen'sis . . . Chilean A.
haeman'tha . . . Purplespot A.
—rose'a . . . Rosy P.A.
lig'tu . . . Purplestreak A.
—pul'chra
Hooker (*hookeri*) hv. A. ligtu
pelegri'na . . . Incalily A.
—al'ba . . . White I.A.
—rose'a . . . Red I.A.
pulchel'la (*psittacina*) . . . Parrot A.
recum'bens
revolu'ta . . . Purplepetal A.
sal'teri . . . Salter A.
splen'dens . . . Showy A.
versicol'or . . . Dwarf Purplespot A.
viola'cea . . . Violet A.

Alstroemeria . . . **Alstroemeria**
Brazilian A. . . . **A. brasiliensis**
Chilean A. . . . **A. chilensis**
Dwarf Purplespot A. . . . **A. versicolor**
Incalily A. . . . **A. pelegrina**
Parrot A. . . . **A. pulchella**
Purplepetal A. . . . **A. revoluta**
Purplespot A. . . . **A. haemantha**
Purplestreak A. . . . **A. ligtu**
Red Incalily A. . . . **A. pelegrina rosea**
Rosy Purplespot A. . . . **A. haemantha r.**
Salter A. . . . **A. salteri**
Showy A. . . . **A. splendens**
Violet A. . . . **A. violacea**
White Incalily A. . . . **A. pelegrina alba**
Yellow A. . . . **A. aurantiaca**

ALTAMIRANO'A . . . **VILLADIA**
See **SUCCULENTS.**

ALTERNAN'THERA (*TELANTHERA*) |w . . . Alternanthera
amoe'na (*Telanthera a.*). Tomthumb A.
¢Amabilis. hv.
¢Rosea
¢Spectabilis
bettzickia'na (*Telanthera b.*) Garden A.
¢Aurea. hv.
¢Aurea Nana (*compacta*)
¢Magnifica
brilliantis'sima
ficoi'dea . . . Rabbitmeat A.
philoxeroi'des |w . . . Alligator A.
versicol'or (*Telanthera v.*) . Copper A.

ALTHAE'A |w
ficifo'lia . . . Figleaf Hollyhock
hirsu'ta
officina'lis |w . . . Marshmallow

ALTHAEA, continued
rose'a |w . . . Hollyhock
¢Allegheny. hv.
¢Newportpink

ALTIN'GIA . . . Altingia
chinen'sis (*Liquidambar c.*) Chinese A.
excel'sa . . . Rasamala A.

Alumbarktree . . . **Stryphnodendron**
Barbatimao A. . . . **S. barbatimam**
Leafy A. . . . **S. polyphyllum**
Roundleaf A. . . . **S. rotundifolium**

Alumroot . . . **Heuchera**
American A. . . . **H. americana**
Coralbells . . . **H. sanguinea**
Hairy A. . . . **H. villosa**
Littleleaf A. . . . **H. parvifolia**
Marbled A. . . . **H. pubescens**
Ovalleaf A. . . . **H. ovalifolia**
Pinkbells . . . **H. lithophila**
Red A. . . . **H. rubescens**
Rough A. . . . **H. hispida**
Roundleaf A. . . . **H. cylindrica**

ALVARADO'A . . . Alvaradoa
amorphoi'des (*mexicana*). Mexican A.

ALYS'SUM . . . Alyssum
alpes'tre
alyssoi'des (*calycinum*) . . . Pale A.
ama'mum Hort.
ardoi'ni
argen'teum (*rostratum*) Yellowtuft A.
atlan'ticum . . . Atlantic A.
borzaea'num
calyc'inum . . . **A. alyssoides**
condensa'tum
cor'sicum . . . Corsican A.
corymbo'sum
cret'icum . . . Cretan A.
edentula'tum
gemonen'se
halimifo'lium
idae'um
inca'num . . . **Berteroa incana**
leucade'um . . . Silver A.
lutes'cens . . . **Lobularia maritima l.**
marit'imum . . . **Lobularia maritima**
mildea'num
moellendorfia'num . Moellendorf A.
monta'num . . . Mountain A.
orienta'le . . . Oriental A.
procum'bens . . . Ground A.
pyrena'icum . . . Pyrenees A.
re'pens . . . Creeping A.
rostra'tum . . . **A. argenteum**
saxat'ile . . . Goldentuft A.
¢Compactum. hv.
¢Double (*florepleno*)
¢Dwarf (*compactum*)
¢Lemon (*luteum; sulphureum*)
¢Silverqueen
¢Variegated (*variegatum*)
spino'sum . . . Spiny A.
Roseum. hv.
stylo'sum
wulfenia'num (*rocheli*)

Alyssum . . . **Alyssum**
Atlantic A. . . . **A. atlanticum**
Corsican A. . . . **A. corsicum**
Creeping A. . . . **A. repens**
Cretan A. . . . **A. creticum**
Goldentuft A. . . . **A. saxatile**
Ground A. . . . **A. procumbens**
Moellendorf A. **A. moellendorfianum**
Mountain A. . . . **A. montanum**
Oriental A. . . . **A. orientale**
Pale A. . . . **A. alyssoides**

Alyssum, continued
Pyrenees A. . . **Alyssum pyrenaicum**
Silver A. . . . **A. leucadeum**
Spiny A. . . . **A. spinosum**
Yellowtuft A. . . . **A. argenteum**

ALYX'IA . . . Alyxia
brevifo'lia . . . Shortleaf A.
buxifo'lia . . . Boxleaf A.
olivaefor'mis . . . Maile A.

AMANI'TA . . . Amanita
caesar'ea . . . Caesars A.
musca'ria . . . Fly A.
phalloi'des . . . Deathcup A.
strobilifor'mis . . . Fircone A.
ver'na . . . Spring A.

AMANITOP'SIS . . . Amanitopsis
vagina'ta . . . Sheathed A.

Amaranth . . . **Amaranthus**
Abyssinian A. . . . **A. abyssinicus**
Josephs-coat A. . . . **A. tricolor**
Love-lies-bleeding . . **A. caudatus**
Powell A. . . . **A. powelli**
Prostrate A. . . . **A. blitoides**
Redroot A. . . . **A. retroflexus**
Slim A. . . . **A. hybridus**
Spiny A. . . . **A. spinosus**
Tumbleweed A. . . . **A. graecizans**

AMARAN'THUS |w . . . Amaranth
abyssin'icus . . . Abyssinian A.
blitoi'des |w . . . Prostrate A.
cauda'tus (*cruentus; paniculatus*)
Love-lies-bleeding
Abyssinian (*abyssinicus*) hv.
Blood (*sanguineus*)
Duss (*dussi*)
Elegance (*elegantissimus*)
Margaret (*margaritae*)
Monster (*monstrosus*)
Redleaf (*atropurpureus*)
Superb (*superbus*)
grae'cizans |w . . . Tumbleweed A.
hy'bridus |w . . . Slim A.
¢Blood Princessfeather. hv.
¢Princessfeather (*hypochondriacus*)
pow'elli |w . . . Powell A.
retroflex'us |w . Redroot A. (*Redroot*)
spino'sus |w . . . Spiny A.
tri'color (*gangeticus; melancholicus*)
Josephs-coat A.
¢Angustissimus (*salicifolius* in part) hv.
¢Chameleon
¢Combustion
¢Moltenfire
¢Russet (*angustior; salicifolius* in part)
¢Splendens
¢Sunshine

∞*AMARCRI'NUM* ∞**CRINODONNA**

AMAREL'LA . . . **GENTIANA**

Amargosa . . . Castela, Allthorn: **Castela texana**

AMARYL'LIS (*HIPPEASTRUM*) Amaryllis
atamas'co . . . **Zephyranthes a.**
au'lica (*H. aulicum*)
—stenopet'ala (*H. a. stenopetalum*)
—tettau'i (*H. a. tettaui*)
au'rea . . . **Lycoris a.**
belladon'na (*equestris; punicea; H. puniceum*) . . . Belladonnalily
belladon'na Herbert, *not* L. **Callicore rosea**

AMARYLLIS, continued
breviflo'ra (*Hippeastrum breviflorum*)
calyptra'ta (*H. calyptratum*)
coran'ica . . . . **Ammocharis c.**
eques'tris . . . . **A. belladonna**
formosis'sima . . . . . **Sprekelia f.**
hall'i . . . . . **Lycoris squamigera**
∞ **john'soni** (*reginae* × *vittatum*)
∞ JOHNSON AMARYLLIS
lute'a . . . . **Sternbergia l.**
praten'sis (*H. pratense*) . MEADOW A.
pro'cera (*H. procerum*) . . . TALL A.
psittaci'na (*H. psittacinum*) PARROT A.
punic'ea . . . . **A. belladonna**
radia'ta . . . . **Lycoris r.**
regi'nae (*H. reginae*) . . . QUEENS A.
reticula'ta (*H. reticulatum*)
—**striatifo'lia** (*H. r. striatifolium*)
ru'tila (*H. rutilum*)
—**croca'ta** (*H. r. crocatum*)
—**ful'gida** (*H. r. fulgidum*)
sarnien'sis . . . . **Nerine s.**
solandriflo'ra (*H. solandriflorum*)
stylo'sa (*H. stylosum*)
vitta'ta (*H. vittatum*) . BARBADOSLILY
ALBERT. (Lem.) *Alberti; Double Belladonna.* HV. Amaryllis
AMERICA. (Heat. 1938.)
ANNE LINDBERGH. (Dom. 1934.)
AUGUST KOCH. (Koch 1935.)
BARONESS SCHROEDER. (Schroeder 1928.)
BERENGARIA. (Heat. 1938.)
BERTHA VASKU. (Vas. 1936.)
BERT MERRILL. (Traub 1934.)
BLACKBEAUTY. (Hol. 1925.)
BRITTANIA. (Heat. 1938.)
CARDINAL. (Chandler)
CAROLYN. (Burns 1936.)
CERISE MAGNIFICUM. (Schroeder 1928.)
CLIVE COOKSON. (Cook. 1936.)
CROESUS. (Chandler)
DAWN. (Heat. 1934.)
Double Belladonna. ALBERT.
DR. TRAUB. (Heat. 1935.)
EDELWEISS. (Hayward 1936.)
EDITH. (Hay. 1935.)
EDWARD HALL. (Heat. 1934.)
ELEANOR ROOSEVELT. (Dom. 1934.)
ELIZABETH TRAUB. (Til. 1935.)
ELLA STEVENS. (Traub & Hughes 1937.)
EMMA PIPER. (Traub & Hughes 1937.)
EMPRESS OF INDIA. (de Graaff)
EOLA. (Heat. 1934.)
ERNESTINE. (Hay. 1935.)
ETHEL DUCKWORTH. (Hay. 1937.)
FAITH. (Heat. 1934.)
FLAME. (Hay. 1935.)
FLORENCE SPRINGER. (Spring. '37.)
FLORIDA. (Til. 1935.)
FRANK WOOTTEN. (Traub 1935.)
FRILLED QUEEN. (Chandler)
FULL MOON. (Hay. 1935.)
GARFIELDI. (Koch 1935.)
GLORIA. (Heat. 1938.)
GLORIOUS. (Heat. 1935.)
GOLIATH. (Hay. 1935.)
GRETA GARBO. (Traub 1935.)
GUARDSMAN. (Chandler)
HARLEQUIN. (Chandler)
HARRY SEARLES. (Searles 1935.)
HELEN. (Heat. 1934.)
HELEN HEATON. (Heat. 1938.)
HELEN JANE. (Til. 1934.)
HELEN TILGHMAN. (Til. 1934.)

AMARYLLIS, continued
HENRY NEHRLING. (Heat. 1935.)
JOHNSON. (John. 1910.)
KIRBY PINK. (Hay. 1935.)
LADY (*Juliet*) DUFF. (Duff 1929.)
LAURA. (Chandler)
LENA HUGHES. (Traub & Hughes 1937.)
MARIE. (Heat. 1934.)
MARINA. (Traub 1936.)
MARS. (Hay. 1935.)
MARY DAVIS. (Hay. 1937.)
MENELIK. (Chandler)
MEPHISTO. (Heat. 1934.) *War.*
MOTHER. (Heat. 1934.)
MRS. (*Donald*) DUDLEY. (Heat. 1935.)
MRS. GARFIELD. (Veitch)
MRS. LAMBERTON. (Heat. 1935.)
NAUTCH GIRL. (Chandler)
NEVOSO. (Hay. 1935.)
ORANGE KING. (Heat. 1935.)
ORANGE PERFECTION. (Heat. '35.)
ORCHID. (Heat. 1935.)
ORLANDO. (Heat. 1934.)
ORLANDO SALMON. (Heat. 1936.)
OSCEOLA. (Til. 1935.)
PALATKA. (Til. 1934.)
PARDY. (Hay. 1935.)
PEACE. (Heat. 1934.)
PINKBEAUTY. (Heat. 1935.)
PINKBLOSSOM. (Holford 1925.)
PRESIDENT ROOSEVELT. (Heat. '34.)
PRINCESS ELIZABETH. (Traub & Hughes 1937.)
PURITY. (Hay. 1935.)
RALPH WHEELER. (Heat. 1935.)
REDEMPEROR. (Heat. 1935.)
REDSUNSET. (Heat. 1936.)
REDWING. (Heat. 1935.)
ROUGE. (Vasku 1936.)
RUBY. (Schroeder 1931.)
Ruby. (Hay. 1935.)
RUTH. (Chandler)
SALMONBEAUTY. (Heat. 1935.)
SALMONQUEEN. (Hay. 1935.)
SCARLETKING. (Chandler)
SCARLETQUEEN. (Chandler)
SIBYL HOUDYSHEL. (Houd.)
STANSTED. (Challis 1935.)
STRAWBERRY GLOW. (Hay. 1935.)
SUNSET. (Heat. 1935.)
THEODORE MEAD. (Heat. 1934.)
VIRGINIA. (Heat. 1935.)
WAR. (Chandler)
War. MEPHISTO.
WHITEBEAUTY. (Heat. 1935.)
WILL ROGERS. (Traub 1935.)
WYNDHAM HAYWARD. (Traub '35.)

AMARYLLIS FAMILY GENERA (AMARYLLIDACEAE)

This Genera list, based on an original prepared by Hamilton P. Traub, Editor of "Herbertia," on behalf of the American Amaryllis Society, is included for convenience of reference. Each genus with its species and varieties will be found elsewhere in regular alphabetical sequence. Indebtedness is acknowledged here to Dr. Traub for aid with numerous liliaceous genera.

Alstroemer'ia . . . . ALSTROEMERIA
Amaryl'lis (*Hippeastrum*) . AMARYLLIS
Ammoch'aris . . . . SANDNYMPH
Argyrop'sis . . . . . **Zephyranthes**
Boma'rea . . . . BOMAREA
Booph'ane (*Buphane*) . COWBANELILY

AMARYLLIS FAMILY GENERA, continued
∞ **Brunsdon'na** (*Brunsvigia* × *Callicore*)
∞ BRUNSDONNA
Brunsvig'ia . . . . . . BRUNSVIGIA
Bu'phane . . . . **Boophane**
Callico're . . . . CALLICORE
Calostem'ma . . . . . . CALOSTEMMA
Chlidan'thus . . . . . . CHLIDANTHUS
Cli'via . . . . KAFIRLILY
∞ **Cooperan'thes** (*Cooperia* × *Zephyranthes*) . . . . . . ∞ COOPERANTHES
Cooper'ia . . . . RAINLILY
∞ **Crinodon'na** (*Amaryllis* × *Crinum*)
∞ CRINODONNA
Cri'num . . . . CRINUM
Cybiste'tes . . . . CYBISTETES
Cyrtan'thus . . . . . . CYRTANTHUS
Elise'na . . . . ELISENA
Eu'charis . . . . EUCHARIS
Eury'cles . . . . EURYCLES
Galan'thus . . . . SNOWDROP
Griffin'ia . . . . GRIFFINIA
Habran'thus . . . . . . HABRANTHUS
Haeman'thus . . . . BLOODLILY
Hes'sea . . . . HESSEA
Hippeas'trum . . . . **Amaryllis**
Hymenocal'lis . . . . HYMENOCALLIS

The term Spiderlily is often used for some species of this genus, but Hamilton P. Traub informs the Editorial Committee that the name has been rejected by the American Amaryllis Society, which sponsors the generic name as a common name, because Spiderlily is also used for Lycoris radiata in the South.

Isme'ne . . . . PERUVIANDAFFODIL
Ixiolir'ion . . . . IXIOLIRION
Leuco'jum . . . . SNOWFLAKE
Lyco'ris . . . . LYCORIS
Narcis'sus . . . . NARCISSUS
Neri'ne . . . . NERINE
Pamian'the . . . . PAMIANTHE
Pancra'tium . . . . . PANCRATIUM
Phaedranas'sa . . . . . QUEENLILY
Pyrolir'ion . . . . FLAMELILY
Spreke'lia . . . . AZTECLILY (*Jacobeanlily; St. Jameslily*)
Stenomes'son . . . . . STENOMESSON
Sternberg'ia . . . . . . STERNBERGIA
Urceoli'na . . . . PITCHERLILY
Vallo'ta . . . VALLOTA (*Scarborolily*)
Zephyran'thes (*Argyropsis*)
ZEPHYRLILY

AMASO'NIA . . . . AMASONIA
calyci'na
punic'ea

AMAZONVINE . . . . . . **Stigmaphyllon**
ARGENTINE A. . . . . . . **S. littorale**
BOGOTA A. . . . . **S. bogotense**
FRINGED A. . . . . **S. ciliatum**
LEDUMLEAF A. . . . . . . **S. ledifolium**

AMBARELLA . . . . **Spondias cytherea**

AMBERBO'A (*VOLUTARELLA*)
AMBERBOA
murica'ta (*Volutarella m.*) . SPINY A.

AMBLYOLE'PIS |w
setig'era |w

AMBRO'SIA |w . . . . . . RAGWEED
ap'tera |w . . . . BLOOD R.
artemisifo'lia (*elatior*) |w . COMMON R.
bidenta'ta |w . . . . . . LANCELEAF R.
cumanen'sis
psilosta'chya |w . . . . WESTERN R.
pu'mila . . . . DWARF R.
trif'ida |w . . . GIANT R. (*Richweed*)

AMELAN'CHIER |w . . Serviceberry
(*Juneberry; Shadblow; Shadbush*)
alnifo'lia |w . . . . . Saskatoon S.
—pu'mila (*A. pumila*) . Dwarf S.S.
amab'ilis . . . . Snowy S.
asiat'ica . . . . Asian S.
bartramia'na (*oligocarpa*). Bartram S.
canaden'sis (*botryapium*) |w
Shadblow S. (*Downy S.*)
cusick'i . . . . Cusick S.
flo'rida |w . . . . Pacific S.
∞ **grandiflo'ra** (*canadensis* × *laevis*)
∞ Apple S.
—rubes'cens . . . . . . Ruddy A.S.
hu'milis . . . . Low S.
interme'dia
lae'vis . . . . Allegany S.
oblongifo'lia (*obovalis*) . . Thicket S.
oligocar'pa . . . . . . **A. bartramiana**
oreoph'ila . . . . . . Mountain S.
ova'lis (*rotundifolia; vulgaris*) Garden S.
polycar'pa . . . . Cluster S.
prunifo'lia (*rubescens*) . . . Redbud S.
pu'mila . . . . **A. alnifolia p.**
pur'pusi
sangui'nea |w . . . . Roundleaf S.
ser'a
∞ **spica'ta** (*oblongifolia* × *?stolonifera*)
∞ Dwarf S.
stolonif'era . . . . . . Running S.
utahen'sis |w . . . . Utah S.
vulga'ris . . . . **A. ovalis**

∞ **AMELASOR'BUS**
∞ **jack'i** (*Amelanchier florida* × *Sorbus sitchensis*) . . . . . . ∞ Sorberry

AMEL'LUS . . . . Amellus
an'nuus . . . . Annual S.

American-mistletoe . . **Phoradendron**
Bigleaf A. . . . . . **P. macrophyllum**
Christmas A. . . . . **P. flavescens**
ColoradoDesert A. . **P. coloradense**
Cypress A. . . . . . . **P. densum**
Fir A. . . . . . . **P. pauciflorum**
Incensecedar A. . . . . **P. libocedri**
Juniper A. . . . . **P. juniperinum**
Mesquite A. . . . **P. californicum**
Pacific A. . . . . **P. villosum**
Pinchscale A. . . . . . . **P. ligatum**

American-oilpalm. **Corozo; C. oleifera**

AMERIM'NON . . . **DALBERGIA**
Ame'sia gigan'tea . . . . . **Epipactis g.**

AMETHYS'TIA
coeru'lea

AMHERS'TIA . . . . . . Amherstia
no'bilis . . . . Flame A.

AMIAN'THIUM (*ZIGADENUS* in part) . . . . Crowpoison
muscaetox'icum (*Chrosperma m.; Zigadenus m.*) . . . . . Crowpoison

AMIC'IA . . . . Amicia
zygome'ris . . . . . . Mexican A.

AMMAN'IA |w . . . . . . Ammania
auricula'ta |w . . . . . . Earleaf A.
coccin'ea |w . . . . Purple A.
koehne'i |w . . . . Koehne A.

AM'MI . . . . Ammi
ma'jus . . . . Greater A.
visna'ga . . . . Toothpick A.

AMMO'BIUM
ala'tum . . . . Wing-everlasting
—grandiflo'rum . . . . . . Big W.

AMMOCH'ARIS . . . . . Sandnymph
coccin'ea . . . . Scarlet S.
coran'ica (*Amaryllis c.*) . . Koran S.
falca'ta . . . . . **Cybistetes longifolia**

AMMO'PHILA . . . . . Beachgrass
See **GRASS GENERA.**

AMO'MIS . . . . **PIMENTA**
caryophylla'ta . . . . . **P. racemosa**
—citrifo'lia . . . . . **P. racemosa c.**

AMO'MUM . . . . Amomum
car'damon . . . . . . Cardamon A.
grana-paradi'si . . . **Aframomum g.**
melegue'ta . . . . . **Aframomum m.**
vitelli'num . . . . . **Alpinia vitellina**

AMOO'RA
nitid'ula

AMOREUX'IA |w
malvaefo'lia |w
palmatif'ida |w

AMOR'PHA |w . . . . . . Amorpha
califor'nica . . . . . California A.
canes'cens |w . . . . . Leadplant A.
croceo-lana'ta . . . Yellowwool A.
fra'grans (*angustifolia*) . Fragrant A.
frutico'sa |w . . . . . . Indigobush A.
—albiflo'ra . . . . White I.A.
—angustifo'lia . . . . Midwest I.A.
—coeru'lea . . . . Cerulean I.A.
—emargina'ta
—hu'milis . . . . . . Ground I.A.
—pen'dula . . . . . Drooping I.A.
—tennessen sis (*A. tennessensis*)
Tennessee I.A.
gla'bra (*montana*). Mountainindigo A.
herba'cea (*pubescens; pumila*)
Clusterspike A.
na'na (*microphylla*) . Dwarfindigo A.
ni'tens . . . . Georgia A.
Some botanists consider this a synonym of the older A. fruticosa.
panicula'ta |w . . . . . Panicled A.
tennessen'sis . . . . . **A. fruticosa t.**
virga'ta

Amorpha . . . . **Amorpha**
California A. . . . . . **A. californica**
Cerulean Indigobush A.
A. fruticosa coerulea
Clusterspike A. . . . . **A. herbacea**
Desertindigo A. . . . **A. occidentalis**
Drooping Indigobush A.
A. fruticosa pendula
Dwarfindigo A. . . . . **A. nana**
Fragrant A. . . . . **A. fragrans**
Georgia A. . . . . **A. nitens**
Ground Indigobush A.
A. fruticosa humilis
Indigobush A. . . . . . **A. fruticosa**
Leadplant A. . . . . . **A. canescens**
Midwest Indigobush A.
A. fruticosa angustifolia
Mountainindigo A. . . . . **A. glabra**
Panicled A. . . . . . . **A. paniculata**
Tennessee Indigobush A.
A. fruticosa tennessensis
White I. A. . . . . . . **A. f. albiflora**
Yellowwool A. . . **A. croceo-lanata**

AMORPHOPHAL'LUS . . Giantarum
campanula'tus . . . . Whitespot G.
gigan'teus . . . . Great G.
rivier'i . . . . **Hydrosme r.**
tita'num . . . . Titan G.

AMPELODES'MA
mauritan'icus (*tenax*)

AMPELOP'SIS (*PSEDERA*) |w
Ampelopsis
Consult also the allied genera Cissus, Parthenocissus, and Vitis.
aconitifo'lia (*dissecta; A. aconitifolia d.; Vitis a.*). . . . . Monkshoodvine
—gla'bra (*A. a. palmiloba; A. palmiloba; A. tripartita*) . Threeleaf M.
arbo'rea (*Vitis a.; V. bipinnata*) |w
Peppervine
bodinier'i (*micans; Vitis m.*)
Bodinier A.
—cine'rea (*A. micans c.*) . Gray B.A.
brevipeduncula'ta (*amurensis; A. heterophylla a.; Vitis b.*) . . . Amur A.
—citrulloi'des (*A. citrulloides; A. heterophylla c.; Vitis h. c.*)
—el'egans (*tricolor; Vitis heterophylla e.*) . . . . Basket A.
—maximowicz'i (*Vitis heterophylla*)
Porcelain A.
chaffanjo'ni (*leeoides; watsoniana*)
corda'ta (*Vitis c.; V. indivisa*) |w
Heartleaf A.
delavaya'na (*A. heterophylla d.; Vitis d.*)
Delavay A.
dissec'ta . . . . **A. aconitifolia**
henrya'na . . . . **Parthenocissus h.**
heterophyl'la amuren'sis
A. brevipedunculata
—citrulloi'des . **A. brevipedunculata c.**
humulifo'lia . . . . Hop A.
hypoglau'ca . . . . **Cissus h.**
japon'ica (*A. serjaniaefolia; Vitis s.*)
Japan A.
leeoi'des . . . . **A. chaffanjoni**
low'i . **Parthenocissus tricuspidata l.**
megalophyl'la (*Vitis m.*). Spikenard A.
mi'cans . . . . **A. bodinieri**
—cine'rea . . . . . . **A. bodinieri c.**
mura'lis Hort. **Parthenocissus quinquefolia murorum**
orienta'lis (*Vitis o.*) . . . Oriental A.
palmilo'ba . . . **A. aconitifolia glabra**
quinquefo'lia . . . **Parthenocissus q.**
—engelmann'i . **Parthenocissus q. e.**
—muro'rum . **Parthenocissus q. m.**
—saintpaul'i . . **Parthenocissus q. s.**
serjaniaefo'lia . . . . . **A. japonica**
thom'soni . . . . . **Parthenocissus t.**
tri'color . **A. brevipedunculata elegans**
tricuspida'ta . . . . **Parthenocissus t.**
triparti'ta . . . **A. aconitifolia glabra**
veitch'i **Parthenocissus tricuspidata v.**
vita'cea . . . **Parthenocissus inserta**
vitifo'lia
watsonia'na . . . . . **A. chaffanjoni**

Ampelopsis . . . . **Ampelopsis**
Amur A. . . . . **A. brevipedunculata**
Basket A. . . . . **A. b. elegans**
Bodinier A. . . . . **A. bodinieri**
Delavay A. . . . . . . **A. delavayana**
Gray Bodinier A. **A. bodinieri cinerea**
Heartleaf A. . . . . **A. cordata**
Hop A. . . . . **A. humulifolia**
Japan A. . . . . **A. japonica**
Monkshoodvine . . . **A. aconitifolia**
Oriental A. . . . . **A. orientalis**
Palmate Monkshoodvine
A. aconitifolia palmiloba
Peppervine . . . . **A. arborea**
Porcelain A.
A. brevipedunculata maximowiczi
Spikenard A. . . . . **A. megalophylla**

AMPHIACHY'RIS
dracunculoi'des . . . . **Gutierrezia d.**
fre'monti . . . . . **Amphipappus f.**

AMPHICAR'PA (*FALCATA*) |w Hogpeanut
bractea'ta (*monoica; Falcata comosa*) |w Southern H
pit'cheri |w . . . . . . Pitchers H

AMPHICAR'PUM (*AMPHICARPON*) Goobergrass
See **GRASS GENERA.**

AMPHICO'ME
argu'ta
emo'di

AMPHIPAP'PUS
fre'monti (*Amphiachyris f.*)

AMSINCK'IA |w . . . . . Fiddleneck
douglasia'na . . . . . . Douglas F.
douglasia'na Auth., *not* DC. **A. intermedia**
interme'dia (*douglasiana* Auth., *not* DC.) |w . . . . Fireweed F.
interme'dia Auth., *not* Fisch. & Mey. **A. spectabilis**
lycopsoi'des . . . . . . Tarweed F.
menzies'i . . . . Menzies F.
retror'sa
spectab'ilis (*intermedia* Auth., *not* Fisch. & Mey.) . . . . Coast F.

AMSO'NIA . . . . Amsonia
angustifo'lia (*ciliata*) . . Feather A.
eastwoodia'na . . . . Eastwood A.
pal'meri . . . . Palmer A.
tabernaemonta'na (*salicifolia*) Willow A.
texa'na . . . . Texas A.

Amugis . **Koordersiodendron pinnatum**

Amuletplant . . . . **Putranjiva**
India A. . . . . **P. roxburghi**

AMYG'DALUS . . . . . . **PRUNUS**
commu'nis . . . . . . **P. amygdalus**
glandulo'sa . . . . **P. texana**
na'na . . . . **P. tenella**
platycar'pa . . . **P. persica compressa**

AMYLOCAR'PUS . . . . . **BACTRIS**
See **PALM GENERA.**

AM'YRIS . . . . Amyris
balsamif'era . . . . . . Balsam A.
elemif'era (*maritima*) . . . . Sea A.

ANAB'ASIS
aphyl'la

Anacahuita . . . . . **Cordia boissieri**

ANACAMP'SEROS
See **SUCCULENTS.**

ANACAMP'SEROS Haw., *not* L. **SEDUM**
See **SUCCULENTS.**

ANACAR'DIUM . . . . . . Cashew
occidenta'le . . . . . . Common C.
rhinocar'pus . . . . . . Guiana C.

ANACH'ARIS (*PHILOTRIA*) |w Waterweed

The genera Anacharis and Elodea are much confused in literature; actually they are distinct, Elodea being confined to South America and Anacharis to North America.

canaden'sis (*Elodea c.; Philotria c.*) |w Canada W.
Gigantea. hv.
linea'ris |w . . . . Narrowleaf W.
occidenta'lis (*Elodea o.*) |w Western W.

ANACY'CLUS
depres'sus
officina'rum
pyreth'rum
radia'tus

ANAETOCHI'LUS **ANOECTOCHILUS**
See **ORCHID GENERA.**

ANAGAL'LIS |w . . . . . Pimpernel
arven'sis |w . . . . Scarlet P.
—caeru'lea
—phoenic'ea
linifo'lia (*grandiflora*) . . Flaxleaf P.

ANAGY'RIS
foe'tida . Mediterranean Stinkbush

ANAMIR'TA . . . . . . Fishberry
coc'culus . . . . Malay F.

ANAMO'MIS . . . . . **EUGENIA**

ANA'NAS
como'sus (*sativus*) . . . . Pineapple

For horticultural varieties, see Pineapple in **FRUIT AND EDIBLE NUT NAMES.**

macrodon'tes . . . . Arghan
magdale'nae . . . . . . **Aechmea m.**
portea'nus

ANAPH'ALIS . . . Pearleverlasting
cuneifo'lia
margarita'cea (*Antennaria m.*) Common P.
—occidenta'lis . . . . Western C.P.
—subalpi'na (*A. subalpina*) Western C.P.
nubig'ena
tripliner'vis

Anarrhi'num crassifo'lium **Linaria origanifolia**

ANASTA'TICA. Resurrectionmustard (*Resurrectionplant*)
hierochun'tica . . . . . Jericho R.

ANATH'ERUM . . . . . **VETIVERIA**
See **GRASS GENERA.**

Anattotree . . . . . **Bixa; B. orellana**

ANCHIE'TEA . Anchietea (*Pirageia*)
saluta'ris . . . . Mercury A.

ANCHIS'TEA . . . **WOODWARDIA**
See **FERN GENERA.**

ANCHU'SA (*PENTAGLOTTIS*) Bugloss
affi'nis
azu'rea (*italica*) . . . . Italian B.
Best of All. hv.
Dropmore
Feltham Pride
Lissadell
Morning Glory
Opal
Picotee
Pride of Dover
barrelier'i . . . . Early B.
capen'sis . . . . Cape B.
—al'ba . . . . White C.B.
ital'ica . . . . **A. azurea**
myosotidiflo'ra . **Brunnera macrophylla**
ochroleu'ca
officina'lis . . . . Common B.
—incarna'ta . . . . Carnation C.B.
sempervi'rens (*Pentaglottis s.*) Evergreen B.
undula'ta
—lamprocar'pa

ANCISTROCAC'TUS . Fishhookcactus
See **CACTUS GENERA.**

ANDI'RA (*VATAIREOPSIS; VOUACAPOUA*) . . . . . Angelintree

Andira is conserved under International Rules.

araro'ba (*Vataireopsis a.; Vouacapoua a.*) . . . . Goa A.
iner'mis (*jamaicensis; Vouacapoua americana*) . . . . Cabbage A.
spectab'ilis . . . . Showy A.
vermifu'ga . . . . . . Brazilian A.

ANDRACH'NE . . . . . Andrachne
col'chica
revercho'ni . . . **Savia phyllanthoides**

ANDROGRA'PHIS
panicula'ta . . . . Kariyat

ANDROM'EDA |w . . . . Andromeda
arbo'rea . . . **Oxydendrum arboreum**
calycula'ta . . . . **Chamaedaphne c.**
cates'baei . . . . **Leucothoe c.**
glaucophyl'la . . . . . . Downy A.
polifo'lia |w . . . . Bogrosemary A.
—na'na . . . . Dwarf B.A.
racemo'sa . . . . **Leucothoe r.**
specio'sa . . . . **Zenobia pulverulenta**

ANDROPO'GON . . . . . Bluestem
See **GRASS GENERA.**

ANDROS'ACE |w . . . Rockjasmine
acu'ta |w
ai'zoon . . . . Aizoon R.
—coccin'ea . . . . . . Scarlet A.R.
alpi'na (*glacialis*) . . . . . Alpine R.
carne'a . . . . Pine R.
Brigantiaca. hv.
Haller (*halleri*)
Laggers (*laggeri*)
chamaejas'me . . . . . Dwarf R.
cilia'ta
folio'sa
hedrean'tha
helve'tica . . . . Swiss R.
lacte'a
lactiflo'ra (*coronopifolia*)
lanugino'sa
—leicht'lini
—yunnanen'sis
max'ima
obtusifo'lia
occidenta'lis |w . . . . . Western R.
primuloi'des . . . . . . Primula R.
puberulen'ta |w
sarmento'sa
—chum'byi
—primuloi'des
—wat'kinsi
sempervivoi'des
septentriona'lis
—subumbella'ta
spinulif'era
villo'sa
—arachnoi'dea
vitalia'na . . . . **Douglasia v.**

ANDROSTEPH'IUM . . Funnellily
caeru'leum (*violaceum*) . . Blue F.

ANE'MIA
See **FERN GENERA.**

ANEM'ONE (*PULSATILLA*) |w Anemone
alpi'na (*acutipetala; Pulsatilla alpina*) Alpine A.
—sulphu'rea (*A. sulphurea*) Sulfur A.A.

ANEMONE, continued
alta'ica . . . . . Irkutsk Anemone
angulo'sa . . . . **Hepatica a.**
apenni'na . . . . . . Apennine A.
—al'ba . . . . White A.A.
balden'sis . . . . Moraine A.
blan'da . . . . Greek A.
—atrocaeru'lea . . . . . Dark G.A.
—rose'a . . . . Rosy G.A.
—scythin'ica
canaden'sis . . . . . . Meadow A.
carolinia'na . . . . . . Carolina A.
cer'nua . . . . Nodding A.
corona'ria . . . . Poppy A.
—floreple'no Hort. . . Double P.A.
¢Skycup. hv. A. coronaria
¢St. Bridget
cylin'drica . . . . Candle A.
decapet'ala . . . . . . Tenpetal A.
deltoi'dea . . . . . . Threeleaf A.
drum'mondi . . . . . . Drummond A.
ful'gens . . . . Flame A.
—multipet'ala . . . . Double F.A.
globo'sa . . . . Pacific A.

Anemone globosa, is perhaps hardly more than a southern form of A. hudsoniana.

hal'leri (*Pulsatilla h.*) . . Haller A.
hirsutis'sima . . . . . **A. ludoviciana**
horten'sis . . . . Garden A.
hudsonia'na . . . . . Hudsonian A.
japon'ica . . . . Japanese A.
—al'ba . . . . White J.A.
—cris'pa . . . . . . Curlleaf J.A.
¢Alice. hv. A. japonica
¢Charmeuse
¢Geante Blanche
¢Honorine Joubert
¢Hupeh (*hupehensis*)
¢Kriemhilde
¢Loreley
¢Louise Uhink
¢Margarete
¢Max Vogel
¢Mount Rose
¢Nigricans
¢Occidentalis
¢Profusion
¢Purple (*atropurpurea*)
¢Richard Arends
¢Rosea
¢Rubra
¢September Queen
¢September Sprite
¢Showy (*splendens*)
¢Superba
¢Whirlwind
lancifo'lia . . . . . Lanceleaf A.
ludovicia'na (*hirsutissima; nuttalliana; A. patens n.; A. p. wolfgangiana; Pulsatilla hirsutissima; P. ludoviciana*) |w . American Pasqueflower
ly'alli . . . . Lyall A.
magellan'ica . . . . . Magellan A.
monta'na (*Pulsatilla m.*). Mountain A.
—al'ba . . . . White M.A.
—ru'bra . . . . Red M.A.
multif'ida . . . . . . Argentine A.
narcissiflo'ra (*zephyra*) Narcissus A.
nemoro'sa . . . European Wood A.
—*quinquefo'lia* . . . **A. quinquefolia**
¢Alba (*florepleno*) hv. A. nemorosa
¢Allen (*alleni*)
¢Bluebonnet
¢Celestial
¢Major
¢Robinson (*robinsoniana*)

ANEMONE nemorosa, continued
¢Rosea (*rubra fl. pl.*)
¢Simplex
nuttallia'na . . . . . . **A. ludoviciana**
occidenta'lis (*Pulsatilla o.*) Western Pasqueflower
orega'na . . . . . Oregon Anemone
palma'ta . . . . . Mediterranean A.
¢Albida. hv.
¢Double
¢Yellow (*lutea*)
parviflo'ra . . . . Arctic A.
pa'tens (*Pulsatilla p.*). Spreading Pasqueflower (*Spreading Anemone*)
—*nuttallia'na* . . . . **A. ludoviciana**
—*wolfgangia'na* . . . **A. ludoviciana**
pennsylvan'ica . . . . **A. canadensis**
praten'sis (*Pulsatilla p.*) . Meadow P.
pulsatil'la (*Pulsatilla vulgaris*) European P.
¢Amoena. hv.
¢Lilac (*lilacina*)
¢Mrs. Vanderelst
¢Red (*rubra*)
¢Variegated (*variegata*)
¢Whiteswan
quinquefo'lia (*A. nemorosa q.*) American Wood A.
ranunculoi'des . . Yellow Wood A.
¢Double (*plena*) hv.
reflex'a . . . . Yenesei A.
ripa'ria . . . . Riverbank A.
rivula'ris . . . . Brook A.
rupic'ola . . . . Malebum A.
sibir'ica . . . . Siberian A.
sphenophyl'la . . . . . Chilean A.
sulphu'rea . . . . **A. alpina s.**
sylves'tris . . . . . . Snowdrop A.
¢Double (*plena*) hv.
tubero'sa . . . . Tuber A.
verna'lis (*Pulsatilla v.*) . Vernal A.
villosis'sima Hort.

Perhaps a hort. var. of A. narcissiflora.

virginia'na . . . . Virginia A.
vitifo'lia . . . . Grapeleaf A.
—tomento'sa . . . . . Hairy G.A.
zeph'yra . . . . . . **A. narcissiflora**

Anemone . . . . **Anemone**

For hort. var. of Anemone, see preceding list.

Alpine A . . . . **A. alpina**
American Pasqueflower **A. ludoviciana**
American Wood A. . . **A. quinquefolia**
Apennine A. . . . . . . **A. apennina**
Arctic A. . . . . **A. parviflora**
Argentine A. . . . . . . **A. multifida**
Brook A. . . . . **A. rivularis**
Candle A . . . . **A. cylindrica**
Carolina A. . . . . . . **A. caroliniana**
Chilean A. . . . . . **A. sphenophylla**
Curlleaf Japanese A. **A. japonica crispa**
Dark Greek A. **A. blanda atrocaerulea**
Double Flame A. **A. fulgens multipetala**
Double Poppy A. **A. coronaria florepleno**
Drummond A. . . . . . **A. drummondi**
European Pasqueflower **A. pulsatilla**
European Wood A. . . . **A. nemorosa**
Flame A. . . . . **A. fulgens**
Garden A. . . . . **A. hortensis**
Grapeleaf A. . . . . **A. vitifolia**
Greek A. . . . . **A. blanda**

Anemone, continued
Hairy Grapeleaf A. **Anemone vitifolia tomentosum**
Haller A. . . . . **A. halleri**
Hudsonian A. . . . . . **A. hudsoniana**
Irkutsk A. . . . . **A. altaica**
Japanese A. . . . . **A. japonica**
Lanceleaf A. . . . . **A. lancifolia**
Lyall A. . . . . **A. lyalli**
Magellan A. . . . . . **A. magellanica**
Malebum A. . . . . **A. rupicola**
Meadow A. . . . . **A. canadensis**
Meadow Pasqueflower. **A. pratensis**
Mediterranean A. . . . . **A. palmata**
Moraine A. . . . . **A. baldensis**
Mountain A. . . . . **A. montana**
Narcissus A. . . . . **A. narcissiflora**
Nodding A. . . . . **A. cernua**
Oregon A. . . . . **A. oregana**
Pacific A . . . . **A. globosa**
Poppy A. . . . . **A. coronaria**
Red Mountain A. . **A. montana rubra**
Riverbank A. . . . . **A. riparia**
Rosy Greek A. . . . **A. blanda rosea**
Siberian A. . . . . **A. sibirica**
Snowdrop A. . . . . . . **A. sylvestris**
Spreading Pasqueflower . **A. patens**
Sulfur Alpine A. **A. alpina sulphurea**
Tenpetal A. . . . . . . **A. decapetala**
Threeleaf A. . . . . **A. deltoidea**
Tuber A. . . . . **A. tuberosa**
Vernal A. . . . . **A. vernalis**
Virginia A. . . . . **A. virginiana**
Western Pasqueflower **A. occidentalis**
White Apennine A.. **A. apennina alba**
White Japanese A. . . **A. japonica a.**
White Mountain A. . **A. montana a.**
Yellow Wood A. . **A. ranunculoides**
Yenesei A. . . . . **A. reflexa**

ANEMONEL'LA (*SYNDESMON*) Anemonella
thalictroi'des (*Syndesmon t.; Thalictrum anemonoides*) . . . . Anemonella

ANEMONOP'SIS
macrophyl'la

ANEMOPAEG'MA
chamberlay'ni (*Bignonia c.*) Goldentrumpet

ANEMOP'SIS
califor'nica |w . . . . Yerbamansa

ANE'THUM
grave'olens . . . . Dill
officina'le . . . . Sulfurroot

ANGEL'ICA |w . . . . . . Angelica
anom'ala . . . . Eumenol A.
—chinen'sis . . . . . Chinese E.A.
archangel'ica (*officinalis; Archangelica o.*) . . . . Garden A.
atropurpu'rea . . . . Purplestem A.
brew'eri . . . . Brewer A.
cur'tisi . . . . Filmy A.
gray'i . . . . Grays A.
heterocar'pa . . . . . . Spanish A.
ly'alli . . . . Lyall A.
officina'lis . . . . . . **A. archangelica**
pinna'ta . . . . Small-leaf A.
rosaefo'lia . . . . Rose A.
sylves'tris . . . . Woodland A.
villo'sa (*Archangelica hirsuta*) Hairy A.
wheel'eri . . . . Wheeler A.

Angelica . . . . **Angelica**
Brewer A. . . . . **A. breweri**

ANGELICA, continued
CHINESE EUMENOL A.
Angelica anomala chinensis
EUMENOL A. . . . . A. anomala
FILMY A. . . . . A. curtisi
GARDEN A. . . . . . A. archangelica
GRAYS A. . . . . A. grayi
HAIRY A. . . . . A. villosa
LYALL A. . . . . A. lyalli
PURPLESTEM A. . . . A. atropurpurea
ROSE A. . . . . A. rosaefolia
SMALL-LEAF A. . . . . . . A. pinnata
SPANISH A. . . . . . A. heterocarpa
WHEELER A. . . . . . . A. wheeleri
WOODLAND A. . . . . . A. sylvestris

ANGELINTREE . . . . Andira
BRAZILIAN A. . . . . . A. vermifuga
CABBAGE A. . . . . A. inermis
GOA A. . . . . A. araroba
SHOWY A. . . . . . . A. spectabilis

ANGELO'NIA . . . . . . ANGELONIA
angustifo'lia
grandiflo'ra
Possibly a hort. form of A. salicariaefolia.
salicariaefo'lia

ANGELS-TEARS . . . Narcissus triandrus

Angels-trumpet . DATURA, FLORIPONDIO: Datura arborea

ANGELWOOD, PARA . Dicorynia paraensis

ANGIOP'TERIS . . . . . VESSELFERN
See FERN GENERA.

ANGOPH'ORA . . . . . GUMMYRTLE
interme'dia . . . . KINO G.
lanceola'ta (*costata*) . . . . RUSTY G.
subvelu'tina

ANGRAE'CUM
See ORCHID GENERA.

ANGULO'A . . . . . . CRADLEORCHID
See ORCHID GENERA.

ANHALO'NIUM . . . ARIOCARPUS
See CACTUS GENERA.

ANI'BA
co'to (*Nectandra c.; Ocotea c.*)
COTOBARK
panuren'sis . . . . CAYENNE LINALOE (*Bois de Rose*)

ANIGOZAN'THOS
flav'ida
hu'milis
man'glesi . . . . . . KANGAROOPAW
ru'fa
vir'idis

ANISACAN'THUS . . . . ANISACANTH
insig'nis . . . . DWARF A.
thur'beri . . . . THURBER A.
wright'i . . . . WRIGHTS A.

ANISE . . . . Pimpinella anisum

ANISETREE . . . . Illicium
BURMA A. . . . . I. majus
CAMBODIA A. . . . . . I. cambodianum
FLORIDA A. . . . . . . I. floridanum
HENRY A. . . . . I. henryi
HIMALAYA A. . . . . I. griffithi
JAPANESE A. . . . . I. anisatum
TRUESTAR A. . . . . I. verum
VARIEGATED JAPANESE A.
I. anisatum variegatum
YELLOW A. . . . . I. parviflorum

ANISOLO'TUS . . . . LOTUS
decum'bens . . . . L. douglasi

ANISOP'TERA . . . . . MERSAWA
thurif'era (*Dipterocarpus thurifer*)
PALOSAPIS M.

ANISOS'TICHUS . . . . BIGNONIA

ANISOTO'ME
latifo'lia

ANJELYWOOD . . . Artocarpus hirsutus

ANNO'NA (*ANONA*)
biflo'ra cine'rea . . . . A. squamosa
cherimo'la . . . . CHERIMOYA
diversifo'lia . . . . ILAMA
forskahl'i . . . . A. squamosa
gla'bra (*A. laurifolia palustris*)
PONDAPPLE (*Alligator Apple*)
longiflo'ra . . . . WILD CHERIMOYA
monta'na . . . MOUNTAIN SOURSOP
murica'ta . . SOURSOP (*Guanabana*)
purpu'rea . . . . SONCOYA
reticula'ta
BULLOCKSHEART CUSTARDAPPLE
scleroder'ma . . . . . . HARDSHELL C.
squamo'sa (*A. biflora cinerea; forskahli*)
SUGARAPPLE (*Custardapple; Sweetsop*)

ANO'DA ⊻ . . . . ANODA
hasta'ta
lavateroi'des ⊻
triangula'ris
wright'i . . . . WRIGHTS A.

ANODEN'DRON
panicula'tum . . . . . CABLECREEPER

ANOECTOCHI'LUS
See ORCHID GENERA.

ANOGEIS'SUS . . . . AXLEWOOD
acumina'ta . . . . YON A.
latifo'lia . . . . BAKLIGUM A.

ANO'GRA . . . . OENOTHERA
albicau'lis . . . . O. pallida

ANOMATHE'CA . . LAPEIROUSIA

ANO'NA . . . . ANNONA

ANOP'TERIS
See FERN GENERA.

ANO'TA
densiflo'ra . . . . ANOTA
viola'cea . . . . VIOLET A.

ANSEL'LIA
See ORCHID GENERA.

ANTELOPEHORN . . . . . . Asclepiodora
SPIDER A. . . . . A. decumbens

ANTENNA'RIA ⊻ . . . . PUSSYTOES
alpi'na . . . . ALPINE P.
a'prica . . . . . ROCKYMOUNTAIN P.
canaden'sis . . . . CANADA P.
carpath'ica . . . . . . CARPATHIAN P.
dimor'pha . . . . LOW P.
dio'ica (*candida; tomentosa*) COMMON P.
—rose'a . . . . A. rosea
lana'ta . . . . WOOLLY P.
luzuloi'des . . . . RUSH P.
magellan'ica . . . . . . MAGELLAN P.
margarita'cea . . . . . Anaphalis m.
me'dia
microphyl'la (*parvifolia*) LITTLELEAF P.
neglec'ta . . . . FIELD P.
neodio'ica . . . . SMALLER P.
obova'ta
plantaginifo'lia ⊻ . . PLANTAINLEAF P.
pulcher'rima . . . . SHOWY P.

ANTENNARIA, continued
racemo'sa . . . RACEME PUSSYTOES
rhodan'tha
rose'a (*A. dioica r.*) . . . . ROSE P.
tomento'sa . . . . A. dioica
umbrinel'la

ANTHAENAN'TIA . . . . SILKYSCALE
See GRASS GENERA.

AN'THEMIS ⊻ . . . . . . CAMOMILE
ai'zoon . . . Achillea ageratifolia a.
altis'sima . . . . TALL C.
ara'bica . . . . . Cladanthus arabicus
arven'sis . . . . FIELD C.
—agres'tis . . . . . . CORNFIELD C.
carpat'ica . . . . . . CARPATHIAN C.
cine'rea . . . . GRAY C.
cot'ula ⊻ . . . . MAYWEED C.
macedon'ica . . . . MACEDONIAN C.
macran'tha . . . . BIGHEAD C.
monta'na . . . . RIVIERA C.
no'bilis . . . ROMAN C. (*English C.*)
₵DOUBLE (*florepleno*) HV.
₵SHOWY (*grandiflora*)
sancti-johan'nis . . . . ST. JOHNS C.
tincto'ria . . . . GOLDEN C.
₵E. (*C.*) BUXTON. HV.
₵KELWAY (*kelwayi*)
₵PALE (*pallida*)
₵ROGER PERRY
₵THORA PERRY
₵WHITERIM (*alba*)

ANTHEPH'ORA
See GRASS GENERA.

ANTHE'RICUM . . . . ANTHERICUM
bichet'i . . . . BICHET A.
como'sum . . . . . Chlorophytum c.
goldia'num . . . . GOLDIE A.
lilia'go . . . . . . ST. BERNARDLILY
lilias'trum . . . . Paradisea l.
mandaia'num . Chlorophytum elatum
ramo'sum
tor'reyi . . . . TORREY A.
vitta'tum . . . Chlorophytum elatum

ANTHOCH'LOA
See GRASS GENERA.

ANTHOLY'ZA . . . . . MADFLOWER
aethio'pica . . . . ETHIOPIAN M.
panicula'ta . . . . PANICLED M.
revolu'ta

ANTHOPO'GON . . . . GENTIANA
el'egans . . . . G. thermalis

ANTHOXAN'THUM . . VERNALGRASS
See GRASS GENERA.

ANTHRIS'CUS . . . . BEAKCHERVIL
cerefo'lium . . . . . . SALADCHERVIL
sylves'tris . . . . WOODLAND B.
vulga'ris (*anthriscus*) . . . BUR B.

ANTHU'RIUM . . . . . . ANTHURIUM
×al'bum . . . . WHITE A.
andraea'num . . . . . . FLAMINGO A.
—gigan'teum . . . . GIANT F.A.
₵JULIUS ROEHRS. HV. A. andraeanum
₵SOUVENIR DEGAND
bogoten'se . . . . BOGOTA A.
brown'i . . . . BROWNS A.
∞car'neum (*andraeanum × nymphaefolium*) . . . . ∞FLESH A.
corda'tum (*Pothos cordatus*)
crystalli'num . . . . CRYSTAL A.
₵VARIEGATED (*variegatus*) HV.
∞ferrieren'se (*andraeanum × ornatum*)
∞FERRIER A.

ANTHURIUM, continued
forget'i . . . . Forgets Anthurium
gran'de . . . . Bolivian A.
hook'eri . . . . Hooker A.
magnif'icum
orna'tum
re'gale . . . . Royal A.
scherzeria'num . . . . . Common A.
¢Bigspathe (*giganteum*) hv.
¢Bloodred (*sanguineum*)
¢Rosegay (*roseum*)
¢Rothschild (*rothschildianum*)
¢Scarletspathe (*maximum*)
¢White (*album*)
sello'um
tetrag'onum
veitch'i . . . . Veitch A.
veluti'num . . . . Satiny A.
warocquea'num
¢Clark (*clarkianum*) hv. Anthurium
¢Duchart (*ducharti*)
¢Illustrious (*illustre*)
¢Lows (*lowi*)
¢Reynolds (*reynoldsianum*)

Anthurium . . . . **Anthurium**
Bogota A. . . . . **A. bogotense**
Bolivian A. . . . . **A. grande**
Browns A. . . . . **A. browni**
Common A. . . . . **A. scherzerianum**
Crystal A. . . . . **A. crystallinum**
∞Ferrier A. . . . . . ∞**A. ferrierense**
Flamingo A. . . . . **A. andraeanum**
∞Flesh A. . . . . ∞**A. carneum**
Forgets A. . . . . **A. forgeti**
Giant Flamingo A.
A. andraeanum giganteum
Hooker A. . . . . **A. hookeri**
Royal A. . . . . **A. regale**
Satiny A. . . . . . . **A. velutinum**
Veitch A. . . . . **A. veitchi**
White A. . . . . **×A. album**

ANTHYL'LIS . . . . . Anthyllis
barba-jo'vis . . . Jupitersbeard A.
hermann'iae . . . . Hermann A.
—aspal'athi
monta'na . . . . Alps A.
—carmin'ea
—ru'bra
tetraphyl'la . . . . Fourleaf A.
vulnera'ria . . . . . Kidneyvetch A. (*Woundwort*)

ANTIA'RIS
toxica'ria . . . . Upastree

ANTIC'LEA . . . . . . **ZIGADENUS**

ANTIDES'MA . . . . . Chinalaurel
bu'nius . . . . Bignay C.
delicat'ulum

ANTIG'ONON . . . . . . Coralvine
lepto'pus . . . . Mountainrose C. (*Rosa-de-Montana*)
—al'bus . . . . White M.C.
macrocar'pus

ANTIPHYL'LA . . . . **SAXIFRAGA**

ANTIRRHI'NUM . . . . Snapdragon
angustifo'lium . . . . **A. siculum**
antirrhiniflo'ra . . . . **Maurandia a.**
asari'na . . . . Wildginger S.
coulteria'num . . . . . . Chaparral S.
glandulo'sum . . . . Sierra S.
glutino'sum . . . . . . Gummy S.
hispan'icum . . . . . . Spanish S.
hu'eti . . . . **A. sempervirens**
latifo'lium . . . . . . Wideleaf S.

ANTIRRHINUM, continued
ma'jus . . . . Common Snapdragon
¢Brilliant. hv.
¢Carmineking
¢Coralpink
¢Crimsonking
¢Fairyqueen
¢Firefly
¢Grandiflorum
¢Maximum
¢Nigrescens
¢Rosedore
¢Torchlight
¢Whitequeen
¢Yellowking
maurandioi'des
Maurandia antirrhiniflora
mol'le . . . . Pyrenees S.
nuttallia'num . . . . . Nuttall S.
orcuttia'num . . . . Orcutt S.
oron'tium . . . . Corn S.
sempervi'rens (*hueti*) . Evergreen S.
sic'ulum (*angustifolium*) . Sicilian S.
specio'sum . . . . **Galvezia speciosa**
va'gans . . . . Coastrange S.

Antpalm . . . . **Korthalsia**
Java A. . . . . **K. junghuhni**
Teysmann A. . . . . **K. teysmanni**

Anttree . . . . **Triplaris**
Caracas A. . . . . **T. caracasana**
Longjohn A. . . . . **T. americana**
Peru A. . . . . . **T. bonplandiana**
Surinam A. . . . . **T. surinamensis**

Anzacwood . . . . **Pomaderris**
Edgerley A. . . . . . . **P. edgerleyi**
Golden-tainui A. . . . . **P. elliptica**
Petaled A. . . . . **P. lanigera**
Rustyvein A. . . . . . . **P. rugosa**
Shrubby A. . . . . **P. phylicaefolia**
Virescent A. . . . . . . **P. apetala**

Apacheplume . . **Fallugia; F. paradoxa**

Aparejograss . . **Muhlenbergia utilis**

APAR'GIA . . . . . **LEONTODON**

APEI'BA
as'pera

Apes-earring . . . . . **Pithecellobium**
Carib A. . . . . **P. caribaeum**
Catclaw A. . . . . . **P. unguiscati**
Ebony A. . . . . **P. flexicaule**
Goldwood A. . . . . . **P. vinhatico**
Guamachil A. . . . . **P. dulce**
Huajillo A. . . . . . **P. brevifolium**
Junghuhn A. . . **P. junghuhnianum**
Ladder A. . . . . **P. scalare**
Raintree A. . . . . **P. saman**
Snowwood A. . . . . **P. pruinosum**
Soaptree A. . . . . **P. trapezifolium**
Tamarind A. . . . . . . **P. arboreum**
Tortoiseshell A. . **P. grandiflorum**

APHANAN'THE
as'pera (*Homoioceltis a.*)

Apha'nes arven'sis . . . **Alchemilla a.**

APHANOPET'ALUM
resino'sum

APHANOSTE'PHUS
skirrob'asis

APHELAN'DRA . . . . . Aphelandra
auranti'aca . . . . Orange A.
squarro'sa (*leopoldi*) Saffronspike A.
tetrag'ona . . . . Scarlet A.

APHYLLAN'THES
monspelien'sis

API'CRA
See **SUCCULENTS.**

A'PIOS ⌊w . . Potatobean (*Groundnut*)
america'na (*tuberosa; Glycine apios*) ⌊w American P.

A'PIUM (*CELERI*) ⌊w . . . Celery
am'mi
grave'olens ⌊w . . . . . . Wild C.
—dul'ce . . . . Garden C.
—rapa'ceum . . . . Celeriac

APLEC'TRUM . . . . . . Puttyroot
See **ORCHID GENERA, HARDY TERRESTRIAL GROUP.**

APLOPAP'PUS (*Bigelovia* in part; *Chrysoma; Diplopappus; Ericameria; Eriocarpum; Haplopappus; Isocoma; Macronema; Oonopsis; Prionopsis; Pyrrocoma; Sideranthus; Stenotopsis; Stenotus; Tonestus*) Goldenweed
acau'lis (*Stenotus a.*) . Stemless G.
acrade'nius (*Bigelovia acradenia; Isocoma a.*) . . . . Paleleaf G.
arbores'cens (*Bigelovia a.; Ericameria a.*) . . . . Fleece G.
baylahu'en
bloom'eri (*Chrysothamnus b.*) Rabbitbrush G.
brachyle'pis Hall, *not* Phil. **A. propinquus**
brickellioi'des . . . . . Brickell G.
ca'nus (*Diplostephium canum; Hazardia cana*) . . . . Hoary G.
cilia'tus (*Prionopsis ciliata*) ⌊w
coop'eri (*monactis; Bigelovia c.*) Cooper G.
cunea'tus (*Ericameria cuneata*) Wedgeleaf G.
eastwood'ae (*Chrysoma fasciculata*) Monterey G.
ericoi'des (*Diplopappus e.; Ericameria e.*) . . . . Heather G.
falca'tus (*Stenotus caespitosus*) Tufted G.
fre'monti (*Oonopsis condensata*) Fremont G.
frutico'sus (*Bigelovia coronopifolia; Isocoma c.; I. fruticosa*) ⌊w Burroweed
green'ei (*Macronema g.*) . Greenes G.
—mol'lis
heterophyl'lus (*Bigelovia heterophylla; Isocoma heterophylla; I. wrighti*) Jimmyweed
integrifo'lius (*Pyrrocoma integrifolia*) Wholeleaf G.
jun'ceus . . . . Rush G.
lanceola'tus (*Pyrrocoma lanceolata*) Lanceleaf G.
laricifo'lius (*Ericameria laricifolia*) Larchleaf G.
linearifo'lius (*Stenotopsis linearifolia; Stenotus linearifolius*) Narrowleaf G.
—inte'rior . . . . Desert G.
macrone'ma (*Macronema discoideum*) Whitestem G.
monac'tis . . . . **A. cooperi**
na'nus (*Ericameria nana*). Dwarf G.
nutt'alli (*Sideranthus grindelioides*) Nuttall G.
pal'meri (*Ericameria p.*) . Palmer G.
par'ishi (*Bigelovia p.*) . . . Parish G.
phylloceph'alus (*rubiginosus*)
pinifo'lius (*Ericameria pinifolia*) Pine G.

APLOPAPPUS, continued
propin'quus (*brachylepis* Hall, *not* Phil.; *Ericameria b.*) CHAPARRAL GOLDENWEED
spinulo'sus . . . . . IRONPLANT G.
squarro'sus . . . . . SAWTOOTH G.
suffrutico'sus (*Macronema suffruticosum*) . . . . . SINGLEHEAD G.
uniflo'rus (*Pyrrocoma uniflora*) PLANTAIN G.
vene'tus (*Isocoma veneta*) DAMIANA G.
—vernonioi'des . . . . . COAST G.

APOC'YNUM . . . . DOGBANE
androsaemifo'lium . . SPREADING D.
—gla'brum (*A. ambigens*)
cannab'inum . . . . HEMP D.
pu'milum . . . . LOW D.
scopulo'rum . . . . CLIFF D.
sibir'icum . . . . PRAIRIE D.

APODY'TES
benien'sis
dimidia'ta

APO'GON . . . . **SERINEA**
hu'milis . . . . **S. oppositifolia**

APONOGE'TON (*OUVIRANDRA*) WATERHAWTHORN
distach'yus . . . . CAPE W.
—gigan'teus . . . . . . GIANT C.W.
fenestra'lis (*Ouvirandra f.*) . LACE W.

APOROCAC'TUS . . . APOROCACTUS
See **CACTUS GENERA.**

APPLE . . . . **Malus**
See also CRABAPPLE; for cultivated varieties of Apple see **FRUIT AND EDIBLE NUT NAMES.**
COMMON A. . . . . **M. pumila**
Mexican A. . . . . . WHITESAPOTE: **Casimiroa edulis**

APPLECACTUS . . . . **Harrisia**
BROOKS A. . . . . **H. brooki**
EARLES A. . . . . **H. earlei**
FERNOW A. . . . . **H. fernowi**
PUERTORICO A. . . **H. portoricensis**
SHELLMOUND A. . . . **H. aboriginum**

APPLEOFPERU. **Nicandra; N. physalodes**

APRICOT . . . . . **Prunus; P. armeniaca**
See also ALMOND, BIRDCHERRY, BUSHCHERRY, CHERRY, CHOKECHERRY, LAURELCHERRY, PEACH, PEACHBRUSH, and PLUM. For cultivated varieties see **FRUIT AND EDIBLE NUT NAMES.**
ANSU A. . . . . . . **P. armeniaca ansu**
BRIANCON A. . . . . . . **P. brigantina**
JAPANESE A. . . . . **P. mume**
MANCHURIAN A. . . **P. mandshurica**
PURPLE A. . . . . **P. dasycarpa**
SIBERIAN A. . . . . **P. sibirica**
SMOOTH JAPANESE A. **P. mume tonsa**
WHITE J. A. . . . . **P. m. alba**

APTE'NIA **MESEMBRYANTHEMUM**
See **SUCCULENTS.**

APULE'IA
prae'cox

AQUARIUM PLANTS
Chiefly this list is based on E. J. Alexander's "Water Plants for Home Cultivation" (Journ. Amer. Mus. Nat. Hist. 34 (3): 207–220, illus. 1934).

ALDROVAN'DA vesiculo'sa WATERBUGTRAP

ALIS'MA plantago-aquat'ica AMERICAN WATERPLANTAIN

AQUARIUM PLANTS, continued

ANACH'ARIS canaden'sis (*Elodea c.; Philotria c.*) CANADA WATERWEED
GIGANTEA. HV.

APONOGE'TON WATERHAWTHORN
distach'yus . . . . CAPE W.
fenestra'lis (*Ouvirandra f.*) . LACE W.

AZOL'LA . . . . AZOLLA
carolinia'na . . . . MOSQUITOFERN
filiculoi'des . . . . . . PACIFIC A.

BACO'PA rotundifo'lia (*Bramia r.; Herpestis r.; Moniera r.*) DISK WATERHYSSOP

BATRA'CHIUM **RANUNCULUS**
trichophyl'lum . **R. aquatilis capillaceus**

BI'DENS beck'i BECKS BEGGARTICKS

BOOT'TIA corda'ta HEARTLEAF BOOTTIA

Bra'mia rotundifo'lia . . **Bacopa r.**

BRASE'NIA schre'beri (*peltata*) SCHREBER WATERSHIELD

BU'TOMUS umbella'tus FLOWERINGRUSH

CABOM'BA . . . . . . FANWORT
aquat'ica . . . . TROPICAL F.
carolinia'na (*aquatica* DC., *not* Aubl.) CAROLINA F.
—pulcher'rima . . . . PURPLE C.F.

CALLI'TRICHE . WATERSTARWORT

CERATOPHYL'LUM demer'sum HORNWORT

CERATOP'TERIS . . WATERFERN
pteridoi'des . . . . . AMERICAN W.
thalictroi'des . . . . . ORIENTAL W.

CHA'RA . . . . . . STONEWORT

COT'ULA coronopifo'lia BIRD BRASSBUTTONS

CRYPTOCORY'NE . CRYPTOCORYNE
cilia'ta . . . . FRAGRANT C.
grif'fithi . . . . BROADLEAF C.
retrospira'lis . . . . . TWISTHOOD C.

CYP'ERUS . . . . . FLATSEDGE
alternifo'lius . . . . . UMBRELLA F.
papy'rus (*Papyrus antiquorum*) PAPYRUS

EICHHORN'IA cras'sipes (*Piaropus c.*) COMMON WATERHYACINTH

ELATI'NE . . . . . . WATERWORT

ELEO'CHARIS canaden'sis CANADA SPIKESEDGE

Elode'a canaden'sis . . **Anacharis c.**

ERIG'ERON . . . . . FLEABANE

ERIOCAU'LON decangula're TENANGLE PIPEWORT

ERYN'GIUM . . . . . . ERYNGO

FONTINA'LIS antipyret'ica FEVER WATERMOSS

Herpes'tis rotundifo'lia . **Bacopa r.**

HIPPU'RIS vulga'ris . MARESTAIL

HOTTO'NIA . . . FEATHERFOIL
infla'ta . . . . AMERICAN F.
palus'tris . . . . EUROPEAN F.

AQUARIUM PLANTS, continued

HYDROCH'ARIS morsus-ra'nae FROGBIT

HYDRO'CLEIS nymphoi'des (*Limnocharis humboldti*) . WATERPOPPY

HYDROCOT'YLE . . PENNYWORT
peduncula'ris . . . . TASMANIAN P.
rotundifo'lia . . . . SHINY P.
vulga'ris . . . . COMMON P.

HYDRO'TRIDA carolinia'na CAROLINA BOGHYSSOP

HYGRORY'ZA (*HYGRORHIZA*) WATERRICE

ISNAR'DIA palus'tris (*Ludwigia p.*) MARSHPURSLANE

ISO'ETES . . . . QUILLWORT

JUN'CUS re'pens . CREEPING RUSH

LEM'NA . . . . . . DUCKWEED

LILAEOP'SIS . . . . LILAEOPSIS

LIMNAN'THEMUM **NYMPHOIDES**

Limnoch'aris humboldt'i **Hydrocleis nymphoides**

LIMNOPH'ILA . . . MARSHWEED

LIMOSEL'LA . . . . . MUDWORT

LITTOREL'LA uniflo'ra EUROPEAN SHOREWEED

LOBE'LIA dortman'na WATER LOBELIA

LUDWIG'IA . . . . . . SEEDBOX
na'tans (*mulertti*) . . . . . WATER S.
The identity of Ludwigia mulertti, of the Aquarium Plants trade, has long been problematical. Under date of June 10, 1941, P. A. Munz, Professor of Botany, Pomona College, Claremont, Calif., an outstanding authority on the Evening-primrose family (*Onagraceae*), communicated this note to W. A. Dayton of the S.P.N. Editorial Com.: "I have borrowed the material of *Ludwigia Mulerttii* from the Bailey Hortorium. It consists of 3 sheets. . . All are *Ludwigia natans* Ell. var. *typica* Fernald & Griscom, so far as I can see. They are certainly not *L. palustris*." The var. typica is, of course, typical L. natans. Some botanists use the original spelling of the generic name, Ludvigia.
palus'tris . . . . **Isnardia p.**

LUDWIGIAN'THA . LUDWIGIANTHA

LYSIMACH'IA nummula'ria MONEYWORT

MARSIL'EA uncina'ta HOOKED PEPPERWORT

MAYA'CA fluviat'ilis RIVER MAYACA

MENYAN'THES trifolia'ta COMMON BOGBEAN

MONIER'A . . . . **BACOPA**

MYRIOPHYL'LUM PARROTFEATHER
pinna'tum . . . . GREEN P.
proserpinacoi'des . . . . . CHILE P.
verticilla'tum . . . . . . CANADA P.

NAI'AS . . . . NAIAD
flex'ilis
—robus'ta

NELUM'BIUM (*NELUMBO*) LOTUS

NITEL'LA . . . . NITELLA

AQUARIUM PLANTS, continued

NU'PHAR adve'na (*Nymphozanthus a.*) . SPATTERDOCK COWLILY

NYMPH'AEA . . . . WATERLILY

NYMPHOI'DES in'dicum (*Limnanthemum i.*) . INDIA FLOATINGHEART

NYMPHOZAN'THUS . **NUPHAR**

ORON'TIUM aquat'icum GOLDENCLUB

OTTE'LIA alismoi'des WATERPLANTAIN OTTELIA

OUVIRAN'DRA . **APONOGETON**

PAPY'RUS . . . . . . **CYPERUS**

PEC'TIS . . . . PECTIS

PELTAN'DRA virgin'ica (*undulata*) VIRGINIA ARROWARUM

PHILO'TRIA . . . **ANACHARIS**

PHYLLAN'THUS flu'itans FLOATING LEAFFLOWER

PIARO'PUS . . . **EICHHORNIA**

PIS'TIA stratio'tes . WATERLETTUCE

PONTEDE'RIA . PICKERELWEED
corda'ta . . . . . . PICKERELWEED
—lancifo'lia . . . . LANCE P.

POTAMOGE'TON . . PONDWEED

PROSERPINA'CA pectina'ta COMBLEAF MERMAIDWEED

Radic'ula nasturtium-aquat'icum **Rorippa n.**

RANUN'CULUS . . . BUTTERCUP

The species most commonly grown in aquaria belong to the aquatic, white-flowered subgenus Batrachium.

aquat'ilis (*Batrachium aquatile*) WATERCROWFOOT B.
—capilla'ceus (*R. trichophyllus; Batrachium trichophyllum*) HAIRLEAF W.B.
—heterophyl'lus . . VARILEAF W.B.

Perhaps not distinct from R. aquatilis.

lenor'mandi . . . . LENORMAND B.

RIC'CIA flu'itans . COMMON RICCIA

RICCIOCAR'PUS na'tans COMMON RICCIOCARPUS

RORIP'PA nasturtium - aquat'icum (*Radicula n.*) . . WATERCRESS

RUP'PIA . . . . . WIDGEONWEED

SAGITTA'RIA te'res SLENDER ARROWHEAD

SALVIN'IA . . . . . . SALVINIA

SCIR'PUS . . . . . . BULRUSH

SCLEROL'EPIS uniflo'ra SCLEROLEPIS

SPHAG'NUM macrophyl'lum LONGLEAF SPHAGNUM

STRATIO'TES aloi'des WATERSOLDIER

SUBULA'RIA aquat'ica WATER AWLWORT

TRA'PA na'tans . WATERCHESTNUT

TRAPEL'LA sinen'sis CHINESE TRAPELLA

UTRICULA'RIA vulga'ris COMMON BLADDERWORT

AQUARIUM PLANTS, continued

VALLISNE'RIA spira'lis SPIRAL WILDCELERY

WEBSTE'RIA submer'sa WATERMEAL

ZANNICHEL'LIA palus'tris COMMON POOLMAT

AQUILA'RIA . . . . . . EAGLEWOOD
agal'locha . . . . . . AGALLOCH E.

AQUILE'GIA |w . . . . . COLUMBINE
akiten'sis . . . . AKITA C.
alpi'na . . . . ALPINE C.
arc'tica . . . . **A. formosa**
bertolo'ni (*reuteri*) . ALPINEROCK C.
bi'color . . . . **A. sibirica**
brevis'tyla . . . . YUKON C.
buergeria'na
califor'nica . . . . . . **A. formosa**
canaden'sis . . . . . AMERICAN C.
chrysan'tha (*thalictrifolia*) GOLDEN C.
coeru'lea . . . . COLORADO C.

The state flower of Colorado. See also hort. var. list below.

dis'color
elegan'tula . . . . WESTERNRED C.
faur'ieri
flabella'ta . . . . FAN C.
flaves'cens . . . . YELLOW C.
formo'sa (*arctica; californica*) SITKA C.
—trunca'ta (*A. truncata*) CALIFORNIA C.
glandulo'sa . . . . ALTAI C.
—jucun'da (*A. jucunda*)
jones'i . . . . JONES C.
lactiflo'ra
leptoce'ras
longis'sima . . . . . LONGSPUR C.
lute'a

Thought to be a hybrid between coerulea and chrysantha.

olymp'ica . . . . . . **A. vulgaris o.**
oxyse'pala . . . . EARLY C.
pauciflo'ra
pineto'rum . . . . PINE C.
pubes'cens
pubiflo'ra
pyrena'ica . . . . PYRENEES C.
reu'teri . . . . **A. bertoloni**
saximonta'na . ROCKYMOUNTAIN C.
sibir'ica (*bicolor*) . . . . SIBERIAN C.
skin'neri . . . . SKINNER C.
∞ **stuart'i** (*glandulosa × vulgaris olympica*) ∞ STUART C.
suave'olens
thalictrifo'lia . . . . . **A. chrysantha**
trunca'ta . . . . . . **A. formosa t.**
viridiflo'ra . . . GREENFLOWER C.
vulga'ris (*stellata*) . . . EUROPEAN C.
—olymp'ica (*A. olympica*). OLYMPIC C.

All the below with one exception are clons.

ALPINE SUPERBA. HV. Aquilegia
BAIKALENSIS
BLUESHADES (*longissima*)
CANDIDISSIMA (*coerulea c.*)
CLEMATIQUILLA
CRIMSONSTAR
DELICATISSIMA
DOUBLE EUROPEAN (*vulgaris floreplено*)
DOUBLE GOLDEN (*chrysantha albaplena*)
DOUBLE SIBERIAN (*sibirica floreplено*)

AQUILEGIA, continued

DOUBLE WHITE EUROPEAN (*vulgaris albaplena*)
DOUBLE WHITEFAN (*flabellata nana alba*)
DWARF AMERICAN (*canadensis nana*)
DWARF SITKA (*formosa nana alba*)
HAYLODGENSIS
HELEN (*coerulea helenae*)
∞ HYBRID COLORADO (*coerulea hybrida*)
JAESCHKANI
LEMON COLORADO (*coerulea citrina*)
MUNSTED (*vulgaris nivea*)
ROSE COLORADO (*coerulea rosea*)
VERVAENE (*vulgaris vervaeneana*)
WHITE ALPINE (*alpina alba*)
WHITE COLORADO (*coerulea alba*)
WHITE GOLDEN (*chrysantha alba*)
YELLOW COLORADO (*coerulea lutea*)

ARABIANTEA . . . . **Catha edulis**

ARABIDOP'SIS
thalia'na (*A. stenophragma t.; Sisymbrium thalianum*) . MOUSEEARCRESS

AR'ABIS |w . . . . ROCKCRESS
aculeola'ta (*purpurascens* Howell, *not* Presl, in part)
albi'da . . . . WALL R.
—floreple'no . . . . . . DOUBLE W.R.
₵BILLARDIER (*billardieri*) HV. A. albida
₵COMPACT (*compacta*)
₵SILVERLEAF (*argentea*)
₵VARIEGATED (*variegata*)
allio'ni
alpi'na . . . . ALPINE R.
₵DOUBLE (*florepleno*) HV.
₵DWARF (*nana compacta*)
₵GRANDIFLORA
₵LISSADELL PINK
₵ROSABELLE
₵ROSE (*rosea*)
₵SUPERB (*superba*)
₵VARIEGATED (*variegata*)
androsa'cea
areno'sa
aubrietioi'des
bellidifo'lia
blepharophyl'la
brachycar'pa . . . . SHORTFRUIT R.
brachycar'pa (T. & G.) Britt., *not* Rupr. **A. divaricarpa**
brew'eri . . . . BREWER R.
bryoi'des . . . . MOSS R.
canes'cens . . . . SILVER R.
carducho'rum
colli'na
corymbiflo'ra
divaricar'pa (*brachycarpa* (T. & G.) Britt., *not* Rupr.)
drum'mondi . . . . DRUMMOND R.
ex'ilis . . . . SLIM R.
ferdinandi-co'burgi
gerard'i . . . . GERARD R.
gla'bra . . . . . TOWERMUSTARD R.
hal'leri . . . . HALLER R.
hirsu'ta . . . . HAIRY R.
—pycnocar'pa (*A. pycnocarpa*) COMMON H.R.
holboell'i . . . . HOLBOELL R.
∞ **kellerer'i** (*bryoides × ferdinandi-coburgi*) . . . . ∞ KELLERER R.
koeh'leri . . . . RED R.
laeviga'ta . . . . SMOOTH R.
lem'moni . . . . LEMMONS R.
lu'cida
VARIEGATED (*variegata*) HV.
ly'alli . . . . LYALL R.
microphyl'la . . . . LITTLELEAF R.

ARABIS, continued
mol'lis . . . . . Downy Rockcress
mura'lis (*rosea*) . . . . Italian R.
nutt'alli (*spathulata* Nutt., *not* DC.) Nuttall R.
orega'na (*purpurascens* Howell, *not* Presl, in part) . . . . Oregon R.
platysper'ma . . . . . . Pioneer R.
procur'rens
purpuras'cens . . . . . Purple R.
purpuras'cens Howell, *not* Presl **A. aculeolata; A. oregana**
pycnocar'pa . . . . . . **A. hirsuta p.**
rose'a . . . . **A. muralis**
spathula'ta Nutt., *not* DC. . **A. nuttalli**
stel'leri . . . . Steller R.
stric'ta . . . . Erect R.
stur'i
∞ **suendermann'i** (*ferdinandi-coburgi* × *procurrens*) . . ∞ Suendermann R.
suffrutes'cens . . . . . Woody R.
suks'dorfi . . . . . . Suksdorf R.
tur'rita

Araca . . . . Guava, Brazilian: **Psidium guineense**

AR'ACHIS |w . . . . Peanut
hypogae'a |w . . Peanut (*Groundnut*)

ARACHNAN'THE
See **ORCHID GENERA.**

ARACH'NIS . . . **ARACHNANTHE**
See **ORCHID GENERA.**

ARAGAL'LUS . . . . **OXYTROPIS**
albiflo'rus A. Nels., *not* Bunge **O. saximontana**

ARA'LIA (*DIMORPHANTHUS*) |w Aralia
au'rea . . . . Yellow A.
balfouria'na . . . . . . **Polyscias b.**
cachemir'ica (*cashmeriana*) Kashmir A.
califor'nica . . . . . California A.
chabrier'i . . **Elaeodendron orientale**
chinen'sis . . . . Chinese A.
corda'ta (*A. edulis*) . . . . . . Udo
ela'ta (*A. chinensis glabrescens; A. c. mandshurica*) . . . . Japanese A.
—**canes'cens** . . . . . . Hoary J.A.
₵Pyramidal (*fastigiata*) hv. A. elata
₵Variegated (*variegata*)
₵Yellowleaf (*aureovariegata*)
elegantis'sima . . . . **Dizygotheca e.**
filicifo'lia . . . . **Polyscias f.**
frutico'sa . . . . **Polyscias f.**
guilfoy'lei . . . . **Polyscias g.**
his'pida |w . . . . Bristly A.
japon'ica . . . . **Fatsia j.**
—*variega'ta* **Fatsia japonica** ₵Variegated
kerchovea'na . . . . **Dizygotheca k.**
maximowicz'i . . **Kalopanax pictus m.**
nudicau'lis |w . . . Wildsarsaparilla
papyrif'era . . **Tetrapanax papyriferus**
pentaphyl'la Sieb. & Zucc. **Acanthopanax sieboldianus**
pentaphyl'la Thunb. **Acanthopanax spinosus**
quinquefo'lia . . **Panax quinquefolium**
racemo'sa |w . . American Spikenard
siebold'i . . . . **Fatsia japonica**
spino'sa |w . Devils-walkingstick (*Herculesclub; Tree Aralia*)
See Zanthoxylum clavaherculis.

trifo'lia
veitch'i . . . . **Dizygotheca v.**

Arartree . . **Tetraclinis; T. articulata**

ARAUCA'RIA . . . . Araucaria
angustifo'lia (*brasiliana*) . Parana A.
arauca'na (*imbricata*) Monkeypuzzle A.
balan'sae . . . . Balansa A.
bid'willi . . . . Bunyabunya A.
columna'ris (*cooki*) . . Columnar A.
cunningham'i . . . . Cunningham A.
excel'sa . . . . Norfolkislandpine
₵Blue (*glauca*) hv.
₵Emerald (*robusta*)
₵Silverstar (*albospica*)
grac'ilis . . . . Slender A.
imbrica'ta . . . . **A. araucana**

ARAU'JIA . . . . . . Bladderflower
sericif'era (*Physianthus albens*) White B.

Arborvitae . . . . **Thuja**
Eastern A. . . . . . **T. occidentalis**
Giant A. . . . . **T. plicata**
Japanese A. . . . . . . **T. standishi**
Korean A. . . . . . . **T. koraiensis**
Oriental A. . . . . **T. orientalis**

ARBU'TUS |w . . . . Madrone
andrach'ne
×**andrachnoi'des** (*andrachne* × *unedo; hybrida*)
arizo'nica . . . . Arizona M.
canarien'sis . . . . Canary M.
croom'i . . . . **A. unedo rubra**
fur'iens (*Gaultheria f.; Pernettya ciliaris*)
menzies'i (*procera*) |w . . Pacific M.
texa'na . . . . Texas M.
une'do . . . . Strawberry M.
—**integer'rima**
—**ru'bra** (*A. croomi*)
xalapen'sis . . . . Mexican M.

ARCEUTHO'BIUM (*RAZOUMOWSKYA*) |w . . . Dwarfmistletoe
pusil'lum (*Razoumowskya p.*) |w Small D.

ARCHANGEL'ICA . . . **ANGELICA**

ARCHONTOPHOE'NIX (*LOROMA*) Kingpalm
See **PALM GENERA.**

ARCTER'ICA . . . . **PIERIS**

ARC'TIUM (*LAPPA*) |w . . Burdock
lap'pa (*Lappa edulis; L. major*) |w Great B.
mi'nus (*Lappa minor*) |w . Smaller B.
tomento'sum . . . . . . Cotton B.

ARCTOME'CON . . . . . Bearpoppy
merria'mi . . . . Desert B.

ARCTOSTAPH'YLOS (*COMAROSTAPHYLIS; XYLOCOCCUS*) |w Manzanita
Some botanists, especially in California, regard Comarostaphylis and Xylococcus as distinct genera.

alpi'na . . . . . . **Arctous alpinus**
anderso'ni (*regismontana*) Heartleaf M.
bi'color (*Xylococcus b.*) . . Mission M.
bracteo'sa . . . . Monterey M.
canes'cens . . . . Hoary M.
cine'rea . . . . Delnorte M.
columbia'na . . . . Hairy M.
confertiflo'ra . . SantaRosaIsland M.
crusta'cea . . . . . . Brittleleaf M.
densiflo'ra . . . . Sonoma M.
diversifo'lia (*Comarostaphylis d.*) Toothed M.

ARCTOSTAPHYLOS, continued
drupa'cea . . . . **A. pringlei d.**
el'egans . . . . Konocti Manzanita
glandulo'sa . . . . . Eastwood M.
glau'ca . . . . Bigberry M.
hispid'ula . . . . Howell M.
hook'eri . . . . Hooker M.
insula'ris . . . . Island M.
laeviga'ta
manzani'ta |w . . . . . Common M.
maripo'sa . . . . . . Mariposa M.
me'dia

Perhaps a hybrid between A. columbiana and A. uva-ursi.

mewuk'ka (*pastillosa*) . . Indian M.
morroen'sis . . . . Morro M.
myrtifo'lia . . . . Ione M.
nevaden'sis |w . . . . . Pinemat M.
nissena'na . . . . Eldorado M.
nummula'ria . . . . Fire M.
obispoen'sis . . . . . Serpentine M
otayen'sis . . . . Otay M.
pajaroen'sis . . . . Pajaro M.
parrya'na . . . . Parry M.
—**pineto'rum** (*A. pinetorum*) . Pine M.
pastillo'sa . . . . **A. mewukka**
pat'ula |w . . . . . . Greenleaf M.
pechoen'sis . . . PechoMountain M.
pilos'ula . . . . . . Stripeberry M.
pring'lei . . . . Pringle M.
—**drupa'cea** (*A. drupacea*)
pu'mila . . . . Dune M.
pun'gens |w . . . . . Pointleaf M.
regismonta'na . . . . . **A. andersoni**
ru'dis . . . . Shagbark M.
sensiti'va . . . . . . Littleberry M.
silvic'ola . . . . . . Silverleaf M.
stanfordia'na . . . . . Stanford M.

Probably a hybrid between A. manzanita and A. stanfordiana.

tomento'sa . . . . Woolly M.
uva-ur'si |w . . . . . . Bearberry (*Kinnikinnick*)
viridis'sima . . . . . . Lompoc M.
vis'cida . . . . . . Whiteleaf M.

ARCTO'TIS . . . . Arctotis
acau'lis . . . . Bushy A.
brevisca'pa . . . . . . Stemless A.
—**auranti'aca**
calendula'cea **Cryptostemma calendulaceum**
fos'teri . . . . Foster A.
gumbleto'ni . . . . . Gumbleton A.
stoechadifo'lia (*grandis*) . African A.

ARCTO'US . . . . Ptarmiganberry
alpi'nus (*Arctostaphylos alpina; Mairania alpina*) |w . . . . Alpine P.
ru'ber (*erythrocarpa*) . . Redfruit P.

ARDIS'IA (*ICACOREA*) . . . Ardisia
acumina'ta
crenula'ta
₵Variegated (*variegata*) hv.
cris'pa (*crenulata*) . . . . Coral A.
japon'ica (*Bladhia j.*) . . . Japanese A.
panicula'ta (*pickeringia; Icacorea paniculata*) . . . . Marble A.
solana'cea . . . . . . Shoebutton A.
wal'lichi . . . . Wallich A.

AR'ECA . . . . Arecapalm
See **PALM GENERA.**

ARECAS'TRUM (*COCOS* in part) Queenpalm
See **PALM GENERA.**

AREGE'LIA . . . Aregelia
marmora'ta . . . Airplant A.
prin'ceps . . . Princely A.
spectab'ilis . . . Showy A.
tris'tis . . . Bitter A.

ARENA'RIA |w . . . Sandwort
aequicau'lis
alpi'na . . . Alpine S.
austria'ca . . . Austrian S.
balear'ica . . . Corsican S.
banat'ica . . . Banatian S.
bauhino'rum . . . Bauhins S.
biflo'ra . . . Twinflower S.
burk'ei . . . Burke S.
caespito'sa . . . **A. verna c.**
capilla'ris
—*formo'sa* . . . **A. formosa**
carolinia'na (*squarrosa*) . Carolina S.
cephalo'tes
compac'ta . . . Compact S.
conges'ta . . . Ballhead S.
cre'tica . . . Crete S.
fend'leri |w . . . Fendler S.
formo'sa (*A. capillaris f.*) . Fescue S.
grac'ilis
graminifo'lia . . . Grassleaf S.
groenland'ica . . . Greenland S.
hook'eri . . . Hooker S.
juniperi'na . . . Juniper S.
king'i . . . Kings S.
laricifo'lia . . . Larchleaf S.
lateriflo'ra |w . . . Bluntleaf S.
ledebouria'na . . . Ledebour S.
longifo'lia . . . Longleaf S.
macran'tha
monta'na . . . Mountain S.
—grandiflo'ra . . . Bigflower M.S.
peploi'des |w . . . Seabeach S.
pun'gens
purpuras'cens . . . Purple S.
racemo'sa
re'pens . . . Creeping S.
rig'ida . . . Stiff S.
rosan'i
rotundifo'lia . . . Roundleaf S.
sajanen'sis . . . Siberian S.
saxif'raga . . . Saxifrage S.
serpyllifo'lia |w . . . Thymeleaf S.
squarro'sa . . . **A. caroliniana**
stevenia'na . . . Steven S.
stric'ta . . . Rock S.
tetraque'tra
tmole'a
uintahen'sis . . . Uinta S.
ver'na . . . Tufted S.
—caespito'sa (*A. caespitosa*) . Moss S.
Goldmoss (*aurea*) hv.

AREN'GA (*SAGUERUS*). Sugarpalm
See **PALM GENERA.**

AREQUI'PA . . . Arequipa
See **CACTUS GENERA.**

ARETHU'SA . . . Arethusa
See **ORCHID GENERA, HARDY TERRESTRIAL GROUP.**

ARGA'NIA
siderox'ylon

ARGEMO'NE |w . . . Pricklepoppy
al'ba . . . White P.
grandiflo'ra . . . Showy P.
interme'dia |w
mexica'na . . . Mexican P.
platyce'ras . . . Crested P.
—his'pida (*A. hispida*) Hedgehog P.
—rose'a . . . Rosy P.

ARGENTI'NA . . . **POTENTILLA**

ARGE'TA. **MESEMBRYANTHEMUM**
See **SUCCULENTS.**

Arghan . . . **Ananas macrodontes**

ARGYRE'IA . . . Asiaglory
obtusifo'lia . . . Bluntleaf A.
specio'sa . . . Woolly A.
splen'dens . . . Silver A.

ARGYRODER'MA
MESEMBRYANTHEMUM
See **SUCCULENTS.**

ARGYROP'SIS . . **ZEPHYRANTHES**

ARGYTHAM'NIA . . . Silverbush
califor'nica . . . California S.
lanceola'ta . . . Lanceleaf S.
sericophyl'la

ARIDA'RIA
MESEMBRYANTHEMUM
See **SUCCULENTS.**

ARIKURYRO'BA (*ARIKURY; COCOS* in part) . . . Arikurypalm
See **PALM GENERA.**

ARIOCAR'PUS (*ANHALONIUM; ENCEPHALOCARPUS; OBREGONIA; ROSEOCACTUS*)
Livingrockcactus (*Livingrock*)
See **CACTUS GENERA.**

ARISAE'MA |w . . . Jackinthepulpit
atroru'bens . . . Common J.
dracon'tium . . . Dragonroot J.
fimbria'tum . . . Plumecalla J.
grif'fithi . . . Griffith J.
serra'tum . . . Japan J.
—blum'ei (*A. japonicum*) . Blumes J.J.
specio'sum . . . Showy J.
stewardso'ni
triphyl'lum |w . . . Indian J.
wallichia'num . . . Wallichian J.

ARISTE'A . . . Aristea
capita'ta . . . Sabreleaf A.
eck'loni . . . Ecklons A.
lu'cida Hort. . . . Blueiris A.

ARIS'TIDA . . . Threeawn
See **GRASS GENERA.**

ARISTOLO'CHIA (*HOCQUARTIA*) |w
Dutchmanspipe
altis'sima . . . Tall D.
brasilien'sis . . . Brazil D.
—macrophyl'la . . . Largeleaf B.D.
califor'nica . . . California D.
chry'sops (*Isotrema c.*)
clemati'tis . . . Birthwort D.
dur'ior (*macrophylla; sipho*)
Common D.
el'egans . . . Calico D.
fimbria'ta . . . Argentine D.
galea'ta . . . Broadblade D.
galeot'ti . . . Mexican D.
gi'gas . . . **A. grandiflora**
—*sturtevant'i* . . . **A. grandiflora s.**
glandulo'sa
glasio'vi
grandiflo'ra (*gigas*) . . . Pelican D.
—hook'eri . . . Hookers P.D.
—sturtevant'i (*A. gigas s.*)
Longtail P.D.
hasta'ta . . . Herb D.
heterophyl'la (*Isotrema h.*)
Yellowmouth D.
kaem'pferi . . . Kaempfer D.
∞ kewen'sis (*brasiliensis* × *trilobata*)

ARISTOLOCHIA, continued
macrophyl'la . . . **A. durior**
macrou'ra
manshurien'sis
Manchurian Dutchmanspipe
moupinen'sis . . . Moupin D.
odoratis'sima . . . Fragrant D.
reticula'ta . . . Texas Snakeroot D.
rin'gens . . . Gaping D.
rotun'da . . . Roundroot D.
ru'gens
sempervi'rens . . . Evergreen D.
serpenta'ria . Virginia Snakeroot D.
si'pho . . . **A. durior**
wat'soni |w . . . Watson D.

ARISTOTE'LIA . . . Wineberry
colenso'i . . . Colenso W.
frutico'sa . . . Shrubby W.
mac'qui . . . Chilean W.
—variega'ta . . . Variegated C.W.
racemo'sa . . . Makomako W.
(*NewZealand W.*)

ARMATOCE'REUS
LEMAIREOCEREUS
See **CACTUS GENERA.**

ARMENI'ACA . . . **PRUNUS**
vulga'ris . . . **P. armeniaca**

ARME'RIA (*STATICE* in part) Thrift
alpi'na . . . **A. montana**
arme'ria . . . **A. maritima**
bupleuroi'des (*Statice b.*) Whitehead T.
∞ caesalpi'na (*caespitosa* × *montana;* × *Statice c.*) . . . ∞ Caesalpina T.
caespito'sa (*Statice c.*) . Pyrenees T.
canes'cens (*Statice c.*) . . . Pale T.
cas'pia . . . **Limonium reticulatum**
cephalo'tes . . . **A. pseudoarmeria**
—*ru'bra* . . . **A. pseudoarmeria r.**
dianthoi'des . . . **A. plantaginea**
elonga'ta (*Statice e.*)
fru'ticans . . . **Limonium f.**
hal'leri (*Statice h.*) . . . Haller T.
jun'cea . . . **A. setacea**
latifo'lia . . . **A. pseudoarmeria**
—*al'ba* . . . **A. pseudoarmeria a.**
—*elegantis'sima*. . **A. pseudoarmeria e.**
—*rose'a* . . . **A. pseudoarmeria r.**
leucoceph'ala (*Statice l.*) . Corsican T.
macrophyl'la **Limonium macrophyllum**
marit'ima (*armeria; vulgaris; Statice a.; S. vulgaris*) . . . Common T.
—al'ba (*Statice armeria a.; S. vulgaris a.*) . . . White C.T.
—lauchea'na (*Statice armeria l.; Statice l.*) . . . Lauche C.T.
—robus'ta (*Statice armeria r.*)
Clump C.T.
—ru'bra (*Statice armeria r.*)
Blood C.T.
—splen'dens (*Statice armeria s.*)
Roseglobe C.T.
mauritan'ica (*Statice m.*) . Algerian T.
monta'na (*alpina; Statice m.*)
Mountain T.
plantagin'ea (*dianthoides; Statice d.; S. plantaginea*) . . . Plantain T.
—gigan'tea (*Statice p.g.*) . Great P.T.
pseudoarme'ria (*cephalotes; latifolia; Statice formosa* Hort.; *S. latifolia; S. pseudoarmeria*) . . . Pinkball T.
—al'ba (*A. latifolia a.*) . . . White P.T.
—elegantis'sima (*A. latifolia e.*)
—rose'a (*A. latifolia r.*)
—ru'bra (*A. cephalotes r.; Statice pseudoarmeria cephalotes*) . Rose P.T.
pun'gens (*Statice p.*). Pinkcluster T.

ARMERIA, continued
purpu'rea (*Statice p.*)
Purplehead Thrift
seta'cea (*juncea; Statice j.*) Rushleaf T.
vulga'ris . . . . **A. maritima**

ARMILLA'RIA . . . . . . Armillaria
matsuta'ke . . . . . Matsutake A.
mel'lea . . . . Honeycolor A.
ventrico'sa . . . . Coarse A.

ARMORA'CIA
lapathifo'lia (*Rorippa armoracia*)
Horseradish

ARNE'BIA . . . . Arnebia
cornu'ta . . . . . Arabprimrose A.
echioi'des . . . Prophetflower A.

AR'NICA . . . . Arnica
alpi'na . . . . Alpine A.
betonicaefo'lia . . . . . Betony A.
chamisso'nis . . . . . . Chamisso A.
clus'i . . . . **Doronicum c.**
cordifo'lia . . . . . . Heartleaf A.
folio'sa . . . . Leafy A.
—inca'na . . . . . . Hoaryleaf A.
ful'gens . . . . Orange A.
latifo'lia . . . . Broadleaf A.
—viscid'ula . . . . . . Sticky B.A.
longifo'lia . . . . Longleaf A.
mol'lis . . . . Hairy A.
monta'na . . . . Mountain A.
nevaden'sis . . . . Nevada A.
par'ryi . . . . Rayless A.
peduncula'ta . . . . Corm A.
sachalinen'sis . . . . . Sakhalin A.

Arnica . . . . **Arnica**
Alpine A. . . . . **A. alpina**
Betony A. . . . . . . **A. betonicaefolia**
Broadleaf A. . . . . **A. latifolia**
Chamisso A. . . . . . . **A. chamissonis**
Corm A. . . . . **A. pedunculata**
Hairy A. . . . . **A. mollis**
Heartleaf A. . . . . . . **A. cordifolia**
Hoaryleaf A. . . . **A. foliosa incana**
Leafy A. . . . . **A. foliosa**
Longleaf A. . . . . **A. longifolia**
Mountain A. . . . . **A. montana**
Nevada A. . . . . **A. nevadensis**
Orange A. . . . . **A. fulgens**
Rayless A. . . . . **A. parryi**
Sakhalin A. . . . . . **A. sachalinensis**
Sticky Broadleaf A.
A. latifolia viscidula

ARNOS'ERIS . . . . . Lambsuccory
min'ima . . . . Small L.

ARO'NIA ⌊w . . . . . . Chokeberry
arbutifo'lia (*erythrocarpa; Pyrus a.*) ⌊w
Red C.
—brilliantis'sima . . . Brilliant C.
—macrocar'pa . . . . . Cherry C.
—pu'mila . . . . Dwarf C.C.
atropurpu'rea . . . . . **A. prunifolia**
erythrocar'pa . . . . . **A. arbutifolia**
melanocar'pa (*nigra; Pyrus n.*) ⌊w
Black C.
—ela'ta . . . . Glossy B.C.
—grandifo'lia . . . . . Great B.C.
prunifo'lia (*atropurpurea; floribunda*) ⌊w
Purplefruit C.

ARPOPHYL'LUM
See **ORCHID GENERA.**

ARRABIDAE'A . . . . Funnelvine
mol'lis . . . . Trinidad F.
rotunda'ta

ARRACA'CIA . . . . . . Arracacia
xanthorrhi'za (*esculenta*) . . . Apio A.

ARRHENA'THERUM . . . Oatgrass
See **GRASS GENERA.**

ARROJADO'A . **CEPHALOCEREUS**
See **CACTUS GENERA.**

Arrowarum . . . . **Peltandra**
Redfruit A. . . . . **P. glauca**
Virginia A. . . . . . . **P. virginica**

Arrowfeather . . . Threeawn, Arrowfeather: **Aristida purpurascens**

Arrowhead . . . . **Sagittaria**
Awlleaf A. . . . . **S. subulata**
Beach A. . . . . **S. natans**
Bigpod A. . . . . . . **S. macrocarpa**
Bulltongue A. . . . . . **S. lancifolia**
Chapman A. . . . . . . **S. chapmani**
Common A. . . . . **S. latifolia**
Delta A. . . . . **S. platyphylla**
Downy A. . . . . **S. pubescens**
Duckpotato A. . . . . . . **S. cuneata**
Engelmann A. . . **S. engelmanniana**
Giant A. . . . . . . **S. montevidensis**
Grassy A. . . . . **S. graminea**
Gregg A. . . . . **S. greggi**
Longbarb A. . . . . **S. longiloba**
Longbeak A. . . . . . **S. longirostra**
Mohrs A. . . . . **S. mohri**
Narrowleaf A. . . . **S. angustifolia**
Oldworld A. . . . . . **S. sagittifolia**
Sandford A. . . . . . . **S. sandfordi**
Shortbeak A. . . . . **S. brevirostra**
Slender A. . . . . **S. teres**
Sticky A. . . . . **S. viscosa**
Stiff A. . . . . **S. rigida**
Strapleaf A. . . . . **S. lorata**
Varileaf A. . . . . **S. heterophylla**
Weatherby A. . . . **S. weatherbiana**

Arrowleaf, Bush **Hofmeisteria pluriseta**

Arrowroot . . . . **Maranta**
Banded A. . . . . . . **M. leuconeura**
Bermuda A. . . . . **M. arundinacea**
Closon A. . . . . **M. closoni**
Spotted A. . . . . **M. goveniana**

Arsenococ'cus ligustri'nus
Lyonia ligustrina

ARTABO'TRYS . . . . . Tailgrape
uncina'tus (*odoratissimus*)
Fragrant T.

ARTEMIS'IA ⌊w
Sagebrush; Wormwood

In the western United States, Sagebrush is universally entrenched in usage—in story, song, place names, literature and scientific publications. Wormwood is equally entrenched for the Old World species, which occur in the Drug Plants and Herbgarden lists as well as elsewhere in this book. In view of this situation, the west-American species of Artemisia are called Sagebrush in this book, and the other species, Wormwood.

abrota'num . . . . . . Oldman W.
(*Southernwood*)
absin'thium . . . . . . Common W.
al'bula . . . . Silverking S.
ambrosiifo'lia
an'nua . Sweet W. (*Sweet Mugwort*)
arbores'cens . . . . . . Shrubby W.
arbus'cula (*A. tridentata a.*) ⌊w. Low S.
argen'tea . . . . Silver W.
atomif'era
austria'ca . . . . Austrian W.
baumgart'eni . . . . Baumgarten W.
bien'nis ⌊w . . . . Biennial W.
bigelo'vi . . . . Bigelow S.
bolan'deri (*A. tridentata b.*)
Bolander S.

ARTEMISIA, continued
borea'lis . . . Northern Wormwood
califor'nica . California Sagebrush
campes'tris . . . . . Sagewort W.
camphora'ta . . . . . . Camphor W.
ca'na ⌊w . . . . Silver S.
canaden'sis . . . . Canada S.
carruth'i . . . . Carruth S.
cauda'ta ⌊w
chamaemelifo'lia
ci'na . . . . Levant W.
dis'color (*incompta*) . . . Sweet S.
diversifo'lia . . . . . . Mixleaf S.
dracunculoi'des . Falsetarragon S.
dracun'culus . . . . Tarragon
filifo'lia . . . . Sand S.
flocco'sa . . . . Woolly S.
franserioi'des . . . . Ragweed S.
frig'ida ⌊w . . . . Fringed S.
glacia'lis . . . . Glacier W.
glau'ca
gnaphalo'des . . . . . . Cudweed S.
grac'ilis . . . . **A. scoparia**
granaten'sis
incomp'ta . . . . **A. discolor**
lacinia'ta
laciniatifor'mis
lactiflo'ra (*A. vulgaris l.*)
Ghostplant W.
longifo'lia . . . . Longleaf S.
ludovicia'na . . . . . . Louisiana S.
marit'ima . . . . Maritime W.
mexica'na ⌊w . . . . . . Mexican S.
michauxia'na . . . . . Michaux S.
minu'ta . . . . Silvermat S.
mox'a . . . . Moxa W.
mutelli'na . . . . . . Silveralp W.
natronen'sis . . . . Alkali S.
neomexica'na . . . NewMexican S.
no'va (*A. tridentata n.*) ⌊w . Black S.
nu'tans
pal'meri . . . . Palmer S.
par'ishi (*A. tridentata p.*) . Parish S.
pedatif'ida . . . . Birdfoot S.
pedemonta'na . . . . Piedmont W.
per'sica . . . . Persian W.
pon'tica . . . . Roman W.
pro'cera
purshia'na . . . . Pursh S.
pycnoceph'ala . . . . Sandhill W.
redo'lens . . . . Chihuahua S.
rig'ida . . . . Stiff S.
rothrock'i (*A. tridentata r.*)
Rothrock S.
rupes'tris . . . . Rock W.
sacro'rum . . . . Russian W.
—vir'idis . . . . Summerfir R.W.
sali'na
schmidtia'na
scopa'ria (*gracilis*) . . Oriental W.
scopulo'rum . . . . Alpine S.
seric'ea
serra'ta . . . . Sawtooth S.
spica'ta . . . . Mountain W.
spines'cens ⌊w . . . . Bud S.
splen'dens . . . . . . AsiaMinor W.
stelleria'na . Beach W. (*Dustymiller*)
sua'vis . . . . French W.
tridenta'ta ⌊w . . . . Big S.
—angustifo'lia . . Narrowleaf B.S.
—arbus'cula . . . . . . **A. arbuscula**
—bolan'deri . . . . . . **A. bolanderi**
—no'va . . . . **A. nova**
—par'ishi . . . . **A. parishi**
—rothrock'i . . . . . . **A. rothrocki**
triparti'ta (*A. tridentata trifida; trifida* Nutt., *not* Turcz.) ⌊w . Threetip S.
vulga'ris . . . . Mugwort W.

ARTEMISIA, continued
vulga'ris heterophyl'la
MIXLEAF MUGWORT WORMWOOD
—lactiflo'ra . . . . . . **A. lactiflora**
wright'i . . . . WRIGHTS SAGEBRUSH

ARTHRAX'ON
See **GRASS GENERA.**

ARTHROCE'REUS **TRICHOCEREUS**
See **CACTUS GENERA.**

ARTHROPO'DIUM
can'didum
cirrha'tum

ARTHROTHAM'NUS . . . . KOMBU
bi'fidus . . . . FORKED K.
kurilen'sis . . . . KURILE K.

ARTICHOKE . . . . . . **Cynara scolymus**
Chinese A.; Japanese A. . . BETONY, ARTICHOKE: **Stachys sieboldi**

ARTOCAR'PUS
Sitodium is an older name for this genus, but Artocarpus is in universal use and is proposed for conservation. Artocarpus is masculine under International Rules, though it is usually treated as feminine in literature.
al'tilis (*communis; incisus*)
BREADFRUIT
blu'mei . . . . JAVA B.
can'noni
chap'lasha . . . . . . CHAPLASH B.
commu'nis . . . . **A. altilis**
elas'ticus
falca'tus
gomezia'nus
heterophyl'lus (*integer; integrifolius*)
JAKFRUIT (*Jackfruit*)
hirsu'tus . . . . . . ANJELYWOOD
hypargyre'us
inci'sus . . . . **A. altilis**
in'teger; integrifo'lius **A. heterophyllus**
lakoo'cha . . . . LAKOOCHA
odoratis'simus . . . . . . MARANG
polyphe'mus . . . . . CHAMPEDAK
rig'idus . . . . MONKEYJACK
super'bus

A'RUM . . . . ARUM
crini'tum . . **Helicodiceros muscivorus**
dracun'culus . . **Dracunculus vulgaris**
gutta'tum . . . . . . **Sauromatum g.**
ital'icum . . . . ITALIAN A.
macula'tum . . . . LORDSANDLADIES
palaesti'num . . . . BLACKCALLA A.
peda'tum . **Sauromatum guttatum p.**
pic'tum
veno'sum . . . . . **Sauromatum v.**

ARUN'CUS . . . . GOATSBEARD
alleghenien'sis . . . . ALLEGANY G.
—pubes'cens . . . . . HAIRY A.G.
sylves'ter (*Spiraea aruncus; S. humboldti*) . . . . SYLVAN G.
¢CUTLEAF (*kneiffi*) HV.

ARUNDINA'RIA . . . . CANE
See **BAMBOO GENERA.**

ARUN'DO . . . . GIANTREED
See **GRASS GENERA.**

AS'ARUM (*HEXASTYLIS*)
WILDGINGER
arifo'lium . . . . ARUM W.
canaden'se . . . . CANADA W.
cauda'tum . . . BRITISHCOLUMBIA W.
europae'um . . . . . EUROPEAN W.
hart'wegi . . . . SIERRA W.
heterophyl'lum

ASARUM, continued
lem'moni . . LEMMONS WILDGINGER
reflex'um . . . . CURLY W.
shuttleworth'i (*macranthum; Hexastylis s.*) . . . . MOTTLED W.
virgin'icum (*Hexastylis virginica*)
VIRGINIA W.

ASCARI'NA
lu'cida

ASCLE'PIAS |w . . . . . . MILKWEED
cordifo'lia . **Gomphocarpus cordifolius**
cornu'ti . . . . **A. syriaca**
curassa'vica . . . BLOODFLOWER M.
eriocar'pa . . . . . . WOOLLYPOD M.
ero'sa . . . . DESERT M.
exalta'ta
fre'monti . . . . KOTOLO M.
galioi'des . . . . POISON M.
hall'i . . . . HALLS M.
incarna'ta |w . . . . . . SWAMP M.
—al'ba . . . . WHITE S.M.
—pul'chra (*A. pulchra*) |w
HAIRY S.M.
—rose'a . . . . PINK S.M.
involucra'ta . . . . . . DWARF M.
lanceola'ta |w . . . . . PACIFIC M.
latifo'lia . . . . . . BROADLEAF M.
mexica'na . . . . MEXICAN M.
phytolaccoi'des . . . . WESTCOAST M.
pul'chra . . . . **A. incarnata p.**
pu'mila . . . . PLAINS M.
purpuras'cens . . . . . . PURPLE M.
ru'bra . . . . RED M.
specio'sa . . . . SHOWY M.
subula'ta . . . . SKELETON M.
sullivant'i . . . . . . SULLIVANT M.
syri'aca (*cornuti*) |w . . . COMMON M.
tubero'sa . . . . . . BUTTERFLY M.
¢VERMILION. HV.
verticilla'ta |w . . . . . WHORLED M.

ASCLEPIODO'RA . . . ANTELOPEHORN
decum'bens . . . . SPIDER A.

ASCOCEN'TRUM
minia'tum

ASCOPHYL'LUM . . . . ROCKWEED
nodo'sum . . . . DRUG R.

ASCOTAI'NIA . . . . **TAINIA**
See **ORCHID GENERA.**

ASCY'RUM |w
hypericoi'des (*crux-andreae; multicaule*) |w . . . . ST.ANDREWSCROSS
stans' . . . ATLANTIC ST.PETERSWORT

ASH . . . . **Fraxinus**
AFGHAN A. . . . **F. xanthoxyloides**
ALGERIAN A. . . . . . . **F. dimorpha**
AUCUBALEAF A.
F. pennsylvanica aucubaefolia
BERLANDIER A. . . . **F. berlandieriana**
BILTMORE A. . . . . . **F. biltmoreana**
BLACK A. . . . . **F. nigra**
BLUE A. . . . . . . **F. quadrangulata**
BUNGE A. . . . . **F. bungeana**
CAROLINA A. . . . . . . **F. caroliniana**
CHINESE A. . . . . **F. chinensis**
EUROPEAN A. . . . . **F. excelsior**
FLORIDA A. . . . . **F. pauciflora**
FLOWERING A. . . . . **F. ornus**
FRAGRANT A. . . . . **F. cuspidata**
GREEN A. **F. pennsylvanica lanceolata**
GREGG A. . . . . **F. greggi**
GRIFFITH A. . . . . **F. griffithi**
HIMALAYAN A. . . . . . . **F. floribunda**
HOOKER A. . . . . **F. hookeri**
JAPANESE A. . . . . . . **F. longicuspis**

ASH, continued
KOREAN A.
Fraxinus chinensis rhynchophylla
LEATHERLEAF A. **F. velutina coriacea**
LOWELL A. . . . . **F. lowelli**
MANCHURIAN A. . . **F. mandshurica**
MARIES A. . . . . **F. mariesi**
NARROWLEAF A. . . . **F. angustifolia**
NUMIDIAN A. . . . . **F. numidica**
OREGON A. . . . . **F. oregona**
PAX A. . . . . **F. paxiana**
PUMPKIN A. . . . . **F. tomentosa**
RED A. . . . . **F. pennsylvanica**
REHDER A. **F. caroliniana rehderiana**
ROUNDLEAF A. . . . . . **F. rotundifolia**
ROUNDLEAF FLOWERING A. **F. ornus r.**
SHAMEL A. . . . . **F. uhdei**
SIEBOLD JAPANESE A.
F. longicuspis sieboldiana
SINGLELEAF A. . . . . . . **F. anomala**
SMALLSEED WHITE A.
F. americana microcarpa
SMOOTH A. . . . . **F. velutina glabra**
SMOOTH OREGON A. . . . **F. oregona g.**
SPAETH A. . . . . **F. spaethiana**
SYRIAN A. . . . . **F. syriaca**
TEXAS A. . . . . **F. texensis**
THICKLEAF WHITE A.
F. americana subcoriacea
TOUMEY A. . . . **F. velutina toumeyi**
TURKESTAN A. . . . . **F. potamophila**
TWOPETAL A. . . . . **F. dipetala**
VELVET A. . . . . **F. velutina**
WALNUTLEAF WHITE A.
F. americana juglandifolia
WHITE A. . . . . **F. americana**

ASIABELL . . . . **Codonopsis**
CLEMATIS A. . . . . . **C. clematidea**
FOREST A. . . . . **C. silvestris**
GREENFLOWER A. . . . **C. viridiflora**
GUINEAFOWL A. . . . . . **C. meleagris**
LANCE A. . . . . **C. lanceolata**
ROUNDLEAF A. . . . . . **C. rotundifolia**
ASIABELLTREE . . . . . . **Radermachia**
GLORY A. . . . . **R. sinica**
GRAND A. . . . . **R. pentandra**
ASIAGLORY . . . . **Argyreia**
BLUNTLEAF A. . . . . . **A. obtusifolia**
SILVER A. . . . . **A. splendens**
WOOLLY A. . . . . **A. speciosa**
ASIAPOPPY . . . . **Roemeria**
SPOTTED A. . . . . **R. refracta**

ASIM'INA . . . . . PAWPAW (*Papaw*)
angustifo'lia . . . . SLIMLEAF P.
inca'na (*grandiflora; speciosa*)
WOOLLY P.
obova'ta . . . . BIGFLOWER P.
parviflo'ra . . . . . SMALLFLOWER P.
pulchel'la . . . . SLIMPETAL P.
pyg'maea . . . . SPRAWLING P.
reticula'ta . . . . . . SEMINOLETEA P.
ru'geli . . . . RUGEL P.
specio'sa . . . . **A. incana**
tetram'era . . . . ST.LUCIE P.
trilo'ba . . . . COMMON P.

ASPAR'AGUS (*MYRSIPHYLLUM*) |w
ASPARAGUS
acutifo'lius
africa'nus . . . . AFRICAN A.
al'bus . . . . WHITE A.
asparagoi'des (*medeoloides; Myrsiphyllum a.*) . . . . SMILAX A.
coop'eri . . . . COOPER A.
cris'pus (*decumbens*) . . DROOPING A.
drepanophyl'lus (*duchesnei*)
falca'tus . . . . . . SICKLETHORN A.

ASPARAGUS, continued
hor'ridus
laric'inus . . . . LARCH ASPARAGUS
lu'cidus . . . . SHINY A.
madagascarien'sis . MADAGASCAR A.
medeoloi'des . . . . **A. asparagoides**
myriocla'dus
officina'lis |w . . . . GARDEN A.
plumo'sus . . . . FERN A.
¢COMPACT (*compacta*) HV.
¢DWARF (*nanus*)
¢HATCHER (*hatcheri*)
¢LARGE (*blampiedi*)
¢WIRESTEM (*tenuissimus*)
pseudosca'ber
racemo'sus
scan'dens . . . . BASKET A.
spreng'eri . . . . SPRENGER A.
tetrag'onus
verticilla'tus
virga'tus

ASPARAGUS . . . . **Asparagus**
AFRICAN A. . . . . **A. africanus**
BASKET A. . . . . **A. scandens**
COOPER A. . . . . **A. cooperi**
DROOPING A. . . . . **A. crispus**
FERN A. . . . . **A. plumosus**
GARDEN A. . . . . **A. officinalis**
LARCH A. . . . . **A. laricinus**
MADAGASCAR A. **A. madagascariensis**
SHINY A. . . . . **A. lucidus**
SICKLETHORN A. . . . . **A. falcatus**
SMILAX A. . . . . . . **A. asparagoides**
SPRENGER A. . . . . **A. sprengeri**
WHITE A. . . . . **A. albus**

Asparagus-fern . . . ASPARAGUS, FERN: **Asparagus plumosus**

ASPA'SIA
See **ORCHID GENERA.**

ASPEN . . . . **Populus**
See also POPLAR.
BIGTOOTH A. . . . . **P. grandidentata**
CHINESE A. . . . . **P. adenopoda**
DAVIDS EUROPEAN A. **P. tremula davidiana**
EUROPEAN A. . . . . . . **P. tremula**
GOLDEN QUAKING A. **P. tremuloides aurea**
HAIRY EUROPEAN A. **P. tremula villosa**
KIDNEYLEAF QUAKING A. **P. tremuloides reniformis**
QUAKING A. . . . . . **P. tremuloides**
SIEBOLD A. . . . . **P. sieboldi**
SOUTHERN BIGTOOTH A. **P. grandidentata meridionalis**
VANCOUVER QUAKING A. **P. tremuloides vancouveriana**
WEEPING BIGTOOTH A. **P. grandidentata penduliformis**
WEEPING EUROPEAN A. **P. tremula pendula**

ASPER'ULA . . . . WOODRUFF
azu'rea; azurea-seto'sa . . **A. orientalis**
capita'ta
cynan'chica (*montana*)
galioi'des . . . . . . BEDSTRAW W.
hexaphyl'la . . . . MISTY W.
hir'ta
humifu'sa
laeviga'ta
longiflo'ra . . . . . LONGFLOWER W.
lute'a . . . . YELLOW W.
monta'na . . . . **A. cynanchica**
nit'ida

ASPERULA, continued
odora'ta . . . . SWEET WOODRUFF
orienta'lis (*azurea; azurea-setosa*) ORIENTAL W.
subero'sa
tincto'ria . . . . DYERS W.

ASPHODEL . . . . **Asphodelus**
ASIA A. . . . . **A. asiaticus**
BRANCHING A. . . . . **A. albus**

ASPHODELI'NE . . . . . JACOBSROD
balan'sae
libur'nica (*Asphodelus liburnicus*)
lute'a (*Asphodelus luteus*). COMMON J.

ASPHODEL'US . . . . . . ASPHODEL
al'bus . . . . BRANCHING A.
asiat'icus . . . . ASIA A.
libur'nicus . . . **Asphodeline liburnica**
lute'us . . . . . . **Asphodeline lutea**
ramo'sus
tenuifo'lius

ASPIDIS'TRA . . . . . ASPIDISTRA
ela'tior (*lurida*) . . . . . COMMON A.
¢PURPLESPOT (*punctata*) HV.
¢STRIPED (*variegata*)

ASPID'IUM
See **FERN GENERA.**

ASPIDOSPER'MA . WHITEQUEBRACHO
polyneur'on
quebracho-blan'co . . . COMMON W.
tomento'sum . . . . WOOLLY W.

ASPLE'NIUM . . . . . SPLEENWORT
See **FERN GENERA.**

AS'PRIS . . . . **AIRA**
See **GRASS GENERA.**

ASSEGAITREE . . . . . **Curtisia faginea**

ASSO'NIA . . . . **DOMBEYA**

ASTAR'TEA
fascicula'ris

ASTE'LIA
nervo'sa

AS'TER (*Bellidiastrum; Diplopappus; Doellingeria; Eucephalus; Galatella; Ionactis; Leucelene; Machaeranthera; Oreostemma; Xylorrhiza*) . ASTER
ab'atus (*tortifolius*) . . . . MOHAVE A.
a'cris (*linifolius; punctatus; sedifolius*) RHONE A.
—na'nus . . . . . . DWARF R.A.
acumina'tus . . . . . ACUMINATE A.
adscen'dens (*denudatus; nelsoni; oxylepis; vallicola*)
alpi'nus (*garibaldi; nivalis; pulchellus; scabris*) . . . . ALPINE A.
—al'bus . . . . WHITE A.A.
—ru'ber . . . . RED A.A.
—specio'sus . . . . . . SHOWY A.A.
—super'bus . . . . . . GREAT A.A.
—wolf'i . . . . WOLFS A.A.
¢ALPINE LEICHTLIN. HV. A. alpinus
¢GIGANTEUS
¢MAGNIFICUS
¢ROSEUS
amel'lus (*amelloides; ibericus; noianus; pseudoamellus; scepusiensis; tinctorius; trinervius*) . . . ITALIAN A.
—bessara'bicus (*A. bessarabicus*) BESSARABIAN A.
—el'egans . . . . LOW I.A.

ASTER, continued
amethysti'nus . . AMETHYST ASTER
amplexifo'lius . . . . **A. integrifolius**
anderso'ni . . . . ANDERSON A.
angus'tus . . . . **A. brachyactis**
a'pricus . . . . **A. foliaceus a.**
azu'reus . . . . AZURE A.
bellidias'trum (*Bellidiastrum micheli*) MICHEL A.
bergeria'nus . . . **Felicia bergeriana**
bessarab'icus . . . . . **A. amellus b.**
bigelo'vi (*townsendi; Machaeranthera b.*) BIGELOW A.
brachyac'tis (*angustus*) |w
brachytrich'us . . . . . HANKOW A.
burk'ei . . . . **A. foliaceus b.**
cabu'licus . . **Microglossa albescens**
can'byi . . . . CANBY A.
canes'cens (*Machaeranthera c.*) HOARY A.
carno'sus . . . . **A. intricatus**
carolinia'nus . . . . . . CAROLINA A.
cassiarab'icus . . . . VOLGA A.
caucas'icus (*monocephalus*) CAUCASIAN A.
chap'mani . . . . SAVANNAH A.
chilen'sis (*chamissonis*) . . PACIFIC A.
cogna'tus . . . COLORADO DESERT A.
commuta'tus
—cras'sulus (*A. crassulus*)
conspic'uus (*macdougali*) . SHOWY A.
cordifo'lius (*pallidulus*) HEARTLEAF A.
—magnif'icus . . . . . SHOWY H.A.
—polyceph'alus
¢HEARTLEAF VERSICOLOR. HV. A. cordifolius
corymbo'sus . . . . . **A. divaricatus**
cras'sulus . . . . **A. commutatus c.**
cur'tisi . . . . CURTIS A.
deco'rus . . . . **A. laevis**
decur'rens . . . . **A. laevis**
delavay'i . . . . DELAVAY A.
denuda'tus . . . . . . **A. adscendens**
diffus'us . . . . **A. lateriflorus**
diplostephioi'des . . HINDUKUSH A.
¢HINDUKUSH LEICHTLIN. HV.
divarica'tus (*corymbosus*) WHITE WOOD A.
doug'lasi
dracunculoi'des (*Galatella d.*) MEDITERRANEAN A.
drum'mondi . . . . . DRUMMOND A.
dumo'sus . . . . BUSHY A.
eat'oni (*A. foliaceus e.*) . EATONS A.
elonga'tus
engelmann'i . . . . ENGELMANN A.
ericoi'des (*multiflorus*) . . HEATH A.
—villo'sus . . . . **A. pilosus**
far'reri . . . . FARRER A.
floribun'dus . . . . . . **A. novibelgi**
folia'ceus . . . . . . LEAFYBRACT A.
—a'pricus (*A. apricus*) . ALPINE L.A.
—burk'ei (*A. burkei*) . . BURKE L.A.
—eat'oni . . . . **A. eatoni**
—fron'deus (*A. frondeus*). . TALL L.A.
for'resti . . . . FORREST A.
fre'monti . . . . FREMONT A.
fron'deus . . . . . . **A. foliaceus f.**
frondo'sus . . . . LEAFY A.
frutico'sus (*Diplopappus fruticulosus*) FRUTICOSE A.
garibald'i . . . . **A. alpinus**
glabrius'culus (*Xylorrhiza glabriuscula*) ALKALI A.
glauco'des (*Eucephalus glaucus*)
grandiflo'rus . . . . GREAT A.
great'ai . . . . . . SANGABRIEL A.

ASTER, continued
haloph'ilus |w
Hotsprings Saltmarsh Aster
Regarded by some botanists as a synonym of A. adscendens, but probably distinct, at least as a variety or form.

harrowia'nus . . . . . Harrows A.
hesper'ius . . . . Siskiyou A.
himala'icus (*himalayensis*) Himalayan A.
iber'icus . . . . **A. amellus**
inci'sus . . . . . . **Calimeris incisa**
integrifo'lius (*amplexifolius*) Thickstem A.
intrica'tus (*carnosus*)
johannen'sis . . . Lake St. John A.
jun'ceus . . . . Rush A.
kum'lieni . . . . . . Kumlien A.
lae'vis (*decorus; decurrens*). Smooth A.
lateriflo'rus (*diffusus*) . . . Calico A.
ledophyl'lus (*Eucephalus l.*)
leucanthemifo'lius (*Machaeranthera leucanthemifolia*) . . . Daisyleaf A.
leucele'ne (*Leucelene ericoides*) Babywhite A.
likiangen'sis . . . . . . Likiang A.
linariifo'lius (*Ionactis l.*) Savoryleaf A.
lindleya'nus . . . . . . Lindley A.
linifo'lius . . . . **A. acris**
linosy'ris . . . . **Linosyris vulgaris**
lip'skyi . . . . Lipsky A.
longifo'lius (*virgineus*) . Longleaf A.
lowriea'nus . . . . Lowrie A.
lu'cidus . . . . Shining A.
maack'i . . . . Hakone A.
macdoug'ali . . . . . **A. conspicuus**
macrophyl'lus (*polyphyllus*) Bigleaf A.
modes'tus . . . . . Fewflower A.
monoceph'alus . . . . **A. caucasicus**
multiflo'rus . . . . . **A. ericoides**
nel'soni . . . . **A. adscendens**
nemora'lis . . . . Bog A.
niv'alis . . . . **A. alpinus**
noia'nus . . . . **A. amellus**
novaean'gliae . . NewEngland A.
—**rose'us** . . . . . . Rosy N.A.
¢Albus. hv. A. novaeangliae
¢Ruber
¢Violaceus
novibel'gi (*floribundus*). NewYork A.
oblongifo'lius . . . . . Aromatic A.
occidenta'lis . . . . . Western A.
ontario'nis . . . . Ontario A.
or'cutti . . . . Orcutt A.
orego'nus . . . . Oregon A.
oxyle'pis . . . . **A. adscendens**
pallid'ulus . . . . . . **A. cordifolius**
paludo'sus . . . Singlestem Bog A.
panicula'tus . . . . . . Panicled A.
par'ryi (*Xylorrhiza p.*) . . Parry A.
pa'tens . . . . Skydrop A.
patterso'ni (*Machaeranthera p.*) Patterson A.
paucicapita'tus (*Eucephalus p.*)
perel'egans (*Eucephalus elegans*) Nuttall A.
pilo'sus (*A. ericoides villosus*)
polyphyl'lus . . . . **A. macrophyllus**
por'teri . . . . Porters A.
Showy (*superbus*) hv.
pseudoamel'lus . . . . . **A. amellus**
ptarmicoi'des . . White Upland A.
pulchel'lus . . . . **A. alpinus**
puncta'tus . . . . **A. acris**
punic'eus . . . . Swamp A.
pyrenae'us . . . . . . Pyrenees A.
rad'ula . . . . Rough A.

ASTER, continued
sagittifo'lius . . . . . Arrow Aster
salicifo'lius . . . . Willowleaf A.
sca'bris . . . . **A. alpinus**
scepusien'sis . . . . . . **A. amellus**
schre'beri . . . . . . Schreber A.
scopulo'rum (*Ionactis alpina*) Crag A.
sedifo'lius . . . . **A. acris**
seric'eus . . . . Silky A.
short'i . . . . Georgia A.
sibir'icus . . . . Siberian A.
sinen'sis . . . **Callistephus chinensis**
spectab'ilis (*speciosus*) . Seaside A.
spino'sus . . . . . Devilweed A.
squarro'sus . . . . **A. walteri**
staticifo'lius . . . . . . Statice A.
stenome'res (*Ionactis s.*) Northwest A.
stra'cheyi . . . . Strachey A.
subcoeru'leus . . . . EastIndies A.
subula'tus |w . Annual Saltmarsh A.
tanacetifo'lius (*Machaeranthera tanacetifolia*) . . . . . . Tansyleaf A.
tatar'icus . . . . Tatarian A.
tenuifo'lius |w . . . . . . Saline A.
thom'soni . . . . Thomson A.
tincto'rius . . . . **A. amellus**
tortifo'lius . . . . **A. abatus**
town'sendi . . . . **A. bigelovi**
tradescant'i . . . . Tradescant A.
triceph'alus . . . . . . Garwhal A.
triner'vius . . . . **A. amellus**
tripoli'um . . . . Tripoli A.
turbinel'lus . . . . . . Prairie A.
umbella'tus (*Doellingeria umbellata*) Flattop A.
undula'tus . . . . Wave A.
vallic'ola . . . . **A. adscendens**
versicol'or . . . . . . Versicolor A.
vesti'tus . . . . Kintong A.
vimin'eus . . . . . Small White A.
virgin'eus . . . . **A. longifolius**
wal'teri (*squarrosus*) . . Walter A.
xylorrhi'za (*Xylorrhiza scopulorum; X. villosa*) . . . . Common Woody A.
yunnanen'sis . . . . . . Yunnan A.

Hort. var. of **Hardy Aster:**

For the horticultural variety list of Aster the Editorial Committee acknowledges its indebtedness to Ray M. Koon, in charge, Waltham Field Station, Massachusetts State College, Waltham, Mass., a recognized specialist.

This is believed to be the most authoritative and up-to-date list of hardy Asters yet published.

Because of the large number of varieties of Aster the common-name list and the hort. var. list have been combined in the special list below. Most, if not all, of the horticultural varieties may be considered as clons, though it is possible some of the natural varieties may come fairly true to parent from seed.

Abbreviations indicating the species to which a hort. var. is reported to belong are as follows:

×	Hybrid
Acr.	A. acris
Alp.	A. alpinus
Amel.	A. amellus
Cord.	A. cordifolius
Dip.	A. diplostephioides
Dum.	A. dumosus
Eric.	A. ericoides
Fol.	A. foliaceus
Grand.	A. grandiflorus
Laev.	A. laevis
Lat.	A lateriflorus
Lin.	Linosyris vulgaris (*A. linosyris*)
Nova.	A. novaeangliae
Novb.	A. novibelgi
Ob.	A. oblongifolius
Ptar.	A. ptarmicoides
Spec.	A. spectabilis
Sub.	A. subcoeruleus
Thom.	A. thomsoni
Trad.	A. tradescanti
Unc.	Unclassified
Vim.	A. vimineus

ASTER, HARDY, continued

Abendroethe. Novb.
Acme. Novb.
Acuminate A. **A. acuminatus.**
Adorable. Novb.
Advance. Amel.
Aerschott. Novb.
A. (*G. N.*) Launder. Eric.
Ahrensburger Zwerg. Amel.
Albus. Nova.
Aldebaran. Cord.
Aldenham Pink. Novb.
Alderman Vokes. Novb.
Alkali A. **A. glabriusculus.**
Alkaline. Unc.
Alpengluhen. Alp.
Alpine A. **A. alpinus.**
Alpine Leafybract A. **A. foliaceus apricus.**
Alpine Leichtlin. Alp.
A. (*M.*) Carr. Novb.
Amethyst A. **A. amethystinus.**
Amethyst. Novb.
Amos Perry. Novb.
Amy. Eric.
Anderson A. **A. andersoni.**
Anita Ballard. Novb.
Anne Thomas. Novb.
Annual Saltmarsh A. **A. subulatus.**
Antwerp. Novb.
Apollo. Sub.
Apollon. Alp.
Archer Hind. Novb.
Ardon. ×.
Aromatic A. **A. oblongifolius.**
Arrow A. **A. sagittifolius.**
Artemis. Sub.
Artis. Unc.
Asa Gray. Unc.
Aster Purple. Unc.
Aurora. ×.
Autumnglow. Novb.
Autumnlady. Amel.
Autumnqueen. Novb.
Aviateur Lindbergh. Unc.
Azure A. **A. azureus.**
Azure. Novb.
Bab Ballard. ×.
Babcock. Nova.
Babys Breath. Ptar.
Babywhite A. **A. leucelene.**
Ballards Crimson. Novb.
Barrs Pink. Nova.
Beacon. Amel.
Beaute Orleanaise. ×.
Beaute Parfaite. Amel.
Beauty of Colwall. Novb.
Beauty of Eisenach. Amel.
Beauty of Ronsdorf. Amel.
Beechwood Beacon. Novb.
Beechwood Belle. Novb.
Beechwood Bride. Novb.
Beechwood Challenger. Novb.
Beechwood Charm. Novb.
Beechwood Chieftain. Novb.
Beechwood Glory. Novb.
Beechwood Glow. Novb.
Beechwood Lady. Novb.
Beechwood Ray. Novb.

ASTER, HARDY, continued
Beechwood Rival. Novb.
Beechwood Triumph. Novb.
Bees Blush. Unc.
Bees Helio. Unc.
Belgian Queen. Novb.
Belle-rose. Unc.
Belle Rotraut. Unc.
Bessarabian A. **A. amellus bessarabicus.**
Bessie Chaplin. Unc.
Bessie Chapman. Amel.
Beth. Eric.
Betty. Sub.
Bigelow A. **A. bigelovi.**
Bigleaf A. **A. macrophyllus.**
Bijou. Amel.
Blanchette. Unc.
Blaustern. Amel.
Blue. Alp.
Bluebaby. ×.
Bluebeard. Unc.
Bluebird. ×.
Bluebouquet. ×.
Bluedazzler. Amel.
Blueeyes. Novb.
Bluegem. Novb.
Bluegown. Novb.
Bluejacket. Novb.
Bluelagoon. Novb.
Blueplume. Novb.
Blueprince. Novb.
Bluestar. Eric.
Bluetenregen. Cord.
Bluetenschirm. Novb.
Blushing Bride. Unc.
Bog A. **A. nemoralis.**
Bonfire. Amel.
Boule Deneige. Amel.
Bouquet Rose. Novb.
Brightest and Best. Novb.
Brighteyes. Novb.
Brightness. Novb.
Brimstone. Eric.
Bruges. Unc.
Brussels. Novb.
Buisson Fleuri. Unc.
Buisson Rose. Unc.
Burbanks Charming. ×.
Burke Leafybract A. **A. foliaceus burkei.**
Bushy A. **A. dumosus.**
Buxtons Dwarf. ×.
Calico A. **A. lateriflorus.**
Campbells Pink. Ob.
Canby A. **A. canbyi.**
Candelabra. Novb.
Capitaine. Novb.
Captain Fryatt. Unc.
Cardinal Mercier. Novb.
Carmen. Novb.
Carolina A. **A. carolinianus.**
Cassiope. Vim.
Caterham Gem. Eric.
Cattleya. Novb.
Caucasian A. **A. caucasicus.**
Celeste. Unc.
Charles Davis. Amel.
Charles Wilson. Novb.
Charmer. Eric.
Charming. Unc.
Chastity. Eric.
Cheznous. ×.
Cheznous Dwarf Pink. ×.
Cheznous Mauve. Novb.
Cheznous Pink. Novb.
Cinderella. Cord.
Clairette. Novb.

ASTER, HARDY, continued
Cleopatra. Novb.
Climax. Novb.
Clio. Unc.
Cloudy Blue. Novb.
Coleorton. Amel.
Col. (*F. R.*) Durham. Novb.
Collarette Rose. Unc.
Colorado Desert A. **A. cognatus.**
Colwall Pink. Novb.
Common Woody A. **A. xylorrhiza.**
Constance. ×.
Coombe Fishacre. Unc.
Coquette. Eric.
Coquetterie. Unc.
Cordibelgi Pioneer. Novb.
Corona. Novb.
Cosette. Unc.
Cote d'Azur. Unc.
Cottage Maid. Novb.
Countess. Novb.
Countess of Dudley. ×.
Crag A. **A. scopulorum.**
Crimson Beauty. Nova.
Crimson King. Nova.
Crimson Star. Nova.
Curtis A. **A. curtisi.**
Dainty. Novb.
Daisyleaf A. **A. leucanthemifolius.**
Daphne. ×.
Dark Beauty. Alp. *Dunkleschone.*
Datschi. Dif.
Daydream. Eric.
Dazzler. Novb.
Decorator. Eric.
Delavay A. **A. delavayi.**
Delight. Eric.
Den Oudens Beauty. Alp.
Desire. Eric.
Deutsche Treue. Amel.
Devilweed A. **A. spinosus.**
Diadem. Unc.
Diana. ×.
Dick Ballard. Novb.
Donny Boy. Unc.
Doris. Eric.
Doris Fisher. Amel.
Dorothy Rowe. Cord.
Dorothy Vokes. ×.
Dr. Eckner. Nova.
Drummond A. **A. drummondi.**
Duchess. Novb.
Dusky Maid. Nova.
Dwarf Rhone A. **A. acris nanus.**
Dwarf White. Unc.
EastIndies A. **A. subcoeruleus.**
Eatons A. **A. eatoni.**
E. (*C.*) Buxton. Unc.
Edith Goodwin. Novb.
Edmond Brochon. Unc.
Edna Mercier. Nova.
Edna Perry. Novb.
Edwin Beckett. Novb.
Effie. Novb.
Eiger. Thom.
Eileen Kelway. Novb.
Elfin. Vim.
Elisabeth Liemann. Amel.
Elizabeth Bright. Novb.
Elsa. Novb.
Elsie Perry. Novb.
Elta. Nova.
Emile Thoury. Novb.
Emil Tobler. Novb.
Emma Bedau. Amel.
Emperor. Unc.
Empress of Colwall. Novb.
Enchantress. Eric.

ASTER, HARDY, continued
Enfant Devitres. Unc.
Engelmann A. **A. engelmanni.**
English Elegance. Unc.
Erectus. Eric.
Erica. Unc.
Erlkonig. Eric.
Erstling. Amel.
Esmee. Novb.
Esther. Novb.
Estrallita. Unc.
Ethel. Amel.
Ethel Ballard. Novb.
Etoile Mauve. Amel.
Evening Star. Vim.
Excelsior. Amel.
Fairy. Vim.
Fanal. Amel.
Farrer A. **A. farreri.**
Favourite. Amel.
Feltham Blue. Novb.
Fewflower A. **A. modestus.**
Finale. Nova.
Finchley White. Novb.
Findelking. Dif.
Fitzpatrick. Cord.
Flattop A. **A. umbellatus.**
Fleuve Bleu. Amel.
Florists Delight. Sub.
Florrie. Eric.
Flossy. Unc.
Forget-Me-Not. Trad.
Forrest A. **A. forresti.**
Framfieldi. Amel.
Frances Sands. Nova.
Freedom. Novb.
Fremont A. **A. fremonti.**
Freude. Alp.
Frikarti. Thom.
Friquet. Amel.
Frohna. Novb.
Fruticose A. **A. fruticosus.**
F. W. Burbridge. Novb.
Gaiete. Amel.
Garibaldi. Alp.
Garwhal A. **A. tricephalus.**
Gayborder Beauty. Novb.
Gayborder Blue. Novb.
Gayborder Charm. Novb.
Gayborder Lilac. Novb.
Gayborder Pink. Novb.
Gayborder Plenty. Novb.
Gayborder Pride. Novb.
Gayborder Prince. Novb.
Gayborder Purple. Novb.
Gayborder Queen. Novb.
Gayborder Rose. Novb.
Gayborder Supreme. Novb.
Gayborder Violet. Novb.
General Leman. Novb.
General Pershing. Amel.
Genevieve Rouillard. Amel.
Georgia A. **A. shorti.**
Gerald Perry. Nova.
Gerbe d'Azure. Unc.
Gertrude. Amel.
Ghent. Unc.
Giganteus. Alp.
Gladys Adams. Eric.
Gladys Forbes. Amel.
Gloire Decronstadt. Nova.
Gloire d'Orleans. Alp.
Gloriosa. Nova.
Glory of Colwall.
Glowworm. Unc.
Gnom. Amel.
Golden Fleece. Eric.
Golden Rain. Unc.

ASTER, HARDY, continued
Golden Spray. Eric.
Golden Star. Vim.
Golden Youth. Unc.
Goldfinch. Unc.
Goldflake. Unc.
Goldilocks. Lin.
Goliath. Alp.
Gorgeous. Novb.
Grace. Unc.
Grace (*Mary*) Lewis. Novb.
Grace Sweet. Novb
Grayish-White. Unc.
Great A. **A. grandiflorus.**
Great Alpine A. **A. alpinus superbus.**
Grey Dawn. Eric.
Greylady. Novb.
Gruppenkoenigin. Amel.
Gute. Alp.
Hakone A. **A. maacki.**
Halo. Nova.
Hameola. Novb.
Hankow A. **A. brachytrichus.**
Harmony. Eric.
Harold Brewerton. Unc.
Harringtons Pink. Nova.
Harrows A. **A. harrowianus.**
Heartleaf A. **A. cordifolius.**
Heartleaf Versicolor. Cord.
Heath A. **A. ericoides.**
Heather Glow. Novb.
Heavenly Blue. Sub.
Hebe. ×.
Heiderose. Novb.
Heinrich Seibert. Amel.
Helen. Unc.
Helen Durward. Laev.
Herbstmyrthe. Novb.
Herbstwunder. Novb.
Hermann Lons. Amel.
H. G. Mills. Amel.
Highland Maid. Unc.
Highland Morning. Unc.
Hilda Ballard. Novb.
Hilda Morris. Nova.
Hillagonda. Novb.
Himalayan A. **A. himalaicus.**
Himmelskoenigin. Unc.
Hindukush A. **A. diplostephioides.**
Hindukush Leichtlin. Dip.
Hoary A. **A. canescens.**
(*Hon.*) Edith Gibbs. Novb.
(*Hon.*) Vicary Gibbs. Novb.
Hortense. Nova.
Hotsprings Saltmarsh A. **A. halophilus.**
Humosa. Unc.
Ideal. Cord.
Imperator. Amel.
Italian A. **A. amellus.**
Ivy Logan. Novb.
Jacqueline Genebrier. Amel.
Jacquot. Unc.
James Kelway. Novb.
Japanese Double White. Unc.
Japonoise. Unc.
J. (*A.*) Raynor. Unc.
Jean Oldham. Novb.
Joan Vaughan. Novb.
Josephine Wells. Novb.
Joseph Laekin. Unc.
Josie. Sub.
Joy. Unc.
J. (*S.*) Baker. Novb.
Julia. ×.
Jungfrau. Thom.
Jupiter. Unc.
J. Wood. Unc.

ASTER, HARDY, continued
Kate Bloomfield. Nova.
Katherine. Eric.
Kaye. Unc.
Kelways Gloriosa. Unc.
Kelways Masterpiece. Novb.
Kentucky Grand. Grand.
Keston. Amel.
Keston Blue. Unc.
King. Unc.
King Albert. Novb.
King Edward VIII. Eric.
King George. Amel.
King of Autumn. Unc.
Kink of Blues. Unc.
King of the Belgians. Novb.
King Solomon. Amel.
Kintong A. **A. vestitus.**
Kitty. Sub.
Kobold. ×.
Konigin. Amel.
Kruffeage. ×.
Kumlien A. **A. kumlieni.**
Lac Degeneve. Unc.
Lady (*Henry*) Maddocks. ×.
Lady Hurley. Unc.
Lady Lloyd. Novb.
Lady Swettenham. Amel.
Lafrance. Amel.
Lake St. John A. **A. johannensis.**
Lamarne. Unc.
L'Amerique. Amel.
Lareine. Amel.
Laura Borton. Novb.
Lavanda. ×.
Lavandal. Novb.
Lavender. Novb.
Lavender Queen. Unc.
Leafy A. **A. frandosus.**
Leafybract A. **A. foliaceus.**
Leichtlini. Unc.
Leuchtfeuer. Unc.
Licktblick. Amel.
Liege. Unc.
Likiang A. **A. likiangensis.**
Lilac Carpet. ×.
Lilacina. Amel.
Lilactime. ×.
Lil Fardell. Nova.
Lily Elsie. Unc.
Lindbergh. Amel.
Lindley A. **A. lindleyanus.**
Linette. Unc.
Lipsky A. **A. lipskyi.**
L'Italie. Amel.
Little Boy Blue. Novb.
Little Gem. Amel.
Little Pink Lady. Novb.
L. M. Meakin. Amel.
Longleaf A. **A. longifolius.**
Los Angeles. Unc.
Lotus Lily. Novb.
Louise. Amel.
Louvain. Novb.
Lovely. Vim.
Low Italian A. **A. amellus elegans.**
Lowrie A. **A. lowrieanus.**
Lt. Warneford, V. C. Novb.
Lusantha. Amel.
Lutetia. Unc.
Maggie Perry. Novb.
Magnificus. Alp.
Maidenhood. Eric.
Maid of Athens. Novb.
Maid of Colwall. Unc.
Malines. Novb.
Mammoth. Novb.
Margaret Ballard. Novb.

ASTER, HARDY, continued
Margery. Novb.
Margery Oliver. Eric.
Marion. Eric.
Marjorie. ×.
Mars. Amel.
Mary Purdy. Unc.
Mauve Cushion. ×.
Mauvequeen. Novb.
Max Pohlig. Amel.
Mayi. Novb.
May Queen. Novb.
Mediterranean A. **A. dracunculoides.**
Melbourne Blue. Novb.
Melbourne Gem. Novb.
Melbourne Glory. Novb.
Melbourne Lad. Novb.
Melbourne Lassie. Novb.
Melbourne Marvel. Novb.
Melbourne Mauve. Novb.
Mesagrande. Unc.
Meyer. *F. K. Meyer.*
Michel A. **A. bellidiastrum.**
Mignon. Amel.
Mischung. Amel.
Miss (*A. E.*) Groll. Amel.
Miss Eisele. Novb.
Miss Meeson. Amel.
Miss (*M.*) Storr. Unc.
Miss Muffet. Novb.
Miss Stafford. Novb.
Miss Willmott. Novb.
Mme. Antoine Rivoire. Amel.
Mme. Besnard. Amel.
Mme. Cacheux. Novb.
Mme. Carroy. Novb.
Mme. (*E.*) Ganguin. Amel.
Mme. Emile Thoury. Novb.
Mme. (*Georges*) Rondeau. Amel.
Mme. (*L.*) Galloides. Amel.
Mme. (*Lionel*) Bruneau. Unc.
Mme. Louis Tillie. Unc.
Mme. Michaud. Unc.
Mme. Philippe Rivoire. Amel.
Mme. Poichauvin. Amel.
Mme. Soyneuse. Unc.
Mme. Theo Cholet. Amel.
Moerheim Beauty. Amel.
Moerheim Gem. Amel.
Mohave A. **A. abatus.**
Monch. Thom.
Monette. Amel.
Mons. Novb.
Montagne Deneige. Novb.
Moonlight. Novb.
Moonstone. Novb.
Morning Star. Unc.
Mother of Pearl. Novb.
Mrs. (*A. E.*) Underdown. Eric.
Mrs. (*A. H.*) Wiggins. Amel.
Mrs. (*A.*) Maddocks. Amel.
Mrs. Berkeley. Acr.
Mrs. (*Davis*) Evans. Novb.
Mrs. (*D.*) Mitchell. Unc.
Mrs. Francis Childers. Nova.
Mrs. F. W. Fitzpatrick. Nova.
Mrs. (*F. W*). Raynor. Nova.
Mrs. (*George*) Munro. Novb.
Mrs. Glossop. Cord.
Mrs. (*H.*) Morris. Novb.
Mrs. (*J. K.*) Holmes. Novb.
Mrs. (*Lewis*) Evans. Novb.
Mrs. McCudden. Unc.
Mrs. M. Storr. Novb.
Mrs. Perry. Amel.
Mrs. (*Ralph*) Wood. Amel.
Mrs. (*S. A.*) de Graeff. Unc.

ASTER, HARDY, continued
MRS. SIMS. Unc.
MRS. (*S. T.*) WRIGHT. Nova.
MT. EVEREST. Novb.
MT. RAINIER. Nova.
MULBERRY. Novb.
MURIEL CHANDLER. Unc.
NAMUR. Novb.
NANCY. ×.
NANCY BALLARD. Novb.
NANCY PERRY. Alp.
NECO. Spec.
NENCO. Unc.
NEWENGLAND A. **A. novaeangliae.**
NEWYORK A. **A. novibelgi.**
NEWYORK AMETHYST. Novb.
NEWYORK AZURE. Novb.
NICOLETTE. Amel.
NIOBE. Novb.
NIXE. Alp.
NORA ROGERS. Novb.
NORDLICHT. Unc.
NORMA. Novb.
NORTHERN ALPHA. Eric.
NORTHERN BRIMSTONE. Eric.
NORTHERN GEM. Unc.
NORTHERN GLORY. Novb.
NORTHERN MIGNONETTE. Eric.
NORTHERN PROGRESS. Eric.
NORTHERN QUEEN. Nova.
NORTHERN RED. Nova.
NORTHERN SATIN. Novb.
NORTHWEST A. **A. stenomeres.**
NOVELTY. Eric.
NURSE CAVELL. Novb.
NUTTALL A. **A. perelegans.**
OCTOBER DAWN. Novb.
OCTOBER GLOW. Unc.
OKTOBERFRUHLINE. Novb.
OKTOBERKIND. Amel.
OLD ENGLAND. Novb.
OLGA KEITH. Novb.
OLIVET. Amel.
OLYMPIC MOUNTAINS. Eric.
ONTARIO A. **A. ontarionis.**
ONWARD. Amel.
OPHIR. Eric.
ORCUTT A. **A. orcutti.**
OREGON A. **A. oregonus.**
OSPREY. Vim.
OTTO RUDOLPH. Amel.
OWEN WELLS. Novb.
PACIFIC A. **A. chilensis.**
PALE BLUE. Alp.
PALMYRA. Novb.
PANICLED A. **A. paniculatus.**
PAPER WHITE. Novb.
PARRY A. **A. parryi.**
PASTEL. Novb.
PATTERSON A. **A. pattersoni.**
PEGGY. Sub.
PEGGY BALLARD. Novb.
PERFECTA. Vim.
PERFECTION. Eric.
PERKEO. Amel.
PERKY. Unc.
PERLE ROSE. Amel.
PERRYS BLUE. Novb.
PERRYS FAVOURITE. Amel.
PERRYS PINK. Unc.
PERRYS PRIDE. Novb.
PERRYS WHITE. Novb.
PETER PAN. ×.
PETUNIA. Novb.
PHOEBUS. Amel.
PHOTOGRAPH. Cord.
PHYLLIS. Novb.
PINK DWARF. ×.

ASTER, HARDY, continued
PINK NYMPH. ×.
PINK OF RONSDORF. Amel.
PINK PEARL. Novb.
PINK PERFECTION. Novb.
PINK PROFUSION. Novb.
PINK PROGRESSIVE. Novb.
PINK PYRAMID. Novb.
PINK ROYAL. Unc.
PIONEER. Novb.
PLUTO. Novb.
PORTERS A. **A. porteri.**
POWDERPUFF. Novb.
PRAIRIE A. **A. turbinellus.**
PRESIDENT. Novb.
PRESIDENT KRUGER. Amel.
PRIMADONNA. Eric.
PRIMUS. Unc.
PRINCESS (*Marie*) LOUISE. Unc.
PROFUSION. Cord.
PROMETHEUS. Amel.
PRUDENCE. Unc.
PURPLE EMPEROR. Novb.
PURPLE KING. Nova.
PURPLE PRINCE. Nova.
PURPLE ROBE. Novb.
PURPURKOENIG. Amel.
PYRENEES A. **A. pyrenaeus.**
QUEEN. Amel.
QUEEN ANNE. Eric.
QUEEN ELIZABETH. Novb.
QUEEN MARY. Novb.
QUEEN OF COLWALL. Novb.
QUEEN OF THE LILACS. Novb.
RACHEL BALLARD. Novb.
RACLUSE. Thom.
RADIANCE. Novb.
RADIANT. Novb.
RAPTURE. Novb.
RED ALPINE A. **A. alpinus ruber.**
REDCLOUD. Nova.
REDFIRE. Amel.
REDROVER. Novb.
REDSTAR. Novb.
REGINA. Amel.
R. (*E.*) HAY. Novb.
REMEMBRANCE. Novb.
REV. (*C.*) NUNN. Novb.
REX. Alp.
RHONE A. **A. acris.**
RICHNESS. Novb.
RINGDOVE. Eric.
RIVERSLEA. Amel.
ROBERT PARKER. Novb.
ROBINSON (*V. C.*). Novb.
ROI DES ASTERS. Unc.
ROI DES ROSES. Unc.
RONALD. ×.
ROSA VONRONSDORF. Amel.
ROSEGEM. Novb.
ROSEMARY. Novb.
ROSE McDONALD. Ple.
ROSEQUEEN. Novb.
ROSETTE. Novb.
ROSEUS. Alp.
ROSY. Eric.
ROSYMORN. Novb.
ROSY NEWENGLAND A. **A. novaeangliae roseus.**
ROTBLUME. Amel.
ROTER ZWERG. Amel.
ROTTRAUT. Unc.
ROUGETTE. Unc.
ROUGH A. **A. radula.**
ROYAL BLUE. Novb.
ROYAL PINK. Novb.
ROYAL PURPLE. Novb.
RUBER. Nova.

ASTER, HARDY, continued
RUBY. Amel.
RUBY TIPS. Novb.
RUDOLPH GOETHE. Amel.
RUE (*des*) HATIVES. Unc.
RUSH A. **A. junceus.**
RUTH BIDE. Novb.
RYECROFT PINK. Nova.
RYECROFT PURPLE. Nova.
SALINE A. **A. tenuifolius.**
SAM BANHAM. Novb.
SANGABRIEL A. **A. greatai.**
SAPHIR. Unc.
SATURN. Novb.
SATURNALE. Amel.
SATURNUS. Amel.
SAVANNAH A. **A. chapmani.**
SAVORYLEAF A. **A. linariifolius.**
SCHNEETANNE. Eric.
SCHOENHEIT. Alp.
SCHOEN ROTTRAUT. Cord.
SCHREBER A. **A. schreberi.**
SEASHELL. Unc.
SEASIDE A. **A. spectabilis.**
SENSATION. Eric.
SHAKESPEARE. Nova.
SHINING A. **A. lucidus.**
SHOWY A. **A. conspicuus.**
SHOWY ALPINE A. **A. alpinus speciosus.**
SHOWY HEARTLEAF A. **A. cordifolius magnificus.**
SIBERIAN A. **A. sibiricus.**
SILBERBLICK. Amel.
SILBERSTEIN. Amel.
SILKY A. **A. sericeus.**
SILVERGEM. Eric.
SILVERSEA. Novb.
SILVERSHEEN. Novb.
SILVERSPRAY. Cord.
SIMPLICITY. Eric.
SINGLESTEM BOG A. **A. paludosus.**
SIRIUS. Novb.
SISKIYOU A. **A. hesperius.**
SKYDROP A. **A. patens.**
SKYLANDS QUEEN. Novb.
SMALL WHITE A. **A. vimineus.**
SMOOTH A. **A. laevis.**
SNOWBALL. Novb.
SNOWDON. Novb.
SNOWDRIFT. Novb.
SNOWFLAKE. ×.
SNOWQUEEN. Unc.
SNOWSPRITE. ×.
SOIR D'AUTOMNE. Unc.
SONIA. Amel.
SONNTAGSKIND. Nova.
SPRINGSIDE SEEDLING. Novb.
STAR OF EISENACH. Sub.
STAR OF SOMERSET. Amel.
STAR OF WARTBURG. Sub.
STARSHOWER. Eric.
STATICE A. **A. staticifolius.**
ST. EGWIN. Novb.
STELLA. Amel.
STELLATA. Amel.
STERNKUGEL. Dum.
STORMCLOUD. Nova.
STRACHEY A. **A. stracheyi.**
STRAWBERRIES AND CREAM. Novb.
SUNKISSED. Novb.
SUNSET. Novb.
SUNSET GLOW. Novb.
SURVIVOR. Nova.
SUZETTE. Amel.
SWAMP A. **A. puniceus.**
SWEETHEART. Cord.
SWEET LAVENDER. Cord.
SYLVIA. Amel.

ASTER, HARDY, continued
SYMPHONY. Eric.
TALL LEAFYBRACT A. **A. foliaceus frondeus.**
TANSYLEAF A. **A. tanacetifolius.**
TANTE JEANNE. Unc.
TAPLOW BLUE. Amel.
TAPLOW SPIRE. Novb.
TARDIVE ROSE. Novb.
TATARIAN A. **A. tataricus.**
TAYLOR. Unc.
TENDRESSE. Unc.
THE GARDEN. Novb.
THE KING. Alp.
THELMA PERRY. Novb.
THE QUEEN. Novb.
THE SHIRLEY. Amel.
THICKSTEM A. **A. integrifolius.**
THOMAS WARE. Unc.
THOMSON A. **A. thomsoni.**
THORA PERRY. Novb.
TOM SAWYER. Unc.
TOMTIT. ×.
TOOLES PINK. Nova.
TOUSLE. Unc.
TOUSSAINT. Unc.
TRADESCANT A. **A. tradescanti.**
TREASURE. Unc.
TREUE. Alp.
TRIPOLI A. **A. tripolium.**
TRIUMPH. Unc.
TROUVAILLE. Unc.
TURQUOISE. Unc.
TWILIGHT. Eric.
ULTRAMARINE. Amel.
UNA. Unc.
VAGA. Unc.
VANITY. Amel.
VENUS. ×.
VEREHRUNG. Alp.
VERSICOLOR A. **A. versicolor.**
VICTOR. ×.
VIKTORIA. Amel.
VIOLA. Laev.
VIOLACEUS. Nova.
VIOLET. Nova.
VIOLETTA. Novb.
VISCOUNTESS GLADSTONE. Unc.
VOKES PINK. Novb.
VOLGA A. **A. cassiarabicus.**
WALKENDENS PINK. Novb.
WALLOON. Novb.
WALTER A. **A. walteri.**
WARGRAVE. Alp.
WARGRAVE PINK. Alp.
WARGRAVE ROSE. Alp.
WAVE A. **A. undulatus.**
W. COPELAND. Unc.
WEDGEWOOD. Novb.
WEINHOLTZI. Amel.
WELLS ADVANCE. Unc.
WELLS FAVOURITE. Amel.
WELLS WHITE. Novb.
WESERPERLE. Amel.
WESTERN A. **A. occidentalis.**
WHITE ALPINE A. **A. alpinus albus.**
WHITEBUTTON. Vim.
WHITECLIMAX. Novb.
WHITEDIANA. Cord.
WHITEFEATHER. Eric.
WHITEHEATHER. Eric.
WHITELADY. Novb.
WHITEPLUME. Unc.
WHITEQUEEN. Novb.

ASTER, HARDY, continued
WHITE UPLAND A. **A. ptarmicoides.**
WHITE WOOD A. **A. divaricatus.**
W. H. POWER. Unc.
WILLIAM BOWMAN. Unc.
WILLIAM PERRY. Unc.
WILLIAM ROBINSON. Amel.
WILLOWLEAF A. **A. salicifolius.**
WINCHELL VARIETY. Novb.
WINCHMORE HILL. Thom.
WOLFS ALPINE A. **A. alpinus wolfi.**
WONDER OF COLWALL. Novb.
WONDER OF STAFA. Thom.
WOOLSTONS BLUE. Unc.
W. ROBINSON. Amel.
WUNDER. Alp.
WYNDLEY. Unc.
YPRES. Novb.
YUNNAN A. **A. yunnanensis.**
YVETTE RICHARDSON. Ple.

Asteracan'tha longifo'lia **Hygrophila spinosa**

ASTIL'BE . . . . ASTILBE
∞ **arend'si**
A polybrid name applied to a group of hybrids of A. davidi with other species.
astilboi'des (*Spiraea a.*) GOATSBEARD A.
biterna'ta (*decandra*) . . FALSE G.A.
chinen'sis . . . . CHINESE A.
—**pu'mila** . . . . DWARF C.A.
da'vidi (*A. chinensis d.; Spiraea d.*) DAVID A.
gran'dis . . . . GREAT A.
₵MAGNIFICA (*rosea magnifica*) HV.
hy'brida . . . . **A. rosea**
japon'ica . . . . JAPANESE A.
₵DWARF (*compacta*) HV.
₵GLADSTONE
₵SNOWCLOUD (*multiflora*)
korea'na
lemoin'ei . . . . LEMOINE A.
rivula'ris
∞ **rose'a** (*chinensis* × *japonica; hybrida*) ∞ ROSE A.
PEACHBLOSSOM. HV.
QUEEN ALEXANDRA
∞ **rubel'la**
Hybrid with A. davidi parentage.
simplicifo'lia . . . . STAR A.
—**car'nea**
thunberg'i
Probably all the varieties listed below are clons.
ALEXANDRA. HV. Astilbe
AMERICA
AMETHYST
AVALANCHE
CERES
DIAMANT
FANOL
FRIEDA KLAPP
GERBE D'ARGENT
GLORIA
GLORIA BRIX
GNOME
GRANAT
GRUNO
HANNA STODT
IRENE ROTTSIEPER
JUNO
KING ALBERT
KOLN
KRISTELL

ASTILBE, continued
LAQUETI
LILLIPUT
MARIE VANSTIRUM
META IMMICK
MOERHEIM
PEACHBLOSSOM
PINKPEARL
PRINCESS JULIANA
PROF. WIELEN
QUEEN ALEXANDRA
RHINELAND
SALLAND
SALMON
SHELLPINK
TEERIE
VENUS
VESTA
WASHINGTON
W. E. GLADSTONE
W. REEVES

ASTRAG'ALUS (*Ctenophyllum; Cystium; Diholcos; Geoprumnon; Hamosa; Homalobus; Kentrophyta; Orophaca; Phaca; Picraena* Stev., *not* Lindl.; *Pterophacos; Rydbergiella; Tium; Xylophacos*) [W]
LOCO; MILKVETCH; POISONVETCH

The harmless species are known as Milkvetch. The species causing locoism are called Loco; poisonous species, causing symptoms very different from locoism, are called Poisonvetch.

aborig'inum . . . . INDIAN M.
aculea'tus
adsur'gens Auth., *not* Pall. . **A. striatus**
agres'tis . . . . PURPLE M.
alloch'rous (*Phaca allochroa*) HALFMOON L.
alopecuroi'des . . . . . FOXTAIL M.
alpi'nus (*Tium alpinum*). . ALPINE M.
amphiox'ys
angustifo'lius
araneo'sus . . . . . . DRYPLAINS M.
arc'tus (*A. preussi a.; A. p. latus*)
arista'tus (*sempervirens*)
arizo'nicus . . . . ARIZONA L.
austri'nus **A. nuttallianus trichocarpus**
beck'withi . . . . . . BECKWITH M.
bigelo'vi . . . . BIGELOW M.
bisulca'tus (*Diholcos b.*) TWOGROOVED L.
blake'i
caespito'sus
calyco'sus
campes'tris A. Gray, *not* L. **A. convallarius**
canaden'sis . . . . . . CANADA M.
ceram'icus (*pictus; Phaca picta*)
ci'cer
col'toni . . . . COLTON L.
confertifo'lius
convalla'rius (*campestris* A. Gray, *not* L.) . . . . TIMBER P.
—**diversifo'lius** (*A. diversifolius; A. junciformis*)
—**hyloph'ilus** (*A. hylophilus*)
crassicar'pus . . . . GROUNDPLUM M.
curvicar'pus . . . . . CURVEPOD L.
decum'bens . . . . . DECUMBENT M.
diffu'sus . . . . DIFFUSE M.
diph'ysus (*Cystium diphysum*) . BLUE L.
diver'gens
diversifo'lius . . . **A. convallarius d.**

Hort. var.; HV. = horticultural variety (or varieties); sp. = species (singular); spp. = species (plural).
₵ = clon; × (as a prefix) = hybrid; × (between scientific plant names) = crossed by; ∞ = polybrid; [W] = plant useful to wildlife.
See Glossary for definitions of clon, hybrid, and polybrid.

ASTRAGALUS, continued
drum'mondi (*Tium d.*) DRUMMOND MILKVETCH
druso'rum
earl'ei . . . . EARL LOCO
ech'inus
falca'tus
flexuo'sus (*Homalobus f.*). FLEXILE M.
frig'idus (*Phaca frigida*)
glaucophyl'lus
gonia'tus . . . . . . NICKLEAF M.
gum'mifer . . . . . TRAGACANTH M.
haydenia'nus (*scobinatulus; Diholcos s.*) HAYDEN POISONVETCH
helioph'ilus
hookeria'nus . . . . . **A. sonneanus**
horn'i . . . . HORN L.
humistra'tus
hyloph'ilus . . . . **A. convallarius h.**
hypoglot'tis
impen'sus . . . . THISTLE M.
juncifor'mis **A. convallarius diversifolius**
lambert'i . . . . **Oxytropis l.**
lentigino'sus (*Cystium lentiginosum*) SPECKLEPOD L.
leucolo'bus
leucophae'us
leucophyl'lus . . . . WOOLLYLEAF L.
lonchocar'pus
lotiflo'rus
massilien'sis . . . . . **A. tragacantha**
menzies'i . . . . MENZIES L.
mexica'nus (*Geoprumnon crassicarpum; G. mexicanum*)
missourien'sis
mollis'simus . . . . . . WOOLLY L.
monspessula'nus
mort'oni . . . . MORTON L.
nothox'ys . . . . SHEEP L.
nuttallia'nus |w
—trichocar'pus (*A. austrinus*) |w
onobry'chis
oocar'pus . . . . EGGPOD L.
palliser'i (*Homalobus p.*). PALLISER P.
patterso'ni (*Rydbergiella p.*) PATTERSON L.
pectina'tus (*Ctenophyllum pectinatum*) NARROWLEAF P.
Reported as containing selenium if grown on shale soils bearing that element.
pic'tus . . . . **A. ceramicus**
praelon'gus . . . . . . **A. sabulosus**
preuss'i . . . . PREUSS M.
—arc'tus . . . . **A. arctus**
—la'tus . . . . **A. arctus**
pursh'i (*Xylophacos p.*) . . PURSH L.
pyg'maeus
remul'cus . . . . TOWLINE L.
ru'byi . . . . **Oxytropis tenella**
rus'byi
sabulo'sus (*praelongus; Rydbergiella praelonga*) . . . STRAIGHTSTEM P.
sarcocol'la
scapo'sus (*Hamosa scaposa*) BARESTEM L.
scobinat'ulus . . . . **A. haydenianus**
semibilocula'ris
sempervi'rens . . . . **A. aristatus**
serot'inus
shortia'nus (*Xylophacos s.*)
sieversia'nus
silera'nus |w
sin'icus
sonnea'nus (*hookerianus*) BALLOONPOD M.
spatula'tus . . . . TUFTED M.
stria'tus (*adsurgens* Auth., *not* Pall.) PRAIRIE M.

ASTRAGALUS, continued
strigo'sus
succulen'tus
taur'icus
tenel'lus . . LOOSEFLOWER MILKVETCH
tetrap'terus (*Pterophacos t.*) FOURWING POISONVETCH
thomp'sonae . . . . THOMPSON LOCO
thur'beri . . . . THURBER L.
tragacan'tha (*massiliensis*)
triphyl'lus (*Orophaca caespitosa*)
utahen'sis (*Xylophacos shortianus; X. utahensis*) . . . . UTAH L.
vesperti'nus (*Xylophacos v.*)
ward'i (*Phaca w.*) . . . . WARD L.
wingata'nus
woot'oni . . . . WOOTON L.
yaquia'nus . . . . YAQUI L.
zi'onis . . . . ZION M.

ASTRANT'IA . . . . . MASTERWORT
bieberstein'i . . . . BIEBERSTEIN M.
carnio'lica
grac'ilis
helliborifo'lia . . . . . . BLACK M.
ma'jor . . . . GREAT M.
mi'nor . . . . DWARF M.

ASTRE'BLA . . . . . MITCHELLGRASS
See **GRASS GENERA.**

ASTRID'IA **MESEMBRYANTHEMUM**
See **SUCCULENTS.**

ASTROCA'RYUM . . . ASTROCARYUM
See **PALM GENERA.**

ASTRO'NIUM . . . . STARTREE
fraxinifo'lium . . . . . ASHLEAF S.
grave'olens . . . . FETID S.

Astrophyl'lum dumo'sum. **Choisya dumosa**

ASTROPHY'TUM . . . . STARCACTUS
See **CACTUS GENERA.**

ASYSTA'SIA
bel'la . . . . **Mackaya b.**
coromandelia'na (*gangetica*)
viola'cea

ATALAN'TIA . . . . . . ATALANTIA
buxifo'lia . . . . **Severinia b.**
ceylon'ica . . . . CEYLON A.
citroi'des
macrophyl'la . GIANT A. (*Giant India A.*)
monophyl'la . . . . INDIA A.
racemo'sa . . . . BOMBAY A.
—hen'ryi . . HENRY B.A. (*Henry A.*)
rotundifo'lia . . . . . ROUNDLEAF A. (*Dwarf Ceylon A.*)

ATAMASCOLILY . **Zephyranthes atamasco**

ATAMOS'CO (ATAMASCO) **ZEPHYRANTHES**

∞ ATEMOYA . . . . . **Annona cherimola ×A. squamosa**

ATHAMAN'TA
creten'sis
matthio'li

Athana'sia an'nua . . . **Lonas inodora**

ATHEROSPER'MA
moscha'tum . AUSTRALIAN-SASSAFRAS

ATHROTAX'IS
cupressoi'des
laxifo'lia
selaginoi'des

ATHY'RIUM
See **FERN GENERA.**

ATITA'RA . . . . . **DESMONCUS**
See **PALM GENERA.**

ATRAG'ENE . . . . . . **CLEMATIS**
america'na . . . . . . **C. verticillaris**

ATRAPHAX'IS (*TRAGOPYRUM*)
billardier'i
buxifo'lia (*Polygonum crispulum*)
frutes'cens (*lanceolata; Polygonum f.*)
muschketow'i (*T. lanceolatum latifolium*)
spino'sa

A'TRIPLEX |w . . . . SALTBUSH
The Old World annuals are known as Orach.
brew'eri . . . . . . **A. lentiformis b.**
canes'cens (*occidentalis*). FOURWING S.
confertifo'lia . . . . . SHADSCALE S.
decum'bens . . . . . . MATSCALE S.
el'egans . . . . . . WHEELSCALE S.
gard'neri (*nuttalli*) . . . GARDNER S.
hal'imus . . . . . MEDITERRANEAN S.
hasta'ta . . . . **A. patula h.**
horten'sis . . . . . GARDEN ORACH
—atrosanguin'ea Hort. . . RED G.O.
hymenely'tra . . . . DESERTHOLLY S.
lentifor'mis . . . . BIG S. (*Lenscale; Quailbush*)
—brew'eri (*A. breweri*) . BREWER B.S.
nutt'alli . . . . **A. gardneri**
occidenta'lis . . . . . . **A. canescens**
par'ryi . . . . PARRY S.
pat'ula |w . . . . FAT-HEN S.
—hasta'ta (*A. hastata*) SPEARLEAF F.S.
polycar'pa |w . . . . CATTLE S.
portulacoi'des . . . . PORTULACA S.
rose'a |w . . . . . TUMBLING ORACH
semibacca'ta . . . . . AUSTRALIAN S.
serena'na
spinif'era
suckleya'na . . . . **Suckleya s.**
tatar'ica . . . . TATARIAN S.
trunca'ta . . . . . WEDGESCALE S.

A'TROPA
belladon'na . . . . . . BELLADONNA

ATTALE'A (*BORNOA*) . . . ATTALEA
See **PALM GENERA.**

AUBRIE'TA . . . . AUBRIETA
deltoi'dea . . . . COMMON A.
¢BOUGAINVILLE (*bougainvillei*) HV.
¢CAMPBELL (*campbelli*)
¢GREEK (*graeca*)
¢HENDERSON (*hendersoni*)
¢LEICHTLIN (*leichtlini*)
¢MOERHEIM (*moerheimi*)
¢OLYMPIC (*olympica*)
¢PURPLELADY (*purpurea*)
¢TRUMPET (*eyrei*)
¢WHITEWELL GEM (*perkinse*)

AUCOU'MEA . . . . OKOUME
klainea'na . . . . KLAINE O.

AUCU'BA (*AUKUBA*) . . . . AUCUBA
chinen'sis . . . . CHINESE A.
crotonifo'lia . . . **A. japonica** ¢CROTON
himala'ica . . . . . HIMALAYAN A.
japon'ica . . . . JAPANESE A.
¢CONCOLOR. HV.
¢CRASSIFOLIA
¢CROTON (*crotonensis; crotonifolia*)
¢DENTATA
¢FRUCTO-ALBO
¢GOLDDUST (*maculata*)
¢GRANDIS
¢LIMBATA
¢LONGIFOLIA

AUCUBA japonica, continued
¢LUTEOCARPA
¢MACROPHYLLA
¢SALICIFOLIA

AUDIBERT'IA . . . . . . **SALVIA**
capita'ta . . . . **S. mohavensis**
grandiflo'ra . . . . . . **S. spathacea**
hu'milis . . . . **S. sonomensis**
inca'na . . . . **S. carnosa**
niv'ea . . . . **S. leucophylla**
polystach'ya . . . . . . **S. apiana**
stachyoi'des . . . . . . **S. mellifera**
—revolu'ta . . . . . . **S. brandegei**

AUDOUIN'IA
capita'ta (*Diosma c.*) . . CAPEHEATH
AUGUSTIN'EA . . . . . **BACTRIS**
See **PALM GENERA.**

AUKU'BA . . . . **AUCUBA**

AU'LAX
cneorifo'lia
pallas'ia

AULOSPER'MUM . . . . . RIBSEED
lon'gipes

AUREOLA'RIA . . . . . OAKLEECH
pedicula'ria (*Agalinis p.; Dasystoma p.; Gerardia p.*) . . . . . ATLANTIC O.
virgin'ica . . . . . . VIRGINIA O.

Auric'ula lute'a . . . . **Primula auricula**

AUSTRALIAHEATH . . . . **Epacris**
COMMON A. . . . . **E. impressa**

AUSTRALIANFLAG . . . . . **Patersonia**
BLUE A. . . . . **P. glauca**
DELL A. . . . . **P. umbrosa**

Australian-pine . BEEFWOOD: **Casuarina**

Australian-rosemary. WESTRINGIA, ROSEMARYBUSH: **Westringia rosmariniformis**

AUSTRALIAN-SASSAFRAS
Atherosperma moschatum

AUSTRALIA-SANDALWOOD . **Eucarya spicata**

AUSTROCAC'TUS
See **CACTUS GENERA.**

AUTUMNCROCUS . . . . . . **Colchicum**
AGRIPPA A. . . . . . . **C. agrippinum**
BORNMUELLER A. . . . **C. bornmuelleri**
BYZANTINE A. . . . . . **C. byzantinum**
COMMON A. . . . . . . **C. autumnale**
DECAISNE A. . . . . . . **C. decaisnei**
LEVANT A. . . . . . . **C. variegatum**
SHOWY A. . . . . **C. speciosum**
YELLOW A. . . . . **C. luteum**

AVE'NA . . . . OAT
See **CEREALS** and **GRASS GENERA.**

AVENS . . . . **Geum**
ALEPPO A. . . . . **G. aleppicum**
BULGARIAN A. . . . . . **G. bulgaricum**
CHILE A. . . . . **G. chiloense**
EWEN A. . . . . **G. eweni**
JANKA A. . . . . **×G. jankae**
JAPANESE A. . . . . . . **G. japonicum**
LARGELEAF A. . . . **G. macrophyllum**
MAGELLAN A. . . . **G. magellanicum**
OREGON A. . . . . . . **G. oregonense**
PYRENEES A. . . . . . **G. pyrenaicum**
WATER A. . . . . **G. rivale**
WHITE A. . . . . **G. canadense**
YELLOW A. . . . . **G. strictum**

AVERRHO'A
bilim'bi . . . . BILIMBI
carambo'la . . . . . . CARAMBOLA

AVICEN'NIA
mari'na (*nitida*) . . BLACKMANGROVE

AVOCADO
For horticultural varieties see **FRUIT AND EDIBLE NUT NAMES.**
AMERICAN A. . . . **Persea americana**
COYO A. . . . . **P. schiedeana**
MEXICAN A. . **P. americana drymifolia**
OAXACA A. . . . . **P. floccosa**
TRAPP A. . . . **P. americana leiogyna**
YAS A. . . . . **P. pittieri**

AVODIRE . . . . **Turraeanthus**
AFRICAN A. . . . . . . **T. africana**

AWLCACTUS . . . . . **Gymnocalycium**
FLEISCHER A. . . **G. fleischerianum**
MONVILLE A. . . . . . **G. monvillei**
STUCKERT A. . . . . . . **G. stuckerti**
SUTTER A. . . . . . **G. sutterianum**

AWLWORT . . . . **Subularia**
WATER A. . . . . **S. aquatica**

AXLEWOOD . . . . **Anogeissus**
BAKLIGUM A. . . . . . . **A. latifolia**
YON A. . . . . **A. acuminata**

AXON'OPUS . . . . . CARPETGRASS
See **GRASS GENERA.**

AX'YRIS
amaranthoi'des . . RUSSIAN PIGWEED

AYE'NIA ⌊W . . . . AYENIA
califor'nica . . . . CALIFORNIA A.
pusil'la ⌊W . . . . DWARF A.

AYLOSTE'RA
See **CACTUS GENERA.**

AYO . . . . . . **Tetrastigma harmandi**

Azadirach'ta in'dica . **Melia azadirachta**

AZA'LEA (**RHODODENDRON**) ⌊W
AZALEA
Because of their outstanding horticultural interest, and because they are popularly (as well as by some botanists) generically distinguished from Rhododendrons, Azaleas are listed separately here, as well as under Rhododendron. *Typically,* Azaleas differ from Rhododendrons chiefly in their deciduous (rather than persistent) leaves; funnelshaped, somewhat 2-lipped, mostly fragrant (rather than regularly companulate, typically inodorous) flowers; and in their typically 5 (rather than 10 or more), long-exserted stamens. But intergrades occur. Azaleastrum is also included in this Azalea list, as it is popularly regarded as an Azalea. Rhodora, another closely related plant, is also included.

alabamen'sis (**Rhododendron alabamense**) . . . . ALABAMA A.
∞*al'bicans* (*mollis × occidentalis;* ∞**R. albicans**) . . . . . . ∞ALBICANS A.
albiflo'ra (**R. albiflorum**) . CASCADES A.
—ple'na (**R. a. plenum**) DOUBLE C.A.
albrecht'i (**R. albrechti**). ALBRECHT A.
amoe'na . . . . *A. obtusa a.*
∞*annelies'ae* (*arborescens × calendulacea;* ∞**R. anneliesae**) . ∞ANNELIESA A.
arbores'cens (**R. arborescens**) SWEET A.
∞*arnoldia'na* . . . . . ∞ *A. obtusa a.*
atlan'tica (**R. atlanticum**) . COAST A.
—luteo-al'ba (**R. a. luteo-album**)
BLUELEAF C.A.
—neglec'ta (**R. a. neglectum**)
PURPLE C.A.
austri'na (**R. austrinum**) . FLORIDA A.
∞*azaleoi'des* (?*nudiflora × pontica;* ∞**R. azaleoides**) . . . ∞PINXTERPONT A.
calendula'cea (*lutea* in part; **R. calendulaceum**) . . . . . . FLAME A.

AZALEA, continued
calendula'cea auran'tia (**R. calendulaceum aurantium**)
ORANGE FLAME AZALEA
—flam'mea . . . . *A. speciosa*
califor'nica (*occidentalis;* **R. occidentale**)
WESTERN A.
canaden'sis . . . . . . **R. canadense**
—al'ba . . . . . . **R. c. albiflorum**
can'dida . . . . . . *A. canescens c.*
canes'cens (**R. canescens**) PIEDMONT A.
—can'dida (*candida;* **R. c. candidum**)
WHITE P.A.
—subgla'bra (**R. c. subglabrum**)
SMOOTH P.A.
daur'ica . . . . **R. dauricum**
fla'va . . . . *A. pontica*
∞*gandaven'sis* (∞*mortieri × pontica;* ∞**R. gandavense**) . . ∞GHENT A.
∞*—ple'na* (∞**R. g. plenum**)
∞DOUBLE G.A.
in'dica (**R. indicum**) . . . INDICA A.
—balsaminaeflo'ra (*A. rollisoni;* **R. i. balsaminaeflorum;** *R. i. rosaeflorum*)
BALSAM I.A.
—crispiflo'ra (**R. i. crispiflorum**)
CURLY I.A.
—lacinia'ta (**R. i. laciniatum**)
FRINGED I. A.
—rosaeflo'ra. A. indica balsaminaeflora
japon'ica (**R. japonicum**). JAPANESE A.
—al'ba grandiflo'ra
A. mucronata noordtiana
—au'rea (**R. j. aureum**) . GOLDEN J.A.
kaemp'feri . . . . *A. obtusa k.*
∞*kosteria'na* (*japonica × mollis;* ∞**R. kosterianum**) . . . ∞KOSTER A.
kuru'me . . . . . *A. obtusa japonica*
ledifo'lia . . . . . . *A. rosmarinifolia*
—noordtia'na . . . . *A. r. noordtiana*
linearifo'lia (**R. linearifolium**) SPIDER A.
—dianthiflo'ra (**R. l. dianthiflorum**)
DIANTHUS S.A.
—macrosep'ala (**R. l. macrosepalum**)
BIGSEPAL S.A.
lu'tea (in part) . . . *A. calendulacea*
microphy'ta (**R. microphytum**)
PINKFLUSH A.
minutiflo'ra (**R. minutiflorum**)
TINYFLOWER A.
∞*mix'ta* (∞*gandavensis × mollis;* ∞**R. mixtum**) . . . . ∞CHINAGHENT A.
mol'lis (*sinensis;* **R. molle**) CHINESE A.
∞*mortier'i* (*calendulacea × nudiflora;* ∞**R. mortieri**) . . . ∞MORTIER A.
mucrona'ta . . . . . *A. rosmarinifolia*
mucronula'ta . . . **R. mucronulatum**
nudiflo'ra (*periclymenoides;* **R. nudiflorum**) . . . . PINXTERBLOOM A.
—al'ba (**R. n. album**) . . WHITE P.A.
—glandif'era (**R. n. glandiferum**)
oblongifo'lia (**R. oblongifolium**)
TEXAS A.
obtu'sa (**R. obtusum**) . . . HIRYU A.
—al'ba (*A. ramentacea;* **R. o. album**)
WHITE A.
—amoe'na (*A. amoena;* **R. o. amoenum**)
AMOENA A.
∞*—arnoldia'na* (*A. o. amoena × A. o. kaempferi;* ∞*A. arnoldiana;* ∞*A. obtusa arnoldiana* vars.; ∞**R. arnoldianum**) . . . . . ∞ARNOLD A.
—japon'ica (*A. kurume;* **R. o. japonicum**) . . . . KURUME A.
Here belong the many Kurume Azaleas, one of the best known of which is HINODEGIRI.

AZALEA, continued
obtu'sa kaemp'feri (*A. kaempferi; Rhododendron kaempferi;* **R. obtusum kaempferi**) . . . . TORCH AZALEA
occidenta'lis . . . . . *A. californica*
∞*pennsylvan'ica* (∞**R. pennsylvanicum**) ∞PENNSYLVANIA A.
pentaphyl'la (**R. pentaphyllum**) FIVELEAF A.
periclymenoi'des . . . . *A. nudiflora*
phoenic'ea . . . . . . *A. pulchra p.*
pon'tica (*flava; R. flavum;* **R. luteum;** *not* A. lutea) . . . . . . PONTIC A.
—*macran'tha* (**R. l. macranthum**) BIGFLOWER P.A.
poukhanen'sis . . . . *A. yedoensis p.*
prinophyl'la . . . . *A. rosea*
procum'bens . . . . . **Loiseleuria p.**
prunifo'lia (**R. prunifolium**) PLUMLEAF A.
pul'chra (**R. pulchrum**) . . LOVELY A.
—*phoenic'ea* (*A. phoenicea; R. phoeniceum;* **R. pulchrum phoeniceum**) PURPLE L.A.
quinquefo'lia (**R. quinquefolium**) CORK A.
ramenta'cea . . . . . *A. obtusa alba*
reticula'ta (**R. reticulatum;** *R. rhombicum*) . . . . ROSE A.
—*pentan'dra* (**R. reticulatum pentandrum;** *R. rhombicum pentandrum*) FIVESTAMEN R.A.
rolliso'ni . . *A. indica balsaminaeflora*
rose'a (*prinophylla; R. prinophyllum;* **R. roseum**) . . . . ROSESHELL A.
rosmarinifo'lia (*ledifolia; mucronata; R. ledifolium; R. l. album;* **R. mucronatum**) . . . . SNOW A.

If Azalea be recognized as a distinct genus, the correct name for this species is A. rosmarinifolia.

—*amethyst'ina* (*A. mucronata a.;* **R. m. amethystinum**) . . AMETHYST S.A.
—*narcissiflo'ra* (*A. mucronata n.;* **R. m. narcissiflorum**) . . NARCISSUS S.A.
—*noordtia'na* (*A. japonica alba grandiflora; A. ledifolia n.; A. mucronata n.;* **R. m. noordtianum**) . . NOORDT S.A.
—*ple'na* (*A. mucronata p.;* **R. m. plenum**) . . . . PEONY S.A.
—*ripen'sis* (*A. mucronata r.;* **R. m. ripense**) . . . . RIVERBANK S.A.
—*sekide'ra* (*A. mucronata s.;* **R. m. sekidera**) . . . . . SEKIDERA S.A.
∞*san'deri* (*obtusa* × *simsi;* ∞**R. sanderi**) ∞SANDER A.
sca'bra (*R. sublanceolatum;* **R. scabrum**) . . . . LUCHU A.
schlippenbach'i (**R. schlippenbachi**) ROYAL A.
semibarba'ta (*Azaleastrum semibarbatum;* **R. semibarbatum**) AUTUMNLEAF A.
serpyllifo'lia (**R. serpyllifolium**) WILDTHYME A.
serrula'ta (**R. serrulatum**) HAMMOCKSWEET A.
sims'i (**R. simsi**) . . . . . INDIAN A.
sinen'sis . . . . *A. mollis*
specio'sa (*A. calendulacea flammea;* **R. speciosum**) . . . . . OCONEE A.
tomento'sa . . . . *A. viscosa t.*
tschonos'ki (**R. tschonoski**) TSCHONOSKI A.
vas'eyi (*Biltia v.;* **R. vaseyi**) PINKSHELL A.
—*al'ba* (**R. v. album**) . . WHITE P.A.
visco'sa (**R. viscosum**) . . . SWAMP A.

AZALEA, continued
visco'sa glau'ca (**R. viscosum glaucum**) BLUELEAF SWAMP AZALEA
—*nit'ida* (**R. v. nitidum**) . SHINY S.A.
—*rhodan'tha* (**R. v. rhodanthum**) PINK S.A.
—*rubes'cens* (**R. v. rubescens**) RUBY S.A.
—*tomento'sa* (*A. tomentosa;* **R. v. tomentosum**) . . . . . WOOLLY S.A.
∞*viscosep'ala* (*mollis* × *viscosa;* ∞*viscocephala;* ∞**R. viscosepalum**) ∞CHINESE SWAMP A.
₵—*da'viesi* (₵**R. v. daviesi**) ₵DAVIES C.A.
wey'richi (**R. weyrichi**) . WEYRICH A.
yedoen'sis (*yodogawa;* **R. yedoense**) YODOGAWA A.
—*poukhanen'sis* (*A. poukhanensis; R. poukhanense;* **R. y. poukhanense**) KOREAN Y.A.

Hort. var. of **Azalea:**

Because of the large number of varieties of Azaleas, the common-name list, the horticultural varieties, and the hybrids have been combined in the special list below. All the horticultural varieties are clons.

Abbreviations indicating the name of the group to which a horticultural variety is reported to belong, or the species from which it is reported to have been derived, in whole or in part, are as follows:

Alb. Albicans (occidentalis × mollis) and hybrids with other species.
Gh. The Ghent hybrids are derivatives of ∞*R. gandavense.* This is a complex group of plants, *R. luteum, R. calendulaceum, R. viscosum, R. nudiflorum,* and other species having been used in the hybridization, resulting in the large number of varieties listed in this group.
Ind. For the purposes of this list, the Indian azaleas comprise hybrids and clonal varieties of *R. simsi, R. indicum, R. mucronatum* (*A. ledifolia*), *R. scabrum,* and *R. pulchrum.* Some of the first Indian azaleas came to the United States as early as 1830. This group is fairly tender and is grown out-of-doors chiefly in the South, though a few varieties can be grown in the North.
Kae. Hybrids and clonal varieties of *R. obtusum kaempferi.*
Kur. Hybrids and clonal varieties of *R. obtusum* and its varieties. Actually here belong the Kaempferi and Sander hybrids, but because these are of comparatively recent origin, their history is fairly accurate, and so it was thought advisable to keep these groups separated from the Kurume azaleas in the following list. E. H. Wilson has given English names, derived from the Japanese, for many of the azaleas in the Kurume group.
Mix. Hybrids and clonal varieties of ∞*R. mixtum.* Here belong the double-flowering Mollis hybrids and those formerly known in the trade as *A. rustica flore pleno.*
Mol. The Mollis hybrids are usually loosely classified in the trade (and here, also) as derivatives of *R. molle, R. japonicum,* ∞*R. kosterianum,* and hybrids among these species.
San. The Sander hybrids result from crosses of *R. obtusum* varieties and some of the Indian azaleas (chiefly *R. simsi*). This is a group of azaleas chiefly for greenhouse forcing. The first member of the group was raised in 1885, but the name "Sander Hybrids" has been given because of the large number of splendid crosses made by Charles Sander, gardener to the late Charles S. Sargent, first Director of the Arnold Arboretum.

(Many other varieties not included in this list will be found in C. G. Bowers' "Rhododendrons and Azaleas," and J. G. Millais' "Rhododendrons and the Various Hybrids.")

ABBREVIATIONS OF NAMES OF ORIGINATORS

B.&A.	Bobbink & Atkins, East Rutherford, N. J.
Carn.	Earl of Carnarvon, Highclere, England.
Dav.	Isaac Davies, Ormskirk, England.
End.	L. H. Endtz, Boskoop, Netherlands.
F.&D.	Felix and Dykuis, Boskoop, Netherlands.
Har.	Hardyzer, Boskoop, Netherlands.
Hat.	T. D. Hatfield, Wellesley, Mass.
Ker.	Johannes Kersbergen, Boskoop, Netherlands.
Kos.	M. Koster and Sons, Boskoop, Netherlands.
Oost.	Oosthoek, Boskoop, Netherlands.
P.M.K.	P. M. Koster, Boskoop, Netherlands.
Rinz	Jacob Rinz, Frankfort, Germany.
V.Hou.	Louis Van Houtte, Ghent, Belgium.
V.Nes	C. B. Van Nes, Boskoop, Netherlands.
V.Noor.	Van Noordt, Boskoop, Netherlands.
Ver.,A.	Ambroise Verschaffelt, Ghent, Belgium.
Vuy.	Charles Vuylstecke, Ghent, Belgium.
Wat.,A.	Anthony Waterer, Woking, Surrey, England.
Wez.	K. Wezelenberg and Son, Hazerswoude, Netherlands.

ABELS. Mol.
ADELAIDE. Mol. (Kos. before 1939.)
ADMIRABLE. Mol.
ADMIRAL DE RUYTER. Gh. (Before 1855.)
ADMIRAL TROMP. Mol.
ADMIRATION. Kur.
ADOLPHE. Gh.
ADRIAAN. Mol. (Kos. before 1939.)
AFTERGLOW. Mol.
AGATHA. Gh.
AGEMAKI. Kur. *Jose.*
AIDA. Mix. (Vuy. about 1888.)
AIOI. Kur. *Fairy Queen* (Kur., *not* Mol.)
AKADAI. Kur.
ALABAMA A. **Rhododendron alabamense.**
ALASKA. (B.&A. about 1935.)
ALBA GRANDIFLORA. Gh.
ALBA MACULATA. Ind.
ALBA ODORATA. Gh.
ALBA PUNCTULATA. Ind.
ALBERT. Ind.
ALBERT ELIZABETH. Ind.
∞ALBICANS A. ∞**R. albicans.**
ALBION. (B.&A. about 1935.)
ALBRECHT A. **R. albrechti.**
ALICE. Kae. (P.M.K.)
ALICE DE STEURS. Mol. (Kos. before 1939.)
ALICE SARGENT. San.
ALICE (*W.*) MULLER. (B.&A. about 1935.)
Allaglow. SAKURA TSUKASA.
ALMA TADEMA. Mol. (Kos. 1896.)
ALPHONSE LAVALLEE. Mol. (V.Hou. 1872.)

AZALEA, continued
ALTACLARENSE. Gh. (Carn. 1829.) *Aurea Grandiflora.*
AMBROISE VERSCHAFFELT. Mol.
America. MATTAPAN.
AMERICANA. Kur. (B.&A. about 1935.)
AMETHYST. *Japonica alba.*
AMETHYST SNOW A. **R. mucronatum amethystinum.**
AMOENA A. **R. obtusum amoenum.**
AMOENA COCCINEA. Kur.
AMOENA SUPERBA. Kur.
ANNA. Mol.
ANNA LOUISE. Gh.
∞ANNELIESA A. ∞**R. anneliesae.**
ANNY. Kae. (P.M.K.)
ANTHENON. Ind.
ANTHONY KOSTER. Mol. (Kos. 1892.)
ANTIGONE. Ind.
APELLES. Mix.
APOLLO. Kae.
Apple Blossom. Howo.
ARDENTISSIMA. Gh. (Before 1872.)
ARETHUSA. Gh. (Rinz before 1885.)
ARIADNE. Mix. (Vuy. about 1888.)
ARIEL. Gh.
∞ARNOLD A. ∞**R. arnoldianum.**
ASAGASUMI. Kur. *Rosy Morn.*
ASAHI. Kur.
ASUKAGAWA. Kur.
ATLANTA. Kae. (P.M.K.)
AUGIGASANA. Kur.
AUGUSTA.
AUGUSTE BULTEMANN. Mol.
AUGUST MECHELYNCK. Gh. (V.Hou. 1873.)
Aurea Grandiflora. ALTACLARENSE.
AURELIA. Gh.
AURORE DE ROYGHEM. Gh. (Before 1869.)
AUTUMNLEAF A. **R. semibarbatum.**
AVALANCHE. Kur.
AYAGOROMO. Kur.
AYA KAMMURI. Kur. *Pinkie.*
∞AZALEODENDRON. ∞**R. azaleodendron.**
AZUMA KAGAMI. Kur. *Pinkpearl.*
AZUMA SHIBORI. Kur.
BABEUF. Mol. (Ker. 1918.)
BACCHUS. Gh.
BAGSHOT FLAME.
BALSAM. *Rosaeflora; Rosiflora.*
BALSAM INDICA A. **R. indicum balsaminaeflorum.**
BARON (*Constant*) DEREBECQUE. Mol. (V.Hou. 1872.)
BARON (*Edmond*) DEROTHSCHILD. Mol.
BARON (*L.*) VONWOLFF. Mol.
BARON (*N. De*) ROTHSCHILD. Ind.
BARON PYCKE. Mol.
BARTHOLS LAZZARI. Gh.
BEAUTE CELESTE. Gh. (Before 1882.)
BEETHOVEN. Mol. (Ker. 1918.)
BELLS OF ARCADY. Kur.
BENIFUDE. Kur. *Sunbeam.*
BENIGIRI. Kur.
BENIKERIN. Kur.
BENIKIRISHIMA. Kur.
BERNARD ANDRE. Ind.
BETSY DEBRUIN. Mol. (Kos. 1895.)
BETSY VANNES. Mol. (Ker. 1918.)
BETTY. Kae. (P.M.K.)
Betty (Kur., *not* Kae.). SUGANO-ITO.
BIGFLOWER PONTIC A. **R. luteum macranthum.**
BIGSEPAL SPIDER A. **R. linearifolium macrosepalum.**
BIJINSUI. Kur. *Littleimp.*

AZALEA, continued
BIJOU DE GANDBRUGGE. Gh. (V.Hou. 1873.)
BIJOU DES AMATEURS. Gh. (Before 1872.)
BLACKHAWK. San.
BLONDINE. Gh.
BLOODRED. Kur.
BLUELEAF. *Viscosa floribunda.*
BLUELEAF COAST A. **R. atlanticum luteo-album.**
BLUELEAF SWAMP A. **R. viscosum glaucum.**
BLUSHBEAUTY. Alb.
BLUSHINGBRIDE. Ind.
BORSIG. Ind.
BOSKOOP BEAUTY. Mol. (Kos. 1898.)
BOTTICELLI. Kur.
BOUQUET DEFLORE. Gh. (A.Ver. before 1869.)
BOUQUET D'ORANGE. Mol. (Kos. 1876.)
BOUQUET ROSE. Kur.
BRIARCLIFFE. Kur.
BRIDESMAID. Kur.
BRIDESMAID. Gh.
BRILLIANT. Kur.
BRILLIANTRED. Mol.
BRONZEUNIQUE. Gh.
BROOKLINE. San.
BYRON. Mix. (Vuy. about 1888.)
CANDLELIGHT. Kur.
CAPTAIN CARSJENS. Mol.
CARDINAL. Gh. (Before 1846.)
Cardinal (Kur., *not* Gh.). TSUTA MOMIJI.
CARDINALIS. Kur.
CARDON. Gh. *Cardoniana.*
CARMEN. Kae. (P.M.K.)
CARMINATA SPLENDENS. Kur.
CARMINEKING. Kur. (B&A. about 1935.)
CARMINEPRINCE. Kur.
Carminequeen. KURAINOHIMO.
CAROLINA SWAMP A. **R. viscosum montanum.**
CASCADES A. **R. albiflorum.**
CATTLEYA. Kur.
CAVENDISHIANA. Ind.
C. B. VANNES. Mol. (V.Nes.)
CENGALTO. Kur.
CERCES. Ind.
C. ESVELD. Mol.
CHARLEMAGNE. Gh.
CHARLES DARWIN. Mol. (Kos. 1896.)
CHARLES DICKENS. Mol. (P.M.K.)
CHARLES ENCKE. Ind.
CHARLES FRANCOIS LUPPIS. Mol. (V. Hou. 1872.)
CHARLES KEKULE. Mol. (V.Hou. 1872.)
CHARLES ROGIER. Mol. (Vuy. about 1888.)
CHARLOTTE. Kae. (P.M.K.)
CHARMER. Ind.
CHEERFULNESS. Kur.
Cherryblossom. TAKASAGO.
CHERRYRIPE. Kur.
Cherub. KIMIGAYO.
CHEVALIER (*A.*) DEREALI. Mol. (V. Hou. 1872.)
CHEVALIER (*J. J.*) GLATT. Mol.
CHICAGO. Mol. (Ker. 1918.)
CHIEFTAIN. Gh.
∞CHINAGHENT A. ∞**R. mixtum.**
CHINESE A. **R. molle.**
∞CHINESE SWAMP A. ∞**R. viscosepalum.**
CHIYONO-AKEBONO. Kur.
CHRISTMASCHEER. Kur.

AZALEA, continued
CHROMATELLA. Gh. (Rinz before 1872.)
CLARA BUTT. Mol. (Wez. 1912.)
CLEOPATRA. Kae. (P.M.K.)
C. MAARSCHALK. Mol. (Kos. 1896.)
COAST A. **R. atlanticum.**
COCCINEA. Kur.
COCCINEA GRANDIFLORA. Gh.
COCCINEA MAJOR. Ind.
COCCINEA SPECIOSA. Gh.
COL. (*F. R.*) DURHAM. Mol. (End. 1925.)
COLUMBUS. Mol. (Ker. 1918.)
COMTE DEFLANDERS. Gh.
COMTE DEGOMER. Mol. (V.Hou. 1872.)
COMTE DEKERCHOVE. Mol.
COMTE DEQUINCY. Mol. (V.Hou. 1872.)
COMTE PAPADOPOLI. Mol. (V.Hou. 1872.)
COMTESSE DEBEAUFORT. Ind.
COMTESSE DEKERCHOVE. Mol. (Before 1878.)
COMTESSE (*Eugenie*) DEKERCHOVE. Ind.
CONCINNA. Ind.
CONSTANCE. (B.&A. about 1935.)
CONSUL CERESOLE. Mol.
CONSUL PECHER. Mol. (V.Hou. 1872.)
COPERNICUS. Mol.
CORALBELLS. Kur.
CORK A. **R. quinquefolium.**
CORNEILLE. Mix.
CORNELIUS ESVELD. Mol. (Ker.)
COTTAGEMAID. Gh.
CRIMSONGLORY. (B&A. about 1935.)
CRIMSONKING. Gh.
CRITERION. Ind.
CROEMINA. Ind.
CRUENTA. Gh.
CUPREA ARDENS. Gh.
CUPREA PULCHELLA. Gh.
CURLY INDICA A. **R. indicum crispiflorum.**
C. VUYLSTEKE. Mol.
CYMODOCEE. Gh. (Before 1855.)
DAGONET. Mol.
DAINTY. Gh.
Dainty. IROHAYAMA.
Damelavender. OMOINE.
DAMIO. Kae.
DANTE (*Gabrielle*) ROSSETTI. Mol. (Ker. 1918.)
DAPHNE. Kur.
DAPHNE RED. Ind.
DAPHNE SALMON. Ind.
DARLING OF THE GODS. Kur.
DAVID TENIERS. Mix.
¢DAVIES CHINESE A. ¢**R. viscosepalum daviesi.**
DAVIESI. Gh. (Dav. before 1873.)
Daybreak. KIRIN.
DEBUTANTE. Kur.
DECORATOR. Gh.
DECUS HORTORUM. Gh. (Before 1872.)
DELICATA. Gh.
DELICATANOVA. Gh.
DELICATISSIMA. Gh.
DELICATISSIMA. Kur.
DESCHRYVER. Ind. *De Schryveriana.*
DESDEMONA. (Kos. 1910.)
DEUTSCHE PERLE. Ind.
DEVONIA. Mol.
DEXTERS PINK. Kur.
DIAMOND. Ind.
DIANTHUS SPIDER A. **R. linearifolium dianthiflorum.**

AZALEA, continued
Dick Crabeth. Mol. (P.M.K.)
Director (*C.*) Ohrt. Gh.
Dixie. Ind.
Domenico Scassi. Mol.
Dominique Vervaene. Ind.
Dorothy Gish. (B.&A. about 1935.)
Double Cascades A. **R. albiflorum plenum.**
∞Double Ghent A. ∞**R. gandavense plenum.**
Double Mauve. Kur.
Dr. (*Asa*) Gray. Gh.
Dr. (*Chas.*) Baumann. Gh.
Dr. Kirtland. Gh.
Dr. (*Leon*) Vignes. Mol. (V.Hou. 1872.)
Dr. Moore. Ind.
Dr. (*M.*) Oosthoek. Mol. (About 1920.)
Dr. Pasteur. Mol. (Kos. 1896.)
Dr. Reichenbach. Mol. (Kos. 1892.)
Dr. Reval. Mol.
Duc Denassau.
Duc Deprovence. Gh.
Duc Derohan. Ind.
Duchess of Portland. Mol.
Duke of Wellington. Ind.
Duke of Windsor. Ind.
Dulcinee. Mol. (Vuy. about 1888.)
Dyogine. Mix.
Earlydawn. Kur.
Eastergreetings. Ind.
Eclaireur. Ind.
Eclatante. Ind.
E. Cuthbert. Mol.
Edison. Mol. (Vuy. about 1888.)
Edward Henry. Mol.
Electa. Gh.
Elegance. Ind.
Elegans. Ind.
Elegans Superba. Ind.
Elf. Kasumigaseki.
Elizabeth. Mol. (Kos. 1876.)
Ellen Cuthbert. Mol. (Kos. 1895.)
Emile. Gh.
Emile Liebig. Mol. (Kos. 1892.)
Emma. Gh.
Empereur du Bresil. Ind. *Emperor of Brazil.*
Empress of India. Ind.
Enchantress. Mol. (Kos. 1938.)
E. Pycke. Mol.
Ernest Bach. Mol. (V.Hou. 1872.)
Ernest Eeckhaute. Ind.
Ernest Thiers. Ind.
Esmeralda. Mol. (Vuy. about 1888.)
Esperance. Mol. (Kos. 1900.)
Eva. Kae. (P.M.K.)
Eveningglow. Mol. (Kos. 1920.)
Eveningstar. Kur.
Excelsior. Mol.
Exquisita. Gh.
Exquisite. Kur.
Fairy. Kur.
Fairy Queen. Mol. (Wez. 1912.)
Fairy Queen (Kur., *not* Mol.). Aioi.
Fama. Gh. (Before 1883.)
Fancy. Tamafuyo.
Fanny. Gh. (Before 1873.)
Fanny Ivery. Ind.
Fascination. Ima Shojo.
F. Dekoninck. Mol.
Fedora. Kae. (P.M.K.)
Felix Deschamps. Gh.
Fenelon. Mix.
Fidelio. Kae. (P.M.K.)
Fielders White. Ind.

AZALEA, continued
Firebird. Kur.
Firebrand. Mol.
Firefly. Hexe.
Fireglow. Mol.
Firelight. (B.&A. about 1935.)
Fiveleaf A. **R. pentaphyllum.**
Fivestamen Rose A. **R. reticulatum pentandrum.**
F. J. Seidel. Mol.
Flag of Truce. Ind.
Flambeau. Ind.
Flamboyant. Gh.
Flame. Suetsumu.
Flame A. **R. calendulaceum.**
Flamealo Incarnata. Gh. (V.Hou. 1887.)
Flamingo. Tamano-utena.
F. L. Atkins. (B.&A. about 1935.)
Flora. Gh.
Floradora. Mol. (Kos. before 1939.)
Floralia. Mol. (Kos. before 1939.)
Florida A. **R. austrinum.**
Floriosa. Glory of Sunninghill.
Flushingqueen. Gh.
Formosa. Ind.
Foster. Ind. *Fosteriana.*
Fragrans. Sweetghent.
Francois Devos. Ind.
Frans Vanderbom. Mol. (Kos. 1892.)
Fraternite. Mol.
Frau (*Hermann*) Seidel. Ind.
Frederic Demerode. Mol. (Vuy. about 1888.)
Frederick Engels. Mol. (Ker. '18.)
Frederick the Great. Ind.
Fred Sanders. Ind.
Frere-Orban. Mol. (Vuy. about 1888.)
Freya. Mix. (Vuy. about 1888.)
Frieda. Kae. (P.M.K.)
Fringed Indica A. **R. indicum laciniatum.**
Frisia. Mol. (P.M.K.)
Fritz Quihoui. (Before 1873.)
Fudesuteyama. *Poppy.*
Fudetsuka. Kur.
(*Fuerst*) Camille Vonrohan. Gh.
(*Fuerstin*) Baro Trysky. Ind.
Fujimanyo. Ind.
Fujimoyo. Ind.
Fulgada. (A.Wat. 1870.)
Futa-ekubo. Kur.
Futae-tsuru. Ind.
Garden Beauty. Kae.
Gartendirektor Walter. Mol.
Garteninspektor Ohrt. Mol. (V.Noor.)
Geant des Batailles. Gh. (Before 1876.)
Geisha. Kur.
Gen. Brialmont. Mol. (Vuy. about 1888.)
Gen. Chasse. Gh. (Before 1869.)
Gen. Drouet. Gh.
Gen. Goffinet. Mol. (Vuy. about 1888.)
Gen. Trauff. Gh. (Before 1882.)
Gen. Vetter. Mol. (Kos. 1896.)
George Cuthbert. Mol.
George Franc. Ind.
George (*Lindley*) Taber. Ind.
George Stephenson. Mol.
Gerda. Kae. (P.M.K.)
∞Ghent A. ∞**R. gandavense.**
Gloire Debelgique. Mol. (Vuy. about 1888.)

AZALEA, continued
Gloriamundi. Gh.
Gloriosa.
Glory. Kur. (B.&A. about 1935.)
Glory of Boskoop. Mol. (Kos. 1896.)
Glory of Sunninghill. Ind. *Floriosa.*
Gog. Mol.
Goldback. Gh.
Golden Japanese A. **R. japonicum aureum.**
Goldsworthnova. Kur.
Goldsworthred. Mol.
Gosho Zakura. *Vanity.*
Graciosa. Mol.
Graf (*Alfred*) Von Nieperg. Gh. (Before 1882.)
Graf Vonmeran. (Rinz or V.Hou. before 1854.)
Grandduc de Luxembourg. Gh. (Before 1855.)
Grandeur Triomphante. Gh. (Before 1872.)
Grandiflora Rubra.
Grand Monarque. Gh.
Gretchen. Kae. (P.M.K.)
Guelder Rose. Gh. (Before 1872.)
Gulf Pride. Ind.
Hachi Katzugi. *Prudence.*
Haeren Lorraine. Ind.
Haerens. Ind. *Haerensiana.*
Hagoromo. Kur.
Hakata Shiro. Ind.
Hamlet. Mol. (Kos. 1896.)
Hammocksweet A. **R. serrulatum.**
Hampton Rose.
Hana Asobi. *Sultan.*
Hanaikada. Kur.
Harriet Horn. Gh.
Harry Veitch. Ind.
Harvest Moon.
Hatsugiri. Kur.
Hatsuhinode. Kur.
Havemeyer. San.
Hayaotomi. Kur.
Hebe. San.
Helena. San.
Helena Degroot. Mol.
Helena Oosthoek. Mol. (1925.)
Helene Thelemann. Ind.
Henri Conscience. Mol. (Vuy. about 1888.)
Henriette. Kae.
Henri Lefever. Ind.
Her Majesty. Kur.
Hermoine. San.
Heroine. (Rinz before 1872.)
Heros Deflandre. Mol. (Vuy. about 1888.)
Heureuse Surprise. Gh. (Before 1869.)
Hexe. San. *Firefly.*
H. H. Hunnewell. Mol.
Hiawatha. San.
Hilda Hedlund. San.
Hinodegiri. Kur.
Hinodenotaka. *Ruby* (Kur., *not* San.)
Hinohakama. Kur.
Hinomayo. Kur.
Hinotsukasa. Kur.
Hiryu A. **R. obtusum.**
Hoikusia. Kur.
Holfordi.
Hollandia. Gh. (P.M.K.)
Holmlea. San.
Homebush.
Hoo. Howo.
Hora. Mix. (Vuy. about 1888.)
Hortensia. Kur.

AZALEA, continued
HORTULANUS (*A.*) FIET. Mol.
HORTULANUS WITTE. Mol. (Kos. 1892.)
HOWO. Kur. *Apple Blossom; Hoo.*
HOWODEN. Kur.
HUGO HARDYZER. Mol.
HUGO KOSTER. Mol. (Kos. 1892.)
HUGO OOSTHOEK. Mol. (1925.)
HUMMINGBIRD. Kur.
IGNAEA NOVA.
ILLUMINATOR.
IL TASSO. Mix. (Vuy. about 1888.)
IMA SHOJO. Kur. *Fascination.*
IMPERATOR. Gh. (Before 1885.)
IMPERATRICE DES INDIES. Ind.
IMPERATRIX. Gh. (Before 1873.)
INDIAN A. **R. simsi.**
INDIAN CHIEF. (B.&A. about 1935.)
INDICA A. **R. indicum.**
Indica rosea. SEKIDERA SNOW A.
IOYANA. Kur.
IRENE. Kur.
IRENE KOSTER. Gh.
IROHAYAMA. Kur. *Dainty.*
ISABELLE VANHOUTTE. Mol. (V.Hou. 1872.)
IVERYANA. Ind.
IVETTE. Kae.
IWATOKAGAMI. Kur.
IZAYOI. Kur.
JACK STRAW. Mol.
JAPANESE A. **R. japonicum.**
Japonica alba. AMETHYST.
J. C. VANTOL. Mol. (1890.)
JEANETTE. Kae.
JEANNE. Mol.
JEANNE (*A.*) KOSTER. Mol. (Kos. '00.)
JEANNE OOSTHOEK. Mol. (1925.)
JEANNETTE (*K.*) SIEMENE. Mol.
JEAN PEETER. Ind.
JEAN VERVAENE. Ind.
JEWEL. (B.&A. about 1935.)
J. (*J.*) DEVINK. Mol. (Kos. 1896.)
JOHANNA GOTTSCHALK. Ind.
JOHN BALL. Mol. (Ker. 1918.)
JOHN CAIRNS. Kae.
JOHN (*Gould*) VEITCH. Ind.
JOHN KERSBERGEN. Mol. (1918.)
JOHN PETERS. Ind.
JOHN RUSKIN. Mol.
Jose. AGEMAKI.
JOSEPH BAUMANN. Gh.
JOSEPHINE KLINGER. Gh. (Before 1882.)
J. T. LOVETT. Ind.
JUBILEE.
JULDA SCHUPP. Gh. (Before 1882.)
JULIANA. Kae. (P.M.K.)
JULIA SECOND. Gh. *Juliana nova.*
JULIUS CAESAR. Gh. (Before 1872.)
JULIUS ROEHRS. Ind.
JUPITER. San.
KASANE KAGARIBI. *Rosita.*
KASUMIGASEKI. Kur. *Elf.*
KATHERINE HAVEMEYER. Kae.
KATHLEEN. Kae. (P.M.K.)
KATSURANOHANA. Kur. *Ruth.*
KEIKAI. Kur. *Madonna.*
KEPLER. Mol. (Ker 1917.)
KIMIGAYO. Kur. *Cherub.*
KING ALBERT. Mol.
KING LEAR. Mol. (Kos. 1895.)
KINJO NOTAMA. Kur.
KINKUJAKU. Kur.
KINNOZAI. Kur.
KIRIN. Kur. *Daybreak.*
KIRISHIMA. Kur.
KIRITSUBO. Kur. *Twilight.*
KITTY. Kae.

AZALEA, continued
KOCHONO-MAI. Kur.
KOENIGIN SOPHIA. Mol. (Kos. 1876.) *Queen Sophia.*
KOKIN-SHITA. Kur.
KONISHIKI. Kur.
KOREAN YODOGAWA A. **R. yedoense poukhanense.**
∞KOSTER A. ∞**R. kosterianum.**
KOSTERS BLOTCHED. Mol. (Kos. '20.)
KOSTERS BRILLIANTRED. Mol. (Kos. 1918.)
KOSTERS DEEPRED. Mol. (Kos. 1920.)
KOSTERS ORANGE. Mol. (Kos. 1920.)
KOSTERS YELLOW. Mol. (Kos. 1920.)
KUMONOHIMO. Kur.
KUMONOHOMARE. Kur.
KUMONO-UYE. Kur. *Kumo-no-vie; Salmonprince.*
KURAINOHIMO. Kur. *Carminequeen.*
KURENOSAKE. Kur.
KURENOYUKI. Kur. *Snowflake.*
KURUME A. **R. obtusum japonicum.**
KYUSHU. Kur.
LADY (*Alice*) DESTUERS. Mol. (Kos. 1910.)
LADY EDITH. Ind.
LADY PIGOTT. Gh.
LADY ROOSEVELT. Ind.
LAELIA. Gh.
LAERTES. Mol. (Kos. 1910.)
LAKME. Kae. (P.M.K.)
LANTANA ALBA. Ind.
LATERITA ALBA. Ind.
L. A. VANHOUTTE. Gh.
LAVENDER AND OLD LACE. Kur.
LAVENDER QUEEN. Kur.
LAVICTOIRE. Ind.
LAWSAL. Ind.
LAWSONI. Ind.
Ledifolia rosea. SEKIDERA SNOW A.
LEIBNITZ. (Rinz before 1872.)
LEMONORA. Mol. (Wez. 1912.)
LETITIEN. Mix. (Vuy. about 1888.)
LILACINA.
Littleimp. BIJINSUI.
L. J. BOBBINK. (B.&A. about 1935.)
LOHENGRIN. Kae. (P.M.K.)
LONNIE SMIT. Mol. (V.Noor. 1905.)
LORD LISTER. Mol.
LORRAINE. Kur.
LOUIS (*A.*) VANHOUTTE. Gh. (V.Hou. 1873.)
LOUISE. Kae. (P.M.K. about 1915.)
LOUISE COUVELIER. Ind.
LOUISE HUNNEWELL. Mol. *Miss Louise Hunnewell.*
LOUIS ENDTZ. Mol.
LOUISE PAYNAERT. Ind.
LOUISE VONBADEN. Ind.
LOUIS HELLEBUYEK. Gh. (V.Hou. 1873.)
LOVELY A. **R. pulchrum.**
L. SPAETH. Mol.
LUCHU A. **R. scabrum.**
LUTEA MAJOR. Mol.
MACROSTEMON. Kur.
Madonna. KEIKAI.
MAGNIFICA. Gh. (Before 1873.)
Maidens Blush. OTOME.
MARCONI. Mol. (Kos. before 1924.)
MARGO KOSTER. Mol. (P.M.K.)
MARIE LOUISE. Ind.
MARIE VERSCHAFFELT. Gh. (Before 1872.)
MARMION. Mol. (Kos. before 1936.)
MARS. San.
MARSHAL BLUCHER. Mol.

AZALEA, continued
MARTHA. Kae.
MARY. Mol. (Kos. 1895.)
MARY CORCORAN. (B.&A. about 1935.)
MARY KOSTER. Mol.
MATHILDE. Gh.
MATTAPAN. Led. *America.*
MAUD. Mol. (Kos. 1895.)
MAUVEBEAUTY. Kur.
MAUVEQUEEN. Kae.
MAXIMILIAN. Ind.
MAXWELL. Ind.
M. DESBOIS. Mol. (Vuy. about 1888.)
MECENE. Mix.
MELANIE. Gh. (Before 1882.)
Melody. OINOMEZAME.
MEMOIRE (*de Louis*) VANHOUTTE. Ind.
METEORE. Gh.
MIGNON. Mol. (Vuy. about 1888.)
MIKADO. Kae.
MILTON. Mix. (Vuy. about 1888.)
MILTONI. Ind.
MINA DENOUDEN. Mol.
MINA VANHOUTTE. Gh.
MINERVA. Gh. (Before 1846.)
MINISTRE THORBECKE. Mol.
(*Miss*) EDITH CAVELL. Mol. (Ker. '18.)
MISS (*E.*) JARRETT. Ind.
Miss Louise Hunnewell. LOUISE HUNNEWELL.
MIYAGINO. Kur.
MIYAKOJISHI. Kur.
M. KOSTER. Mol. (Kos. 1876.)
MME. (*Anthony*) KOSTER. Mol.
MME. (*Arthur*) DEWARELLES. Mol. (V.Hou. 1872.)
MME. (*Camille*) VANLANGEHOVE. Ind.
MME. (*Caroline Legrelle*) D'HANIS. Mol.
MME. DOMINIQUE. Ind.
MME. FREY. Ind.
MME. (*Gustave*) GUILLEMOT. (V.Hou. 1872.)
MME. (*Herman*) SEIDEL. Ind.
MME. (*Iris*) LEFEBVRE. Ind.
MME. (*John*) HAERENS. Ind.
MME. (*Joseph*) VERVAENE. Ind.
MME. L. VANHOUTTE. Ind.
MME. (*Marie*) LOUISE. Kur.
MME. MAYER. Mol. (Kos. 1902.)
MME. (*Mesman*) VANDERLOO. Mol.
MME. MORREUX. Ind.
MME. MOSER. Gh.
MME. PERICAT.
MME. PETRICK. Ind.
MME. PETRICK SUPERBA. Ind.
MME. THIBAUT. Gh.
MME. VANDERCRUYSSEN. Ind.
MOLLIS ALBA. Mol. (Kos. 1888.)
MONS. THIBAUT. Ind.
MONTBLANC. Kur.
MORNINGGLOW. Kur.
∞MORTIER A. ∞**R. mortieri.**
MOSSIEANA. Kur.
MOSSPOINT RED. Ind.
MOTHEROFPEARL. (B.&A. about 1935.)
MOUNTAIN LAUREL. Kur.
MOUNT KIRISHIMA.
MR. (*Arthur*) DEWARELLES. Mol.
MR. DESBOIS. Gh.
MR. L. (*J.*) ENDTZ. Mol.
MRS. A. (*E.*) ENDTZ. Mol. (End. '00.)
MRS. (*Anthony*) KLUIS. Mol.
MRS. ANTHONY KOSTER. Mol. (Kos. 1898.)
MRS. CARMICHAEL. Kur.
MRS. (*H.*) DENOUDEN. Mol.
MRS. HELEN KOSTER. Mol. (Kos. before 1939.)

AZALEA, continued
Mrs. (*H.*) White. Gh.
Mrs. (*J.*) Dykuis. Mol. (F.&D. '27.)
Mrs. (*John*) Russell. Mol. (Kos. before 1939.)
Mrs. L. (*J.*) Endtz. Mol. (End. '00.)
Mrs. (*Norman*) Luff. Mol. (Kos. before 1939.)
Mrs. (*Oliver*) Slocock. Mol.
Mrs. Oosthoek. Mol. (Oost. 1925.)
Mrs. Peter Koster. Mol. (Kos. about 1933.)
Mrs. (*Stewart*) Paton. Mol.
Mrs. Turner. Ind.
Mrs. Walter. Mol.
Mrs. (*W. R.*) Coe. (B.&A. about '35.)
Multatuli. Mol. (Ker. 1918.)
Multiflora. Mol.
Murasaki Botan. *Purple Peony.*
Muriel. San.
Murillo. Mix. (Vuy. about 1888.)
Nancy Waterer. Gh. (A.Wat. 1870.)
Naniwagata. Kur. *Paintedlady.*
Narcissiflora. Mol. (Rinz. or V.Hou. before 1872.)
Narcissus Snow A. **R. mucronatum narcissiflorum.**
Narumi Shibori. Kur.
Natalie. San.
Natalie (*Mai*) Coe. (B.&A. about 1935.)
Nelly Vannoordt. Mol. (V.Noor. 1895.)
Nereide. Gh.
Nero. Gh.
Newwhite. Ind.
Nicholas Beets. Mol. (Kos. 1892.)
Niobe. Ind.
Nishikigasane. Kur.
Nishikinomori. Kur.
Noordt Snow A. **R. mucronatum noordtianum.**
Nora. Kae.
Nora Lee. Ind.
Norma. Mix.
Norma. Kae. (P.M.K.)
Northstar. San.
Nosegay. Gh.
Obergartner Nietner. Mol.
Oberon. Kae. (P.M.K.)
Oconee A. **R. speciosum.**
Oimatsu. Kur.
Oinomezame. Kur. *Melody.*
Oldivory. Shin Seikai.
Oldwine. Kur.
Omoine. Kur. *Damelavender.*
Omurasaki. Ind.
Ophelia. Mol. (Kos. 1905.)
Opherie. Gh. (Rinz before 1872.)
Optima.
Orangebeauty. Kur.
Orangeblossom. Kur.
Orangeblotched. Mol.
Orange Flame A. **R. calendulaceum aurantium.**
Orangeking. (B.&A. about 1935.)
Orangequeen. Kur.
Orchid. Ind.
Orchid Lavender. Ind.
Orpheus. Gh.
Oryukyu Shibori. Kur.
Osakazuki. Kur.
Osaraku. *Penelope.*
Osaraku Seedling. *Winsome.*
Oswald Dekerchove. Mol. (Vuy. about 1888.)
Othello. Kae. (P.M.K. about 1915.)
Otome. Kur. *Maidens Blush.*

AZALEA, continued
Otto Lilienthal. Mol. (Ker. 1918.)
Pagoda. Kur.
Paintedlady. Naniwagata.
Pallas. Gh.
Paul Schame. Ind.
Paul Weber. Ind.
Pax. Ind.
Peachblossom. Mol.
Peachblossom. Kur. Saotome.
Peachblow. Kur.
Penelope. Osaraku.
∞Pennsylvania A. ∞**R. pennsylvanicum.**
Peony Snow A. **R. mucronatum plenum.**
Percy (*Bysshe*) Shelley. Mol. (Ker. 1918.)
Perfecta. Gh.
Perfection. Ind.
Perfection Derentz. Ind.
Peril. Mol.
Perle Delabelgique. Ind.
Persil.
Peter Koster. Mol. (Kos. 1895.)
Peter Vannoordt. Mol. (V.Noor. 1895.)
Pharailde Mathilde. Ind.
Phidias. Mix. (Vuy. about 1888.)
Phoebe. Mix. (Vuy. about 1888.)
Phoenica. Gh.
Piedmont A. **R. canescens.**
Pinkandsilver. Kur.
Pinkbeauty. Mol.
Pinkbeauty. (B.&A. about 1935.)
Pinkflush A. **R. microphytum.**
Pinkie. Aya Kammuri.
Pinklady. (B.&A. about 1935.)
Pinkpearl. Azuma Kagami.
Pinkperfection.
Pinkruffles. (B.&A. about 1935.)
Pinkshell A. **R. vaseyi.**
Pink Swamp A. **R. viscosum rhodanthum.**
Pinktreasure. Kae.
Pinxterbloom A. **R. nudiflorum.**
∞Pinxterpont A. ∞**R. azaleoides.**
Planting Fields. (B.&A. about '35.)
Plumleaf A. **R. prunifolium.**
Pluto. Ind.
Pocahontas. (B.&A. about 1935.)
Pontic A. **R. luteum.**
Poppy. Fudesuteyama.
Praestantissima. Ind.
Praxitile. Gh.
President Clay. Ind.
President (*Ghellinck*) Dewalle. Ind.
President (*Oswald*) Dekerchove. Ind.
President (*Victor*) Denhecke. Ind.
Prestantissima. Gh.
Pride of Dorking. Ind.
Pride of Mobile. Ind. *Watermelon Pink.*
Prince Adrienne. Gh.
Prince Albert. Mol. (Vuy. about 1888.)
Prince Alexander. Mol.
Prince Baudouin. Mol. (Vuy. about 1888.)
Prince (*Camille*) Derohan. (Before 1905.)
Prince Delight. Kur.
Prince d'Orange. Gh.
Prince (*Henri de*) Paybas. Gh.
Prince Henry. Mol.
Prince of Orange. Mol. (Wes. '12.)
Prince of Wales. Ind.
Princess Alice. Ind.

AZALEA, continued
Princess Clementine. Ind.
Princesse Adrienne. Gh.
Princess Juliana. Mol. (1920.)
Professor Amundsen. Mol.
Professor (*Aug.*) Forel. Gh.
Professor Rontgen. Mol. (Kos. 1896.)
Professor Walters. Ind.
Professor (*W.*) Koster. Mol. (Kos. 1876.)
Proteus. Gh.
Prudence. Hachi Katzugi.
Pucelle. Gh.
Purity. Yorozuyo.
Purple Coast A. **R. atlanticum neglectum.**
Purple King. Kae.
Purple Lovely A. **R. pulchrum phoeniceum.**
Purple Peony. Murasaki Botan.
Queen Alexandria. Mol. (Kos. 1895.)
Queen of England. Gh.
Queen Sophia. Koenigin Sophia.
Queen Victoria. Gh. (Before 1872.)
Quentin Metsys. Mix.
Racine. Mix.
Ramefutacea. Kur.
Ramentacea. Kur.
Raphael. Ind.
Raphael Desmet. Gh. (Before 1889.)
Rashomon. Kur.
Redamoena. Kur.
Redlight. *Sanguinea.*
Redrobin. Waka Kayede.
Reine Despaybas. Ind.
Reine Desroses. Ind.
Reine Desrouges. Gh.
Reine Louise. Gh.
Remarquable. Gh.
Rembrandt. Gh. (Before 1869.)
Rhapsody. (B.&A. about 1935.)
Ribiera. Mix.
Richardissima. Gh.
Richardson Sweet A. **R. arborescens richardsoni.**
Rivena. Mix.
Riverbank Snow A. **R. mucronatum ripense.**
Robespierre. Mol. (Ker. 1918.)
Roi Dehollande. Ind.
Roi Desbelges. Gh. (Before 1869.)
Roi Desfeux. Gh.
Rosaeflora. Balsam.
Rose. Kae.
Rose A. **R. reticulatum.**
Rosea. Gh.
Rosea Floreplena. Gh.
Roseapurpurea. Ind.
Rosecherry. Gh.
Rose d'Amour. Gh.
Rose Dehollande. Gh. (Rinz before 1872.)
Rosemarie. Gh.
Rosequeen. San. (B.&A. about 1935.)
Roseshell A. **R. roseum.**
Rosetaffeta. Shin Tokinohagasane.
Rosetta. Gh.
Rosiflora. Balsam.
Rosita. Kasane Kagaribi.
Rosy. Mol. (1900.)
Rosy Morn. Asagasumi.
Royal A. **R. schlippenbachi.**
Royalred. Ind.
Rubens. Mix.
Rubra Magnifica. Ind.
Ruby. San.

AZALEA, continued
Ruby (Kur., *not* San.). HINODENOTAKA.
RUBYDUST. (B.&A. about 1935.)
RUBY SWAMP A. **R. viscosum rubescens.**
RUDYARD KIPLING. Mol. (Kos. '02.)
Ruth. KATSURANOHANA.
RUTHERFORDIANA. (B.&A. about 1935.)
SAKON. Kur.
SAKUNTULA. Ind.
SAKURAGASANE. Kur.
SAKURAGATA. Ind.
SAKURA TSUKASA. Kur. *Allaglow.*
SALLY. Mol. (V.Hou. 1869.)
SALMON. Ind.
SALMONBEAUTY. Kur.
SALMONEA. Mol.
SALMONGLOW. Mol. (B.&A. about 1935.)
SALMONIANA RUBRA. Mol.
SALMONJOY. (B.&A. about 1935.)
SALMONKING. Kur. (B.&A. about '35.)
Salmonprince. KUMONO-UYE.
SALMONQUEEN. Kur.
SALMONSPRAY. Kur. (B.&A. about 1935.)
SAMUEL (*Taylor*) COLERIDGE. Mol.
∞SANDER A. ∞**R. sanderi.**
SANG DEGENTBRUGGE. Gh. (V.Hou. 1873.)
Sanguinea. REDLIGHT.
SANTOI. Kur. *Shin Utena.*
SAOTOME. Kur.

The preempted name Peachblossom has been misapplied to this var.

SAVILLE.
Scarletprince. YAYEHIRYU.
SEBASTOPOL. Mol. (Kos. 1896.)
SEIQUA. Ind.
SEKIDERA SNOW A. **R. mucronatum sekidera.**
SENGE TAURENXANA. Kur.
Seraphim. TANCHO.
SESOSTRIS. Gh.
SHAKESPEARE. Mol.
SHEBA. Alb.
SHIKUBUSHIMA. Ind.
SHIN SEIKAI. Kur. *Oldivory.*
SHIN TOKINOHAGASANE. Kur. *Rosetaffeta.*
Shin Utena. SANTOI.
SHINY SWAMP A. **R. viscosum nitidum.**
SHIRATAKI. Kur.
SHIRO BOTAN. Kur.
SIGISMUND RUCKER. Ind.
SIMON MARDNER. Ind.
SIR WALTER SCOTT. Mol. (Ker. '18.)
SMOOTH PIEDMONT A. **R. canescens subglabrum.**
SNOW A. **R. mucronatum.**
SNOWBANK. (B.&A. about 1935.)
SNOWBIRD. Kur.
SNOWDRIFT. Mol.
Snowflake. KURENOYUKI.
SNOWQUEEN. (B.&A. about 1935.)
SOIOKI.
SOI YOHI. *Sprite; Sui Oki; Sui Yohi.*
SOLEIL D'ORANGE. Gh.
SOUTHGATE WONDER. Mol.
SOUVENIR (*de Louis*) VANHOUTTE. Mol.
SOUVENIR (*de Pres.*) CARNOT. Gh.
SOUVENIR (*du Prince*) ALBERT. Ind.
SPIDER A. **R. linearifolium.**
Sprite. SOI YOHI.
STADTGARTNER MACHTIG. Mol. (V. Noor. 1900.)

AZALEA, continued
S. T. COLERIDGE. Mol.
STELLA. Mol.
SUBLANCEOLATA. Ind.
SUETSUMU. Kur. *Flame.*
SUGANO-ITO. Kur. *Betty* (Kur., *not* Kae.).
Sui Oki; Sui Yohi. SOI YOHI.
SUKATA. Kur.
Sultan. HANA ASOBI.
Sunbeam. BENIFUDE.
SUNSET. Mix. (Wez. 1912.)
Sunset. (B.&A. about 1935.)
SUNSTAR. Kur.
SUPERBA. Gh.
SURUGA MANYO. Kur.
SUZUKI. San.
SWAMP A. **R. viscosum.**
SWEET A. **R. arborescens.**
SWEETBRIAR. Kur.
SWEETGHENT. Gh. *Fragrans.*
TAGONO-URA. Kur.
TAKASAGO. Kur. *Cherryblossom.*
TAMAFUYO. Kur. *Fancy.*
TAMANOTAKA. Kur.
TAMANO-UTENA. Kur. *Flamingo.*
TAM NO ITO. Kur.
TANCHO. Kur. *Seraphim.*
TAUKEN. Kur.
TEBOTAN. Kur.
TEMPERANCE. Ind.
TENIERS. Mix.
TERUKIMI. Kur.
TEXAS A. **R. oblongifolium.**
THAIS. Kae. (P.M.K.)
THE BRIDE.
THEODORE REIMERS. Ind.
THERESE. Mol. (Kos. 1876.)
THISBE. Gh.
THISER. Gh.
THOMAS MOORE. Mol. (Ker. 1918.)
THOMAS NEWCOMBER. Mol.
TINYFLOWER A. **R. minutiflorum.**
T. J. SEIDEL. Mol. (Kos. 1892.)
TOBINOHAGASANE. Kur.
TOKO NATSU. Kur.
TORCH A. **R. obtusum kaempferi.**
TRICOLOR VANAKEN. Gh.
TRIOMPHE DEGAUD. Gh.
TRIUMPHE. Ind.
TSARINE.
TSCHONOSKI A. **R. tschonoski.**
TSUTA MOMIJI. *Cardinal* (Kur., *not* Gh.).
TUBANTIA. Mol. (P.M.K. before '39.)
Twilight. KIRITSUBO.
UMMU. Kur.
UNCAS. San.
UNIQUE. Gh. (Before 1882.)
VANDYKE. Mix.
VANHOUTTE FLOREPLENO. Gh. (V.Hou. 1870.)
Vanity. GOSHO ZAKURA.
VELASQUEZ. Mix. (Vuy. about 1888.)
VENUS. San.
VERONICA CONCORDIA. Mol.
VERSICOLOR. Gh. (Before 1885.)
VERVAENEANA. Ind. *Vervaene.*
VERVAENEANA ALBA.
VERVAENEANA SALMONEA.
VESTA. Gh.
VESUVIUS. Kur.
VICTORIA. Mol. (V.Hou. 1869.)
VIOLA. Ind.
VIOLACEA RUBRA. Ind.
VIOLETTA. Kur.
VIRGILE. Mix. (Vuy. 1888.)
Viscosa floribunda. BLUELEAF.

AZALEA, continued
VITTATA FORTUNEI. Ind.
VIVID. San.
VULCAN. Gh.
VULCANO. Gh.
VUYLSTEKE. San. *Vuylstekeana.*
WAKA KAYEDE. Kur. *Redrobin.*
WAKAMATSU. Ind.
WALTER CRANE. Mol. (Ker. 1918.)
Watermelon Pink. PRIDE OF MOBILE.
WATT TYLER. Mol.
W. (*C.*) BRYANT. Gh.
W. (*E.*) GLADSTONE. Mol. (Kos. '02.)
W. (*E.*) GUMBLETON. Mol. (V.Hou. 1872.)
WESTERN A. **R. occidentale.**
WEYRICH A. **R. weyrichi.**
WHITE A. **R. obtusum album.**
WHITE PIEDMONT A. **R. canescens candidum.**
WHITE PINKSHELL A. **R. vaseyi album.**
WHITE PINXTERBLOOM A. **R. nudiflorum album.**
WHITE SWAN. Kur.
WILDTHYME A. **R. serpyllifolium.**
WILHELMINA. Kae.
WILLIAM III. Mol. (Kos. 1876.)
WILLIAM BULL. Ind.
WILLY. Kae.
WILSON SAUNDERS. Ind.
Winsome. OSARAKU SEEDLING.
WOODDOVE. Kur.
WOOLLY SWAMP A. **R. viscosum tomentosum.**
YACHIYO. Kur.
YAMATO BOTAN. Kur.
Yayegiri. YAYEHIRA.
YAYEHIME. Kur.
YAYEHIRA. Kur. *Yayegiri.*
YAYEHIRYU. Kur. *Scarletprince.*
YELLOWBEAUTY. Mol. (Before 1932.)
YELLOWPRINCE. Mol. (Kos. before 1939.)
YEZONISHUKI. Kur.
YODOGAWA A. **R. yedoense.**
YOROZUYO. Kur. (B.&A. about 1935.) *Purity.*
YOZAKURA. Kur.
YULETIDE. (B.&A. about 1935.)
ZAMPA. Kae. (P.M.K.)
ZEELANDIA. Mol. (P.M.K. before 1939.)

AZALEAS'TRUM **RHODODENDRON**

AZALEODENDRON **×Rhododendron azaleodendron**

AZA'RA . . . . AZARA
browne'ae . . . . BROWNES A.
celastri'na . . . . SANTIAGO A.
denta'ta . . . . CUTLEAF A.
gil'liesi . . . . GOLDEN A.
integrifo'lia . . . . . GOLDSPIRE A.
—variega'ta . . . VARIEGATED G.A.
lanceola'ta . . . . . . LANCELEAF A.
microphyl'la . . . . . . BOXLEAF A.
—variega'ta . . . . VARIEGATED B.A.

AZOL'LA . . . . AZOLLA
See **FERN GENERA.**

AZOREL'LA
peduncula'ta

AZTECLILY . . . **Sprekelia formosissima**
PALE A. . . . . **S. f. glauca**

AZTE'KIUM
See **CACTUS GENERA.**

BABASSU . . . . . . **Orbignya oleifera**
MARTIUS B. . . . . **O. martiana**

BABIA'NA . . . . BABOONROOT
dis'ticha . . . . HYACINTH B.
mucrona'ta (*Gladiolus ringens* Thunb. in part)
plica'ta . . . . CARNATION B.
stric'ta . . . . ERECT B.
—rubrocya'nea . . REDTHROAT E.B.
—sulphu'rea (*B. sulphurea; Gladiolus ringens* Thunb. in part) SULFUR E.B.

BABOONROOT . . . . **Babiana**
CARNATION B. . . . . . . **B. plicata**
ERECT B. . . . . **B. stricta**
HYACINTH B. . . . . . . **B. disticha**
REDTHROAT ERECT B.
B. stricta rubrocyanea
SULFUR E. B. . . . . **B. s. sulphurea**

BABYBONNETS . . . . **Coursetia**
ROSARY B. . . . . . . **C. glandulosa**
TEXAS B. . . . . **C. axillaris**

BABYSBREATH . . **Gypsophila paniculata**

BABYSTEARS . . . **Helxine; H. soleiroli**

BAC'CHARIS |w . . . . . BACCHARIS
angustifo'lia |w . . . NARROWLEAF B.
brachyphyl'la . . . . SHORTLEAF B.
coridifo'lia . . . . MIOMIO B.
doug'lasi |w . . . . . . DOUGLAS B.
emo'ryi . . . . EMORY B.
genistelloi'des
glomeruliflo'ra |w . . . SOUTHERN B.
glutino'sa . . . . . SEEPWILLOW B.
halimifo'lia |w . . . . . EASTERN B.
moritzia'na . . . . . . MORITZ B.
patago'nica . . . . PATAGONIA B.
pilula'ris . . . . KIDNEYWORT B.
plum'merae . . . . . PLUMMER B.
pteronioi'des (*ramulosa*) YERBADEPASMO B.
salici'na . . . . WILLOW B.
sarothroi'des . . . . BROOM B.
sergiloi'des . . . . SQUAW B.
triner'vis
—rhexioi'des
vimin'ea . . . . MULEFAT B.

BACCHARIS . . . . **Baccharis**
BROOM B. . . . . . . **B. sarothroides**
DOUGLAS B. . . . . **B. douglasi**
EASTERN B. . . . . . . **B. halimifolia**
EMORY B. . . . . **B. emoryi**
KIDNEYWORT B. . . . . . **B. pilularis**
MIOMIO B. . . . . . . **B. coridifolia**
MORITZ B. . . . . . . **B. moritziana**
MULEFAT B. . . . . **B. viminea**
NARROWLEAF B. . . . **B. angustifolia**
PATAGONIA B. . . . . . **B. patagonica**
PLUMMER B. . . . . . . **B. plummerae**
SEEPWILLOW B. . . . . . **B. glutinosa**
SHORTLEAF B. . . . . **B. brachyphylla**
SOUTHERN B. . . . **B. glomeruliflora**
SQUAW B. . . . . **B. sergiloides**
WILLOW B. . . . . **B. salicina**
YERBADEPASMO B. . . **B. pteronioides**

BACKHOUS'IA . . . . . BACKHOUSIA
citriodo'ra . . . . CITRON B.

BACO'PA (*MONIERA* B. Juss. *ex* P. Br., *not* Loefl.) |w . . . WATERHYSSOP
Bacopa Aubl. (1775) is conserved over Moniera B. Juss. *ex* P. Br. (1756).
carolinia'na |w . . . . CAROLINA W.
monnier'ia |w . . . . . COASTAL W.
rotundifo'lia (*Bramia r.; Herpestis r.; Moniera r.*) |w . . . . . . DISK W.

BAC'TRIS (*AMYLOCARPUS; AUGUSTINEA; PYRENOGLYPHIS*) . . . . SPINYCLUBPALM
See **PALM GENERA.**

BACULA'RIA . . . . **LINOSPADIX**
See **PALM GENERA.**

BAECK'EA
camphoros'mae
platyceph'ala
virga'ta

BAELFRUIT . . . . **Aegle; A. marmelos**

BAEOMET'RA
columella ris (*Tulipa breyniana* L.)

BAER'IA (*ACTINOLEPIS* in part) |w GOLDFIELDS
arista'ta (*coronaria; Actinolepis c.*) EVERLASTING G.
chrysosto'ma (*gracilis*) . BRANCHY G.
macran'tha . . . . TUBER G.
marit'ima . . . . MARITIME G.
platycar'pa |w . . . . BROADFRUIT G.

BAGPOD . . . **Glottidium; G. vesicarium**

BAGTIKAN . . . . **Parashorea**
COMMON B. . . . . . **P. malaanonan**
MINDANAO B. . . . . . . **P. warburgi**
TAVOY B. . . . . **P. stellata**

BAHI'A . . . . BAHIA
dissec'ta (*Villanova d.*) . RAGLEAF B.
oppositifo'lia (*Picradeniopsis o.*) PLAINS B.

BAHIAGRASS . . . . **Paspalum notatum**

Bahia-Piassava. . . ATTALEA, PIASSAVA: **Attalea funifera**

BAIKIAE'A
pluriju'ga . . . . . RHODESIANTEAK

BAI'LEYA . . . . BAILEYA
multiradia'ta . . . . . . DESERT B.
peren'nis . . . . . . LEAFYSTEM B.

BAILLON'IA (*DIOSTEA*) . BAILLONIA
jun'cea (*Diostea j.; Verbena j.*) RUSH B.

Bakupari . . . . RHEEDIA, BAKUPARI: **Rheedia brasiliensis**

BALA'KA . . . . BALAKA
See **PALM GENERA.**

BALANI'TES . . . . . . BALANITES
roxburgh'i . . . . . . ROXBURGH B.

BALANOCAR'PUS
heim'i

BALATA . . . . **Manilkara**
COMMON B. . . . . **M. bidentata**
PANAMA B. . . . . . . **M. darienensis**
PEKOLA . . . . **M. kauki**
ROXBURGH B. . . . **M. roxburghiana**

BALAUS'TION . . . . . BALAUSTION
pulcher'rimum . . . . . SOLITARY B.

BALDCYPRESS . . . . **Taxodium**
COMMON B. . . . . **T. distichum**
MONTEZUMA B. . . . **T. mucronatum**
POND B. . . . . **T. ascendens**

BALDRUSH . . . . **Psilocarya**
SHINY B. . . . . **P. nitens**

BALLFERN . . . . **Davallia bullata**

BALLMUSTARD . . . . **Neslia paniculata**

BALLOONFLOWER
Platycodon; P. grandiflorum

BALLOONPEA . . . . **Sutherlandia**
CAPE B. . . . . **S. frutescens**
SMOOTH C. B. . . . . **S. f. communis**
WOOLLY C. B. . . . . **S. f. tomentosa**

BALLO'TA . . . . BALLOTA
ni'gra (*foetida*) . . . . BLACK B.

BALM . . . . **Melissa**
COMMON B. . . . . . . **M. officinalis**
GOLDEN C. B. . . . . . . **M. o. aurea**

BALMTREE . . . . **Myroxylon**
ECUADOR B. . . . . . . **M. peruiferum**
PERUBALSAM B. . . . . . **M. pereirae**
TOLUBALSAM B. . . . . **M. balsamum**

BALO'GHIA
lu'cida

BALSA . . . . **Ochroma**
WESTINDIES B. . . . . **O. pyramidale**

BALSAM
GARDEN B. . . . **Impatiens balsamina**
ILLURIN-BALSAM DANIELLA
Daniella oliveri

BALSAMAPPLE . . **Momordica balsamina**

BALSAMOCIT'RUS . BALSAMOCITRUS
daw'ei . . . . BALSAMOCITRUS

BALSAMORHI'ZA |w . . BALSAMROOT
deltoi'des . . . . PUGET B.
hirsu'ta . . . . HAIRY B.
hook'eri . . . . HOOKER B.
inca'na . . . . HOARY B.
macrophyl'la . . . . . . CUTLEAF B.
sagitta'ta . . . . ARROWLEAF B.
terebintha'cea . . . . TURPENTINE B.

BALSAMPEAR . . . **Momordica charantia**

BALSAMROOT . . . . **Balsamorhiza**
ARROWLEAF B. . . . . . . **B. sagittata**
CUTLEAF B. . . . . . **B. macrophylla**
HAIRY B. . . . . **B. hirsuta**
HOARY B. . . . . **B. incana**
HOOKER B. . . . . **B. hookeri**
PUGET B. . . . . **B. deltoides**
TURPENTINE B. . . . **B. terebinthacea**

BALSAMSCALE . . . . **Elyonurus**
PANAMERICAN B. . . . **E. tripsacoides**
WOOLSPIKE B. . . . . **E. barbiculmis**

BAMBOO . **Bambusa; Chimonobambusa; Phyllostachys; Pleioblastus; Pseudosasa; Thamnocalamus; Thyrsostachys**
Until Bamboo names are better standardized botanically, it seems necessary, for the present at least, to use the name in a tribal rather than generic sense.

ARROW B. . . . **Pseudosasa japonica**
BEECHEY B. . . **Bambusa beecheyana**
BLACK B. . . . . **Phyllostachys nigra**
BUDDHA B. . . . . **B. ventricosa**
CASTILLO B. . . . . . **Phyllostachys bambusoides castillonis**
COMMON B. . . . . **B. vulgaris**
FALCONER B. **Thamnocalamus falconeri**
FERN B. . . . . **Pleioblastus distichus**
GOLDEN B. . . . **Phyllostachys aurea**
GREENSTRIPE COMMON B.
B. vulgaris vittata
GREEN SULFUR B.
Phyllostachys sulphurea viridis
GROUND B. . . . **Pleioblastus pumilus**
HEDGE B. . . . . **B. multiplex**
HENON B. **Phyllostachys nigra henonis**
HENRY B. . . . . **Phyllostachys henryi**
HOOKER B.
Chimonobambusa hookeriana
JAPANESE TIMBER B.
Phyllostachys bambusoides
LOW B. . . . . **Pleioblastus humilis**
MARBLE B. . . . . **C. marmorea**
MOSO B. . . **Phyllostachys pubescens**
NEVIN B. . . . **Phyllostachys nevini**
NINGALA B. . . . . **C. falcata**
POWDERY B. . . . . **B. chungi**

BAMBOO, continued
PUNTINGPOLE B. . **Bambusa tuldoides**
PYGMY B. . . **Pleioblastus pygmaeus**
RAMROD B. . . . **Pleioblastus hindsi**
SIAM B. . . **Thyrsostachys siamensis**
SILVERSTRIPE SIMON B.
Pleioblastus simoni variegatus
SIMON B. . . . . **Pleioblastus simoni**
SPATHE B. **Thamnocalamus spathiflorus**
SQUARE B.
Chimonobambusa quadrangularis
SULFUR B. . . **Phyllostachys sulphurea**
THORNY B. . . . . . **B. arundinacea**
TORTOISESHELL B.
Phyllostachys pubescens heterocycla
VIOLET B. . **Phyllostachys violascens**
WRINKLED B.
Phyllostachys bambusoides marliacea

BAMBOOFERN . . **Coniogramme japonica**

BAMBOO GENERA

An attempt has been made to incorporate into this list those bamboo names which are likely to be encountered in horticultural literature, and I think it can fairly be said to include most of the bamboos that have been successfully introduced or have come to be cultivated to any extent in the United States.

The traditional approach to the taxonomy of the bamboos, placing the major emphasis upon the reproductive, rather than upon the vegetative organs, has resulted in a tangle of difficulties, so that to this day there are relatively few species that can be identified in the field with certainty. The new approach, laying greater emphasis on vegetative characters, is gradually changing this, but there is much bad work to be undone before the names can be put in order, and identification made easier. The reader is warned, therefore, that many of the names here given are provisional only, and may have to be changed in the future.

The writer is indebted to Mr. R. A. Young, of the Bureau of Plant Industry, for his collaboration in the preparation of this list.—F. A. MCCLURE, Professor of Economic Botany, Lingnan University, Canton, China.

ARUNDINA'RIA . . . . CANE
ama'bilis . . . . TONKIN C.
an'ceps
angula'ta
Misidentification of Chimonobambusa quadrangularis.
aurico'ma . . . . . **A. viridi-striata**
chrysan'tha . . . . **Sasa c.**
deb'ilis . . . . CLUSTER C.
falca'ta . . . . **Chimonobambusa f.**
The name Arundinaria falcata has also been misused in Florida for FERNLEAF HEDGE BAMBOO, a variety of Bambusa multiplex.
falconer'i . . . . **Thamnocalamus f.**
fastuo'sa . . . . . **Semiarundinaria f.**
fortun'ei . . . . **Pleioblastus f.**
gigan'tea (*macrosperma*) . . GIANT C.
hinds'i . . . . **Pleioblastus h.**
—*gramin'eus* . . . . . **Pleioblastus g.**
hookeria'na . . **Chimonobambusa h.**
hu'milis . . . . . . **Pleioblastus h.**
japon'ica . . . . . . **Pseudosasa j.**
longiauri'ta. **Indocalamus longiauritus**
macrosper'ma . . . . . **A. gigantea**
marmore'a . . . **Chimonobambusa m.**
muriel'ae . . . . **Sinarundinaria m.**
nagashi'ma . . . . . **Pleioblastus n.**
narihi'ra . **Semiarundinaria fastuosa**
nepalen'sis . . . . . . NEPAL C.
nit'ida . . . . **Sinarundinaria n.**

BAMBOO GENERA (ARUNDINARIA), continued
no'bilis . . **Thamnocalamus falconeri**
pu'mila . . . . **Pleioblastus pumilus**
pygmae'a . . **Pleioblastus pygmaeus**
ragamow'ski . . . . **Sasa tessellata**
si'moni . . . . **Pleioblastus s.**
—*variega'ta*
Pleioblastus simoni variegatus
spathiflo'ra
Thamnocalamus spathiflorus
tec'ta . . . . SWITCH CANE
—**decid'ua** . . . . . BILTMORE S.C.
variega'ta . . . **Pleioblastus fortunei**
veitch'i . . . . **Sasa v.**
viridi-stria'ta (*auricoma; Bambusa auricoma; B. viridi-striata; Sasa a.*)

BAMBU'SA . . . . BAMBOO
alphonse-kar'ri . . . **B. multiplex** HV.
angula'ta
Misidentification of Chimonobambusa quadrangularis.
angustifo'lia **Pleioblastus angustifolius**
argen'tea Hort. . . . . . **B. multiplex**
—*stria'ta* Hort. . . . **B. multiplex** HV.
argenteo-stria'ta . . . **B. multiplex** HV.
arundina'cea . . . . . THORNY B.
au'rea . . . . **Phyllostachys a.**
aurico'ma **Arundinaria viridi-striata**
balcoo'a
The bamboos thus far introduced into the United States under this name have been misidentified.
beecheya'na **Sinocalamus beecheyanus**
castillo'ni
Phyllostachys bambusoides c.
chrysan'tha . . . . **Sasa c.**
chung'i . . . . POWDERY B.
dis'ticha . . . . **Pleioblastus distichus**
falca'ta . . . . . **Chimonobambusa f.**
fastuo'sa . . . . . **Semiarundinaria f.**
fortun'ei . . . . **Pleioblastus f.**
heno'nis . . . **Phyllostachys nigra h.**
kumasa'ca . . . **Shibataea kumasasa**
longispicula'ta
macrocul'mis . . . **Dendrocalamus m.**
marmore'a . . . **Chimonobambusa m.**
meta'ke . . . . **Pseudosasa japonica**
mul'tiplex (*argentea* Hort.; *nana*)
HEDGE B.
₵ALPHONSE KARR (*alphonse-karri; nana alphonse-karri*) HV.
₵FERNLEAF (*disticha; nana; nana gracillima*)
₵SILVERSTRIPE (*nana argentea striata; nana variegata; vittata-argentea; argenteo-striata*)
₵STRIPESTEM FERNLEAF (*disticha striata; nana viridi-striata; striata*)
Dwarf variety with slender, pink-ish-to-yellowish, green-striped culms.
₵WILLOWY
Tall, very slender, delicate-stemmed, drooping variety.
narihi'ra . **Semiarundinaria fastuosa**
ni'gra . . . . **Phyllostachys n.**
polymor'pha
pu'mila . . . . **Pleioblastus pumilus**
pygmae'a . . **Pleioblastus pygmaeus**
quadrangula'ris . **Chimonobambusa q.**
quilio'i . **Phyllostachys bambusoides**
ragamow'ski
Doubtful; probably Sasa tessellata.
ruscifo'lia . . . **Shibataea kumasasa**
senanen'sis . . . . **Sasa s.**
si'moni . . . . **Pleioblastus s.**

BAMBOO GENERA (BAMBUSA), continued
stria'ta . . . . . **B. vulgaris vittata**
tessella'ta . . . . **Sasa t.**
thouars'i . . . . **B. vulgaris**
The name B. thouarsi is also frequently misapplied to B. tuldoides.
tul'da
tuldoi'des . . PUNTINGPOLE BAMBOO
Commonly miscalled B. thouarsi in Florida and elsewhere.
variega'ta . . . **Pleioblastus fortunei**
veitch'i . . . . **Sasa v.**
ventrico'sa . . . . BUDDHA B.
verticilla'ta . . . . . . **Gigantochloa v.**
In Florida the name B. verticillata has been misapplied to the Alphonse Karr var. of Bambusa multiplex.
vilmorin'i
Doubtful; probably Pleioblastus distichus.
vimina'lis
Doubtful; probably Shibataea kumasasa.
violas'cens . . . . . **Phyllostachys v.**
viridi-glauces'cens . . **Phyllostachys v.**
viridi-stria'ta . . . . . . **Arundinaria v.**
vulga'ris . . . . COMMON B.
—**vitta'ta** (*B. striata*)
GREENSTRIPE C.B.

CEPHALOSTA'CHYUM
pergrac'ile

CHIMONOBAMBU'SA
falca'ta (*Arundinaria f.; Bambusa f.*)
NINGALA BAMBOO
hookeria'na (*Arundinaria h.*)
HOOKER B.
marmore'a (*Arundinaria m.; Bambusa m.*) . . . . MARBLE B.
quadrangula'ris (*Bambusa q.*)
SQUARE B.

CHUSQUE'A . . . . CHUSQUEA
abietifo'lia . . . . . . FIRLEAF C.
cum'ingi . . . . CUMING C.
qui'la . . . . QUILA
valdivien'sis . . . . . VALDIVIA C.

DENDROCAL'AMUS
DENDROCALAMUS
hamilto'ni . . . . . HAMILTON D.
latiflo'rus
latifo'lius
These two specific names have been applied erroneously in Florida and California to a large handsome species suspected of being Bambusa oldhami (Sinocalamus o.) from Formosa.
macrocul'mis (*Bambusa m.*)
membrana'ceus
sikkimen'sis . . . . . . SIKKIM D.
stric'tus

GIGANTOCHLO'A . GIANTGRASS
as'pera . . . . ROUGH G.
verticilla'ta (*Bambusa v.*)

INDOCAL'AMUS
longiauri'tus (*Arundinaria longiaurita*)

MELOCAN'NA . . . MELOCANNA
hu'milis . . . . LOW M.

PHYLLOSTA'CHYS
Some botanists prefer to regard Phyllostachys as masculine.
au'rea (*Bambusa a.*) GOLDEN BAMBOO
bambusoi'des (*mazeli; quilioi; reticulata; Bambusa q.*)
JAPANESE TIMBER B.
—**castillo'ni** (*Bambusa c.*) CASTILLO B.

BAMBOO GENERA (PHYLLOSTACHYS), continued
bambusoi'des marlia'cea (*P. marliacea*) WRINKLED BAMBOO
ed'ulis . . . . **P. pubescens**
flexuo'sa
heno'nis . . . . **P. nigra h.**
hen'ryi . . . . HENRY B.
heterocy'cla . . . . . **P. pubescens h.**
kumasa'sa . . . . **Shibataea k.**
marlia'cea . . . . **P. bambusoides m.**
maze'li . . . . . . **P. bambusoides**
mi'tis . . . . . **P. sulphurea viridis**
nevi'ni . . . . NEVIN B.

The bamboo introduced from China in 1908 by the U. S. Department of Agriculture, and later distributed under the name P. nevini has since been pronounced by the Royal Botanical Gardens, Kew, England, to be apparently not of that species but of some undetermined one.

ni'gra (*Bambusa n.*) . . . . BLACK B.
₵BLACKSPOT (*punctata*) HV.
₵MUCHISASA
₵WILLOWY
—heno'nis (*P. henonis; P. puberula; Bambusa h.*) . . . . . . HENON B.
₵BORY (*boryanus*) HV.
pubes'cens (*edulis*) . . . . MOSO B.
—heterocy'cla (*P. heterocycla*) TORTOISESHELL B.
quilio'i; reticula'ta . . **P. bambusoides**
ruscifo'lia . . . . **Shibataea kumasasa**
sulphu'rea . . . . SULFUR B.
—vir'idis (*P. mitis*) . . GREEN S. B.
violas'cens (*Bambusa v.*) . VIOLET B.
viridi-glauces'cens (*Bambusa v.*)

PLEIOBLAST'US
angustifo'lius (*Bambusa angustifolia*)
argenteo-stria'tus (*Bambusa argenteostriata; Sasa a.*)
dis'tichus (*Bambusa disticha; Pseudosasa d.; Sasa d.*) . . FERN BAMBOO
fortun'ei (*Arundinaria f.; A. variegata; Bambusa f.; B. variegata; Sasa v.*)
gramin'eus (*Arundinaria hindsi g.*)
hinds'i (*Arundinaria h.; Thamnocalamus h.*) . . . . RAMROD B.
hu'milis (*Arundinaria h.; Sasa h.*) LOW B.
nagashi'ma (*Arundinaria n.*)
pu'milus (*Arundinaria pumila; Bambusa p.; Sasa p.*) . . GROUND B.
pygmae'us (*Arundinaria pygmaea; Bambusa p.*) . . . . . . PYGMY B.
si'moni (*Arundinaria s.; Bambusa s.*) SIMON B.
—variega'tus (*Arundinaria s. variegata*) SILVERSTRIPE S.B.

PSEUDOSA'SA
dis'ticha . . . . **Pleioblastus distichus**
japon'ica (*Arundinaria j.; Bambusa metake; Sasa j.*) . ARROW BAMBOO

SA'SA . . . . SASA
argenteo-stria'ta **Pleioblastus argenteo-striatus**
This name has been used inadvertently for B. multiplex HV. Silverstripe.
aurico'ma . **Arundinaria viridi-striata**
chrysan'tha (*Arundinaria c.; Bambusa c.*) . . . . AUREATE S.
dis'ticha . . . . **Pleioblastus distichus**
hu'milis . . . . **Pleioblastus h.**
japon'ica . . . . **Pseudosasa j.**
pu'mila . . . . **Pleioblastus pumilus**
pygmae'a . . **Pleioblastus pygmaeus**
senanen'sis (*Bambusa s.*). . . SENAN S.

BAMBOO GENERA (SASA), continued
₵NEBULOSA (*Arundinaria palmata; A. paniculata n.; Bambusa p.*) HV.
tessella'ta (*Arundinaria ragamowski; Bambusa t.*) . . . BROADLEAF SASA
variega'ta . . . **Pleioblastus fortunei**
veitch'i (*Arundinaria v.; Bambusa v.*) VEITCH S.

SCHIZOSTA'CHYUM
biflo'rum
blum'ei
brachycla'dum
funghom'i
latifo'lium
lumampa'o
pseudoli'ma

SEMIARUNDINA'RIA
fastuo'sa (*Arundinaria f.; A. narihira; Bambusa f.; B. narihira*) NARIHIRA CANE

SHIBATAE'A . . . . SHIBATAEA
kumasa'sa (*Bambusa kumasaca; B. ruscifolia; Phyllostachys kumasasa; P. ruscifolia*) . . . . KUMA S.
The original spelling of this name is kumasaca, but that appears to be an obvious misspelling of the Japanese name kumasasa.

SINARUNDINA'RIA . CHINACANE
muriel'ae (*Arundinaria m.*) MURIEL C.
nit'ida (*Arundinaria n.*) GLOSSYLEAF C.

SINOCAL'AMUS . . SINOCALAMUS
beecheya'nus (*Bambusa beecheyana*) BEECHEY S.
latiflo'rus (*Dendrocalamus l.*)

THAMNOCAL'AMUS
arista'tus
falconer'i (*Arundinaria f.; A. nobilis*) FALCONER BAMBOO
hinds'i . . . . **Pleioblastus h.**
spathiflo'rus (*Arundinaria spathiflora*) SPATHE B.

THYRSOSTA'CHYS
siamen'sis . . . . . SIAM BAMBOO
Bamboos thus far introduced into the United States under this name have been misidentified.

BAMBU'SA . . . . BAMBOO
See **BAMBOO GENERA.**

BANANA . . . . **Musa**
ABACA B. . . . . **M. textilis**
ABYSSINIAN B. . . . . . . **M. ensete**
ARNOLD B. . . . . **M. arnoldiana**
COMMON B. . **M. paradisiaca sapientum**
DWARF B. . . . . **M. nana**
INDIA B. . . . . **M. rosacea**
JAPANESE B. . . . . **M. basjoo**
PLANTAIN B. . . . . . **M. paradisiaca**
QUEENSLAND B. . . . . . . **M. banksi**
SUMATRANA B. . . . . **M. sumatrana**

BANANASHRUB . . . . **Michelia fuscata**

BANEBERRY . . . . **Actaea**
BLACK B. . . . . **A. spicata**
GREEN B. . . . . **A. viridiflora**
IVORY B. . . . . **A. eburnea**
RED B. . . . . **A. rubra**
WESTERN B. . . . . **A. arguta**
WHITE B. . . . . **A. alba**

BANISTER'IA . **BANISTERIOPSIS; HETEROPTERIS**
argen'tea . . . . . . **Heteropteris a.**
caa'pi . . . . **Banisteriopsis c.**
laurifo'lia . . . . . **Banisteriopsis l.**

BANISTERIOP'SIS (*BANISTERIA* in part)
argen'tea . . . . . . **Heteropteris a.**
caa'pi (*Banisteria c.*) . . . . . . CAAPI
laurifo'lia (*Banisteria l.*)

BANKS'IA . . . . BANKSIA
bax'teri . . . . BAXTER B.
ca'leyi . . . . CALEY B.
coccin'ea . . . . SCARLET B.
denta'ta
ericifo'lia (*ericaefolia*) . HEATHLEAF B.
good'i . . . . GOODS B.
gran'dis . . . . GREATCONE B.
integrifo'lia . . . . . ENTIRELEAF B.
lemannia'na . . . . . . LEMANN B.
littora'lis . . . . SHORE B.
margina'ta . . . . . HONEYSUCKLE B.
meiss'neri . . . . MEISSNER B.
menzies'i . . . . MENZIES B.
nu'tans . . SCRUBHONEYSUCKLE B.
occidenta'lis . . . . . . WESTERN B.
priono'tes
pulchel'la
quercifo'lia . . . . . . OAKLEAF B.
re'pens . . . . CREEPING B.
serra'ta . . . . REDWOOD B.
solan'dri . . . . SOLANDER B.
specio'sa . . . . SHOWY B.
sphaerocar'pa
verticilla'ta . . . . . WHORLLEAF B.

BANKS'IA Forst., *not* L. f. . **PIMELEA**

BANKSIA . . . . **Banksia**
BAXTER B. . . . . **B. baxteri**
CALEY B. . . . . **B. caleyi**
CREEPING B. . . . . **B. repens**
ENTIRELEAF B. . . . . **B. integrifolia**
GOODS B. . . . . **B. goodi**
GREATCONE B. . . . . . . **B. grandis**
HEATHLEAF B. . . . . . . **B. ericifolia**
HONEYSUCKLE B. . . . **B. marginata**
LEMANN B. . . . . . . **B. lemanniana**
MEISSNER B. . . . . . . **B. meissneri**
MENZIES B. . . . . **B. menziesi**
OAKLEAF B. . . . . . . **B. quercifolia**
REDWOOD B. . . . . **B. serrata**
SCARLET B. . . . . **B. coccinea**
SCRUBHONEYSUCKLE B. . . **B. nutans**
SHORE B. . . . . **B. littoralis**
SHOWY B. . . . . **B. speciosa**
SOLANDER B. . . . . **B. solandri**
WESTERN B. . . . . . . **B. occidentalis**
WHORLLEAF B. . . . . . **B. verticillata**

Banyan . . . . FIG, BANYAN; **Ficus benghalensis**

BAOBAB . . . . . . **Adansonia digitata**

BA'PHIA . . . . CAMWOOD
nit'ida . . . . SHINY C.
racemo'sa . . . . BUSH C.

BAPTIS'IA [W] . . . . . . WILDINDIGO
al'ba . . . . WHITE W.
austra'lis . . . . BLUE W.
bractea'ta . . . . CREAM W.
leucan'tha . . . . ATLANTIC W.
leucophae'a . . . . PLAINS W.
perfolia'ta . . . . GEORGIA W.
tincto'ria . . . . YELLOW W.

Barbadoscherry . MALPIGHIA, BARBADOSCHERRY: **Malpighia glabra**

BARBADOS-GOOSEBERRY **Pereskia aculeata**

BARBADOSLILY . . . . **Amaryllis vittata**

BARBADOSNUT . . . . . **Jatropha curcas**

BARBADOS-OLIVE. . **Bontia; B. daphnoides**

BARBARE'A (*CAMPE*) |w WINTERCRESS
orthoce'ras (*Campe o.*) . . . ERECTPOD W.
plantagin'ea . . . . . PLANTAIN W.
ple'na . . . . DOUBLE W.
rupic'ola . . . . SARDINIAN W.
ver'na |w . . . . EARLY W.
vulga'ris |w . . . . BITTER W.

BARBERRY . . . . **Berberis**
AETNA B. . . . . **B. aetnensis**
ALLEGANY B. . . . . **B. canadensis**
AMUR B. . . . . . . **B. amurensis**
ANDES B. . . . . **B. montana**
ASIATIC B. . . . . **B. asiatica**
BEANS B. . . . . **B. beaniana**
BERGMANN B. . . . **B. bergmanniae**
BIGFLOWER B. . . . . . **B. oblonga**
BIGFRUIT CINNAMONSTEM B.
B. virescens macrocarpa
BLACK B. . . . . . . **B. gagnepaini**
BLOODBEAD B. . . . . . **B. oritrepha**
Boxleaf B. . . . . . . MAGELLAN B.
BOXTHORN B. . . . . . . **B. lycium**
CAUCASIAN B. . . . . **B. chinensis**
CHALKLEAF B. . . . . **B. dictyophylla**
∞ CHENAULT B. . . . . ∞ **B. chenaulti**
CHILEAN B. . . . . . . **B. chilensis**
CHROMEFLOWER B. . . . **B. polyantha**
CINNAMONSTEM B. . . . **B. virescens**
COLORADO B. . . . . . . **B. fendleri**
CORAL JAPANESE B.
B. thunbergi maximowiczi
COX B. . . . . **B. coxi**
CRETAN B. . . . . **B. cretica**
CROW B. . . . . . . **B. empetrifolia**
CURLLEAF B. . . . . . **B. replicata**
CUTLEAF B. . . . . **B. circumserrata**
DAINTY B. . . . . **B. concinna**
DARWIN B. . . . . **B. darwini**
DIELS B. . . . . **B. dielsiana**
∞ DROOPING B. . . . . . ∞ **B. declinata**
DWARF DARWIN B. . **B. darwini nana**
DWARF MAGELLAN B. . **B. buxifolia n.**
DWARF WINTERGREEN B.
B. julianae n.
EDGEWORTH B. . . . **B. edgeworthiana**
EGGFRUIT WILSON B.
B. wilsonae stapfiana
EUROPEAN B. . . . . . **B. vulgaris**
∞ FALSE BLACK B.
∞ **B. hybrido-gagnepaini**
FAXON B. . . . . **B. faxoniana**
Fendler B. . . . . COLORADO B.
GIRALD B. . . . . **B. giraldi**
GLOBE WILSON B. **B. wilsonae globosa**
GREEN HOOKERS B. . **B. hookeri viridis**
GROUND B. . . . . . . **B. parvifolia**
HAKODATE B. . **B. amurensis japonica**
HAWTHORN B. . . . . **B. crataegina**
HEDGEHOG B. . . . . **B. heterophylla**
HENRY B. . . . . **B. henryana**
HIMALAYAN B. . . . . . **B. umbellata**
HOLLY B. . . . . **B. ilicifolia**
HOLLYGREEN B. . . . . . **B. pruinosa**
HOOKERS B. . . . . **B. hookeri**
INKFRUIT B. . . . . . . **B. hakeoides**
JAMES B. . . . . **B. jamesiana**
JAPANESE B. . . . . . . **B. thunbergi**
JASPERBELLS B. . . . **B. linearifolia**
JAVA B. . . . . **B. xanthoxylon**
JETBEAD B. . . . . . . **B. atrocarpa**
KANSU B. . . . . . . **B. kansuensis**
KEW B. . . . . **B. kewensis**
KOREAN B. . . . . **B. koreana**
LECOMTE B. . . . . **B. lecomtei**
LITTLELEAF RED-PEDICEL B.
B. sanguinea microphylla

BARBERRY, continued
∞ LOLOG B. . . . ∞ **Berberis lologensis**
LONGSPINE B. . . . . . . **B. potanini**
MAGELLAN B. . . . . . **B. buxifolia**
∞ MEEHAN B. . . . . . . ∞ **B. meehani**
∞ MENTOR B. . . . . ∞ **B. mentorensis**
MONEYLEAF B. . . . . **B. nummularia**
NETVEIN B. . . . . . . **B. reticulata**
∞ NOTCHED B. . . . . ∞ **B. emarginata**
∞ OTTAWA B. . . . . ∞ **B. ottawensis**
PALELEAF B. . . . . . . **B. candidula**
PALLID B. . . . . **B. pallens**
PENDANT B. . **B. francisci-ferdinandi**
PINKBERRY B.
B. wilsonae subcaulialata
POIRET B. . . . . **B. poireti**
PRATT B. . . . . . **B. aggregata pratti**
PROSTRATE DARWIN B.
B. darwini prostrata
∞ PURPLEBEAD B. . ∞ **B. macracantha**
PURPLEBERRY B. . . **B. bretschneideri**
PYGMY MAGELLAN B.
B. buxifolia pygmaea
REDBEAD B. . . . . . . **B. angulosa**
REDDROP B. . . . . . . **B. diaphana**
RED-PEDICEL B. . . . . **B. sanguinea**
∞ REHDER B. . . . . . ∞ **B. rehderiana**
∞ ROSEMARY B. . . . ∞ **B. stenophylla**
SALMON B. . . . . **B. aggregata**
SARGENT B. . . . . . **B. sargentiana**
∞ SCARLETBEAD B. . . ∞ **B. rubrostilla**
SHANSI B. . . . . **B. mitifolia**
∞ SHARPLEAF DROOPING B.
∞ **B. declinata oxyphylla**
SHINY B. . . . . × **B. lucida**
SIBERIAN B. . . . . **B. sibirica**
SIEBOLD B. . . . . **B. sieboldi**
SIKKIM B. . . . . **B. insignis**
SOULIE B. . . . . . . **B. soulieana**
∞ SPAETH B. . . . . . . ∞ **B. spaethi**
SPINETOOTH B. . . . . . . **B. aristata**
SPINY BERGMANN B.
B. bergmanniae acanthophylla
SPINY MAGELLAN B.
B. buxifolia spinosissima
TAIWAN B. . . . . **B. morrisonensis**
TANGUT B. . . . . . **B. dasystachya**
TAROUCAN B. . . **B. silva-taroucana**
THIBETAN B. . . . . . . **B. thibetica**
THINSTEM B. . . . . . **B. leptoclada**
THREESPINE B. . **B. triacanthophora**
TISCHLER B. . . . . **B. tischleri**
TSARONG B. . . . . . **B. tsarongensis**
TURKESTAN B. . . . . **B. heteropoda**
∞ VANFLEET B. . . . . ∞ **B. vanfleeti**
VEITCH B. . . . . **B. veitchi**
VERNA B. . . . . **B. vernae**
∞ VILMORIN B. . . . . . ∞ **B. vilmorini**
VIOLETBEAD B. . . . **B. hypokeriana**
WALLICH B. . . . . . **B. wallichiana**
WARTY B. . . . . . . **B. verruculosa**
WILDFIRE B. . . . . **B. gilgiana**
WILSON B. . . . . **B. wilsonae**
WINTERGREEN B. . . . . **B. julianae**
YELLOWSPIKE B. . . . **B. brachypoda**
YUNNAN B. . . . . . **B. yunnanensis**

BARETTA . . . . . **Helietta parvifolia**

BARKCLOTHTREE . . . . **Brachystegia**
SPIKE B. . . . . **B. spicaeformis**

BARKER'IA
See **ORCHID GENERA.**

BARK'LYA . . . . BARKLYA
syringifo'lia . . . . LILAC B.

BARKTREE, ANGOSTURA
Galipea officinalis

BARLER'IA . . . . BARLERIA
caeru'lea . . . . . VEINYBRACT B.
crista'ta . . . . BLUEBELL B.
ela'ta . . . . BIG B.

BARLEY . . . . . **Hordeum; H. vulgare**
See also **CEREALS.**
ANCESTRAL TWOROW B.
H. spontaneum
BEARDLESS B. **H. vulgare trifurcatum**
BOBTAIL B. . **H. jubatum caespitosum**
BULBOUS B. . . . . . . **H. bulbosum**
FOXTAIL B. . . . . **H. jubatum**
LITTLE B. . . . . **H. pusillum**
MEADOW B. . . . . . . **H. nodosum**
MEDITERRANEAN B. **H. gussonianum**
MEXICAN B. . . . . . **H. adscendens**
MONTANA B. . . . . **H. montanense**
MOUSE B. . . . . **H. murinum**
NORTHERN MEADOW B.
H. nodosum boreale
Prairie B. . . . . MONTANA B.
SEASIDE B. . . . . **H. marinum**
SIXROW B. . . . . . **H. hexastichon**
TWOROW B. . . . . . . **H. distichon**
Wall B. . . . . MOUSE B.

BARNADE'SIA
spino'sa

BARNYARDGRASS . **Echinochloa crusgalli**
ALKALI B. . . . . . . **E. c. zelayensis**
BEARDLESS B. . . . . . . **E. c. mitis**

BAROS'MA . . . . BUCHU
betuli'na . . . . SHORT B.
crenula'ta . . . . OVALLEAF B.
ova'ta . . . . EGGLEAF B.
pulchel'la . . . . SHOWY B.
scopa'ria
serratifo'lia . . . . . . LONGLEAF B.

BARRELCACTUS . . . . **Ferocactus**
ALAMOS B. . . . . . **F. alamosanus**
BLUEGLOBE B. . . . . **F. glaucescens**
CALIFORNIA B. . . . . **F. acanthodes**
MELONBARRELS . **F. melocactiformis**
ORCUTT B. . . . . **F. orcutti**
PRINGLE B. . . . . **F. pringlei**
SOUTHWEST B. . . . . . **F. wislizeni**
TOWNSEND B. . . . **F. townsendianus**
TURBAN B. . . . . . . **F. viridescens**

BARRELPALM . . . **Colpothrinax wrighti**

BARRENSTRAWBERRY
Waldsteinia fragarioides

BARRINGTO'NIA . . . BARRINGTONIA
acutan'gula . . . . CHEE B.
specio'sa (*asiatica*) . . . . INDIA B.

BARTO'NIA Muhl. (1801) . . BARTONIA
virgin'ica . . . . VIRGINIA B.

BARTO'NIA Pursh. (1812)
MENTZELIA

BARTSCHEL'LA **MAMMILLARIA**
See **CACTUS GENERA.**

BARTS'IA . . . . . . **ODONTITES**

BARTSIA . . . . **Odontites**
RED B. . . . . **O. rubra**

BARYX'YLUM . . **PELTOPHORUM**

BASEL'LA . . . . VINESPINACH
al'ba . . . . WHITE V.
Perhaps not more than a var. or form of B. rubra.
ru'bra . . . . RED V.

BASIL . . . . **Ocimum**
AMERICAN B. . . . . **O. micranthum**
EASTINDIES B. . . . **O. gratissimum**
FEVER B. . . . . **O. viride**
GUINEA B. . . . . **O. guineense**
HOARY B. . . . . **O. canum**
HOLY B. . . . . **O. sanctum**
JAPANESE B. . . . . . . **O. crispum**
LEAST B. . . . . **O. minimum**
PURPLE L. B. . . . . **O. m. purpureum**
PURPLE SWEET B. . **O. basilicum p.**
SLIMFLOWER B. . . . **O. tenuiflorum**
SWEET B. . . . . **O. basilicum**
TREE B. . . . . **O. suave**

BASKETFERN . . . **Nephrolepis pectinata**

BASKETGRASS . . **Oplismenus hirtellus**

BASKETIVY . . . . **Cymbalaria**
KENILWORTHIVY . . . . **C. muralis**
LIVERLEAF B. . . . **C. hepaticaefolia**
SHAGGY B. . . . . **C. pilosa**
TOADFLAX B. . . . . **C. aequitriloba**

BASKETVINE . . . . . . **Aeschynanthus**
LOBBS B. . . . . **A. lobbianus**
LOBECUP B. . . . . . **A. grandiflorus**
MARBLED B. . . . . . **A. marmoratus**
SCARLET B. . . . . **A. pulcher**
SUMATRA B. . . . . . **A. boschianus**

BAS'SIA All. (1766) . . . . . BASSIA
hirsu'ta . . . . HAIRY B.
hyssopifo'lia (*Kochia h.*) . FIVEHOOK B.

BAS'SIA Koen. *ex* L. (1771)
MADHUCA
latifo'lia . . . . **M. indica**

BASSWOOD
Forestry name for LINDEN: **Tilia**

Bastardtoadflax . COMANDRA: **Comandra**

BATEMAN'NIA
See **ORCHID GENERA.**

BA'TIS |w . . . . SALTWORT
marit'ima |w . . . . . MARITIME S.

BATODENDRON . . . **VACCINIUM**

Batokoplum . LOUVI: **Flacourtia inermis**

BATRA'CHIUM . . . **RANUNCULUS**
heterophyl'lum
R. aquatilis heterophyllus
trichophyl'lum . . . **R. a. capillaceus**

BAU'ERA . . . . BAUERA
rubioi'des

BAUHIN'IA . . . . BAUHINIA
aculea'ta (*ungula*)
acumina'ta . . . . SNOWY B.
cornicula'ta
corymbo'sa
cumanen'sis
densiflo'ra
fa'beri . . . . FABER B.
fasseglen'sis
forfica'ta . . . . BELL B.
gal'pini . . . . RED B.
godefroy'i . . . . . . GODEFROY B.
heterophyl'la
megalan'dra
mexica'na . . . . PATAVACA B.
mollicel'la
monan'dra (*kappleri; krugi*)
BUTTERFLY B.
paulet'ia . . . . . RAILWAYFENCE B.

BAUHINIA, continued
petersia'na
pic'ta . . . . . MOTTLED BAUHINIA
polycar'pa
purpu'rea (*triandra*) . . . PURPLE B.
—al'ba
racemo'sa
reticula'ta
saigonen'sis . . . . SAIGON B.
tomento'sa . . . . . . ST.THOMAS B.
trian'dra . . . . **B. purpurea**
un'gula . . . . **B. aculeata**
vahl'i . . . . MALUCREEPER B.
variega'ta . . . . BUDDHIST B.
GREENVEIN (*candida*) HV.
walla'cei . . . . WALLACE B.
yunnanen'sis . . . . . . YUNNAN B.

BAUHINIA . . . . **Bauhinia**
BELL B. . . . . **B. forficata**
BUDDHIST B. . . . . . . **B. variegata**
BUTTERFLY B. . . . . . **B. monandra**
FABER B. . . . . **B. faberi**
GODEFROY B. . . . . . . **B. godefroyi**
MALUCREEPER B. . . . . . . **B. vahli**
MOTTLED B. . . . . **B. picta**
PATAVACA B. . . . . . . **B. mexicana**
PURPLE B. . . . . **B. purpurea**
RAILWAYFENCE B. . . . **B. pauletia**
RED B. . . . . **B. galpini**
SAIGON B. . . . . . . **B. saigonensis**
SNOWY B. . . . . **B. acuminata**
ST.THOMAS B. . . . . . **B. tomentosa**
WALLACE B. . . . . **B. wallacei**
YUNNAN B. . . . . . **B. yunnanensis**

Bay, True . . . . . LAUREL, GRECIAN:
Laurus nobilis

BAYBERRY . . . . **Myrica**
See also WAXMYRTLE.
NORTHERN B. . . . **M. pensylvanica**

BAYCEDAR . . . . **Suriana; S. maritima**

BAYRUMTREE . . . **Pimenta racemosa**

BEACHGRASS . . . . **Ammophila**
AMERICAN B. . . . **A. breviligulata**
EUROPEAN B. . . . . . . **A. arenaria**

BEACHHEATHER . . . . . . **Hudsonia**
MOUNTAIN B. . . . . . **H. montana**
WOOLLY B. . . . . . . **H. tomentosa**

BEADLILY . . . . **Clintonia**
QUEENCUP B. . . . . **C. uniflora**
RED B. . . . . **C. andrewsiana**
SPECKLED B. . . . . **C. umbellulata**
YELLOW B. . . . . **C. borealis**

BEADPLANT . . . **Nertera granadensis**

BEADRUBY . . . . **Maianthemum**
CANADA B. . . . . . . **M. canadense**
TWOLEAF B. . . . . **M. bifolium**

BEADTREE . . . . **Adenanthera**
LADYCOOT B. . . . . **A. microsperma**
SANDAL B. . . . . **A. pavonina**

BEAKCHERVIL . . . . . . **Anthriscus**
BUR B. . . . . **A. vulgaris**
SALADCHERVIL . . . . **A. cerefolium**
WOODLAND B. . . . . . . **A. sylvestris**

BEAKGRAIN . . . . **Diarrhena**
AMERICAN B. . . . . . **D. americana**

BEAKRUSH . . . . **Rhynchospora**
HORNED B. . . . . . . **R. corniculata**
LITTLESEED B. . . . . **R. microcarpa**
PLUMED B. . . . . **R. plumosa**

BEAN . . . . **Phaseolus**
ADSUKI B. . . . . **P. angularis**
BUSH KIDNEY B. . **P. vulgaris humilis**
DWARF SIEVA B. **P. lunatus lunonanus**
HAMMOCK B. . . . . . . **P. smilacifolius**
KIDNEY B. . . . . **P. vulgaris**
LIMA B. . . . . **P. limensis**
Lyon B. . . . . VELVETBEAN, CHINESE:
Stizolobium niveum
MALAY B. . . . . **P. trinervius**
METCALFE B. . . . . **P. metcalfei**
MOTH B. . . . . **P. aconitifolius**
MUNG B. . . . . **P. aureus**
MUNGO B. . . . . **P. mungo**
NARROWLEAF B. . . . **P. angustifolius**
RICE B. . . . . **P. calcaratus**
SCARLET RUNNER B. . . **P. coccineus**
SIEVA B. . . . . **P. lunatus**
SLIMLEAF B. . . . . **P. angustissimus**
SNAIL B. . . . . **P. caracalla**
TEPARY B. . . **P. acutifolius latifolius**
TEXAS B. . . . . **P. acutifolius**
THICKET B. . . . . . . **P. polystachys**
WILLOWLEAF SIEVA B.
P. lunatus salicis

BEANCAPER . . . . **Zygophyllum**
SYRIAN B. . . . . **Z. fabago**

BEARBERRY . . **Arctostaphylos uva-ursi**

BEARGRASS . . . . **Xerophyllum**
COMMON B. . . . . **X. tenax**
DOUGLAS B. . . . . **X. douglasi**
TURKEYBEARD B. . . **X. asphodeloides**

BEARMAT . . . **Chamaebatia foliolosa**
SOUTHERN B. . . . . . **C. f. australis**

BEARPOPPY . . . . **Arctomecon**
DESERT B. . . . . **A. merriami**

BEARSFOOTFERN . . **Humata tyermanni**

BEAUCAR'NEA
recurva'ta
—tubercula'ta

BEAUFOR'TIA . . . . BRUSHMYRTLE
decussa'ta . . . . . . SWANRIVER B.
orbifo'lia . . . . ORBLEAF B.
purpu'rea . . . . PURPLE B.
spar'sa
squarro'sa

BEAUMONT'IA . . . HERALDTRUMPET
grandiflo'ra . . . . EASTER H.
jerdonia'na

BEAUTYBERRY . . . . **Callicarpa**
AMERICAN B. . . . . . **C. americana**
BODINIER B. . . . . . . **C. bodinieri**
CHENAULT B. . . . . . . **C. chenaulti**
FUZZY B. . . . . **C. mollis**
GIRALD B. . . . . **C. bodinieri giraldi**
JAPANESE B. . . . . **C. japonica**
LONGLEAF B. . . . . **C. longifolia**
MALAY B. . . . . **C. cana**
PURPLE B. . . . . **C. dichotoma**
WHITE AMERICAN B.
C. americana lactea

BEAUTYBUSH . . . **Kolkwitzia amabilis**

BEAUTYLEAF . . . . **Calophyllum**
BRAZIL B. . . . . **C. brasiliense**
CALABA B. . . . . . **C. b. antillanum**
CEYLON B. . . . . **C. calaba**
CEYLONPOON B. . . . **C. tomentosum**
INDIAPOON B. . . . . **C. inophyllum**

Hort. var.; HV.=horticultural variety (or varieties); sp.=species (singular); spp.=species (plural).
₵=clon; × (as a prefix)=hybrid; × (between scientific plant names)=crossed by; ∞=polybrid; |w=plant useful to wildlife.
See Glossary for definitions of clon, hybrid, and polybrid.

BEAUTYLEAF, continued
MADAGASCAR B. Calophyllum tacamahaca
PENANGPOON B. . . C. angustifolium
REKO B. . . . . C. rekoi

BEB'BIA . . . . BEBBIA
jun'cea . . . . RUSH B.
—as'pera . . . . SWEET R.B.

BECKMAN'NIA . . . . SLOUGHGRASS
See **GRASS GENERA.**

BECKWITH'IA . . . **RANUNCULUS**

Bedbuggrass . . . . . BUGSEEDGRASS: **Coridochloa cimicina**

BEDSTRAW . . . . **Galium**
BOG B. . . . . **G. labradoricum**
BOLANDER B. . . . . . . **G. bolanderi**
CATALINA B. . . . . . **G. catalinense**
CATCHWEED B. . . . . . **G. aparine**
CLAYTONS B. . . . . . . **G. claytoni**
COAST B. . . . . . . **G. hispidulum**
DOWNY B. . . . . **G. pubens**
DYE B. . . . . **G. tinctorium**
HAIRY B. . . . . **G. pilosum**
HALL B. . . . . **G. halli**
LANCELEAF WILDLICORICE **G. lanceolatum**
MARSH B. . . . . **G. palustris**
MATTHEWS B. . . . . **G. matthewsi**
MUNZ B. . . . . **G. munzi**
NARROWLEAF B. . . **G. angustifolium**
NEEDLE B. . . . . . . **G. andrewsi**
NITGRASS . . . . . **G. ventricosum**
NORTHERN B. . . . . . . **G. boreale**
NORTHERN WILDLICORICE **G. kamtschaticum**
NUTTALL B. . . . . . . **G. nuttalli**
PARISH B. . . . . **G. parishi**
ROTHROCK B. . . . . **G. rothrocki**
ROUGH B. . . . . . . **G. asprellum**
SHRUBBY B. . . . . . **G. multiflorum**
SMALL B. . . . . **G. trifidum**
SWEETSCENTED B. . . . . **G. triflorum**
TWINLEAF B. . . . . . . **G. bifolium**
WHITE B. . . . . **G. mollugo**
YELLOW B. . . . . **G. verum**

BEEBALM . . . . **Monarda**
LEMON B. . . . . **M. citriodora**
MINTLEAF B. . . . . **M. menthaefolia**
OSWEGO B. . . . . **M. didyma**
PONY B. . . . . **M. pectinata**
RAMALEY B. . . . . **M. ramaleyi**
REDPURPLE WILDBERGAMOT B. **M. fistulosa rubra**
RUSSELL B. . . . . . **M. russelliana**
SOFT WILDBERGAMOT B. **M. fistulosa mollis**
SPOTTED B. . . . . . . **M. punctata**
WHITE WILDBERGAMOT B. **M. fistulosa alba**
WILDBERGAMOT B. . . . **M. fistulosa**

BEECH . . . . **Fagus**
AMERICAN B. . . . . **F. grandifolia**
CAROLINA B. . . . . **F. g. caroliniana**
ENGLER B. . . . . . . **F. engleriana**
EUROPEAN B. . . . . . . **F. sylvatica**
JAPANESE B. . . . . **F. japonica**
ORIENTAL B. . . . . . . **F. orientalis**
SIEBOLD B. . . . . **F. sieboldi**

BEECHDROPS . . . . **Epifagus**
VIRGINIA B. . . . . . . **E. virginiana**

BEECHFERN
BROAD B. . **Dryopteris hexagonoptera**
NARROW B. . . . . . **D. phegopteris**

BEEFWOOD . . . . **Casuarina**
COAST B. . . . . **C. stricta**
CUNNINGHAM B. . **C. cunninghamiana**

BEEFWOOD, continued
ERECT B. . . . . **Casuarina suberosa**
FOREST B. . . . . **C. torulosa**
FRASER B. . . . . **C. fraseriana**
HORSETAIL B. . . . . **C. equisetifolia**
SCALYBARK B. . . . . **C. lepidophloia**
STUNTED B. . . . . **C. distyla**

BEET . . . . **Beta**
COMMON B. . . . . **B. vulgaris**
LEAF B. . . . . **B. cicla**
SUGAR B. . . . . . . **B. saccharifera**

BEFA'RIA (*BEJARIA*) . . BEFARIA
racemo'sa . . . . . TARFLOWER B.

Beggartickgrass . . THREEAWN, SINGLE: **Aristida orcuttiana**

BEGGARTICKS . . . . **Bidens**
BEARDED B. . . . . **B. aristosa**
BECKS B. . . . . **B. becki**
BUR B. . . . . **B. tripartita**
COREOPSIS B. . . . . . . **B. polylepis**
CROWN B. . . . . **B. coronata**
DEVILS B. . . . . **B. frondosa**
DISCOID B. . . . . . . **B. discoidea**
DITCHSUNFLOWER . **B. trichosperma**
EATONS B. . . . . **B. eatoni**
FERNLEAF B. . . . . **B. ferulaefolia**
LEAFYBRACT B. . . . . . . **B. comosa**
NODDING B. . . . . **B. cernua**
NORTHERN B. . . . . **B. hyperborea**
PURPLESTEM B. . . . . . **B. connata**
RAILWAY B. . . . . **B. pilosa**
SMOOTH B. . . . . **B. laevis**
SPANISHNEEDLES . . . **B. bipinnata**
SWAMP B. . . . . . . **B. bidentoides**
TALL B. . . . . **B. vulgata**
WHITE B. . . . . **B. leucantha**

BEGGARTICKTREE, SAHARA **Warionia saharae**

BEGO'NIA . . . . BEGONIA

For the treatment of Begonia below, the Editorial Committee is indebted to Bessie Raymond Buxton, Peabody, Mass. Mrs. Buxton's book "Begonias" is the standard manual for growers of this very large and popular plant group. The list has necessarily been somewhat modified to conform to STANDARDIZED PLANT NAMES style, including the addition of a limited number of common names. About 1,500 species of Begonia have been described by botanists and the number is being continually augmented by exploration, some of the least-known portions of the earth's surface, botanically speaking, possessing a rich Begonia flora. The genus is widely distributed in warmer countries, both in the northern and southern, as well as in the eastern and western, hemispheres. As might be anticipated, under the circumstances mentioned, the genus is botanically very complex, still imperfectly known, and much additional investigation will be required before it can be satisfactorily monographed with the nomenclature and synonymy reasonably well settled.

ac'ida (*braziliensis* Hort.)
aconitifo'lia
acutang'ula
acutifo'lia (*acuminata*)
adscen'dens
aequa'ta
aequilatera'lis
affi'nis
ag'rial
agusanen'sis
alaeci'da
al'ba
albobractea'ta
albococcin'ea (*grahamiana*)

BEGONIA, continued
albomacula'ta
alboren'sis
alchemilloi'des
alepen'sis
alnifo'lia
altis'sima
altoperuvia'na
alvarez'i
amab'ilis
am'pla
anaimalaien'sis (*anamalayana*)
andamen'sis
andi'na
andrea'na
anemonoi'des
angilogen'sis
angula'ris (*crenulata; hastata; zebrina*)
—ala'ta
angula'ta
—angustifo'lia
angustilim'ba
angustilo'ba (*dentata*)
anisop'tera
anisosep'ala
annobonen'sis
anodaefo'lia
antioquen'sis
apayaoen'sis
ap'tera
arbores'cens (*confertiflora; dimitiata, patens*)
areola'ta
argen'tea . . . . . . **B. maculata a**
argentinen'sis
argyrostig'ma . . . . . . **B. maculata**
arnottia'na . . . . **B. cordifolia**
asarifo'lia
asperifo'lia
asplenifo'lia
assam'ica
a'tricha
attenua'ta . . . . **B. herbacea**
aucubaefo'lia . . . . . **B. incarnata**
au'gustae
augustin'ei
aurantia'ca . . . . **B. cinnabarina**
auricula'ta
aurifor'mis . . . . **B. incana**
axilla'ris
axillipa'ra
azuen'sis
bacca'ta
bahien'sis
bak'eri
balan'sae
balansaea'na
bang'i
barahonen'sis
baramen'sis
barban'a
barba'ta
barbella'ta
bar'keri
bar'oni
bates'i
bau'manni
bavien'sis
bec'cari
beccaria'na
beddom'ei
bell'i
bernier'i
beryl'lae
besleriaefo'lia
bi'color . . . . **B. gracilis**
bidenta'ta (*langsdorffi*)
bifo'lia

BEGONIA, continued
biliranen'sis
bilocula'ris
binuangen'sis
biol'leyi
bipet'ala
bipinden'sis
bipinnatif'ida
biserra'ta
boisia'na
boivinia'na
bolivien'sis
×**—sulphu'rea**
—superb'a
bollea'na
bol'steri
bombyci'na . . . . **B. isoptera**
bo'ni
borneen'sis
bouchea'na
bouthainen'sis
bowringia'na . . . . . . **B. laciniata**
brachycla'da
brachypo'da
bractea'ta
bracteo'sa
brandisia'na
brasil'a (*dasypoda; hirtella*)
brasilia'na
brasilien'sis . . . . BRAZIL BEGONIA
brazilien'sis Hort. . . . . **B. acida**
bretschneideria'na
brevicau'lis
brevic'yma
brev'ipes
brevipet'ala
brevirimo'sa
brid'gesi
broussonetiaefo'lia
bruneel'i
buch'holzi
buddleiaefo'lia
bui-monta'na
bulbillif'era (*bulbifera*)
bulbo'sa
bulla'ta
bur'bidgei
bur'killi
caespito'sa
caf'fra . . . . **B. dregei**
calabar'ica
calcar'ea
calcic'ola
caldero'ni
califor'nica
calophyl'la
camiguinen'sis
capen'sis (*diptera*)
capen'sis Blanco, *not* L. **B. rhombicarpa**
capil'lipes
capitulifor'mis
cardiocar'pa
cardioph'ora
carleto'ni
carno'sa
carnos'ula
caroliniaefo'lia (*rotata*)
carpinifo'lia
casiguranen'sis
castaneaefo'lia
castillo'i
catarac'tarum
cathaya'na
cathcar'ti (*nemophila*)
This name is often misapplied to one of the forms of B. xanthina.
cauda'ta

BEGONIA, continued
caudilim'ba
cavaler'iei
cavallyen'sis
cebadillen'sis
celeb'ica
chaetocar'pa
chepoen'sis
chevalier'i
chiriqui'na
cilia'ta
cilia'ta Pav., *not* H.B.K. **B. subciliata**
ciliibracteo'la
ciliif'era
ciliobractea'ta
cinnabari'na (*aurantiaca*)
—albovitta'ta
circumloba'ta
cladocar'pa
clarke'i
clival'is
clypeifo'lia
coba'na
coccin'ea (*rubra*) . SCARLET BEGONIA
colli'na
collis'iae
colora'ta
columna'ris
coma'ta
comoren'sis
complica'ta
concanen'sis
conchaefo'lia . . . . **B. warscewiczi**
concin'na
confertiflo'ra . . . . **B. arborescens**
conges'ta
conrau'i
consanguin'ea
contrac'ta
convalliodo'ra
convolvula'cea
coop'eri
cope'landi
copeya'na
coralli'na . . . . CORAL B.
corda'ta
cordifo'lia (*arnottiana*)
—insula'ris
coria'cea
coria'cea Hassk., *not* DC. **B. peltifolia**
coronen'sis
corredora'na
cow'elli
crassicau'lis
cras'sipes
crena'ta (*minima*)
crenatiflo'ra
crenula'ta . . . . **B. angularis**
crini'ta
crispipi'la
crista'ta
cruen'ta
cuben'sis . . . . . . **B. wrightiana**
cubinco'la
cultra'ta
cum'ingi (*philippinensis*)
cumingia'na
cunea'ta . . . . **B. spathulata**
cuneatifo'lia
cuningham'ei
cur'tisi
cuspida'ta
cyathoph'ora
cyclophyl'la
daeda'lea . . . . . . **B. strigillosa**
dasycar'pa
dasypo'da . . . . **B. brasila**

BEGONIA, continued
dav'isi . . . . . . DAVIS BEGONIA
dealba'ta
debil'is
decaisnea'na
decan'dra
declina'ta
deco'ra
delava'yi
delicat'ula
delicio'sa
demis'sa
×**densiflo'ra**
denta'ta . . . . **B. angustiloba**
dentatilo'ba
denticula'ta
depaupera'ta . . . . . **B. rhizocarpa**
derycxia'na . . . . **B. nelumbiifolia**
diade'ma
dichot'oma
dichro'a
dielsia'na
digy'na
dimidia'ta . . . . . . **B. arborescens**
dipet'ala . . . . . . **B. malabarica d.**
dip'tera . . . . **B. capensis**
dis'color . . . . **B. grandis**
discre'ta
diversifo'lia . . . . **B. gracilis**
djamuen'sis
dolabrif'era
dolichot'richa
domingen'sis
dominica'lis
donkelaaria'na
du'bia
duclou'xi
duruen'sis
dusen'i
ealen'sis
eberhard'ti
ebolowen'sis
echinosep'ala
ecilia'ta
ecuadorien'sis . . . . . ECUADOR B.
This palmatifid-leaved Ecuador species has apparently never been published botanically. Unfortunately, the name B. ecuadoriensis has sometimes been misapplied to B. acida.
edano'i
ed'ulis
egreg'ia
eiromisch'a
elaeagnifo'lia
ela'ta
elatostematoi'des
elatostem'ma
el'egans
elian'i
elliot'i
ellip'tica . . . . **B. glabra**
el'meri
emin'i
eng'leri (*engleriana*)
epibater'ium
—angustiala'ta
epilobioi'des
epiphyt'ica
episcopal'is
erec'ta
eriocau'lis (*tomentosa*)
eriocau'lon
erman'i
—uligino'sa
ermin'ea
—obtu'sa

BEGONIA, continued
erubes'cens
erythrocar'pa
∞ **erythrophyl'la** (*hydrocotylifolia* × *manicata*)
erythrot'richa
esculen'ta
esquiro'li
estrellen'sis
evansia'na
—al'ba
everet'ti
exala'ta
excel'sa
ex'ilis
fagifo'lia
fagopyroi'des
—fendleria'na
falcifo'lia
falcilo'ba
fal'lax
fascicula'ta
fasciculiflo'ra
faurea'na . . . . . FAURES BEGONIA
favar'geri
fen'icis
ferrugin'ea
festi'va
fibro'sa
fie'brigi
filibracteo'sa
fil'ipes
fimbria'ta
fimbristip'ula
findlaysonia'na
fissisep'ala
fissurar'um
flaccidis'sima
flexicau'lis
flex'ula
floccif'era
folio'sa (*microphylla*)
forbes'i
forgetia'na
foxworth'yi
fran'cois
franco'nis
frag'ilis
frig'ida
froebel'i
—na'na
∞ **—vernal'is** (*dregei* × *froebeli*)
fruticel'la
frutico'sa
∞ **fuchsifolio'sa** (*foliosa* × *fuchsioides*)
fuchsioi'des (*miniata*)
ful'gens
fulvovillo'sa
furfura'cea
fus'ca
fusiala'ta
fusibul'ba
galeottia'na
garagaka'na
gard'neri
garret'ti
gaudichau'di
gemel'la
gemmip'ara
gemmirhi'za
genicula'ta
gentil'i
geoffra'yi
geranifo'lia
geranioi'des
geranioi'des Hort., *not* Hook.
gigan'tea (*silhetensis*)

BEGONIA, continued
gil'gi
gilgia'na
gitingen'sis
glaber'rima
gla'bra (*elliptica; moritziana; scandens*)
glabricau'lis
gladiifo'lia
glandulif'era
glau'ca
glaucophyl'la
× **globo'sa**
goegoen'sis
gonio'tis
goudo'ti
gouroa'na
gracilicau'lis
gracil'ipes
gracilipetiola'ta
grac'ilis (*bicolor; diversifolia*) SLENDER BEGONIA
gracil'lima
grahamia'na . . . . **B. albo-coccinea**
grandipet'ala
gran'dis (*discolor*)
∞ *gran'dis* Hort., *not* Dryand. (*rex* × *splendida*)
grantia'na
gra'ta
grenatiflo'ra
grewiaefo'lia
—jamesonia'na
—pavonia'na
grif'fithi
gris'ea
guaduen'sis
gueritzia'na
gunneraefo'lia
guyanen'sis
haagea'na (*scharffi*)
halconen'sis
han'iffi
har'mandi
harrowia'na
hasskar'li
hasskarlia'na
has'sleri
hasta'ta . . . . **B. angularis**
hataco'a
haullevillea'na
havilan'di
haya'tae
hed'dei
hedera'cea . . . . **B. herbacea**
hederaefo'lia
hemsleya'na
henri'quesi
hen'ryi
heracleifo'lia (*jatrophaefolia; radiata*)
—ni'grans
—puncta'ta
herba'cea (*attenuata; hederacea*)
hernandioi'des
herveya'na
heterocli'nis
heterodon'ta
heterophyl'la
heteropo'da
hey'dei
hieron'ymi
hilaria'na
hirsuticau'lis
hirsu'tula
hirtel'la . . . . **B. brasila**
his'pida
hispidis'sima
hoegea'na

BEGONIA, continued
holoseric'ea
hol'tonis
holttu'mi
hom'blei
hookeria'na
horsfield'i
hortico'la
hu'beri
huge'li
hullet'ti
humboldtia'na
humilicau'lis
hu'milis . . . . . TRINIDAD BEGONIA
hydrocotylifo'lia
hygroph'ila
hymenophyl'la
hypogae'a
hypolipa'ra
ig'nea
ignora'ta
imperfec'ta
imperia'lis . . . . IMPERIAL B.
—macula'ta
—smaragdi'na . . . . . GREEN I.B.
× **—venulo'sa**
inca'na (*auriformis*)
incarna'ta (*aucubaefolia; insignis; seemanniana*)
—grandiflo'ra
—papillo'sa
—ru'bra
incer'ta
inci'sa
incisoserra'ta
incondi'ta
infla'ta
injoloen'sis
inophyl'la
inoste'gia
insig'nis . . . . **B. incarnata**
insula'rum
integer'rima
integrifo'lia
intermix'ta
involucra'ta
irides'cens
isabelen'sis
isop'tera (*bombycina*)
—hirsu'ta
isopteroi'dea
ja'gori
jamesonia'na
jatrophaefo'lia . . . **B. heracleifolia**
john'stoni
jo'sephi
—macrocar'pa
junghuhnia'na
juntasen'sis
jussiaeicar'pa
kanien'sis
karwinskya'na
kellermann'i
kellia'na
kenien'sis
kerr'i
kersting'i
kingia'na
kisulua'na
klain'ei
klem'mei
kloss'i
komoen'sis
koor'dersi
kotoen'sis
kouytcheouen'sis
kriben'sis

BEGONIA, continued
kummer'iae
kunstleria'na
labor'dei
lac'era
lacinia'ta (*bowringiana*)
—nepalen'sis
lacinio'sa
lacuno'sa
lae'vis
lagunen'sis
lanceola'ta
lancifo'lia
lancilim'ba
langbianen'sis
langsdorf'fi . . . . **B. bidentata**
lantaniaefo'lia
lanugino'sa
∞ **lapeyrou'sei** (*hydrocotylifolia* × *incarnata*)
laporteifo'lia
latipetiola'ta
latistip'ula
lauri'na Hort. . . . . **B. ottonis**
lauterbach'i
lecom'tei
ledermann'i
lehmbach'i
∞ **leodien'se** (*echinosepala* × *princeps*)
lep'ida
lepidel'la
lepido'ta . . . . **B. manicata**
lepro'sa
leptan'tha
leptopo'da
leptotri'cha
leucan'tha
leuconeu'ra
leucostic'ta
leyten'sis (*wenzeli*)
libanen'sis
liebmann'i (*reptans*)
ligno'sa
limprich'ti
lindenia'na
lindleya'na (*vitifolia* Lindl., *not* Schott)
linea'ta
lipingen'sis
littler'i
lobb'i
lobbia'na
lobula'ta
locella'ta
loher'i
loloen'sis
lomen'sis
longibrac'ta
longicau'lis
∞ **longicy'ma** (*schmidtiana* × *semperflorens*)
longifo'lia
longino'da
lon'gipes
—laticorda'ta
—petiola'ta
longiros'tris
longiscar'pa
longistip'ula
longovillo'sa
lophop'tera
loranthoi'des
lowia'na
lub'bersi
lu'dicra
lugar'si
lushaien'sis
lux'i

BEGONIA, continued
luxu'rians
luzonen'sis
ly'alli
lynchea'na . . . . **B. roezli**
macahen'sis
macgreg'ori
ma'cra
macrier'a
macrocar'pa
macrophyl'la . . . . **B. nelumbiifolia**
—max'ima . . . . . . **B. n. maxima**
macropo'da
macrop'tera (*villosa* Gardn., *not* Lindl.)
—grandiflo'ra
—pal'udum
—pohlia'na
—pulcher'rima
—racemo'sa
macrosty'la
macro'tis
macru'ra
macula'ta (*argyrostigma*) SPOTTED BEGONIA
—argen'tea (*B. argentea*)
—elegantis'sima
—pic'ta
—wight'i
maestren'sis
magnif'ica
magnifo'lia
mair'ei
majungaen'sis
malabar'ica
—dipet'ala (*B. dipetala*)
malindangen'sis
malmquistia'na
—angustifo'lia
—latifo'lia
malva'cea
mameia'na
manica'ta (*lepidota; schizolepis*)
—aureo-macula'ta
—cris'pa . . . . CURLY B.
manillen'sis
mann'i
maracayuen'sis
marmora'ta
∞ **marmore'a** (*rubrovenia* × *xanthina*)
martaban'ica
mar'tini . . . . MARTIN B.
martinicen'sis
masarangen'sis
mascarien'sis
mauran'diae
max'ima
maxwellia'na
maynen'sis
mearn'si
megacar'pa
megalan'tha
megaphyl'la
megap'tera
megapteroi'dea
meis'sneri
membrana'cea
meriden'sis
mer'rilli
mer'riti
metal'lica . . . . STEEL B.
mex'iae
mexica'na
meyenia'na
meysselia'na
microcar'pa
microphyl'la . . . . **B. foliosa**
microp'tera

BEGONIA, continued
microsper'ma
mildbrae'di
mindanaen'sis
mindoren'sis
minia'ta . . . . **B. fuchsioides**
min'ima . . . . **B. crenata**
minjemen'sis
modes'ta
modestiflo'ra
mod'ica
mol'leri
mol'lis
monadelph'a
monan'tha
monophyl'la
monop'tera
monta'na
montic'ola
moritzia'na . . . . **B. glabra**
moszkow'ski
mouhotia'na
moulmeinen'sis
mucronistip'ula
multan'gula
—glabra'ta
multibulbillo'sa
multidenta'ta
multiflo'ra
—erec'ta
muri'na
muruden'sis
myrian'tha
na'na
natalen'sis . . . . . . **B. suffruticosa**
naumonien'sis
ndongen'sis
neglec'ta
—caules'cens
negrosen'sis
nelumbiifo'lia (*derycxiana; macrophylla*)
—max'ima (*B. maxima*)
nemoph'ila . . . . **B. cathcarti**
neocomen'sium
nepalen'sis
—microp'teron
nicaraguen'sis
nigres'cens
nigritar'um
nit'ida . . . . . . GLOSSY BEGONIA
—odora'ta (*B. odorata*)
niv'ea
northia'na
nossibe'a
nota'ta
notioph'ila
nu'ri
oaxaca'na (*plagiata*)
—pilo'sula
oblanceola'ta
oblonga'ta
oblongifo'lia
obovatistip'ula
obovoi'dea
obtusifo'lia
obver'sa
octopet'ala
odora'ta . . . . **B. nitida o.**
ol'bia
oligan'tha
oligocar'pa
oligophyl'la
opuliflo'ra
orbicula'ta
orchidiflo'ra
orega'na
∞ **orna'ta** (*dregei* × *sutherlandi*)

BEGONIA, continued
ornithocar'pa
∞ **ottonia'na** (*conchaefolia* × *coriacea*)
otto'nis (*laurina* Hort.)
oxyan'thera
oxycan'tha
oxylo'ba
oxyphyl'la
oxysper'ma
∞ **pa'la** (*peltata* × *ricinifolia*)
palawanen'sis
palea'cea
palea'ta
palmar'is
—jur'genseni
pal'meri
paludic'ola
palus'tris
panayen'sis
panicula'ta
pantheri'na
papua'na
paraguayen'sis
parcifo'lia
par'ishi
par'va
parvilim'ba
parvipelta'ta . . . . . . **B. peltifolia**
par'vula
pastoen'sis
pa'tens . . . . **B. arborescens**
paulen'sis
pauper'cula
pavonia'na
pavoni'na
pearce'i . . . . . . PEARCE BEGONIA
peda'ta
pedatifi'da
peeke'li
peltifo'lia (*coriacea* Hassk. *not* DC.; *parvipeltata; peltata*)
pen'dula
penin'sulae
pentaphragmifo'lia
peperomio'des
peraken'sis
periste'gia
perpusil'la
perrier'i
peruvia'na
petalo'des
pet'rae
petroph'ila
petropolita'na
philippinen'sis . . . . . **B. cumingi**
phoeniogram'ma
phrixophyl'la
phyllomania'ca
pic'ta . . . . NEPAL B.
There is also a hort. var., probably of B. coccinea, known as PICTA.
pier'rei
pilderifo'lia
pilo'sa
pinamalayen'sis
pineto'rum
pittier'i
plagia'ta . . . . **B. oaxacana**
plagioneu'ra
platanifo'lia
platyphyl'la
platyp'tera
plebe'ja
pleiopet'ala
plumier'i
poculif'era
poeci'la

BEGONIA, continued
poeppigia'na
pog'gei
pohlia'na
poikilan'tha . . . . . **B. quadrialata**
polyan'tha
polycar'pa
polygona'ta
polygonifo'lia
polygonoi'des
polypet'ala
—elwe'siae
—sel'lae
popenoe'i
popul'nea
por'teri
portilla'na
portoricen'sis
potamoph'ila
praeclar'a
prieu'rei
prin'ceae
pring'lei
prismatocar'pa
procridifo'lia
procum'bens
prolif'era
prolix'a
prome'thea
propin'qua
prunia'ta
pryeria'na
pseudimpa'tiens
pseudisop'tera
pseudolatera'lis
∞ **pseudophyllomania'ca** (*heracleifolia* × *incarnata*)
pseudovi'ola
pubes'cens
pubipedicel'la
pulchel'la
pululahua'na
pu'mila
pu'milo
purdiea'na
pusil'la
pustula'ta
put'ti
pycnan'tha
pyr'rha
quadriala'ta (*poikilantha*)
quercifo'lia
quinta'si
rab'ili
racemiflo'ra
racemo'sa
radia'ta . . . . . . **B. heracleifolia**
rad'icans
ragozi'ni
ra'jah
ramenta'cea
ramo'si
randaien'sis
renifo'lia
repan'da
rep'tans . . . . **B. liebmanni**
reticula'ta
retu'sa
rex . . . . . . ASSAMKING BEGONIA
rheifo'lia
rhipsaloi'des
rhizocar'pa (*depauperata*)
rhodan'tha
rhoeph'ila
rhombicar'pa (*capensis* Blanco, *not* L.)
rhopalocar'pa
×**rich'ardi**

BEGONIA, continued
richardsia'na
rieck'ei
riedel'i
rig'ida
rimar'um
ripic'ola
robinso'ni
robus'ta (*splendida* Hort.)
There is also a hort. var., probably of B. fuchsioides, known as ROBUSTA.
roez'li (*lyncheana*)
romeen'sis
rosa'cea
rosaeflo'ra
rose'a
rossman'niae
rostra'ta
rota'ta . . . . . **B. caroliniaefolia**
rotun'da
rotundifo'lia
roxburgh'i
roy'lei
ru'bida
ru'bra . . . . **B. coccinea**
rubricau'lis
rubrifo'lia
rubromargina'ta
rubronerva'ta
rubroner'via
rubropilo'sa
rubrosetulo'sa
rubrove'nia
ru'fa
rufipi'la
rugo'sa
rupes'tris
rupic'ola
salazien'sis
salicifo'lia
samaren'sis
sandalifo'lia
sanguin'ea
santorosen'sis
sarasino'rum
sarawaken'sis
sarcocar'pa
sarcophyl'la
sassandren'sis
satrap'is
saxat'ilis
saxic'ola
saxif'raga
saxifragifo'lia
sca'brida
scan'dens . . . . **B. glabra**
scapig'era
schaef'eri
scharf'fi . . . . **B. haageana**
scharffia'na
—mi'nor
schiaph'ila
schizole'pis . . . . **B. manicata**
schlech'teri
schlumbergeria'na
schmidtia'na
schottia'na
schultz'ei
schulzia'na
scin'tillans
scortechi'mi
scutella'ta . . . . . . **B. warscewiczi**
scutifo'lia
scu'tulum
seemannia'na . . . . . **B. incarnata**
sel'loi
semiova'ta

BEGONIA, continued
semperflo'rens . Perpetual Begonia
—hook'eri
—sel'lowi
ser'eti
serot'ina
ser'pens
serratifo'lia
serratipet'ala
serrulatoa'la
sessilan'thera
sessilifo'lia
setif'era
seto'sa
setulo'sa
seychellen'sis
sharpea'na
siamen'sis
sibthorpioi'des
sikkimen'sis
silheten'sis . . . . **B. gigantea**
smilac'ina
smith'iae
so'cia
socotra'na . . . . Socotra B.
sodiro'i
sogeren'sis
solanan'thera
solu'ta
somervil'lei
sootepen'sis
sordidis'sima
sparsipi'la
spathula'ta (*cuneata*)
spelun'cae
sphenocar'pa
spica'ta
spilotophyl'la
sprucea'na
squamo'sa
squamulo'sa
squarro'sa
stand'leyi
staudt'i
stenophyl'la
stenop'tera
stictopo'da
stigmo'sa
strachwitz'i
strictiner'vis
strictipetiolar'is
strigillo'sa (*daedalea*)
strigulo'sa
subacutoala'ta
subalpes'tris
subcilia'ta (*ciliata* Pav., *not* H.B.K.)
subcos'ta
subcuculla'ta
subcyclophyl'la
subfalca'ta
subhu'milis
subloba'ta
subnummularifo'lia
suborbicula'ta
subpelta'ta
subperfolia'ta
subprostra'ta
subrectan'gula
subscuta'ta
subtrunca'ta
subvillo'sa (*villosa* Klotzsch, *not* Lindl.)
subvir'idis
suffrutico'sa (*natalensis*)
—gueinzia'na
sulca'ta
surculig'era
sutherland'i

BEGONIA, continued
sylvat'ica
sylves'tris
syphilit'ica
tafien'sis
taiwania'na
talien'sis
tampi'nica
tawaen'sis
tayaben'sis
telfair'iae
ten'era (*thwaitesi*)
tenericau'lis
tenuicau'lis
tenuifo'lia
tenuipi'la
tessaricar'pa
teusch'eri
teuszia'na
teysmannia'na
thaspingen'sis
thi'mei
thimo'tei
thomea'na
thom'soni
thwaite'si . . . . **B. tenera**
tiliaefo'lia
tiomanen'sis
togoen'sis
tomento'sa . . . . . . **B. eriocaulis**
tondu'zi
tonkinen'sis
tor'resi
torricellen'sis
trachyp'tera
trianae'i
trichocar'pa
trichochi'la
trichopo'da
tricor'nis
tricosep'ala
tricuspida'ta
triflo'ra
trigonocar'pa
trigonop'tera
trilo'ba
triradia'ta
trispathula'ta
trisulca'ta
tropaeolifo'lia
trullaefo'lia
truncico'la
tuerckheim'i
udisilves'tris
u'lei
uligino'sa
—er'mani
ulmifo'lia
umbella'ta
umbraculif'era
unduaven'sis
undula'ta
uniala'ta
uniflo'ra
unifo'lia
unilateral'ia
urdaneten'sis
urophyl'la
ur'ticae
—his'pida
urticifo'lia
uruapen'sis
uva'na
va'gans
va'ginans
valden'sium
val'eri

BEGONIA, continued
val'ida
vanderckhove'ni
vandewat'eri
vanoverbergh'i
variab'ilis
varia'na
veitch'i
veller'ea
veno'sa
ver'dicki
∞ **verschaffeltia'na** (*caroliniaefolia* × *manicata; verschaffelti*)
ves'tita
villipetio'la
villo'sa
villo'sa Gardn., *not* Lindl. **B. macroptera**
villo'sa Klotzsch, *not* Lindl. **B. subvillosa**
vincentia'na
violaefo'lia
viridiflo'ra
vitifo'lia
—gran'dis
vitifo'lia Lindl., *not* Schott **B. lindleyana**
∞ **vi'vicans** Hort. (*incarnata* × *sedeni*)
vui'jcki
wa'dei
wageneria'na
wake'fieldi
wallichia'na
wal'persi
war'burgi
warburgia'na
waria'na
war'puri
warscewicz'i (*conchaefolia; scutellata*) Shell Begonia
watt'i
web'eri
weddellia'na
weigall'i
wellmann'i
wen'geri
wen'zeli . . . . **B. leytensis**
whyte'i
wil'liamsi
wil'soni
wollas'toni
woll'nyi
wood'i
worthia'na
wray'i
wrightia'na (*cubensis*)
xanthi'na
—gandaven'sis
—lazu'li
× **—marmore'a**
—pictifo'lia
yap'pi
yunnanen'sis
zamboangen'sis
zebri'na . . . . **B. angularis**
zobiaen'sis
zollingeria'na

Hort. var. of **Begonia:**

It may be assumed that most if not all of the horticultural varieties listed below are clons selected from polybrids and must be propagated vegetatively if it is desired to maintain identity with the parent without variations. The clon sign is therefore omitted.

It is quite probable, moreover, that the horticultural variety names listed which are preceded by the polybrid sign ∞ represent, as a matter of fact, clons

BEGONIA, continued

selected from the polybrid hybridization; example, ∞ABEL CARRIERE (*evansiana* × *rex*). Normally the name ABEL CARRIERE should be the group or polybrid name and represent the product of a single cross or any number of crosses between *evansiana* and *rex;* therefore, if a clon name was intended, a polybrid name should have been supplied for the cross *evansiana* × *rex*.

Lacking definite information as to the facts, the editors prefer to treat such names normally as polybrids, and affix the proper symbol ∞.

ABBREVIATIONS OF BEGONIA CLASSIFICATION

Acon.	**B. aconitifolia.**
Bert.	∞BERTINI.
Bol.	**B. boliviensis.**
Chei.	∞CHEIMANTHA.
Cocc.	**B. coccinea.**
Cyp.	∞CYPRAEA.
Dreg.	∞DREGEI.
Duc.	∞DUCHARTREI.
Grac.	**B. gracilis.**
Her.	**B. heracleifolia.**
Hiem.	∞HIEMALIS.
Imp.	**B. imperialis.**
Inc.	**B. incarnata.**
Luc.	∞LUCERNA.
Met.	**B. metallica.**
Mult.	**B. multiflora.**
Rex.	∞REXCULTORUM.
Ric.	∞RICINIFOLIA.
Rosae.	**B. rosaeflora.**
Schar.	**B. scharffiana.**
Semp.	**B. semperflorens.**
Soc.	**B. socotrana.**

ABBREVIATIONS OF NAMES OF INTRODUCERS

Aren.	George Arends, Ronsdorf, Ger.
Ben.	Ernst Benary, Erfurt, Germany.
Berry	Roy Berry, Torrance, Calif.
Bin.	Binot.
Bow.	Miss Constance Bower, San Diego, Calif.
Bru.	G. de Bruant, Frankfort, Ger.
Chev.	Auguste Chevalier (pere), and Charles Chevalier (fils).
Crozy	Crozy.
Des.	Desbois.
Dut.	Dutrie.
Ed.	W. W. Edgar, Watertown, Mass.
Few.	Mrs. E. M. Fewkes, San Diego, Calif.
Fleet.	Mrs. Orrell Fleetwood, Calif.
Gibbs	Clarence Gibbs, Lynn, Mass.
Grant	Wm. Grant, San Diego, Calif.
Gray	Mrs. E. K. Gray, San Diego, Calif.
Haage & Schm.	Haage & Schmidt, Erfurt, Ger.
Has.	Justus Carl Haaskarl, Germany.
Hein.	Heineman, Erfurt, Germany.
Hen.	Henderson.
Karl.	Karlsons.
Lem.	V. Lemoine & Son, Nancy, France.
Liege	Liege (city).
Lind.	Linden.
Lion.	Lionnet, France.
Lotte	Lotte.
Mal.	M. Arthur Mallet, France.
Peace	Mrs. Mary Peace, Calif.
Pete.	Wm. A. Peterson, Chicago, Ill.
Rob.	A. D. Robinson, San Diego, Calif.
Rod.	Mrs. C. A. Rodenburg, Santa Monica, Calif.
Schm.	Schmidtt.
Shep.	Mrs. Theodosia Shepherd, Ventura, Calif.
Sut.	Sutton & Sons, Reading, Eng.
Swi.	Mrs. Ross Swisher, Sycamore, Pa.
Thib. & Ket.	Thibaut & Keteleer.
Till.	Mrs. George Tillman, Rockville, Md.
Trav.	Harold Traver, M.D., Conn.
Val.	Vallerand.
Van H.	Louis Benoit Van Houtte, Ghent, Belgium.
Ved.	Chauncey Vedder, San Diego, Calif.
Vei.	James G. Veitch, England.
Vers.	Ambrose Verschaffelt, Belgium.
Wai.	Mrs. Frank Waite, San Diego, Calif.
Wal.	W. A. Wallow, Calif.
W. Bull	William Bull, England.
Weitz	Weitz.
Wil.	William.

∞ABEL CARRIERE (*evansiana* × *rex*). (Svahn 1875.)
A. D. DAVIS. Rex. (Rob.)
ADONIS. Soc. (1887.)
AGATHACOMPACTA. Soc. (Vei. 1907.)
∞ALATACOCCINEA (∞SEDENI × *veitchi*). (Lem. 1871.)
ALBIDASETULOSA. (Has.)
ALICE MANNING.
∞ALLERYI (*gigantea* × *metallica*).
ALMA MILLIKEN. (Swi.)
∞ALPENGLUHEN (*diadema* × *rex*). (Dut.)
ALPHONSE.
ALTRINGHAM PINK. Soc.
ALZASCO. Luc. (Rob. 1934.)
∞AMELIA (∞CARRIEREI × *lyncheana*). (Bru. 1885.)
ANGELWING. Cocc.
ANNABELLE. (Ved. 1922.)
ANNIE LAURIE. Cocc. (Rob.)
∞ARGENTEOGUTTATA (*albopicta* × *olbia*). (Lem. 1888.) *Trout.*
ARLINE. Cocc. (Rob.)
∞ARTHUR MALLET (ELDORADO × *subpeltata*). (Lion. 1886.)
∞*Ascotiensis* (*fuchsioides* × *semperflorens*). CORBEILLE DEFEU.
ASTOLAT. (Gray 1926.)
ASTRIDA. (Chev. 1936.)
ATROPURPUREA COMPACTA.
AUDREE. Cocc. (Rob.)
AUGUST NONIN. (1895.)
BAVARIA. (1884.)
BAYERN.
∞BEATRICE (*coccinea* × *Gloire Dejouy*). (Shep.)
BEAUTYOFHALE. Soc.
Beefsteak. ∞FEASTI.
Beefsteak Upright. BESSIE BUXTON.
BELLAGIO. Luc. (Rob. 1934.)
BENNETRUBRA. Cocc. (Rob. 1932.)
BERKLEYI.
∞BERLIN (CREDNERI COMPACTA × *metallica*). (Aren.)
Bertha Dechateau-Rocher. CORBEILLE DEFEU.
BERTHA MCGREGOR. Rex.
Bertha Vonlothringen. ∞PERLE LORRAINE.
∞BERTINI (*boliviensis* × *veitchi*).
BERTINI LICHTROSA.
BESSIE BUXTON. *Beefsteak Upright; Flambeau; Upright Feasti.*
BIJOU DEJARDIN. Semp.
BINOTI. (Bin. 1909.)
BISMARCKIANA. (Vei. 1886.)
BLUTENMEER. Grac.
BOSNIE.
BOULE DENEIGE. Semp. (Lem. 1898.)
BOUQUET BLANC. (Lem. 1904.)
BOWDEN BEAUTY. Soc.
BRAEMAR.
BRONZE DENANCY. (Lem. 1901.)
BRONZE QUEEN.

BEGONIA, continued

∞BUISSON ROSE (*gracilis* × *polyantha*). (Lem. 1902.)
BUNCHI.
CALEDONIA. Soc. (1901.)
CALLA LILY.
CAMILLE PARMENTIER. (1924.)
∞CANDELABRE (*haageana* × *metallica*). (Lem. 1900.)
CAPT. NEMO. (Rob.)
CARLOTTA. (Rod. 1939.)
CARMEN. Grac. (Hein. 1929.)
CARMINE. Semp.
∞CAROLINAE (*acuminata* × *nitida*).
CAROLINE SCHMIDTT. (Schm. 1875.)
∞CARRIEREI (*schmidtiana* × *semperflorens;* ×*bruanti* Hort.; ×*smithi* Hort.)
∞CHAMBERSI (*pearcei* × ∞SEDENI).
CHARLES WAGNER. (1895.)
CH. CHEVALIER. (1924.)
×CHEIMANTHA.
∞CHELSONI (*boliviensis* × ∞SEDENI).
CHIALA-ALBA. (Grant 1930.)
CHIALA-ROSEA. (Grant 1930.)
CHRISTMAS CHEER. Semp.
CLEMENTA.
CLEMMENCE. Cocc. (Rob.)
CLIBRANS PINK. Soc.
CLIBRANS RED. Soc.
CODELARGO. Luc. (Rob. 1934.)
∞COLOGNE (CREDNERI COMPACTA × *metallica*). (Aren. 1927.)
COMTE DELIMMINGHE.
COMTE DEMIRIBEL. (Bru. 1896.)
CONBOW. (Bow. 1928.)
CONSTANCE. Luc. (Rob.)
COPPERY GOLD.
CORAIL. (Lem. 1901.)
CORAIL ROSE. (Lem. 1872.)
∞CORALLINA DELUCERNA (*coccinea* × *teuscheri*). (1892.)
CORAL RUBRA.
CORBEILLE DEFEU. (Lem. 1891.) ∞*Ascotiensis; Bertha Dechateau-Rocher; Vesuvius.*
CORINTHIAN PINK. Cocc. (Rob.)
CORKSCREW.
∞CORONATA (*caroliniaefolia* × *polyantha*).
COUNTESS OF PORTLAND.
∞CREDNERI (*metallica* × *scharffiana*).
×CROFTONI.
CROWFOOT.
CRYSTAL WHITE. (Wai. 1930.)
CYPRAEA. Met.
DAPHNE. (Shep.)
DARK STAR.
DAWN. (Ved. 1928.)
DAZZLER. Soc.
DEAREST MAE. (Shep.)
DECKERS SELECT. (1919.) *Deckers Robusta.*
∞DEGRELLINA (*corallina* × *dregei*).
∞DEURINGERI (*cinnabarina* × *incarnata*).
DEWDROP.
DIELYTRA. Cocc. (Rob. 1930.)
∞DIGSWELLIANA (*fuchsioides* × *semperflorens*). *Sandersi; Sandersoni.*
∞DIRECTEUR (*Henri*) CHEVALIER (*metallica* × *princeps*). (Liege 1938.)
DISCOLOR MARMOREA. (Mal. 1863.)
DOLFUSS.
DOROTHY GRANT. (Grant 1928.)
∞DREGEI.
DREGEI SINUATA.
∞DRESDEN (CREDNERI COMPACTA × *metallica*). (Aren. 1927.)

BEGONIA, continued
Dresden. Semp.
Dr. Nachtingal. (Haage & Schm. 1886.)
∞Druryi (Cypraea × *sanguinea*). (Bow. 1932.)
∞Duchartrei (*pearcei* × *subpeltata*).
Duke of Cambridge.
Eclipse. Soc.
∞Ed Pynaert (*evansiana* × *rex*). (1880.)
Elaine. Luc. (Grant 1928.)
Eldorado.
Elegance. Semp.
Elithe. Cocc. (Rob. 1934.)
Elsmeri.
Elva S. (Swi.)
∞Emeraude (*boliviensis* × *veitchi*). (Van H. 1870.)
Emily Clibran. Soc.
∞Emperor (*clarkei* × *veitchi*). (Vei. 1875.)
Enchantress. Semp.
Erectacristata. (1896.)
Erectagrandiflora. (1903.)
Erectaviridis. (1908.)
∞Erfordia (*schmidtiana* × Vernon). (Haage & Schm. 1893.)
Erna. Cocc. (Rob.)
Ethel Calloway. (Gray.)
E. Vallerand. Inc. (Lem. 1881.)
∞Excelsior (∞Chelsoni × *cinnabarina*). (Vei. 1875.)
Exquisite. Soc. (1931.)
Fair Rosamunde. (Shep.)
Fascination. Soc.
∞Feasti (*hydrocotylifolia* × *manicata*). (?Feast. 1880.) *Beefsteak; erythrophylla.*
Feu Debengal. (Lem. 1904.)
Feuermeer. Semp.
Feuerzauber. Grac.
Fireflame.
Fireking. *Goegoensis.*
Fischers Ricinifolia. Ric.
Flambeau. Bessie Buxton.
Flamboyant.
Flammarion. (Shep.)
∞Florida Incomparabilis (*rosea* × *schmidtiana*). (Haage & Schm. 1883.)
Florida Species.
∞Forckeli (*coccinea* × *sanguinea*).
Frau (*Helena*) Harms.
Frieda Grant. (Grant 1928.)
Froebeli Incomparabilis.
Frondosa. (Few.)
Frutescans. (Rob.)
Fulgurant. (Lem. 1901.)
∞Gabrielle Petit (*corallina* × *undulata*). (1917.)
Gambetta. (Lem. 1907.)
∞Gandavensis (*rubrovenia* × *xanthina*).
∞Gemmata (*decora* × *rex*).
∞Gen. (*Comte*) Demiribel (*albo-picta* × *coccinea*). (1896.)
Geneva. Luc. (Wai.)
∞Gen. Jacques (*scharffiana* × *venosa*). (1918.)
Gen. Leman. (1917.)
Gigantea Carminea. (Lem. 1884.)
Gigantea Duplex. (1914.)
Gigantea Odorata.
∞Gigantea Rosea (*roezli* × *semperflorens*). (Lem. 1883.)
Gilsoni. (1880.)
Gloire Dechatelaine. (1905.)
Gloire Dejouy.

BEGONIA, continued
∞Gloire Delorraine (∞Dregei × *socotrana*). Chei. (Lem. 1892.)
Gloire Delouveciennes.
Gloire Delucerna. ∞Lucerna.
Gloire Demoordrecht.
Gloire Denancy. (Lem.)
Gloire Desceaux. Soc. (Thib. & Ket. 1884.)
Gloria.
Glory of Cincinnati. Chei. (Soc.) (Pete. 1910.)
Goegoensis. Fireking.
Goethe. Mult.
Goliath. Semp. (Lem. 1895.)
Grace. Cocc. (Rob.)
∞Gracilis (*schmidtiana* × *semperflorens*).
Grants Duchartrei. Duc. (Grant 1928.)
Grayola. (Gray 1925.)
Greyfeather.
Gruba. Semp.
Guineaswing.
Gustav Lund. *Westport Beauty.*
Haageana Drosti.
∞Hamburg (Credneri Compacta × *metallica*). (Aren. 1927.)
Hebe. (Shep.)
Helena. (1928.)
Helen (*W.*) King. Luc. (Rob. 1920.)
∞Heracleicotyle (*heracleifolia* × *hydrocotylifolia*). *Mrs. Townsend.*
×Hiemalis.
A group name for all socotrana × tuberous hybrids.
Hildegarde Schneider. Acon.
Hollyhock.
Ideala. Soc. (Vei. 1901.)
Illustrata.
Immense. Ric.
Indianarian. Semp.
Indian Maid. Semp.
Indian Ricinifolia.
∞Ingrami (*fuchsioides* × *nitida*).
The name B. robusta is often misapplied to this hybrid.
Interlaken. Luc. (Rob. 1934.)
×Intermedia (*boliviensis* × *veitchi*).
Janice Milliken. (Swi.)
Jaurezi.
Jean. Cocc. (Rob.)
∞Jean Lotte (∞Duchartrei × *metallica*). (Lotte 1902.)
Jinnie May. Cocc. (Rob. 1925.)
Kallista.
Kathi. (Gray.)
Kenzipalmata. (Gray.)
Kewensis.
K. O. Sessions. Rex. (Rob.)
Kulu. (Gray.)
Lady Lou. Cocc. (Rob. 1934.)
Lady Mac. Chei. (Ed. 1925.)
Lady Roberts. Soc.
Lady Waterlow.
Laetevirens.
Lafayette. (Lem. 1889.)
Laneige.
×Langeana.
Lecco. Luc. (Rob. 1934.)
Lecorrege. (Lem. 1873.)
×Legia.
Lemaouti. (Val. 1889.)
Lemoinei. (Lem. 1874.)
Leon Delaville. (1895.)
×Leopoldi.
∞Lesoudsi (*diadema* × *rex*). (Bru. 1888.)

BEGONIA, continued
∞Lettonica (*heracleifolia* × *nelumbiifolia*).
Lillian S. Cocc. (Rob.)
Lobata Variegata.
Loma Alta. (Few. 1935.)
Louise. Cocc. (Rob.)
Lucendro. Luc. (Rob. 1934.)
∞Lucerna (*rubra* × *teuscheri*). (1903.) *Gloire Delucerna.*
Lucianae. (Bru. 1889.)
Lucille. Soc. (Trav. 1936.)
Lucy Clibran. Soc.
Lugano. Luc. (Rob. 1920.)
Luminosa Compacta.
Luminosa Robusta.
Luteanana. (1890.)
Mabelle E. Luc. (Rob.)
Macbethi. Dreg.
Macbethi Pink.
Maculata Deliciosa.
Maggiore. Luc. (Rob. 1934.)
Margaritacea. (Vei. 1895.)
∞Margaritae (*echinosepala* × *metallica*).
Marge. Cocc. (Rob.)
Marginata. (1897.)
Marian. Ric.
Marietta.
Marion Louise. Rex. (Rob.)
∞Marjorie Daw (*coccinea* × *glaucophylla*). (Shep. 1900.)
Marjorie Gibbs. (Gibbs 1918.)
Marshalli.
Martha. Cocc. (Rob.)
Mary. Cocc. (Rob.)
Massange Delouvrex. (1875.)
∞Massiliensis (*cinnabarina* × *veitchi*).
×Mastodonte.
May Queen. Cocc. (Gray.)
Medora. (1926.)
Melanie. Imp.
Melior. Chei. (Pete. 1914.)
Mermaid. Semp. (Rob.)
M. Hardy. (Vei. 1895.)
Mignon. Soc. (Ben. 1911.)
Mikado.
Mira. (Des. 1885.)
Miranda.
Mireille.
∞Mme. Charrat (*corallina* × ∞Dregei).
Mme. (*Ch.*) Leuridan.
∞Mme. Delesseps (∞Argenteoguttata × *olbia*).
Mme. (*Fanny*) Giron. (Sch. 1875.) *Red Pollard.*
Mme. Henneau. (1936.)
Mme. Lionnet. (Vei. 1895.)
Mme. Mandrot. Bert.
Mme. Thibaut. (Lion. 1886.)
∞Mme. Wagner (*griffithi* × *rubrovenia*). (Vers. 1858.)
Model. (Vei. 1873.)
Monarch. (Vei. 1875.)
Moonbeam. Rex. (Rob.)
Moonlight.
Mouilliereana.
∞Mrs. (*Fred*) Scripps (*luxurians* × *scharffiana*). (1934.)
Mrs. John Heal. Soc. (1895.)
∞Mrs. (*Margaret E.*) Ham (*bracteata* × *luminosa*). (1935.)
∞Mrs. (*Mary*) Peace (*caroliniaefolia* × Ricinifolia). (Peace 1920.)
∞Mrs. Master (*pearcei* × ∞Sedeni). (W. Bull 1873.)
Mrs. J. A. Peterson. Soc. (Pete. 1915.)

BEGONIA, continued
Mrs. Schinkel. Cocc. (Rob.)
Mrs. Townsend. ∞ Heracleicotyle.
Mrs. (*W. A.*) Wallow. (Wal. 1928.)
Mrs. (*W. D.*) Harney. Cocc. (Rob.)
Mrs. W. L. Frevert. Rex. (Rob.)
Mrs. (*W. S.*) Kimball. (1913.)
∞ Munich (Credneri Compacta × *metallica*). Aren.
Musetta. (Rod. 1939.)
Mussolini. Luc. (Rob.)
Narcissiflora.
Neely Gaddis. (Gray 1923.)
Nelly Bly. Cyp. (Gray 1923.)
Neuchatel. Luc. (Rob. 1934.)
NewHampshire.
Noemi Mallet. (Lion. 1885.)
Noordi. (Gray 1923.)
Nuage Rose. (Lem. 1904.)
Nydia Starr. (Gray.)
Octavie Mallet. (Lion. 1886.)
Optima. Hiem.
Orange King. Hiem. (1931.)
Orrell. Luc. (Fleet. 1920.)
Otto Forster. Imp.
Otto Hacker.
∞ Ourqueen (*laciniata* × *rex*).
∞ Palomar (*peltifolia* × Ricinifolia). (Bow. 1937.)
Palu. Luc. (Rob.)
Papa Chevalier. (1921.)
Patriae. Soc. (Lem. 1908.)
Patsy Jean. (Swis.)
Paul Bruant. (Bru. 1888.)
Peachglow.
Peachleaf. Washington Street.
Peerless.
Perle Degard.
∞ Perle Lorraine (*polyantha* × *strigillosa*). (Lem. 1901.) *Bertha Vonlothringen.*
Picta.
Picta Marmorata. (1903.)
Picta Rosea.
Pink Cane.
Pink Perfection. Hiem.
Poincare. Rex. (Rob.)
∞ Polygonheracle (*heracleifolia* × *polygonata*). (Chev. 1938.)
∞ Pres. Carnot (*coccinea* × *olbia*). (Crozy 1884.)
∞ President (*coccinea* × *olbia*). (1892.)
President Deboureuilles. (Vei. 1895.)
Pres. Oury. (1921.)
∞ Prestoniensis (*cinnabarina* × *incarnata*).
Preussen.
Primadonna. Grac.
Prince. (1934.)
Prince Deliege. (1934.)
Prince Eugen. (Karl. 1928.)
Princeps.
∞ Princess Beatrice (*rosea* × *schmidtiana*). (Sut. 1886.)
Princess Clementine.
Prince Troubetzkoi. (Vers. 1858.)
Prof. Burvenich. (1890.)
∞ Prof. Gravis (*corallina* × *dichroa*) ('24.)
∞ Prof. Monoyer (*manicata* × *nelumbifolia*). (1938.)
Prunifolia. (Rob. 1920.)
Prunifolia Pink.
Pulvinata.
Queen.
Queenofwhites. (Hen. 1879.)
Queen Victoria. (1878.)

BEGONIA, continued
∞ Ramolo (*peltifolia* × Ricinifolia). (Bow. 1937.)
Redargentea. (Wai. 1927.)
Redcompta.
Red Pollard. Mme. (*Fanny*) Giron.
∞ Redveined Peltata (*peltifolia* × Ricinifolia). (Bow. 1937.)
× Reichenheimi.
∞ Rexcultorum.
Rhizocaulis.
Richard Robinson. (Rob. 1925.)
× Ricinifolia.
Rigi. Luc. (Rob.)
Robego. Cocc. (Rob.)
∞ Robert Emmet (*grandis* × *reichenheimi*). (Mal. 1863.)
Robusta.
× Rodwelli.
Rody. (Rod. 1939.)
Roezli Rosea.
∞ Roi Albert (*caroliniaefolia* × *roezli*). (1934.)
Roi Leopold. (1860.)
Rosabella. (Ben. 1926.)
Rosalind. Soc.
Rose. Cocc. (Rob.)
∞ Roseagigantea (*roezli* × *semperflorens*). (1883.)
Roseasuperba. Rosae. (Vei. 1878.)
Rose Queen. Soc.
Rosie Murphiski. Luc. (Rob.)
Rossi. (Rob. 1920.)
Royalty. (Wil.)
Rubego. (Rob.)
Rubellina. *Rubella.*
Rubrabamboo. (Shep.)
Rubraodorata. Cocc. (Rob.)
Rubrapink.
Rubrasuperba. (W. Bull. 1873.)
∞ Rubris (*rosaeflora* × ∞ Sedeni).
∞ Rutilans (*davisi* × *gracilis*).
Sachsen.
Sandersi; Sandersoni. ∞ Digswelliana.
Sarabelle. Luc. (Rob.)
Scandens.
Schmidtiana Rosea.
Schwabenland. (Sch. 1933.)
Sea Nymph. (Rob.)
Seashell. Semp. (Shep.)
∞ Sedeni (*boliviensis* × *veitchi*).
Semperflorens Elegans.
Semperflorens Gigantea.
Semperflorens Rosea.
Semperflorens Roseomultiflora.
Semperflorens Sturzi.
Shasta. Cocc. (Rob. 1930.)
Shasta Pink. Cocc. (Rob. 1930.)
Shrimp. Cocc. (Rob. 1930.)
Silvadore. (Few. 1937.)
Silverfleece.
× *Smithi.* ∞ Carrierei.
∞ Souvenir (*de Francois*) Gaulin (*coccinea* × *olbia*). (Crozy 1891.)
Speculata.
∞ Splendida Argentea (*robusta* × *xanthina*). (Van H.)
∞ Stella (∞ Sedeni × *veitchi*). (Vei. 1873.)
∞ Stuttgart (Credneri Compacta × *metallica*). (Aren. 1927.)
Subpeltata Nigra.
Subpeltata Nigricans.
∞ Suncana (*incana* × Sunderbruchi). (Till. 1938.)
Sunderbruchi. Her.

BEGONIA, continued
∞ Sunrise (*boliviensis* × ∞ Sedeni). (W. Bull. 1878.)
Superba-azella. (Gray 1926.)
Superbakathi. (Gray 1925.)
Superbakenzi. (Gray 1925.)
Superbalemorna. (Gray 1925.)
Suretta. Luc. (Rob. 1934.)
Sylvia. Inc. (Shep. 1900.)
Tanager. Semp. (Rob.)
Tanay. Luc. (Rob.)
Templini. (1901.)
The Pearl. Hein.
∞ Topaz (*boliviensis* × *veitchi*). (Van H. 1870.)
Triomphe Delemoine (*daedalea* × *socotrana*). (Lem. 189–.)
Triomphe Del'est. (Lem. 1905.)
∞ Triomphe Delorraine (*roezli* × *socotrana*). (Lem. 1887.)
∞ Triomphe Denancy (*daedalea* × *socotrana*). (Lem. 189–.)
Trout. ∞ Argenteoguttata.
∞ Tuberhybrida.
Turnford Hall. Soc.
Umbrata.
Undemille. Schar. (Rob.)
Undine. (Rob. 1900.)
Upright Feasti. Bessie Buxton.
Van-Ex. (Berry 1935.)
Vedderi. (Ved. 1922.)
∞ Veitchs Carmine (*coccinea* × ∞ Dregei). (Vei. 1895.)
Velma S. Cocc. (Rob.)
∞ Velvetqueen (*decora* × *laciniata*). (Lem. 1914.)
Ventura. (Weitz 1939.)
Venusta. (Lem. 1914.)
Vernon. Semp.
× Versaliensis.
Vesuve. (Lem. 1898.)
Vesuvius. Corbeille Defeu.
Viaude. (1897.)
Victoria. (Lind. 1859.)
Victor Lemoine. Inc. (1875.)
Viscountess Doneraile. (Vei. 1876.)
Washington Street. *Peachleaf.*
∞ Weltoniensis (∞ Dregei × *sutherlandi*).
Westport Beauty. Gustav Lund.
× Wettsteini.
Whitequeen. Rosae. (Hen. 1878.)
Wintercheer. Soc.
Wintermarchen. Semp.
∞ Woodmani (*pearcei* × *veitchi*).
Worthiana. Bol. (1874.)
Yosemite.
∞ Yvan Braconnier (∞ Dregei × *richardsiana*).
Zauberin. Semp. (Schm. 1927.)
Zelma. Cocc.
Zurich.

Begonia . . . . **Begonia**
Assamking B. . . . . **B. rex**
Brazil B. . . . . . . **B. brasiliensis**
Coral B. . . . . **B. corallina**
Curly B. . . . . **B. manicata crispa**
Davis B. . . . . **B. davisi**
Ecuador B. . . . . **B. ecuadoriensis**
Faures B. . . . . **B. faureana**
Glossy B. . . . . **B. nitida**
Green Imperial B. **B. imperialis smaragdina**
Imperial B. . . . . . . **B. imperialis**
Martin B. . . . . **B. martini**
Nepal B. . . . . **B. picta**
Pearce B. . . . . **B. pearcei**

BEGONIA, continued
Perpetual B. **Begonia semperflorens**
Scarlet B. . . . . . . **B. coccinea**
Shell B. . . . . . . **B. warscewiczi**
Slender B. . . . . **B. gracilis**
Socotra B. . . . . . . **B. socotrana**
Spotted B. . . . . . . **B. maculata**
Steel B. . . . . **B. metallica**
Trinidad B. . . . . **B. humilis**

BEILSCHMIED'IA . . . . . Slugwood
tarai'ri . . . . Taraire S.
ta'wa . . . . Tawa S.

BELAMCAN'DA (*GEMMINGIA; PARDANTHUS*)
chinen'sis (*Gemmingia c.; Pardanthus c.; P. sinensis*) . . Blackberrylily

BE'LIS . . . . . . **CUNNINGHAMIA**

Belladonna . . . . **Atropa belladonna**

Belladonnalily **Amaryllis belladonna**
Cape B. . . . . Callicore: **Callicore**

Bellflower . . . . **Campanula**
Allegany B. . . . . . . **C. divaricata**
Allioni B. . . . . **C. allioni**
Alpine B. . . . . **C. alpina**
American B. . . . . **C. americana**
American Harebell . . **C. petiolata**
Anatolian B. . . . . **C. macrostyla**
Armenian B. . . . **C. phyctidocalyx**
Aucher B. . . . . **C. aucheri**
Azores B. . . . . **C. vidali**
Bearded B. . . . . **C. barbata**
Bedstraw B. . . . . **C. aparinoides**
Behring B. . . . . . . **C. lasiocarpa**
Betony B. . . . . . **C. betonicaefolia**
Big Dalmatian B.
C. portenschlagiana major
Bluebell . . . . **C. rotundifolia**
Bluebells of Scotland . **C. r. superba**
Bluenod B. . . . . . **C. kolenatiana**
Bluestar B. . . . . **C. ramosissima**
Bristly B. . . . . . . **C. speciosa**
California B. . . . **C. prenanthoides**
Canterburybells . . . **C. medium**
Carpathian B. . . . . . **C. carpatica**
Chimney B. . . . . . . **C. pyramidalis**
Cliff B. . . . . **C. petraea**
Coventrybells . . . **C. trachelium**
Creeping B. . . . . **C. rapunculoides**
Cup-and-saucer B.
C. medium calycanthema
Dahurian B. . **C. glomerata dahurica**
Dalmatian B. . . **C. portenschlagiana**
Danesblood B. . . . . . **C. glomerata**
Diamond B. . . . . **C. rhomboidalis**
Dusky B. . . . . **C. pulla**
Elatines B. . . . . **C. elatines**
Erinus B. . . . . **C. erinus**
Flaxleaf B. . . . . **C. linifolia**
Fragile B. . . . . **C. fragilis**
Fuzzy B. . . . . **C. mollis**
Grassleaf B. . . . . . **C. ardonensis**
Great B. . . . . **C. latifolia**
Greek B. . . . . **C. drabifolia**
Grossek B. . . . . **C. grosseki**
Hurghalt B. . **C. latifolia hurghalti**
Italian B. . . . . **C. isophylla**
Kashmir B. . . . . . **C. cashmiriana**
∞ Kew B. . . . . ∞ **C. kewensis**
Leutwein B. . . . . . . **C. leutweini**
Lowcluster B. **C. glomerata acaulis**
Marsh B. . . . . **C. uliginosa**
Michaux B. . . . . **C. michauxioides**
Milky B. . . . . **C. lactiflora**
Near East B. . . . . . **C. propinqua**
Olympic B. . . . . **C. latiloba**

Bellflower, continued
Olympic Bluebell
Campanula rotundifolia olympica
Parry Bellflower . . . **C. parryi**
Peachleaf B. . . . . **C. persicifolia**
Pink Cup-and-saucer B.
C. medium rosea
Piper B. . . . . **C. piperi**
Portuguese B. . . **C. primulaefolia**
Poscharsky B. . . **C. poscharskyana**
Pyrenees B. . . . . . . **C. pyrenaica**
Radde B. . . . . **C. raddeana**
Rainer B. . . . . **C. raineri**
Rambling B. . . . . . . **C. patula**
Rampion B. . . . . . **C. rapunculus**
Robinson Bluebell
C. rotundifolia robinsoni
Robson B. . . . . **C. robsoni**
Sarmatian B. . . . . . **C. sarmatica**
Saxifrage B. . . . . . . **C. saxifraga**
Scheuchzer B. . . . . **C. scheuchzeri**
Shaggy B. . . . . **C. pilosa**
Showycluster B. **C. glomerata superba**
Siberian B. . . . . **C. sibirica**
Singlenod B. . . . . . **C. caespitosa**
Solitary B. . . . . **C. carnica**
Spiked B. . . . . **C. spicata**
Spotted B. . . . . **C. punctata**
Spurred B. . . . . **C. alliariaefolia**
Stansfield B. . . . . . **C. stansfieldi**
Steven B. . . . . **C. steveni**
Stone B. . . . . **C. saxatilis**
Swiss B. . . . . **C. cenisia**
Tongue B. . . . . **C. lingulata**
Top B. . . . . . **C. carpatica turbinata**
Tridentleaf B. . . . . . . **C. tridentata**
Velvet Bluebells of Scotland
C. rotundifolia velutina
Violet B. . . . . **C. bellidifolia**
Waldstein B. . . . **C. waldsteiniana**
White Bluebell . **C. rotundifolia alba**
White Canterbury-bells
C. medium a.
White Carpathian B. **C. carpatica a.**
White Chimney B. . **C. pyramidalis a.**
White Great B. . . . **C. latifolia a.**
White Italian B. . . . **C. isophylla a.**
White Olympic B. . . . **C. latiloba a.**
White Singlenod B. **C. caespitosa a.**
White Spotted B. . . . **C. punctata a.**
Wocke B. . . . . **C. wockei**
Wonder B. . . . . **C. mirabilis**
Yellowspike B. . . . **C. thyrsoides**
Zoys B. . . . . **C. zoysi**

BELLIDIAS'TRUM . . . **ASTER**
michel'i . . . . . . **A. bellidiastrum**

BEL'LIS . . . . Daisy
an'nua . . . . Spanish D.
peren'nis . . . . English D.
¢Golden (*lutea*) hv.
¢Helichrysoides
¢Monstrosa
rotundifo'lia . . . . . Morocco D.
—caerules'cens . . . Blueray M.D.

BEL'LIUM . . . . Bellium
bellidioi'des . . . . Stolon B.
—**niva'le** (*B. nivale*)
minu'tum . . . . Tiny B.

Bellvine . . . . **Rhodochiton**
Purple B. . . . . **R. volubile**

BELOPERO'NE . . . . . Beloperone
califor'nica . . . . . California B.
como'sa
gutta'ta . . . . . . Rattlesnake B.
tomento'sa

BELO'TIA . . . . Belotia
mexica'na . . . . Mexican B.

BENINCA'SA . . . . . . Waxgourd
his'pida (*cerifera*) . . . . Chinese W.

Bentgrass . . . . **Agrostis**
Alaska B. . . . . . . **A. aequivalvis**
Alpine B. . . . . **A. humilis**
Arctic B. . . . . **A. borealis**
Arcticwinter B.
A. hiemalis geminata
Autumn B. . . . . . . **A. perennans**
Awned Colonial B. **A. tenuis aristata**
Awned Spike B. **A. exarata monolepis**
Baker B. . . . . **A. bakeri**
Big Spike B. . . . **A. exarata ampla**
Black B. . . . . **A. nigra**
Blasdale B. . . . . . . **A. blasdalei**
California B. . . . . **A. californica**
Cloud B. . . . . **A. nebulosa**
Cocoos B. . Hort. *strain* of **A. palustris**
Colonial B. . . . . **A. tenuis**
Coos Bay B.
Hort. *strain* of **A. palustris**
Creeping B. . . . . . . **A. palustris**
Dune B. . . . . **A. pallens**
Elliott B. . . . . . . **A. elliottiana**
Halls B. . . . . **A. halli**
Henderson B. . . . . **A. hendersoni**
Howell B. . . . . **A. howelli**
Idaho B. . . . . **A. idahoensis**
Italian B. . . . . **A. interrupta**
Longtongue B. . . . **A. longiligula**
Metropolitan B.
Hort. *strain* of **A. palustris**
Oregon B. . . . . . . **A. oregonensis**
Pacific B. . . . . . . **A. retrofracta**
Pringle B. . . . . . **A. halli pringlei**
RhodeIsland B.
Hort. *strain* of **A. tenuis**
Ross B. . . . . **A. rossae**
Seashore B. Hort. *strain* of **A. palustris**
Seaside B. Hort. *strain* of **A. palustris**
Sequoia B. . . . . **A. lepida**
Sixweeks B. . . . . **A. exigua**
Spike B. . . . . **A. exarata**
Thin B. . . . . **A. diegoensis**
Thurber B. . . . . . . **A. thurberiana**
Velvet B. . . . . **A. canina**
Washington B.
Hort. *strain* of **A. palustris**
Water B. . . . . **A. verticillata**
Wind B. . . . . **A. spica-venti**
Winter B. . . . . **A. hiemalis**

BENTHAMAN'THA
caribae'a
ed'wardsi

BENTHA'MIA . . . . . **CORNUS**
fragif'era . . . . **C. capitata**
japon'ica . . . . **C. kousa**

BENTINCK'IA . . . . . . Bentinckia
See **PALM GENERA.**

BEN'ZOIN . . . . **LINDERA**
aestiva'le . . . . **L. benzoin**
—xanthocar'pum . **L. b. xanthocarpa**
grandifo'lium . . . . . **L. megaphylla**

BERBERIDOP'SIS . . . . Chilevine
coralli'na . . . . Coral C.

BER'BERIS . . . . Barberry

The thanks of the Editorial Committee are extended to S. B. Fracker, L. M. Ames, and others for criticism and valuable suggestions on this Barberry list.

The Mahonias (Mahonia, syn. Odostemon), which are united by some very conservative botanists with Barberry, are

BERBERIS, continued
here regarded as a distinct genus and are listed separately.

actinacan'tha
acumina'ta . **B. gagnepaini; B. veitchi**
ae'mulans
aetnen'sis . . . . Aetna Barberry
aggrega'ta (*giraldi* Veitch, *not* Hesse) Salmon B.
—pratt'i (*B. brevipaniculata; B. pratti*) Pratt B.

The B. brevipaniculata of horticulture is B. aggregata pratti.

—recurva'ta
amuren'sis (*B. vulgaris a.*) . Amur B.
—japon'ica (*B. regeliana*) Hakodate B.
angulo'sa . . . . . . Redbead B.
approxima'ta . . . . **B. dictyophylla a.**
aquifo'lium . . . . . . **Mahonia a.**
arido-ca'lida
arista'ta . . . . Spinetooth B.
—coria'ria (*B. coriaria; B. a. floribunda*, in part)
arista'ta Sims, *not* DC. . . **B. chitria**
asiat'ica (*hypoleuca*) . . Asiatic B.
atrocar'pa (*levis* Bean, *not* Franch.) Jetbead B.
atropurpu'rea . . . . **B. vulgaris a.**
∞ *aurico'ma* . . . . . ∞ **B. ottawensis**
beal'ei . . . . **Mahonia b.**
beania'na (*veitchi* Hort.) . . Beans B.
bergman'niae . . . . Bergmann B.
—acanthophyl'la . . . . Spiny B.B.
boscha'ni
brachyp'oda . . . . Yellowspike B.
brachyp'oda Schneid., *not* Maxim. **B. mitifolia**
bretschnei'deri . . . Purpleberry B.
brevipanicula'ta . . **B. aggregata pratti**
buxifo'lia (*dulcis*) . . . Magellan B.
—na'na . . . . Dwarf M.B.
—pyg'maea . . . . . Pygmy M.B.
—spinosis'sima . . . . Spiny M.B.
califor'nica . . . . **Mahonia dictyota**
callian'tha
canaden'sis . . . . . Allegany B.
candid'ula (*B. wallichiana pallida*) Paleleaf B.
∞ **chenault'i** (*gagnepaini* × *verruculosa*) ∞ Chenault B.
chilen'sis . . . . Chilean B.
chinen'sis (*serotina; sinensis* Desf., *not* DC. *nor* Koch.) . . Caucasian B.
chi'tria (*aristata* Sims, *not* DC.)
chocho'co . . . . **Mahonia c.**
circumserra'ta . . . . . Cutleaf B.
concin'na . . . . Dainty B.
congestiflo'ra
—hakeoi'des . . . . . **B. hakeoides**
consim'ilis
coria'ria . . . . **B. aristata c.**
cor'yi . . . **B. wilsonae subcaulialata**
cox'i . . . . Cox B.
crataegi'na . . . . . Hawthorn B.
cre'tica . . . . Cretan B.
dar'wini . . . . Darwin B.
—na'na . . . . Dwarf D.B.
—prostra'ta . . . Prostrate D.B.
dasystach'ya . . . . . Tangut B.
dealba'ta
∞ **declina'ta** (*?canadensis* × *vulgaris*) ∞ Drooping B.
∞ **—oxyphyl'la** (*?amurensis* × *canadensis*) ∞ Sharpleaf D.B.
densiflo'ra . . . . **B. turcomanica d.**
diaph'ana . . . . Reddrop B.

BERBERIS, continued
dictyoneu'ra
dictyophyl'la . Chalkleaf Barberry
—approxima'ta (*B. approximata*)
—epruino'sa
dictyo'ta . . . . **Mahonia d.**
dielsia'na . . . . Diels B.
dul'cis . . . . **B. buxifolia**

The name B. dulcis is sometimes misapplied also to the Currant Barberry, hort. var. of B. vulgaris.

dumic'ola
durobreven'sis
edgeworthia'na . . . Edgeworth B.
el'egans Hort. . . . . . **B. lycium**
∞ **emargina'ta** (*sibirica* × *vulgaris*) ∞ Notched B.
₵Britzensis. hv.
empetrifo'lia . . . . Crow B.
fascicula'ris . . . **Mahonia pinnata**
faxonia'na . . . . Faxon B.
fend'leri . . . . Colorado B.
fortun'ei . . . . **Mahonia f.**
francisci-ferdinand'i . . Pendant B.
fre'monti . . . . **Mahonia f.**
gagnepain'i (*acuminata* Stapf, *not* Franch.) . . . . Black B.
gilgia'na (*pubescens*) . . Wildfire B.
gir'aldi . . . . Girald B.
gir'aldi Hort. . . . . . **B. suberecta**
gir'aldi Veitch, *not* Hesse **B. aggregata**
grac'ilis . . . . **Mahonia g.**
haematocar'pa . . . . . **Mahonia h.**
hakeoi'des (*B. congestiflora h.*) Inkfruit B.
hartweg'i . . . . **Mahonia h.**
henrya'na . . . . Henry B.
heterophyl'la . . . . . Hedgehog B.
heterophyl'la Zabel., *not* Juss. ∞ **Mahonia h.**
heterop'oda . . . . . Turkestan B.
—oblon'ga . . . . **B. oblonga**
hook'eri (*wallichiana* Hook, *not* DC.) Hookers B.
—latifo'lia . . . . . . **B. xanthoxylon**
—vir'idis . . . . Green H.B.
∞ **hybrido-gagnepain'i** (*candidula* × *gagnepaini*) . . . ∞ False Black B.
hypokeria'na . . . . . Violetbead B.
hypoleu'ca . . . . **B. asiatica**
ilicifo'lia . . . . Holly B.
ilicifo'lia Hort., *not* Forst. ∞ **Mahoberberis neuberti**
ilien'sis
insig'nis . . . . Sikkim B.
—tongloen'sis
jamesia'na . . . . James B.
japon'ica Hort. . . . . . **B. thunbergi**
See also note on Mahonia japonica.
julia'nae . . . . Wintergreen B.
—na'na . . . . Dwarf W.B.
kansuen'sis . . . . Kansu B.
kewen'sis . . . . Kew B.
knight'i . . . . **B. xanthoxylon**
korea'na . . . . Korean B.
∞ **laxiflo'ra** (*?chinensis* × *vulgaris*)
₵Langeana (*B. langeana*) hv.
₵Oblanceolata
lecom'tei . . . . Lecomte B.
lepidifo'lia
lepto'clada . . . . . Thinstem B.
le'vis
le'vis Bean, *not* Franch. . **B. atrocarpa**
liechtenstein'i . . . . . **B. potanini**
linearifo'lia . . . . . Jasperbells B.
∞ **lologen'sis** (*darwini* × *linearifolia*) ∞ Lolog B.

BERBERIS, continued
×**lu'cida** . . . . . Shiny Barberry
lycioi'des
ly'cium (*elegans* Hort.; *ruscifolia*) Boxthorn B.
∞ **macracan'tha** (*aristata* × *vulgaris*) ∞ Purplebead B.
∞ **mee'hani** (*amurensis* × *?chinensis*) ∞ Meehan B.
∞ **mentoren'sis** (*julianae* × *thunbergi*) ∞ Mentor B.

This is Plant Patent No. 99. The plant in cultivation is a clon.

mitifo'lia (*brachypoda* Schneid., *not* Maxim.) . . . . Shansi B.
monta'na . . . . Andes B.
morrisonen'sis . . . . . Taiwan B.
mouillaca'na
nepalen'sis . . . **Mahonia napaulensis**
nervo'sa . . . . **Mahonia n.**
∞ *neuber'ti* . . . . . ∞ **Mahoberberis n.**
nevi'ni . . . . **Mahonia n.**
∞ **notab'ilis** (*heteropoda* × *?vulgaris*)
nummula'ria . . . . . Moneyleaf B.
—pyrocar'pa
oblon'ga (*B. heteropoda o.*) Bigflower B.
oritre'pha . . . . . . Bloodbead B.
orthobot'rys
∞ **ottawen'sis** (*thunbergi* × *vulgaris*; ∞ *auricoma*) . . . . ∞ Ottawa B.
—purpu'rea
pal'lens . . . . Pallid B.
parvifo'lia . . . . Ground B.
pinna'ta . . . . **Mahonia p.**
piperia'na . . . . **Mahonia p.**
poiret'i (*sinensis* DC. in part, *not* Desf. *nor* Koch.) . . . . Poiret B.
polyan'tha . . . . Chromeflower B.
potani'ni (*liechtensteini*) Longspine B.
—serra'ta
pratt'i . . . . **B. aggregata p.**
∞ **provincia'lis** (*sibirica* × *vulgaris?*)
pruino'sa . . . . . Hollygreen B.
pubes'cens . . . . **B. gilgiana**
pu'mila . . . . **Mahonia p.**
regelia'na . . **B. amurensis japonica**
∞ **rehderia'na** (*?canadensis* × *fendleri*) ∞ Rehder B.
re'pens . . . . **Mahonia r.**
replica'ta . . . . Curlleaf B.
reticula'ta . . . . Netvein B.
∞ **rubrostil'la** (*?aggregata* × *wilsonae*) ∞ Scarletbead B.
₵Autumn Beauty. hv.
₵Comet
₵Fireflame
₵Sibbertoet Coral
₵The Sparkler
ruscifo'lia . . . . **B. lycium**
sanguin'ea . . . . . Red-pedicel B.
—microphyl'la . . . Littleleaf R.B.
sargentia'na . . . . . . Sargent B.
serot'ina . . . . **B. chinensis**
sibir'ica . . . . Siberian B.
siebold'i . . . . Siebold B.
silva-tarouca'na . . . . Taroucan B.
sinen'sis . . . . **B. chinensis; B. poireti; B. thunbergi**
souliea'na (*stenophylla* Hance, *not* Lindl.) . . . . Soulie B.
∞ **spaeth'i** (*?chitria* × *?*) . . ∞ Spaeth B.
stapfia'na . . . . **B. wilsonae s.**
∞ **stenophyl'la** (*darwini* × *empetrifolia*) ∞ Rosemary B.
₵Autumn (*autumnalis*) hv.

BERBERIS, continued
¢BRILLIANT
¢BROADLEAF (*latifolia*)
¢CORALLINA
¢CRAWLEY GEM
¢DRABLEAF (*glauca*)
¢EVERFLOWERING (*semperflorens*)
¢IRWIN (*irwini*)
¢SCARLET (*coccinea*)
¢SLENDER (*gracilis*)
stenophyl'la Hance, *not* Lindl. . . . **B. soulieana**
subcauliala'ta . . . . **B. wilsonae s.**
suberec'ta (*giraldi* Hort.)
suble'vis (*B. wallichiana microcarpa*)
swa'seyi . . . . **Mahonia s.**
talien'sis
thibet'ica . . . THIBETAN BARBERRY
thunberg'i (*japonica* Hort.; *sinensis* K. Koch, *not* Desf. *nor* DC.) ⊔w JAPANESE B.
—atropurpu'rea . . . REDLEAF J.B.
—maximowicz'i . . . . CORAL J.B.
¢ARGENTEO-MARGINATA. HV. B. thunbergi
¢BOX (*minor; B. t. dawsoni*)
¢DWARF (*compacta*)
¢FLAME (*pluriflora*)
¢TRUEHEDGE COLUMNBERRY (*erecta*)
This is Plant Patent No. 110 and is a clon.
¢VARIEGATED (*tricolor*)
tisch'leri . . . . TISCHLER B.
triacanthoph'ora . . THREESPINE B.
trifolia'ta . . . **Mahonia trifoliolata**
tsarongen'sis . . . . . . TSARONG B.
turcoma'nica
—densiflo'ra (*B. densiflora*)
—integer'rima
umbella'ta . . . . . . HIMALAYAN B.
∞**vanfleet'i** (*veitchi* × *vulgaris*) ∞VANFLEET B.
veitch'i (*acuminata* Veitch, *not* Franch.) VEITCH B.
veitch'i Hort. . . . . . . **B. beaniana**
ver'nae . . . . VERNA B.
verruculo'sa . . . . . . WARTY B.
∞**vilmori'ni** (*diaphana* × *pruinosa*) ∞VILMORIN B.
vires'cens . . . . CINNAMONSTEM B.
—macrocar'pa . . . . BIGFRUIT C.B.
vulga'ris ⊔w . . . . EUROPEAN B.
—amuren'sis . . . . **B. amurensis**
¢CURRANT (*dulcis*) HV. B. vulgaris
¢GOLDEDGE (*aureo-marginata*)
¢PURPLE (*atropurpurea*)
¢SEEDLESS (*enuclea*)
¢SILVEREDGE (*marginata*)
¢WHITEFRUIT (*alba*)
¢YELLOW (*lutea*)
wallichia'na . . . . . . WALLICH B.
This name is sometimes misapplied to B. julianae and B. sargentiana. The true B. wallichiana of botanists is not yet in the trade.
wallichia'na Hook., *not* DC. **B. hookeri**
—microcar'pa . . . . . **B. sublevis**
—pal'lida . . . . . . **B. candidula**
wilcox'i . . . . **Mahonia w.**
wil'sonae . . . . WILSON B.
—globo'sa . . . . . . GLOBE W.B.
—stapfia'na (*B. stapfiana*) EGGFRUIT W.B.
—subcauliala'ta (*B. coryi; B. subcaulialata*) . . . . . PINKBERRY B.
xanthox'ylon (*B. hookeri latifolia; knighti*) . . . . JAVA B.
yunnanen'sis . . . . . . YUNNAN B.

BERCHE'MIA ⊔w . . . . SUPPLEJACK
giraldia'na . . . . GIRALD S.
hypochrys'a . . . . . UNDERGOLD S.
linea'ta . . . . STRIPED S.
polyphyl'la . . . . . . LITTLELEAF S.
racemo'sa . . . . JAPANESE S.
scan'dens ⊔w . . . . . . ALABAMA S.

BERGE'NIA (*MEGASEA*) . BERGENIA
cordifo'lia (*Saxifraga c.*) HEARTLEAF B.
crassifo'lia (*Saxifraga c.*). LEATHER B.
¢ORBICULAR (*orbicularis; Saxifraga o.*) HV.
¢VANHOUTTE (*vanhouttei; Saxifraga v.*)
ligula'ta (*Saxifraga l.*) . STRAPLEAF B.
—leichtlin'i (*Saxifraga leichtlini*)
—rose'a . . . . PINK S.B.
—specio'sa . . . . SHOWY S.B.
purpuras'cens (*Saxifraga p.*) PURPLE B.
strach'eyi (*Saxifraga s.*). STRACHEY B.

BERGERAN'THUS **MESEMBRYANTHEMUM**
See **SUCCULENTS.**

BERGEROCAC'TUS
See **CACTUS GENERA.**

BER'GIA ⊔w . . . . BERGIA
texa'na ⊔w . . . . TEXAS B.

BERLANDIE'RA
lyra'ta

BERMUDAGRASS . . . **Cynodon dactylon**

BERNARD'IA . . . . . . BERNARDIA
myricaefo'lia . . . . . SOUTHWEST B.

BER'RYA . . . . BERRYA
cordifo'lia . . . TRINCOMALIWOOD
quinquelocula'ris

BERRYLOBELIA . . . . **Pratia**
BEGONIALEAF B. . . . **P. begonifolia**
BIGTOOTH B. . . . . . . **P. macrodon**
CHATHAM B. . . . . . . **P. arenaria**
MAT B. . . . . **P. angulata**

BERRYRUE. **Cneoridium; C. dumosum**

Berseem . . . . . . CLOVER, EGYPTIAN: **Trifolium alexandrinum**

BERTERO'A . . . FALSEALYSSUM
inca'na (*Alyssum incanum*). HOARY F.

BERTHOLLET'IA
excel'sa . . . BRAZILNUT (*Niggertoe*)

BERTOLO'NIA . . . . . BERTOLONIA
macula'ta . . . . . . PURPLEVEIN B.
marmora'ta . . . . COPPER B.
pubes'cens . . . . . CHOCOLATE B.

BER'ULA ⊔w . . . . BERULA
erec'ta ⊔w . . . . STALKY B.

BESCHORNER'IA
yuccoi'des

BES'SERA (*PHARIUM*) . CORALDROPS
Some botanists put this genus in Milla.
el'egans (*Milla e.; Pharium e.*) SHOWY C.

BES'SEYA . . . . . . **SYNTHYRIS**

BE'TA ⊔w . . . . BEET
cic'la . . . . LEAF B.
saccharif'era . . . . . . SUGAR B.
vulga'ris ⊔w . . . . . COMMON B.
—marit'ima

BETELNUTPALM . . . . **Areca cathecu**

BETON'ICA . . . . . . **STACHYS**
superb'a . . . . **S. grandiflora s.**

BETONY . . . . **Stachys**
ALPINE B. . . . . **S. alpina**
ARTICHOKE B. . . . . . . **S. sieboldi**
BIG B. . . . . **S. grandiflora**
COMMON B. . . . . . . **S. officinalis**
CORSICA B. . . . . **S. corsica**
FIELDNETTLE B. . . . . . **S. arvensis**
FLORIDA B. . . . . . . **S. floridana**
GREEK B. . . . . **S. scardica**
HEDGENETTLE B. . . . . . . **S. annua**
HIMALAYA B. . . . . **S. sericea**
LAVENDERLEAF B.. . **S. lavandulaefolia**
MARSH B. . . . . **S. palustris**
MAUVE BIG B. **S. grandiflora superba**
MOUSEEAR B. . . . . . **S. germanica**
MT. TMOLUS B. . . . . . . **S. tmolea**
OREGON B. . . . . **S. ciliata**
PUFFNETTLE B. . . . . . . **S. bullata**
ROSY BIG B. . **S. grandiflora robusta**
ROUGHNETTLE B. . . . . . . **S. aspera**
SHADE B. . . . . **S. agraria**
SLENDERLEAF B. . . . . **S. tenuifolia**
TEXAS B. . . . . **S. coccinea**
WHITESPOT B. . . . . . . **S. sylvatica**
WOOLLY B. . . . . **S. lanata**

BET'ULA . . . . BIRCH
alaska'na . . **B. papyrifera neoalaskana**
al'ba (in large part) **B. pendula; B. pubescens**
See also B. platyphylla.
albo-sinen'sis . . . CHINAPAPER B.
—septentriona'lis . . . . BROWN C.B.
alnoi'des . . . . ALDER B.
atra'ta
∞**aura'ta** (*papyrifera* × *pubescens; hybrida*)
×**borggrevea'na**
chinen'sis . . . . CHINESE B.
∞**coeru'lea** (*coerulea-grandis* × *populifolia*) . . . . . . ∞BLUELEAF B.
coerulea-grand'is (*B. c. blanchardi*) BLANCHARD B.
coria'cea . . . . . SCANDINAVIAN B.
corylifo'lia
costa'ta
cylindrosta'chya
davur'ica . . . . DAHURIAN B.
delavay'i . . . . DELAVAY B.
—for'resti . . . . . . FORRESTS D.B.
east'woodae . . . . YUKON B.
er'mani . . . . ERMANS B.
—subcorda'ta
fontina'lis (*occidentalis*) ⊔w . WATER B.
—pi'peri (*B. piperi*) . . PIPER W.B.
for'resti . . . . FORRESTS B.
frutico'sa . . . . ALTAI B.
glandulif'era
glandulo'sa . . . . BOG B.
globospi'ca
gros'sa . . . JAPANESE CHERRY B.
hall'i . . . . HALLS B.
hu'milis
hy'brida . . . . ∞ **B. aurata**
×**interme'dia** (*nana* × *pubescens*)
∞**jack'i** (*lenta* × *pumila*) . ∞JACKS B.
jacquemontia'na . . JACQUEMONT B.
japon'ica . . . . **B. platyphylla j.**
—kamtschat'ica . . . **B. platyphylla k.**
—mandshu'rica . . . **B. platyphylla m.**
—szechuan'ica . . . **B. platyphylla s.**
kena'ica . . . . . . **B. papyrifera k.**
×**koehn'ei** (*papyrifera* × *pendula*)
len'ta ⊔w . . . . SWEET B.
—lacinia'ta . . . . . CUTLEAF S.B.

BETULA, continued
luminif'era
lute'a ⌊w . . . . . . Yellow Birch
—allegheniens'sis . . Allegany Y.B.
—macrole'pis
mandshu'rica . . . . **B. platyphylla m.**
—japon'ica . . . . **B. platyphylla j.**
—kamtschat'ica . . . **B. platyphylla k.**
—szechuan'ica . . . **B. platyphylla s.**
maximowiczia'na . . . Monarch B.
medwediew'i
middendorf'fi . . . Middendorff B.
na'na ⌊w . . . . . Dwarf Arctic B.
neoalaska'na . . . . **B. papyrifera n.**
ni'gra ⌊w . . . . River B.
occidenta'lis . . . . . . **B. fontinalis**
odora'ta . . . . **B. pubescens**
papyrif'era . . . . Paper B.
—an'drewsi . . . . . Andrews P.B.
—cordifo'lia . . . . Mountain P.B.
—eloba'ta . . . . Gaspe P.B.
—kena'ica (*B. kenaica*) ⌊w . Kenai P.B.
—mi'nor . . . . Dwarf P.B.
—montanen'sis . . . Montana P.B.
—neoalaska'na (*B. alaskana; B. neoalaskana*) . . . . . Alaska P.B.
—occidenta'lis . . . Western P.B.
—subcorda'ta . Northwestern P.B.
pen'dula (*alba* in part; *B. a. pendula; verrucosa*) . . European White B.
—oycovien'sis . . . . Shrubby W.B.
₵Cutleaf (*alba gracilis; a. laciniata; pendula gracilis*) hv. B. pendula Dalecarlia (*dalecarlica; B. laciniata*)
₵Purpleleaf (*alba purpurea; pendula purpurea*)
₵Pyramidal (*alba fastigiata; a. pyramidalis fastigiata*)
₵Slender (*tristis*)
₵Sticky (*viscosa*)
₵Youngs (*youngi*)
pi'peri . . . . **B. fontinalis p.**
platyphyl'la . . . . Asian White B.
—japon'ica (*B. japonica; B. mandshurica j.*) . . . . Japanese W.B.
—kamtschat'ica (*B. japonica k.; B. mandshurica k.*) Kamchatka W.B.
—mandshu'rica (*B. japonica m.; B. mandshurica*) . . . Manchu W.B.
—szechuan'ica (*B. japonica s.; B. mandshurica s.*) . Szechwan W.B.

Varieties kamtschatica and mandshurica have also been regarded, in the past, as varieties of *B. alba* L., a species not now recognized by botanists.

populifo'lia ⌊w . . . . Gray B.
₵Cutleaf (*laciniata*) hv.
₵Purple (*purpurea*)
₵Weeping (*pendula*)
potani'ni . . . . Potanin B.
pubes'cens (*alba; odorata*)
pu'mila . . . . Low B.
∞ **pur'pusi** . (*?lutea × pumila × glandulifera*) . . . . . ∞ Minnesota B.
rotundifo'lia ⌊w . . . . . Ground B.
∞ **sand'bergi** (*papyrifera × pumila glandulifera*) . . . . . ∞ Sandberg B.
schmidt'i . . . . Schmidts B.
turkestan'ica . . . . . Turkestan B.
u'tilis . . . . Himalaya B.
—pratt'i
verruco'sa . . . . . . **B. pendula**

BEURE'RIA . . . . Beureria
ova'ta . . . . Strongback B.

BEVERAGES (Plant Sources of)
See **ECONOMIC PLANTS, BEVERAGES.**

BIANCAE'A . . . . **CAESALPINIA**

BICU'CULLA . . . . . **DICENTRA**

BI'DENS ⌊w . . . . . . Beggarticks
aristo'sa ⌊w . . . . . . Bearded B.
atrosanguin'ea . **Cosmos diversifolius**
beck'i ⌊w . . . . Becks B.
bidentoi'des ⌊w . . . . . . Swamp B.
bipinna'ta ⌊w . . . . Spanishneedles
cer'nua ⌊w . . . . Nodding B.
como'sa ⌊w . . . . . Leafybract B.
conna'ta ⌊w . . . . . Purplestem B.
corona'ta ⌊w . . . . Crown B.
dahlioi'des . . . **Cosmos diversifolius**
discoi'dea (*Coreopsis discoides*) ⌊w Discoid B.
ea'toni . . . . Eatons B.
ferulaefo'lia . . . . . . Fernleaf B.
frondo'sa ⌊w . . . . Devils B.
grandiflo'ra
hu'milis
hyperbo'rea . . . . . Northern B.
lae'vis ⌊w . . . . Smooth B.
leucan'tha . . . . White B.
mi'tis ⌊w
pilo'sa . . . . Railway B.
polyle'pis (*involucrata; Coreopsis i.*) Coreopsis B.
trichosper'ma . . Ditchsunflower
triparti'ta . . . . Bur B.
vulga'ta ⌊w . . . . Tall B.

BIFRENA'RIA
See **ORCHID GENERA.**

BIGELO'VIA . . . . **APLOPAPPUS; CHRYSOTHAMNUS**
coronopifo'lia . . . . . **A. fruticosus**

BIGNO'NIA (*ANISOSTICHUS; PYROSTEGIA*) . . . . . Bignonia

Most of the horticultural varieties listed in the past as Bignonias are now referred to the genus Campsis, which see.

aequinoctia'lis . . . . . . **Cydista a.**
allia'cea . . **Adenocalymna alliaceum**
buccinato'rius . . . **Phaedranthus b.**
callistegioi'des . . . . **Clytostoma c.**
capreola'ta (*Anisostichus capreolatus; Doxantha capreolata*) . . Crossvine (*Quartervine*)
—atrosanguin'ea . . . Redpurple C.
chamberlayn'i . . . **Anemopaegma c.**
chere're . **Phaedranthus buccinatorius**
chinen'sis . . . **Campsis grandiflora**
fimbria'ta . **Stereospermum fimbriatum**
grandiflo'ra . . . . . . **Campsis g.**
hy'brida . . . ∞ **Campsis tagliabuana**
leucox'yla Vell. . . . **Tabebuia pallida**
leucox'ylon L. . **Tabebuia pentaphylla**
magnif'ica
pal'lida . . . . **Tabebuia p.**
pentaphyl'la . . . . . . **Tabebuia p.**
rad'icans . . . . **Campsis r.**
smith'i . . . . **Tecoma s.**
specio'sa . . **Clytostoma callistegioides**
stans' . . . . **Stenolobium s.**

BIGNONIA, continued
tweedia'na; unguis-cat'i **Doxantha unguis-cati**
venus'ta . . . . **Pyrostegia v.**
Bigroot . . . . **Megarrhiza**
California B. . . . . . **M. californica**
Oregon B. . . . . **M. oregana**

BIHA'I . . . . **HELICONIA**

BIJ'LIA
ca'na

BIKU'KULLA . . . . . . **DICENTRA**

Bilberry, Bog . **Vaccinium uliginosum**

BILDERDY'KIA . . **POLYGONUM**

Bilimbi . . . . **Averrhoa bilimbi**

BILLARDIE'RA . . . . . Billardiera
longiflo'ra . . . . Droopflower B.
—al'ba . . . . White D.B.
scan'dens . . . . Twinebranch B.

BILLBER'GIA . . . . Airbrom
amoe'na . . . . Showy A.
cap'pei . . . . Cappes A.
forgetia'na . . . . Forget A.
libonia'na . . . . Libon A.
mor'eli . . . . Morel A.
nu'tans . . . . Bluerim A.
pyramida'lis (*thyrsoidea*) Violetrim A.
rhodocya'nea . . . **Aechmea fasciata**
sanderia'na . . . . Sander A.
specio'sa . . . . Bluetip A.
zebri'na . . . . Zebra A.

Billian . . . . **Eusideroxylon**
Borneo B. . . . . **E. zwageri**

Billiondollar Grass . Japanesemillet: **Echinochloa crusgalli frumentacea**

Bil'tia va'seyi (*Azalea v.*) **Rhododendron v.**

Bimblebox . Eucalyptus, Poplarleaf: **Eucalyptus populifolia**

BINGHAM'IA (*HAAGEOCEREUS; PSEUDOESPOSTOA*)
See **CACTUS GENERA.**

BIO'TA . . . . **THUJA**

Birch . . . . **Betula**
Alaska Paper B. **B. papyrifera neoalaskana**
Alder B. . . . . **B. alnoides**
Allegany Yellow B. **B. lutea allegheniensis**
Altai B. . . . . **B. fruticosa**
Andrews Paper B. **B. papyrifera andrewsi**
Asian White B. . . . **B. platyphylla**
Blanchard B. . . **B. coerulea-grandis**
∞ Blueleaf B. . . . . . . ∞ **B. coerulea**
Bog B. . . . . **B. glandulosa**
Brown Chinapaper B. **B. albo-sinensis septentrionalis**
Chinapaper B. . . . . **B. albo-sinensis**
Chinese B. . . . . **B. chinensis**
Cutleaf Sweet B. . **B. lenta laciniata**
Dahurian B. . . . . . . **B. davurica**
Delavay B. . . . . **B. delavayi**
Dwarf Arctic B. . . . . . . **B. nana**
Dwarf Paper B. . **B. papyrifera minor**
Ermans B. . . . . **B. ermani**
European White B. . . **B. pendula**
Forrests B. . . . . **B. forresti**

Hort. var.; hv. = horticultural variety (or varieties); sp. = species (singular); spp. = species (plural).
₵ = clon; × (as a prefix) = hybrid; × (between scientific plant names) = crossed by; ∞ = polybrid; ⌊w = plant useful to wildlife.
See Glossary for definitions of clon, hybrid, and polybrid.

Birch, continued
Forrests Delavay B. **Betula delavayi forresti**
Gaspe Paper B. **B. papyrifera elobata**
Gray B. . . . . . . **B. populifolia**
Ground B. . . . . . **B. rotundifolia**
Halls B. . . . . **B. halli**
Himalaya B. . . . . **B. utilis**
∞ Jacks B. . . . . **∞ B. jacki**
Jacquemont B. . **B. jacquemontiana**
Japanese Cherry B. . . . **B. grossa**
Japanese White B. **B. platyphylla japonica**
Kamchatka W. B. **B. p. kamtschatica**
Kenai Paper B. **B. papyrifera kenaica**
Low B. . . . . **B. pumila**
Manchu White B. **B. platyphylla mandshurica**
Middendorff B. . . **B. middendorffi**
∞ Minnesota B. . . . . . . **∞ B. purpusi**
Monarch B. . . . **B. maximowicziana**
Montana Paper B. **B. papyrifera montanensis**
Mountain P. B. . . . **B. p. cordifolia**
Northwestern P. B. **B. p. subcordata**
Paper B. . . . . . . **B. papyrifera**
Piper Water B. . **B. fontinalis piperi**
Potanin B. . . . . **B. potanini**
River B. . . . . **B. nigra**
∞ Sandberg B. . . . . . **∞ B. sandbergi**
Scandinavian B. . . . . **B. coriacea**
Schmidts B. . . . . . . **B. schmidti**
Shrubby White B. **B. pendula oycoviensis**
Sweet B. . . . . **B. lenta**
Szechwan White B. **B. platyphylla szechuanica**
Turkestan B. . . . . **B. turkestanica**
Water B. . . . . **B. fontinalis**
Western Paper B. **B. papyrifera occidentalis**
Yellow B. . . . . **B. lutea**
Yukon B. . . . . . . **B. eastwoodae**

Birdbeak . . . . **Cordylanthus**
Bushy B. . . . . **C. ramosus**
Coastal B. . . . . . . **C. maritimus**
DeathValley B. . . . . **C. eremicus**
Wright B. . . . . **C. wrighti**

Birdcherry
See also Almond, Apricot, Bushcherry, Cherry, Chokecherry, Laurelcherry, Peach, Peachbrush, and Plum.
European B. . . . . **Prunus padus**
Harbinger E. B. . . **P. p. commutata**
Himalayan B. . . . . . **P. cornuta**
Korean B. . . . . . **P. padus laxa**
Palefruit European B. **P. p. leucocarpa**
Smallflower E. B. . **P. p. parviflora**
Yellow E. B. . . **P. p. chlorocarpos**

Birdlip . . . . **Ornithochilus**
Burmese B. . . . . **O. fuscus**

Bird-of-paradise-flower . . **Strelitzia**
Lance B. . . . . **S. parvifolia**
Queens B. . . . . **S. reginae**

Bird-of-paradise-flower . . Poinciana, Paradise: **Poinciana gilliesi**

Birdsnestfern . . . **Asplenium nidus**

Birdsnest Grass . . . . . . Gypgrass: **Sporobolus nealleyi**

Biriba . . . . **Rollinia deliciosa**

BISCHOF'IA . . . . . . Bishopwood
javan'ica (*trifoliata*) . . . . . Java B.

Biscuitroot
Bicolor B. . **Lomatium leptocarpum**

Biscuitroot, continued
Cous B. . . . . . . **Lomatium cous**
Geyer B. . . . . **L. geyeri**
Wallowa B. . . . . **L. circumdatum**
Wyeth B. . . . . . . **L. ambiguum**

BISCUTEL'LA
laeviga'ta
Bishopscap . . . Miterwort: **Mitella**

Bishopwood . . . . **Bischofia**
Java B. . . . . **B. javanica**

BISMARCK'IA . . . . . Bismarckia
See **PALM GENERA.**

Bisnaga . . . . . **Echinocactus visnaga**

Bistort . . . . **Polygonum**
See also Cornbind, Fleeceflower, Knotweed, Ladysthumb, Smartweed.
American B. . . . . **P. bistortoides**
European B. . . . . . . **P. bistorta**
Viviparous B. . . . . . **P. viviparum**

BISTOR'TA . . . . **POLYGONUM**
officina'lis . . . . **P. bistorta**

Bitterbrush . . . . **Purshia**
Antelope B. . . . . . **P. tridentata**
Desert B. . . . . . **P. t. glandulosa**

Bitterbush . . . . **Picramnia**
Florida B. . . . . . . **P. pentandra**
Jamaica B. . . . . . **P. antidesma**

Bittercress . . . . **Cardamine**
Angled B. . . . . **C. angulata**
Bulb B. . . . . **C. bulbosa**
Cuckoo B. . . . . **C. pratensis**
Double C. B. . . . . . . **C. p. plena**
Douglass B. . . . . . . **C. douglassi**
Heartleaf B. . . . . . **C. cordifolia**
Pennsylvania B. . . . . . **C. hirsuta**

Bitterorange
Celebes B. . . . . **Citrus celebica**
Ichang B. . . . . . **C. ichangensis**
Kerrs Melanesia B. **C. macroptera kerri**
Khasia B. . . . . **C. latipes**
Mauritius B. . . . . . . **C. hystrix**
Melanesia B. . . . . **C. macroptera**
Smallflower B. . . . **C. micrantha**
Smallfruit B. . . **C. m. microcarpa**

Bittersweet . . . . **Celastrus**
American B. . . . . . **C. scandens**
Anglestem B. . . . . . **C. angulata**
Christmas Oriental B. **C. orbiculata punctata**
Glaucous B. . . . . **C. glaucophylla**
Hooker B. . . . . **C. hookeri**
Korean B. . . . . . . **C. flagellaris**
Loesener B. . . . . . . **C. loeseneri**
Oriental B. . . . . . . **C. orbiculata**
Pale B. . . . . **C. hypoleuca**
Panicled B. . . . . . . **C. paniculata**

Bittertree . . . . **Picrodendron**
Jamaica B. . . . . . . **P. baccatum**

Bitterweed . . . Sneezeweed, Bitter: **Helenium tenuifolium**

Bitterwood . . . . **Trichilia**
Acurel B. . . . . . **T. oblanceolata**
Bagre B. . . . . **T. triphylla**
Catigua B. . . . . **T. catigua**
Mafura B. . . . . **T. emetica**
Musk B. . . . . **T. moschata**
Pimenteira B. . . . . **T. alta**
Trinidad B. . . . . . **T. cruegeriana**
White B. . . . . . . **T. spondioides**

BIX'A . . . . Anattotree
orella'na . . . . Anattotree

Blackberry . . . . **Rubus**
See also Dewberry and Raspberry. For horticultural varieties cultivated for their fruit, see **FRUIT AND EDIBLE NUT NAMES.**
Allegany B. . . . . **R. allegheniensis**
Broadleaf Evergreen B. **R. leucostachys**
Cutleaf B. . . . . **R. laciniatus**
Delicious B. . . . . . **R. pergratus**
Dwarf Red B. . . . . **R. pubescens**
Elmleaf B. . . . . . . **R. ulmifolius**
European B. . . . . . **R. fruticosus**
Evergreen Thornless B. **R. ulmifolius inermis**
Glandstem B. . . . . **R. glandicaulis**
Highbrush B. . . . . **R. ostryifolius**
Himalaya B. . . . . **R. procerus**
Link B. . . . . **R. linkianus**
Rands B. . . . . **R. canadensis randi**
Sand B. . . . . **R. cuneifolius**
Setose B. . . . . **R. setosus**
Swamp B. . . . . **R. hispidus**
Tataramoa B. . . . . . . **R. australis**
Thornless B. . . . . . **R. canadensis**
Trailing B. . . . . **R. macropetalus**
Tree B. . . . . **R. probabilis**
Vermont B. . . . . **R. vermontanus**
Yankee B. . . . . . . **R. frondosus**

Blackberrylily . **Belamcanda chinensis**

Blackboy . . . . Grasstree, Preiss: **Xanthorrhoea preissi**

Blackbristlepalm **Roscheria; R. melanochaetes**

Blackbrush . . **Coleogyne ramosissima**

Blackbryony . . . . **Tamus**
Common B. . . . . . . **T. communis**

Blackcalabash **Enallagma; E. cucurbitina**

Blackeyedsusan . . . **Rudbeckia hirta**

Blackfoot . . . . **Melampodium**
Plains B. . . . . . . **M. leucanthum**

Blackmangrove . . **Avicennia marina**

Blackpalm **Astrocaryum standleyanum**

Blackthorn . . . . . **Prunus spinosa**
See also Sloe.

Blackvarnishtree **Holigarna longifolia**

Blackwood, African **Dalbergia melanoxylon**

Bladderfern . . . . **Cystopteris**
Berry B. . . . . **C. bulbifera**
Brittle B. . . . . **C. fragilis**

Bladderflower . . . . **Araujia**
White B. . . . . **A. sericifera**

Bladdernut . . . . **Staphylea**
American B. . . . . **S. trifolia**
Bumalda B. . . . . **S. bumalda**
Chinese B. . . . . . . **S. holocarpa**
Colchis B. . . . . **S. colchica**
Dwarf American B. **S. trifolia pauciflora**
European B. . . . . **S. pinnata**
French B. . **S. colchica coulombieri**
Himalayan B. . . . . **S. emodi**
Kochs B. . . . **S. colchica kochiana**
Pink Chinese B. . **S. holocarpa rosea**
Sierra B. . . . . **S. bolanderi**

Bladderpod . . . . **Lesquerella**
Engelmann B. . . . . **L. engelmanni**
Globe B. . . . . **L. globosa**
Silver B. . . . . **L. argentea**

Bladdersage . . . . **Salazaria**
Mexican B. . . . . **S. mexicana**

BLADDERSENNA . . . . **Colutea**
CILICIAN B. . . . . **C. cilicica**
COMMON B. . . . . . **C. arborescens**
DWARF B. . . . . **C. a. bullata**
∞ HYBRID B. . . . . **∞ C. media**
ORIENTAL B. . . . . . . **C. orientalis**
PERSIAN B. . . . . **C. persica**
SLENDER B. . . . . **C. gracilis**

BLADDERWORT . . . . . . **Utricularia**
AWN B. . . . . **U. subulata**
COMMON B. . . . . **U. vulgaris**
FIBER B. . . . . **U. fibrosa**
FLOATING B. . . . . . . **U. inflata**
FLORIDA B. . . . . . . **U. floridana**
HORNED B. . . . . **U. cornuta**
LESSER B. . . . . **U. minor**
MARTINIQUE B. . . . . . **U. montana**
PURPLE B. . . . . **U. purpurea**
RUSH B. . . . . **U. juncea**

BLADEKELP . . . . **Laminaria**
SUGAR B. . . . . . . **L. saccharina**

Blad'hia japon'ica . . . . . . **Ardisia j.**

BLANDFORD'IA . . . CHRISTMASBELLS
margina'ta . . . . . . TASMANIA C.
no'bilis . . . . GOSFORD C.

Blazingstar
See **MENTZELIA.**

BLECH'NUM (*LOMARIA*) . BLECHNUM
See **FERN GENERA.**

BLEEDINGHEART . . . . . . **Dicentra**
CALIFORNIA B. . . . . **D. pauciflora**
COMMON B. . . . . . . **D. spectabilis**
CREAM B. . . . . . . **D. ochroleuca**
DUTCHMANS-BREECHES . **D. cucullaria**
FRINGED B. . . . . **D. eximia**
GOLDEARDROPS B. . . . **D. chrysantha**
LITTLE B. . . . . **D. pusilla**
OREGON B. . . . . **D. oregana**
PACIFIC B. . . . . **D. formosa**
SQUIRRELCORN . . . . **D. canadensis**
STEERSHEAD B. . . . . . **D. uniflora**
WHITE COMMON B. **D. spectabilis alba**
WHITE FRINGED B. . . . **D. eximia a.**

BLEPHARIDACH'NE . DESERTGRASS
See **GRASS GENERA.**

BLEPHARIGLOT'TIS . **HABENARIA**
See **ORCHID GENERA, HARDY TERRESTRIAL GROUP.**

BLEPHARONEU'RON
See **GRASS GENERA.**

BLEPHI'LIA
cilia'ta
hirsu'ta

BLESSEDTHISTLE . **Cnicus; C. benedictus**

BLET'IA
See **ORCHID GENERA.**

BLETIL'LA . . . . BLETILLA
See **ORCHID GENERA.**

BLIGH'IA . . . . AKEE
sa'pida (*Cupania s.*) . . . . AKEE

BLI'TUM . . . . **CHENOPODIUM**

BLOLLY . . . . **Torrubia**
LONGLEAF B. . . . . . . **T. longifolia**

BLOODLEAF . . . . **Iresine**
HERBST B. . . . . **I. herbsti**
JUBASBUSH B. . . . . **I. celosia**
LINDEN B. . . . . **I. lindeni**

BLOODLILY . . . . **Haemanthus**
BASEBALL B. . . . . . . **H. puniceus**
GREENBRACT LEAFY B.
H. magnificus insignis

BLOODLILY, continued
HAIRY WHITE B.
Haemanthus albiflos pubescens
KATHARINE B. . . . . . **H. katharinae**
LEAFY B. . . . . **H. magnificus**
LINDENS B. . . . . **H. lindeni**
LITTLELEAF SCARLET B.
H. coccineus coarctatus
NATAL B. . . . . **H. natalensis**
SALMON B. . . . . . . **H. multiflorus**
SCARLET B. . . . . . . **H. coccineus**
SNOW B. . . . . **H. candidus**
TIGER B. . . . . **H. tigrinus**
WHITE B. . . . . **H. albiflos**

BLOODROOT . **Sanguinaria; S. canadensis**

BLOODTRUMPET . . . . . **Phaedranthus**
MEXICAN B. . . . . **P. buccinatorius**

BLOODWOODTREE . . . . **Haematoxylon**
BRAZIL B. . . . . . . **H. brasiletto**
LOGWOOD . . . . **H. campechianum**

BLOOMER'IA . . . . . . BLOOMERIA
cleve'landi . . . . . CLEVELAND B.
cro'cea (*aurea*) . . . DARKSTRIPE B.

BLOWOUTGRASS . **Redfieldia; R. flexuosa**

BLOWWIVES . . . **Achyrachaena mollis**

BLUEBEARD . . . . **Caryopteris**
COMMON B. . . . . **C. incana**
MONGOLIAN B. . . . . **C. mongholica**

BLUEBELL . . . **Campanula rotundifolia**
OLYMPIC B. . . . . . **C. r. olympica**
ROBINSON B. . . . . . **C. r. robinsoni**
WHITE B. . . . . **C. r. alba**

BLUEBELLCREEPER . . . . . . **Sollya**
AUSTRALIAN B. . . . **S. heterophylla**

BLUEBELLS . . . . **Mertensia**
FRANCISCAN B. . . . **M. franciscana**
GREENLEAF B. . . . . . . **M. viridis**
LANCELEAF B. . . . . **M. lanceolata**
LEAFY B. . . . . **M. foliosa**
MOUNTAIN B. . . . . **M. ciliata**
OBLONGLEAF B. . . . **M. oblongifolia**
PANICLE B. . . . . . **M. paniculata**
SEA B. . . . . **M. maritima**
SHORTSTYLE B. . . . . **M. brevistyla**
SIERRA MOUNTAIN B.
M. ciliata stomatechoides
SMALL B. . . . . **M. longiflora**
SPINDLEROOT B. . . . . **M. fusiformis**
TALL B. . . . . **M. leonardi**
TWEEDY B. . . . . **M. tweedyi**
VIRGINIA B. . . . . . . **M. virginica**
YELLOWSTONE B. . . . . . **M. amoena**

BLUEBELLS OF SCOTLAND
Campanula rotundifolia superba
VELVET B. OF S. . . . **C. r. velutina**

BLUEBERRY . . . . **Vaccinium**
For hort. var. see **FRUIT AND EDIBLE NUT NAMES.**
∞ ATLANTIC B. . . . . **∞ V. atlanticum**
BIG WHORTLEBERRY **V. membranaceum**
BLUERIDGE B. . . . . . **V. pallidum**
BOG BILBERRY . . . . **V. uliginosum**
BOX B. . . . . **V. ovatum**
CANADA B. . . . . . . **V. canadense**
CAUCASIAN WHORTLEBERRY
V. arctostaphylos
CHERRY B. . . . . **V. praestans**
COLOMBIAN B. . . . . **V. floribundum**
COMMON DEERBERRY . **V. stamineum**
COWBERRY . . . . **V. vitis-idaea**
CRANBERRY . . . . **V. macrocarpum**
CREEPING B. . . . . . **V. crassifolium**
DELAVAY B. . . . . **V. delavayi**
DELICIOUS B. . . . . . . **V. deliciosum**
DINGLEBERRY . . **V. erythrocarpum**

BLUEBERRY, continued
DOWNY B. . . **Vaccinium atrococcum**
DWARF B. . . . . **V. cespitosum**
ENTIRELEAF HIGHBUSH B.
V. corymbosum caesariense
FARKLEBERRY . . . . . **V. arboreum**
FORMOSA B. . . . . **V. merrillianum**
GEORGIA B. . . . . **V. melanocarpum**
GROUND B. . . . . **V. myrsinites**
GROUSE WHORTLEBERRY **V. scoparium**
HAIRY W. . . . . **V. hirsutum**
HIGHBUSH B. . . . . **V. corymbosum**
HIMALAYA B. . . . . **V. dunalianum**
JAPANESE B. . . . . . . **V. japonicum**
KANSU B. . . . . . . **V. moupinense**
KOREAN B. . . . . **V. koreanum**
LOWBUSH B. . . . . **V. angustifolium**
MISSOURI FARKLEBERRY
V. arboreum glaucescens
MOUNTAIN COWBERRY
V. vitisidaea minus
MYRTLE LOWBUSH B.
V. angustifolium myrtilloides
MYRTLE WHORTLEBERRY . **V. myrtillus**
OLDHAM B. . . . . **V. oldhami**
ORIENTAL B. . . . . . . **V. bracteatum**
OVALLEAF WHORTLEBERRY
V. ovalifolium
PALELEAF HIGHBUSH B.
V. corymbosum glabrum
RABBITEYE B. . . . . . . **V. virgatum**
REDJAP B. . . . . **V. hirtum**
RED WHORTLEBERRY . **V. parvifolium**
ROCKYMOUNTAIN W. . **V. oreophilum**
SHORE COWBERRY . **V. vitisidaea majus**
SMALLCLUSTER RABBITEYE B.
V. virgatum tenellum
SMALL CRANBERRY . . . **V. oxycoccos**
SMALLS B. . . . . **V. smalli**
SMOOTHLEAF LOWBUSH B.
V. angustifolium laevifolium
SOUTHERN DEERBERRY . **V. neglectum**
SPRENGEL B. . . . . . . **V. sprengeli**
SZECHWAN B. . . . . **V. fragile**
TALLER DWARF B.
V. cespitosum arbuscula
THIBET B. . . . . . . **V. nummularia**
WESTERNBOG B. . . . **V. occidentale**
WESTERN SMALL CRANBERRY
V. oxycoccos intermedium
WHITEBERRY LOWBUSH B.
V. angustifolium leucocarpum
WHITEFRUIT DOWNY B.
V. atrococcum l.
WHITEFRUIT HIGHBUSH B.
V. corymbosum albiflorum
WHITEFRUIT MYRTLE WHORTLEBERRY
V. myrtillus leucocarpum

BLUECURLS . . . . **Trichostema**
FORKED B. . . . . . . **T. dichotomum**
PARISH B. . . . . **T. parishi**
VINEGAR B. . . . . . **T. lanceolatum**
WOOLLY B. . . . . **T. lanatum**

BLUE-EYEDGRASS . . . . **Sisyrinchium**
ARGENTINE B. . . . . . . **S. striatum**
ATLANTIC B. . . . . . **S. atlanticum**
BERMUDA B. . . . . . **S. bermudianum**
BRAZIL B. . . . . . . **S. pachyrhizum**
COLORADO B. . . . . **S. alpestre**
COMMON B. . . . . . **S. angustifolium**
DOUGLAS B. . . . . **S. douglasi**
GOLDEN B. . . . . . . **S. californicum**
IDAHO B. . . . . **S. idahoense**
MONTANA B. . . . . . **S. occidentale**
SPOKANE B. . . . . **S. boreale**
TEXAS B. . . . . **S. varians**
WESTERN B. . . . . **S. bellum**

Bluegrass . . . . **Poa**
Alaska B. . . . . . **P. paucispicula**
Alkali B. . . . . **P. juncifolia**
Alpine B. . . . . **P. alpina**
Annual B. . . . . **P. annua**
Arctic B. . . . . **P. arctica**
Autumn B. . . . . . **P. autumnalis**
Big B. . . . . **P. ampla**
Bigelow B. . . . . . . **P. bigelovi**
Bog B. . . . . **P. leptocoma**
Bolander B. . . . . . **P. bolanderi**
Bulbous B. . . . . . . **P. bulbosa**
Canada B. . . . . . . **P. compressa**
Canby B. . . . . **P. canbyi**
Chapman B. . . . . **P. chapmaniana**
Chisos B. . . . . **P. involuta**
Cusick B. . . . . **P. cusicki**
Douglas B. . . . . . . **P. douglasi**
Dune B. . . . . **P. confinis**
Early B. . . . . . . **P. cuspidata**
Fendler B. . . . . Mutton B.
Fowl B. . . . . **P. palustris**
Greenland B. . . . . . . **P. glauca**
Grove B. . . . . **P. alsodes**
Hotsprings B. . . . . . **P. laxiflora**
Howell B. . . . . **P. howelli**
Inland B. . . . . **P. interior**
Kellogg B. . . . . . . **P. kelloggi**
Kentucky B. . . . . . **P. pratensis**
Leiberg B. . . . . **P. leibergi**
Letterman B. . . . . **P. lettermani**
Longtongue Mutton B.
P. longiligula
Mt.Stuart B. . . . . . **P. curtifolia**
Mt.Washington B. . . . . **P. laxa**
Mutton B. . . . . . **P. fendleriana**
Nevada B. . . . . . **P. nevadensis**
NewMexico B. . . . **P. occidentalis**
Nodding B. . . . . **P. reflexa**
Oregon B. . . . . . **P. vaseyochloa**
Patterson B. . . . . . **P. pattersoni**
Pine B. . . . . **P. scabrella**
Plains B. . . . . **P. arida**
Pringle B. . . . . **P. pringlei**
Roughstalk B. . . . . . **P. trivialis**
SanBernardino B. . **P. atropurpurea**
Sandberg B. . . . . . . **P. secunda**
Seacliff B. . . . . . **P. unilateralis**
Seashore B. . . . . **P. macrantha**
Siskiyou B. . . . . . **P. rhizomata**
Skyline B. . . . . **P. epilis**
Slender B. . . . . . . **P. gracillima**
Sudetic B. . . . . **P. sudetica**
Tartar B. . . . . **P. tartarica**
Texas B. . . . . . **P. arachnifera**
Timberline B. . . . . . **P. rupicola**
Torrey B. . . . . . . **P. languida**
Tracy B. . . . . **P. tracyi**
Trinius B. . . . . . **P. stenantha**
Wasatch B. . . . . **P. curta**
Wheeler B. . . . . . . **P. nervosa**
Wolfs B. . . . . **P. wolfi**
Wood B. . . . . . . **P. nemoralis**
Woodland B. . . . . . **P. sylvestris**

Bluegum
Sydney B. Eucalyptus, Sydney Blue: **Eucalyptus saligna**

Tasmanian B. Eucalyptus, Tasmanian Blue: **E. globulus**

Bluejoint . . . Reedgrass, Bluejoint: **Calamagrostis canadensis**
Macoun B. . . . Reedgrass, Macoun Bluejoint: **C. c. macouniana**
Rough B. . . . . Reedgrass, Rough Bluejoint: **C. c. scabra**

Bluestem . . . . **Andropogon**
Angleton B. . . . . . . **A. annularis**
Australian B. . . . . **A. intermedius**
Awnless B. . . . . . **A. exaristatus**
Big B. . . . . **A. furcatus**
Bushy B. . . . . . . **A. glomeratus**
Cabanis B. . . . . **A. cabanisi**
Cane B. . . . . **A. barbinodis**
Colorado B. Bluestem Wheatgrass
Creeping B. . . . . . **A. stolonifer**
Delhi B. . . . . **A. foveolatus**
EastIndies B. . . . . **A. ischaemum**
Elliott B. . . . . **A. elliotti**
Florida B. . . . . . . **A. floridanus**
Gulf B. . . . . **A. maritimus**
Gulf Yellowsedge B.
A. virginicus hirsutior
India B. . . . . . . **A. carricosus**
Little B. . . . . **A. scoparius**
Low B. . . . . **A. pumilus**
Mohrs B. . . . . **A. mohri**
NewMexico B.
A. scoparius neomexicanus
Pinhole B. . . . . . **A. perforatus**
Pitted B. . . . . **A. pertusus**
Prairie B. . . . . Little B.
Sand B. . . . . **A. halli**
Sandhill B. . . . . Sand B.
SantaFe B. . . **A. hirtiflorus feensis**
Seacoast B. . . . . . . **A. littoralis**
Shortspike B. . . **A. brachystachyus**
Silky B. . . . . **A. sericeus**
Silver B. . . . . . **A. saccharoides**
Slender B. . . . . **A. tener**
Slim B. . . . . . **A. perangustatus**
Texas B. . . . . **A. cirratus**
Tracy B. . . . . **A. tracyi**
Wiry B. . . . . **A. gracilis**
Wrights B. . . . . **A. wrighti**
Yellowsedge B. . . . **A. virginicus**

Bluets . . . . **Houstonia**
Common B. . . . . . . **H. caerulea**
Creeping B. . . . . **H. serpyllifolia**
Florida B. . . . . . . **H. floridana**
Longleaf B. . . . . . **H. longifolia**
Purple B. . . . . . . **H. purpurea**
Tiny B. . . . . **H. minima**
Wrights B. . . . . **H. wrighti**

Blueweed . . Vipersbugloss, Common: **Echium vulgare**

BLUM'EA . . . . Blumea
lac'era . . . . Malay B.

BLUMENBACH'IA (*SALOA*) Stinglily
insig'nis . . . . Redspot S.
lateri'tia . . . . **Cajophora l.**

BOCCO'NIA . . . . Bocconia
arbore'a . . . . Tree B.
corda'ta . . . . **Macleaya c.**
frutes'cens . . . SouthAmerican B.
japon'ica . . . . **Macleaya cordata**
microcar'pa . . . . . . **Macleaya m.**

BOE'BERA . . . . **DYSSODIA**

BOEHME'RIA |w . . . Falsenettle
argen'tea . . . . Silverspot F.
cylin'drica |w . . . . Smallspike F.
macrophyl'la . . . . Bigleaf F.
niv'ea (*Urtica utilis*) . . . . Ramie
—tenacis'sima . . . . Rhea R.
platyphyl'la . . . . African F.
rugulo'sa
ur'era

BOENNINGHAUSE'NIA . . Chinarue
albiflo'ra . . . . White C.

BOERHAA'VIA |w . . . . Spiderling
annula'ta . . . . Wetleaf S.
coccin'ea . . . . Scarlet S.
erec'ta . . . . Erect S.
wat'soni |w . . . . Watson S.

Bogasphodel . . . . **Narthecium**
California B. . . . **N. californicum**
NewJersey B. . . . **N. americanum**

Bogbean . . . . **Menyanthes**
Common B. . . . . . . **M. trifoliata**

Boghyssop, Carolina
Hydrotrida caroliniana

Bogorchid, White . **Habenaria dilatata**

Bois de Rose . . . . Linaloe, Cayenne: **Aniba panurensis**

BOISDUVA'LIA . . . Spikeprimrose
densiflo'ra (*Godetia d.; Oenothera d.*)
Dense S.
stric'ta . . . . Brook S.

BOLAN'DRA . . . . Bolandra
orega'na . . . . Oregon B.

BOLDE'A; BOLDU' . . . . **PEUMUS**
fra'grans . . . . **P. boldus**

Boldutree . . . . . **Peumus boldus**

BOLE'TUS . . . . Boletus
bi'color
chrysen'teron
ed'ulis . . . . Edible B.
felle'us . . . . Bitter B.
granula'tus
lute'us

BOL'LEA . . . **ZYGOPETALUM**
See **ORCHID GENERA**.

BOLTO'NIA . . . . Boltonia
asteroi'des (*glastifolia*) . . White B.
latisqua'ma . . . . Violet B.
—na'na . . . . Dwarf V.B.

BOLUSAN'THUS
specio'sus (*Lonchocarpus s.*)

BOMA'REA . . . . Bomarea
acutifo'lia
bridgesia'na . . . . Bridges B.
caldasia'na . . . . Caldas B.
—macrophyl'la . . . . Bigleaf C.B.
car'deri . . . . Spotted B.
chontalen'sis
ed'ulis . . . . Edible B.
multiflo'ra . . . . . Denseflower B.
oligan'tha . . . . Inca B.
ova'ta
patacocen'sis (*conferta*) . . Andes B.
salsil'la (*oculata*) . . . . Salsilla B.
shuttleworth'i . . . . . Eggtuber B.
werck'lei . . . . Orange B.

BOM'BAX . . . . Bombax
buonopozen'ce
cei'ba . . . . Malabar B.
flam'meum . . . . Flame B.
malabar'icum . . **Salmalia malabarica**

BOMBYCIDEN'DRON
vidalia'num

Boneset . . . **Eupatorium perfoliatum**

BON'TIA . . . . Barbados-olive
daphnoi'des . . . . . Barbados-olive

Bonyberry . . . . **Osteomeles**
Chinese B. . . . . . . **O. schwerinae**
Littleleaf C. B. . . **O. s. microphylla**
Polynesian B. . . . **O. anthyllidifolia**
Roundleaf B. . . . . . **O. subrotunda**

BOOJAMTREE . . . . **Idria; I. columnaris**

BOOPH'ANE (*BUPHANE*) COWBANELILY
dis'ticha

BOOT'TIA . . . . BOOTTIA
corda'ta . . . . HEARTLEAF B.

BORA'GO . . . . BORAGE
laxiflo'ra . . . . CORSICAN B.
officina'lis . . . . COMMON B.
orienta'lis . . . . . **Trachystemon o.**

BORAS'SUS
See **PALM GENERA.**

BORNEOCAMPHOR . . . . **Dryobalanops**
COMMON B. . . . . . . **D. aromatica**

BOR'NOA . . . . **ATTALEA**
See **PALM GENERA.**

BORO'NIA . . . . BORONIA
ala'ta . . . . WING B.
ela'tior . . . . TALL B.
heterophyl'la . . . . . VARIEDLEAF B.
megastig'ma . . . . SWEET B.
purdiea'na . . . . PURDY B.
spathula'ta . . . . BATTLEDORE B.
vimi'nea

BORRE'RA . . . . BORRERA
ash'neyi . . . . CHUTCHELEERA B.
fla'vicans . . . . YELLOW B.

BORRICH'IA |W . . . . . SEA-OXEYE
arbores'cens |W . . . . . . TREE S.
frutes'cens |W . . . . . . BUSHY S.

BORZICAC'TUS
See **CACTUS GENERA.**

BOSBERRY . . . . **Bosea**
AMHERST B. . . . . **B. amherstiana**
VARIEGATED A. B. . . . **B. a. variegata**

Bos'cia undula'ta . . **Vepris lanceolata**

BO'SEA . . . . BOSBERRY
amherstia'na . . . . . AMHERST B.
—variega'ta . . . VARIEGATED A.B.

BOSSE'KIA . . . . **RUBUS**

BOSSIAE'A . . . . SUNBUSH
aquifo'lium . . . . HOLLY S.
bilo'ba . . . . TWOLOBE S.
buxifo'lia . . . . BOXLEAF S.
eriocar'pa . . . . . . WOOLLEAF S.
orna'ta . . . . SHOWY S.

BOSTONFERN
Nephrolepis exaltata bostoniensis
For the varieties of Bostonfern, see **NEPHROLEPIS.**

BOSWEL'LIA . . . . FRANKINCENSE
car'teri . . . . BIBLE F.
frerea'na . . . . ELEMI F.
serra'ta . . . . INDIA F.

Botree . . FIG, BOTREE: **Ficus religiosa**

BOTRY'CHIUM . . . . . GRAPEFERN
See **FERN GENERA.**

BOTRYOSTE'GE . . **TRIPETALEIA**

BOTTLEBRUSH . . . . . . **Callistemon**
AUSTRALIAN WILLOW B.
C. salignus australis
BRILLIANT B. . . . . . **C. splendens**
CUNNINGHAM B. . . . **C. cunninghami**
GREEN B. . . . . . . **C. viridiflorus**
GREEN WILLOW B. . . **C. salignus v.**
HYBRID B. . . . . . . **×C. hybridus**
LEMON B. . . . . . . **C. lanceolatus**

BOTTLEBRUSH, continued
NARROWLEAF B. . **Callistemon linearis**
PINELEAF B. . . . . . . **C. pinifolius**
SCARLET B. . . . . . . **C. coccineus**
SHOWY B. . . . . **C. speciosus**
STIFF B. . . . . **C. rigidus**
STOUT B. . . . . **C. robustus**
WILLOW B. . . . . **C. salignus**

BOTTLEBRUSHGRASS . **Hystrix; H. patula**
CALIFORNIA B. . . . . **H. californica**

BOTTLEPALM . . **Hyophorbe amaricaulis**

BOTTLETREE . . . . . . **Brachychiton**
BARREL B. . . . . . . **B. rupestris**
BIDWILL B. . . . . **B. bidwilli**
FIRE B. . . . . **B. luridus**
FLAME B. . . . . **B. acerifolius**
KURRAJONG B. . . . . . **B. populneus**
LACEBARK B. . . . . . . **B. discolor**

BOUGAINVIL'LEA (*BUGINVILLEA*)
BOUGAINVILLEA
The name of this genus was originally spelled Buginvillea, but Bougainvillea is conserved over Buginvillea.

berberidifo'lia . . BARBERRYLEAF B.
brasilien'sis . . . . . **B. spectabilis**
campanula'ta . . . . BLUEBELL B.
gla'bra . . . . LESSER B.
₵CYPHERS (*cypheri*) HV.
₵PAPERFLOWER (*sanderiana*)
₵VARIEGATED (*variegata*)
infes'ta
lehmannia'na . . . . . LEHMANN B.
lindleya'na . . . . . . LINDLEY B.
malmea'na
modes'ta
pachyphyl'la . . . . THICKLEAF B.
peruvia'na . . . . PERU B.
prae'cox . . . . EARLY B.
reful'gens . . . . SHINY B.
Perhaps not more than a var. or form of B. spectabilis.

rosea-specio'sa . . . . SHOWYROSE B.
spectab'ilis (*brasiliensis*) . . BRAZIL B.
₵BRICKRED (*lateritia*) HV.
₵CRIMSON LAKE
₵PRAETORIUS
spino'sa . . . . SPINY B.
stipita'ta
troll'i . . . . TROLLS B.
₵CATALINA ROSE (*rosa-catalina*) HV.

₵CAUCASIAN (*caucasica*) HV. Bougainvillea
₵GRAND (*formosa*)
₵HARRIS (*harrisi*)
HARVARD NO. 1
₵MAGNIFICA
MAUD CHETTLEBURG
MRS. BUTT
₵OFFICINALIS
THOMAS (*thomasi*)

BOUGAINVILLEA . . . . **Bougainvillea**
BARBERRYLEAF B. . **B. berberidifolia**
BLUEBELL B. . . . . **B. campanulata**
BRAZIL B. . . . . . . **B. spectabilis**
EARLY B. . . . . **B. praecox**
LEHMANN B. . . . . **B. lehmanniana**
LESSER B . . . . **B. glabra**
LINDLEY B. . . . . . . **B. lindleyana**
PERU B. . . . . **B. peruviana**
SHINY B. . . . . **B. refulgens**
SHOWYROSE B. . . **B. rosea-speciosa**
SPINY B. . . . . **B. spinosa**
THICKLEAF B. . . . . **B. pachyphylla**
TROLLS B. . . . . **B. trolli**

BOUNCINGBET . . **Saponaria officinalis**

BOURBONTEA ORCHID **Angraecum fragrans**

BOURRE'RIA . . . . . . STRONGBARK
ova'ta . . . . OVALLEAF S.

BOUSSINGAUL'TIA . . MADEIRAVINE
ramo'sa (*baselloides*) MIGNONETTE M.

BOUTELOU'A . . . . GRAMA
See **GRASS GENERA.**

BOUVAR'DIA . . . . . . BOUVARDIA
hum'boldti . . . . SWEET B.
hy'brida . . . . HYBRID B.
leian'tha
longiflo'ra
ternifo'lia (*triphylla*) . . SCARLET B.

BOWDICH'IA
nit'ida
virgilioi'des . . . . ALCORNOCO

BOWE'NIA . . . . BOWENIA
See **CYCAD GENERA.**

BOWERPLANT, BRAZIL
Adhatoda cydoniaefolia

BOWIE'A (*SCHIZOBASOPSIS*)
BOWIEA
Bowiea is conserved under International Rules.

kilimandschar'ica . . KILIMANJARO B.
volu'bilis (*Schizobasopsis v.*)
COMMON B.

Probably the below are all clons:
ALFRED NEUNER. HV. Bowiea
BRIDAL WREATH
BRIDESMAID
BRILLIANT
CANDIDISSIMA
DAZZLER
ELEGANS
FLAVESCENS
FLAVESCENS DOUBLE (*florepleno*)
JASMINOIDES
KING OF (*the*) SCARLETS
MAIDENS BLUSH
MRS. ROBERT GREEN
PRESIDENT CLEVELAND
PRESIDENT GARFIELD
PRIORY BEAUTY
PURITY
SANG LORRAINE
THE BRIDE
THOMAS MEEHAN
TRIOMPHE DE NANCY
VICTOR LEMOINE
VREELAND (*Vreelandi; davidsoni*)
VULCAN
WHITE BOUQUET

BOWKER'IA . . . . . SLIPPERTREE
gerrardia'na . . . . . . GERRARD S.
triphyl'la . . . . . . NARROWLIP S.

BOWMANSROOT . . . **Gillenia trifoliata**

BOX . . . . **Buxus**
CHINESE LITTLELEAF B.
B. microphylla sinica
COMMON B. . . . . **B. sempervirens**
HARLANDS B. . . . . **B. harlandi**
JAPANESE LITTLELEAF B.
B. microphylla japonica
KOREAN L. B. . . . . **B. m. koreana**
LITTLELEAF B. . . . . **B. microphylla**
MACOWAN B. . . . . . **B. macowani**
SPANISH B. . . . . . . **B. balearica**
WALLICHIAN B. . . . **B. wallichiana**

BOXELDER . . . . **Acer negundo**
ARIZONA B. . . . . **A. n. arizonicum**
CALIFORNIA B. . . **A. n. californicum**
INLAND B. . . . . . . **A. n. interius**
TEXAS B. . . . . . . **A. n. texanum**
VIOLET B. . . . . . **A. n. violaceum**

BOXLILY . . . . **Philesia**
MAGELLAN B. . . . **P. magellanica**

BOXORANGE . . . . **Severinia**
BOUQUET B. . . . . . **S. paniculata**
CHINESE B. . . . . . . **S. buxifolia**
DWARF C. B. . . . **S. b. subinermis**
NARROWLEAF B. . . . . . **S. linearis**
PHILIPPINE B. . . . . . . **S. disticha**

BOYKIN'IA . . . . BOYKINIA
ela'ta (*occidentalis*) . SANTALUCIA B.
james'i . . . . JAMES B.
ma'jor . . . . SIERRA B.
rotundifo'lia . . . . SANGABRIEL B.
tellimoi'des (*Saxifraga t.*) JAPANESE B.

BRACHIA'RIA . . . . . SIGNALGRASS
See **GRASS GENERA.**

BRACHYCE'REUS
See **CACTUS GENERA.**

BRACHYCHI'TON . . . BOTTLETREE
acerifo'lius (*Sterculia acerifolia*)
FLAME B. (*Flametree*)
bid'willi (*Sterculia b.*) . . BIDWILL B.
dis'color (*Sterculia d.*) . LACEBARK B.
lur'idus (*Sterculia lurida*) . . FIRE B.
popul'neus (*Sterculia diversifolia*)
KURRAJONG B.
rupes'tris (*Sterculia r.*) . BARREL B.

BRACHYCO'ME
iberidifo'lia . . . . SWANRIVERDAISY

BRACHYELY'TRUM . . . SHORTHUSK
See **GRASS GENERA.**

BRACHYGLOT'TIS
rangio'ra
repan'da
—variega'ta

BRACHYLAE'NA
denta'ta
ellip'tica

BRACHYPO'DIUM . . FALSEBROME
See **GRASS GENERA.**

BRACHYSE'MA . . . . . . PEABUSH
acumina'tum
lanceola'tum . . . . . LANCELEAF P.

BRACHYSTE'GIA . . BARKCLOTHTREE
spicaefor'mis . . . . . . SPIKE B.

BRACKEN . . . . **Pteridium**
EASTERN B. . . . . . **P. latiusculum**
TAILED B. . . . . **P. caudatum**
WESTERN B. . **P. aquilinum pubescens**

BRACKETPLANT . . **Chlorophytum elatum**
VARIEGATED B. . . . **C. e. variegatum**

BRADBUR'YA . . **CENTROSEMA**

BRAGAN'TIA . . . . . . BRAGANTIA
wal'lichi . . . . ALPAMROOT B.

BRAHE'A (*ACOELORRAPHE* in part)
BRAHEAPALM
See **PALM GENERA.**

BRAKE . . . . **Pteris**
ALEXANDRA B. . . . . **P. cretica** HV.
AUSTRALIAN B. . . . . . **P. tremula**
CHARLESWORTH B. . **P. multifida** HV.
CHILDS B. . . . . . . **P. cretica** HV.

BRAKE, continued
CHINESE B. . . . . . . **Pteris vittata**
CRESTED SPIDER B. . **P. multifida** HV.
CRETAN B. . . . . **P. cretica**
DRINKWATER B. . . . **P. cretica** HV.
DUTRE B. . . . . **P. cretica** HV.
FOREST B. . . . . **P. umbrosa**
GAUTHER B. . . . . . **P. cretica** HV.
MAYS B . . . . **P. cretica** HV.
MOORES B.. . **Anopteris hexagona** HV.
OUVRARD B. . . . . **P. multifida** HV.
RIBBON B. . . . . . . **P. cretica** HV.
RIVERTON B. . . . . . **P. cretica** HV.
RUSTY B. . . . . **B. longifolia**
SIEBOLD B. . . . . . **P. ensiformis** HV.
SPIDER B. . . . . **P. multifida**
STRIPED B. . . . **P. quadriaurita** HV.
SWORD B. . . . . **P. ensiformis**
TALL CRETAN B. . . . **P. cretica** HV.
TRISECT B. . . . . **P. tripartita**
VICTORIA B. . . . **P. ensiformis** HV.
WILSON B. . . . . . . **P. cretica** HV.
WIMSETT B. . . . . . **P. cretica** HV.

BRAMBLE, ARCTIC . . . **Rubus arcticus**

BRAMBLEPALM . . . . **Desmoncus**
PICMOC B. . . . . **D. horridus**

Bra'mia rotundifo'lia . . . . **Bacopa r.**

BRASE'NIA W . . . . . WATERSHIELD
schre'beri (*peltata*) W . SCHREBER W.

BRASILIOPUN'TIA . . **OPUNTIA**
See **CACTUS GENERA.**

BRASSAI'A
actinophyl'la (*Schefflera a.*)

BRASSAVO'LA
See **ORCHID GENERA.**

BRASSBUTTONS . . . . **Cotula**
BIRD B. . . . . . . **C. coronopifolia**
NEWZEALAND B. . . . . **C. squalida**
SOUTHERN B. . . . . . **C. australis**

BRAS'SIA . . . . SPIDERORCHID
See **ORCHID GENERA.**

BRAS'SICA (*SINAPIS*) W
aceph'ala . . . . . . **B. oleracea a.**
—botry'tis . . . . . . **B. oleracea b.**
adpres'sa . . . . . . **B. geniculata**
al'ba . . . . **B. hirta**
albogla'bra . . . CABBAGE MUSTARD
arven'sis . . . . **B. kaber**
botry'tis . . . . . . **B. oleracea b.**
campes'tris W . . . . . BIRD RAPE
—oleif'era . . . . . OILNAVEW B.R.
capita'ta . . . . . . **B. oleracea c.**
caulora'pa . . **B. oleracea gongylodes**
chinen'sis. PAKCHOI (*Chinese Cabbage*)
cre'tica
elonga'ta
genicula'ta (*adpressa*)
hir'ta (*alba; Sinapis a.*)
WHITE MUSTARD
insula'ris
japon'ica . . . . . . JAPANESE M.
jun'cea (*rugosa; Sinapis j.*) . INDIA M.
—crispifo'lia (*japonica* Hort.)
POTHERB M.
ka'ber (*arvensis; Sinapis a.*) W
CHARLOCK
napobras'sica . . . . . . RUTABAGA
na'pus W . . . . WINTER RAPE
narino'sa
ni'gra W . . . . . . BLACK MUSTARD
olera'cea W . . . . . WILD CABBAGE
—aceph'ala (*B. acephala*) . . . KALE
(*Borecole; Collard*)

BRASSICA oleracea acephala, continued
FLANDRE. HV.
JERSEYWINTER
MARROW
PAIMIER
POITEAU
SARTHE
—botry'tis (*B. acephala b.; B. botrytis*)
CAULIFLOWER
¢BROCCOLI. HV.
—capita'ta (*B. capitata*) . . CABBAGE
—gemmif'era . . BRUSSELS SPROUTS
—gongylo'des (*B. caulorapa*)
KOHLRABI
—ital'ica . . . ASPARAGUS BROCCOLI
—tronchu'da . . PORTUGUESE KALE
parachinen'sis . . . FALSE PAKCHOI
pekinen'sis (*pe-tsai*) . . PETSAI (*Celery Cabbage; Chinese C.; Peking C.*)
ra'pa . . . . TURNIP
rugo'sa . . . . **B. juncea**

BRASSOCATTLAE'LIA
See **ORCHID GENERA.**

BRASSOCAT'TLEYA
See **ORCHID GENERA.**

BRASSO-CATTLEYA-LAE'LIA
BRASSOCATTLAELIA
See **ORCHID GENERA.**

BRASSOLAE'LIA
See **ORCHID GENERA.**

BRAUNE'RIA . . . . **ECHINACEA**

Brava, Cocuiza . . FURCREA, HUMBOLDT: **Furcraea humboldtiana**

BRAVAI'SIA
floribun'da . . . . . . JIGGERWOOD

BRAVO'A
geminiflo'ra . . MEXICAN TWINBLOOM

BRA'YERA . . . . **HAGENIA**
anthelmin'tica . . . . **H. abyssinica**

Brazilcherry PITANGA: **Eugenia uniflora**

Braziliancherry . . . . . GRUMICHAMA: **Eugenia dombeyi**

BRAZILIAN-SATINWOOD
Euxylophora paraensis

BRAZILNUT . . . **Bertholletia excelsa**

BRAZILTRUMPET . . . . **Odontadenia**
REDTUBE B. . . . . . . **O. speciosa**

BRAZILWOOD . . **Caesalpinia brasiliensis**
PRICKLY B. . . . . **C. echinata**

BREADFRUIT . . . . . **Artocarpus altilis**
CHAPLASH B. . . . . . . **A. chaplasha**
JAVA B. . . . . **A. blumei**

BREADNUTTREE . . . . **Brosimum**
COW B. . . . . **B. utile**
PARA B. . . . . **B. paraense**
RAMON B. . . . . **B. alicastrum**

BREATH-OF-HEAVEN . . . . **Coleonema**
PINK B. . . . . **C. pulchrum**
WHITE B. . . . . **C. album**

BREVOOR'TIA . . FLORALFIRECRACKER
ida-ma'ia (*coccinea; Brodiaea c.*)
FLORALFIRECRACKER

BREWER'IA W . . . . . . BREWERIA
humistra'ta W

BREY'NIA . . . . BREYNIA
nivo'sa (*Phyllanthus nivosus*)
SNOWBUSH B.
—atropurpu'rea . . . PURPLE S.B.

BREYNIA, continued
nivo'sa roseo-pic'ta
¢KHEDIVE (*atropurpurea*) HV. B. nivosa
¢MOTTLED (*roseopicta*)

BRICKEL'LIA (*COLEOSANTHUS*) BRICKELLIA
argu'ta . . . . PUNGENT B.
—odontole'pis . . . . SHARPTOOTH B.
califor'nica (*wrighti* A. Gray, *not* Rothr.; *Coleosanthus californicus*) CALIFORNIA B.
deserto'rum . . . . . . DESERT B.
floribun'da (*wrighti* Rothr., *not* A. Gray; *Coleosanthus floribundus*) BIGLEAF B.
frutes'cens . . . . RIGID B.
glabra'ta (*Coleosanthus glabratus*)
grandiflo'ra (*Coleosanthus grandiflorus*) TASSELFLOWER B.
green'ei . . . . MOUNTAIN B.
inca'na . . . . WHITE B.
knappia'na . . . . . . WILLOW B.
longifo'lia . . . . . . LONGLEAF B.
microphyl'la . . . . . LITTLELEAF B.
multiflo'ra . . . . INYO B.
ne'vini . . . . NEVIN B.
oblongifo'lia
—linifo'lia (*B. mohavensis*) MOHAVE B.
wat'soni . . . . WATSON B.
wright'i A. Gray, *not* Rothr. **B. californica**
wright'i Rothr., *not* A. Gray **B. floribunda**

BRICKELLIA . . . . **Brickellia**
BIGLEAF B. . . . . . . **B. floribunda**
CALIFORNIA B. . . . . **B. californica**
DESERT B. . . . . . . **B. desertorum**
INYO B. . . . . **B. multiflora**
LITTLELEAF B. . . . . **B. microphylla**
LONGLEAF B. . . . . . **B. longifolia**
MOHAVE B. . **B. oblongifolia linifolia**
MOUNTAIN B. . . . . . . **B. greenei**
NEVIN B. . . . . **B. nevini**
PUNGENT B. . . . . . . **B. arguta**
RIGID B. . . . . . . **B. frutescens**
SHARPTOOTH B. . **B. arguta odontolepis**
TASSELFLOWER B. . . **B. grandiflora**
WATSON B. . . . . . . **B. watsoni**
WHITE B. . . . . **B. incana**
WILLOW B. . . . . **B. knappiana**

BRIDE'LIA . . . . BRIDELIA
mono'ica . . . . . . PIKPOKTSAI B.
monta'na . . . . BARK B.
retu'sa

BRISTLEFERN. **Trichomanes boschianum**

BRISTLEGRASS . . . . **Setaria**
BLACK B. . . . . . **S. nigrirostris**
BRAZIL B. . . . . . . **S. rariflora**
COAST B. . . . . . **S. corrugata**
CORAL B. . . . . **S. macrosperma**
EASTINDIES B. . . . . . **S. barbata**
GIANT B. . . . . **S. magna**
GREEN B. . . . . **S. viridis**
GRISEBACH B. . . . . **S. grisebachi**
HAIRYLEAF B. . . . . **S. villosissima**
HOOKED B. . . . . . **S. verticillata**
KNOTROOT B. . . . . **S. geniculata**
LIEBMANN B. . . . . . **S. liebmanni**
PLAINS B. . . . . . **S. macrostachya**
SICILIAN HOOKED B. **S. verticillata ambigua**
SOUTHWESTERN B. . . . **S. scheelei**

BRISTLEGRASS, continued
WESTINDIES B. . . . **Setaria setosa**
YELLOW B. . . . . . . **S. lutescens**

BRISTLETHISTLE . . . . . . **Carduus**
ACANTHUS B. . . . . **C. acanthoides**
CURLY B. . . . . **C. crispus**
KERNER B. . . . . **C. kerneri**
MUSK B. . . . . **C. nutans**

BRITO'A
ac'ida . . . . PARAGUAVA

BRITTLEBUSH, WHITE . **Encelia farinosa**

BRITTONAS'TRUM . **AGASTACHE**

BRI'ZA . . . . QUAKINGGRASS
See **GRASS GENERA.**

BROADBEAN . . . . **Vicia faba**

¢BROCCOLI . . ¢**of Brassica oleracea botrytis**
ASPARAGUS B. . . . . . **B. o. italica**

BRODIAE'A (*CALLIPRORA; DICHELOSTEMMA; HESPEROSCORDUM; HOOKERA; STROPHOLIRION; TRITELEIA*) |W BRODIEA
brid'gesi . . . . BRIDGES B.
califor'nica (*Hookera c.*) CALIFORNIA B.
can'dida . . . . PALE B.
capita'ta (*Dichelostemma capitatum*) BLUEDICKS B.
coccin'ea . . . . **Brevoortia ida-maia**
conges'ta . . . . . **Brodiaea pulchella**
corona'ria (*grandiflora*) . HARVEST B.
cro'cea . . . . GOLDEN B.
doug'lasi (*Hookera d.; Triteleia grandiflora*) . . . . DOUGLAS B.
east'woodae Hort. . . **B. peduncularis**
grandiflo'ra . . . . . . **B. coronaria**
henderso'ni . . . . . HENDERSON B.
hyacinthi'na (*lactea; Hesperoscordum hyacinthinum*) |W . . . HYACINTH B.
ixioi'des (*Calliprora i.*) PRETTYFACE B.
—splen'dens (*Calliprora i. s.*)
lac'tea . . . . **B. hyacinthina**
lax'a (*Triteleia l.*) . . . GRASSNUT B.
—max'ima . . . . BIG G.B.
—mi'nor . . . . LITTLE G.B.
lilac'ina (*Triteleia l.*) . . . . LILAC B.
mi'nor (*purdyi; Hookera m.*) MINOR B.
multiflo'ra
peduncula'ris (*eastwoodae* Hort.; *Triteleia p.*)
pulchel'la (*congesta; Dichelostemma pulchellum*) . . . . . . PURPLEHEAD B.
stella'ris (*Hookera s.*) . . . . STAR B.
terres'tris . . . . GROUND B.
uniflo'ra (*Leucocoryne u.; Milla u.; Triteleia u.*) . . . . . SOLITARY B.
viola'cea (*Triteleia v.*) . . . VIOLET B.
volu'bilis (*Stropholirion californicum* Torr., *not B. californica* Lindl.) VINE B.

BRODIEA . . . . **Brodiaea**
BIG GRASSNUT B. . . **B. laxa maxima**
BLUEDICKS B. . . . . . **B. capitata**
BRIDGES B. . . . . . . **B. bridgesi**
CALIFORNIA B. . . . . **B. californica**
DOUGLAS B. . . . . . . **B. douglasi**
GOLDEN B. . . . . **B. crocea**
GRASSNUT B. . . . . **B. laxa**
GROUND B. . . . . . **B. terrestris**
HARVEST B. . . . . . **B. coronaria**
HENDERSON B. . . . **B. hendersoni**
HYACINTH B. . . . . **B. hyacinthina**
LILAC B. . . . . **B. lilacina**

BRODIEA, continued
LITTLE GRASSNUT B. **Brodiaea laxa minor**
MINOR B. . . . . **B. minor**
PALE B. . . . . **B. candida**
PRETTYFACE B. . . . . . **B. ixioides**
PURPLEHEAD B. . . . . **B. pulchella**
SOLITARY B. . . . . . . **B. uniflora**
STAR B. . . . . **B. stellaris**
VINE B. . . . . **B. volubilis**
VIOLET B. . . . . **B. violacea**

BROME . . . . **Bromus**
ALASKA B. . . . . . . **B. sitchensis**
ALEUTIAN B. . . . . . **B. aleutensis**
AUSTRALIAN B. . . . . **B. arenarius**
Austrian B.; Awnless B. . . SMOOTH B.
BALD B. . . . . **B. racemosus**
Big B. . . . . MOUNTAIN B.
BROOM B. . . . . **B. scoparius**
California B. . . . . . MOUNTAIN B.
CANADA B. . . . . **B. purgans**
CHEATGRASS B. . . . . **B. tectorum**
CHESS B. . . . . **B. secalinus**
CHILEAN B. . . . . **B. trinii**
CHINOOK B. . . . . **B. laevipes**
COLUMBIA B. . . . . . . **B. vulgaris**
Common B. . . . . SMOOTH B.
Downy B. . . . . . . CHEATGRASS B.
EARLEAF B. . . . . . . **B. latiglumis**
FIELD B. . . . . **B. arvensis**
FOXTAIL B. . . . . **B. rubens**
FRINGED B. . . . . **B. ciliatus**
HAIRY B. . . . . . . **B. commutatus**
HALL ORCUTT B. . **B. orcuttianus halli**
Hungarian B. . . . . . . SMOOTH B.
JAPANESE B. . . . . . . **B. japonicus**
KALM B. . . . . **B. kalmi**
LONGARM RIPGUT B. **B. rigidus gussonei**
MEADOW B. . . . . **B. erectus**
MEDITERRANEAN B. . **B. macrostachys**
MOUNTAIN B. . . . . . **B. carinatus**
NODDING B. . . . . . . **B. anomalus**
ORCUTT B. . . . . . **B. orcuttianus**
PACIFIC B. . . . . **B. pacificus**
PANAMINT B. . . . **B. trinii excelsus**
Porter B. . . . . NODDING B.
POVERTY B. . . . . **B. sterilis**
PUMPELLY B. . . . . **B. pumpellianus**
PYGMY B. . . . . . . **B. molliformis**
RATTLE B. . . . . . **B. brizaeformis**
Red B. . . . . FOXTAIL B.
RESCUE B. . . . . . . **B. catharticus**
Richardson B. . . . . . . FRINGED B.
RIPGUT B. . . . . **B. rigidus**
Russian B. . . . . SMOOTH B.
SLIMLEAF B. . . . . **B. breviaristatus**
SMOOTH B. . . . . **B. inermis**
SOFT B. . . . . **B. mollis**
SPANISH B. . . . . . **B. madritensis**
SUKSDORF B. . . . . . . **B. suksdorfi**
SUNSHINE B. **B. commutatus apricorum**
TALL B. . . . . **B. grandis**
TEXAS B. . . . . **B. texensis**
TWEEDY B. **B. pumpellianus tweedyi**
WEEPING B. . . . . **B. frondosus**
WOOLLY NODDING B. **B. anomalus lanatipes**

Bromegrass . . . . . . BROME: **Bromus**

BROME'LIA . . . . BROMELIA
fastuo'sa
magdale'nae . . . ARGHAN FIBER B.
pin'guin . . . . PINGUIN B.

BRO'MUS . . . . BROME
See **GRASS GENERA.**

Brookgrass . . . . **Catabrosa aquatica**

Broom . . . . **Cytisus**
Ardoin B. . . . . **C. ardoini**
Austrian B. . . . . **C. austriacus**
∞ Beans B. . . . . ∞ **C. beani**
Bigflower B. . . . . . . **C. supinus**
Canary B. . . . . **C. canariensis**
∞ Dallimore B. . . . . ∞ **C. dallimorei**
Easter B. . . . . **C. racemosus**
Greek B. . . . . **C. triflorus**
Ground B. . . . . . **C. procumbens**
Heuffel Austrian B.
C. austriacus heuffeli
Hillebrandt B. . . . **C. hillebrandti**
Hungarian B. . . . . . . **C. leiocarpus**
Leafy Madeira B.
C. maderensis magnifoliosus
Madeira B. . . . . **C. maderensis**
Montpelier B. . . **C. monspessulanus**
Pale Portuguese B. **C. albus pallidus**
Portuguese B. . . . . **C. albus**
Prostrate B. . . . . . . **C. decumbens**
Provence B. . . . . **C. purgans**
Purple B. . . . . **C. purpureus**
Rochel B. . . . . **C. rocheli**
Scotch B. . . . . **C. scoparius**
Sessile B. . . . . . . **C. sessilifolius**
Spike B. . . . . **C. nigricans**
Sweet B. . . . . **C. fragrans**
Teneriffe B. . . . . **C. filipes**
∞ Warminister B. . . . . ∞ **C. praecox**
Whitespanish B. . . . **C. multiflorus**
Yellow Sessile B.
C. sessilifolius leucanthus

Broomcorn **Sorghum vulgare technicum**

Broomcrowberry . . **Corema conradi**

Broomrape . . . . **Orobanche**
Clover B. . . . . **O. minor**
Hemp B. . . . . **O. ramosa**
Louisiana B. . . . . **O. ludoviciana**

Broomsedge . . Bluestem: **Andropogon**

Broomtree . . . . **Kingia**
Australian B. . . . . . **K. australis**

Broomweed . Snakeweed, Tarragon: **Gutierrezia dracunculoides**

Broomwort . . . . **Scoparia**
Sweet B. . . . . **S. dulcis**

BROS'IMUM . . . . Breadnuttree
alicas'trum . . . . Ramon B.
aublet'i . . . . **Piratinera guianensis**
paraen'se . . . . Para B.
u'tile (*galactodendron*) . . . . Cow B.

BROUGHTO'NIA
See **ORCHID GENERA.**

BROUSSONET'IA (*PAPYRIUS*) |w
Papermulberry
Broussonetia L'Her. *not* Orteg., is conserved under International Rules.
kazino'ki . . . . Kazinoki P.
papyrif'era (*Papyrius p.*) |w Common P.
¢Cutleaf (*laciniata*) hv.
¢Variegated (*variegata*)
¢Whitefruit (*leucocarpa*)

BROUSSONET'IA Orteg., *not* L'Her. **SOPHORA**

BROWAL'LIA . . . . Browallia
america'na (*demissa; elata*)
Amethyst B.
grandiflo'ra (*roezli*) . . Bigflower B.
jameso'ni . . . . . . **Streptosolen j.**

BROWALLIA, continued
specio'sa . . . . Lovely Browallia
—al'ba . . . . White L.B.
—ma'jor (*B. major*) . . . Major L.B.
visco'sa (*pulchella*) . . . . Sticky B.

BROWN'EA . . . . Flamebean
capitel'la . . . . Orange F.
coccin'ea . . . . Scarlet F.
gran'diceps . . . . Glory F.
latifo'lia . . . . . . Broadleaf F.
macrophyl'la . . . . Great F.
rosa-de-mon'te (*rosea*)
Mountainrose F.

Browneyedsusan . **Rudbeckia triloba**

Browngum . . . Eucalyptus, Beakpod: **Eucalyptus multiflora**

BROWNIN'GIA . . . . . . **CEREUS**
See **CACTUS GENERA.**

Browntopmillet . **Panicum ramosum**

BRUCKENTHA'LIA . . . Spikeheath
spiculifo'lia (*Erica s.*) . . Spikeheath

BRUGMAN'SIA . . . . . **DATURA**

BRUNEL'LA . . . . **PRUNELLA**

BRUNFEL'SIA (*FRANCISCEA*)
Raintree
america'na . . . . Franciscan R.
calyci'na . . . . Brazil R.
—exim'ia . . . . Fading B.R.
—floribun'da (*Franciscea f.*)
Whiteeye B.R.
—macran'tha . . . Bluering B.R.
capita'ta
hopea'na . . . . Manaca R.
hydrangeaefor'mis . . . . Mire R.
latifo'lia . . . . . . Broadleaf R.
macrophyl'la . . . . . . Bigleaf R.

BRU'NIA
stoko'ei

BRUN'NERA . . . . . . Brunnera
macrophyl'la (*Anchusa myosotidiflora*)
Heartleaf B. (*Siberian Bugloss*)

BRUNNICH'IA |w . . Buckwheatvine
cirrho'sa |w . . . . . American B.

∞**BRUNSDON'NA** (*BRUNSVIGIA* × *CALLICORE*) . . . ∞ Brunsdonna
¢Alba (*multiflora alba*). (Bradley 1870.) hv.
¢Harbord
¢Haythor
¢Intermedia
¢Multiflora
¢Ovieto
¢Parker (*parkeri*)
¢Rosea (*multiflora rosea*). (Bradley 1870.)
¢Vantubergen (*tubergeni*)
¢White Parker (*parkeri alba*)
¢Zwanenburg

BRUNSVIG'IA . . . . . . Brunsvigia
gigan'tea (*josephinae*) . . . Giant B.
orienta'lis . . . . Cape B.

Brushmyrtle . . . . **Beaufortia**
Orbleaf B. . . . . . . **B. orbifolia**
Purple B. . . . . **B. purpurea**
SwanRiver B. . . . . . **B. decussata**

Brussels Sprouts
Brassica oleracea gemmifera

BRY'A . . . . Cocuswood
eb'enus . . . . Ebony C.

BRYAN'THUS
muscifor'mis

BRYO'NIA . . . . Bryony
al'ba . . . . White B.
dio'ica . . . . Redberry B.
lacinio'sa . . . . . . **Bryonopsis l.**

BRYONOP'SIS . . . . . Bryonopsis
lacinio'sa (*Bryonia l.*) . . Cutleaf B.

Bryony . . . . **Bryonia**
Redberry B. . . . . **B. dioica**
White B. . . . . **B. alba**

BRYOPHYL'LUM . . **KALANCHOE**
See **SUCCULENTS.**

∞ Buartnut
The commercial nut of ∞ Walnut, Bixby: ∞ **Juglans bixbyi.**

BUCHENA'VIA
capita'ta

BU'CHLOE (*BULBILIS*)
See **GRASS GENERA.**

Buchu . . . . **Barosma**
Eggleaf B. . . . . **B. ovata**
Longleaf B. . . . . . **B. serratifolia**
Ovalleaf B. . . . . . . **B. crenulata**
Short B. . . . . **B. betulina**
Showy B. . . . . **B. pulchella**

BU'CIDA . . . . Bucida
angustifo'lia . . . . Narrowleaf B.
buce'ras (*Terminalia b.*) . Oxhorn B.

Buckbean . . . . **Menyanthes trifoliata**

Buckberry . . . . **Gaylussacia ursina**

Buckeye . . . . **Aesculus**
See also Horsechestnut.
∞ Arboretum B. . . . . ∞ **A. mutabilis**
∞ Arkansas B. . . . . . . ∞ **A. bushi**
∞ Arnold B. . . . . . ∞ **A. arnoldiana**
Bottlebrush B. . . . . **A. parviflora**
California B. . . . . . **A. californica**
Carolina Yellow B.
A. octandra vestita
∞ Dupont B. . . . . . . ∞ **A. duponti**
Ellwanger B.
A. woerlitzensis ellwangeri
Etowah Painted B.
A. neglecta pubescens
Flame B. . . . . **A. splendens**
Georgia Painted B.
A. neglecta georgiana
∞ Hybrid B. . . . . ∞ **A. hybrida**
Late Bottlebrush B.
A. parviflora serotina
∞ Maryland Hybrid B. ∞ **A. marylandica**
∞ Mississippi B. . . ∞ **A. mississippiensis**
Oconee Painted B.
A. neglecta tomentosa
Ohio B. . . . . **A. glabra**
Oklahoma B. . . . . . **A. g. monticola**
Painted B. . . . . **A. neglecta**
Pale Ohio B. . . . . **A. glabra pallida**
Purple Yellow B.
A. octandra purpurascens
Rabun Painted B.
A. neglecta lanceolata
Red B. . . . . **A. pavia**
Sargent Ohio B. . **A. glabra sargenti**
Scarlet Woolly B. . **A. discolor mollis**
Shrubby W. B. . . . . . **A. d. koehnei**
Texas B. . . . . **A. arguta**
Tricolor Purple B.
A. octandra virginica
Whitebark Ohio B.
A. glabra leucodermis

Buckeye, continued
Woerlitz B. . . **Aesculus woerlitzensis**
Woolly B. . . . . . . **A. discolor**
Yellow B. . . . . . . **A. octandra**
Yellow Woolly B.
A. discolor flavescens

BUCK'LEYA . . . . Piratebush
distichophyl'la . . . . . Piratebush

Buckthorn . . . . **Rhamnus**
Alder B. . . . . **R. alnifolia**
Alpine B. . . . . **R. alpina**
Broadleaf B. . . . . . **R. latifolia**
Broadleaf Glossy B. . **R. frangula l.**
California B. . . . . **R. californica**
Carniolian B. . . . . . . **R. fallax**
Carolina B. . . . . . **R. caroliniana**
Cascara B. . . . . . **R. purshiana**
Caucasian B. . . . . . **R. imeretina**
Chinese B. . . . . **R. utilis**
Cliff B. . . . . **R. rupestris**
Common B. . . . . . **R. cathartica**
Cutleaf Hedge B.
R. dumetorum crenoserrata
Dahurian B. . . . . . . **R. davurica**
Dwarf B. . . . . **R. pumila**
Dyers B. . . . . **R. tinctoria**
Entireleaf Italian B.
R. angustifolia integrifolia
Glossy B. . . . . **R. frangula**
Great Redberry B. **R. crocea insularis**
Hairy Common B.
R. cathartica pubescens
Hedge B. . . . . . . **R. dumetorum**
Hollyleaf Redberry B.
R. crocea ilicifolia
∞Hybrid B. . . . . ∞**R. hybrida**
Italian B. . . . . . . **R. alaternus**
Japanese B. . . . . . . **R. japonica**
Korean B. . . . . . **R. koraiensis**
Lanceleaf B. . . . . **R. lanceolata**
Lebanon B. . . . . . **R. libanotica**
Littleleaf B. . . . . . **R. parvifolia**
Lokao B. . . . . **R. globosa**
Manchurian Schneider B.
R. schneideri manshurica
Narrowleaf Glossy B.
R. frangula angustifolia
Nippon B. . . . **R. davurica nipponica**
Oriental B. . . . . **R. crenata**
Persianberry B. . . . **R. infectoria**
Petioled B. . . . . . . **R. petiolaris**
Plumleaf B. . . . . . **R. prunifolia**
Purple B. . . . . **R. purpurea**
Redberry B. . . . . **R. crocea**
Ribleaf B. . . . . **R. costata**
Rock B. . . . . **R. saxatilis**
Rosthorns B. . . . . . **R. rosthorni**
SanDiego Redberry B.
R. crocea pilosa
Sargent R. . . . . . **R. sargentiana**
Scabrous Slenderleaf B.
R. leptophylla scabrella
Schneider B. . . . . **R. schneideri**
Sharptooth B. . . . . . . **R. arguta**
Slenderleaf B. . . . **R. leptophylla**
Slimleaf Italian B.
R. alaternus angustifolia
Smith B. . . . . **R. smithi**
Thickleaf California B.
R. californica crassifolia
Twiggy B. . . . . **R. virgata**
Whiteleaf B. . . . . **R. tomentella**
Wrinkleleaf B. . . . . **R. rugulosa**

Buckwheat . . . . **Fagopyrum**
See also **CEREALS.**
Common B. . . . . . **F. sagittatum**
Tartary B. . . . . . . **F. tataricum**

Buckwheattree . **Cliftonia monophylla**

Buckwheatvine . . . . . **Brunnichia**
American B. . . . . . **B. cirrhosa**

BUDDLE'IA . . . . . Butterflybush
albiflo'ra (*hemsleyana*)
alternifo'lia . . . . . Fountain B.
america'na . . . . . American B.
asiat'ica . . . . Asian B.
auricula'ta
can'dida
caryopteridifo'lia
col'villei . . . . Colville B.
—kewen'sis . . . . Kew C.B.
cris'pa . . . . Curly B.
curviflo'ra . . . . **B. japonica**
da'vidi (*variabilis*) . . Orangeeye B.
—amplis'sima
—magnif'ica (*B. magnifica*) **Oxeye B.**
—nanhoen'sis
—serot'ina
—super'ba . . . . Juno B.
—veitchia'na
—wil'soni . . . . Wilson B.
Distinction. hv. B. davidi
Hartweg (*hartwegi*)
Ile de France
Mauve Queen
Pink Pearl
fallowia'na . . . . . . Fallows B.
—al'ba . . . . White F.B.
∞**farquhar'i** (*asiatica × officinalis*)
∞Farquhar B.
far'reri . . . . Farrer B.
—pal'lida . . . . Pale F.B.
for'resti . . . . Forrest B.
globo'sa . . . . Globe B.
helioph'ila
hemsleya'na . . . . . . **B. albiflora**
∞**hy'brida** (*asiatica × davidi*) ∞Hybrid B.
¢Eva Dudley. hv.
∞**interme'dia** (*japonica × lindleyana*)
∞Wisteria B.
¢Wingstem (*insignis*) hv.
japon'ica (*curviflora*) . . Japanese B.
lindleya'na . . . . . . Lindley B.
—sinuato-denta'ta
madagascarien'sis . Madagascar B.
magnif'ica . . . . **B. davidi m.**
marrubiifo'lia . . . . . Woolly B.
microphyl'la . . . . Littleleaf B.
myrian'tha
niv'ea . . . . Snowy B.
—yunnanen'sis . . . . Yunnan S.B.
officina'lis . . . . Pale B.
panicula'ta . . . . . . Panicle B.
salvifo'lia
scordioi'des . . . . . Escobilla B.
stenosta'chya
utahen'sis . . . . Utah B.
variab'ilis . . . . **B. davidi**
∞**weyeria'na** (*davidi × globosa*)
∞Weyer B.
¢Goldenglow. hv.
¢Moonlight

Buffaloberry . . . . . **Shepherdia**
Roundleaf B. . . . **S. rotundifolia**
Russet B. . . . . . **S. canadensis**
Silver B. . . . . . . **S. argentea**

Buffalogourd **Cucurbita foetidissima**

Buffalograss . . **Buchloe dactyloides**
False B. . . . . **Munroa squarrosa**

Bugbane . . . . **Cimicifuga**
American B. . . . . **C. americana**
Cohosh B. . . . . . . **C. racemosa**

Bugbane, continued
Cordate B. . . **Cimicifuga cordifolia**
Cutleaf B. . . . . **C. laciniata**
Dahurian B. . . . . . . **C. davurica**
Japanese B. . . . . . . **C. japonica**
Kamchatka B. . . **C. foetida simplex**
Skunk B. . . . . **C. foetida**
Tall B. . . . . **C. elata**

BUGINVIL'LEA . **BOUGAINVILLEA**

Bugle . . . . **Ajuga**
Brockbank B. . . . . **A. brockbanki**
Carpet B. . . . . **A. reptans**
Geneva B. . . . . . . **A. genevensis**
Groundpine B. . . . **A. chamaepitys**
Tottenham B. . . . . **A. tottenhami**
White Carpet B. . . **A. reptans alba**

Buglelily . . . . **Watsonia**
Beatrice B. . . . . . . **W. beatricis**
Brickred B. . . . . . . **W. pillansi**
Bulbil B. . . . . . . **W. bulbillifera**
Fragrant B. . . . . . **W. marginata**
Irisleaf B. . . . . **W. iridifolia**
Longleaf B. . . . . . **W. longifolia**
Meriana B. . . . . . . **W. meriana**
Rosewand B. . . . . . **W. densiflora**
Rosy B. . . . . **W. rosea**
Scarlet B. . . . . . . **W. coccinea**
Shortleaf B. . . . . . **W. brevifolia**
Taperpetal B. . . . . . **W. angusta**
Versfeld B. . . . . . . **W. versfeldi**
Wordsworth B. . **W. wordsworthiana**

Bugleweed . . . . **Lycopus**
American B. . . . . **L. americanus**
European B. . . . . **L. europaeus**
Virginia B. . . . . . . **L. virginicus**

Bugloss . . . . **Anchusa**
Cape B. . . . . **A. capensis**
Carnation Common B.
A. officinalis incarnata
Common B. . . . . . . **A. officinalis**
Early B. . . . . **A. barrelieri**
Evergreen B. . . . . **A. sempervirens**
Italian B. . . . . **A. azurea**
Siberian B. . Brunnera, Heartleaf:
Brunnera macrophylla
White Cape B. . . **A. capensis alba**

Bugseedgrass **Coridochloa; C. cimicina**

BUL'BILIS . . . . **BUCHLOE**
See **GRASS GENERA.**

BULBI'NE
See **SUCCULENTS.**

BULBINEL'LA
hook'eri (*Chrysobactron h.*)
robus'ta

BULBOCO'DIUM . Meadowsaffron
ver'num . . . . Spring M.

BULBOPHYL'LUM
See **ORCHID GENERA.**

BULBOSTY'LIS (*STENOPHYL-LUS*) Lw
capilla'ris Lw

Bulletwood . . . . **Mimusops**
Elengi B. . . . . **M. elengi**
Heckel B. . . . . **M. heckeli**
Kafir B. . . . . **M. caffra**

Bullgrass . **Muhlenbergia emersleyi**

Bullich . . . . Eucalyptus, Bigpod:
Eucalyptus megacarpa

BULNE'SIA . . . . Bulnesia
arbo'rea . . . . Verawood B.

Bulrush . . . . **Scirpus**
Alkali B. . . . . **S. paludosus**
American B. . . . . **S. americanus**
California B. . . . . **S. californicus**
Cuban B. . . . . **S. cubensis**
Deerhair B. . . . . **S. caespitosus**
Great B. . . . . **S. lacustris**
Green B. . . . . . . **S. atrovirens**
Halls B. . . . . **S. halli**
Keeled B. . . . . . . **S. carinatus**
Leafy B. . . . . . . **S. polyphyllus**
Nevada B. . . . . . . **S. nevadensis**
Olney B. . . . . **S. olneyi**
Panicled B. . . . . . **S. microcarpus**
Red B. . . . . **S. rufus**
River B. . . . . **S. fluviatilis**
RockyMountain B. **S. saximontanus**
Saltmarsh B. . . . . . . **S. robustus**
Slender B. . . . . **S. heterochaetus**
Smiths B. . . . . **S. smithi**
Softstem B. . . . . **S. validus**
Tabernaemontanus B.
S. tabernaemontani
Torrey B. . . . . **S. torreyi**
Tule B. . . . . **S. acutus**
Weak B. . . . . **S. debilis**
Weeping B. . . . . . . **S. cernuus**
Woodland B. . . . . . **S. sylvaticus**
Woolgrass B. . . . . . **S. cyperinus**

BUME'LIA |w . . . . Bumelia
angustifo'lia . . . Saffronplum B.
lanugino'sa |w . . Woollybucket B.
—al'bicans . . . . . . Gum W.B.
—rig'ida
lycioi'des |w . . . . . Buckthorn B.
montic'ola . . . . Brazos B.
obtusifo'lia . . . . . . Ibiranira B.
ten'ax . . . . Tough B.

Bunchflower
Melanthium; M. virginicum

Bunchgrass
Beardless B. . . . . Pine Dropseed
Big B. . . . . Bearded Bluebunch Wheatgrass
Big Buffalo B. . . Big Rough Fescue
Bigplume B. . . . . . Alkali Sacaton
Blue B. . . . . Idaho Fescue
Buffalo B. . . . . Rough F.
Feather B. . . . Green Needlegrass; Green Fescue; Mountain Muhly
Mountain B. . . . Arizona Fescue
Pine B. . . . . . Mountain Muhly
Wire B. . . . . Bearded Bluebunch Wheatgrass

Bundleflower . . . . . **Desmanthus**
Illinois B. . . . . . . **D. illinoensis**
James B. . . . . **D. cooleyi**
Rayado B. . . . . **D. virgatus**

BU'PHANE . . . . **BOOPHANE**

BUPHTHAL'MUM . . . . . Oxeye
grandiflo'rum . . . . . Showy O.
salicifo'lium . . . . Willowleaf O.
speciosis'simum (*Telekia speciosissima*) Tall O.
specio'sum (*cordifolium; Telekia cordifolia*) . . . . Heartleaf O.

BUPLEU'RUM |w . . . . . Thorowax
frutico'sum . . . . Shrub T.
ranunculoi'des
rotundifo'lium |w . . . Roundleaf T.

BURCHEL'LIA
capen'sis

Burclover
California B. . . **Medicago hispida**

Burclover, continued
Fivecoil B.
Medicago hispida reticulata
Threecoil B. . . . . **M. h. confinis**
Toothed B. . . . . **M. h. denticulata**

Burcucumber . . . . **Sicyos**
Wall B. . . . . **S. angulatus**

Burdekinplum . **Pleiogynium solandri**

Burdock . . . . **Arctium**
Cotton B. . . . . . . **A. tomentosum**
Great B. . . . . **A. lappa**
Smaller B. . . . . **A. minus**

Burgrass . . . . **Tragus**
Spike B. . . . . . **T. berteronianus**
Stalked B. . . . . . **T. racemosus**

Burhead . . . . **Echinodorus**

Buripalm . . . . **Corypha utan**

Burity . . . . . Mauritia, Fiber: **Mauritia flexuosa**

BURKILLAN'THUS . . . . Ghostlime
malaccen'sis . . . . Malay G.

BURLINGTO'NIA (*RODRIGUEZIA*)
See **ORCHID GENERA.**

Burmareed . . **Neyraudia reynaudiana**

Burnet . . . . **Poterium; Sanguisorba**
American B. . . . . . **S. canadensis**
Garden B. . . . . . . **S. officinalis**
Japanese B. . . . . **S. obtusa**
Menzies B. . . . . . . **S. menziesi**
Prairie B. . . . . **S. annua**
Siberian B. . . . . . . **S. tenuifolia**
Sitka B. . . . . **S. sitchensis**
Small B. . . . . **S. minor**
Spiny B. . . . . **P. spinosum**

Burningbush
Eastern B. . . . . Wahoo, Eastern: **Euonymus atropurpureus**
Western B. . . . Wahoo, Western: **E. occidentalis**

Burnweed . . . . **Erechtites**
American B. . . . . **E. hieracifolia**
Australian B. . . . **E. prenanthoides**
Bushmans B. . . . . **E. arguta**

Burreed . . . . **Sparganium**
American B. . . . . **S. americanum**
Giant B. . . . . . . **S. eurycarpum**
Least B. . . . . **S. minimum**
Narrowleaf B. . . **S. angustifolium**
Water B. . . . . **S. fluctuans**

Burrobrush . . . . . . **Hymenoclea**
Singlewhorl B. . . . . **H. monogyra**
White B. . . . . **H. salsola**

Burrofat . . . . **Isomeris**
Tree B. . . . . **I. arborea**

Burrograss . **Scleropogon; S. brevifolius**

Burroweed . . . **Aplopappus fruticosus**

BUR'SA . . . . **CAPSELLA**

Bursage . . . . **Franseria**
Ambrosia B. . . . . **F. ambrosioides**
Hollyleaf B. . . . . **F. ilicifolia**
SanDiego B. . . . **F. chenopodiifolia**
Skeletonleaf B. . . . . . **F. discolor**
Slimleaf B. . . . . . . **F. tenuifolia**
Triangle B. . . . . . . **F. deltoidea**
White B. . . . . **F. dumosa**
Woolly B. . . . . . . **F. eriocentra**
Woollyleaf B. . . . **F. tomentosa**

BURSA'RIA . . . . Bursaria
inca'na . . . . Hoary B.
pan'toni . . . . Panton B.
spino'sa . . . . Sweet B.

BUR'SERA (*ELAPHRIUM*) Bursera
excel'sa
glabrifo'lia (*aloexylon; Elaphrium glabrifolium*) . . . . . . Linaloe B.
grave'olens
microphyl'la (*Elaphrium microphyllum*) Elephant B.
penicilla'ta (*delpechiana; Elaphrium penicillatum*)
simaru'ba . . . . Gumbolimbo
spino'sa . . . . Spiny B.

Burstwort . . . . **Herniaria**
Common B. . . . . **H. glabra**
Gray B. . . . . **H. cinerea**
Hairy B. . . . . **H. hirsuta**
Syrian B. . . . . **H. incana**
Velvety B. . . . . **H. latifolia**

Bushbeech . . . . **Gmelina**
Bristly B. . . . . **G. hystrix**
Leichhardt B. . . . . **G. leichhardti**
Malay B. . . . . **G. arborea**

Bushcherry
See also Almond, Apricot, Birdcherry, Cherry, Chokecherry, Laurelcherry, Peach, Peachbrush, and Plum.

Chinese B. . . . . **Prunus japonica**
Engler C. B. . . . . . **P. j. engleri**
Nakai C. B. . . . . **P. j. nakai**
Thunberg C. B. . . . **P. j. thunbergi**

Bushhoneysuckle . . . . . **Diervilla**
Dwarf B. . . . . **D. lonicera**
Georgia B. . . . . **D. rivularis**
Southern B. . . . . . **D. sessilifolia**

Bushmanspoison . . . . **Acokanthera**
Abyssinian B. . . . . **A. abyssinica**
Ouabaio B. . . . . **A. ouabaio**
True B. . . . . **A. venenata**
Wintersweet B. . . . **A. spectabilis**

Bushmint . . . . **Hyptis**
Emory B. . . . . **H. emoryi**

Bushpoppy . . . . . . **Dendromecon**
Island B. . . . . **D. harfordi**
Stiff B. . . . . **D. rigida**

Bushsunflower . . . . **Simsia**
Stinking B. . . . . **S. foetida**

Bustic . . . . **Dipholis**
Willow B. . . . . **D. salicifolia**

Butchersbroom . **Ruscus; R. aculeatus**

BU'TEA
monosper'ma (*frondosa*) Bengal Kino

BU'TIA (*COCOS* in part) . Butiapalm
See **PALM GENERA.**

Butiapalm . . . . **Butia**
Acorn B. . . . . **B. bonneti**
Bigfruit B. . . . **B. capitata pulposa**
Brazilian B. . . . . . . **B. capitata**
Dotfruit B. . . . . **B. punctata**
Greenleaf B. . **B. capitata virescens**
Nehrling B. . . . **B. c. nehrlingiana**
Perfume B. . . . . . . **B. c. odorata**
Woolly B. . . . . . . **B. eriospatha**

BUTNER'IA . . . **CALYCANTHUS**

BU'TOMUS |w . . . Floweringrush
umbella'tus |w . . . Floweringrush

Butter-and-eggs . . Toadflax, Butter-and-eggs: **Linaria vulgaris**

Butterbough . . . **Exothea paniculata**

Butterbur . . . . **Petasites**
Giant Japanese B.
P. japonica gigantea
Japanese B. . . . . . . **P. japonica**

BUTTERBUR, continued
PALMATE B. . . . Petasites palmata
PURPLE B. . . . . P. hybrida
SNOWLEAF B. . . . . P. nivea
SWEET B. . . . . P. fragrans

BUTTERCUP . . . . Ranunculus
ACONITE B. . . . . . R. aconitifolius
ALLEGANY B. . . . . R. allegheniensis
ALPINE B. . . . . . . R. adoneus
ANDERSON B. . . . . . R. andersoni
ANEMONE B. . . . . R. anemonoides
BIG TONGUE B. . R. lingua grandiflorus
BLISTER B. . . . . . R. sceleratus
BOLANDER B. . . . . . . R. bolanderi
BONGARD B. . . . . . . R. bongardi
BRISTLY B. . . . . . . R. hispidus
BROTERS B. . . . . . . R. broteri
BULB B. . . . . R. bulbosus
CALIFORNIA B. . . . . R. californicus
CORN B. . . . . R. arvensis
CREAM B. . . . . . . R. tenuicaulis
CREEPING B. . . . . R. repens
CREEPING SPEARWORT B.
R. flammula reptans
CRENATE B. . . . . . . R. crenatus
DWARF PLANTAINLEAF B.
R. alismaefolius alismellus
FIGROOT B. . . . . . . R. ficaria
GLACIER B. . . . . . . R. glacialis
GRASSY B. . . . . . . R. gramineus
GREAT STRAIGHTBEAK B.
R. orthorhyncus platyphyllus
HAIRLEAF WATERCROWFOOT B.
R. aquatilis capillaceus
HOOKED B. . . . . . R. recurvatus
ILLYRIAN B. . . . . . . R. illyricus
IVY B. . . . . R. hederaceus
LABRADOR B. . . . . R. ovalis
LAPP B. . . . . R. lapponicus
LENORMAND B. . . . . R. lenormandi
LITTLELEAF B. . . . . . R. abortivus
LOBB B. . . . . R. lobbi
LONGBEAK B. . . . . R. longirostris
LYALL B. . . . . R. lyalli
MACAULEY B. . . . . . R. macauleyi
MEDITERRANEAN B. R. ophioglossifolius
MORAINE B. . . . . . . R. alpestris
MOUNTAIN B. . . . . . R. montanus
NINELEAF B. . . . . . R. triternatus
PARNASSUS B. . . . R. parnassifolius
PENNSYLVANIA B. . R. pennsylvanicus
PERSIAN B. . . . . . . R. asiaticus
PLANTAINLEAF B. . . . R. alismaefolius
PYRENEES B. . . . . . . R. pyrenaeus
SAGEBRUSH B. . . . . R. glaberrimus
SEGUIERS B. . . . . . . R. seguieri
SHARP B. . . . . . . R. acriformis
SHORE B. . . . . . . R. cymbalaria
SPEARWORT B. . . . . . . R. flammula
STICKTIGHT B. . . . . . R. parviflorus
STRAIGHTBEAK B. . . R. orthorhyncus
SUKSDORF B. . . . . . . R. suksdorfi
SWAMP B. . . . R. septentrionalis
TALL B. . . . . R. acris
TONGUE B. . . . . R. lingua
TUFTED B. . . . . . . R. fascicularis
VARILEAF WATERCROWFOOT B.
R. aquatilis heterophyllus
WATERCROWFOOT B. . . B. aquatilis
WESTERN B. . . . . R. occidentalis
WILDWOOD B. . . . . . R. nemorosus
YELLOWEYE B. . . . R. amplexicaulis

BUTTERFIELDFERN
Cyrtomium falcatum HV.

BUTTERFLYBUSH . . . . . Buddleia
AMERICAN B. . . . . . B. americana
ASIAN B. . . . . B. asiatica

BUTTERFLYBUSH, continued
COLVILLE B. . . . . Buddleia colvillei
CURLY B. . . . . B. crispa
ESCOBILLA B. . . . . B. scordioides
FALLOWS B. . . . . . . B. fallowiana
∞ FARQUHAR B. . . . . ∞ B. farquhari
FARRER B. . . . . B. farreri
FORREST B. . . . . B. forresti
FOUNTAIN B. . . . . . B. alternifolia
GLOBE B. . . . . B. globosa
∞ HYBRID B. . . . . ∞ B. hybrida
JAPANESE B. . . . . B. japonica
JUNO B. . . . . . . B. davidi superba
KEW COLVILLE B. B. colvillei kewensis
LINDLEY B. . . . . . . B. lindleyana
LITTLELEAF B. . . . . B. microphylla
MADAGASCAR B. B. madagascariensis
ORANGEEYE B. . . . . . . B. davidi
OXEYE B. . . . . . . B. d. magnifica
PALE B. . . . . B. officinalis
PALE FARRER B. . . B. farreri pallida
PANICLE B. . . . . . . B. paniculata
SNOWY B. . . . . B. nivea
UTAH B. . . . . B. utahensis
∞ WEYER B. . . . . . . ∞ B. weyeriana
WHITE FALLOWS B. B. fallowiana alba
WILSON B. . . . . B. wilsoni
∞ WISTERIA B. . . . . ∞ B. intermedia
WOOLLY B. . . . . . B. marrubiifolia
YUNNAN SNOWY B.
B. nivea yunnanensis

BUTTERFLYFLOWER . . . . Schizanthus
CARMINE WINGLEAF B.
S. pinnatus carmineus
GRAHAM B. . . . . S. grahami
LILAC WINGLEAF B. S. pinnatus lilacinus
ORANGE-ROSE B. . . . . . S. retusus
SLIM B. . . . . S. gracilis
WHITE WINGLEAF B.
S. pinnatus candidissimus
WINGLEAF B. . . . . . . S. pinnatus
∞ WISETON B. . . . ∞ S. wisetonensis

BUTTERFLYPALM . . . Chrysalidocarpus
LUCUBA B . . . . . . C. lucubensis
MADAGASCAR B. C. madagascariensis
YELLOW B. . . . . . . C. lutescens

BUTTERFLYPEA . . . . . Centrosema
BRAZIL B. . . . . . . C. brasilianum
COASTAL B. . . . . . C. virginianum
FLORIDA B. . . . . . . C. arenicola

BUTTERNUT . . . . . Juglans cinerea

BUTTERSEED . . . . . Butyrospermum
SHEA B. . . . . B. parki

BUTTERTREE
ILLIPE B. . . . . . . Madhuca indica
MOWRA B. . . . . . . M. longifolia

BUTTERWORT . . . . . . Pinguicula
BIGFLOWER B. . . . . P. grandiflora
COMMON B. . . . . P. vulgaris
MOUNTAIN B. . . . . P. alpina
TALL B. . . . . P. elatior
YELLOW B. . . . . P. lutea

BUTTONBUSH . . . . . . Cephalanthus
COMMON B. . . . . . C. occidentalis
SOUTHERN B. . . . . C. o. pubescens

BUTTONCACTUS . Epithelantha micromeris

BUTTONFLOWER . . . . Hibbertia
TOOTHLEAF B. . . . . . . H. dentata
TWINING B. . . . . H. volubilis

BUTTONMANGROVE . Conocarpus erecta

BUTTONPLANT . . . . . . Spermacoce
SMOOTH B. . . . . S. glabra

BUTTONWEED . . . . Diodia
ROUGH B. . . . . D. teres
VIRGINIA B. . . . . . . D. virginiana

BUTYROSPER'MUM . . BUTTERSEED
park'i . . . . SHEA B.

BUX'US . . . . Box
balear'ica . . . . SPANISH B.
har'landi . . . . . . HARLANDS B.
macow'ani . . . . . . MACOWAN B.
microphyl'la . . . . . LITTLELEAF B.
—**japon'ica** (*B. japonica*)
JAPANESE L.B.
—**korea'na** . . . . . KOREAN L.B.
—**si'nica** . . . . . . CHINESE L.B.
¢KINGSVILLE DWARF (*compacta*) HV.
B. microphylla
sempervi'rens . . . . . COMMON B.
¢BULLATA. HV.
¢ELEGANTISSIMA
¢FORGETMENOTLEAF (*myosotidifolia*)
¢GOLDEDGE (*marginata*)
¢GOLDEN (*aureovariegata*)
¢GOLDEN WEEPING (*aureopendula*)
¢HANDSWORTH (*handsworthi*)
¢MYRTLELEAF (*myrtifolia*)
¢PROSTRATE (*prostrata*)
¢PYRAMID (*pyramidata*)
¢ROSEMARY (*rosmarinifolia*)
¢ROUNDLEAF (*rotundifolia*)
¢SILVER (*argenteo-variegata*)
¢TRUEDWARF (*suffruticosa*)
TRUETREE (*arborescens*)
¢VARIEGATA
¢VARIEGATED OLIVE (*elegans*)
¢WEEPING (*pendula*)
¢WILLOW (*angustifolia*)
wallichia'na . . . . WALLICHIAN B.

BYRNES'IA . . **GRAPTOPETALUM**
See **SUCCULENTS.**

BYRSON'IMA . . . . . . BYRSONIMA
crassifo'lia
lu'cida . . . . LONGKEY B.
spica'ta

CAAPI . . . . . . Banisteriopsis caapi

CABBAGE . . Brassica oleracea capitata
Celery C. . . PETSAI: B. pekinensis
Chinese C. . . PAKCHOI: B. chinensis;
PETSAI: B. pekinensis
Peking C. . . PETSAI: B. pekinensis
WILD C. . . . . B. oleracea

CABELLUDA . . . . Eugenia tomentosa

CABLECREEPER Anodendron paniculatum

CABOM'BA |w . . . . FANWORT
aquat'ica . . . . TROPICAL F.
carolinia'na (*aquatica* DC., *not* Aubl.) |w
CAROLINA F.
—**pulcher'rima** . . . . . PURPLE C.F.
—**rosaefo'lia** . . . . . . ROSE C.F.

CABRA'LEA . . . . CABRALEA
congera'na . . . . . CANCHARANA C.
Caca'lia re'pens . . Senecio succulentus
CACAO . . . . Theobroma cacao

CACCI'NA
glau'ca

CAC'TUS . . . . . **MAMMILLARIA; MELOCACTUS**

CACTUS GENERA
See also **SUCCULENTS.**

This list is based on a nomenclatural revision by Elzada U. Clover, of the Department of Botany, University of Michigan, of an original furnished by the Cactus and Succulent Society of America through its Treasurer, R. W. Poindexter.

CACTUS GENERA, continued

Dr. Poindexter reports that, on the recommendation of the Nomenclature Committee of the Society, the classification of the original list was essentially Backeberg & Knuth's modifications of the Britton & Rose system and corresponded to that in present horticultural practice; also that it consists of all plants actually known by himself and colleagues to be in cultivation. Dr. Clover, an outstanding student of Cacti, takes a nomenclatural ground somewhat between the radical treatment of Britton & Rose and the very conservative treatment of Vaupel (in Engler & Prantl), though nearer to the former than the latter. The warm thanks of the Editorial Committee are extended to Doctors Poindexter and Clover, as well as to Messrs. W. T. Marshall and Scott Haselton who advised with them and furnished valuable suggestions. For convenience of reference, the genera and species of Cacti are here brought together in one consolidated list.

With Cacti there is encountered a somewhat different situation from that in general horticulture in that Cacti are primarily purchased by collectors who are most interested in those that are rare and difficult to obtain.

For this and other quite obvious reasons the Editorial Committee believes it would serve no useful end to bestow vernacular or common names on any great number of species of either Cacti or Succulents but suggests that the botanical names alone are usually sufficient and far more preferable.

ACANTHOCALYC'IUM
chionan'thum (*Echinopsis chionantha; Lobivia c.*)
formo'sum (*Echinopsis formosa*)
klimpelia'num (*Echinopsis klimpeliana; Lobivia k.*)
spiniflo'rum (*Echinopsis spiniflora; Lobivia s.*)
thionan'thum (*Echinopsis thionantha; Lobivia t.*)
viola'ceum (*Echinopsis violacea*)

ACANTHOCE'REUS ACANTHOCEREUS
acutan'gulus (*Cereus a.*)
florida'nus (*Cereus f.*)
hor'ridus (*Cereus h.*)
macula'tus
pentag'onus (*Cereus baxaniensis; C. pentagonus*) . BARBWIRE A. (*Dildoe*)

ACANTHORHIP'SALIS
micran'tha (*Rhipsalis m.*)

ANCISTROCAC'TUS FISHHOOKCACTUS
brevihama'tus (*Echinocactus b.*)
megarhi'zus (*Echinocactus m.*) BIGROOT F.
scheer'i (*Echinocactus s.*) . SCHEER F.

ANHALO'NIUM **ARIOCARPUS**
engelmann'i . . . . . . **A. fissuratus**
prismat'icum . . . . **A. retusus**
sulca'tum . . . **A. kotschoubeyanus**

APOROCAC'TUS . APOROCACTUS
conzat'ti . . . . CONZATTI A.
flagellifor'mis (*Cereus f.*) RATTAIL A.
flagrifor'mis
lepto'phis . . . . SNAKE A.
martia'nus (*Cereus m.*)

AREQUI'PA . . . . . AREQUIPA
leucot'richa (*Echinocactus leucotrichus*)

CACTUS GENERA, continued

ARIOCAR'PUS (*ANHALONIUM; ENCEPHALOCARPUS; OBREGONIA; ROSEOCACTUS*) . . . LIVINGROCKCACTUS (*Livingrock*)
dene'gri (*Obregonia d.*)
discifor'mis (*Echinocactus d.; E. turbiniformis; Mammillaria d.; Strombocactus d.; S. turbiniformis*)
fissura'tus (*Anhalonium engelmanni; A. fissuratum; Mammillaria fissurata; Roseocactus fissuratus*) . CHAUTLE L.
furfura'ceus
kotschoubeya'nus (*Anhalonium kotschoubeyanum; A. sulcatum; Roseocactus k.*) . . . . . . KOTSCHOUBEY L.
lloyd'i (*Roseocactus l.*) . . . LLOYD L.
retu'sus (*prismaticus; Anhalonium prismaticum*) . . . COBBLERSTHUMB L.
scapharos'trus
strobilifor'mis (*Encephalocarpus s.*)
trig'onus

ARMATOCE'REUS **LEMAIREOCEREUS**

ARROJADO'A **CEPHALOCEREUS**

ARTHROCE'REUS **TRICHOCEREUS**

ASTROPHY'TUM . . STARCACTUS
aster'ias (*Echinocactus a.*) SEAURCHIN S.
capricor'ne (*Echinocactus capricornis*) GOATHORN S.
myriostig'ma (*Echinocactus m.*) BISHOPSHOOD S.
orna'tum (*Echinocactus ornatus*)

AUSTROCAC'TUS
berti'ni (*Cereus b.*)

AYLOSTE'RA
fie'brigi (*Echinocactus f.*)
spegazzinia'na (*Rebutia s.*)

AZTE'KIUM
rit'teri (*Echinocactus r.*)

BARTSCHEL'LA **MAMMILLARIA**

BERGEROCAC'TUS
emo'ryi (*Cereus e.; Echinocereus e.*) VELVETCACTUS

BINGHAM'IA (*HAAGEOCEREUS; PSEUDOESPOSTOA*)
acran'tha (*Cereus acranthus; Haageocereus a.*)
chosicen'sis (*Cereus c.; C. melanostele; Haageocereus c.; Pseudoespostoa c.*)
decum'bens (*Cereus d.; Haageocereus d.*)
hum'boldti . . . . . **Borzicactus h.**
icosag'ona . . **Borzicactus icosagonus**
lareden'sis (*Cereus l.; Haageocereus l.*)
pacalaen'sis (*Cereus p.; Haageocereus p.*)
platinospi'na (*Cereus platinospinus; Haageocereus p.*)
pseudomelanoste'le (*melanostele; Cereus p.; Haageocereus p.*)
versic'olor (*Cereus v.; Haageocereus v.*)

BORZICAC'TUS
acanthu'rus (*Cereus a.*)
eriot'richus (*Cereus e.*) . CRAWLDEVIL
faustia'nus (*Cereus f.*)
hum'boldti (*Binghamia h.; Cereus h.*)
icosag'onus (*Binghamia icosagona; Cereus icosagonus*)
jajoia'nus (*Cereus j.*)
se'pium (*Cereus s.*)

CACTUS GENERA, continued

BRACHYCE'REUS
thouars'i (*Cereus t.*)

BRASILIOPUN'TIA **OPUNTIA**

BROWNING'IA . . . **CEREUS**

CAC'TUS . . **MAMMILLARIA; MELOCACTUS**
intor'tus . . . . **Melocactus i.**
macracan'thus . . . . **Melocactus m.**
missourien'sis . . . **Coryphantha m.**
panicula'tus . **Neoabbottia paniculata**

CARNEGIE'A . . . . **CEREUS**

CEPHALOCE'REUS (*ARROJADOA; STEPHANOCEREUS*) CEPHALOCEREUS
albispi'nus . . . . . . **Pilocereus a.**
alen'sis . . . . **Pilocereus a.**
arra'bidae . . . . . . **Pilocereus a.**
bahamen'sis . . . . . **Pilocereus b.**
barbaden'sis . . . . . **Pilocereus b.**
brooksia'nus . . . . . **Pilocereus b.**
catingic'ola . . . . . **Pilocereus c.**
chrysacan'thus . . . . **Pilocereus c.**
chrysomal'lus . . . . . **Pachycereus c.**
chrysoste'le . . . . . . **Pilocereus c.**
come'tes . . . . **Pilocereus c.**
deer'ingi . . . . **Pilocereus d.**
dybow'ski . . . . DYBOWSKY C.
euphorbioi'des . . . . . **Pilocereus e.**
fluminen'sis (*melocactus*) . . RIO C.
fri'ci . . . . **Pilocereus f.**
glauces'cens . . . . . **Pilocereus g.**
gounel'lei . . . . . . **Pilocereus g.**
hapalacan'thus . . . . **Pilocereus h.**
hoppenstedt'i (*Pilocereus h.*) HOPPENSTEDT C.
keyen'sis . . . . **Pilocereus k.**
lanugino'sus . . . . . . **Pilocereus l.**
leucoste'le (*Cereus l.; Stephanocereus l.*) ROLLINGPIN C.
macroceph'alus . . . . **Pilocereus m.**
max'oni . . . . **Pilocereus m.**
mills'paughi . . . . . **Pilocereus m.**
minen'sis . . . . **Pilocereus m.**
monoclo'nos . . . . . **Pilocereus m.**
no'bilis . . . . **Pilocereus n.**
pal'meri . . . . **Pilocereus p.**
pentaedroph'orus . . . **Pilocereus p.**
phaeacan'thus . . . . **Pilocereus p.**
polyg'onus . . . . . . **Pilocereus p.**
polylo'phus . . . . . . **Pilocereus p.**
pur'pusi . . . . **Pilocereus p.**
rhodan'thus (*Arrojadoa rhodantha; Cereus rhodanthus*)
ro'bini . . . . **Pilocereus r.**
roye'ni . . . . **Pilocereus r.**
russelia'nus . . . . . . **Pilocereus r.**
salvadoren'sis . . . . . **Pilocereus s.**
sartoria'nus . . . . . . **Pilocereus s.**
sen'ilis (*Cereus s.; Pilocereus s.*) OLDMANCACTUS
sublana'tus . . . . . . **Pilocereus s.**
swartz'i . . . . **Pilocereus s.**
u'lei . . . . **Pilocereus u.**
urbania'nus . . . . . . **Pilocereus u.**

CE'REUS (*Browningia; Carnegiea; Corryocactus; Dendrocereus; Epiphyllanthus; Erdisia; Escontria; Eulychnia; Leptocereus; Piptanthocereus; Stetsonia*) . . . CEREUS
acanthu'rus . . . . . **Borzicactus a.**
ac'ifer . . . . **Echinocereus a.**
acran'thus . . . **Binghamia acrantha**
acutan'gulus . . . . **Acanthocereus a.**

CACTUS GENERA (CEREUS), continued

adscen'dens . . . **Eriocereus a.**
ae'thiops . . . **C. coerulescens**
aggrega'tus . . **Coryphantha aggregata**
alacriporta'nus (*C. peruvianus a.*)
alamosen'sis . . . **Rathbunia a.**
amecamen'sis . . . **Heliocereus a.**
anguin'eus . . . **Cleistocactus a.**
anisit'si . . . **Monvillea a.**
areola'tus . . . **Cleistocactus a.**
argentinien'sis . Argentine Cereus
assur'gens (*Leptocereus a.*)
atropurpu'reus . **Eriocereus tortuosus**
au'reus Meyen, *not* Salm-Dyck **C. meyeni**
auric'olor . . . **Trichocereus a.**
azu'reus (*Piptanthocereus a.*)
bau'manni . . . **Cleistocactus b.**
bavo'sus . . **Lemaireocereus hollianus**
baxanien'sis **Acanthocereus pentagonus**
beneck'ei . . . **Lemaireocereus b.**
berlandier'i . . **Echinocereus blancki**
berti'ni . . . **Austrocactus b.**
bertramia'nus . . . **Trichocereus b.**
bifor'mis . . . **Disocactus b.**
biol'leyi . . . **Weberocereus b.**
blanck'i . . . **Echinocereus b.**
boeckmann'i . . . **Selenicereus b.**
bonpland'i . . . **Eriocereus b.**
brachypet'alus (*Corryocactus b.*)
brevispi'nus . . . **Selenicereus b.**
brevis'tylus (*Corryocactus b.*)
bridg'esi . . . **Trichocereus b.**
brittonia'nus . . **Monvillea maritima**
bronxen'sis . . . **Hylocereus b.**
brook'i . . . **Harrisia b.**
buchtien'i . . . **Cleistocactus b.**
cae'sius
caespito'sus **Echinocereus reichenbachi**
calcara'tus . . . **Hylocereus c.**
candela'brum . **Lemaireocereus weberi**
candela'ris (*Browningia c.*)
can'dicans . . . **Trichocereus c.**
cartwrightia'nus . **Lemaireocereus c.**
casta'neus . . . Chestnut C.
cavendish'i . . . **Monvillea c.**
celsia'nus . . . **Oreocereus c.**
cephalomacros'tibas **Trichocereus c.**
chacoa'nus . . . Chaco C.
chalybae'us (*Piptanthocereus c.*)
chen'de . . . **Lemaireocereus c.**
chi'chipe . . . **Lemaireocereus c.**
childs'i
chiloen'sis . . . **Trichocereus c.**
chiotil'la (*Escontria c.*)
chloran'thus . . . **Echinocereus c.**
chosicen'sis . . . **Binghamia c.**
chrysomal'lus . . . **Pachycereus c.**
cineras'cens . . . **Echinocereus c.**
coccin'eus DC. (1828) . **Mediocactus c.**
coccin'eus Engelm. (1849) **Echinocereus c.**
coccin'eus Salm-Dyck (1828) **Heliocereus elegantissimus**
co'chal **Myrtillocactus geometrizans c.**
coerules'cens (*aethiops*)
colubri'nus . . **Cleistocactus baumanni**
columna-traja'ni . . . **Pachycereus c.**
conglomera'tus . . . **Echinocereus c.**
coniflo'rus . . . **Selenicereus c.**
conoi'deus . . . **Echinocereus c.**
coquimba'nus . . . **Trichocereus c.**
cory'ne (*Stetsonia c.*)
costaricen'sis . . . **Hylocereus c.**
ctenoi'des . . . **Echinocereus c.**
cuben'sis . . . **Harrisia eriophora**
cuscoen'sis . . . **Trichocereus c.**

CACTUS GENERA (CEREUS), continued

dasyacan'thus . . . **Echinocereus d.**
daya'mi
decum'bens . . . **Binghamia d.**
defic'iens . . . **Lemaireocereus d.**
diffu'sus . . . **Monvillea diffusa**
donkelaar'i . . . **Selenicereus d.**
du'bius . . . **Echinocereus d.**
dumortier'i . . . **Lemaireocereus d.**
dybow'ski . . . Dybowsky Cereus
earl'ei . . . **Harrisia e.**
ebur'neus . . . **Lemaireocereus e.**
ehrenberg'i . . . **Echinocereus e.**
emo'ryi . . . **Bergerocactus e.**
engelmann'i . . . **Echinocereus e.**
enneacan'thus . . . **Echinocereus e.**
erioph'orus . . . **Harrisia eriophora**
eriot'richus . . . **Borzicactus e.**
er'uca . . . **Machaerocereus e.**
euphorbioi'des . . . **Pilocereus e.**
exten'sus . . . **Hylocereus e.**
fascicula'ris . . . **Trichocereus f.**
faustia'nus . . . **Borzicactus f.**
fend'leri . . . **Echinocereus f.**
fernow'i . . . **Harrisia f.**
fimbria'tus . . . **Harrisia fimbriata**
flagellifor'mis . . . **Aporocactus f.**
florida'nus . . . **Acanthocereus f.**
forbe'si . . . **C. validus**
fossula'tus . . . **Oreocereus f.**
fra'grans . . . **Harrisia f.**
fulvispi'nus . **Trichocereus terschecki**
galapagen'sis . . . **Jasminocereus g.**
gates'i . . . **Lophocereus g.**
gau'meri . . . **Pachycereus g.**
gemma'tus . **Pachycereus marginatus**
geome'trizans . . . **Myrtillocactus g.**
—*co'chal* . . . **Myrtillocactus g. c.**
gigan'teus (*Carnegiea gigantea*)
Saguaro (*Giantcactus*)
gla'ber . . . **Werckleocereus g.**
gladia'tus . . . **Trichocereus g.**
glazio'vi . . . **Leocereus g.**
godingia'nus . . . **Lemaireocereus g.**
grac'ilis . . . **Harrisia g.**
grandiflo'rus . . . **Selenicereus g.**
gran'dis . . . **Pachycereus g.**
grantia'nus (*Leptocereus g.*)
gregg'i . . . **Peniocereus g.**
grise'us . . **Lemaireocereus eburneus**
guatemalen'sis . . . **Hylocereus g.**
guelich'i . . . **Eriocereus g.**
gummo'sus . . . **Machaerocereus g.**
hama'tus . . . **Selenicereus g.**
hankea'nus . . . Hanke C.
hass'leri . . . **Mediocactus coccineus**
hendriksenia'nus . . . **Oreocereus h.**
herzogia'nus . . . **Cleistocactus h.**
hexag'onus
hildmannia'nus . . . Hildmann C.
hirschtia'nus . . . **Nyctocereus h.**
hollia'nus . . . **Lemaireocereus h.**
honduren'sis . . . **Selenicereus h.**
hor'ridus . . . **Acanthocereus h.**
huasch'a . . . **Trichocereus h.**
hum'boldti . . . **Borzicactus h.**
hu'milis . . . **Lemaireocereus h.**
huntingtonia'nus . . Huntington C.
hy'strix . . . **Lemaireocereus h.**
icosag'onus . . . **Borzicactus i.**
iner'mis . . . **Selenicereus i.**
insula'ris . . . **Monvillea i.**
intrica'tus . . **Trichocereus strigosus**
iquiquen'sis (*Eulychnia l.*)
irra'dians . **Selenicereus boeckmanni**
jajoia'nus . . . **Borzicactus j.**
jamaca'ru . . . Mandacaru C.
johns'toni . . . **Peniocereus j.**

CACTUS GENERA (CEREUS), continued

jusbert'i . . . **Eriocereus j.**
kunthia'nus . . . **Selenicereus k.**
lae'tus . . . **Lemaireocereus l.**
lamprochlo'rus . . . **Trichocereus l.**
lamprosper'mus
lana'tus . . . **Pilocereus l.**
lareden'sis . . . **Binghamia l.**
lemair'ei . . . **Hylocereus l.**
leo'ni (*Leptocereus l.*) . Leon Cereus
litora'lis . . . **Lemaireocereus l.**
macdonald'iae . . . **Selenicereus m.**
macrog'onus . . . **Trichocereus m.**
macrosti'bas (*Neoraimondia m.*)
mamilla'tus . . . **Echinocereus m.**
margina'tus . . . **Pachycereus m.**
marmora'tus . . **Monvillea marmorata**
martia'nus . . . **Aporocactus m.**
mar'tini . . . **Eriocereus m.**
max'imus (*Erdisia maxima*) Great C.
max'oni . . . **Pilocereus m.**
melanoste'le . **Binghamia chosicensis**
melanot'richus (*Corryocactus m.*)
Blackhair C.
melanu'rus . . . **Leocereus m.**
mey'eni (*aureus* Meyen, *not* Salm-Dyck; *Erdisia m.*) . . . Meyen C.
microsphae'ricus . . **C. obtusangulus**
mojaven'sis . . . **Echinocereus m.**
monacan'thus . . . **Hylocereus m.**
monta'nus . . . **Lemaireocereus m.**
moritzia'nus . . . **Pilocereus m.**
mur'rilli . . . **Selenicereus m.**
nash'i . . . **Harrisia fimbriata**
nick'elsi Hort. . **Pilocereus polylophus**
nudiflo'rus (*Dendrocereus n.*)
nycticau'lis . **Selenicereus pteranthus**
obtusan'gulus (*microsphaericus; Epiphyllanthus m.; E. obtusangulus; Epiphyllum microsphaericum*)
obtu'sus
ocam'ponis . . . **Hylocereus o.**
octacan'thus . . . **Echinocereus o.**
ol'fersi . . **Pilocereus euphorbioides**
pacalaen'sis . . . **Binghamia p.**
pachano'i . . . **Trichocereus p.**
pal'meri . . . **Pilocereus p.**
panamen'sis . . . **Weberocactus p.**
panicula'tus **Neoabbottia paniculata**
pasaca'na . . . **Trichocereus p.**
paucispi'nus **Echinocereus triglochidiatus**
pecten-aborig'inum . . **Pachycereus p.**
pectina'tus . . . **Echinocereus p.**
penicilla'tus
pentag'onus . . . **Acanthocereus p.**
pentalo'phus . . . **Echinocereus p.**
pernambucen'sis . . Pernambuco C.
peruvia'nus . . . Peru C.
—*alacriporta'nus* . . **C. alacriportanus**
phatnosper'mus **Monvillea phatnosperma**
phoenic'eus . **Echinocereus coccineus**
platinospi'nus **Binghamia platinospina**
po'co . . . **Trichocereus p.**
polyacan'thus . . . **Echinocereus p.**
polylo'phus . . . **Pilocereus p.**
polyrhi'zus . . . **Hylocereus p.**
pomanen'sis . . . **Eriocereus p.**
portoricen'sis . . . **Harrisia p.**
posel'geri . . . **Wilcoxia p.**
potts'i . . . **Peniocereus greggi**
prin'glei . . . **Pachycereus p.**
procum'bens **Echinocereus pentalophus**
pruino'sus . . . **Lemaireocereus p.**
pseudomelanoste'le . . **Binghamia p.**
pteran'thus . . . **Selenicereus p.**
pubiflo'rus

CACTUS GENERA (CEREUS), continued
pur'pusi . . . . **Hylocereus p.**
quadricosta'tus (*Leptocereus q.*)
queretaroen'sis . . **Lemaireocereus q.**
re'geli . . . . **Eriocereus r.**
reichenbachia'nus
Echinocereus reichenbachi
repan'dus Haw., *not* Mill.
Harrisia gracilis
rhodan'thus . . . . **Cephalocereus r.**
rhodoleucan'thus
Monvillea rhodoleucantha
roe'meri . . . **Echinocereus coccineus**
roe'meri Engelm., *not* Muhlenpf.
Echinocereus octacanthus
roez'li . . . . **Cleistocactus r.**
rondonia'nus . . . . **Trichocereus r.**
rostra'tus . . . **Selenicereus hamatus**
roye'ni . . . . **Pilocereus r.**
ru'ficeps . . . . **Pachycereus r.**
saxic'ola . . . . **Monvillea s.**
scheer'i . . . . . . **Echinocereus s.**
schickendant'zi . . . **Trichocereus s.**
schmoll'i . . . . **Wilcoxia s.**
schott'i . . . . **Lophocereus s.**
—monstro'sus . . **Lophocereus s. m.**
schrank'i . . . . **Heliocereus s.**
scopa'rius . . . . **Pilocereus s.**
sen'ilis . . . . **Cephalocereus s.**
se'pium . . . . **Borzicactus s.**
serica'tus . . . . **Pilocereus s.**
serpenti'nus . . . . . **Nyctocereus s.**
seta'ceus . . . **Mediocactus coccineus**
sha'feri . . . . . . **Trichocereus s.**
silves'tri . . . . . . **Chamaecereus s.**
smaragdiflo'rus . . . **Cleistocactus s.**
smithia'nus . . **Monvillea smithiana**
sonoren'sis . . **Rathbunia alamosensis**
spachia'nus . . . . **Trichocereus s.**
speciosis'simus . **Heliocereus speciosus**
specio'sus K. Schum., *not* Sweet
Heliocereus s.
spegazzi'ni . . . . **Monvillea s.**
spinibar'bis (*Eulychnia s.*)
spinulo'sus . . . . . **Selenicereus s.**
splen'dens . **Nyctocereus serpentinus**
squamo'sus
squarro'sus (*Erdisia squarrosa*)
stella'tus . . . . . **Lemaireocereus s.**
stenog'onus
stenop'terus . . . . . **Hylocereus s.**
stramin'eus . . . . **Echinocereus s.**
straus'i . . . . . . **Cleistocactus s.**
stria'tus . . . . . . **Wilcoxia striata**
strigo'sus . . . . . **Trichocereus s.**
tephracan'thus . . . . **Eriocereus t.**
terscheck'i . . . . . . **Trichocereus t.**
testu'do . . . . **Deamia t.**
tetrag'onus
thelegonoi'des . . . . **Trichocereus t.**
thelego'nus . . . . . **Trichocereus t.**
thouars'i . . . . . . **Brachycereus t.**
thur'beri . . . . . **Lemaireocereus t.**
tominen'sis . . . . . **Cleistocactus t.**
tondu'zi . . . . . **Werckleocereus t.**
tortuo'sus . . . . **Eriocereus t.**
treleas'ei . . . . . **Lemaireocereus t.**
triangula'ris Haw. . . . **Hylocereus t.**
triangula'ris Hort. **Hylocereus undatus**
tricosta'tus . . . **Hylocereus undatus**
triglochidia'tus . . . **Echinocereus t.**
trig'onus . . **Hylocereus costaricensis**
troll'i . . . . **Oreocereus t.**
tunil'la . . . . . . **Weberocactus t.**
tupizen'sis . . . . . **Cleistocactus t.**
unda'tus . . . . **Hylocereus u.**
urbania'nus . . . . **Selenicereus u.**
uyupampen'sis . . . **Trichocereus u.**

CACTUS GENERA (CEREUS), continued
va'gans . . . . **Selenicereus v.**
val'idus (*forbesi; Piptanthocereus v.*)
variab'ilis
venezuelen'sis . . . . . **Hylocereus v.**
versic'olor . . . . **Binghamia v.**
viperi'nus . . . . . **Wilcoxia viperina**
viridiflo'rus . . . . **Echinocereus v.**
vollia'nus . . . . . . **Trichocereus v.**
web'eri . . . . . **Lemaireocereus w.**
werck'lei . . . . **Selenicereus w.**
werdermannia'nus . . **Trichocereus w.**
xanthocar'pus YELLOWBERRY CEREUS

CHAMAECE'REUS
silves'tri (*Cereus s.*) . . PEANUTCACTUS

CHIAPA'SIA . **EPIPHYLLUM**

CHILE'NIA . **PYRRHOCACTUS**
heteracan'tha
Stenocactus heteracanthus

CLEISTOCAC'TUS
anguin'eus (*Cereus a.*)
areola'tus (*Cereus a.*)
bau'manni (*Cereus b.; C. colubrinus*)
FIRECRACKER-CACTUS
buchtie'ni (*Cereus b.*)
herzogia'nus (*Cereus h.*)
roez'li (*Cereus r.*)
smaragdiflo'rus (*Cereus s.*)
straus'i (*Cereus s.*)
tominen'sis (*Cereus t.*)
tupizen'sis (*Cereus t.*)

COCHEMIE'A
ha'lei (*Mammillaria h.*)
marit'ima (*Mammillaria m.*)
pond'i (*Mammillaria p.*)
posel'geri (*Mammillaria p.; M. roseana*)
setispi'na (*Mammillaria s.*)

CONSOLE'A . . . . **OPUNTIA**

COPIAPO'A
cineras'cens
margina'ta

CORRYOCAC'TUS . . **CEREUS**

CORYNOPUN'TIA . . **OPUNTIA**

CORYPHAN'THA (*ESCOBARIA; NEOBESSEYA*) CORYPHANTHA
aggrega'ta (*Cereus aggregatus; Echinocactus a.; Echinocereus a.; Mammillaria aggregata*) . . . . GOLFBALL C.
alverso'ni (*Echinocactus a.; Mammillaria radiosa*) . . . ALVERSON C.
an'dreae (*Echinocactus a.*)
arizo'nica (*Echinocactus arizonicus; Mammillaria arizonica*) ARIZONA C.
begui'ni . . . . **Neolloydia b.**
bel'la (*Echinocactus bellus; Escobaria bella*)
bumam'ma (*Echinocactus bumammus; Mammillaria bumamma*)
chaf'feyi (*Echinocactus c.; Escobaria c.*)
chihuahuen'sis (*Echinocactus c.; Escobaria c.*)
chloran'tha (*Echinocactus chloranthus*)
cla'va (*Echinocactus clavus; Mammillaria clava*)
conoi'dea . . . . . . **Neolloydia c.**
cornif'era (*Echinocactus corniferus; Mammillaria cornifera*)
cuben'sis (*Echinocactus c.*)
daemonoce'ras (*radians; Echinocactus r.; Mammillaria r.*)
dasyacan'tha (*Echinocactus dasyacanthus; Escobaria dasyacantha*)
des'erti (*Echinocactus d.*) FOXTAIL C.

CACTUS GENERA (CORYPHANTHA), continued
diffic'ilis (*Echinocactus d.*)
durangen'sis (*Echinocactus d.*)
DURANGO CORYPHANTHA
echinoi'dea (*Echinocactus echinoideus*)
echi'nus (*Echinocactus e.; Mammillaria e.*)
elephant'idens (*Echinocactus e.; Mammillaria e.*)
erec'ta (*Echinocactus erectus; Mammillaria erecta*)
georg'i (*Echinocactus g.*) . GEORGES C.
gladiispi'na (*Echinocactus gladiispinus*)
grandiflo'ra . . . . . **Neolloydia g.**
guerkea'na (*Echinocactus guerkeanus*)
horrip'ila . . . . . . **Neolloydia h.**
knuthia'na . . **Thelocactus knuthianus**
lloyd'i (*Escobaria l.*)
macrom'eris (*Echinocactus m.; Mammillaria m.*)
missourien'sis (*Cactus m.; Echinocactus m.; Mammillaria m.; M. nuttalli; Neobesseya m.*) . . . . MISSOURI C.
muehlenpfordt'i (*scheeri; Echinocactus m.* Poselger, *not* Fennel; *E. validus; Mammillaria scheeri* Muhlenpf., 1847, *not* Muhlenpf., 1845)
neomexica'na (*Echinocactus neomexicanus; Mammillaria neomexicana*)
SPINYSTARS C.
nick'elsae (*Echinocactus n.; Mammillaria n.*)
notestei'ni (*Echinocactus n.; Neobesseya n.*)
octacan'tha (*Echinocactus octacanthus; Mammillaria octacantha*)
pal'lida (*Echinocactus pallidus*)
pal'meri (*Echinocactus rosei*) PALMER C.
pectina'ta
poselgeria'na (*Echinocactus poselgerianus; Mammillaria valida* Purp., *not* Weber)
pseudechi'nus (*Echinocactus p.*)
pycnacan'tha (*Echinocactus pycnacanthus*)
ra'dians . . . . . . **C. daemonoceras**
recurva'ta (*Echinocactus recurvatus; Mammillaria recurvata; M. recurvispina* Engelm., *not* De Vriese)
retu'sa (*Echinocactus retusus*)
robustispi'na (*Echinocactus robustispinus; Mammillaria browni; M. robustispina*) . . . . SPIKESPINE C.
run'yoni (*Echinocactus r.; Escobaria r.*)
RUNYON C.
salm-dyckia'na (*Echinocactus delaetianus; E. salm-dyckianus* Poselger, *not* Pfeiffer)
sau'eri . . . . **Thelocactus s.**
scheer'i . . . . . **C. muehlenpfordti**
sim'ilis (*Echinocactus s.; Mammillaria s.; Neobesseya s.*)
sneed'i (*Echinocactus s.; Escobaria s.*)
SNEED C.
sulca'ta (*Echinocactus sulcatus*)
NIPPLE C.
tuberculo'sa (*Echinocactus strobiliformis; E. tuberculosus; Escobaria tuberculosa; Mammillaria s.; M. tuberculosa*)
vivip'ara (*Echinocactus radiosus; E. viviparus; Mammillaria vivipara*)
wiss'manni (*Echinocactus w.; Mammillaria similis robustior; Neobesseya w.*) . . . . . . WISSMANN C.

DEAM'IA
testu'do (*Cereus t.*)

CACTUS GENERA, continued

DENDROCE'REUS . . . CEREUS

DENMO'ZA . ECHINOCACTUS

DISCOCAC'TUS

alte'olens (tricornis; Echinocactus a.)
placentifor'mis (besleri; insignis; Melocactus b.)

DISOCAC'TUS

bifor'mis (Cereus b.; Epiphyllum biforme; Phyllocactus biformis)

DOLICHOTHE'LE . . . MAMMILLARIA

ECCREMOCAC'TUS

bra'dei

ECHINOCAC'TUS (DENMOZA; HOMALOCEPHALA) . . . ECHINOCACTUS

acantho'des . . . Ferocactus a.
acutis'simus . . . Pyrrhocactus a.
aggrega'tus . . . Coryphantha aggregata
alamosa'nus . . . Ferocactus a.
alba'tus . . . Ferocactus a.
alte'olens . . . Discocactus a.
alverso'ni . . . Coryphantha a.
an'dreae . . . Coryphantha a.
anfractuo'sus . . . Stenocactus a.
a'pricus . . . Notocactus a.
arechavaleta'i . . . Malacocarpus a.
arizo'nicus . . . Coryphantha arizonica
aster'ias . . . Astrophytum a.
aureicen'trus . . . Parodia aureicentra
aureispi'nus . . . Parodia aureispina
begui'ni . . . Neolloydia b.
bel'lus . . . Coryphantha bella
bi'color . . . Thelocactus b.
brevihama'tus . . . Ancistrocactus b.
buek'i . . . Thelocactus b.
bumam'mus . . . Coryphantha bumamma
caespito'sus . . . Notocactus c.
capricor'nis . . . Astrophytum capricorne
castaneoi'des . . . Pyrrhocactus c.
casta'neus . . . Frailea castanea
cataphrac'tus . . . Frailea cataphracta
ceratis'tes . . . Trichocereus c.
chaf'feyi . . . Coryphantha c.
chihuahuen'sis . . . Coryphantha c.
chilen'sis . . . Pyrrhocactus c.
chloran'thus . . . Coryphantha chlorantha
chrysacan'thion . . . Parodia c.
cine'reus
cla'vus . . . Coryphantha clava
colombia'nus . . . Frailea colombiana
colora'tus . . . Ferocactus c.
concin'nus . . . Notocactus c.
conoi'deus . . . Neolloydia conoidea
conothe'los . . . Thelocactus c.
coptonog'onus . . . Stenocactus c.
cornif'erus . . . Coryphantha cornifera
cornig'erus . . . Ferocactus latispinus
covil'lei . . . Ferocactus c.
crassihama'tus . . . Ferocactus c.
crispa'tus . . . Stenocactus c.
cuben'sis . . . Coryphantha c.
cum'ingi . . . Weingartia c.
curvispi'nus . . . Pyrrhocactus c.
cylindra'ceus . . . Ferocactus acanthodes
dasyacan'thus . . . Coryphantha dasyacantha
delaetia'nus . . . Coryphantha salm-dyckiana
denuda'tus . . . Gymnocalycium d.
des'erti . . . Coryphantha d.
diffic'ilis . . . Coryphantha d.
digue'ti . . . Ferocactus d.
discifor'mis . . . Ariocarpus d.

CACTUS GENERA (ECHINOCACTUS), con.

durangen'sis . . . Coryphantha d.
echid'ne . . . Ferocactus e.
echinoi'deus . . . Coryphantha echinoidea
electracan'thus . . . Ferocactus melocactiformis
elephant'idens . . . Coryphantha e.
emo'ryi . . . Ferocactus covillei
erec'tus . . . Coryphantha erecta
erina'ceus . . . Malacocarpus e.
erythroceph'alus (Denmoza erythrocephala)
faustia'nus . . . Parodia faustiana
fidaia'na . . . Weingartia f.
fie'brigi . . . Aylostera f.
flavovi'rens . . . Ferocactus f.
florico'mus . . . Notocactus f.
ford'i . . . Ferocactus f.
fossula'tus . . . Thelocactus f.
fus'cus . . . Neoporteria fusca
georg'i . . . Coryphantha g.
gibbo'sus . . . Gymnocalycium gibbosum
gladia'tus . . . Stenocactus g.
gladiispi'nus . . . Coryphantha gladiispina
glauces'cens . . . Ferocactus g.
grac'ilis . . . Ferocactus g.
gracil'limus . . . Frailea gracillima
graess'neri . . . Notocactus g.
grahlia'nus . . . Frailea grahliana
grandiflo'rus . . . Neolloydia grandiflora
gran'dis
gros'sei . . . Notocactus g.
gru'soni . GOLDBALLCACTUS (Goldenball)
guerkea'nus . . . Coryphantha guerkeana
haag'ei Hort. . . Lobivia neohaageana
hamatocan'thus . . . Hamatocactus h.
haselberg'i . . . Notocactus h.
hasta'tus . . . Stenocactus h.
has'tifer . . . Thelocactus h.
hayn'ei . . . Matucana h.
heloph'orus

Obscurely described; perhaps a synonym of E. ingens.

heteracan'thus . . . Stenocactus h.
heterochro'mus . . . Thelocactus pottsi
hexaedroph'orus . . . Thelocactus h.
horizonthalo'nius |w . . . DEVILSHEAD ECHINOCACTUS
hu'milis Rumpl., not Pfeiffer . . . Neoporteria fusca
in'gens

See note under E. helophorus.

intor'tus . . . Melocactus i.
john'soni . . . Thelocactus j.
johnstonia'nus . . . Ferocactus j.
jussieu'i . . . Neoporteria j.
knuthia'nus . . . Thelocactus k.
lamello'sus . . . Stenocactus l.
lan'cifer . . . Stenocactus l.
latispi'nus . . . Ferocactus l.
lecon'tei . . . Ferocactus acanthodes
leninghaus'i . . . Notocactus l.
leucacan'thus . . . Thelocactus l.
leucan'thus . . . Echinopsis leucantha
leucot'richus . . . Arequipa leucotricha
lloyd'i . . . Stenocactus l.
longihama'tus . . . Hamatocactus hamatocanthus
lophothe'le . . . Thelocactus l.
maas'si . . . Parodia m.
macdow'elli . . . Thelocactus m.
macrodis'cus . . . Ferocactus m.
macrohe'le . . . Strombocactus m.
macrom'eris . . . Coryphantha m.
mammillarioi'des . . . Pyrrhocactus m.
mammulo'sus . . . Notocactus m.
mandrag'ora . . . Thelocactus m.
maths'soni . . . Ferocactus crassihamatus

CACTUS GENERA (ECHINOCACTUS), continued

megarhi'zus . . . Ancistrocactus m.
melocactifor'mis . . . Ferocactus m.
microm'eris . . . Epithelantha m.
microsper'mus . . . Parodia microsperma
minus'culus . . . Lobivia minuscula
missourien'sis . . . Coryphantha m.
most'i . . . Gymnocalycium m.
muehlenpfordt'i Poselger, not Fennel . . . Coryphantha m.
multicosta'tus . . . Stenocactus m.
multiflo'rus . . . Gymnocalycium m.
murica'tus . . . Notocactus m.
mutab'ilis . . . Parodia m.
myriostig'ma . . . Astrophytum m.
napi'nus . . . Neoporteria napina
neomexica'nus . . . Coryphantha neomexicana
neumannia'nus . . . Weingartia neumanniana
nick'elsae . . . Coryphantha n.
nicola'i . . . Notocactus schumannianus
ni'dulans . . . Thelocactus n.
ni'gricans . . . Neoporteria n.
nigrihor'ridus . . . Pyrrhocactus n.
nivo'sus . . . Parodia nivosa
notestein'i . . . Coryphantha n.
obrepan'dus . . . Echinopsis obrepanda
obvalla'tus . . . Stenocactus o.
octacan'thus . . . Coryphantha octacantha
or'cutti . . . Ferocactus o.
orna'tus . . . Astrophytum ornatum
otto'nis . . . Notocactus o.
pal'lidus . . . Coryphantha pallida
pal'meri . . . E. platyacanthus p.
papyracan'thus . . . Toumeya papyracantha
pauciareola'tus . . . Malacocarpus p.
pectina'tus . . . Echinocereus p.
peruvia'nus . . . Oroya peruviana
pfeif'feri . . . Ferocactus glaucescens
phymatothe'le . . . Thelocactus p.
pilispi'nus . . . Neolloydia pilispina
pilo'sus . . . Ferocactus stainesi
platyacan'thus
—grand'is . MONSTER ECHINOCACTUS
—pal'meri (E. palmeri)
polyancis'trus . . . Sclerocactus p.
polyceph'alus . . . COTTONTOP E.
poselgeria'nus . . . Coryphantha poselgeriana
potts'i . . . Thelocactus p.
prin'glei . . . Ferocactus p.
pseudechi'nus . . . Coryphantha p.
pseudomacroche'le . . . Strombocactus p.
pulcher'rimus . . . Frailea pulcherrima
pu'milus . . . Frailea pumila
pycnacan'thus . . . Coryphantha pycnacantha
ra'dians . . . Coryphantha daemonoceras
radio'sus . . . Coryphantha vivipara
rectispi'nus . . . Ferocactus r.
recurva'tus . . . Coryphantha recurvata
recur'vus . . . Ferocactus nobilis
reich'ei . . . Neoporteria r.
retu'sus . . . Coryphantha retusa
rhodacan'thus (Denmoza rhodacantha; Echinopsis r.) . . . REDSPINE E.
rinconen'sis . . . Thelocactus r.
rit'teri . . . Aztekium r.
robustispi'nus . . . Coryphantha robustispina
robus'tus . . . Ferocactus r.
rose'i . . . Coryphantha palmeri
run'yoni . . . Coryphantha r.
salm-dyckia'nus Poselger, not Pfeiffer . . . Coryphantha salm-dyckiana
sanguiniflo'rus . . . Gymnocalycium venturianum

CACTUS GENERA (ECHINOCACTUS), con.
sau'eri . . . . **Thelocactus s.**
saussier'i . . . . . . **Thelocactus s.**
scheer'i . . . . . . **Ancistrocactus s.**
schickendant'zi . . **Gymnocalycium s.**
schilinzkya'nus . **Frailea schilinzkyana**
schmiedickea'nus . . **Strombocactus s.**
schumannia'nus . . . **Notocactus s.**
schwebsia'nus . . **Parodia schwebsiana**
sco'pa . . . . **Notocactus s.**
setispi'nus . . . . . **Hamatocactus s.**
si'leri . . . . **Utahia s.**
sim'ilis . . . . **Coryphantha s.**
simp'soni . . . . . . **Pediocactus s.**
sneed'i . . . . **Coryphantha s.**
staines'i . . . . **Ferocactus s.**
strausia'nus . . . . . **Pyrrhocactus s.**
strobilifor'mis **Coryphantha tuberculosa**
stue'meri . . . . **Parodia s.**
subgibbo'sus . . . . **Pyrrhocactus s.**
submammulo'sus . . . **Notocactus s.**
subterra'neus . . . . . **Thelocactus s.**
sulca'tus . . . . **Coryphantha sulcata**
tabula'ris . . . . . . **Notocactus t.**
tephracan'thus **Malacocarpus sellowi**
tetrax'iphus **Stenocactus heteracanthus**
texen'sis (*Homalocephala t.*)
Devilshead Echinocactus
tilcaren'sis . . . . **Parodia t.**
townsendia'nus . . . . **Ferocactus t.**
tuberculo'sus . **Coryphantha tuberculosa**
turbinifor'mis . **Ariocarpus disciformis**
umadea've . . . . . **Pyrrhocactus u.**
uncina'tus . . . . . . **Thelocactus u.**
unguispi'nus . . . . . **Thelocactus u.**
val'idus . **Coryphantha muehlenpfordti**
vandera'eyi . . . . **Ferocactus echidne**
vaupelia'nus . . . . . **Stenocactus v.**
viereck'i . . . . **Neolloydia v.**
violaciflo'rus . . . . . **Stenocactus v.**
viridiflo'rus . . . . **Echinocereus v.**
viscainen'sis . . . . . **Ferocactus v.**
visna'ga . . . . Bisnaga
vivip'arus . . . **Coryphantha vivipara**
vorwerckia'nus . . . **Malacocarpus v.**
wagneria'nus . . . . **Thelocactus w.**
whip'plei . . . . . **Sclerocactus w.**
wislize'ni . . . . . . **Ferocactus w.**
wiss'manni . . . . . **Coryphantha w.**

ECHINOCE'REUS . Echinocereus
a'cifer (*Cereus a.*)
aggrega'tus . . **Coryphantha aggregata**
albispi'nus . . . . . Whitespine E.
amoe'nus . . . . . . **E. pulchellus a.**
arizo'nicus . . . . Arizona E.
bai'leyi . . . . Bailey E.
barthelowa'nus
blanck'i (*berlandieri; Cereus berlandieri; C. blancki*)
brandegee'i . . . . . Brandegee E.
caespito'sus . . . . **E. reichenbachi**
can'dicans . . . . . **Trichocereus c.**
chloran'thus (*Cereus c.*)
Brownpitaya E.
cineras'cens (*glycimorphus; Cereus c.*)
coccin'eus (*phoeniceus; Cereus c.* Engelm., *not* DC. *nor* Salm-Dyck; *C. phoeniceus; C. roemeri*)
conglomera'tus (*Cereus c.*)
conoi'deus (*Cereus c.*)
ctenoi'des (*Cereus c.*)
dasyacan'thus (*Cereus d.*)
Yellowpitaya E.
delae'ti
du'bius (*Cereus d.*)
ehrenberg'i (*Cereus e.*) Ehrenberg E.
emo'ryi . . . . . . **Bergerocactus e.**

CACTUS GENERA (ECHINOCEREUS), con.
engelmann'i (*Cereus e.*)
Engelmann Echinocereus
enneacan'thus (*Cereus e.*)
fend'leri (*Cereus f.*) . . . . Fendler E.
fitch'i . . . . Fitch E.
glycimor'phus . . . . **E. cinerascens**
gonacan'thus . . . . **E. triglochidiatus**
gran'dis
knippelia'nus
leptacan'thus . . . . . **E. pentalophus**
lloyd'i . . . . Lloyd E.
longise'tus
lu'teus . . . . **E. subinermis**
mamilla'tus (*Cereus m.*)
marit'imus
mer'keri . . . . Merker E.
mojaven'sis (*Cereus m.*) . Mohave E.
octacan'thus (*roemeri; Cereus o.; C. roemeri* Engelm., *not* Muhlenpf.)
oklahomen'sis . . . . . Oklahoma E.
pacif'icus . . . . Pacific E.
pal'meri . . . . Palmer E.
papillo'sus (*texensis* Runge, *not* Jacobi)
Alicoche E.
paucispi'nus . . . . **E. triglochidiatus**
pectina'tus (*Cereus p.; Echinocactus p.*)
pen'silis
pentalo'phus (*leptacanthus; procumbens; Cereus pentalophus; C. procumbens*)
perbel'lus
phoenic'eus . . . . **E. coccineus**
polyacan'thus (*Cereus p.*)
posel'geri . . . . **Wilcoxia p.**
procum'bens . . . . . . **E. pentalophus**
pulchel'lus
—**amoe'nus** (*E. amoenus*)
purpu'reus
reichenbach'i (*caespitosus; texensis* Jacobi, *not* Runge; *Cereus c.; C. reichenbachianus*) . . . . Lace E.
rigidis'simus . . . . . . Rainbow E.
roe'meri . . . . **E. octacanthus**
roet'teri . . . . Roetter E.
ros'ei . . . . Rose E.
salm-dyckia'nus
sarissoph'orus
scheer'i (*Cereus s.*) . . . . Scheer E.
sciu'rus . . . . Squirrel E.
stramin'eus (*Cereus s.*)
subiner'mis (*luteus*)
texen'sis Jacobi . . . **E. reichenbachi**
texen'sis Runge, *not* Jacobi **E. papillosus**
triglochidia'tus (*gonacanthus; paucispinus; Cereus p.; C. triglochidiatus*)
Claretcup E.
viereck'i . . . . Viereck E.
viridiflo'rus (*Cereus v.; Echinocactus v.*)
Greenpitaya E.

ECHINOFOSSULOCAC'TUS
STENOCACTUS

ECHINOMAS'TUS
THELOCACTUS

ECHINOP'SIS . Hedgehogcactus
allegraia'na . . . . **Lobivia a.**
ancistroph'ora
andalgalen'sis . . . . . . **Lobivia a.**
atrovi'rens . . . . **Lobivia a.**
au'rea . . . . **Lobivia a.**
backeberg'i . . . . **Lobivia b.**
binghamia'na . . . . . . **Lobivia b.**
bolivien'sis . . . . **Lobivia b.**
breviflo'ra . . . . **Lobivia b.**
bridg'esi . . . . Bridges H.
caespito'sa . . . . **Lobivia c.**
calo'chlora
campylacan'tha . . . . . **E. leucantha**

CACTUS GENERA (ECHINOPSIS), continued
chionan'tha
Acanthocalycium chionanthum
chrysan'tha . . . . **Lobivia c.**
cinnabari'na . . . . **Lobivia c.**
cor'bula . . . . **Lobivia c.**
cordoben'sis
Cordova Hedgehogcactus
cylin'drica . . . . **Lobivia c.**
drijveria'na . . . . **Lobivia d.**
euan'thema . . . . **Lobivia e.**
eyrie'si
famatimen'sis . . . . . . **Lobivia f.**
fe'rox . . . . **Lobivia f.**
formo'sa . **Acanthocalycium formosum**
gemma'ta . . . . **E. turbinata**
haagea'na . . . . **Lobivia h.**
haematan'tha . . . . . . **Lobivia h.**
hamatacan'tha
hermannia'na . . . . . . **Lobivia h.**
hertrichia'na . . . . . . **Lobivia h.**
higginsia'na . . . . **Lobivia h.**
hos'sei . . . . **Lobivia h.**
huot'ti
inca'ica . . . . **Lobivia i.**
intricatis'sima
jajoia'na . . . . **Lobivia j.**
johnsonia'na . . . . **Lobivia j.**
klimpelia'na
Acanthocalycium klimpelianum
kratochvilia'na (*Lobivia graulichi*)
lateri'tia . . . . **Lobivia l.**
leucan'tha (*campylacantha; salpigophora; Echinocactus leucanthus*)
leucorhodan'tha
leucorho'don . . . . **Lobivia l.**
lobivioi'des
longispi'na . . . . **Lobivia l.**
mamillo'sa
mieck'leyi
mirab'ilis
mistien'sis . . . . **Lobivia m.**
mul'tiplex
nealea'na . . . . **Lobivia n.**
neohaagea'na . . . . **Lobivia n.**
ni'gra . . . . Black H.
ni'gricans . . . . . . **Neoporteria n.**
obrepan'da (*Echinocactus obrepandus*)
oruren'sis . . . . **Lobivia o.**
oxygo'na
pelecyrha'chis
pent'landi . . . . **Lobivia p.**
polyancis'tra
polyceph'ala . . . . **Lobivia p.**
pseudocachen'sis . . . . . **Lobivia p.**
pugionacan'tha . . . . . . **Lobivia p.**
pyg'maea . . . . **Lobivia p.**
rebutioi'des . . . . **Lobivia r.**
rhaphidacan'tha . . . . . **Lobivia r.**
rhodacan'tha
Echinocactus rhodacanthus
rhodo'tricha
rubes'cens . . . . **Lobivia r.**
salpigoph'ora . . . . . . **E. leucantha**
salten'sis . . . . **Lobivia s.**
sanguiniflo'ra . . . . . . **Lobivia s.**
schrei'teri . . . . **Lobivia s.**
sha'feri . . . . **Lobivia s.**
silves'tri . . . . Silvestri H.
smrzia'na
spiniflo'ra **Acanthocalycium spiniflorum**
sublimiflo'ra . . . . **Lobivia s.**
thionan'tha
Acanthocalycium thionanthum
tubiflo'ra (*zuccarini*)
turbina'ta (*gemmata*)
viola'cea . **Acanthocalycium violaceum**
wegheia'na . . . . **Lobivia w.**

CACTUS GENERA, continued
ENCEPHALOCAR'PUS **ARIOCARPUS**
EPIPHYLLAN'THUS **CEREUS**
microsphae'ricus . . **C. obtusangulus**
EPIPHYLLOP'SIS **SCHLUMBERGERA**
EPIPHYL'LUM (*CHIAPASIA; NOPALXOCHIA; PHYLLOCACTUS*) . . . . EPIPHYLLUM (*Leafcactus*)
angu'liger (*Phyllocactus a.*)
bifor'me . . . . **Disocactus biformis**
brid'gesi . . . . . **Schlumbergera b.**
crena'tum (*Phyllocactus crenatus* Lem., *not* Walp.)
dar'rahi . . . . DARRAH E.
gaert'neri . . . . . **Schlumbergera g.**
guatemalen'se . . . . GUATEMALA E.
hook'eri (*Phyllocactus h.*) HOOKER E.
lat'ifrons
makoya'num **Schlumbergera gaertneri**
microsphae'ricum **Cereus obtusangulus**
oxypet'alum (*Phyllocactus acuminatus; P. grandis; P. latifrons*) BROADLEAF E.
phyllanthoi'des (*Nopalxochia p.; Phyllocactus p.*)
pittier'i . . . . PITTIER E.
russellia'num **Schlumbergera russelliana**
—*gaert'neri* . . . **Schlumbergera g.**
stenopet'alum (*Phyllocactus stenopetalus*)
stric'tum (*Phyllocactus strictus*)

Hort. var. of **Epiphyllum:**

According to American usage, the true species of Epiphyllums are called *Epiphyllums.* In European usage, Epiphyllums are usually called *Phyllocacti,* particularly the horticultural hybrids. There is a tendency in America to call the species Epiphyllums and the hybrids Phyllocacti, on the ground that the hybrids are not true Epiphyllums in that they are hybridized with plants of other genera, usually either Selenicereus or Heliocereus.
R. W. POINDEXTER

All the following are clons.
ADELE MURIETTA
ADONIS
AGATHE
AIDA
ALBUS (*Perfectus*) SUPERBISSIMUS
ALPHA
AMBER QUEEN
ARGUS
ARIADNE
AURANTIACUS SUPERBUS
AUTUMN
BELLA
BOHEMIENNE
BRILLIANT
BRONZE
BUFF. (Steele)
CASTNERI
CLEOPATRA
CONWAYS GIANT
COOPERI
COPPERCOLOR
CORAL
DELICIOSA
DEUTSCHE KAISERIN
A group of hybrids.
EDEN. (Poindexter)
EREBUS
ETOILE DE CONTICH

CACTUS GENERA (EPIPHYLLUM), con.
EVRARTI
FIESTA. (Steele)
FLAMINGO. (Steele)
FORTUNA. (Steele)
FOSE DE LAET
FRANCOIS VERHAERT
GAMUT. (Steele)
GARNET. (Steele)
GLORIA
HANS REHM
HEKLA
HENNA
HERMOSISSIMUS
HERMOSUS
HYPATICA
IMPERATOR
IVORY. (Steele)
JANET
JENKINSONI
JULES SCHLUMBERGER
KATHARINA
KEITHI
LACKNERI
LATONA
LE DAUPHIN
LILACINUS
LOHENGRIN. (Steele)
LONDONI
MADONNA. (Steele)
MAGENTA
MAGNOLIA
MARTHA KNEBLE
MEDAILLE D'OR
MIRANDA
MISS EVANS
MME. DE LAET
MME. SALLIER
MONTEZUMA
MOONLIGHT. (Steele)
(*Mr.*) FERD. SCHLUMBERGER
NIOBE
ORION
OTUMBA
PAULA KNEBLE
PEACHBLOW
PEACOCKI
PFAU
PHOEBE. (Steele)
PINK NYMPH
POINSETTIA
POLYGLOT
POPOCATAPETL
PRIMA DONNA
ROSEA SUPERBA
ROSE PERFECTION
ROSETTA
ROTHER COOPERI
ROYAL FLUSH. (Steele)
SACUNTALA
SCARLET GIANT
SUNBURST. (Steele)
TRIOMPHE D'ANTHIEUSE
TRIOMPHE DE GUEBVILLERS
URANUS
VALENCIA. (Steele)
VAN HOFFINI
VIVE ROUGE
VIVIANNA. (Steele)
WANDA

EPITHELAN'THA
microm'eris (*Echinocactus m.; Mammillaria m.*) . . . . BUTTONCACTUS
ERDIS'IA . . . . . . **CEREUS**
ERIOCE'REUS
adscen'dens (*Cereus a.*)
bonpland'i (*Cereus b.; Harrisia b.*)

CACTUS GENERA (ERIOCEREUS), con.
guelich'i (*Cereus g.*)
jusbert'i (*Cereus j.*)
mar'tini (*Cereus m.; Harrisia m.*)
pomanen'sis (*Cereus p.*)
re'geli (*Cereus r.*)
tephracan'thus (*Cereus t.*)
tortuo'sus (*Cereus atropurpureus; C. tortuosus; Harrisia tortuosa*)
ERIOSY'CE . **TRICHOCEREUS**
sandil'lon . . . . **T. ceratistes**
ERYTHRORHIP'SALIS
pilocar'pa (*Rhipsalis p.*)
ESCOBA'RIA **CORYPHANTHA**
ESCON'TRIA . . . . . **CEREUS**
ESPOSTO'A . . . **PILOCEREUS**
EULY'CHNIA . . . **CEREUS**
FACHEIRO'A . . **PILOCEREUS**
FEROCAC'TUS . . BARRELCACTUS
acantho'des (*lecontei; Echinocactus a.; E. cylindraceus; E. lecontei*) CALIFORNIA B.
alamosa'nus (*Echinocactus a.*) ALAMOS B.
colora'tus (*Echinocactus c.*)
covil'lei (*Echinocactus c.; E. emoryi*)
crassihama'tus (*Echinocactus c.; E. mathssoni*)
digue'ti (*Echinocactus d.*)
echid'ne (*Echinocactus e.; E. vanderaeyi*)
flavovi'rens (*Echinocactus f.*)
ford'i (*Echinocactus f.*)
glauces'cens (*Echinocactus g.; E. pfeifferi*) . . . . BLUEGLOBE B.
grac'ilis (*Echinocactus g.*)
hamatocan'thus . . . **Hamatocactus h.**
hor'ridus
john'soni . . . . . . **Thelocactus j.**
johnstonia'nus (*Echinocactus j.*)
latispi'nus (*Echinocactus cornigerus; E. latispinus*)
lecon'tei . . . . **F. acanthodes**
macrodis'cus (*Echinocactus m.*)
melocactifor'mis (*Echinocactus electracanthus; E. melocactiformis*) MELONBARRELS
no'bilis (*Echinocactus recurvus*)
or'cutti (*Echinocactus o.*) . ORCUTT B.
pilo'sus . . . . **F. stainesi**
pring'lei (*Echinocactus p.*) PRINGLE B.
rectispi'nus (*Echinocactus r.*)
robus'tus (*Echinocactus r.*)
staines'i (*pilosus; Echinocactus p.; E. stainesi*)
townsendia'nus (*Echinocactus t.*) TOWNSEND B.
uncina'tus . . . . . . **Thelocactus u.**
virides'cens (*Echinocactus v.*) TURBAN B.
viscainen'sis (*Echinocactus v.*)
wislize'ni (*Echinocactus w.*) SOUTHWEST B.
FRAIL'EA . . . . FRAILEA
casta'nea (*Echinocactus castaneus*) CHESTNUT F.
cataphrac'ta (*Echinocactus cataphractus*)
colombia'na (*Echinocactus colombianus*) COLOMBIA F.
da'daki
gracil'lima (*Echinocactus gracillimus*)
grahlia'na (*Echinocactus grahlianus*)
pulcher'rima (*Echinocactus pulcherrimus*)

CACTUS GENERA (FRAILEA), continued
pu'mila (*Echinocactus pumilus*)
pyg'maea
schilinzkya'na (*Echinocactus schilinzkyanus*)

GRUSO'NIA . . . . . . GRUSONIA
bradtia'na (*Opuntia b.*) . THICKET G.
santamari'a . . . . SANTAMARIA G.

GYMNOCALYC'IUM . AWLCACTUS
andre'ae
anisit'si
bodenbenderia'num
bruch'i
capillen'se
castellano'si
chubuten'se
dam'si
denuda'tum (*Echinocactus denudatus*)
fleischeria'num . . . . FLEISCHER A.
gibbo'sum (*Echinocactus gibbosus*)
guerkea'num
hos'sei
hybopleu'rum
joossensia'num
leea'num
lorica'tum
megalothe'los
mihanovi'chi
monvil'lei . . . . . . MONVILLE A.
mos'ti (*Echinocactus m.*)
multiflo'rum (*Echinocactus multiflorus*)
ochoterena'i
oenan'themum
pflan'zi
platen'se
prolif'erum
quehlia'num
saglio'nis
schickendant'zi (*Echinocactus s.*)
stuck'erti . . . . . . STUCKERT A.
sutteria'num . . . . SUTTER A.
venturia'num (*sanguiniflorum; Echinocactus sanguiniflorus*)
weissia'num

HAAGEOCE'REUS **BINGHAMIA**

HAMATOCAC'TUS
hamatocan'thus (*Echinocactus h.; E. longihamatus; Ferocactus h.*)
The name frequently appears as hamatacanthus, but the original spelling is hamatocanthus.
setispi'nus (*Echinocactus s.*)
uncina'tus . . . . . . **Thelocactus u.**
—wright'i . . . . **Thelocactus u. w.**

HARRIS'IA . . . . APPLECACTUS (*Pricklyapple*)
aborig'inum . . . . SHELLMOUND A.
bonpland'i . . . . . . **Eriocereus b.**
brook'i (*Cereus b.*) . . . BROOKS A.
earl'ei (*Cereus e.*) . . . . EARLES A.
erioph'ora (*Cereus cubensis; C. eriophorus*)
fernow'i (*Cereus f.*) . . . FERNOW A.
fimbria'ta (*Cereus fimbriatus; C. nashi*)
fra'grans (*Cereus f.*)
grac'ilis (*Cereus g.; C. repandus* Haw., *not* Mill.)
mar'tini . . . . **Eriocereus m.**
portoricen'sis (*Cereus p.*) PUERTORICO A.
tortuo'sa . . . . **Eriocereus tortuosus**

CACTUS GENERA, continued
HATIO'RA . . . . . **RHIPSALIS**

HELIOCE'REUS
amecamen'sis (*Cereus a.*)
cinnabari'nus (*Cereus c.*)
elegantis'simus (*Cereus coccineus* Salm-Dyck, *not* DC. *nor* Engelm.)
schrank'i (*Cereus s.*)
specio'sus (*Cereus speciosissimus; C. speciosus* K. Schum., *not* Sweet)

HICKE'NIA . . . . **PARODIA**

HOMALOCEPH'ALA **ECHINOCACTUS**

HYLOCE'REUS NIGHTBLOOMING-CEREUS
antiguen'sis (*Cereus a.*) . ANTIGUA N.
bronxen'sis (*Cereus b.*)
calcara'tus (*Cereus c.*)
costaricen'sis (*Cereus c.; C. trigonus*) COSTARICA N.
cuben'sis
exten'sus (*Cereus e.*)
guatemalen'sis (*Cereus g.*) GUATEMALA N.
lemair'ei (*Cereus l.*) . . . LEMAIRE N.
monacan'thus (*Cereus m.*) ONESPINE N.
ocampo'nis (*Cereus o.*)
polyrhi'zus (*Cereus p.*)
pur'pusi (*Cereus p.*) . . . PURPUS N.
stenop'terus (*Cereus s.*)
triangula'ris (*Cereus t.* Haw., *not* Hort.)
trigo'nus
unda'tus (*Cereus triangularis* Hort., *not* Haw.; *C. tricostatus; C. undatus*) COMMON N.
venezuelen'sis (*Cereus v.*)

JASMINOCE'REUS
galapagen'sis (*Cereus g.*)

LEMAIREOCE'REUS (*ARMATOCEREUS*)
beneck'ei (*Cereus b.*)
cartwrightia'nus (*Armatocereus c.; Cereus c.*)
chen'de (*Cereus c.*)
chi'chipe (*Cereus c.*)
defic'iens (*Cereus d.*)
dumortie'ri (*Cereus d.*)
ebur'neus (*griseus; Cereus e.; C. griseus*)
er'uca . . . . . . **Machaerocereus e.**
godingia'nus (*Armatocereus g.; Cereus g.*)
gummo'sus . . . . **Machaerocereus g.**
hollia'nus (*Cereus bavosus; C. hollianus*)
hu'milis (*Cereus h.*)
hys'trix (*Cereus h.*)
lae'tus (*Armatocereus l.; Cereus l.*)
litora'lis (*Cereus l.*)
margina'tus . . . . **Pachycereus m.**
monta'nus (*Cereus m.*)
pruino'sus (*Cereus p.*)
queretaroen'sis (*Cereus q.*)
stella'tus (*Cereus s.*)
thur'beri (*Cereus t.*)
treleas'ei (*Cereus t.*)
web'eri (*Cereus candalabrum; Cereus w.*)

LEOCE'REUS
bahien'sis
glazio'vi (*Cereus g.*)
melanu'rus (*Cereus m.*)

CACTUS GENERA, continued
LEPIS'MIUM
commu'ne . . . **Rhipsalis squamulosa**
crucifor'me (*Rhipsalis cavernosa*)

LEPTOCE'REUS . . . **CEREUS**

LEUCHTENBER'GIA
prin'cipis . . . . . . AGAVE-CACTUS

LOBIV'IA (*REBUTIA* in part)
allegraia'na (*Echinopsis a.*)
andalgalen'sis (*Echinopsis a.*)
atrovi'rens (*Echinopsis a.*)
au'rea (*Echinopsis a.*)
aureiflo'ra (*Mediolobivia a.; Rebutia a.*)
backeberg'i (*Echinopsis b.*)
binghamia'na (*Echinopsis b.*)
bolivien'sis (*Echinopsis b.*)
breviflo'ra (*Echinopsis b.*)
caespito'sa (*Echinopsis c.*)
chionan'tha **Acanthocalycium chionanthum**
chrysacan'tha (*Rebutia c.*)
chrysan'tha (*Echinopsis c.*)
cinnabari'na (*Echinopsis c.*)
cor'bula (*Echinopsis c.*)
cylin'drica (*Echinopsis c.*)
drijveria'na (*Echinopsis d.*)
duursmaia'na . . . **Mediolobivia d.**
el'egans . . . . . . **Mediolobivia e.**
euan'thema (*Echinopsis e.*)
famatimen'sis (*Echinopsis f.*)
fe'rox (*Echinopsis f.*)
grandiflo'ra (*Rebutia g.*)
grau'lichi . **Echinopsis kratochviliana**
haagea'na (*Echinopsis h.*)
haematan'tha (*Echinopsis h.*)
hermannia'na (*Echinopsis h.*)
hertrichia'na (*Echinopsis h.*)
higginsia'na (*Echinopsis h.*)
hos'sei (*Echinopsis h.*)
inca'ica (*Echinopsis i.*)
jajoia'na (*Echinopsis j.*)
jansenia'na
johnsonia'na (*Echinopsis j.*)
klimpelia'na **Acanthocalycium klimpelianum**
knuthia'na (*Rebutia k.*)
lateri'tia (*Echinopsis l.*)
leucorho'don (*Echinopsis l.*)
longise'ta (*Rebutia l.*)
longispi'na (*Echinopsis l.*)
minus'cula (*Echinocactus minusculus; Rebutia minuscula*)
mistien'sis (*Echinopsis m.*)
nealea'na (*Echinopsis n.*)
neohaagea'na (*Echinocactus haagei* Hort.; *Echinopsis n.; Rebutia haagei*, nom. nud.)
oruren'sis (*Echinopsis o.*)
pent'landi (*Echinopsis p.*)
polyceph'ala (*Echinopsis p.*)
pseudocachen'sis (*Echinopsis p.*)
pugionacan'tha (*Echinopsis p.*)
pyg'maea (*Echinopsis p.*)
rebutioi'des (*Echinopsis r.*)
rhaphidacan'tha (*Echinopsis r.*)
rubes'cens (*Echinopsis r.*)
salten'sis (*Echinopsis s.*)
sanguiniflo'ra (*Echinopsis s.*)
schrei'teri (*Echinopsis s.*)
sen'ilis (*Rebutia s.*)
sha'feri (*Echinopsis s.*)
spiniflo'ra **Acanthocalycium spiniflorum**

Hort. var.; HV. = horticultural variety (or varieties); sp. = species (singular); spp. = species (plural).
₵ = clon; × (as a prefix) = hybrid; × (between scientific plant names) = crossed by; ∞ = polybrid; [W] = plant useful to wildlife.
See Glossary for definitions of clon, hybrid, and polybrid.

CACTUS GENERA (LOBIVIA), continued
stein'manni (*Rebutia s.*)
sublimiflo'ra (*Echinopsis s.*)
thionan'tha
Acanthocalycium thionanthum
violaciflo'ra (*Rebutia v.*)
wegheia'na (*Echinopsis w.*)
xanthocar'pa (*Rebutia x.*)

LOPHOCE'REUS
gates'i (*Cereus g.*)
schott'i (*Cereus s.; Pilocereus s.*)
—monstro'sus (*Cereus s. m.*)
TOTEMPOLE-CACTUS

LOPHOPH'ORA . . . . . PEYOTE
lew'ini
wil'liamsi . . . . MESCALBUTTON P.
zieg'leri

MACHAEROCE'REUS
er'uca (*Cereus e.; Lemaireocereus e.*)
CREEPINGDEVIL-CACTUS
gummo'sus (*Cereus g.; Lemaireocereus g.*)

MAIHUE'NIA . . . . MAIHUENIA
andic'ola . . . . ANDES M.
patago'nica (*Opuntia p.*) PATAGONIA M.
philip'pi . . . . PHILIPPI M.
poep'pigi . . . . POEPIG M.

MALACOCAR'PUS
arechavaleta'i (*Echinocactus a.*)
erina'ceus (*Echinocactus e.*)
leninghaus'i . . . . . Notocactus l.
mammulo'sus . . . . . Notocactus m.
otto'nis . . . . Notocactus o.
pauciareola'tus (*Echinocactus p.*)
sello'wi (*tephracanthus; Echinocactus t.*)
submammulo'sus . . . Notocactus s.
tabula'ris . . . . . . Notocactus t.
vorwerckia'nus (*Echinocactus v.*)

MAMILLOP'SIS **MAMMILLARIA**

MAMMILLA'RIA (*Bartschella; Cactus* in part; *Dolichothele; Mamillopsis; Neomammillaria; Pelecyphora; Phellosperma; Porfiria; Solisia*)
MAMMILLARIA
aggrega'ta . . . . . Coryphantha a.
al'bicans . . . . PALE M.
albic'oma
angula'ris . . . . . . M. compressa
applana'ta (*Neomammillaria a.*)
FLATTENED M.
ar'ida . . . . DESERT M.
arizo'nica . . . . . Coryphantha a.
armilla'ta (*Neomammillaria a.*)
assellifor'mis (*Pelecyphora a.*)
HATCHET M.
balsasen'sis
baxteria'na . . . . . . BAXTER M.
bi'color . . . . . M. geminispina
blossfeldia'na . . . . BLOSSFELD M.
bocasa'na (*Neomammillaria b.*)
BOCASA M.
—iner'mis . . . . . POWDERPUFF M.
boedekeria'na . . . . BOEDEKER M.
bogoten'sis . . . . . . BOGOTA M.
bombyci'na
brandeg'eei (*gabbi*)
brown'i . . Coryphantha robustispina
bullardia'na . . . . . BULLARD M.
bumam'ma . . . . . Coryphantha b.
calacan'tha
campot'richa
can'dida (*Neomammillaria c.*)
WHITEHAIR M.
capen'sis

CACTUS GENERA (MAMMILLARIA), con.
caperis'ia
car'nea (*Neomammillaria c.*)
BLOOD MAMMILLARIA
celsia'na (*Neomammillaria c.*)
centricir'rha
cephaloph'ora
cerati'tes . . . . Neolloydia c.
cerralbo'a
chapinen'sis (*woburnensis*)
chinoceph'ala
cirrhif'era
cla'va . . . . Coryphantha c.
clava'ta . . . . Neolloydia c.
colli'na
col'linsi . . . . MESA M.
compres'sa (*angularis; Neomammillaria c.*)
conoi'dea . . . . . . Neolloydia c.
cornif'era . . . . . Coryphantha c.
crucig'era
dealba'ta . . . . . WHITEWASH M.
decip'iens (*Neomammillaria d.*)
densispi'na . . . . DENSESPINE M.
denuda'ta (*Neomammillaria d.*)
digue'ti (*Mamillopsis d.*)
dio'ica (*Neomammillaria d.*)
discifor'mis . . . . . Ariocarpus d.
dis'color . . . . PIEBALD M.
dolichocen'tra . . . . . M. tetracantha
dona'ti
durispi'na
echina'ria (*Neomammillaria e.*)
echi'nus . . . . . . Coryphantha e.
el'egans (*Neomammillaria e.*)
elephant'idens . . . . Coryphantha e.
elonga'ta (*?minima; tenuis; Neomammillaria e.*) LACE M.
—stella-aura'ta . . GOLDENSTAR M.
erec'ta . . . . Coryphantha e.
evermannia'na . . . . EVERMANN M.
fascicula'ta (*Neomammillaria f.*)
fer'tilis . . . . FERTILE M.
fissura'ta . . . Ariocarpus fissuratus
flavovi'rens
frag'ilis . . . . THIMBLE M.
frailea'na
gabb'i . . . . M. brandegeei
gates'i
geminispi'na (*bicolor; nivea; Neomammillaria g.*)
gigan'tea (*Neomammillaria g.*)
GREATSPREAD M.
grac'ilis
gra'hami . . . . M. microcarpa
grandiflo'ra . . . . . Neolloydia g.
guelzowia'na
gummif'era (*Neomammillaria g.*)
GUM M.
haagea'na . . . . HAAGE M.
hahnia'na . . . . GRANNY M.
ha'lei . . . . Cochemiea h.
hamiltonhoy'tea
heesea'na . . . . . . M. petterssoni
herre'rae . . . . HERRERA M.
hey'deri (*Neomammillaria h.*)
HEYDER M.
hidalgen'sis
horrip'ila . . . . . . Neolloydia h.
hutchisonia'na . . . . HUTCHISON M.
john'stoni . . . . . . JOHNSTON M.
karwinskia'na . . . KARWINSKY M.
kewen'sis . . . . KEW M.
klissingia'na . . . . . KLISSING M.
kunzea'na . . . . KUNZE M.
lana'ta
lasiacan'tha (*Neomammillaria l.*)

CACTUS GENERA (MAMMILLARIA), con.
len'ta
leo'na . . . . M. pottsi
lesaunie'ri
lloyd'i . . . . . LLOYD MAMMILLARIA
longic'oma
longiflo'ra
longimam'ma (*Dolichothele l.*)
macdou'gali (*Neomammillaria m.*)
MACDOUGAL M.
macrom'eris . . . . Coryphantha m.
magnimam'ma (*Neomammillaria m.*)
mai'niae (*Neomammillaria m.*)
mammilla'ris (*simplex*)
marit'ima . . . . . . Cochemiea m.
marshallia'na . . . . MARSHALL M.
mazatlanen'sis . . . . MAZATLAN M.
meiacan'tha (*Neomammillaria m.*)
melanocen'tra (*Neomammillaria m.*)
mendelia'na . . . . MENDEL M.
microcar'pa (*grahami; Neomammillaria m.*) . . . . FISHHOOK M.
microhe'lia
microheliop'sis
microm'eris . . . . Epithelantha m.
microthe'le
mil'leri (*Neomammillaria m.*)
min'ima
Apparently synonymous with M. elongata.
missourien'sis . . . Coryphantha m.
moelleria'na . . . . . MOELLER M.
mul'ticeps (*Neomammillaria m.*)
multifor'mis
mys'tax (*mutabilis; N. mystax*)
neomexica'na . . . . Coryphantha n.
nick'elsae . . . . . Coryphantha n.
niv'ea . . . . M. geminispina
nivo'sa . . . . SNOWY M.
nune'zi
nutt'alli . Coryphantha missouriensis
ochoterre'nae
octacan'tha . . . . . Coryphantha o.
oliv'iae (*Neomammillaria o.*) OLIVIA M.
or'cutti . . . . ORCUTT M.
ortiz-rubio'na
pacif'ica . . . . PACIFIC M.
pain'teri . . . . PAINTERS M.
pal'meri (*Neomammillaria p.*)
PALMER M.
parkinso'ni (*N. p.*) . . PARKINSON M.
pectina'ta (*Pelecyphora p.; Solisia p.*)
peninsula'ris
perbel'la (*Neomammillaria p.*)
petroph'ila
pettersso'ni (*heeseana; Neomammillaria p.*) . . . . . PETTERSSON M.
phaeacan'tha
phellosper'ma (*tetrancistra; Phellosperma t.*)
phitauia'na
phymatothe'le
pilispi'na . . . . Neolloydia p.
plumo'sa (*Neomammillaria p.*)
FEATHERBALL M.
polye'dra (*Neomammillaria p.*)
pond'i . . . . Cochemiea p.
posel'geri . . . . . . Cochemiea p.
potts'i (*leona*)
prae'li
pring'lei . . . . PRINGLE M.
prolif'era (*pusilla; Neomammillaria prolifera*)
pseudopectina'ta (*Pelecyphora p.*)
pseudoperbel'la
pur'pusi . . . . Pediocactus simpsoni
pyg'maea . . . . PYGMY M.
ra'dians . Coryphantha daemonoceras
radio'sa . . . Coryphantha alversoni

CACTUS GENERA (MAMMILLARIA), con.
recurva'ta . . . . . **Coryphantha r.**
recurvispi'na Engelm., *not* De Vriese **Coryphantha recurvata**
rhapidacan'tha . . **Neolloydia clavata**
rhodan'tha (*Neomammillaria r.*)
ritteria'na . . RITTER MAMMILLARIA
robustispi'na . . . . **Coryphantha r.**
rosea'na . . . . **Cochemiea poselgeri**
rues'ti
run'yoni . . . . RUNYON M.
sar'tori
scheer'i Muhlenpf. 1847, *not* Muhlenpf. 1845 . **Coryphantha muehlenpfordti**
schiedea'na
schmoll'i
schu'manni (*Bartschella s.*) SCHUMANN M.
schwartz'i (*Porfiria coahuilensis; P. schwartzi*)
seitzia'na (*Neomammillaria s.*)
sempervi'vi (*caput-medusae; Neomammillaria s.*)
sen'ilis (*Mamillopsis s.*)
setispi'na . . . . . . **Cochemiea s.**
shel'doni . . . . SHELDON M.
sim'ilis . . . . . . **Coryphantha s.**
—*robus'tior* . **Coryphantha wissmanni**
sim'plex . . . . . . **M. mammillaris**
simp'soni . . . . . . **Pediocactus s.**
sinistrohama'ta
sle'vini . . . . SLEVIN M.
so'lisi
sphacela'ta
sphae'rica (*Dolichothele s.*) NIPPLE M.
spinosis'sima (*Neomammillaria s.*)
stand'leyi . . . . . . STANDLEY M.
strobilifor'mis **Coryphantha tuberculosa**
supertex'ta
swing'lei . . . . SWINGLE M.
ten'uis . . . . **M. elongata**
tetracan'tha (*dolichocentra; Neomammillaria t.*)
tetrancis'tra . . . . **M. phellosperma**
trichacan'tha
trohar'ti
tuberculo'sa . . . . . **Coryphantha t.**
uberifor'mis (*Dolichothele u.*)
uncina'ta (*Neomammillaria u.*)
valdezia'na (*Pelecyphora v.*)
val'ida Purp., *not* Weber **Coryphantha poselgeriana**
verhaertia'na
viereck'i . . . . VIERECK M.
viperi'na . . . . VIPER M.
viridiflo'ra . . . GREENFLOWER M.
vivip'ara . . . . . **Coryphantha v.**
wal'theri . . . . WALTHER M.
wil'coxi (*Neomammillaria w.*) WILCOX M.
wild'i (*Neomammillaria w.*) WILDS M.
winteri'ae . . . . WINTERS M.
woburnen'sis . . . . **M. chapinensis**
wright'i (*Neomammillaria w.*) WRIGHTS M.
xanthi'na . . . . GOLDEN M.
zahnia'na . . . . ZAHN M.
zeilmannia'na . . . . . ZEILMANN M.
zephyranthoi'des (*Neomammillaria z.*)
zeyeria'na . . . . ZEYER M.
zuccarinia'na . . . . . ZUCCARINI M.

MATUCA'NA
hay'nei (*Echinocactus h.*)

MEDIOCAC'TUS
coccin'eus (*Cereus c.* DC., *not* Salm-Dyck *nor* Engelm.; *C. hassleri; C. setaceus*)

CACTUS GENERA, continued

MEDIOLOBIV'IA (*REBUTIA* in part)
aureiflo'ra . . . . **Lobivia a.**
boedekeria'na
duursmaia'na (*Lobivia d.; Rebutia d.*)
el'egans (*Lobivia e.; Rebutia e.*)

MELOCAC'TUS (*CACTUS* in part) MELONCACTUS
an'toni . . . . ANTON M.
bahien'sis . . . . BAHIA M.
bes'leri . . **Discocactus placentiformis**
broad'wayi . . . . . BROADWAY M.
cae'sius . . . . GRAY M.
depres'sus . . . . **M. violaceus**
intor'tus (*Cactus i.; Echinocactus i.*) TURKSCAP M.
lemair'ei . . . . LEMAIRE M.
macracan'thus (*Cactus m.*)
matanza'nus . . . . . MATANZAS M.
max'oni . . . . MAXON M.
mique'li . . . . MIQUEL M.
ne'ryi . . . . NERY M.
o'reas
peruvia'nus . . . . . PERUVIAN M.
town'sendi . . . . . . TOWNSEND M.
viola'ceus (*depressus; melocactoides*) VIOLET M.
zuccari'ni . . . . ZUCCARINI M.

MI'LA
caespito'sa . . . . **Notocactus c.**
kubea'na
nealea'na

MONVIL'LEA
anisi'tsi (*Cereus a.*)
cavendish'i (*Cereus c.*)
diffu'sa (*Cereus diffusus*)
insula'ris (*Cereus i.*)
marit'ima (*Cereus brittonianus*)
marmora'ta (*Cereus marmoratus*)
phatnosper'ma (*Cereus phatnospermus*)
rhodoleucan'tha (*Cereus rhodoleucanthus*)
saxic'ola (*Cereus s.*)
smithia'na (*Cereus smithianus*)
spegazzi'ni (*Cereus s.*)

MYRTILLOCAC'TUS
geomet'rizans (*Cereus g.*) GARAMBULLO
—**co'chal** (*Cereus c.; C. geometrizans c.*) COCHAL

NEOABBOT'TIA
panicula'ta (*Cactus paniculatus; Cereus p.*)

NEOBES'SEYA **CORYPHANTHA**

NEOLLOYD'IA
begui'ni (*Coryphantha b.; Echinocactus b.*)
cerati'tes (*Mammillaria c.*)
clava'ta (*Mammillaria c.; M. rhapidacantha*)
conoi'dea (*Coryphantha c.; Echinocactus conoideus; Mammillaria c.*)
grandiflo'ra (*Coryphantha g.; Echinocactus grandiflorus; Mammillaria grandiflora*)
horrip'ila (*Coryphantha h.; Mammillaria h.*)
knuthia'na . . **Thelocactus knuthianus**
pilispi'na (*Echinocactus pilispinus; Mammillaria pilispina*)
rosea'na

Probably a synonym of Cochemiea poselgeri.

CACTUS GENERA (NEOLLOYDIA), con.
sau'eri . . . . **Thelocactus s.**
texen'sis
viereck'i (*Echinocactus v.*)

NEOMAMMILLA'RIA **MAMMILLARIA**

NEOPORTE'RIA
chilen'sis . . . . . **Pyrrhocactus c.**
fus'ca (*Echinocactus fuscus; E. humilis* Rumpl., *not* Pfeiffer)
jussieu'i (*Echinocactus j.*)
napi'na (*Echinocactus napinus; Notocactus n.*)
ni'dus
ni'gricans (*Echinocactus n.; Echinopsis n.*)
reich'ei (*Echinocactus r.*)
sen'ilis
subgibbo'sa . **Pyrrhocactus subgibbosus**

Neoraimon'dia macrosti'bas **Cereus m.**

NOPA'LEA . . . . NOPALCACTUS
au'beri (*Opuntia a.*) . . . . AUBER N.
cochenil'lifer (*cochenillifera; Opuntia c.*) COCHINEAL N.

This species was originally published by Linnaeus as Cactus cochenillifer; the specific adjective is usually misspelled in literature.

dejec'ta (*Opuntia d.*) . . PANAMA N.
inaper'ta

NOPALXO'CHIA **EPIPHYLLUM**

NOTOCAC'TUS
a'pricus (*Echinocactus a.*)
caespito'sus (*Echinocactus c.; Mila caespitosa*)
concin'nus (*Echinocactus c.*)
floric'omus (*Echinocactus f.*)
graess'neri (*Echinocactus g.*)
gros'sei (*Echinocactus g.*)
haselberg'i (*Echinocactus h.*)
leninghaus'i (*Echinocactus l.; Malacocarpus l.*)
mammulo'sus (*Echinocactus m.; Malacocarpus m.*)
mueller-mel'chersi
murica'tus (*Echinocactus m.*)
napi'nus . . . . . **Neoporteria napina**
otto'nis (*Echinocactus o.; Malacocarpus o.*)
schumannia'nus (*Echinocactus nicolai; E. schumannianus*)
sco'pa (*Echinocactus s.*)
submammulo'sus (*Echinocactus s.; Malacocarpus s.*)
tabula'ris (*Echinocactus t.; Malacocarpus t.*)
velenov'ski

NYCTOCE'REUS
hirschtia'nus (*Cereus h.*)
serpenti'nus (*Cereus s.; C. splendens*) SERPENTCACTUS

OBREGO'NIA . . **ARIOCARPUS**

OPUN'TIA (*BRASILIOPUNTIA; CONSOLEA; CORYNOPUNTIA; TEPHROCACTUS*) PRICKLYPEAR; CHOLLA

The flatstemmed species (subgenus Platyopuntia), which are frequently valuable emergency stock feed, especially when the spines are singed off, are designated Pricklypear. The cylindricalstemmed species (subgenus Cylindropuntia), which are often serious pests on stock range, are called Cholla.

CACTUS GENERA (OPUNTIA), continued
acanthocar'pa . . BUCKHORN CHOLLA
acicula'ta
albiflo'ra . . . . **O. salmiana**
alca'hes
andic'ola (*Tephrocactus andicolus*)
aoracan'tha (*Tephrocactus aoracanthus*)
arbores'cens . . . . . . **O. imbricata**
au'beri . . . . **Nopalea a.**
auranti'aca . ORANGERED PRICKLYPEAR
au'rea . . . . GOLDEN P.
basila'ris . . . . . . BEAVERTAIL P.
bernardi'na . . . . . . **O. parryi**
bigelo'vi . . . ARIZONA JUMPING P.
boldingh'i
brachycla'da
bradtia'na . . . . **Grusonia b.**
brasilien'sis (*Brasiliopuntia b.*)
bruch'i (*Tephrocactus b.*)
bulbispi'na (*Corynopuntia b.*)
cacana'pa . . . . . . **O. lindheimeri**
calmallia'na
caman'chica . . . . **O. phaeacantha**
cani'na . . . . DOG P.
castil'lae . . . . . . **O. megacantha**
catacan'tha . . . . . . **O. rubescens**
chlorot'ica |w . . . DOLLARJOINT P. (*Dollarcactus*)
chol'la . . . . MEXICALI C.
clavarioi'des
clava'ta (*Corynopuntia c.*)
clavelli'na
cochenillif'era . **Nopalea cochenillifer**
compres'sa (*opuntia*)
curassa'vica
cylin'drica . . . . . . ECUADOR C.
da'visi . . . . JEFFDAVIS C.
decum'bens (*puberula*) . GROUND P.
dejec'ta . . . . **Nopalea d.**
demis'sa . . . . **O. occidentalis**
dille'ni (*horrida*) . . . . . DILLEN P.
dobbiea'na . . . . DOBBIE P.
echinocar'pa (*deserta*) . STRAWTOP P.
eich'lami . . . . EICHLAM P.
ela'ta
ela'tior (*nigricans*) . . . CHIMNEY P.
emo'ryi . . . . **O. stanlyi**
engelmann'i |w . . . ENGELMANN P.
erectocla'da
erina'cea (*ursina*) . GRIZZLYBEAR P.
exalta'ta
ficus-in'dica . . . . INDIANFIG
flocco'sa (*senilis*)
frag'ilis . . . . BRITTLE P.
ful'gida . . . . SONORA JUMPING C.
—mammilla'ta
fulvispi'na . . . . . . **O. leucotricha**
fuscoa'tra
go'mei . . . . **O. lindheimeri**
gosselinia'na
grandiflo'ra . . . . . BIGFLOWER P.
haloph'ila (*Tephrocactus halophilus*)
herrfeldt'i . . . . . . HERRFELDT P.
hor'rida . . . . **O. dilleni**
humifu'sa . . . . **O. vulgaris**
hu'milis . . . . **O. tuna**
humistra'ta
hyptiacan'tha
hystrici'na
igno'ta (*Tephrocactus ignotus*)
imbrica'ta (*arborescens; vexans*) |w WALKINGSTICK C.
iner'mis . . . . **O. stricta**
invic'ta (*Corynopuntia i.*)
klein'iae . . . . CANDLE C.
lae'vis . . . . SMOOTH P.

CACTUS GENERA (OPUNTIA), continued
leptocau'lis (*frutescens*) |w . . TESAJO
leucot'richa (*fulvispina*) AARONSBEARD PRICKLYPEAR (*Aaronsbeard*)
lindhei'meri (*cacanapa; gomei*)
linguifor'mis . . . . COWSTONGUE P.
litora'lis
macdougalia'na . . MACDOUGAL P.
mackensen'i . . . . . MACKENSEN P.
macracan'tha (*Consolea m.*)
macrocen'tra |w
megacan'tha (*castillae*) . MISSION P.
megarhi'za
mesacan'tha . . . . . . **O. vulgaris**
microda'sys . . . . . GOLDPLUSH P.
microdis'ca
millspaugh'i (*Consolea m.*)
missourien'sis . . . . **O. polyacantha**
mistien'sis (*Tephrocactus m.*)
moelleria'na
mojaven'sis . . . . . . MOHAVE P.
monacan'tha . . . . . . **O. vulgaris**
—variega'ta . . . . . . **O. vulgaris**
monilifor'mis (*Consolea m.*)
multiflo'ra . . . . **O. tuna**
na'na . . . . **O. vulgaris**
ni'gricans . . . . **O. elatior**
occidenta'lis (*demissa*) . WESTERN P.
opun'tia . . . . **O. compressa**
ova'ta (*Tephrocactus ovatus*)
par'ishi (*Corynopuntia p.*) PARISH CHOLLA
par'ryi (*bernardina*)
patago'nica . . . . **Maihuenia p.**
pent'landi (*Tephrocactus p.*)
perri'ta . . . . **O. tunicata**
phaeacan'tha (*camanchica*)
pilif'era . . . . SOFTHAIR P.
pol'lardi . . . . POLLARD P.
polyacan'tha (*missouriensis; schweriniana*) |w . . . . PLAINS P.
polyan'tha . . . . **O. tuna**
potts'i . . . . MEXICANROSE P.
prolif'era . . . . . . SANDIEGO C.
puber'ula . . . . . . **O. decumbens**
pu'mila
pycnan'tha
quimi'lo
rafines'quei . . . . **O. vulgaris**
ramosis'sima . . . . . HOLYCROSS C.
re'pens
retror'sa
rhodan'tha (*xanthostemma*)
robus'ta
rubes'cens (*catacantha; Consolea r.*)
ru'fida . . . . BLIND P.
salmia'na (*albiflora*)
santa-ri'ta . . . . . . SANTARITA P.
scheer'i . . . . SCHEERS P.
schott'i (*Corynopuntia s.*) SCHOTTS C.
schu'manni . . . . . . SCHUMANN P.
schwerinia'na . . . . **O. polyacantha**
sen'ilis . . . . **O. floccosa**
soederstromia'na
soeh'rensi
spathula'ta . . . . **Pereskiopsis s.**
sphae'rica (*Tephrocactus sphaericus*)
spino'sior
spinosis'sima (*Consolea s.*)
stan'lyi (*emoryi; Corynopuntia s.*) STANLY C.
stenopet'ala . . . . NARROWPETAL P.
streptacan'tha
stric'ta (*inermis*)
subula'ta (*Pereskia s.*)
sulphu'rea . . . . SULFUR P.
te'res
tetracan'tha . . . . . FOURSPINE C.

CACTUS GENERA (OPUNTIA), continued
tomento'sa
tortispi'na . TWISTSPINE PRICKLYPEAR
treleas'ei . . . . . . TRELEASE P.
tu'na (*humilis; multiflora; polyantha*) TUNA P. (*Tuna*)
tunica'ta (*perrita*)
ursi'na . . . . **O. erinacea**
va'seyi . . . . VASEY P.
veluti'na . . . . VELVET P.
verschaffelt'i . VERSCHAFFELT CHOLLA
versic'olor
vesti'ta
vex'ans . . . . **O. imbricata**
vivip'ara
vulga'ris (*humifusa; mesacantha; monacantha; O. m. variegata; nana; rafinesquei*) |w . . . . COMMON P.
web'eri (*Tephrocactus w.*)
whip'plei . . . . WHIPPLE C.
whitneya'na . . . . . . WHITNEY P.
xanthostem'ma . . . . **O. rhodantha**

OREOCE'REUS
celsia'nus (*Cereus c.*)
doelzia'nus
fossula'tus (*Cereus f.*)
hendriksenia'nus (*Cereus h.*)
troll'i (*Cereus t.*)

ORO'YA
neoperuvia'na
peruvia'na (*Echinocactus peruvianus*)

PACHYCE'REUS
chrysomal'lus (*Cephalocereus c.; Cereus c.*)
columna-traja'ni (*Cereus c.*) TRAJANSCOLUMN
gau'meri (*Cereus g.*)
gran'dis (*Cereus g.*)
margina'tus (*Cereus gemmatus; C. marginatus; Lemaireocereus m.*) ORGANPIPE-CACTUS
pecten-aborig'inum (*Cereus p.*) HAIRBRUSHCACTUS
pring'lei (*Cereus p.*)
ru'ficeps (*Cereus r.*)

PARODI'A (*HICKENIA*)
aureicen'tra (*Echinocactus aureicentrus*)
aureispi'na (*Echinocactus aureispinus*)
chrysacan'thion (*Echinocactus c.*)
faustia'na (*Echinocactus faustianus*)
maas'si (*Echinocactus m.*)
microsper'ma (*Echinocactus microspermus; Hickenia microsperma*)
mutab'ilis (*Echinocactus m.*)
nivo'sa (*Echinocactus nivosus*)
sanguiniflo'ra
schwebsia'na (*Echinocactus schwebsianus*)
stue'meri (*Echinocactus s.*)
tilcaren'sis (*Echinocactus t.*)

PEDIOCAC'TUS
simp'soni (*Echinocactus s.; Mammillaria purpusi; M. simpsoni*) SNOWBALLCACTUS
—mi'nor
—robus'tior

PEIRES'KIA . . . **PERESKIA**
PELECY'PHORA **MAMMILLARIA**

PENIOCE'REUS
gregg'i (*Cereus g.; C. pottsi*) DEERHORNCACTUS
johns'toni (*Cereus j.*)

CACTUS GENERA, continued

· **PERES'KIA** (*PEIRESKIA; RHODOCACTUS*) . . . . PERESKIA

The name Pereskia is variously spelled. It is used in honor of N. C. F. de Peiresc (1580–1637).

aculea'ta (*pereskia*) BARBADOS-GOOSEBERRY
ble'o
Name often misapplied to P. grandifolia.
conzat'ti
grandifo'lia (*Rhodocactus grandifolius*)
sacharo'sa (*amapola*)
spathula'ta . . . . . . **Pereskiopsis s.**
subula'ta . . . . **Opuntia s.**
tampica'na . . . . TAMPICO P.
zehnt'neri . . . . **Quiabentia z.**

PERESKIOP'SIS
aquo'sa
cha'pistle
digue'ti
gates'i
por'teri (*brandegeei*)
spathula'ta (*Opuntia s.; Pereskia s.*)
veluti'na

PFEIF'FERA
ianothe'le (*cereiformis; Rhipsalis c.*)

PHELLOSPER'MA **MAMMILLARIA**
tetrancis'tra . . . . **M. phellosperma**

PHYLLOCAC'TUS **EPIPHYLLUM**
acumina'tus . . . . . **E. oxypetalum**
bifor'mis . . . . **Disocactus b.**
gran'dis; lat'ifrons . . **E. oxypetalum**
russellia'nus **Schlumbergera russelliana**

PILOCE'REUS (*ESPOSTOA; FACHEIROA*) . . . . PILOCEREUS

This genus is somewhat doubtfully distinct from the older Cephalocereus.

albispi'nus (*Cephalocereus a.*) WHITESPINE P.
alen'sis (*Cephalocereus a.*) SIERRADELALO P.
arra'bidae (*exerens; Cephalocereus a.*) BRAZILCOAST P.
bahamen'sis (*Cephalocereus b.*) BAHAMAS P.
barbaden'sis (*Cephalocereus b.*) BARBADOS P.
brooksia'nus (*Cephalocereus b.*) BROOKS P.
catingic'ola (*Cephalocereus c.*) CATINGA P.
chrysacan'thus (*Cephalocereus c.*) GOLDSPINE P.
chrysoste'le (*Cephalocereus c.*)
come'tes (*Cephalocereus c.*)
deer'ingi (*Cephalocereus d.*) MATACUMBE P.
euphorbioi'des (*Cephalocereus e.; Cereus e.; C. olfersi*) . . . . . . SPURGE P.
ex'erens . . . . **P. arrabidae**
fric'i (*Cephalocereus f.*)
glauces'cens (*Cephalocereus g.*)
gounel'lei (*Cephalocereus g.*) GOUNELLE P.
hapalacan'thus (*Cephalocereus h.*)
hoppenstedt'i . . . . **Cephalocereus h.**
houllet'i . . . . **P. palmeri**
keyen'sis (*Cephalocereus k.*) KEYWEST P.
lana'tus (*Cereus l.; Espostoa lanata*)
lanugino'sus (*Cephalocereus l.*) CURACAO P.
leucoceph'alus . . . . WHITELOCK P.

CACTUS GENERA (PILOCEREUS), con.

macroceph'alus (*Cephalocereus m.*) TEHUACAN PILOCEREUS
max'oni (*Cephalocereus m.; Cereus m.*) MAXON P.
millspaugh'i (*Cephalocereus m.*) MILLSPAUGH P.
minen'sis (*Cephalocereus m.*)
monoclo'nos (*Cephalocereus m.*) HAITI P.
moritzia'nus (*Cereus m.*)
no'bilis (*strictus; Cephalocereus n.*)
pal'meri (*houlleti; Cephalocereus p.; Cereus p.*) . . . . . . PALMER P.
pentaedroph'orus (*Cephalocereus p.*) VERACRUZ P.
phaeacan'thus (*Cephalocereus p.*) BAHIA P.
polyg'onus (*Cephalocereus p.*) POLYGON P.
polylo'phus (*Cephalocereus p.; Cereus nickelsi* Hort.; *C. polylophus*)
pur'pusi (*Cephalocereus p.*) . PURPUS P.
robi'ni (*Cephalocereus r.*) . ROBINS P.
roye'ni (*Cephalocereus r.; Cereus r.*) ROYEN P.
russelia'nus (*Cephalocereus r.*) RUSSEL P.
salvadoren'sis (*Cephalocereus s.*) SALVADOR P.
sartoria'nus (*Cephalocereus s.*) SARTORIUS P.
schott'i . . . . **Lophocereus s.**
scopa'rius (*Cereus s.*) . . . BROOM P.
sen'ilis . . . . . . **Cephalocereus s.**
serica'tus (*Cereus s.; Espostoa sericata*)
stric'tus . . . . **P. nobilis**
sublana'tus (*Cephalocereus s.*)
swartz'i (*Cephalocereus s.*) . SWARTZ P.
u'lei (*Cephalocereus u.; Facheiroa u.*) ULE P.
urbania'nus (*Cephalocereus u.*) URBANS P.

PIPTANTHOCE'REUS **CEREUS**

PORFI'RIA . **MAMMILLARIA**
coahuilen'sis . . . . . **M. schwartzi**

PSEUDOESPOS'TOA **BINGHAMIA**

PSEUDORHIP'SALIS
acumina'ta
ala'ta
himantoc'lada (*Rhipsalis h.*)

PTEROCAC'TUS . . WINGCACTUS
fish'eri . . . . FISHER W.
tubero'sus . . . . TUBER W.

PYRRHOCAC'TUS (*CHILENIA*)
acutis'simus (*Chilenia acutissima; Echinocactus acutissimus*)
castaneoi'des (*Chilenia c.; Echinocactus c.*)
chilen'sis (*Chilenia c.; Echinocactus c.; Neoporteria c.*)
curvispi'nus (*Echinocactus c.*)
heteracan'thus . . . . **Stenocactus h.**
hor'ridus
mammillarioi'des (*Echinocactus m.*)
nigrihor'ridus (*Chilenia nigrihorrida; Echinocactus nigrihorridus*)
strausia'nus (*Echinocactus s.*)
subgibbo'sus (*Chilenia subgibbosa; Echinocactus subgibbosus; Neoporteria subgibbosa*)
umadea've (*Echinocactus u.*)

QUIABENT'IA . . . . QUIABENTIA
chacoen'sis . . . . CHACO Q.
zehnt'neri (*Pereskia z.*) ZEHNTNER Q.

CACTUS GENERA, continued

RATHBUN'IA . . RATHBUNCACTUS
alamosen'sis (*sonorensis; Cereus a.; C. sonorensis*) . . . . SONORA R.
ker'beri . . . . KERBER R.

REBU'TIA . . . . . **LOBIVIA; MEDIOLOBIVIA**
haag'ei nom. nud. . . **L. neohaageana**
speggazinia'na . . . . . **Aylostera s.**

RHIPSALIDOP'SIS
rose'a (*Rhipsalis r.*)

RHIP'SALIS (*HATIORA*) RHIPSALIS
bambusoi'des (*Hatiora b.*) BAMBOO R.
capillifor'mis . . . . . TREEHAIR R.
cassu'tha (*cassytha*) . . MISTLETOE R.
caverno'sa . . **Lepismium cruciforme**
cereifor'mis . . . **Pfeiffera ianothele**
cerus'cula (*saglionis*)
clava'ta
coria'cea
crispa'ta
cylin'drica (*Hatiora c.*)
dissim'ile (*Lepismium d.*)
ellip'tica
gaert'neri . . . . **Schlumbergera g.**
grandiflo'ra
himantoc'lada . . **Pseudorhipsalis h.**
houlletia'na
jamaicen'sis . . . . . . JAMAICA R.
leucorha'phis
mesembrianthemoi'des
micran'tha . . . **Acanthorhipsalis m.**
pachyp'tera
paradox'a (*Lepismium paradoxum*) CHAIN R.
pentap'tera . . . . . FIVEWING R.
pilocar'pa . . . . **Erythrorhipsalis p.**
prismat'ica
puniceo-dis'ca (*Lepismium puniceodiscum*)
rhom'bea
rose'a . . . . **Rhipsalidopsis r.**
russellia'na . . . . **Schlumbergera r.**
saglio'nis . . . . **R. ceruscula**
salicornioi'des (*Hatiora s.*) . CORAL R.
squamulo'sa (*Lepismium commune*)
trigo'na (*Lepismium trigonum*) TRIANGLE R.
warmingia'na . . . . WARMINGS R.

RHODOCAC'TUS . . **PERESKIA**

ROSEOCAC'TUS . **ARIOCARPUS**

SCHLUMBER'GERA (*EPIPHYLLOPSIS; ZYGOCACTUS*) CRABCACTUS
bridg'esi (*Epiphyllum b.; Rhipsalis b.*) BRIDGES C.
gaert'neri (*Epiphyllopsis g.; Epiphyllum g.; E. makoyanum; E. russellianum g.; Rhipsalis g.*) . EASTERCACTUS
russellia'na (*Epiphyllum russellianum; Phyllocactus russellianus; Rhipsalis russelliana*) . . . . . RUSSELL C.
trunca'ta (*Zygocactus truncatus*) CHRISTMASCACTUS

SCLEROCAC'TUS
polyancis'trus (*Echinocactus p.*) PINEAPPLE-CACTUS
whip'plei (*Echinocactus w.*)

SELENICE'REUS . . . . MOONLIGHTCACTUS (*Snakecactus*)
boeckmann'i (*Cereus b.; C. irradians*) BOECKMANN M.

CACTUS GENERA (SELENICEREUS), con.
brevispi'nus (*Cereus b.*)
coniflo'rus (*Cereus c.*) CONEFLOWER MOONLIGHTCACTUS
donkelaar'i (*Cereus d.*) SLIMSTEM M.
grandiflo'rus (*Cereus g.*) QUEENOFTHENIGHT
hama'tus (*Cereus h.; C. rostratus*)
honduren'sis (*Cereus h.*) HONDURAS M.
iner'mis (*Cereus i.*) . . SPINELESS M.
kunthia'nus (*Cereus k.*) . KUNTH M.
macdonald'iae (*Cereus m.*) LADYOFTHENIGHT
mur'rilli (*Cereus m.*) . MURRILL M.
pteran'thus (*nycticaulis; Cereus n.; C. pteranthus*) . . . . . BIGBLOOM M.
spinulo'sus (*Cereus s.*)
urbania'nus (*Cereus u.*) . URBANS M.
va'gans (*Cereus v.*)
werck'lei (*Cereus w.*)

SOLIS'IA . . **MAMMILLARIA**

SPEGAZZIN'IA . **WEINGARTIA**

STENOCAC'TUS (*ECHINOFOSSULOCACTUS*)
alba'tus (*Echinocactus a.; Echinofossulocactus a.*)
anfractuo'sus (*Echinocactus a.; Echinofossulocactus a.*)
ar'rigens
coptonog'onus (*Echinocactus c.; Echinofossulocactus c.*)
crispa'tus (*Echinocactus c.; Echinofossulocactus c.*)
gladia'tus (*Echinocactus g.*)
hasta'tus (*Echinocactus h.*)
heteracan'thus (*tetraxiphus; Chilenia heteracantha; Echinocactus heteracanthus; E. tetraxiphus; Echinofossulocactus h.; Pyrrhocactus h.*)
lamello'sus (*Echinocactus l.*)
lan'cifer (*Echinocactus l.*)
lloyd'i (*Echinocactus l.*)
multicosta'tus (*Echinocactus m.; Echinofossulocactus m.*)
obvalla'tus (*Echinocactus o.*)
tetrax'iphus . . . . . **S. heteracanthus**
vaupelia'nus (*Echinocactus v.*)
violaciflo'rus (*Echinocactus v.*)

STEPHANOCE'REUS **CEPHALOCEREUS**

STETSO'NIA . . . . **CEREUS**

STROMBOCAC'TUS
discifor'mis . . . . . **Ariocarpus d.**
macrohe'le (*Echinocactus m.*)
pseudomacroche'le (*Echinocactus p.*)
schmiedickea'nus (*Echinocactus s.*)
turbinifor'mis . **Ariocarpus disciformis**

STROPHOCAC'TUS
witt'i

TACIN'GA
funa'lis

TEPHROCAC'TUS . **OPUNTIA**

THELOCAC'TUS (*ECHINOMASTUS*)
bi'color (*Echinocactus b.*)
buek'i (*Echinocactus b.*)
conothe'los (*Echinocactus c.*)
dasyacan'thus (*Echinomastus d.*)
erectocen'trus (*Echinomastus e.*)
fossula'tus (*Echinocactus f.*)
has'tifer (*Echinocactus h.*)
hexaedroph'orus (*Echinocactus h.*)
intertex'tus (*Echinomastus i.*)
john'soni (*Echinocactus j.; Ferocactus j.*)

CACTUS GENERA (THELOCACTUS), con.
knuthia'nus (*Coryphantha knuthiana; Echinocactus knuthianus; Neolloydia knuthiana*)
kraus'ei (*Echinomastus k.*)
leucacan'thus (*Echinocactus l.*)
lophothe'le (*Echinocactus l.*)
macdow'elli (*Echinocactus m.; Echinomastus m.*)
mandrag'ora (*Echinocactus m.*)
ni'dulans (*Echinocactus n.*)
phymatothe'le (*Echinocactus p.*)
porrec'tus
Perhaps hardly more than a var. of T. leucacanthus.
potts'i (*Echinocactus heterochromus; E. pottsi*)
rinconen'sis (*Echinocactus r.*)
sau'eri (*Coryphantha s.; Echinocactus s.; Neolloydia s.*)
saussie'ri (*Echinocactus s.*)
subterra'neus (*Echinocactus s.*)
uncina'tus (*Echinocactus u.; Ferocactus u.; Hamatocactus u.*)
—**wright'i** (*Hamatocactus u. w.*)
unguispi'nus (*Echinocactus u.; Echinomastus u.*)
wagneria'nus (*Echinocactus w.*)

TOU'MEYA
papyracan'tha (*Echinocactus papyracanthus*)

TRICHOCE'REUS (*ARTHROCEREUS; ERIOSYCE*)
auric'olor (*Cereus a.*)
bertramia'nus (*Cereus b.*)
brid'gesi (*Cereus b.*)
can'dicans (*Cereus c.; Echinocereus c.*)
cephalomacros'tibas (*Cereus c.*)
ceratis'tes (*Echinocactus c.; Eriosyce c.; E. sandillon*)
chiloen'sis (*Cereus c.*)
coquimba'nus (*Cereus c.*)
cuscoen'sis (*Cereus c.*)
fascicula'ris (*Cereus f.*)
gladia'tus (*Cereus g.*)
hua'scha (*Cereus h.*)
korethroi'des (*Eriosyce k.*)
lamprochlo'rus (*Cereus l.*)
macrog'onus (*Cereus m.*)
microsphae'ricus (*Arthrocereus m.*)
pachano'i (*Cereus p.*)
pasaca'na (*Cereus p.*)
po'co (*Cereus p.*)
rondonia'nus (*Arthrocereus r.; Cereus r.*)
schickendant'zi (*Cereus s.*)
sha'feri (*Cereus s.*)
spachia'nus (*Cereus s.*)
strigo'sus (*Cereus intricatus; C. strigosus*)
terscheck'i (*Cereus fulvispinus; C. terschecki*)
thelegonoi'des (*Cereus t.*)
theleg'onus (*Cereus t.*)
uyupampen'sis (*Cereus u.*)
vollia'nus (*Cereus v.*)
werdermannia'nus (*Cereus w.*)

UTA'HIA
si'leri (*Echinocactus s.*)

WEBEROCE'REUS
biol'leyi (*Cereus b.*)
panamen'sis (*Cereus p.*)
tunil'la (*Cereus t.*)

WEINGART'IA (*SPEGAZZINIA*)
cum'ingi (*Echinocactus c.; Spegazzinia c.*)

CACTUS GENERA (WEINGARTIA), con.
fidaia'na (*Echinocactus f.; Spegazzinia f.*)
neumannia'na (*Echinocactus neumannianus; Spegazzinia neumanniana*)

WERCKLEOCE'REUS
gla'ber (*Cereus g.*)
tondu'zi (*Cereus t.*)

WILCOX'IA
austra'lis Hort.
A very distinct species.
posel'geri (*Cereus p.; C. tuberosus; Echinocereus p.*)
schmoll'i (*senilis; Cereus s.*)
stria'ta (*Cereus striatus*)
viperi'na (*Cereus viperinus*)

WILMAT'TEA
minutiflo'ra

WIT'TIA . . . . WITTIA
amazo'nica . . . . . . AMAZON W.

ZEHNTNEREL'LA
squamulo'sa

ZYGOCAC'TUS **SCHLUMBERGERA**

CADILLO . . . . **Urena lobata**

CAESALPIN'IA (*BIANCAEA; LIBIDIBIA*) . . . . CAESALPINIA
brasilien'sis . . . . . BRAZILWOOD
coria'ria (*Libidibia c.*) . . . DIVIDIVI
cris'ta (*bonducella; Guilandina c.*) NICKERNUT C.
digy'na . . . . TOWRI
echina'ta . . . PRICKLY BRAZILWOOD
gil'liesi . . . . **Poinciana g.**
japon'ica . . . . JAPAN C.
mexica'na . . . . . . MEXICAN C.
nu'ga (*Ticanto n.*) . . WOODGOSSIP C
pauciflo'ra
prae'cox . . . . BREAGUM C.
pulcher'rima . . . . . . **Poinciana p.**
re'gia . . . . **Delonix r.**
sap'pan (*Biancaea s.*) . . . SAPPAN C.
sepia'ria (*Biancaea s.*) . MYSORETHORN
spino'sa (*Coulteria tinctoria*) SPINY C.
tincto'ria

CAESALPINIA . . . . **Caesalpinia**
BRAZILWOOD . . . . . . **C. brasiliensis**
BREAGUM C. . . . . **C. praecox**
DIVIDIVI . . . . **C. coriaria**
JAPAN C. . . . . **C. japonica**
MEXICAN C. . . . . . . **C. mexicana**
MYSORETHORN . . . . . **C. sepiaria**
NICKERNUT C. . . . . . . **C. crista**
PRICKLY BRAZILWOOD . . **C. echinata**
SAPPAN C. . . . . **C. sappan**
SPINY C. . . . . **C. spinosa**
TOWRI . . . . **C. digyna**
WOODGOSSIP C. . . . . . . **C. nuga**

CAILLIE'A (*DICHROSTACHYS*)
glomera'ta (*Dichrostachys nutans*)

Cainito . . . . . STARAPPLE, CAINITO: **Chrysophyllum cainito**

Cajan . . . PIGEONPEA: **Cajanus cajan**

CAJA'NUS
ca'jan (*indicus*) . PIGEONPEA (*Cajan*)

CAJEPUTTREE **Melaleuca leucadendron**

CAJOPH'ORA . . . . . TINGLELILY
lateri'tia (*Blumenbachia l.*) TWINING T.

CAKI'LE . . . . SEAROCKET
eden'tula . . . . AMERICAN S.

CALABARBEAN . . . **Physostigma**
DEADLY C. . . . **P. venenosum**

CALABASHTREE . . . **Crescentia**
COMMON C. . . . **C. cujete**
CROSSLEAF C. . . . **C. alata**

CALACI'NUM . **MUEHLENBECKIA**

CALA'DIUM . . . CALADIUM
bi'color . . . COMMON C.
esculen'tum . . . **Colocasia esculenta**
hum'boldti (*argyrites*) . HUMBOLDT C.
pictura'tum . . . MOTTLED C.
schom'burgki . . . SCHOMBURGK C.

CALAMAGROS'TIS . . . REEDGRASS
See **GRASS GENERA.**

Calamint . . . SAVORY, CALAMINT: **Satureia calamintha**

CALAMIN'THA . . . **SATUREIA**
leucopo'dium . . . **S. vulgaris**
officina'lis . . . **S. calamintha**

Calamondin . . ORANGE, CALAMONDIN: **Citrus mitis**

CALAMOVIL'FA . . . SANDREED
See **GRASS GENERA.**

CALAMPE'LIS . **ECCREMOCARPUS**

CAL'AMUS . . . RATTANPALM
See **PALM GENERA.**

Calamus . . SWEETFLAG: **Acorus calamus**

CALANDRI'NIA |w . . ROCKPURSLANE
arizo'nica |w . . . ARIZONA R.
bur'ridgei . . . BURRIDGE R.
caules'cens |w . . . DESERT R.
—menzies'i (*C. menziesi; C. speciosa*) REDMAIDS R.
grandiflo'ra . . . COMMON R.
umbella'ta . . . PERUVIAN R.

CALAN'THE
See **ORCHID GENERA.**

CALAPPAPALM . **Actinorhytis calapparia**

CALATHE'A . . . CALATHEA
allou'ia . . EDIBLE C. (*Topee Tambo*)
bachemia'na (*Maranta kegeliana*) BACHEMIAN C.
bel'la . . . STEMLESS C.
bi'color . . . **Maranta b.**
chantrier'i . . . CHANTRIER C.
dis'color . . . TWOCOLOR C.
exim'ia . . . SHOWY C.
fascia'ta . . . SILVERBAR C.
illus'tris (*Maranta i.*) WHITEMARGIN C.
insig'nis (*Maranta i.*) OLIVEBLOTCH C.
legrellia'na . . . LEGRELLE C.
leopardi'na . . . LEOPARD C.
liet'zei (*Maranta conspicua*) LIETZE C.
lindenia'na (*Maranta lindeni*) LINDENS C.
loui'sae . . . LOUISA C.
lucia'na (*Maranta l.*) . . . LUCIA C.
makoya'na (*Maranta m.*) . MAKOY C.
medio-pic'ta . . . WHITERIB C.
mi'cans . . . WHITEFEATHER C.
musa'ica . . . TRANSVERSE C.
orna'ta . . . BIGLEAF C.
—roseilinea'ta . . . ROSELINE B.C.
pavon'i (*tubispatha*) . . . PAVONS C.
pictura'ta . . . **C. vandenheckei**
prin'ceps . . . DUSKYBAND C.
pulchel'la (*Maranta p.*) GREENBAND C.
roseo-pic'ta (*Maranta r.*) REDMARGIN C.
sanderia'na (*Maranta s.*) . SANDERS C.
smaragdi'na . **Monotagma smaragdinum**

CALATHEA, continued
splen'dida . . . SPLENDID CALATHEA
tubispa'tha . . . **C. pavoni**
undula'ta . . . WHITESTRIPE C.
vandenheck'ei (*picturata; Maranta vandenhecki*) . . . VANDENHECK C.
veitchia'na . . . VEITCH C.
vitta'ta (*Maranta v.*)
wal'lisi . . . WALLIS C.
warscewicz'i . . . WARSCEWICZ C.
zebri'na (*Maranta z.*) . . . ZEBRA C.
—bino'ti . . . BIG Z.C.

CALATHEA . . . **Calathea**
BACHEMIAN C. . . . **C. bachemiana**
BIGLEAF C. . . . **C. ornata**
BIG ZEBRA C. . . **C. zebrina binoti**
CHANTRIER C. . . . **C. chantrieri**
DUSKYBAND C. . . . **C. princeps**
EDIBLE C. . . . **C. allouia**
GREENBAND C. . . . **C. pulchella**
LEGRELLE C. . . . **C. legrelliana**
LEOPARD C. . . . **C. leopardina**
LIETZE C. . . . **C. lietzei**
LINDENS C. . . . **C. lindeniana**
LOUISA C. . . . **C. louisae**
LUCIA C. . . . **C. luciana**
MAKOY C. . . . **C. makoyana**
OLIVEBLOTCH C. . . . **C. insignis**
PAVONS C. . . . **C. pavoni**
REDMARGIN C. . . . **C. roseo-picta**
ROSELINE BIGLEAF C. **C. ornata roseilineata**
SANDERS C. . . . **C. sanderiana**
SHOWY C. . . . **C. eximia**
SILVERBAR C. . . . **C. fasciata**
SPLENDID C. . . . **C. splendida**
STEMLESS C. . . . **C. bella**
TRANSVERSE C. . . . **C. musaica**
TWOCOLOR C. . . . **C. discolor**
VANDENHECK C. . . **C. vandenheckei**
VEITCH C. . . . **C. veitchiana**
WALLIS C. . . . **C. wallisi**
WARSCEWICZ C. . . . **C. warscewiczi**
WHITEFEATHER C. . . . **C. micans**
WHITEMARGIN C. . . . **C. illustris**
WHITERIB C. . . . **C. medio-picta**
WHITESTRIPE C. . . . **C. undulata**
ZEBRA C. . . . **C. zebrina**

CALCEOLA'RIA (*FAGELIA*) |w CALCEOLARIA
al'ba . . . WHITE C.
biflo'ra . . . TWOFLOWER C.
chelidonioi'des
clibran'i . . . **¢C. profusa**
crenatiflo'ra . . . COMMON C.
dar'wini . . . DARWIN C.
×*fruticohy'brida* Hort.
Possibly forms of C. integrifolia.
grac'ilis . . . STICKYLEAF C.
×**herbeohy'brida** (*herbacea; hybrida; youngi*) . . . VOSS C.
Possibly forms of C. crenatiflora.
integrifo'lia (*rugosa*) . . . BUSH C.
—angustifo'lia . . NARROWLEAF B.C.
—viscosis'sima . . . STICKY B.C.
ligno'sa . . . WOODY C.
¢**med'fordi** Hort. . . . MEDFORD C.
mexica'na . . . MEXICAN C.
pinna'ta . . . FEATHER C.
polyrrhi'za
¢**profu'sa** Hort. (*clibrani*) . CLIBRAN C.
rugo'sa . . . **C. integrifolia**
scabiosaefo'lia . . . BEDDING C.
tenel'la
umbella'ta
¢**veitch'i** Hort. . . . VEITCH C.

CALCEOLARIA, continued
verticilla'ta |w NORTHAMERICAN CALCEOLARIA
viola'cea . . . **Jovellana v.**
young'i . . . ×**C. herbeohybrida**
¢SINCLAIR (*sinclairi*) HV. Calceolaria
¢STEWART (*stewarti*)

CALCEOLA'RIA Loefl., *not* L. **HYBANTHUS**

CALCEOLARIA . . . **Calceolaria**
BEDDING C. . . . **C. scabiosaefolia**
BUSH C. . . . **C. integrifolia**
CLIBRAN C. . . . **¢C. profusa**
COMMON C. . . . **C. crenatiflora**
DARWIN C. . . . **C. darwini**
FEATHER C. . . . **C. pinnata**
MEDFORD C. . . . **¢C. medfordi**
MEXICAN C. . . . **C. mexicana**
NARROWLEAF BUSH C. **C. integrifolia angustifolia**
NORTHAMERICAN C. . . **C. verticillata**
SINCLAIR C. . . . **C. sinclairi**
STICKY BUSH C. **C. integrifolia viscosissima**
STICKYLEAF C. . . . **C. gracilis**
TWOFLOWER C. . . . **C. biflora**
VEITCH C. . . . **¢C. veitchi**
VOSS C. . . . ×**C. herbeohybrida**
WHITE C. . . . **C. alba**
WOODY C. . . . **C. lignosa**

CA'LEA . . . CALEA
glomera'ta . . . COLOMBIAN C.
zacatechi'chi . . . BITTERS C.

CALEN'DULA . . . CALENDULA
eriocar'pa
hy'brida . . . ∞**Dimorphotheca h.**
maderen'sis . . . MADEIRA C.
marit'ima . . . SICILY C.
officina'lis . . . POTMARIGOLD C.
BUTTERCUP (*chrysantha*) HV.
pluvia'lis . . **Dimorphotheca annua**
sic'ula
Possibly a race of C. officinalis.
stella'ta
suffrutico'sa . . . SHRUBBY C.
tra'gus . . **Dimorphotheca aurantiaca**

CALIFORNIALAUREL **Umbellularia; U. californica**

California-nutmeg. TORREYA, CALIFORNIA: **Torreya californica**

CALIFORNIAPITCHER **Darlingtonia; D. californica**

CALIFORNIAPOPPY **Eschscholtzia californica**
DOUGLAS C. . . . **E. c. douglasi**

CALIME'RIS
This genus is perhaps doubtfully distinguished from Aster.
inci'sa (*incisaefolia; Aster incisus*)

Calinguero . . . MOLASSESGRASS: **Melinis minutiflora**

CAL'LA |w . . . CALLA
aethio'pica . . . **Zantedeschia a.**
elliottia'na . . . **Zantedeschia e.**
palus'tris |w . . . WILD C.

CALLALILY . . . **Zantedeschia**
BLACKTHROAT C. . . **Z. melanoleuca**
COMMON C. . . . **Z. aethiopica**
GOLDEN C. . . . **Z. elliottiana**
ROSE C. . . . **Z. rehmanni**

CALLIAN'DRA |w . . . CALLIANDRA
califor'nica . . . CALIFORNIA C.
eriophyl'la . . . FALSEMESQUITE C.

CALLIANDRA, continued
guil'dingi . . TRINIDAD CALLIANDRA
houstonia'na (*houstoni*) PANBOTANO C.
hu'milis . . . . DWARF C.
portoricen'sis . . . PUERTORICO C.
reticula'ta |w . . . . . . NETVEIN C.
schott'i . . . . SCHOTT C.
surinamen'sis . . . . . SURINAM C.
tweed'i (*Inga pulcherrima*) TWEED C.

CALLICAR'PA |w . . . . BEAUTYBERRY
america'na |w . . . . AMERICAN B.
—lacte'a (*C. a. alba*) . . WHITE A.B.
bodinier'i . . . . . . BODINIER B.
—girald'i . . . . GIRALD B.
ca'na (*sinensis*) . . . . . MALAY B.
chenault'i . . . . . . CHENAULT B.
dichot'oma (*gracilis; koreana; purpurea*) . . . . . . PURPLE B.
japon'ica (*mimurazaki*) . JAPANESE B.
—augusta'ta
—leucocar'pa
korea'na . . . . **C. dichotoma**
longifo'lia . . . . . . LONGLEAF B.
mimuraza'ki . . . . **C. japonica**
mol'lis . . . . FUZZY B.
purpu'rea . . . . **C. dichotoma**
rubel'la
sinen'sis . . . . **C. cana**

CALLICHLA'MYS
ripa'ria

Callichro'a doug'lasi . . **Layia calliglossa**

CALLICO'MA . . . . . . CALLICOMA
serratifo'lia . . . . . . SAWLEAF C.

CALLICO'RE . . . CALLICORE (*Cape Belladonnalily*)
rose'a (*Amaryllis belladonna* Herbert, *not* L.) . . . . ROSE C.
—bi'color
—blan'da
—ma'jor
—max'ima
—mi'nor
—pal'lida
—purpu'rea
—ru'bra
—stric'ta
BAPTISTI. HV. C. rosea
G. H. FRANCES
PERFECTA

Calliglos'sa doug'lasi . . **Layia calliglossa**

CALLIGO'NUM
aphyl'lum (*pallasia*)

CALLIOP'SIS . . . . **COREOPSIS**
bi'color; el'egans; marmora'ta **C. tinctoria**

CALLIPRO'RA . . . . . **BRODIAEA**

CALLIRHO'E . . . . . POPPYMALLOW
digita'ta . . . . FINGER P.
involucra'ta (*verticillata*) . . . LOW P.
leiocar'pa (*pedata; Malva p.*) . TALL P.
papa'ver
triangula'ta . . . . . CLUSTERED P.

CALLISTEM'MA . **CALLISTEPHUS**

CALLISTE'MON . . . . BOTTLEBRUSH
acumina'tus
brachyan'drus
coccin'eus . . . . SCARLET B.
cunningham'i . . . CUNNINGHAM B.
×hy'bridus . . . . HYBRID B.
L. H. Bailey reports this name to be of uncertain application.

CALLISTEMON, continued
lanceola'tus (*citrinus; Metrosideros floribunda; M. semperflorens*) LEMON BOTTLEBRUSH
laterit'ius
linea'ris . . . . . . NARROWLEAF B.
phoeni'ceus
pinifo'lius . . . . . . PINELEAF B.
rig'idus . . . . STIFF B.
robus'tus . . . . STOUT B.
rugulo'sus
salig'nus . . . . WILLOW B.
—austra'lis . . . AUSTRALIAN W.B.
—viridiflo'rus . . . . GREEN W.B.
specio'sus . . . . SHOWY B.
splen'dens . . . . . . BRILLIANT B.
vimina'lis
viridiflo'rus . . . . GREEN B.

CALLIS'TEPHUS (*CALLISTEMMA*) CHINA-ASTER
Callistephus is conserved under International Rules.
chinen'sis (*Aster sinensis; Callistemma chinense*) . . . . . COMMON C.
Many hort. var. of China-aster are in cultivation but their names are not yet standardized.

CALLI'TRICHE |w . . WATERSTARWORT
autumna'lis |w . . . . . AUTUMN W.
hermaphrodi'tica
heterophyl'la |w . . . . . LARGER W.
palus'tris |w . . . . . . COMMON W.
stagna'lis . . . . POND W.

CALLI'TRIS . . . . . . CYPRESSPINE
actinostro'bus **Actinostrobus pyramidalis**
acumina'ta
arbo'rea . **Widdringtonia juniperoides**
austra'lis . . . . **C. oblonga**
calcara'ta
cupressifor'mis (*rhomboidea; Frenela r.*) DROOPING C.
drum'mondi . . . . . DRUMMOND C.
glau'ca . . . . **C. robusta**
juniperoi'des . . . . . . JUNIPER C.
muel'leri . . . . MUELLER C.
oblon'ga (*australis*) . OBLONGCONE C.
quadrival'vis . . **Tetraclinis articulata**
rhomboi'dea . . . . **C. cupressiformis**
robus'ta (*glauca; verrucosa*) STURDY C.
roe'i . . . . ROES C.
schwarz'i . . . . SCHWARZ C.
tasman'ica . . . . . . TASMANIAN C.
verruco'sa . . . . **C. robusta**
whyt'ei . . . . . . **Widdringtonia w.**

CALLU'NA . . . . HEATHER
vulga'ris (*Erica v.*) . . . . SCOTCH H.
¢ALPORT (*alporti*) HV.
¢ARGENTEA
¢ATRORUBENS
¢BRONZE (*cuprea*)
¢BRUSH (*rigida*)
¢COCCINEA
¢COMPACTA
¢DECUMBENS
¢DIFFUSA
¢DOUBLE (*florepleno; plena*)
¢FLESH (*carnea*)
¢FOX (*foxi*)
¢GOLDLEAF (*aurea*)
¢GRACILIS
¢HAMMOND WHITE
¢H. E. BEALE
¢HIRSUTA
¢HUMOSA
¢HYPNOIDES

CALLUNA vulgaris, continued
¢KEVERNENSIS
¢MAJOR
¢MONSTROSA
¢MOSS (*nana*)
¢MOSS COMPACT
¢MOSS WHITE
¢MULTIPLEX
¢ROSEA
¢RUBRA
¢SEARLE (*searlei*)
¢STRICTA
¢TENELLA
¢TENUIS
¢VARIEGATA
—al'ba . . WHITE SCOTCH HEATHER
¢DWARF (*minor*) HV.
¢ERECT (*erecta*)
¢SEARLE WHITE
¢SILKY (*pilosa*)
¢SPIKE (*spicata*)
¢STIFF (*rigida*)
¢TALL (*elata*)

CALOCAR'PUM (*SAPOTA*)
sapo'ta (*mammosum; Lucuma mammosa*) . . . . SAPOTE
vi'ride . . . . GREEN S.

CALOCE'PHALUS . . GARLANDFLOWER
brown'i . . . . BROWNS G.

CALOCHOR'TUS . . . . . MARIPOSA (*Mariposalily; Mariposatulip*)
The Latin nomenclature of the plants listed below accords with the treatment of Marion Ownbey in "A Monograph of the Genus Calochortus" (Annals Mo. Bot. Gard. 27:371–560. 1940). Many California authorities object to the use of Mariposa as a common name except for members of the section Mariposa. These authorities chiefly use Fairylantern, Globetulip, Pussyears, and Startulip for the subsection Pulchelli, section Cyclobothra, subsection Elegantes, and subsections Nitidi—Nudi, respectively. The Editorial Committee believes that the use of so many common names for this genus results in confusion. It might be better to use Calochortus (or Calochort) as an English generic name for the whole group.
al'bus . . . . WHITE M. (*White Fairylantern*)
PEARL. HV.
PINK (*rubellus*)
al'bus Hort., *not* Dougl. . . **C. nuttalli**
amab'ilis (*C. pulchellus a.*) LOVELY M. (*Golden F.*)
amoe'nus . . PURPLE M. (*Purple F.*)
apicula'tus
au'reus . . . . . . **C. nuttalli aureus**
barba'tus (*flavus*)
ben'thami . . . . . **C. monophyllus**
catali'nae . . . . CATALINA M.
citri'nus Baker, *not* Hort. . **C. weedi**
citri'nus Hort., *not* Baker . **C. luteus**
clava'tus . . . . . . CLUBHAIR M.
coeru'leus (*maweanus* in part) SKYBLUE M. (*Skyblue Pussyears*)
—mawea'nus . . . . **C. tolmiei**
colli'nus . . . . **C. umbellatus**
con'color . . . . . GOLDENBOWL M.
davidsonia'nus . . . . . **C. splendens**
douglasia'nus . . . . . DOUGLAS M. (*Douglas Startulip*)
dunn'i . . . . DUNNS M.
el'egans . . . . NORTHWESTERN M. (*Northwestern Pussyears*)
eurycar'pus . . . . **C. nitidus**

CALOCHORTUS, continued
excava'tus
fla'vus . . . . **C. barbatus**
flexuo'sus . . WEAKSTEM MARIPOSA
green'ei . . . . GREENES M.
gunniso'ni . . . . . . GUNNISON M.
how'elli . . . . HOWELLS M.
invenus'tus . . . . PLAINS M.
ken'nedyi . . . . DESERT M.
leicht'lini . . . . SMOKY M.
This has been confused in the past with C. nuttalli.
lilac'inus . . . . **C. uniflorus**
lobb'i . . LOBBS M. (*Lobbs Pussyears*)
longebarba'tus . . . . LONGHAIR M. (*Longhair Startulip*)
lute'us (*citrinus* Hort., *not* Baker; *C. luteus c.* in part; *C. venustus c.* Hort., *not* Baker) . . . . . . YELLOW M.
—*citri'nus* . . **C. luteus; C. superbus**
—*ocula'tus* S. Wats., *not* Purdy **C. vestae**
—*ocula'tus* Purdy, *not* S. Wats. **C. superbus**
—*ves'tae* . . . . **C. vestae**
lute'us Nutt., *not* Dougl. . . **C. nuttalli**
lute'us × super'bus
ly'alli . . LYALL M. (*Lyall Startulip*)
macrocar'pus . . . . SAGEBRUSH M.
mawea'nus . . **C. coeruleus; C. tolmiei**
—*ma'jor* . . . . **C. tolmiei**
—*ro'seus* . . . . **C. tolmiei**
min'imus . LEAST M. (*Least Startulip*)
monophyl'lus (*benthami*) . ONELEAF M. (*Yellow Pussyears*)
nit'idus (*eurycarpus; umbellatus* A. Nels., *not* Wood) . BROADFRUIT M.
nu'dus (*shastensis*) . . . SIERRA M. (*Sierra Startulip*)
nutt'alli (*albus* Hort., *not* Dougl.; *luteus* Nutt., *not* Dougl.) . . SEGOLILY M. (*Segolily*)
—**au'reus** (*C. aureus*) . GOLDEN S.M.
obispoen'sis (*C. weedi o.*) . OBISPO M. (*Obispo Globetulip*)
pal'meri (*paludicola*) . . PALMERS M.
persis'tens . . . . . PERSISTENT M. (*Persistent Startulip*)
plum'merae (*C. weedi purpurascens* in part) . . . . PLUMMER M. (*Plummer Globetulip*)
pulchel'lus . . . GOLDENLANTERN M. (*Mt. Diablo Fairylantern*)
—*amab'ilis* . . . . **C. amabilis**
pur'dyi . . . . **C. tolmiei**
shasten'sis . . . . **C. nudus**
splen'dens (*davidsonianus; C. s. rubra*) LILAC M.
super'bus (*C. luteus citrinus* in part; *C. l. oculatus* Purdy, *not* S. Wats.; *C. venustus citrinus* Baker, *not* Hort.; *C. v. oculatus* Hort.; *C. v. superbus*) VIVID. HV.
tol'miei (*C. coeruleus maweanus; maweanus* in part; *C. maweanus major; C. maweanus roseus; purdyi*) TOLMIE M. (*Tolmie Pussyears*)
umbella'tus (*collinus*) . . OAKLAND M. (*Oakland Startulip*)
umbella'tus A. Nels., *not* Wood **C. nitidus**
uniflo'rus (*lilacinus*) . MONTEREY M. (*Monterey S.*)
venus'tus (*C. v. purpurascens; C. v. roseus*) . . . . . . CHARMING M.
—*citri'nus* Baker, *not* Hort. **C. superbus**

CALOCHORTUS, continued
venus'tus citri'nus Hort., *not* Baker **C. luteus**
—*ocula'tus* Hort. . . . . . **C. superbus**
—*purpuras'cens; ro'seus* . **C. venustus**
—*super'bus* . . . . **C. superbus**
—*ves'ta* . . . . **C. vestae**
ELDORADO. HV. C. venustus
ves'tae (*C. luteus oculatus* S. Wats., *not* Purdy; *C. l. vestae; C. venustus vesta*)
weed'i (*citrinus* Baker, *not* Hort.) WEEDS MARIPOSA (*Weeds Globetulip*)
—*obispoen'sis* . . . . **C. obispoensis**
—*purpuras'cens* . . . **C. plummerae; C. weedi vestus**
—**ves'tus** (*C. w. purpurascens* in part)

CALODEN'DRUM . . . CAPECHESTNUT
capen'se . . . . . . CAPECHESTNUT

CALONCO'BA . . . . . . CALONCOBA
angolen'sis . . . . ANGOLA C.
brev'ipes
ficifo'lia (*Oncoba f.*) . . . FIGLEAF C.
gro'tei . . . . GROTE C.

CALONYC'TION . . . . MOONFLOWER
aculea'tum (*Ipomoea bona-nox; I. grandiflora; I. noctiflora*) LARGE M.
murica'tum . . . . SMALL M.
tu'ba (*Ipomoea t.*) . . . TRUMPET M.

CALOPHA'CA
grandiflo'ra
wolga'rica

CALOPHYL'LUM . . . BEAUTYLEAF
angustifo'lium . . . PENANGPOON B.
brasilien'se . . . . BRAZIL B.
—**antilla'num** (*C. antillanum; C. calaba* Jacq., *not* L.; *C. inophyllum* Sieb. *ex* Presl, *not* L. *nor* Lam.; *C. jacquini*) CALABA B.
cala'ba L. . . . . CEYLON B.
cala'ba Jacq. **C. brasiliense antillanum**
inophyl'lum L. . . . . . INDIAPOON B.
inophyl'lum Lam. . . . . **C. tacamahaca**
inophyl'lum Sieb. *ex* Presl **C. brasiliense antillanum**
reko'i . . . . REKO B.
tacamahac'a (*inophyllum* Lam., *not* L. *nor* Sieb.) . . . . MADAGASCAR B.
tomento'sum . . . . CEYLONPOON B.

CALOPO'GON . . GRASSPINK ORCHID
See **ORCHID GENERA, HARDY TERRESTRIAL GROUP.**

CALOPOGO'NIUM
caeru'leum . . . . JICAMA

CALOSTEM'MA . . . . CALOSTEMMA
al'bum . . . . WHITE C.
lute'um . . . . YELLOW C.
purpu'reum . . . . . . PURPLE C.

CALOTHAM'NUS . . . . . NETBUSH
as'per . . . . ROUGH N.
chrysan'therus . . . . . GOLDEN N.
giles'i . . . . GILES N.
homalophyl'lus . . CRIMSONSPIKE N.
longis'simus . . . . DWARF N.
quadrif'idus . . CRIMSONCLUSTER N.
rupes'tris . . . . CLIFF N.
sanguin'eus . . . . BLOOD N.

CALOT'ROPIS . . . . . CALOTROPE
gigan'tea . . . . AKUND C.
pro'cera . . . . FAFTAN C.

CALPUR'NIA . . . . CALPURNIA
au'rea (*lasiogyne*) . . . . GOLDEN C.
sylvat'ica . . . . . . WOODLAND C.

CAL'THA ⌊w . . . . . MARSHMARIGOLD
biflo'ra (*howelli*) . . TWINFLOWER M.
chelido'ni . . . . . . CELANDINE M.
leptosep'ala (*rotundifolia*) ⌊w ELKSLIP M.
—**grandiflo'ra** . . . . BIG E.M.
na'tans ⌊w . . . . . . FLOATING M.
palus'tris ⌊w . . . . . . COMMON M.
¢DOUBLE (*monstrosa-pleno*) HV.
¢SEMIDOUBLE (*semiplena*)
¢WHITE (*alba*)
polypet'ala . . . . GREAT M.

CALTROP . . . . **Kallstroemia**
HAIRY C. . . . . **K. hirsutissima**

CALUMBAROOT . . . **Jateorhiza palmata**

CALUMBAWOOD . **Coscinium fenestratum**

CALVA'TIA . . . . CALVATIA
cyathifor'mis . . . . CUP C.
gigan'tea . . . . GIANT C.

CALYCAN'THUS (*BUTNERIA*) SWEETSHRUB
fer'tilis (*glaucus*) . . . . . . PALE S.
—**fe'rax** . . . . SMOOTH P.S.
—**na'nus** . . . . CAROLINA S.
flor'idus . . . . COMMON S.
—**ova'tus** . . . . . BROADLEAF C.F.
occidenta'lis (*macrophyllus*) CALIFORNIA S.
prae'cox . . . . **Chimonanthus p.**

CALYCOPHYL'LUM . CALYCOPHYLLUM
candidis'simum . . . . DEGAME C.
multiflo'rum . . . . . ARGENTINE C.
sprucea'num . . . . . . MULATTO C.

CALYCOTO'ME . . . . . CALYCOTOME
spino'sa . . . . SPINY C.
villo'sa . . . . HAIRY C.

CALYP'SO (*CYTHEREA*) . . CALYPSO
See **ORCHID GENERA, HARDY TERRESTRIAL GROUP.**

CALYPTRAN'THES . . . LIDFLOWER
pal'lens . . . . PALE L.
zuzy'gium . MYRTLE-OF-THE-RIVER L.

CALYPTROCA'LYX . CALYPTROCALYX
See **PALM GENERA.**

CALYPTROSTIG'MA . . **WEIGELA**

CALYSTE'GIA . . . **CONVOLVULUS**
pubes'cens . . . . . . **C. hederaceus**

CAL'YTRIX (*CALYTHRIX*) FRINGEMYRTLE
sullivan'i . . . . SULLIVAN F.
tenuifo'lia . . . . . . SHORTLEAF F.
tetrag'ona . . . . HAIRCUP F.

CAMARO'TIS
See **ORCHID GENERA.**

CAMAS . . . . **Camassia**
ATLANTIC C. . . . . **C. scilloides**
AZURE C. . . . . **C. azurea**
BLUE LEICHTLIN C. **C. leichtlini caerulea**
COMMON C. . . . . **C. quamash**
CUSICK C. . . . . **C. cusicki**
LEICHTLIN C. . . . . . . **C. leichtlini**
SUKSDORF C. . . . . . . **C. suksdorfi**
WHITE LEICHTLIN C. **C. leichtlini alba**

CAMAS'SIA (*QUAMASIA*) ⌊w . CAMAS
azu'rea . . . . AZURE C.
cu'sicki (*Quamasia c.*) . . . CUSICK C.

CAMASSIA, continued
esculen'ta; fra'seri; hyacin'thia **C. scilloides**
leicht'lini (*Quamasia l.*) LEICHTLIN CAMAS
—al'ba . . . . WHITE L.C.
—caeru'lea . . . . . . BLUE L.C.
qua'mash (*esculenta* Lindl., *not* (Ker.) Rob.; *Quamasia q.*) . . COMMON C.
scilloi'des (*esculenta* Rob., *not* Lindl.; *fraseri; hyacinthia*) . . ATLANTIC C.
suksdorf'i . . . . SUKSDORF C.

CAMELI'NA |w . . . . FALSEFLAX
denta'ta . . . . FLATSEED F.
microcar'pa |w . . . . LITTLEPOD F.
sati'va . . . . BIGSEED F.

CAMEL'LIA (*THEA*) . CAMELLIA; TEA

Botanists have decreed that Teas are Camellias, although a few regard them as distinct but *closely allied* genera. Horticulturally and economically, however, a wide gulf separates these two groups. The Camellia, whose beauty and fragrance is a chief charm of Southern gardens and of Northern hothouses and floral establishments, is grown for ornament. Teas, on the other hand, and especially Common Tea (Camellia sinensis, synonym Thea sinensis), are for use, providing a beverage of worldwide popularity which has given its name to an evening meal, and made these plants an outstanding agricultural crop of the Orient.

Botanically, the differences between Camellias and Teas are minor.

cuspida'ta (*Thea c.*) . . TAPERLEAF T.
drupif'era . . . . . . HIMALAYAN C.
hongkongen'sis . . . . HONGKONG C.
japon'ica (*T. japonica*) . . COMMON C. (*Japanese C.*)
—al'ba . . . . WHITE C.C.
—anemoniflo'ra . . . ANEMONE C.C.
—apucaeform'is . . . SPLITLEAF C.C.
oleo'sa (*C. sasanqua o.; T. oleosa*) OILTEA C.
reticula'ta . . . . . . NETVEIN C.
sasan'qua (*T. sasanqua*) . SASANQUA C.
—anemoniflo'ra . . . ANEMONE S.C.
—kiss'i (*T. kissi*) . . . . . KISSI S.C.
—oleo'sa . . . . **C. oleosa**
sinen'sis (*thea; T. sinensis*) COMMON T.
—assam'ica (*T. sinensis a.*) ASSAM T.
—bohe'a (*T. sinensis b.*) . BOHEA T.
—cantonien'sis (*T. sinensis c.*) CANTON T.
—vir'idis (*T. sinensis v.*) . GREEN T.

Common names and hort. var. (clons) of **Camellia:**

To H. Harold Hume, Dean of the College of Agriculture, Gainesville, Fla., the thanks of the Editorial Committee are given for providing an authoritative list of Camellia japonica and C. sasanqua hybrids. Dean Hume states that the Sasanqua Group is quite new in America and in consequence most of these plants bear Japanese names.

Undoubtedly many new horticultural varieties will soon appear, and hybridizers and introducers are urged to bestow on them appropriate "fancy" or vernacular names in conformance with International Rules and STANDARDIZED PLANT NAME practice.

For convenience of reference, the names of botanical species and varieties are combined with those of horticultural varieties in the appended list. The botanical names can be distinguished from those of hort. var. by the addition of the letter C. (or the word Tea), followed by the boldface Latin name. All the hort. var. in the list below are clons.

Jap. C. japonica.
Sas. C. sasanqua.

ADOLPH AUDUSSON. Jap.
ADRIAN LEBRUN. Jap.
ADZUMA-SHIBORI. Jap.
AINFA EGERIA. Jap.
AKA-SUMIKURA. Jap.
AKA-TAKUKAI. Jap.
AKEBONO. Jap.
AKEBONO-SHIBORI. Sas.
AKI-GESHIKI. Sas.
AKI-NO-YAMA. Jap.
ALBA CASSORETTI. Jap.
ALBA COMPACTA. Jap.
ALBA PLENA. Jap.
Alba Plena Fimbriata. FIMBRIATA.
ALLEN. Jap.
ALLINGHAM. Jap.
ALOHA. Jap.
ALTHAEIFLORA. Jap.
AMABILIS. Jap.
AMA-NO-KAWA. Jap.
AMA-NO-SHITA. Jap.
AMERICANA. Jap.
ANEMONE COMMON C. **C. japonica anemoniflora.**
ANEMONE SASANQUA C. **C. sasanqua anemoniflora.**
ANGELO BOTTI. Jap.
ANGELO COCCHI. Jap.
ANITA. Jap.
ANNA BRUNEAU. Jap.
ANNA FROST. Jap.
ANNA ZUCCHINI. Jap.
APPLEBLOSSOM. Jap., Sas.
ARCHIDUC MAXIMILIAN. Jap.
AREJISHI. Jap.
ARNALDA DE BRESIA. Jap.
ASAHI-ZURU. Sas.
ASSAM TEA. **C. sinensis assamica.**
AUGUSTA WILSON. Jap.
AUGUSTE DELFOSSE. Jap.
AURORA. Jap.
AUSTILL PINK. Jap.
AYA-NISHIKI. Jap.
BAHAUD-LITOU. Jap. *Souv. de Bahaud-Litou.*
BARONNE LEGUAY. Jap.
BEALI ROSEA. Jap.
BEAUTE DE NANTES. Jap.
BELLA D'ARGLIONE. Jap.
BELLA LAMBERTI. Jap.
BELLA ROMANA. Jap.
BELLE JEANETTE. Jap.
BELLE JUDITA. Jap.
BELLE ROSE. Jap.
BELLIFORMIS NOVA. Jap.
BENI-KIRIN. Jap.
BENI-KORAKO. Jap.
BENTEN. Jap.
BICOLOR DE (*la*) REINE. Jap.
BIHOW. Jap.
BLACK PRINCE. Jap.
BLANCHETTE. Sas.
BOHEA TEA. **C. sinensis bohea.**
BONOMIANA. Jap.
BOULE DE NEIGE. Jap.
BRETTI. Jap.
BRIAR ROSE. Sas.
BRIOMAROTTI. Jap.
BROOKLYANA. Jap.
BROWNS RED. Jap.
CALDWELL RED. Jap.
CALDWELL VARIEGATED. Jap.
CALDWELL WHITE. Jap.
CALEB COPE. Jap.
CAMILLE BORGHESE. Jap. *Dom Camille Borghese.*
CAMILLE BROZZONI. Jap.
CAMPBELLI. Jap.
CANDIDA. Jap.
CANDIDA ELEGANTISSIMA. Jap.
CANDIDISSIMA. Jap.
CANTON TEA. **C. sinensis cantoniensis.**
CAPITAL OF CHINA. Sas.
CAPRICE. Jap.
CARLOTTA GRISI. Jap. *Imbricata Rubraplena.*
CARNEA. Jap.
CARPENTRI. Jap.
CARSWELLIANA. Jap.
CARYOPHYLLOIDES. Jap.
CATHERINE CATHCART. Jap.
CATHERINE LONGHI. Jap.
CENTIFOLIA ALBA. Jap.
CENTIFOLIA RUBRA. Jap.
CHANDLERI ELEGANS. Jap.
CHEERFUL. Jap.
CHEERFULNESS. Jap.
CHEROKEE. Jap.
CHIFFON. Jap.
CHIRI. Sas.
CHITOSE GIKU. Jap.
CHIYOTA NISHIKI. Jap.
CHIYO-SURU. Sas.
CHRISTINE LEE. Jap.
CHUYA-SHIBORI. Sas.
CLARKE RED. Jap.
CLEOPATRA. Sas.
CLIVIANA. Jap.
(*C. M.*) HOVEY. Jap.
COLETTE VAN WASSENHOVE. Jap. *Souv. de Mme. Colette Van Wassenhove.*
COLLETTI. Jap.
Colonel Firey. MATHOTIANA RUBRA.
COLVILLI STRIATA. Jap.
COMMON C. **C. japonica.**
COMMON TEA. **C. sinensis.**
COMPACTA ALBA. Jap.
COMTE BONTOURLIN. Jap.
COMTE DE CHAMBARD. Jap.
COMTE DE GOMER. Jap.
COMTE DE PARIS. Jap.
COMTESSE CALLENIE. Jap.
COMTESSE NIEUPORT. Jap.
CONCORDIA. Jap.
CONSPICUA. Jap.
(*Contessa*) LAVINIA MAGGI. Jap.
COQUETTI. Jap.
CORRADINO. Jap.
COUNTESS OF DERBY. Jap.
COUNTESS OF ORKNEY. Jap.
COVINA. Jap.
CRAWFORDI. Jap.
CREPE DE CHINE. Jap.
CRUCIATA. Jap.
CUP OF BEAUTY. Jap.
DAIKAGURA. Jap.
DANIEL WEBSTER. Jap.
DANTE. Jap.
DARSI. Jap.
DAVIESI. Jap.
DEBUTANTE. Jap. *Sara C. Hastie.*
DE LA REINE. Jap.
DE L'ISLE. Jap.
DELORME. Jap.
DE NOTARIS. Jap.
DERBIANA. Jap.
DEVONIA. Jap.
DIVERSIFLORA PLENA. Jap.

CAMELLIA, continued
Dixie. Jap.
Dobrielle. Jap.
(*Dom*) Camille Borghese. Jap.
Donkelaari. Jap.
Downing. Jap. *H. A. Downing.*
Dr. (*Oldwig*) Thayer. Jap.
Dryad. Iride.
Duc de Brabant. Jap.
Duc de Bretagne. Jap.
Duchesse de Berry. Jap.
Duchesse de Caze. Jap.
Duchesse de Montpensier. Jap.
Duchesse d'Orleans. Jap.
Duchess of Exeter. Jap.
Ecstasy. Jap.
Edith Churchwell. Jap.
Elena Nobile. Jap. *Napa Red.*
Elisa Centurioni. Jap.
Elizabeth. Jap.
Emelie Gavazzi. Jap.
Emperor. Jap.
Emperor of Russia. Jap.
Empress of India. Jap.
Empress of Russia. Jap.
Eugene Lizze. Jap.
Fanny Bolis. Jap.
Feasti. Jap.
Festiva. Jap.
Fimbriata. Jap. *Alba Plena Fimbriata.*
Fireball. Jap.
Flora. Jap.
Floreplena Atrorubens. Jap.
Francine. Jap.
Frans Vandamme. Jap.
Fucatus. Jap.
Fuji-no-mine. Sas.
Fuku-no-kami. Sas.
Fuyajo. Jap.
Gaston Allery. Jap. *Souv. de Gaston Allery.*
General (*George*) Washington. Jap.
General Lafayette. Jap.
General Lamoriciere. Jap.
Genji-guruma. Sas.
Genji-karako. Jap.
Giardina Schmitz. Jap.
Gigantea. Jap.
Gilbeaus Pink. Jap.
Gin-no-sai. Sas.
Gin-ryo. Sas.
Giovanni Santarelli. Jap. *Prof. Giovanni Santarelli.*
Gloire de Nantes. Jap.
Gloire de Paulina. Jap.
Goishi. Jap.
Gondo-shibori. Jap.
Gordoni. Jap.
Gosho-guruma. Jap.
Gosho-nishiki. Sas.
Gosho-zakura. Sas.
Governor Mouton. Jap.
Grandiflora. Jap.
Grandiflora Rosea. Jap.
Grandis. Jap.
Green Tea. **C. sinensis viridis.**
Guthriana. Jap.
(*H. A.*) Downing. Jap.
Haemanthus. Jap.
Hagoromo. Jap.
Haku-bai. Jap.
Haku-botan. Jap.
Haku-cho. Jap.
Hakuo. Jap.
Haku-rakuten. Jap.
Haku-ryo. Jap.
Haku-tsuru. Jap.
Hana-daijin. Sas.

CAMELLIA, continued
Hana-fuki. Sas.
Hana-guruma. Jap.
Harlequin. Jap.
Hashidate. Sas.
Hassaku-tsubaki. Jap.
Hatsu-arashi. Jap.
Hatsu-nishiki. Sas.
Hatsu-sakura. Jap.
Hatsu-shime. Jap.
Hatsu-yuki. Sas.
Hebe. Sas.
Hectotiana. Jap.
Henri Favre. Jap.
Henri Guichard. Jap. *Souv. d'Henri Guichard.*
Henry (*VIII*) Eighth. Jap.
Hermes. Jap.
Hermosa. Jap.
Hichi-fuku-jin. Sas.
Himalayan C. **C. drupifera.**
Hinode-gumo. Sas.
Hi-no-hakama. Sas.
Hinomaru. Jap.
Hiodoshi. Sas.
Hi-otome. Jap.
Hi-owsho. Jap.
Hiryo. Sas.
Hiryo-nishiki. Sas.
Hishi-karaito. Jap.
Hito-hiryo. Sas.
Hito-maro. Sas.
Hito-sugi. Jap.
Hollifolia. Jap.
Homare-no-nishiki. Sas.
Hongkong C. **C. hongkongensis.**
Honjo-shiro. Jap.
Horkens. Jap.
Hoshi-guruma. Jap.
Hoshi-hiryo. Sas.
Hote-asobi. Sas.
Hovey. Jap. *C. M. Hovey.*
Howmei. Sas.
Ichimonji. Jap.
Idaten-shibori. Jap.
Ignescens. Jap.
Il Cygno. Jap.
Il Giogello. Jap.
Il Tramonto. Jap.
Il 22 Marzo. Jap.
Imbricata. Jap.
Imbricata Rubraplena. Carlotta Grisi.
Imperator. Jap.
Imperatrice Eugenie. Jap.
Imperialis. Jap.
Imura. Jap.
Incarnato. Jap.
Inconstant Beauty. Jap.
Involutus. Jap.
Iride. Jap. *Dryad.*
Isabella Spinola. Jap.
Italiana. Jap.
Iwane-shibori. Jap.
Jacksoni. Jap.
Japanese C. Common C.
Jardin d'Hiver. Jap.
Jarvis Red. Jap.
Jefferson (*II*). Jap.
Jenny Lind. Jap.
John Bennett. Jap. *Rev. John Bennett.*
John (*G.*) Drayton. Jap.
Jubilee. Jap.
Judith. Jap.
Julia Drayton. Jap.
Julia Jahnz. Jap. *Mrs. Julia Jahnz.*
Justine Heurtin. Jap.
Kagiri. Jap.

CAMELLIA, continued
Kagoshima. Jap.
Kaidomaru. Sas.
Kamakura. Sas.
Kamohoami. Jap.
Kanzaki-murui. Jap.
Kari-gorome. Jap.
Kasugano. Jap.
Kayoi-dori. Jap.
Kenny. Jap.
Kiku-dzuki. Jap.
Kiku-togi. Jap.
Kilwingtonia. Jap.
Kimberley. Jap.
Kimigayo. Jap.
Kingyo. Jap.
Kinkasan. Sas.
Kinnosai. Sas.
Kishiu-tsukasa. Jap.
Kissi Anemone C. **C. sasanqua kissi.**
Kiyosu. Jap.
Kokinkan. Sas.
Konron-koku. Jap.
Kon-wabisuki. Jap.
Koshi-no-yuki. Jap.
Kossuth. Jap.
Kowei. Jap.
Kow-gyoku. Sas.
Kumasaka. Jap.
Kurai-no-himo. Jap.
Kureha. Sas.
Kuro. Jap.
Kyokko. Jap.
Kyo-nishiki. Sas.
Lady (*Audrey*) Buller. Jap.
Lady Campbell. Jap.
Lady Clare. Jap.
Lady Derby. Jap.
Lady Desaumerez. Jap.
Lady Frances. Jap.
Lady Humes Blush. Jap.
Lady Vansetti. Jap.
Lallarook. Jap.
La Niobe. Jap.
La Pace. Jap.
Latifolia. Jap.
Laurelleaf. Jap.
Lavinia Maggi. Jap. *Contessa Lavinia Maggi.*
Leeana Superba. Jap.
Leila. Jap.
Leon Leguay. Jap.
Leopold. Jap.
Leucantha. Jap.
Lewellyn Red. Jap.
Lewellyn Variegated. Jap.
Lilyi. Jap.
Linda Barry. Jap.
Linda Rosazza. Jap.
Lineata. Jap.
Lorraine. Jap.
Lucida. Jap.
Ludovicianus. Jap.
Madge (*Burt*) Miller. Jap.
Madonna. Jap.
Magnoliaeflora. Jap.
Maidens Blush. Jap., Sas.
Maid of Orleans. Jap.
Marchioness of Salisbury. Jap.
Margharita Caleonie. Jap.
Marghuttina. Jap.
Marguerite Gouillon. Jap.
Maria Antonietta. Jap.
Marianna Gaete. Jap.
Maria Theresa. Jap.
Marie Morren. Jap.
Marquisa. Jap.
Marquise d'Exeter. Jap.

CAMELLIA, continued
Masayoshi. Jap.
Mathilda. Jap.
Mathotiana. Jap.
Mathotiana Alba. Jap.
Mathotiana Rubra. Jap. *Colonel Firey; Purpledawn; Purple Emperor; Wm. S. Hastie.*
Matsukasa. Jap.
Mazuchelli. Jap.
Meigetsu. Sas.
Mihata. Jap.
Mikenjaku. Jap.
Minamoto. Jap.
Mine-no-yuki. Sas.
Minerva. Jap.
Minina. Sas.
Miodoroki. Sas.
Missima. Jap.
Miyuki-nishiki. Jap., Sas.
Mme. (*Appoline*) Guichard. Jap.
Mme. Cachet. Jap.
Mme. (*Canaert*) d'Hamale. Jap.
Mme. (*Charles*) Blard. Jap.
Mme. de Chambard. Jap.
Mme. Feters. Jap.
Mme. Haas. Jap.
Mme. Lebois. Jap.
Mme. Pepin. Jap.
Mme. Picouline. Jap.
Mme. Verschaffelt. Jap.
Momijigari. Jap.
Momo Chidori. Jap.
Monjisu. Jap.
Monjisu Red. Jap.
Monsieur Faucillon. Jap.
Monsieur Paugam. Jap.
Monstruosa Rubra. Jap.
Mont Blanc. Jap.
Montironi. Jap.
Montironi Rosea. Jap.
Mrs. (*Abby*) Wilder. Jap.
Mrs. Cope. Jap.
Mrs. (*F.*) Sander. Jap.
(*Mrs.*) Julia Jahnz. Jap.
Mrs. Luerman. Jap.
Mrs. (*T. H.*) McHatton. Jap.
Mrs. (*Wm.*) Thompson. Jap.
Murui-shibori. Jap.
Myorenji. Jap.
Nana-komachi. Jap.
Napa Red. Elena Nobile.
Napoleon d'Italie. Jap.
Neddyboy. Jap.
Negishi-ko. Sas.
Neige d'Oree. Jap.
Netvein C. **C. reticulata.**
Nishiki-mino. Jap.
Nishiki-no-tsukasa. Jap.
Nobilissima. Jap.
Nobilissima Rosea. Jap.
Noisetti. Jap.
Nonpareil. Jap.
Ochroleuca. Jap.
Ohzora. Jap.
Oiltea C. **C. oleosa.**
Oki-no-hame. Jap.
Omigoromo. Sas.
Onor del Monte. Jap.
Optima. Jap.
Oranda-gasa. Jap.
Oridono-nishiki. Jap.
Osaka-zuki. Sas.
Otome. Jap.
Otome Red. Jap.
Otome White. Jap.
Paeoniflora. Jap.
Palazzo Turzi. Jap.

CAMELLIA, continued
Panache. Jap.
Paolina Guichardini. Jap.
Peachblossom. Jap.
Perfecta Variegata. Jap.
Perfection White. Jap.
Philippo Parlatore. Jap. *Prof. Philippo Parlatore.*
Pictorum Rosea. Jap.
Picturata. Jap.
Pink Perfection. Jap.
Pirzio Secondo. Jap.
Pomponia. Jap.
Pope Pius IX. Jap.
Prenilland. Jap.
President Allard. Jap.
Preston Rose. Jap.
Prince Albert. Jap.
Prince de Salerne. Jap.
Prince (*Eugene*) Napoleon. Jap.
Princessa Bacciochi. Jap.
Princess Clothilde. Jap.
Principa Dorea. Jap.
Prof. (*C. S.*) Sargent. Jap.
(*Prof.*) Giovanni Santarelli. Jap.
(*Prof.*) Philippo Parlatore. Jap.
Prosper Vial. Jap.
Prymee. Jap.
Punctata Boutourlin. Jap.
Punctata Major. Jap.
Purpledawn; Purple Emperor. Mathotiana Rubra.
Quartette. Jap.
Queen Bessie. Jap.
Queen of Hearts. Jap.
Queen Victoria. Jap.
Rainy Sun. Jap.
Rasen-zome. Jap.
Reine des Fleurs. Jap.
Reine Marie-Henriette. Jap.
Renjonotama. Jap.
(*Rev.*) John Bennett. Jap.
Rogetsu. Jap.
Rogetsu-nishiki. Jap.
Roi Leopold. Jap.
Romany. Jap.
Rosea. Sas.
Rosita. Jap.
Rouge. Jap.
Rubens. Jap.
Rubescens Major. Jap.
Rubra Virginalis. Jap.
Sacco. Jap.
Sacco Nova. Jap.
Sacco Vera. Jap.
Sakuraba-genji. Jap.
Sanbow. Jap.
Sangdon. Jap.
Sanko-nishiki. Jap.
Sara C. Hastie. Debutante.
Sarah Frost. Jap.
Sarasa-shibori. Sas.
Sasanqua C. **C. sasanqua.**
Secchuka. Jap.
Seiganji. Jap.
Semidouble Blush. Jap.
Setsuzan. Sas.
Shibori-karako. Jap.
Shibori-no-rogetsu. Jap.
Shibori-wabisuke. Jap.
Shikishima. Sas.
Shinonome. Sas.
Shio-ginu. Jap.
Shira-giku. Jap.
Shira-nuhi. Jap.
Shiro-bokuhan. Jap.
Shiro-kagura. Jap.
Shiro-karako. Jap.

CAMELLIA, continued
Shiro-takukai. Jap.
Shiro-wabisuke. Jap.
Shishigashira. Sas.
Shokko. Jap.
Shokko-nishiki. Jap.
Shuchuka. Sas.
Shungyo-ko. Jap.
Shuzan. Jap.
Snow. Sas.
Snowdrift. Jap.
Snowmaiden. Jap.
Snowwhite. Jap.
Sode-gakushi. Jap.
Solaris. Jap.
Somegawa Red. Jap.
Somegawa Variegated. Jap.
Somnambula. Jap.
Sophia. Jap.
Sophia Chiarugi. Jap.
(*Souv. de*) Bahaud-Litou. Jap.
(*Souv. de*) Gaston Allery. Jap.
(*Souv. d'*) Henri Guichard. Jap.
(*Souv. de Mme.*) Colette Van Wassenhove. Jap.
(*Souvenir d'*) Une Amie. Jap.
Sovereign. Jap.
Sowa-no-sakae. Sas.
Spectabilis. Jap.
Splitleaf Common C. **C. japonica apucaeformis.**
St. Andre. Jap.
Stiles Perfection. Jap.
Storyi. Jap.
Striata. Jap.
Suibijin. Jap.
Sunrise. Jap.
Superbissima. Jap.
Sweetiana Vera. Jap.
Sylvia. Jap.
Taihei. Jap.
Taimei-Nishiki. Sas.
Taisho-Nishiki. Sas.
Takara-Awase. Sas.
Tanya. Jap., Sas.
Taperleaf Tea. **C. cuspidata.**
Targioni. Jap.
Taroan. Jap.
Tenninkwan. Jap.
Teutonia. Jap.
Theresa Mossine. Jap.
Tillmani. Jap.
T. K. Variegated. Jap.
Tokoyama. Jap.
Tornielli. Jap.
Totenko. Sas.
Toyennishiki. Sas.
Toyo Nishiki. Jap.
Traversi Plenissima. Jap.
Tricolor Desiebold. Jap.
Tricolor Imbricata. Jap.
Triomphant. Jap.
Trois Marie. Jap.
Tsuda Shibori. Sas.
Tsukino Kasa. Sas.
Tsukino Miyako. Jap.
Tsumaorigasa. Sas.
Tsuzuranishiki. Sas.
Tsyunotama. Sas.
Tutcheria Spectabilis. Jap.
Umegaki. Jap.
Une Amie. Jap. *Souvenir d'Une Amie.*
Unica. Jap.
Unifa Deltebro. Jap.
Usuotome. Jap.
Valtaveridiana. Jap.
Variabilis. Jap.
Variegata. Jap.

CAMELLIA, continued
Vedrine. Jap.
Ville Denantes. Jap.
Virgina Franco. Jap.
Vittorio Emanuele (II). Jap.
Wago-jin. Sas.
Warratah. Jap.
Waterloo. Jap.
White Butterfly. Yamato-nishiki.
White Common C. **C. japonica alba.**
White Kagura. Jap.
Wilderi. Jap.
Wm. S. Hastie. Mathotiana Rubra.
Woodruff. Jap.
Yae-gasumi. Jap.
Yamato-kagami. Sas.
Yamato-nishiki. Sas. *White Butterfly.*
Yezo-nishiki. Jap.
Yezo-shibori. Jap.
Yobiko-dori. Jap.
Yodo-noasahi. Jap.
Yohei-haku. Jap.
Yuki-botan. Jap.
Yuki-no-nogame. Sas.
Zoraide Wanzi. Jap.
Camelthorn . . . **Alhagi pseudalhagi**
CAMOEN'SIA . . . . Showvine
max'ima . . . . Big S.
Camomile . . . . **Anthemis**
Bighead C. . . . . . **A. macrantha**
Carpathian C. . . . . . **A. carpatica**
Cornfield C. . . . **A. arvensis agrestis**
English C. . . . . Roman C.
Field C. . . . . **A. arvensis**
Golden C. . . . . **A. tinctoria**
Gray C. . . . . **A. cinerea**
Macedonian C. . . . **A. macedonica**
Mayweed C. . . . . . . **A. cotula**
Riviera C. . . . . . . **A. montana**
Roman C. . . . . **A. nobilis**
St.Johns C. . . . **A. sancti-johannis**
Tall C. . . . . **A. altissima**
CAMPAN'ULA ⌊W . . . . Bellflower
abieti'na
acau'lis
Probably a form of C. glomerata.
alliariaefo'lia . . . . . . Spurred B.
allio'ni . . . . Allioni B.
alpi'na . . . . Alpine B.
amab'ilis . . . . . **C. phyctidocalyx**
america'na . . . . . American B.
aparinoi'des . . . . . Bedstraw B.
ardonen'sis . . . . . Grassleaf B.
arva'tica . . **Wahlenbergia hederacea**
at'tica . . . . **C. drabifolia**
au'cheri . . . . Aucher B.
barba'ta . . . . Bearded B.
bellidifo'lia . . . . Violet B.
betonicaefo'lia . . . . . Betony B.
bononien'sis
caespito'sa (*bellardi; pusilla*)
Singlenod B.
—**al'ba** . . . . White S.B.
car'nica . . . . Solitary B.
carpa'tica . . . . Carpathian B.
—**al'ba** . . . . White C.B.
₵Chinacup. hv.
₵Exquisite
₵Nana
₵Pallida
—**turbina'ta** (*C. turbinata*) . . Top B.
₵Isabel. hv. C. carpatica
cashmiria'na . . . . . Kashmir B.
cec'ili . . . . **P. propinqua grandiflora**
ceni'sia . . . . Swiss B.
cervica'ria
—**transylva'nica**

CAMPANULA, continued
colli'na
divarica'ta (*flexuosa*)
Allegany Bellflower
drabifo'lia (*attica*) . . . . Greek B.
elati'nes . . . . Elatines B.
elatinoi'des
el'egans
eri'nus . . . . Erinus B.
exci'sa
flexuo'sa . . . . **C. divaricata**
formanekia'na
fra'gilis . . . . Fragile B.
garga'nica
—**al'ba**
—**eri'nus**
—**hirsu'ta**
₵W. H. Paine. hv. C. garganica
glomera'ta . . . . . Danesblood B.
—**acau'lis** . . . . . Lowcluster B.
—**dahur'ica** . . . . . Dahurian B.
—**super'ba** . . . . Showy Cluster B.
grandiflo'ra **Platycodon grandiflorum**
gran'dis . . . . **C. latiloba**
gros'seki . . . . Grossek B.
imereti'na
isophyl'la . . . . Italian B.
—**al'ba** . . . . White I.B.
—**may'i**
istria'ca
∞ **kewen'sis** (*excisa* × *Wahlenbergia hederacea*) . . . . ∞ Kew B.
kolenatia'na . . . . . . Bluenod B.
—**na'na**
—**turbina'ta**
₵Riverslea Beauty. hv. C. kolenatiana
₵Whitestar
lactiflo'ra . . . . Milky B.
—**al'ba**
₵Magnifica. hv.
—**coeru'lea**
₵Magnifica. hv.
lana'ta
lasiocar'pa . . . . Behring B.
latifo'lia . . . . Great B.
—**al'ba** . . . . White G.B.
—**hurghalt'i** . . . . . . Hurghalt B.
—**macran'tha** (*C. macrantha*)
₵Brantwood. hv. C. latifolia
latilo'ba (*grandis*) . . . . Olympic B.
—**al'ba** . . . . White O.B.
leutwein'i . . . . Leutwein B.
lingula'ta . . . . Tongue B.
linifo'lia . . . . Flaxleaf B.
longesty'la
lo'reyi . . . . **C. ramosissima**
macran'tha . . . . . . **C. latifolia m.**
macrorrhi'za
macrosty'la . . . . . Anatolian B.
marcheset'ti
me'dium . . . . Canterburybells
—**al'ba** . . . . White C.
—**calycan'thema** . Cup-and-saucer B.
—**rose'a** . . . . Pink C.B.
michauxioi'des . . . . . Michaux B.
mirab'ilis . . . . Wonder B.
mol'lis (*velutina*) . . . . . Fuzzy B.
mura'lis . . . . . **C. portenschlagiana**
no'bilis . . . . **C. punctata**
pallasia'na . . . . **C. pilosa**
par'ryi . . . . Parry B.
pat'ula . . . . Rambling B.
pentago'nia . . . . . **Specularia p.**
persicifo'lia . . . . . . Peachleaf B.
Coerulea. hv.
Coronata
Double

CAMPANULA persicifolia, continued
Everest
Fairy
Fleur Deneige
Grandiflora
Lavender Queen
Lissadell
Macrantha
Moerheim
Petticoat (*grandiflora*)
Pfitzer
Pride of Exmouth
Splendida
Telham Beauty
Verdun
White
petiola'ta (*rotundifolia* Auth., *not* L.)
American Harebell
petrae'a . . . . Cliff Bellflower
phyctidoca'lyx (*amabilis*) Armenian B.
pilo'sa (*pallasiana*) . . . Shaggy B.
pi'peri . . . . Piper B.
portenschlagia'na (*muralis*)
Dalmatian B.
—**ma'jor** . . . . Big D.B.
poscharskya'na . . . Poscharsky B.
prenanthoi'des . . . . California B.
primulaefo'lia . . . Portuguese B.
propin'qua . . . . . . Near East B.
—**grandiflo'ra** (*C. cecili*)
pseudo-rain'eri
Probably a hybrid.
pul'la . . . . Dusky B.
G. T. Wilson. hv.
pulloi'des
Perhaps a hybrid.
puncta'ta (*nobilis*) . . . Spotted B.
—**al'ba** . . . . White S.B.
Marian Gehring. hv. C. punctata
pusil'la . . . . **C. caespitosa**
pyramida'lis . . . . . Chimney B.
—**al'ba** . . . . White C.B.
pyrena'ica . . . . . . Pyrenees B.
raddea'na . . . . Radde B.
rain'eri . . . . Rainer B.
ramosis'sima (*loreyi*) . Bluestar B.
rapunculoi'des . . . . Creeping B.
rapun'culus . . . . . . Rampion B.
rhomboida'lis . . . . . Diamond B.
rob'soni . . . . Robson B.
rotundifo'lia . . . . Bluebell
—**al'ba** . . . . . . White Bluebell
—**olym'pica** . . . Olympic Bluebell
—**robinso'ni** . . Robinson Bluebell
—**super'ba** . . Bluebells of Scotland
—**velu'tina** . . . Velvet B. of S.
Prairiequeen. hv. C. rotundifolia
Purplegem
rotundifo'lia Auth., *not* L. **C. petiolata**
sarma'tica . . . . . . Sarmatian B.
saxat'ilis . . . . Stone B.
saxif'raga . . . . . . Saxifrage B.
scabrel'la
scheuch'zeri . . . . Scheuchzer B.
sibir'ica . . . . Siberian B.
specio'sa . . . . Bristly B.
spec'ulum **Specularia speculum-veneris**
spica'ta . . . . Spiked B.
stans'fieldi . . . . . . Stansfield B.
stenoco'don
ste'veni . . . . Steven B.
subpyrena'ica
thes'sala
thyrsoi'des . . . . Yellowspike B.
tommasinia'na . . . **C. waldsteiniana**
trache'lium . . . . Coventrybells
tridenta'ta . . . . Tridentleaf B.

CAMPANULA, continued
turbina'ta . . . . . . **C. carpatica t.**
uligino'sa |w . . MARSH BELLFLOWER
veluti'na . . . . **C. mollis**
versicol'or
vidal'i . . . . AZORES B.
waldsteinia'na (*tommasiniana*)
WALDSTEIN B.
wock'ei . . . . WOCKE B.
zoy'si . . . . ZOYS B.

CAM'PE . . . . **BARBAREA**

CAM'PHORA . . **CINNAMOMUM**
officina'rum . . . . . . **C. camphora**

CAMPHORFUME . . . . . **Camphorosma**
MEDITERRANEAN C. . **C. monspeliaca**

CAMPHOROS'MA . . . CAMPHORFUME
monspelia'ca . . MEDITERRANEAN C.

CAMPHORTREE **Cinnamomum camphora**
NEPAL C. . . . . . **C. glanduliferum**

CAMPION . . . . **Lychnis**
ARCTIC C. . . . . **L. alpina**
ARKWRIGHT C. . . . ×**L. arkwrighti**
BRILLIANT C. . . . . . . **L. fulgens**
CLAMMY C. . . . . **L. viscaria**
CORSICA C. . . . . **L. corsica**
CROWN C. . . . . **L. coronata**
DRUMMOND C. . . . . **L. drummondi**
EVENING C. . . . . **L. alba**
FLOWEROFJOVE . . . . . **L. flosjovis**
HAAGE C. . . . . . . ×**L. haageana**
MALTESECROSS C. . . **L. chalcedonica**
PYRENEES C. . . . . . . **L. pyrenaica**
RAGGEDROBIN . . . . . **L. floscuculi**
RED C. . . . . **L. dioica**
ROSE C. . . . . **L. coronaria**
ROSEOFHEAVEN . . . . . **L. coelirosa**

CAMPOMANE'SIA . . **ABBEVILLEA**

CAMPSID'IUM
valdivia'num

CAMP'SIS |w . . . TRUMPETCREEPER
grandiflo'ra (*chinensis; Bignonia c.; B. grandiflora; Tecoma g.*) CHINESE T.
—**thunberg'i** (*Tecoma t.*)
THUNBERG C.T.
rad'icans (*Bignonia r.; Tecoma r.*) |w
COMMON T. (*Trumpetvine*)
¢DWARF (*minor*) HV.
¢EARLY (*praecox*)
¢PURPLE (*atropurpurea*)
¢SHOWY (*speciosa*)
¢YELLOW (*flava*)
∞ **tagliabua'na** (*grandiflora × radicans; Bignonia hybrida; Campsis h.; Tecoma intermedia*) . . ∞HYBRID T.
¢MME. GALEN. HV.

CAMPTOSO'RUS . . . WALKINGFERN
See **FERN GENERA**.

CAMPTOTHE'CA
acumina'ta

CAMPULO'SUS . . . . . **CTENIUM**
See **GRASS GENERA**.

CAMPYLAN'THUS
salsoloi'des
—**penduli'nus**

CAMPYLO'TROPIS . . CLOVERSHRUB
macrocar'pa (*Lespedeza chinensis; L. macrocarpa*) . . . . CHINESE C.

CAMWOOD . . . . **Baphia**
BUSH C. . . . . **B. racemosa**
SHINY C. . . . . **B. nitida**

CANAIGRE . . . **Rumex hymenosepalus**

CANAN'GA (*CANANGIUM*)
odora'ta . . . . YLANGYLANG

CANAN'GIUM . . . . **CANANGA**

CANARA'LIA
macropleu'ra

CANARI'NA . . . . . CANARYBELL
campan'ula . . . . PURPLESPOT C.

CANA'RIUM . . . . . CANARYTREE
commu'ne . . . . . JAVAALMOND C.
euphyl'lum . . . . . . ANDAMAN C.
luzon'icum . . . . ELEMI C.
ova'tum . . . . PILINUT C. (*Pilauai*)
schweinfur'thi . . . . PAPO C.
stric'tum . . . . BLACKDAMAR C.

CANARYBELL . . . . **Canarina**
PURPLESPOT C. . . . **C. campanula**

CANARYCLOVER . . . . . . **Dorycnium**
BRANCHING C. . . . **D. suffruticosum**
HAIRY C. . . . . **D. hirsutum**
HERB C. . . . . . . **D. herbaceum**
UPRIGHT C. . . . . **D. rectum**

CANARYGRASS . **Phalaris; P. canariensis**
BULB C. . . . . **P. tuberosa**
CALIFORNIA C. . . . . . **P. californica**
CAROLINA C. . . . . . **P. caroliniana**
CUTSCALE C. . **P. paradoxa praemorsa**
HOOD C. . . . . **P. paradoxa**
LEMMON C. . . . . **P. lemmoni**
LITTLESEED C. . . . . **P. minor**
REED C. . . . . . **P. arundinacea**
SHORTSPIKE C. . . **P. brachystachys**
TIMOTHY C. . . . . . . **P. angusta**

CANARYTREE . . . . **Canarium**
ANDAMAN C. . . . . . **C. euphyllum**
BLACKDAMAR C. . . . . **C. strictum**
ELEMI C. . . . . . . **C. luzonicum**
JAVAALMOND C. . . . . **C. commune**
PAPO C. . . . . . **C. schweinfurthi**
PILINUT C. . . . . **C. ovatum**

CANAVA'LIA . . . . JACKBEAN
ensifor'mis . . COMMON J. (*Maljoe*)
gladia'ta . . . SWORD J. (*Swordbean*)
obtusifo'lia . . . . . . GROUND J.
plagiosper'ma . . . . . CLIMBING J.

CANDLENUTTREE . **Aleurites moluccana**

CANDLEPLANT . . . **Kleinia articulata**

CANDLETREE . . . . **Parmentiera**
FOOD C. . . . . **P. edulis**
PANAMA C. . . . . **P. cereifera**
YELLOWTAPER C. . . . . **P. aculeata**

CANDOL'LEA . . . . CANDOLLEA
cuneifor'mis (*Hibbertia c.*)
WEDGELEAF C.

CANDYTUFT . . . . **Iberis**
COMBLEAF C. . . . . . . **I. pectinata**
EVERGREEN C. . . . **I. sempervirens**
GIBRALTAR C. . . . . . **I. gibraltarica**
GLOBE C. . . . . **I. umbellata**
JORDAN C. . . . . **I. jordani**
PRUIT C. . . . . **I. pruiti**
REDFLUSH TENORE C.
S. tenoreana petraea
ROCK C. . . . . **I. saxatilis**
ROCKET C. . . . . **I. amara**
SICILIAN C. . . . . . **I. semperflorens**
SWEET C. . . . . **I. odorata**
TAURUS C. . . . . **I. taurica**
TENORE C. . . . . . . **I. tenoreana**

CANE . . . . **Arundinaria**
See also **BAMBOO GENERA** and SUGARCANE.
BILTMORE SWITCH C. **A. tecta decidua**

CANE, continued
CLUSTER C. . . . **Arundinaria debilis**
GIANT C. . . . . **A. gigantea**
NARIHIRA C. **Semiarundinaria fastuosa**
NEPAL C. . . . . **A. nepalensis**
SWITCH C. . . . . **A. tecta**
TONKIN C. . . . . **A. amabilis**

CANEL'LA . . . . CANELLA
wintera'na . . . . . . CINNAMON C.

CANIS'TRUM . . . . . . CANISTRUM
amazon'icum . . . . . . AMAZON C.
auranti'acum . . . . GREENSPOT C.
lin'deni . . . . LINDENS C.

CAN'NA . . . . CANNA
achi'ras . . . . **C. lanuginosa**
altenstein'i . . . . **C. latifolia**
angustifo'lia . . . . **C. flaccida**
annae'i . . . . **C. glauca**
aureovitta'ta . . . . . . **C. limbata**
buek'i . . . . **C. pedunculata**
car'nea . . . . **C. variabilis**
cearen'sis . . . . **C. polyclada**
chinen'sis (*nepalensis*) . CHINESE C.
cinnabari'na (*fulgida*) . CINNABAR C.
coccin'ea (*rubra*) . . . . SCARLET C.
coccin'ea Link, *not* Mill . . . **C. indica**
commuta'ta . . . . **C. lutea**
cro'cea . . . . **C. indica**
densiflo'ra . . . . **C. lutea**
dis'color (*rotundifolia*) . . . BRICK C.
ed'ulis (*esculenta; rubricaulis*)
EDIBLE C.
excel'sa . . . . **C. paniculata**
exig'ua . . . . **C. humilis**
exim'ia . . . . **C. polyclada**
fintelmann'i . . . . . FINTELMANN C.
flac'cida (*angustifolia; glauca* Walt., *not* L.) |w
flaves'cens . . . . **C. orientalis**
floribun'da . . . **C. limbata; C. lutea**
formo'sa . . . . BOUCHE C.
ful'gida . . . . **C. cinnabarina**
gemel'la . . . . **C. latifolia**
∞ **general'is** . . ∞COMMON GARDEN C.
gigan'tea . . . . **C. latifolia**
glau'ca (*annaei; lanceolata; mexicana; schlechtendaliana; stolonifera*)
glau'ca Walt., *not* L. . . . **C. flaccida**
heliconifo'lia . . . . TEXAS C.
—**xalapen'sis** (*C. xalapensis*)
DWARF T.C.
hu'milis (*exigua*) . . . . INDOCHINA C.
in'dica (*coccinea* Link, *not* Mill; *crocea; patens* Roscoe, *not* Hook.; *spectabilis; tenuiflora*) . . . . INDIA C.
iridiflo'ra . . . . IRIS C.
lae'ta . . . . **C. limbata**
lagunen'sis . . . . REDSPOT C.
lambert'i (*poeppigi*) . . . . LAMBERT C.
lanceola'ta . . . . **C. glauca**
lanugino'sa (*achiras*) . . . . INCA C.
latifo'lia (*altensteini; gemella; gigantea; macrophylla; neglecta*) BROADLEAF C.
leptochi'la . . . . **C. speciosa**
leucocar'pa . . . . . PRIMROSE C.
liliiflo'ra . . . . . . HONEYSUCKLE C.
limba'ta (*aureovittata; floribunda* in part; *laeta; patens* Hook.; *recurvata; variegata; ventricosa*) . . PARANA C.
longifo'lia . . . . LONGLEAF C.
lute'a (*commutata; densiflora; floribunda* in part; *maculata; sulphurea* Hort.)
YELLOW C.
—**auranti'aca** . . . . ORANGE Y.C.
macrophyl'la . . . . **C. latifolia**

CANNA, continued

macula'ta . . . . **C. lutea**
mexica'na . . . . **C. glauca**
moritzia'na . . . . **C. pallida**
neglec'ta . . . . **C. latifolia**
nepalen'sis . . . . **C. chinensis**
orchio'des . . . . . ORCHID CANNA
₵AUSTRIA. HV.
₵ITALIA
orienta'lis (*flavescens*) . . . MALAY C.
pal'lida (*moritziana*) . . . SULFUR C.
panicula'ta (*excelsa*) . . . ANDEAN C.
pa'tens . . . . **C. indica; C. limbata; C. selloi** Hort.
peduncula'ta (*bueki; reflexa*) TRINIDAD C.
poep'pigi . . . . **C. lamberti**
polycla'da (*cearensis; eximia*) BRAZILIAN C.
polymorph'a . . . . **C. speciosa**
portoricen'sis . . . . . . **C. sylvestris**
recurva'ta . . . . **C. limbata**
reeves'i . . . . REEVES C.
reflex'a . . . . **C. pedunculata**
rotundifo'lia . . . . . . **C. discolor**
ru'bra . . . . **C. coccinea**
rubricau'lis . . . . **C. edulis**
rubrolu'tea Hort. . . . . . PANSY C.
sanguin'ea **C. speciosa; C. warscewiczi**
schlechtendalia'na . . . . . **C. glauca**
sello'i Hort. (**patens** Baker). SELLO C.
specio'sa (*leptochila; polymorpha; sanguinea* Hort.; *saturate-rubra*) HIMALAYA C.
spectab'ilis . . . . **C. indica**
stolonif'era . . . . **C. glauca**
sulphu'rea Hort. . . . . . . **C. lutea**
sylves'tris (*portoricensis*) CARIBBEAN C.
tenuiflo'ra . . . . **C. indica**
tine'i . . . . TINE C.
variab'ilis (*carnea*) . . . VARIABLE C.
variega'ta; ventrico'sa . . . **C. limbata**
viola'cea . . . . VIOLET C.
warscewicz'i (*sanguinea* Warsc., *not* Hort.) . . . . . WARSCEWICZ C.
xalapen'sis . . . . **C. heliconifolia x.**

Common names and hort. var. (clons) of **Canna:**

The Editorial Committee acknowledges with sincere thanks the coöperation of Robert Pyle, West Grove, Pa., in supplying this list of modern horticultural varieties of Canna.

In using names from this list the clon sign ₵ should precede hort. var. names; example, ₵ABRAHAM LINCOLN; but should not precede species and variety common names; example, ANDEAN C.

ABRAHAM LINCOLN.
ADMIRAL AVELLAN.
ADMIRAL SCHLEY.
ADOLF ERNST.
A. EISENBARTH.
AFRICA.
A. GASQUET.
A. H. BAHLMANN.
Alba Rosea Grandiflora. PEACHBLOW.
ALBERTA.
ALBINO.
ALFRED MAUTHIER.
ALGERIE.
ALLEMANIA.
ALLIGATOR.
ALPHONSE BOUVIER.
ALSACE.
AMBASSADOR.
AMERICA.

CANNA, continued

AMERICAN BEAUTY.
AMERICAN FLAG.
AMI PICHON.
ANDEAN C. **C. paniculata.**
Andenken an Hans Muehle. HANS MUEHLE.
Andenken an Karl Schmidt. KARL SCHMIDT.
Andenken an Woldemar Neubert. WOLDEMAR NEUBERT.
Andenken an W. Pfitzer. W. PFITZER.
ANDREAS HOFER.
ANNIE LAURIE.
ANTHEOR.
ANTOINE CROZY.
ANTOINE WINTZER.
ANTONIE SCHOTT.
APHRODITE.
APRICOT.
ASSAUT.
AUGUSTA.
Augusta. CUBA.
AURIBEAU.
AURORA.
AUSTRIA.
A. W. KUHN.
AYMARD. *J. Aymard.*
BALTIMORE.
BARON SEQUIER.
BEACON.
BEAUTE DESMARCHES.
BEAUTE POITEVINE.
BEFREIUNG.
BERCKMANS. *P. J. Berckmans.*
BETSY ROSS.
BIOT.
BISZTRA.
BLACKBEAUTY.
BLACKBEAUTY IMP.
BLACKPRINCE.
BLACKWARRIOR.
BLANCHE WINTZER.
BLAZINGTORCH.
BOUCHE C. **C. formosa.**
BRACIA HOSER.
BRANDYWINE.
BRAZILIAN C. **C. polyclada.**
BRICK C. **C. discolor.**
BRILLIANT.
BROADLEAF C. **C. latifolia.**
BRONZE OLYMPIC.
BURBANK.
BUTTERCUP.
CABOS. *J. D. Cabos.*
CAGNE.
CALIENTE.
CALIFORNIA. *Klondike.*
CANARYBIRD.
CANDELABRA.
CANNES.
CAP D'ANTIBES.
CARIBBEAN C. **C. sylvestris.**
CARILLON.
CARMINEBEAUTY.
CASTAGNIES.
CAVALAIRE.
CELESTIN DUBOST. *Mme. Celestin Dubost.*
CHABANNE. *Secretaire Chabanne.*
CHAMELEON.
CHAMPION.
CHAPPAQUA.
CHARGE.
CHARGUERAUD. *Souvenir de Chargueraud.*
CHARLES HENDERSON.
CHAUTAUQUA.

CANNA, continued

CHEERFULNESS.
CHEROKEE.
CHICAGO.
CHINESE C. **C. chinensis.**
CINNABAR C. **C. cinnabarina.**
CITY OF PORTLAND.
CLARA BARTON.
CLEOPATRA.
CLOTHOFGOLD.
COGOLIN.
COLUMBIA.
COMMANDER BYRD.
∞COMMON GARDEN C. ∞**C. generalis.**
COMTE CHOISEL. *Comte Horace Choisel.*
COMTE DEBOUCHAUD.
COMTE DESACHS.
CONARD JUNIOR.
CONOWINGO.
CONQUEROR.
COPPERGIANT.
CORONET.
CORONET IMP.
CORRIDA.
COUNT CHANDON. *Count Raoul Chandon.*
COURSEGOULES.
CRAMPBEL. *Explorateur Crampbel.*
CRIMSONBEDDER.
CUBA. *Augusta.*
CUPID.
CZERNA.
DAKAR.
DAMAS.
DAVID HARUM.
DAYBREAK.
DAZZLER.
DEFENDER.
DELEUIL. *J. A. Deleuil.*
DELICIOUS.
DEPUTE RAVARIN.
DIRECTEUR POTIER.
DIRECTOR HOLTZE.
DISCOLOR.
DISTINCTION.
DR. ACKERKNECHT. *Dr. E. Ackerknecht.*
DRAGON.
DR. BALZ. *Prof. Dr. Balz.*
DR. BOSCH. *Dr. Ing. Robert Bosch.*
DR. BUEDINGER.
DR. CAVET.
DR. DOCK.
DR. DURR. *Dr. Ing. Durr.*
Dr. E. Ackerknecht. DR. ACKERKNECHT.
DR. ECKENER.
Dr. Eugen Trauffer. DR. TRAUFFER.
DR. GRAFF. *Dr. Erwin Graff.*
DR. HEMPEL. *Justizrat Dr. Hempel.*
Dr. Ing. Durr. DR. DURR.
Dr. Ing. Robert Bosch. DR. BOSCH.
DR. MARCUS.
DR. MENE.
DR. NANSEN.
DR. TRAUFFER. *Dr. Eugen Trauffer.*
DRUIDHILL.
DR. VIDAL.
DUCHESS OF MARLBOROUGH.
DUCHESS OF YORK.
DUKE OF MARLBOROUGH.
DUKE OF YORK.
DUTCHER. *John B. Dutcher.*
DWARF TEXAS C. **C. heliconifolia xalapensis.**
EASTERN BEAUTY.
EDIBLE C. **C. edulis.**
EDOUARD ANDRE.
EDWARD W. BOK.

CANNA, continued
Egandale.
E. G. Hill.
Ehrenfels.
Eisele. *J. D. Eisele.*
Eldorado.
Elise Clair. *Souvenir d'Elise Clair.*
Elizabeth. *Grobherzogin Elizabeth.*
Elizabeth Hoss.
Emden.
Emma.
Empress of India.
Enavant.
Enchantress.
Ernest Ludwig. *Grand Duke Ernest Ludwig.*
Ernst Sonntag.
Eureka.
Evolution.
Explorateur Crampbel. Crampbel.
Express.
Eze.
Fairpersian.
Fairyqueen.
Fanal.
F. A. Richers. Richers.
Favorite.
Felix Ragout.
Feuermagazin.
Feuermeer.
Feuerzauber.
F. F. Hunt.
Fierycross.
Fintelmann C. **C. fintelmanni.**
Firebird.
Firebrand.
Flagoftruce.
Flamingo.
Flashlight.
Florence Vaughan.
Florence Vaughan Imp.
Florida.
F. Neuvessel.
Fontan.
Francois Porcher. *Souvenir de Francois Porcher.*
Francois Relf.
Franz Buchner.
Franz Vonstuck.
Frau C. Siebert. Frau Siebert.
Frau Gartendirektor Siebert. Frau Siebert.
Frau Hultsch. *Frau Daisy Hultsch.*
Frau Klein. *Frau Dr. Klein.*
Frau Siebert. *Frau C. Siebert; Frau Gartendirektor Siebert.*
Frau Wendhausen.
F. R. Pierson.
Fuerst Bismarck.
Gaiety.
Gaikwar of Baroda.
Garam.
Garteninspektor Junge. Junge.
Garteninspektor Nebler. Nebler.
Gartenschonheit.
G. A. Stroehlein. Stroehlein.
General Dankl.
Generalmajor von Teichmann. Vonteichmann.
General Merkel.
George Washington.
Germania.
Giantbronze.
Giantcrimson.
Gladiator.
Gladioflora.
Gloriosa.
Goldbank.

CANNA, continued
Goldbird.
Goldencity.
Goldeneagle.
Goldengate.
Goldengem.
Goldenpearl.
Goldenrod.
Goldensceptre.
Goldenstar.
Goldenwedding.
Goldkrone.
G. O. Quintus.
Gourdon.
Governor Roosevelt.
Governor Vonzimmer.
Graf Buelow.
Graf Dekerchove. *Graf Oswald De-Kerchove.*
Graf Rechberg. *Graf Otto v. Rechberg.*
Graf Schaffgotsch.
Graf Waldersee.
Grand Duke Ernest Ludwig. Ernest Ludwig.
Grasse.
Grobherzogin Elizabeth. Elizabeth.
Gruppenstolz.
Gustav Gumpber.
Halleys Comet.
Halli.
Hamburg. *Hansestadt Hamburg.*
Hanoi.
Hans Muehle. *Andenken an Hans Muehle.*
Hans Werthmuller.
Harlequin.
Harmony.
Harry Laing.
Heidenreich. *Stadrat Heidenreich.*
Hermann A. Hesse.
Herzblut.
Hiawatha.
Himalaya C. **C. speciosa.**
Hindenburg.
Hollywood.
Honeysuckle C. **C. liliiflora.**
Honolulu.
Hugo Devries. *Prof. Hugo de Vries.*
Hungaria.
H. Wehrenpfennig.
H. Wendland.
Hydepark.
Inca C. **C. lanuginosa.**
India C. **C. indica.**
Indiana.
IndoChina C. **C. humilis.**
Ingeborg.
Inspector Ehman.
Iris C. **C. iridiflora.**
Italia.
Jackson. *J. Jacksoni.*
Jacksonville Fire.
James Veitch. *James H. Veitch.*
James Wood.
Jane Addams.
Janus.
J. Aymard. Aymard.
J. A. Deleuil. Deleuil.
J. B. Van Der Schoot. Vanderschoot.
J. C. Vaughan. Vaughan.
J. D. Cabos. Cabos.
J. D. Eisele. Eisele.
Jean Tissot.
Jennie Fannline. *Jennie Walls Fannline.*
Jerseyrose.
J. Jacksoni. Jackson.

CANNA, continued
J. Lochner. Lochner.
John B. Dutcher. Dutcher.
John Farquhar.
John Laing.
John White.
Juanita.
Junge. *Garteninspektor Junge.*
Jupiter.
Justizrat Dr. Hempel. Dr. Hempel.
Karl Merck.
Karl Schmidt. *Andenken an Karl Schmidt.*
Kate Deemer. *Kate F. Deemer.*
Kate Grey.
King Humbert.
King Midas.
Klondike. California.
Koenigin Der Gelben.
Konsul Vellnagel. *Konsul W. Vellnagel.*
Koros.
Krelage. *Souvenir de J. H. Krelage.*
Kronus.
Lafayette.
Lafrance.
Lahneck.
Lairds Favorite.
Lalonde.
Lambert C. **C. lamberti.**
Laroya.
Laturbie.
Lavalette.
Lavesubie.
Lehalleur. *Leon Pepin Lehalleur.*
Lelavandou.
Leonard Vaughan.
Leonie Vinnot. *Souvenir de Leonie Vinnot.*
Leon Vassilliere. Vassilliere.
Leopard.
Lepaillon.
Lepradet.
Levens.
Liberation.
Liebesglut.
Lincroft.
Littlegem.
Lochner. *J. Lochner.*
Longleaf C. **C. longifolia.**
Lorraine.
Lorraine Imp.
Louis Colomb.
Louise.
Louise Cayeux.
Louisiana.
Louis Reverchon.
Loveliness.
L. Patry. Patry.
Luceran.
Lucienne Guillaud.
Ludwig Tesdorf.
Luray.
Maidensblush.
Maidoforleans.
Malaussene.
Malay C. **C. orientalis.**
Mandarin.
Mandelieu.
Maranta.
Marechal Vaillante.
Maroc.
Mars.
Martha Washington.
Marvel.
Mary Thilow.
Maurice Mussey.
Melpomene.

CANNA, continued
Menelek.
Menton.
Mephisto.
Meteor.
Mine d'Or.
Minnehaha.
Mirifique.
Miss Sara Hill. Sara Hill.
Mlle. Berat.
Mlle. Brunner. *Mlle. Berthine Brunner.*
Mlle. Frey.
Mlle. Lombard. *Mlle. Merienne Lombard.*
Mme. Aynard. *Mme. J. Aynard.*
Mme. Blanc. *Mme. Alfred Blanc.*
Mme. Celestin Dubost. Celestin Dubost.
Mme. Crozy.
Mme. Druz. *Mme. Louis Druz.*
Mme. Ferdinand Cayeux.
Mme. Hardy. *Souvenir de Mme. Hardy.*
Mme. J. Aynard. Mme. Aynard.
Mme. Leclerc. *Mme. Leon Leclerc.*
Mme. Mesmer.
Mme. Montefiore.
Mme. Opten.
Mme. Sallier.
Mme. Victor Cayeux.
Mohawk.
Monaco.
Mons. Desloges. *Mons. Jarry Desloges.*
Montana.
Mont Blanc.
Mont Blanc Imp. Snowtop.
Montezuma.
Montreal.
Montrouge.
Montthabor.
Morningglow.
Morningstar.
Mougins.
MountEtna.
Mrs. Antoine Wintzer. Mrs. Wintzer.
Mrs. Carl Kelsey. Mrs. Kelsey.
Mrs. Conard. *Mrs. Alfred F. Conard.*
Mrs. C. W. Ward. Mrs. Ward.
Mrs. Dreer. *Mrs. William F. Dreer.*
Mrs. DuPont. *Mrs. Pierre S. DuPont.*
Mrs. Fairman Rogers. Mrs. Rogers.
Mrs. George A. Stroehlein. Mrs. Stroehlein.
Mrs. Gray. *Mrs. Kate Gray.*
Mrs. Hoover. *Mrs. Herbert Hoover.*
Mrs. Kate F. Deemer.
Mrs. Kelsey. *Mrs. Carl Kelsey.*
Mrs. Pierre S. DuPont. Mrs. DuPont.
Mrs. Rogers *Mrs. Fairman Rogers.*
Mrs. Stone. *Mrs. William Stone.*
Mrs. Stroehlein. *Mrs. George A. Stroehlein.*
Mrs. Ward. *Mrs. C. W. Ward.*
Mrs. William F. Dreer. Mrs. Dreer.
Mrs. Wintzer. *Mrs. Antoine Wintzer.*
Mrs. Woodrow Wilson.
Musaefolia.
Nebler. *Garteninspektor Nebler.*
Nera.
NewYork.
Niagara.
Nice.
Nigricans.
Nokomis.
Oceanus.
Olifant.
Olympia.

CANNA, continued
Olympic.
Orangebedder.
Orangekoenigin.
Orangequeen.
Orange Yellow C. **C. lutea aurantiaca.**
Orchid C. **C. orchiodes.**
Ostrich.
Othello.
Ottawa.
Ottawa Imp.
Palm Beach.
Panache Rouge.
Panama.
Pandora.
Pansy C. **C. rubrolutea.**
Paola Radaelli.
Papa Canna.
Papa Nardy.
Parana C. **C. limbata.**
Parthenope.
Patrie.
Patry. *L. Patry.*
Paul Bruant.
Paul Grotz.
Paul Hempel.
Paulina.
Paul Lorenz.
Paul Marquant.
Peachblow. *Alba Rosea Grandiflora*
Pennsylvania.
Perle von Schwaben.
Philadelphia.
P. Huettig.
Pierson Premier.
Pillaroffire.
Pink Ehmani.
Pinkgem.
P. J. Berckmans. Berckmans.
Pluto.
Pocahontas.
Poncedeleon.
Poppy.
Praesident Mayer.
Premier.
President. *The President.*
President Carnot. *Praesident Carnot; Souvenir du President Carnot.*
President Cleveland.
President Faure.
President McKinley.
Primrose.
Primrose C. **C. leucocarpa.**
Prince Igor.
Prince of India.
Princeton.
Prof. Dr. Balz. Dr. Balz.
Professor Roeber.
Prof. Hugo de Vries. Hugo Devries.
Queen Charlotte.
Queen Eleanor.
Queen Helen.
Queen of Holland.
Raede Caroly.
Rainbow.
Razzle Dazzle.
Redcross.
Redindian.
Redspot C. **C. lagunensis.**
Reeves C. **C. reevesi.**
Richard Wallace.
Richers. *F. A. Richers.*
Robert Christie.
Robusta.
Roidesrouges.
Roisoleil.
Roquebillieres.

CANNA, continued
Roquesteron.
Rosalba.
Rosamond Coles.
Rosea Gigantea.
Rosemawr.
Roseofmay.
Rosequeen.
Roseunique.
Rosl Holl.
Roslindale.
Rubin.
Saigon.
Salamander.
Salmonqueen.
Sam Trelease.
Sam Trelease Imp.
SanDiego.
Saorge.
Sara Hill. *Miss Sara Hill.*
Sardanapal.
Saturnus.
Scarlet C. **C. coccinea.**
Schmids Beste.
Schwabenstreich.
Secretaire Chabanne. Chabanne.
Sello C. **C. selloi.**
Semaphore.
Senator Millaud.
Sensation.
Sfax.
Shenandoah.
Sir Lawrence. *Sir Trevor Lawrence.*
Snowqueen.
Snowtop. *Mont Blanc Imp.*
Somali.
Sophie Buchner.
Sospel.
Soudan.
Souvenir d'Antoine Crozy. Antoine Crozy.
Souvenir de Chargueraud. Chargueraud.
Souvenir de Francois Porcher. Francois Porcher.
Souvenir de J. H. Krelage. Krelage.
Souvenir de Leonie Vinnot. Leonie Vinnot.
Souvenir d'Elise Clair. Elise Clair.
Souvenir de Mme. Hardy. Mme. Hardy.
Souvenir du President Carnot. President Carnot.
Splendor.
Stadrat Heidenreich. Heidenreich.
Stadt Fellbach.
Starlight.
Statue of Liberty.
Stella Kanst.
St. Johns.
St. Louis.
Striped Beauty.
Stroehlein. *G. A. Stroehlein.*
Stuttgartia.
Suedfunk.
Sulfur C. **C. pallida.**
Sunbeams.
Sungold.
Sunnyjim.
Sunray.
Sunset.
Sunsetglow.
Susquehanna.
S. Wright. *S. T. Wright.*
Szava.
Tananarive.
Tango.
Tarrytown.
Temes.

CANNA, continued
Tennyson.
Texas C. **C. heliconifolia.**
The Ambassador.
The Gem.
Theoule.
The President. President.
Timbuctoo.
Tine C. **C. tinei.**
Tirol.
Tocsin.
Transylvania.
Trinidad C. **C. pedunculata.**
Triomphe.
Triumph.
Uhlberg.
Uncle Sam.
Vainqueur.
Valbonne.
Vandenberg.
Vanderschoot. *J. B. Van Der Schoot.*
Variable C. **C. variabilis.**
Varouna.
Vassilliere. *Leon Vassilliere.*
Vaughan. *J. C. Vaughan.*
Vence.
Venus.
Vermilion.
Vicepresident Luizet.
Victory.
Violet C. **C. violacea.**
Virginia.
Vonteichmann. *Generalmajor von Teichmann.*
Vorwarts.
Vulcan.
Wabash.
Walhalla.
Warscewicz C. **C. warscewiczi.**
Wawa.
WestGrove.
WestVirginia.
Wilhelm Beck.
Wilhelm Bofinger.
William Griesinger.
William Saunders.
Willy Reinhardt.
Wilmer Atkinson.
Windmar.
Winona.
Winsome.
Wintzers Colossal.
Woldemar Neubert. *Andenken an Woldemar Neubert.*
Wonderful.
W. Pfitzer. *Andenken an W. Pfitzer.*
W. Watson.
Wyoming.
Yellowbird.
Yellow C. **C. lutea.**
Yellowcrozy.
Yellow King Humbert.
Zenith.
Zephyr.

CAN'NABIS |w . . . . Hemp
sati'va (*gigantea; indica*) |w . Hemp
Giant (*gigantea*) hv.

Cannonballtree . . . . . **Couroupita**
Guiana C. . . . . **C. guianensis**

CANO'TIA . . . . Canotia
holacan'tha . . . . Canotia

Cantaloup
Cucumis melo cantalupensis

Canterburybells . **Campanula medium**
White C. . . . . **C. m. alba**

CANTHAREL'LUS . . Cantharellus
auranti'acus . . . . False C.
ciba'rius . . . . . . Chanterelle C.

CAN'THIUM . . . . . . Canthium
dicoc'cum . . . . . . Butulang C.
parviflo'rum . . . Littleflower C.

CAN'TUA . . . . Cantua
bi'color . . . . . . Yellowtube C.
buxifo'lia . . . . Magicflower C.
—tri'color

Canyon-sunflower . . . . **Venegasia**
Common C. . . . . . **V. carpesioides**

Capechestnut **Calodendrum; C. capense**

Capecowslip . . . . **Lachenalia**
Great Nodding C. **L. pendula superba**
Nodding C. . . . . **L. pendula**
Orchid C. . . . . . . **L. orchioides**
Singleleaf C. . . . . . . **L. unifolia**
Tricolor C. . . . . **L. tricolor**

Cape-gooseberry . . . . Groundcherry, Peruvian: **Physalis peruviana**

Capeheath . . . . **Audouinia capitata**

Cape-honeysuckle . **Tecomaria capensis**

Capejasmine . . **Gardenia jasminoides**
Fortunes C. . . . . **G. j. fortuniana**

Capemarigold . . . . **Dimorphotheca**
Annual C. . . . . **D. annua**
Bedding C. . . . . . . **D. ecklonis**
Blueeyed C. . . . . **D. sinuata**
Chrysanthemumleaf C.
D. chrysanthemifolia
Gaping Rain C. . **D. pluvialis ringens**
Rain C. . . . . **D. pluvialis**
Scarletorange C. . . . . **D. cuneata**
Showy C. . . . . . . **D. spectabilis**
Winter C. . . . . . . **D. aurantiaca**

Cape-primrose . . . . . **Streptocarpus**
Dunns C. . . . . **S. dunni**
∞Kew C. . . . . ∞**S. kewensis**
Wendland C. . . . . . **S. wendlandi**

Caper . . . . **Capparis**
Common C. . . . . **C. spinosa**
Dog C. . . . . **C. flexuosa**
Jamaica C. . . . **C. cynophallophora**
Simulo C. . . . . **C. coriacea**

CAPERO'NIA |w
palus'tris |w

Capim Gordura . . . . Molassesgrass: **Melinis minutiflora**

CAPNOI'DES . . . . . **CORYDALIS**

CAP'PARIS . . . . Caper
coria'cea . . . . Simulo C.
cynophalloph'ora (L. 1753, *not* 1759; *jamaicensis*) . . . . . Jamaica C.
flexuo'sa (*cynophallophora* L. 1759, *not* 1753) . . . . Dog C.
spino'sa (*rupestris*) . . . Common C.

CAPRIO'LA . . . . . . **CYNODON**
See **GRASS GENERA.**

CAPSEL'LA |w . . . Shepherdspurse
bursa-pasto'ris (*Bursa b.*) |w
Shepherdspurse

CAP'SICUM |w . . . . . . Redpepper
frutes'cens (*annuum; baccatum*) |w
Bush R.
See note under var. typicum.
—abbrevia'tum (*C. abbreviatum*)
Ornamental B.R.
—cerasifor'me . . . . . Cherry R.
—conoi'des . . . . . . Tabasco R.
Coralgem. hv.

CAPSICUM, continued
frutes'cens fascicula'tum
Cluster Redpepper
—gros'sum . . . . . Sweetbell R.
—lon'gum (*C. longum*) . . Long R.
Cayenne. hv.
Chilli
Red
Yellow
—typ'icum . . . . Bird R.
This is the typical form of this very variable species.

Capulasan . . . . Pulasan: **Nephelium mutabile**

CARAGA'NA . . . . Peashrub
altaga'na . . . . **C. microphylla**
arbores'cens . . . . . . Siberian P.
—redow'ski . . . . . . **C. fruticosa**
₵Dwarf (*nana*) hv. C. arborescens
₵Lorberg (*lorbergi*)
₵Weeping (*pendula*)
auranti'aca . . . . Dwarf P.
Upright Dwarf. hv.
bois'i . . . . Bois P.
brevifo'lia . . . . . . Shortleaf P.
brevispi'na . . . . . . Shortspine P.
chamla'gu . . . . **C. sinica**
crassicau'lis . . . . . Thickstem P.
cuneifo'lia . . . . ∞**C. sophoraefolia**
decor'ticans . . . . Afghanistan P.
franchetia'na . . . . . Franchet P.
fru'tex (*frutescens*) . . . Russian P.
—latifo'lia . . . . . Broadleaf R.P.
—macran'tha . . . . Bigflower R.P.
frutico'sa (*C. arborescens redowski*)
Shrubby P.
gerardia'na (*spinosissima*) Gerard P.
grandiflo'ra . . . . . . Caucasian P.
juba'ta . . . . Shagspine P.
maximowiczia'na . . . Maximowicz P.
microphyl'la (*altagana*) Littleleaf P.
—megalan'tha . . . . . . Showy L.P.
oreoph'ila . . . . Silkyleaf P.
pekinen'sis . . . . Peking P.
pyg'maea . . . . Pygmy P.
si'nica (*chamlagu*) . . . Chinese P.
∞**sophoraefo'lia** (*arborescens × microphylla; cuneifolia*) ∞Sophoraleaf P.
The plant in cultivation is probably a clon of the original polybrid.
spino'sa . . . . Spiny P.
spinosis'sima . . . . . **C. gerardiana**
sukien'sis . . . . Himalaya P.
tibet'ica . . . . Thibet P.

CARAL'LIA . . . . Carallia
brachia'ta . . . . India C.

CARALLU'MA
See **SUCCULENTS.**

Carambola . . . **Averrhoa carambola**

CARA'PA . . . . Crabwood
grandiflo'ra . . . . Uganda C.
guianen'sis . . . . Guiana C.
moluccen'sis . . . . . . Molucca C.

CARA'RA . . . . **CORONOPUS**
corono'pus . . . . . . **C. procumbens**

Carat . . . . . . Palmetto, Trinidad: **Sabal mauritiaeformis**

Caraway . . . . **Carum carvi**

CARDAM'INE |w . . . . Bittercress
angula'ta |w . . . . Angled B.
asarifo'lia
bulbo'sa . . . . Bulb B.
cordifo'lia . . . . . . Heartleaf B.

CARDAMINE, continued
curvisili'qua |w
douglass'i . Douglass Bittercress
hirsu'ta (*pennsylvanica*) Pennsylvania B.
infaus'ta |w
paucisec'ta . . . . **Dentaria californica**
praten'sis (*Dentaria digitata*) |w Cuckoo B.
—ple'na . . . . Double C.B.

Cardamon . **Elettaria; E. cardamomum**

CARDA'RIA (*HYMENOPHYSA*) Whitetop
dra'ba (*Lepidium d.*) . Pepperweed W.
fenestra'ta (*Hymenophysa f.*) Turkestan W.
macrocar'pa (*Hymenophysa m.*) Persian W.
pubes'cens (*Hymenophysa p.*) Hairy W.
—elonga'ta . . . . Longstalk H.W.

CARDIAN'DRA
alternifo'lia

Cardinalberry . . . . **Rhodosphaera**
Big C. . . . . **R. rhodanthema**

Cardinalflower . . **Lobelia cardinalis**
Western C. . . . . **L. splendens**

Cardinalsguard . . . . **Pachystachys**
Blackstick C. . . . . . **P. coccinea**

CARDIOSPER'MUM |w . . Heartseed
grandiflo'rum . . . . . . Showy H.
halicaca'bum |w . . . Balloonvine H.
hirsu'tum . . . . Hairy H.

Cardoon . . . . **Cynara cardunculus**

CAR'DUUS . . . . . Bristlethistle
acanthoi'des . . . . . Acanthus B.
arven'sis . . . . . . **Cirsium arvense**
benedic'tus . . . . **Cnicus b.**
cris'pus . . . . Curly B.
discol'or . . . . **Cirsium d.**
ker'neri . . . . Kerner B.
lanceola'tum . . . . **Cirsium l.**
maria'nus . . . . **Silybum marianum**
nu'tans . . . . Musk B.
pycnoceph'alus (*arabicus*)
undula'tus . . . . **Cirsium undulatum**

CARDWEL'LIA
subli'mis Lacewood (*Goldspanglewood*)

CA'REX |w . . . . Sedge
abrup'ta . . . . . . Abruptbeak S.
acu'ta |w
ala'ta |w . . . . Wingseed S.
albursi'na . . . . Whitebear S.
amplifo'lia |w . . . . . . Bigleaf S.
angus'tior |w
aper'ta |w
aquat'ilis |w . . . . Water S.
athero'des |w
athrosta'chya . . . Slenderbeak S.
atra'ta . . . . Black S.
au'rea . . . . Golden S.
bar'barae . . . . SantaBarbara S.
bel'la
bolan'deri . . . . BolanderS.
brev'ior |w
buchan'ani . . . . . Buchanan S.
cephaloph'ora |w . . . Woodbank S.
chloroph'ila |w
chordorrhi'za |w . . . . Cordroot S.
co'mans . . . . NewZealand Hair S.
como'sa |w
conoi'dea |w
craw'fordi |w . . . . . Crawford S.

CAREX, continued
crini'ta |w . . . . . Fringed Sedge
cristatel'la |w
cruscor'vi |w . . . . . Crowfoot S.
cryptole'pis |w
cu'sicki |w . . . . Cusick S.
decompos'ita |w
dian'dra |w
doug'lasi . . . . Douglas S.
ebe'nea . . . . Ebony S.
eleoch'aris (*stenophylla* Auth., *not* Wahl.) . . . . . . Needleleaf S.
emo'ryi |w . . . . Emory S.
eurycar'pa |w . . . . . Widefruit S.
exser'ta . . . . Shorthair S.
exsicca'ta |w
exten'sa |w
festivel'la |w . . . . . . Ovalhead S.
filifo'lia |w . . . . . Threadleaf S.
flexuo'sa |w
follicula'ta |w
frank'i |w . . . . Franks S.
fra'seri (*Cymophyllus f.*) . . Fraser S.
geoph'ila
gey'eri |w . . . . Elk S.
gigan'tea |w . . . . Giant S.
glareo'sa |w
gracil'lima |w
gran'dis |w
heleonas'tes |w
helioph'ila . . . . Sun S.
hinds'i |w . . . . Hinds S.
hood'i . . . . Hood S.
hormatho'des |w
hyalinole'pis |w
hystrici'na |w . . . . Bottlebrush S.
illo'ta . . . . Sheep S.
incur'va |w
inte'rior |w . . . . Inland S.
intumes'cens |w
japon'ica . . . . **C. morrowi**
kel'loggi |w . . . . Kellogg S.
lachenal'i |w . . . . . . Lachenal S.
lacus'tris |w
laevicon'ica |w
lanugino'sa |w . . . . Woolly S.
lasiocar'pa |w . . . . . Woolfruit S.
liddon'i . . . . **C. petasata**
limo'sa |w . . . . Mud S.
lolia'cea |w . . . . Ryegrass S.
lupulifor'mis |w . . . . . Hoplike S.
lupuli'na |w . . . . Hop S.
lu'rida |w . . . . Lurid S.
lyng'baei |w
mar'cida . . . . **C. praegracilis**
mari'na |w . . . . Sea S.
merten'si . . . . Mertens S.
microp'tera . . . . . . Smallwing S.
milia'ris |w
mor'rowi (*japonica*) . . . Morrows S.
nardi'na |w
nebrasken'sis |w . . . . Nebraska S.
ni'gricans . . . . . . Black Alpine S.
nubic'ola . . . . Cloud S.
obnup'ta
oklahomen'sis |w . . . . Oklahoma S.
oligosper'ma |w . . . . . Fewseed S.
pachystach'ya . . . . . . Chamisso S.
palea'cea |w
petasa'ta (*liddoni*) . . . . Liddon S.
phaeoceph'ala . . . . . . Dunhead S.
plantagine'a . . . . . . Plantainleaf S.
praegrac'ilis (*marcida*)
prai'rea |w . . . . Prairie S.
pres'li . . . . Presl S.
pseudocype'rus |w
rariflo'ra |w
raynolds'i . . . . Raynolds S.

CAREX, continued
rec'ta |w
ripa'ria |w . . . . Streambank Sedge
ross'i . . . . Ross S.
rostra'ta |w . . . . Beaked S.
sali'na |w . . . . Salt S.
sart'welli |w . . . . Sartwell S.
scopa'ria |w . . . . Broom S.
shel'doni |w . . . . Sheldon S.
sicca'ta . . . . Silvertop S.
simula'ta |w
sitchen'sis |w . . . . Sitka S.
stenophyl'la Auth., *not* Wahl. **C. eleocharis**
ster'ilis |w
stipa'ta |w
stric'ta |w
stric'tior |w
tenel'la |w
teneraefor'mis . . . . . Sierraslim S.
tol'miei . . . . Tolmie S.
tra'cyi |w . . . . Tracy S.
triangula'ris |w
tribuloi'des |w . . . . Bristlebract S.
trichocar'pa . . . . . . Hairyseed S.
—arista'ta . . . . Awned H.S.
va'ria |w
verruco'sa |w . . . . Warty S.
vesica'ria |w . . . . Blister S.
vica'ria |w
virid'ula |w . . . . Green S.
vulpinoi'dea |w . . . . Fox S.

CA'REYA . . . . Careya
arbo'rea . . . . Kumbi C.

CA'RICA . . . . Papaya
candamarcen'sis . . . . Mountain P.
papay'a . . . . Papaya
quercifo'lia . . . . Oakleaf P.

CARINIA'NA . . . . Cariniana
domes'tica (*Couratari d.*) . Goyaz C.
One of the species called Jequitiba in the lumber trade.
excel'sa (*Couratari estrellensis*) Giant C.
pyrifor'mis . . . . Albarco C.
This is, erroneously and unfortunately, sometimes miscalled Colombian Mahogany, a genus to which it is not related.

CARIS'SA . . . . Carissa
These plants, when grown for hedges, are often called Hedgethorns.
ardui'na (*acuminata; bispinosa*) Amatungula C.
caran'das . . . . Karanda C.
—dul'cis . Sweet K.C. (*Perunkila*)
ed'ulis . . . . Egyptian C.
grandiflo'ra . . . . Natalplum C.
ova'ta . . . . Australian C.
spina'rum . . . . Ceylon C.

CARLI'NA . . . . Carlina
acanthifo'lia . . . . . . Whitewool C.
acau'lis . . . . Smooth C.

CARLOWRIGHT'IA |w . Carlowrightia
arizo'nica |w . . . . Arizona C.
linearifo'lia . . . . Heath C.

CARLUDOVI'CA . . . . Carludovica
atrovi'rens
hu'milis
lauchea'na (*Ludovia l.*)
palma'ta . Hat C. (*Panama Hatpalm*)
plica'ta

CARMICHAE'LIA
austra'lis
en'ysi

CARMICHAELIA, continued
flagellifor'mis
grandiflo'ra
—divarica'ta
odora'ta
pet'riei
uniflo'ra
williams'i

CARNATION . . **Dianthus caryophyllus**
See also PINK; for hort. var. see **DIANTHUS.**

CARNAUBAPALM . . . **Copernicia cerifera**

CARNEGIE'A . . . . . . **CEREUS**
See **CACTUS GENERA.**

CAROA . . . . **Neoglaziovia variegata**

CAROB . . . . **Ceratonia siliqua**

CAROLINAJESSAMINE
Gelsemium sempervirens

Carolina-vanilla . . TRILISA, VANILLA: **Trilisa odoratissima**

CARPAN'THEA
MESEMBRYANTHEMUM
See **SUCCULENTS.**

CARPENTE'RIA . . . . CARPENTERIA
califor'nica . . . . . CARPENTERIA

CARPETGRASS . . . . **Axonopus**
BIG C. . . . . **A. furcatus**
COMMON C. . . . . **A. affinis**
TROPICAL C. . . . . . **A. compressus**

CARPETWEED . **Mollugo; M. verticillata**

CARPHOCHAE'TE
bigelo'vi

CARPI'NUS [w] . . . . . . HORNBEAM
bet'ulus . . . . EUROPEAN H.
—carpiniz'za . . . CARPINIZZA E.H.
¢COLUMN (*columnaris*) HV. C. betulus
¢CUTLEAF (*incisa*)
¢OAKLEAF (*quercifolia*)
¢PURPLE (*purpurea*)
¢PYRAMID (*fastigiata; pyramidalis*)
¢WEEPING (*pendula*)
carolinia'na (*americana*) [w]
AMERICAN H.
The northern form of this species is distinguished by some botanists as C. caroliniana virginiana.

corda'ta . . . . HEARTLEAF H.
exim'ia . . . . KOREAN H.
fargesia'na . . . . FARGES H.
henrya'na . . . . HENRY H.
japon'ica . . . . JAPANESE H.
laxiflo'ra . . . . LOOSEFLOWER H.
—da'vidi . . . . . . DAVIDS L.H.
—macrosta'chya
orienta'lis . . . . . . ORIENTAL H.
tschonos'ki (*yedoensis*) . . YEDDO H.
turczanino'vi
—ovalifo'lia (*C. polyneura*)

CARPOBRO'TUS
MESEMBRYANTHEMUM
See **SUCCULENTS.**

CARPODE'TUS . . . . . PUTAWETA
serra'tus . . . . PUTAWETA

CARPODI'NUS
dul'cis

Carrageen . IRISHMOSS: **Chondrus crispus**

CARRICILLO . . . . . . **Olyra latifolia**

CARRIER'EA
calyci'na

CARRIONFLOWER . . . . **Stapelia**
STARFISH C. . . . . **S. asterias**

CARROT . . . . **Daucus**
GARDEN C. . . . . **D. carota sativa**
SOUTHWESTERN C. . . . **D. pusillus**
WILD C. . . . . **D. carota**

CARTHA'MUS
lana'tus
leucocau'los
tincto'rius . . . . SAFFLOWER

CA'RUM [w]
bulbocas'tanum . . . . . EARTHNUT (*Groundnut*)
car'vi [w] . . . . CARAWAY
cop'ticum . . **Trachyspermum ammi**
gaird'neri . . . . . . **Perideridia g.**
orega'num . . . . **Perideridia oregana**

CA'RYA (*HICORIA*) [w] . . HICKORY
For horticultural varieties of Hickories and Pecans, see **FRUIT AND EDIBLE NUT NAMES.**
al'ba K. Koch . . . . **C. tomentosa**
al'ba Nutt. . . . . **C. ovata**
ama'ra . . . . **C. cordiformis**
aquat'ica (*Hicoria a.*) [w] . . WATER H.
—austra'lis (*Hicoria a. a.*)
NARROWLEAF W.H.
ash'ei (*Hicoria a.*) . . . HAMMOCK H.
This Florida Hickory, listed in Sudworth's Check List, requires further study; its specific status is uncertain.
∞**brown'i** (*cordiformis* × *pecan*; ∞*Hicoria b.*) . . . . . . ∞BROWNS H.
¢SEARS CREEK (*varians; H. b. v.*) HV.
buck'leyi . . . . **C. texana**
—arkansa'na . . . . **C. t. arkansana**
—villo'sa . . . . **C. t. villosa**
carolinae-septentriona'lis (*Hicoria c.*)
CAROLINA H.
cathayen'sis (*Hicoria c.*) CATHAY H.
cordifor'mis (*amara; Hicoria c.; H. minima*) . . . . . . BITTERNUT H.
—elonga'ta (*Hicoria c. e.*) ASHE B.H.
—latifo'lia (*Hicoria c. l.*)
BROADLEAF B.H.
×**demaree'i** (*cordiformis* × *ovalis*)
DEMAREE H.
×**dun'bari** (*?laciniosa* × *ovata; Hicoria d.*) . . . . DUNBAR H.
fernowia'na (*myristicaeformis* Auth., *not* Nutt.; *Hicoria f.*) . FERNOW H.
florida'na (*Hicoria f.*) . . . SCRUB H.
gla'bra (*porcina; Hicoria g.*) PIGNUT H.
—megacar'pa (*Hicoria g. m.*)
COAST P.H.
illinoen'sis (*pecan* Engl. & Graebn., *not* Nutt.; *Hicoria p.*) [w] . . . . PECAN
lacinio'sa (*sulcata; Hicoria l.*)
SHELLBARK H.
×**la'neyi** (*cordiformis* × *ovata; Hicoria l.*)
LANEY H.
×**—chateaugayen'sis** (*cordiformis* × *ovata; Hicoria l. c.*) . . . . . CANADA H.
×**lecon'tei** (*texana* (LeConte) C.DC., *not* Buckl.; *texana* (LeConte) Britt.)
BITTER PECAN
Elbert L. Little, Jr., has recently published this new name for Bitter Pecan, C. texana (LeC.) C.DC. (1862) being antedated by C. texana Buckl. (1860).

CARYA, continued
leioder'mis (*Hicoria l.*) SWAMP HICKORY (*Louisiana H.*)
—callico'ma (*Hicoria l. c.*) RUDDY S.H.
—mollis'sima (*C. mollissima; Hicoria l. m.; Hicoria m.*) . MISSISSIPPI S.H.
microcar'pa . **C. ovalis; C. ovata nuttalli**
myristicaefor'mis (*Hicoria m.*)
NUTMEG H.
myristicaefor'mis Auth., *not* Nutt.
C. fernowiana
×**nussbaum'eri** (*laciniosa* × *pecan; Hicoria n.*) . . . . . NUSSBAUMER H.
ova'lis (*microcarpa* in part; *Hicoria m.; H. ovalis*) . . . . RED H.
—borea'lis (*Hicoria o. b.*)
MICHIGAN R.H.
—hirsu'ta (*Hicoria o. h.*)
CAROLINA R.H.
—mol'lis (*Hicoria o. m.*) . OHIO R.H.
—obcorda'ta (*Hicoria o. o.*)
NORTHERN R.H.
—obova'lis (*Hicoria o. o.*)
PEARNUT R.H.
—odora'ta (*Hicoria o. o.*)
ROUNDNUT R.H.
ova'ta (*alba* Nutt., *not* K. Koch; *Hicoria o.*) . . . . . . SHAGBARK H.
—complana'ta (*Hicoria o. c.*)
MOUNTHOPE S.H.
—ellipsoida'lis (*Hicoria o. e.*)
MISSOURI S.H.
—fraxinifo'lia (*Hicoria o. f.*)
ASHLEAF S.H.
—nutt'alli (*C. microcarpa* in part; *Hicoria m.; Hicoria o. n.*)
LITTLENUT S.H.
—pubes'cens (*Hicoria o. p.*)
SOUTHERN S.H.
¢HALES (*halesi*) HV. C. ovata
pal'lida (*Hicoria p.*) . . . SAND H.
pecan' Engl. & Graebn., *not* Nutt.
C. illinoensis
porci'na . . . . **C. glabra**
×**schneck'i** (*pecan* × *tomentosa; Hicoria s.*) . . . . SCHNECK H.
sinen'sis (*Hicoria s.*) . . CHINESE H.
sulca'ta . . . . **C. laciniosa**
texa'na (*buckleyi; Hicoria b.*) BLACK H.
—arkansa'na (*C. buckleyi a.; Hicoria b. a.*) . . . . . . ARKANSAS B.H.
—villo'sa (*C. buckleyi v.; Hicoria b. v.*)
VALLEY B.H.
texa'na (LeConte) C.DC., *not* Buckl.
×**C. lecontei**
tomento'sa (*alba* K. Koch, *not* Nutt.; *Hicoria a.; H. tomentosa*)
MOCKERNUT H.
—ficoi'des (*Hicoria t. f.*) . FIG M.H.
—subcoria'cea (*Hicoria t. s.*) GULF M.H.

CARYO'CAR
nucif'erum . . SAWARRINUT (*Pekeanut; Peruvianalmond; Souarinut*)
villo'sum . . . . PIQUIA-ETE

CARYOPHYL'LUS . . . . **EUGENIA**
aromat'icus . **Syzygium aromaticum**
jam'bos . . . . **Syzygium j.**
malaccen'sis . **Syzygium malaccense**

CARYOP'TERIS . . . . . BLUEBEARD
×**clandonen'sis** (*incana* × *mongholica*)
glutino'sa

Hort. var.; HV. = horticultural variety (or varieties); sp. = species (singular); spp. = species (plural).
¢ = clon; × (as a prefix) = hybrid; × (between scientific plant names) = crossed by; ∞ = polybrid; [w] = plant useful to wildlife.
See Glossary for definitions of clon, hybrid, and polybrid.

CARYOPTERIS, continued
inca'na (*mastacanthus; tangutica*) Common Bluebeard
mongho'lica . . . . . Mongolian B.
₵White (*incana candida*) hv. Caryopteris

CARYO'TA . . . . . . Fishtailpalm
See **PALM GENERA.**

Casabanana . . . . . **Sicana odorifera**

CASEA'RIA
esculen'ta
spino'sa

Cashew . . . . **Anacardium**
Common C. . . . . . **A. occidentale**
Guiana C. . . . . . . **A. rhinocarpus**

CASIMIRO'A
ed'ulis . . . . Whitesapote (*Casimiroa; Mexican Apple*)
tetrame'ria . . . . Woollyleaf W.

Casimiroa . . . . . . Whitesapote: **Casimiroa edulis**

CASSAN'DRA . **CHAMAEDAPHNE**

Cassava
Aipi C. . . . . **Manihot aipi**
Common C. . . . . . **M. esculenta**

CAS'SIA ⌊w . . . . Senna
acutifo'lia (*senna*) . . Alexandria S.
ala'ta (*Herpetica a.*) . . Ringworm S.
angustifo'lia . . . . Congo S.
arma'ta . . . . Desert S.
artemisioi'des . . . . Wormwood S.
auricula'ta . . . . Avaram S.
austra'lis . . . . . . Southern S.
bacilla'ris
bauhinioi'des ⌊w
bearea'na
bicapsula'ris
biflo'ra
brasilien'sis . . . . . Brazilian S.
chamaecris'ta **Chamaecrista fasciculata**
cine'rea . . . . . . **Chamaecrista c.**
corymbo'sa (*floribunda*) . Flowery S.
coves'i . . . . Hairy S.
didymobo'trya
eremoph'ila
excel'sa
—angustifo'lia
fis'tula (*Cathartocarpus f.*) Goldenshower S.
floribun'da . . . . . . **C. corymbosa**
flor'ida . . . . **C. siamea**
glau'ca . . . . . Glossyshower S.
gran'dis . . . . Pinkshower S.
hebecar'pa (*marilandica* Am. Auth.) American S.
hirsu'ta
javan'ica . . . . . Appleblossom S.
laeviga'ta (*grandiflora; Adipera l.*) Smooth S.
leptocar'pa ⌊w . . . . . . Slimpod S.
lindheimeria'na
margina'ta
marilan'dica (*medsgeri*) ⌊w . . Wild S.
marilan'dica Am. Auth. . **C. hebecarpa**
moscha'ta
multiju'ga
nairoben'sis
nic'titans . **Chamaecrista procumbens**
nodo'sa . . . . Jointwood S.
obtusifo'lia . . . . **C. tora**
occidenta'lis ⌊w . . . . . . Coffee S.
pilif'era
polyan'tha
roemeria'na

CASSIA, continued
sen'na . . . . **C. acutifolia**
siam'ea (*florida*) . . Siamese Senna
siberia'na . . . . Siberian S.
so'phera
spectab'ilis
splen'dida . . . . Goldenwonder S.
suffrutico'sa
suratten'sis
tomento'sa . . . . Woolly S.
to'ra (*obtusifolia*) ⌊w . . . . Sickle S.
wislize'ni . . . . . . Wislizenus S.

Cassiabarktree . **Cinnamomum cassia**

Cassiaflowertree **Cinnamomum loureiri**

CASSIN'IA (*DIPLOPAPPUS*) Cassinia
au'rea . . . . Golden C.
ful'vida (*Diplopappus chrysophyllus*) Goldenheath C.
leptophyl'la . . . . Silverheath C.
retor'ta . . . . Twisted C.
vauvillier'si
—al'bida

CASSI'OPE ⌊w . . . . Cassiope
fastigia'ta . . . . . . Himalaya C.
hypnoi'des . . . . Arctic C.
lycopodioi'des ⌊w . . . . Alaska C.
mertensia'na ⌊w . . . . Mertens C.
stelleria'na ⌊w . . . . . Starry C.
tetrag'ona ⌊w . . . . . Firemoss C.

CASTA'LIA . . . . . **NYMPHAEA**
See **WATERLILY GENERA.**

CASTA'NEA ⌊w . . . . . . Chestnut
For horticultural varieties of Chestnut grown for their nuts, see **FRUIT AND EDIBLE NUT NAMES.** The species, often shrubs or small trees, with small burs and solitary nuts are known as Chinkapin (*Chinquapin*).
alabamen'sis . . Alabama Chinkapin
alnifo'lia . . . Trailing Chinkapin
—florida'na . . . . . . **C. floridana**
—margaret'ta . . . . . **C. floridana m.**
america'na . . . . **C. dentata**
ash'ei . . . . Ashe Chinkapin
∞**blaringhem'i** (*dentata* × *sativa*) ∞Blaringhem Chestnut
The following is probably a hv.
₵Paragon. hv.
∞**bur'banki** (*mollissima* × *pumila*) ∞Burbank C.
∞**couder'ci** (*crenata* × *sativa*) ∞Couderc C.
crena'ta (*japonica*) . . . Japanese C.
da'vidi . . . . **C. seguini**
denta'ta (*americana*) ⌊w . American C.
∞**endicott'i** (*crenata* × *dentata*) ∞Endicott C.
∞**fleet'i** (*crenata* × *pumila*) ∞Vanfleet C.
florida'na (*C. alnifolia f.*) Florida Chinkapin
—margaret'ta (*C. alnifolia m.*) Margaret F.C.
Perhaps indistinguishable from C. ashei.
hen'ryi (*vilmoriniana*) Henry Chinkapin
japon'ica . . . . **C. crenata**
mollis'sima . . Chinese Chestnut (*Hairy C.*)
Giant. hv.
∞**mor'risi** (*alnifolia* × *mollissima*) ∞Morris C.
₵Tamba. *Giant Japanese Chestnut.* hv.

CASTANEA, continued
∞**neglec'ta** (*dentata* × *pumila*) ∞Chinknut
₵Rush. hv.
ozarken'sis . . . Ozark Chinkapin
∞**pulchel'la** (*pumila* × *sativa*) ∞Pulchella Chestnut
pu'mila ⌊w . . . Allegany Chinkapin
sati'va (*vesca; vulgaris*) . . European Chestnut (*Spanish C.*)
—prolif'era . . . Narrowleaf E.C.
₵Asplenifolia. hv. C. sativa
₵Column (*fastigiata*)
₵Purpleleaf (*purpurea*)
₵Pyramid (*pyramidalis*)
₵Silverleaf (*argenteo-variegata*)
₵Whitemargin (*albo-marginata*)
seguin'i (*davidi*) . Seguin Chinkapin
vilmorinia'na . . . . **C. henryi**

CASTANOP'SIS Evergreenchinkapin
cauda'ta . . . . Chinese E.
chrysophyl'la . . . . Giant E.
—mi'nor (*C. minor*) . . . Golden E.
cuspida'ta (*Quercus c.*) . Japanese E.
sclerophyl'la
sempervi'rens (*C. chrysophylla s.*) Sierra E.

CASTANOSPER'MUM
austra'le . . . Moretonbaychestnut

CASTE'LA . . . . Castela
nicholso'ni . . . . . . Nicholson C.
texa'na (*C. nicholsoni t.*) Allthorn C. (*Amargosa*)

CASTIL'LA (*CASTILLOA*) . Gumtree
elas'tica (*Castilloa e.*) . . Panama G.

CASTILLE'JA ⌊w . . . . . Paintedcup
affi'nis
angustifo'lia (*hispida*) Northwestern P.
bradbur'yi . . . . Bradbury P.
califor'nica
coccin'ea . . . Indian Paintbrush
colli'na
confu'sa
fla'va . . . . . Yellow Paintedcup
foliolo'sa . . . . Woolly P.
his'pida . . . . **C. angustifolia**
hololeu'ca . . . . Shrubby P.
indivi'sa . . . . Texas P.
inte'gra . . . . Wholeleaf P.
latifo'lia
lau'ta . . . . . . Yellowstone P.
linariaefo'lia . . . . . . Wyoming P.
lindheim'eri
lute'a (*villosa*) . . . . . . Hairy P.
luteovi'rens . . . Yellowgreen P.
mar'tini
minia'ta . . . . Scarlet P.
occidenta'lis . . . . Western P.
oreop'ola . . . . Magenta P.
palles'cens . . . . Pale P.
parviflo'ra
—doug'lasi
pilo'sa . . . . White P.
pineto'rum . . . . Pine P.
rhexifo'lia . . . . . . Splitleaf P.
stenan'tha
sulphu'rea . . . . Sulfur P.
villo'sa . . . . **C. lutea**

CASTILLO'A . . . . . . **CASTILLA**

Castorbean . . **Ricinus; R. communis**
African C. . . . . **R. c. africanus**
Bigfruit C. . . . **R. c. macrocarpus**
Bigleaf C. . . . **R. c. macrophyllus**

CASTORBEAN, continued
BOURBON C. Ricinus communis borboniensis
CAMBODIA C. . . . **R. c. cambodgensis**
GIBSON C. . . . . **R. c. gibsoni**
HYBRID C. . . . . . **×R. c. hybridus**

CASUARI'NA . . . . . BEEFWOOD (*Australian-pine*)
cunninghamia'na . . CUNNINGHAM B.
dis'tyla . . . . STUNTED B.
equisetifo'lia . . . . . HORSETAIL B.
fraseria'na . . . . FRASER B.
glau'ca
hor'rida
lepidophloi'a . . . . . SCALYBARK B.
leptocla'da
monta'na
rumph'ii
stric'ta (*quadrivalvis*) . . . COAST B.
subero'sa . . . . ERECT B.
torulo'sa (*tenuissima*) . . . FOREST B.

CATABRO'SA
See **GRASS GENERA.**

CATALINAGRASS
Dissanthelium californicum

CATAL'PA (*MACROCATALPA*) |w CATALPA
bignonioi'des (*syringaefolia*) |w SOUTHERN C.
¢GOLDEN (*aurea*) HV.
¢KOEHNES (*koehnei*)
¢UMBRELLA (*nana*)
bun'gei . . . . . . MANCHURIAN C.
The name Catalpa bungei is commonly misapplied to the Umbrella Catalpa, a horticultural variety of C. bignonioides.
—heterophyl'la
far'gesi . . . . FARGES C.
—duclouxi'i . . . . . . DUCLOUX C.
∞ **hy'brida** (*bignonioides* × *ovata; teasiana*) ∞ TEAS C.
¢JAPANESE (*japonica*) HV.
¢PURPLELEAF (*purpurea*)
longis'sima (*Macrocatalpa l.*) HAITI C.
ova'ta (*kaempferi*) . . . CHINESE C.
¢GOLDEN (*flavescens*) HV.
specio'sa . . . . . . NORTHERN C.
syringaefo'lia . . . . **C. bignonioides**

CATANAN'CHE . . . . . CUPIDSDART
caeru'lea . . . . BLUE C.
BICOLOR. HV.
MAJOR
WHITE (*alba*)

CATAPO'DIUM
See **GRASS GENERA.**

CATASE'TUM
See **ORCHID GENERA.**

CATCHBIRDTREE
AUSTRALASIA C. . **Pisonia brunoniana**
MALAY C. . . . . **P. excelsa**
Catchfly . . . . SILENE: **Silene**
The name Catchfly, however, is apropos only for those Silenes which are conspicuously viscid.
CATCHFLYGRASS . . **Leersia lenticularis**

CATES'BAEA . . . . . . LILYTHORN
spino'sa . . . . HEDGE L.

CA'THA . . . . . ARABIANTEA (*Kat*)
ed'ulis . . . . ARABIANTEA (*Kat*)
Cathar'tia betonicifo'lia . . **Meconopsis b.**
Cathartocar'pus fis'tula . . . . **Cassia f.**

CATHARTOLI'NUM . . . . **LINUM**

CATHCART'IA
villo'sa

CATHES'TECUM
See **GRASS GENERA.**
Catinguero . . . . . . MOLASSESGRASS: **Melinis minutiflora**
CA'TIS . . . . **EUTERPE**
See **PALM GENERA.**
CATIVO . . . . . **Prioria; P. copaifera**
CATNIP . . . . **Nepeta cataria**
CATSEAR . . . . **Hypochoeris**
SMOOTH C. . . . . **H. glabra**
SPOTTED C. . . . . . . **H. radicata**
CATTAIL . . . . **Typha**
COMMON C. . . . . . . **T. latifolia**
ELEPHANTGRASS C. . . **T. elephantina**
NARROWLEAF C. . . . **T. angustifolia**
Cattailmillet . . . . . . PEARLMILLET: **Pennisetum glaucum**

CAT'TLEYA
See **ORCHID GENERA.**

CAU'CALIS |w
microcar'pa |w . . . . FALSECARROT
nodo'sa . . . . **Torilis n.**

CAULAN'THUS
crassicau'lis . THICKSTEM WILDCABBAGE
infla'tus . . . . **Streptanthus i.**
CAULIFLOWER **Brassica oleracea botrytis**

CAULOPHYL'LUM
thalictroi'des . . . . . BLUE COHOSH

CAVENDISH'IA
urichia'na

CAYAPO'NIA
globo'sa
penduli'na . . . . . **Dermophylla p.**
Cayennecherry . PITANGA: **Eugenia uniflora**

CAYLU'SEA
abyssin'ica

CEANO'THUS |w . . . . . CEANOTHUS
america'nus |w JERSEYTEA C. (*Redroot*)
—interme'dius
arbo'reus . . . . FELTLEAF C.
austromonta'nus . . . . . **C. foliosus**
azu'reus Desf., *not* Hort. . **C. coeruleus**
azu'reus Hort., *not* Desf. ∞ **C. delilianus**
∞ **burk'woodi** (*delilianus* ¢INDIGO × *floribundus* Hort., *not* Hook.) ∞ BURKWOOD C.
coeru'leus (*azureus* Desf., *not* Hort.) AZURE C.
confu'sus . . . . RINCON C.
cordula'tus MOUNTAIN WHITETHORN C.
crassifo'lius . . . . HOARYLEAF C.
cunea'tus |w . . . . . BUCKBRUSH C.
cya'neus . . . . SANDIEGO C.
decum'bens . . . . . **C. diversifolius**
∞ **delilia'nus** (*americanus* × *coeruleus; azureus* Hort., *not* Desf.; *hybridus* Hort.) . . . . ∞ DELISLE C.
¢ARNOULD (*arnouldi*) HV.
¢CIEL DEPROVENCE
¢GLOIRE DEPLANTIERES
¢GLOIRE DEVERSAILLES
¢INDIGO
¢LEON SIMON
¢VICTOR JOUIN
denta'tus . . . . CROPLEAF C.

CEANOTHUS, continued
denta'tus floribun'dus
—impres'sus . . . . . . **C. impressus**
¢BRILLIANT. HV. C. dentatus
divarica'tus . . . . . **C. oliganthus**
divarica'tus Auth., *not* Nutt. **C. leucodermis**
diver'gens MOUNT ST. HELENA CEANOTHUS
diversifo'lius (*decumbens*) TRAILING C.
fend'leri |w . . . . . . FENDLER C.
fer'risae . . . . COYOTE C.
floribun'dus
Name often misapplied to a garden hybrid.
folio'sus (*austromontanus*) WAVYLEAF C.
fresnen'sis (*C. rigidus f.*) FRESNOMAT C.
glorio'sus . . . . . . POINTREYES C.
—exalta'tus
gregg'i |w . . . . DESERT C.
—perplex'ans . . . . CUPLEAF D.C.
—vesti'tus (*C. vestitus*) MOHAVE D.C.
hy'bridus Hort. . . . . . ∞ **C. delilianus**
—rig'idus . . . . **C. rigidus**
impres'sus (*C. dentatus i.*)
inca'nus . . . COAST WHITETHORN C.
insula'ris . . . . . **C. megacarpus i.**
integer'rimus |w . . . DEERBRUSH C.
The blue-flowered form of this species is commonly called Bluebrush.
jep'soni . . . . JEPSON C.
lem'moni . . . . LEMMONS C.
leucoder'mis (*divaricatus* Auth., *not* Nutt.) CHAPARRAL WHITETHORN C.
lobbia'nus . . . . LOBB C.
H. E. McMinn, Professor of Botany, Mills College, Oakland, Calif., who has made a special study of this species, reports that it is not a hybrid as hitherto supposed by some botanists.
mar'tini . . . . MARTIN C.
megacar'pus (*macrocarpus* Nutt., *not* Cav.) . . . . BIGPOD C.
—insula'ris (*C. insularis*)
mogollo'nicus . . . . MOGOLLON C.
oligan'thus (*divaricatus*) . . HAIRY C.
ova'tus |w . . . . INLAND C.
∞ **pal'lidus** (? ∞ *delilianus* × *ovatus*) ∞ PALLIDUS C.
¢DOUBLE (*plenus*) HV. ∞ C. pallidus
¢MARIE SIMON
¢ROSEUS
pal'meri . . . . PALMER C.
papillo'sus . . . . . WARTYLEAF C.
—rowea'nus . . MT. TRANQUILLON C.
par'ryi . . . . PARRY C.
parvifo'lius . . . . . LITTLELEAF C.
pineto'rum . . . . KERN C.
prostra'tus . . . . . SQUAWCARPET C.
purpu'reus . . . . . . HOLLYLEAF C.
ramulo'sus . . . . COAST C.
reclina'tus . . . . . . SNAKEROOT C.
rig'idus (*C. hybridus r.*) MONTEREY C.
—fresnen'sis . . . . . **C. fresnensis**
sanguin'eus |w . . . . REDSTEM C.
∞ **serrula'tus** (*cordulatus* × *prostratus*) ∞ CASCADELAKE C.
sonomen'sis . . . . . . SONOMA C.
soredia'tus . . . . . . JIMBRUSH C.
spino'sus . . . . REDHEART C.
thyrsiflo'rus . . . . BLUEBLOSSOM C.
—chand'leri . . . . . CHANDLER B.C.
—gri'seus . . . . GRAY B.C.
tomento'sus . . . . . WOOLLYLEAF C.
∞ **veitchia'nus** (*rigidus* × *thyrsiflorus*) ∞ VEITCH C.

CEANOTHUS, continued
veluti'nus |w . Snowbrush Ceanothus
—laeviga'tus . . . . Varnishleaf C.
verruco'sus . . . . . Wartystem C.
vesti'tus . . . . **C. greggi v.**
¢Arboreus-hybridus. hv. Ceanothus
¢Ceres
¢Doublewhite (*alboplenus*)
¢Henri Defosse
¢Lucie Simon
¢Perlerose
¢Pierre Pignon
¢Richesse
¢Roseus Carmineus
¢Topas

Ceanothus . . . . **Ceanothus**
Azure C. . . . . **C. coeruleus**
Bigpod C. . . . . . . **C. megacarpus**
Blueblossom C. . . . . **C. thyrsiflorus**
Buckbrush C. . . . . . . **C. cuneatus**
∞ Burkwood C. . . . . ∞ **C. burkwoodi**
∞ Cascadelake C. . . . ∞ **C. serrulatus**
Chandler Blueblossom C.
C. thyrsiflorus chandleri
Chaparral Whitethorn C.
C. leucodermis
Coast C. . . . . **C. ramulosus**
Coast Whitethorn C. . . **C. incanus**
Coyote C. . . . . **C. ferrisae**
Cropleaf C. . . . . **C. dentatus**
Cupleaf Desert C.
C. greggi perplexans
Deerbrush C. . . . . **C. integerrimus**
∞ Delisle C. . . . . . . ∞ **C. delilianus**
Desert C. . . . . **C. greggi**
Feltleaf C. . . . . **C. arboreus**
Fendler C. . . . . **C. fendleri**
Fresnomat C. . . . . . **C. fresnensis**
Gray Blueblossom C.
C. thyrsiflorus griseus
Hairy C. . . . . **C. oliganthus**
Hoaryleaf C. . . . . **C. crassifolius**
Hollyleaf C. . . . . . **C. purpureus**
Inland C. . . . . **C. ovatus**
Jepson C. . . . . **C. jepsoni**
Jerseytea C. . . . . . **C. americanus**
Jimbrush C. . . . . . . **C. sorediatus**
Kern C. . . . . **C. pinetorum**
Lemmons C. . . . . **C. lemmoni**
Littleleaf C. . . . . . **C. parvifolius**
Lobb C. . . . . **C. lobbianus**
Martin C. . . . . **C. martini**
Mogollon C. . . . **C. mogollonicus**
Mohave Desert C. . **C. greggi vestitus**
Monterey C. . . . . **C. rigidus**
Mountain Whitethorn C.
C. cordulatus
Mount St. Helena C. . **C. divergens**
Mt.Tranquillon C.
C. papillosus roweanus
∞ Pallidus C. . . . . . . ∞ **C. pallidus**
Palmer C. . . . . **C. palmeri**
Parry C. . . . . **C. parryi**
Pointreyes C. . . . . . . **C. gloriosus**
Redheart C. . . . . **C. spinosus**
Redstem C. . . . . . . **C. sanguineus**
Rincon C. . . . . **C. confusus**
SanDiego C. . . . . **C. cyaneus**
Snakeroot C. . . . . . . **C. reclinatus**
Snowbrush C. . . . . . . **C. velutinus**
Sonoma C. . . . . . . **C. sonomensis**
Squawcarpet C. . . . . **C. prostratus**
Trailing C. . . . . . **C. diversifolius**
Varnishleaf C. **C. velutinus laevigatus**
∞ Veitch C. . . . . . . ∞ **C. veitchianus**
Wartyleaf C. . . . . . **C. papillosus**
Wartystem C. . . . . . **C. verrucosus**

Ceanothus, continued
Wavyleaf C. . . . **Ceanothus foliosus**
Woollyleaf C. . . . **C. tomentosus**
Cearubberplant . . **Manihot glaziovi**

CE'BATHA . . . . **COCCULUS**

CECRO'PIA . . . . Pumpwood
(*Snakewoodtree; Trumpettree*)
adeno'pus . . . . Ambay P.
obtu'sa . . . . Medicinal P.
palma'ta . . . . Silverleaf P.
pelta'ta . . . . Shieldleaf P.

Cedar . . . . **Cedrus**
The common name Cedar is widely misapplied, especially to species and varieties of **Chamaecyparis** (Falsecypress; *Whitecedar; Yellowcedar*), **Cryptomeria** (*Japanese-cedar*), **Cupressus** (Cypress; *Whitecedar*), **Juniperus** (Juniper; *Redcedar*), **Libocedrus** (Incensecedar), and **Thuja** (Arborvitae; *Redcedar; Whitecedar*). This illustrates the importance of the principle adopted by the Joint Committee that a common name properly belonging to one genus should not be used for a plant of another genus, except as part of a compound word; thus for **Chamaecyparis thyoides,** Falsecypress is correct, *not* White Cedar.
Atlas C. . . . . **C. atlantica**
Blue A. C. . . . . **C. a. glauca**
Cedar-of-Lebanon . . . . **C. libani**
Cyprian C. . . . . **C. brevifolia**
Deodar C. . . . . **C. deodara**

Cedar-of-Lebanon . . . **Cedrus libani**

CE'DRELA . . . . Cedrela
The closely related Old World genus Toona is united with Cedrela by some botanists.
austra'lis . . . . **Toona a.**
fis'silis
mexica'na . . . . Mexican C.
odora'ta . . . . Cigarbox C.
serra'ta . . . . **Toona s.**
sinen'sis . . . . **Toona s.**
too'na . . . . **Toona ciliata**

CEDRONEL'LA . . . . . Cedronella
ca'na . . . . **Agastache c.**
mexica'na . . . . **Agastache m.**
triphyl'la (*canariensis*) . . Canary C.

CE'DRUS . . . . Cedar
atlan'tica . . . . Atlas C.
—glau'ca . . . . Blue A.C.
¢Golden (*aurea*) hv. C. atlantica
¢Sentinel (*fastigiata*)
¢Silver (*argentea*)
¢Weeping (*pendula*)
brevifo'lia (*C. libani b.*) . Cyprian C.
deoda'ra . . . . Deodar C.
¢Compact (*compacta*) hv.
¢Creeping (*prostrata*)
¢Fountain (*fontinalis*)
¢Golden (*aurea*)
¢Green (*viridis*)
¢Hardy (*verticillata*)
¢Longleaf (*robusta*)
¢Silver (*argentea*)
¢Weeping (*pendula*)
li'bani (*libanotica*). Cedar-of-Lebanon
Blue (*glauca*) hv.
Dwarf (*nana*)
Pendant (*pendula*)
Sargent (*sargenti*)

CE'IBA (*ERIODENDRON*) . . Ceiba
aesculifo'lia . . . . . . Pochote C.
pentan'dra (*casearia; E. anfractuosum*)
Kapok C.

Celandine . . . . **Chelidonium**
Greater C. . . . . **C. majus**
Celandine-poppy **Stylophorum diphyllum**

CELAS'TRUS |w . . . . Bittersweet
angula'ta (*latifolia*) . . Anglestem B.
articula'ta . . . . **C. orbiculata**
flagella'ris . . . . Korean B.
gemma'ta
glaucophyl'la . . . . . . Glaucous B.
hoesen'eri
hook'eri . . . . Hooker B.
hypoleu'ca (*hypoglauca*) . . . Pale B.
latifo'lia . . . . **C. angulata**
loesen'eri . . . . Loesener B.
orbicula'ta (*articulata*) . . Oriental B.
—puncta'ta . . . . . . Christmas O.B.
panicula'ta . . . . Panicled B.
rosthornia'na
rugo'sa
scan'dens |w . . . . . American B.
strigillo'sus

CEL'ERI . . . . **APIUM**

Celeriac . **Apium graveolens rapaceum**

Celery . . . . **Apium**
Celeriac . . **A. graveolens rapaceum**
Garden C. . . . . **A. g. dulce**
Wild C. . . . . **A. graveolens**

Celerypine . . . . **Phyllocladus**
Mountain C. . . . . **P. alpinus**
Tanekaha C. . . . **P. trichomanoides**
Tasmania C. . . . . **P. rhomboidalis**
Toatoa C. . . . . **P. glaucus**

CELMI'SIA . . . . Celmisia
coria'cea . . . . . . Leatherleaf C.
gracilen'ta
graminifo'lia
holoseri'cea
longifo'lia . . . . Longleaf C.
munro'i
petiola'ta
spectab'ilis . . . . Showy C.
verbascifo'lia

CELO'SIA . . . . Cockscomb
argen'tea . . . . Feather C.
—crista'ta (*C. cristata*). Common F.C.
Childs (*childsi*) hv.
Dwarf Fieryfeather
Dwarf Goldenfeather
Flameoffire
Pyramid (*pyramidalis*)
Thompson (*thompsoni*)
floribun'da
hut'toni . . . . Hutton C.
Aurantiaca. hv. Celosia
Chrysantheflora
Kermesina
Spicata

CEL'SIA . . . . Celsia
arctu'rus . . . . Bearstail C.
cre'tica . . . . Cretan C.

CEL'TIS |w . . . . Hackberry
austra'lis . . . . European H.
bion'di
—heterophyl'la (*C. leveillei*)
brev'ipes . . . . **C. laevigata b.**
bungea'na (*davidiana*) . . . Bunge H.
cani'na . . . . **C. occidentalis c.**
caucas'ica . . . . Caucasian H.
cerasif'era
corda'ta . . . . **C. occidentalis**
doug'lasi (*rugulosa*) |w . . Douglas H.
georgia'na . . . . **C. pumila g.**
glabra'ta
jessoen'sis

CELTIS, continued
julia'nae
koraien'sis . . . KOREAN HACKBERRY
la'bilis
laeviga'ta (*mississippiensis*) lw
SUGAR H.
—**appos'ita** . . . . KENTUCKY S.H.
—**brachyphyl'la** . . . UVALDE S.H.
—**brev'ipes** (*C. brevipes*) ARIZONA S.H.
—**small'i** (*C. smalli*) . . SMALLS S.H.
—**texa'na** (*C. texana*) . . TEXAS S.H.
leveil'lei . . . . **C. biondi heterophylla**
lindheim'eri . . . . LINDHEIMER H.
mississippien'sis . . . . **C. laevigata**
occidenta'lis (*cordata*) lw . COMMON H.
—**cani'na** (*C. canina*) . . . . DOG H.
—**crassifo'lia** . . . . . . BIGLEAF H.
orienta'lis Mill., *not* L. . **C. tourneforti**
pal'lida . . . . SPINY H.
pel'lae
pu'mila . . . . SMALL H.
—**georgia'na** (*C. georgiana*) GEORGIA H.
reticula'ta lw . . . . . . NETLEAF H.
—**vesti'ta** . . . . . OKLAHOMA H.
rugulo'sa . . . . **C. douglasi**
sinen'sis . . . . CHINESE H.
small'i . . . . **C. laevigata s.**
soyau'xi . . . . NIGERIAN H.
ta'la
texa'na . . . . **C. laevigata t.**
tournefort'i (*orientalis* Mill., *not* L.)
ORIENTAL H.

CEN'CHRUS . . . . SANDBUR
See **GRASS GENERA.**

CENTAU'REA (*AETHEOPAPPUS*) lw
CENTAUREA
alpi'na . . . . ALPINE C.
america'na lw . . BASKETFLOWER C.
arena'ria
argen'tea . . . . **C. gymnocarpa**
atropurpu'rea
babylon'ica . . . . SYRIAN C.
benedic'ta . . . . **Cnicus benedictus**
calcitra'pa lw
cinera'ria (*candidissima*) DUSTYMILLER
clemen'tei . . . . . . SPANISH C.
conif'era . . . . **Leuzea c.**
crista'ta . . . . CRESTED C.
crocody'lium
cya'nus . . . . CORNFLOWER
cynaroi'des (*Rhaponticum c.*)
PYRENEES C.
dealba'ta . . . . PERSIAN C.
depres'sa
dilu'ta
erioph'ora
fritsch'i
glastifo'lia
gymnocar'pa (*argentea; plumosa*)
VELVET C.
iber'ica . . . . IBERIAN C.
imperia'lis . . . . ROYAL C.
ja'cea . . . . BROWNSCALE C.
macroceph'ala . . . . . . GLOBE C.
maculo'sa . . . . SPOTTED C.
WHIRLWIND. HV.
melanoceph'ala
meliten'sis lw . . . . MALTA C.
monta'na . . . . . MOUNTAINBLUET
CITRINA. HV.
COERULEA
MAJOR (*grandiflora*)
PINK (*carnea*)
PURPLE (*purpurea*)
ROSE (*rosea*)
SULFUR (*sulphurea*)
WHITE (*alba*)

CENTAUREA, continued
moscha'ta (*odorata; suaveolens*)
SWEETSULTAN
nervo'sa
ni'gra . . . . . . BLACK CENTAUREA
CREAM (*variegata*) HV.
orienta'lis (*rigidifolia*) . CAUCASIAN C.
oxyle'pis
phry'gia
pi'cris . . . . **C. repens**
plumo'sa . . . . . . **C. gymnocarpa**
praeal'ta
pulcher'rima (*Aetheopappus pulcherrimus*) . . . . ROSE C.
re'pens (*picris*) . . . . . RUSSIAN C.
rigidifo'lia . . . . **C. orientalis**
ruthe'nica . . . . . . RUTHENIAN C.
rutifo'lia
salonita'na
scabio'sa . . . . SCABIOSA C.
solstitia'lis . . . . YELLOW C.
sor'dida
splen'dens
stenophyl'la
suaveo'lens . . . . **C. moschata**
verbascifo'lia

CENTAUREA . . . . **Centaurea**
ALPINE C. . . . . **C. alpina**
BASKETFLOWER C. . . . **C. americana**
BLACK C. . . . . **C. nigra**
BROWNSCALE C. . . . . . . **C. jacea**
CAUCASIAN C. . . . . . . **C. orientalis**
CORNFLOWER . . . . **C. cyanus**
CRESTED C. . . . . **C. cristata**
DUSTYMILLER . . . . . . **C. cineraria**
GLOBE C. . . . . . **C. macrocephala**
IBERIAN C. . . . . **C. iberica**
MALTA C. . . . . **C. melitensis**
MOUNTAINBLUET . . . . . . **C. montana**
PERSIAN C. . . . . **C. dealbata**
PYRENEES C. . . . . . . **C. cynaroides**
ROSE C. . . . . **C. pulcherrima**
ROYAL C. . . . . **C. imperialis**
RUSSIAN C. . . . . **C. repens**
RUTHENIAN C. . . . . . . **C. ruthenica**
SCABIOSA C. . . . . **C. scabiosa**
SPANISH C. . . . . **C. clementei**
SPOTTED C. . . . . **C. maculosa**
SWEETSULTAN . . . . **C. moschata**
SYRIAN C. . . . . **C. babylonica**
VELVET C. . . . . **C. gymnocarpa**
YELLOW C. . . . . **C. solstitialis**

CENTAURI'DIUM . . **XANTHISMA**
drum'mondi . . . . . . **X. texanum**

CENTAU'RIUM (*ERYTHRAEA*)
CENTAURIUM
bey'richi
confer'tum
mas'soni (*Erythraea diffusa*)
pulchel'lum (*Erythraea ramosissima*)
umbella'tum (*Erythraea centaurium*)
DRUG C.
venus'tum (*Erythraea venusta*) PINK C.

CENTEL'LA lw
asiat'ica lw

CENTIPEDEGRASS **Eremochloa ophiuroides**

Centipedeplant . . . . . RIBBONBUSH:
Homalocladium; H. platycladum

CENTRADE'NIA
floribun'da

CENTRAN'THUS . . . CENTRANTHUS
al'bus
A name sometimes applied erroneously to the white hort. vars. of C. macrosiphon and of C. ruber.

CENTRANTHUS, continued
angustifo'lius
calcit'rapa
macrosi'phon
SPURVALERIAN CENTRANTHUS
WHITE (*albus*) HV.
ru'ber (*Valeriana coccinea; V. rubra*)
JUPITERSBEARD C.
WHITE (*albus*) HV.

CENTROLO'BIUM . PORCUPINEPODTREE
paraen'se . . . . PARA P.

CENTROPO'GON
lucya'nus
surinamen'sis

CENTROSE'MA (*BRADBURYA*) lw
BUTTERFLYPEA
arenic'ola . . . . FLORIDA B.
brasilia'num . . . . BRAZIL B.
plumier'i
pubes'cens
virginia'num (*grandiflora; Bradburya virginiana*) lw . . . . . COASTAL B.

CEPHAE'LIS
acumina'ta
ipecacuan'ha (*Psychotria i.*)
tomento'sa

CEPHALAN'THERA (*EBUROPHYTON*) . . . . . PHANTOMORCHID
See **ORCHID GENERA, HARDY TERRESTRIAL GROUP.**

CEPHALAN'THUS lw . . BUTTONBUSH
occidenta'lis lw . . . . . COMMON B.
—**angustifo'lius**
—**pubes'cens** . . . . SOUTHERN B.

CEPHALA'RIA . . . . . CEPHALARIA
alpi'na . . . . YELLOW C.
balea'rica . . . . BALEARIC C.
centauroi'des
leucan'tha
radia'ta
rig'ida
syria'ca
tatar'ica . . . . TATARIAN C.
tchihat'chewi
transylvan'ica

CEPHALOCE'REUS (*ARROJADOA; STEPHANOCEREUS*)
CEPHALOCEREUS
See **CACTUS GENERA.**

CEPHALOPHYL'LUM
MESEMBRYANTHEMUM
See **SUCCULENTS.**

CEPHALOSTA'CHYUM
See **BAMBOO GENERA.**

CEPHALOTAX'US . . . . PLUMYEW
fortu'ni . . . . CHINESE P.
harringto'nia (*C. drupacea pedunculata*)
—**drupa'cea** (*C. drupacea*)
—**fastigia'ta** (*C. drupacea f.; C. h. koraiana*)
—**na'na** (*C. drupacea n.; C. nana*)
—**sinen'sis** (*C. drupacea s.*)
oli'veri

CERAS'TIUM lw . . . . . CERASTIUM
alpi'num . . . . ALPINE C.
—**lana'tum**
arven'se lw . . . . STARRY C.
WHITEMAT (*compactum*) HV.
bieberstein'i . . . . . . TAURUS C.
boissier'i (*gibraltaricum*) . SPANISH C.
caespito'sum
glacia'le . . . . **C. uniflorum**

CERASTIUM, continued
grandiflo'rum (*argenteum*)
lerchenfeldia'num
stric'tum |w . . COMMON CERASTIUM
thom'asi . . . . THOMAS C.
tomento'sum (*columnae*) SNOW-IN-SUMMER
uniflo'rum (*glaciale*) . . . . ICY C.
visco'sum |w . . . . STICKY C.
vulga'tum |w . . . . BIG C.

CERA'SUS . . . . **PRUNUS**

Cerasus, the section of the genus Prunus which contains the true Cherries, is regarded by some botanists as a distinct genus.

cap'ollin . . . . **P. serotina salicifolia**
capronia'na . . . . **P. cerasus**
integrifo'lia . . . . **P. lyoni**
mol'lis . . . . **P. prunifolia**
occidenta'lis . . . . . **P. ilicifolia o.**

CERATIO'LA |w . . . . . SANDHEATH
ericoi'des |w . . . . . . SANDHEATH

CERATOCAR'PUS
arena'rius

CERATO'NIA . . . . CAROB
sili'qua . . . CAROB (*St. Johnsbread*)

CERATOPET'ALUM . . . COACHWOOD
apet'alum . . . . . . FRAGRANT C.
gummif'erum . . . . CHRISTMAS C.

CERATOPHYL'LUM |w . HORNWORT
demer'sum |w . . . . . HORNWORT

CERATOP'TERIS . . . . WATERFERN
See **FERN GENERA.**

CERATOSTIG'MA . . . CERATOSTIGMA
grif'fithi . . . . GRIFFITH C.
mi'nus (*polhilli*) . . . CREEPING C.
plumbaginoi'des (*Plumbago larpentiae*) BLUE C.
willmottia'num . . . . WILLMOTT C.

CERATOTHE'CA
trilo'ba

CERATOZA'MIA . . . . HORNCONE
See **CYCAD GENERA.**

CER'BERA . . . . . CERBERUSTREE
frutico'sa
odol'lam . . . . ODOLLAM C.
tan'ghin . . . . ORDEAL C.
theve'tia . . . . . **Thevetia nereifolia**

CERBERUSTREE . . . . **Cerbera**
ODOLLAM C. . . . . **C. odollam**
ORDEAL C. . . . . **C. tanghin**

CERCIDIPHYL'LUM . . KATSURATREE
japon'icum . . . . . KATSURATREE
—sinen'se . . . . CHINESE K.

CERCID'IUM |w . . . . . PALOVERDE
flo'ridum (*torreyanum; Parkinsonia torreyana*) |w . . . . BLUE P.
flo'ridum Auth., *not* Benth. **C. macrum**
ma'crum (*floridum* Auth., *not* Benth.) BORDER P.
microphyl'lum (*Parkinsonia microphylla*) . . . . . . LITTLELEAF P.
texa'num . . . . TEXAS P.

CER'CIS |w . . . . REDBUD
canaden'sis |w . . . . . EASTERN R.
—al'ba . . . . WHITE E.R.
—glabrifo'lia . . . . . SMOOTH E.R.
—pubes'cens . . . . . . HAIRY E.R.
¢DOUBLE (*plena*) HV. C. canadensis
chinen'sis (*japonica*) . . CHINESE R.

CERCIS, continued
occidenta'lis |w . CALIFORNIA REDBUD
orbicula'ta . . . . UTAH R.
racemo'sa . . . . RACEME R.
renifor'mis (*texensis*) . . . TEXAS R.
siliquas'trum . . . . JUDASTREE
¢WHITE (*alba*) HV.

CERCOCAR'PUS |w MOUNTAINMAHOGANY
alnifo'lius . . . . . . ALDERLEAF M.
argen'teus . . . . SILVER M.
arizo'nicus . . . . ARIZONA M.
betuloi'des (*betulifolius*) BIRCHLEAF M.
breviflo'rus . . . . . . WRIGHT M.
doug'lasi

Perhaps hardly more than a var. or form of C. betuloides.

exim'ius

Perhaps hardly more than a var. or form of C. paucidentatus.

intrica'tus . . . . . LITTLELEAF M.
ledifo'lius . . . . CURLLEAF M.
minutiflo'rus . . . . . . SANDIEGO M.
monta'nus (*parvifolius*) |w . TRUE M.
paucidenta'tus . . . . . SHAGGY M.
trask'iae . . . . . . CATALINA M.
Cerda'na alliodo'ra . . . . . **Cordia a.**

CEREALS

This list of Cereals was prepared for this edition of STANDARDIZED PLANT NAMES by various specialists of the Bureau of Plant Industry, and chiefly of the Division of Cereal Crops and Diseases, U. S. Department of Agriculture, under the general oversight of M. A. McCall and John H. Martin of that Division and Bureau, to all of whom the Editorial Committee wishes to express its appreciation.

EDITORIAL COMMITTEE

The names of the varieties of the cereal crops (except Corn) are listed herewith. The varieties listed include all those grown commercially in the United States except for some of minor importance. They also include a few varieties of certain of the crops which are not grown commercially but which are referred to frequently in the literature because of their use as parents in breeding new varieties or as differential host varieties in studies of disease resistance or for other purposes. Recent comprehensive classifications of Wheat and Sorghum varieties, referred to later, have been published. Partial classifications of varieties of Oats and Barley were published less recently but taxonomic studies of these two crops as well as of Flax have been undertaken by the crop specialists who have supplied the lists of varieties and synonyms. The lists of varieties of the other cereals are based upon agronomic studies of numerous varieties by crop specialists who also are familiar with the particular crop as grown throughout the United States.

J. H. MARTIN

BARLEY. Hordeum vulgare.

The varieties of Barley grown commercially or used in Barley research and improvement in the United States are listed below. Descriptions of many of these varieties are given in the following article: Harlan, H. V. and Martini, M. L., "Problems and Results in Barley Breeding" U. S. Dept. Agr. Yearbook Sep. 1571: 303–346. 1937. Descriptions of new improved varieties of Barley registered by the American Society of Agronomy are published in the Journal of that Society.

G. A. WIEBE

CEREALS (BARLEY), continued
ACE.
ALASKA.
ALGERIAN.
ALPHA.
AREQUIPA.
ARIVAT.
ARLINGTON AWNLESS.
ATLAS.
Bay Brewing. COAST.
Beardless 5. TENNESSEE BEARDLESS 5.
Beardless 6. TENNESSEE BEARDLESS 6.
BEECHER.
BELDI GIANT.
BLACK HULL-LESS.
BLUE.
BOLIVIA.
BRANDON.
BYNG.
CALIFORNIA COAST. *Bay Brewing; California Feed; Coast.*
California Feed. COAST.
CALIFORNIA MARIOUT. *Mariout.*
CHARLOTTETOWN 80.
CHEVRON.
CLUB MARIOUT. *Golden Mariout; Mariout; Oregon Mariout.*
COAST. *Bay Brewing; California Feed.*
Coast × Lion F. C. 1110. LICO.
COLSESS.
COMFORT.
COMPANA.
DEFICIENS.
Early Beardless. MISSOURI EARLY BEARDLESS.
ESAW.
EZOND.
FEATHERSTON.
FLYNN.
FRANKLIN MALT. *Malt.*
GATAMI.
Giant White Hull-less. NEPAL.
GLABRON.
Golden Mariout. CLUB MARIOUT.
GOLDFOIL.
Guymayle. HIMALAYA.
HANNA.
HANNCHEN.
HAN RIVER.
HEIL HANNA.
HERO.
HIMALAYA. *Guymayle.*
Hooded 5. TENNESSEE BEARDLESS 5.
Hooded 6. TENNESSEE BEARDLESS 6.
HORN.
Hyatter. WARD.
IMPROVED MANCHURIA. *Minnesota 184.*
KENTUCKY NO. 1.
KENTUCKY NO. 2.
KENTUCKY NO. 11. *Kentucky Smooth-awned.*
LICO. *Coast × Lion F. C. 1110.*
LION.
Malt. FRANKLIN MALT.
MANCHURIA. *Mandscheuri; Manshury; Mensury.*
Manchuria. O.A.C. 21.
Manshury. MANCHURIA.
Mariout. CALIFORNIA MARIOUT; CLUB MARIOUT.
MARNOBARB. *Nobarb.*
MELOY.
Mensury. MANCHURIA.
MICHIGAN WINTER.
Minnesota 184. IMPROVED MANCHURIA.
MINSTURDI.
MISSOURI EARLY BEARDLESS. *Early Beardless.*

CEREALS (BARLEY), continued

NAKANO WASE.
NEPAL. *Giant White Hull-less; White Hull-less.*
NEWEL.
NOBARB.
Nobarb. MARNOBARB.
O.A.C. No. 7.
O.A.C. 21. *Manchuria.*
ODERBRUCKER.
ODESSA.
Oklahoma Winter. WARD.
OLLI.
Oregon Mariout. CLUB MARIOUT.
OREL.
OTTAWA E 25.
PALMELLA BLUE.
PEATLAND.
Pedigree 38. WISCONSIN BARBLESS.
PERUVIAN.
PIDOR.
PONTIAC.
PROSPECT. *Sans Barb 2.*
REGAL.
RENO.
REX.
RUFFLYN.
SANALTA.
Sans Barb 2. PROSPECT.
SANTIAM.
SHORT COMFORT.
Smyrna. WHITE SMYRNA.
SPARTAN.
STAVROPOL.
Tapp Winter. WINTER CLUB.
TENNESSEE BEARDLESS 5. *Beardless 5; Hooded 5; Tennessee Hooded 5.*
TENNESSEE BEARDLESS 6. *Beardless 6; Hooded 6; Tennessee Hooded 6.*
TENNESSEE WINTER.
TENNESSEE WINTER SEL. 52.
TREBI.
UNION BEARDLESS.
UNION WINTER.
Utah Winter. WINTER CLUB.
VAUGHN.
VELVET.
VELVON.
VICTORY.
WARD. *Hyatter; Oklahoma Winter.*
White Hull-less. NEPAL.
WHITE SMYRNA. *Smyrna.*
WINTER CLUB. *Tapp Winter; Utah Winter; White Winter.*
WINTEX.
WISCONSIN BARBLESS. *Pedigree 38; Wisconsin Pedigree 38.*
WISCONSIN WINTER.
YORK.

BUCKWHEAT. **Fagopyrum** species.

Cultivated Buckwheat in the United States is of two species, viz., the commonly grown so-called Common Buckwheat (**Fagopyrum sagittatum**) and Tartary Buckwheat (**F. tataricum**). The so-called Winged (or Notchseeded) Buckwheat (**F. emarginatum**) is merely a type of the hort. var., Japanese, of **F. sagittatum.**

J. H. MARTIN

Sag. Fagopyrum sagittatum
Tat. F. tataricum

JAPANESE. Sag. *Common.*
SILVERHULL. Sag. *Common Gray.*
TARTARY. Tat. *Bloomless; Calcutta; Duckwheat; Hulless; Indiawheat; Marina; Mountain; Rye Buckwheat; Siberian; Wildgoose.*

CEREALS, continued

CORN. **Zea mays.**

Various estimates indicate that not less than 1000 different varieties of corn are grown in the United States. No one has assembled or classified a complete collection of these varieties. Consequently it is impossible to compile an accurate comprehensive list of the recognized corn varieties and their synonyms. A partial list would be inadequate, so corn varieties are not included in this book.

Corn is largely cross-pollinated and thus no open-pollinated variety is pure and uniform. Natural and human selection often quickly change the prevailing type in a corn variety. Thus a given named variety may be very different as grown in different localities or by different growers. On many farms open-pollinated varieties of corn are being replaced as rapidly as suitable adapted hybrids are developed by breeders. The varieties of corn recommended by each of the 48 State agricultural experiment stations for growing in their respective States are listed in the following article: Jenkins, M. T., "Corn Improvement." U. S. Dept. Agr. Yearbook Sep. 1574: 455–522. 1937.

The leading corn hybrids also are listed in the above article. The leading varieties of popcorn are described in the following bulletin: Brunson, A. M. and Bower, C. W., "Popcorn." U. S. Dept. Agr. Farmers' Bulletin 1679: 1–18. 1931. Varieties of sweetcorn are listed in the following article: Tapley, W. T., Enzie, W. D. and Van Eseltine, G. P., "The Vegetables of New York": Part 1, Legumes, Cucurbits, Corn, Alliums; Part III, Sweet Corn: 1–111. Report New York State Agricultural Experiment Station for the Year ending July 30, 1934.

J. H. MARTIN and M. T. JENKINS

FLAX. **Linum usitatissimum.**

Flax (**Linum usitatissimum L.**) is of two types which differ largely in length of stem. Seed Flax produces the linseed used in making linseed oil, while Fiber Flax is grown primarily for the long fibers in the stems which are used for linen manufacture. The varieties of Flax are listed and described in the following article: Dillman, A. C., "Improvement in Flax." U. S. Dept. Agr. Yearbook, Sep. 1579: 745–784. 1937.

A. C. DILLMAN and B. B. ROBINSON

Fib. Fiber Flax
Sd. Seed Flax

ABYSSINIAN. Sd. *Abyssinian Yellow.*
Argentine in part. MALABRIGO; RIO.
BISON. Sd.
BOLLEY GOLDEN. Sd. *Golden.*
BUDA. Sd.
CIRRUS. Fib.
CONCURRENT. Fib.
CROWN. Fib. *Liral 4.*
GOSSAMER. Fib.
J. W. S. Fib.
LINOTA. Sd.
MALABRIGO. Sd. *Argentine.*
MONARCH. Fib. *Liral 3.*
NEWLAND. Sd.
PINNACLE. Fib.
PUNJAB. Sd.
REDWING. Sd.
RIO. Sd. *Argentine.*
ROMAN WINTER. Sd.
ROYAL. Sd.
SMOKY GOLDEN. Sd.
VIKING. Sd.
WALSH. Sd.

CEREALS, continued

OAT. **Avena** species.

The cultivated varieties of Oat are grouped below into three species, viz., **Avena byzantina** C. Koch, Red Oat; **A. sativa** L., Common Oat; and **A. nuda** L., Naked (or Hull-less) Oat. The **A. sativa** species is divided into two subspecies: (1) **diffusa,** Tree Oat, and (2) **orientalis,** Side Oat, on the basis of the arrangement of the panicle branches. Varieties listed without an abbreviated symbol are common Tree Oat, **A. sativa diffusa.** Many of the Oat varieties are listed and the origin given in the following article: Stanton, T. R., "Superior germ plasm in Oats." U. S. Dept. Agr. Yearbook. Sep. 1572: 347–414. 1937.

New improved varieties are registered by the American Society of Agronomy and the Bureau of Plant Industry, cooperating. These have been described in the Journal of that Society.

T. R. STANTON

Byz. Avena byzantina.
Nud. A. nuda.
Or. A. sativa orientalis.

Abundance. SWEDISH SELECT.
Acton. SILVERMINE.
Alaska. TOBOLSK.
Alber. RED ALGERIAN.
ALBION. *Iowa No. 103; Nebraska No. 21; Ohio No. 7009; White Cross.*
Alexander. SILVERMINE.
Algerian. RED ALGERIAN.
ALMERIA. *Belgian Black Winter.*
American Banner. SILVERMINE.
American Beauty. LINCOLN.
ANTHONY.
Appler. RED RUSTPROOF.
Archangel. SWEDISH SELECT.
Argentina. RED ALGERIAN.
AURORA. *Yellow Peruvian.*
AWNLESS CULRED. Byz.
AWNLESS MONARCH.
AWNLESS PROBSTEIER. *Beardless Probsteier; Yellow Nasgaard* in part.
Bancroft. RED RUSTPROOF.
Banner. SILVERMINE.
Bannock. VICTORY.
Barley Oat. CANADIAN.
Beardless Probsteier. AWNLESS PROBSTEIER.
BELAR. Byz.
Belgian Black Winter. ALMERIA.
Belgian Winter. WINTER TURF.
Belgium. SILVERMINE.
BELYAK. *White Belyak.*
Berger. RED ALGERIAN.
Beseler. SWEDISH SELECT.
BICKNELL.
BIG BOY. *Coker Norton No. 20–93.*
Big Four. SILVERMINE.
BLACK ALGERIAN. Byz.
Black Anthony. OLD ISLAND BLACK.
Black Beauty. BLACK TARTAR.
BLACK BELL I. *Black Bell II; Black Norway; Orion; Sirius.*
BLACK DIAMOND.
Black Edgecomb. HATCHETT.
Black Egyptian. BLACK TARTAR.
Black Egyptian. VICTOR.
Black Great Mogul. GREAT MOGUL.
BLACK MESDAG. *Black President; Improved Black President; Mesdag.*
Black Mogul. GREAT MOGUL.
Black Norway. BLACK BELL I.
Black President. BLACK MESDAG.
Black Prolific. BLACK TARTAR.
BLACK RIVAL.

CEREALS (OAT), continued
Black Russian. Boswell.
Black Tartar. Or. *Black Beauty; Black Egyptian; Black Prolific; Garton Black; Molds Enobled.*
Bliss Side. White Tartar.
Bohemian. Chinese.
Bond. Byz.
Boone. *Control; Tama; Vicland.*
Boswell. *Black Russian.*
Bountiful. Victor.
Brunker. Byz.
Bumpercrop. Swedish Select.
Burt. Byz. *Early Harvest; Early Ripe; Early Six Weeks; Fourth of July; Gamlin; June; Little Red Rustproof; May.*
Calcutta. Byz. *Indian; Palestine.*
California Black. Coastblack.
California Red. Red Rustproof.
Canada Cluster. Tartar King.
Canadian. *Barley Oat; Potato.*
Capa. *Pampa; Uruguay.*
Cape. Red Algerian.
Carleton. Kherson.
Carter Prize Cluster. Tartar King.
Cartier. Silvermine.
Cassel. Byz. *Sterilis Selection; Sterisel.*
Castleton. *Castleton Potato.*
Chinese. Nud. *Bohemian; Disco; Kilby.*
Cliff. Red Rustproof.
Clinton. *Lasalle* in part; *Silvermine Selection.*
Clydesdale. Swedish Select.
Coastblack. Byz. *California Black; Commercial Black.*
Coker No. 32-1.
Coker No. 33-19. Fulgrain.
Coker No. 33-47.
Coker Fulghum No. 4. Fulghum.
Coker Norton No. 20-93. Big Boy.
Colburt. Monarch.
Cole. *Sixty-Day* in part.
College Algerians. Red Algerian.
College Success; College Wonder. Silvermine.
Colorado No. 37. Swedish Select.
Columbia. Byz.
Columbian. Lincoln.
Comewell. Silvermine.
Commercial Black. Coastblack.
Control. Boone.
Cock. Red Rustproof.
Cornellian. *White Queen.*
Corriente. Sparrowbill.
Crown. Golden Rain.
Culberson.
Culred. Byz.
Custis. Lee.
Czar of Russia. Silvermine.
Damier. Red Rustproof.
Danish Island.
Daubeney. *Iowa No. 444; O.A.C. No. 3; Trojan.*
Diamond. Liberty.
Dibble Heavyweight. Swedish Select.
Disco. Chinese.
Dwarf Culberson.
Eagle. Victory.
Early Champion. *Early Ohio.*
Early Dakota. Silvermine.
Early Gothland. Gothland.
Early Harvest. Burt.
Early Joanette. *Early Joanette Hybrid.*
Early Miller. Silvermine.
Early Mountain.
Early Ohio. Early Champion.

CEREALS (OAT), continued
Early Red Rustproof. Byz. *Early Red Texas.*
Early Ripe. Burt.
Early Siberian. Tobolsk.
Early Six Weeks. Burt.
Edkin. Kherson.
Elder. Wayne.
Empire. Silvermine.
English Wonder. Scottish Chief.
Erban; Esa. Silvermine.
Ferguson No. 71; Ferguson No. 922. Red Rustproof.
Fortuna. Golden Rain.
Forward. Silvermine.
Fourth of July. Burt.
Fowlds. Nakota.
Franklin. Byz.
Frankside. Tartar King.
Fulghum. Byz. *Coker Fulghum No. 4; Frazier; Kanota; Kareela; King; Marett Fulghum; Nicholson Improved Extra-Early Red Rustproof; Sinclair.*
Fulgrain. Byz. *Coker No. 33-19.*
Fulmer. Byz.
Fulton. Byz.
Fulwin. Byz.
Funk. Silvermine.
Gamlin. Burt.
Garton Black. Black Tartar.
Garton Gray. Or.
Garton No. 5. *Garton No. 691; Kiami; Leader; Record; Yielder* in part.
Garton No. 306; Garton No. 396; Garton No. 453. Victor.
Garton No. 473.
Garton No. 691. Garton No. 5.
Garton No. 748. Or.
Garton No. 784. Or.
Garton No. 1174. Victor.
Garton Yellow. Or.
Gerlach. Silvermine.
German Rustproof. Green Russian.
Golden Giant. Or. *Giant French Hybrid; Giant Yellow; Jaune Geant a Grappes; Yellow Flanders; Yellow Tartar.*
Golden Rain. *Crown; Fortuna; Gold Rain; Golden Drop; Golden Rain II; Svalof Golden; Von Lochow; Wasa.*
Goldmine. Green Russian.
Gopher.
Gothland. *Early Gothland; Minnesota No. 295.*
Granary Filler; Gray Moore. Silvermine.
Gray Winter; Grazing. Winter Turf.
Great American. Silvermine.
Great Mogul. *Black Great Mogul; Black Mogul; Stormogul.*
Green Mountain. Or.
Green Russian. *German Rustproof; Goldmine; Hancock; Iogren; Keystone; Morota; Patterson; Rainbow; Schoolmam.*
Greens Ruakura. Ruakura.
Hairy Culberson.
Hajira. Kherson.
Hancock. Green Russian.
Hastings Hundred Bushel. Red Rustproof.
Hatchett. *Black Edgecomb; Hatchett Blackwinter.*
Hawkeye. State Pride.
Hay.
Hudson. *Sixty-Day Selection.*
Huron. Victory.
Hutcheson Selection. Tech.

CEREALS (OAT), continued
Hvitling. Victory.
Idamine. Silvermine.
Improved Black President. Black Mesdag.
Indian. Calcutta.
Iogold.
Iogren. Green Russian.
Iowa No. 103. Albion.
Iowa No. 105. Richland.
Iowa No. 444. Daubeney.
Iowar.
Irish Victor. *Maine No. 340.*
Isbell New Johnson. Scottish Chief.
Ithacan. Silvermine.
Jackson. Lee.
Japan. *Japan Selection.*
Jaune Geant a Grappes. Golden Giant.
Joanette. *Jostrain; Longfellow.*
Johnson. Scottish Chief.
June. Burt.
Kanota; Kareela. Fulghum.
Keystone. Green Russian.
Kherson. *Carleton; Edkin; Hajira; Orloff; Seventyfive-Day; Sixty-Day* in part.
Kiami. Garton No. 5.
Kilby. Chinese.
King. Fulghum.
Lasalle, in part. Clinton; Swedish Select.
Laurel. Liberty.
Leader, in part. Garton No. 5; Marvelous.
Lee. *Custis; Jackson; Randolph.*
Legacy. Silvermine.
Lenroc.
Liberty. Nud. *Diamond; Laurel.*
Ligowa. Swedish Select.
Lincoln. *American Beauty; Columbian; Myrick; New Sensation; Sensation; Siberian* in part; *Standwell; Wideawake.*
Little Red Rustproof. Burt.
Longfellow. Joanette.
Longs White Tartar. Tartar King.
Madrid.
Maine No. 340. Irish Victor.
Mammoth; Mammoth Cluster. Storm King.
Marett Fulghum. Fulghum.
Marion. Silvermine.
Markton. *South Dakota 334.*
Marvelous. *Leader* in part; *New Banker.*
May. Burt.
McGehee; Mercier. Red Rustproof.
Mesdag. Black Mesdag.
Miami. Swedish Select.
Minnesota No. 281. Silvermine.
Minnesota No. 295. Gothland.
Minnesota No. 368. Silvermine.
Minota.
Molds Enobled. Black Tartar.
Monarch. *Colburt; Suwanee.*
Mongolian. Nud.
Montana No. 30. Swedish Select.
Morota. Green Russian.
Mortgage Lifter. Swedish Select.
Myrick. Lincoln.
Nakota. Nud. *Fowlds; South Dakota No. 165.*
National. Swedish Select.
Navarro. Byz. *Three Grain Mesh.*
Nebraska No. 21. Albion.
New Banker. Marvelous.
New Era. Silvermine.
New Market. Swedish Select.

CEREALS (OAT), continued
New Nortex. Red Rustproof.
New Sensation. Lincoln.
Nicholson Improved Extra-Early Red Rustproof. Fulghum.
Nicol. Silvermine.
Nidar.
Nortex. Red Rustproof.
North Finnish.
O.A.C. No. 3. Daubeney.
O.A.C. No. 72. *Siberian* in part.
O.A.C. No. 144. *Ohio No. 201*.
Ohio No. 7009. Albion.
Old Island Black. *Black Anthony; Prince Edward Island*.
Oregon Gray. Winter Turf.
Oriental. Or.
Orion. Black Bell I.
Orloff. Kherson.
Palestine. Calcutta.
Pampa. Capa.
Patterson. Green Russian.
Potato. Canadian.
President. Swedish Select.
Prince Edward Island. Old Island Black.
Pringle Progress. Silvermine.
Probsteier. *Yellow Nasgaard* in part.
Progress. Silvermine.
Rainbow. Green Russian.
Randolph. Lee.
Record. Garton No. 5.
Red Algerian. Byz. *Alber; Algerian; Argentina; Berger; Cape; College Algerians; River Plate; Sidonian; Smyrna*.
Red Rustproof. Byz. *Appler; Bancroft; California Red; Cliff; Cook; Damier; Ferguson No. 71; Ferguson No. 922; Hastings Hundred Bushel; McGehee; Mercier; New Nortex; Nortex; Red Rustresistant; Texas Red*.
Regenerated Swedish Select. Swedish Select.
Richland. *Iowa No. 105; Richland No. 52*.
River Plate. Red Algerian.
Roosevelt. Swedish Select.
Ruakura. Byz. *Greens Ruakura; Ruakura Rustproof; Ruakura Rustresistant*.
Rusota. Silvermine.
Sandy. *Sandwich*.
Schoenen. Silvermine.
Schoolmam. Green Russian.
Schumacker No. 7. Or.
Scottish Chief. *English Wonder; Isbell New Johnson; Johnson; Scottish Chieftain; Upright*.
Seager. Victory.
Segetal. Byz. *Volgen*.
Seizure. Or.
Senator. Storm King.
Sensation. Lincoln.
Seventyfive-Day. Kherson.
Shadeland Challenge. Sparrowbill.
Shadeland Climax. Swedish Select.
Shadeland Eclipse; Shadeland Wonder. Sparrowbill.
Siberian, in part. Lincoln; O.A.C. No. 72.
Sidonian. Red Algerian.
Silvermine. *Acton; Alexander; American Banner; Banner; Belgium; Big Four; Cartier; College Success; College Wonder; Comewell; Czar of Russia; Early Dakota; Early Miller; Empire; Erban; Esa; Forward: Funk; Gerlach;*

CEREALS (OAT), continued
Granary Filler; Gray Moore; Great American; Idamine; Ithacan; Legacy; Marion; Minnesota No. 281; Minnesota No. 368; New Era; Nicol; Pringle Progress; Progress; Rusota; Schoenen; Spooner; Thousand Dollar; Three Grain; Twentieth Century; Vanguard; Wayne; Welcome; Wisconsin Wonder; Wolverine; Worthy.
Silvermine Selection. Clinton.
Sinclair. Fulghum.
Sirius. Black Bell I.
Sixty-Day, in part. Cole; Kherson.
Sixty-Day Selection. Hudson.
Smyrna. Red Algerian.
South Dakota No. 165. Nakota.
South Dakota 334. Markton.
Sparrowbill. *Corriente; Shadeland Challenge; Shadeland Eclipse; Shadeland Wonder*.
Spooner. Silvermine.
Sporen. Winter Turf.
Standwell. Lincoln.
Star. Victory.
State Pride. *Hawkeye; Wisconsin Pedigree No. 7*.
Sterilis Selection; Sterisel. Cassel.
Storm King. Or. *Mammoth; Mammoth Cluster; Senator; Waverly*.
Stormogul. Great Mogul.
Sunrise. Byz.
Superb. Tartar King.
Support. Winter Turf.
Suwanee. Monarch.
Svalof Golden. Golden Rain.
Svalof Victory. Victory.
Swedish Select. *Abundance; Archangel; Beseler; Bumpercrop; Clydesdale; Colorado No. 37; Dibble Heavyweight; Lasalle* in part; *Ligowa; Miami; Montana No. 30; Mortgage Lifter; National; Newmarket; President; Regenerated Swedish Select; Roosevelt; Shadeland Climax; Wisconsin Pedigree No. 5*.
Swedish Victory. Victory.
Tabor.
Tama. Boone.
Tartarian. White Tartar.
Tartar King. Or. *Canada Cluster; Carter Prizecluster; Frankside; Longs White Tartar; Superb; Tartar Knight; White Plume*.
Tech. *Hutcheson Selection; V.M.I. No. 1*.
Tennex. Byz.
Terry.
Texas Red. Red Rustproof.
Thousand Dollar; Three Grain. Silvermine.
Three Grain Mesh. Navarro.
Tobolsk. *Alaska; Early Siberian*.
Trisperma. Byz.
Trojan. Daubeney.
Twentieth Century. Silvermine.
Tyrone Tawny.
Upright. Scottish Chief.
Uruguay. Capa.
Vanguard. Silvermine.
Vicland. Boone.
Victor. *Black Egyptian; Bountiful; Garton No. 306; Garton No. 396; Garton No. 453; Garton No. 1174*.
Victoria. Byz.
Victory. *Bannock; Eagle; Huron; Hvitling; Seager; Star; Svalof Victory; Swedish Victory*.

CEREALS (OAT), continued
Virginia Gray. Winter Turf.
V. M. I. No. 1. Tech.
Volgen. Segetal.
Von Lochow; Wasa. Golden Rain.
Waverly. Storm King.
Wayne. *Elder*.
Wayne; Welcome. Silvermine.
White Belyak. Belyak.
White Bonanza.
White Cross. Albion.
White Maine.
White Plume. Tartar King.
White Queen. Cornellian.
White Tartar. Or. *Bliss Side; Tartarian; White Russian; White Tartarian*.
Wideawake. Lincoln.
Winter Turf. *Belgian Winter; Gray Winter; Grazing; Oregon Gray; Sporen; Support; Virginia Gray*.
Wisconsin Pedigree No. 5. Swedish Select.
Wisconsin Pedigree No. 7. State Pride.
Wisconsin Wonder; Wolverine; Worthy. Silvermine.
Yakutsk.
Yellow Flanders. Golden Giant.
Yellow Nasgaard, in part. Awnless Probsteier; Probsteier.
Yellow Peruvian. Aurora.
Yellow Tartar. Golden Giant.
Yielder. Garton No. 5.

PROSO. **Panicum miliaceum.**

Also called Broomcorn, Early Fortune, Hershey, Hog, and Manitoba Millet.

Black Voronezh.
Deerbrook.
Early Fortune.
Hansen White Siberian. *Hansen; Siberian; White Siberia*.
Manitoba. Yellow Manitoba.
Orenburger. Turghai.
Red Lump.
Red Russian. *Tambov*.
Siberian. Hansen White Siberian.
Turghai. *Orenburger; Red Turghai*.
White French.
White Siberia. Hansen White Siberian.
Yellow Manitoba. *Manitoba*.

RICE. **Oryza sativa.**

The rice varieties grown in the United States, belonging to a single species, are listed and described briefly in the following article: Jones, J. W., "Improvement in Rice." U. S. Dept. Agr. Yearbook Sep. 1573. 415–454. 1937.

J. W. Jones

Acadia.
American Patna. Rexoro.
Arkansas Fortuna.
Asahi.
Blue Rose.
Calady. *California Blue Rose*.
Caloro.
Colusa.
Delitus.
Early Prolific. *Early Blue Rose*.
Early Wataribune.
Edith.
Fortuna. *Texas Fortuna*.
Honduras.
Improved Blue Rose.

CEREALS (RICE), continued
IOLA.
KAMEJI.
LADY WRIGHT.
NIRA.
ONSEN.
REXORO. *American Patna.*
SHINRIKI.
SHOEMED.
STORM PROOF.
SUPREME BLUE ROSE.
Texas Fortuna. FORTUNA.
WATARIBUNE.
ZENITH.

RYE. Secale cereale.

The named varieties of rye grown in the United States, or of recent experimental interest, are listed below. Rye is largely cross-pollinated, many plants even being self-sterile. Consequently no variety of rye is completely pure, and most varieties are extremely variable in seed color and other observable characters. Thus the identification of most so-called varieties of rye is difficult, if not impossible.

J. W. TAYLOR and B. B. BAYLES

ABRUZZES. *Abruzzi.*
ADVANCE. *Dean.*
BALBO.
Brooks. FRENCH.
DAKOLD. *North Dakota No. 959.*
Dean. ADVANCE.
DOUBLE CHROMOSOME. *Tetraploid.*
Florida. SOUTH GEORGIA.
FRENCH. *Brooks.*
GIANT WINTER.
IMPERIAL. *White Rye; Wisconsin Pedigree No. 6.*
IVANOF. *Wisconsin Pedigree No. 3.*
KANSAS WINTER.
MAMMOTH WHITE.
Minnesota No. 2. SWEDISH.
North Dakota No. 959. DAKOLD.
PETKUS. *Wisconsin Pedigree No. 1.*
PIEDMONT.
PROLIFIC.
RARITAN.
ROSEN.
RUSSIAN NO. 9.
SCHLANSTEDT. *Wisconsin Pedigree No. 2; 12; 19.*
SOUTH GEORGIA. *Florida.*
STAR.
SWEDISH. *Minnesota No. 2.*
Tetraploid. DOUBLE CHROMOSOME.
VERN.
White Rye. IMPERIAL.
Wisconsin Pedigree No. 1. PETKUS.
Wisconsin Pedigree No. 3. IVANOF.
Wisconsin Pedigree No. 6. IMPERIAL.
Wisconsin Pedigree No. 2; 12; 19. SCHLANSTEDT.

SORGHUM. Sorghum vulgare.

This species includes three groups, viz., (1) Grain Sorghums (Durra, Hegari, Kafir, Kaoliang, Milo, Shallu, etc.), (2) Sorgos (Sweet or Saccharine Sorghums, known popularly as "Cane"), sometimes listed as **S. vulgare saccharatum,** and (3) Broomcorn, sometimes listed as **S. vulgare technicum.** The origin, history and description of most of the varieties listed below are given in the following: Vinall, H. N., Stephens, J. C., and Martin, J. H., "Identification, History, and Distribution of Common Sorghum Varieties" (U. S. Dept. Agr. Tech. Bul. 506: 1–102. 59 pl. 26 figs. July 1936). Some of the newer varieties have been registered and described by the American Society of Agronomy.

J. H. MARTIN

Bro. Broomcorn.
Dur. Durra.
Kaf. Kafir.
Kao. Kaoliang.
Mil. Milo.
Sha. Shallu.
Sor. Sorgo.

Acme. EVERGREEN DWARF.
African Millet. SOURLESS.
AJAX.
Aksarben Special. CALIFORNIA GOLDEN.
Algeria. BISHOP.
ATLAS. Sor.
Austrian. EVERGREEN.
BEAVER. *Combine Maize; Hog Maize.*
BISHOP. *Algeria; Bishop Kafir.*
Black Amber. MINNESOTA AMBER.
Black Chaff; Blackhull White. STANDARD BLACKHULL.
BLACK SPANISH. Bro. *Black Jap; Extra Early Japanese; Japanese Broomcorn.*
BLACKSPANISH DWARF. Bro.
BROWN. Dur. *Brown Egyptian Corn; Brown Gyp.*
Buff. FARGO.
CALIFORNIA GOLDEN. Bro. *Aksarben Special.*
California Wheat. SHALLU.
CHEYENNE. *Cheyenne Sweet-stalked Kafir.*
CHILTEX. *Chiltex Kafir.*
CHINESE AMBER. Sor.
CLUB. *Club Kafir.*
Club Head. SUMAC.
COES. *Improved Coes.*
COLLIER. Sor.
COLMAN. Sor. *Honey Drip; Red Orange; Sugar Drip.*
Combine Maize. BEAVER.
Combine Milo. WHEATLAND.
Crookneck Maize. DWARF YELLOW *mil.*
DAKOTA AMBER. Sor.
DARLO.
DARSO. *Maizo.*
DAWN. Kaf. *Dwarf Kafir.*
DAY. Mil.
DENTON. Sor.
DESERT BISHOP. *Desert Maize.*
DOUBLE DWARF. Mil.
DOUBLE DWARF YELLOW. Mil. *Extra Dwarf; Rabbit Maize.*
DWARF ASHBURN. Sor.
DWARF BLACKHULL. Kaf. *Dwarf Kafir; Santa Fe; Sharon Blackhull; Texas Blackhull; Western Blackhull.*
Dwarf Evergreen. EVERGREEN DWARF.
DWARF FETERITA. *Dwarf Spur.*
DWARF FREED.
Dwarf Hegari. HEGARI.
Dwarf Kafir. Kaf. DAWN; DWARF BLACKHULL.
Dwarf Maize. DWARF YELLOW MILO.
Dwarf Spur. DWARF FETERITA.
DWARF WHITE. Mil.
DWARF WHITE DURRA. Dur. *Hoeflings Curlyleaf White Gyp.*
DWARF YELLOW. Mil. *Crookneck Maize; Dwarf Maize; Heileman; Red Maize; Red Milo.*
Early Amber; Early Black Amber. MINNESOTA AMBER.
Early Blackhull. SUNRISE.
EARLY KALO.

CEREALS (SORGHUM), continued
Early Orange. ORANGE; WACONIA ORANGE.
EARLY SUMAC. Sor.
EARLY WHITE. Mil. *Fortyday; Little Sweet; Seventyday; Sugar Milo; Sweet Maize.*
EASON. Kaf.
Egyptian Corn. WHITE DURRA.
Egyptian Rice Corn; Egyptian Wheat. SHALLU.
EVERGREEN. Bro. *Austrian; Illinois Favorite; Missouri Evergreen; Standard; Tennessee Evergreen; White Italian.*
EVERGREEN DWARF. Bro. *Acme; Dwarf Evergreen; Long Brush Dwarf; Oklahoma Dwarf; Western Dwarf.*
Extra Dwarf. DOUBLE DWARF YELLOW.
Extra Early Japanese. BLACK SPANISH.
FARGO. Kaf. *Buff; Fargo Milo; Fargo Straightneck; Straight Maize; Straightneck Maize.*
Farmer Jones. JONES.
FINNEY. Mil. *Resistant.*
FOLGER. Sor. *Folgers Early.*
Fortyday. EARLY WHITE.
FREED. Sor. *Freed Sorgo; White Cane.*
FREMONT. Sor.
Golden Drip. SUGAR DRIP.
GOOSENECK. Sor. *Texas Seeded Ribbon Cane.*
GROHOMA. *New Grain; Stockman No. 1.*
Gyp Corn. WHITE DURRA.
HEGARI. *Dwarf Hegari; Higear; Higeary; Higrain Wheat.*
Heileman. DWARF YELLOW.
HIGHLAND. Kaf.
Higrain Wheat. HEGARI.
Hoeflings Curlyleaf White Gyp. DWARF WHITE DURRA.
Hog Maize. BEAVER.
HONEY. Sor. *Japanese Cane; Japanese Honey Drip; Japanese Ribbon Cane; JapaneseSeededRibbonCane; Sprangle Top.*
Honey Drip. COLMAN; HONEY; RED AMBER.
HYDRO. Kaf.
Illinois Favorite. EVERGREEN.
Improved Coes. COES.
Japanese Broomcorn. BLACK SPANISH.
Japanese Cane. HONEY.
JAPANESE DWARF. Bro. *Jap Dwarf; Sterling Dwarf; Whisk Dwarf.*
Japanese Extra Early. BLACK SPANISH.
Japanese Honey Drip. HONEY.
Japanese Ribbon Cane. HONEY; SUGAR DRIP.
Japanese Seeded Ribbon Cane. HONEY.
Jerusalem Corn. WHITE DURRA.
JONES. Sor. *Farmer Jones.*
KALO. *Yellow Kafir.*
KANSAS ORANGE. Sor.
LEOTI. Sor. *Leoti Red.*
Link Hybrid. SAPLING.
Little Sweet. EARLY WHITE.
Long Brush Dwarf. EVERGREEN DWARF.
Maizo. DARSO.
MANCHU BROWN. Kao.
MANKO. *Maizola; Manko Maize.*
MCLEAN. Sor.
Mexican Wheat. SHALLU.
MINNESOTA AMBER. Sor. *Black Amber; Early Amber; Early Black Amber; Minnesota Early Amber.*
Missouri Evergreen. EVERGREEN.
New Grain. GROHOMA.

CEREALS (SORGHUM), continued

Oklahoma Dwarf. EVERGREEN DWARF.
Oklahoma 101. WHITE DARSO.
ORANGE. Sor. *Early Orange.*
PEARL. Kaf.
PINK KAFIR. Kaf.
PLANTER. Sor. *Planters Friend.*
PREMO.
QUADROON.
Rabbit Maize. DOUBLE DWARF YELLOW.
RED AMBER. Sor. *Honey Drip.*
Red Egyptian Corn. STANDARD YELLOW.
RED KAFIR. Kaf.
Red Maize; Red Milo. DWARF YELLOW.
Red Orange. COLMAN.
Red Top. SUMAC.
REED. Kaf.
Resistant. FINNEY.
REX. Sor. *Red X.*
RICE. Kaf.
Rice Corn. WHITE DURRA.
Rox Orange. WACONIA ORANGE.
Saccaline. SAPLING.
Sagrain. SCHROCK.
Santa Fe. DWARF BLACKHULL.
SAPLING. Sor. *Link Hybrid; Saccaline; Straightneck Sorgo.*
SCARBOROUGH. Bro. *Scarbaugh; Scarboro; Scarbough; Scarbro.*
Schribar Corn. STANDARD FETERITA.
SCHROCK. *Sagrain.*
Seventyday. EARLY WHITE.
SHALLU. Sha. *California Wheat; Egyptian Rice Corn; Egyptian Wheat; Mexican Wheat.*
Sharon Blackhull. DWARF BLACKHULL.
Silver Drip. SUGAR DRIP.
SOONER. Mil. *Sixty Day; Sixty Day Maize.*
SOURLESS. Sor. *African Millet; White Orange.*
Sprangle Top. HONEY.
SPUR FETERITA.
Standard. EVERGREEN.
STANDARD BLACKHULL. Kaf. *Black Chaff; Blackhull White.*
STANDARD FETERITA. *Schribar Corn.*
STANDARD WHITE. Mil. *White Maize.*
STANDARD YELLOW. Mil. *Red Egyptian Corn; Standard Maize; Standard Red Maize.*
Sterling Dwarf. JAPANESE DWARF.
Stockman No. 1. GROHOMA.
Straight Maize; Straightneck Maize. FARGO.
Straightneck Sorgo. SAPLING.
SUGAR DRIP. Sor. *Golden Drip; Japanese Ribbon Cane; Silver Drip.*
Sugar Drip. COLMAN.
Sugar Milo. EARLY WHITE.
SUMAC. Sor. *Club Head; Red Top.*
SUNRISE. Kaf. *Early Blackhull.*
Sweet Maize. EARLY WHITE.
Tennessee Evergreen. EVERGREEN.
Texas Blackhull. DWARF BLACKHULL.
Texas Seeded Ribbon Cane. GOOSENECK.
WACONIA AMBER. Sor.
WACONIA ORANGE. Sor. *Early Orange; Rox Orange; Yellow Orange.*
Western Blackhull. DWARF BLACKHULL.
Western Dwarf. EVERGREEN DWARF.
WHEATLAND. Mil. *Combine Milo.*
Whisk Dwarf. B. JAPANESE DWARF.
WHITE AFRICAN. Sor. *White Mammoth.*
White Cane. FREED.
WHITE DARSO. *Oklahoma 101.*

CEREALS (SORGHUM), continued

WHITE DURRA. Dur. *Egyptian Corn; Gyp Corn; Jerusalem Corn; Rice Corn; White Egyptian Corn; White Gyp.*
White Italian. EVERGREEN.
WHITE KAFIR. *Whitehulled Kafir Corn.*
White Maize. STANDARD WHITE.
White Mammoth. WHITE AFRICAN.
White Orange. SOURLESS.
WONDER.
Yellow Kafir. KALO.
Yellow Orange. WACONIA ORANGE.

WHEAT. **Triticum** species.

In the list of varieties of wheat shown below, some of the recognized varietal names in the lefthand column are followed by a letter. The durum wheats (*T. durum* Desf.) are indicated by the letter (d) and the club wheats (*T. compactum* Host) by the letter (c). Following the names of the varieties of emmer, spelt, Polish wheat, Poulard wheat and timopheevi, the botanical species is given. Where no letter or name is given to indicate the species, the varieties are common wheat belonging to the species *Triticum aestivum* L. (*T. vulgare* Vill.). The commercial varieties of American wheats are classified and described in the following publication: Clark, J. A. and Bayles, B. B., "Classification of Wheat Varieties in the United States in 1939." U. S. Dept. Agr. Tech. Bul. (in press).

Nearly all new improved varieties of merit are registered by the American Society of Agronomy. Descriptions and histories of the new registered varieties are published annually by the Journal of that Society.

J. A. CLARK and B. B. BAYLES

Abundance. GOLDCOIN.
Accession 33. WABASH.
ACME. (d).
Acme. FULCASTER; MEDITERRANEAN.
Acme Bred. FULCASTER.
Advance. RED WAVE.
Alabama Bluestem. PURPLESTRAW.
ALASKA (*T. turgidum* L.) Poulard Wheat. *Egyptian; Eldorado; Jerusalem; King Tut; Many Headed; Many Spiked; Miracle; Mortgage Lifter; Multiple Headed; Mummy; Reed; Seven Headed; Seven Headed Sinner; Smyrna; Syrian; Taos; Wheat of Miracle; Wheat 3,000 Years Old; Wild Goose.*
Alberta Red. TURKEY.
ALBIT. (c)
ALICEL. (c) *Fortyfold-Hybrid 128 (white chaff).*
ALLEN. *Red Allen; Wolf Hybrid.*
ALTON. *Ghirka Winter; Smooth Head.*
Amber. MARTIN.
American Banner. DAWSON.
American Bronze. PROSPERITY.
Anti-rust. RUDY.
APEX.
ARCO. *Pecavet.*
ARDITO.
Argentine. TURKEY.
Arizona Baart. BAART.
Armstrong. MARTIN.
ARNAUTKA. (d) *Goose; Johnson; Nicaragua; Pierson; Wild Goose.*
ASHKOF.
ASHLAND.
ATHENA. *Fortyfold-Federation.*
Auburn. DIEHL-MEDITERRANEAN.
Australian. PACIFIC BLUESTEM.
Australian Club. RED RUSSIAN; SQUAREHEADS MASTER; SURPRISE.

CEREALS (WHEAT), continued

BAART. *Arizona Baart; Columbia; Diener Hybrids; Diener No. 18; Early Baart; White Columbia.*
BAART 38.
BALDROCK.
Baldwin. GOENS.
Bartel's Best. REDHULL.
Bay. SURPRISE.
Bearded Bluestem. FULCASTER.
Bearded Fife. PRESTON.
Bearded Purplestraw. FULCASTER.
Beardless Turkey. MOSIDA; NEWTURK.
Beechwood. POOLE; RED MAY.
Beechwood Hybrid. POOLE.
Beloturka. KUBANKA.
Ber Ban. FULTZ.
BERKELEY ROCK.
BIG CLUB. (c) *Big Four; Chile Club, Crookneck Club; Montezuma Club; Oregon Club; Salt Lake Club.*
BIG CLUB 37. (c).
Big Four. BIG CLUB.
Big Ten. DIEHL-MEDITERRANEAN.
Bishop's Pride. WHITE WINTER.
Black-bearded Durum. PELISS.
Black Chaff. BLACKHULL.
Black Don; Black Durum; Black Emmett. KAHLA.
BLACKHULL. *Black Chaff; Clark's Black Hull; Clark's Black Hulled; Superhard; Superhard Blackhull.*
Black Mediterranean. RUDY.
Black Sea. HARVEST QUEEN.
Black Swamp. KAHLA.
Black Tea. JAVA.
Blankenship. FULCASTER.
Blount's Lambrigg. GYPSUM.
BLUECHAFF. (c) *Blue Chaff Calvert Club.*
Blue Ribbon. PRESTON.
Blue Ridge. FULCASTER.
Bluestem. CHINA; FULCASTER; FULTZ; HAYNES BLUESTEM; MEDITERRANEAN; PACIFIC BLUESTEM; POOLE; PURPLESTRAW.
Bluestem Fultz. FULTZ.
Bolton Bluestem. HAYNES BLUESTEM.
Brandon 123. GREAT NORTHERN.
BREVIT.
BRILL.
Bronze Turkey. REDHULL.
Brown Squarehead. SQUAREHEADS MASTER.
Bulgarian. HUSTON; TURKEY.
Bull Moose. GRANDPRIZE.
BUNYIP.
Burbank's Quality. FLORENCE.
Burbank's Super. JONES FIFE.
Burrhead. FULTZO-MEDITERRANEAN.
California Club; California Gem; California Glory. SURPRISE.
California Red. POOLE.
Canadian. FULCASTER; HARVEST QUEEN.
Canadian Club. JAVA.
Canadian Fife. HARVEST QUEEN; RED FIFE.
Canadian Hybrid. JONES FIFE; RED MAY.
Canadian Progress. PROGRESS.
CANADIAN RED. *Canadian Spring.*
CANAWA.
CANUS.
CARINA.
CARLEEDS. *Nordhougen.*
Celebrated K. B. No. 2. CLIMAX.
CERES.
Champion. FULCASTER.

CEREALS (WHEAT), continued

CHEYENNE. *Fly Proof; Nebraska No. 50.*
CHIEFKAN. *Chiefton; Kanhull.*
Chile. PACIFIC BLUESTEM.
Chile Club. BIG CLUB.
CHINA. *Bluestem; Lebanon Valley; Mortgage Lifter; Pennsylvania Bluestem.*
China Tea. JAVA.
CLARKAN. *Clark's No. 40.*
Clark's Black Hull; Clark's Black Hulled. BLACKHULL.
Clark's No. 40. CLARKAN.
Clawson. GOLDCOIN; RED CLAWSON.
Cleathers Red. REDHULL.
CLIMAX. *Celebrated K. B. No. 2; Grecian; Jones Climax; K. B. No. 2; Pennsylvania Standard; Wilson; Wilson Special.*
Climax. PRESTON.
Club; Club Head. FULTZO-MEDITERRANEAN.
Colorado Special. GYPSUM.
Columbia. BAART; FULTZO-MEDITERRANEAN.
COMET.
Conoway. REDHULL.
COOPERATORKA. *Kooperatka; Kooperatorka; Russian Turkey.*
Corn (wheat). FULCASTER; WHITE POLISH.
CORONATION.
Crail Fife. JONES FIFE.
Crimean. TURKEY.
Crookneck Club. BIG CLUB.
Cumberland Valley. FULCASTER.
Cummings. GOENS.
CURRAWA.
CURRELL. *Currell's Prolific; Dunbar; Gill; Golden Chaff; Pearl Prolific; Perfection; Prettybone; Prolific; Red Gill; Red Odessa; Red Prolific; Tennessee Prolific.*
D-1. MONAD.
D-5; D-fife. PENTAD.
DAWSON. *American Banner; Dawson Golden Chaff; Golden Bronze; Golden Chaff; Improved Amber; White Winter.*
DEFIANCE. *Pringle's Defiance.*
Defiance. GIPSY; TURKEY.
DEMOCRAT.
DENTON.
DICKLOW. *Irwin Dicklow; Jim Holly.*
DIEHL-MEDITERRANEAN. *Auburn; Big Four; Big Ten; Eclipse; Hybrid Mediterranean; Michigan Bronze; Michigan Brown; Miller's Choice; Shepherd's Perfection; Shepherd's Prolific; Spade.*
Diener Hybrids; Diener No. 18. BAART.
Dietz; Dietz Longberry; Dietz Longberry Red. FULCASTER.
Disco. RUBY.
Dixie. JAVA.
DIXON. *Ghirka; Humpback II; Johnson; Smooth Humpback.*
Double Head; Duck Bill. FULTZO-MEDITERRANEAN.
Duffy. FULCASTER.
Dunbar. CURRELL.
Dunlap; Dunlop. GOENS.
Durum No. 5. PENTAD.
Dutch. PROSPERITY.
EAGLE CHIEF.
Early Baart. BAART.
EARLY BLACKHULL. *Early Hardy (Blackhull); Early Russian; Haeberle; Haeberle's Early.*
Early Harvest. RED MAY.

CEREALS (WHEAT), continued

Early Iowa; Early Java. JAVA.
Early May. FLINT; RED MAY; RICE.
Early Oakley. OAKLEY.
Early Ontario. FULTZO-MEDITERRANEAN.
EARLY PREMIUM. *Missouri Early Premium.*
Early Purplestraw. PURPLESTRAW.
Early Red. GOENS.
Early Red Clawson. RED CLAWSON.
Early Rice. RICE.
Early Ripe. GOENS; RED MAY.
Early Rudy. RUDY.
Early Russian. EARLY BLACKHULL.
Early Triumph. RED BOBS.
Early Wonder. HUSTON.
Ebersole. FULCASTER.
Eclipse. DIEHL-MEDITERRANEAN.
Economy. FULTZ; FULTZO-MEDITERRANEAN.
Eden. FULCASTER.
Egyptian. ALASKA; GIPSY; TURKEY.
Egyptian Amber. FULCASTER.
EICKMEYER. *Improved Fortyfold; Shatterproof Fortyfold.*
Eldorado. ALASKA; GOLDCOIN.
ELGIN. (c)
ENID. *Enid Strain; Red Krienke.*
Enterprise. RED MAY.
ERECT.
ESCONDIDO.
Ebersole. FULCASTER.
Excelsior. SURPRISE.
Extra Early Oakley. OAKLEY.
Famine. FULCASTER.
Farmers Friend. FULCASTER; GIPSY.
Farmers Pride. FULTZO-MEDITERRANEAN.
Farmers Trust. MEDITERRANEAN.
FEDERATION.
Fife. JONES FIFE; RED FIFE.
Fishhead. JONES FIFE.
Flat Top. FULTZO-MEDITERRANEAN.
FLINT. *Early May; Little May; Little Red; Little Red May; May; Rappahannock; Red Davie; Red May.*
FLOMAR.
FLORENCE. *Burbank's Quality; Qualintine; Quality; Russian Qualintine; Siberian; Sommers Triple Cross.*
Fly Proof. CHEYENNE.
Fortyfold. GOLDCOIN.
Fortyfold-Federation. ATHENA.
Fortyfold-Hybrid 128. ALICEL.
Forty-to-one. FULCASTER.
FORWARD.
Four Row Fultz. FULTZO-MEDITERRANEAN.
FRONDOSO.
FRONTEIRA.
FULCASTER. *Acme; Acme Bred; Bearded Bluestem; Bearded Purplestraw; Blankenship; Blue Ridge; Bluestem; Canadian; Champion; Corn; Cumberland Valley; Dietz; Dietz Longberry; Dietz Longberry Red; Duffy; Ebersole; Eden; Egyptian Amber; Ebersole; Famine; Farmers Friend; Forty-to-one; Georgia Red; Golden Chaff; Golden King; Goose; Greening; Half Bushel; Improved Acme; Ironclad; Jokisch; Kansas Mortgage Lifter; Kentucky Giant; Kentucky Wonder; Lancaster; Lancaster-Fulcaster; Lincoln; Martha Washington; Marvelous; Michigan Red Line; Millennium; Millennium Dawn; Miracle; Moores Prolific; Multiplier; New Light; New Marvel; Number 10; Peck; Prices Wonder; Rattlejack; Red Wonder; Russellite; Russell's Wonder; Stoner Stooling; Three Peck; Turkish Amber; Tuscan Island; Two Peck; Winter King; Wonderful.*
FULHIO. *Ohio No. 127.*
FULTZ. *Ber Ban; Bluestem; Bluestem Fultz; Economy; Grains o'Gold; Halver; Hickman; High Grade; Illinois Rustproof; Improved English; Improved Fultz; Jersey Fultz; Little Red Jersey; McKennon; New Economy; Nixon; Orange Blossom; Perpetuated Fultz; Roosevelt; Rust Proof; Shamrock; Slickhead; Snow; Tennessee Fultz; Tipton Red; Winter Pearl.*
FULTZO-MEDITERRANEAN. *Burrhead; Club; Club Head; Columbia; Doublehead; Duck Bill; Early Ontario; Economy; Farmers Pride; Flat Top; Four Row Fultz; Harper; New Columbia; Russian Red; Scotts Square Head; Square Head; Square Top; Stub Head; Velvet Chaff.*
GALGALOS.
GARNET.
GASTA.
Georgia Bluestem. PURPLESTRAW.
Georgia Red. FULCASTER; PURPLESTRAW.
German Amber. MEALY; VALLEY.
German Red. RED RUSSIAN.
Gharnovka. KUBANKA.
Ghirka. DIXON; JAVA.
Ghirka Winter. ALTON.
Gill. CURRELL.
GIPSY. *Defiance; Egyptian; Farmers Friend; Gipsy Queen; Golden Straw; Grains o'Gold; Lebanon; Niagara; Reliable.*
GLADDEN. *Number 6100.*
Gleason. GREESON.
GOENS. *Baldwin; Cummings; Dunlap; Dunlop; Early Red; Early Ripe; Going; Hall; Miller's Pride; Owen; Red Chaff; Red Chaff Bearded; Red Hall; Russian Red Chaff; Shelby Red Chaff.*
Gold Bullion. GOLDCOIN.
GOLDCOIN. *Abundance; Clawson; Eldorado; Fortyfold; Gold Bullion; Gold Medal; Goldmine; Golden Chaff; Improved No. 6; International No. 6; Junior No. 6; Klondike; New Soules; Niagara; Number 6; Oregon Goldmine; Plymouth Rock; Prizetaker; Prizewinner; Rochester No. 6; Soules; Superlative; Twentieth Century; White Century; White Clawson; White Eldorado; White Rock; White Russian; White Soules; White Surprise; Winter King.*
GOLDEN.
Golden. RUBY.
GOLDEN BALL. *Solid Stem Durum; Spanish; Viking.*
Golden Bronze. DAWSON.
Golden Chaff. CURRELL; DAWSON; FULCASTER; GOLDCOIN; GRANDPRIZE.
Golden Drop, Golden Fife. PRESTON.
Golden Gate Club. SURPRISE.
Golden Grain. REDHART.
Golden King. FULCASTER.
Golden Straw. GIPSY.
Golden Van. HARVEST QUEEN.
Gold Medal; Goldmine. GOLDCOIN.
Goose. ALASKA; ARNAUTKA; FULCASTER.
Grains o'Gold. FULTZ; GIPSY.

CEREALS (WHEAT), continued

GRANDPRIZE. *Bull Moose; Golden Chaff; New Genesee; St. Louis Grand Prize; Velvet Head.*
Grass. ODESSA.
GREAT NORTHERN. *Brandon 123; Newmarq.*
Great Western. MEDITERRANEAN.
Grecian. CLIMAX.
Greening. FULCASTER.
GREESON. *Gleason; Greensboro.*
GYPSUM. *Blount's Lambrigg; Colorado Special.*
Haeberle; Haeberle's Early. EARLY BLACKHULL.
Half Bushel. FULCASTER.
Hall. GOENS.
Halver. FULTZ.
HARD FEDERATION.
HARD FEDERATION 31.
HARDIRED.
Hard Winter. TURKEY.
Hardy Northern. RUSSIAN.
Harper. FULTZO-MEDITERRANEAN.
Harvest King. POOLE.
HARVEST QUEEN. *Black Sea; Canadian; Canadian Fife; Golden Van; Imported Scotch; Italian Wonder; Kansas Queen; May Queen; New 100; Oregon Red; Prairie Queen; Prizetaker; Red Cross; Salzer's Prizetaker; Virginia Reel; Winter Queen.*
Hastings Prolific. LEAP.
HAYNES BLUESTEM. *Bluestem; Bolton Bluestem; Marvel Bluestem; Minnesota No. 169; Velvet Bluestem.*
Hedge Prolific. POOLE.
Hickman; High Grade. FULTZ.
HOHENHEIMER.
Holland. WILHELMINA.
HONOR.
HOOD. (c)
HOPE.
Humpback II. DIXON.
Hundred-and-one. TURKEY.
Hundred Mark, in part. POOLE; PROSPERITY.
Hungarian. TURKEY.
HUSSAR.
HUSTON. *Bulgarian; Early Wonder; Little Red; Ninety-Day; Red Spring; Swamp.*
Hybred. IOBRED.
Hybrid Mediterranean. DIEHL-MEDITERRANEAN.
HYBRID 63. (c) *Turkey Hybrid; White Hybrid.*
HYBRID 123. (c) *Red Hybrid; Red Walla.*
HYBRID 128. (c) *Washington Hybrid 128; White Hybrid.*
HYBRID 143. (c) *Shot Club.*
Hydro Prolific. POOLE.
HYMAR. (c)
IDAED.
Illinois No. 1. JAVA.
ILLINOIS NO. 2. *Progeny No. 2.*
Illinois Rustproof. FULTZ.
ILRED. *Turkey 10-110.*
Imperial Club. SURPRISE.
Imported Scotch. HARVEST QUEEN.
Improved Acme. FULCASTER.
Improved Amber. DAWSON.
Improved English. FULTZ.
Improved Fortyfold. EICKMEYER.
Improved Fultz. FULTZ.
Improved No. 6. GOLDCOIN.
Improved Turkey. TURKEY.
Indiana Red Wave. RED WAVE.

CEREALS (WHEAT), continued

Indiana Swamp. VALLEY.
International No. 6. GOLDCOIN.
International No. 8; Invincible. PROSPERITY.
IOBRED. *Hybred; Iowa Bred; Red Russian.*
IOTURK.
IOWIN.
Ironclad. FULCASTER.
Ironclad Blackhull. REDHULL.
Irwin Dicklow. DICKLOW.
Italian Wonder. HARVEST QUEEN.
JAVA. *Black Tea; Canadian Club; China Tea; Dixie; Early Iowa; Early Java; Ghirka; Illinois No. 1; Kearney County; Siberian; Swedish; Tea Leaf.*
JENKIN. (c) *Jenkin's Club.*
Jersey Fultz. FULTZ.
Jerusalem. ALASKA.
Jim Holly. DICKLOW.
Johnson. ARNAUTKA; DIXON; PRESTON.
Johnson's Early Fife. PRESTON.
Jokisch. FULCASTER.
Jones Climax. CLIMAX.
JONES FIFE. *Burbank's Super; Canadian Hybrid; Crail Fife; Fife; Fishhead; Jones Winter Fife; Silver King; Super; Velvet Chaff; Winter Fife.*
Jones Longberry; Jones Longberry No. 1; Jones Red Wave. RED MAY.
Jones Winter Fife. JONES FIFE.
Junior No. 6. GOLDCOIN.
KAHLA. (d) *Black Don; Black Durum; Black Emmett; Black Swamp; Purple Durum; Red Swamp; Sloat.*
Kanhull. CHIEFKAN.
KANRED. *P-762.*
Kanred. UTAH KANRED.
Kansas Mortgage Lifter. FULCASTER.
Kansas Queen. HARVEST QUEEN.
KARMONT.
KAWVALE.
K. B. No. 2. CLIMAX.
Kearney County. JAVA.
Kentucky Bluestem. POOLE.
Kentucky Giant. FULCASTER; RUDY.
Kentucky Wonder. FULCASTER.
Key's Prolific. MEDITERRANEAN.
KHAPLI. (*T. dicoccum* Shrank)
Kharkof. TURKEY.
King Tut. ALASKA.
KITCHENER.
Klondike. GOLDCOIN.
KOMAR. *Number 1656; Number 1656.84.*
Kooperatka; Kooperatorka. COOPERATORKA.
KOTA. *R. B. R. 3.*
KRUSE.
KUBANKA. (d) *Beloturka; Gharnovka; Pererodka; Taganrog; Yellow Gharnovka.*
Ladd Durum. PENTAD.
LADOGA. *Spring Turkey.*
Lancaster; Lancaster-Fulcaster. FULCASTER.
Lancaster Red. MEDITERRANEAN.
Landreth. MARTIN.
LEAP. *Hastings Prolific; Leap's Prolific; Woods Prolific; Woolf.*
LEAPLAND.
Lebanon. GIPSY.
Lebanon Valley. CHINA.
Lehigh. MEDITERRANEAN.
LEMHI.
Lincoln. FULCASTER.
Little May. FLINT; RICE.

CEREALS (WHEAT), continued

Little Red. FLINT; HUSTON.
Little Red Jersey. FULTZ.
Little Red May. FLINT.
LOFTHOUSE. *Winter La Salle; Winter Nellis.*
LOROS.
Lost Freight. TURKEY.
LYNN.
MACKEY.
MAJOR.
Malakof; Malcome. TURKEY.
Mammoth Ball. RED MAY.
MAMMOTH RED.
Many Headed; Many Spiked. ALASKA.
MARQUILLO. *Minnesota No. 2202.*
MARQUIS.
Martha Washington. FULCASTER.
MARTIN. *Amber; Armstrong; Landreth; Martin Amber; Satisfaction; Silver Chaff; White Amber.*
MARVEL. *Overby.*
Marvel Bluestem. HAYNES BLUESTEM.
Marvelous. FULCASTER.
May. FLINT; RED MAY; RICE.
May Queen. HARVEST QUEEN.
McKennon. FULTZ.
MEALY. *German Amber; Velvet Chaff; Velvet Head; White Velvet Chaff.*
MEDITERRANEAN. *Acme; Bluestem; Farmers Trust; Great Western; Key's Prolific; Lancaster Red; Lehigh; Miller; Millers Pride; Missouri Bluestem; Mortgage Lifter; Red Chaff; Red Mediterranean; Red Sea; Red Top; Rocky Mountain; Standby; Swamp.*
MERCURY.
MERIT.
Michigan Amber. RED MAY.
Michigan Bronze; Michigan Brown. DIEHL-MEDITERRANEAN.
Michigan Red. PROSPERITY.
Michigan Red Line. FULCASTER.
Michigan Wonder. RED MAY.
MICHIKOF.
Millennium; Millennium Dawn. FULCASTER.
Miller. MEDITERRANEAN.
Miller's Choice. DIEHL-MEDITERRANEAN.
Miller's Pride. GOENS; MEDITERRANEAN.
MINDUM. (d)
MINHARDI.
Minnesota No. 169. HAYNES BLUESTEM.
Minnesota No. 188. PRESTON.
Minnesota No. 1507. MINTURKI.
Minnesota No. 2202. MARQUILLO.
Minnesota Red Cross; Minnesota Reliable. TURKEY.
MINTURKI. *Minnesota No. 1507.*
Miracle. ALASKA; FULCASTER.
Missouri Bluestem. MEDITERRANEAN.
Missouri Early Premium. EARLY PREMIUM.
MONAD. (d) D-1.
Montana Deal. RED RUSSIAN.
MONTANA NO. 36.
Montezuma Club. BIGCLUB.
Moore's Prolific. FULCASTER.
Mortgage Lifter. ALASKA; CHINA; MEDITERRANEAN; POOLE.
MOSIDA. *Beardless Turkey.*
Mountain Purplestraw. PURPLESTRAW.
Multiple Headed. ALASKA.
Multiplier. FULCASTER.
Mummy. ALASKA.
NABOB.
Nebraska No. 50. CHEYENNE.

CEREALS (WHEAT), continued
NEBRASKA No. 60.
NEBRED.
Neverfail. OAKLEY.
New Columbia. FULTZO-MEDITERRANEAN
New Economy. FULTZ.
New Genesee. GRANDPRIZE.
New Light. FULCASTER.
Newmarq. GREAT NORTHERN.
New Marvel. FULCASTER.
New 100. HARVEST QUEEN.
New Soules. GOLDCOIN.
NEWTURK. *Beardless Turkey.*
Niagara. GIPSY; GOLDCOIN; VALLEY.
Nicaragua. ARNAUTKA.
Nick Special. REDHULL.
NIGGER. *Winter Green; Winter John; Winter King.*
Ninety-Day. HUSTON; SONORA.
Nissley; Nissley's Hybrid. POOLE.
NITTANY. *Penn. No. 44.*
Nixon. FULTZ.
NODAK. (d)
Nordhougen. CARLEEDS; PROGRESS.
Norwood. OAKLEY.
Number 6. GOLDCOIN.
Number 8. PROSPERITY.
Number 10. FULCASTER.
Number 1656; Number 1656.84. KOMAR.
Number 6100. GLADDEN.
OAKLEY. *Early Oakley; Extra Early Oakley; Neverfail; Norwood.*
Ocean Wave. POOLE.
ODESSA. *Grass.*
Ohio No. 127. FULHIO.
Old Dutch. RED WAVE.
ONAS.
Orange. RED MAY.
Orange Blossom. FULTZ.
Oregon Club. BIG CLUB.
Oregon Goldmine. GOLDCOIN.
Oregon Red. HARVEST QUEEN.
Oregon Red Chaff. RED CHAFF.
Oregon White. WHITE WINTER.
OREGON ZIMMERMAN. *Zimmerman.*
ORO.
Overby. MARVEL.
Owen. GOENS.
P-762. KANRED.
PACIFIC BLUESTEM. *Australian; Bluestem; Chile; Palouse Bluestem; White Australian; White Bluestem; White Chile; White Elliott; White Lammas.*
PACIFIC BLUESTEM 37.
Palouse Bluestem. PACIFIC BLUESTEM.
Pearl Prolific. CURRELL.
Pecavet. ARCO.
Peck. FULCASTER.
PELISS. (d) *Black Bearded; Pelissier.*
Penn. No. 44. NITTANY.
Pennsylvania Bluestem. CHINA.
Pennsylvania Standard. CLIMAX.
PENTAD. (d) *D-5; Durum No. 5; D-fife; Ladd Durum; Red Durum; Resistant Fife; Rust Proof.*
Pererodka. KUBANKA.
Perfection. CURRELL.
Perpetuated Fultz. FULTZ.
Pierson. ARNAUTKA.
PILCRAW. *Pilcraw Enormous; Thompson; Thompson Club; White Russian.*
PILOT.
Pioneer Turkey. TURKEY.
Plymouth Rock. GOLDCOIN.
POOLE. *Beechwood; Beechwood Hybrid; Bluestem; California Red; Harvest King; Hedge Prolific; Hundred Mark;*

CEREALS (WHEAT), continued
Hydro Prolific; Kentucky Bluestem; Mortgage Lifter; Nissley; Nissley's Hybrid; Ocean Wave; Red Amber; Red California; Red Chaff; Red Fultz; Red King; Red Russell; Royal Red Clawson; Sweet Water Valley; Wagner; Winter King.
PORTAGE.
POSO. (c) *Small Club.*
POWER. *Power's Fife; Station No. 66.*
POWERCLUB. *Power's Club.*
Prairie Queen. HARVEST QUEEN.
PREMIER.
PRESTON. *Bearded Fife; Blue Ribbon; Climax; Golden Drop; Golden Fife; Johnson; Johnson's Early Fife; Minnesota No. 188; Red Fife; Velvet Chaff.*
Prettybone. CURRELL.
Price's Wonder. FULCASTER.
Pride of California. SURPRISE.
Pride of Indiana. RED MAY.
Pringle's Defiance. DEFIANCE.
Pringle's Surprise. SURPRISE.
Prizetaker. GOLDCOIN; HARVEST QUEEN.
Prizewinner. GOLDCOIN.
Progeny No. 2. ILLINOIS NO. 2.
PROGRESS. *Canadian Progress; Nordhougen; Prosper.*
Prolific. CURRELL.
PROPO. *Proper.*
Prosper. PROGRESS.
PROSPERITY. *American Bronze; Dutch; Hundred Mark; International No. 8; Invincible; Michigan Red; No. 8; Red Victory; Silver Chaff; Twentieth Century; Zinn's Golden.*
PURDUE NO. 1.
Purdue No. 4. RED MAY.
PURKOF.
Purple Durum. KAHLA.
PURPLESTRAW. *Alabama Bluestem; Bluestem; Early Purplestraw; Georgia Bluestem; Georgia Red; Mountain Purplestraw; Ripley.*
Qualintine; Quality. FLORENCE.
Queen of New York. RUDY.
Queen Wilhelmina. WILHELMINA.
RAMONA.
Rappahannock. FLINT.
Rattlejack. FULCASTER.
R. B. R. 3. KOTA.
Reed. ALASKA.
Red Allen. ALLEN.
Red Amber. POOLE; RED MAY.
RED BOBS. *Early Triumph.*
Red California. POOLE.
RED CHAFF. (c) *Oregon Red Chaff; Red Chaff Club.*
Red Chaff. GOENS; MEDITERRANEAN; POOLE; REDHULL; RED WAVE; SONORA; SQUAREHEADS MASTER.
Red Chaff Bearded. GOENS.
RED CLAWSON. *Clawson; Early Red Clawson; Zellers Valley.*
Red Cross. HARVEST QUEEN; RED MAY.
Red Davie. FLINT.
Red Durum. PENTAD.
RED FIFE. *Canadian Fife; Fife; Saskatchewan Fife; Scotch Fife.*
Red Fife. PRESTON.
Red Fultz. POOLE.
Red Gill. CURRELL.
Red Hall. GOENS.
REDHART. *Golden Grain.*

CEREALS (WHEAT), continued
REDHULL. *Bartel's Best; Bronze Turkey; Cleathers Red; Conoway; Ironclad Blackhull; Nick Special; Red Chaff; Rupp.*
Red Hybrid. HYBRID 123.
RED INDIAN.
Red Ivory. RED WAVE.
Red King. POOLE.
Red Krienke. ENID.
RED MAY. *Beechwood; Canadian Hybrid; Early Harvest; Early May; Early Ripe; Enterprise; Jones Longberry; Jones Longberry No. 1; Jones Red Wave; Mammoth Ball; May; Michigan Amber; Michigan Wonder; Orange; Pride of Indiana; Purdue No. 4; Red Amber; Red Cross; Red Republic; Republican Red.*
Red May. FLINT; RICE.
Red Mediterranean. MEDITERRANEAN; SEA ISLAND.
Red Odessa. CURRELL.
Red Prolific. CURRELL.
Red Republic. RED MAY.
Red Rice. RICE.
RED ROCK.
Red Russell. POOLE.
RED RUSSIAN. *Australian Club; German Red; Montana Deal; Red Walla; Squarehead.*
Red Russian. IOBRED; SQUAREHEADS MASTER; TURKEY.
Red Sea. MEDITERRANEAN.
Red Spring. HUSTON.
Red Swamp. KAHLA.
Red Top. MEDITERRANEAN.
Red Victory. PROSPERITY.
Red Wafer. RED WAVE.
Red Walla. HYBRID 123; RED RUSSIAN.
RED WAVE. *Advance; Indiana Red Wave; Jones Red Wave; Old Dutch; Red Chaff; Red Ivory; Red Wafer; Ruble; Rust Proof; Waif; Waverly; Worlds Fair.*
RED WINTER. Sp.
Red Winter. TURKEY.
Red Wonder. FULCASTER; TURKEY.
Reed. ALASKA.
REGENT.
Reliable. GIPSY.
RELIANCE.
RELIEF.
RENOWN.
Republican Red. RED MAY.
REQUA.
Resistant Fife. PENTAD.
REWARD.
REX.
RICE. *Early May; Early Rice; Little May; May; Red May; Red Rice; White Rice.*
RIDIT. *Selection C; Smutless.*
RINK.
RIO.
Ripley. PURPLESTRAW.
RIVAL.
Rochester No. 6. GOLDCOIN.
Rocky Mountain. MEDITERRANEAN.
Romanella. TURKEY.
Roosevelt. FULTZ.
Royal Red Clawson. POOLE.
Ruble. RED WAVE.
RUBY. *Disco; Golden.*
RUDY. *Antirust; Black Mediterranean; Early Rudy; Kentucky Giant; Queen of New York.*
Rupp. REDHULL.

CEREALS (WHEAT), continued
Russellite; Russell's Wonder. FULCASTER.
RUSSIAN. *Hardy Northern.*
Russian. TURKEY.
Russian Amber. VALLEY.
Russian Qualintine. FLORENCE.
RUSSIAN RED.
Russian Red. FULTZO-MEDITERRANEAN.
Russian Red Chaff. GOENS.
Russian Turkey. COOPERATORKA.
Rust Proof. FULTZ; PENTAD; RED WAVE; VALLEY.
Salt Lake Club. BIG CLUB.
Salzer's Prizetaker. HARVEST QUEEN.
Saskatchewan Fife. RED FIFE.
Satisfaction. MARTIN.
Scotch Fife. RED FIFE.
Scott's Squarehead. FULTZO-MEDITERRANEAN.
SEA ISLAND. *Red Mediterranean; Texas Red.*
Selection C. RIDIT.
Seven Headed; Seven Headed Sinner. ALASKA.
SEVIER.
Shamrock. FULTZ.
Shatterproof Fortyfold. EICKMEYER.
Shelby Red Chaff. GOENS.
SHEPHERD.
Shepherd's Perfection; Shepherd's Prolific. DIEHL-MEDITERRANEAN.
Shot Club. HYBRID 143.
Siberian. FLORENCE; JAVA.
SIBLEY 81.
Silver Chaff. MARTIN; PROSPERITY; SURPRISE.
Silver Club. SURPRISE.
Silver King. JONES FIFE.
Slickhead. FULTZ.
Sloat. KAHLA.
Small Club. POSO.
Smith Club. SURPRISE.
Smooth Head. ALTON.
Smooth Humpback. DIXON.
Smutless. RIDIT.
Smyrna. ALASKA.
Snow. FULTZ.
Solid Stem Durum. GOLDEN BALL.
Sommer's Triple Cross. FLORENCE.
SONORA. *Ninety-Day; Red Chaff; White Sonora.*
SONORA 37.
Soules. GOLDCOIN.
Spade. DIEHL-MEDITERRANEAN.
Spanish. GOLDEN BALL.
SPELMAR. (d)
"Speltz." VERNAL.
Spring Turkey. LADOGA.
Squarehead. RED RUSSIAN.
Square Head. FULTZO-MEDITERRANEAN.
SQUAREHEADS MASTER. *Australian Club; Brown Squarehead; Redchaff; Red Russian.*
Square Top. FULTZO-MEDITERRANEAN.
Standby. MEDITERRANEAN.
Station No. 66. POWER.
St. Louis Grand Prize. GRANDPRIZE.
Stoner; Stooling. FULCASTER.
Stub Head. FULTZO-MEDITERRANEAN.
STURGEON.
Super. JONES FIFE.
Super-Hard; Superhard Blackhull. BLACKHULL.
Superlative. GOLDCOIN.
SUPREME.
SURPRISE. *Australian Club; Bay; California Club; California Gem; California Glory; Excelsior; Golden Gate Club; Imperial Club; Pride of California; Pringle's Surprise; Silver Chaff; Silver Club; Smith Club; University Gem; White Russian.*
Swamp. HUSTON; MEDITERRANEAN.
Swedish. JAVA.
Sweet Water Valley. POOL
Syrian. ALASKA.
Taganrog. KUBANKA.
Taos. ALASKA.
Tauranian. TURKEY.
Tea Leaf. JAVA.
TENMARQ.
Tennessee Fultz. FULTZ.
Tennessee Prolific. CURRELL.
Texas Red. SEA ISLAND.
THATCHER.
Theiss. TURKEY.
THEW.
Thompson; Thompson Club. PILCRAW.
THORNE. *T. N. 1006.*
Three Peck. FULCASTER.
TIMOPHEEVI (*T. timopheevi* Zhuk.)
Tipton Red. FULTZ.
TOUSE. *White Touse.*
TRIPLET.
TRUMBULL.
TURKEY. *Alberta Red; Argentine; Bulgarian; Crimean; Defiance; Egyptian; Hard Winter; Hundred-and-one; Hungarian; Improved Turkey; Kharkof; Lost Freight; Malakof; Malcome; Minnesota Red Cross; Minnesota Reliable; Pioneer Turkey; Red Russian; Red Winter; Red Wonder; Romanella; Russian; Tauranian; Theiss; Turkey Red; Turkish Red; Ulta; Wisconsin No. 18; World's Champion; Zuni.*
Turkey Hybrid. HYBRID 63.
Turkey Red. TURKEY.
Turkey 10–110. ILRED.
Turkish Amber. FULCASTER.
Turkish Red. TURKEY.
Tuscan Island. FULCASTER.
Twentieth Century. GOLDCOIN; PROSPERITY.
Two Peck. FULCASTER.
UKRAINKA.
ULKA.
Ulta. TURKEY.
UNION. (c)
University Gem. SURPRISE.
UTAC. (c)
UTAH KANRED. *Kanred.*
VALLEY. *German Amber; Indiana Swamp; Niagara; Russian Amber; Rust Proof.*
VALPRIZE.
Velvet Bluestem. HAYNES BLUESTEM.
Velvet Chaff. FULTZO-MEDITERRANEAN; JONES FIFE; MEALY; PRESTON.
Velvet Head. GRANDPRIZE; MEALY.
VERNAL (*T. dicoccum* Shrank). *"Speltz"; Yaroslav.*
VESTA.
Viking. GOLDEN BALL.
Virginia Reel. HARVEST QUEEN.
V. P. I. 112.
V. P. I. 131.
WABASH. *Accession 33.*
Wagner. POOLE.
Waif. RED WAVE.
Washington Hybrid 128. HYBRID 128.
Waverly. RED WAVE.
WEBSTER.
Wheat of Miracle. ALASKA.
Wheat 3000 Years Old. ALASKA.
White Amber. MARTIN.
White Australian; White Bluestem. PACIFIC BLUESTEM.
White Century. GOLDCOIN.
White Chile. PACIFIC BLUESTEM.
White Clawson. GOLDCOIN.
White Columbia. BAART.
White Eldorado. GOLDCOIN.
White Elliott. PACIFIC BLUESTEM.
WHITE FEDERATION.
WHITE FEDERATION 38.
White Holland. WILHELMINA.
White Hybrid. HYBRID 63; HYBRID 128
White Lammas. PACIFIC BLUESTEM.
WHITE POLISH (*T. polonicum* L.). *Cor* (*wheat*).
White Rice. RICE.
White Rock. GOLDCOIN.
White Russian. GOLDCOIN; PILCRAW SURPRISE.
White Sonora. SONORA.
White Soules; White Surprise. GOLDCOIN
White Touse. TOUSE.
White Velvet Chaff. MEALY.
WHITE WINTER. *Bishop's Pride; Orego White; Wold's White Winter.*
White Winter. DAWSON.
Wild Goose. ALASKA; ARNAUTKA.
WILHELMINA. *Holland; Queen Wilhelmina; White Holland.*
Wilson; Wilson Special. CLIMAX.
Winter Fife. JONES FIFE.
Winter Green; Winter John. NIGGER.
Winter King. FULCASTER; GOLDCOIN NIGGER; POOLE.
Winter Lasalle; Winter Nellis. LOFTHOUSE.
Winter Pearl. FULTZ.
Winter Queen. HARVEST QUEEN.
Wisconsin No. 18. TURKEY.
WISCONSIN PEDIGREE NO. 2.
Wold's White Winter. WHITE WINTER.
Wolf Hybrid. ALLEN.
Wonderful. FULCASTER.
Woods Prolific; Woolf. LEAP.
World's Champion. TURKEY.
Worlds Fair. RED WAVE.
Yaroslav. VERNAL.
Yellow Gharnovka. KUBANKA.
YEOMAN.
YOGO.
YORKWIN.
Zellers Valley. RED CLAWSON.
Zimmerman. OREGON ZIMMERMAN.
Zinns Golden. PROSPERITY.
Zuni. TURKEY.

CE'REUS (*Browningia; Carnegiea; Corryocactus; Dendrocereus; Epiphyllanthus; Erdisia; Escontria; Eulychnia; Leptocereus; Piptanthocereus; Stetsonia*) . . . . CEREUS
See **CACTUS GENERA.**

CEREUS . . . . **Cereus**
ARGENTINE C. . . . **C. argentiniensis**
BLACKHAIR C. . . . **C. melanotrichus**
CHACO C. . . . . . . **C. chacoanus**
CHESTNUT C. . . . . . **C. castaneus**
DYBOWSKY C. . . . . . **C. dybowski**
GREAT C. . . . . **C. maximus**
HANKE C. . . . . . . **C. hankeanus**
HILDMANN C. . . **C. hildmannianus**
HUNTINGTON C. . **C. huntingtonianus**
LEON C. . . . . **C. leoni**
MANDACARU C. . . . . . **C. jamacaru**
MEYEN C. . . . . **C. meyeni**
PERNAMBUCO C. . **C. pernambucensis**

Cereus, continued
Peru C. . . . . . Cereus peruvianus
Saguaro . . . . C. giganteus
Yellowberry C. . . C. xanthocarpus

Ceriman . . . . . **Monstera deliciosa**

CERIN'THE . . . . Honeywort
ma'jor
retor'ta . . . . Greek H.

CEROCHLA'MYS
MESEMBRYANTHEMUM
See **SUCCULENTS.**

CEROPE'GIA . . . . Ceropegia
See **SUCCULENTS.**

CEROP'TERIS . **PITYROGRAMMA**
See **FERN GENERA.**

Ceratham'nus inodo'rus . **Myrica inodora**

CEROX'YLON . . . . Waxpalm
See **PALM GENERA.**

CERVICI'NA . . **WAHLENBERGIA**

CES'TRUM (*HABROTHAMNUS*)
Cestrum (*Jessamine*)
auranti'acum . . . . Orange C.
diur'num . . . . Day C.
el'egans (*Habrothamnus e.*) Purple C.
—**smith'i**
fascicula'tum (*Habrothamnus fasciculatus*) . . . . Early C.
—**new'elli** (*C. newelli*) . . . Red E.C.
laurifo'lium
noctur'num . . . Nightblooming C.
par'qui . . . . Chilean C.
santanderia'num

CETRA'RIA
island'ica . . . . . . Icelandmoss
juniperi'na . . . . . . Junipermoss

Ceylongooseberry . . . . Kitembilla:
Dovyalis hebecarpa

Ceylonmoss . . . . **Gracilaria**
Agar C. . . . . **G. lichenoides**

Chaconia . . . . **Warszewiczia**
Orangegold C. . . . . . **W. coccinea**

CHAENAC'TIS Chaenactis (*Falseyarrow*)
doug'lasi . . . . Douglas C.
glabrius'cula

CHAENOME'LES . Floweringquince
cathayen'sis . . . . . . **C. lagenaria c.**
japon'ica (*maulei; Cydonia m.; Pyrus j.* Thunb., *not* Sims; *P. maulei*)
Japanese F.
—**alpi'na** (*C. maulei a.; Cydonia sargenti*) . . . . Alpine J.F.
₵Tricolor. hv. C. japonica
lagena'ria (*Cydonia japonica* Loisel., *not* Pers.; *Pyrus j.* Sims, *not* Thunb.; *P. lagenaria*) . . . . . Common F.
—**cathayen'sis** (*C. cathayensis; Cydonia c.*)
—**wil'soni**

Presumably the following hort. var. of C. lagenaria are all clons.

Alba
Appleblossom
Apricot
Atrococcinea
Atrococcinea Plena
Atropurpurea
Aurora
Baltzi
Boule Defeu
Cardinalis
Columbia

CHAENOMELES lagenaria, continued
Contorta
Double Scarlet (*sanguinea plena*)
Double Vermillion
Eximia
Falconet Charlot
Florepleno
Foliis Rubris
Frutico-alba
Gaujardi
Grandiflora
Kermesina Semiplena
Knaphill Scarlet
Macrocarpa
Marmorata
Moerloosi. Pinkstripe
Nivalis
Nivea Extus Coccinea
Phyllis Moore
Pinkstripe (*moerloosi*)
Pygmaea
Rosea Grandiflora
Roseaplena
Rubra
Rubra Grandiflora
Sanguinea
Sanguinea Semiplena
Semperflorens
Simon
Umbellata
Umbilicata
Versicolor
Versicolor Lutescens

maul'ei . . . . **C. japonica**
—*alpi'na* . . . . . . **C. japonica a.**
sinen'sis (*Cydonia s.; Pseudocydonia s.*)
Chinese F.
∞ **super'ba** (*japonica × lagenaria; Cydonia maulei s.*)
₵Rosy (*rosea*) hv.
₵Scarlet (*perfecta*)
₵White (*alba*)

CHAENOSTO'MA (*SUTERA*)
Chaenostoma
fastigia'tum (*Sutera cephalotes*) Head C.
his'pidum (*Sutera brachiata*) . Hairy C.
polyan'thum (*Sutera polyantha*)
Annual C.

CHAEROPHYL'LUM . . . . Chervil
bulbo'sum . . . . . Turniproot C.
procum'bens . . . . . Spreading C.

CHAETOCA'LYX
parviflo'ra

CHAETOCH'LOA . . . . . **SETARIA**
See **GRASS GENERA.**

CHAETOMOR'PHA |w
cannabi'na |w
li'num
melago'nium |w

Chaffseed . . . . **Schwalbea**
American C. . . . . . **S. americana**

Chainfern . . . . **Woodwardia**
European C. . . . . . **W. radicans**
Giant C. . . . . **W. fimbriata**
Mexican C. . . . . . . **W. spinulosa**
Netvein C. . . . . . . **W. areolata**
Virginia C. . . . . . . **W. virginica**

CHAL'CAS . . . . **MURRAYA**

Chalicevine . . . . **Solandra**
Bugle C. . . . . **S. longiflora**
Goldcup C. . . . . **S. guttata**
Lovely C. . . . . . . **S. spectabilis**
Milkcup C. . . . . **S. nitida**
Showy C. . . . . **S. grandiflora**

CHAMAEBA'TIA
foliolo'sa . Bearmat (*Mountainmisery*)
—**austra'lis** (*C. australis*) Southern B.

CHAMAEBATIA'RIA
millefo'lium . Tansybush (*Desertsweet*)

CHAMAECERA'SUS . . **LONICERA**

CHAMAECE'REUS
See **CACTUS GENERA.**

CHAMAECIS'TUS . **LOISELEURIA**

CHAMAECRIS'TA . . . Partridgepea
This genus is united by some botanists with Cassia.

cine'rea (*Cassia c.*) . . . Seashore P.
fascicula'ta (*Cassia chamaecrista*)
Showy P.
flavico'ma . . . . . Yellowlocks P.
leptade'nia . . . . Greenman P.
procum'bens (*nictitans* Auth.; *Cassia n.*)
Sensitive P.
wright'i . . . . Wrights P.

CHAMAECYP'ARIS |w . Falsecypress
lawsonia'na (*Cupressus l.*) Lawson F.
(*PortOrford Whitecedar*)
—**erec'ta** (*C.l. erecta viridis*) Erect L.F.
₵Bluecolumn (*erecta glauca*) hv. C. lawsoniana
₵Bluejacket
₵Bowler (*bowleri*)
₵Cream (*albospica*)
₵Darley (*darleyensis*)
₵Depken (*depkeni*)
₵Drummond (*drummondi*)
₵Dwarf (*nana*)
₵Elegantissima
₵Ellwood (*ellwoodi*)
₵Filiformis
₵Fletcher (*fletcheri*)
₵Forsteck (*forsteckiana*)
₵Fountain (*gracilis*)
₵Fraser (*fraseri*)
₵Golden (*lutea*)
₵Hillier (*hillieri*)
₵Intertexta
₵Littleblue (*minima glauca*)
₵Lycopod (*lycopodioides*)
₵Patula
₵Rogers
₵Scarab (*allumi*)
₵Schongariana
₵Sentry (*pyramidalis*)
₵Shaw (*shawi*)
₵Silver (*argentea*)
₵Silverqueen
₵Silvertip (*argenteovariegata*)
₵Smith (*smithi*)
₵Steel (*glauca*)
₵Stewartgolden (*stewarti*)
₵Sulfur (*sulphurea*)
₵Triomphe Deboskoop
₵Veitch (*glauca veitchi*)
₵Weeping (*pendula*)
₵Westermann
₵Whitesentry (*pyramidalis alba*)
₵Wissel (*wisseli*)
₵Yellowcolumn (*erecta aurea*)
₵Youngs (*youngi*)
nootkaten'sis (*Cupressus n.*) |w
Nootka F.
₵Blue (*glauca*) hv.
₵Compact (*compacta*)
₵Sanders (*sanderi*)
₵Silver (*argenteovariegata*)
₵Weeping (*pendula*)
₵Yellowleaf (*lutea*)

CHAMAECYPARIS, continued
obtu'sa (*Cupressus o.*) HINOKI FALSECYPRESS
—**formosa'na** . . . . FORMOSA H.F.
₵ACUTELEAF (*acuta*) HV. C. obtusa
₵BREVIRAMEA
₵CLUBMOSS (*lycopodioides*)
₵COLUMN (*erecta*)
₵COMPACT (*compacta*)
₵CRIPPS (*crippsi*)
₵DWARF (*nana*)
₵DWARFGOLD (*nana aurea*)
₵FERNSPRAY (*filicoides*)
₵GOLDEN (*aurea*)
₵GOLDENSIDE (*tetragona aurea*)
₵GREAT (*magnifica*)
₵PYGMY (*pygmaea*)
₵SANDERS (*ericoides*)
₵SILVERTIP (*albospicata*)
₵SLENDER (*gracilis*)
₵TETRAGONA
₵WEEPING (*pendula*)
₵YELLOWTIP (*gracilis aurea*)
pisif'era (*Cupressus p.*) . . SAWARA F.
₵DWARFPLUME (*plumosa nana*) HV.
₵DWARFTHREAD (*filifera nana*)
₵GLOBE (*globosa*)
₵GOLDEN (*aurea*)
₵GOLDPLUME (*plumosa aurea*)
₵GRAYMOSS (*squarrosa veitchi*)
₵MIDGET (*minima*)
MOSS (*squarrosa*)
₵PLUME (*plumosa*)
₵SIEBOLD (*sieboldi*)
₵SILVERTIP (*plumosa aurea*)
₵SULFURPLUME (*plumosa sulphurea*)
THREAD (*filifera*)
₵YELLOWDWARF (*nana aurea*)
₵YELLOWTHREAD (*filifera aurea*)
thyoi'des (*sphaeroides*) WHITECEDAR F.
₵ANDELY (*andelyensis*) HV.
₵BLUE (*glauca*)
₵HEATH (*ericoides*)
₵VARIEGATED (*variegata*)

CHAMAEDAPH'NE (*CASSANDRA*) LEATHERLEAF
calycula'ta (*Andromeda c.; Cassandra c.*) LEATHERLEAF
—**angustifo'lia**
—**na'na** . . . . DWARF L.

CHAMAEDORE'A CHAMAEDOREA; PACAYA
See **PALM GENERA.**

CHAMAELAU'CIUM
cilia'tum

CHAMAELIR'IUM
lute'um . . . . FAIRYWAND

CHAMAENE'RION . . **EPILOBIUM**

CHAMAEPERICLY'MENUM **CORNUS**

CHAMAEPEU'CE . . . . **CIRSIUM**

CHAMAE'ROPS. MEDITERRANEANPALM (*Hairpalm*)
See **PALM GENERA.**

CHAMAESY'CE . . . **EUPHORBIA**
See **SUCCULENTS.**

CHAMBEYRO'NIA (*KENTIOPSIS* in part) . . . . CHAMBEYRONIAPALM
See **PALM GENERA.**

CHAMISE . . . . **Adenostoma**
GREASEWOOD C. . . . **A. fasciculatum**
REDSHANK C. . . . . **A. sparsifolium**

Chamomil'la matrica'ria **Matricaria chamomilla**

CHAMPEDAK . . **Artocarpus polyphemus**

CHAPARRALPEA . . . . . . **Pickeringia**
CALIFORNIA C. . . . . . **P. montana**
FUZZY C. C. . . . . **P. m. tomentosa**

CHAPMAN'NIA . . . . ALICIA
florida'na . . . . FLORIDA A.

CHA'RA [W] . . . . STONEWORT
corona'ta . . . . CROWN S.
crini'ta . . . . FEMALE S.
frag'ilis . . . . BRITTLE S.

CHA'RIEIS
heterophyl'la (*Kaulfussia amelloides*)

CHARLOCK . . . . **Brassica kaber**

CHASMATOPHYL'LUM **MESEMBRYANTHEMUM**
See **SUCCULENTS.**

CHASTETREE . . . . **Vitex**
CUTLEAF C. . . . **V. negundo incisa**
FIVELEAF C. . . . . **V. quinata**
GUIANA C. . . . . . . **V. divaricata**
HARDY LILAC C. **V. agnuscastus latifolia**
LILAC C. . . . . **V. agnuscastus**
MOLAVE C. . . . . **V. parviflora**
NEGUNDO C. . . . . **V. negundo**
NEWZEALAND C. . . . . . **V. lucens**
SIMPLELEAF SHRUB C. **V. rotundifolia**
TIMOR C. . . . . **V. littoralis**
WHITE C. . . . **V. agnuscastus alba**

CHAULMOOGRATREE . . . **Hydnocarpus**
COMMON C. . . . **H. anthelminthicus**
WIGHT C. . . . . . . **H. wightianus**

CHAWSTICK . . . . **Gouania lupuloides**

CHAYO'TA . . . . **SECHIUM**

CHAYOTE . . . . . **Sechium; S. edule**

Cheat . . . . BROME: **Bromus**

Checkerbloom . . . . CHECKERMALLOW, FOOTHILL: **Sidalcea malvaeflora**

CHECKERMALLOW . . . . . . **Sidalcea**
BIRD C. . . . . . . **S. glaucescens**
FOOTHILL C. . . . . . **S. malvaeflora**
HENDERSON C. . . . . **S. hendersoni**
NELSON C. . . . . **S. nervata**
NEWMEXICAN C. . . **S. neomexicana**
OREGON C. . . . . **S. oregana**
PLAINS C. . . . . . . **S. campestris**
SMALL NEWMEXICAN C. **S. neomexicana parviflora**
SPIKE C. . . . . **S. spicata**
WHITE C. . . . . **S. candida**

Checkertree . . . . . . MOUNTAINASH, CHECKERTREE: **Sorbus torminalis**

CHEEGRASS . . . . . **Stipa splendens**

CHEILAN'THES . . . . . . LIPFERN
See **FERN GENERA.**

CHEIRAN'THUS . . . WALLFLOWER
allio'ni . . . . . **Erysimum asperum**
alpi'nus . . . . ALPINE W.
cheir'i . . . . COMMON W.
×**kewen'sis** . . . . KEW W.
linifo'lius . . . **Erysimum linifolium**
mey'eri . . . . MEYER W.
mutab'ilis
semperflo'rens . . . . MOROCCO W.
senoner'i . . . . GREEK W.

CHEIRIDOP'SIS **MESEMBRYANTHEMUM**
See **SUCCULENTS.**

CHEIRIN'IA . . . . **ERYSIMUM**
inconspic'ua . . . . . **E. parviflorum**

CHELIDO'NIUM . . . . CELANDINE
ma'jus . . . . GREATER C.
—**lacinia'tum**

CHELO'NE [W] . . . . . . TURTLEHEAD
barba'ta . . . . **Penstemon barbatus**
gla'bra (*alba*) [W] . . . . . WHITE T.
ly'oni . . . . PINK T.
nemoro'sa . . **Penstemon nemorosus**
obli'qua . . . . ROSE T.

CHENOPO'DIUM (*BLITUM*) [W] GOOSEFOOT
al'bum [W] . . . . LAMBSQUARTERS G.
amaranti'color
ambrosioi'des [W] . . . WORMSEED G.
—**anthelmin'ticum** (*C. anthelminticum*) DRUG W.G.

The commercial (drug trade) type of this plant (var. anthelminticum) is not constantly distinguishable from typical forms of the species because of natural intergrades.

atrip'licis . . . . . **C. purpurascens**
atrovi'rens
berlandier'i . . . . . . PITSEED G.
bonus-hen'ricus . GOODKINGHENRY G.
bo'trys . . . . . JERUSALEMOAK G.
califor'nicum
capita'tum (*Blitum c.*) . . . BLITE G.
fre'monti . . . . FREMONT G.
glau'cum [W] . . . . . . OAKLEAF G.
hirci'num
hy'bridum [W] . . . . MAPLELEAF G.
inci'sum (*cornutum*) . . . RAGLEAF G.
leptophyl'lum [W] . . . . SLIMLEAF G.
mura'le [W] . . . . . NETTLELEAF G.
paga'num [W] . . . . . . PIGWEED G.
polysper'mum
purpuras'cens (*atriplicis*)
quino'a . . . . QUINOA
ru'brum [W] . . . . RED G.
ur'bicum . . . . CITY G.

CHERIMOYA . . . . **Annona cherimola**
WILD C. . . . . **A. longiflora**

CHERRIES, ORIENTAL FLOWERING, **Prunus** species.

The Editorial Committee wishes to acknowledge its indebtedness to Paul Russell for this valuable revision of the clons of Oriental Flowering Cherry.

Abbreviations indicating the name of the species to which a hort. var. is reported to belong, or the species from which it is reported to have been derived in whole or in part, are as follows:

Sarg. P. sargenti.
Ser. P. serrulata.
Sub. P. subhirtella.
Yed. P. yedoensis.

STATEMENT OF AUTHOR

Observations in the field and careful examination of the literature for several years indicate clearly the necessity for a conservative treatment of the horticultural varietal names of the Oriental (or Japanese) Flowering Cherries. Great confusion in the horticultural nomenclature of these

CHERRIES, ORIENTAL FLOWERING, continued

cherries has resulted chiefly from two factors: (1) Japanese horticulturists have applied distinct names to scores of forms differing only very slightly from each other, the difference often due to unusual cultural conditions or environment; (2) English and American and also Japanese nurserymen have applied the same name to different varieties, or have created new names without good reason.

For the benefit of American nurserymen, therefore, it has been considered best to limit these names to those varieties which are now, or are likely to become, established in the United States or in Europe, and which are reasonably distinct. In many instances it has been possible to indicate synonyms, but names of doubtful standing have purposely been omitted. Varietal names published in American and Japanese literature frequently have been too briefly characterized to distinguish the variety.

PAUL RUSSELL,
DIVISION OF PLANT EXPLORATION AND INTRODUCTION, BUREAU OF PLANT INDUSTRY, U. S. DEPARTMENT OF AGRICULTURE.

In using this list the clon sign ₵ should precede hort. var. names but not species names.

AKEBONO. Yed.
Aki-higan. JUGATSU-ZAKURA.
ALBO-PLENA. Ser. *Double Chinese.*
AMANOGAWA. Ser. *Tanabata.*
ARIAKE. Ser.
Asagi. UKON.
ASANO. Ser.
Beni-fugen. FUGENZO.
BENI-HIGAN. Sub.
Beni-kan C. TAIWAN C.
BOTAN-ZAKURA. Ser. *Moutan.*
Brentwood. TAKASAGO.
Cheals Weeping. KIKU-SHIDARE.
Chigo-higan. JUGATSU-ZAKURA.
Chisima C. TAKANE C.
Chiyo-higan. JUGATSU-ZAKURA.
DAIKOKU. Ser.
Double Chinese. Ser. ALBO-PLENA.
Eureka Weeping. SHIDARE-HIGAN.
FUGENZO. Ser. *Beni-fugen; James H. Veitch; Kofugen.*
FUJI C. (*Mame C.*). **P. incisa.**
FUKU-ROKUJU. Ser.
GIJO-ZAKURA. Ser.
GOSHO-ZAKURA. Ser. *Gozio-zakura.*
Gozanoma-nioi. TAKI-NIOI.
GYOIKO. Ser. *Gioiko.*
HIGAN C. Sub. *Kizo-zakura; Ko-higan C.*
HIGURASHI. Ser.
Hoki-zakura. TAIZAN-FUKUN.
HOKUSAI. Ser.
HORINJI. Ser.
HOSOKAWA. Ser. *Hosokawa-nioi.*
ICHIYO. Ser.
James H. Veitch. FUGENZO.
JO-NIOI. Ser.
JUGATSU-ZAKURA. Sub. *Aki-higan; Chigo-higan; Chiyo-higan; Yaye-higan.*
KABA-ZAKURA. Ser.
Kan-hi C. TAIWAN C.
Kanzan. KWANZAN.
KIKU-SHIDARE. Ser. *Cheals Weeping; Lidera-Nova; Oriental Weeping; Shidare-zakura.*
Kirin. KWANZAN.
Kizo-zakura. HIGAN C.
Kofugen. FUGENZO.

CHERRIES, ORIENTAL FLOWERING, continued

Ko-higan C. HIGAN C.
Kojima. SHIROTAE.
KURUMA-YAMA. Ser.
KWANZAN. Ser. *Kanzan; Kirin; Seki-yama; Sekizan.*
Lidera-Nova. KIKU-SHIDARE.
Mame C. FUJI C.
MIKURUMA-GAESHI. Ser.
Mine C. TAKANE C.
MOMI-JIGARI. Sub.
Mount Fuji. SHIROTAE.
Moutan. BOTAN-ZAKURA.
Musha-Zakura. TAKASAGO.
OHNANDEN. Ser. *Nanden.*
Oh-yama-zakura. OSHIMA-ZAKURA.
OJOCHIN. Ser.
Oku-miyako. SHOGETSU.
ORIENTAL C. **P. serrulata.**
Oriental Weeping. KIKU-SHIDARE.
OSHIMA-ZAKURA. Ser. *Oh-yama-zakura; Takigi-zakura.*
Park Weeping. SHIDARE-HIGAN.
Pink Pearl. TANKO-SHINJU.
SARGENT C. **P. sargenti.**
Seki-yama. KWANZAN.
Sekizan. KWANZAN.
SENDAI-ITO-ZAKURA. Sub.
SHIBORI. Ser.
SHIDARE-HIGAN. Sub. *Eureka Weeping; Park Weeping.*
SHIDARE-YOSHINO. Yed.
Shidare-zakura. KIKU-SHIDARE.
SHIRAYUKI. Ser.
SHIRO-FUGEN. Ser. *Victory.*
SHIRO-HIGAN. Sub.
SHIROTAE. Ser. *Kojima; Mount Fuji; Sirotae.*
SHOGETSU. Ser. *Oku-miyako.*
SHUJAKU. Ser.
Siebold. TAKASAGO.
Sirotae. SHIROTAE.
TACHI-HIGAN. Sub.
TAI-HAKU-ZAKURA. Ser.
TAIWAN C. (*Beni-kan C.; Kan-hi C.; Usu-kan C.*). **P. campanulata.**
TAIZAN-FUKUN. Ser. *Hoki-zakura.*
TAKANE C. (*Chisima C.; Mine C.*). **P. nipponica.**
TAKASAGO. *Brentwood; Musha-Zakura; Siebold; Watereri.*
Takigi-zakura. OSHIMA-ZAKURA.
TAKI-NIOI. Ser. *Gozanoma-nioi.*
Tanabata. AMANOGAWA.
TANKO-SHINJU. Ser. *Pink Pearl.*
TEMARI. Ser.
TORANO-O. Ser.
UKON. Ser. *Asagi.*
USU-BENI-HIGAN. Sub.
Usu-kan C. TAIWAN C.
Victory. SHIRO-FUGEN.
WASHINO-O. Ser.
Watereri. TAKASAGO.
YAE-MURASAKI. Ser.
YAMA-ZAKURA. Sarg.
Yaye-higan. JUGATSU-ZAKURA.
YEDO-ZAKURA. Ser.
YOSHINO C. **P. yedoensis.**

CHERRY . . . . **Prunus**

See also ALMOND, APRICOT, BIRDCHERRY, BUSHCHERRY, CHOKECHERRY, LAUREL-CHERRY, PEACH, PEACHBRUSH, and PLUM. For cultivated varieties see **FRUIT AND EDIBLE NUT NAMES.**

ALMOND C. . . . . . **P. glandulosa**
APPALACHIAN SAND C.
P. pumila susquehanae

CHERRY, continued

BESSEY C. . . . . . . **Prunus besseyi**
BITTER C. . . . . **P. emarginata**
BLACK C. . . . . **P. serotina**
BRISTLELEAF MAME C. **P. incisa serrata**
BUNGE C. . . . . **P. humilis**
CAPULIN BLACK C.
P. serotina salicifolia
CATALINA C. . . . . **P. lyoni**
CONRADINA C. . . . . **P. conradinae**
∞ DESFONTAINES C. . ∞ **P. fontanesiana**
DIELS C. . . . . **P. dielsiana**
∞ DUKE C. . . . . ∞ **P. effusa**
FUJI C. . . . . **P. incisa**
GROUND C. . . . . . . **P. fruticosa**
HAWTHORN C. . . . . **P. crataegifolia**
HELENA C. . . . . . . **P. helenae**
HIGAN C. . . . . . . **P. subhirtella**
HIMALAYAN C. . . . . **P. rufa**
HOLLYLEAF C. . . . . . . **P. ilicifolia**
JACQUEMONT C. . . **P. jacquemonti**
∞ JUDD C. . . . . ∞ **P. juddi**
KURILE TAKANE C.
P. nipponica kurilensis
LITTLE C. . . . . . . **P. microcarpa**
MAHALEB C. . . . . . . **P. mahaleb**
MANCHU C. . . . . . **P. tomentosa**
MANITOBA PIN C.
P. pensylvanica saximontana
MARASCA SOUR C. **P. cerasus marasca**
∞ MAURER C. . . . . ∞ **P. maureri**
MAZZARD C. . . . . **P. avium**
MEDITERRANEAN GROUND C.
P. prostrata
MIYAMA C. . . . . **P. maximowiczi**
Nanking C. . . . . MANCHU C.
NOPETAL C. . . . . **P. apetala**
ORIENTAL C. . . . . . . **P. serrulata**
PALEFRUIT MANCHU C.
P. tomentosa leucocarpa
PIN C. . . . . . . **P. pensylvanica**
PINK ALMOND C. . **P. glandulosa rosea**
PLUMLEAF C. . . . . . **P. prunifolia**
RACEMOSE C. . . . . **P. buergeriana**
SAND C. . . . . **P. pumila**
SARGENT C. . . . . . . **P. sargenti**
SHINY BLACK C.
P. serotina cartilaginea
SHRUBBY SOUR C. **P. cerasus frutescens**
SIEBOLD C. . . . . **P. sieboldi**
∞ SOURBUSH C. . . . . . . ∞ **P. eminens**
SOUR C. . . . . **P. cerasus**
SPRAWLING SAND C. **P. pumila depressa**
SPRENGER C. . . . . . . **P. sprengeri**
TAIWAN C. . . . . **P. campanulata**
TAKANE C. . . . . . . **P. nipponica**
TALL HIGAN C.
P. subhirtella ascendens
TATSIEN C. . . . . . **P. tatsienensis**
TWISTSTEM LITTLE C.
P. microcarpa tortuosa
UNDERBLUE BLACK C.
P. serotina montana
UNDERBROWN ORIENTAL C.
P. serrulata spontanea
UNDERGRAY C. . . . . **P. canescens**
UNDERWOOL C. . . . . . . **P. incana**
∞ UTAH C. . . . . ∞ **P. utahensis**
WESTERN HOLLYLEAF C.
P. ilicifolia occidentalis
WHITE ALMOND C. **P. glandulosa alba**
WHITEFLOWERED MANCHU C.
P. tomentosa endotricha
WILD MAZZARD C. . **P. avium actiana**
WILLOWLEAF M. C. . **P. a. salicifolia**
WILLOWLEAF SOUR C. . **P. cerasus s.**
WILLOWOAK BLACK C.
P. serotina phelloides

CHERRY, continued
YELLOW MAHALEB C. **Prunus mahaleb xanthocarpa**
YOSHINO C. . . . . . . **P. yedoensis**

Cherrylaurel . . LAURELCHERRY: **Prunus** spp. (subgenus Laurocerasus)

CHERRYORANGE . . . . . . **Citropsis**
ANGOLA C. . . . . . . **C. angolensis**
CAMEROON C. . . . . . **C. zenkeni**
EASTAFRICAN C. . . **C. schweinfurthi**
GABON C. . . . . . . **C. gabonensis**
GILLET C. . . . . . . **C. gilletiana**
IKONGU C. . . . . **C. latialata**
IVORYCOAST C. . . . . **C. mirabilis**
KASAI C. . . **C. gabonensis lacourtiana**
LETESTU C. . . . . **C. letestui**
WESTAFRICAN C. . . . . **C. articulata**

CHERRYPALM . . . . . **Pseudophoenix**
BUCCANEER C. . . . . . **P. vinifera**
SARGENT C. . . . . . . **P. sargenti**

CHERVIL . . . . . **Chaerophyllum**
SPREADING C. . . . . **C. procumbens**
TURNIPROOT C. . . . . . **C. bulbosum**

Chess . . . . BROME: **Bromus**
Introduced annual spp. of Bromus are often called Chess, especially B. secalinus.

CHESTNUT . . . . **Castanea**
See also CHINKAPIN.
AMERICAN C. . . . . . . **C. dentata**
∞ BLARINGHEM C. . . . **∞ C. blaringhemi**
∞ BURBANK C. . . . . . **∞ C. burbanki**
CHINESE C. . . . . . **C. mollissima**
∞ CHINKNUT . . . . . . **∞ C. neglecta**
∞ COUDERC C. . . . . . **∞ C. couderci**
∞ ENDICOTT C. . . . . . **∞ C. endicotti**
EUROPEAN C. . . . . . . **C. sativa**
Hairy C. . . . . CHINESE C.
JAPANESE C. . . . . . . **C. crenata**
∞ MORRIS C. . . . . **∞ C. morrisi**
NARROWLEAF EUROPEAN C. **C. sativa prolifera**
∞ PULCHELLA C. . . . . **∞ C. pulchella**
Spanish C. . . . . . . EUROPEAN C.
∞ VANFLEET C. . . . . **∞ C. fleeti**

CHIA
CALIFORNIA C. . . **Salvia columbariae**
MEXICAN C. . . . . . . **S. hispanica**

CHIAPA'SIA . . . . **EPIPHYLLUM**
See **CACTUS GENERA.**

CHIASTOPHYL'LUM . **COTYLEDON**
See **SUCCULENTS.**

CHICKENCORN **Sorghum vulgare drummondi**

CHICKPEA . . . . **Cicer**
GRAM C. . . . . **C. arietinum**

CHICKRASSY, CHITTAGONG **Chukrasia tabularis**

CHICKWEED . . . . . **Stellaria media**

CHICORY . . . . **Cichorium**
COMMON C. . . . . **C. intybus**

Chilauni . . . GUGERTREE, DARJEELING: **Schima wallichi**

CHILEBELLS . . . . **Lapageria**
RED C. . . . . **L. rosea**
WHITE C. . . . . **L. r. albiflora**

CHILEGUAVA . . . . . **Ugni; U. molinae**

CHILEHAZEL . . . . . **Gevuina avellana**

CHILEJASMINE . **Mandevilla suaveolens**

CHILENETTLE . . . . **Loasa**
TRICOLOR C. . . . . **L. tricolor**

CHILE'NIA . . . **PYRRHOCACTUS**
See **CACTUS GENERA.**

Chilenut. CHILEHAZEL: **Gevuina avellana**

CHILESTAR . . . . **Leucocoryne**
GLORY-OF-THE-SUN C. . . . **L. ixioides**

CHILEVINE . . . . **Berberidopsis**
CORAL C. . . . . **B. corallina**

CHILIO'TRICHUM
rosmarinifo'lium

CHILOP'SIS |w . . . DESERTWILLOW
linea'ris (*saligna*) |w . DESERTWILLOW
WHITE (*alba*) HV.

CHIMA'PHILA . . . . . PIPSISSEWA
macula'ta . . . . STRIPED P.
menzies'i . . . . MENZIES P.
umbella'ta . COMMON P. (*Princespine*)
—cisatlan'tica
—occidenta'lis . . . . . WESTERN P.

CHIMAYA . . . . **Cymopterus fendleri**

CHIMONAN'THUS (*MERATIA*)
prae'cox (*fragrans; Calycanthus p.; Meratia p.*) . . . . WINTERSWEET
—grandiflo'rus

CHIMONOBAMBU'SA
See **BAMBOO GENERA.**

CHINA-ASTER . . . . **Callistephus**
COMMON C. . . . . . . **C. chinensis**

CHINABELLS . . . . **Alniphyllum**
FORTUNES C. . . . . . . **A. fortunei**

CHINABERRY . . . **Melia; M. azedarach**
MARGOSA . . . . . . **M. azadirachta**
UMBRELLA C. **M. azedarach umbraculiformis**

CHINACANE . . . . . . **Sinarundinaria**
GLOSSYLEAF C. . . . . . . **S. nitida**
MURIEL C. . . . . . . **S. murielae**

CHINACYPRESS **Glyptostrobus; G. pensilis**

CHINAFIR . . . . **Cunninghamia**
COMMON C. . . . . . **C. lanceolata**
FORMOSA C. . . . . **C. konishi**

CHINAGREEN . . . . **Aglaonema simplex**

CHINALAUREL . . . . **Antidesma**
BIGNAY C. . . . . **A. bunius**

CHINARUE . . . . . **Boenninghausenia**
WHITE C. . . . . **B. albiflora**

Chinese-date . . . . JUJUBE, COMMON: **Zizyphus jujuba**

CHINESELANTERN . . . . . . **Quincula**
PLAINS C. . . . . **Q. lobata**

CHINESEPOPPY, YELLOW **Meconopsis integrifolia**

CHINKAPIN
ALABAMA C. . **Castanea alabamensis**
ALLEGANY C. . . . . **C. pumila**
ASHE C. . . . . **C. ashei**
FLORIDA C. . . . . **C. floridana**
HENRY C. . . . . **C. henryi**
MARGARET FLORIDA C. **C. floridana margaretta**
OZARK C. . . . . . . **C. ozarkensis**
SEGUIN C. . . . . **C. seguini**
TRAILING C. . . . . **C. alnifolia**

CHINKERICHEE
CAPE C. . . **Ornithogalum thyrsoides**
GOLDEN C. C. . . . . . **O. t. aureum**
KEW C. . . . . **×O. kewense**

∞ CHINKNUT . . . **∞ Castanea neglecta**

Chinograss . . . . GRAMA, GYP: **Bouteloua breviseta**

CHIOCOC'CA . . . . MILKBERRY
al'ba (*racemosa*) . . . . DAVIDS M.

CHIOG'ENES |w . . . . PEARLBERRY
hispid'ula (*serpyllifolia*) |w CREEPING P.

CHIONAN'THUS |w . . . FRINGETREE
retu'sus . . . . CHINESE F.
virgin'icus |w . . . . WHITE F.
—marit'imus (*C. v. pubescens*)

CHIO'NE . . . . CHIONE
gla'bra . . . . SMOOTH C.

CHIONODOX'A . . GLORYOFTHESNOW
lucil'iae . . . . . GLORYOFTHESNOW
GIGANTEA. HV.
GRANDIFLORA
SARDENSIS
TMOLUSI

CHIONO'PHILA . . . . . SNOWLOVER
james'i . . . . JAMES S.

CHIRI'TA
lavandula'cea

CHIRO'NIA . . . . STARPINK
bacciff'era
ixif'era . . . . CHIRONIA S.
linoi'des

CHIVE . . . . **Allium schoenoprasum**
SIBERIAN C. . . . . . **A. s. sibiricum**

CHLIDAN'THUS . . . CHLIDANTHUS
fra'grans . . . . PERU C.

CHLO'RA . . . . YELLOWWORT
perfolia'ta . . . . COMMON Y.

CHLORAN'THUS
gla'ber (*brachystachys*)

CHLO'RIS . CHLORIS; WINDMILLGRASS
See **GRASS GENERA.**

CHLORIS . . . . **Chloris**
ANNUAL C. . . . . **C. radiata**
ARGENTINE C. . . . . **C. berroi**
BURYSEED C. . . . . . **C. chloridea**
Curlytop C. HOODED WINDMILLGRASS
FOURSPIKE C. . . . . . . **C. neglecta**
FRINGED C. . . . . **C. ciliata**
MANYSPIKED C. . . . **C. polydactyla**
MOROCCAN C. . . . . **C. prieuri**
SALTMARSH C. . . . . . . **C. glauca**
SHOWY C. . . . . **C. virgata**
STIFFLEAF C. . . . . . . **C. petraea**
TWOSPIKE C. . . . . . . **C. floridana**
WEEPING C. . . . . **C. distichophylla**

CHLOROCO'DON (*MONDIA*) MUNDIROOT
white'i (*Mondia w.*) . . . WHITES M.

CHLOROG'ALUM (*LAOTHOE*) SOAPPLANT
pomeridia'num (*Laothoe pomeridiana*) AMOLE S.

CHLORO'PHORA . . . . FUSTICTREE
excel'sa . . . . IROKO F.
tincto'ria . . . . DRUG F.

CHLOROPHY'TUM
capen'se
como'sum (*Anthericum c.*)
ela'tum (*Anthericum mandaianum; A. vittatum*) . . . . BRACKETPLANT
—variega'tum . . . . VARIEGATED B.

CHLOROX'YLON . . . . SATINWOOD
swiete'nia . . . . CEYLON S.

CHOCOLATETREE . . . . . . **Theobroma**
CACAO . . . . **T. cacao**
MONKEY C. . . . . . **T. angustifolia**
NICARAGUA C. . . . . **T. bicolor**

CHOI'SYA . . . . . Mexicanorange
dumo'sa (*Astrophyllum dumosum*) Starleaf M.
terna'ta . . . . Ternate M.

Chokeberry . . . . **Aronia**
Black C. . . . . . **A. melanocarpa**
Brilliant C. **A. arbutifolia brilliantissima**
Cherry C. . . . . . **A. a. macrocarpa**
Dwarf C. C. . . . . . **A. a. pumila**
Glossy Black C. **A. melanocarpa elata**
Great B. C. . . . . **A. m. grandifolia**
Purple C. . . . . . **A. atropurpurea**
Purplefruit C. . . . . **A. prunifolia**
Red C. . . . . **A. arbutifolia**

Chokecherry . . . . **Prunus**
See also Almond, Apricot, Birdcherry, Bushcherry, Cherry, Laurelcherry, Peach, Peachbrush, and Plum.
Alabama C. . . . . **P. alabamensis**
Amber Common C. **P. virginiana leucocarpa**
Amur C. . . . . **P. maacki**
Black Common C. **P. virginiana melanocarpa**
Broadleaf C. C. . . . **P. v. duerincki**
Common C. . . . . . . **P. virginiana**
Georgia C. . . . . . . **P. cuthberti**
Gila C. . . . . . . **P. virens rufula**
Grays C. . . . . **P. grayana**
Meyer C. . . . . **P. meyeri**
Nepal C. . . . . . . **P. napaulensis**
South Alabama C. . . . **P. australis**
Southwestern C. . . . . **P. virens**
Western Common C. **P. virginiana demissa**
Wilson C. . . . . **P. wilsoni**

Cholla . . . . **Opuntia**
See also Pricklypear.
Buckhorn C. . . . . **O. acanthocarpa**
Candle C. . . . . **O. kleiniae**
Ecuador C. . . . . . . **O. cylindrica**
Fourspine C. . . . . **O. tetracantha**
Holycross C. . . . **O. ramosissima**
JeffDavis C. . . . . **O. davisi**
Mexicali C. . . . . **O. cholla**
Parish C. . . . . **O. parishi**
SanDiego C. . . . . **O. prolifera**
Sonora Jumping C. . . . **O. fulgida**
Stanly C. . . . . **O. stanlyi**
Verschaffelt C. . . **O. verschaffelti**
Walkingstick C. . . . **O. imbricata**
Whipple C. . . . . **O. whipplei**

CHOME'LIA
brasilia'na

CHONDODEN'DRON
tomento'sum . . . . . Pareiraroot

CHONDRIL'LA . . . Skeletonweed
jun'cea . . . . Rush S.

CHONDRORHYN'CHA
See **ORCHID GENERA.**

CHON'DRUS lw . . . . Irishmoss
cris'pus lw . . Irishmoss (*Carrageen*)

CHORIS'IA . Chorisia (*Palo Borracho*)
insig'nis . . . . Samohu C.
specio'sa . . . . . Floss-silktree

CHORIZAN'THE
staticoi'des . . . . . . Turksrug

CHORIZE'MA . . . . Flamepea
corda'tum . . . . Heartleaf F.
ilicifo'lium . . . . Holly F.

CHORIZEMA, continued
va'rium . . . . . . Bush Flamepea
—**grandiflo'rum** (*C. grandiflorum*) Showy B.F.

Chorogi . . . . . Betony, Artichoke: **Stachys sieboldi**

CHOSE'NIA
bracteo'sa (*Salix eucalyptoides*)

Christmasbells . . . . . . **Blandfordia**
Gosford C. . . . . **B. nobilis**
Tasmania C. . . . . **B. marginata**

Christmasberry . . **Photinia arbutifolia**
Catalina C. . . . . **P. a. macrocarpa**
Orange C. . . . . **P. a. chrysocarpa**

Christmasbush . . . . . . **Alchornea**
Cordate C. . . . . **A. cordata**
Heartleaf C. . . . . . **A. cordifolia**
Hollyleaf C. . . . . . **A. ilicifolia**

Christmascactus **Schlumbergera truncata**

Christmasfern **Polystichum acrostichoides**

Christmasrose . . . **Helleborus niger**

Chrosper'ma muscaetox'icum **Amianthium m.**

CHRYSACTIN'IA
mexica'na . . . . Damianita

CHRYSALIDOCAR'PUS Butterflypalm
See **PALM GENERA.**

CHRYSAM'PHORA **DARLINGTONIA**

CHRYSAN'THEMUM (*ISMELIA; LEUCANTHEMUM; PYRETHRUM*) lw . Chrysanthemum
achilleaefo'lium . . . . Yarrow C.
alpi'num (*Leucanthemum a.*) Alpine C.
amali'ae . . . . Amalia C.
anethifo'lium . . . . Dill C.
arc'ticum . . . . Arctic C.
atra'tum (*coronopifolium*) . Swiss C.
atrococcin'eum . . . . . **C. carinatum**
balsami'ta . . . . **C. majus**
—*tanacetoi'des* . . . . . **C. majus t.**
broussonet'i (*Ismelia b.*) Broussonet C.
carina'tum (*atrococcineum; bicolor; burridgeanum; dunetti; tricolor*) Annual C.
¢Burridge (*burridgeanum*) hv.
caucas'icum (*Pyrethrum c.*) Caucasian C.
cinerariaefo'lium (*Pyrethrum c.*) Dalmatian Pyrethrum
Source of Dalmatian insect powder.
coccin'eum (*roseum; Pyrethrum carneum; P. hybridum*) Florists Pyrethrum
corea'num . . . . **C. sibiricum**
corona'rium . . . . Crowndaisy C.
coronopifo'lium . . . . . . **C. atratum**
corymbo'sum (*Pyrethrum c.*) Mediterranean C.
dunett'i . . . . **C. carinatum**
fontanes'i (*Hymentostemma f.*) Desfontaines C.
frutes'cens . . . . Marguerite C.
gla'brum . . . . **C. paludosum**
hispan'icum (*Pyrethrum h.*) Spanish C.
horto'rum . . . . . . **C. morifolium**
in'dicum (*japonicum*) . . Mother C.
inodo'rum . . . . **Matricaria inodora**

CHRYSANTHEMUM, continued
lacus'tre (*latifolium*) Portuguese Chrysanthemum
leucan'themum (*Leucanthemum grandiflorum; L. vulgare*) lw Oxeyedaisy (*Woundwort*)
—**pinnatif'idum** . . . . . Field O.
macrophyl'lum (*Tanacetum m.*) Tansy C.
ma'jus (*balsamita; Tanacetum b.*) Costmary C.
—**tanacetoi'des** (*C. balsamita t.*) Rayless C.C.
marsch'alli . Caucasian Pyrethrum
Perhaps not distinct from P. coccineum.
maw'i . . . . Morocco C.
max'imum . . . . . . Pyrenees C.
¢Chrysanthemumdaisy. hv.
¢Glory of the Wayside
¢King Edward VII
¢Robinson (*robinsoni*)
¢Shastadaisy
¢The Speaker
morifo'lium (*hortorum; sinense*) Florists C.
multicau'le . . . . Clump C.
myco'nis . . . . Mycon C.
nippon'icum (*Leucanthemum n.*) Nippon Oxeyedaisy
nivel'lei . . . . Nivelle C.
pal'lens . . . . Cevennes C.
paludo'sum (*glabrum*) . . . Swamp C.
parthe'nium (*Matricaria capensis; M. eximia; M. parthenoides*) Feverfew C.
¢Aureum. hv.
¢Crispum
¢Glaucum
¢Laciniatum
¢Selaginoides
praeal'tum (*parthenifolium*)
ptarmicaeflo'rum . Canary Islands C.
rose'um . . . . **C. coccineum**
rotundifo'lium . . . . Hungarian C.
seg'etum . . Corn C. (*Cornmarigold*)
sibir'icum (*coreanum; Leucanthemum s.*) Korean C.
sinen'se . . . . **C. morifolium**
tchihatchew'i . . . . . **Matricaria t.**
tri'color . . . . **C. carinatum**
uligino'sum (*Pyrethrum u.*) Giantdaisy
visco'sum . . . . Sulfur C.
vulga're . . . . **Tanacetum v.**

Common names and hort. var. (clons) of **Chrysanthemum:**

The following list of clons is made up from the first edition of Standardized Plant Names and from lists received from the following sources: Arno H. Nehrling, Secretary (1937–38) and G. H. Poesch, Present Secretary, Chrysanthemum Society of America; the late Elmer D. Smith, Chrysanthemum specialist and hybridizer, Adrian, Mich.; John C. Wister, Philadelphia, Pa., "Hardy Chrysanthemums at Swarthmore"; and Alex Cumming, Jr., Chrysanthemum specialist and hybridizer, Bristol, Conn., to all of whom the Editorial Committee wishes to extend its gratitude.

Because of the large number of horticultural varieties of Chrysanthemum the hort. var. list and the common-name list have been combined in the special list below. All hort. var. names below represent clons.

Classification

An.	Anemone.
A. S.	Anemone Single.
Ast.	Aster.
Bab.	Baby.

CHRYSANTHEMUM, continued

Bab. Pom.	Baby Pompon.
But.	Button.
Co.	Compact.
Con.	Commercial.
Dec.	Decorative.
Dis.	Disbud.
Dbl. Loo.	Double Loose.
Dbl. Rou.	Double Round.
Dup. Har.	Duplex Hardy.
Dwf.	Dwarf.
Exh.	Exhibition.
Fan. Jap.	Fantastic Japanese.
Hairy.	Hairy.
Har.	Hardy.
Har. Hyb.	Hardy Hybrid.
Har. Sin.	Hardy Single.
Inc.	Incurved.
Jap.	Japanese.
Jap. An.	Japanese Anemone.
Jap. Inc.	Japanese Incurved.
Jap. Odd.	Japanese Oddity.
Jap. Tub.	Japanese Tube.
Kor.	Korean.
Kor. Har.	Korean Hardy.
Kor. Sd.	Korean Semidouble.
Kor. Sin.	Korean Single.
Lrg. An.	Large Anemone.
Lrg. Dbl.	Large Double.
Lrg. Flo.	Large Flower.
Lrg. Pom.	Large Pompon.
Med. Pom.	Medium Pompon.
Odd.	Oddity.
Pom.	Pompon.
Pom. An.	Pompon Anemone.
Pot Pla.	Pot Plant.
Pot Var.	Pot Variety.
Qui.	Quilled.
Ref.	Reflexed.
Rev. Pom.	Reverse Pompon.
Sd.	Semidouble.
Sin.	Single.
Sin. Co.	Single Compact.
Sin. Dup.	Single Duplex.
Sin. Stu.	Single Sturdy.
Sm. Flo.	Small Flower.
Sm. Pom.	Small Pompon.
Sm. Sin.	Small Single.
Spi.	Spidery.
Spi. Odd.	Spidery Oddity.
Spo.	Sport.
Spo. Erm.	Sport Ermalinda.
Spo. Lil.	Sport Lillian.
Sp. Pet.	Spoon Petals.

Abbreviations of Names of Originators or Introducers

ABC	American Bulb Co., Chicago, Ill.
ABG	ABG-Pep.
Alb.	Alberthamp.
And.	Anderson Floral Co., Columbus, Neb.
Arb.	Arbini, San Rafael, Calif.
Ask.	Askenback Bros., Clifton, N. J.
A.&M.	Askenback & Muller.
B.&A.	Bobbink & Atkins, East Rutherford, N. J.
Bay S.	Bay State Nurseries, North Abington, Mass.
Bea.	Beasley.
Bebb	Bebb Floral Co., Muskogee, Okla.
Berg.	Francis H. Bergen, Summit, N. J.
Bert.	Bertanzel.
Bin.	Bindy.
Bird	Bird.
B.R.	Blue Rapids.
Bra.	Braun.
Bre.	Jos. Breck & Sons, Boston, Mass.
Bret.	Bretmeyer.
Bris.	Bristol Nurseries, Bristol, Conn.
Bro.	Tom Browne, Detroit, Mich.
Bro.T.E.	Mrs. Theodore E. Brown.
Bru.	Bruant Nursery, Poitiers, France.
Brun.	Brunning, Melbourne, Australia.
B.-S.	Baur-Steinkamp & Co., Indianapolis, Ind.
Cal.	Calvat.
Call	Call's Nurseries, Perry, Ohio.
Can.	H. Cannell & Sons, Swanley, Kent, England.
Car.	Carpenter.
C.C.F.	Cleveland Cut Flower Co., Newton Falls, Ohio.
Cool	Cool Crest Floral Co.
Cor.	Corliss Bros., Inc., Gloucester, Mass.
C.-P.	Conard-Pyle Co., West Grove, Pa.
Cra.	Robert Craig Co., Norwood, Pa.
Cri.	Crisey.
Cro.	Crozey.
Dai.	Daikoku.
Dal.	Dale Estate, Brampton, Ont., Canada.
Dan.	Danzig.
Dav.	Davis.
Dee.	Deemer Floral Co., Bowling Green, Ky.
Del.	Deloux.
DeM.	DeMack.
DeP.	V. R. DePetris, Grosse Pointe Farms, Mich.
D.H.J.	Dot.-Hill-Jab.
Dom.	Domotro.
Don.	Donaldson.
Dor.	Dorner.
Dre.	Henry A. Dreer, Philadelphia, Pa.
Duc.	William C. Duckham, Madison, N. J.
Eb.	Ebhen.
Ehman	Ehman.
Eng.	Engleman.
Engel	W. J. Engel, Columbus, Ohio.
Esp.	Espy's.
Eve.	Everitt.
Fab.	Faber.
Farn.	George L. Farnum, Media, Pa.
Farq.	R. & J. Farquhar Co., Boston, Mass.
Fen.	E. W. Fengar, Irvington, N. J.
Fer.	Ferguson.
Few.	Fewkes.
F.F.	Fight Floral Co., New York, N. Y.
For.	Forest Nursery Co., McMinnville, Tenn.
Fost.	Fosterman.
Frank	George Frank Nursery, East Rochester, N. Y.
Freis	Freis.
Frey	Frey & Frey, Lincoln, Neb.
Frey,A.	Alois Frey.
Fri.	Friedly Co.
F.W.	Fort Worth Botanic Garden.
Gar.	Garrett-Olsen Co., San Fernando, Calif.
Gas.	Gasser.
Gasu.	Gasurella.
Gaut.	Gaut.
G.&C.	Gray & Cole, Ward Hill, Mass.
G.F.	Grotto Floral Co.
G.&O.	G. & O.
Goa.	Goacher (England). See Wells.
Godf.	Godfrey, W. J. Exmouth, England.
Gre.C.	Greenwood Cemetery.
Gri.	Grimes.
Gri.S.	D. S. Grimes Sons.
Gro.	Groshner.
Groff	Geo. K. Groff, Lancaster, Pa.
Hal.	H. V. Hallock, Son & Thorpe, Queens, L. I., N. Y.
Hale	Hale.
Har.	Harkness.
Has.	H. G. Hastings Co., Atlanta, Ga.
Hen.	Alex Henderson, Inc., Chicago, Ill.
Hen.,P.	Peter Henderson & Co., New York, N. Y.
Hes.	Hession.
Hil.	Hillis.
Hill	Jos. Hill & Co., Richmond, Ind.
Imp.	Imported.
Int.	Introducer.
Jab.	Jablonsky.
Jae.	Adolf Jaenicke, Supt. Parks, Fort Wayne, Ind.
Jam.	James & Son.
Jap.	Japan.
Jep.	Jepson.
Joh.	C. W. Johnson, Morgan Park, Ill.
Jon.	H. S. Jones, Ltd., Hithergreen, Lewisham, London, England.
Kell.	R. M. Kellogg Co., Three Rivers, Mich.
Kels.	Harlan P. Kelsey, Inc., East Boxford, Mass.
Keu.	Keubler.
K.-M.	Kelbey-Mahew.
Kni.	Tom Knipe, Kokomo, Ind.
Knig.	Knight.
Koch	August Koch, Garfield Park, Chicago, or Otto Koch, N. J. State Hosp., Morris Plains, N. J.
Kra.	Kramer Bros., Ontario, Calif.
Kri.	Kridel.
Lac.	Lacroix.
Lam.	Lamborn Floral Co., Alliance, Ohio.
Laub	Laub.
Lem.	Lemoine.
L.&F.	V. Lemoine & Fils, Nancy, France.
Lib.	Liberty.
Lin.	Linton.
Liv.	Livingston Seed Co., Columbus, Ohio.
Lotze	Lotze.
L.&S.	Lowe & Shawyer, Uxbridge, Middlesex, England.
Lux.	Keith Luxford.
Man.	Joseph Manda Co., West Orange, N. J.
Mand.	Mandel.
Mar.	W. E. Marshall & Co., New York, N. Y.
Mas.	Masson.
May	John M. May, Summit, N. J.
Mayh.	Mayhew.
McL.	E. W. McLellan Co., San Francisco, Calif.
Mil.	Milne.
M.M.	Mesh-Mesh.
Mor.	Morrison.
Mt.G.	Mt. Greenwood.
Mul.,A.	Albert Muller, Long Island Head Gardener.
Mul.,J.	J. L. Muller.
Mur.	R. H. Murphey, Urbana, Ohio.
Muto	K. A. Muto & Sons, San Fernando, Calif.
Nag.	Naginoc.
Naw.	C. F. Nawrocki, Milwaukee, Ore.
Nic.	Nicholls.
Nonin	A. Nonin, Chatillon-Sous-Bagneux, Seine, France.
Nor.	Normandie.
N.Y.E.S.	New York Experimental Station.
Park	G. W. Park, Greenwood, S. C.
Pat.	Patton & Co.
Pau.	F. Pautke, Grosse Pointe, Mich.
Pea.	G. Pearson.
P.F.	Park Floral Co.
Pier.	A. N. Pierson, Inc., Cromwell, Conn.
P.&M.	Pitcher & Manda, Orange, N. J.
Poc.	Pockett.
Pol.	Pollock.
Pre.	Preisach.
Put.	Putnam.
Que.	Quetier.
Raw.	Rawson.
Rin.	Ivar Rindahl, Rome, N. Y.
Rit.	W. H. Ritter, Philadelphia, Pa.
Rob.	Robertson.
Roe.	Roeser.
Rose	Rose.
Rowe	Rowe.
Roz.	Rozian.
S.C.	Smith & Co.
Sch.	Schaeffer.
Schen.	Schenley Park, Pittsburgh, Pa.

CHRYSANTHEMUM, continued

Sco.	I. W. Scott Co., Inc., Pittsburgh, Pa.
Sey.	Seymour.
She.	Shephard.
Shi.	Shibuya, Mountain View, Calif.
Sie.	Sievers.
Sil.	Silsbury.
Smi.	Elmer D. Smith, Adrian, Mich.
Smi.F.	Smith Floral Co., Lansing, Mich.
Smi.S.	E. D. Smith & Sons, Winona, Ont., Canada.
S.N.	Styers Nursery, Concordville, Pa.
Som.	Somerset Rose Nursery, New Brunswick, N. J.
Spa.	Thos. H. Spaulding, Orange, N. J.
S.S.B.	A. Smith Stein Bros.
Sta.	Stafford Conservatories, Stafford Springs, Conn.
Ste.	Steffen.
Stout	Stout.
Str.	Straud.
Sty.	Styer's Nurs.
Sun.	Sunnyslope Mum Gardens, San Gabriel, Calif.
Tho.	A. W. Thorpe, Litchfield, England (probably); Hallock & Thorpe, Queens, N. Y., or John Thorpe (Hallock & Thorpe), Queens, N. Y.
Tho.	Thorpe & Son.
Thom.	Thompson.
T.&K.	T & K.
T.N.	Texas Nursery Co.
Tob.	Tobin.
Totty	C. H. Totty, Madison, N. J.
Tra.	Traischel.
Tur.	Turner Bros., West Long Branch, N. J.
U.Ill.	University of Illinois, Urbana, Ill.
U.S.D.A.	U. S. Department of Agriculture, Washington, D. C.
Vau.	Vaughan's Seed Store, Chicago, Ill.
Wai.	W. H. Waite, Eatontown, N. J.
W.B.&B.	Weiter, Borst & Borst.
Wei.	Weiland.
Wells	W. Wells & Co., Merstham, Surrey, England (including varieties raised by Goacher).
W.G.	Wayside Gardens, Mentor, Ohio.
Whe.	James Wheeler & Son, Natick, Mass.
Whi.	White.
Wil.	Wilde.
Woo.	H. Woolman, Birmingham, England.
Yod.	Yoder Bros., Barberton, Ohio.
Yosh.	Yoshiike (Japanese Nursery), Oakland, Calif.
You.	Youdath Perennial Gardens, Mentor, Ohio.

Perhaps the greater number of the horticultural varieties (clons) in the following list belong to C. morifolium (*hortorum*), Florists Chrysanthemum, a cultigen (treated often as a species), supposed to be of Chinese origin. In recent years, however, remarkable progress has been made in hardier types by using a number of species for hybridizing. These include C. arcticum, C. coccineum, C. indicum, C. maximum, C. nipponicum, C. sibiricum (*coreanum*), and perhaps others. All names in this list represent clons except the common names of species or natural varieties.

A. Barham. Dec. (B.&A.-Totty 1914.)
Abelard. Pom. (T.&K. 1936.)
Aberdeen. Pom. (Bay S.)
A. (*B.*) Hood. Sin. (Totty-Godf. 1927.)
Absolute. Sin. (Totty-Godf. 1928.)
Acto. Pom. (Smi. 1901.)
Ada (*B.*) Gosling. Jap. (Totty-Jon.'27.)
Ada Brooker. Com. (Hill 1924.)

CHRYSANTHEMUM, continued

Adams. Har. (You. 1938.)
Ada Sweet. Pom. (Smi.-Frey 1909.)
Adelaide. Lrg. Pom. (Totty 1921.)
Adelphia. Lrg. Pom. (Smi. 1922.)
Adenlair. An. (Smi. 1927.)
Adironda. But. (Smi. 1918.)
Admiral Beatty. Inc. (Totty 1921.)
Admiration. An. (Smi. 1935.)
Adonis. Jap. (Smi. 1910.)
Adorable. Pom. (And. 1938.)
Adrians Pride. Lrg. Flo. (Smi. 1922.)
Aduana. Ref. (Smi. 1918.)
Aesthetic. Inc. (Smi. 1912.)
Afterglow. Sd. (England 1930.)
Agate. Pom. (Smi. 1937).
Agatha. Pom. (Smi. 1931.)
Agnes (*Selkirk*) Clark. Sin. (Bri.)
Agrippina. Pom. (Bay S.)
Akron. Har. (You. 1938.)
Aladdin. Har. Lrg. Pom. (Bre. 1932.) *Mrs. Phil Page.*
Alaska. Inc. (Dom. 1896.)
Alban. An. (And. 1937.)
Albatross. Com. (B.-S. 1939.)
Albert Jessurun. Sin. (Totty 1925.)
Albert Muller. Har. Lrg. Pom. (A.&M. 1936.)
Alecia. Pom. (Smi. 1929.)
Aleck. Pom. (Smi. 1929.)
Aletta. Med. Pom. (Smi. 1925.)
Alex Donaldson. Pom. (Totty-Don. 1925.)
Algonquin. Har. (U.S.D.A. 1938.)
Alice. Pom. (DeP. 1937.)
Alice Barham. Dbl. Loo. (Nonin 1914.)
Alice Benson. Inc.
Alice Day. Jap. Inc. (Totty-Poc. 1916.)
Alice Dunn. An. (Gar. 1940.)
Alice Howell. Sin. (Pier. 1918.)
Alice Tashima. Odd. (Sun. 1938.)
Aline. Sin. (Totty 1925.)
Allen Anderson. Sin. (And. 1931.)
Alma. Pom. (Smi. 1907.)
Aloma. Sin. (Totty 1930.)
Aloysia. An. (Smi. 1935.)
Alpine C. **C. alpinum.**
Amalia C. **C. amaliae.**
Ambassador. Com. (B.-S. 1931.)
Amber Beauty. Har. (Kell.-Smi. 1925.)
Amberstar. Sin. (Dre. 1934.)
Amelia. Har. (Cri. 1931.) *Azaleamum.*
Amethyst Queen. Har. (K.&S. 1935.)
Amos. Pom. (B.-S. 1931.)
Amoskeag. Sin. (U.S.D.A. 1938.)
A. Neilson. Pom. (Bay S.)
Angeline. Sin. (Fab. 1935.)
Angelo. Pom. (Smi. 1920.)
Aniwa. Pot. Var. (Smi. 1926.)
Anna. Sin. (Smi. 1909.)
Anna Danzig. Spo. (Dan. 1925.)
Anna (*H.*) Condict. Sin. (Totty 1922.)
Anna Kaskas. Inc. (DeP.)
Anna Kuhn. Lrg. Pom. (Totty 1925.)
Anna (*Louise*) Pierce. Dbl. Loo.
Anna Mary. Sm. Flo. (Farq.)
Anneta. Pom. (Smi. 1920.)
Annette. Bab. (Smi. 1936.)
Anne (*V.*) Dort. Sin. (Totty-Berg.'34.)
Ann Miller. Har. (Smi. 1937.)
Annual C. **C. carinatum.**
Anoka. Pom. (Smi. 1919.)
Antarctic. Con. (B.-S. 1940.)
Antigo. An. (Smi. 1936.)
Antigone. Lrg. Flo. (Smi. 1915.)
Antique. Spo. (Totty 1912.)
Antoine Lanquetet. Dec. (B.&A.)
Aphrodite. Kor. Sin. Har. (Bris. 1936.)

CHRYSANTHEMUM, continued

Apollo. Kor. Sin. (Bris. 1936.)
Appeal. Kor. Sin. (Dre. 1937.)
Apple Blossom. Sin. (Gar. 1938.)
Apricot. Har. (You. 1938.)
Apricot May Wallace. Com. (Woo. Imp. 1937.)
Apricot Queen. Com. (Smi. 1935.)
Aquitaine. Har. (Smi. Imp.; Nonin'09.)
Araby. Sin. (Totty 1923.)
Arcadia. Pom. (DeP. 1938.)
Arctic C. **C. arcticum.**
Arcturus. Har. (Dre. 1938.)
Ardice. An. (Gar. 1940.)
Ardith. Pom. (Smi. 1933.)
Ariana. Dis. (Smi. 1930.)
Arlee. Lrg. Sin. (Smi. 1910.)
Arlene. Pom. (Gar. 1939.)
Arlyn. Pom. (Smi. 1932.)
Armistice Day. (Totty 1931.)
Armorel. Dbl. Loo. (Dre. 1932.)
Artemis. Sin. (Totty 1918.)
Arthola. Com. (Smi. 1936.)
Arthur Clark. Sin. (Gar. 1939.)
Artisan. Jap. (Smi. 1919.)
Artista. Lrg. Flo. (Smi. 1916.)
Artistic Queen. Jap. Inc. (Smi. 1912.)
Arvede Barine. Hairy. (Hill Imp. Bru. 1911.)
Astrid. Har. Sin. (Whe.-S.N. 1936.)
Athalie. Sin. (Sey. 1938.)
Attraction. Sin. (Dre. 1929.)
August Dasse. Inc. (Hill; Imp. 1912.)
Aureum. **C. parthenium** hv.
Autocrat. Jap. Inc. (Totty 1916.)
Autocrat. Har. (Dre. 1938.)
Autumn. Sin. (C.-P. 1935.)
Autumn Beauty. Dec. (Totty.)
Autumn Glints. Rev. Pom. (B.-S. '26.)
Autumn Glow. Lrg. Flo. Inc. (Dor. 1893.)
Autumn Glow. Dbl. (1906.)
Autumn Glow. Med. Sd. Har.
Autumn Gold. Dec. (Totty-Jon. 1933.)
Autumn Leaf. Har. (Dre. 1934.)
Autumn Queen. Pom. (Hen. Imp. 1888.)
Autumn Queen. Jap. (Smi. Imp. 1892.)
Avalon. Pom. (DeP. 1937.)
Azaleamum. Amelia.
Azelda. An. (Smi. 1914.)
Azora. Pom. (Smi.)
Baby. But. (Cra. 1905.)
Baby Charles. Sin. (Totty 1928.)
Baby Doll. But. (Smi. 1920.)
Baby Marguerite. But. Spo. Bab. (Cra. 1909.)
Baby Pink. Har. (You. 1938.)
Balandus. Dis. (Smi. 1933.)
Baldwin Scarlet. Pom. (Totty 1916.)
Ball of Gold. Lrg. Pom. (Smi. 1928.)
Baltimore. But. (Totty.)
Barbara. Har. (You. 1938.)
Barbara Cumming. Dbl. Loo. (Bris.'30.)
Barbara Davis. Com. (Pier.; Gas. 1917.)
Barnegat. Har. (U.S.D.A. 1938.)
Beatrice. Pom. (Totty-Kni. 1936.)
Beatrice Asmus. An. (Smi.-Frey 1909.)
Beatrice Lilly. Exh. (Totty 1936.)
Beautiful Lady. An. (Smi. 1932.)
Beauty of Truro. Hairy. (Smi.; Dav. 1897.)
Becky McLane. But. (Pier.-Joh. 1919.)
Bella Pink. Har. (You. 1938.)
Bella Red. Har. (You. 1938.)
Bella Yellow. Har. (You. 1938.)
Belle Mauve. Dbl. Loo. (France before 1920.)

CHRYSANTHEMUM, continued
Bellingham. An. (Smi.-Smi. 1926.)
Belva. An. (And. 1940.)
Benoit. Pom. (Smi. 1926.)
Ben Tashima. Exh. (Sun. 1940.)
Benten. Jap. (Totty 1918.) *Goddess of Beauty.*
Benua. Pom. (Smi. 1925.)
Ben Wells. Lrg. Flo.
Berneita. An. (Smi. 1925.)
Berta. Ref. (Totty; Jon. 1926.)
Berta Crowell. Odd. (Gar. 1939.)
Bertha Fairs. Sin. (Totty; Wells.'18.)
Bessie Flight. An.
Bessie Laroche. Sin. (Totty; Shi.'26.)
Bess Witt. Spi. (Sun. 1940.)
Beth. Pom. (Totty-Joh. 1913.)
Betsey Ross. Inc. (Smi. 1918.)
Betty Price. Pom. (Totty; DeP.1929.)
Betty Rose. An. (DeP.)
Betty Watkins. Pom. (Smi.)
Beuneta. Pom. (DeP.)
Bigbaby. But. (Smi.)
Billancourt. Dec. (Totty 1915.)
Billie Burke. But. (Smi. 1921.)
Birdine. An. (Smi. 1935.)
Birmingham. Exh. (Totty; Jon. 1933.)
Bishop. (Muto 1940.)
Bizarre. An. (Smi. 1937.)
Blackhawk. (Hill 1898.)
Blanche. An.
Blaze. Sin. (Yod. 1940.)
Blazing Gold. Com. (B.-S. 1939.)
Blazingstar. Sin. (Smi. 1913.)
Blushing Bride. Har. (You. 1938.)
Bobbie. Pom. (U.Ill.)
Bobette. Pom. (And. 1940.)
Bob Pulling. Lrg.Flo. (Totty; Jon.'15.)
Bob White. Har. (You. 1938.)
Bohemia. Lrg. Flo. (P.&M. 1890.)
Bokhara. Pom. (B.-S. 1925.)
Bol d'Or. Lrg. Flo. (Totty 1917.)
Bona. An. (And. 1937.)
Bonfire. Har. (You. 1938.)
Bannaffon De Luxe. Com. (Smi. 1938.)
Bonnibel. Lrg. Pom. (Smi. 1932.)
Bonnie Maid. Pom. (B.-S.)
Border Beauty. Dec. (Totty.)
Boston. Lrg. Flo. Sd. Har. (Bay S.)
Bradshaw. Lrg. Flo. (Farq.)
Brick. Dbl. Rou. Pot. Pla. (Rit. 1926.)
Bridal Bells. Pom. (Smi. 1937.)
Bridesmaid. Sin. (Dre. 1929.)
Bridgewater Velvet. Sin. (Imp. 1938.)
Bright Eyes. But. (Smi. 1920.)
Bright Light. Dec.
Brighton. An. (And. 1939.)
Bright Spot. Pom. (And. 1937.)
Brilliant. Sin. (Dre. 1928.)
Bristolite. Pom. (Bris. 1934.)
Bronze Acto. Pom. (And.)
Bronze Beauty. Pom. (F.F. 1935.)
Bronze Beauty. Har. (K.-M. 1936.)
Bronze Beauty. Com. (B.-S. 1939.)
Bronze Buckingham. Sin. (Totty; Fen. 1918.)
Bronze Buttercup. Dbl. Loo. (Imp. Godf.)
Bronze Button. But. (W.G.)
Bronze Charm. An. (And. 1940.)
Bronze Climax. Climax Bronze.
Bronzecup. An. (Smi. 1930.)
Bronze Doty. Lrg. Pom. (Mul. 1922.)
Bronze Doty 2nd. Pom. (Totty 1922.)
Bronze Dream. (Muto 1940.)
Bronze Ermalinda. Pom. (Smi.)

CHRYSANTHEMUM, continued
Bronze Frick. Inc. (Smi.)
Bronze Frick. Helen Frick.
Bronze Garza Supreme. An. (Gar. (1939.)
Bronzegem. Com. (B.-S. 1937.)
Bronze Goacher. Dbl. Loo. (Goa.)
Bronze Gold Lode. Com. (Smith F. 1938.)
Bronze Gootcher. Lrg. Dbl. (Imp. Wells.)
Bronze Groff von Oriole. An.
Bronze May Wallace. (Muto 1940.)
Bronze Mistletoe. Spo. (Dee. 1925.)
Bronze Molly. Lrg. Sin. (Totty 1921.)
Bronze Norma. Spo. (M.-M. 1935.)
Bronze Norma. An. (Smi.)
Bronze Normandie. Pom. (Bri. 1931.)
Bronze November. Pom. (Bris.)
Bronze Perfection. Pom. (PF., Wei. 1930.)
Bronzeprince. Pom.
Bronze Princess. Pom. (And. 1940.)
Bronzequeen. Har. (Totty. U.Ill. 1924.)
Bronze Sceptre. (Muto 1940.)
Bronze Source d'Or. Dec. (Pier.)
Bronze Supreme. An. (Naw. 1937.)
Bronze Turner. Spo. (Totty; Rob. 1924.)
Bronze Tuxedo. An. (Yod. 1938.)
Bronze Unaka. Jap. Inc. (Totty; Fen. 1918.)
Bronze Usona. Spo. Pom. (Smi. 1932.)
Bronze Volunteer. An. (Yod.)
Bronzito. Pom. (Smi.; Smi. 1923.)
Broussonet C. **C. broussoneti.**
Brownbeauty. Pom. (Smi. 1925.)
Brownbess. Sm. Pom.
Brownbessie. Pom. (Pier.)
Brownbessie. But.
Brownbutton. But. (Smi.)
Browne Tom. Com. (Smi. 1929.)
Brown Eyes. Pom. (And. 1940.)
Brownie. Bab. But. (Smi.; U.Ill. '35.)
Brown Stephen. Exh. (Totty; Poc.'23.)
Brune Poitevine. Dec. Double. Loo. (Nonin 1916.)
Brunnhilde. Har. Sin. (Sty. 1939.)
Brutus. Jap. Ref. (May; May 1901.)
Buddy. Pom. An. (Totty; U.Ill. 1927.)
Buena. But. or Bab. Pom. (Smi. 1919.)
Buffbeauty. Sd. (Dre. 1929.)
Buffqueen. An. (Smi. 1926.)
Bunbu. Odd. (Imp. 1938.)
Burgundy Red. Sin. (Gar. 1940.)
Burridge. **C. carinatum** hv.
Butlers Caprice. Pom. (Totty; Wells 1913.)
Buto. Com. (And. 1938.)
Buttercup. Pom. (Bris. 1936.)
Buttonrose. But. (Smi. 1920.)
Califloral Beauty. Pom. (Muto 1940.)
Califloral Pride. Pom. (Muto 1940.)
California. Pom. (Totty; Shi. 1923.)
Calif. Bronze Daisy. Sin. (Meh. 1940.)
Calif. Gold. Sin. (Kra. 1940.)
Calif. Peach. Sin. (Kra. 1940.)
Calif. Red Daisy. Sin. (Meh. 1940.)
Calif. Yellow Daisy. Sin. (Meh. 1940.)
Caliph. Har. (Bris. 1938.)
Calumet. Lrg. Flo. (Smi. 1915.)
Calypso. An. (Smi. 1935.)
Cameoqueen. Har. (Kell. 1936.)
Camilla. Inc. Com. (Smi. 1930.)

CHRYSANTHEMUM, continued
Campfire. Pom. (Yod.; DeP. 1935.)
Canary. Har. (You. 1938.)
Canary. Pom. (B.-S. 1940.)
CanaryIslands C. **C. ptarmicaeflorum.**
Candida. Jap. Dbl. Loo. (Totty; L.&S. 1923.)
Canova. Pom. Pot. Var. (Smi. 1925.)
Caprice Deprintemps. Dec. (Totty; Del.; Nonin 1908.)
Caprice Purple. Pom.
Caprice White. Pom.
Captain Cook. Pom. (Totty 1919.)
Capt. Blood. Pom. (And. 1940.)
Captivation. An. (Smi. 1927.)
Cardonia. Inc. (B.-S.)
Carlotta. Sin. (Totty 1917.)
Carmelite. Har. Lrg. Flo. (B.&A.; Totty 1913.)
Carmen. Sin. (DeP. 1938.)
Carmine. Sin. (Dre. 1929.)
Carnelia. Sin. (DeP.)
Carolina Lee. Pom. (Smi. 1938.)
Caroline Mastic. Sin. (Totty; U.S.D.A. 1931.)
Caroline Robbins. Sin. (Totty; Ski.'26.)
Carrie. Har. Dec. Dbl. Loo. (Wells 1904.) *Glory of Seven Oaks; Seven Oaks.*
Carrie Beinecke. Jap.Exh. (Totty'27.)
Catherine. An. (Gar. 1938.)
Catherine Livingstone. Sin. (Smi.; Liv. 1910.)
Catherine Neff. Sin. (Gar. 1939.)
Catriona. Sin. (Totty; Jon. 1925.)
Caucasian C. **C. caucasicum.**
Caucasian Pyrethrum. **C. marschalli.**
Cavalier. Sin. (Bri. 1934.)
Cavalier. Sin. (Dre. 1934.)
Cazlonia. Pom. (Smi. 1933.)
Cecile. Bab. (Smi. 1936.)
Ceddie Mason. Sin. (Totty 1912.)
Celebration. Jap. Inc. (Hill 1919.)
Celebrity. Com. (Muto 1940.)
Celestra. Inc. (B.-S. 1929.)
Ceres. Kor. Sin. (Bris. 1934.)
Cerise Queen. Sm. Flo. (Farq.)
Certainty. Com. (Imp.-Woo. 1937.)
Ceta. Pom. (Smi. 1918.)
Cevennes C. **C. pallens.**
Chadwick Bronze. Inc. (Smi.)
Chadwick Improved. Jap. Inc. (Smi. 1909.)
Chadwick White. Inc. (Smi.)
Chaldon. Dec. (Totty; Wells 1913.)
Challenger. Lrg. Sin. (Smi. Imp.'36.)
Champagne. Dbl. Loo. (Nonin 1908.)
Champagne. Dec. (Hill Imp.; Nonin'09.)
Champ d'Or. Dec. (B.&A.)
Charles Fairs. Sin. (Totty; Smi.'21.)
Charles H. Totty. Lrg. Flo. (Hill; Wells; Poc. 1909.)
Charles Rager. Inc. (Freis 1907.)
Charles Totty. Dec. (Smi.S.; Del. 1892.)
Charles (*W.*) Johnson. Com. (Smi.'31.)
Charlo. Sin. (Gar. 1940.)
Charlotte Waite. Sin. (Totty; Wai.'17.)
Charm. Sin. (P. Hen. 1935.)
Charming Prince. Com. (And. 1935.)
Charter Oak. Sin. (Pier.; Fos. 1920.)
Chattanooga. Inc. (Smi.; Smi. 1927.)
Cheerfulness. Sm. Pom. (Dre. 1934.)
Cherokee. Exh. (Smi.; Smi. 1924.)
Chestnut. Pom. An. (Vau.; U.Ill.'21.)
Chestnut Burr. Med. Pom. (Dre.'34.)
Cheyenne. Jap. Inc. (Smi. 1919.)
Chibuya Bonmatton. (G.&O. 1938.)

CHRYSANTHEMUM, continued
Chicago Pearl. Pom. (W.B.&B. '23.)
Chieftain. Inc. (Hill Imp. Eng. 1914.) *Ivy Gay.*
Chinarose. An. (DeP.)
Chochard Rose. Com. (Totty; Nonin 1924.) *Rose Chochard.*
Christina. Inc.
Christmas Cheer. Pom. (Smi. 1937.)
Christmas Glow. Sin. (Hill; Jon. 1923.) *Winter Glow.*
Christmas Gold. But. (Fri. 1919.)
Christy Mathewson. Jap. (Smi.'12.)
Chrome Emerald. An. (DeP. 1937.)
Chrysanthemumdaisy. **C. maximum** hv.
Chrysolora. Dbl. Loo. Inc. (Smi.'11.)
Cincinnatus. Inc. (B.-S. 1926.)
Cinderella. Sin. (B.-S. 1916.)
Citronella. Inc. (B.-S. 1923.)
Citrus Queen. An. (Smi. 1937.)
Clara (*B.*) Ford. Kor. Sin. (Smi. 1926.)
Clara Jameson. Pom. (Totty 1919.)
Clare. But. (Smi. 1922.)
Claremont. Pom. (Kra.)
Claret. Med. Pom. (Smi.; U.Ill. 1925.)
Clarice. Pom. (Smi. 1920.)
Claudette. Bab. (Smi. 1935.)
Clemencia. Jap. An. (Totty 1917.)
Cleopatra. Sin. (1935.)
Cleveland. Har. (You. 1938.)
Climax Bronze. Pom. (Roe. 1929.) *Bronze Climax.*
Clio. Kor. Sin. (Dre. 1936.)
Clista. Bab. But. (Smi. 1935.)
Clorinda. Pom. (Smi. 1910.)
Clump C. **C. multicaule.**
Clytie. Lrg. Sin. (Totty; Jon. 1933.)
Coahoma. Com. (B.-S. 1933.)
Coed. An. (Vau.; U.Ill. 1921.)
Col. Frederick M. Alger. Com. (DeP. 1937.)
Col. (*Horace M.*) Hickman. Exh. (Totty; Kni. 1936.)
Colonel (*D.*) Appleton. Inc. (Pier.; Mar. 1900.)
Colorado. Spo. *Mrs. Godfrey.*
Columbus Dispatch. Inc. (Smi. 1933.)
Comanche. Pom. (Smi. 1937.)
Comeleto. Dbl. Loo. Com. (Smi. 1907.)
Comet. Com. (B.-S. 1940.)
Cometo. Med. Pom. (Smi. 1919.)
Companion. Har. (You. 1938.)
Comtesse Decariel. Jap. Inc. (Spa.; Del. 1891.)
Coney. Har. (You. 1938.)
Connie Dick. Pom. (Totty 1918.) *Yellow Doty.*
Conquest. Exh. (Smi. 1935.)
Coppercity. Spo. (Rin. 1931.) *Louise Davenport.*
Copperclad. Pom. (And. 1936.)
Cora. Har. (You. 1938.)
Coralblaze. An. (Totty; DeP. 1936.)
Cora Mae. (Gar. 1939.)
Cora Peck Buhl. Pom. (Smi. 1923.)
Cordell. Sin. (Gar. 1939.)
Cordova. Pom. (Smi. 1930.)
Corinne. Pom. (Totty 1937.)
Corn C. (*Cornmarigold*). **C. segetum.**
Corneto. Exh. (Smi. 1923.)
Cornmarigold. **C. segetum.**
Corona. Inc. (B.-S. 1926.)
Corporal (*J. Fred*) Piper. Lrg. Flo. (Totty 1919.)
Coryphee. Sin. (Gar. 1938.)
Cosmos. Sin. (Dre. 1924.)
Costmary C. **C. majus.**
Countess Edgmont. Sin. (Totty 1922.)

CHRYSANTHEMUM, continued
Country Girl. Sin. (Bris. 1935.)
Country Maiden. Exh. (Sun. 1940.)
Cranfordia. Dec. Dbl. Loo. (Totty Imp.; Wells 1915.)
Cranford Pink. Dec. (Totty Imp.'14.)
Cranford White. Dec. (Pier.)
Cranford Yellow. Dec. (Totty Imp.; Wells 1914.)
Creole. Pom. (B.-S. 1937.)
Crimson Conquest. Sin. (Totty; Jon. 1933.)
Crimsonglory. Har. Pom. (Smi. 1935.)
Crimson Glow. Ref. (Totty; Jon. 1926.)
Crimson Lustre. Pom. (Smi.; Smi.'29.)
Crimson Perfection. Exh. (Hill Imp. 1925.)
Crimson Pride. Pom. (Totty; Wells'13.)
Crimson Quintus. Dec. (Totty Imp.; Wells 1913.)
Crimson Source d'Or. Dec. (Totty.)
Crimson Splendor. Har. Lrg. Flo. (Bris. 1933.)
Crispum. **C. parthenium** hv.
Crista. But. (Smi. 1922.)
Crocus. Jap. (Smi. 1906.)
Crowndaisy C. **C. coronarium.**
Crusader. An. (Smi.; U.Ill. 1935.)
Crystal Dome. Inc. (B.-S.; B.-S. 1927.)
Crystal Gem. Lrg. Flo. (Smi. 1915.)
Crystal Jewel. Pom. (And. 1935.)
Crystal Queen. Com. (Smi. 1928.)
Crystal White. Pom. (B.-S.)
Cydonia. Har. (Dre. 1938.)
Cyril Kock. Sin. (Totty 1928.)
Cyril Thorne. Sin. (Gar. 1939.)
Daikoku. Jap.? (Totty 1918.)
Daily Mail. Inc. (Totty; Wells; Poc. 1914.)
Dainty. Sm. Sin. (Totty; Wai. 1918.)
Dainty. Sin. (Dre. 1929.)
Dainty. Sin. (Hen. 1935.)
Dainty Maid. But. (Smi. 1922.)
Dainty Miss. Sin. (Gar. 1938.)
Daisy. Pom. (P.&M. 1891.)
Dalmatian Pyrethrum. **C. cinerariaefolium.**
Damon. Pom. (Totty; Kni. 1936.)
Dan Bradshaw. Sin. (Gar. 1939.)
Dante. Pom. (Totty; Kni. 1936.)
Daphne. Sin. (Bri. 1934.)
Darkpink Jewell. Pom. (Yod. 1938.)
Darkpink Norma. Pom. (Yod.)
Dark Yellow Mefo. Com. (Gri. S. 1938.)
Dasira. Sin. Com. (Bris.; Smi.)
David B. Oliver. Exh. (Smi. 1935.)
David I. Kelly. Exh. Ref. (Kni.; Totty 1936.)
David Rust. Dbl. Loo. (Rit. 1929.)
Dawn. Lrg. Flo. (Farq.)
Dawn. Hasegawa.
Daybreak. Har. Sin. Dup. (Bris. 1932.)
Dazzle. Sin. (Smi.; U.Ill. 1922.)
Dazzler. Sin. (Dre. 1929.)
Deanna. Har. (Smi. 1937.)
Debutante. Dec. (Totty; Imp.; Wells 1915.)
December Beauty. Inc. (Smi. 1920.)
December Bronze. (Muto 1940.)
December Crystal. Com. (And. 1936.)
December Gem. Jap. (Cy.; Smi. 1911.)
December Glory. Com. Inc. (Smi. 1923.)
December Glory. Pom. (Kra. 1938.)
December Gold. Dec. (Hill; Imp.; Wells 1910.)

CHRYSANTHEMUM, continued
December Queen. Jap. Inc. (Smi. 1917.)
Delight. Ref. (Totty 1919.)
Delmar. Pot. Var. Dbl. Loo. (Smi. 1925.)
Delphine Dodge. Pom. (Pier.; Pau.'17.)
Del Rey. Sin. (Gar. 1940.)
Denice. Pom. (Smi. 1929.)
Derigold. Pom. (B.-S. 1938.)
Desert Song. Sin. (Totty; Jon. 1935.)
Desfontaines C. **C. fontanesi.**
Detroit News. Inc. (Smi. 1926.)
Diana. Har. (Totty; Imp.; Nonin 1913.)
Diana. Kor. Sin. (Bris. 1934.)
Diantha. An. (Smi. 1913.)
Dick Witterstaetter. Ref. (Smi.'11.)
Dill C. **C. anethifolium.**
Dinizulu. Sm. Flo. (Farq.)
Distinction. Inc. (B.-S. 1925.)
Distinction. Spo. (B.-S. 1931.)
Distinction. Pom. (Dre. 1934.)
Divine. Har. (You. 1938.)
Dolly Duncan. Lrg. Sin. (Totty.)
Dolora. But. Pom. (Smi. 1931.)
Donald. Pom. Sm. (Totty; Joh. 1913.)
Donalda. An. (Smi. 1933.)
Donaldina. Exh. (Smi. 1931.)
Donald Wells. Sin. (Wells.)
Dorianda. Com. (Smi. 1930.)
Doris. Sm. Pom. (Joh. 1913.)
Dorothy. Har. (Totty; Nonin 1914.)
Dorothy Ann. Har. (You. 1938.)
Dorothy Crighton. Sin. (Totty; Wil. 1932.)
Dorothy Gish. But. (Smi.)
Dorothy Nehrling. Pom. (Smi. 1937.)
Dorothy Turner. Pom. (Bris. 1930.)
Dorris Louise. An. (And. 1940.)
Dot. Spo. (D-H-J. 1933.)
Dotson. Pom. (Smi. 1925.)
Doty. Spo. Lil. (Sco. 1916.)
Dr. (*Borden*) Taylor. Sin. (1916.)
Dr. (*C.V.*) Bryant Pom. (Totty 1929.)
Dream. Pom. (Totty; U.Ill. 1927.)
Dr. Enguehard. Lrg. Flo. (Pier.; Man. Nonin 1904.)
Dr. (*J.M.*) Inglis. Jap. (Totty; Jon.'26.)
Dr. (*Marcus A.*) Curry. Sin. (Totty; Koch 1927.)
Dr. Mills. Sin. (Totty; Koch 1927.)
Drops of Gold. Pom. (Totty; Jon.'35.)
Dr. W. R. Pettit. Pom. (Kni. 1936.)
Dubonnet. Odd. (Gar. 1938.)
Duchess of Westminster. Jap. (Totty; Jon. 1926.)
Duke. Har. (You. 1938.)
Dundee. Lrg. Flo. (Farq.)
Durbin. Har. (You. 1938.)
Dusky Maid. Pom. (B.-S. 1939.)
Earliest of All. Pom. (Totty 1930.)
Earliwhite. Pom. (B.-S.)
Earl Kitchner. Lrg. Flo. (Totty; Imp.; Wells 1915.)
Early Bronze. Har. Pom. (G.&C.'26.)
Early Frost. (Hill; Dor. 1915.)
Early Garza Supreme. An. (Rowe.)
Early Monarch. Inc. (Smi. 1929.)
Early Morn. Dbl. Loo. Pom. (Dre.'34.)
Early Quality. Com. (And. 1939.)
Early Rose. Inc.? (Smi.; Smi. 1916.)
Early Yellow. Pom. (Ask. 1937.)
Eclipse. Sin. (Muto 1940.)
Ecstasy. Pom. (B.-S. 1937.)
Ed D. Duffield. Exh. (Totty; Poc.'25.)
Eddie Knopping. Inc. Jap.? (Totty'19.)
Eden. (Nonin 1908.)
Eden Nonin. Dec. (B.&A. Imp.; Nonin.)
Edgar Sanders. Inc. (Smi. 1902.)

CHRYSANTHEMUM, continued
Edgar (*S.*) Kelly. Com. (Smi. 1926.)
Edina. Pom. (Smi. 1918.)
Edith Cavell. Exh. (Totty; Jon. 1933.)
Edith Newberry. Pom. (DeP. 1931.)
Edna. Pom. (May 1899.)
Edwin Seidewitz. Inc. (Lotze 1914.)
Eileen. Sin. (Totty; Wil. 1932.)
Eileen. Pom. (Totty; Kni. 1936.)
Eilene Masson. Sin. (Mas. 1927.)
Elberon. Inc. (Smi. 1913.)
El Dorado. Har. (DeP. 1938.)
Eleanor. Jap. An. (Totty; Sch. 1913.)
Eleanor Beardslee. An. (Totty; Thom. 1931.)
Electra. Com. (B.-S. 1932.)
Elegance. Sin. (Dre. 1937.)
Elegant. Har. (You. 1938.)
Elena. Dbl. (Smi. 1934.)
Elf. Sin. (P.Hen. 1935.)
Elizabeth. Sin. (Totty; Jon. 1935.)
Elizabeth. But. (B.-S.)
Elizabeth. An. (Totty 1936.)
Elizabeth Firestone. Sin. (Pier '18.)
Elizabeth Jamison. Jap.? (Totty; Hill 1920.)
Elizabeth McDowell. Sin.
Elizabeth Peterson. Pom.
Elkton. But. (Totty.)
Elora. Pom. (B.-S.)
Elreno. Pom. (Smi. 1923.)
Elsa. Sin. (Totty 1915.)
Elva Scoville. Spo. (Pier. 1916.)
E. M. Benson. (Totty; Poc. 1916.)
E.M.Byrnes. Exh. (Totty-U.S.D.A.'11.)
Ember. Har. (Bris. 1937.)
Embers. Sin. (Gar. 1938.)
Emberta. Inc.
Emelie. Bab. (Smi. 1936.)
Emmet. Har. Sin. (Smi.-U.S.D.A.1936.)
Emperor. Sin. (Muto 1940.)
Empire. Har. (You. 1938.)
Enchantress. Sin. Sd. (Dre. 1934.)
Envers Pride. Pom. (Gar. 1940.)
E. N. Ward. Exh. (Totty; Poc. 1929.)
Erligold. Sin. (Gar. 1939.)
Ermalinda. Med. Pom. (Smi. 1923.)
Ermalinda. Sm. Pom. Har.
Ermine. Sm. Flo. (Farq.)
Ernest Cooper. Lrg. An.
Esme Waters. Sin. (Totty; Godf.1927.)
Espys Darkpink Supreme. An. (Esp.)
Espys White Supreme. An. (Esp.)
Esther Longyear Murphy. Sin. (DeP. 1937.)
Estrelita. An. (Smi. 1930.)
Ethel. Sm. Pom. But. Bab. (Smi.1923.)
Ethel Blades. Dec. (B.&A.)
Ethel (*May*) Johnson. Sin. (Totty'23.)
Etoile d'Or. But. (Nonin 1906.)
Eugene Langaulet. Pom. An. (Hill; Wells 1915.)
Eureka. Sin. (Gar. 1938.)
Eva Legallienne. An. Jap. (Totty; Sch. 1935.)
Evelyn. Pom.
Evelyne Lethbridge. Sin. (Gar. 1938.)
Evelyn L. Baer. Pom. (Bra. 1934.)
Eveningglow. Com. Inc. (Smi. 1935.)
Eveningstar. Inc. (Smi.)
Excellence. Lrg. Flo. (Farq.)
Excelsior. Lrg. Sin. Med. Pom. (Totty; Imp.; Can. 1915.)
Exquisite. Sd. (Dre. 1934.)
Exquisite. An. (And. 1940.)
Fairy. Pom. (And. 1935.)
Fairy. Sin. (Hen. 1935.)

CHRYSANTHEMUM, continued
Fairy. Kor. Sin. (Dre. 1937.)
Fairyland. Odd. (Sun. 1938.)
Fairy Queen. Pom. Hairy. (Yosh. Imp. 1893.)
Fairy Queen. Sin. (DeP. 1937.)
Faith. An. (And. 1936.)
Faith Engel. An. (Engel 1939.)
Fanny. Har. (You. 1938.)
Fantasia. Jap. An. (Smi. 1927.)
Fascination. Sin. (Pier. 1916.)
Fascination. An. (And. 1937.)
Favorite. Inc. (Hill; Godf. 1923.)
Fawn. Sin. (Yod. 1940.)
Fawney. Har. (You. 1938.)
Featherbrook. Pom. (Totty 1937.)
Fee Parisian. Dbl. Loo. (Nonin 1908.)
Felice. Pom. (Smi. 1924.)
Felicity. Lrg. Sin.
Fernridge. Sin. (Totty; Berg. 1918.)
Fetterman. (Rit. 1926.)
Feverfew C. **C. parthenium.**
Fez. Pom. (Bri. 1936.)
Fiana. Dbl. Rou. Pom. (Smi. 1930.)
Field of Snow. Sd. Pom.
Field Oxeyedaisy. **C. leucanthemum pinnatifidum.**
Fiesta. Sin. (Gar. 1938.)
Fireball. Pom. (Smi.)
Firebird. Pom. Dbl. Loo. (Smi. 1920.)
Firebrand. Sin. (Dre. 1934.)
Fireflame. Kor.Sin. (Dre.1937.)
Firefly. An. (And. 1935.)
Firefly. Sin. (Gar. 1938.)
Firelight. Dbl. Loo. (Totty; Imp.; Nonin 1914.)
Firstdawn. Jap. (Totty; Poc. 1929.)
F. J. Taggart. Hairy. (Smi. 1903.)
Flame. Pom. (B.-S. 1933.)
Flashlight. Dbl. Loo. (Smi. 1934.)
Fleuve Rouge. Dec. (B.&A.)
Flora. Pom. (Hill 1919.)
Flora. Pom. (B.-S. 1928.)
Floradora. Pot. Var. An. (Smi. 1928.)
Florence. Har. (You. 1938.)
Florence Bahn. Jap. (Totty 1928.)
Florence McNeeley. Dbl. Loo. (Rit. 1925.)
Florence Stanton. Dec. (Totty; Wells 1913.)
Florera. An. (Smi. 1923.)
Florham Queen. Pom. (Totty 1921.)
Florists C. **C. morifolium.**
Florists Pyrethrum. **C. coccineum.**
Flossie. Sin. (Totty; Jon. 1925.)
Flossie. Har. (You. 1938.)
Floyd Gibbons. But. Com. (Smi.1931.)
Fondest. Har. (You. 1938.)
Fortuna. Kor. Sin. (Dre. 1936.)
Frances Huckvale. Lrg. Pom. (Totty; U.S.D.A. 1920.)
Frances Whittlesey. Dbl. Har. Dec. Loo. (Bri. 1931.)
Francine. Exh. (Smi. 1927.)
Francine. Sin. (Totty; Wil. 1932.)
Francis. Dec. (B.&A.)
Francis Jolliffe. Lrg. Flo. (Scott; Imp. Sil. 1911.)
Frank Durant. Exh. (Smi. 1926.)
Frank R. Sellers. Odd. (Gar. 1938.)
Frank Wilcox. Pom.
Frank Wilcox, Jr. But. (Smi. 1920.)
Fred J. Lrg. Flo. (Farq.)
Freida. An. (And. 1935.)
Frenzy. Pom. (Bay S.)
Freya. Har. (Sty. 1939.)
Frick. Spo. (And. 1929.)
Friendly Call. Com. (And. 1937.)

CHRYSANTHEMUM, continued
Friendly Rival. Com.Inc. (Smi.1928.)
Frison d'Or. Hairy. (Smi.; Imp.; Roz. 1909.)
F. S. Vallis. Lrg. Flo. (Gay; Hill; Smi.; Col. 1903.)
Fugi. Jap. Odd. (Totty; Imp. 1918.)
Fujiyama. Qui. (Rit. 1926.)
Fumiko Tashima. Odd. (Sun. 1940.)
Fusan. Har. (Smi. 1938.)
Gaiety. Exh. (Totty; DeP. 1931.)
Gaiety. Sin. (Muto 1940.)
Galatea. Pom. (Totty; Kni. 1936.)
Gallant Knight. Spi. (Sun. 1940.)
Galva. Pom. (Smi. 1935.)
Ganna. Dbl.Loo.Pom.Har. (Smi.1931.)
Garden Club of America. Jap. (Totty; U.S.D.A. 1927.)
Garfield. Pom. (You. 1938.)
Garnet. An. (U.Ill.)
Garnet Gem. Har. (Kel.; Smi. 1935.)
Garnet King. Com. Ref. (Smi. 1928.)
Garry. Sin. (Gar. 1940.)
Garza. An. (P.&M. 1894.)
Gaston Quineaux. Dec. (Totty; Nonin 1917.)
Gayboy. Com. (And. 1937.)
Gem Sept. Sin. (Totty 1927.)
Gene Anderson. Sin. (And. 1932.)
General Allenby. Ref. (Totty; Poc. 1922.)
Genevieve. Lrg. Sin. (Totty 1922.)
Genial. Har. (You. 1938.)
Gental. Har. (You. 1938.)
George Carpenter. Sin. (Totty 1934.)
George Hawkins. Lrg. An. (Smi. S.; Can. 1892.)
George Heuster. Dbl. Loo. (Rit.'26.)
George (*J.*) Ball. Dis. (Smi. 1930.)
George (*J.*) Bruzard. Lrg. Flo. (Smi.; Car. 1910.)
George (*W.*) Childs. Ref. (Tho.S.1892.)
Geraldine. Pom. (Smi. 1937.)
Geronimo. Sin. (U.S.D.A. 1938.)
Gertrude Wilson. Pom. An. (Smi.; Frey 1909.)
Giantdaisy. **C. uliginosum.**
Gilda. Pom. (Smi. 1922.)
Ginza. Pom. (Smi. 1930.)
Gipsy. Sin. (Pier. 1916.)
Gizella. Har. (You. 1938.)
Glada. Har. Dec. Dbl. Loo. (Smi.1930.)
Gladness. Har. (You. 1938.)
Gladys Pearson. Com. Inc. (Smi.'25.)
Gladys Spaulding. Lrg. An. (Spa.1888.)
Glaucum. **C. parthenium** hv.
Gleam. An. (Yod. 1940.)
Glenartney. Jap. (Totty 1921.)
Glencove. Jap. (Smi. 1911.)
Glenview. Jap. (Pier. 1905.)
Glitters. Com. Ref. (B.-S. 1933.)
Globe d'Or. Jap. Inc. Sd. (Spa. Imp.; Bru. 1897.)
Gloire Defrance. Lrg. Flo. (Farq.; Imp. from France.)
Glomero. Dbl. Loo. Har. (Smi. 1933.)
Gloria. Inc. (Smi. S. 1909.)
Gloriana. Sin. (Totty 1919.)
Glorietta. Har. (Smi. 1935.)
Glorious. Inc. (B.-S. 1921.)
Glory. Inc. (Smi. 1923.)
Glory of Seven Oaks. Carrie.
Glory of the Pacific. (Totty; Yosh. 1895.)
Glory of the Wayside. **C.maximum** hv.
Glow. Pom. (Bri. 1936.)
Goachers Crimson. Dec. (Smi.; Hill; Wells 1904.)

CHRYSANTHEMUM, continued
Goddess of Beauty. Benten.
Godfrey Bronze. Sin. (Totty; Godf. 1923.)
Godfrey Bronze. Spo. Sd. (Totty; Godf. 1930.)
Godfrey Favorite. Sin. (Totty; Godf. 1923.)
Godfrey Perfection. An. (Totty; Godf. 1915.)
Godfrey Triumph. Sin. (Totty; Godf. 1927.)
God of Wealth. (Dai.; Totty Imp. 1918.)
Goldaisy. Har. (You. 1938.)
Gold Christmas. Pom. (1918.)
Goldcoin. Pom. (Smi. 1926.)
Golddame. Dbl. Loo.
Golddrop. Pom. (B.-S. 1928.)
Golden Age. Pom. (Smi.)
Golden Arbini. Com. (Arb. 1938.)
Golden Boy. Com. (Muto 1940.)
Golden Bronze. Inc.
Golden Celebration. Ref. Sport of Celebration. (B.-S. 1928.)
Golden Chadwick. Inc. (Vau. 1903.)
Golden Champion. Nagirroc.
Golden Climax. Pom. (Pier.; Joh. 1914.)
Golden Crest. Pom. (Smi. 1925.)
Golden Elberon. Inc. Sport of Elberon. (S.S.B. 1920.)
Golden Fairy. Pom. (And. 1937.)
Golden Feather. Dec. (Pier.; Totty 1917.) *Source d'Or.*
Golden Fez. Pom. (Groff 1937.)
Golden Firebrand. But. (Totty.)
Golden Fleece. But. (DeP.)
Golden Fringe. But. (Smi.)
Golden Gate. Dbl. (Dre. 1934.)
Golden Gem. Pom. (And. 1934.)
Golden Gleam. Ref. (Pier. 1916.)
Golden Gleam. Sin. (U.Ill.)
Golden Glory. Inc.
Golden Glorymum. Har. (Mur. 1937.)
Golden Glow. Inc. (Smi. 1908.)
Golden Harp. Exh. (Sun. 1940.)
Golden Herald. Inc. Pom. (Totty; DeP. 1932.)
Golden Lida Thomas. An. (Hes. 1915.)
Golden Majestic. Spo. Inc. (Hill 1930.)
Golden Marvel. Jap. (Totty; Jon. 1927.)
Golden Measure. Inc. (B.-S. 1927.)
Golden Mensa. Sin. Spo. (Totty; Wells 1914.)
Golden Mistletoe. Spo. (Pier. 1919.)
Golden (*Mrs.*) Ross. Inc. (Smi.)
Golden Nymph. Pom. But. (Smi. 1924.)
Golden Oak. Pom. (B.-S. 1938.)
Golden October. Jap. (B.-S. 1926.)
Golden Oride. Sin. (Smi. 1925.)
Golden Oriole. Sin. (Smi. 1925.)
Golden Pearson. Spo. (B.-S.Pier.'31.)
Golden Pearson. Inc. (Smi.)
Golden Pheasant. An. (Smi. 1927.)
Golden Pockett. Spo. (1932.)
Golden Queen. Inc. (Smi. 1915.)
Golden Ring. Com. (Smi. 1923.)
Golden Robin. Jap. (Smi. 1913.)
Golden Sceptre. Pom. (Smi. 1926.)
Golden Seal. Sin. (Totty; Jon. 1933.)
Golden Seal. Sin. (Smi. Imp. 1936.)
Golden Shower. Jap. (Smi. S. Imp. 1900.)

CHRYSANTHEMUM, continued
Golden Shower. Sin. (DeP. 1937.)
Golden Splendor. Pom. (Smi. 1935.)
Golden Spray. Pom. (B.-S. 1937.)
Golden Star. Har. Pom. (Totty; U.Ill. 1924.)
Golden State. An. (Smi. 1926.)
Golden Sun. Sin. to Sd. (Totty; Jon. 1925.)
Golden Tints. Inc. (B.-S.)
Golden Topaz. Com. Inc. (Smi. 1932.)
Golden Tower. Har. (You. 1938.)
Golden Treasure Island. Pom. (Muto 1940.)
Golden Triumph. Com. (And. 1935.)
Golden Trophy. Pom. (Muto 1940.)
Golden Varsity. But. Sport of Varsity. (C.C.F.; Alb. 1935.)
Golden Wave. Inc. (Smi. 1929.)
Golden Wedding. Inc. (Hen. Imp. 1893.)
Golden West. Pom. (Pier.; Joh. 1914.)
Goldfinch. Pom. (B.-S.)
Goldlace. Sin. (Dre. 1929.)
Gold Lode. Com. Ref. (B.-S. 1927.)
Goldmine. Pom. (Smi. 1928.)
Goldmine. But. (B.-S.)
Goldnugget. Pom. (B.-S. 1922.)
Gold Standard. Sd. (Dre. 1934.)
Goldtips. Com. (B.-S. 1930.)
Goldtips. Pom. (Smi.)
Good News. Spo. Inc. (Yod. 1935.)
Gorgeous. Dbl. Loo. (Rit. 1927.)
Governor Green. Com.Inc. (Smi.'28.)
Governor (*Harry*) Moore. Exh. (Totty; Poc. 1926.)
Governor Lake. Pom. (Smi.)
Grace. Sin. (P.Hen. 1925.)
Grace Calhoun. Sin. (Totty; Shi.'26.)
Grace Coolidge. Inc. (Totty; U.S. D.A. 1926.)
Graceland. Sin. An. (Smi. 1928.)
Grace Sturgis. Exh. Ref. (Totty; Fer. 1928.)
Graf Vonfleming. Jap. An. (Totty; Sch. 1917.)
Graf Vonoriola. Jap. An. (Totty; Sch. 1917.)
Grandmere. An. (Gar. 1939.)
Granny Scovill. Har. Dec. (Bris. 1934.)
Grant (*B.*) Schley. Sin. (Totty.)
Grenada. Pom. (Totty; DeP. 1932.)
Grenadier. Sin. Stu. Pom. Har. (Bris. 1933.)
Greta. Pom. Lrg. (Smi. 1928.)
Greta. Pom. (B.-S.)
Gretchen. Dbl. Loo. (Wells 1908.)
Gretchen Piper. Sin. (Totty; Koch '27.)
Greystone. Pom. (Pier.; Whi. 1914.)
Gwen Patton. Pom. (Sun. 1940.)
Gypsy Girl. Sin. (Bris. 1928.)
Gypsy Girl. Sin. (Gar. 1938.)
Hachimanzan. Odd. (Sun. 1940.)
Hajnalka. Har. (You. 1938.)
Halo. Sin. (Dre. 1934.)
Hamburgh. Jap. (Has.; Laub 1920.)
Hamburgh Late White. (Totty.)
Happiness. Kor. Sin. (Dre. 1937.)
Harbinger. Sin. (Dre. 1934.)
Harding. Har. (You. 1938.)
Harrie. Dec. (Totty Imp.; Wells 1913.)
Harriet Sykes. Pom. (Totty 1921.)
Harry (*E.*) Converse. Lrg. Flo. (Totty; Wells 1911.)
Harvard. Ref. (Smi.; Poc. 1912.)
Harvest. Sin. Sd. (Dre. 1934.)
Harvester. Har. (Dre. 1938.)

CHRYSANTHEMUM, continued
Harvest Home. Har. Dbl. Lrg. Loo. (Totty; Tho. 1913.)
Harvest Moon. Jap. Pom. (Yosh.; Sie. 1891.)
Harvest Moon. Exh. (B.-S. 1939.)
Hasegawa. Sin. (Kra. 1938.) *Dawn,* not of Farq.
Hasegawa Gold. Pom. (Kra.)
Hasegawa Orange. Sin. (Kra. 1938.)
Hasegawa Poinsettia. Sin. (Kra.)
Hashegawa Yellow. Pom. (Gar.; Olsen 1935.)
Hazen (*S.*) Pingree. Com. (Smi. 1936.)
H. B. Wells. Exh. (Totty; Poc. 1923.)
Healsville. Sin. (Totty; Wil. 1932.)
Hearts of Gold. An. (Totty; DeP.'29.)
Hebe. Sin. (Bris. 1935.)
Hebe. Sin. (B.-S.)
Helen. Har. (You. 1938.)
Helena. Har. (Totty; Wells 1913.)
Helena Flint. Pom. (Totty 1922.)
Helena Pockett. Exh. (Totty 1938.)
Helene. Pom. (Totty; Kni. 1936.)
Helen Frick. Spo. (P.F. 1935.) *Bronze Frick.*
Helen Hubbard. Pom. Sin. (Pier. 1920.)
Helen Lecron. Sin. (Totty 1937.)
Helen Lee. Inc.? (Smi. 1917.)
Helen Newberry. Pom. (Bret.; Pau. 1912.)
Helen Page Wodell. Sin. (Totty '34.)
Helen Tait. Pom. (U.Ill. 1931.)
Helios. Sin. (Totty 1918.)
Helios. Dbl. Loo. (Gaut 1918.)
Heloise. Pom. (Totty; Kni. 1936.)
Henrietta. Dis. Pom. (Smi. 1936.)
Henri Vincent. Jap. (Totty 1919.)
Herada. An. (And. 1937.)
Hercules. Odd. (Sun. 1938.)
Hester. Sin. (Totty; Wil. 1932.)
Hestia. Kor. Sd. (Dre. 1936.)
H.E.Trueman. Exh. (Totty Imp. 1936.)
Heuster. Dbl. (Rit. 1926.)
Hiawatha. Lrg. Pom. (C.-P. 1936.)
High Lights. Pom. (Smi. 1935.)
Hijos. Pom.? (B.&A.)
Hilda Bergen. Inc. (Berg.)
Hilda Bergen. Com. (Totty 1929.)
Hilda Canning. But. Bab. Pom. (Pier.; Mt.G. 1917.)
Hilga. Har. Dbl. (Smi. 1933.)
Hillier. Loo. (Rit. 1930.)
Hilo. Exh. (Sun. 1940.)
H. Marie Totty. Sin. (Totty 1917.)
Holdona. Har. Dbl. (Smi. 1935.)
Holmes White. Har. (Totty Imp.; Dav. 1913.)
Homestead. Dbl. Loo.
Honeydew. Exh. (Hill 1923.)
Honeydew. Inc. (Smi.)
Hon. J. R. Mann. Ref. (Totty; U.S.D.A. 1926.)
Hope Engel. An. (Engel 1939.)
Hortense Malgot. Dec. (Totty; Nonin 1915.)
H. R. H. Lrg. Pom. (Totty Imp. 1925.)
Hugh Mitchell. Exh. (Imp.-Woo. 1937.)
Hungarian C. **C. rotundifolium.**
Ida. Sin. Dbl. Pom. (Totty Imp. 1924.)
Ida (*Catharine*) Skiff. Lrg. Sin. (Totty 1918.)
Ideal Pink. Har. (You. 1938.)
Idolf. Pom. (Smi. 1918.)
Igloo. Har. (Sty. 1939.)
Illco. Har. Sin. (Smi.; U.S.D.A. 1936.)

CHRYSANTHEMUM, continued
Illona. Pom. (Smi. 1915.)
Ilo. Exh. (Totty; U.S.D.A. 1936.)
Immaculate. Com. Inc. (B.-S. 1933.)
Imogene. Com. (Smi. 1933.)
Imperial Gold. But. Exh. (Smi. 1930.)
Improved Goldenglow. (Totty 1922.)
Indian. Lrg. Flo. Dbl. Loo. (Dre.)
Indianapolis Bronze. Com. (B.-S. 1940.)
Indianapolis Pink. Com. (B.-S. 1938.)
Indianchief. Com. (DeP. 1938.)
Indianhill. Pom. (Totty 1921.)
Indianmaid. Sin. (Dre. 1934.)
Indian Maid. Sin. (Gar. 1938.)
Indianola. Inc. (B.-S. 1928.)
Indian Princess. Odd. (Sun. 1938.)
Indian Summer. Sd. (Dre. 1934.)
Indian Summer. Kor. Loo. Dbl. (Bris. 1936.)
Indian Summer. Har. (Bris. 1937.)
Indicum. Sm. Sin. (Totty Imp. Jap.; Smi. 1908.)
Indolf. Pom. (Smi.)
Indomitable. Dbl. Rou.
Innocence. Kor. Sin. (Bris. 1934.)
Innocensia. Jap. An. (Totty; Sch.'17.)
Intensity. Ref. (Smi. 1900.)
Intensity. Har. (Dre. 1938.)
Iowa. Exh. (U.S.D.A. 1937.)
Irene. Sin. (Totty 1915.)
Irene. Med. Pom. Dwf. (Smi. 1923.)
Irene Rich. Dis. Pom. (Smi. 1932.)
Iridescent. Pom. (B.-S.)
Iroquois. Pom. (Smi. 1938.)
Isotta. Har.Dbl.Loo.Dwarf. (Smi.'28.)
Itaska. Lrg. Sin. (Smi. 1910.)
Iva. Lrg. Pom. (Smi. 1908.)
Ivor Grant. Sin. (Totty; Godf. 1915.)
Ivy Gay. Chieftain.
Izalco. An. (Smi. 1918.)
Izalco. Dis. (Smi. 1935.)
Jack Bannister. Dbl. Loo. Dec. (Wells before 1915.)
Jakie. Pom. (DeP. 1937.)
James Boone. Sm. Flo. (Farq.)
James Fraser. Ref. Exh. (Totty; Poc. 1914.)
James Hampson. Dec. (Totty 1932.)
Jane Cuthbert. Sin. (Totty;Wil.1932.)
Jane Harte. Spo. An. Sin. (Totty; Mor. 1930.)
Jane Kelsey. Kor. (Kels.)
Jane Kelsey. Har. (Cor. 1938.)
January Gold. Inc. (Smi. 1920.)
Japanese Maiden. Odd. (Smi. 1932.)
Japanese Red. Sin. (Kra. 1938.)
Jay. Har. (You. 1938.)
J. B. Deal. Exh. (Totty; Poc. 1925.)
Jean. Sin. (Smi. 1926.)
Jean Cumming. Har. Dec. (Bris. 1931.)
Jeanine. Pom. (Totty; Kni. 1936.)
Jeanne Shelly Adams. Sin.(Totty'26.)
Jean Treadway. Har.Dec. (Bris.1933.)
Jemima. Pom. (B.-S.)
Jena. Har. (You. 1938.)
Jerry. An. (And. 1936.)
Jersey. Lrg. Flo. (Farq.)
Jersey Beauty. Sm. Pom.
Jersey Gem. Pom.
Jewell. Pom. (B.-S. 1931.)
Jiggs. Sd. (Rit. 1925.)
Jimmie. Dec. (B.&A.)
Jimmy Walker. Ref. (Totty; Poc.'26.)
Jitsujetui. Jap. Odd. (Hill Imp.; Wells 1909.)
Joan. Pom. (Smi. 1933.)
Joan Edwards. Sin. (Totty; Wells'13.)

CHRYSANTHEMUM, continued
Joanne. An. (Gar. 1938.)
Joan of Arc. Ref. (Totty; Wells 1918.)
Joan Piper. Sin. (Totty 1923.)
Joan Wells. Pom. (Yod.)
Joe Beuerlein. Sin. (Bris. 1938.)
John Balmer. Jap. (Totty; Jon. 1923.)
John Bunyan. Lrg. An. (Smi.; Owen 1895.)
John Burton. (Smi. 1904.)
John (*S.*) Bush. Exh. (Totty; Poc.'25.)
John Shields. An. (Totty.)
Johnson. Pom. (You. 1938.)
Johnson Favorite. Pom. (Bay S.)
Jolo. Pom. (Smi. 1927.)
Jose. Sin. (Totty; Wil. 1932.)
Josephine. Sin. (Totty Imp.; Wells'13.)
Josephine. Har. (You. 1938.)
Josephine Foley. Jap.Inc. (Smi.1916.)
Josephine Lawler. Inc.
Josephine Scholtman. Sin. (Totty'18.)
Joseph (*P.*) Day. Exh. (Totty; Poc.'24.)
Josetta. Pot. Var. (Smi. 1926.)
Joyce Strowlger. Sin. (Totty;Jon.'25.)
J. R. Booth. Ref. (Nag.; Totty 1923.)
Jubilee. Com. (B.-S. 1939.)
Judith Anderson. Med. Pom. But. (Bris. 1936.)
Julia. Sin. (Totty 1924.)
Julia. Har. (You. 1938.)
Julia Dewitt. Med. Pom. (Totty; U.S.D.A. 1920.)
Juliana. Lrg. Pom. (Smi. 1918.)
Julia Quinlan. Sin. (Totty 1927.)
Julie Lagravere. Pom.
Julio. Pom. (Gar. 1940.)
Julius Saxon. Har. (You. 1938.)
Junior. Har. (You. 1938.)
Juno. Jap. An. (Totty 1917.)
Juno. Kor. Sin. (Dre. 1936.)
Justine Miller. But. (Smi.)
Justrite. Inc. (B.-S. 1929.)
Juva Nicholson. Pom.
J. W. Jr. Pom. (Totty; U.S.D.A. 1929.)
J. W. Prince. Inc. (B.-S.)
Kaino. Pom. (Muto 1940.)
Kariya Bronze. Pom. (Muto 1940.)
Kariya White. Pom. (Muto 1940.)
Katherine Harley. Sin. (Pier. 1920.)
Katherine Russell. Jap. (Totty; U.S.D.A. 1931.)
Katherine Twigg. Lrg.Flo. (Totty'20.)
Kathleen. An. (Totty 1936.)
Kathleen May. Sin. (Totty 1919.)
Kathleen Thompson. Dec. (Totty; Wells 1913.)
Kay Tashima. Odd. (Sun. 1938.)
Kegon No Taki. Odd. (Imp. 1938.)
Kenneth. Pom. (B.&A.; Smi.)
Kenny Boy. Com. (Sun. 1940.)
Kewanee. Inc. (Smi. 1915.)
Keystone. Com. Inc. (Smi. 1932.)
Kimie Tashima. Sin. (Sun. 1940.)
King Cushion. Har. (You. 1937.)
King Edward VII. **C. maximum** hv.
King Midas. Har. (Bris. 1937.)
King of Plumes. Odd. (Hill; Wells '09.)
King Tut. Com. (And. 1938.)
Kitty Bourne. Lrg. Flo. (Totty; Wells 1907.)
Kitty Riches. Sin. (Totty 1922.)
Klondike. Pom. (May; May 1901.)
Koleta. Pom. (Smi. 1918.)
Korean C. **C. sibiricum.**
Kramer's Buff Orange. Sin. (Kra. 1938.)
Kramer's Mori Apricot. Sin. (Kra. 1940.)

CHRYSANTHEMUM, continued
Kramer's Mori White. Sin. (Kra. 1940.)
Kristina. Sin. (Sty. 1939.)
Kuzuka. Har. An. (Smi. 1935.)
Laciniatum. **C. parthenium** hv.
Lady Astor. M.P. Sin. (Totty; Jon. 1921.)
Lady Astor. Sin. (Smi. 1936.)
Lady Beatrice. Har. (Kri. 1933.)
Lady Brunton. Dec. (Totty; Jon.'33.)
Lady Esther. Con. (And. 1935.)
Lady Frances. Har. (Kri.; Kri. 1933.)
Lady Frank Clarke. Exh. (Poc. 1938.)
Lady Hopetoun. Lrg. Flo. (Hill; Brun. 1903.)
Lady Lavonne. Har. (Kri. 1933.)
Lady Lee. Lrg. Sin.
Lady Lu. Sin. (S.C.; Alois; Frey 1909.)
Lady Lydia. Dec. (Totty.)
Lady Naylor. Lrg. Flo. (Farq.)
Ladysmith. Sm. Sin. (Totty; Wells'07.)
Lady Violet. Br. (Jae. 1930.)
Lady White. Com. (And. 1938.)
Laelia. An. (Vau.; U.Ill. 1921.)
Lafrance. Exh. Inc. (Smi. 1930.)
Lagaronne. Dbl. Loo. (Hill Imp. 1897.)
L'Aisne. Dec. (Totty Imp.; Godf.1913.)
Lamour. Har. (You. 1938.)
Laneta. Pom. (Smi. 1918.)
Lanona. An. (Smi. 1932.)
Laona. Sin. (Smi. 1926.)
Lapurite. Pom. (Smi.)
Larchmont. Sin. (Totty 1922.)
L'Argentuillais. Dbl. Loo. (Tra.'08.)
L'Argentuillais. Dec. (Hill Imp.; Tra. 1909.)
Lasomme. Dec. (Totty; Godf. 1913.)
Lasomme. Dbl. Loo. (Nonin 1914.)
Last Call. Sin. (Totty 1935.)
Lavender Gem. Inc. (Smi. 1928.)
Lavender Gown. Odd. (Sun. 1940.) *Osho Yushi.*
Lavender Lady. Kor. Dbl. (Bris.)
Lavender Queen. An. (Totty; Sch.'33.)
Lavera. Pom. (B.-S. 1935.)
Legal Tender. Pom. (B.-S. 1931.)
Leilah. Pom. (Smi. 1919.)
Lelia. But. (Totty.)
Lemonade. Sin. (Dre. 1934.)
Lemonade. Com. (Smi. 1935.)
Lemon Queen. Com. Inc. (Smi. 1929.)
L'Enfant des Deux Mondes. Sport. Hairy. (Hill; Cro. 1893.)
Lenox. Inc. (Smi. 1911.)
Leocadie Gentils. Hairy. (Smi. S.; Que. 1899.)
Lepactole. Dec. (B.&A.)
Leroy. Pom. (Pre. 1925.)
Leroy Zang. Inc.
Leslie. Pom. (Wells 1908.)
Letha. Bab. Pom. (Smi. 1935.)
Letitia. Pom. (B.-S. 1933.)
Liberty. Sin. (Jep. 1926.)
Liberty Bond. Inc. (Smi. 1918.)
Lida Thomas. An. (Frey 1902.)
Lighthouse. Sin. (Kra. 1938.)
Lilac. Cap. Dec. (Totty; Wells 1913.)
Lilac Caprice. Pom. (Totty 1913.)
Lillian Doty. Lrg. Dis. Pom. (Int. Totty 1914.)
Lilyan. Har. (1935.)
Lily Neville. Lrg. Sin. (Totty 1919.)
Lina Earp. (Totty 1930.)
Lincoln. Har. (You. 1938.)
Linda-Lou. An. (B.-S. 1940.)
Little America. An. (Totty 1936.)

CHRYSANTHEMUM, continued
LITTLE BARBEE. Sin. But. (Smi. Imp.; Godf. 1910.)
LITTLE BILLY. But. (Smi.)
LITTLE BOB. Har. Bab. But. (Imp.)
LITTLE DOT. But.
LITTLE GEM. But. (Smi. 1917.)
LITTLE PRINCESS. An. (You. 1938.)
LITTLE TOT. But. (Smi. 1920.)
LITTLE TRUANT. Bab. (Smi. 1928.)
LIZZIE ADCOCK. Dec. (Totty.)
LIZZIE ROBERTSON. Exh. (Hill; Dav.'23.)
LOIS. Pom. Sport Bronzito. (Hill 1932.)
LONG ISLAND BEAUTY. An. (Kra. 1940.)
LORD SOMERS. Pot. Pla. (Totty; Jon. 1933.)
LORELEI. Dbl. Har. Dec. (Smi. 1933.)
LORELIE. Sin. (Gar. 1938.)
LORETTA. Har. (You. 1938.)
LORIS. Pom. (Kra. 1938.)
LORRAINE MEECH. Pom. (Pier. 1920.)
LOS ANGELES. Sin. (Gar. 1938.)
LOUCELLA. An. (Smi. 1931.)
LOUISA POCKETT. Lrg. Flo. (Totty; Poc. 1917.)
Louisa Pockett. Exh. Ref. (Totty; Poc. 1918.)
LOUIS BOEHMER. Hairy. (Yosh. 1893.)
LOUISE DAVENPORT. Pom. (Pier. 1922.)
Louise Davenport. COPPERCITY.
LOUISE MAYO. Sin. (Totty; Jon. 1925.)
LOUISE PARKER. Sin. (Totty 1937.)
LOUISE SCHLING. Kor. Sd. Sin. (Bris. 1934.)
LOUIS FRIED. Pom. (Gar. 1939.)
LOUIS MORI. Sin. (Totty 1927.)
LOUIS SPEARS. Sin. (Totty; Godf.1918.)
LOVELIGHT. Kor. Sin. (Dre.)
LOVELY LADY. Sin. (Gar. 1938.)
LOYALTY. Jap. Inc. (Smi. 1919.)
LUAN. Sm. Flo. (Farq.)
LUCIA. Pom. (B.-S. 1922.)
LUCIE. Har. (You. 1938.)
LUCIFER. Dbl. Loo.
LUCILE. Pom. (Hill 1919.)
LUCINDA. Pom. (B.-S. 1928.)
LUCKY STAR. Sin. (DeP. 1938.)
LUCRETA. Pom. (B.-S. 1922.)
LUELLA. Pom. (B.-S. 1922.)
LUGANO. Pom.
LUSTRE. Inc. (B.-S. 1928.)
LUTEAS. Pot. Var. Inc. (Smi. 1932.)
LYNDHURST. Sm. Flo. (Farq.)
MABEL SEYMOUR. Sin. (Totty; Wil.'32.)
MABEL TONE. Sin. (Totty 1937.)
MADAM LUNT. Har. (Totty 1925.)
MADISON. Ref. (Smi. 1913.)
Madison. Exh. (Totty 1931.)
MADUSE. Dec. (L.&F. 1896.)
MA FERGUSON. Com. (Smi. 1925.)
MAGATHA. Pom. (Smi. 1936.)
MAIDENS BLUSH. Sin. (Dre. 1929.)
MAID OF KENT. Sm. Pom. (Pier. Can.)
MAJESTIC. Exh. Inc. (Hill; Dan. 1923.)
MAJOR BONAFFON. Inc. (Dor. 1894.)
MAJOR BONNATTON. Spo. (Dor. 1923.)
MAJOR (*Edward*) BOWES. Inc. (Smi.'36.)
MAMORU TASHIMA. Odd. (Sun. 1938.)
MANANTICO. Har. (U.S.D.A. 1938.)
MANCHUKUO. Pom. (B.-S. 1938.)
MANDARIN. Har. (Bris. 1938.)
MANITOU. Exh. (Smi. 1928.)
Manitou. Sin. (C.-P. 1936.)
MANKATO. Ref. (Smi. 1915.)
M. ANTONIN MARMONTEL. Jap. Exh. (Smi. S.; Hill Imp.; Nonin 1905.)
MAPLELEAF. An. (Vau.; U.Ill. 1921.)
MARCELLA. Pom. (Smi. 1932.)

CHRYSANTHEMUM, continued
MARGARET GRAHAM. Com. (B.-S.1929.)
MARGARET MACDONNELL. Jap. (Totty; Jon. 1927.)
MARGARET TERESA. Pom. (Pre. 1925.)
MARGARET WAITE. Spo. Sin. (Godf.; Pier. 1916.)
MARGARET WALKER. Sin. (Totty; Wells 1931.)
MARGARET (*W.*) WARNER. Sin. (Totty; Shi. 1926.)
MARGARET ZANG. Spo. (Lam. 1931.) *Yellow Pearson.*
MARGO. An. (Smi. 1931.)
MARGOT. Pom. But. (Smi. 1925.)
MARGUERITE C. **C. frutescens.**
MARGUERITE CLARK. But. (Smi. 1920.)
MARIANA. Pom. (Hill 1917.)
MARIAN (*H.*) UFFINGER. Inc.
MARIE. Bab. (Smi. 1936.)
MARIE ANDERSON. Sin. (And.)
MARIE ANTOINETTE. Lrg. Flo. Pom. (Farq.)
MARIE DEPETRIS. Inc. (DeP. 1928.)
MARIE DUPONT. Dbl. Loo.
MARIE KRAMER. Pom. (Kra. 1940.)
MARIE LOUISE. An. (And. 1940.)
MARIE TASHIMA. Odd. (Sun. 1938.)
MARIETTA. An. (Smi. 1929.)
MARIGOLD. Lrg. Flo. (Smi. 1915.)
MARILYN. Pom. (Smi. 1932.)
MARILYN SHANTIC. Har. (You. 1938.)
MARION H. UTTIGER. Exh. (Totty; Poc. 1930.)
MARION SEMLER. Exh. (Totty; Mil.'25.)
MARION SHILLABER. Har. (Totty 1925.)
MARIPOSA. Com. (DeP. 1937.)
MARISA. Har. (Smi. 1935.)
MARITZA. An. (Smi. 1933.)
MARKETEER. Com. (B.-S. 1938.)
MARK TWAIN. Inc. (Smi. 1936.)
MARLENE. Pom. (Totty; Kni. 1936.)
MARNE. Jap. (Totty; Jon. 1927.)
MARS. Kor. Sin. (Bris. 1934.)
MARTINA. Har. (You. 1938.)
MARY. Pom. (Totty; Joh. 1913.)
MARY ANN. Har. (Totty; U.Ill. 1924.)
Mary Ann. Pom. (Totty; U.Ill. 1925.)
MARY COLLADAY. An. (Str. 1912.)
MARY DAVIS. Sin. (Totty; Jon. 1925.)
MARY DONELLAN. Inc. Jap. (Smi.; Totty; Wells 1908.)
MARY FERGUSON. Pom. (Totty; Fer.'23.)
MARY HILLIER. Dbl. Loo. (Rit. 1930.)
MARY JANE. Lrg. Pom. (C.-P. 1935.)
MARY L. CLARK. Exh. (Smi. 1925.)
MARY (*Lennon*) HALL. Pom. (U.S.D.A.)
MARY LOU. Exh. (And. 1934.)
MARY MASON. Lrg. Flo. (Wells; Poc.'08.)
MARY PICKFORD. But. (Smi. 1921.)
MARY YOUDATH. Har. (You. 1938.)
MASAKA. Dis. Pom. (Smi. 1935.)
MASONS BRONZE. Lrg. Sin. (Smi. Imp. 1936.)
MASTERPIECE. Pom. (Dor. 1935.)
MATADOR. An. (And. 1935.)
MATAWAN. Har. (U.S.D.A. 1938.)
MAUD DEAN. Inc. (Hill 1893.)
MAUREEN. An. (Totty 1936.)
MAUVEQUEEN. Jap. (Smi. 1928.)
MAUVE SAM CASWELL. Odd. (Gar.1938.)
MAYBELLE. Dec. (Totty; ? 1932.)
MAYELLEN. Sd. An. Har. (Smi. 1925.)
MAYFIELD SUNRISE. Dec. (Totty; Jon. 1933.)
MAYOR J. W. SMITH. Sin. (Totty; DeP. 1928.)
MAY SUYDAM. Dec. Lrg. Pom. (B.&A.)

CHRYSANTHEMUM, continued
MAY WALLACE. Com. (Smi. Imp. 1936.)
MCKINLEY. Har. (You. 1938.)
MCNIECE. Ref.
MEDITERRANEAN C. **C. corymbosum.**
MEFO. Inc. (Smi. 1926.)
Mefo. Spo. (P.F.; Gri. 1932.)
MEG. Lrg. Sin. (Totty; Dav. 1913.)
MEGAN. Com. (B.-S. 1924.)
MELBA. Sin. (Totty; DeP. 1928.)
MEMORIES. Pom. (And. 1940.)
MENSA. Lrg. Sin. (Totty; Dav. 1913.)
MENTOR. Har. (You. 1938.)
MERCURY. Kor. Sin. (Bris. 1934.)
MERIDA. Jap. Com. (Smi. 1927.)
MERSTHAM JEWEL. Sin. (Totty; Wells 1911.)
META I. BERGEN. Sin. (Totty 1930.)
MEUDON. Lrg. Flo. (Totty; Wells; Poc. 1914.)
MEUDON SURPRISE. Lrg.Flo. (Totty'20.)
M. GRAINIER. Sd.
MIDDAY. An. (And. 1936.)
MIDGUARD. An. (And. 1937.)
MIDNIGHT SUN. Inc. (Smi.)
MILDRED JAMES. Pom. (Jam. 1927.)
MILDRED PRESBY. Sin. (Totty 1919.)
MILLICENT PIPER. Lrg. Sin. (Totty; Wells 1917.)
MILLIE. An.
MILO ASTELL. Pot. Var. (Totty 1935.)
MILTON. An. (And. 1937.)
MIMICO. Pom. (Smi. 1918.)
MIMOSA. But. (B.&A.)
MINEWA. Com. (Smi. 1937.)
MINGONETTE. Jap. Odd. (1909.)
MINNEHAHA. Pom. (Totty 1936.)
MINNESOTA. Sin. (Smi.; Frey 1909.)
MINONG. Sm. Pom. (Smi. 1926.)
MINTA. Pom. (Smi. 1911.)
MINTJE. Dbl. Rou. (Smi. 1930.)
MINUET. Sin. (Gar. 1938.)
MIRABEAU. But. (B.&A.)
MIRAMAR. Pom. (Smi. 1918.)
MISS (*Anola*) WRIGHT. Inc. (Smi. 1917.)
MISS (*A.*) WISBY. Amb. (Totty; Jon. 1933.)
MISS (*B.*) HAMILTON. Dec. (B.&A.; Totty; Nonin 1916.)
MISS CHICAGO. Inc. (B.-S. 1928.)
MISS CLAY FRICK. Spo. (Totty 1907.) *Wm. Duckham.*
MISS (*Elvia*) SCOVILLE. Lrg. Flo. (Pier. 1916.)
MISS (*Emily*) MORRISON. Exh. (Totty; Poc. 1924.)
MISS EMMA. Lrg. Flo. (Farq.)
MISS (*Emma*) ROOPE. (Sco.; Jon. 1915.)
MISS (*Eva*) HUDD. Com. (Totty; Jon. 1933.)
MISS (*F.*) COLLIER. Ast.?
MISS (*Gladys*) WOODERSON. Ref. (Totty; Poc. 1922.)
MISS (*Grace*) DURKIN. Jap. Inc. (Totty 1916.)
MISS HAZEL. Sin. (Totty; Poc. 1926.)
MISS (*Helen*) ANDRE. Pom. (Pier.1920.)
MISS (*Helen*) BORMAN. An. (Totty1924.)
MISS HELEN FRICK. Inc. (Smi. 1904.)
MISS (*Helen*) TAIT. Har. (Totty; U.Ill. 1924.)
MISS ISABELLE. Sin. (Pier. 1915.)
MISS JOLIET. Pom. (Jep.; Mt.G. 1926.)
MISS (*Katherine*) SIMMONS. An. (Smi.; Frey 1909.)
MISS (*Mary*) ISABELLE. Sin. (Totty'28.)
MISS (*Mary*) POPE. (Totty Imp.; Godf. 1912.)

CHRYSANTHEMUM, continued

Miss (*Millicent*) Rogers. Exh. (Totty; Poc. 1924.)
Miss (*Nellie L.*) Parker. Exh. (Jep.; Mt.G. 1925.)
Miss Prim. Lrg. Pom. (C.-P. 1935.)
Miss (*Rita*) Mitchell. Exh. (Totty; Poc. 1925.)
Miss (*Ruth*) Bergen. Sin. (Totty 1917.)
Miss (*Ruth*) Twombley. Ref. (Totty; Poc. 1921.)
Mistletoe. Com. (Hill; Dor. 1914.)
Mite Nice. Com. (And. 1935.)
Mitzi. Pom. But. (Smi. 1922.)
Mlle. Jeanne Nonin. Inc. (Totty; Hill 1905.)
Mme. (*D.*) L'Argentage. (Dre.)
Mme. Drouard. Ast. (Totty; Wells'13.)
Mme. Marquis. (Totty; Nonin 1914.)
Model. Pom. (B.&A.)
Model of Perfection. Pom. (Dre.)
Modena. Pom. (Smi. 1933.)
Modernistic. Har. (You. 1938.)
Modesto. Inc. (Smi. 1896.)
Modesty. Sin. (Dre. 1934.)
Mohawk Chief. Com. Inc. (Smi. 1929.)
Mohican. Har. (Smi. 1938.)
Mojave. Sin. (Gar. 1939.)
Molly Godfrey. Sin. (Totty; Godf. 1927.)
Molly Hunt. Sin. (Totty; Jon. 1925.)
Molly Owens. Sin. (Gar. 1939.)
Molly Whitmore. Sin. (Pier. 1919.)
Mona. Sin. (Totty; U.S.D.A. 1931.)
Monadel. Pom. (Smi. 1937.)
Monarch. Inc. (Hill 1923.)
Monroe. Pom. (You. 1938.)
Monument. Spo. (Hill; Eng. 1932.)
Monument. Inc. (B.-S.)
Moonbeam. Sin. (Dre. 1934.)
Moonbeam. Har. (You. 1938.)
Moonlight. Sin. (Dre. 1934.)
Morningglow. Pom. (B.-S. 1926.)
Morocco C. **C. mawi.**
Morristown. Lrg. Flo. (Smi. 1911.)
Mother C. **C. indicum.**
Mother of Pearl. Pom. (Kra. 1939.)
Mother Sebree. Sin. (Gar. 1939.)
Mr. Allen. Com. (And. 1935.)
Mr. (*Chas.*) Seasongood. Jap. Inc. (Totty; Poc. 1926.)
Mr. (*F. S.*) Vallis. Lrg. Flo. (May; Hill; Smi.; Cal. 1903.)
Mr. Rux. Dec. (B.&A.)
Mrs. (*Adolph*) Haenicke. Har. (Kri. 1933.)
Mrs. (*A.*) Hiles. Sin. (Totty Imp. 1927.)
Mrs. A. Holden. Exh. (Imp.-Woo. 1937.)
Mrs. (*A. J.*) Staehlin. Com. Inc. (Smi. 1933.)
Mrs. A. Kramer. Sin. (Kra. 1938.)
Mrs. (*Albert*) Phillips. Sin. (Totty 1917.)
Mrs. (*Alex*) Laurie. Com. Inc. (Smi. 1930.)
Mrs. (*Alfred G.*) Wilson. An. (Totty; DeP.)
Mrs. (*Alice*) Burke. Exh. (Hill; Hill '23.)
Mrs. (*A. L.*) Warner. Exh. (Totty; Poc. 1923.)
Mrs. (*B.*) Carpenter. Sport of Mrs. Algernon. (Totty; Jon. 1926.)
Mrs. (*B. D.*) Spillman. Ref. Exh. (Totty; Poc. 1932.)
Mrs. (*B. S.*) Mechling. An. (Totty; Sch. 1935.)
Mrs. (*Calvin*) Coolidge. Sin. (U.S.D.A.)
Mrs. (*C. C.*) Mason. Exh. (Totty; Wells; Poc. 1915.)

CHRYSANTHEMUM, continued

Mrs. (*Charles*) Cleary. Sin. (Totty'19.)
Mrs. (*Charles C.*) Mickle. Sin. (Totty; Wells 1916.)
Mrs. (*Charles*) Fox. Jap. (Totty; Jon. 1926.)
Mrs. (*Charles H.*) Curtis. Lrg. Flo. Jap. (Totty; Poc. 1922.)
Mrs. (*Charles H.*) Peck. Jap. (Totty 1923.)
Mrs. (*Charles H.*) Stout. Pom. (Totty; Stout 1923.)
Mrs. (*Charles H.*) Totty. Lrg. Flo. (Totty; Wells; Hill; Smi.; Poc. 1909.)
Mrs. (*Charles W.*) Johnson. Jap. Inc. (Totty; Joh. 1920.)
Mrs. (*Chester*) Robinson. Pom. (Totty 1920.)
Mrs. (*Clifford*) Brigham. Sin. (Totty; Berg. 1922.)
Mrs. (*C. S.*) McKinney. Sin. (Totty 1922.)
Mrs. Darling. Sin.
Mrs. (*David*) Lloyd-George. Sin. Lrg. Flo. (Totty; Wil. 1921.)
Mrs. (*David*) Syme. Lrg. Flo. (Totty; Wells; Poc. 1910.)
Mrs. (*David*) Timmons. Sin. (Rit. 1929.)
Mrs. (*Dean*) Emery. Dec. (B.&A.)
Mrs. (*D. F.*) Roy. Com. Inc. (Totty; Poc. 1913.)
Mrs. (*E. D.*) Godfrey. Sin. (Totty; Wai. 1912.)
Mrs. (*Ed*) Harding. Sin. (Totty 1926.)
Mrs. (*E. H.*) Wells. Sd. (Totty.)
Mrs. (*E.*) Kershaw. Inc. (Totty 1921.)
Mrs. (*Ellen*) Mackay. Exh. (Totty; DeM. 1924.)
Mrs. (*Ernest*) Wild. Lrg. Flo. (Totty; Wells; Poc. 1914.)
Mrs. (*E.*) Roberts. Sd. (Wells 1907.)
Mrs. (*F. D.*) Roosevelt. Inc. (DeP.)
Mrs. (*F. E.*) Lewis. Exh. (Totty; Poc. 1925.)
Mrs. (*Felix*) Fuld. Exh. (Totty; Poc. 1925.)
Mrs. (*F. Gordon*) Dexter. Lrg. An. (P.&M. 1894.)
Mrs. (*F. H.*) Bergen. Dbl. Loo. (Berg. 1916.)
Mrs. (*F. Norris*) Collins. Sin. (Totty 1923.)
Mrs. (*Francis*) Bergen. Pom. Har. (Totty; Berg. 1916.)
Mrs. (*Frank*) Beu.
Mrs. (*Frank H.*) Traendly. Exh. (Totty; Poc. 1918.)
Mrs. (*Frank J.*) Tanher. An. (Totty'29.)
Mrs. (*Frank*) Wilcox. But. (Totty.)
Mrs. Fred G. Marshall. An. (Gar. 1938.)
Mrs. (*George*) Hunt. Jap. Inc.
Mrs. (*George*) Munro. Com. (Hill '24.)
Mrs. (*G. G.*) Mason. Ref. (Totty; Poc.; Wells 1913.)
Mrs. (*Gilbert*) Drabble. Lrg. Flo. (Totty 1912.)
Mrs. (*G. Lloyd*) Wigg. Lrg. Flo. (Totty 1913.)
Mrs. Godfrey. Colorado.
Mrs. Greening. Dec. (Totty; Wells 1913.)
Mrs. (*G. W.*) Wickersham. Lrg. Pom. (Totty 1922.)
Mrs. (*Harold*) Wells. Exh. (Totty; Wells 1932.)
Mrs. Harrison Craig. Dec. (Totty; Cra. 1907.)

CHRYSANTHEMUM, continued

Mrs. (*Harry*) Turner. Lrg. Flo. (Totty; Wells; Poc. 1912.)
Mrs. (*H.*) Craig. Dbl. Loo. (Totty 1917.)
Mrs. (*H. E.*) Kidder. Com. Inc. (Smi. 1930.)
Mrs. (*Henry*) Evans. Jap. (Totty; Poc. 1928.)
Mrs. (*Henry F.*) Vincent. Pom. (Totty; U.S.D.A. 1920.)
Mrs. (*Henry R.*) Rea. Com. (Smi.'35.)
Mrs. (*H.*) Harrison. Sm. Pom. (Totty.)
Mrs. Higgy. Pom. Sport of Loraine Meech. (G.F. 1935.)
Mrs. Hilda Hayward. Exh. (Muto 1940.)
Mrs. (*H. J.*) Ballagh. An. (Totty; DeP. 1929.)
Mrs. (*H. J.*) Jones. Jap. (Sco. Imp. Jon. 1914.)
Mrs. (*H. S.*) Firestone. Lrg. Flo. (Totty; Wells; Poc. 1918.)
Mrs. (*H.*) Shoebridge. Sin. (Totty; Wells 1916.)
Mrs. (*Jacob*) Wellauer. An. (Smi.; Frey 1909.)
Mrs. (*James*) Kelly. Jap. (Totty; Jon. 1926.)
Mrs. (*J. A.*) Miller. Jap. (Totty; Smi.; May 1905.)
Mrs. (*J. B.*) Menchin. Sin. (Totty; Jon. 1925.)
Mrs. (*J. C.*) Neill. Inc. (Smi. 1908.)
Mrs. (*J. E.*) Dunne. Jap. (Smi.; Hill; Totty; Wells; Poc. 1906.)
Mrs. Jeffries. Lrg. Flo. (Totty 1921.)
Mrs. (*J.*) Fielding. Dec. (B.&A.)
Mrs. (*J. G.*) Fetterman. Dbl. Loo. (Rit. 1926.)
Mrs. (*J.*) Gibson. Lrg. Flo. Exh. (Totty; Wells; Poc. 1916.)
Mrs. (*J. Leslie*) Davis. Inc. (Tur.; Totty; Call 1920.) *Pinkturner.*
Mrs. (*John A.*) Stewart, Jr. Sin. (Totty; Eve. 1916.)
Mrs. (*John*) Gilpin. Dbl. Loo. Qui. (Rit. 1928.)
Mrs. (*J. S.*) Roberts. An. (Smi. 1937.)
Mrs. (*Jules C.*) Leeds. Jap. (Totty; Poc. 1927.)
Mrs. (*J.*) Wells. Ref. (Smi.; Wells; Poc.)
Mrs. (*J. Willis*) Buhl. Lrg. Flo. (Totty; Wells; Poc. 1918.)
Mrs. (*J. Willis*) Martin. Dbl. Loo. Pom. (Totty 1925.)
Mrs. (*L.*) Birchard. Med. Pom. Dec.
Mrs. (*Louis B.*) Tim. Inc. (Totty; DeM. 1924.)
Mrs. (*Lou*) Thompson. Sin. (Totty; Godf. 1914.)
Mrs. (*Marcus A.*) Curry. Sin. (Totty; Koch 1927.)
Mrs. (*Mary*) Hooker. Pom. (Bris.)
Mrs. (*Max*) Behr. Sin. (Totty; Godf. 1918.)
Mrs. McColby. Pom. (U.S.D.A. 1937.)
Mrs. (*Morgan G.*) Bulkeley. Pom. (Bris. 1938.)
Mrs. (*Nellie*) Kleris. Lrg. Pom. (Totty 1919.)
Mrs. Nellie (*T.*) Ross. Com. Inc. (Smi. 1925.)
Mrs. (*N. G.*) Moore. Pom. (Smi. Gasu. 1935.)

CHRYSANTHEMUM, continued
Mrs. (*O. H.*) Kahn. Lrg. Flo. (Totty; Wells; Poc. 1909.)
Mrs. (*Owen*) Winston. Jap. An. (Totty.)
Mrs. (*Paul*) Moore. Lrg. Flo. (Totty; Poc.; Wells 1914.)
Mrs. Peary. Lrg. Flo. (Farq.)
Mrs. Phil Page. Aladdin.
Mrs. Porter. Lrg. Flo. (Farq.)
Mrs. (*R. C.*) Pulling. Lrg. Flo. (Totty; Jon. 1914.)
Mrs. (*R. Hooper*) Pearson. Dec. (Smi. S.; Dav. 1907.)
Mrs. (*R. M.*) Calkins. Com. (Smi.'26.)
Mrs. Roberts. Ast. (Dre.)
Mrs. (*Roland*) Voight. Pom. (Totty; Fer. 1923.)
Mrs. Roswell Easton. Pom. (Totty 1937.)
Mrs. (*Sam P.*) Rotan. Har. (Dre. 1938.)
Mrs. Shimmins. Lrg. An. (Smi.)
Mrs. Stephen Van Hoesen. Pom. (Totty 1938.)
Mrs. (*T. W.*) McNeice. Ref. (Hill; Smi. S.; Brun. 1904.)
Mrs. (*U. P.*) Hedrick. Lrg. Sin. Smi. (N.Y.E.S. 1918.)
Mrs. (*Ward E.*) Olney. Exh. (Totty; Poc. 1926.)
Mrs. (*W. C.*) Emmett. Exh. (Totty; Poc. 1923.)
Mrs. (*W.*) Dennis. Exh. (Totty; Wells; Poc. 1918.)
Mrs. (*W. E.*) Buckingham. Sin. Sd. (Totty; Wells 1917.)
Mrs. (*W.E.*) Chipman. Sin. (Totty '26.)
Mrs. (*W. E.*) Tricker. Exh. (Totty; Wells 1913.)
Mrs. (*W. H.*) Waite. Sin. (Totty; Wai. 1918.)
Mrs. (*W.H.*) Walker. Exh. (Sco.1915.)
Mrs. (*William*) Thaw, Jr. Com. Inc. (B.-S. 1935.)
Mrs. Will Lake. Har. (F.W. 1937.)
Mrs. (*Woodrow*) Wilson. Lrg. Flo. (Hill; U.S.D.A. 1921.)
Mrs. (*W. J.*) Engel. Sport. of G. Pearson. (Engel; Pea. 1931.)
Mrs. W. W. Waterston. Odd. (Gar. 1938.)
Mt. Etna. Inc. (And. 1936.)
Muldoon. Dbl. Rou. Har. Pom. (Smi. 1931.)
Muriel. Pom. (Smi. 1936.)
Murillo. Har. Dec. (Smi. 1925.)
Muskogee. Har. (U.S.D.A. 1938.)
Muskoka. Pom. Dis. (Smi. 1921.)
Mycon C. **C. myconis.**
Myers Perfection. But. (Totty.)
My Michigan. Inc. (Smi. 1924.)
My Pride. Pom.
Nacola. Har. (Smi. 1936.)
Nacora. Dbl. Loo. Sin. (Smi. 1926.)
Nadia. Pom. An. (Smi. 1924.)
Nadine. Lrg. Flo. (Totty; Poc. 1922.)
Nagirroc. Lrg. Flo. (Totty; Poc. 1917.) *Golden Champion.*
Nagona. Sin. (McL. 1940.)
Nagoya. Ref. (Smi. 1899.)
Nakota. Lrg. Flo. (Smi. 1913.)
Nancy Copeland. Har. (Bris. 1937.)
Nancy Sanford. Inc. (Smi. 1926.)
Naomah. Inc. (Smi. 1910.)
Naponee. Lrg. Flo. (Smi. 1918.)
Nartica. Har. (DeP. 1938.)
Natick. Pot. Var. (1927.)

CHRYSANTHEMUM, continued
Natoma. Sin. (Gar. 1940.)
Navada. Pom. (Smi. 1924.)
Nellie Blake. Dec. Dbl. Loo. (Totty.)
Nellie Irwin. Pom. (Pier. 1920.)
Nellie Pockett. Jap. Inc. (Smi; May; Poc. 1901.)
Nellie Rainsford. But. (B.&A.)
Nelma Putnam. Pom. Sm. (Totty; U.S.D.A. 1920.)
Nemo. Bab. (Smi. 1925.)
Neo. Har. (You. 1938.)
Neola. Pom. (Smi. 1915.)
Nerissa. Lrg. Flo. (Smi. 1914.)
Netty. Pom. (Pre. 1925.)
New Gold. An. (And. 1937.)
NewJersey. Exh. (Hill 1923.)
New Philadelphia. Pom. (You. 1938.)
NewYork. Pom. (Pier. 1922.)
Niagara. Exh. Inc. (Hill 1932.)
Nightingale. Spi. (Imp. from Japan 1940.)
Nina Blick. Dec. (Pier.)
Nio. But. (Smi. 1906.)
Niobe. Kor. Sin. (Dre. 1936.)
Nioto. Inc. (DeP.)
Niphetos. Com. (Hill 1917.)
Nippon. Pom. (Totty 1916.)
Nippon Oxeyedaisy. **C. nipponicum.**
Nita. Sin. (Gar. 1938.)
Nivelle C. **C. nivellei.**
Niveus. Jap. (Smi. 1893.)
Niza. Pom. (Smi. 1915.)
Nokomis. Pot. An. (Smi. 1925.)
Nokomis. Dbl. (C.-P. 1936.)
Nordi. Pom. (Smi. 1916.)
Norine. Pom. (Smi. 1925.)
Norma. An. (Totty; DeP. 1929.)
Normandie. Dec. Dbl. Loo. (Smi. Imp.; Nonin 1909.)
Normandie. Spo. (Nor.; Pier. 1917.)
Normandie Gold. Pom. (Pier. 1922.)
Normandie Pearl. Pom. (Pier. 1919.)
Norrine. Pom.
North Cape. Har. (Sty. 1939.)
Noveltie. An.
November Bride. Pom. (Muto 1940.)
November Glow. Jap. Inc. (Smi. 1918.)
Nubian. Pom. (B.-S. 1928.)
Nuggets. Sm. Pom. (B.-S. 1922.)
Nunobiki. Odd. (Sun. 1940.)
Nysa. Kor. Sin. (Dre. 1936.)
Oakleaf. Inc. Sport of Gladys Pearson. (Bin. 1931.)
Oconto. Lrg. Flo. Dbl. Loo. (Smi. 1914.)
Octararo. Har. (Smi. 1935.)
October Dawn. Dbl. Loo. (Bris. 1930.)
October Frost. Lrg. Flo. (Smi. 1906.)
October Girl. Har. Dec. (Bris. 1930.)
October Glow. Com. (And. 1935.)
October Gold. Dbl. Loo. (Wells 1913.)
October Herald. Lrg. Flo. Com. (Smi. 1917.)
October King. Jap. Inc. (Totty; Duc. 1917.)
October Maple. Odd. (Sun. 1940.)
October Pride. Com. (And. 1938.)
October Queen. Lrg. Flo. (Smi. 1916.)
October Rose. Com. Inc. (B.-S. 1925.)
Odessa. Inc. (Smi. 1914.)
Ohio State. Pom. An. (Hill; Engle '33.)
Okeda. Exh. Inc. (Smi. 1933.)
Okitsu. Odd. (Imp. 1938.)
Oldgold. Sin. (Brun. 1905.)
Oldgold. Sin. (Vau.; U.Ill. 1921.)

CHRYSANTHEMUM, continued
Old Gold. Har. (You. 1938.)
Old Homestead. Jap. Lrg. Flo. Har. Med. (May; May 1893.)
Oldrose. An. (Totty; Sch. 1917.)
Oldrose. Com. Inc. (B.-S. 1931.)
Olga. Har. (Smi. 1932.)
Olive. Exh. (Totty; Poc. 1923.)
Olivia. Pom. (Smi. 1927.)
Olivia. Pom. (B.-S.)
Olivia Post. Sin. (Lin. 1938.)
Oliviette. Exh. (Smi. 1930.)
Onargo. Pom. (Smi.)
Oneta. Ref. Pot. (Smi. 1932.)
Oo-Loo-Loo. Exh. (Sey. 1937.)
Opal. Dbl. (Dre. 1934.)
Opal. Har. (Dre. 1935.)
Ora. Sm. Flo. (Farq.)
Orangeglow. An. (Totty; Sch. 1933.)
Orangeglow. An. (Smi.)
Orange Glow. Pom. (Bay S. 1940.)
Orange Perfection. Sd. (Dre. 1934.)
Orange Prince. Pom. (Smi. 1928.)
Orange Queen. Inc. (Smi. 1921.)
Orange Sunset. Har. (You. 1938.)
Orange Wonder. Har. (Dre. 1938.)
Orchid Beauty. An. (Totty; DeP.'35.)
Orchidgem. Sin. (Yod. 1938.)
Orchidqueen. Com. (B.-S. 1937.)
Orchid Tips. Har. (Kell.; Smi. 1935.)
Orea. Pom. (Smi. 1902.)
Orion. Kor. Sin. (Bris. 1935.)
Ortha. Odd. (Gar. 1939.)
Oscoda. Com. Inc. (Smi. 1933.)
Osho Yushi. Lavender Gown.
Otsego. Har. (U.S.D.A. 1938.)
Ottawa. Pom. (Smi. 1938.)
Otto Blum. An. (Gar. 1938.)
Ouray. Sm. Pom. (Smi. 1919.)
Oxeyedaisy. **C. leucanthemum.**
Pacific Rose. Sin. (Gar. 1938.)
Pacific Supreme. Jap. (Smi. 1908.)
Padoka. But. Dwf. Pom. (Smi. 1926.)
Pagosa. Pom. (Smi. 1928.)
Pagosa. Pom. (B.-S.)
Pale Moon. Kor. Dbl.
Pandora. Ref. (B.-S. 1920.)
Panola. Har. Sin. (Smi. 1936.)
Papillion. Spi. (Gar. 1939.)
Pasadena. Pom. (Kra. 1938.)
Passumpsic. Sin. (U.S.D.A. 1938.)
Patricia Grace. Jap. Tub. Petal. (Totty; Bert. 1928.)
Patsy Dowd. But. (Smi.)
Patsy Sturgis. Sin. (Bro. T. E. 1939.)
Patty. Jap.
Patty York. Pom. (Gar. 1939.)
Pauline Wilcox. Dbl. Loo. Pom. (Pier. 1920.)
Pawnee Scout. Sin. (And. 1932.)
Peach Blossom. Har. (You. 1938.)
Pearl. Pom. (Yod. 1940.)
Pearl Cluster. Sm. Flo. (Farq.)
Pearl White. Har. (You. 1938.)
Peggy (*Ann*) Hoover. Jap.
Peggy Poesch. Pom. (Engel 1939.)
Pelias. Pom. (Totty; Kni. 1936.)
Penelope. Pom. (Totty; Kni. 1936.)
Penguin. Pom. (DeP. 1938.)
Pepita. An. Jap. (Totty.)
Perfection White. Com. (Smi. 1913.)
Perfection Yellow. Com. (Put.; Dav. 1915.)
Perfecto. Pom. (Smi. 1938.)
Perle Chatillonaise. Dec. (Totty; Wells 1913.)
Perry Winifred. Sin. (Totty Imp.'27.)
Persia. Sin. (Dre. 1934.)

CHRYSANTHEMUM, continued
Persian Red. Sin. (Totty; Wil. 1932.)
Persian Rose. Pom. (DeP. 1938.)
Peter John. Ref. Sport of Thanksgiving Pink. (Smi. Imp. 1936.)
Peter Pan. Pom. (And. 1937.)
Peter Pearson. An. (Smi. 1926.)
Petite. Pom. Bab. But. (Totty; U.Ill. 1927.)
Petite Louise. Dbl. Loo. (Nonin 1914.)
Petit Enfant. Pom. (Gar. 1939.)
Petit Jean. Dbl. Loo. (Nonin 1914.)
Petit Jean. Sin. (Totty; Nonin 1915.)
Petit Louis. Har. (Totty Imp.; Wells 1913.)
Peto. Lrg. Flo. (Farq.)
Philip Ricci. Lrg. Flo. Jap. (Totty; Poc. 1921.)
Phintias. Pom. (Totty; Kni. 1936.)
Phryne. Com. (Totty; Lux. 1935.)
Phyllis. Inc. Exh. (Totty; Poc. 1925.)
Phyllis Bryant. Sin. (Totty; Godf. 1914.)
Phyllis Lawlor. Sin. (Totty 1919.)
Phyllis Tyson. Har. An. (Totty 1924.)
Piccola. Har. (You. 1938.)
Pigmy. Pom. (Smi. 1920.)
Pink Anemone. (Totty 1924.)
Pinkbeauty. Spi. Odd. (Totty Imp. 1928.)
Pinkbeauty. Sin. (Dre. 1929.)
Pinkbeauty. Inc. (DeP.)
Pink Cactus. Har. (You. 1938.)
Pinkchief. Com. Inc. (B.-S. 1932.)
Pinkcranford. Dec. (Totty Imp. 1914.)
Pinkdaisy. Sin. (B.-S. 1922.)
Pinkdame. Dbl. Loo. (Tho.)
Pink Dawn. Com. (Smi. 1938.)
Pinkdelight. Com. Inc. (Smi. 1931.)
Pinkdot. Pom. (B.-S. 1924.)
Pinkdot. Sarda.
Pinkfairy.
Pinkgarza. An. (Totty; Bird 1912.)
Pinkgem. Inc. (Smi.; Smi. 1912.)
Pinkglobe. Com. (Smi. 1933.)
Pinkglobe. Inc. (B.-S.)
Pinkie. Odd. (Sun. 1938.)
Pinklady. An. (Pier.; Hale.)
Pinklustre. Har. (Bris. 1937.)
Pink Matchsticks. (Gar. 1939.)
Pink Mensa. Sin. (Gar. 1939.)
Pinkmistletoe. (Smi.?)
Pinkpopcorn. Har. Pom. (Totty 1924.)
Pinkreliance. Com. (Smi. 1929.)
Pinkrosette. Com. (Hill 1921.)
Pink Sensation. Odd. (Sun. 1938.)
Pinksimplicity. Sin. (Pier.; Gre.C.'17.)
Pink Skiff. Sin. (Gar. 1939.)
Pinkspoon. Sin.
Pinksupreme. An. (Smi. 1930.)
Pink Thistle. Spi. (Gar. 1940.)
Pinktreasure. Inc. (Smi.)
Pink Treasure Island. Pom. (Muto 1940.)
Pinkturner. Mrs. (*J. Leslie*) Davis.
Pink Welcome. An. (Gar. 1938.)
Pirate Gold. Pom. (B.-S. 1939.)
Pirate Princess. Pom. (And. 1935.)
Pocketts Crimson. Lrg. Flo. (Totty 1909.)
Pocketts Surprise. Jap. Inc. (Totty; Hill; Smi.; Wells; Poc. 1909.)
Pohatcong. Har. (U.S.D.A. 1938.)
Polly Duncan. Lrg. Sin. (Totty; Wells 1913.)
Polly Rose. (Totty; Rose 1899.)
Pomona. An. (Smi. 1919.)

CHRYSANTHEMUM, continued
Portia. Sin. (Totty; Wells 1918.)
Portuguese C. **C. lacustre.**
Portula. Pom. (Gar. 1939.)
Poughkeepsie. Lrg. Flo. (Smi. 1911.)
Poultons Climax. Jap. (Totty; Jon. 1926.)
Prairie Gold. Pom. (And. 1935.)
Prairie Rose. Sin. (And. 1932.)
Pres. Hoover. Sin. (Totty; U.S.D.A. 1932.)
President (*John*) Everitt. Lrg. Flo. (Totty; Eve. 1917.)
President Taft. Jap. Inc. (Smi. 1909.)
Pride of Richmond. Com. (Hill; Hill 1928.)
Pride of Riga. But. (Gro. 1932.)
Pride of Sunnyslope. Com. (Sun. 1940.)
Pride of Tokyo. Odd. Jap. (Smi. 1931.)
Primrose. An. (Smi.; Dor. 1923.)
Prince Cushion. Har. (You. 1938.)
Prince Littlefield.
Princess. Sin. (Dre. 1934.)
Princess. An. (Smi.)
Princess Ileana. An. (Smi. 1927.)
Princess Teru. Exh. (Smi. 1931.)
Princeton. Pom. (Yod.; DeP. 1935.)
Priscilla. Inc. (B.-S. 1920.)
Private (*James*) Gresham. Ref. (Totty 1922.)
Private (*Merlie*) Hay. Ref. (Totty'22.)
Profusion. Sin. (Dre. 1934.)
Progress. Inc. (B.-S. 1920.)
Prosperity. Pom. (DeP. 1940.)
Provence. Dbl. Loo. (Nonin 1909.)
Provence. Ast. ? Dec. (Smi.)
Psyche. Kor. Sin. (Dre. 1936.)
Puck. Pom. (Totty; Kni. 1936.)
Puritan. An. (Smi.; Dor. 1923.)
Puritan. Sin. (Dre. 1934.)
Puritan Surprise. An. (And. 1935.)
Purple Caprice. Dec. (Totty 1913.)
Purpleking. Lrg. Flo. (Smi. 1918.)
Purple Princess. Odd. (Gar. 1938.)
Purplequeen. An. (Smi.; U.Ill. 1935.)
Purpurea. Pom. (Muto 1940.)
Pygmalion. Pom. (Totty; Kni. 1936.)
Pygmy Gold. Dwf. Pom.
Pyrenees C. **C. maximum.**
Quakerlady. Med. Pom.
Quakermaid. Jap. Inc. (B.-S. 1927.)
Queen. Sin. (Smi. 1914.)
Queen Cushion. Har. (You. 1937.)
Queen Marie. Exh. (Smi. 1927.)
Queen Mary. Lrg. Flo. (Totty; Wells; Poc. 1913.)
Queen of the Whites. But. (Totty; Sil. 1904.)
Quinola. Pom. (May 1901.)
Quiz. Har. (You. 1938.)
Radiant. Sin. (Smi.; U.Ill. 1935.)
Rag Doll. Har. (You. 1938.)
Rally. Pom. (And. 1937.)
Ramapo. Jap. (Cy.; Totty; Sch. 1912.)
Ramona. Har. (You. 1938.)
Rapture. Dbl. Loo. (Dre. 1934.)
Rapture. Har. (Dre. 1938.)
Rayless Costmary C. **C. majus tanacetoides.**
Rayonnante. Jap. Tub. (Totty; Lac. 1908.)
R. B. Mellon. Inc. (Totty; DeP. 1936.)
R. Collins. Sin. (Totty Imp. 1928.)
Reality. Com. Inc. (Smi. 1932.)
Realization. Pom. (Pol. 1935.)
Red Beauty. Pom. Sport of Dorothy Turner. (Bra. 1934.)

CHRYSANTHEMUM, continued
Redbeu. Dec.
Redbird. An. Sin. (Vau.; U.Ill. 1921.)
Red Bird. Har. (You. 1938.)
Red Doty. Pom. (Totty 1922.)
Redflare. Dbl. Loo. Pom. Dec. (Smi. 1933.)
Red Glare. Har. (You. 1938.)
Red Glitters. Com. (Muto 1940.)
Red Graf Von Oriola. An. (Gar. 1938.)
Redlight. Lrg. Sin. (Smi. 1911.)
Redlight. Ref. Pot. Var. (1932.)
Red Majestic. Spo. Inc. (Totty; Lux. 1923.)
Red Melba. Sin. (Yod.)
Red Rolinda. An. (Yod.)
Red Rover. Sin. (Totty; Jon. 1933.)
Redskin. Kor. Sin. (Dre. 1934.)
Red Welcome. An. (Gar. 1938.)
Redwing. Har. (You. 1938.)
Redwings. Pom. (Smi. 1932.)
Reflexed Louisa Pockett. Lrg. Flo. (Totty; Wells; Poc. 1918.)
Regina. Com. (And. 1935.)
Reginald Godfrey. Sin. (Totty; Godf. 1926.)
Reginald Vallis. Jap. (Smi.; Totty; Wells 1907.)
Rena. Pom. (Totty 1919.)
Rev. (*Horace*) Bushnell. Pom. (Bris. 1938.)
Rev. M. Inglis. Jap. (Totty; Jon.'26.)
Rheingold. Har. (Sty. 1939.)
Rhoda. Sm. Flo. Pom. (Farq.)
Rhoda. Pom. (And. 1937.)
Richard Delafield. Sin. (Totty; Eve. 1916.)
Rich Gold. Pom. (And. 1939.)
Richmond. Com. (Hill 1917.)
Richred. Sin. (Totty 1929.)
Ridgewood. Sin. (Totty 1926.)
Riorita. An.
Rita. Pom. (Totty; Joh. 1913.)
Rita Clifton. Sin. (Totty 1938.)
R. Marion Hatton. Dbl. Dec. Har. (Bris. 1931.)
R. M. Calkins. Inc. (Smi.)
R. M. Grey. Hairy. (P.&M. 1894.)
Roberta Copeland. Har. Dec. (Bris. 1939.)
Robert Bacon. Sin. (Kra. 1938.)
Robert Wallace. Sin. (Totty 1937.)
Robin Hood. Pom. (B.-S. 1935.)
Robinson. **C. maximum** hv.
Rocket. Odd. (Sun. 1938.)
Rockford. Har. (You. 1938.)
Rock Gem. Har. (You. 1938.)
Rodell. Pom. (Smi. Imp. 1925.)
Rodell Improved. Spo. (F.F. Ehman 1935.)
Rodi. Pom. (Smi. 1915.)
Roi Deprecoces. Pom. (Bay S.)
Rolinda. An. (Hill; DeP. 1933.)
Romaine Warren. Dbl. Loo. (Pau.'17.)
Romanbronze. Pom.
Romangold. Inc. (Smi. 1911.)
Romantic. An. (Smi. 1937.)
Romany. Har. (Bris. 1937.)
Romola. Pom. Dis. (Smi. 1935.)
Rosabella. Com. (B.-S. 1940.)
Rosamund. Kor. Sin. (Dre. 1937.)
Rosanda. Lrg. Flo. (Smi. 1921.)
Rosa Raisa. Inc. (Smi. 1923.)
Rose a Dore. Pom. (And. 1938.)
Rose Betty. An. (Totty; DeP. 1929.)
Rose Charm. Com. Pom. (B.-S. 1924.)
Rose Chochard. Chochard Rose.

CHRYSANTHEMUM, continued
Rose Day. Lrg. Flo. (Totty; Poc. 1921.)
Rose Delight. Inc. (Smi. 1922.)
Rose (*F.*) Ricci. Sin. (1927.)
Roseglory. Com. Inc. (B.-S. 1930.)
Roseglow. Com. (B.-S. 1926.)
Rose Jewell. Sin. (Gar. 1938.)
Roselandia. Sin. (Muto 1940.)
Roselea. Pom. (Smi. 1931.)
Roselite. Har. (Gar. 1939.)
Rose Madder. An. (Totty; Sch. 1923.)
Rose Mandel. Inc. (Mand.)
Rosemarie. Com. Ref. (Smi. 1928.)
Rose Marie. Har. (You. 1938.)
Rose (*M.*) Daly. Sin. (Totty 1919.)
Rose Modernistic. Har. (You. 1938.)
Rosena. Inc. Exh. (Smi. 1924.)
Rose Pearl. Pom. (B.-S. 1940.)
Rose Perfection. Inc. (Smi. 1920.)
Rose Pockett. Jap. Inc. (Totty; Hill; Smi.; Wells; Poc. 1909.)
Rosequeen. Sd. (Dre. 1934.)
Roseroyal. An. (Smi. 1926.)
Rose Surprise. Sin. (Gar. 1938.)
Rose Trevenna. But. Pom. (Totty; Wells 1907.)
Roseus. Pom. (Smi. 1937.)
Rose Walker. Inc. (Totty; Wells '17.)
Rosie. Dec. (Pier.)
Rosinante. Pom. (Dre.)
Rosydawn. Pom. (Smi. 1926.)
Rosy Dot. Pom. (Smi. 1938.)
Rosygem. Har. Dec. (Smi. 1932.)
Rosymaid. Sin. (Dre. 1934.)
Roszika. Dbl. Har. Pom. (Smi. 1934.)
Roupel Beauty. Lrg. Flo. (Farq.)
Rowenna. Pom. (Smi. 1924.)
Roxie. Pom. (You. 1938.)
Royal. Har. (Gar. 1938.)
Royalmahogany. Har. (Kell.; Smi. 1935.)
Royalqueen. Pom. (Smi. 1933.)
Royalred. Har. (Kell.; T. N.)
Rubyqueen. Sin. (Sco.; Imp.; Jon.'14.)
Rufus. Sm. Flo. (Farq.)
Ruth. Sm. Pom. (Joh. 1913.)
Ruth Bergen Dort. Dec. (1932.)
Ruth C. Dennison. Sin. (Totty 1924.)
Ruth Cumming. Dec. Har. Dbl. Loo. (Pier. 1920.)
Ruth (*E.*) Adams. Sin. (Totty 1926.)
Ruth Hatton. Pom. Dec. (Bris. 1930.)
Saladin. Har. (Bris. 1938.)
Sally. Har. (You. 1938.)
S. A. Naceur Bey. Inc. Jap. (Smi.; Hill; Cal. 1908.)
San Antonio. Pom. (Kra. 1940.)
San Carlos. Sin. (Kra. 1940.)
San Diego. Pom. (Kra. 1940.)
Sandra. Har. (Smi. 1938.)
San Gabriel. Spi. (Sun. 1940.)
San Marino. Spi. (Sun. 1940.)
Sappho. Kor. Sin. (Dre. 1936.)
Sarah. Sin. (Totty 1924.)
Sarah Fisher. Pom. (Pat. 1927.)
Sarah Townsend. Pom. (Pier. 1922.)
Saranac. Har. (Smi. 1935.)
Sarda. Pom. (Smi. 1933.) *Pinkdot.*
Sardi Vorro. Pom. (Totty 1921.)
Satisfaction. Lrg. An.
Saturn. Har. Sin. (Bris. 1936.)
Savanta. Pot. Var. Pom. (Smi. 1931.)
Savina. Dbl. Loo. Pom. (Smi. 1925.)
Seagull. Pom. (B.-S. 1932.)
Seashell. Sin. (U.S.D.A. 1926.)
Secretary H. Mortimer Brockway. An. (And. 1940.)
Secretary Nehrling. Inc. (Smi.)

CHRYSANTHEMUM, continued
Selaginoides. **C. parthenium** hv.
Seminole. Har. (U.S.D.A. 1938.)
Seminole Chief. Exh. (Smi. 1926.)
Sensation. Sin. (Dre. 1935.)
Sepia Prince. Odd. (Sun. 1938.)
September Gem. Sin. (Totty 1927.)
September Queen. Dbl. Loo. Har. Dec. (Smi. 1920.)
Sequoia. Har. (Dre. 1938.)
Sergeant (*Wm. E.*) Young. **Lrg. Flo.** (Totty 1919.)
Seven Oaks. Carrie.
Shaker Lady. Med. Pom. (Totty 1921.)
Shasta. An. (B.-S. 1940.)
Shastadaisy. **C. maximum** hv.
Sheila. Pom. (Smi. 1930.)
Sheilah. Pom. (B.-S. 1939.)
Shenandoah. Har. (You. 1938.)
Shirley. Sin. (Gar. 1938.)
Shirley Anderson. Sin. (And. 1932.)
Shirley Pride. Exh. Dbl. Loo. (Woo. Imp.)
Shirly. Sin. (Dre. 1932.)
Sidney Mitchell. Pom. (Totty 1919.)
Siegfried. Har. (Sty. 1939.)
Silverball. Med.Pom.Dis. (Smi.1928.)
Silverbells. Pom. (B.-S. 1937.)
Silverdawn. Com. Inc. (Totty; DeP. 1931.)
Silver Dollar. (Smi. 1938.)
Silver Emblem. (DeP. 1940.)
Silverking. Ref. (Smi. 1915.)
Silversheen. Com. Inc. (Smi. 1925.)
Silverstar. Pom. (Smi. 1931.)
Silverstar. An. (Totty; DeP. 1932.)
Silvertips. Pom. (B.-S. 1930.)
Sincerity. An. (And. 1937.)
Sipper. An. (And. 1937.)
Sir (*E.*) Letchworth. Lrg. Flo. (Totty; Wells 1920.)
Sir Michael. Lrg. Flo. (Farq.)
Skibo. Med. Pom. But. (Smi. 1905.)
Smith Advance. Lrg. Flo. (Smi.)
Smith Cameo. Inc. (Smi.)
Smith Imperial. Inc. (Smi. 1917.)
Smiths Brilliant. Ref. (Smi. 1927.)
Smiths Challenge. Inc. (Smi. 1928.)
Smiths Early White. Ref. Inc. (Smi. 1931.)
Smiths Enchantress. Ref. (Smi. 1925.)
Smith Sensation. Inc. (Smi. 1912.)
Smiths Innocence. An. (Smi.)
Smiths Late White. Jap. Inc. (Smi. (1926.)
Smiths Peerless. Com.Inc.(Smi.1924.)
Smiths Purity. An. (Smi. 1928.)
Smiths Superlative. Ref. (Smi. 1932.)
Smith Sublime. Inc. (Smi. 1920.)
Snappy. Sd. (Dre. 1934.)
Snowater. Sp. Pet. (Hen. 1935.)
Snowbank. Lrg. Pom.
Snowbird. Lrg. Pom. Dis. (Smi. 1931.)
Snowbound. Com. (B.-S. 1925.)
Snowcloud. Pom. (B.-S. 1933.)
Snowcrest. Pom. (B.-S. 1922.)
Snowdrift. Med. Pom. (Spa. 1888.)
Snowdrift. Dbl. (Dre. 1934.)
Snowdrop. Sm. Pom. (Int. Hal. 1890.)
Snowflake. Lrg. Sin. (Totty 1914.)
Snowstar. Sin. (Hen. 1935.)
Snowwhite. Com.Ref.Inc. (B.-S.1924.)
Solonore. Pom. (DeP.)
Sonia. Har. (Smi. 1938.)
Sonoma. Har.Dec.Dbl.Loo. (Smi.1931.)
Sorona. An. (Smi. 1925.)
Source d'Or, Crimson. Dec. (Totty; Wells 1913.)

CHRYSANTHEMUM, continued
Source d'Or. Golden Feather.
Southampton. Exh. (Totty; Jon. 1933.)
Souvenier. Har. (You. 1938.)
Souvenir. Odd. (Sun. 1938.)
Spanish C. **C. hispanicum.**
Spanish Gold. Pom. (Totty; DeP.1935.)
Sparkler. An. (And. 1938.)
Spotless. Com. Inc. (Smi. 1936.)
Springfield. Com. (Lib.; C.C.F.1930.)
Spring Hill. Jap. An. (Totty.)
Stanley Ven. Sin. (Totty; Wells 1914.)
Stardust. Pom. (Sta. 1936.)
Star Dust. Sin. (Muto 1940.)
Stately White. Com.Inc. (B.-S.1935.)
Steffins Delight. Pom. (Ste. 1930.)
Stellaris. Kor. Sin. (Dre. 1937.)
St. Elmo. Lrg. Flo. (Farq.)
Stewart Smith. Sin. (Totty 1938.)
St. Louis Gold. Pom.
Stoplight. An. (Smi. 1929.)
Stormpetrel. Pom. (B.-S. 1925.)
Sue Sally Jones. Spi. (Sun. 1940.)
Sulfur C. **C. viscosum.**
Sulphur. Har. (You. 1938.)
Sulphur Frills. An. (And. 1936.)
Sultan. Kor. Sin. (Dre. 1937.)
Sunbeam. Inc. (Smi. 1920.)
Sunbright. Sin. (Dre. 1934.)
Sunburst. Har. (DeP. 1937.)
Sunflower. Sin. (Dre. 1934.)
Sunglow. Jap. Inc. (Smi. 1919.)
Sungold. Jap. Ref. (Smi. 1923.)
Sunkist. Har. Sm. Pom. (Smi. 1934.)
Sunlight. Sin. (Totty 1929.)
Sunlite. Sin. (Gar. 1939.)
Sunnyboy. Sin.Pom. (Yod.; DeP.1935.)
Sunny Boy. Pom. (Cor. 1937.)
Sunny's Beauty. Odd. (Sun. 1938.)
Sunnyslope. Com. (Sun. 1940.)
Sunray. Inc. (Smi. 1920.)
Sunset. Sin. Sport of Prince Littlefield. (Kra. 1936.)
Sunset. Pom. (Kra. 1938.)
Sunshine. Jap. But. (Totty; Wells '12.)
Suntan. Dec. (And.)
Supreme. Sin. (Totty; Wells 1918.)
Surprise. Lrg. Flo. (Hen. Fost. 1892.)
Surprise. Lrg. An. (Hill; Owen 1897.)
Susanne Miller. An. (A.B.G. 1931.)
Susanne Miller. An. (DeP.)
Susan Willard. Spi. (Gar. 1939.)
Susie. Har. (You. 1938.)
Susquehanna. Pom. (Bay S.)
Suwanee. Har. (U.S.D.A. 1938.)
Swamp C. **C. paludosum.**
Swan. An. (Yod. 1940.)
Sweet Auburn. Sin. (Totty; Jon.1925.)
Swiss C. **C. atratum.**
Sydney Mitchell. Med. Pom. (Totty 1919.)
Sylvan Tints. Com. (Smi. 1925.)
Sylvia. Lrg. Flo. (Farq.)
Sylvia Slade. Sin. (Totty; Hill; Wells 1910.)
Symphony. Har. (Bris. 1938.)
Symphony. An. (Muto 1940.)
Tachibana. Jap. Odd. (Totty; Jap.'18.)
Taft. Har. (You. 1938.)
Tagoya. Sin. (DeP.)
Tango. Pom. (And. 1939.)
Tansy C. **C. macrophyllum.**
Tasiva. Dbl. Dec. Dwf. Har. Loo. (Smi. 1928.)
Taxpayer. Sin. (Bea. 1930.)
T. Carrington. Lrg. Flo. (May; Poc. 1900.)
Tekonsha. Lrg. Flo. Com. (Smi. 1915.)

CHRYSANTHEMUM, continued
Tennyson. Sm. Flo. (Farq.)
Thalia. Kor. Sin. Sd. (Dre. 1936.)
Thanksgiving Bronze. Sin. (Smi.)
Thanksgiving Gem. Pom. (Smi. 1933.)
Thanksgiving Glory. Com. (Smi.'30.)
Thanksgiving Pink. (B.-S. 1921.)
Thanksgiving Queen. Lrg. Flo. (Smi. 1911.)
The Belle. An. (Smi.; U.Ill. 1922.)
The Chief. An. (Vau.; U.Ill. 1921.)
The Chief. Har. (Dre. 1935.)
The Czar. Pom. (B.&A.)
The Dean. Odd. (Totty; U.Ill. 1926.)
The Favorite. Pot. Var. (Totty; Jon. 1933.)
Thelma. Pom. (Totty 1919.)
The Melba. Sport of Louisa Pockett. (Totty; Poc. 1932.)
The Moor. Har. (Bris. 1937.)
The Peer. Com. (Smi. 1932.)
The Speaker. **C. maximum** hv.
The Titan. An. (DeP.)
The Torch. Sd. Dbl. (Dre. 1934.)
Thetta Quay Franks. Jap. (Totty; U.S.D.A. 1927.)
The Urchin. Dec. (Bris.)
Thor. Har. (You. 1930.)
Thorp. Har. (You. 1938.)
Thos. (*W.*) Pockett. Inc. (Poc.)
Thyra. Pom. (Smi.)
Tiger. Jap. Inc. (Smi. 1916.)
Tillie. Har. (You. 1938.)
Timothy Eaton. Jap. Inc. (Hill; Cra.; Hil. 1901.)
Tints of Gold. Dec.? Dbl.Loo. (Totty.)
Tip Top. Pom. (And. 1940.)
Titanic. Lrg. Flo. (Smi. 1919.)
Titian Beauty. Jap. An. (Totty 1917.)
Tobins Late Yellow. Inc. (Tob.)
Tokio Improved. Pom. (Gar. 1940.)
Tokyo. Jap. Ref. (B.-S. 1920.)
Tom Browne. Inc. (Smi.)
Tom Higginbottom. Com. (G. F. 1935.)
Tom Pearson. Pom. (Totty; DeP. 1936.)
Tom Preston. Sin. (Gar. 1939.)
Tonquin. Pom. (Smi. 1933.)
Tony. Pom. (Dre. 1929.)
Topaz. Pom. (Kra.)
Topknot. An. (Smi.)
Topsy. Lrg. Pom. (C.-P. 1935.)
Toth. Har. (You. 1938.)
Touchdown. Pom. (Som. 1937.)
Towantic. Com. (Smi. 1924.)
Trail Blazer. Sin. (And. 1932.)
Traveler. Pom. (Totty 1921.)
Treasure Island. Com. (And. 1934.)
Treasure Island. Pom. (Muto 1940.)
Treasure Trove. Har. (Bay S. 1940.)
Triomphe d'Or. Lrg. Flo. (Farq.)
Triumph. An. (Smi. 1926.)
Trojan. Sm. Flo. (Farq.)
Tronesta. An. (Smi. 1925.)
Turner Bronze. Inc.
Tuscoba. An. (Smi. 1926.)
Tuxedo. Ref. (Smi. 1892.)
Tuxedo. An. (Totty; Sch. 1933.)
Tyler. Har. (You. 1938.)
Unaka. Inc. (Smi. 1911.)
Unalga. Pom. (Smi. 1925.)
Uncle Dan. Sin. (Totty; Koch 1927.)
Unique. Spi. (Totty; Sch. 1933.)
Unique. Sin. Sd. (Dre. 1934.)
Unique. Jap. (Smi.)
Urith. But. (Totty.)
Usona. Pom. (Smi. 1927.)
Usona Bronze (Bronze Usona). Sport of Usona. (Smi. 1932.)

CHRYSANTHEMUM, continued
Utopia. Har. (You. 1938.)
Uvalda. Lrg. Pom. (Smi. 1919.)
Valencia. Sin. (Yod; DeP. 1935.)
Valeria. Har. (You. 1938.)
Varsity. But. Pom. (U.Ill.)
Vasco. Pom. (Smi. 1919.)
Vayenne. Pom. An. (Cy.)
Venus. Com. (B.-S. 1923.)
Venus. Kor. Har. Sin. (Bris. 1936.)
Vera Victoria. Pom. (Totty; U.S.D.A. 1929.)
Vermont. Inc. (Totty 1919.)
Verona. Dbl. Loo. An. (Smi. 1929.)
Veronica. Sin. (Totty 1917.)
Veronica. Har. (You. 1938.)
Vesta. Kor. Sin. Sd. Hyb. (Dre. 1936.)
Victoria. Har. (You. 1938.)
Victoria Mori. Sin. (Totty 1927.)
Victory. Lrg. Flo. Inc. (Smi. 1919.)
Viking. Har. (Sty. 1939.)
Viola. Dbl. (She. 1893.)
Viola. Pom. (May; May 1900.)
Virginal. An. (DeP. 1937.)
Virginia Holden. Sin. (Pier.; Mt.G. 1917.)
Vivian. Pom. (Smi. 1938.)
Vivian. Har. (You. 1938.)
Vivian Cook. Lrg. Sin. (Totty 1917.)
Vivian Martin. Pom. An. (Smi. 1921.)
Vivid. Har. Sin. (Dre. 1932.)
Volunteer. An. (Pier.; Pau. 1919.)
Vulcan. Kor. Sin. (Bris. 1935.)
W. A. Bilney. (Hill; Dav. 1925.)
Waco. But. (Smi. 1907.)
Wallanda. An. (Smi. 1932.)
Wally. Pom. (Totty 1937.)
Wanda. Lrg. Pom. (Smi. 1918.)
Warrior. Sd. Sin. (Dre. 1934.)
Washington. Har. (You. 1938.)
Weedot. Bab. Pom. But. (Smi. 1928.)
Weewah. An. Jap. (Totty 1917.)
Welcome. An. (Totty; U.Ill. 1926.)
Wells Crimson. Har. (Totty; Wells'13.)
Wells Excelsior. Sin. (Pier.)
Wells Late Buff. Sport of Wells Late. (1932.)
Wells Late Pink. Lrg. Flo. (Smi.; Totty; Hill; Wells; Poc. 1910.)
Wells Scarlet. Dec. (Pier.)
Wells White. (Totty Imp.; Wells '12.)
Wembly. Dbl. Loo. (Woo.)
Wendalia. Lrg. Flo. (Farq.)
Western Beauty. Pom. (Smi.; Totty.)
Westernking. Inc. (Smi. 1897.)
Westernstar. An. (And. 1937.)
Western Sun. An. (Muto 1940.)
W. H. Chadwick. Inc. (Raw. 1898.)
W. H. Evard. Inc. (Totty; Poc. 1929.)
White Anemone. An. (Ask. 1937.)
Whiteball. Pom. (Totty; Jon. 1933.)
White Beautiful Lady. An. (Muto 1940.)
White Berneita. An. Sport of Berneita. (A.B.C.; And. 1933.)
White Bonnaffon. Inc. (Smi. 1900.)
Whitecap. Dec. (Totty.)
Whitecaps. Pom. (B.-S. 1925.)
Whitechief. Inc. (B.-S.)
White Chieftain. Sport of Chieftain. Inc. (Hill; Hill; Dal. 1915.)
White Cluster. An. (And. 1939.)
White Countess. Ast. (Dre.)
White Cranford. Dec. (Pier.)
Whitedaisy. Sin.
White Distinction. Inc.
Whitedoty. Lrg. Pom. (Sco. 1916.)

CHRYSANTHEMUM, continued
Whiteeagle. Ref. (And. 1935.)
White Elberon. Inc. Sport of Elberon. (Keu. 1920.)
White Enchantress. Sport of Enchantress. (And. 1931.)
White Ermalinda. Pom. (Smi.)
White Feather. Har. (Totty; U.Ill.'24.)
White Gem. Pom. (And. 1937.)
White Godfrey. Sin.
White Grant. Exh. (Hill 1923.)
White Gull. Pom. (Smi. 1937.)
White Helen Frick. Inc. (Smi. 1910.)
White Izola. An. (Bebb.)
White Jewell. Pom.
Whitemagic. Har. Sport of Cameo Queen. (Kel.; Mayh. 1936.)
Whitemagic. Sm. Pom. (Can.)
White Matchsticks. Odd. (Gar. 1938.)
White Mensa. Sin.
White Midget. But. (Smi. 1920.)
White Mistletoe Imp. (Mistletoe, White Imp.). Spo. (Smi.; Har. 1930.)
White Mrs. Filkins. Dec. (Totty.)
White Nerissa. Sport of Nerissa. (Smi. Schen. 1935.)
White Norma. An. Spo. (Smi. 1935.)
White Pearl. Pom. (B.-S. 1940.)
White Popcorn. Pom. (Totty 1925.)
White Prince. Com. Inc. (Smi. 1925.)
White Seidewitz. Jap. Inc. (Hill; Knig. 1919.)
White Sensation. Odd. (Sun. 1938.)
White Surprise. Jap. (Smi. 1921.)
Whiteswan. Hairy. (Yosh. 1895.)
Whitethread. Fan. Jap. (Totty; Jap. Imp. 1928.)
White Wisteria. Sport of Fuji. (Totty Imp. 1928.)
Whittier. Inc. (Smi.)
W. H. Lincoln. Pot. Var. (Few. Imp. 1889.)
W. H. Waite Imp. Inc. Sport of W. H. Waite. (Smi. 1930.)
Wildfire. Pom. (DeP. 1938.)
Wilfreda. Jap. An. (Totty; Sch. 1917.)
Willa Templin. Exh. (Sun. 1940.)
William Didden. Inc.
William Hazelhurst. Inc.
William (*H.*) Waite. Lrg. Flo. (Totty; Poc. 1917.)
William McCabe. Odd. (Sun. 1938.)
William Rigby. Lrg. Flo. (Totty; Wells; Poc. 1916.)
William Sobey. Ast. Med. Pom. (Dre.)
William Turner. Inc. (Totty 1911.)
William Vert. Ref. (Totty 1914.)
William Westlake. But. Med. Pom. (Int.; Spa. 1893.)
Wilson. Pom. (You. 1938.)
Windlass. Lrg. Flo. (Farq.)
Windsor Gold. Inc. (Yod.)
Windsor Gold. Com. (Imp. 1938.)
Winnetka. Pom. Har. Ast. (Smi. 1914.)
Winnie Ann. Odd. (Sun. 1938.)
Winter Glow. Christmas Glow.
Wm. Duckham. Miss Clay Frick.
W. N. Rudd. Jap. (Jep. Mt.G. 1926.)
Woalfs Pink. Exh. (Totty; Poc. 1915.)
Woburn. Sin.
Wolverine. Dec. Har. Dbl. Loo. (Smi. 1923.)
Woodside. Exh. (Poc.; Totty 1915.)
W. Woodmason. Lrg. Flo. (Totty; Wells; Poc. 1910.)
Yanoma. Ref. (Smi. 1896.)

CHRYSANTHEMUM, continued
Yarrow C. **C. achilleaefolium.**
Yellow Advance. Ref. (Totty.)
Yellow Ambassador. Inc. Sport of Ambassador. (1935.)
Yellow Anemone. (Totty 1924.)
Yellow Arcadia. Pom. (Muto 1940.)
Yellow Armistice Day. (Muto 1940.)
Yellow Bacon. (Muto 1940.)
Yellowbird. Pom. (Smi. 1930.)
Yellow Blanche. An. (Yod.)
Yellow Caprice. (Totty; Smi. 1913.)
Yellow Chattanooga. Inc. (Smi.)
Yellow Chattanooga Imp. Com. (Yod. 1940.)
Yellow Chieftain. Sport of White Chieftain. (Totty; Shi. 1928.)
Yellow Cordova. Com. (Yod. 1938.)
Yellow Cranford. Dec. (Totty Imp. 1914.)
Yellow Daintymaid. Com. (Yod. 1938.)
Yellow Decemberglory. Inc. Sport of December Glory. (Smi.; Bro. '35.)
Yellowdot. But. Bab. (Smi. 1931.)
Yellowdot. Sport of Pinkdot. Pom. (Hill; Jab. 1933.)
Yellow Doty. Pom. (Muto 1940.)
Yellow Doty. Connie Dick.
Yellow Earlyfrost. (Totty 1910.)
Yellow Estrelita. An. (Yod. 1938.)
Yellow Favorite. Spo. (Hill Imp.; Jon. 1935.)
Yellow Fellow. Pom. (B.-S. 1925.)
Yellow Frost. Lrg. Pom. (Hill 1924.)
Yellow Garza. An. (Totty; Bird 1912.)
Yellow Garza Supreme. Sport of Garza Supreme. (B.R. 1931.)
Yellowgem. Sm. Flo. (Farq.)
Yellowgem. Pom. (Bris. 1932.)
Yellow Glorianna. Sport of Glorianna. (Totty 1924.)
Yellow Godfrey. Sin.
Yellowgold. Com. Inc. (B.-S. 1931.)
Yellowgown. Com. (Smi. Imp. 1936.)
Yellow Mefo. Spo. (Gri. S. 1933.)
Yellow Mefo. Inc. (Yod.)
Yellow Monument. Inc.
Yellow Muskoka. Lrg. Pom. Spo. (Smi. 1931.)
Yellow NewYork. Pom.
Yellow Normandie. Dec. (Pier. 1907.)
Yellow Normandie. Dbl. Loo. (Pier.'17.)
Yellow Pearson. Margaret Zang.
Yellow Pockett. Lrg.Flo. (Totty '21.)
Yellow Prince. An. (Totty; Sch.'17.)
Yellow Quaker Maid. Sport of Frank. (Frank 1933.)
Yellow Rolinda. An. (Yod.)
Yellow Silverstar. Spo. Pom. (Smi. 1935.)
Yellowstone. Com. Inc. (And. 1936.)
Yellow Supreme. An. (Naw. 1937.)
Yellow Triumphant. Dec. (Totty; Wells 1913.)
Yellow Turner. Inc. (Totty; Smi. Poc.; Nic.; Smi. 1916.)
Yolanda. An. (And. 1940.)
Youdath's Eggshell. Har. (You. 1938.)
Youdath's Pink Bouquet. Har. (You. 1938.)
Youdath's Pride. Har. (You. 1938.)
Youdath's Quilled. Har. (You. 1938.)
Youdath's Rose. Har. (You. 1938.)
Youdath's Vivid. Har. (You. 1938.)
Youdath's White. Har. (You. 1938.)

CHRYSANTHEMUM, continued
Youdath's Yellow. Har. (You. 1938.)
Yukon. Inc. (B.-S. 1925.)
Yuletide. Pom. (Smi. 1923.)
Yuletide White. Pom.
Yuletide Yellow. Pom.
Yuvawn. Pom. (Smi. 1929.)
Yvonne. Sin. (Totty; Eve. 1915.)
Yvonne. Bab. Pom. (Smi. 1936.)
Zaza. Dbl. Loo. Har. (Smi. 1931.)
Zelia. Dbl. Loo. Pom. (Smi. 1920.)
Zenobia. But. (May 1900.)
Zetha. Pot. Var. (Smi. 1927.)
Zoe. Pom. (B.-S. 1933.)
Zora. Pom. (Smi. 1915–6.)
Zoraida. Lrg. An. (Smi. 1899.)
Zoroka. Pom. (Smi. 1935.)

Chrysobac'tron hook'eri . . **Bulbinella h.**

CHRYSOBA'LANUS . . . Cocoplum
ica'co . . . . Icaco C.
—pellocar'pa (*C. pellocarpa*) Smallfruit C.

Chrysobot'rya odora'ta . **Ribes odoratum**

CHRYSOCO'MA
coma-au'rea . . . Goldhair-plant
lino'syris . . . **Linosyris vulgaris**

CHRYSO'GONUM . . . . Goldenstar
virginia'num . . . . . . Goldenstar

CHRYSO'MA . . . . **APLOPAPPUS**
fascicula'ta . . . . . . **A. eastwoodae**

CHRYSOPHYL'LUM . . . Starapple
africa'num . . . . African S.
caini'to . . . . . Cainito S. (*Cainito*)

This species furnishes the edible Starapple of commerce.

magalis-monta'num
olivifor'me . . . . . . Satinleaf S.

CHRYSOPO'GON

See GRASS GENERA.

CHRYSOP'SIS |w . . . . Goldaster
brew'eri . . . . Brewer G.
falca'ta . . . . Sickleleaf G.
folio'sa . . . . Leafy G.
gossypi'na . . . . Cottony G.
graminifo'lia . . . . . Grassleaf G.
his'pida . . . . Rough G.
maria'na . . . . Maryland G.
orego'na . . . . Oregon G.
stenophyl'la |w . . . Narrowleaf G.
villo'sa . . . . Hairy G.
—rut'teri . . . . Rutters H.G.

CHRYSOSPLE'NIUM |w Goldsaxifrage
alternifo'lium . . Alternateleaf G.
america'num |w . . . . American G.
beringia'num |w . . . . Bering G.
oppositifo'lium . . . Oppositeleaf G.

CHRYSOTHAM'NUS (*BIGELOVIA*) |w Rabbitbrush
al'bidus . . . . Alkali R.
bloom'eri . . . . **Aplopappus b.**
depres'sus . . . . Dwarf R.
grave'olens (*C. nauseosus g.; Bigelovia g.*) . . . . Greenplume R.
green'ei . . . . Greenes R.
how'ardi . . . . Howard R.
hu'milis . . . . Low R.
lanceola'tus . . . . . Lanceleaf R.
linifo'lius . . . . Flaxleaf R.
nauseo'sus . . . . Rubber R.
—grave'olens . . . . . **C. graveolens**

CHRYSOTHAMNUS, continued
nevaden'sis . Nevada Rabbitbrush
panicula'tus . . . . . . Desert R.
par'ryi . . . . Parry R.
pinifo'lius . . . . . Pineneedle R.
puber'ulus . . . . Downy R.
pulchel'lus . . . . . . Southwest R.
specio'sus . . . . Tall R.
stenophyl'lus . . . . . . Small R.
teretifo'lius . . . . . Roundleaf R.
turbina'tus
viscidiflo'rus . . . . . . Douglas R.
—pu'milus (*C. pumilus*) . . Low D.R.
—serrula'tus (*C. serrulatus*) Sawtooth D.R.
—tortifo'lius (*C. tortifolius*) Twistleaf D.R.

Chuckawallabush . . . **Halliophytum**
Halls C. . . . . **H. halli**

Chufa . . . . . . Flatsedge, Chufa: **Cyperus esculentus**

CHUKRA'SIA
tabula'ris . . Chittagong Chickrassy

CHUNCO'A . . . . . . **TERMINALIA**

Chuncoa is now regarded by most botanists as a subgenus of Terminalia. Unfortunately it has sometimes been confused with Buchenavia.

CHUSQUE'A . . . . Chusquea

See BAMBOO GENERA.

CHYLIS'MIA . . . . **OENOTHERA**

CHY'SIS

See ORCHID GENERA.

CIBO'TIUM (*CYBOTIUM*) . Cibotium

See FERN GENERA

CIC'CA . . . . . . **PHYLLANTHUS**
dis'ticha . . . . **P. acidus**

CI'CER . . . . Chickpea
arieti'num . . . . Gram C.

CICHO'RIUM . . . . Chicory
endiv'ia . . . . Endive
in'tybus . . . . Common C.
¢Rosy (*roseum*) hv.
¢White (*album*)

∞ Cicitrange . . . . . ∞ Citrange × **Poncirus trifoliata**

CICU'TA |w . . . . . Waterhemlock
bolan'deri |w . . . . . Bolander W.
bulbif'era |w . . . . Bulb W.
califor'nica . . . . California W.
cur'tissi |w . . . . Curtiss W.
doug'lasi . . . . Douglas W.
macula'ta |w . . . . . . Spotted W.
occidenta'lis |w . . . . Western W.
va'gans |w . . . . Tuber W.
viro'sa . . . . European W.

CIENFUGO'SIA (*FUGOSIA*).
hakeaefo'lia (*Fugosia h.*)

CIMICIF'UGA . . . . Bugbane
aceri'na . . . . **C. japonica**
america'na . . . . . . American B.
cordifo'lia (*C. racemosa c.*) Cordate B.
davur'ica . . . . Dahurian B.
ela'ta . . . . Tall B.
foe'tida . . . . Skunk B.
—sim'plex (*C. racemosa s.*) Kamchatka B.
japon'ica (*acerina; Actaea j.; Pityrosperma acerinum*) . . . Japanese B.
lacinia'ta . . . . Cutleaf B.

CIMICIFUGA, continued
racemo'sa COHOSH BUGBANE (*Richweed*)
—*cordifo'lia* . . . . . . **C. cordifolia**
—*sim'plex* . . . . **C. foetida s.**

CINCHO'NA . . . . CINCHONA
calisa'ya . . . . . . YELLOWBARK C.
ledgeria'na . . . . LEDGERBARK C.
officina'lis . . . . . MEDICINAL C.
pal'lida . . . . PALE C.
succiru'bra . . . . . . REDBARK C.

CINERA'RIA Hort. . . . **SENECIO**
The florists' Cineraria appear to be various hybrids of Senecio cineraria and S. cruentus.
grandiflo'ra . . . . **S. cruentus**
marit'ima . . . . **S. cineraria**
stella'ta . . . . **S. cruentus**

CINERARIA, COMMON . **Senecio cruentus**

CIN'NA . . . . WOODREED
See **GRASS GENERA.**

CINNAMO'MUM (*CAMPHORA*) CINNAMON
bur'mani (*burmanni*) . . . MALAY C.
campho'ra (*Camphora officinarum; Laurus c.*) . . . . . . CAMPHORTREE
cas'sia . . . . . . CASSIABARKTREE
culila'wan . . . CULIBAN CINNAMON
glandulif'erum (*Laurus glandulifera*) NEPAL CAMPHORTREE
loureir'i . . . . CASSIAFLOWERTREE
massoi'a . . . MASSOIA CINNAMON
peduncula'tum (*japonicum*) JAPANESE C.
tama'la . . . . HIMALAYA C.
zeylan'icum . . . . . CEYLON C.

CINNAMON . . . . **Cinnamomum**
CAMPHORTREE . . . . . **C. camphora**
CASSIABARKTREE . . . . . **C. cassia**
CASSIAFLOWERTREE . . . **C. loureiri**
CEYLON C. . . . . . . **C. zeylanicum**
CULIBAN C. . . . . . . **C. culilawan**
HIMALAYA C. . . . . **C. tamala**
JAPANESE C. . . . . **C. pedunculatum**
MALAY C. . . . . **C. burmani**
MASSOIA C. . . . . . . **C. massoia**
NEPAL CAMPHORTREE **C. glanduliferum**

CINNAMONFERN **Osmunda cinnamomea**

CINNAMONVINE . . . **Dioscorea batatas**

CINQUEFOIL . . . . **Potentilla**
ALBERTA C. . . . **P. pseudorupestris**
ALPS C. . . . . **P. frigida**
ANISELEAF C. . . . **P. pimpinelloides**
APENNINE C. . . . . . **P. apennina**
BAKER C. . . . . **P. bakeri**
BEAUTY C. . . . . . . **P. pulcherrima**
BICOLOR C. . . . . . . **×P. bicolor**
BIENNIAL C. . . . . . . **P. biennis**
BIGFLOWER BUSH C. **P. fruticosa grandiflora**
BIGFLOWER C. . . . . . . **P. fissa**
BLASCHKE C. . . . . **P. blaschkeana**
BLUELEAF C. . . . . **P. glaucophylla**
BREWER C. . . . . **P. breweri**
BROOK C. . . . . **P. rivalis**
BUCCOAN C. . . . . . **P. buccoana**
BURNET C. . . . . **P. sanguisorba**
BUSH C. . . . . **P. fruticosa**
CALABRIAN SILVER C. **P. argentea calabra**
CARPET C. . . . . **P. supina**

CINQUEFOIL, continued
CAUCASIAN C. . **Potentilla adscharica**
CHINESE BUSH C. **P. fruticosa albicans**
CLIFF C. . . . . **P. rupestris**
CLUSIUS C. . . . . . . **P. clusiana**
COLOMBIAN C. . . . . . **P. andicola**
CONTINENTAL C. . . . . . . **P. hirta**
CREAMY BUSH C. **P. fruticosa ochroleuca**
CREEPING C. . . . . **P. reptans**
DAHURIAN BUSH C. **P.fruticosa dahurica**
DETOMMAS C. . . . . **P. detommasi**
DOMBEY C. . . . . . . **P. dombeyi**
DOWNY C. . . . . . . **P. intermedia**
DRUMMOND C. . . . . **P. drummondi**
DWARF BUSH C. . **P. fruticosa pumila**
ELEGANT C. . . . . . . **P. concinna**
FANLEAF C. . . . . . **P. flabellifolia**
FARRER BUSH C. . **P. fruticosa farreri**
∞ FLORISTS C. . . . . . . **∞ P. hybrida**
FRIEDRICHSEN BUSH C. **×P. fruticosa friedrichseni**
GAY C. . . . . **P. jucunda**
GLAND C. . . . . . . **P. glandulosa**
GOLDEN C. . . . . **P. aurea**
GRIFFITH C. . . . . **P. griffithi**
HAIRY C. . . . . **P. villosa**
HAIRY NORWEGIAN C. **P. norvegica hirsuta**
HIMALAYA BUSH C. **P. fruticosa rigida**
HIMALAYAN C. . . . **P. atrosanguinea**
HOOKER C. . . . . . **P. hookeriana**
∞ HOPWOOD C. . . . **∞ P. hopwoodiana**
HORSE C. . . . . **P. hippiana**
HUDSONBAY C. . . . . . **P. dissecta**
KLEIN C. . . . . **P. kleiniana**
KURDISH C. . . . . **P. kurdica**
LADYSMANTLE C. . . **P. alchemilloides**
LANKLEAF C. . . . . . **P. stenophylla**
LARGE BREWER C. **P. breweri expansa**
LEBANON C. . . . . . . **P. libanotica**
LETTERPETAL C. . . **P. grammopetala**
LEVIER C. . . . . **P. levieri**
LITTLELEAF BUSH C. **P. fruticosa parvifolia**
∞ MACNAB C. . . . . **∞ P. macnabiana**
MANCHURIAN BUSH C. **P. fruticosa mandschurica**
MAROON C. . . . . . . **P. perfecta**
MARSH C. . . . . **P. palustris**
MATSUMURA C. . . . . **P. matsumurae**
MEYER C. . . . . **P. meyeri**
MONTENEGRIN C. . . **P. montenegrina**
MONTPELIER C. . . **P. monspeliensis**
NEPAL C. . . . . **P. nepalensis**
NIPPON C. . . . . . **P. cryptotaeniae**
NORTHWEST C. . . . . . . **P. gracilis**
NORWEGIAN C. . . . . . **P. norvegica**
NUTTALL C. . . . . **P. nuttalli**
OLDFIELD C. . . . . . **P. canadensis**
ORANGESPOT C. . . . . . **P. alpestris**
PACIFIC C. . . . . **P. pacifica**
PENNSYLVANIA C. . . **P. pensylvanica**
PETTY C. . . . . **P. pumila**
PLATTE C. . . . . **P. plattensis**
PRIMROSE C. . . . . . **P. chrysantha**
PURDOM BUSH C. **P. fruticosa purdomi**
PURPLE C. . . . . **P. purpurea**
PYGMY CLIFF C. **P. rupestris pygmaea**
PYRENEES BUSH C. **P. fruticosa pyrenaica**
PYRENEES C. . . . . . **P. pyrenaica**
RUBY UNDERSNOW C. **P. argyrophylla atrosanguinea**

CINQUEFOIL, continued
∞ RUSSELL C. . **∞ Potentilla russelliana**
RUSTY C. . . . . **P. cinerea**
SALESOV C. . . . . . **P. salesoviana**
SASKATCHEWAN C. . . . . **P. effusa**
SAXIFRAGE C. . . . . . **P. saxifraga**
SEVENLEAF C. . . . . **P. heptaphylla**
SHINY C. . . . . **P. fulgens**
SHOWY C. . . . . **P. speciosa**
SIBERIAN C. . . . . **P. gelida**
SILVER C. . . . . **P. argentea**
SILVERWEED C. . . . . . **P. anserina**
SINGLEFLOWER C. . . . . **P. uniflora**
SLIMLEAF BUSH C. **P. fruticosa tenuiloba**
SLIMSTEM C. . . . . **P. filipes**
SMALL NEPAL C. **P. nepalensis minor**
SNOWLINE C. . . . . **P. nitida**
SNOWY C. . . . . **P. nivalis**
SPANISH C. . . . . . **P. nevadensis**
SPRING C. . . . . **P. verna**
STAGHORN C. . . . . . . **P. multifida**
STRAWBERRY C. . . . . **P. fragiformis**
SULFUR C. . . . . **P. recta**
SUMMIT C. . . . . **P. propinqua**
SUNNY C. . . . . . . **P. grandiflora**
THURBER C. . . . . **P. thurberi**
TORMENTILLA C. . . . . . **P. erecta**
TRANSCASPIAN C. . . . **P. transcaspia**
TWIGGY C. . . . . **P. virgata**
TWOFORK C. . . . . **P. bifurca**
UNDERSNOW C. . . . **P. argyrophylla**
VARILEAF C. . . . . . **P. diversifolia**
VEITCH BUSH C. . **P. fruticosa veitchi**
VILMORIN B. C. . . **P. f. vilmoriniana**
WALTHERS C. . . . . . . **P. curviseta**
WARRENS SULFUR C. **P. recta warreni**
WHITE C. . . . . **P. alba**
WHITE CLIFF C. . . . **P. rupestris a.**
WINELEAF C. . . . . . . **P. tridentata**
WOOLLYFRUIT C. . . . . **P. eriocarpa**

CIPADES'SA
baccif'era

CIPU'RA . . . . CIPURA
martinicen'sis . . . . . **Trimeza m.**
paludo'sa . . . . TRINIDAD C.

CIRCAE'A . . . . CIRCAEA (*Enchanters-nightshade*)
alpi'na . . . . ALPINE C.
canaden'sis . . . . . . CANADIAN C.
latifo'lia . . . . BROADLEAF C.
lutetia'na . . . . PARIS C.

Cirio . BOOJAMTREE: **Idria; I. columnaris**

CIRRHOPET'ALUM
See **ORCHID GENERA.**

CIR'SIUM (*CHAMAEPEUCE*) ⱳ THISTLE
altis'simum ⱳ . . . . TALL T.
andrews'i ⱳ . . . . . . ANDREWS T.
arven'se (*Carduus arvensis*) ⱳ CANADA T.
—**hor'ridum**
—**integrifo'lium**
—**mi'te**
—**vesti'tum**
cilia'tum
cris'pum . . . . CURLY T.
diacan'thum (*Chamaepeuce diacantha*) SILVERLINE T.
dis'color (*Carduus d.*) . . . FIELD T.
drum'mondi . . . . . DRUMMOND T.

Hort. var.; HV. = horticultural variety (or varieties); sp. = species (singular); spp. = species (plural).
₵ = clon; × (as a prefix = hybrid; × (between scientific plant names) = crossed by; ∞ = polybrid; ⱳ = plant useful to wildlife.
See Glossary for definitions of clon, hybrid, and polybrid.

CIRSIUM, continued
ed'ule |w . . . . . . INDIAN THISTLE
erioceph'alum
folio'sum . . . . ELK T.
hill'i . . . . HILLS T.
lanceola'tum (*Carduus l.*) |w . BULL T.
mu'ticum |w . . . . SWAMP T.
occidenta'le . . . . . . WESTERN T.
—candidis'simum . SNOWWOOL W.T.
—coul'teri . . . . . COULTER W.T.
—venus'tum . . . . . SCARLET W.T.
pu'milum . . . . . . FRAGRANT T.
purpura'tum
syri'acum (*Notobasis syriaca*) SYRIAN T.
undula'tum (*Carduus undulatus*) WAVYLEAF T.
velenov'skyi . . . . VELENOVSKY T.

CISSAM'PELOS
parei'ra

CIS'SUS |w . . . . TREEBINE
See also allied genera **AMPELOPSIS** and **VITIS.**
ac'ida (*Vitis a.*) . . . . . ACID T.
antarc'tica (*Vitis a.*) . KANGAROO T.
capen'sis (*Vitis c.*) . . EVERGREEN T.
dis'color (*Vitis d.*) . . . BEGONIA T.
gongylo'des (*Vitis g.; V. pterophora*) MARBLE T.
hypoglau'ca (*Ampelopsis h.; Vitis h.*)
inci'sa (*Vitis i.*) |w . . . . IVY T.
oblon'ga (*Vitis o.*) . QUEENSLAND T.
quadrangula'ris (*Vitis q.*) WINGED T.
rhombifo'lia (*Vitis r.*) . VENEZUELA T.
sicyoi'des . . . . . WATERWITHE T.
stria'ta (*Vitis s.; V. sempervirens*) STRIPED T.

CISTAN'THERA
papaverif'era . . . . DANTA

CIS'TUS . . . . ROCKROSE
al'bidus . . . . WHITELEAF R.
—al'bus
algarven'sis . . **Halimium ocymoides**
∞ **canes'cens** (*albidus* × *villosus*) ∞ PURPLE R.
₵ALBUS. HV.
× **corbarien'sis** (*populifolius* × *salvifolius*)
A natural hybrid.
∞ **crispa'tus** (*crispus* × *villosus creticus*)
cris'pus . . . . . . WRINKLELEAF R.
∞ **cy'prius** (*ladaniferus* × *laurifolius*) ∞ SPOTTED R.
₵ALBUS. HV.
× **florenti'nus** (*monspeliensis* × *salvifolius*) . . . . . FLORENTINE R.
A natural hybrid.
∞ **glau'cus** (*laurifolius* × *monspeliensis*)
heterophyl'lus
∞ **hetier'i** (*ladaniferus* × *laurifolius* × *monspeliensis*) . . . . ∞ HETIER R.
The cultivated plant is presumably a clon of this polybrid.
hirsu'tus . . . . HAIRY R.
ladanif'erus . . . . GUM R.
—albiflo'rus (*immaculatus* Hort.) WHITE G.R.
—macula'tus . . CRIMSONSPOT G.R.
—petiola'tus . . . . . AFRICAN G.R.
laurifo'lius . . . . LAUREL R.
× **loret'i** . . . . LORETS R.
—albiflo'rus . . . . . WHITE L.R.
∞ **lusitan'icus** (*?hirsutus* × *ladaniferus*) ∞ PORTUGUESE R.
₵DECUMBENS. HV.

CISTUS, continued
monspelien'sis MONTPELIER ROCKROSE
∞ **ni'gricans** (*monspeliensis* × *populifolius*)
∞ **obtusifo'lius** (*hirsutus* × *salvifolius*)
parviflo'rus
∞ **platyse'palus** (*hirsutus* × *monspeliensis*)
populifo'lius . . . . . POPLARLEAF R.
∞ **pulverulen'tus** (*albidus* × *crispus*)
∞ **purpu'reus** (*ladaniferus* × *villosus*) ∞ ORCHIDSPOT R.
salvifo'lius . . . . SALVIA R.
∞ **skan'bergi** (*monspeliensis* × *parviflorus*) . . . . . . ∞ SKANBERG R.
∞ **vergui'ni** (*ladaniferus* × *salvifolius*) ∞ VERGUIN R.
villo'sus
—cor'sicus
—cre'ticus
—tau'ricus

CITHAREX'YLUM . . . . FIDDLEWOOD
berlandier'i . . . . BERLANDIER F.
frutico'sum (*cinereum* L., *not* Jacq.) FLORIDA F.
ilicifo'lium . . . . . . HOLLYLEAF F.
spino'sum (*cinereum* Jacq., *not* L.) SPINY F.
trista'chyum . . . . THREESPIKE F.

∞ CITRADIA . . . . **Citrus aurantium** × **Poncirus trifoliata**

∞ CITRANDIRIN . . **Citrus reticulata** × **Poncirus trifoliata**

∞ CITRANGE . . . . **Citrus sinensis** × **Poncirus trifoliata**

∞ CITRANGEDIN . . . . ∞ CITRANGE × ∞ KUMANDARIN

∞ CITRANGEQUAT . . . ∞ CITRANGE × **Fortunella** spp.

∞ CITRANGEREMO . . . ∞ CITRANGE × **Eremocitrus glauca**

∞ CITREMON . . . . **Citrus reticulata** × **Poncirus trifoliata**

CITRON . . . . **Citrus medica**
ETHROG C. . . . . **C. m. ethrog**
FINGER C. . . . . **C. m. sarcodactylis**
SOUR C. . . . . **C. m. acida**

CITRONELLAGRASS **Cymbopogon nardus**

CITRONMELON **Citrullus vulgaris citroides**

CITROP'SIS . . . . . CHERRYORANGE
angolen'sis . . . . . . ANGOLA C.
articula'ta . . . . . WESTAFRICAN C.
gabonen'sis . . . . GABON C.
—lacourtia'na . . . . KASAI C.
gilletia'na . . . . GILLET C.
latiala'ta . . . . IKONGU C.
letes'tui . . . . LETESTU C.
mirab'ilis . . . . . . IVORYCOAST C.
schweinfurth'i . . EASTAFRICAN C.
zen'keri . . . . CAMEROON C.

CITRUL'LUS |w . . . . . CITRULLUS
colocyn'this . . . . . COLOCYNTH
vulga'ris |w . . . . . . WATERMELON
—citroi'des . . . . . CITRONMELON

∞ CITRUMELO . . . . **Citrus paradisi** × **Poncirus trifoliata**

∞ CITRUMQUAT . . . **Fortunella** spp. × **Poncirus trifoliata**

CIT'RUS |w
For hort. var. of Citrus Fruits see **FRUIT AND EDIBLE NUT NAMES.** See also **CITRUS GENERA AND CITRUS HYBRIDS.**
aurantifo'lia (*limetta* in part) . . LIME

CITRUS, continued
auran'tium (*amara; bigaradia; vulgaris*) |w . SOUR ORANGE (*Seville O.*)
—myrtifo'lia . . . . MYRTLELEAF O.
berga'mia . . . . . . BERGAMOT O.
This is probably a hybrid, and not a natural botanical species.
celeb'ica . . CELEBES BITTERORANGE
delicio'sa . . . . **C. reticulata**
excel'sa . . . . . PHILIPPINE LEMON
gran'dis (*decumana; maxima*) . PUMMELO (*Pompelmous; Shaddock*)
hys'trix . . . . MAURITIUS BITTERORANGE (*Cabuyao*)
ichangen'sis . ICHANG BITTERORANGE
in'dica . . . . INDIA WILD ORANGE
japon'ica . . . . **Fortunella j.**
lat'ipes . . . KHASIA BITTERORANGE
limet'ta . . . . **C. aurantifolia**
limon' (*limonia*) . . . . . . LEMON
macrop'tera MELANESIA BITTERORANGE
—kerr'i . . . . KERRS M.B.
margari'ta . . . . . . **Fortunella m.**
max'ima . . . . **C. grandis**
—uvacar'pa . . . . **C. paradisi**
med'ica . . . . CITRON
—ac'ida . . . . SOUR C.
—eth'rog . . . . ETHROG C.
—sarcodac'tylis . . . . FINGER C.
micran'tha SMALLFLOWER BITTERORANGE
—microcar'pa . . . . SMALLFRUIT B.
mi'tis . . . . . CALAMONDIN ORANGE
no'bilis . . . . KING ORANGE
Dr. Swingle reports that this is probably the name of a hybrid.
—unshi'u (*C. trifoliata u.*) SATSUMA ORANGE
paradi'si (*C. maxima uvacarpa*) GRAPEFRUIT
reticula'ta (*deliciosa; C. nobilis d.*) MANDARIN ORANGE
The Mandarin includes the so-called Tangerine varieties of Orange.
sinen'sis |w . . . . SWEET ORANGE
tachiba'na . JAPANESE TACHIBANA O.
taiten'sis . . TAHITI O. (*Otaheite O.*)
trifolia'ta . . . . **Poncirus t.**
—unshi'u . . . . **C. nobilis u.**
vulga'ris . . . . **C. aurantium**

CITRUS GENERA AND CITRUS HYBRIDS

For the botanical treatment of Citrus genera and hybrids in this edition of STANDARDIZED PLANT NAMES the Editorial Committee is chiefly indebted to Walter T. Swingle, Bureau of Plant Industry, U. S. Department of Agriculture, who has given permission to extract names from the manuscript of his "The Botany of Citrus and Its Wild Relatives of the Orange Subfamily" (Chapter 4, Vol. 1, "The Citrus Industry," University of California Press, 1941). Dr. Swingle's monograph is the first complete write-up of the subfamily since 1861 and includes 2 tribes, 6 subtribes, 33 genera and 203 species. All of the genera and species are keyed out, with detailed descriptions and discussion, together with 50 text figures. Dr. Swingle feels confident that increasingly great attention will be paid in the near future to the use of wild relatives of Citrus and of Citrus hybrids for rootstocks. Many are of extraordinary interest because of special qualities, such as hardiness, drought-, saltsoil- and salt-spray-tolerance, depth and spread of root system, resistance to disease, etc.

CITRUS GENERA AND CITRUS HYBRIDS, continued
Afraegle . . . . **AFRAEGLE**
Atalantia . . . . . . **ATALANTIA**
Baelfruit . . . . **AEGLE**
Balsamocitrus **BALSAMOCITRUS**
Boxorange . . . . . . **SEVERINIA**
Cherryorange . . . . **CITROPSIS**
∞ Cicitrange
∞ Citrange × **Poncirus trifoliata**
∞ Citradia
Citrus aurantium × P. trifoliata
∞ Citrandirin
C. reticulata × P. trifoliata
∞ Citrange . **C. sinensis × P. trifoliata**
∞ Citrangedin
∞ Citrange × ∞ Kumandarin
∞ Citrangequat
∞ Citrange × **Fortunella spp.**
∞ Citrangeremo
∞ Citrange × **Eremocitrus glauca**
∞ Citremon . . . . **Citrus reticulata × Poncirus trifoliata**
∞ Citrumelo **C. paradisi × P. trifoliata**
∞ Citrumquat . . . **Fortunella spp. × Poncirus trifoliata**
Citrus . . . . **CITRUS**
Here belong Citron, Grapefruit, Lemon, Lime, Orange, Pummelo, etc.
Clymenia . . . . . . **CLYMENIA**
Desertlime . . . . **EREMOCITRUS**
∞ Eremolemon
Citrus limon × Eremocitrus glauca
∞ Eremoradia **C. aurantium × E. glauca**
∞ Eremorange **C. sinensis × E. glauca**
∞ Faustrimedin . . ∞ Kumandarin × ∞ **Microcitrus australasica**
Feroniella . . . . . **FERONIELLA**
Fingerlime **MICROCITRUS** (in part)
See also Wildlime.
Ghostlime . . **BURKILLANTHUS**
Glycosmis . . . . . **GLYCOSMIS**
Hardyorange . . Trifoliate-orange
Hesperethusa . . **HESPERETHUSA**
∞ Ichandarin
Citrus ichangensis × C. reticulata
∞ Ichangelo
C. grandis × C. ichangensis
Jasminorange . . . . . **MURRAYA**
∞ Kumandarin
Citrus reticulata × Fortunella spp.
Kumquat . . . . . **FORTUNELLA**
∞ Lemandarin
Citrus limon × C. reticulata
∞ Lemonime **C. aurantifolia × C. limon**
Limeberry . . . . . **TRIPHASIA**
∞ Limequat . . . **Citrus aurantifolia × Fortunella spp.**
Luvunga . . . . **LUVUNGA**
Merope . . . . **MEROPE**
Merrillia . . . . . . **MERRILLIA**
Micromelum . . . **MICROMELUM**
Monanthocitrus
MONANTHOCITRUS
Orangeaster . **PLEIOSPERMIUM**
∞ Orangequat . **Citrus nobilis unshiu × Fortunella spp.**
Oxanthera . . . . **OXANTHERA**
Pamburus . . . . . . **PAMBURUS**
Paramignya . . . **PARAMIGNYA**
∞ Procimequat
Fortunella hindsi × ∞ Limequat
∞ Rofaustrime . . **Microcitrus australasica × M. australis**
Swamporange . . . **LIMNOCITRUS**
Tabog . . . . **SWINGLEA**
∞ Tangelo **Citrus paradisi × C. reticulata**

CITRUS GENERA AND CITRUS HYBRIDS, continued
∞ Tangerine . . **Citrus reticulata** HV.
∞ Tangor . **C. reticulata × C. sinensis**
Trifoliate-orange (*Hardyorange*)
PONCIRUS
Wampee . . . . **CLAUSENA**
Wenzelia . . . . **WENZELIA**
Wildlime . **MICROCITRUS** (in part)
See also Fingerlime.
Woodapple . . . . **FERONIA**

CLADAN'THUS
ara'bicus (*Anthemis arabica*)

CLA'DIUM . . . . **MARISCUS**

CLADO'NIA
rangiferi'na . . . . . Reindeermoss

CLADO'PHORA lw
arc'ta
callico'ma
frac'ta
glomera'ta
grac'ilis
rupes'tris

CLADOTHAM'NUS
pyrolaeflo'rus

CLADRAS'TIS . . . . . Yellowwood
amuren'sis . . . . **Maackia a.**
lute'a (*tinctoria; Virgilia l.*)
American Y.
platycar'pa (*Sophora p.*) . Japanese Y.
sinen'sis . . . . Chinese Y.
wil'soni . . . . Wilson Y.

Clammyweed . . . . **Polanisia**
Roughseed C. . . . **P. trachysperma**
Stinking C. . . . . . **P. graveolens**

CLARK'IA (*EUCHARIDIUM*) Clarkia
brew'eri (*Eucharidium b.*)
concin'na (*Eucharidium concinnum; E. grandiflorum*)
concin'na . **Eucharidium concinnum**
el'egans (*unguiculata*) . . . . Rose C.
—al'ba
pulchel'la

Clary . . . Sage, Clary: **Salvia sclarea**

CLAUDO'PUS . . . . . . Claudopus
ni'dulans . . . . Nestcap C.

CLAUSE'NA (*CLAUCENA*) . Wampee
anisum-o'lens . . . . . Aniseoil W.
denta'ta
—dul'cis . . . . India W.
lan'sium (*punctata; wampi*)
Chinese W.

CLAV'ICEPS . . . . Claviceps
purpu'rea . . . . Ergot C.

CLAVI'JA
longifo'lia (*ornata*)

Clawfern . . . . **Onychium**
Japanese C. . . . . . **O. japonicum**

CLAYTO'NIA lw . . . . Springbeauty
carolinia'na . . . . . . Carolina S.
chamisso'i (*Montia c.*) . . Water S.
lanceola'ta . . . . . . Lanceleaf S.
megarrhi'za . . . . Alpine S.
nevaden'sis (*Montia n.*) . Nevada S.
parvifo'lia (*Montia p.*) . Littleleaf S.
perfolia'ta (*Montia p.*) lw
Minerslettuce
tubero'sa . . . . Tuber S.
virgin'ica . . . . Virginia S.

Clearweed . . . . **Pilea**
Artillery C. . . . . . **P. microphylla**
Canada C. . . . . **P. pumila**
Creepingcharley C.
P. nummulariaefolia

CLEISTOCAC'TUS
See **CACTUS GENERA.**

CLEISTOCA'LYX Blume **SYZYGIUM**

CLEISTOCA'LYX Steud.
RHYNCHOSPORA

CLEISTOG'ENES
See **GRASS GENERA.**

CLEM'ATIS (*ATRAGENE; VIORNA*)
Clematis
acutan'gula . . . . . Wingsepal C.
addiso'ni (*Viorna a.*) . . Addison C.
aethusifo'lia . . . . . Longplume C.
—latisec'ta
afolia'ta
albico'ma
alpi'na (*Atragene a.*) . . . Alpine C.
—carunculo'sa . . . **C. chiisanensis c.**
—occidenta'lis . . . **C. pseudoalpina**
—sibir'ica (*C. a. alba* Hort.; *C. sibirica; Atragene s.*)
anemoniflo'ra . . . . . . **C. montana**
angustifo'lia . . . . Narrowleaf C.
apiifo'lia . . . . October C.
—obtusidenta'ta
arista'ta . . . . Australian C.
—den'nisae (*C. sanderi*) Dennis A.C.
ar'mandi . . . . Armand C.
—biondia'na
—farquharia'na (*C. a. grandiflora*)
Farquhar A.C.
∞ **aromat'ica** (*flammula × integrifolia;* × *C. coerulea odorata* Hort.; × *davurica;* × *Viorna a.*) . . . . ∞ Aromatic C.
austra'lis
azu'rea . . . . **C. patens**
bald'wini (*Viorna b.*) . . Baldwin C.
balear'ica (*calycina*) . . Balearic C.
barbella'ta . . . . Barbel C.
benthamia'na (*terniflora* Benth., *not* DC.) . . . . Bentham C.
×*bergero'ni* Hort. . . . ∞ **C. eriostemon**
brachia'ta . . . . . Anglebranch C.
brachyu'ra . . . . Seoul C.
brevicauda'ta . . . . Shortplume C.
—tenuisep'ala
buchanania'na . . . . Buchanan C.
calyc'ina . . . . **C. balearica**
campaniflo'ra . . . . Bellflower C.
catesbya'na (*holosericea; C. virginiana c.*) . . . . Catesby C.
×*chand'leri* Hort. . . ∞ **C. eriostemon**
chiisanen'sis . . . . . . Chiisan C.
—carunculo'sa (*C. alpina c.*)
chinen'sis . . . . Chinese C.
chrysoco'ma . . . . . . Goldwool C.
—seric'ea (*C. montana s.; C. spooneri*)
Silky G.C.
cirrho'sa . . . . Vernal C.
coccin'ea . . . . **C. texensis**
—ma'jor . . . . **C. texensis m.**
coeru'lea . . . . **C. patens**
—grandiflo'ra . . . . . **C. patens g.**
×*—odora'ta* Hort. . . . ∞ **C. aromatica**
colenso'i
columbia'na . . . . **C. verticillaris c.**
conna'ta . . . . Goldnod C.
crassifo'lia . . . . . . September C.
cris'pa (*cylindrica; simsi* Sweet, *not* Auth.; *Viorna c.*) . . . . Curly C.
—wal'teri
crux-fla'va . . . . . . **C. orientalis**

CLEMATIS, continued
davidia'na . . . . **C. heracleaefolia d.**
×*davur'ica* . . . . . . ∞**C. aromatica**
delavay'i . . . . Delavay Clematis
dioscoreaefo'lia . . . **C. paniculata d.**
∞**divarica'ta** (*?integrifolia* × *viorna;* ×*C. integrifolia pinnata* Hort.)
doug'lasi (*hirsutissima; Viorna d.*) Douglas C.
—scott'i
drum'mondi . . . . . . Drummond C.
∞**durand'i** (*integrifolia* × *jackmani;* ×*C. integrifolia d.* Hort.; ×*C. i. semperflorens*) . . . . ∞Durand C.
erec'ta . . . . **C. recta**
erioph'ora (*Viorna e.*) . . Wyoming C.
erio'poda . . . . **C. tangutica**
∞**erioste'mon** (*integrifolia* × *viticella;* ×*bergeroni* Hort.; ×*chandleri* Hort.; ×*hendersoni* Hort.; ×*intermedia* Hort.)
farges'i . . . . Farges C.
—souli'ei . . . . Soulie C.
fasciculiflo'ra . . . . . Clustered C.
finetia'na (*pavoliniana*) . . Fineti C.
flam'mula (*pallasi*) . . . . Plume C.
—robus'ta . . . . . . **C. paniculata**
—rotundifo'lia (*C. fragrans*) Roundleaf P.C.
—rubel'la (*C. rubella*) . Painted P.C.
×*—rubro-margina'ta* ∞**C. violacea** ₵Redrim
flor'ida (*japonica*) . . . . Cream C.
—fortun'ei . . . . **C. patens f.**
—ple'na . . . . . . Double C.C.
—siebold'i (*C. f. bicolor; C. sieboldi*)
—stand'ishi . . . . . . **C. patens s.**
×*—veno'sa* . . . . ∞**C. venosa**
₵Belle of Woking. hv. C. florida
₵John (*Gould*) Veitch
foe'tida
fortun'ei . . . . **C. patens f.**
fra'grans . **C. flammula rotundifolia**
×*francofurten'sis* . . . . . ∞**C. guascoi**
fre'monti (*Viorna f.*) . . Fremont C.
frutico'sa . . . . Shrubby C.
—loba'ta
fus'ca (*Viorna f.*) . . . . Stanavoi C.
—viola'cea (*C. janthina*) . Violet S.C.
gattinger'i (*Viorna g.*) . Gattinger C.
gebleria'na . . . . . . **C. songarica**
gentianoi'des
glau'ca (*C. orientalis g.*) Yellowbell C.
—akebioi'des . . . . . Triple Y.C.
—angustifo'lia (*C. intricata*) Mongol Y.C.
—phaean'tha . . . . . Violet Y.C.
∞**globulo'sa** Hort. (*scotti* × *texensis*)
gouria'na (*C. vitalba g.*) . Gourian C.
—finet'i
gracilifo'lia . . . . Graceful C.
gra'ta (*C. vitalba g.*) . . Himalayan C.
—argentilu'cida (*C. g. grandidentata*)
—lobula'ta . . . . Lobeleaf H.C.
grave'olens . . . . **C. orientalis**
∞**guasco'i** (*patens* × *viticella;* ×*francofurtensis*) . . . . . ∞Guasco C.
×*hakonen'sis* . . . . . ∞**C. jackmani**
×*henderso'ni* Hort. . . . ∞**C. eriostemon**
×*hen'ryi* Hort.

The homonymous name ×C. henryi Hort. (see C. lawsoniana henryi) is commonly applied in the trade to the hybrid Henry Clematis, and should not be confused with C. henryi Oliv., a Chinese species allied to C. orientalis and not in cultivation.

CLEMATIS, continued
heracleaefo'lia (*tubulosa*) Tube Clematis
—davidia'na (*C. davidiana*) Fragrant T.C.
—ichangen'sis . . . . . Ichang T.C.
—stans' . . . . **C. stans**
Cote d'Azur. hv. C. heracleaefolia
hexasep'ala
hilar'i
hirsutis'sima . . . . . . **C. douglasi**
holoseric'ea . . . . . . **C. catesbyana**
indivi'sa . . . . . NewZealand C.
—loba'ta . . . . Lobed N.C.
integrifo'lia (*Viorna i.*) . Solitary C.
×*—durand'i* Hort. . . . . ∞**C. durandi**
—ol'gae
×*—pinna'ta* Hort. . . . ∞**C. divaricata**
×*—semperflo'rens* . . . . ∞**C. durandi**
×*interme'dia* Hort. . . ∞**C. eriostemon**
intrica'ta . . . **C. glauca angustifolia**
∞**jack'mani** (*lanuginosa* × *viticella;* ×*hakonensis;* ×*splendida*) ∞Jackman C.
All the following are clons.
Alba. hv.
Alexandra
Devoniensis
Francois Morel
Fulgens
Gipsyqueen
Jackman Rubra
Lafrance
Magnifica
Mme. (*Baron*) Veillard
Mme. (*Edouard*) Andre
Mme. Grange
Modesta
Mrs. (*James*) Bateman
Mrs. Moore
Prince of Wales
Purpurea Hybrida
Reine des Bleus
Rubella
Rubroviolacea
Splendida
Star of India
Superba
Thomas Moore
Tunbridgensis
Velutina-purpurea
Ville de Lyon
janthi'na . . . . . **C. fusca violacea**
japon'ica . . . . **C. florida**
∞**jeuneia'na** (*armandi* × *finetiana*)
∞**jouinia'na** (*heracleaefolia* × *vitalba*) ∞Jouin C.
₵Spingarn. hv.
juba'ta
kermesi'na Hort. **C. viticella** ₵Kermes
korea'na . . . . Korean C.
—lute'a
lancifo'lia
lanugino'sa . . . . Ningpo C.
All the following are clons.
Alba Magna. hv.
Candida
Excelsior
Lady (*Caroline*) Neville
Marie Lefebvre
Mme. (*Emile*) Sorbet
Mme. Thibaut
Mme. Vanhoutte
Nivea
Perfection
Princess of Wales
Robert Hanbury
Sensation
(*The*) President
Violacea

CLEMATIS, continued
lasian'dra . . . Mandarin Clematis
lasian'tha . . . . Pipestem C.
laval'lei . . . . **C. stans l.**
∞**lawsonia'na** (*lanuginosa* × *patens*) ∞Lawson C.
∞**—gablen'zi** (×*C. patens g.*) ∞Gablenz C.
∞**—hen'ryi** (×*C. henryi* Hort.) ∞Henry C.
∞**—symesia'na** (×*C. symesiana*) ∞Symes C.
₵Gem. hv. ∞C. lawsoniana
₵Gloire de St. Julien
₵Imperatrice Eugenie
₵Jeanne d'Arc
₵Otto Froebel
leiocar'pa . . . . **C. uncinata**
ligusticifo'lia [w] Western Virginsbower
—califor'nica . . . . California V.
macropet'ala . . . . . . Bigpetal C.
mandchur'ica . . **C. recta mandshurica**
marmora'ta Hort. **C. viticella** ₵Marbled
mendoci'na . . . . . Mendocino C.
meyenia'na . . . . Meyen C.
—heterophyl'la . . **C. quinquefoliolata**
microphyl'la . . . . . Tinyleaf C.
missourien'sis . . . **C. virginiana m.**
monta'na (*anemoniflora; C. m. alba; odorata* Hort.) . . . . Anemone C.
—grandiflo'ra . . . . . Large A.C.
—lilaci'na . . . . . . Lilac A.C.
—ru'bens . . . . Pink A.C.
—seric'ea . . . . . **C. chrysocoma s.**
—wil'soni (*C. repens*) . Wilson A.C.
₵Perfecta. hv. C. montana
₵Undulata
∞**mor'eli** (*crispa* × *texensis; pitcheri* × *texensis*) . . . . ∞Morel C.
nu'tans . . . . . . Woodvine C.
nu'tans Bean, *not* Royle **C. rehderiana**
—thyrsoi'dea . . . . . . **C. rehderiana**
nu'tans Royle, *not* Crantz . **C. roylei**
ochroleu'ca (*ovata; Viorna o.*) Chrome C.
odora'ta Hort. . . . . . . **C. montana**
orienta'lis (*crux-flava; graveolens*) Oriental C.
—glau'ca . . . . **C. glauca**
—tangu'tica . . . . . . **C. tangutica**
ova'ta . . . . **C. ochroleuca**
pal'lasi . . . . **C. flammula**
panicula'ta (*C. flammula robusta; C. recta p.*) . . . . Sweetautumn C.
—dioscoreaefo'lia (*C. dioscoreaefolia*) Yamleaf S.C.
∞**parviflo'ra** (*campaniflora* × *viticella;* ×*revoluta*)
pa'tens (*azurea* Hort.; *coerulea*) Lilac C.
—fortun'ei (*C. florida f.; C. fortunei*) Fortunes L.C.
×*—gablen'zi* . . . . ∞**C. lawsoniana g.**
—grandiflo'ra (*C. coerulea g.*) Large L.C.
—stand'ishi (*C. florida s.; C. standishi*) Standish L.C.
All the following are clons.
Albert Victor. hv. C. patens
Amalia
Countess of Lovelace
Duchess of Edinburgh
Fair Rosamond
Helena
John Murray
Lady Lanesborough
Lord Lanesborough

CLEMATIS patens, continued
Louisa
Louis Vanhoutte
Marcel Moser
Marie
Miss Bateman
Montrosa
Mrs. (*G.*) Jackman
Mrs. (*James*) Baker
Nelly Moser
Ostrichplume
Snowdrift
Sophia
Stella
(*The*) Queen
Vesta
Violacea
Waverly
pavolinia'na . . . . . . **C. finetiana**
∞ **pellier'i** (*integrifolia* × *jackmani*)
piero'ti . . . . . Pierot Clematis
pitch'eri (*simsi* Auth, *not* Sweet; *Viorna p.*) . . . . Pitcher C.
—sargent'i . . . . . . Sargent P.C.
pratt'i . . . . Pratt C.
pseudoalpi'na (*C. alpina occidentalis; Atragene p.*) . RockyMountain C.
∞ **pseudococcin'ea** (*jackmani* × *texensis*) ∞ Redjack C.
₵Countess of Onslow. hv.
₵Duchess of Albany
₵Duchess of York
pseudoflam'mula
pubes'cens . . . . . . Mexican C.
quinquefoliola'ta (*C. meyeniana heterophylla*) . . . . . Woodbine C.
ranunculoi'des . . . . Buttercup C.
rec'ta (*erecta*) . . . . Ground C.
—mandshur'ica (*C. mandchurica; C. terniflora* DC., *not* Benth.) Manchurian G.C.
—panicula'ta . . . . . **C. paniculata**
—ple'na . . . . . . Double G.C.
rehderia'na (*nutans* Bean, *not* Royle; *C. n. thyrsoidea*) . . . Rehder C.
re'pens . . . . . **C. montana wilsoni**
reticula'ta (*Viorna r.*) . . Netleaf C.
×*revolu'ta* . . . . ∞ **C. parviflora**
royl'ei (*nutans* Royle, *not* Crantz)
rubel'la . . . . **C. flammula r.**
×*rubro-margina'ta* ∞ **C. violacea** ₵Redrim
san'deri . . . . . **C. aristata dennisae**
scott'i . . . . Scott C.
serratifo'lia . . . . Hermitgold C.
sibir'ica . . . . **C. alpina s.**
siebold'i . . . . **C. florida s.**
sims'i . . . . **C. crispa; C. pitcheri**
smilacifo'lia . . . . . . Smilax C.
songa'rica (*gebleriana*) . . Sungari C.
—gebleria'na . . . . Gebler S.C.
—integrifo'lia
×*splen'dida* . . . . . ∞ **C. jackmani**
spoon'eri . . . . . **C. chrysocoma sericea**
×*—rose'a* . . ∞ **C. vedrariensis** ₵Rosea
stand'ishi . . . . **C. patens s.**
stan'leyi (*stanleyana* Hort.) Transvaal C.
stans' (*C. heracleaefolia s.*) . Japtube C.
—laval'lei (*C. lavallei*) . Lavalle J.C.
suksdorf'i . . . . Suksdorf C.
×*symesia'na* . . . . . . ∞ **C. lawsoniana s.**
tangu'tica (*eriopoda; C. orientalis t.*) Golden C.
—far'reri
—obtusius'cula
terniflo'ra . . . . . . **C. benthamiana; C. recta mandshurica**

CLEMATIS, continued
texen'sis (*coccinea; C. viorna c.; Viorna c.*) . . . . . . Scarlet Clematis
—ma'jor (*C. coccinea m.*) Large S.C.
thunberg'i . . . . . . Thunberg C.
troutbeckia'na . . . . Troutbeck C.
trullif'era . . . . Chengtu C.
tubulo'sa . . . . . . **C. heracleaefolia**
uncina'ta (*leiocarpa*)
—retu'sa
∞ **vedrarien'sis** (*chrysocoma* × *montana;* ×*verriensis*) . . . . ∞ Vedrarie C.
₵Rosea (×*C. spooneri r.*) hv.
veitchia'na . . . . Veitch C.
∞ **veno'sa** (*florida* × *viticella;* ×*C. florida v.;* ×*C. viticella v.*) . . ∞ Veiny C.
₵Louise Carriere. hv.
versicol'or (*Viorna v.*) . Manycolor C.
verticilla'ris (*Atragene americana*) Rock C.
—columbia'na (*C. columbiana*) Columbian R.C.
∞ **viola'cea** (*flammula* × *viticella*) ∞ Violet C.
₵Redrim (*rubro-marginata;* ×*C. flammula r.;* ×*C. rubro-marginata*) hv.
vior'na (*Viorna v.*) Leatherflower C. (*Leatherflower*)
—coccin'ea . . . . **C. texensis**
virginia'na . . . . . Virginsbower
—catesbya'na . . . . . **C. catesbyana**
—missourien'sis (*C. missouriensis*) Missouri V.
vital'ba . . . . Travelersjoy
—gouria'na . . . . **C. gouriana**
—gra'ta . . . . **C. grata**
viticel'la . . . . Italian C.
—albiflo'ra (*C. v. alba*) . White I.C.
—coeru'lea . . . . Blue I.C.
—na'na . . . . Dwarf I.C.
—purpu'rea (*C. v. rubra*) Purple I.C.
×*—veno'sa* . . . . ∞ **C. venosa**
₵Ascotiensis. hv. C. viticella
₵Double (*multiplex; C. v. flore-pleno* Hort.; *C. v. pulchella*)
₵Italian Rubra
₵Kermes (*kermesina; C. kermesina* Hort.)
₵Lady Bovill
₵Lilacina Floribunda
₵Marbled (*marmorata; C. marmorata* Hort.)
yunnanen'sis . . . . . . Yunnan C.

Hort. var. (clons) of **Clematis:**

For the following list the Editorial Committee is largely indebted to the late J. E. Spingarn, a noted grower and hybridizer of this genus.

Admiration
Alba
Alba Magna
Albert Victor
Alexandra
Amalia
Amy Spingarn
Ascotiensis
Belle Nantaise
Belle of Woking
Bluegem
Boskoop (*C. boskoop* Hort.; *C. distorta; integrifolia* × *viticella*)
Candida
Comtesse de Bouchaud
Cote d'Azur
Countess of Lovelace
Countess of Onslow
Countess of York
Crimson King
Devoniensis
Double
Double Armand (*armandi florepleno*)
Duchess of Albany
Duchess of Edinburgh
Duchess of York
Duke of Edinburgh
Duke of Portland
Durand (*durandi*)
Edouard Desfosse
Elsa Spaeth
Excelsior
Fair Rosamond
Fairyqueen
Francois Morel
Fulgens
Gem
Gipsyqueen
Gloire de St. Julien
Grace Darling
Helena
Henry (*henryi*)
Hybrida Sieboldi
Imperatrice Eugenie
Italian Rubra
Jackman (*jackmani*)
Jackman Rubra
Jeanne d'Arc
John (*Gould*) Veitch
John Murray
Kermes (*kermesina*)
King George V
King of the Belgians
Lady Bovill
Lady (*Caroline*) Neville
Lady Lanesborough
Lafrance
Lanuginosa Candida
Lasurstern
Lawson (*lawsoniana*)
Lilacina
Lilacina Floribunda
Lord Lanesborough
Lord Neville
Lord Northcliffe
Louisa
Louise Carriere
Louis Vanhoutte
Magnifica
Marbled
Marcel Moser
Marie
Marie Lefebvre
Miss Bateman
M. Koster
Mme. (*Baron*) Veillard
Mme. (*Edouard*) Andre
Mme. (*Emile*) Sorbet
Mme. Grange
Mme. Thibaut
Mme. Vanhoutte
Modesta
Montrosa
Mrs. Cholmondeley
Mrs. (*G.*) Jackman
Mrs. Hope
Mrs. (*James*) Baker
Mrs. (*James*) Bateman
Mrs. Moore
Nelly Moser
Nivea
Ostrichplume
Otto Froebel
Perfecta
Perfection

CLEMATIS, continued
Perle d'Azur
President
Prince of Wales
Princess of Wales
Prins Hendrik
Purple Armand (*armandi purpurea*)
Purpurea Hybrida
Queen
Ramona
Red Jackman (*jackmani rubra*)
Redrim
Reine des Bleus
Robert Hanbury
Rosea
Rubella
Rubroviolacea
Sensation
Siebold (*hybrida sieboldi*)
Sir (*Garnet*) Wolseley
Snowdrift
Sophia
Spingarn
Splendida
Standish (*patens standishi*)
Star of India
Stella
Superba
Symesiana (*lawsoniana symesiana*)
(*The*) President
(*The*) Queen
Thomas Moore
Tunbridgensis
Undulata
Velutina-purpurea
Vesta
Ville de Lyon
Ville de Paris
Violacea
Violet Jackman (*jackmani superba*)
Waverly
White Jackman (*jackmani alba*)
William Kennett

Clematis . . . . **Clematis**
Addison C. . . . . **C. addisoni**
Alpine C. . . . . **C. alpina**
Anemone C. . . . . **C. montana**
Anglebranch C. . . . . . **C. brachiata**
Armand C. . . . . **C. armandi**
∞ Aromatic C. . . . . . ∞ **C. aromatica**
Australian C. . . . . . . **C. aristata**
Baldwin C. . . . . **C. baldwini**
Balearic C. . . . . **C. balearica**
Barbel C. . . . . . . **C. barbellata**
Bellflower C. . . . **C. campaniflora**
Bentham C. . . . . **C. benthamiana**
Bigpetal C. . . . . . **C. macropetala**
Blue Italian C. **C. viticella coerulea**
Buchanan C. . . . **C. buchananiana**
Buttercup C. . . . **C. ranunculoides**
California Virginsbower
C. ligusticifolia californica
Catesby C. . . . . . **C. catesbyana**
Chengtu C. . . . . . . **C. trullifera**
Chiisan C. . . . . . **C. chiisanensis**
Chinese C. . . . . . . **C. chinensis**
Chrome C. . . . . . **C. ochroleuca**
Clustered C. . . . **C. fasciculiflora**
Columbian Rock C.
C. verticillaris columbiana
Cream C. . . . . **C. florida**
Curly C. . . . . **C. crispa**
Delavay C. . . . . . . **C. delavayi**
Dennis Australian C.
C. aristata dennisae
Double Cream C. . . **C. florida plena**
Double Ground C. . . . **C. recta p.**

Clematis, continued
Douglas C. . . . **Clematis douglasi**
Drummond C. . . . . **C. drummondi**
∞ Durand C. . . . . . ∞ **C. durandi**
Dwarf Italian C. . **C. viticella nana**
Farges C. . . . . **C. fargesi**
Farquhar Armand C.
C. armandi farquhariana
Fineti C. . . . . **C. finetiana**
Fortunes Lilac C. **C. patens fortunei**
Fragrant Tube C.
C. heracleaefolia davidiana
Fremont C. . . . . **C. fremonti**
∞ Gablenz C. . ∞ **C. lawsoniana gablenzi**
Gattinger C. . . . . . **C. gattingeri**
Gebler Sungari C.
C. songarica gebleriana
Golden C. . . . . . . **C. tangutica**
Goldnod C. . . . . **C. connata**
Goldwool C. . . . . **C. chrysocoma**
Gourian C. . . . . . . **C. gouriana**
Graceful C. . . . . . **C. gracilifolia**
Ground C. . . . . **C. recta**
∞ Guasco C. . . . . . . ∞ **C. guascoi**
∞ Henry C. . . ∞ **C. lawsoniana henryi**
Hermitgold C. . . . **C. serratifolia**
Himalayan C. . . . . **C. grata**
Ichang Tube C.
C. heracleaefolia ichangensis
Italian C. . . . . **C. viticella**
∞ Jackman C. . . . . . ∞ **C. jackmani**
Japtube C. . . . . **C. stans**
∞ Jouin C. . . . . . . ∞ **C. jouiniana**
Korean C. . . . . . . **C. koreana**
Large Anemone C.
C. montana grandiflora
Large Lilac C. . . . . . **C. patens g.**
Large Scarlet C. **C. texensis major**
Lavalle Japtube C. **C. stans lavallei**
∞ Lawson C. . . . . ∞ **C. lawsoniana**
Leatherflower C. . . . . **C. viorna**
Lilac Anemone C.
C. montana lilacina
Lilac C. . . . . **C. patens**
Lobed NewZealand C.
C. indivisa lobata
Lobeleaf Himalayan C.
C. grata lobulata
Longplume C. . . . . **C. aethusifolia**
Manchurian Ground C.
C. recta mandshurica
Mandarin C. . . . . . **C. lasiandra**
Manycolor C. . . . . . **C. versicolor**
Mendocino C. . . . . **C. mendocina**
Mexican C. . . . . . . **C. pubescens**
Meyen C. . . . . **C. meyeniana**
Missouri Virginsbower
C. virginiana missouriensis
Mongol Yellowbell C.
C. glauca angustifolia
∞ Morel C. . . . . ∞ **C. moreli**
Narrowleaf C. . . . **C. angustifolia**
Netleaf C. . . . . **C. reticulata**
NewZealand C. . . . . . **C. indivisa**
Ningpo C. . . . . . . **C. lanuginosa**
October C. . . . . **C. apiifolia**
Oriental C. . . . . . . **C. orientalis**
Painted Plume C.
C. flammula rubella
Pierot C. . . . . **C. pieroti**
Pink Anemone C. **C. montana rubens**
Pipestem C. . . . . . . **C. lasiantha**
Pitcher C. . . . . **C. pitcheri**
Plume C. . . . . **C. flammula**
Pratt C. . . . . **C. pratti**
Purple Italian C.
C. viticella purpurea
∞ Redjack C. . . ∞ **C. pseudococcinea**

Clematis, continued
Rehder C. . . **Clematis rehderiana**
Rock C. . . . . **C. verticillaris**
RockyMountain C. . **C. pseudoalpina**
Roundleaf Plume C.
C. flammula rotundifolia
Sargent Pitcher C.
C. pitcheri sargenti
Scarlet C. . . . . **C. texensis**
Scott C. . . . . **C. scotti**
Seoul C. . . . . . . **C. brachyura**
September C. . . . . **C. crassifolia**
Shortplume C. . . **C. brevicaudata**
Shrubby C. . . . . . . **C. fruticosa**
Silky Goldwool C.
C. chrysocoma sericea
Smilax C. . . . . . . **C. smilacifolia**
Solitary C. . . . . **C. integrifolia**
Soulie C. . . . . **C. fargesi souliei**
Stanavoi C. . . . . **C. fusca**
Standish Lilac C. **C. patens standishi**
Suksdorf C. . . . . . . **C. suksdorfi**
Sungari C. . . . . . . **C. songarica**
Sweetautumn C. . . . **C. paniculata**
∞ Symes C. ∞ **C. lawsoniana symesiana**
Thunberg C. . . . . . **C. thunbergi**
Tinyleaf C. . . . . **C. microphylla**
Transvaal C. . . . . . **C. stanleyi**
Travelers-joy . . . . . . **C. vitalba**
Triple Yellowbell C.
C. glauca akebioides
Troutbeck C. . . . **C. troutbeckiana**
Tube C. . . . . . . **C. heracleaefolia**
∞ Vedrarie C. . . . ∞ **C. vedrariensis**
∞ Veiny C. . . . . . . ∞ **C. venosa**
Veitch C. . . . . . . **C. veitchiana**
Vernal C. . . . . **C. cirrhosa**
∞ Violet C. . . . . . . ∞ **C. violacea**
Violet Stanavoi C. . . **C. fusca v.**
Violet Yellowbell C.
C. glauca phaeantha
Virginsbower . . . . **C. virginiana**
Western Virginsbower
C. ligusticifolia
White Italian C.
C. viticella albiflora
Wilson Anemone C.
C. montana wilsoni
Wingsepal C. . . . . **C. acutangula**
Woodbine C. . . **C. quinquefoliolata**
Woodvine C. . . . . . . **C. nutans**
Wyoming C. . . . . . **C. eriophora**
Yamleaf Sweetautumn C.
C. paniculata dioscoreaefolia
Yellowbell C. . . . . . **C. glauca**
Yunnan C. . . . . **C. yunnanensis**

CLEMATOCLE'THRA . Vineclethra
integrifo'lia
lasiocla'da

CLEMENT'SIA . . . . . **SEDUM**
See **SUCCULENTS.**

CLEO'ME |w . . . . . Spiderflower
aculea'ta . . . . . . Prickly S.
anom'ala
arbo'rea
gigan'tea . . . . Giant S.
glabra'ta . . . . Sambo S.
his'pida |w . . . . . . Hairy S.
lu'tea . . . . Yellow S.
polyg'ama
serrula'ta (*Peritoma serrulatum*) |w
Bee S.
speciosis'sima
spino'sa (*pungens*) |w . . . Spiny S.
stylo'sa

CLERODEN'DRON (*CLERODENDRUM*) . . . . . GLORYBOWER
balfour'i . . . . **C. thomsonae**
—variega'tum . . . . **C. thomsonae v.**
bung'ei (*foetidum*) . . . . ROSE G.
colebrookia'num . . . COLEBROOK G.
commerso'ni . . . . COMMERSON G.
cyrtophyl'lum . . . MAYFLOWER G.
fal'lax . . . . . . **C. speciosissimum**
fra'grans . . . . . . FRAGRANT G.
—pleniflo'rum . . . . DOUBLE F.G.
gla'brum . . . . NATAL G.
inci'sum
—macrosi'phon
japon'icum (*squamatum*) . JAPANESE G.
myricoi'des
nu'tans
siphonan'thus . **Siphonanthus indicus**
speciosis'simum (*fallax*) . . . JAVA G.
×specio'sum (*splendens × thomsonae*)
splen'dens
squama'tum . . . . . **C. japonicum**
suspen'sum
thom'sonae (*balfouri*) BLEEDINGHEART G.
—delec'tum . . . . SUNSHINE B.G.
—far'gesi . . . . . . FARGES B.G.
—variega'tum (*C. balfouri v.*) VARIEGATED B.G.
trichot'omum . . . . HARLEQUIN G.

CLE'THRA . . . . CLETHRA
acumina'ta . . . . . CINNAMON C.
alnifo'lia . . . . SUMMERSWEET C.
—panicula'ta
—rose'a . . . . PINK S.C.
arbo'rea . . . LILY-OF-THE-VALLEY C.
barbiner'vis (*canescens*) . JAPANESE C.
delavay'i . . . . DELAVAY C.
far'gesi . . . . FARGES C.
monosta'chya
tomento'sa . . . . . . WOOLLY C.

CLEY'ERA . . . . CLEYERA
japon'ica (*Eurya ochnacea*) . JAPAN C.
—tri'color (*fortunei; Ternstroemia f.*)

CLIAN'THUS . . . . . . PARROTBEAK
dampier'i . . . . . . GLORYPEA P.
punic'eus . . . . RED P.
—al'bus . . . . ALBINO R.P.

CLIBA'DIUM
glabres'cens
surinamen'se
sylves'tre

CLIFFBRAKE . . . . **Pellaea**
AUSTRALIAN C. . . . . . . **P. falcata**
BIRDSFOOT C. . . . . **P. mucronata**
BREWERS C. . . . . **P. breweri**
BRIDGES C. . . . . **P. bridgesi**
DWARF C. . . . . **P. pumila**
GREEN C. . . . . **P. viridis**
NEWZEALAND C. . . . **P. rotundifolia**
PURPLE C. . . . . . . **P. atropurpurea**
SIERRA C. . . . . . . **P. brachyptera**

CLIFFROSE . . . . **Cowania**
STANSBURY C. . . . . **C. stansburiana**

CLIFTO'NIA . . . . BUCKWHEATTREE
monophyl'la (*ligustrina; nitida*) BUCKWHEATTREE

CLIMBINGDAHLIA . . . **Hidalgoa wercklei**

CLIMBINGFERN . . . . **Lygodium**
FEATHERY C. . . . . . . **L. scandens**
JAPANESE C. . . . . . **L. japonicum**
MALAY C. . . . . . . **L. circinatum**

CLINOPO'DIUM
aci'nos . . . . **Satureia a.**

CLINOPODIUM, continued
calamin'tha . . . . . . **Satureia c.**
coccin'eum (*Satureia coccinea*)
georgia'num (*Satureia caroliniana*)
nep'eta . . . . **Satureia n.**
vulga're . . . . . . **Satureia vulgaris**

CLINOSTIG'MA
See **PALM GENERA.**

CLINTO'NIA . . . . BEADLILY
andrewsia'na . . . . RED B.
borea'lis . . . . YELLOW B.
el'egans . . . . **Downingia e.**
pulchel'la . . . . . . **Downingia p.**
uden'sis
umbellula'ta (*umbellata*) . SPECKLED B.
uniflo'ra . . . . QUEENCUP B.

CLISTOYUC'CA . . . . . . **YUCCA**

CLITOCY'BE . . . . . . CLITOCYBE
dealba'ta
illu'dens . . . . JACK-O'-LANTERN C.
monadel'pha
mul'ticeps . . . . . . MANYHEAD C.
ochropurpu'rea . . . . PURPLEGILL C.

CLITO'RIA . . . . . . PIGEONWINGS
cajanifo'lia . . . . TROPIC P.
dendri'na . . . . BIG P.
maria'na . . . . ATLANTIC P.
terna'tea . . . . ASIAN P.

CLI'VIA . . . . KAFIRLILY
×cyrtanthiflo'ra (*miniata × nobilis; Imantophyllum cyrtanthiflorum*)
gar'deni
minia'ta . . . . SCARLET K.
—fla'va
no'bilis . . . . GREENTIP K.

CLOAKFERN . . . . **Notholaena**
BULB C. . . . . **N. sinuata**
LITTLE B. C. . . . . . **N. s. crenata**
SLENDER C. . . . . **N. aurea**
STAR C. . . . . **N. standleyi**
ZIGZAG C. . . . . **N. fendleri**

CLOCKVINE . . . . **Thunbergia**
BENGAL C. . . . . . . **T. grandiflora**
BLACKEYED C. . . . . **T. alata**
BUSH C. . . . . **T. erecta**
LAUREL C. . . . . **T. laurifolia**
MYSORE C. . . . . . . **T. mysorensis**
ORANGE C. . . . . **T. gibsoni**
SCARLET C. . . . . **T. coccinea**
SWEET C. . . . . **T. fragrans**
VOGEL C. . . . . **T. vogeliana**
WHITE BUSH C. . . . **T. erecta alba**
WIGHT C. . . . . **T. wightiana**

CLOUDBERRY . . . **Rubus chamaemorus**

CLOVEBARKTREE **Dicypellium caryophyllatum**

CLOVER . . . . **Trifolium**
ALPINE C. . . . . **T. alpinum**
ALSIKE C. . . . . **T. hybridum**
ARIZONA C. . . . . . **T. arizonicum**
AZTEC C. . . . . **T. amabile**
BECKWITH C. . . . . . . **T. beckwithi**
BIGHEAD C. . . . **T. macrocephalum**
BIGLEAF C. . . . . **T. howelli**
BLADDER C. . . . . . . **T. amplectens**
BOLANDER C. . . . . . . **T. bolanderi**
BRACTED C. . . . . . . **T. bracteatum**
BRANDEGEE C. . . . . . **T. brandegei**
BREWER C. . . . . **T. breweri**
BUFFALO C. . . . . **T. reflexum**
BURDOCK C. . . . . . **T. lappaceum**
CAROLINA C. . . . . **T. carolinianum**
CARPET C. . . . . . . **T. monanthum**

CLOVER, continued
CLAMMY C. . . **Trifolium obtusiflorum**
CLUSTER C. . . . . . **T. glomeratum**
COCKLEBUR C. . . . . . . **T. supinum**
COLUMBIA C. . . . . . **T. fimbriatum**
COVILLE C. . . . . **T. covillei**
CRIMSON C. . . . . . . **T. incarnatum**
CROOKED C. . . . . . . **T. angulatum**
CUP C. . . . . **T. cyathiferum**
CUTCOLLAR C. . . . . **T. lacerum**
DEPAUPERATE C. . . **T. depauperatum**
DOUGLAS C. . . . . **T. douglasi**
DWARF C. . . . . **T. nanum**
EGYPTIAN C. . . . . **T. alexandrinum**
ELMERDREW C. . . **T. longipes elmeri**
FENDLER C. . . . . **T. fendleri**
FINELEAF C. . . . . . **T. angustifolium**
FIVELEAF C. . . . . **T. andersoni**
FOOTHILL C. . . . . **T. ciliolatum**
FOXTAIL C. . . . . **T. rubens**
GAMBEL C. . . . **T. fucatum gambeli**
HALLS C. . . . . **T. halli**
HANSEN C. . . . . **T. hanseni**
HAYDEN C. . . . . **T. haydeni**
HOLLYLEAF C. . . . . **T. gymnocarpon**
HOP C. . . . . **T. agrarium**
HUNGARIAN C. . . . . **T. pannonicum**
KINGS C. . . . . **T. kingi**
KNOTTED C. . . . . **T. striatum**
KURA C. . . . . **T. ambiguum**
LANKY C. . . . . **T. oliganthum**
LEMMONS C. . . . . **T. lemmoni**
LITTLEHEAD C. . . **T. microcephalum**
LONGSTALK C. . . . . **T. longipes**
LOST C. . . . . . **T. appendiculatum**
LOW HOP C. . . . . . **T. procumbens**
MACRAE C. . . . . **T. macraei**
Mignonette C. . . . . . . LOW HOP C.
MONO C. . . . . **T. monoense**
MONTANA C. . . . . . **T. montanense**
MOUNTAIN C. . . . . . . **T. montanum**
NODHEAD C. . . . . **T. cernuum**
OREGON C. . . . . **T. oreganum**
PARRY C. . . . . **T. parryi**
PERSIAN C. . . . . . . **T. resupinatum**
PINOLE C. . . . . **T. bifidum**
PINPOINT C. . . . . . . **T. gracilentum**
PUFF C. . . . . **T. fucatum**
PURPLEGLOBE C. . . . . . . **T. alpestre**
PURPLELEAF WHITE C. **T. repens purpureum**
PUSSY C. . . . . **T. plumosum**
RABBITFOOT C. . . . . **T. arvense**
RANCHERIA C. . . . **T. albopurpureum**
RED C. . . . . **T. pratense**
ROUGH C. . . . . **T. scabrum**
RUSBY C. . . . . **T. rusbyi**
RYDBERG C. . . . . **T. rydbergi**
Shaftal C. . . . . PERSIAN C.
SHOWY C. . . . . **T. elegans**
SIERRA C. . . . . . . **T. wormskjoldi**
SOLITARY C. . . . . **T. uniflorum**
SONOMA C. . . . . **T. grayi**
Soursalt C. . . . . CLAMMY C.
SPINDLEROOT C. . . . . . . **T. arcuatum**
STELLATE C. . . . . **T. stellatum**
STRAWBERRY C. . . . . . . **T. fragiferum**
SUBTERRANEAN C. . . . **T. subterraneum**
SUCKLING C. . . . . **T. dubium**
TEASEL C. . . . . **T. parviflorum**
THREAD C. . . . . **T. filiforme**
THRIFT C. . . . . **T. stenolobum**
TOMCAT C. . . . . **T. tridentatum**
TWIN C. . . . . **T. latifolium**
UTAH C. . . . . **T. macilentum**
WHIPROOT C. . . . . . **T. dasyphyllum**
WHITE C. . . . . **T. repens**
WHITETIP C. . . . . **T. variegatum**

CLOVER, continued
WILLOW C. . . . **Trifolium salictorum**
WOOLLY C. . . . . **T. tomentosum**
WOOLLYHEAD C. . . **T. eriocephalum**
WYOMING C. . . . . **T. anemophilum**
ZIGZAG C. . . . . **T. medium**

CLOVERSHRUB . . . . . **Campylotropis**
CHINESE C. . . . . **C. macrocarpa**

CLOVETREE . . **Syzygium aromaticum**

CLUBAWNGRASS . . . . **Corynephorus**

CLUBMOSS . . . . **Lycopodium**
BILLARDIER C. . . . . . **L. billardieri**
CAROLINA C. . . . . **L. carolinianum**
CARPET C. . . . . . . **L. prostratum**
FIR C. . . . . **L. selago**
FOXTAIL C. . . . . **L. alopecuroides**
GROUNDCEDAR
L. complanatum flabelliforme
GROUNDPINE . . . . . . **L. obscurum**
RUNNINGPINE . . . . . . **L. clavatum**
SHINING C. . . . . . . **L. lucidulum**
SLENDER GROUNDCEDAR. **L. tristachyum**
SOUTHERN C. . . . . **L. adpressum**
STAGHORN C. . . . . . . **L. cernuum**

CLU'SIA . . . . CLUSIA
al'ba . . . . WHITE C.
fla'va . . . . KEYWEST C.
intertex'ta . . . . . . MOUNTAIN C.
rose'a . . . . COPEY C.

CLUSTERPALM . . . . . **Actinophloeus**
MACARTHUR C. . . . **A. macarthuri**
PURPLELEAF C. . . . . . . **A. nicolai**
SANDER C. . . . . . . **A. sanderianus**

CLUSTERPEA . . . . **Dioclea**
BOYKIN C. . . . . . . **D. multiflora**
SCARLET C. . . . . . **D. glycinoides**

CLYME'NIA . . . . CLYMENIA
polyan'dra . . . . CLYMENIA

CLYTOSTO'MA . . . . TRUMPETVINE
callistegioi'des (*Bignonia c.; B. speciosa*)
ARGENTINE T.
purpu'reum (*purpurea*) . URUGUAY T.

CNEORI'DIUM . . . . . BERRYRUE
dumo'sum . . . . BERRYRUE

CNEO'RUM . . . . . . SPURGEOLIVE
tricoc'con . . . . . . SPURGEOLIVE

CNES'TIS
ferrugi'nea

CNI'CUS . . . . . . BLESSEDTHISTLE
benedic'tus (*Carduus b.; Centaurea benedicta*) . . . . . BLESSEDTHISTLE
cynarioi'des (*Serratula cyranoides*)

Cnid'ium officina'le . . . . **Selinum o.**

CNIDOS'COLUS . . . TREADSOFTLY

Cnidoscolus Pohl (1827), in general use, has been proposed for conservation over the earlier Bivonea Raf. (1814) and two other names by Louis C. Wheeler, American University, Washington, D. C. (Contrib. Gray Herb. 124: 51-2. 1939). Dr. Wheeler is expert in the Spurge family (Euphorbiaceae) to which the genus belongs.

stimulo'sus (*Jatropha stimulosa*) lw
RISKY T.
texa'nus (*J. texana*) lw . . TEXAS T.
u'rens (*J. urens*) . . . . . DRUG T.

COACHWOOD . . . . . . **Ceratopetalum**
CHRISTMAS C. . . . **C. gummiferum**
FRAGRANT C. . . . . **C. apetalum**

COBAE'A . . . . COBAEA
macrosto'ma (*lutea*) . . GUATEMALA C.
scan'dens . . . . . . PURPLEBELL C.
—al'ba . . . . WHITEBELL C.

Cobnut . . . . FILBERT, COB:
Corylus avellana grandis

COCAINETREE . . . . . **Erythroxylum**
HUANUCO C. . . . . **E. coca**
PERUVIAN C. . . . **E. novogranatense**
TRUJILLO C. . . . . . **E. truxillense**

COCCIN'IA . . . . IVYGOURD
cordifo'lia (*indica*) . . . . . INDIA I.

COCCOCYP'SELUM
guianen'se

COCCOLO'BIS (*COCCOLOBA*)
SEAGRAPE
diversifo'lia . . . . . . MIXLEAF S.
florida'na (*laurifolia*) . . . PIGEON S.
grandifo'lia (*pubescens*) GRANDLEAF S.
krug'i . . . . KRUGS S.
uvif'era . . . . COMMON S.

COCCOTHRI'NAX (*THRINAX* in part; *THRINCOMA; THRINGIS*)
SILVERPALM
See **PALM GENERA.**

COC'CULUS (*CEBATHA; EPIBATERIUM*) lw . . . . . SNAILSEED
caroli'nus (*Cebatha carolina; Epibaterium carolinum*) lw . . CAROLINA S.
diversifo'lius . . . . **Sinomenium acutum**
laurifo'lius . . . . . . LAURELLEAF S.
tril'obus . . . . JAPANESE S.

COCHAL . . . . **Myrtillocactus geometrizans cochal**

COCHEMIE'A
See **CACTUS GENERA.**

COCHLEA'RIA . . . . SCURVYWEED
officina'lis . . . . COMMON S.
saxat'ilis . . . . **Kernera s.**

COCHLIO'DA
See **ORCHID GENERA.**

COCHLOSPER'MUM (*MAXIMILIANEA*) SHELLSEED
religio'sum (*gossypium*) . . COTTON S. (*Whitesilk Cotton*)
vitifo'lium . . . . . YELLOWSILK S.

COCKLEBUR . . . . **Xanthium**
BEACH C. . . . . **X. echinatum**
ITALIAN C. . . . . **X. italicum**
ORIENTAL C. . . . . . . **X. orientale**
PALOALTO C. . . . . **X. calvum**
SPINY C. . . . . **X. spinosum**

COCKSCOMB . . . . **Celosia**
COMMON FEATHER C.
C. argentea cristata
FEATHER C. . . . . **C. argentea**
HUTTON C. . . . . **C. huttoni**

COCKSEGGS . . **Salpichroa rhomboidea**

Cocksfoot . . ORCHARDGRASS: **Dactylis**

COCKSPUR . . . . **Echinochloa**
COAST C. . . . . **E. walteri**
FLORIDA C. . . . . . . **E. paludigena**
GULF C. . . . . **E. crus-pavonis**

COCONUT . . . . . **Cocos; C. nucifera**

COCOPLUM . . . . **Chrysobalanus**
ICACO C. . . . . **C. icaco**
SMALLFRUIT C. . . . . **C. i. pellocarpa**

CO'COS . . . . COCONUT
See **PALM GENERA**

COCUSWOOD . . . . **Brya**
EBONY C. . . . . **B. ebenus**

Codarioca'lyx gy'rans . . **Desmodium g.**

CODIAE'UM (*PHYLLAUREA*)
LEAFCROTON
variega'tum (*pictum; C. variegatum p.; Phyllaurea variegata*) VARIEGATED L.

Probably all of the below are clons.

ADONIS (*superbum*) HV. Codiaeum
AIGBURTHIENSE
ALBALINEATUM
ALBICANS
AMABILE
ANDRE (*andreanum*)
ANGUSTISSIMUM (*angustifolium*)
ANIETUMENSE
APPENDICULATUM
AUCUBAEFOLIUM
AUREOLINEATUM
AUREOMACULATUM
AUREUM
BANANA (*musaicum*)
BARON ADOLPH SEILLIERE
BARON FRANK SEILLIERE
BARONNE (*James*) DEROTHSCHILD. *Baron Rothschild*
BARRYI
B. COMPTE
BEAUTY
BELLULUM
BERGMAN (*bergmani*)
BRAGAEANUM
BRILLIANTISSIMUM
BROOMFIELDI
BRUXELLENSE
BURTONI
CARRIEREI
CAUDATUM TORTILE
CHALLENGER. *Challengeri?; Imperator?*
CHANTRIERI
CHELSONI
CHILDSONI
CHRYSOPHYLLUM
CLOUDY (*fuscatum*)
COMPTE DEGERMINY
CONTORTUM
COOPERI
CORNUTUM
COUNTESS. *Countess Superba?*
CRAIGI
CROESUS
CRONSTADT (*cronstadti*)
CROWN PRINCE
CZAR ALEXANDER III
DAVISI
DAYSPRING
DELIGHT
DISRAELI
DODGSONAE
DORMANNIANUM
DROUETI
DUVALI
DUVIVIERI
EARL OF DERBY

Perhaps the same as LORD DERBY.

EARLSCOURT
EBURNEUM
EDMONT (*edmontense*)
ELEGANS
ELEGANTISSIMUM
ELONGATUM
ELVIRA
ELYSIAN
EMINENS

CODIAEUM, continued
EUTERPE
EVANS (*evansianum*)
EXCELSIOR
EXCURRENS
EXQUISITE
EYREI
FASCIATUM
FASCINATUM
FLAMBEAU
FLAMINGO
FORMOSUM
Fuscatum. CLOUDY
GLORIOSUM. *Prince of Wales*
GOEDENOUGHTI
GOLDEN QUEEN
GOLDEN RING
GOLDIEI
GRANDI
GRAYI
HAMMONDI
HANBURYANUM
HARWOOD (*harwoodianum; triumphans h.*)
HASTIFERUM
HAWKERI
HENRYANUM
HERMON
HEROICUM
HILLEANUM
HOOKERIANUM (*hookeri*)
ILLUSTRE
IMPERATOR
Perhaps the same as CHALLENGER.
IMPERIALE
Inimitabile. NONESUCH
INSIGNE
INTERRUPTUM
INTERRUPTUM ELEGANS
INVICTUM
IRREGULARE
JAMESI
JOHANNIS (*taeniosum*)
JUBILEE
JUNIUS
KATHARINA
KATON (*maculatum katoni*)
LACTEUM
LADY ZETLAND
LAINGI
LANCIFOLIUM
LATIMACULATUM
LEOPARD (*maculatum*)
LETZAR
LIMBATUM
LORD BELHAVEN
LORD DERBY. *Earl of Derby?*
LYRATUM
MACFARLANEI
MACROPHYLLUM
Maculatum. LEOPARD
Maculatum Katoni. KATON
MADAME SEILLIERE
MAGNIFICENT
MAGNIFICUM
MAGNOLIAEFOLIUM
MAJESTICUM
MAKOYANUM
MARQUIS DE CASTELLANE
MARQUIS DE GUADIARO
MASSANGEANUM
MAXIMUM
MEDIUM VARIEGATUM
MEMPHIS
MME. LUCIEN LINDEN
MONARCH
MONTEFONTAINENSE (*montfortiense*)

CODIAEUM, continued
MOOREANUM
MORTI
MRS. (*Chas.*) HEINE
MRS. (*Craige*) LIPPINCOTT
MRS. DORMAN
MRS. (*H. F.*) WATSON
MRS. ICETON
MRS. MCLEAD
MRS. SWAN
MULTICOLOR
Musaicum. BANANA
Mutabile. PRINCEPS
NESTOR
NEVILLIAE
NEWMANNI
NOBILE
NONESUCH (*inimitabile*)
ORNATUM
ORVILLA
OVALIFOLIUM
PARADOXUM
PENNINCKI
PHILLIPSI
PICTUM
PICTURATUM
PILGRIM
PRINCE HENRY
Prince of Wales. GLORIOSUM
PRINCEPS (*mutabile*)
PRINCESS MATILDA
PRINCESS OF WALES
PRINCESS WALDECK
PUCCIANUM
Punctatum. SPECKLED
PUNCTATUMAUREUM
QUEEN VICTORIA
RECURVATUM
RECURVIFOLIUM
REGINAE
REID (*reidi*)
REX
RODECKIANUM
ROSEOPICTUM
RUBERRIMUM
RUBROLINEATUM
RUBROSTRIATUM
RUSSELLI
SANDERI
SCEPTRE
SCHATTI
SINITZIANUM
SOLLERI
SPECKLED (*punctatum*)
SPIRALE
SPLENDENS
SPLENDIDUM
STEWARTI
SUNSHINE. *Sunbeam?*
SUPERBIENS
SUPERBISSIMUM
Superbum. ADONIS
Taeniosum. JOHANNIS
THOMSON (*thomsoni*)
TORQUETUM
TORRIGIANUM
TORTILE
TOURNFORDENSE
TRICOLOR
TRILOBUM
TRIUMPHANS
Triumphans Harwoodianum. HARWOOD
TRUFFAUTI
UNDULATUM
VAN OOSTERZEEI
VARIABILE
VEITCHI

CODIAEUM, continued
VERVAETI
VICTORY
VITTATUM
VOLUTUM
WARRENI
WEISMANI
WIGMANNI
WILLIAMSI
WILSONI
YOUNGI

CODONOCAR'PUS . . MEDICINETREE
cotinifo'lia . . . . . . MUSTARD M.

CODONOP'SIS . . . . . . ASIABELL
clemati'dea . . . . . . CLEMATIS A.
lanceola'ta . . . . LANCE A.
melea'gris . . . . GUINEAFOWL A.
ova'ta
pilo'sula
rotundifo'lia . . . . ROUNDLEAF A.
silves'tris . . . . FOREST A.
viridiflo'ra . . . . GREENFLOWER A.

COE'LIA
See **ORCHID GENERA.**

COELOCOC'CUS . . **METROXYLON**
See **PALM GENERA.**

COELOGLOS'SUM . . **HABENARIA**
See **ORCHID GENERA.**

COELOGY'NE
See **ORCHID GENERA.**

COELOPLEU'RUM |w
gmel'ini |w
lu'cidum

COFFE'A . . . . COFFEE
ara'bica . . . . ARABIAN C.
—excel'sa . . . . CONGO C.
SANRAMON. HV. C. arabica
cane'phora
lauren'ti . . . . LAWRENCE C.
liber'ica . . . . LIBERIAN C.
robus'ta . . . . ROBUST C.
stenophyl'la . . . SIERRALEONE C.
zangueba'riae (*zanzibarensis*)
ZANZIBAR C.

COFFEE . . . . **Coffea**
ARABIAN C. . . . . **C. arabica**
CONGO C. . . . . **C. a. excelsa**
LAWRENCE C. . . . . . **C. laurenti**
LIBERIAN C. . . . . **C. liberica**
ROBUST C. . . . . **C. robusta**
SIERRALEONE C. . . . **C. stenophylla**
ZANZIBAR C. . . . . **C. zanguebariae**

COFFEEFERN . **Pellaea andromedaefolia**

COFFEETREE . . . . . . **Gymnocladus**
CHINESE C. . . . . . . **G. chinensis**
KENTUCKY C. . . . . . . **G. dioicus**

Cogongrass . . . . . SATINTAIL, COGON:
Imperata cylindrica

COGSWEL'LIA . . . . **LOMATIUM**
anom'ala . **L. triternatum anomalum**
bi'color . . . . **L. leptocarpum**
jones'i . . . . **L. macdougali**
platyphyl'la . . . . . . **L. nudicaule**

COHOSH, BLUE
Caulophyllum thalictroides

COHUNE PALM . . . . **Orbignya cohune**
Source of Cohunenuts of commerce.

CO'IX . . . . JOBSTEARS
lacrymajo'bi . . . . JOBSTEARS
YELLOWSTRIPE (*aurea zebrina*) HV.

CO'LA . . . . COLANUT
acumina'ta (*nitida*) . . . . SUDAN C.

COL'CHICUM . . . . AUTUMNCROCUS
agrippi'num . . . . . . AGRIPPA A.
autumna'le . . . . . . COMMON A.
DOUBLE (*florepleno*) HV.
GIANT (*major*)
PURPLE (*atropurpureum*)
SMALL (*minor*)
WHITE (*album*)
bornmuel'leri . . BORNMUELLER A.
byzanti'num . . . . . BYZANTINE A.
decais'nei . . . . . . DECAISNE A.
lute'um . . . . YELLOW A.
specio'sum . . . . . . SHOWY A.
GRECIAN (*illyricum*) HV.
RUBYQUEEN (*atrorubens*)
SNOWQUEEN (*album*)
variega'tum . . . . . . LEVANT A.

COLDE'NIA [w] . . . . . . COLDENIA
canes'cens [w] . . . . . SPREADING C.
nutt'alli . . . . NUTTALL C.
pal'meri . . . . PALMER C.
plica'ta . . . . DESERTMAT C.

COLEAN'THUS . . . . . MUDGRASS
See **GRASS GENERA.**

COLEOG'YNE
ramosis'sima . . . . . . BLACKBRUSH

COLEONE'MA . . BREATH-OF-HEAVEN
al'bum (*Diosma alba*) . . . WHITE B.
pul'chrum . . . . PINK B.

COLEOSAN'THUS . . **BRICKELLIA**

COLEOSPA'DIX
See **PALM GENERA.**

CO'LEUS . . . . COLEUS
amboin'icus (*aromaticus*)
SPANISHTHYME C.
autra'ni
blu'mei . . . . COMMON C.
—verschaffelt'i . . VERSCHAFFELT C.
There are many HV. of this species besides the clon listed below.
₵ORNATUS. HV. C. blumei
lanugino'sus
persoon'i . . . . PERSOON C.
pu'milus . . . . DWARF C.
rehneltia'nus . . . . . . REHNELT C.
—super'bus . . . . SHOWY R.C.
shiren'sis
thyrsoi'deus . . . . BUSH C.

COLEWORT . . . . **Crambe**
HEARTLEAF C. . . . . . . **C. cordifolia**
SEAKALE C. . . . . **C. maritima**
SPANISH C. . . . . **C. hispanica**

COLLE'TIA . . . . COLLETIA
arma'ta . . . . ARMED C.
crucia'ta . . . . . . ANCHORBUSH C.
ephe'dra . . . . PERU C.
infaus'ta (*horrida; spinosa*)
CYLINDER C.
serratifo'lia . . . . **Discaria s.**

COLLIN'IA . . . **CHAMAEDOREA**
See **PALM GENERA.**

COLLIN'SIA [w] . . . . . . COLLINSIA
bartsiaefo'lia (*bartsiae*) . . SEASIDE C.
bi'color . . . . PAGODA C.
CANDIDISSIMA. HV.
MULTICOLOR
PURPUREA
grandiflo'ra . . . . . . BLUELIPS C.

COLLINSIA, continued
parviflo'ra (*tenella* (Pursh) Piper, *not* Benth.) . LITTLEFLOWER COLLINSIA
tenel'la (*Tonella collinsoides*)
SLENDER C.
tincto'ria . . . . . BROWNSTAIN C.
ver'na . . . . . BLUE-EYED-MARY C.

COLLINSO'NIA [w] . . . . HORSEBALM
canaden'sis [w] . . . . CITRONELLA H.
(*Richweed*)

COLLO'MIA . . . . **GILIA**
micran'tha . . . . . . **Microsteris m.**

COLLYB'IA . . . . COLLYBIA
radica'ta . . . . ROOTED C.
velu'tipes . . . . . . VELVETSTEM C.

COLOCA'SIA (*LEUCOCASIA*)
ELEPHANTSEAR
antiquo'rum (*C. esculenta a.*) . . TARO
—euchlo'ra
—fontanes'i . . . DESFONTAINES T.
—illus'tris . . . . IMPERIAL T.
esculen'ta (*Caladium esculentum*)
DASHEEN
in'dica . . . . GREEN T.
neo-guineen'sis . . **Schismatoglottis n.**
BLACK CALADIUM (*illustris; antiquorum i.*) HV. Colocasia

COLOCYNTH . . . **Citrullus colocynthis**

COLPOTHRI'NAX . . . BARRELPALM
See **PALM GENERA.**

COLQUHOU'NIA
vesti'ta

COLTSFOOT . . . . **Tussilago**
COMMON C. . . . . **T. farfara**

COLUBRI'NA . . . . . . COLUBRINA
arbores'cens (*colubrina; ferruginea*)
WILDCOFFEE C.
califor'nica . . . . . CALIFORNIA C.
cuben'sis . . . . CUBA C.
ferrugino'sa . . . . BAHAMA C.
gla'bra . . . . SMOOTH C.
reclina'ta . . . . . SOLDIERWOOD C.
texen'sis . . . . TEXAS C.

COLUMBINE . . . . **Aquilegia**
AKITA C. . . . . **A. akitensis**
ALPINE C. . . . . **A. alpina**
ALPINEROCK C. . . . . . . **A. bertoloni**
ALTAI C. . . . . **A. glandulosa**
AMERICAN C. . . . . . . **A. canadensis**
CALIFORNIA C. . . **A. formosa truncata**
COLORADO C. . . . . **A. coerulea**
EARLY C. . . . . **A. oxysepala**
EUROPEAN C. . . . . **A. vulgaris**
FAN C. . . . . **A. flabellata**
GOLDEN C. . . . . **A. chrysantha**
GREENFLOWER C. . . . . . **A. viridiflora**
JONES C. . . . . **A. jonesi**
LONGSPUR C. . . . . . . **A. longissima**
OLYMPIC C. . . . **A. vulgaris olympica**
PINE C. . . . . **A. pinetorum**
PYRENEES C. . . . . **A. pyrenaica**
ROCKYMOUNTAIN C. . . **A. saximontana**
SIBERIAN C. . . . . **A. sibirica**
SITKA C. . . . . **A. formosa**
SKINNER C. . . . . **A. skinneri**
∞STUART C. . . . . **∞A. stuarti**
WESTERNRED C. . . . . . **A. elegantula**
YELLOW C. . . . . **A. flavescens**
YUKON C. . . . . **A. brevistyla**

COLUMNBERRY, TRUEHEDGE . **Berberis thunbergi** ₵ERECTA

COLUM'NEA . . . . . . COLUMNEA
glorio'sa . . . . COSTARICA C.
rotundifo'lia . . . . . ROUNDLEAF C.
tu'lae
varrieren'sis

COLUSAGRASS . . **Anthochloa colusana**

COLU'TEA . . . . . . BLADDERSENNA
arbores'cens . . . . COMMON B.
—bulla'ta (*pygmaea*) . . DWARF B.
breviala'ta
cilic'ica (*longialata*) . . . CILICIAN B.
grac'ilis . . . . SLENDER B.
is'tria (*halepica*)
∞**me'dia** (*arborescens* × *orientalis*)
∞HYBRID B.
The cultivated shrub, often mislabeled C. orientalis, is presumably a clon.
melanoca'lyx
orienta'lis (*cruenta*) . . ORIENTAL B.
per'sica . . . . PERSIAN B.
pyg'maea . . . **C. arborescens bullata**

COLVIL'LEA . . . . COLVILLEA
racemo'sa . . . . GLORY C.

COMAN'DRA [w] . . . . . . COMANDRA
(*Bastardtoadflax; Falsetoadflax*)
liv'ida . . . . NORTHERN C.
richardsia'na . . . . . . RICHARDS C.
umbella'ta (*nudiflora; pallida*)
COMMON C.

COMAROSTAPH'YLIS
ARCTOSTAPHYLOS

Coma'rum palus'tre . **Potentilla palustris**
salesso'wi . . . . . . **P. salesoviana**

COMBBUSH . . . . **Petrophila**
LONGSTALK C. . . . . . **P. pedunculata**
PRETTY C. . . . . **P. pulchella**
QUEENSLAND C. . . . . . . **P. sessilis**
ROUNDLEAF C. . . . . **P. media**
SHUTTLEWORTH C. **P. shuttleworthiana**
SLIMLEAF C. . . . . **P. linearis**
TWINLOBE C. . . . . **P. biloba**

COMBGRASS . . . . **Ctenium**
FLORIDA C. . . . . . . **C. floridanum**

COMBRE'TUM . . . . . COMBRETUM
coccin'eum (*Grislea coccinea*)
SCARLET C.
como'sum . . . . FLAME C.
farino'sum . . . . MEALY C.
frutico'sum (*loeflingi; microphyllum*)
LOEFLING C.
grandiflo'rum . . . . . . SHOWY C.
mucrona'tum
panicula'tum . . . . . . PANICLED C.
secun'dum . . . . TRINIDAD C.
smeath'mani . . . . . SMEATHMAN C.
Regarded by some botanists as a synonym of C. mucronatum.
sunda'icum . . . . SUNDAI C.

COMBSEED . . . . **Pectocarya**
SHORTLEAF C. . . . . **P. penicillata**
SLIM C. . . . . **P. linearis**

COMESPER'MA
spino'sum

COMFREY . . . . **Symphytum**
CAUCASIAN C. . . . . **S. caucasicum**
COMMON C. . . . . . . **S. officinale**
PRICKLY C. . . . . **S. asperum**
TUBER C. . . . . **S. tuberosum**

COMMELI'NA [w] . . . . DAYFLOWER
angustifo'lia . . . . NARROWLEAF D.
coeles'tis . . . . MEXICAN D.

COMMELINA, continued
commu'nis |w . . Common Dayflower
cris'pa |w . . . . . . Curlyleaf D.
dianthifo'lia (*linearis*) . . Birdbill D.
el'egans |w
erec'ta |w . . . . Erect D.
hirtel'la |w . . . . Hairy D.
nudiflo'ra (*sellowiana*) . Creeping D.
sikkimen'sis . . . . Sikkim D.
tubero'sa . . . . Tuber D.
virgin'ica |w . . . . . . Virginia D.

COMMI'PHORA . . . . Myrrhtree
abyssin'ica . . . . . Abyssinian M.
africa'na . . . . African M.
erythrae'a . . . . Bisabol M.
ka'taf . . . . Opopanax M.
mu'kul . . . . Mukul M.
myrrh'a . . . . Common M.
opobalsa'mum . . . . . Mecca M.

Compassplant . . **Silphium laciniatum**

Composite

Any plant belonging to the enormous Composite family (Compositae, or Asteraceae), as an Aster or Sunflower.

COMPSO'A . . . . **TRICYRTIS**

COMPTO'NIA |w . . . . Sweetfern
peregri'na (*asplenifolia; Myrica a.* in part) |w . . . . . . Sweetfern
—asplenifo'lia (*Myrica a.* in part) Littleleaf S.

CONAN'DRON
ramondioi'des

CONAN'THUS . . . . **NAMA**

CONDA'LIA |w . . . . . . Condalia
linea'ta . . . . Striped C.
lycioi'des (*Zizyphus l.*) Southwestern C.
—canes'cens . . . . . . Desert S.C.
mexica'na . . . . Mexican C.
obova'ta |w . . . . . . Bluewood C.
obtusifo'lia (*Zizyphus o.*) |w Lotewood C.
par'ryi (*Zizyphus p.*) . . . Parry C.
spathula'ta |w . . . . Knifeleaf C. (*Squawbush*)

Condorvine . . **Marsdenia cundurango**

Conebush . . . . **Isopogon**
Anemoneleaf C. . . **I. anemonifolius**
Anethum C. . . . . . **I. anethifolius**
Horny C. . . . . **I. roseus**
Roundhead C. . . **I. sphaerocephalus**

Coneflower . . . . **Rudbeckia**
Blackeyedsusan . . . . . . **R. hirta**
Browneyedsusan . . . . **R. triloba**
California C. . . . . **R. californica**
Clasping C. . . . . **R. amplexicaulis**
Cutleaf C. . . . . **R. laciniata**
Erfurt C. . . . . **R. bicolor superba**
Great C. . . . . **R. maxima**
Niggerhead . . . . . **R. occidentalis**
Orange C. . . . . **R. fulgida**
Pinewoods C. . . . . . . **R. bicolor**
Showy C. . . . . **R. speciosa**
Sweet C. . . . . . . **R. subtomentosa**

Conehead . . . . **Strobilanthes**
Bedding C. . . . . . . **S. isophyllus**
Burma C. . . . . **S. dyerianus**
Zigzag C. . . . . . . **S. anisophyllus**

Confederate-jasmine
Starjasmine, Chinese: **Trachelospermum jasminoides**

CON'GEA . . . . Congea
tomento'sa . . . . . . Woolly C.

CONICO'SIA **MESEMBRYANTHEMUM**
See **SUCCULENTS.**

Conifer

Any tree or shrub, as a Pine or Fir, belonging to the Conifer family (Coniferae, or Pinaceae).

CONIOGRAM'ME
See **FERN GENERA.**

CONIOSELI'NUM . Hemlockparsley
chinen'se . . . . . Appalachian H.

CO'NIUM
macula'tum . . . . Poisonhemlock

This is undoubtedly the plant to which, historically and etymologically, the English plant name Hemlock properly belongs. Unfortunately, however, the North American-Asiatic coniferous tree genus Tsuga (unknown in England when this country was settled by English-speaking peoples) has usurped the name Hemlock, which has become so entrenched in usage that the misnomer can probably never be dislodged. This makes it necessary to rename the true Hemlock "Poisonhemlock." Attention is called to the significance of this name: Anglo-Saxon *hem* (meadow, or border) and *lok* or *lich* (death, or corpse), the former surviving in such a phrase as the "hem of a skirt," and the latter in the "lich gate" of a cemetery. "Meadow death" is an appropriate name for a deadly plant (like Conium maculatum) growing in meadows or meadow borders, but is eminently inappropriate for the tree genus Tsuga, which is neither an inhabitant of meadows nor poisonous.

CONNA'RUS . . . . . . Zebrawood
guianen'sis . . . . Guiana Z.

CONOCAR'PUS
erec'ta . . . . . Buttonmangrove

CONOCLI'NIUM . . **EUPATORIUM**

CONOPHYL'LUM **MESEMBRYANTHEMUM**
See **SUCCULENTS.**

CONOPHY'TUM **MESEMBRYANTHEMUM**
See **SUCCULENTS.**

CONRADI'NA . . . . . Conradina
canes'cens . . . . . . Bluesage C.
verticilla'ta . . . . . Whorled C.

CONRIN'GIA . . . . . . Haresear
orienta'lis . . . . Treacle H.

CONSOLE'A . . . . . . **OPUNTIA**
See **CACTUS GENERA.**

CONVALLA'RIA . . Lilyofthevalley
maja'lis . . . . . Lilyofthevalley
—fortun'ei . . . . Fortunes L.
—rose'a . . . . Pink L.

CONVOL'VULUS (*CALYSTEGIA; RHODORHIZA*) |w . . Glorybind
althaeoi'des . . Mediterranean G.
arven'sis |w . . . . . European G.
au'reus . . . . Golden G.
canta'brica . . . . . Cantabrian G.
cneo'rum
cupania'nus . . . . **C. tricolor**
elonga'tus . . . . Solitary G.
farino'sus
flor'idus (*Rhodorhiza florida*) Canary G.
hedera'ceus (*Calystegia pubescens*) Ivy G.
inca'nus . . . . Nebraska G.

CONVOLVULUS, continued
japon'icus (*Calystegia japonica*) Rose Glorybind
luteo'lus . . . . **C. purpuratus**
macroste'gius (*occidentalis*) California G.
ma'jor . . . . . . **Ipomoea purpurea**
mauritan'icus . . . . . Morocco G.
pentapetaloi'des . . . Crawling G.
polymor'phus . . . . . Variable G.
purpura'tus (*luteolus* Gray, *not* Spreng.) Pacific G.
purpu'reus . . . . **Ipomoea purpurea**
scammo'nia . . . . . Scammony G.
scopa'rius (*Rhodorhiza scoparia*)
se'pium (*Calystegia s.*) |w . Hedge G.
sic'ulus . . . . Baby G.
soldanel'la (*Calystegia s.*) . Seashore G.
spithamae'us (*Calystegia s.*) |w
tri'color (*cupanianus*) . . . Dwarf G.
undula'tus

Coolweed . . . . Clearweed, Canada: **Pilea pumila**

Coontie . . . . . . **Zamia integrifolia**
St. Johns C. . . . . **Z. pumila**

∞**COOPERAN'THES** (*COOPERIA* × *ZEPHYRANTHES*) ∞Cooperanthes
₵Alipore Beauty. hv.
₵Autumntint
₵Balletgirl
₵Canarybird
₵Clara
₵Dogstar
₵Emperor
₵Enchantress
₵Goldfinch
₵Goliath
₵Hereward
₵His Majesty
₵Ida
₵Jupiter
₵Lancaster
₵Mary
₵Peter Pan
₵Prince of Wales
₵Queen Mary
₵Rheingold
₵Salmon
₵Satyr
₵Star of Alipore
₵Whitequeen

COOPER'IA . . . . Rainlily
al'bicans . . . . White R.
drum'mondi . . . . Eveningstar R.
—chloroso'len . . . Greentip E.R.
kansen'sis . . . . Kansas R.
peduncula'ta . . . . . Redtinge R.
small'i . . . . Smalls R.
traub'i . . . . Traub R.

Coowarrabox . . Eucalyptus, Cambage: **Eucalyptus cambageana**

COPAIF'ERA . . . . . Copaltree
coleosper'ma . . . . . Rhodesian C.
conjuga'ta (*gorskiana; Gorskia c.*) Inhambane C.
copallif'era (*guibortiana*) SierraLeone C.
demeus'ei . . . . Congo C.
langs'dorfi . . . . Balsam C.
mopa'ne . . . . Mopane C.
officina'lis . . . . . . Copaiba C.
salikoun'da
tessmann'i . . . . . . Tessmann C.

Copal, Accra . . Daniella, Ogeagum: **Daniella ogea**

Copaltree . . . . **Copaifera**
Balsam C. . . . . **C. langsdorfi**
Congo C. . . . . **C. demeusei**
Copaiba C. . . . . . . **C. officinalis**
Inhambane C. . . . . **C. conjugata**
Mopane C. . . . . . . **C. mopane**
Rhodesian C. . . . **C. coleosperma**
SierraLeone C. . . . **C. copallifera**
Tessmann C. . . . . . **C. tessmanni**

COPERNIC'IA . . . . . Copernicia
See **PALM GENERA.**

Copernicia . . . . **Copernicia**
Bailey C. . . . . **C. baileyana**
Brittons C. . . . . . . **C. brittonorum**
Burret C. . . . . . . **C. burretiana**
Caranda C. . . . . . . **C. australis**
Carnaubapalm . . . . . **C. cerifera**
Clark C. . . . . **C. clarki**
Cowell C. . . . . **C. cowelli**
Torres C. . . . . **C. torreana**
Yarey C. . . . . **C. yarey**

COPIAPO'A
See **CACTUS GENERA.**

Copperleaf . . . . **Acalypha**
Balfour C. . . . . **A. balfouri**
California C. . . . . . **A. californica**
Chenille C. . . . . . . **A. hispida**
Hophornbeam C. . . . **A. ostryaefolia**
Lindheimer C. . . . . **A. lindheimeri**
NewMexico C. . . . **A. neomexicana**
Painted C. . . . . . **A. wilkesiana**
Poirets C. . . . . **A. poireti**
Slender C. . . . . . . **A. gracilens**
Virginia C. . . . . . . **A. virginica**

Coppertip . . . . **Crocosmia**
Golden C. . . . . **C. aurea**

COPRI'NUS . . . . Coprinus
atramenta'rius . . . . . Inkcap C.
coma'tus . . . . . Shaggymane C.
mica'ceus . . . . Shiny Inkcap C.

COPROS'MA . . . . Coprosma
acero'sa . . . . Needle C.
areola'ta
bau'eri (*baueriana*) . . . . Hedge C.
—craw'fordi . . . . Crawford H.C.
—margina'ta
—stock'i . . . . Stocks H.C.
—variega'ta . . . . Blotched H.C.
cunea'ta . . . . . Clusterberry C.
cunningham'i . . . Cunningham C.
kirk'i . . . . Kirks C.
lu'cida . . . . Shiny C.
macrocar'pa . . . . . Bigfruit C.
microcar'pa . . . . Littlefruit C.
parviflo'ra . . . . Littleflower C.
pe'triei . . . . Petries C.
propin'qua
ramulo'sa . . . . Crawling C.
rhamnoi'des . . . . . Buckthorn C.
rig'ida . . . . . . Yellowberry C.
robus'ta . . . . Robust C.
—angusta'ta
rotundifo'lia . . . . . . Orbleaf C.
rugo'sa . . . . Blueberry C.
spathula'ta . . . . Ebonyberry C.
tenuicau'lis
tenuifo'lia

Coprosma . . . . **Coprosma**
Bigfruit C. . . . . . . **C. macrocarpa**
Blotched Hedge C.
C. baueri variegata

Coprosma, continued
Blueberry C. . . . . **Coprosma rugosa**
Buckthorn C. . . . . . **C. rhamnoides**
Clusterberry C. . . . . **C. cuneata**
Crawford Hedge C.
C. baueri crawfordi
Crawling C. . . . . . . **C. ramulosa**
Cunningham C. . . . **C. cunninghami**
Ebonyberry C. . . . . **C. spathulata**
Hedge C. . . . . **C. baueri**
Kirks C. . . . . **C. kirki**
Littleflower C. . . . **C. parviflora**
Littlefruit C. . . . . **C. microcarpa**
Needle C. . . . . **C. acerosa**
Orbleaf C. . . . . . **C. rotundifolia**
Petries C. . . . . **C. petriei**
Robust C. . . . . **C. robusta**
Shiny C. . . . . **C. lucida**
Stocks Hedge C. . . **C. baueri stocki**
Yellowberry C. . . . . . . **C. rigida**

COP'TIS |w . . . . Goldthread
asplenifo'lia . . . . Ferny G.
groenlan'dica . . . . . . Common G.
lacinia'ta . . . . Cutleaf G.
occidenta'lis . . . . . . Western G.
trifo'lia |w . . . . Alaska G.

Coracanmillet . . . . . Ragimillet: **Eleusine coracana**

Coralbean . . . . **Erythrina**
Brotero C. . . . . **E. broteroi**
Bucare C. . . . . . . **E. poeppigiana**
Cockspur C. . . . . . **E. crista-galli**
Common C. . . . **E. corallodendrum**
Coralline C. . . . . . **E. coralloides**
Eastern C. . . . . **E. herbacea**
Goldman C. . . . . . . **E. goldmani**
Himalayan C. . . . . **E. arborescens**
Hume C. . . . . **E. humeana**
India C. . . . . **E. indica**
Senegal C. . . . . . **E. senegalensis**
Variegated C. . . . . . . **E. variegata**
Western C. . . . . **E. flabelliformis**

Coralbells . . . **Heuchera sanguinea**

Coralberry
∞ Chenault C.
∞ **Symphoricarpos chenaulti**
Chinese C. . . . . **S. sinensis**
Indiancurrant C. . . **S. orbiculatus**

Coralblow . . . . **Russelia**
Coralplant . . . . **R. equisetiformis**
Fountainplant . . . . . **R. lemoinei**
Hybrid C. . . . . . **R. elegantissima**
Leafy C. . . . . **R. sarmentosa**

Coralbush . . . . **Templetonia**
Leafless C. . . . . **T. egena**
Mueller C. . . . . **T. muelleri**
Red C. . . . . **T. retusa**
Yellow C. . . . . **T. sulcata**

Coraldrops . . . . **Bessera**
Showy C. . . . . **B. elegans**

CORALLORRHI'ZA . . . . Coralroot
See **ORCHID GENERA, HARDY TERRESTRIAL GROUP.**

Coralplant . . . **Russelia equisetiformis**

Coralroot . . . . **Corallorrhiza**
Crestedcoralroot **Hexalectris spicata**
Early Coralroot . . . . . . **C. trifida**
Hooded C. . . . . **C. striata**
Late C. . . . . **C. odontorhiza**
Pacific C. . . . . . . **C. mertensiana**
Spotted C. . . . . **C. maculata**
Wister C. . . . . **C. wisteriana**

Coralvine . . . . **Antigonon**
Mountainrose C. . . . . . **A. leptopus**
White M. C. . . . . **A. l. albus**

CORCHOROP'SIS
crena'ta

CORCHO'RUS . . . . Jute
capsula'ris . . . . Roundpod J.
japon'icus . . . . . **Kerria japonica**
olito'rius . Potherb J. (*Jews-mallow*)

CORDEAU'XIA
ed'ulis . . . . Yebbnut

Cordgrass . . . . **Spartina**
Alkali C. . . . . **S. gracilis**
Big C. . . . . **S. cynosuroides**
California C. . . . . . . **S. leiantha**
Gulf C. . . . . **S. spartinae**
Marshhay C. . . . . **S. patens**
Prairie C. . . . . **S. pectinata**
Saltmarsh C.; Saltmeadow C.
Marshhay C.
Sand C. . . . . **S. bakeri**
Smooth C. . . . . . . **S. alterniflora**
Townsend C. . . . . . **S. townsendi**
Tufted Marshhay C.
S. patens caespitosa

COR'DIA . . . . Cordia
al'ba . . . . White C.
alliodo'ra (*cerdana; frondosa; Cerdana a.*) . . . . Onion C.
boissier'i . . . . Anacahuita
colococ'ca . . . . Manjack C.
fragrantis'sima . . . . . Fragrant C.
francis'ci . . . . Sandpaper C.
frondo'sa . . . . **C. alliodora**
gla'bra . . . . Nopo C.
goeldia'na . . . . Goeldi C.
grandiflo'ra . . . . . Bigflower C.
lute'a . . . . Yellow C.
macleo'di . . . . MacLeod C.
myx'a . . . . Sebastanplum C.
ni'tida . . . . Glossy C.
obli'qua
sebeste'na (*Sebesten s.*) Geigertree C.
trem'ula

Cordia . . . . **Cordia**
Anacahuita . . . . **C. boissieri**
Bigflower C. . . . . . **C. grandiflora**
Fragrant C. . . . . **C. fragrantissima**
Geigertree C. . . . . . **C. sebestena**
Glossy C . . . . **C. nitida**
Goeldi C. . . . . **C. goeldiana**
MacLeod C. . . . . . . **C. macleodi**
Manjack C. . . . . . . **C. colococca**
Nopo C. . . . . **C. glabra**
Onion C. . . . . **C. alliodora**
Sandpaper C. . . . . . . **C. francisci**
Sebastanplum C. . . . . . . **C. myxa**
White C. . . . . **C. alba**
Yellow C. . . . . **C. lutea**

COR'DULA . . . . . . Slipperorchid
See **ORCHID GENERA.**

CORDYLAN'THUS (*ADENOSTEGIA*) |w . . . . Birdbeak
ere'micus (*Adenostegia eremica*)
DeathValley B.
marit'imus |w . . . . . . Coastal B.
mol'lis |w
ramo'sus (*Adenostegia ramosa*)
Bushy B.
wright'i (*Adenostegia w.*) . Wright B.

CORDYLI'NE . . . . Dracena
The common name for Cordyline, "Dracena," should not be confused with the common name for the closely allied Dracaena, "Dracaena."
austra'lis (*Dracaena a.*) . . Giant D. (*Tikouka*)
₵Doucet (*douceti*) hv.

CORDYLINE, continued
banks'i . . . . . . BANKS DRACENA
indivi'sa (*Dracaena i.*) . . BLUE D.
₵**norwoodien'sis** Hort. . MANYSTRIPE D.
pumil'io . . . . . . SLIMPANICLE D.
ru'bra . . . . LILAC D.
stric'ta . . . . . AUSTRALIAN D.
—**grand'is**
termina'lis (*Dracaena t.*) . COMMON D.
—**amab'ilis** . . . . . . AMABILIS D.
₵BAPTIST (*baptisti*) HV. C. terminalis
₵DRAGONSBLOOD
₵HYBRID (*hybrida*)
₵IMPERIAL (*imperialis*)
₵METALLIC (*metallica*)
₵RAYO
₵ROSYRIB (*nigro-rubra*)
₵YOUNGS (*youngi*)

Probably all of these are clons.
ANDREIRA. HV. Cordyline
ATROPURPUREA
BERTHA ANDRE
EMERALD (*knerki*)
FIREBRAND
GEN. PERSHING
GOV. TOWNER
HAAGE (*haageana*)
HARMONY
JANET CRAIG
KELLERI
LENTIGNOSA
LORD WOLSELEY
MARGARET STOREY
MME. EUGENE ANDRE
MRS. RUFUS SCOTT
PRES. HOOVER
PRINCE ALBERT
PUERTORICO
REDCLOUD
REDWING
ROTH (*rothiana*)
TORCH
TRICOLOR
VARIEGATED
VEITCH (*veitchi*)

CORE'MA . . . . BROOMCROWBERRY
con'radi . . . . . BROOMCROWBERRY

COREOP'SIS (*CALLIOPSIS; LEPTOSYNE*) |w . . . . . COREOPSIS
atkinsonia'na . . . . ATKINSON C.
auricula'ta . . . . EARED C.
₵SUPERB (*superba*) HV.
bi'color . . . . C. **tinctoria**
bigelo'vi (*Leptosyne b.*) . BIGELOW C.
calliopsi'dea (*Leptosyne c.*) CALIFORNIA C.
cardaminefo'lia |w . . . CARDAMINE C.
corona'ta . . . . **C. nuecensis**
delphinifo'lia . . . . . LARKSPUR C.
discoi'des . . . . . **Bidens discoidea**
doug'lasi (*Leptosyne d.; L. californica*) DOUGLAS C.
drum'mondi (*picta*) . GOLDENWAVE C.
gigan'tea (*Leptosyne g.*) . . GIANT C.
grandiflo'ra (*floribunda; C. lanceolata g.*) BIGFLOWER C.
₵BIGDOUBLE (*florepleno*) HV.
₵MAYFIELD GIANT
₵PERRYS
₵SUPERB (*auricula superba*)
×**hy'brida** . . . . GOLDEN GIANT C.
involucra'ta . . . . **Bidens polylepis**
lanceola'ta (*Calliopsis l.*) . LANCE C.
—*grandiflo'ra* . . . . **C. grandiflora**
₵MAYFIELD GIANT. HV. C. lanceolata

COREOPSIS, continued
ma'jor (*senifolia*) . TREFOIL COREOPSIS
marit'ima (*Leptosyne m.*) . PACIFIC C.
microphyl'la . . . . . . TINYLEAF C.
nuecen'sis (*coronata; Calliopsis c.*) CROWN C.
palma'ta . . . . FINGER C.
pic'ta . . . . **C. drummondi**
radia'ta (*Calliopsis r.*) . . . QUILL C.
rose'a . . . . ROSE C.
—**na'na** . . . . DWARF R.C.
senifo'lia . . . . **C. major**
still'mani (*Leptosyne s.*) . STILLMAN C.
tincto'ria (*bicolor; Calliopsis b., elegans, marmorata,* and *tinctoria*). PLAINS C.
—**atropurpu'rea** . . . PURPLE P.C.
trip'teris . . . . ATLANTIC C.
verticilla'ta (*tenuifolia*) THREADLEAF C.

COREOPSIS . . . . **Coreopsis**
ATKINSON C. . . . . **C. atkinsoniana**
ATLANTIC C. . . . . . . **C. tripteris**
BIGELOW C. . . . . . . **C. bigelovi**
BIGFLOWER C. . . . . **C. grandiflora**
CALIFORNIA C. . . . **C. calliopsidea**
CARDAMINE C. . . **C. cardaminefolia**
CROWN C. . . . . **C. nuecensis**
DOUGLAS C. . . . . . . **C. douglasi**
DWARF ROSE C. . . . **C. rosea nana**
EARED C. . . . . **C. auriculata**
FINGER C. . . . . **C. palmata**
GIANT C. . . . . **C. gigantea**
GOLDEN G. C. . . . . . ×**C. hybrida**
GOLDENWAVE C. . . . **C. drummondi**
LANCE C. . . . . **C. lanceolata**
LARKSPUR C. . . . . **C. delphinifolia**
PACIFIC C. . . . . **C. maritima**
PLAINS C. . . . . **C. tinctoria**
PURPLE P. C. . . . **C. t. atropurpurea**
QUILL C. . . . . **C. radiata**
ROSE C. . . . . **C. rosea**
STILLMAN C. . . . . . . **C. stillmani**
THREADLEAF C. . . . **C. verticillata**
TINYLEAF C. . . . . . **C. microphylla**
TREFOIL C. . . . . **C. major**

CORETHROGY'NE . . COTTONASTER
califor'nica . . . . . CALIFORNIA C.
filaginifo'lia . . . . . . CUDWEED C.

CORIANDER . . . **Coriandrum sativum**

CORIAN'DRUM . . . . . CORIANDER
sati'vum . . . . CORIANDER

CORIA'RIA . . . . CORIARIA
japon'ica . . . . JAPANESE C.
myrtifo'lia . . . . MYRTLE C.
ruscifo'lia (*sarmentosa*) NEWZEALAND C. (*Tutu; Wineberry*)
termina'lis . . . . SIKKIM C.
—**xanthocar'pa** . . YELLOWFRUIT S.C.
thymifo'lia . . . . THYMELEAF C.

CORIDOCH'LOA . . BUGSEEDGRASS
See **GRASS GENERA.**

Coridothy'mus capita'tus . . **Thymus c.**

CORISPER'MUM . . . . . TICKSEED
hyssopifo'lium . . . . HYSSOPLEAF T.

CORKTREE . . . . **Phellodendron**
AMUR C. . . . . **P. amurense**
CHINESE C. . . . . . . **P. chinense**
JAPANESE C. . . . . . **P. japonicum**
LAVALLE C. . . . . **P. lavallei**
PEARFRUIT C. . . . . . **P. piriforme**
SAKHALIN C. . . . **P. sachalinense**
SMOOTH CHINESE C. **P. chinense glabriusculum**

CORKWING . . . . **Phellopterus**
BIGROOT C. . . . . . **P. macrorhizus**
UTAH C. . . . . **P. utahensis**

CORKWOOD . . . . **Leitneria**
FLORIDA C. . . . . **L. floridana**

CORMONE'MA
ovalifo'lium

CORN
CHICKENCORN **Sorghum vulgare drummondi**
INDIAN C. (MAIZE) . . . . **Zea mays**
POD C. . . . . **Z. m. tunicata**

CORNBIND . . . . **Polygonum**
See also BISTORT, FLEECEFLOWER, KNOTWEED, LADYSTHUMB, SMARTWEED.
DULLSEED C. . . . . **P. convolvulus**
HEDGE C. . . . . **P. scandens**

CORNCOCKLE . . . . **Agrostemma**
COMMON C. . . . . **A. githago**

CORNFLOWER . . . **Centaurea cyanus**

CORNICULA'RIA . . . CORNICULARIA
aculea'ta . . . . PRICKLY C.
—**spadi'cea** . . . . . . BROWN P.C.

Cornmarigold. CHRYSANTHEMUM, CORN: **Chrysanthemum segetum**

CORNSALAD . . . . **Valerianella**
EUROPEAN C. . . . . . . **V. olitoria**
ITALIAN C. . . . . **V. eriocarpa**
NUTTALL C. . . . . **V. nuttalli**
PRICKLY C. . . . . **V. echinata**
TOOTHED C. . . . . **V. dentata**
WOODS C. . . . . . . **V. woodsiana**

CORNSMUT . . . . **Ustilago zeae**

CORNUCO'PIAE
cuculla'tum

COR'NUS (*BENTHAMIA; CHAMAEPERICLYMENUM; SVIDA*) |w . . . . DOGWOOD
al'ba . . . . TATARIAN D.
—**sibir'ica** (*C. sibirica*) . SIBERIAN D.
₵CREAMEDGE (*argenteo-marginata*) HV. C. alba
₵MOTTLED (*gouchaulti*)
₵PURPLETWIG (*kesselringi*)
₵WESTONBIRD
₵YELLOWEDGE (*spaethi*)
alternifo'lia |w . . . . . . PAGODA D.
₵SILVERLEAF (*argentea*) HV.
amo'mum (*caerulea; sericea*) |w SILKY D. (*Squawbush*)
∞**arnoldia'na** (*obliqua* × *paniculata*) ∞ ARNOLD D.
asperifo'lia (*candidissima*) |w ROUGHLEAF D.
austra'lis
—**koe'nigi**
bai'leyi |w . . . . BAILEY D.
brachypo'da . . . . . **C. macrophylla**
bretschnei'deri . . BRETSCHNEIDER D.
caeru'lea . . . . **C. amomum**
califor'nica . . . . . CALIFORNIA D.
canaden'sis (*Chamaepericlymenum canadense*) |w . . . . BUNCHBERRY D.
candidis'sima . . . . . **C. asperifolia**
capita'ta (*Benthamia fragifera*) EVERGREEN D.
circina'ta . . . . **C. rugosa**
controver'sa . . . . GIANT D.
₵VARIEGATED. HV.
corea'na . . . . KOREAN D.
∞**du'bia** (*amomum* × *paucinervis*)
∞**dun'bari** (*asperifolia* × *macrophylla*)

CORNUS, continued
flo'rida (*Cynoxylon floridum*) |w Flowering Dogwood
—xanthocar'pa . Yellowberry F.D.
¢Double (*plena; pluribracteata*) hv. C. florida
¢Redflowering (*rubra*)
¢Varileaf (*welchi*)
¢Weeping (*pendula*)
¢Willowleaf (*salicifolia*)
foem'ina (*femina*) . Stiffcornel D.
glabra'ta . . . . . . Brown D.
hems'leyi . . . Hemsley Cornel D.
hes'sei . . . . Hesse D.
∞ **hor'seyi** . . . . ∞ Horsey D.
kou'sa (*Benthamia japonica*). Kousa D.
—chinen'sis . . . . . Chinese K.D.
macrophyl'la (*brachypoda*) Largeleaf D.
mas' (*mascula*) Corneliancherry D.
—na'na . . . . Dwarf C.D.
—*na'na* Dipp., *not* Carr.. . **C. pumila**
¢Variegated (*elegantissima*) hv. C. mas
¢Whiteedge (*variegata*)
¢Whitefruit (*alba*)
¢Yellowfruit (*flava*)
¢Yellowleaf (*aurea*)
mon'beigi . . . . Monbeig D.
nutt'alli |w . . . . Pacific D.
¢Winkenwerder (*winkenwerderi*) hv.
obli'qua (*purpusi*) . . . . Pale D.
oblon'ga
occidenta'lis |w . . . . Western D.
officina'lis . . . Japanesecornel D.
panicula'ta. . . . . . . **C. racemosa**
pauciner'vis . . . . . Littleleaf D.
poliophyl'la
pubes'cens (*Svida p.*)
pu'mila (*C. mas nana* Dipp., *not* Carr.)
pur'pusi . . . . **C. obliqua**
racemo'sa (*paniculata*) |w . Gray D.
rugo'sa (*circinata*) |w . Roundleaf D.
sanguin'ea . . . . Bloodtwig D.
¢Deepred (*atrosanguinea*) hv.
¢Greentwig (*viridissima*)
¢Piebald (*variegata*)
seric'ea . . . . **C. amomum**
ses'silis . . . . . . Blackfruit D.
sibir'ica . . . . **C. alba s.**
stolonif'era |w . . . . Redosier D. (*Squawbush*)
—coloraden'sis . . . Colorado R.D.
—flavira'mea . . Yellowtwig R.D.
—ni'tida . . . . Greentwig R.D.
¢Kelseydwarf. hv. C. stolonifera
wal'teri . . . . Walter D.
Corojo . . . . . . Acrocomia, Cuban: **Acrocomia armentalis**

CORO'KIA . . . . Corokia
buddleoi'des
—linea'ris
cheese'manni . . . Cheesemann C.
cotoneas'ter . . . . Cotoneaster C.
macrocar'pa . . . . . . Bigfruit C.
virga'ta

CORONA'RIA . . . . . . **LYCHNIS**

CORONIL'LA . . . . Coronilla
cappado'cica (*iberica*) Cappadocian C.
emeroi'des
em'erus . . . . . Scorpionsenna C.
glau'ca . . . . Honey C.
¢Variegated (*variegata*) hv.
jun'cea . . . . Rush C.
min'ima . . . Small Crownvetch C.

CORONILLA, continued
monta'na . . Mountain Coronilla
scorpioi'des . . . . . . Scorpion C.
securida'ca . . . **Securigera coronilla**
valenti'na
va'ria . . . . Crownvetch C.

CORONO'PUS (*CARARA*) |w Wartcress
did'ymus (*Carara didyma*) |w Swine W.
procum'bens (*Carara coronopus*) Creeping W.

CORO'ZO (*ALFONSIA*) American-oilpalm
See **PALM GENERA.**
Corozo . . . Acrocomia, PuertoRico: **Acrocomia media**

CORPUSCULA'RIA **MESEMBRYANTHEMUM**
See **SUCCULENTS.**

COR'REA . . . . Correa
al'ba . . . . White C.
bauerlen'i . . . . . . Bauerlen C.
ru'bra . . . . Red C.
—leucocla'da
specio'sa (*bicolor*) . . . Broadleaf C.
ventrico'sa

CORRYOCAC'TUS . . . . . **CEREUS**
See **CACTUS GENERA.**

CORTADE'RIA . . . Pampasgrass
See **GRASS GENERA.**

CORTINA'RIUS . . . . Cortinarius
cinnamo'meus
lilaci'nus

CORTINEL'LUS . . . . Cortinellus
edo'des (*berkelyanus*) . . Shiitake C.

CORTU'SA
matthi'oli

CORYD'ALIS (*CAPNOIDES*) |w Corydalis
al'leni . . . . Allen C.
au'rea (*Capnoides aureum*) Golden C.
bractea'ta
brande'gei . . . . . . Brandegee C.
bulbo'sa . . . . Bulb C.
capnoi'des
casea'na (*Capnoides caseanum*) Fitweed C.
cheilanthifo'lia . . . . . . Chinese C.
curvisili'qua
densiflo'ra
fla'vula
glau'ca . . . . . . **C. sempervirens**
lute'a . . . . Yellow C.
monta'na |w . . . . . Mountain C.
no'bilis (*Capnoides n.*) . Siberian C.
ochoten'sis
ochroleu'ca
ophiocar'pa
orthocar'pa
pal'lida
rose'a . . . . Rosy C.
rupes'tris
scou'leri . . . . Scouler C.
sempervi'rens (*glauca*) . . . Pale C.
—rose'a
thalictrifo'lia . . . . Meadowrue C.
tubero'sa . . . . Tuber C.
wil'soni . . . . Wilson C.
Corydalis . . . . **Corydalis**
Allen C. . . . . **C. alleni**
Brandegee C. . . . . . **C. brandegei**

Corydalis, continued
Bulb C. . . . . . . **Corydalis bulbosa**
Chinese C. . . . . **C. cheilanthifolia**
Fitweed C. . . . . **C. caseana**
Golden C. . . . . **C. aurea**
Meadowrue C. . . . **C. thalictrifolia**
Mountain C. . . . . **C. montana**
Pale C. . . . . **C. sempervirens**
Rosy C. . . . . **C. rosea**
Scouler C. . . . . **C. scouleri**
Siberian C. . . . . **C. nobilis**
Tuber C. . . . . **C. tuberosa**
Wilson C. . . . . **C. wilsoni**
Yellow C. . . . . **C. lutea**

CORYLOP'SIS . . . . Winterhazel
glabres'cens (*gotoana*) . Fragrant W.
grif'fithi . . . . Griffith W.
pauciflo'ra . . . . . . Buttercup W.
platypet'ala
sinen'sis . . . . Chinese W.
—glandulif'era
spica'ta . . . . Spike W.
veitchia'na . . . . Veitch W.
willmot'tiae . . . . . Willmott W.
wil'soni . . . . Wilson W.
yunnanen'sis . . . . . . Yunnan W.

COR'YLUS |w . . . . Filbert (*Hazel*)

U. S. Department of Agriculture policy favors use of the term Filbert, rather than Hazel for these species. The nuts are known in commerce as Filberts or occasionally Hazelnuts, the former preferred in the trade. Hazel, of course, the original English name for these shrubs, has given rise to a color name, and, in the famous floral alphabet of the Celts, stood for the letter H. Filbert is of French origin, the nuts becoming ripe about the time of St. Philibert's Day (August 22).

For varieties of Filbert grown for their nuts, see **FRUIT AND EDIBLE NUT NAMES.**

america'na |w . . . . American F.
∞ **america'na** × **max'ima** . . ∞ Amax F.
avella'na . . . . . . European F.
—gran'dis . . . . . Cob F. (*Cobnut*)
—pon'tica . . . . . . Caucasian F.
¢Curly (*contorta*) hv. C. avellana
¢Cutleaf (*laciniata*)
¢Golden (*aurea*)
¢Oakleaf (*quercifolia*)
¢Purple (*atropurpurea*)
¢Weeping (*pendula*)
califor'nica . . . . . California F.
chinen'sis . . . . Chinese F.
colur'na . . . . Turkish F.
∞ **colurnoi'des** (*avellana* × *colurna*) ∞ Colurnoid F.
cornu'ta (*rostrata*) |w . . . Beaked F.
fe'rox . . . . Himalaya F.
heterophyl'la . . . . . . Siberian F.
—sutchuenen'sis . . . Szechwan F.
—yunnanen'sis . . . . . Yunnan F.
max'ima . . . . Giant F.
¢Lambert. hv.
¢Purple Giant (*purpurea*)
∞ **mildreden'sis** (*americana* × *avellana*) ∞ Mildred F.
rostra'ta . . . . **C. cornuta**
sieboldia'na . . . . . . Japanese F.
—mandshur'ica . . . . Manchu F.
∞ **spines'cens** (*avellana* × *tibetica*) ∞ Spiny F.
tibet'ica . . . . Tibetan F.
∞ **vilmori'ni** (*avellana* × *chinensis*) ∞ Vilmorin F.

CORYNAN'THE . . . . Corynanthe
johim'be . . . . Yohimbe C.

CORYNE'PHORUS . Clubawngrass
See **GRASS GENERA.**

CORYNOCAR'PUS . . . . Karakanut
laeviga'ta . . . . . . NewZealand K.

CORYNOPUN'TIA . . . . **OPUNTIA**
See **CACTUS GENERA.**

CORY'PHA . . . . Corypha
See **PALM GENERA.**

CORYPHAN'THA (*ESCOBARIA; NEOBESSEYA*) . . . Coryphantha
See **CACTUS GENERA.**

Coryphantha . . . . . . **Coryphantha**
Alverson C. . . . . . . **C. alversoni**
Arizona C. . . . . . . **C. arizonica**
Durango C. . . . . . **C. durangensis**
Foxtail C. . . . . . . **C. deserti**
Georges C. . . . . **C. georgi**
Golfball C. . . . . . . **C. aggregata**
Missouri C. . . . . **C. missouriensis**
Nipple C. . . . . **C. sulcata**
Palmer C. . . . . **C. palmeri**
Runyon C. . . . . **C. runyoni**
Sneed C. . . . . **C. sneedi**
Spikespine C. . . . . **C. robustispina**
Spinystars C. . . . **C. neomexicana**
Wissmann C. . . . . **C. wissmanni**

CORYTHOLO'MA . . . Corytholoma
cardina'lis (*Gesneria c.; G. macrantha*) Cardinal C.

COSCI'NIUM
fenestra'tum . . . . . Calumbawood

COSMI'DIUM . . **THELESPERMA**
geban'ga . . . . **T. elatum**

COS'MOS . . . . Cosmos
bipinna'tus . . . . . Common C.
cauda'tus . . . . Tailed C.
diversifo'lius (*Bidens atrosanguinea; B. dahlioides*) . . . . . . Black C.
sulphu'reus . . . . . Yellow C.

COSSO'NIA
africa'na

COS'TUS . . . . Spiralflag
ig'neus
malortiea'nus (*zebrinus*)
specio'sus . . . . . . Canereed S.

COTI'NUS . . . . Smoketree
america'nus (*cotinoides; Rhus americana; R. cotinoides*) . American S.
coggyg'ria (*coccygea; cotinus; Rhus cotinus*) . Common S. (*Aaronsbeard*)
ȻPurple (*atropurpurea*) hv.
ȻWeeping (*pendulus*)

Cotobark . . . . **Aniba coto**

COTONEAS'TER |w . . Cotoneaster
acumina'ta . . . . . Sharpleaf C.
acutifo'lia . . . . . . Peking C.
—villo'sula . . . . . . Hairy P.C.
adpres'sa . . . . . . Creeping C.
—prae'cox (*C. praecox*) . Early C.
af'finis . . . . . . Brownberry C.
—bacilla'ris
ambig'ua
amoe'na
angustifo'lia . . . . . **Pyracantha a.**
apicula'ta . . . . . . Cranberry C.
applana'ta . . . . . . **C. dielsiana**
bulla'ta . . . . Hollyberry C.
—floribun'da . . . . . Vilmorin C.
—macrophyl'la . . . . . Bigleaf C.
buxifo'lia
This plant is often confused with C. rotundifolia.
—vel'laea

COTONEASTER, continued
conges'ta (*C. microphylla glacialis; pyrenaica*) . Pyrenees Cotoneaster
conspic'ua . . . . Wintergreen C.
—deco'ra (*C. decora*) . Necklace C.
coop'eri . . . . Cooper C.
cotoneas'ter . . . . . . **C. integerrima**
crenula'ta . . . . . . **Pyracantha c.**
∞ **cris'pi** (*frigida × pannosa*) ∞ Crisps C.
dam'meri (*humifusa*) . Bearberry C.
—rad'icans . . . . Littleleaf B.C.
davidia'na . . . . . **C. horizontalis**
dielsia'na (*applanata*) . . . Diels C.
—el'egans (*C. schneideri*). Coral D.C.
—ma'jor . . . . Big D.C.
—minia'ta . . . . **C. zabeli m.**
dis'ticha (*rotundifolia*)
divarica'ta . . . . . . Spreading C.
foveola'ta . . . . Glossy C.
franchet'i . . . . . . Franchet C.
—cineras'cens
frig'ida . . . . Himalayan C.
—aldenhamen'sis . Aldenham H.C.
—vicar'i
ȻYellowberry (*fructuluteo*) hv. C. frigida
glabra'ta . . . . Smooth C.
glaucophyl'la . . . Brightbead C.
—serot'ina (*C. parneyi; C. serotina*)
glomerula'ta . . . . Crimsonbead C.
harrovia'na . . . . . . Harrow C.
hebephyl'la . . . . . Cherryred C.
henrya'na . . . . Henry C.
himala'icus . . . . . . Littleleaf C.
horizonta'lis (*davidiana*) . . Rock C.
—perpusil'la (*C. perpusilla*) Ground C.
—wil'soni (*C. wilsoni* Hort., *not* Nakai) Wilson C.
ȻVariegated (*variegata*) hv. C. horizontalis
humifu'sa . . . . **C. dammeri**
hupehen'sis . . . . Hupeh C.
igna'va . . . . Turkestan C.
integer'rima (*cotoneaster; vulgaris*) European C.
lac'tea
Has been grown for several years under name of Cotoneaster parneyi; identified as Cotoneaster lactea by Eric Walther.
lind'leyi . . . . Lindley C.
lu'cida (*sinensis*) . . . . . Hedge C.
melanocar'pa (*nigra*)
—commix'ta
—laxiflo'ra
microphyl'la . . . . . Rockspray C.
—cochlea'ta
—glacia'lis . . . . . . **C. congesta**
—thymifo'lia (*C. thymifolia*) Thyme R.C.
moupinen'sis . . . . . . Moupin C.
multiflo'ra (*reflexa*)
—calocar'pa
—granaten'sis
ni'gra . . . . **C. melanocarpa**
ni'tens . . . . Pinkblush C.
nummula'ria . . . . . **C. racemiflora**
obscu'ra . . . . . . Bloodberry C.
—cornifo'lia . . . . . . Purple B.C.
oligocar'pa . . . . Redblob C.
panno'sa . . . . . . Silverleaf C.
—na'na . . . . Dwarf S.C.
par'neyi . . **C. glaucophylla serotina**
perpusil'la . . . . . **C. horizontalis p.**
prae'cox . . . . **C. adpressa p.**
prostra'ta . . . . . . **C. rotundifolia**
pyrena'ica . . . . **C. congesta**
racemiflo'ra (*nummularia*) Redbead C.
—desfontain'i

COTONEASTER, continued
racemiflo'ra microcar'pa
Little Rockspray Cotoneaster
—nummula'ria
—roylea'na (*C. r. orbicularis*)
—soongor'ica (*C. soongorica*) Sungari R.C.
—veitch'i . . . . Veitch R.C.
reflex'a . . . . **C. multiflora**
reticula'ta . . . . Jetbead C.
rhytidophyl'la . . . Orangebead C.
rose'a . . . . Redcurrant C.
rotundifo'lia (*prostrata*) . . Redbox C.
The name C. rotundifolia has often been misapplied to C. disticha.
—lana'ta (*C. wheeleri*) . Woolly R.C.
salicifo'lia . . . . . Willowleaf C.
—flocco'sa . . . . Hardy W.C.
—rugo'sa (*C. rugosa*) . Woolly W.C.
schnei'deri . . . **C. dielsiana elegans**
serot'ina . . . . . **C. glaucophylla s.**
silves'tri . . . . Silvestri C.
sim'onsi . . . . Simons C.
sinen'sis . . . . **C. lucida**
soongor'ica . . . . . **C. racemiflora s.**
tenui'pes . . . . Slender C.
thymifo'lia . . . . . **C. microphylla t.**
tomento'sa . . . . . Brickberry C.
turbina'ta . . . . . Brightberry C.
uniflo'ra . . . . . . Singleberry C.
verruculo'sa . . . . Scarletbead C.
vulga'ris . . . . **C. integerrima**
ward'i . . . . Wards C.
∞ **watere'ri** (*frigida × henryana*) ∞ Waterer C.
The cultivated shrub is presumably a clon of this.
wheel'eri . . . . **C. rotundifolia lanata**
wil'soni Hort., *not* Nakai **C. horizontalis w.**
C. wilsoni Nakai, a Formosan species not in culture.
za'beli . . . . . . Cherryberry C.
—minia'ta (*C. dielsiana m.*) Little C.C.

Cotoneaster . . . . . . **Cotoneaster**
Aldenham Himalayan C. **C. frigida aldenhamensis**
Bearberry C. . . . . . . **C. dammeri**
Big Diels C. . . . . **C. dielsiana major**
Bigleaf C. . . **C. bullata macrophylla**
Bloodberry C. . . . . . . **C. obscura**
Brickberry C. . . . . . **C. tomentosa**
Brightbead C. . . . **C. glaucophylla**
Brightberry C. . . . . . **C. turbinata**
Brownberry C. . . . . **C. affinis**
Cherryberry C. . . . . . . **C. zabeli**
Cherryred C. . . . . . **C. hebephylla**
Cooper C. . . . . **C. cooperi**
Coral Diels C. **C. dielsiana elegans**
Cranberry C. . . . . . . **C. apiculata**
Creeping C. . . . . . . **C. adpressa**
Crimsonbead C. . . . **C. glomerulata**
∞ Crisps C. . . . . ∞ **C. crispi**
Diels C. . . . . **C. dielsiana**
Dwarf Silverleaf C. **C. pannosa nana**
Early C. . . . **C. adpressa praecox**
European C. . . . . . **C. integerrima**
Franchet C. . . . . **C. francheti**
Glossy C. . . . . **C. foveolata**
Ground C. **C. horizontalis perpusilla**
Hairy Peking C. **C. acutifolia villosula**
Hardy Willowleaf C. **C. salicifolia floccosa**
Harrow C. . . . . **C. harroviana**
Hedge C. . . . . **C. lucida**
Henry C. . . . . **C. henryana**
Himalayan C. . . . . **C. frigida**

COTONEASTER, continued
HOLLYBERRY C. . Cotoneaster bullata
HUPEH C. . . . . . . C. hupehensis
JETBEAD C. . . . . . . C. reticulata
LINDLEY C. . . . . . . C. lindleyi
LITTLE CHERRYBERRY C.
C. zabeli miniata
LITTLELEAF BEARBERRY C.
C. dammeri radicans
LITTLELEAF C. . . . . C. himalaicus
LITTLE REDBEAD C.
C. racemiflora microcarpa
MOUPIN C. . . . . C. moupinensis
NECKLACE C. . C. conspicua decora
ORANGEBEAD C. . . C. rhytidophylla
PEKING C. . . . . C. acutifolia
PINKBLUSH C. . . . . . C. nitens
PURPLE BLOODBERRY C.
C. obscura cornifolia
PYRENEES C. . . . . . . C. congesta
REDBEAD C. . . . . . C. racemiflora
REDBLOB C. . . . . . C. oligocarpa
REDBOX C. . . . . . C. rotundifolia
REDCURRANT C. . . . . C. rosea
ROCK C. . . . . . . C. horizontalis
ROCKSPRAY C. . . . . C. microphylla
SCARLETBEAD C. . . . C. verruculosa
SHARPLEAF C. . . . . C. acuminata
SILVERLEAF C. . . . . . C. pannosa
SILVESTRI C. . . . . . . C. silvestri
SIMONS C. . . . . C. simonsi
SINGLEBERRY C. . . . . . C. uniflora
SLENDER C. . . . . . . C. tenuipes
SMOOTH C. . . . . . . C. glabrata
SPREADING C. . . . . C. divaricata
SUNGARI REDBEAD C.
C. racemiflora soongorica
THYME ROCKSPRAY C.
C. microphylla thymifolia
TURKESTAN C. . . . . . . C. ignava
VEITCH REDBEAD C.
C. racemiflora veitchi
VILMORIN C. . . C. bullata floribunda
WARDS C. . . . . C. wardi
∞ WATERER C. . . . . . ∞ C. watereri
WILLOWLEAF C. . . . . C. salicifolia
WILSON C. . . C. horizontalis wilsoni
WINTERGREEN C. . . . . C. conspicua
WOOLLY REDBOX C.
C. rotundifolia lanata
WOOLLY WILLOWLEAF C.
C. salicifolia rugosa

COTTAGRASS. Cottea; C. pappophoroides

COT'TEA . . . . COTTAGRASS
See **GRASS GENERA.**

COTTON . . . . Gossypium
ARABIAN C. . . . . G. stocksi
ASIATIC TREE C. . . . G. arboreum
AUSTRALIAN C. . . . . . . G. sturti
BOURBON C. . . . G. purpurascens
CHINA C. . . G. arboreum nanking
DAVIDSON C. . . . . G. davidsoni
FIJI C. . . . . G. taitense
HAWAIIAN C. . . . . G. tomentosum
INDIA LARGEBOLL C.
G. arboreum assamicum
INDIA SMALLBOLL C. . G. a. soudanense
KIRKS C. . . . . G. kirki
LEVANT C. . . . . . . G. herbaceum
SEAISLAND C. . . . . G. barbadense
THURBER C. . . . . . . G. thurberi
UPLAND C. . . . . . . G. hirsutum

COTTONASTER . . . . . . Corethrogyne
CALIFORNIA C. . . . . . C. californica
CUDWEED C. . . . . . C. filaginifolia

Cottongrass . . COTTONTOP: Trichachne

COTTONROSE . . . . . Gifola germanica

COTTONSEDGE . . . . . . Eriophorum
BROADLEAF C. . . . . . E. latifolium
NARROWLEAF C. . . E. angustifolium
SHEATHED C. . . . . . E. vaginatum
VIRGINIA C. . . . . . . E. virginicum

COTTONTHISTLE . . . . . Onopordum
CURLYBRACT C. . . . . O. bracteatum
EGYPTIAN C.
O. sibthorpianum alexandrinum
HYDRA C. . . . . . O. polycephalum
ILLYRIAN C. . . . . . . O. illyricum
MOORS C. . . . . O. arabicum
SCOTCH C. . . . . . . O. acanthium
TAURUS C. . . . . O. tauricum
TURKISH C. . . . O. sibthorpianum

COTTONTOP . . . . Trichachne
ARIZONA C. . . . . . . T. californica
SHORTLEAF C. . . . . . T. hitchcocki
TEXAS C. . . . . T. patens

Cottontop FLUFFGRASS: Triodia pulchella

COTTONWEED . Diotis; D. candidissima

Cottonwood . . . . . . POPLAR: Populus
Black C.. CALIFORNIA P.: P. trichocarpa
Northern B.C. PACIFIC P.: P. t. hastata

COT'ULA |w . . . . BRASSBUTTONS
au'rea . . . . Matricaria a.
austra'lis . . . . . . SOUTHERN B.
coronopifo'lia |w . . . . . BIRD B.
dioi'ca
squa'lida . . . . . . NEWZEALAND B.

COTYLE'DON (*CHIASTOPHYLLUM*) COTYLEDON
See **SUCCULENTS.**

COUE'PIA . . . . COUEPIA
grandiflo'ra . . . . . . RIGIDNUT C.

Coulter'ia tincto'ria Caesalpinia spinosa; Poinciana conzatti

COUMAROU'NA . . . . DIPTERYX

COURAN'TIA . . . . . ECHEVERIA
See **SUCCULENTS.**

COURATA'RI . . . . . . COURATARI
domes'tica . . . . Cariniana d.
estrellen'sis . . . . Cariniana excelsa
exig'ua
guianen'sis . . . . . . GUIANA C.
tauar'i . . . . . CIGARETTEBARK C.

COURBARIL . . . Hymenaea courbaril

COUROUPI'TA . . CANNONBALLTREE
guianen'sis . . . . GUIANA C.

COURSE'TIA . . . . . . BABYBONNETS
axilla'ris . . . . TEXAS B.
glandulo'sa (*microphylla*) . ROSARY B.

COUTA'REA
hexan'dra

COVENTRYBELLS Campanula trachelium

COVIL'LEA . . . . LARREA

COWA'NIA |w . . . . CLIFFROSE
stansburia'na (*mexicana*) |w STANSBURY C.

COWBANE . . . . Oxypolis
FENDLER C. . . . . O. fendleri
LEAFLESS C. . . . . . . O. filiformis
PACIFIC C. . . . . . O. occidentalis
STIFF C. . . . . O. rigidior

COWBANELILY . . . . Boophane

COWBERRY . . . Vaccinium vitis-idaea
MOUNTAIN C. . . . . V. v. minus
SHORE C. . . . . V. v. majus

COWLILY . . . . Nuphar
ARROW C. . . . . . . N. sagittifolium
EUROPEAN C. . . . . N. luteum
JAPANESE C. . . . . . . N. japonicum
LEAST C. . . . . N. minimum
LETTUCE C. . . . . N. microphyllum
PAINTED C. . . . . . N. variegatum
REDDISK C. . . . . . N. rubrodiscum
ROCKYMOUNTAIN C. . N. polysepalum
SPATTERDOCK C. . . . . . N. advena

COWPARSNIP . . . . Heracleum
BIGLEAF C. . . H. mantegazzianum
CAUCASIAN C. . . . . H. pubescens
COMMON C. . . . . H. lanatum
GIANT C. . . . . H. villosum
HOGWEED C. . . . . H. sphondylium

COWPEA . . . . Vigna
CATJANG C. . . . . V. catjang
COMMON C. . . . . V. sinensis
HAIRY C. . . . . V. pilosa
SEASHORE C. . . . . V. marina
YARDLONG C. . . . V. sesquipedalis

COWPLANT, AUSTRALIAN
Gymnema sylvestre

COWSEYE . . . . . . Odontospermum
CANARIES C. . . . . . . O. sericeum
SWEET C. . . . . O. aquaticum

COWWHEAT . . . . . . Melampyrum
NARROWLEAF C. . . . . . M. lineare

COYOL. . . . . . Acrocomia mexicana

COYOTILLO . . . . Karwinskia
CALDERON C. . . . . . K. calderoni
HUMBOLDT C. . . . K. humboldtiana

CRABAPPLE . . . . Malus
For hort. var. grown for their fruits see **FRUIT AND EDIBLE NUT NAMES.**

∞ ARNOLD C. . . . . . ∞ M. arnoldiana
BIGFRUIT C. . . . . . M. platycarpa
BILTMORE C. . . . . . . M. glabrata
BUNCOMBE C. . . . . . M. bracteata
∞ CHERRY C. . . . . . . ∞ M. robusta
CHINESE FLOWERING C. M. spectabilis
CHINESE PEARLEAF C.
M. prunifolia rinki
COMMON APPLE . . . . . . M. pumila
CUTLEAF C. . . . . . M. toringoides
∞ DAWSON C. . . . . ∞ M. dawsoniana
DUNBAR C. . . . . . M. glaucescens
FLORENTINE C. . . . . M. florentina
FORMOSA C. . . . . . . M. formosana
HALLS C. . . . . M. halliana
∞ HARTWIG C. . . . . . ∞ M. hartwigi
HONAN C. . . . . . . M. honanensis
JACK C. . . . . . . M. baccata jacki
JAPANESE FLOWERING C. M. floribunda
KANSU C. . . . . M. kansuensis
¢ KELSEY C. . . . . M. floribunda HV.
LANCELEAF C. . . . . . . M. lancifolia
LOUISIANA C. M. ioensis creniserrata
∞ MAGDEBURG C. ∞ M. magdeburgensis
MANCHURIAN C.
M. baccata mandshurica
∞ MIDGET C. . . . . ∞ M. micromalus
MISSOURI C. . . . . M. ioensis bushi
OREGON C. . . . . M. fusca
PALMER C. . . . M. ioensis palmeri
PEARLEAF C. . . . . . M. prunifolia
PRAIRIE C. . . . . M. ioensis
PRATTS C. . . . . M. pratti
∞ PURPLE C. . . . . . . ∞ M. purpurea
REHDER SWEET C.
M. coronaria elongata
SARGENT C. . . . . M. sargenti
∞ SCHEIDECKER C. . ∞ M. scheideckeri
SIBERIAN C. . . . . M. baccata

CRABAPPLE, continued
Sikkim C. . . . . Malus sikkimensis
∞Soulard C. . . . . . ∞M. soulardi
Southern C. . . . M. angustifolia
Texas C. . . . . M. ioensis texana
Tibetan C. . . . . . M. transitoria
Toringo C. . . . . . M. sieboldi
Wild Sweet C. . . . M. coronaria
∞Yellow Autumn C. . ∞M. sublobata
Yunnan C. . . . . M. yunnanensis
∞Zumi C. . . . . ∞M. zumi

Crabcactus . . . . . Schlumbergera
Bridges C. . . . . . S. bridgesi
Christmascactus . . . S. truncata
Eastercactus . . . . S. gaertneri
Russell C. . . . . . S. russelliana

Crabgrass . . . . Digitaria
This name is applied to the creeping species. See also Fingergrass.
Big Smooth C.
D. ischaemum mississippiensis
Blanket C. . . . . . . D. serotina
Florida C. . . . . . . D. floridana
Hairy C. . . . . . . D. sanguinalis
Jamaica C. . . . . . D. horizontalis
Shore C. . . . . D. littoralis
Smooth C. . . . . . D. ischaemum
Spreading C. . . . . D. decumbens
Violet C. . . . . . . D. violascens

Crabwood . . . . Carapa
Guiana C. . . . . . . C. guianensis
Molucca C. . . . . . C. moluccensis
Uganda C.. . . . . . C. grandiflora

CRAC'CA . . . . **TEPHROSIA**

Cradleorchid . . . . Anguloa
Clowes C. . . . . A. clowesi
Ivory C. . . . . . . A. c. eburnea
Rucker C. . . . . A. ruckeri

CRAM'BE . . . . Colewort
cordifo'lia . . . . . Heartleaf C.
hispan'ica . . . . Spanish C.
marit'ima . . . . Common C.

Cranberry . Vaccinium macrocarpum
Small C. . . . . V. oxycoccos
Western S. C. . . V. o. intermedium

Cranberrybush . . Viburnum: **Viburnum,** especially **V. trilobum**
American C. . . . . American Cranberrybush V.: **V. trilobum**
European C. . . . . European Cranberrybush V.: **V. opulus**
Sargent C. . . . . Sargent Cranberrybush V.: **V. sargenti**

Cranberrygourd . . Abobra tenuifolia

Craneflyorchid . . . . . . Tipularia
American C. . . . . . . T. unifolia

CRANIOLA'RIA . . . . Craniolaria
an'nua (*Martynia craniolaria*) Annual C.
argenti'na . . . . . . Argentine C.
integrifo'lia (*Martynia i.*)

Crapefern . . . Leptopteris superba

Crapejasmine . . Ervatamia coronaria

Crapemyrtle . . . . . Lagerstroemia
Andaman C. . . . . . L. hypoleuca
Batitinan C. . . . . . L. piriformis
Common C. . . . . L. indica
Littleflower C. . . . L. parviflora
Queen C. . . . . L. speciosa

CRASPE'DIA
uniflo'ra

CRASSI'NA . . . . . . **ZINNIA**

CRASSOCE'PHALUM . . **GYNURA**

CRAS'SULA . . . . Crassula
See **SUCCULENTS.**

Crassula . . . . Crassula
Alston C. . . . . C. alstoni
Clubmoss C. . . . . C. lycopodioides
Columnar C. . . . . . C. columnaris
Cooper C. . . . . C. cooperi
Coral C. . . . . C. corallina
Horned C. . . . . C. cornuta
Keyleaf C. . . . . C. clavifolia
Milky C. . . . . C. lactea
Schmidt C. . . . . C. schmidti
Silver C. . . . . C. argentea
Thorowort C. . . . . . C. perfoliata
Woolly C. . . . . . . C. tomentosa

∞**CRATAEGOMES'PILUS** (*CRATAEGUS + MESPILUS* or *CRATAEGUS × MESPILUS*) ∞Hawmedlar
×**dar'dari** (*Crataegus monogyna × M. germanica*) . . . . Bronvaux H.
×—**asniere'si** (*C. asnieresi*) Asnieres H.
∞**gillot'i** (*Crataegus monogyna × M. germanica*) . . . . ∞Gillot H.
∞**grandiflo'ra** (*Crataegus oxyacantha × M. germanica; Crataegus grandiflora*) ∞Bigflower H.

CRATAE'GUS |w . . . . . Hawthorn
abbrevia'ta
accli'vis
acerifo'lia . . . . . **C. phaenopyrum**
acutifo'lia . . . . St.Louis H.
aestiva'lis . . . . May H.
—**maloi'des** . . . . . Hawcreek H.
al'gens . . . . Buncombe H.
alta'ica . . . . Altai H.
ambig'ua . . . . Russian H.
amica'lis
amnic'ola
anno'sa
anom'ala
antiplas'ta
apiifo'lia Michx., *not* Med. **C. marshalli**
apiomor'pha
appos'ita . . . . . . Delaware H.
—**bissell'i** (*C. bisselli*) . Bissell D.H.
a'prica . . . . Beadle H.
araiocla'da
arbo'rea . . . . . Montgomery H.
arbores'cens . . . . . . **C. viridis**
arduen'nae . . . . . . Chicago H.
arkansa'na . . . . . Arkansas H.
arnoldia'na . . . . . . Arnold H.
ash'ei . . . . Ashe H.
asperifo'lia (*C. brainerdi a.*) Niagara H.
assur'gens
atroru'bens
azaro'lus . . . . Azarole H.
barrya'na . . . . Barry H.
basil'ica
berberifo'lia . . . Barberryleaf H.
berlandier'i . . . . Berlandier H.
bissell'i . . . . **C. apposita b.**
blan'da
boyn'toni . . . . Boynton H.
brachyacan'tha . . . . Blueberry H.
brachyphyl'la
brain'erdi asperifo'lia . **C. asperifolia**
brazo'ria . . . . Brazos H.
brit'toni . . . . Britton H.
buck'leyi . . . . Buckley H.
bush'i . . . . Bushes H.
callicar'pa
calpoden'dron (*chapmani; tomentosa*) Pear H.

CRATAEGUS, continued
canaden'sis . . . Canada Hawthorn
can'byi . . . . Canby H.
carrier'ei . . . . ∞**C. lavallei**
cerro'nis (*erythropoda*) . . Cerro H.
champlainen'sis . . . Champlain H.
chap'mani . . . . . **C. calpodendron**
cherokeen'sis . . . . Cherokee H.
chippewaen'sis . . . . Chippewa H.
chlorosar'ca . . . . Blackfruit H.
choriophyl'la
chrysocar'pa . . . . . Fireberry H.
—**phoeni'cea** (*C. rotundifolia*) Eastern F.H.
coccin'ea . . . . **C. intricata**
coccinioi'des . . . . Kansas H.
cocks'i . . . . Cocks H.
colli'na . . . . Sandhill H.
coloraden'sis . . . . . Colorado H.
consanguin'ea
corda'ta . . . . . . **C. phaenopyrum**
corus'ca
crenula'ta . . . . . . **Pyracantha c.**
croci'na
crusgal'li |w . . . . Cockspur H.
—**capilla'ta** . . . Wilmington C.H.
—**oblonga'ta** . . Pennsylvania C.H.
—**pyracanthifo'lia** . . . Redhip C.H.
—**splen'dens** . . . . . . Showy C.H.
cunea'ta . . . . Nippon H.
cu'prea . . . . Bronzy H.
dallasia'na . . . . Dallas H.
dawsonia'na . . . . Dawson H.
delec'ta
delos'i . . . . Bunch H.
dena'ria . . . . Mississippi H.
de'pilis
deweya'na . . . . Dewey H.
diffu'sa
dilata'ta
disjunc'ta
dis'par
disper'sa
doug'lasi |w . . . . Douglas H.
drymo'phila
dsungar'ica . . . . Mongol H.
dun'bari . . . . Dunbar H.
durobriven'sis . . . . Christmas H.
eames'i . . . . Eames H.
edi'ta . . . . Sabine H.
ed'ura
e'gani . . . . Egans H.
ellwangeria'na . . . . Ellwanger H.
engelmann'i . . . . Engelmann H.
enuclea'ta
erec'ta . . . . Bottom H.
erythrop'oda . . . . . . **C. cerronis**
fecun'da . . . . Missouri H.
fe'ra
flabella'ta . . . . Fanleaf H.
fla'va . . . . Yellow H.
florida'na . . . . . Jacksonville H.
foe'tida . . . . Russet H.
fontanesia'na
formo'sa
fructuo'sa . . . . . Westchester H.
frutico'sa . . . . . . Lowhedge H.
gault'i . . . . Gault H.
gemmo'sa
georgia'na . . . . Georgia H.
glabrius'cula
grandiflo'ra . ∞**Crataegomespilus g.**
gra'vida
gregg'i . . . . Gregg H.
harbiso'ni . . . . Harbison H.
held'reichi . . . . Heldreich H.
∞**hiema'lis** (*?crusgalli × pentagyna*)
hill'i . . . . Hills H.

CRATAEGUS, continued
holmesia'na . . Holmes Hawthorn
—tard'ipes
—vil'lipes
hudson'ica . . . . Hudson H.
igna'va
illinoien'sis . . . . . . Illinois H.
indu'ta . . . . . . Turkeyapple H.
in'fera . . . . October H.
in'gens
inte'gra
integrilo'ba
intermix'ta . . . . . Hannibal H.
intrica'ta (*coccinea*) . . . Thicket H.
invi'sa
jones'ae
kansuen'sis . . . . Kansu H.
kel'loggi . . . . Kellogg H.
kingstonen'sis . . . . Kingston H.
korolkow'i . . . . **C. wattiana**
la'cera
lacrima'ta . . . . . . Pensacola H.
lalan'di . . . **Pyracantha coccinea l.**
∞ **lambertia'na** (*?nigra* × *sanguinea*) ∞ Lambert H.
la'neyi . . . . Laney H.
lanugino'sa
lau'ta . . . . Franklin H.
∞ **laval'lei** (*crusgalli* × *pubescens; carrierei*) . . . . ∞ Lavalle H.
lawrencen'sis. LawrenceCounty H.
letterman'i . . . . Letterman H.
lima'ria
limno'phila . . . . . Wakulla H.
lobula'ta
luco'rum
luxurio'sa
macracan'tha . . . . . . Spike H.
macrosper'ma
mansfielden'sis . . . . Mansfield H.
margaret'ta . . . . . Margaret H.
—brown'i
marietten'sis . . . . . Marietta H.
mar'shalli (*apiifolia* Michx., *not* Med.) Parsley H.
maximowicz'i . . . Maximowicz H.
∞ **me'dia** (*monogyna* × *oxyacantha*)
meridiona'lis
mexica'na . . . . . . **C. pubescens**
micran'tha
microcar'pa . . . . . **C. spathulata**
mi'tis
modes'ta . . . . Baby H.
mohr'i . . . . Mohrs H.
mol'lis . . . . Downy H.
monogy'na . . . . . Singleseed H.
₵Doublered (*rubroplena*) hv.
₵Doublewhite (*alboplena*)
₵Pyramidal (*stricta*)
₵Rose (*rosea*)
₵Singlered (*punicea*)
₵Weepingpink (*roseapendula*)
₵Weepingwhite (*pendula*)
montiva'ga . . . . . JeffDavis H.
multiflo'ra . . . . . . Inkberry H.
nemora'lis . . . . Wood H.
neolondinen'sis
ni'gra . . . . . European Black H.
ni'tida . . . . Glossy H.
noelen'sis
∞ **no'tha** (*apiifolia* × *brachyphylla*)
nu'da
ohioen'sis . . . . Ohio H.
opa'ca . . . . Riverflat H.
opi'ma
orienta'lis . . . . Silver H.
ova'ta

CRATAEGUS, continued
oxyacan'tha (*oxyacanthoides*) |w English Hawthorn
₵Doublepink (*roseaplena*) hv.
₵Doublered (*coccineaplena*)
₵Doublewhite (*plena*)
₵Goldfruit (*aurea*)
₵Pauls Scarlet (*pauli*)
₵Princeps Simplex
₵Redrim (*bicolor*)
₵Singlepink (*rosea*)
₵Singlered (*coccinea punicea*)
pallia'ta
pal'meri . . . . Palmer H.
pan'da
paucispi'na
pausia'ca
pedicella'ta . . . . . . Ontario H.
—glorio'sa
peni'ta
pennsylva'nica . . Pennsylvania H.
pentagy'na
pentan'dra
peorien'sis . . . . Peoria H.
∞ **peregri'na** (*mollis* × *nigra*) ∞ Peregrina H.
× **persis'tens**
pertomento'sa
phaenopy'rum (*acerifolia; cordata; populifolia*) . . . . . Washington H.
₵Pyramidal (*fastigiata*) hv.
phaneroneu'ra . . . PikeCounty H.
pinnatif'ida . . . . . . Chinese H.
—ma'jor . . . . Large C.H.
poliophyl'la
praten'sis . . . . Prairie H.
prin'glei . . . . Pringle H.
pro'cera
pruino'sa . . . . Frosted H.
prunifo'lia . . . . . . Plumleaf H.
pubes'cens (*mexicana*)

Prof. Rehder follows Stapf's treatment (Kew Bulletin, pp. 289-298, 1914) here. Other authors, however, regard mexicana as a distinct species and, apparently, this matter requires further field study.

—stipula'cea (*C. stipulacea*)
puncta'ta . . . . Dotted H.
—au'rea (*C. xanthocarpa*) Yellow D.H.
—canes'cens . . . . . . Albany H.
—microphyl'la
pyracan'tha . . **Pyracantha coccinea**
querci'na
ravenel'i . . . . Ravenel H.
recur'va
rega'lis . . . . Piedmont H.
rivula'ris |w . . . . River H.
robesonia'na (*spissiflora*) Robeson H.
ro'bur
rotundifo'lia **C. chrysocarpa phoenicea**
rubicun'da
ru'fula . . . . Pond H.
salig'na . . . . Willow H.
sanguin'ea . . . . Redhaw H.
sar'genti . . . . Sargent H.
sen'ta
se'ra
serta'ta
signa'ta . . . . Pineland H.
silves'tris
smith'i . . . . Smith H.
sorbifo'lia . . . . Sorbus H.

Thought to be a hybrid between C. oxyacantha and some other Crataegus.

sor'dida
spathula'ta (*microcarpa*) |w Littlehip H.

CRATAEGUS, continued
spissiflo'ra . . . . **C. robesoniana**
stenose'pala
stipula'cea . . . . . **C. pubescens s.**
stipulo'sa . . . Ecuador Hawthorn
sublobula'ta . . . . . Augustine H.
submol'lis . . . . Quebec H.
suborbicula'ta
subpilo'sa . . . Eureka Springs H.
succulen'ta . . . . Fleshy H.
sutherlanden'sis . . Sutherland H.
—spines'cens
swanen'sis . . . . Swan H.
tanacetifo'lia . . . . . Tansyleaf H.
ter'sa . . . . Opelousas H.
texa'na . . . . Texas H.
tomento'sa . . . . . **C. calpodendron**
treleas'ei . . . . Trelease H.
triflo'ra . . . . . Threeflower H.
tris'tis
triumpha'lis
uniflo'ra . . . . . . Oneflower H.
uni'qua
veg'eta
velu'tina
venus'ta
venus'tula
verruculo'sa
viburnifo'lia
victori'ni
vir'idis (*arborescens*) . . . Green H.
vir'ilis
visen'da
vul'sa
war'neri . . . . Warner H.
wattia'na (*korolkowi*) . . . Watts H.
wil'soni . . . . Wilson H.
xanthocar'pa . . . **C. punctata aurea**
young'i . . . . Youngs H.

CRAWFUR'DIA
japon'ica
triner'vis

Crawldevil . . **Borzicactus eriotrichus**

Crazyweed . . . . **Oxytropis**
Bessey Pointvetch . . **O. besseyi**
Blankinship C. . . **O. blankinshipi**
Creamflower C. . . **O. ochroleuca**
Droppod C. . . . . **O. deflexa**
Hairy C. . . . . **O. villosa**
Haresfoot C. . . . . . . **O. lagopus**
Lambert C. . . . . **O. lamberti**
Plains C. . . . . **O. campestris**
RockyMountain C. **O. saximontana**
Ruby C. . . . . **O. tenella**
Showy C. . . . . **O. splendens**
Silky C. . . . . **O. sericea**
Spike C. . . . . **O. macouni**
St.Johns C. . . . . . **O. johannensis**
Ural C. . . . . **O. uralensis**
Whorled C. . . . . . . **O. richardsoni**
Yellowhair C. . . . . **O. viscidula**

Creamnut . . . . Monkeypottree, Sapucaianut: **Lecythis zabucajo**

Creeper . . . . **Parthenocissus**
Bigleaf Thicket C. **P. inserta macrophylla**
Engelmann Virginia C. **P. quinquefolia engelmanni**
Himalaya C. . . . . . **P. himalayana**
Japanese C. . . . . . **P. tricuspidata**
Littleleaf Virginia C. **P. quinquefolia minor**
Lows Japanese C. **P. tricuspidata lowi**
Purple J. C. . . . . . **P. t. purpurea**
Ragleaf Thicket C. **P. inserta laciniata**

CREEPER, continued
REDLEAF HIMALAYA C. **Parthenocissus himalayana rubrifolia**
REDTWIG VIRGINIA C. **P. quinquefolia hirsuta**
SEVENLEAF C. . . . . **P. heptaphylla**
SILVERVEIN C. . . . . . **P. henryana**
ST. PAUL VIRGINIA C. **P. quinquefolia saintpauli**
THICKET C. . . . . **P. inserta**
THOMSON C. . . . . . . **P. thomsoni**
VEITCH JAPANESE C. **P. tricuspidata veitchi**
VIRGINIA C. . . . . . **P. quinquefolia**
WALL V. C. . . . . . **P. q. murorum**

CREEPINGDEVIL-CACTUS **Machaerocereus eruca**

CREMNO'PHILA
nu'tans

CREOSOTEBUSH . . . . **Larrea**
COVILLE C. . . . . **L. tridentata**
SPREADING C. . . . . . **L. divaricata**

CRE'PIS ⌊w . . . . . . HAWKSBEARD
acumina'ta . . . . . . TAPERTIP H.
barba'ta . . . . **Tolpis b.**
bien'nis . . . . ROUGH H.
bun'gei
capilla'ris (*virens*) . . . . SMOOTH H.
dioscor'idis
glau'ca
glomera'ta
grandiflo'ra
interme'dia . . . . GRAY H.
montic'ola . . . . SISKIYOU H.
na'na (*Youngia n.*) . . . . TINY H.
occidenta'lis ⌊w . . . . WESTERN H.
ru'bra . . . . RED H.
runcina'ta . . . . . DANDELION H.
scopulo'rum . . . YELLOWSTONE H.
seto'sa
tecto'rum . . . . . NARROWLEAF H.
vir'ens . . . . **C. capillaris**

CRESCEN'TIA . . . . CALABASHTREE
ala'ta (*Parmentiera a.*) CROSSLEAF C.
cuje'te . . . . COMMON C.

Cress, Garden . . . . . PEPPERWEED, GARDENCRESS: **Lepidium sativum**

CRESTEDCORALROOT . **Hexalectris spicata**

CRIMSONBEAD . . . . . . **Alseuosmia**
BIGLEAF C. . . . . . . **A. macrophylla**
HOLLY C. . . . . **A. ilex**
OAKLEAF C. . . . . . **A. quercifolia**

CRIMSONFLAG . . . . . . **Schizostylis**
BASUTO C. . . . . **S. coccinea**

CRINKLEAWN . **Trachypogon montufari**

CRINODEN'DRON (*TRICUSPIDARIA*) . . . . LILYTREE
depen'dens (*Tricuspidaria d.*) WHITE L.
pata'gua (*hookerianum; lanceolatum; Tricuspidaria lanceolata; T. patagua*) RED L.

∞**CRINODON'NA** (*AMARYLLIS* × *CRINUM;* ∞*AMARCRINUM*) ∞CRINODONNA
₵**cor'si** (*Amaryllis belladonna* × *Crinum moorei*)
₵**how'ardi** (*Amaryllis belladonna* × *Crinum moorei;* ×*Amarcrinum h.*)

CRI'NUM ⌊w . . . . CRINUM
amab'ile . . . . SUMATRA C.
america'num ⌊w . . . . FLORIDA C.
asiat'icum (*toxicarium*) . . GRAND C.

CRINUM, continued
augus'tum . . . MAURITIUS CRINUM
baines'i . . . . BAINES C.
bulbif'erum (*capense; longifolium*) HARDY C.
campanula'tum . . . . . FUNNEL C.
cris'pum . . . . TRANSVAAL C.
erubes'cens . . . . CARIB C.
fimbria'tulum . . . . . ANGOLA C.
flac'cidum . . . . . DARLINGLILY C.
forbesia'num . . . . FORBES C.
gigan'teum . . . . . . FRAGRANT C.
kirk'i . . . . KIRK C.
kunthia'num . . . . . COLOMBIAN C.

C. kunthianum of gardens is the hybrid Herbert.

longiflo'rum . . . . . . JAMAICA C.
longifo'lium . . . . . **C. bulbiferum**
macow'ani . . . . . . MACOWAN C.
moor'ei . . . . LONGNECK C.
—al'bum . . . . WHITE L.C.
peduncula'tum . . . . . MURRAY C.
rattray'i Hort. . . . . . UGANDA C.
sanderia'num . . . . . . SANDER C.
sca'brum . . . . . . GREENTUBE C.
toxica'rium . . . . . . **C. asiaticum**
yemenen'se . . . . YEMEN C.
yunnanen'se . . . . . . YUNNAN C.
zeylan'icum . . . . . . CEYLON C.

CECIL HOUDYSHEL. HV. Crinum
ELLEN BOSANQUET
EMPRESS OF INDIA
GORDON WAYNE
HARLEMENSE
J. C. HARVEY
KRELAGEI
LOUIS BOSANQUET
MRS. HENRY NEHRLING
MRS. JAMES HENDRY
PEACHBLOW
POWELLI ALBUM
POWELLI ROSEUM
SOPHIA NEHRLING
VIRGINIA LEE
VIRGINICUM
WHITE QUEEN
ZIMMERMANI

CRINUM . . . . **Crinum**
ANGOLA C. . . . . . . **C. fimbriatulum**
BAINES C. . . . . **C. bainesi**
CARIB C. . . . . **C. erubescens**
CEYLON C. . . . . . . **C. zeylanicum**
COLOMBIAN C. . . . . **C. kunthianum**
DARLINGLILY C. . . . . **C. flaccidum**
FLORIDA C. . . . . . **C. americanum**
FORBES C. . . . . . **C. forbesianum**
FRAGRANT C. . . . . . **C. giganteum**
FUNNEL C. . . . . **C. campanulatum**
GRAND C. . . . . **C. asiaticum**
GREENTUBE C. . . . . . **C. scabrum**
HARDY C. . . . . . . **C. bulbiferum**
JAMAICA C. . . . . . **C. longiflorum**
KIRK C. . . . . **C. kirki**
LONGNECK C. . . . . . . **C. moorei**
MACOWAN C. . . . . . **C. macowani**
MAURITIUS C. . . . . . **C. augustum**
MURRAY C. . . . . **C. pedunculatum**
SANDER C. . . . . . **C. sanderianum**
SUMATRA C. . . . . . . **C. amabile**
TRANSVAAL C. . . . . . . **C. crispum**
UGANDA C. . . . . **C. rattrayi**
WHITE LONGNECK C.. **C. moorei album**
YEMEN C. . . . . **C. yemenense**
YUNNAN C. . . . . . **C. yunnanense**

CRISTA'RIA
glaucophyl'la

CRISTATEL'LA ⌊w
james'i ⌊w

CRITH'MUM . . . . SAMPHIRE
marit'imum . . . . SAMPHIRE

CROCAN'THEMUM . . . FROSTWORT

Some botanists maintain that Crocanthemum is a synonym of Helianthemum. Pending further study of the matter, it seems desirable to maintain Crocanthemum as a valid genus in this book, following the usage of Rehder's Manual, the U. S. Pharmacopoeia, and the National Formulary.

canaden'se (*Helianthemum c.*) ⌊w CANADA F.
green'ei (*Helianthemum g.*) GREENES F.
scopa'rium (*Helianthemum s.*) ⌊w BUSH F.
suffrutes'cens (*Helianthemum s.*) AMADOR F.

CROCI'DIUM
multicau'le

CROCOS'MIA . . . . . . COPPERTIP
au'rea . . . . GOLDEN C.

CRO'CUS . . . . CROCUS
ae'rius
astu'ricus
au'reus . . . . **C. moesiacus**
balan'sae
biflo'rus . . . . SCOTCH C.
—a'dami
—argen'teus
—pusil'lus
—wel'deni
bo'ryi
—marathoni'seus
—tournefort'i
byzanti'nus (*iridiflorus*). BYZANTINE C.
cambessedes'i
cancella'tus
—al'bus
cas'pius
chrysan'thus
—fuscotinc'tus
etrus'cus
flei'scheri . . . . . . FLEISCHER C.
hadria'ticus
—chrysobele'nicus
—wil'helmi
hyema'lis
imper'ati . . . . EARLY C.
—al'bus
iridiflo'rus . . . . . . **C. byzantinus**
karducho'rum
korolkow'i
laeviga'tus
—fontenay'i
longiflo'rus . . . . LONGFLOWER C.
—meliten'sis
me'dius
min'imus
moesia'cus (*aureus*)
nudiflo'rus
ochroleu'cus
olivier'i
pulchel'lus
salz'manni . . . . . . SALZMANN C.
sati'vus . . . . SAFFRON C.
—cartwrightia'nus
—pal'lasi
sie'beri . . . . SIEBER C.
—purpu'reus . . . . . . PURPLE S.C.
specio'sus
—aitchiso'ni
—al'bus
—globo'sus

CROCUS, continued
×**stella'ris**
susia'nus . . . CLOTHOFGOLD CROCUS
tau'ri . . . . TAURUS C.
tomasinia'nus
ver'nus . . . . COMMON C.
—al'bus
versicol'or . . . . CLOTHOFSILVER C.
vitelli'nus
—grave'olens
zona'tus

CROCUS . . . . **Crocus**
BYZANTINE C. . . . . **C. byzantinus**
CLOTHOFGOLD C. . . . . **C. susianus**
CLOTHOFSILVER C. . . . **C. versicolor**
COMMON C. . . . . **C. vernus**
EARLY C. . . . . **C. imperati**
FLEISCHER C. . . . . . **C. fleischeri**
LONGFLOWER C. . . . **C. longiflorus**
PURPLE SIEBER C.
C. sieberi purpureus
SAFFRON C. . . . . **C. sativus**
SALZMANN C. . . . . . **C. salzmanni**
SCOTCH C. . . . . **C. biflorus**
SIEBER C. . . . . **C. sieberi**
TAURUS C. . . . . **C. tauri**

CROSSAN'DRA
infundibulifor'mis (*undulaefolia*)

CROSSOSO'MA . . . . . CROSSOSOMA
bigelo'vi . . . . BIGELOW C.
califor'nicum . . . . . CALIFORNIA C.

CROSSVINE . . . . . **Bignonia capreolata**
REDPURPLE C. . . **B. c. atrosanguinea**

CROSSWORT . . . . **Crucianella**
COMMON C. . . . . **C. stylosa**
HERB C. . . . . **C. herbacea**

CROTALA'RIA [w] . . . . CROTALARIA
agatiflo'ra . . . . . . CANARYBIRD C.
anagyroi'des
angula'ta (*rotundifolia*) [w]
RABBITBELLS C.
can'dicans
capen'sis . . . . CAPE C.
inca'na . . . . SHACKSHACK C.
interme'dia
jun'cea . . . . SUNN C.
laburnifo'lia . . . . . RATTLEBOX C.
lanceola'ta . . . . . . LANCELEAF C.
marit'ima . . . . . . COASTPLAIN C.
mucrona'ta (*striata*) . . . STRIPED C.
pu'mila (*lupulina*) [w] . . . . LOW C.
pursh'i [w] . . . . PURSH C.
retu'sa
retz'i . . . . RETZ C.
rotundifo'lia . . . . **C. angulata**
sagitta'lis [w] . . . . ARROW C.
spectab'ilis (*sericea*) . . . SHOWY C.
stria'ta . . . . **C. mucronata**
verruco'sa

CROTALARIA . . . . **Crotalaria**
ARROW C. . . . . **C. sagittalis**
CANARYBIRD C. . . . . . **C. agatiflora**
CAPE C. . . . . **C. capensis**
COASTPLAIN C. . . . . . **C. maritima**
LANCELEAF C. . . . . . **C. lanceolata**
LOW C. . . . . **C. pumila**
PURSH C. . . . . **C. purshi**
RABBITBELLS C. . . . . . **C. angulata**
RATTLEBOX C. . . . . **C. laburnifolia**
RETZ C. . . . . **C. retzi**
SHACKSHACK C. . . . . **C. incana**

CROTALARIA, continued
SHOWY C. . . . **Crotalaria spectabilis**
STRIPED C. . . . . . . **C. mucronata**
SUNN C. . . . . **C. juncea**

CRO'TON [w] . . . . CROTON

The plants known to horticulturists as Croton belong not to the genus Croton of botanists but to the genus Codiaeum, which see for a few of the many horticultural varieties.

califor'nicus . . . . . CALIFORNIA C.
capita'tus [w] . . . . WOOLLY C.
corymbulo'sus . . LEATHERWEED C.
dolichosta'chyus
elute'ria
fruticulo'sus . . . . BUSH C.
glandulo'sus [w]
gossypiifo'lius . . . CANDLETREE C.
malam'bo . . . . MALAMBOBARK C.
monanthogy'nus [w]
neomexica'nus . . . NEWMEXICAN C.
puncta'tus
pun'gens
texen'sis [w] . . . . TEXAS C.
tig'lium . . . . PURGING C.
torreya'nus [w] . . . . . . TORREY C.

CROWBERRY . . . . **Empetrum**
BLACK C. . . . . **E. nigrum**
PURPLE C. . . . . **E. atropurpureum**

Crowfoot . . . . ANEMONE, MEADOW: **Anemone canadensis;** BUTTERCUP: **Ranunculus** spp.; DEERVETCH, BIRDSFOOT: **Lotus corniculatus;** GERANIUM: **Geranium** spp.; GROUNDCEDAR: **Lycopodium complanatum flabelliforme;** GROUNDPINE: **Lycopodium obscurum;** MARSHMARIGOLD, COMMON: **Caltha palustris;** ORCHIS, MALE: **Orchis mascula;** ORCHIS, SPOTLEAF: **Orchis maculata;** PLANTAIN, CROWFOOT: **Plantago coronopus.**

CROWFOOTGRASS . . . **Dactyloctenium**
DURBAN C. . . . . . **D. aegyptium**

CROWNBEARD . . . . **Verbesina**
GOLDEN C. . . . . . **V. encelioides**
GRAVELWEED C. . . **V. helianthoides**
LINDEN C. . . . . **V. lindeni**
MEXICAN C. . . . . **V. crocata**
WHITE C. . . . . **V. virginica**
YELLOW C. . . . . . **V. occidentalis**

CROWPOISON
Amianthium; A. muscaetoxicum

CRUCIANEL'LA . . . . . CROSSWORT
herba'cea . . . . HERB C.
stylo'sa . . . . COMMON C.

Crucifer
Any plant belonging to the Crucifer, or Mustard family (Cruciferae, or Brassicaceae).

CRUPI'NA . . . . CRUPINA
vulga'ris . . . . COMMON C.

CRU'SEA [w]
tricoc'ca [w]

CRYOPHY'TUM
MESEMBRYANTHEMUM
See **SUCCULENTS.**

CRYOSO'PHILA (*ACANTHORRHIZA*) . . . . ROOTSPINEPALM
See **PALM GENERA.**

CRYP'SIS . . . . PRICKLEGRASS
See **GRASS GENERA.**

CRYPTAN'DRA
arbutiflo'ra

CRYPTAN'THA (*CRYPTANTHE; KRYNITZKIA; OREOCARYA*) [w]
CRYPTANTHA
barbig'era
flac'cida [w]
interme'dia
james'i (*Oreocarya suffruticosa*)
JAMES C.
leiocar'pa (*Krynitzkia l.*)
racemo'sa . . . . FORGETMENOT C.
shel'doni (*Oreocarya glomerata*)
SHELDON C.

CRYPTAN'THUS
acau'lis
beuck'eri
zona'tus
ZEBRINA. HV.

CRYPTOCA'RYA . . . CRYPTOCARYA
austra'lis . . . . GRAY C.
mi'ersi . . . . BELLOTA C.
ru'bra (*peumus; Peumus r.*) . RED C.
wood'i . . . . WOODS C.

CRYPTOCORY'NE . . . CRYPTOCORYNE
cilia'ta . . . . FRAGRANT C.
corda'ta
grif'fithi . . . . BROADLEAF C.
retrospira'lis . . . . . TWISTHOOD C.
wil'lisi

CRYPTOGAMS, ECONOMIC

The so-called nonvascular cryptogams (including among others, Algae, Fungi, Lichens, Liverworts, and Mosses) embrace many plants of great economic importance as food for man and beast; as sources of drugs and other chemicals, dyestuffs, packing materials, etc.; as the causative organisms in human, animal, and plant diseases; in symbiotic relationships whereby important higher plants are able to maintain life; as soil- and land-building and soil-protective organisms, and in many other ways. It is not feasible in the limited space available here to give more than a token list of this vast host of plants, but it seems highly important not to ignore them entirely. The literature on these great groups of plants, and especially Fungi, is of course enormous. The very restricted list which appears below has been collated from a number of sources.

The Editorial Committee is indebted to John A. Stevenson, In Charge, Mycological Collections of the Bureau of Plant Industry, Washington, D. C., for suggesting that those actively interested in the outstanding works in this field consult, among others, the following works: *Anderson, Paul J.*, "Check List of Diseases of Economic Plants in the United States," U. S. Dept. Agr. Bul. 1366, 1920. *Arthur, J. C.*, "Manual of the Rusts in the United States and Canada," Purdue Univ., 1934. *Boyce, John S.*, "Forest Pathology," McGraw-Hill Book Co., N. Y., 1938. *Charles, Vera K.*, "Some Common Mushrooms and How to Know Them," U. S. Dept. Agr. Circ. 143, 1931. *Clements, F. E.* and *Shear, C. L.*, "Genera of Fungi," The H. W. Wilson Co., N. Y., 1931. *Coker, W. C.*, "The Clavarias of the United States and Canada," Univ. of N. C. Press, Chapel Hill, N. C., 1923.

CRYPTOGAMS, ECONOMIC, continued

Coker, W. C. and *Couch, J. N.*, "The Gasteromycetes of the Eastern United States and Canada," Univ. of N. C. Press, Chapel Hill, N. C., 1928. *Dodge, C. W.*, "Medical Mycology," C. V. Mosby Co., St. Louis, 1933. *Felt, Ephraim Porter* and *Rankin, W. Howard*, "Insects and Diseases of Ornamental Trees and Shrubs," Macmillan Co., N. Y., 1932. *Fink, B.*, "The Lichen Flora of the United States," Univ. Mich. Press, Ann Arbor, 1935. *Fink, Bruce*, "The Lichens of Minnesota," Contributions U. S. Nat. Herbarium vol. 14, pt. 1. pp. 1–270, 1910. *Fitzpatrick, H. W.*, "The Lower Fungi," McGraw-Hill Book Co., N. Y., 1930. *Guilliermond, Alexandre*, "The Yeasts," Translated and rev. by Fred W. Tanner, John Wiley & Sons, N. Y., 1920. *Gussow, H. T.* and *Odell, W. S.*, "Mushrooms and Toadstools," Ministry of Agriculture, Ottawa, Canada, 1927. *Heald, F. D.*, "Manual of Plant Diseases," McGraw-Hill Book Co., N. Y., rev. 1936. *Kauffman, C. H.*, "The Agaricaceae of Michigan," Applicable to Northern U. S., 2 vols. Mich. Geol. and Biol. Survey, Lansing, 1918. *Krieger, L. C. C.*, "A Popular Guide to the Fungi (Mushrooms) of New York State," Applicable to Northern U. S., N. Y. State Mus. Handbook 11, Albany, 1935. *MacBride* and *Martin*, "The Myxomycetes," Macmillan Co., N. Y., 1938. *Mairet, Ethel M.*, "Vegetable Dyes," Ryerson Press, Toronto, Canada, 1939. *McIlvaine, Charles* and *Macadam, R. K.*, "Toadstools, Mushrooms, Fungi, Edible and Poisonous; One Thousand American Fungi," Bobbs-Merrill Co., Indianapolis, Ind., 1912. *Patterson, F. W.* and *Charles, V. K.*, "Mushrooms and Other Common Fungi," U. S. Dept. Agr. Bul. 175, 1915. *Rolfe, R. T.* and *Rolfe, F. W.*, "The Romance of the Fungus World," Chapman and Hall, Ltd., London, 1925. *Seymour, A. B.*, "Host Index of the Fungi of North America," Harvard Univ. Press, Cambridge, Mass., 1919. *Smith, E. F.*, "Bacterial Diseases of Plants," W. B. Saunders Co., Philadelphia, 1920. *Stevens, F. L.*, "Plant Disease Fungi," Macmillan Co., N. Y., 1925. *Stevenson, John A.*, "Foreign Plant Diseases, a Manual of Economic Plant Diseases Which Are New to or Not Widely Distributed in the United States," U. S. Dept. Agr. Misc. Pub., 1926. *Thom, C.*, "The Penicillia," Williams & Wilkins Co., Baltimore, 1930. *Thom, C.* and *Church, M. B.*, "The Aspergilli," Williams & Wilkins Co., Baltimore, 1930. *Tiffany, Lewis Hanford*, "Algae the Grass of Many Waters," Charles C. Thomas, Publisher, Springfield, Ill., 1938. *Youngken, Heber W.*, "A Text Book of Pharmacognosy," P. Blakiston's Son & Co., Inc., Philadelphia, 4th ed., 1936.

Edi. Edible Poi. Poisonous

ALGAE

ALA'RIA spp. Edi. WINGKELP (*Kombu; Murlin*)

ARTHROTHAM'NUS spp. Edi. KOMBU

CHON'DRUS cris'pus. Edi. IRISHMOSS (*Carrageen*)

DIL'SEA ed'ulis. Edi. . DULSE
See Rhodymenia.

EUCHEU'MA spp. Edi. JELLYALGA
Contributing sources to commercial Agar.

FU'CUS . . . . . ROCKWEED
serra'tus . . . CARTWRACK R.
vesiculo'sus . . BLADDERWRACK R.

GELID'IUM cor'neum. Edi. COMMON AGAR (*Agar-Agar; Tongusa*)

CRYPTOGAMS (ALGAE), continued

GIGARTI'NA mamillo'sa

GLOIOPEL'TIS spp. . GLUE-ALGA (*Funori*)

GRACILA'RIA spp. . CEYLONMOSS

HALI'DRYS siliquo'sa DRUG SEAOAK

LAMINA'RIA spp. . BLADEKELP

LI'MU ko'la. Edi. CEREMONIAL LIMU

MACROCYS'TIS pyrif'era GIANTKELP
Reported to reach occasional lengths of 700 feet, making it the longest of all living organisms.

OEDOGO'NIUM . OEDOGONIUM
autumna'le . . . . . . AUTUMN O.
bosc'i . . . . BOSC O.
gran'de . . . . GREAT O.
landsbor'oughi . LANDSBOROUGH O.
rufes'cens . . . . . . REDDISH O.
stagna'le . . . . . . STAGNANT O.

PORPHY'RA spp. Edi. . LAVER (*Mori; Redlaver; Slack*)

PTILO'TA spp.

RHODYME'NIA palma'ta. Edi. IRISHDULSE SEAKALE
See Dilsea.

SARGAS'SUM spp. . SARGASSO

SPIROGY'RA protec'ta COMMON PONDSCUM

TOLYPEL'LA . . . TOLYPELLA
fimbria'ta
prolif'era

UL'VA spp. Edi. . . SEALETTUCE (*Greenlaver*)

VAUCHE'RIA . . . GREENFELT
gemina'ta . . . . . TWINEGG G.
ses'silis
terres'tris . . . . LAND G.

FUNGI

AGAR'ICUS . . . . . AGARICUS
arven'sis. Edi. . . . . . HORSE A.
campes'tris. Edi. COMMON MUSHROOM A.
placomy'ces. Edi. . . FLATCAP A.
rod'mani. Edi. . . . . RODMANS A.
silvic'ola. Edi. . . . . FOREST A.
subrufes'cens. Edi.

AMANI'TA . . . . . AMANITA
caesar'ea. Edi. . . . CAESARS A.
musca'ria. Poi. . . . . . FLY A.
phalloi'des. Poi. . . DEATHCUP A.
strobilifor'mis . . . . FIRCONE A.
ver'na . . . . SPRING A.

AMANITOP'SIS vagina'ta SHEATHED AMANITOPSIS

ARMILLA'RIA . . . ARMILLARIA
matsuta'ke . . . MATSUTAKE A.
mel'lea. Edi. . . HONEYCOLOR A.
ventrico'sa . . . . . . COARSE A.

BOLE'TUS . . . . BOLETUS
bi'color. Edi.
chrysen'teron
ed'ulis. Edi. . . . . . . EDIBLE B.
felle'us . . . . BITTER B.
granula'tus
lute'us. Edi.

CALVA'TIA . . . . . CALVATIA
cyathifor'mis. Edi. . . . . CUP C.
gigan'tea. Edi. . . . . . GIANT C.

CRYPTOGAMS (FUNGI), continued

CANTHAREL'LUS CANTHARELLUS
auranti'acus . . . . . . FALSE C.
ciba'rius. Edi. . CHANTERELLE C.

CLAUDO'PUS ni'dulans NESTCAP CLAUDOPUS

CLAV'ICEPS purpu'rea. Poi. ERGOT CLAVICEPS

CLITOCY'BE . . . CLITOCYBE
dealba'ta
illu'dens. Poi. JACK-O'-LANTERN C.
monadel'pha. Edi.
mul'ticeps. Edi. . . MANYHEAD C.
ochropurpu'rea . . PURPLEGILL C.

COLLYB'IA . . . . . COLLYBIA
radica'ta. Edi. . . . . ROOTED C.
velu'tipes. Edi. . VELVETSTEM C.

COPRI'NUS . . . . . COPRINUS
atramenta'rius. Edi. . INKCAP C.
coma'tus. Edi. . . SHAGGYMANE C.
mica'ceus. Edi. SHINY INKCAP C.

CORTINA'RIUS . CORTINARIUS
cinnamo'meus. Edi.
lilaci'nus. Edi.

CORTINEL'LUS edo'des (*berkelyanus*) . SHIITAKE CORTINELLUS

DAEDA'LEA querci'na OAK DAEDALEA

ENDO'THIA parasit'ica CHESTNUTBLIGHT ENDOTHIA

FISTULI'NA hepat'ica. Edi. BEEFSTEAK FISTULINA

FO'MES . . . . FOMES
applana'tus . . . . . . SHELF F.
lu'cidus . . . . . . LACQUERED F.
officina'lis (*Polyporus o.*). LARCH F.

GA'LERA tener'a. Edi. LAWN GALERA

GEAS'TER hygromet'ricus BAROMETER EARTHSTAR

HYD'NUM . . . . . HYDNUM
coralloi'des. Edi. . . . . CORAL H.
erina'ceum. Edi. . SATYRSBEARD H.

HYGROPH'ORUS. HYGROPHORUS
chrys'odon. Edi. . . GOLDTOOTH H.
coccin'eus . . . . . . SCARLET H.
con'icus. Poi. . . . . . CONIC H.
hypothe'jus. Edi.

HYPHOLO'MA . . HYPHOLOMA
appendicula'tum. Edi.
perplex'um . . . PERPLEXING H.
sublaterit'ium. Suspected. BRICKTOP H.

ITHYPHAL'LUS impu'dicus STINKHORN ITHYPHALLUS

LACTA'RIUS . . . . LACTARIUS
delicio'sus. Edi. . . DELICIOUS L.
in'digo. Edi. . . . . . . INDIGO L.

LENTI'NUS . . . . . LENTINUS
lecomt'ei . . . . HAIRY L.
lepid'eus . . . . SCALY L.

LEPIO'TA . . . . . . LEPIOTA
america'na. Edi. . . AMERICAN L.
mor'gani. Poi. . . . GREENGILL L.
nauci'na. Edi. . . . . SMOOTH L.
pro'cera. Edi. . . . . PARASOL L.

LYCOP'ERDON pyrifor'me. Edi. PEAR LYCOPERDON

CRYPTOGAMS (FUNGI), continued

MARAS'MIUS . . . Marasmius
orea'des. Edi. . . . Fairyring M.
ro'tula . . . . . Collared M.

MERU'LIUS lac'rymans
Weeping Merulius

MORCHEL'LA esculen'ta. Edi.
Common Morel

MU'TINUS cani'nus
Dogstinkhorn Mutinus

MYCE'NA galericula'ta. Edi.
Peakcap Mycena

NAUCO'RIA semiorbicula'ris.
Edi. . . Halfball Naucoria

OMPHA'LIA campanel'la. Edi.
Bell Omphalia

PANAEO'LUS retiru'gis
Wrinkled Panaeolus

PA'NUS styp'ticus. Poi.
Bitter Panus

PHOLIO'TA . . . . . Pholiota
adipo'sa. Edi. . . . . Fatty P.
capera'ta. Edi. . . . Wrinkled P.
margina'ta. Suspected
squarro'sa. Edi. . . . . Scaly P.

PLEURO'TUS . . . Pleurotus
ostrea'tus. Edi. . . . Oyster P.
sap'idus. Edi. . . . . . Sapid P.

PLU'TEUS cervi'nus. Edi.
Fawncolor Pluteus

POLYP'ORUS . . . Polyporus
berk'eleyi . . . . . Berkeley P.
betuli'nus . . . . Birch P.
cro'ceus . . . . Whitepiperot P.
frondo'sus . . . Oakstrawrot P.
sulphu'reus . . . . Sulfur P.

POLYS'TICTUS . Polystictus
cinnabari'nus
pergame'nus
versicol'or

PSATHYREL'LA dissemina'ta.
Edi. . . . . . Psathyrella

PUCCIN'IA gram'inis
Stemrust Puccinia

RUS'SULA . . . . . Russula
emet'ica. Poi. . . . . Emetic R.
vires'cens. Edi. . . . Green R.

SACCHAROMY'CES cerevis'iae
Brewers Yeast

STE'REUM frustulo'sum
Honeycombrot Stereum

STROBILOMY'CES strobila'ceus
Porecone Strobilomyces

STROPHA'RIA semigloba'ta. Poi.
Poison Stropharia

TERFEZ'IA spp. Terfas (*Kamea*)

TRICHOLO'MA . Tricholoma
eques'tre. Edi. . . Equestrian T.
nu'dum. Edi.
persona'tum. Edi. . . Blewits T.
rus'sula. Edi. . . . . . . Red T.
ter'reum

TU'BER melanos'porum. Edi.
Perigord Truffle

USTILA'GO ze'ae (*maydis*)
Cornsmut

VOLVA'RIA . . . . . Volvaria
bombyci'na . . . . . . Silky V.
volva'cea. Padi V. (*Strawmushroom*)

CRYPTOGAMS, continued
LICHENS

ALECTO'RIA juba'ta
Rockhair Alectoria

BORRE'RA . . . . . Borrera
ash'neyi . . . . Chutcheleera B.
fla'vicans . . . . Yellow B.

CETRA'RIA
island'ica . . . . . Icelandmoss
juniperi'na . . . . . Junipermoss

CLADO'NIA rangiferi'na
Reindeermoss

CORNICULA'RIA aculea'ta spadic'ea . . . Brown Prickly Cornicularia

EVER'NIA . . . . . Evernia
fla'vicans . . . Yellowbrown E.
prunas'tri . . . . . Staghorn E.
vulpi'na . . . . Wolfbane E.

GYROPH'ORA . . Gyrophora
cylin'drica . . . . . Cylinder G.
deus'ta . . . . . . Scorched G.
pustula'ta . . . . . . Blister G.

ISID'IUM . . . . Isidium
coralli'num . . Coralcrottle I.
west'ringi . . . . . Westrings I.

LECANO'RA . . . . Lecanora
candela'ria . . . Candelaria L.
esculen'ta . . . . Manna L.
haemato'ma . . . . Bloodspot L.
palles'cens . . . . Pale L.
parel'la . . . . . . Crabseye L.
tatar'ea . . . . Litmus L.

LECID'EA . . . . . . Lecidea
atrovi'rens . . . . Map L.
sanguina'ria . . . . Bloodred L.

LEPRA'RIA . . . . . Lepraria
chlori'na . . . . . Brimstone L.
ioli'thus . . . . Violet L.

NEPHRO'MA par'ilis
Chocolate Nephroma

PARME'LIA . . . . . Parmelia
capera'ta . . . . . Wrinkled P.
ceratophyl'la . . . . . . Horny P.
conspers'a . . . . . Sprinkled P.
omphalo'des . . Blackcrottle P.
parieti'na . . . . Wall P.
perla'ta
physo'des . . . Darkcrottle P.
saxat'ilis . . . Stonecrottle P.

RAMALI'NA . . . . Ramalina
farina'cea . . . . Mealy R.
scopulo'rum . . . . Ivory R.

ROCCEL'LA tincto'ria
Litmus Roccella

SOLORI'NA cro'cea
Saffron Solorina

STIC'TA . . . . Sticta
croca'ta . . . . Yellow S.
pulmona'ria (*Lobaria p.*)
Lungwort S.
scrobicula'ta . . . . . . Pitted S.

UMBILICA'RIA . Umbilicaria
pustula'ta . . . . Blister U.
velle'a . . . . Fleecy U.

URCEOLA'RIA . Urceolaria
calca'rea . . . . . Limestone U.
cine'rea . . . . Ashy U.
scrupo'sa . . . . Jagged U.

CRYPTOGAMS (LICHENS), continued

US'NEA . . . . Usnea
barba'ta . . . . Bearded U.
flor'ida . . . . Florida U.
plica'ta . . . . Pleated U.

LIVERWORTS

MARCHAN'TIA polymor'pha
Common Marchantia

MOSSES

POLYT'RICHUM. Haircapmoss
commu'ne . . . . . . Common H.
juniperi'num . . . . . Juniper H.

SPHAG'NUM spp. . Sphagnum

CRYPTOGRAM'MA . . . Rockbrake
See **FERN GENERA.**

CRYPTOLE'PIS
el'egans
longiflo'ra

CRYPTOME'RIA . . . Cryptomeria
japon'ica . . . . Cryptomeria
The typical form of the species is the so-called var. japonica, Japanese Cryptomeria.
—sinen'sis (*C. fortunei; C. kawai*)
Chinese C.
¢Araucaria (*araucarioides*) hv. Cryptomeria
¢Cave (*compacta*)
¢Crested (*cristata*)
¢Dacrydium (*dacrydioides*)
¢Dwarf (*nana*)
¢Jundai-Sugi
¢Lobb (*lobbi*)
¢Plume (*elegans*)
¢Prickly (*pungens*)
¢Selaginella (*selaginoides*)
¢Slender (*elegans gracilis*)
¢Spiral (*spiralis*)
¢Vilmorin (*vilmoriniana*)

CRYPTOSTE'GIA . . . . Rubbervine
grandiflo'ra . . . . Palay R.
madagascarien'sis . Madagascar R.

CRYPTOSTEM'MA
calendula'ceum (*Arctotis calendulacea*)

CTENAN'THE
kummeria'na
lubbersia'na
oppenheimia'na (*Maranta o.*)
seto'sa

CTE'NIUM (*CAMPULOSUS*)
Combgrass
See **GRASS GENERA.**

CTENOPHYL'LUM . **ASTRAGALUS**

Cucumber . . . . . **Cucumis sativus**

CU'CUMIS |w
acutan'gulus . . . . **Luffa acutangula**
angu'ria |w (*erinaceus; grossulariaeformis*) . . WestIndian Gherkin
dipsa'ceus . . . . . . Teaselgourd
flexuo'sa . . . . . . **C. melo flexuosus**
me'lo |w . . . . Muskmelon
—cantalupen'sis . . . . Cantaloup (*Cantaloupe*)
—du'daim (*C. odoratissimus*)
Dudaim Melon
—flexuo'sus (*C. flexuosa*) . Snake M.
metulif'erus
myriocar'pus . . . Gooseberrygourd
sati'vus |w . . . . Cucumber

CUCUR'BITA |w
ficifo'lia (*melanosperma*)
Malabargourd

CUCURBITA, continued
foetidis'sima (*perennis*) |w BUFFALOGOURD
max'ima |w . . . . WINTER SQUASH
moscha'ta . . . . CUSHAW
pe'po |w . . . . PUMPKIN
—melope'po (*C. melopepo; C. p. condensa*) . . . . BUSH P.
—ovif'era (*C. ovifera*) YELLOWFLOWERGOURD
peren'nis . . . . . **C. foetidissima**

CUDRA'NIA (*VANIERIA*)
javanen'sis (*Vanieria j.*)
tricuspida'ta (*Maclura t.; Vanieria t.*)

CUDWEED . . . . **Gnaphalium**
CLAMMY C. . . . . . . **G. decurrens**
COTTONBATTING C. . . . **G. chilense**
FRAGRANT C. . . . . **G. obtusifolium**
LOW C. . . . . **G. uliginosum**
PURPLE C. . . . . . . **G. purpureum**
WOOD C. . . . . **G. sylvaticum**

CULVERSPHYSIC **Veronicastrum virginicum**

CU'MINUM . . . . CUMIN
cy'minum . . . . CUMIN

CUNI'LA . . . . STONEMINT
origanoi'des (*mariana*) MARYLAND S. (*Maryland Dittany*)

CUNNINGHAM'IA (*BELIS*) CHINAFIR
konish'i . . . . FORMOSA C.
lanceola'ta (*sinensis; Belis l.*) COMMON C.
¢BLUE (*glauca*) HV.

CUNO'NIA . . . . CUNONIA
capen'sis . . . CAPE C. (*Red Alder*)

CUPA'NIA . . . . CUPANIA
anacardioi'des
cunningham'i . . . . . **Diploglottis c.**
gla'bra . . . . FLORIDA C.
sap'ida . . . . **Blighia s.**
scorbicula'ta
siderox'ylon

CUPFERN . . . . **Dennstaedtia**
GLOSSY C. . . . . . . **D. adiantoides**

CUPFLOWER . . . . **Nierembergia**
DWARF C. . . . . . **N. hippomanica**
SLENDER C. . . . . **N. gracilis**
TALL C. . . . . **N. frutescens**
WHITE C. . . . . **N. rivularis**

CUPGRASS . . . . **Eriochloa**
BEARDED C. . . . . **E. aristata**
CANYON C. . . . . **E. lemmoni**
EVERGLADES C. **E. michauxi simpsoni**
HAIRY C. . . . . **E. villosa**
LONGLEAF C. . . . . . . **E. michauxi**
LOUISIANA C. . . . . . . **E. punctata**
NELSON C. . . . . **E. nelsoni**
PRAIRIE C. . . . . **E. contracta**
SMALL SOUTHWESTERN C. **E. gracilis minor**
SOUTHWESTERN C. . . . . . **E. gracilis**
TEXAS C. . . . . **E. sericea**
TROPICAL C. . . . . **E. procera**

CU'PHEA (*PARSONSIA*) |w CUPHEA
compac'ta . . . . . . **C. miniata c.**
cya'nea (*strigulosa*) . . . . VIOLET C.
em'inens . . . . **C. micropetala**
heterophyl'la
hookeria'na . . . . HOOKER C.
hyssopifo'lia . . . . . . HYSSOP C.
ig'nea . . . . **C. platycentra**
jorullen'sis (*tricolor*) BEETLESAGE C.
lanceola'ta (*silenoides; zimapani*) LANCELEAF C.

CUPHEA, continued
micropet'ala (*eminens*) TINYPETAL CUPHEA
minia'ta (*llavea*) . . . CINNABAR C.
—compac'ta (*C. compacta*) . BUNCH C.
petiola'ta (*Parsonsia p.*) |w CLAMMY C.
platycen'tra (*ignea*) . CIGARFLOWER C.
roez'li . . . . ROEZLI C.
silenoi'des . . . . . . **C. lanceolata**
strigulo'sa . . . . **C. cyanea**
tri'color . . . . **C. jorullensis**
visco'sa . . . . STICKY C.
zimapa'ni . . . . **C. lanceolata**

CUPHEA . . . . **Cuphea**
BEETLESAGE C. . . . . **C. jorullensis**
BUNCH C. . . . **C. miniata compacta**
CIGARFLOWER C. . . . **C. platycentra**
CINNABAR C. . . . . **C. miniata**
CLAMMY C. . . . . **C. petiolata**
HOOKER C. . . . . . . **C. hookeriana**
HYSSOP C. . . . . . . **C. hyssopifolia**
LANCELEAF C. . . . . . **C. lanceolata**
ROEZLI C. . . . . **C. roezli**
STICKY C. . . . . **C. viscosa**
TINYPETAL C. . . . . . **C. micropetala**
VIOLET C. . . . . **C. cyanea**

CUPIDSDART . . . . **Catananche**
BLUE C. . . . . **C. caerulea**

∞ **CUPRESSOCY'PARIS** (*CHAMAECYPARIS × CUPRESSUS*)
Known only in the following cross.

∞ **ley'landi** (*Chamaecyparis nootkatensis × Cupressus macrocarpa; ∞ Cupressus l.*)
The cultivated tree is presumably a clon of this cross.

CUPRES'SUS . . . . CYPRESS
arizo'nica . . . . ARIZONA C.
—boni'ta (*C. glabra*) . SMOOTH A.C.
Some botanists maintain that C. arizonica bonita and C. glabra are distinct.
¢BLUE (*glauca*) HV. C. arizonica
¢COMPACT (*compacta*)
¢DWARF (*nana*)
¢PYRAMIDAL (*pyramidalis*)
ba'keri (*C. macnabiana b.*) . MODOC C.
califor'nica . . . . **C. goveniana**
cashmeria'na . . . . . . KASHMIR C.
duclouxia'na (*torulosa*) . BHUTAN C.
¢CORNEY (*corneyana*) HV.
¢LOFTY (*majestica*)
¢WIGHT (*wightiana*)
excel'sa . . . **C. lusitanica benthami**
forbes'i . . . . TECATE C.
Tecate Cypress has been confused with the larger and much more commonly cultivated Guadalupe Cypress.
formosen'sis . . . . . . FORMOSA C.
fu'nebris . . . . MOURNING C.
—ericoi'des
gla'bra . . . . . **C. arizonica bonita**
govenia'na (*californica*) . . GOWEN C.
—sar'genti . . . . **C. sargenti**
¢BLUE (*californica; pygmaea*) HV. C. goveniana
guadalupen'sis (*C. macrocarpa g.*) GUADALUPE C.
See note on C. forbesi.
¢BLUE (*glauca*) HV.
lawsonia'na . . . . **Chamaecyparis l.**
∞ *ley'landi* . . . . ∞ **Cupressocyparis l.**
lusitan'ica (*glauca; lindleyi*) MEXICAN C. (*Portuguese C.*)
The common name Portuguese C., as well as the specific name lusitanica, are misnomers, as the tree is native to Mexico.

CUPRESSUS, continued
lusitan'ica ben'thami BENTHAM MEXICAN CYPRESS
—knightia'na (*C. knightiana*) KNIGHT M.C.
Perhaps not distinct from var. benthami.
¢BLUE (*glauca*) HV. C. lusitanica
¢SILVER (*argentea*)
¢WHIP (*flagellifera*)
macnabia'na . . . . MACNAB C.
—ba'keri . . . . **C. bakeri**
—nevaden'sis (*C. nevadensis*) PIUTE M.C.
¢SULFUR (*sulphurea*) HV. C. macnabiana
macrocar'pa (*lambertiana; C. macrocarpa l.*) . . . . . . MONTEREY C.
—guadalupen'sis . . **C. guadalupensis**
¢COLUMNAR (*fastigiata*) HV. C. macrocarpa
¢CRIPPS (*crippsi*)
¢GOLDEN (*lutea*)
¢LAMBERT (*lambertiana*)
¢VARIEGATED (*variegata*)
nootkaten'sis . . . **Chamaecyparis n.**
obtu'sa . . . . . **Chamaecyparis o.**
pisif'era . . . . **Chamaecyparis p.**
pyg'maea (*C. goveniana p.*) MENDOCINO C.
sar'genti (*C. goveniana s.*) SARGENT C.
—dut'toni . . . . DUTTON C.
sempervi'rens . . . . . . ITALIAN C.
PYRAMIDAL (*fastigiata; pyramidalis; stricta*) HV.
SPREADING (*horizontalis*)
torulo'sa . . . . **C. duclouxiana**

CUPSCALE . . . . **Sacciolepis**
AMERICAN C. . . . . **S. striata**
INDIA C. . . . . **S. indica**

CURCU'LIGO
capitula'ta (*recurvata*)
latifo'lia

CURCU'MA . . . . TURMERIC
angustifo'lia
lon'ga . . . . COMMON T.
petiola'ta
zedoa'ria . . . . ZEDOARY T.

CURI'MA . . . . **AIPHANES**
See **PALM GENERA.**

CURLYGRASS . . . . . **Schizaea pusilla**

CURLYMESQUITE . . . **Hilaria belangeri**

CURME'RIA . . . **HOMALOMENA**

CURRANT . . . . **Ribes**
See also GOOSEBERRY.
Alaska Black C. . . . TRAILING B.C.
ALPINE C. . . . . **R. alpinum**
AMERICAN BLACK C. **R. americanum**
AMERICAN RED C. . . . . . **R. triste**
ASIATIC C. . . . . **R. tenue**
∞ BETHMONT C. . . . . ∞ **R. bethmonti**
Blood C. . . . . WINTER C.
BUGLE C. . . . . **R. gracillimum**
California Black C. . . . . . STINK C.
CARPATHIAN C. **R. petraeum carpathicum**
∞ CARRIERE C. . . . . . ∞ **R. carrierei**
CATALINA C. . . . . . **R. viburnifolium**
CELERYLEAF EUROPEAN BLACK C. **R. nigrum apiifolium**
CHAPARRAL C. . . . . . **R. malvaceum**
CHERRY RED C. **R. sativum macrocarpum**
CHILEAN C. . . . . **R. gayanum**

CURRANT, continued
CHINESE WINTERBERRY C. **Ribes fasciculatum chinense**
CLOVE C. . . . . **R. odoratum**
COLORADO C. . . . . . **R. coloradense**
COMMON RED C. . . . . **R. sativum**
CRATERLAKE C. . **R. erythrocarpum**
CUTLEAF ALPINE C. **R. alpinum laciniatum**
CUTLEAF EUROPEAN BLACK C. **R. nigrum heterophyllum**
DIKUSCHA C. . . . . . . **R. dikuscha**
EARLY ALPINE C. **R. alpinum pumilum**
EPIPHYTE C. . . . . . **R. ambiguum**
EUROPEAN BLACK C. . . . **R. nigrum**
∞FONTENAY C. . . ∞**R. fontenayense**
∞FUTURUM C. . . . . . ∞**R. futurum**
GOLDEN C. . . . . **R. aureum**
∞GONDUIN C. . . . . . ∞**R. gonduini**
GOOSEBERRY C. . . . **R. montigenum**
∞GORDON C. . . . . ∞**R. gordonianum**
GREEN EUROPEAN BLACK C. **R. nigrum chlorocarpum**
HALLS C. . . . . **R. halli**
HENRY C. . . . . **R. henryi**
HIMALAYA C. . . . . . **R. emodense**
∞HOUGHTON C. . ∞**R. houghtonianum**
HUDSONBAY C. . . **R. hudsonianum**
JAPANESE C. . . . . . **R. japonicum**
∞KOEHNE C. . . . ∞**R. koehneanum**
LAUREL C. . . . . . **R. laurifolium**
MANCHURIAN C. . . **R. manshuricum**
MAPLELEAF C. . . . . **R. acerifolium**
MESCALERO C. . . . **R. mescalerium**
MEYER C. . . . . **R. meyeri**
MORENO C. . . . . **R. canthariforme**
NEPAL C. . . . . **R. glaciale**
NORTHERN RED C. . . . **R. rubrum**
NUTMEG C. . . . . . **R. glutinosum**
ORIENTAL C. . . . . . . **R. orientale**
PALELEAF WAX C. **R. cereum farinosum**
PINK WINTER C. **R. sanguineum carneum**
PRICKLY C. . . . . **R. lacustre**
Redflowering C. . . . . . . WINTER C.
ROCK C. . . . . **R. petraeum**
ROTHROCK C. . . . . **R. wolfi**
RUBY WINTER C. **R. sanguineum atrorubens**
RUSSIAN C. . . . . . **R. multiflorum**
∞SAUNDERS C. . . . . . ∞**R. saundersi**
SCARLET WINTER C. **R. sanguineum splendens**
SHINYLEAF ORIENTAL C. **R. orientale heterotrichum**
SIBERIAN C. . . . . . **R. diacanthum**
SIERRA C. . . . . . . **R. nevadense**
SIKKIM C. . **R. emodense urceolatum**
SKUNK C. . . . . . **R. glandulosum**
SMOOTH SIBERIAN C. **R. diacanthum inerme**
SQUAW C. . . . . **R. inebrians**
STICKY C. . . . . . **R. viscosissimum**
STINK C. . . . . . . **R. bracteosum**
Swamp C. . . . . PRICKLY C.
∞TAWNY C. . . . . . ∞**R. fuscescens**
TRAILING BLACK C. . . **R. laxiflorum**
TREE C. . . . . **R. moupinense**
VILMORIN C. . . . . . . **R. vilmorini**
∞WALLICH C. . . . . . ∞**R. wallichi**
WARSCEWICZ C. . . . **R. warscewiczi**
WARTY HIMALAYA C. **R. emodense verruculosum**
WAX C. . . . . **R. cereum**
WESTERN BLACK C. . . . **R. petiolare**
WHITEFLOWER C. . . . **R. indecorum**

CURRANT, continued
WHITE NUTMEG C. **Ribes glutinosum albidum**
WHITE WINTER C. **R. sanguineum albescens**
WILSON WISTARIA C. **R. longeracemosum wilsoni**
WINTERBERRY C. . . **R. fasciculatum**
WINTER C. . . . . . **R. sanguineum**
WISTARIA C. . . **R. longeracemosum**
YELLOWBERRY GOLDEN C. **R. aureum chrysococcum**
YELLOW EUROPEAN BLACK C. **R. nigrum xanthocarpum**
YELLOWLEAF ALPINE C. **R. alpinum aureum**
YELLOWLEAF WINTER C. **R. sanguineum brocklebanki**

CURRYLEAFTREE . . . **Murraya koenigi**

CURTIS'IA
fagi'nea . . . . ASSEGAITREE

CUSCU'TA |w . . . . DODDER
america'na . . . . . . LOVEVINE D.
arven'sis . . . . **C. pentagona**
Cuscuta arvensis was published as a synonym.
cor'yli . . . . HAZEL D.
epili'num . . . . FLAX D.
epithy'mum . . . . . . CLOVER D.
grono'vi |w . . . . . GRONOVIUS D.
indeco'ra . . . BIGSEED ALFALFA D.
obtusiflo'ra |w
pentag'ona (*arvensis*) |w
planiflo'ra . LITTLESEED ALFALFA D.
sali'na |w . . . . SALTMARSH D.
suave'olens (*C. racemosa chiliana*) CHILE D.

CUSHAW . . . . . **Cucurbita moschata**
CUSTARDAPPLE
BULLOCKSHEART C. . **Annona reticulata**
HARDSHELL C. . . . . **A. scleroderma**
Custardapple . . . . . . SUGARAPPLE: **Annona squamosa**

CUTAN'DIA
See **GRASS GENERA.**

CUTGRASS . . . . **Leersia**
BUNCH C. . . . . . . **L. monandra**
CLUBHEAD C. . . . . . **L. hexandra**
RICE C. . . . . **L. oryzoides**

CUTHBER'TIA
gramin'ea

CYANAN'THUS . . . . CYANANTHUS
delavay'i . . . . DELAVAY C.
inca'nus . . . . HOARY C.
loba'tus

CYANAS'TRUM
cordifo'lium

Cyanophyl'lum magnif'icum **Miconia magnifica**

CYANOP'SIS . . . . CYANOPSIS
tetragonolo'ba

CYANO'TIS
somalien'sis

CYA'THEA . . . . TREEFERN
See **FERN GENERA.**

CYATHO'DES
acero'sa

CYBIS'TAX . . . . PRIMAVERA
donnell-smith'i (*Tabebuia d.*) PRIMAVERA

CYBISTE'TES . . . . . . CYBISTETES
longifo'lia (*Ammocharis falcata*)

CYCAD GENERA

The Editorial Committee acknowledges with thanks valuable suggestions received in the preparation of this list from the following persons: Charles J. Chamberlain, Adriane S. Foster, A. W. Haupt, William Hertrich, and H. A. Van Hermann.

BOWE'NIA . . . . . . BOWENIA
serrula'ta (*B. spectabilis s.*) TURNIPSTEM B.
spectab'ilis . . . . CARROTSTEM B.

CERATOZA'MIA . . HORNCONE
kusteria'na . . . . . . KUSTER H.
latifo'lia . . . . BROADLEAF H.
mexica'na (*longifolia*) . . MEXICO H.
miquelia'na . . . . BLUE H.
pur'pusi . . . . PURPUS H.

CY'CAS . . . . CYCAS
beddom'ei . . . . MADRAS C.
cairnsia'na . . . . CAIRNS C.
circina'lis . . . . CROZIER C.
kennedya'na . . . . . KENNEDY C.
me'dia . . . . NUT C. (*Gaveu*)
micholitz'i . . . . . . MICHOLITZ C.
neocaledo'nica . . . NEWGUINEA C.
normanbya'na . . . . NORMANBY C.
pectina'ta . . . . NEPAL C.
revolu'ta . . . . SAGO C.
Usually called Sago Palm, but the true Sago Palm is Metroxylon rumphii.
riuminia'na . . . . . PHILIPPINE C.
rumph'ii . . . . RUMPHIUS C.
siamen'sis . . . . SIAM C.
tonkinen'sis . . . . TONKIN C.
wade'i . . . . WADE C.
Cycas zeylanica, a trade name, has no botanical standing.

DION' (*DIOON*) . . . . . . DION
chamal' . . . . CHAMAL D.
ed'ule . CHESTNUT D. (*Tiotamal*, Mex.)
pino'i (*dohenyi* Hort.; *tomentosum*)
pur'pusi . . . . PURPUS D.
spinulo'sum . . . . GIANT D.

ENCEPHALAR'TOS . KAFIRBREAD
altenstein'i . . . . ALTENSTEIN K.
brachyphyl'lus (*E. caffer b.*). ZULU K.
caf'fer (*caffra*)
cycadifo'lius . . . . GLOBE K.
ghellinck'i . . . . PINLEAF K.
hilldebrandt'i . . HILLDEBRANDT K.
hor'ridus . . . . SPINY K.
kosien'sis . . . . KOSIBAY K.
lat'ifrons . . . . . . BROADLEAF K.
laurentia'nus . . . . CONGO K.
lehmann'i . . . . LEHMANN K.
longifo'lius . . . . . . LONGLEAF K.
—angustifo'lius . . . . NARROW L.K.
—hook'eri . . . . HOOKER L.K.
—revolu'tus . . . . . . ROLLED L.K.
pun'gens . . . . SHARPLEAF K.
septentriona'lis . . . . NORTHERN K.
villo'sus . . . . WOOLLY K.

MACROZA'MIA . . . MACROZAMIA
coralli'pes . . . . . . CORALFOOT M.
den'isoni (*peroffskyana*) . DENISON M.
doug'lasi . . . . DOUGLAS M.
flexuo'sa . . . . ZIGZAG M.
fra'seri . . . . FRASER M.
heterom'era
hope'i . . . . GIANT M.

CYCAD GENERA (MACROZAMIA), con.
macdon'nelli . . . . . MONSTERSEED MACROZAMIA
miquel'i . . . . MIQUEL M.
moor'ei . . . . MOORE M.
paulo-guliel'mi . . . WOOLLYCONE M.
peroffskya'na . . . . . . **M. denisoni**
platyra'chis . . . . BROADSHAFT M.
spira'lis . . . . SPIRAL M.

MICROCY'CAS . . . MICROCYCAS
caloco'ma CORCHO M. (*Palma Corcho*)

STANGE'RIA . . . . FERNCYCAD
erio'pus (*paradoxa*) . . . STRANGE F.

ZA'MIA . . . . ZAMIA
angustifo'lia . . . . . BAHAMAS Z.
angustis'sima . . . . SLIMLEAF Z.
costaricen'sis . . . . COSTARICA Z.
cycadifo'lia
florida'na
furfura'cea . . . . SCURFY Z.
integrifo'lia . . . . COONTIE
kickx'i . . . . KICKX Z.
latifo'lia . . . . HONDURAS Z.
latifoliola'ta
lawsonia'na . . . . . . LAWSON Z.
leibold'i . . . . LEIBOLD Z.
lin'deni . . . . ECUADOR Z.
loddiges'i (*mexicana; terrestris*) LODDIGES Z.
me'dia
montic'ola . . . . . . MOUNTAIN Z.
portoricen'sis . . . PUERTORICO Z.
pseudoparasit'ica . . TREETRUNK Z.
pu'mila . . . . . ST.JOHNS COONTIE
pyg'maea . . . . PYGMY Z.
silic'ea . . . . SAND Z.
silvat'ica
silvic'ola
skin'neri . . . . PANAMA Z.
spar'tea . . . . BROOM Z.
terres'tris . . . . **Z. loddigesi**
umbro'sa . . . . . UNDERSHRUB Z.

CY'CAS . . . . CYCAS
See **CYCAD GENERA.**

CYCAS . . . . **Cycas**
CAIRNS C. . . . . . . **C. cairnsiana**
CROZIER C. . . . . . . **C. circinalis**
KENNEDY C. . . . . . **C. kennedyana**
MADRAS C. . . . . **C. beddomei**
MICHOLITZ C. . . . . . **C. micholitzi**
NEPAL C. . . . . **C. pectinata**
NEWGUINEA C. . . **C. neocaledonica**
NORMANBY C. . . . **C. normanbyana**
NUT C. . . . . **C. media**
PHILIPPINE C. . . . . **C. riuminiana**
RUMPHIUS C. . . . . . . **C. rumphii**
SAGO C. . . . . **C. revoluta**
SIAM C. . . . . **C. siamensis**
TONKIN C. . . . . . . **C. tonkinensis**
WADE C. . . . . **C. wadei**

CYCLADE'NIA . . . . CYCLADENIA
hu'milis . . . . SMOOTH C.
tomento'sa . . . . . . WOOLLY C.

CY'CLAMEN . . . . . CYCLAMEN
africa'num (*macrophyllum*) FLORISTS C.
∞ **at'kinsi** (*coum × sibiricum*) ∞ ATKINS C.
The plant in cultivation is probably a clon of this polybrid.
ROSE (*roseum*) HV.
co'um
ROSE (*roseum*) HV.
¢WHITE (*album*)
europae'um . . . . . EUROPEAN C.

CYCLAMEN, continued
ibe'ricum . . . . IBERIAN CYCLAMEN
¢RUBRUM. HV.
in'dicum (*hederaefolium; persicum*) IVYLEAF C.
¢GIANT (*giganteum*) HV.
¢ROCOCO
ROSE (*roseum*)
¢WHITE (*album*)
libanot'icum
macrophyl'lum . . . . **C. africanum**
neapolita'num . . . . NEAPOLITAN C.
¢WHITE (*album*) HV.
repan'dum . . . . SPRING C.

CYCLANTHE'RA . . . CYCLANTHERA
explo'dens . . . . . . ARTILLERY C.
peda'ta . . . . PRICKLE C.

CYCLAN'THUS
biparti'tus

CYCLOLO'MA ⌊w . . . . RINGWING
atriplicifo'lium ⌊w . . . . TUMBLE R.

CYCLO'PHORUS (*NIPHOBOLUS*) FELTFERN
See **FERN GENERA.**

CYCLO'PIA
tenuifo'lia

CYCLOSPA'THE **PSEUDOPHOENIX**
See **PALM GENERA.**

CYCNO'CHES . . . . . . SWANORCHID
See **ORCHID GENERA.**

CYDIS'TA . . . . CYDISTA
aequinoctia'lis (*Bignonia a.*)

CYDO'NIA . . . . QUINCE
cathayen'sis. **Chaenomeles lagenaria c.**
japon'ica Loisel., *not* Pers. **Chaenomeles lagenaria**
maul'ei . . . **Chaenomeles japonica**
—*super'ba* . . . . **×Chaenomeles s.**
oblong'a (*vulgaris*) . . . COMMON Q.
¢APPLE (*maliformis*) HV.
¢COLUMNAR (*pyramidalis*)
¢MARBLED (*marmorata*)
¢PEAR (*pyriformis*)
¢PORTUGUESE (*lusitanica*)
sargent'i. **Chaenomeles japonica alpina**
sinen'sis . . . . **Chaenomeles s.**
vulga'ris . . . . **C. oblonga**
For other spp. and var. often listed under Cydonia, see **CHAENOMELES.**
For varieties of the Common Quince cultivated for their fruit see QUINCE under **FRUIT AND EDIBLE NUT NAMES.**

CYLICODIS'CUS
gabunen'sis

CYLINDROPHYL'LUM
calamifor'me

CYMBALA'RIA . . . . . BASKETIVY
aequitrilo'ba (*Linaria a.*). TOADFLAX B.
hepaticaefo'lia (*Linaria h.*) LIVERLEAF B.
mura'lis (*Linaria cymbalaria*) KENILWORTHIVY (*Aaronsbeard*)
¢ALBA. HV.
¢MAXIMA
¢ROSEA
pilo'sa (*Linaria p.*) . . . SHAGGY B.
Cym'bia occidenta'lis . . . . **Krigia o.**

CYMBID'IUM
See **ORCHID GENERA.**

CYMBOPO'GON
See **GRASS GENERA.**

CYMODO'CEA ⌊w . . MANATEEGRASS
manato'rum ⌊w . . . . . . GULF M.
Cymophyl'lus fra'seri . . . . . **Carex f.**

CYMOP'TERUS (*OREOXIS*) ⌊w
fend'leri . . . . CHIMAYA

CYNAN'CHUM . . . . SWALLOWWORT
acuminatifo'lium (*Vincetoxicum acuminatum; V. japonicum*) MOSQUITOTRAP S.
erec'tum . . . . . **Marsdenia erecta**
ni'grum (*Vincetoxicum n.*). . BLACK S.
vincetox'icum (*Vincetoxicum officinale*) WHITE S.

CY'NARA
cardun'culus . . . . CARDOON
sco'lymus . . . ARTICHOKE (*Globe A.*)
¢BURBANK. HV.

CY'NODON (*CAPRIOLA*) DOGTOOTHGRASS
See **GRASS GENERA.**

CYNOGLOS'SUM . . HOUNDSTONGUE
ama'bile . . . . CHINESE H.
—al'bum . . . . WHITE C.H.
furca'tum
glochidia'tum . . . . **C. wallichi**
gran'de . . . . PACIFIC H.
linifo'lium . . . **Omphalodes linifolia**
nervo'sum . . . . GREAT H.
occidenta'le . . . . . . WESTERN H.
officina'le . . . . COMMON H.
virgin'icum . . . . . WILDCOMFREY H.
wal'lichi (*glochidiatum*) . WALLICH H.
zeylan'icum . . . . . . CEYLON H.

CYNOMA'RATHRUM . . DOGPARSLEY
nutt'alli . . . . NUTTALL D.

CYNOME'TRA
triniten'sis

CYNOSU'RUS . . . . DOGTAIL
See **GRASS GENERA.**

Cynox'ylon flor'idum . . **Cornus florida**

CYN'THIA . . . . **KRIGIA**

CYPEL'LA . . . . CYPELLA
her'berti . . . . HERBERT C.
plum'bea

CYP'ERUS (*PAPYRUS*) ⌊w FLATSEDGE
acumina'tus ⌊w . . . . TAPERLEAF F.
adeno'phorus . . . . BRAZILIAN F.
alternifo'lius ⌊w . . . UMBRELLA F.
—**grac'ilis** . . . . . SLENDER U.F.
¢STRIPED (*variegatus*) HV. C. alternifolius
arista'tus ⌊w . . . . . . BEARDED F.
articula'tus ⌊w . . . . . JOINTED F.
cellulo'sa ⌊w
compres'sus ⌊w
cylin'dricus ⌊w . . . . . CYLINDER F.
denta'tus ⌊w . . . . . TOOTHLEAF F.
dian'drus ⌊w
diffor'mis ⌊w
echina'tus ⌊w
engelmann'i ⌊w . . . . ENGELMANN F.
erythrorhi'zos ⌊w
esculen'tus ⌊w . . CHUFA F. (*Chufa*)
fendleria'nus ⌊w . . . . FENDLER F.
fe'rax ⌊w
filici'nus ⌊w . . . . FERN F.
flaves'cens ⌊w
flavico'mus ⌊w

CYPERUS, continued
gates'i |w . . . . GATES FLATSEDGE
has'pan |w
hel'vus |w
hochstet'teri |w . . . HOCHSTETTER F.
inflex'us |w
ir'ia |w
longispica'tus |w . . . LONGSPIKE F.
lon'gus . . . . GALINGALE F.
melanosta'chys |w
microdon'tus |w
natalen'sis . . . . NATAL F.
odora'tus |w
papy'rus (*Papyrus antiquorum*) PAPYRUS
pol'lardi |w . . . . . . POLLARD F.
pseudoveg'etus |w
retrifrac'tus |w
rivula'ris |w . . . . BROOK F.
rotun'dus |w . . . . . NUTGRASS F.
schwei'nitzi |w . . . . SCHWEINITZ F.
strigo'sus |w
tegetifor'mis . . . . CHINESEMAT F.
uniflo'rus |w . . . . . ONEFLOWER F.
vi'rens . . . . GREEN F.

CYPHOMAN'DRA
beta'cea . . . . TREETOMATO

CYPRESS . . . . **Cupressus**
ARIZONA C. . . . . . . **C. arizonica**
BENTHAM MEXICAN C. **C. lusitanica benthami**
BHUTAN C. . . . . . **C. duclouxiana**
DUTTON C. . . . **C. sargenti duttoni**
FORMOSA C. . . . . . **C. formosensis**
GOWEN C. . . . . **C. goveniana**
GUADALUPE C. . . . **C. guadalupensis**
ITALIAN C. . . . . . **C. sempervirens**
KASHMIR C. . . . . **C. cashmeriana**
KNIGHT MEXICAN C. **C. lusitanica knightiana**
MACNAB C. . . . . . **C. macnabiana**
MENDOCINO C. . . . . . **C. pygmaea**
MEXICAN C. . . . . . . **C. lusitanica**
MODOC C. . . . . **C. bakeri**
MONTEREY C. . . . . **C. macrocarpa**
MOURNING C. . . . . . **C. funebris**
PIUTE MACNAB C. **C. macnabiana nevadensis**
Portuguese C. . . . . . MEXICAN C.
SARGENT C. . . . . . . **C. sargenti**
SMOOTH ARIZONA C. **C. arizonica bonita**
TECATE C. . . . . **C. forbesi**

CYPRESSPINE . . . . **Callitris**
DROOPING C. . . . **C. cupressiformis**
DRUMMOND C. . . . **C. drummondi**
JUNIPER C. . . . . **C. juniperoides**
MUELLER C. . . . . . . **C. muelleri**
OBLONGCONE C. . . . . **C. oblonga**
ROES C. . . . . **C. roei**
SCHWARZ C. . . . . . . **C. schwarzi**
STURDY C. . . . . **C. robusta**
TASMANIAN C. . . . . **C. tasmanica**

CYPRIPE'DIUM . . . . . LADYSLIPPER
See **ORCHID GENERA, HARDY TERRESTRIAL GROUP.**

CYRIL'LA . . . . CYRILLA
antilla'na . . . . . . ANTILLES C.
racemiflo'ra . . . . . AMERICAN C.

CYRTAN'THUS . . . . CYRTANTHUS
angustifo'lius . . . NARROWLEAF C.
contrac'tus
mack'eni . . . . . . MACKEN C.
obli'quus . . . . . CAPECOLONY C.
o'bri'eni . . . . OBRIEN C.
ochroleu'cus . . . . . YELLOW C.

CYRTANTHUS, continued
parviflo'rus LITTLEFLOWER CYRTANTHUS
sanguin'eus . . . . BLOOD C.
₵HERMIONE. HV. Cyrtanthus

CYRTO'MIUM . . . . . . BOWFERN
See **FERN GENERA.**

CYRTOPO'DIUM
See **ORCHID GENERA.**

CYRTOSTACH'YS . SEALINGWAXPALM
See **PALM GENERA.**

CYS'TIUM . . . . . **ASTRAGALUS**

CYSTOP'TERIS (*FILIX*) BLADDERFERN
See **FERN GENERA.**

CYTHERE'A . . . . . . **CALYPSO**
See **ORCHID GENERA, HARDY TERRESTRIAL GROUP.**

CY'TISUS . . . . BROOM
acutan'gulus
ad'ami . . . . **₵Laburnocytisus a.**
al'bus (*leucanthus*) . PORTUGUESE B.
—pal'lidus . . . . PALE P.B.
alpi'nus . . . . . **Laburnum alpinum**
ardoi'ni (*Genista a.*) . . . . ARDOIN B.
austria'cus . . . . AUSTRIAN B.
—heuf'feli (*C. heuffeli*). HEUFFEL A.B.
battandier'i
∞ **bean'i** (*ardoini* × *purgans*) ∞ BEANS B.
canarien'sis (*Genista c.*) . CANARY B.
—ramosis'simus (*C. attleyanus; C. ramosissimus*)
can'dicans . . . . **C. monspessulanus**
capita'tus . . . . **C. supinus**
carlier'i . . . **C. nigricans elongatus**
cilia'tus
∞ **dallimor'ei** (*multiflorus* × *scoparius* ₵PARADISE) . . . ∞ DALLIMORE B.
decum'bens (*Genista d.; G. halleri*) PROSTRATE B.
demis'sus
diffu'sus
elonga'tus (*C. ratisbonensis e.*)
emeriflo'rus (*glabrescens*)
fi'lipes . . . . TENERIFFE B.
fra'grans (*Genista f.; Spartocytisus nubigenus*) . . . . SWEET B.
grandiflo'rus Hort. **C. scoparius prostratus**
heuf'feli . . . . . . **C. austriacus h.**
hillebrandt'i . . . . HILLEBRANDT B.
hirsu'tus (*leucotrichus*)
hispan'icus . . . **Genista hispanica**
jun'ceus . . . . . **Spartium junceum**
∞ **kewen'sis** (*ardoini* × *multiflorus*)
The plant in cultivation is probably a clon of this polybrid.
labur'num . . **Laburnum anagyroides**
—purpuras'cens **₵Laburnocytisus adami**
leiocar'pus . . . . . . HUNGARIAN B.
leucan'thus . . . . **C. albus**
leuco'trichus . . . . . . **C. hirsutus**
linifo'lius
maderen'sis . . . . . . MADEIRA B.
—magnifolio'sus (*C. stenopetalus*) LEAFY M.B.
monosper'mus
monspessula'nus (*candicans*) MONTPELIER B.
multiflo'rus (*albus* of some Auth.; *Spartium multiflorum*) WHITESPANISH B.

CYTISUS multiflorus, continued
₵KILLARNEY. HV.
₵WHITEGEM
ni'gricans . . . . . . SPIKE BROOM
—elonga'tus (*carlieri*)
perez'i
∞ **prae'cox** (*multiflorus* × *purgans; Genista praecox*) . . ∞ WARMINISTER B.
₵EASTER (*albus*) HV.
₵LUTEUS
procum'bens . . . . . . GROUND B.
prolif'erus
pur'gans . . . . PROVENCE B.
purpu'reus . . . . PURPLE B.
₵ALBOCARNEUS. HV.
₵ALBUS
₵ATROPURPUREUS
₵ELONGATUS
₵ERECTUS
₵INCARNATUS
racemo'sus (*Genista racemosa*) EASTER B.
radia'tus . . . . . . **Genista radiata**
ramosis'simus . . . **C. canariensis r.**
ratisbonen'sis
—biflo'rus
—elonga'tus . . . . . . **C. elongatus**
₵HORNIFLORUS. HV. C. ratisbonensis
rochel'i . . . . ROCHEL B.
sagitta'lis . . . . **Genista s.**
scopa'rius (*Genista scoparia; Spartium scoparium*) . . . . SCOTCH B.
—prostra'tus (*C. grandiflorus*)
₵ALBUS. HV. C. scoparius
₵BURKWOOD
₵BUTTERFLY
₵C. E. PEARSON
₵CORNISH CREAM
₵DAISY HILL
₵DONALD SEEDLING
₵DOROTHY WALPOLE
₵DOUBLE (*plenus*)
₵ENCHANTRESS
₵FIREFLY
₵FULGENS
₵GEOFFREY SKIPWITH
₵GOLDEN SUNLIGHT
₵HIBERNIA
₵KILLARNEY
₵LADY MOORE
₵LORD LAMBOURNE
₵MARIE BURKWOOD
₵MAYFLY
₵MOONLIGHT (*sulphureus*)
₵PARADISE (*andreanus*)
₵PETER PAN
₵PINKBEAUTY
₵WEEPING (*pendulus*)
sessilifo'lius . . . . . . SESSILE B.
—leucan'thus . . . . YELLOW S.B.
stenopet'alus **C. maderensis magnifoliosus**
supi'nus (*capitatus*) . . BIGFLOWER B.
triflo'rus . . . . GREEK B.
∞ **versicol'or** (*hirsutus* × *purpureus*)
₵HILLER (*hilleri*) HV.

DABOE'CIA . . . . . IRISHHEATH
canta'brica (*polifolia*) . . . . BELL I.
₵ALBA. HV.
₵ATROPURPUREA
₵BICOLOR
₵NANA
₵PALLIDA

DACRY'DIUM . . . . . DACRYDIUM
bid'willi . . . . BIDWILL D.
colenso'i . . . . COLENSO D.

DACRYDIUM, continued
cupressi'num . . Rimu Dacrydium
frank'lini . . . . . Huonpine D.
interme'dium . . . . Fire D.
kirk'i . . . . Kirk D.
westlan'dicum . . . . Westland D.

DAC'TYLIS . . . . . . Orchardgrass
See **GRASS GENERA.**

DACTYLOCTE'NIUM . Crowfootgrass
See **GRASS GENERA.**

DACTYLOP'SIS
MESEMBRYANTHEMUM
See **SUCCULENTS.**

DAEDALACAN'THUS
ERANTHEMUM

DAEDA'LEA . . . . Daedalea
querci'na . . . . Oak D.

DAEMON'OROPS . . . Devilrattan
See **PALM GENERA.**

Daffodil
Common D.
Narcissus pseudo-narcissus
∞Nonesuch D. . ∞**N. incomparabilis**
Petticoat D. . . . **N. bulbocodium**
Tenby D. . . . . . . **N. obvallaris**

DAHL'IA . . . . Dahlia
coccin'ea . . . . Fire D.
excel'sa (*arborea*) . . . . . Tree D.
glabra'ta . . . . **D. mercki**
grac'ilis . . . . Dwarf D.
imperia'lis . . . . . Candelabra D.
juar'ezi . . . . Cactus D.
max'oni . . . . Maxon D.
merck'i (*glabrata*) . . . . Bedding D.
pinna'ta . . . . Aztec D.
rose'a . . . . Old Garden D.
variab'ilis

A group of garden hybrids, probably among D. coccinea, D. pinnata, and D. rosea. These hybrids appear also in nature.

The Editorial Committee wishes to record its warm appreciation of the fine list of Dahlia hort. var. prepared for this edition of Standardized Plant Names by Charles H. Connors, Professor of Ornamental Horticulture, State College of Agriculture, Rutgers University, New Brunswick, N. J., and to express its keen regret that space limitations have precluded the use of this list. Dr. Connors, who is Chairman of the Committee on Nomenclature for the American Dahlia Society, based his list largely upon the list prepared by J. B. S. Norton of the University of Maryland for the former (1923) edition of Standardized Plant Names. Dr. Norton later became Chairman of the Committee on Nomenclature and published privately in 1924 a list of "7000 Dahlias in Cultivation." These two published lists should be consulted by the reader interested in hort. var. of Dahlia.

Dahoon . . . . **Ilex cassine**
Alabama D. . . . . **I. c. angustifolia**
Myrtle D. . . . . . **I. c. myrtifolia**

Daisy . . . . **Bellis**
Blueray Morocco D.
B. rotundifolia caerulescens
English D. . . . . . . **B. perennis**
Morocco D. . . . . . **B. rotundifolia**
New Holland D. . . . . Vittadinia, Australian: **Vittadinia australis**
Spanish D. . . . . **B. annua**

Daisybush . . . . **Olearia**
Akeake D. . . . **O. avicenniaefolia**
Akiraho D. . . . . . **O. paniculata**
Bighead Myrsine D.
O. myrsinoides erubescens
Branny D. . . . . . **O. furfuracea**
Chatham D. . . . . . **O. chathamica**
Coinleaf D. . . . **O. nummularifolia**
Colenso D. . . . . **O. colensoi**
Fragrant D. . . . **O. fragrantissima**
Haast D. . . . . **O. haasti**
Heketara D. . . . . **O. cunninghami**
Hollyleaf D. . . . . . . **O. ilicifolia**
Leatherleaf D. . . . . **O. coriacea**
Musktree D. . . . . . **O. argophylla**
Musky D. . . . . **O. moschata**
Myrsine D. . . . . **O. myrsinoides**
Oliveleaf D. . . . . . . **O. oleifolia**
Ridge Tasmanian D.
O. stellulata lirata
Solander D. . . . . **O. solandri**
Sweet D. . . . . **O. suavis**
Tasmanian D. . . . . . **O. stellulata**
Teteaweka D. . . . . **O. angustifolia**
Thickleaf D. . . . . **O. pachyphylla**
Thomson D. . . . . . . **O. thomsoni**
Traills D. . . . . **O. trailli**
Travers D. . . . . **O. traversi**
Twiggy D. . . . . **O. ramulosa**
Wilcox D. . . . . **O. wilcoxi**

DALBER'GIA (*AMERIMNON*)
Rosewood
thecearen'sis . . . . Ceara R.
cochinchinen'sis
dyeria'na
granadil'lo . . . . . Granadillo R.
grevea'na . . . . . Madagascar R.
hupea'na
hypoleu'ca . . . . . . CostaRica R.
latifo'lia . . . . EastIndian R.
melanox'ylon . African Blackwood
mimosoi'des
ni'gra . . . . Black R.
retu'sa . . . . Panama R.
sis'soo (*Amerimnon s.*) . . . Sissoo
stevenso'ni . . . . . Honduras R.

DA'LEA (*PAROSELA*) |w . . Dalea
alopecuroi'des . . . . . Foxtail D.
amoe'na . . . . Navaho D.
arbores'cens . . . . . . Mohave D.
argyrae'a (*Parosela a.*) . . Silver D.
au'rea |w . . . . Silktop D.
califor'nica . . . . . California D.
emo'ryi . . . . Emory D.
ennean'dra
formo'sa . . . . Feather D.
fre'monti . . . . Fremont D.
frutes'cens (*Parosela f.*) . . Black D.
gregg'i . . . . Gregg D.
james'i . . . . James D.
john'soni . . . . . Desertbeauty D.
lana'ta
mol'lis . . . . Hairy D.
na'na . . . . Dwarf D.
par'ryi (*Parosela p.*) . . . . Parry D.
pogonan'thera . . . . . Bearded D.
polyade'nia . . . . Nevada D.
polygonoi'des . . . . . Sixweeks D.
sanctae-cru'cis . . . . Holycross D.
schott'i . . . . Mesa D.
scopa'ria . . . . Broom D.
spino'sa . . . . . . Smokethorn D.
wright'i . . . . Wright D.

Dalea . . . . **Dalea**
Bearded D. . . . . **D. pogonanthera**
Black D. . . . . **D. frutescens**

Dalea, continued
Broom D. . . . . **Dalea scoparia**
California D. . . . . . **D. californica**
Desertbeauty D. . . . . **D. johnsoni**
Dwarf D. . . . . **D. nana**
Emory D. . . . . **D. emoryi**
Feather D. . . . . **D. formosa**
Foxtail D. . . . . . **D. alopecuroides**
Fremont D. . . . . **D. fremonti**
Gregg D. . . . . **D. greggi**
Hairy D. . . . . **D. mollis**
Holycross D. . . . . **D. sanctae-crucis**
James D. . . . . **D. jamesi**
Mesa D. . . . . **D. schotti**
Mohave D. . . . . . . **D. arborescens**
Navaho D. . . . . **D. amoena**
Nevada D. . . . . . . **D. polyadenia**
Parry D. . . . . **D. parryi**
Silktop D. . . . . **D. aurea**
Silver D. . . . . **D. argyraea**
Sixweeks D. . . . . **D. polygonoides**
Smokethorn D. . . . . . . **D. spinosa**
Wright D. . . . . **D. wrighti**

DALECHAMP'IA . . . Dalechampia
roezlia'na . . . . Roezls D.
—al'ba . . . . White R.D.
tiliaefo'lia (*pruriens*) . . Cowitch D.

DALIBAR'DA . . . . Dalibarda
re'pens (*Rubus dalibarda*)
Starviolet D.

Dallisgrass . . . **Paspalum dilatatum**

DAMASO'NIUM |w . . Damasonium
califor'nicum |w . . . California D.

Damiana . . . . Turnera, Damiana: **Turnera diffusa**

The term Damiana is also used by Spanish-speaking people for certain other Composites reputed to possess aphrodisiac properties.

Damianita . . **Chrysactinia mexicana**

DAMMA'RA . . . . . . **AGATHIS**

Dammarpine . . . . **Agathis**
Big D. . . . . **A. robusta**
Kauri D. . . . . **A. australis**
Palmerston D. . . . **A. palmerstoni**
White D. . . . . **A. alba**

DAMNACAN'THUS
in'dicus

DA'NAE . . . . . Alexandrialaurel
androg'yna . . . . **Semele a.**
racemo'sa (*Ruscus racemosus*)
Alexandrialaurel

Dancinggirls . . . **Mantisia saltatoria**

Dandelion . . . . **Taraxacum**
Common D. . . . . . . **T. officinale**
Rough D. . . . . . **T. ceratophorum**
Smooth D. . . . . . . **T. laevigatum**

Dangleberry . . **Gaylussacia frondosa**

DANIEL'LA . . . . Daniella
o'gea . . Ogeagum D. (*Accra Copal*)
oliver'i . . . . . Illurin-balsam D. (*Illurin-balsam*)
thurif'era SierraLeone-frankincense

Danta . . . **Cistanthera papaverifera**

DANTHO'NIA . . . . Danthonia
See **GRASS GENERA.**

Danthonia . . . . **Danthonia**
Australian D. . . **D. semiannularis**
Bandicoot D. . . . . . . **D. robusta**
California D. . . . . **D. californica**

DANTHONIA, continued
Downy D. . . . Danthonia sericea
Elephant D. . . . . D. elephantina
Flatstem D. . . . . D. compressa
Haaschare D. . . . . D. purpurea
Hairy California D.
D. californica americana
Hairy D. . . . . D. pilosa
Onespike D. . . . . D. unispicata
Parry D. . . . . D. parryi
Poverty D. . . . . . . D. spicata
Timber D. . . . . . D. intermedia
Wallaby D. . . . . . D. penicillata
Yellow D. . . . . . D. flavescens

DAPHNAN'DRA . . . . Daphnandra
micran'tha . . . . . . Sassafras D.

DAPH'NE . . . . Daphne
acutilo'ba . . . . . . Sharpleaf D.
alpi'na . . . . Alpine D.
alta'ica . . . . Mongolian D.
arbus'cula
auranti'aca
blagaya'na . . . . Balkan D.
∞**burk'woodi** (*caucasica* × *cneorum*)
∞Burkwood D.
cannabi'na
caucas'ica . . . . . . Caucasian D.
cneo'rum . . . . Rose D.
₵Largeleaf (*major*) hv.
₵Littleleaf (*minor*)
₵Silverleaf (*variegata*)
₵Verlot (*verloti*)
White (*alba*)
colli'na
—neapolita'na (*D. neapolitana*)
∞**fionia'na** (*cneorum* × *collina ?*)
genk'wa . . . . Lilac D.
₵Fortunes (*fortunei*) hv.
girald'i . . . . Giraldi D.
gl mera'ta
gni'dium . . . . Spurgeflax D.
∞**houttea'na** (*laureola* × *mezereum*)
∞**hy'brida** (*collina* × *odora*)
kamtschat'ica . . . Kamchatka D.
laureo'la . . . . Spurgelaurel D.
—philip'pi
meze'reum . . . . . February D.
₵Alba. hv.
₵Double (*plena*)
₵Grandiflora
₵Red (*rubra*)
neapolita'na . . . . . . **D. collina n.**
odo'ra . . . . Winter D.
₵Rosequeen. hv.
₵Rubra
₵White
₵Yellowedge (*marginata*)
oleoi'des . . . . Olive D.
petrae'a
pon'tica . . . . Pontic D.
pseudo-meze'reum
retu'sa
seric'ea
stria'ta
tangu'tica

Daphne . . . . **Daphne**
Alpine D. . . . . **D. alpina**
Balkan D. . . . . . . **D. blagayana**
∞Burkwood D. . . . . ∞**D. burkwoodi**
Caucasian D. . . . . . **D. caucasica**
February D. . . . . **D. mezereum**

Daphne, continued
Giraldi D. . . . . . Daphne giraldi
Kamchatka D. . . . D. kamtschatica
Lilac D. . . . . D. genkwa
Mongolian D. . . . . . . D. altaica
Olive D. . . . . D. oleoides
Pontic D. . . . . D. pontica
Rose D. . . . . D. cneorum
Sharpleaf D. . . . . . D. acutiloba
Spurgeflax D. . . . . D. gnidium
Spurgelaurel D. . . . . D. laureola
Winter D. . . . . D. odora

DAPHNIPHYL'LUM
hu'mile
macropo'dum

Darlingplum . . . . **Reynosia**
Northern D. . . **R. septentrionalis**

DARLINGTO'NIA (*CHRYSAMPHORA*) . . Californiapitcher
califor'nica . . Californiapitcher

Darnel . . . . . Ryegrass, Darnel: **Lolium temulentum**

DARWIN'IA . . . . Darwinia
citriodo'ra
oederoi'des
schuermann'i
thymoi'des . . . . Thyme D.

Dasheen . . . . . **Colocasia esculenta**

DASIPH'ORA . . . . **POTENTILLA**

DASYLIR'ION |w . . . . Sotol
acro'trichum . . . . . . Brushtip S.
The usual spelling, acrotriche, appears to be incorrect.
glaucophyl'lum . . . . . Blueleaf S.
graminifo'lium . . . . Grassleaf S.
longis'simum (*quadrangulatum*)
Squareleaf S.
par'ryi . . . . **Nolina p.**
serratifo'lium . . . . . Sawtooth S.
texa'num . . . . Texas S.
whee'leri . . . . Wheeler S.

DASYSTEPH'ANA . . **GENTIANA**

DASYSTO'MA . . . **AUREOLARIA**

Date . . . . . **Phoenix; P. dactylifera**
Abyssinian D. . . . . **P. abyssinica**
Canary D. . . . . . **P. canariensis**
Ceylon D. . . . . **P. zeylanica**
Cliff D. . . . . **P. rupicola**
Dwarf D. . . . . **P. humilis**
Hance D. . . . . **P. hanceana**
Malayan D. . . . . . . **P. paludosa**
Roebelen D. . . **P. humilis loureiri**
Senegal D. . . . . . . **P. reclinata**
Shrubby D. . . . . **P. pusilla**
Stemless D. . . . . **P. acaulis**
Sugar D. . . . . **P. sylvestris**

DATIS'CA
cannabi'na

Dattock . . . . **Detarium**
Senegal D. . . . . **D. senegalense**

DATU'RA |w . . . . Datura
aegyp'tica . . . . **D. metel**
arbo'rea (*Brugmansia a.*) . . Floripondio D. (*Angels-trumpet; Maikoa*)

DATURA, continued
can'dida . . . . Thornapple Datura
ceratocau'la
chloran'tha . . . . Yellow D.
cornig'era (*knighti*) . . . Horned D.
denoter'i (*coccinea*)
fe'rox
me'tel (*aegyptica; cornucopia; fastuosa*)
Hindu D.
₵Alba. hv.
₵Caerulea
₵Huberiana
meteloi'des (*wrighti*) |w . . Sacred D.
quercifo'lia . . . . . . Oakleaf D.
sanguin'ea (*Brugmansia s.*) Scarlet D.
stramo'nium (*tatula*) Jimsonweed D.
—iner'mis . . . . . Spineless J.D.
suave'olens . . . . Angeltears D.
wright'i . . . . **D. meteloides**

DAUBENTO'NIA |w . . . Rattlebox
cavanil'lesi (*longifolia; Sesbania c.*) |w
Longleaf R.
drum'mondi (*Sesbania d.*)
Drummond R.
punic'ea (*Sesbania p.*)
trip'etti (*Sesbania t.*) . Glorypea R.

DAUCOPHYL'LUM
tenuifo'lium

DAU'CUS |w . . . . Carrot
caro'ta |w . . . . Wild C.
—sati'va . . . . Garden C.
Garden Carrot applies to the forms of Daucus carota as a cultivated vegetable, Wild Carrot as a weed, and Queen-Annes-Lace as an ornamental.
pusil'lus |w . . . Southwestern C.

DAVAL'LIA . . . . Davallia
See **FERN GENERA**.

DAVID'IA . . . . Dovetree
involucra'ta . . . . Dovetree
—vilmorinia'na . . . . Vilmorin D.

DAVIES'IA . . . . Daviesia
corda'ta . . . . Cordate D.
latifo'lia . . . . Broadleaf D.

Dawnflower . . . . . **Orthrosanthus**
Chimborazo D. . **O. chimboracensis**

Dayflower . . . . **Commelina**
Birdbill D. . . . . . **C. dianthifolia**
Creeping D. . . . . . . **C. nudiflora**
Common D. . . . . . . **C. communis**
Curlyleaf D. . . . . **C. crispa**
Erect D. . . . . **C. erecta**
Hairy D. . . . . **C. hirtella**
Mexican D. . . . . **C. coelestis**
Narrowleaf D. . . . **C. angustifolia**
Sikkim D. . . . . . . **C. sikkimensis**
Tuber D. . . . . **C. tuberosa**
Virginia D. . . . . **C. virginica**

Daylily . . . . **Hemerocallis**
For hort. var. of Daylily see **HEMEROCALLIS.**
Citron D. . . . . **H. citrina**
Double Early D.
H. dumortieri flore-pleno
Dwarf D. . . . . **H. nana**
Early D. . . . . **H. dumortieri**
Foldleaf D. . . . . **H. plicata**

Hort. var.; hv. = horticultural variety (or varieties); sp. = species (singular); spp. = species (plural).
₵ = clon; × (as a prefix) = hybrid; × (between scientific plant names) = crossed by; ∞ = polybrid; |w = plant useful to wildlife.
See Glossary for definitions of clon, hybrid, and polybrid.

DAYLILY, continued
FORRESTS D. . . Hemerocallis forresti
GRASSLEAF D. . . . . . . H. minor
GREAT MIDDENDORFF D.
H. middendorffi major
KOREAN D. . . . . . . H. coreana
LEMON D. . . . . H. flava
LONGTUBE D. . . . . . H. longituba
LONGTUBE TAWNY D. . . . H. fulva l.
MANYFLOWER D. . . . H. multiflora
MIDDENDORFF D. . . H. middendorffi
ORANGE D. . . . . . H. aurantiaca
ROSETAWNY D. . . . . H. fulva rosea
STOUT D. . . . . . . H. exaltata
TAWNY D. . . . . H. fulva
THUNBERG D. . . . . H. thunbergi

DEADNETTLE . . . . Lamium
ARCHANGEL D. . . . . L. galeobdolon
HENBIT D. . . . . . L. amplexicaule
ORVALA D. . . . . L. orvala
PURPLE D. . . . . . L. purpureum
SPOTTED D. . . . . . L. maculatum
WHITE D. . . . . L. album
WHITE SPOTTED D. . L. maculatum a.

DEAM'IA
See **CACTUS GENERA.**

DEATHCAMAS . . . . Zigadenus
ATLANTIC D. . . . . . Z. glaberrimus
FOOTHILL D. . . . . . Z. paniculatus
FREMONT D. . . . . . . Z. fremonti
GRASSY D. . . . . . . Z. gramineus
MEADOW D. . . . . . Z. venenosus
MOUNTAIN D. . . . . . . Z. elegans
NUTTALL D. . . . . . . Z. nuttalli
PINEBARREN D. . . Z. leimanthoides
PINK D. . . . . . . Z. angustifolius
SMALL MEADOW D.
Z. venenosus micranthus

DEATHCARROT . . . . Thapsia
GARGAN D. . . . . . . T. garganica

DEBREGEA'SIA
longifo'lia (*velutina*)

DECAIS'NEA
farges'i

DECKE'NIA . . . . . . DECKENPALM
See **PALM GENERA.**

DE'CODON |w . . . WATERWILLOW
verticilla'tus (*Nesaea verticillata*) |w
WATERWILLOW

DECUMA'RIA . . . . . . DECUMARIA
bar'bara . . . . SOUTHEAST D.
sinen'sis . . . . CHINESE D.

DEERBERRY
COMMON D. . Vaccinium stamineum
SOUTHERN D. . . . V. neglectum

DEERFERN . . . . . Blechnum spicant

DEERGRASS . . . Muhlenbergia rigens

DEERHORNCACTUS . Peniocereus greggi

DEERIN'GIA
amaranthoi'des (*baccata; celosioides*)
¢VARIEGATED (*variegata*) HV.

DEERVETCH . . . . Lotus
ARABIAN D. . . . . . . L. arabicus
BENTHAM D. . . . . . . L. benthami
BIG D. . . . . . . L. crassifolius
BIRDSFOOT D. . . . . L. corniculatus
BROOM D. . . . . . . L. scoparius
CHAPARRAL D. . . . . L. grandiflorus
CHILEAN D. . . . . L. subpinnatus
COAST D. . . . . L. formosissimus
CORALGEM D. . . . . L. bertholeti
DESERT D. . . . . L. tomentellus

DEERVETCH, continued
DOUGLAS D. . . . . . Lotus douglasi
FOOTHILL D. . . . . . L. humistratus
LITTLEFLOWER D. . . L. micranthus
LONGBRACT D. . . L. longebracteatus
MAT D. . . . . L. eriophorus
MEADOW D. . . . . . . L. pinnatus
RIVERBAR D. . . . . . L. denticulatus
RUSH D. . . . . L. junceus
SHRUBBY D. . . . . L. rigidus
SILVER D. . . . . . . L. argophyllus
SLENDERPOD D. . . L. angustissimus
SOFT D. . . . . L. mollis
SPANISHCLOVER D. . . L. americanus
SQUAREPOD D. . . L. tetragonolobus
ST. JAMES D. . . . . . . L. jacobaeus
STREAM D. . . . . L. oblongifolius
TORREY S. D. . . . . . L. o. torreyi
WETLAND D. . . . . . . L. uliginosus
WHITELEAF D. . . . . L. leucophyllus
WRIGHT D. . . . . L. wrighti

DEGUE'LIA . . . . **DERRIS**

DEINAN'THE
caeru'lea

DE'LONIX
re'gia (*Caesalpinia r.; Poinciana r.*)
FLAMBOYANTTREE
(*Royal Poinciana*)

This African genus has been confused in the past with the largely tropical-American genus Poinciana.

DELOSPER'MA
MESEMBRYANTHEMUM
See **SUCCULENTS.**

DELOST'OMA
rose'um

DELPHIN'IUM . . . . . . LARKSPUR

This list of Larkspurs has been assembled chiefly from the 1923 ed. of STANDARDIZED PLANT NAMES, E. I. Wilde's "Studies of the Genus Delphinium," L. H. Bailey's "The Garden of Larkspurs," "Hortus," and "The Standard Cyclopedia of Horticulture," W. L. Jepson's "Manual of the Flowering Plants of California," and U. S. Forest Service range plant records. The hort. var. list was chiefly compiled by R. C. Allen of the American Delphinium Society.

abieto'rum . . . . . . **D. occidentale**
aconi'ti . . . . MONKSHOOD L.
acutilo'bum . . . . . SHARPLOBE L.
aitchiso'ni . . . . AITCHISON L.
aja'cis (*candelabrum; gayanum*)
ROCKET L.
albes'cens . . . . **D. virescens**
albiflo'rum . . . . WHITEBLOOM L.
albocoeru'leum . . . . BLUEWHITE L.
albomargina'tum . . WHITEMARGIN L.
alpes'tre . . . . ALPINE L.
alpi'num . . . . **D. elatum a.**
altis'simum . . . . . . HIMALAYAN L.
amab'ile (*coelestinum* Rydb., *not* Franch.) . . . . LOVELY L.
aman'i . . . . AMAN L.
ambig'uum . . . . . DOUBTFUL L.
amoe'num
amplibractea'tum . . . MOGOLLON L.
anderso'ni (*burkei; leonardi*)
ANDERSON L.
antho'ra . . . . **Aconitum a.**
anthoroi'deum
anthriscifo'lium . . . . CHERVIL L.
apachen'se . . . . APACHE L.
apet'alum . . . . NAKED L.

DELPHINIUM, continued
apicula'tum . . SHARPLEAF LARKSPUR
arcua'tum . . . . BOWED L.
armenia'cum . . . . . . ARMENIAN L.
autumna'le . . . . AUTUMN L.
axilliflo'rum . . . . AXILFLOWER L.
azu'reum . . . . . **D. carolinianum**

The name D. azureum is often loosely used in hort. for numerous hort. var. with bright blue flowers.

balan'sae . . . . BALANSA L.
barba'tum . . . . BEARDED L.
bar'beyi (*D. scopulorum subalpinum; subalpinum*) . . . . . . BARBEY L.
∞ **bar'lowi** (*?elatum × grandiflorum; D. hybridum b.*) . . . . ∞ BARLOW L.

Most of the material now labeled barlowi is D. cheilanthum formosum.

batali'ni . . . . BATALIN L.
batangen'se . . . . BATANG L.
beesia'num . . . . BEESIAN L.
bi'color (*glareosum*) . . . . LITTLE L.
—montanen'se . . . . MONTANA L.L.
bicornu'tum . . . . . . TWOHORN L.
biterna'tum . . . . . BITERNATE L.
blais'delli . . . . BLAISDELL L.
block'manae . . . . . BLOCKMAN L.
bonat'i . . . . BONAT L.
bonvalot'i . . . . BONVALOT L.
bor'basi . . . . BORBAS L.
bove'i . . . . BOVE L.
brachycen'trum
bracteo'sum . . . . . . BRACTED L.
brevicor'ne . . . . . SHORTHORN L.
brown'i . . . . BROWNS L.

L. H. Bailey thinks this may be a form of scopulorum.

brunonia'num . . . . MUSK L.
buchar'icum . . . . . . BUCHARIC L.
bulleya'num . . . . BULLEYS L.
burk'ei . . . . **D. andersoni**
buschia'num . . . . BUSCH L.
calcic'ola . . . . LIME L.
califor'nicum . . . . . CALIFORNIA L.
call'eri . . . . CALLER L.
camaonen'se
campo'rum . . . . . . **D. virescens c.**
camptocar'pum
campylocen'trum
campylopo'dum
candelab'rum . . . . **D. ajacis**
can'didum . . . . CANDID L.
canmoren'se . . . . . . CANMORE L.
cappado'cicum . . . . CAPPADOCIA L.
cardina'le . . . . CARDINAL L.
cardiopet'alum . . . . **D. halteratum c.**
carolinia'num (*azureum; nortonianum; D. c. nortonianum*) . . CAROLINA L.
—penard'i . . . . **D. virescens**
—vimin'eum . . . . . **D. virescens v.**
carum'nae
cashmeria'num . . . . . KASHMIR L.
—walk'eri . . . . . . WALKERS K.L.
caucas'icum . . . . . . **D. speciosum**

Some authorities regard this as a var. of D. speciosum or even a distinct species.

cavalerien'se . . . . CAVALIER L.
ceratopho'rum
cerefo'lium . . . . WAXLEAF L.
chamisso'nis . . . . . . CHAMISSO L.
chefoen'se . . . . CHEFOO L.
cheilan'thum (*sylvaticum*) GARLAND L.
—coelesti'num . . . . SKYBLUE G.L.
—formo'sum . . . . HARDY G.L.

See note under D. formosum. Here belong the BELLADONNA hort. var. See HV. list, p. 156.

DELPHINIUM, continued
chilliwace'nae CHILLIWACEN LARKSPUR
chrysot'richum . . . . . GOLDHAIR L.
cilia'tum . . . . FRINGED L.
cine'reum . . . . ASHEN L.
cockerell'i . . . . . COCKERELL L.
coelesti'num . . . . . CELESTIAL L.
coelesti'num Rydb., *not* Franch.
D. amabile
coerules'cens
coeru'leum . . . . . CERULEAN L.
cogna'tum
coleop'odum
columbia'num (*nuttalli; pauciflorum* Nutt., *not* D. Don) . . COLUMBIA L.
commuta'tum . . . . CHANGING L.
confertiflo'rum . . DENSEFLOWER L.
confer'tum . . . . CROWDED L.
confu'sum
consol'ida . . . . FORKING L.
corymbo'sum . . . . . CORYMB L.
cossonia'num . . . . . . COSSON L.
crassicau'le . . . . . THICKSTEM L.
crassifo'lium . . . . . THICKLEAF L.
cuculla'tum . . . . . **D. occidentale**
∞ **culto'rum** . . . . . . ∞ FLORISTS L.
cunea'tum . . . . WEDGE L.
cuyamac'ae . . . . . CUYAMACA L.
cya'neum
cyanorei'os
cyphoplec'trum
dasyan'thum
dasycar'pum . . . . . . THICKPOD L.
dasycau'lon . . . . . CLUBSTEM L.
dasystach'yon
da'vidi . . . . DAVID L.
deco'rum . . . . . YELLOWTINGE L.
—*pa'tens* . . . . **D. patens**
delavay'i . . . . DELAVAY L.
delica'tum . . . . . **D. urceolatum**
densiflo'rum
denuda'tum
depaupera'tum (*diversifolium*) SLIM L.
desert'i . . . . DESERT L.
dictyocar'pum . . . . . NETPOD L.
dinar'icum . . . . DINARIC L.
dis'color
An untenable name, *fide* L. H. Bailey.
dissec'tum . . . . . . DISSECTED L.
dis'tichum . . . . . . TWOSPIKE L.
divarica'tum
diver'sicolor . . . . . MANYCOLOR L.
diversifo'lium . . . . **D. depauperatum**
du'bium
dumeto'rum . . . . HEDGE L.
ehrenberg'i . . . . . EHRENBERG L.
ela'tum (*intermedium; palmatum*) BEE L.
—**alpi'num** (*D. alpinum; D. intermedium a.*) . . . . ALPINE B.L.
—**duhmberg'i** (*D. duhmbergi*)
DUHMBERG B.L.
See list of hort. var. of D. elatum hybrids.

el'egans . . . . ELEGANT L.
elonga'tum . . . . . . LENGTHY L.
emargina'tum . . . . . MARGINED L.
emil'iae . . . . EMILY L.
engleria'num . . . . . . ENGLER L.
eriocar'pum . . . . WOOLLYFRUIT L.
erios'tylum . . . . . WOOLLYSTYLE L.
esquirol'i . . . . ESQUIROL L.
exalta'tum . . . . TALL L.
exig'uum . . . . PUNY L.
exser'tum
farges'i . . . . FARGES L.
fis'sum . . . . CLEFT L.
This is frequently confused with D. hybridum.

DELPHINIUM, continued
flam'meum . . . . FLAME LARKSPUR
fla'vum . . . . YELLOW L.
flexuo'sum . . . . . . FLEXUOUS L.
floribun'dum . . . . FREEFLOWER L.
foet'idum . . . . SKUNK L.
folio'sum . . . . LEAFY L.
formo'sum . . . . HARDY L.
L. H. Bailey reports that the material labeled "formosum" is chiefly D. cheilanthum formosum, which is not this species.

for'resti . . . . FORRESTS L.
freyn'i . . . . FREYN L.
frig'idum . . . . ARCTIC L.
gautier'i . . . . GAUTIER L.
gaya'num . . . . **D. ajacis**
george'i . . . . GEORGES L.
geraniifo'lium . . . . GERANIUM L.
gey'eri . . . . GEYER L.
gilgia'num . . . . GILG L.
girald'i . . . . GIRALD L.
glacia'le . . . . GLACIER L.
glandulo'sum
glareo'sum . . . . **D. bicolor**
glauces'cens
glau'cum . . . . . **D. scopulorum g.**
goetzea'num . . . . GOETZE L.
gombault'i . . . . . . GOMBAULT L.
gomming'geri . . . GOMMINGGER L.
grac'ile
gracilen'tum (*sonnei*) . . . SONNE L.
grandiflo'rum (*sibiricum*) . SIBERIAN L.
—**al'bum** . . . . WHITE S.L.
—**azu'reum** . . . . AZURE S.L.
—**chinen'se** (*D. sinense*) SLENDER S.L.
—**mi'nor** . . . . DWARF S.L.
L. H. Bailey reports that the trade name "pumilum" seems to be applied to dwarf forms of this species.

greene'i . . . . GREENES L.
gyala'num
haltera'tum . . . MEDITERRANEAN L.
—**cardiopet'alum** (*D. cardiopetalum*)
HEARTPETAL M.L.
hama'tum
han'seni . . . . HANSEN L.
hebeg'ynum
hel'leri . . . . HELLER L.
henderso'ni . . . . . HENDERSON L.
hen'ryi . . . . HENRY L.
hesper'ium . . . . COAST L.
hirschfeldia'num . . . HIRSCHFELD L.
hirticau'le . . . . . . FUZZYSTEM L.
hispan'icum . . . . SPANISH L.
hohenack'eri . . . . HOHENACKER L.
humuli'num . . . . HOP L.
hyb'ridum . . . . MONGREL L.
—*bar'lowi* . . . . ∞ **D. barlowi**
L. H. Bailey recommends elimination of D. hybridum for the present, as it covers at least three different larkspurs. See D. cultorum and fissum.

ilien'se
inca'num . . . . HOARY L.
inconspic'uum . . . . . . MODEST L.
inflex'um
inimitab'ile . **D. elatum** HV. INIMITABLE
interme'dium . . . . **D. elatum**
—*alpi'num* . . . . **D. elatum a.**
intrica'tum
irono'rum
ithaburen'se
jugo'rum
jun'ceum . . . . RUSH L.
karategin'i . . . . . . KARATEGIN L.
keteleer'i . . . . KETELEER L.
kingia'num . . . . KING L.

DELPHINIUM, continued
kurd'icum . . . . . KURD LARKSPUR
labrangen'se
lacost'ei . . . . LACOSTE L.
lanig'erum
lankongen'se . . . . . . LANKONG L.
latisep'alum . . . . . WIDEPETAL L.
laxiflo'rum . . . . . . **D. villosum l.**
leiocar'pum . . . . SMOOTHFRUIT L.
leonard'i . . . . **D. andersoni**
lep'idum . . . . SCALY L.
leptophyl'lum . . . . . THINLEAF L.
leroy'i . . . . LEROY L.
leucophae'um **D. menziesi ochroleucum**
likiangen'se . . . . LIKIANG L.
lilaci'num . . . . LILAC L.
linarioi'des . . . . . . TOADFLAX L.
lineariIo'bum . . . NARROWLOBE L.
lip'ski . . . . LIPSKY L.
longipeduncula'tum . . LONGSTALK L.
long'ipes
loscos'i . . . . LOSCOS L.
lupo'rum . . . . COYOTE L.
lute'um . . . . **D. nudicaule l.**
lycoctonifo'lium
lycocto'num . . . . . WOLFBANE L.
maackia'num . . . . MAACK L.
macedon'icum . . . MACEDONIAN L.
This sp. is perhaps hardly more than a var. or form of D. olopetalum.

macrocen'tron . . . EASTAFRICAN L.
macroceph'alum . . . LONGHEAD L.
macropet'alum . . . . LONGPETAL L.
macrophyl'lum . . . . LONGLEAF L.
macroserat'ile
macrostach'yum . . . LARGESPIKE L.
mair'ei . . . . MAIRE L.
mari'ae . . . . MARIA L.
marit'imum . . . . SEASIDE L.
mauritan'icum . . . MAURETANIA L.
maximowicz'i . . . MAXIMOWICZ L.
maydellia'num . . . . . MAYDELL L.
megacar'pum . . . . . . BIGPOD L.
menzies'i (*nelsoni; pauperculum; pinetorum*) . . . . MENZIES L.
—**ochroleu'cum** (*D. leucophaeum; D. ochroleucum*) . . . . . CREAM M.L.
micran'thum . . . LITTLEFLOWER L.
micropet'alum . . . . SMALLPETAL L.
middendorff'i . . . MIDDENDORFF L.
midzoren'se . . . . . MIDZOREN L.
minu'tum . . . . TINY L.
mirab'ile . . . . MARVEL L.
mitzugen'se . . . . . MITZUGEN L.
moerheim'i Hort.
See hort. var. list.

mol'le . . . . SOFT L.
monta'num . . . . . . MOUNTAIN L.
mosoynen'se
multiflo'rum . . . . MANYFLOWER L.
nacladen'se
na'num . . . . BABY L.
narbonen'se . . . . . NARBONNE L.
neglec'tum
nel'soni . . . . **D. menziesi**
nevaden'se . . . . NEVADA L.
nor'toni . . . . NORTON L.
nortonia'num . . . . **D. carolinianum**
novomexica'num . . NEWMEXICAN L.
nudicau'le . . . . ORANGE L.
—**lute'um** (*D. luteum*) . GOLDEN O.L.
nutt'alli . . . . . . **D. columbianum**
nuttallia'num . . . . . NUTTALL L.
obcorda'tum
occidenta'le (*abietorum; cucullatum; quercetorum* Greene, *not* Boiss.)
DUNCECAP L.

DELPHINIUM, continued
ochroleu'cum . . . . . **D. menziesi o.**
officina'le . . . MEDICINE LARKSPUR
oligan'thum . . . . FEWFLOWER L.
oliveria'num . . . . OLIVER L.
olopet'alum
orega'num . . . . OREGON L.
oreoph'ilum
orienta'le . . . . ORIENTAL L.
orna'tum . . . . ORNATE L.
orthocen'trum
osset'icum
oxysep'alum . . . . . SHARPPETAL L.
pachycen'trum
pallidiflo'rum . . . PALEFLOWER L.
palmatif'idum
palma'tum . . . . **D. elatum**
paludic'ola
panicula'tum . . . . . . PANICLE L.
paphlagon'icum . PAPHLAGONIAN L.
paradox'um . . . . . . STRANGE L.
par'ishi . . . . PARISH L.
par'ryi . . . . PARRY L.
parviflo'rum . . . . SMALLFLOWER L.
pa'tens (*D. decorum p.*) SPREADING L.
pauciflo'rum Nutt., *not* D. Don **D. columbianum**
pauper'culum . . . . . **D. menziesi**
pedatisec'tum . . . . BIRDSFOOT L.
pedifor'me
pellu'cidum . . . . . . DOTTED L.
penard'i . . . . **D. virescens**
penicilla'tum . . . . . . PENCILLED L.
pentag'ynum . . . . . FIVESTYLE L.
peregri'num . . . . . PEREGRINE L.
per'sicum . . . . PERSIAN L.
phryg'ium . . . . PHRYGIAN L.
pic'tum . . . . PAINTED L.
pilo'sulum
pineto'rum . . . . **D. menziesi**
ple'num
pogonan'thum
poltarat'zki
polycla'don
pon'ticum . . . . PONTIC L.
potani'ni . . . . POTANIN L.
praten'se . . . . MEADOW L.
przewal'ski
pseudoperegri'num
pubes'cens
pubiflo'rum
punic'eum
pur'domi . . . . PURDOM L.
pur'pusi . . . . PURPUS L.
pusil'lum
pycnocen'trum
pyl'zowi . . . . PYLZOW L.
pyramida'tum . . . . . . PYRAMID L.
querceto'rum . . . . OAKWOODS L.
querceto'rum Greene, *not* Boiss. **D. occidentale**
ramo'sum . . . . . . BRANCHED L.
rav'eyi . . . . RAVEY L.
recurva'tum . . . . . . RECURVED L.
requien'i . . . . REQUIEN L.
reticula'tum
revolu'tum. . . . . . REVOLUTE L.
rig'idum . . . . STIFF L.
robertia'num . . . . . . ROBERT L.
robus'tum . . . . GIANT L.
rose'um . . . . ROSY L.
ross'icum . . . . . . RUSSIAN L.
rugulo'sum . . . . . WRINKLED L.
ruspolia'num
∞**ruys'i** (*elatum × nudicaule*) ∞RUYS L.
Hort. var. of hybrids with ∞D. ruysi: PINK SENSATION
sacca'tum . . . . SACCATE L.

DELPHINIUM, continued
saniculaefo'lium . SANICLE LARKSPUR
sapello'nis . . . . SAPELLO L.
savatier'i . . . . SAVATIER L.
scabriflo'rum
scapo'sum . . . . . . BARESTEM L.
schlagintweit'i
schmalhaus'eni . . SCHMALHAUSEN L.
schroedingeria'num
scopulo'rum . . . TALLMOUNTAIN L.
—**glau'cum** (*D. glaucum*) . SIERRA L.
—*stachyd'eum* . . . . **D. stachydeum**
—*subalpi'num* . . . . . . **D. barbeyi**
semibarba'tum
sertif'erum
sibir'icum . . . . . **D. grandiflorum**
sierrae-blan'cae . WHITEMOUNTAIN L.
simonkaia'num
sim'plex
sinen'se . . **D. grandiflorum chinense**
sintenis'i . . . . SINTENIS L.
siwanen'se . . . . SIWAN L.
skir'manti
Possibly a synonym of D. orientale.

somchet'icum
son'nei . . . . **D. gracilentum**
sordidecaerules'cens
sordi'dum . . . . SORDID L.
soulie'i . . . . SOULIE L.
sparsiflo'rum. . . . . . . SPARSE L.
specio'sum (*caucasicum; D. s. caucasicum*) . . . . CAUCASIAN L.
—**glabra'tum**. . . . . SMOOTH C.L.
spirocent'rum
spu'rium
stachyd'eum (*D. scopulorum s.*) ROCKYMOUNTAIN L.
stapelios'mum . . . . . CARRION L.
staphisa'gria . . . . STAVESACRE L.
stenosep'alum . . . NARROWPETAL L.
stocksia'num. . . . . . . STOCKS L.
stric'tum . . . . STRICT L.
sua've . . . . SWEET L.
subalpi'num . . . . **D. barbeyi**
subglobo'sum . . . . SUBGLOBOSE L.
subnu'dum
sulca'tum . . . . GROOVED L.
sulphu'reum . . . . . . SULFUR L.
Perhaps not more than a form of D. zalil.

sutchuenen'se
sylvat'icum . . . . . **D. cheilanthum**
syncar'pum
szechuan'icum . . . . SZECHWAN L.
szowitsia'num
talien'se . . . . TALIEN L.
tangut'icum . . . . . . TANGUT L.
tatsienen'se . . . . . . TATSIEN L.
teheran'icum. . . . . . TEHERAN L.
ten'i
tenuisec'tum . . . . . CARROTLEAF L.
tenuis'simum
terna'tum . . . . TERNATE L.
thessalon'icum . . . . . SALONIKI L.
thibet'icum . . . . . . THIBETAN L.
thirkea'num
tirolien'se . . . . . . **D. villosum t.**
tomentel'lum . . . . . . FLANNEL L.
tomento'sum . . . . . TOMENTOSE L.
tongolen'se . . . . TONGOL L.
trelease'i . . . . TRELEASE L.
tribracteola'tum . . THREEBRACT L.
trichoph'orum
tri'color . . . . TRICOLOR L.
tricor'ne . . . . ROCK L.
trifoliola'tum . . . . THREELEAF L.
trigonelloi'des . . . . FENUGREEK L.

DELPHINIUM, continued
triloba'tum . THREELOBE LARKSPUR
tris'te . . . . BITTER L.
trolliifo'lium . . . COLUMBIARIVER L.
tsarongen'se
tubero'sum . . . . TUBER L.
tuntasia'num
turkestan'icum . . . . TURKESTAN L.
turkmen'um . . . . . . TURCOMAN L.
uechtritzia'num . . . . ALBANIA L.
uligino'sum . . . . BOG L.
umbro'sum . . . . DELL L.
uncina'tum . . . . HOOKED L.
urceola'tum (*delicatum*)
vanderwey'eri . . VANDERWEYER L.
variega'tum . . . . ROYAL L.
veluti'num . . . . VELVET L.
veneno'sum . . . . DEATH L.
venulo'sum . . . . VEINY L.
vesti'tum
vicioso'i
villo'sum . . . . HAIRY L.
—**laxiflo'rum** (*D. laxiflorum*) LOOSEFLOWER H.L.
—**tirolien'se** (*D. tiroliense*) TYROLEAN H.L.
vimin'eum . . . . **D. virescens v.**
vires'cens (*albescens; D. carolinianum penardi; penardi; D. v. penardi*) PLAINS L.
—**campo'rum** (*D. camporum*)
—**vimin'eum** (*D. carolinianum v.; D. vimineum*)
virga'tum
vir'ide . . . . GREEN L.
virides'cens . . . . CHELAN L.
vis'cidum . . . . STICKY L.
visco'sum . . . . CLAMMY L.
vitifo'lium . . . . GRAPE L.
ward'i. . . . . WARD L.
well'byi . . . . WELLBY L.
willameten'se . . . WILLAMETTE L.
winkleria'num . . . . . WINKLER L.
wislizen'i . . . . . . WISLIZENUS L.
woot'oni . . . . WOOTON L.
xantholeu'cum . . YELLOWWHITE L.
xylorrhi'zum . . . . YELLOWROOT L.
yunnanen'se . . . . YUNNAN L.
zal'il . . . . ZALIL L.
See note under D. sulphureum.

Hort. var. (clons) of **Delphinium,** LARKSPUR:

LIST OF ABBREVIATIONS
B. Belladonna hybrids.
El. D. elatum hybrids.
R. ∞D. ruysi hybrids.

ADMIRATION. El.
ADVANCEMENT. El.
AFGHAN QUEEN. El.
AFTERGLOW. El.
(*A. J.*) MOIR. El.
ALBERT DE MUN. El.
ALICE ANDRIST. El.
ALICE ARTINDALE. El.
ALICE BLUE. El.
ALICE PULLEINE. El.
ALLIFFE. El.
AMETHYST. El.
AMOS PERRY. El.
Andenken an August Koenemann. AUGUST KOENEMANN.
ANDREW CARNEGIE. El.
ANGELS BREATH. El.
ANNA. El.
ANN BAKER. El.
ANNE HATHAWAY. El.
ARIEL. El.

DELPHINIUM, continued
Arnold Bocklin. B.
Artis. B.
Ascot. El.
Atropurpureum. El.
August Koenemann. El. *Andenken an August Koenemann.*
Avelina. El.
Avon. El.
Azure Fairy. B.
Azure Queen. B.
Baldershage. El.
Barbara Lloyd. El.
Barwickgem. B.
Beau Sabreur. El.
Beauty. El.
Bee Elliott. El.
Beethoven. El.
Bel Amour. El.
Bellamosum. B.
Berengarica. El.
Berghimmel. El.
Bessie Chapman. El.
Betty. El.
Betty Wells. El.
Blackbird. El.
Blackeyed Bride. El.
Blanche Decastille. El.
Bluebatik. El.
Bluebeauty. El.
Bluebees. B.
Bluebird. El.
Blueboy. El.
Blue Butterfly. El.
Blue Danube. El.
Bluegown. El.
Blue Grotto. B.
Bluelake. El.
Blue Majesty. El.
Bluemarvel. El.
Blueprince. El.
Blueprincess. El.
Bluequeen. El.
Blueribbon. El.
Bluerosette. El.
Bluespire. El.
(*B. M.*) Gurteen. El.
Bowdonboy. El.
Bowdongirl. El.
Bridalgown. El.
Bridesmaid. El.
Brightboy. El.
Britannic. El.
Brunton. B. *Mr. J. S. Brunton.*
Burgundy. El.
Cambria. El.
Cambridge. El.
Campanula. El.
Candelabre. El.
Candeur. El.
Capri. B.
Carmen.
Caron. El.
Caronia. El.
Carrie. El.
Caucasicum. El.
Cecil Henderson. El.
Cedric. El.
Celtic. El.
Chaminade. El.
Charles. El.
Charles Green. El.
Charles Nungusser. El.
Charlesta. El.
Charming. El.
Chief Grandin. El.
Christine. El.
Claret. El.

DELPHINIUM, continued
Clarissa. El.
Cliveden Beauty. B.
Cobalt. B.
Cobalt Blue. El.
Codsall Girl. El.
Codsall Lad. El.
Codsall Purple. El.
Colibri. El.
(*Col. Sir*) Wyndham Murray. El.
Concord. El.
Concours. El.
Conspicua. El.
Constance. El.
Constance Barber. El.
Coquette. El.
Cornflower Blue. El.
Corry. El.
Countess Cowley. El.
County Girl. El.
Cranfield. El.
Craterlake Blue. El.
(*C. W.*) Nathes. El.
Daintiness. El.
Daniel Osiris. El.
Dante. B.
Dark Lantern. El.
Dawn. El.
Daydream. El.
(*D. B.*) Crane. El.
Dein Blaues Wunder. El.
Delta. El.
Desert Twilight. El.
Diadem.
Dierdre. El.
Dina. El.
Dominion. El.
Donald Allen. El.
Doreen (*Margaret*) Robinson. El.
Doris. El.
Doris Ashby. El.
Dorothy Ackroyd. El.
Dorothy Boissier. El.
Dove. El.
Dozanna. El.
Dreams. El.
Dreams of Beauty. El.
(*Dr.*) James Black. El.
Duchess of Portland. El.
Duke of Connaught.
Durbar II. El.
Dusky Monarch. El.
Edmund Spencer. El.
Edric. El.
Edward Bromet. El.
Edwin Markham. El.
Eileen (*May*) Robinson. El.
Elizabeth Rickett. El.
Elsie. El.
Elstead Blue. B.
Ena.
Enid Wilson. El.
Enzianturm. El.
Ethereal. El.
Eurydice. El.
Eve. El.
Evelyn (*M.*) Cole. El.
Evelyn Richie. El.
Evening. El.
Eventide. El.
Excalibur. El.
Excelsior.
Exquisite Rose. El.
Fairlady. El.
Famille Rose. El.
Felicite.
F. Koppius. El.
Folkdance. El.

DELPHINIUM, continued
Formosum. El.
Fragonard. El.
Francois Nagels. El.
Freda.
F. S. Clay. El.
F. W. Smith. El.
Galahad. El.
Genius. El.
Gentian Blue. El.
Gentianet. El.
George Cochran. El.
George Moore. El.
Gerald House. El.
Geraldine Kelway. El.
Gertrude Raphael. El.
Gladys Jones. El.
Gloria. El.
Gloriosa. El.
Glory. El.
Glory of the Garden. El.
Glory of Wales. El.
Godfrey. El.
Goldengown. El.
Grace. El.
Graham Seton. El.
Gregalach. El.
Grille.
Gypsoni. B.
Hallgarten.
Happiness. El.
Happy Thought. El.
Harlequin. El.
Harmony. El.
Harry Smetham. El.
Havelland. El.
Hawarden Castle. El.
Hector Lemaire. El.
Henri Fabre. El.
Hermione. El.
Hewitts Superb. El.
Hilary Hanson. El.
Horatius. B.
Howard H. Crane. El.
Hunsdon Dell. El.
Hybridum. El.
Iceberg. El.
Ida R. Elliot. El.
Ideal. El.
Idyll. El.
Inimitable. El.
Intensity. El.
Intermedium. El.
Isis. B.
Isla. El.
Italia. El.
Ivorine. El.
Jack Salmon. El.
James Black. El.
Jane Boisser. El.
Jean. El.
Jean Smith. El.
Jenny Jones. El.
John Milton. El.
Joy Bells. El.
Julia.
Juliet. El.
June. El.
June Boisseri. El.
J. Vandermeulen. El.
J. W. Kelway. El.
Karl Foerster. El.
Kate Greenaway. El.
Kathleen Vaughan. El.
Kelways Blue Ensign. El.
Kelways Delicious. El.
Kelways Premier. El.
Kelways Splendour. El.

DELPHINIUM, continued
Kelways Superb. El.
King Arthur. El.
Kingfisher. El.
King George. El.
King of Delphiniums. El.
Kirchenfenster. El.
Kitty Wardell. El.
Knight of Somerset. El.
(*K. T.*) Caron. El.
La Basse. El.
La Bourdonnais. El.
La Danube. El.
Lady Amy. El.
Lady Augusta. El.
Lady Barbara. El.
Lady Bath. El.
Lady Belinda. El.
Lady Bertha. El.
Lady Bowles. El.
Lady Clara. El.
Lady Derby. El.
Lady Diana. El.
Lady Dorothy. El.
Lady Edith. El.
Lady Eleanor. El.
Lady Elizabeth. El.
Lady Emsley Carr. El.
Lady Fayre. El.
Lady Grace. El.
Lady Guinevere. El.
Lady Gwendoline. El.
Lady Holt. El.
Lady Irene. El.
Lady Janet. El.
Lady Joan. El.
Lady Kathleen. El.
Lady Macbeth. El.
Lady Margaret. El.
Lady May. El.
Lady Rodney. El.
Lady Rose. El.
Lady Stone. El.
Lady Sue. El.
Lady Teressa. El.
Lamartine. B.
Lancelot. El.
Langport Cross. El.
Laura Fairbrother. El.
Laurent. El.
Laurentic. El.
Lavanda. El.
Lavengro. El.
Legionaire. El.
Lemon Gem. El.
Leslie Gibson. El.
Leviathan. El.
Libellule. El.
Lilian Bishop. El.
Lilian Veale. El.
Lize. El.
Lizzie Vanveen. El.
Locarno. El.
Loddonguard. El.
Lord Derby. El.
Lord Lansdowne. El.
Lorenzo de Medici. El.
Lorna. El.
Lucania. El.
Lucretia. El.
Lumen. El.
Luxor. El.
Maackianum. El.
Maclaine of Lochbuie. El.
Madge. El.
Magicmoon. El.
Maiden Erleigh. El.
Maid Marian. El.

DELPHINIUM, continued
Mandarin. El.
Manzanita. El.
Margaret Rose. El.
Marjorie Ferguson. El.
Marshall Foch. El.
Massenet. El.
Mauve Glory. El.
Mauve Mantle. El.
Mauve Radiance. El.
Mavis. El.
Mercurius. El.
Merlin. B.
Mevrouw Visserhooft. El.
Millicent Blackmore. El.
Minerva.
Minister. El.
Minister Deckers. El.
Miranda. El.
Miss (*O.*) Grant. El.
Miss Ruth. El.
Miss (*W. B.*) Mackintosh. El.
Mistland Blue. El.
Mme. Violet Geslin.
Moerheimi. *D. moerheimi* Hort.
Monarch of All. El.
Monarch of Wales. El.
Monica. El.
Mon Pere. El.
Mosaique. El.
Mountain Shadows. El.
Mozart. El.
Mr. J. S. Brunton. Brunton.
Mrs. (*A. J.*) Macself. El.
Mrs. (*A. J.*) Watson. El.
Mrs. (*Allen*) Clark. El.
Mrs. (*A.*) Mansfield. El.
Mrs. (*Colin*) McIvor. El.
Mrs. Creighton. El.
Mrs. Dunn. El.
Mrs. Edmundson. El.
Mrs. (*Edwin*) Bostock. El.
Mrs. (*Foster*) Cunliffe. El.
Mrs. (*G. D.*) Gold. El.
Mrs. (*George*) Gibson. B. El.
Mrs. Gowen. El.
Mrs. Hargreaves. El.
Mrs. (*H. A.*) Tippetts. El.
Mrs. (*H.*) Kaye. El.
Mrs. (*James*) Kelway. El.
Mrs. (*John*) Harkness. El.
Mrs. (*J. S.*) Brunton. El.
Mrs. (*J. S.*) Courtauld. El.
Mrs. (*Newton*) Lees. El.
Mrs. (*Norman*) Holden. El.
Mrs. (*Olga*) Abel. El.
Mrs. Page. El.
Mrs. (*Paul*) Nelke. El.
Mrs. (*Peter*) Blair. El.
Mrs. (*Philip*) Runciman. El.
Mrs. Pitt. El.
Mrs. (*R. E.*) Docwra. El.
Mrs. Sampson. El.
Mrs. Shirley. El.
Mrs. (*Thomas*) Carlile. El.
Mrs. Thomson. B.
Mrs. (*T. J.*) Jones. El.
Mrs. (*Townley*) Parker. El.
Mrs. Trotter. El.
Mrs. Vanegmond. El.
Mrs. Webber. El.
Mrs. Wilson. El.
Mrs. (*W. R.*) Dykes. El.
Mrs. (*W.*) Wells. El.
Musea.
Musis Sacrum. B.
My Lady. El.
Naomi. El.

DELPHINIUM, continued
Naples. B.
Nassau.
Natalie. El.
Nautilus. El.
Nell Gwyn. El.
Neptune. El.
Nettie. El.
Newblue. El.
Niederwald.
Nora Ferguson. El.
Norah Hotblack. El.
Norman. El.
Oberon. El.
Oenone Lang. El.
Olivia. El.
Olympic. El.
Olympus. El.
Omega. El.
Opal. El.
Opalshire. El.
Orchid. El.
Orion. B.
Othello. El.
Owen Butler. El.
Oxford. El.
Painters Dream. El.
Palmyre. El.
Pandora. El.
Pannonia. El.
Pansy Violet. El.
Pastel. El.
Pasteur. El.
Patricia. El.
Pearl Necklace. El.
Peggy Hetherington El.
Perfect Joy. El.
Persimmon. B.
Phantom. B.
Philip Butler. El.
Phyllis. El.
Pierre Louys. El.
Pierre Petit. El.
Pierre Precieuse. El.
Pilkington. El.
Pinkdelight. El.
Pinklady. El.
Pink Sensation. R.
Pompadour. El.
Porthos. El.
Posie. El.
Primrose. El.
Prince Charming. El.
Prince of Wales. El.
Princess. El.
Princess Elizabeth. El.
Princess Mary. El.
Progress. El.
Prometheus. El.
Proserpine. El.
Puccini. El.
Pudors Dream. El.
Pudors Sapphire. B.
Pudors White Wonder. El.
Purple Emperor. El.
Purple King. El.
Purple Prince. El.
Purple Shadows. El.
Purple Splendour. El.
Purple Starlight. El.
Purpurritter. El.
Queenie. El.
Queen Mary. El.
Queen Mauve. El.
Queen of Bath. El.
Queen of Delphiniums. El.
Queen of July. El.
Queen of Spangles. El.

DELPHINIUM, continued
Queen of the Belgians. El.
Rainbow. El.
Rama. El.
Randolph. El.
(*R. A.*) Pilkington. El.
Reddawn. El.
Red Rama. El.
Rene Gilbert. El.
Rev. (*Chas.*) Storr. El.
Rev. (*E.*) Lascelles.
Rev. (*J. J.*) *Stubbs*. Stubbs.
Rex Oregonus. El.
Rhapsody. El.
Rich (&) Rare. El.
Rijnlandia. El.
Rijnstrom. El.
Robbie. El.
Robert Cox. El.
Romeo. El.
Rosemarie. El.
Roseself. El.
Rosette. El.
Rossini. El.
Royalpurple. El.
Royalspires. El.
Royalspray. El.
Royalvelvet. El.
Ruffled Beauty. El.
Sally Place. El.
SanJoaquin. El.
Sapphire. El.
Sarah Barber. El.
Satan. El.
Seaking. El.
Sealandia. El.
Seidenspinner.
Semiplena. B.
Shipsmast. El.
Sibelius. El.
(*Sir*) Arthur Hazlerigg. El.
(*Sir*) Austen Chamberlain. El.
(*Sir*) Douglas Haig. El.
(*Sir*) Neville Pearson. El.
Skyblue Knight. El.
Smoke of War. El.
Snowflake. El.
Snowqueen. El.
Socrate. El.
Somerset County. El.
Sonia Hotblack. El.
(*Souvenir de Jean*) Bourgerette. El.
Splendens. El.
Stanley. El.
Stanley Baldwin. El.
Star of Langport. El.
Star of Somerset. El.
Statuaire Rude. El.
St. George. El.
Stratford Pioneer. El.
Stubbs. *Rev.* (*J. J.*) *Stubbs.*
Sultan. El.
Summercloud. El.
Summersky. El.
Sunrise. El.
Sunrise Pink. El.
Sylph. El.
Tapestry Blue. El.
Tessa. El.
The Alake. El.
The Bishop. El.
The Bride. El.
The Comet. El.
The Muse. El.
Theodora. B.
The Shah. El.
The Sirdar. El.
Tinkabel. B.

DELPHINIUM, continued
Titania. El.
Toboggan. El.
Tom Hewitt. El.
Tomthumb.
Tosti. El.
Tower of Pearls. El.
Trails End. El.
Tristram. El.
Trueblue. El.
Truncatum. El.
Twilight. El.
Ulrica. El.
Ursula. El.
Valkyrie. El.
Vanveens Triumph. El.
Velasquez. El.
Velvabee. El.
Venetian Nights. El.
Venus. El.
Verdi. El.
Verona. El.
Vesta. El.
Viking. El.
Villain. El.
Violet. El.
Violet Queen. El.
Violet Robinson. El.
Virgo. El.
Viscountess Harcourt. El.
Wales. El.
Walter (*T.*) Ware. El.
(*W. B.*) Cranfield. El.
Weber. El.
Wedding Bells. El.
W. E. Fryer. El.
Welcome. El.
Welsh Beauty. El.
Welsh Boy. El.
Welsh Maiden. El.
Welshman. El.
Wendy. B.
White Company. El.
White Majesty. El.
Whitesister. El.
Whitespire. El.
Whitestar. El.
Whitethroat. El.
Whittlesford. B. El.
Wild Wales. El.
Will Shakespeare. El.
Willy O'Brien. El.
Winifred. El.
Winsome. El.
Wrexham Bride. El.
Wrexham Dandy Boy. El.
Wrexham Favorite. El.
Wrexham Glory. El.
Wrexham Lady. El.
Yvette Guibert. El.
Zephyr. El.
Zinfandel. El.

DEMAZE'RIA . . . **DESMAZERIA**
See **GRASS GENERA.**

DEN'DRIUM . . . **LEIOPHYLLUM**
hu'geri . . . . . **L. buxifolium h.**
prostra'tum . . . . **L. buxifolium p.**

DENDRO'BIUM
See **ORCHID GENERA.**

DENDROCAL'AMUS Dendrocalamus
See **BAMBOO GENERA.**

DENDROCE'REUS . . . **CEREUS**
See **CACTUS GENERA.**

DENDROCHI'LUM
See **ORCHID GENERA.**

DENDROME'CON . . . . Bushpoppy
har'fordi . . . . Island B.
rig'ida . . . . Stiff B.

DENDROPO'GON . . **TILLANDSIA**

DE'NEA . . . . **HOWEA**
See **PALM GENERA.**

DENMO'ZA . . . **ECHINOCACTUS**
See **CACTUS GENERA.**

Dennettgrass . . . Wildrye, Virginia: **Elymus virginicus**

DENNSTAED'TIA . . . . . Cupfern
See **FERN GENERA.**

DENTA'RIA . . . . Toothwort
califor'nica (*Cardamine paucisecta*) California T.
digita'ta . . . . **Cardamine pratensis**
diphyl'la . . . . . . Crinkleroot T.
lacinia'ta . . . . Cutleaf T.
macrocar'pa . . . . . . Cascade T.
max'ima . . . . Large T.
tenel'la . . . . Oregon T.

DERMOPHYL'LA . . . . . Skinleaf
penduli'na (*Cayaponia p.*) . Tayuya S.

DER'RIS (*DEGUELIA*) . Jewelvine
ellip'tica . . . . Tubaroot J.
malaccen'sis . . . . . . Malacca J.
pterocar'pus
scan'dens (*Deguelia s.*) . . Malay J.
timorien'sis . . . . Timor J.
trifolia'ta (*uliginosa*) . Trifoliate J.

DESCHAMP'SIA (*AIRA* Auth., *not* L.) . . . . Hairgrass
See **GRASS GENERA.**

DESCURAI'NIA (*SISYMBRIUM* in part; *SOPHIA*) ⌊w . Tansymustard
halicto'rum
—**andrena'rum** (*Sophia a.*)
inci'sa (*Sisymbrium incisum; Sophia incisa*) ⌊w . . . . . Western T.
longipedicella'ta (*Sisymbrium incisum filipes; Sophia filipes; S. longipedicellata; S. pinnata* Howell, *not* Britt. & Br.) . . . . Slimstem T.
menzies'i (*Sisymbrium canescens; S. pinnatum*) ⌊w . . . . Menzies T.
—**ochroleu'ca** (*Sophia o.*) ⌊w Creamy M.T.
pinna'ta (*Sisymbrium sophia*) Pinnate T.
richardso'ni (*Sisymbrium incisum hartwegianum*) . . . . Richardson T.
serra'ta (*Sophia s.*) . . . Toothed T.
sophi'a (*Sophia parviflora*) Flixweed T.

Desertcandle . . . . **Eremurus**
Bunge D. . . . . **E. bungei**
Chinese D. . . . . . . **E. chinensis**
Elwes D. . . . . **E. elwesi**
Giant D. . . . . **E. robustus**
Himalayan D. . . . . **E. himalaicus**
Kaufmann D. . . . . **E. kaufmanni**
Olga D. . . . . **E. olgae**
Orange D. . . . . . **E. aurantiacus**
Shelford D. . . . . . . **E. shelfordi**
Taurus D. . . . . **E. tauricus**
∞ Tubergen D. . . . . ∞ **E. tubergeni**
Turkestan D. . . . **E. turkestanicus**
White Olga D. . . . **E. olgae albus**

Desertgold . . . . **Geraea**

Desertgrass . . . . **Blepharidachne**
Bigelow D. . . . . **B. bigelovi**
King D. . . . . **B. kingi**

DESERTLILY . **Hesperocallis; H. undulata**
DESERTLIME . . . **Eremocitrus glauca**
DESERTNUT . . . . **Eremocarya**
DESERTRUE . . . . **Thamnosma**
  MOHAVE D. . . . . . . **T. montana**
  TEXAS D. . . . . **T. texana**
Desertsweet . . . . TANSYBUSH: **Chamaebatiaria millefolium**
Deserthorn . . . WOLFBERRY: **Lycium**
DESERTWILLOW , **Chilopsis; C. linearis**
DESFONTAI'NEA
  spino'sa
DESMAN'THUS (*ACUAN*) |w BUNDLEFLOWER
  coo'leyi (*jamesi; Acuan j.*) |w JAMES B.
  depres'sus
  illinoen'sis (*Acuan i.*) |w ILLINOIS B.
  virga'tus . . . . . . RAYADO B.
DESMAZE'RIA (*DEMAZERIA*) DEMAZERIA
  See **GRASS GENERA.**
DESMO'DIUM (*MEIBOMIA*) |w TICKCLOVER
  acumina'tum (*grandiflorum*) LARGEFLOWER T.
  angustifo'lium . . . NARROWLEAF T.
  —gramin'eum
  batocau'lis
  bi'color . . . . **Lespedeza b.**
  bigelo'vi . . . . BIGELOW T.
  bracteo'sum
  canaden'se . . . . . CANADA T.
  canes'cens (*Meibomia c.*) . HOARY T.
  cilia're (*obtusum*) |w . . LITTLELEAF T.
  cilia'tum . . . . **Rhynchosia puberula**
  cineras'cens Hutchins., *not* Franch. **D. spicatum**
  dil'leni |w . . . . . . DILLEN T.
  floribun'dum (*sambuense*)
  formo'sum . . . . . SWEETPEA T.
  gra'hami . . . . . . GRAHAM T.
  gy'rans (*Codariocalyx g.*) TELEGRAPH T.
  japon'icum . . . **Lespedeza japonica**
  laeviga'tum . . . . . SMOOTH T.
  mariland'icum . . . . MARYLAND T.
  neo-mexica'num . . NEWMEXICO T.
  nudiflo'rum |w . . . . BARESTEM T.
  obtu'sum . . . . **D. ciliare**
  panicula'tum |w . . . . PANICLED T.
  penduliflo'rum . **Lespedeza thunbergi**
  polycar'pum (*purpureum*) BEGGARWEED T.
  rhombifo'lium |w . . DIAMONDLEAF T.
  rig'idum
  ros'ei
  rotundifo'lium . . . . ROUNDLEAF T.
  sambuen'se . . . . . **D. floribundum**
  sessilifo'lium . . . . . . SESSILE T.
  spica'tum (*cinerascens* Hutchins., *not* Franch.) . . . . . . SPIKE T.
  tenuifo'lium |w . . . . SLIMLEAF T.
  tiliaefo'lium . . . . LINDENLEAF T.
  tortuo'sum (*Meibomia purpurea; M. tortuosa*) |w . . . . CHEROKEE T.
  viridiflo'rum |w . . . VELVETLEAF T.
DESMON'CUS (*ATITARA; DESMONCHUS*) . . . BRAMBLEPALM
  See **PALM GENERA.**
Desmotham'nus lu'cidus . **Lyonia lucida**
DETA'RIUM . . . . . . DATTOCK
  senegalen'se . . . . . . SENEGAL D.

DEUT'ZIA . . . . DEUTZIA
  al'bida
∞ **candela'brum** (*gracilis* × *sieboldiana*)
  ₵ERECTA. HV.
  ₵SUPERB (*fastuosa*)
∞ **can'dida** (∞*lemoinei* × *sieboldiana*)
  The plant in cultivation is probably a clon of this polybrid.
∞ **car'nea** (*rosea grandiflora* × *sieboldiana*)
  ₵DENSIFLORA. HV.
  ₵LACTEA
  ₵STELLATA
  compac'ta . . . . COMPACT D.
  corea'na . . . . KOREAN D.
  corymbo'sa . . . . . HIMALAYA D.
  crena'ta . . . . **D. scabra**
  dis'color
  —ma'jor
∞ **elegantis'sima** (*purpurascens* × *sieboldiana*) . . . . ∞ ELEGANT D.
  ₵ARCUATA. HV.
  ₵FASCICULATA
∞ **excel'lens** (*rosea grandiflora* × *vilmorinae; D. discolor e.*) . . ∞ CHOICE D.
  glabra'ta
  globo'sa . . . . GLOBE D.
  glomeruliflo'ra
  grac'ilis . . . . SLENDER D.
  ₵YELLOWLEAF (*aurea*) HV.
  grandiflo'ra . . . . EARLY D.
  hypoglau'ca
  hypoleu'ca
∞ **kalmiaeflo'ra** (*parviflora* × *purpurascens*) . . . . ∞ KALMIA D.
∞ **lemoin'ei** (*gracilis* × *parviflora*) ∞ LEMOINE D.
  The plant in cultivation may be a clon of this polybrid.
  ₵COMPACTA. HV.
  ₵MONTROSE
  longifo'lia . . . . . . LONGLEAF D.
  —far'reri . . . . FARRER L.D.
  ₵ELEGANS. HV. D. longifolia
  ₵VEITCH (*veitchi*)
∞ **magnif'ica** (*scabra* × *vilmorinae*) ∞ SHOWY D.
  ₵EBURNEA. HV.
  ₵ERECTA
  ₵FORMOSA
  ₵LATIFLORA
  ₵LONGIPETALA
  ₵SUPERBA
∞ **maliflo'ra** (∞*lemoinei* × *purpurascens*)
  ₵AVALANCHE. HV.
  ₵BOULEROSE
  ₵FLEUR DE POMMIER
  mol'lis
  monbeig'i . . . . MONBEIG D.
∞ **myrian'tha** (*parviflora* × *setchuenensis*) ∞ CHERRYBLOSSOM D.
  parviflo'ra . . . . . MONGOLIAN D.
  —amuren'sis
  —ovatifo'lia
  pul'chra . . . . . . EVERGREEN D.
  purpuras'cens . . . . . REDBUD D.
  reflex'a . . . . CURLY D.
  rehderia'na . . . . . . REHDER D.
∞ **rose'a** (*gracilis* × *purpurascens*) ∞ ROSEPANICLE D.
  ₵BELLFLOWER (*campanulata*) HV.
  ₵CARMINE (*carminea*)
  ₵LARGE (*grandiflora*)
  ₵MANYFLOWER (*multiflora*)
  ₵PINKCHOICE (*eximia*)
  ₵SHELL (*floribunda*)
  ₵WHITE (*venusta*)
  ru'bens
  sca'bra (*crenata*) . . . . . FUZZY D.

DEUTZIA scabra, continued
  ₵ANGUSTIFOLIA. HV.
  ₵DOUBLE (*florepleno*)
  ₵DOUBLEROSE (*florepleno rosea*)
  ₵FORTUNES (*fortunei*)
  ₵MACROCEPHALA
  ₵MARMORATA
  ₵PRIDE OF ROCHESTER
  ₵PUNCTATA
  ₵WATERER
  ₵WEEPING (*suspensa*)
  schneideria'na . SCHNEIDER DEUTZIA
  —laxiflo'ra
  setchuenen'sis . . . . SZECHWAN D.
  ₵CORYMB (*corymbiflora*) HV.
  sieboldia'na . . . . SIEBOLD D.
  —dippelia'na . . . . . DIPPELS S.D.
  stamin'ea
  —brunonia'na
  taiwanen'sis . . . . . . FORMOSA D.
  vilmori'nae . . . . . VILMORIN D.
∞ **wil'soni** (?*discolor* × *mollis*) ∞ WILSON D.
  Presumably all the following are clons.
  AZALEAEFLORA. HV. Deutzia
  CONSPICUA
  CONTRASTE
  ELEGANTISSIMA
  EMINENS
  FASTUOSA
  GRACILLIMA
  INSIGNIS
  JOCONDE
  MACROTHYRSA
  MAGICIAN
  MAGNIFICA
  MAGNIFICA ERECTA
  MIRABILIS
  MONTROSE
  PERLEROSE
  STAPHYLEOIDES
DEUTZIA . . . . **Deutzia**
∞ CHERRYBLOSSOM D. . . ∞ **D. myriantha**
∞ CHOICE D. . . . . ∞ **D. excellens**
  COMPACT D. . . . . **D. compacta**
  CURLY D. . . . . **D. reflexa**
  DIPPELS SIEBOLD D. **D. sieboldiana dippeliana**
  EARLY D. . . . . **D. grandiflora**
∞ ELEGANT D. . . . . ∞ **D. elegantissima**
  EVERGREEN D. . . . . **D. pulchra**
  FARRER LONGLEAF D. **D. longifolia farreri**
  FORMOSA D. . . . . . **D. taiwanensis**
  FUZZY D. . . . . **D. scabra**
  GLOBE D. . . . . **D. globosa**
  HIMALAYA D. . . . . . . **D. corymbosa**
∞ KALMIA D. . . . . . ∞ **D. kalmiaeflora**
  KOREAN D. . . . . **D. coreana**
∞ LEMOINE D. . . . . ∞ **D. lemoinei**
  LONGLEAF D. . . . . **D. longifolia**
  MONBEIG D. . . . . **D. monbeigi**
  MONGOLIAN D. . . . . . . **D. parviflora**
  REDBUD D. . . . . . . **D. purpurascens**
  REHDER D. . . . . **D. rehderiana**
∞ ROSEPANICLE D. . . . . . . ∞ **D. rosea**
  SCHNEIDER D. . . . **D. schneideriana**
∞ SHOWY D. . . . . ∞ **D. magnifica**
  SIEBOLD D. . . . . . . **D. sieboldiana**
  SLENDER D. . . . . **D. gracilis**
  SZECHWAN D. . . . **D. setchuenensis**
  VILMORIN D. . . . . . . **D. vilmorinae**
∞ WILSON D. . . . . ∞ **D. wilsoni**
DEVILPEPPER . . . . **Rauwolfia**
  FOURLEAF D. . . . . . **R. tetraphylla**
  JAVA D. . . . . **R. serpentina**
  TRINIDAD D. . . . . . . **R. canescens**

DEVILRATTAN . . . . . . **Daemonorops**
GIANT D. . . . . **D. grandis**
PALEMBANG D. . . . **D. palembanicus**
SUMATRA-DRAGONSBLOOD . . **D. draco**

DEVILSCLAWS . . . . **Proboscidea**
COMMON D. . . . . . . **P. jussieui**
NEWMEXICO D. . . . . **P. parviflora**
SWEET D. . . . . **P. fragrans**

DEVILSCLUB . . . . **Oplopanax**
AMERICAN D. . . . . . **O. horridus**

DEVILSPOTATO . . . **Echites umbellata**

DEVILSTONGUE . . . . **Hydrosme rivieri**

DEVILS-WALKINGSTICK . **Aralia spinosa**

DEWBERRY . . . . **Rubus**
See also BLACKBERRY and RASPBERRY.

CALIFORNIA D. . . . . . **R. ursinus**
CAUCASIAN D. . . . . **R. nemorosus**
DIVERSE-SPINE D. . . . **R. biformis**
EASTERN D. . . . . **R. oriens**
EUROPEAN D. . . . . **R. caesius**
GRAPELEAF CALIFORNIA D.
R. ursinus vitifolius
LUCRETIA D. . **R. flagellaris roribaccus**
NORTHERN D. . . . . . **R. flagellaris**
SNOW D. . . . . **R. nivalis**
SOUTHERN D. . . . . . . **R. trivialis**
TRIFOLIOLATE D. . . . . **R. trifrons**
TURKESTAN D.
R. caesius turkestanicus

DIA'CRIUM . . . . **EPIDENDRUM**
See **ORCHID GENERA.**

DIA'LIUM
guineen'se . . . . VELVET-TAMARIND
lauri'num
main'gayi

DIAMONDFLOWER . . . . . **Ionopsidium**
PORTUGAL D. . . . . . . **I. acaule**

DIANEL'LA . . . . DIANELLA
caeru'lea . . . . . . CERULEAN D.
ensifo'lia (*Dracaena e.*) SWORDLEAF D.
interme'dia
revolu'ta . . . . ROSETTE D.
tasman'ica . . . . . . TASMANIAN D.

DIAN'THERA |w . . . . . DIANTHERA
america'na |w . . . . AMERICAN D.
nodo'sa . . . . JOINTED D.
pectora'lis . . . . . CARPENTERS D.

DIAN'THUS |w . . PINK; CARNATION
acau'lis . . . . **D. sylvestris frigidus**
acicula'ris . . . . . . RUMANIAN P.
—*spiculifo'lius* . . . . **D. spiculifolius**
∞**all'woodi** (*caryophyllus* × *plumarius*)
∞ALLWOOD P.
alpes'tris . . . . . . CLOUDLAND P.
alpi'nus . . . . ALPINE P.
—**al'bus** . . . . WHITE A.P.
anatol'icus . . . . . . ANATOLIAN P.
arbo'reus . . . . TREE P.
arena'rius . . . . FINLAND P.
₵BEATRICE. HV.
₵CRIMSONKING
ar'idus . . . . DESERT P.
arme'ria |w . . . . . DEPTFORD P.
—**pseudarme'ria**
arros'ti
×**arvernen'sis** . . . . . AUVERGNE P.
Thought to be a natural hybrid, one of whose parents is D. monspessulanus.

DIANTHUS, continued
atkinso'ni . . . . . ATKINSON PINK
atroru'bens . . . **D. carthusianorum a.**
attenua'tus . . . . . ROSETUFT P.
banat'icus . . . . BEARD P.
barba'tus . . . . . . SWEETWILLIAM
—**alpi'nus** . . . . ALPINE S.
₵COPPER RED. HV.
₵HOLBORN GLORY
₵NEWPORT PINK
₵PINK BEAUTY
₵SCARLET BEAUTY
—**dunnett'i** . . . . . . DUNNETT S.
—**ocula'tus** . . . . EYED S.
—**rose'us** . . . . ROSY S.
—**salamo'ni** . . . . . . SOLOMON S.
₵CRIMSON (*atrosanguineus*) HV. D. barbatus
₵DUSKY (*nigrescens; nigricans*)
₵DWARF (*nanus*)
₵SCARLET (*atrococcineus*)
₵TUFTED (*compactus*)
₵WHITE (*albus*)
boissier'i . . . . BOISSIER P.
boyd'i . . . . BOYD P.
brachyan'thus . . . . BRANCHED P.
brevicau'lis . . . . MT.TAURUS P.
cae'sius . . . . **D. gratianopolitanus**
callizo'nus . . . . ZONED P.
caloceph'alus
campes'tris . . . . FIELD P.
capita'tus
carthusiano'rum . . CARTHUSIAN P.
—**atroru'bens** (*D. atrorubens*)
—**gigan'teus** (*D. giganteus*)
—**pu'milus** (*D. subneglectus*)
—**tenuifo'lius** (*D. tenuifolius*)
caryophyl'lus CLOVE PINK; CARNATION
—**atroru'bens**
—**gigan'teus**
—**moesia'cus**
—**na'nus**
—**pontede'riae**
—**pu'milus**
—**rupic'ola**
—**sabuleto'rum**
—**sangui'neus**
—**saxig'enus**
—**subfastigia'tus**
₵GRENADIN. HV. D. caryophyllus
₵SALMONQUEEN
chinen'sis (*fischeri; montanus* in part; *sinensis*) . . . . CHINESE P.
—**heddewig'i** (*D. diadematus; D. gardnerianus; D. hartwegi; D. heddewigi; D. laciniatus; D. mirabilis; D. nobilis; D. ochroleucus; D. superbissimus*) . . . . . RAINBOW C.P.
₵SPLENDENS. HV.
₵VESUVIUS
₵WHITE (*albus*)
—**lacinia'tus** . . . . . FRINGED C.P.
cilia'tus
cinnabari'nus . . . . CINNABAR P.
colli'nus . . . . HILLSIDE P.
compac'tus
controver'sus
crini'tus
croa'ticus . . . . CROATIAN P.
cruen'tus . . . . BLOOD P.
cyr'i . . . . CYR P.
deltoi'des (*procumbens*) . MAIDEN P.
—**glau'cus**

DIANTHUS, continued
deltoi'des serpyllifo'lius (*D. serpyllifolius*)
₵BRILLIANT. HV. D. deltoides
₵MAJOR STERNS
₵WHITEMAIDEN
diffu'sus
erythroco'leus
fimbria'tus
fisch'eri . . . . **D. chinensis**
fra'grans . . . . . FRAGRANT PINK
freyn'i . . . . **D. glacialis f.**
frig'idus . . . . **D. sylvestris f.**
frutico'sus . . . . SHRUBBY P.
furca'tus . . . . FORKED P.
—**leresch'ei**
gal'licus . . . . FRENCH P.
gardneria'nus. **D. chinensis heddewigi**
gel'idus . . . . FROST P.
gigan'teus . . . **D. carthusianorum g.**
glacia'lis . . . . ICE P.
—**freyn'i** (*D. freyni*) . . FREYNS P.
₵WHITE (*freyni*) HV.
—**neglec'tus**
glutino'sus . . . . STICKY P.
grac'ilis
granit'icus . . . . GRANITE P.
gratianopolitan'us (*caesius; suavis*)
—**icom'be** (*D. caesius i.*)
₵PRICHARDS. HV.
—**sema'i** (*D. caesius s.*)
₵DOUBLE (*plenus*) HV.
—**splen'dens** (*D. caesius s.*)
—**superb'us** (*D. caesius s.*)
₵CHEDDAR (*caesius grandiflorus; grandiflorus*) HV.
hartweg'i . . **D. chinensis heddewigi**
heddewig'i . . . . **D. chinensis h.**
hir'tus
hoelt'zeri . . . . HOELTZER P.
in'teger . . . . **D. strictus**
japon'icus . . . . JAPANESE P.
knapp'i . . . . . HARDY GARDEN P.
lacinia'tus . . **D. chinensis heddewigi**
latifo'lius Hort. . . . . . . BUTTON P.
A cultigen.
∞**lauchea'nus** (*barbatus* × *deltoides*)
∞LAUCHEAN P.
leptopet'alus
liboschitzia'nus
libur'nicus
longicau'lis
microle'pis
mirab'ilis . . **D. chinensis heddewigi**
monspessula'nus . . MONTPELIER P.
monta'nus . . **D. chinensis; D. seguieri**
myrtiner'vius
nardifor'mis
neglec'tus . . . . GLACIER P.
₵ROYS (*roysi*) HV.
nit'idus
no'bilis . . . **D. chinensis heddewigi**
noea'nus
ochroleu'cus . **D. chinensis heddewigi**
pal'lens
panci'ci (*velenovskyi*)
pelvifor'mis
petrae'us . . . . ROCK P.
pinifo'lius . . . . PINELEAF P.
pluma'rius (*scoticus*) . . . GRASS P.
—**albiflo'rus** . . . . . . WHITE G.P.
—**perramo'sus**
—**semperflo'rens.** EVERBLOOMING G.P.

Hort. var.; HV. = horticultural variety (or varieties); sp. = species (singular); spp. = species (plural).
₵ = clon; × (as a prefix) = hybrid; × (between scientific plant names) = crossed by; ∞ = polybrid; |w = plant useful to wildlife.
See Glossary for definitions of clon, hybrid, and polybrid.

DIANTHUS plumarius, continued
¢DOUBLE (*florepleno*) HV. D. plumarius
¢DWARF (*nanus*)
¢HYLAND QUEEN
¢KING OF THE BLACKS
¢MRS. SINKINS
¢SCOTCH (*scotius*)
¢SPRINGBEAUTY
procum'bens . . . . . . **D. deltoides**
pro'lifer . . . . . . CHILDING PINK
pubes'cens . . . . . . DOWNY P.
re'pens . . . . BERING P.
requien'i
rupic'ola . . . . CRAG P.
scot'icus . . . . **D. plumarius**
seguier'i (*montanus* in part) RAGGED P.
serpyllifo'lius . . . . **D. deltoides s.**
sinen'sis . . . . **D. chinensis**
spiculifo'lius (*D. acicularis s.*)
spino'sus . . **Acanthophyllum pungens**
squarro'sus
sternberg'i . . . . . . STERNBERG P.
stric'tus (*integer*) . . . . . ERECT P.
—**beb'ius**
—**in'teger**
sua'vis . . . . **D. gratianopolitanus**
subacau'lis
subneglec'tus
D. carthusianorum pumilus
sundermann'i . . . SUNDERMANN P.
superbis'simus. **D. chinensis heddewigi**
superb'us . . . . LILAC P.
—**longicalyci'nus**
¢DWARF (*nanus*) HV. D. superbus
¢LOVELINESS (*speciosus*)
sylves'tris . . . . WOOD P.
—**frig'idus** (*D. acaulis; D. frigidus*)
tenuifo'lius . . . **D. carthusianorum t.**
trifascicula'tus
tris'tis . . . . BITTER P.
tymphres'teus
velenov'skyi . . . . **D. pancici**
versicol'or . . . . . . VERSICOLOR P.
vis'cidus . . . . STICKY P.
—**grisebach'i** (*D. grisebachi*)
GRISEBACH S.P.
¢PARNASSUS. HV. D. viscidus
waldstein'ei . . . . . WALDSTEIN P.
wim'meri . . . . WIMMER P.
zona'tus . . . . BANDED P.

Hort. var. (clons) of **Dianthus caryophyllus,** CARNATION:

The Editorial Committee is indebted to the American Carnation Society and to A. F. J. Baur, Editor of its Carnation Register, for this list.

Special attention is called to the inexcusable duplication of horticultural variety names in the Carnation trade. No less than 46 instances occur where homonyms have been used. This pernicious trade practice which at once is untenable and unfair, must cease if plant naming is to become stable.

The rule that a common or horticultural variety name, once accepted and established, shall not again be used for any other plant in the same species or class must be adopted if plant-name chaos is not to continue.

ABBREVIATIONS OF NAMES OF ORIGINATORS

Agar.	Hon. Francis Agar, England.
Al.	Alegatiere, French.
AlC.	C. H. Allen, Floral Park, N. Y.
AlJ.	Jas. Allen, Paterson, N. J.
Allw.	Allwood Bros., England.
Amer.	American Rose Co., Washington, D. C.

DIANTHUS, continued

And.	D. W. Andrews, East River, Mass.
Arn.	W. B. Arnold, Rockland, Mass.
Aul	Caspar Aul, Cleveland, Ohio.
BakC.	C. F. Baker, Utica, N. Y.
BakR.	Sir Rand. Baker, England.
Ban.	Banyard.
Bar.	M. Barnard, Northbrook, Pa.
Baum	C. L. Baum, Knoxville, Tenn.
Bell	Bertie E. Bell.
Bem.	John W. Bement.
Ber.	Bergman.
Bert.	Bertine.
Berta.	C. F. Bertanzel, Roslyn, L. I., N. Y.
Berte.	Bertermann Bros.
Bes.	C. Besold.
Beu.	Peter Beuerlein.
Bin.	G. W. Binstead, Summit, N. J.
BKB.	B. K. & B. Floral Co., Richmond, Ind.
B&L.	Blackmore & Langdon, England.
Bla.	E. Blameuser, Niles Center, Ill.
Blake	F. S. Blake, Rochdale, Mass.
Blau.	Jas. J. Blauveldt, Pearl River, N. Y.
Blo.	Bloomsburg Floral Co., Bloomsburg, Pa.
Bo.	W. A. Bock, N. Cambridge, Mass.
Bod.	A. Bodin, San Rafael, Calif.
Boe.	Boehringer Bros., Bay City, Mich.
Boh.	Bohne Bros.
Bol.	Miss Bolton, England.
Bou.	Bound Brook Nurs., Bound Brook, N. J.
Boy.	A. E. Boyce, Wellesville, N. S.
B.P.I.	Experiment Greenhouses, B.P.I., U.S.D.A.
Br.	Paul F. Brigham.
Bra.	Brandlein.
Brei.	J. Breitmeyer & Sons, Mt. Clemens, Mich.
Bren.	Geo. Brenkert, Denver, Colo.
Bri.	Brinker.
Brin.	Geo. Brinton & Sons, Wilmington, Del.
BroA.	A. C. Brown, Springfield, Ill.
BroF.	Thos. F. Brown, Detroit, Mich.
B&Sm.	Baur & Smith, Indianapolis, Ind.
B&St.	Baur & Steinkamp, Indianapolis, Ind.
Buc.	F. G. Buchholtz.
Bur.	H. Burnett, England.
BurJ.	J. Burton, Philadelphia, Pa.
BurJ.H.	J. H. Burton, Glenville, Pa.
Burn.	Lord Burnham, England.
Burr.	J. G. Burrow, Fishkill, N. Y.
Bux.	Geo. Buxton, Nashua, N. H.
B&W.	Bassett & Washburn, Chicago, Ill.
Cap.	Thos. Capers, Wellesley, Mass.
Car.	D. Carmichael, Wellesley, Mass.
Carr	Geo. F. Carr, Kingston, Pa.
Carro.	Thos. Carroll, Sutor, Mo.
C&H.	Crabb & Hunter, Grand Rapids, Mich.
Cham.	J. C. Chambers, Toughkenamon, Pa.
Char.	Charlton.
Ches.	Chestnut Floral Co.
Chi.	Chicago Carnation Co., Joliet, Ill.
Chit.	H. E. Chitty, Paterson, N. J.
Chr.	Geo. F. Christy, Clifton Heights, Pa.
C&K.	Campbell & Kennedy.
Cl.	Howard Clarke.
Cla.	Geo. Clarke, England.
Clo.	J. E. Cloud, Avondale, Pa.
Cly.	Clyde Carnationery, Clyde, Ohio.
Cock.	J. D. Cockcroft, Northport, N. Y.
CoE.	E. H. Coleman, England.
Col.	Thos. Coles, S. Natick, Mass.
Con.	Conrad.
Cond.	Frank Condito.
Cook	H. A. Cook, Shrewsbury, Mass.
Coop.	Lady Cooper.

DIANTHUS, continued

CoP.	P. A. Coleman, England.
Cot.	Cottage Gardens Co., Queens, N. Y.
Crei.	Creighton.
Cul.	H. J. Cullwick, England.
Cum.	Cummings, Woburn, Mass.
Cush.	Cushings, Quidnick, R. I.
Cut.	Cutbush & Son, England.
Dai.	Dailledouze Bros., Brooklyn, N. Y.
DaiZ.	Dailledouze Zeller & Co., Flatbush, N. Y.
Dan.	W. J. Dance, England.
Dau.	John Dauber.
Dav.	Davis.
DavB.	Davis Bros., Bloomsburg, Pa.
Daw.	W. J. Dawson, Willimantic, Conn.
Dem.	A. C. Demeusey, Brooklyn, N. Y.
Der.	Ctsse. Derby, England.
DeW.	F. H. DeWitt, Wooster, Ohio.
Die.	R. Diener & Co., Mountain View, Calif.
Dil.	J. L. Dillon, Bloomsburg, Pa.
Din.	F. Dinda, Farmingdale, N. Y.
Dix.	Mrs. Dixon, England.
Dor.	F. Dorner & Sons Co., Lafayette, Ind.
Dow.	Downs Park Nurs., England.
Dud.	H. G. Dudley, England.
Dut.	A. F. Dutton, England.
Ea.	L. C. Eastburn, Kennett Square, Pa.
Ed.	Edwards.
EGC.	Elitch Gardens Co., Denver, Colo.
Ei.	H. Eichholz, Waynesboro, Pa.
Eis.	C. Eisele.
El.	Elder Bros., Indianapolis, Ind.
Eld.	B. Eldridge, Belvidere, Ill.
Els.	F. G. Elsner, Barrington, Mass.
Eng.	C. Engelmann, England.
Ess.	Essex Hts. Fl. Co.
Essl.	J. G. & A. Essler, Saddle River, N. J.
Eve.	Evenden Bros., Williamsport, Pa.
Fai.	Geo. Fairbairn & Son, England.
Fair.	Fairhaven & Son, England.
Farr	A. C. Farr.
Faw.	Fawcett.
F&B.	Fillow & Banks.
Fear.	F. Fearnley, England.
Fed.	H. C. Feder, Redondo Beach, Calif.
Few.	E. E. Fewkes.
F&F.	Fick & Faber, San Francisco, Calif.
Fie.	Field.
FieH.	H. W. Field, Northampton, Mass.
Fil.	S. B. Fillow, Westport, Conn.
FisP.	P. Fisher, Ellis, Mass.
FisR.	R. Fisher, Great Neck, N. Y.
FisS.	S. Fisher, Framingham, Mass.
Fle.	M. S. Fleming, Ocean Heights, N. J.
Flo.	Florex Gardens, North Wales, Pa.
Fra.	W. Frank & Sons, Portland, Ind.
Frey	C. H. Frey, Lincoln, Neb.
Fri.	C. M. Frick, Philadelphia, Pa.
GAOA.	Guardian Angel Orphan Asylum, Chicago, Ill.
Gass.	J. M. Gasser, Cleveland, Ohio.
G&G.	Grimm & Gorley, St. Louis, Mo.
Gi.	H. H. Given, Denver, Colo.
Go.	S. J. Goddard, Framingham, Mass.
Goe.	J. B. Goetz, Saginaw, Mich.
Good.	F. W. Gooding, England.
Gore	Gore & Whitney, England.
Grah.	Graham.
Gran.	J. Grande & Sons, Indianapolis, Ind.
Gras.	A. O. Grassl, B.P.I., U.S.D.A.
Grave	E. T. Grave, Richmond, Ind.
Grea.	Thos. Greaves, Montebello, Mass.

DIANTHUS, continued

Gro. H. Grout, Springfield, Mass.
Gude Gude Bros., Washington, D. C.
Gui. E. Guile, England.
Hae. C. J. Haettel.
Hai. J. Haines, Bethlehem, Pa.
Hake A. Hake, Manchester, Pa.
Hall W. E. Hall, Clyde, Ohio.
Han. J. Hancock & Sons, Grand Haven, Mich.
Har. J. Hartje, Indianapolis, Ind.
Harms Harms Park Fl. Co., Chicago, Ill.
Harr. Harrison.
Harw. F. C. Harwood, England.
Hau. Hausmann Bros., Hilton, N. J.
H&B. Harmon & Burr, Sowens, N. Y.
H&E. Hartje & Edler, Indianapolis, Ind.
He. Jos. Heacock & Co., Wyncote, Pa.
Hea. Heath & Son, England.
Hei. Ph. Heilig, Franklin, Pa.
Hem. Hempstead.
Hemus Walter Hemus.
Hen. P. Henderson, New York, N. Y.
Heng. Hengenstenberg.
Henn. W. Hennes.
Hens. Henshaw Floral Co.
Herb P. Herb, Mt. Healthy, Ohio.
Herm. W. Hermes, England.
Herr. A. Herrington, Madison, N. J.
Hes. H. Hession, Brooklyn, N. Y.
Hess Conrad Hess, Baltimore, Md.
Hi. Highland Park Greenhouses, Highland Park, Ill.
HillE. E. G. Hill & Co., Richmond, Ind.
Hill J. Jos. Hill & Co., Richmond, Ind.
Hing. Hingham Flower Co.
H&L. Hopp & Lemke, Grand Rapids, Mich.
Hoff. Hoffman, Pawtucket, R. I.
Hol. T. P. A. Holford, England.
Holl. Hollywood Gardens, Hollywood, Wash.
How. Howland.
H&T. Hallock & Thorpe.
Hud. Hudson & Welch, Lyndonville, N. Y.
H&W. Henderson & Welsh.
Ing. Ingleside Nurs., Alhambra, Calif.
Ir. R. J. Irwin.
Jab. A. Jablonsky, Olivette, Mo.
JahB. Jahn Bros., New Bedford, Mass.
JahH. H. A. Jahn, New Bedford, Mass.
Jen. Jennings.
JohC. C. B. Johnson, Woburn, Mass.
JohE. E. T. Johnston, England.
Ke. P. Kellen, Niles Center, Ill.
Kel. E. Kelly, England.
Kin. L. A. Kintzele.
Kir. W. Kircher, Defiance, Ohio.
Kirk Kirk.
Kirs. Kirschner.
Kle. W. Kleinheinz, Ogontz, Pa.
Kni. H. B. Knight, Newark, N. J.
Knipe Tom Knipe.
Kno. Chas. Knopf Fl. Co., Richmond, Ind.
Know. A. B. Knowlton, N. Grafton, Mass.
Knu. S. Knudsen, Boulder, Colo.
Kra. F. H. Kramer, Washington, D.C.
Krau. M. E. Krauss, New Haven, Conn.
Kre. Kretchmar Bros., W. Nyack, N. Y.
Ku. J. Kuhn, Philadelphia, Pa.
Lake E. G. Lake, Wellesley Hills, Mass.
Lan. M. H. Lancashire, England.
Lar. Larkin, Toughkenamon, Pa.
Law. Wm. Lawrence, England.
Lax. Laxton Bros., England.
LeC. F. H. LeCluse, Blue Point, L. I., N. Y.
Len. S. Lenton, Piru City, Calif.
Lew. W. L. Lewis.
Lom. R. T. Lombard, Wayland, Mass.
Lons. E. Lonsdale, Philadelphia, Pa.

DIANTHUS, continued

Love G. W. Love, Unionville, Pa.
Low Stuart Low, Jr., England.
Lowe J. E. Lowe.
Lu. Max Luthi.
L&W. Littlefield & Wyman.
Mai. O. Mailander, Niles Center, Ill.
Mal. Hugh Maloy.
Mam. H. Mamitch, Englewood, N. J.
Mar. L. E. Marquisee, Syracuse, N. Y.
Mars. E. D. Marshall.
Marv. I. G. Marvin, Wilkes-Barre, Pa.
Mas. H. T. Mason, England.
Mat. H. Mathias, England.
Max. Maxfield.
May J. N. May, Summit, N. J.
McC. McCallum.
McCo. E. McConnell, Sharon, Pa.
McG. J. McGowan, Orange, N. J.
Mc&S. McDonald & Steele, Crawfordsville, Ind.
Mer. S. M. Merwarth, Easton, Pa.
Mi. F. W. Miles.
Mia. Miami Flora Co., Dayton, Ohio.
Mid. L. Midgley, Westboro, Mass.
Mil. Miller & Son, Bracondale, Ont.
Milno J. Milno & Son, Fairbury, Ill.
Mit. A. Mitting, Morris, Ill.
Mo. H. Molatsch, Bay Ridge, N. Y.
Moo. L. A. Moore, Unionville, Pa.
Mor. Morris Floral Co., Morris, Ill.
M&S. Myers & Samtman, Philadelphia, Pa.
M&T. Messmore & Turner, England.
Mu. Muller.
Mun. Munro, Inc., Westerly, R. I.
Mur. J. Murchie, Sharon, Pa.
Murp. Wm. Murphy, Cincinnati, Ohio.
Murr. P. Murray.
Nau. Chas. Nauman, Cleveland, Ohio.
Nel. E. A. Nelson, Indianapolis, Ind.
New. Newport Nurseries, England.
Nic. Wm. Nicholson, Framingham, Mass.
Nie. H. A. Niemeyer, Erie, Pa.
Niq. F. Niquet, Patchogue, N. Y.
No. D. C. Noble, Columbia City, Ind.
Pal. W. J. Palmer & Son, Buffalo, N. Y.
Park Park Floral Co.
Pass. I. A. Passmore, West Chester, Pa.
Pat. Patten & Co., Tewksbury, Mass.
PaT. Thos. Page, England.
PaW. W. H. Page, England.
Pem. A. A. Pembroke, Beverley, Mass.
Pen. C. J. Pennock, Kennett Square, Pa.
Pet. Swan Peterson, Gibson City, Ill.
P&F. Price & Fife, England.
Pfe. J. L. Pfeuffer, Troington, N. Y.
Pho. Phoenix Nurseries, Bloomington, Ill.
Pi. N. D. Pierce, Norwood, R. I.
PieA. A. N. Pierson Co., Cromwell, Conn.
PieF. F. R. Pierson, Tarrytown, N. Y.
Pil. G. Pillsbury.
Pond J. S. Pond.
Pye R. C. Pye, Nyack, N. Y.
Pyf. Pyfer.
Pyle J. H. Pyle.
Rah. A. Rahner, Willisca, Iowa.
Rass. A. Rassmussen, New Albany, Ind.
Rath H. C. Rath, Flushing, N. Y.
Re. Redondo Beach Co., Redondo Beach, Calif.
Rei. J. Reimels, Woodhaven, N. Y.
Rey. J. A. Reynolds, Troy, N. Y.
Roh. H. D. Rohrer, Lancaster, Pa.
Rop. A. Roper, Tewksbury, Mass.
Rowe W. A. Rowe, Kirkwood, Mo.
Rudd W. N. Rudd, Morgan Park, Ill.
Sak. J. G. Sakswich, New Hyde Park, N. Y.
Sal. W. G. Saltford, Poughkeepsie, N. Y.
Scha. Chas. A. Schaeffer, York, Pa.

DIANTHUS, continued

Scho. J. G. Scholl, Burlington, N. Y.
Schr. H. Schrade, Saratoga Springs, N. Y.
Schra. F. Schramm, Park Ridge, Ill.
Schro. B. Schroeter, Detroit, Mich.
Schu. Schuphelt.
Schw. H. Schwarz, Central Park, N. Y.
Sco. Scott Bros., Elmsford, N. Y.
Sea. Lady Seaforth.
See. Mrs. Seeley, England.
S&H. Stuart & Haugh, Anderson, Ind.
Shaw Stephen Shaw.
Shel. W. R. Shelmire, Avondale, Pa.
Sho. J. G. Sholl.
Shum. W. H. Shumway, Berlin, Conn.
Shup. Shuphelt.
Sie. J. H. Sievers, San Francisco, Calif.
Sim Wm. Sim, S. Berwick, Maine.
Simm. W. P. Simmons, Geneva, Ohio.
SmA. A. Smith, England.
SmG. Geo. Smith, Manchester, Vt.
SmN. N. Smith & Son, Adrian, Mich.
SmW. W. J. Smith, England.
SnJ. Jennie P. Snow.
SnW. W. J. Snow, Waterbury, Conn.
Sor. A. Sorensen.
Spe. F. R. Specht, Rochester, N. Y.
Spi. Aug. Spies, New Springville, N. Y.
S&S. Scheiden & Schoos, Chicago, Ill.
Star. Mrs. C. S. Starr, Avondale, Pa.
Starr Chas. T. Starr, Avondale, Pa.
Stei. J. Steidle, Olivette, Mo.
Stev. Stevenson Bros., Govanstown, Md.
Sto. Stollery Bros., Chicago, Ill.
Str. F. Strolisky.
Stro. Strout's, Biddeford, Me.
SwayE. E. Swayne, Kennett Square, Pa.
SwayW. Wm. Swayne, Kennett Square, Pa.
Sym. H. Symonds, Decorah, Iowa.
Tai. Jos. Tailey & Son, Wellesley, Mass.
Tay. Taylors Greenhouses, Dunkirk, N. Y.
Tei. G. Teilman, Marion, Ind.
Tem. Temple.
Tho. Thorpe, Jr., Pearl River, N. J.
Thom. Thompson Bros., Kennett Square, Pa.
ThomJ. J. D. Thompson Car. Co., Joliet, Ill.
Thor. F. R. Thornton, Streator, Ill.
Tie. M. Tierney, Highlands, N. J.
Tim. F. W. Timme, Chicago, Ill.
Tow. Jos. Towell, Paterson, N. J.
T&S. Traendly & Schenck, New York, N. Y.
Tu. J. B. Tudro, Alderbend, N. J.
Uss. Ussing.
VdS. C. F. Van der Sluys, England.
Vei. R. Veitch & Son, England.
Ves. W. J. & M. S. Vesey, Ft. Wayne, Ind.
Vet. Vetch.
Vick F. W. Vick, Rochester, N. Y.
Vict. Victoria Ltd.
VR. E. J. Van Reyper, Belleville, N. J.
Wa. A. R. Walker, Flint, Mich.
Wake A. Wake.
Wal. W. E. Wallace, England.
Wall Chas. Wall, England.
Wan. Wanoka Greenhouses, Barneveld, N. Y.
War. C. Warburton, Fall River, Mass.
Ward G. W. Ward, Queens, L. I., N. Y.
Wat. C. F. Waters, England.
Wea. Elmer Weaver, Bird in Hand, Pa.
WebC. Chas. Weber, Lynbrook, N. Y.
WebF. F. Weber, Chicago, Ill.
WebH. H. Weber, Brooklyn, N. Y.
WebHS. H. Weber & Sons, Oakland, Md.
Webs. J. D. Webster, England.
Wei. Weidemann Bros., Wilsonville, Ore.

DIANTHUS, continued

Weil.	M. Weiland, Evanston, Ill.
Weis.	Weisshaar Bros., Indianapolis, Ind.
Wells	W. Wells & Co., England.
Wels.	Welsing.
West	G. West, England.
WFE.	Wisconsin Fl. Exchange, Milwaukee, Wisc.
Whee.	Jas. Wheeler, Natick, Mass.
Whi.	White.
Whit.	F. E. Whitney, Fishkill on Hudson, N. Y.
Wi.	L. Wight, Framingham, Mass.
Will.	J. E. Williams.
Wils.	Wilson Bros.
Win.	M. Winandy, Chicago, Ill.
Wink.	E. Winkler, Wakefield, Mass.
Wit.	R. Witterstaetter, Cincinnati, Ohio.
Wood	Wood Bros., Fishkill, N. Y.
Wool.	H. Woolman, England.
Woot.	E. Wooten, England.
Wor.	Wormald, Jr., England.
Wri.	Lathrop Wright.
You.	Young & Co., England.
Zell.	Chas. Zeller, Flatbush, N. Y.
Zwei.	N. Zweifel, Milwaukee, Wisc.

Abington. (L&W. 1917.)
Abraham Lincoln. (1895.)
Abundance. (HillE. 1896.)
Abundance. (FisR. 1906.)
A. C. Fitzpatrick. (Simm.)
Achievement. (Beu. 1934.)
Acquisition. (Lom. 1895.)
Acquisition. (Wri.)
Ada. (Dav. 1891.)
Ada Byron. (FisS. 1893.)
Adalaide Kresken. (Herb 1894.)
Adelaide.
Admirable. (DaiZ. 1866.)
Admiral Dewey. (Ei. 1899.)
Admiral Walker. (Bou. 1915.)
Admiration. (Kno. 1910.)
Admiration. (Beu. 1934.)
Adonis. (DaiZ. 1866.)
Adonis. (Wit. 1903.)
Afonwen. (SmW. 1911.)
Afterglow. (Wit. 1911.)
Aggie Ross. (JohC. 1925.)
Aglae. (DaiZ. 1866.)
Agnes Snow. (SnW. 1895.)
Aida. (Sim 1934.)
Alaska. (Chit.)
Alba. (Dor. 1902.)
Albasuperba. (BurJ. 1898.)
Albatross. (Wit. 1903.)
Albino. (Eng. 1914.)
Alb. Manders. (Wat. 1911.)
Alegatiere. (Al. 1881.)
Alexandra. (Uss. 1891.)
Alhambra. (Ing. 1895.)
Alice Coombs. (Rop. 1913.)
Alice Roosevelt. (Wels. 1902.)
Alison. (P&F. 1918.)
Allwhite. (Gras. 1937.)
Allwood. (Beu. 1934.)
Allwoods Rosalind. (Allw. 1917.)
Alma. (Aul. 1900.)
Al. Malaiken. (Ing. 1895.)
Almira. (Shum. 1909.)
Alvina. (Ei. 1909.)
Amabilis. (DaiZ. 1866.)
Amateur. (DaiZ. 1866.)
Amazon. (Hake. 1897.)
Amelia Gude. (Gude 1927.)
America. (HillE. 1899.)
American Flag. (Ber. 1890.)
American Florist.
A. M. Herr. (Dor.)
Amy. (1880.)

DIANTHUS, continued
Amy Phipps. (Simm. 1888.)
Amy Robsart. (Max. 1930.)
Andalusia. (France 1884.)
Andrew Carnegie. (Chi. 1908.)
Angelus. (Shel. 1891.)
Anita. (Sim 1936.)
Anna (*C.*) Eastburn. (Ea. 1899.)
Anna Webb. (FisS. 1885.)
Annie Laurie. (Boh. 1930.)
Annie Lonsdale. (M&S. 1895.)
Annie Wiegand. (Dor. 1902.)
Antarctic. (Sim 1934.)
Apollo. (1902.)
Appleblossom. (Wan. 1909.)
Arabella. (Bou. 1915.)
Arawana. (PieA. 1917.)
Arctic. (Sim 1925.)
Argyle. (Sto. 1896.)
Aristocrat. (Wit. 1907.)
Armazindy. (HillE. 1896.)
A. S. Montgomery. (You. 1911.)
Astoria. (Bert. 1862.)
Astoria. (DaiZ. 1866.)
Atlantis. (Sim 1934.)
Attraction. (DaiZ. 1866.)
Attraction. (Dor. 1891.)
Augusta Rath. (Rath 1897.)
Augusta Williams. (Rath 1897.)
Aurora. (SwayE. 1892.)
Aurora. (Bur. 1911.)
Avalanche. (Pye 1906.)
Averill Furneas. (Bur. 1916.)
Aviator. (Chi. 1916.)
Avondale. (Starr 1880.)
Avondale. (S&H. 1901.)
Baltimore. (Hess 1895.)
Banner. (Faw. 1893.)
Barbara Brigham. (Br. 1938.)
Barbara Farr. (Farr 1936.)
Barnum. (DaiZ. 1866.)
Barss Debrienen. (Low 1911.)
Bayard Taylor. (Starr.)
Baystate. (Rop. 1906.)
Beacon. (FisP. 1907.)
Beatrice. (B&Sm. 1905.)
Beatrice White. (1884.)
Beaubrummel. (Chi. 1907.)
Beauideal. (Pi. 1901.)
Beauty. (HillE. 1882.)
Beauty of Oxford. (1889.)
Bedford Bells. (Lax. 1916.)
Bella. (Eng. 1914.)
Bellevista. (AlJ. 1900.)
Belle Washburn. (B&W. 1916.)
Ben Haliday. (Europe.)
Ben Hur. (Dor. 1892.)
Benora. (FisP. 1912.)
Berkshire Hills. (Eng. 1938.)
Bernice. (Know. 1916.)
Bertha Rath. (Rath 1897.)
Bertha Soper. (1890.)
Bertha Stahl. (Ed. 1893.)
Bess. (Weis. 1895.)
Beth. (Lu. 1932.)
Bettina. (Wi. 1895.)
Betty Jane. (Jab. 1922.)
Betty Lou. (B&St. 1924.)
Bidwell. (Len. 1893.)
Bishton Wonder. (Allw. 1915.)
Blackchief. (Low 1909.)
Blackknight. (Tho. 1886.)
Blackprince. (1885.)
Blanche. (Dor. 1893.)
Blaze. (BPI. 1938.)
Blizzard. (Star. 1888.)
Blondin. (DaiZ. 1866.)
Bohemian Girl. (C&K.)

DIANTHUS, continued
Boissy. (France 1886.)
Bon Ami. (Chi. 1910.)
Bonanza. (Sim 1933.)
Bonfire. (HillE. 1911.)
Bonhomme Richard. (Chi. 1901.)
Bonita. (Vict. 1931.)
Bonniebride. (Blake 1902.)
Bonniedoon. (Hen. 1879.)
Bonniemaid. (Dor. 1907.)
Bonny. (VdS. 1914.)
Bonton. (Blake 1898.)
Bostonmarket. (FisP. 1903.)
Bountiful. (Kir. 1933.)
Bouton d'Or. (Daiz. 1895.)
Brandywine. (Love 1901.)
Bride of Erlescourt. (Mil. 1895.)
Bridesmaid. (Bur. 1910.)
Bridesmaid. (Dor.)
Brightspot. (Zwei. 1909.)
Brilliant. (Low 1918.)
British Triumph. (Eng. 1911.)
Brooklyn. (WebC. 1911.)
Brower. (1895.)
Brunette. (Lons.)
Bruno. (VdS. 1914.)
Brussells. (Starr 1881.)
Brutus. (DaiZ. 1866.)
Brutus. (Shel. 1893.)
Bryant. (Simm.)
Buddie. (Str. 1930.)
Burgundy. (BPI. 1938.)
Burroughs Scarlet. (JohE. 1909.)
Buster. (Len. 1892.)
Butler. (1895.)
Buttercup. (Starr 1878.)
Caesar. (Shel. 1891.)
Calico. (Starr 1884.)
California Giant. (Die. 1912.)
California Gold. (Sie. 1901.)
Calypso. (Bur. 1913.)
Cameo. (Sim 1934.)
Campfire. (Wei. 1924.)
Canada. (1891.)
Canary. (DaiZ. 1866.)
Canarybird. (Schr. 1910.)
Canary of Sanrafael. (Bod. 1916.)
Cancase. (DaiZ. 1866.)
Candace. (Har. 1906.)
Caprice. (See. 1915.)
Capt. (*D.*) McPherson. (Cul. 1916.)
Capt. King. (Pen. 1895.)
Cardinal. (Wit. 1905.)
Cardinal. (FisS.)
Cardinalis. (Shel. 1897.)
Carmen. (Bur. 1912.)
Carnival. (Eng. 1914.)
Carola. (Eng. 1909.)
Casa Blanca. (Re. 1895.)
Catharin Paul. (1884.)
Cattleya Mauve. (Beu. 1934.)
Cavour. (DaiZ. 1866.)
Cecilia Schwake. (Rath 1897.)
Centennial. (Hen. 1877.)
Century. (Starr 1886.)
Cerisequeen. (Brei. 1898.)
Cerisewinsor. (Bla. 1915.)
Challenger. (Hof.)
Chamoise. (Die. 1914.)
Champion. (Dor. 1913.)
Charles Dana. (Cot. 1896.)
Charles Fulford. (Good. 1911.)
Charles Henderson. (Tho. 1884.)
Charles Sumner. (Bo. 1868.)
Charles T. Starr. (Star. 1895.)
Charles Wall. (Wall. 1914.)
Charmer. (1885.)
Charming. (Gran. 1927.)

DIANTHUS, continued
Charming. (Beu. 1934.)
CHASTITY. (Starr 1890.)
C. H. BARNETT. (You. 1914.)
CHEERFUL. (Hau. 1924.)
CHELSEA. (Dut. 1916.)
CHELTONIA. (You. 1909.)
CHERRY LIPS. (Dor. 1891.)
CHERRYRED. (Wel. 1914.)
CHERRYRIPE. (1884.)
CHESTER PRIDE. (Ed. 1877.)
CHICAGO. (Chi. 1900.)
CHICOT. (Chi. 1902.)
CHIEF DENISON. (Die. 1914.)
CHIEF KOKOMO. (Knipe 1930.)
CHINCHITA. (Re. 1895.)
CHRISTABEL. (Woot. 1914.)
CHRISTMAS. (Starr 1890.)
CHRISTMAS CHEER. (Ei. 1910.)
CHRISTMAS EVE. (Cot. 1914.)
CHRISTMAS ROSE. (Hei. 1900.)
CHUSCO. (Re. 1895.)
CINDERELLA. (Fai. 1912.)
CINNEBAR. (Low 1912.)
CIREE. (Eng. 1914.)
CITRUS. (Len. 1895.)
C. J. CLARK. (Simm. 1884.)
CLARA BARTON. (Kre. 1900.)
CLARA MAWER. (Ess. 1892.)
CLARA MORRIS. (Simm. 1886.)
CLARIBEL WORTH. (Boy. 1909.)
CLARISSE. (DaiZ. 1866.)
CLARKS BOUNTIFUL. (Cl. 1937.)
CLEOPATRA. (1895.)
CLIFTON FISHER. (FisS. 1886.)
CLIMAX. (Wan. 1907.)
CLIO. (Pen. 1897.)
CLOTHOFGOLD. (1888.)
COLLEEN. (Eng. 1915.)
COLOSSUS. (Low 1911.)
COLUMBIA. (Tho. 1886.)
Columbia. (Blake 1906.)
COMET. (DaiZ. 1866.)
Comet. (ThomJ. 1915.)
COMFORT. (Mer. 1912.)
COMMONWEALTH. (Rop. 1915.)
CONCHSHELL. (Gro. 1898.)
CONGRESS. (Law. 1913.)
CONQUEST. (Cap. 1900.)
CONSTANCE. (Bell 1911.)
COQUETTE. (Eng. 1918.)
CORA COLLINS. (Bri. 1909.)
CORNELL. (Marv. 1916.)
CORONATION. (Bell 1911.)
CORONET. (Sim 1937.)
CORSAIR. (Chit. 1895.)
COTTAGEMAID. (Cot. 1914.)
COUNTESS OF MARCH. (Bur. 1910.)
COUNTESS OF PEMBROKE.
COUNTESS OF WILTON.
COUR DELAVAELA. (Eng. 1895.)
CREOLE. (Dor. 1891.)
CRESSBROOK. (War. 1901.)
CRIMSONCORONET. (Crei. 1892.)
CRIMSONGLOW. (DaiZ. 1906.)
CRIMSONKING.
CRIMSONSPORT. (Dil. 1898.)
CRIMSONVELVET. (1887.)
CRIMSONWAVE. (Len. 1895.)
CRISIS. (Dav. 1905.)
CRUSADER. (Chi. 1904.)
CRYPTA. (Len. 1895.)
CRYSTAL. (FisS. 1895.)
CRYSTALWHITE. (Cot. 1916.)
C. SCHMIDT. (1890.)
DAHEIM. (PieF. 1904.)
DAINTYQUEEN. (Sim 1937.)
DAIRYMAID. (Beu. 1934.)

DIANTHUS, continued
DAISY. (1875.)
DAISYBELL. (Shel. 1895.)
DANDY. (Ir. 1928.)
DAPHNE. (Bur. 1910.)
DARDS. (1896.)
DARKNESS. (DaiZ. 1866.)
DAWN. (Starr 1886.)
DAYBREAK. (Simm. 1891.)
DAYBREAK PERFECTION. (Boe. 1902.)
DAYDREAM. (Wal. 1917.)
DAYSTAR. (Hol. 1914.)
DAZZLE. (Dor. 1891.)
DEAN HOLE. (May 1895.)
DEBUTANTE. (Die. 1913.)
DECORAH. (Sym. 1914.)
DEFENDER. (FisP. 1896.)
DEFIANCE. (DaiZ. 1866.)
Defiance. (Rudd 1908.)
DEFONTANNE. (DaiZ. 1866.)
DELAWARE. (Brin. 1893.)
DELICACY. (Sim 1937.)
DELICATE. (1888.)
DELICE. (Dud. 1915.)
DELIGHTFUL. (Len. 1893.)
DELLA FOX. (M&S. 1896.)
DELRAY. (Wink. 1930.)
DEMOCRACY. (Gude 1919.)
DENVER. (Bren. 1919.)
DEROO MITTING. (Mit. 1899.)
DESTINY. (Allw. 1917.)
DETERMINATION. (Ei. 1927.)
DIADEM. (1870.)
DIADEME. (DaiZ. 1866.)
DIAMOND. (Brin. 1893.)
DICTATOR. (Kin. 1936.)
DIMITY. (Beu. 1934.)
DITCHLING. (Beu. 1934.)
DOLLY VARDON. (Hen. 1882.)
DONALD. (Stro. 1919.)
DONNA LEE. (DavB. 1931.)
DORINDA. (Few. 1892.)
DORIS. (Go. 1916.)
DOROTHY. (Shel. 1891.)
Dorothy. (Grave 1901.)
DOROTHY FORBES. (Hei. 1900.)
DOROTHY GORDON. (He. 1909.)
DOROTHY MANDELL. (Cook 1899.)
DOROTHY WHITNEY. (Dor. 1902.)
DR. DELAMO. (Re. 1895.)
DREAM. (Hol. 1859.)
DR. (*E. P.*) LAWRENCE. (Rath 1897.)
DR. LAMBORN. (Len. 1893.)
DR. PATZKI. (Re. 1895.)
DR. SAM. (Baum 1914.)
DR. SMART. (Dor. 1893.)
DR. WARDER. (Shel. 1895.)
DUBARRY. (BurJ.H. 1924.)
DUCHESS OF DEVONSHIRE. (You. 1909.)
DUKE OF ORANGE. (Starr 1878.)
DUKE OF YORK. (Shel. 1899.)
EARLYDAWN. (Dor. 1927.)
EARLYROSE. (Dor. 1927.)
EARLY SUNRISE. (L&W. 1937.)
EASTERN BEAUTY. (L&W. 1917.)
EASTERN MAIL. (Allw. 1917.)
EASTERN QUEEN. (Wood.)
EASTERN STAR. (FisP. 1901.)
E. A. WOOD. (Dor.)
ECLIPSE. (1881.)
EDELWEISS. (Shel. 1891.)
EDITH FOSTER. (1896.)
EDITH WATERS. (Wat. 1912.)
EDNA. (Zwei. 1919.)
EDNA CRAIG. (Dor. 1893.)
EDWARD LONSDALE. (Dor. 1891.)
EDWARDSI. (1866.)

DIANTHUS, continued
EDW. BISSELL. (Pho.)
EDW. PAGE. (PaT. 1917.)
E. G. GILLETT. (Cly. 1910.)
E. G. HILL. (Tho. 1887.)
EGYPT. (WebH. 1901.)
E. H. WILSON. (Dor. 1932.)
ELDORADO. (Shel. 1895.)
ELEANOR. (You. 1936.)
ELEANOR AMES. (Car. 1900.) ***May Whitney.***
ELECTRA. (Eng. 1911.)
ELEGANCE. (Bur. 1912.)
ELIZABETH. (Shum. 1909.)
ELMA. (Nie. 1901.)
ELM CITY. (Krau. 1900.)
ELMONT. (1888.)
ELSENHAM BEAUTY. (CoP. 1914.)
ELSIE BOYD. (Low 1912.)
ELSIE EVANS. (West. 1911.)
ELSIE GRAY. (And. 1911.)
EMILY L. TAPLIN. (Burr. 1891.)
EMMA LOWRY. (1896.)
EMMA (*M.*) THOMPSON. (1896.)
EMMA QUINLAN. (Rath 1897.)
EMMA WOCHER. (Wit. 1896.)
EMPEROR. (Lan. 1911.)
EMPIRE DAY. (SmA. 1911.)
EMPRESS. (Bar. 1898.)
EMPRESS OF MOROCCO. (1881.)
ENCHANTRESS. (FisP. 1903.)
ENCHANTRESS SUPREME. (DaiZ. 1913.)
ENID. (Wal. 1919.)
ENQUIRER. (Wit. 1902.)
ERMINIE. (Starr 1888.)
ESPERANCE. (DaiZ. 1866.)
ESTELLE. (Wit. 1901.)
ESTHER. (Dor. 1893.)
ETHEL. (1896.)
ETHEL CROCKER. (Sie. 1900.)
ETHEL WARD. (Cot. 1904.)
ETHEL (*W.*) RIGO. (Hens. 1936.)
ETNA. (Mat. 1911.)
ETOILE MARIE. (DaiZ. 1866.)
EUGENE DAILLEDOUZE. (1896.)
EULALIA. (Shel. 1895.)
EUPHEMIA. (Shup.)
EUREKA. (Dil. 1900.)
Eureka. (Starr.)
Eureka. (Mid. 1914.)
EVALINA. (Wit. 1897.)
EVANGELINE. (Dor. 1892.)
EVANSTON. (Weil. 1899.)
EVENING STAR. (1896.)
E. V. LOW. (McG. 1893.)
EXCELSIOR. (Brin. 1893.)
EXQUISITE. (1892.)
Exquisite. (Allw. 1917.)
FAIRHARVARD. (Hes. 1920.)
FAIRMAID. (Rop. 1902.)
FAIRMOUNT. (Allw. 1911.)
FAIR ROSAMOND. (1884.)
FAIRY PRINCESS. (Tho. 1884.)
FAIRYQUEEN. (JohC. 1927.)
FAITH. (Ei. 1927.)
FANCY. (Starr 1883.)
FANNY. (Eng. 1912.)
FASCINATION. (Tho. 1882.)
FAUST. (Cock. 1907.)
FAVORITE. (Sim 1938.)
F. BURKI. (Mur. 1905.)
F. CREIGHTON. (Crei. 1890.)
FERD MANGOLD. (Tho. 1884.)
Ferd Mangold. (Simm. 1886.)
F. GOODING. (Good. 1911.)
F. H. KRAMER. (Kra. 1905.)
FIANCEE. (Dor. 1905.)
FIDELIA. (See. 1915.)

DIANTHUS, continued
Field of Gold. (Starr 1878.)
Fiesta. (Sim 1938.)
Firebrand. (Fie. 1881.)
Firefly. (Han. 1899.)
Fireglow. (Low 1911.)
Firelight. (Pen. 1893.)
Fishkill. (Wood.)
Fitzpatrick. (1885.)
F. Johnson. (Tai. 1891.)
Flambeau. (B&Sm. 1905.)
Flame. (Vict. 1931.)
Flaming June. (You. 1916.)
Flamingo. (Mar. 1904.)
Flatbush. (DaiZ. 1866.)
Flora. (Sim. 1925.)
Flora Hill. (HillE. 1896.)
Florence Bevis. (Grah.)
Florence Eddie. (Vick. 1896.)
Florence Fisher. (FisS.)
Florence Vanriper. (VR. 1893.)
Floriana. (F&B. 1902.)
Flushing. (Rath 1897.)
F. McGregor. (Dor. 1893.)
Fortuna. (Bur. 1910.)
Fortune. (DaiZ. 1866.)
Fort Wayne. (Ves. 1897.)
Fragrance. (DaiZ. 1903.)
Fragrance. (Beu. 1934.)
Fred Dorner. (Dor. 1891.)
Fred Weir. (Mo. 1896.)
Freedom. (FisP. 1897.)
Gaiety. (HillE. 1902.)
Gardenia. (Sim 1937.)
Garnet Beauty. (Cl. 1937.)
Gauntlet. (Hen. 1876.)
Gayety. (Hake 1897.)
Gayety. (Law. 1914.)
Gen. Burnside. (1896.)
Gen. (*Chas.*) Miller. (Hei. 1901.)
Gen. Custer. (Shel. 1891.)
Genesee. (H&B. 1898.)
Geneva. (Simm. 1890.)
Genevieve. (Pat. 1909.)
Genevieve Lord. (WebH. 1900.)
Gen. Gomez. (Cot. 1898.)
Gen. Grant. (DaiZ. 1866.)
Gen. Joffre. (Cla. 1916.)
Gen. Maceo. (Cot. 1899.)
Gen. Sherman. (1896.)
Gen. Washington. (Zell.)
George Thorpe. (Tho. 1884.)
Germania. (Germany 1886.)
Gertrude. (Weis. 1895.)
G. H. Crane. (Dor. 1899.)
G. Henshaw. (Low 1914.)
Giant Laddie. (Pem. 1930.)
Gibbonsii. (1880.)
Gibson Beauty. (Pet. 1905.)
Glacier. (Cot. 1896.)
Gladys Ray. (Bar. 1896.)
Glare. (Law. 1914.)
Glendale. (Ves. 1906.)
Gloria. (FieH. 1913.)
Gloriosa. (Dor. 1910.)
Glorious. (1890.)
Glory. (BPI. 1938.)
Glory of Venice.
Glowworm. (Schw.)
Goldenbeauty. (Cot. 1901.)
Goldeneagle. (Cot. 1904.)
Goldenflag. (You. 1916.)
Goldengate. (Starr 1889.)
Goldengem. (Love 1896.)
Goldenglory. (Hea. 1909.)
Goldenglow. (Bla. 1925.)
Goldenidol. (Allw. 1917.)
Goldenray. (Dor. 1912.)

DIANTHUS, continued
Goldentriumph. (Pond 1892.)
Goldenwest. (Wils. 1934.)
Goldenwonder. (L&W. 1930.)
Goldfinch. (Dor. 1895.)
Goldnugget. (Dor. 1898.)
Goldsmith. (1892.)
Gorgeous. (FisP. 1912.)
Gov. Deneen. (BroaA. 1909.)
Gov. Griggs. (Tow. 1899.)
Gov. Lowndes. (WebH. 1903.)
Gov. Markham. (Re. 1895.)
Gov. Roosevelt. (Cot. 1901.)
Gov. Russell. (Cum. 1893.)
Gov. Wolcott. (FisP. 1902.)
Grace. (Rop. 1914.)
Grace Battles. (Lons. 1893.)
Grace Bollinger. (1896.)
Grace Darling. (Cham. 1892.)
Grace Fardon. (Simm. 1889.)
Grace Page. (PaW. 1917.)
Grace Wilder. (Tai. 1881.)
Granite State. (Bux. 1910.)
Granthorpe Beauty. (Dix. 1911.)
Graves Seedling.
Greatheart. (Shaw 1933.)
Grenadier. (Der. 1915.)
Grenadier. (Europe.)
Grizel. (P&F. 1917.)
Guardian Angel. (GAOA.)
Guide. (DaiZ. 1866.)
Guiding Star. (Simm.)
Guinivere. (Bem. 1937.)
Gunner. (Der. 1916.)
Guy Allwood. (Beu. 1934.)
Gypsy. (Schra. 1924.)
Gypsyking. (Sim 1938.)
Hanworth. (Henn. 1918.)
Happiness. (Dem. 1926.)
Happy Day. (Wake 1898.)
Happy Day. (Dor. 1922.)
Harlequin. (Eng. 1909.)
Harlowarden. (Chi. 1903.)
Harriett. (Starr 1880.)
Harriett Thorpe. (Tho. 1884.)
Harrisons White. (Harr. 1897.)
Harry Fenn. (Cot. 1902.)
Harry Palmer. (Pal.)
Harvard. (Cock. 1907.)
Harvard Crimson. (Blake 1905.)
Harvester. (B&St. 1921.)
Hattie Starritt. (Pat. 1909.)
Hector. (Wri. 1891.)
Helen Galvin. (Wri. 1893.)
Helen Goddard. (Go. 1906.)
Helen Keller. (Lons. 1894.)
Helen (*M.*) Gould. (PieF. 1908.)
Heliotrope Monsine. (Woot. 1914.)
Henrietta.
Henrietta Sargent. (Tai.)
Herbert Thwaites. (Will. 1930.)
Her Majesty. (Chi. 1903.)
Hermosa. (Go. 1937.)
Hero. (ThomJ. 1914.)
Hesper. (Wri. 1893.)
Hiawatha. (Pen. 1897.)
Hilda. (Weis. 1895.)
Hilda Brenkert. (EGC. 1927.)
Hinsdale. (1876.)
Hinzes Red. (Brei. 1879.)
Hinzes White. (Brei. 1879.)
His Majesty. (Wall. 1914.)
H. N. Higinbotham. (Chi. 1902.)
Holmes. (Simm.)
Hon. J. Boscawen. (You. 1911.) J. Boscawen.
Hon. Lady A. Need. (You. 1909.) Lady Need.

DIANTHUS, continued
Hon. Mrs. F. Agar. (Agar 1909.) Mrs. Agar.
Hon. T. B. Reed. (1896.) T. B. Reed.
Hon. Wm. McKinley. (1896.) William McKinley.
Hoosier. (Dor. 1893.)
Hoosier Lad. (Dor. 1909.)
Hoosier Maid. (Rass. 1901.)
Hope Henshaw. (PieA. 1921.)
Hugh Graham. (Grah. 1885.)
Iago. (McG. 1893.)
Ian. (P&F. 1918.)
Ida. (Woot. 1896.)
Ida Feder. (Re. 1895.)
Ida May. (Con.)
Ida McKinley.
Ideal. (Len. 1893.)
Ilona. (Buc. 1932.)
Immaculate. (1914.)
Imogen. (1884.)
Imperial. (Hai. 1904.)
Improved Pink Abundance. (Ke. 1938.)
Indiana. (Dor. 1892.)
Indiana Market. (B&Sm. 1903.)
Indianapolis. (B&Sm. 1904.)
Ingleside. (Ing. 1895.)
Innocence. (Dor. 1891.)
Innocence. (HillE. 1903.)
Irene. (C&H. 1901.)
Isabelle, Ctsse. of Aberdeen. (Kel. 1914.)
Ivanhoe. (Sim 1938.)
Ivory. (1896.)
Ivory. (JohC. 1926.)
Ivy Seely. (See. 1915.)
Jack Frost. (Shel. 1898.)
Jacquard. (DaiZ. 1866.)
Jahns Scarlet. (JahH. 1897.)
James Corbett. (Re. 1895.)
James Dean. (1896.)
James Madison. (1878.)
James Perkins. (Simm. 1886.)
James White. (JahH. 1892.)
James (*W.*) Riley. (Berte. 1910.)
Jane Sutherland. (JohC. 1931.)
Janette. (H&W. 1919.)
Jaquiminot. (Whee.)
J. B. Jaquier. (France 1890.)
J. B. Kidd. (Simm. 1886.)
J. Boscawen. (You. 1911.)
J. C. Ainsworth. (Fed. 1895.)
J. C. Sibley. (Hei. 1900.)
Jealousie. (DaiZ. 1866.)
Jeanette. (Tho. 1882.)
Jeanne Morell.
Jean Sisley. (France 1882.)
Jennie. (Ke. 1925.)
Jennie Parker. (London 1892.)
Jessica. (WebHS. 1906.)
Jewell. (Sim 1926.)
J. Gould. (Tho. 1884.)
J. J. Harrison. (Simm. 1886.)
Joan. (New. 1914.)
Joan Marie. (Flo. 1931.)
John Briry. (Sim 1938.)
John (*E.*) Haines. (Hai. 1906.)
John Habermehl. (Ku. 1901.)
John McCullough. (Simm. 1886.)
John Page. (PaT. 1918.)
John (*R.*) Renere. (JahB. 1892.)
Johnsons Crimson. (JohC. 1925.)
John Thorpe. (Dor.)
John Young. (Cot. 1896.)
Joseph Eaton, Jr. (JahB. 1892.)
Josephine. (Len. 1895.)
Joseph Jefferson. (Pen. 1897.)

DIANTHUS, continued
Joseph Manley. (Cot. 1902.)
Joy. (Bla. 1914.)
J. R. Freeman. (Starr 1890.)
Juanita. (Fil. 1908.)
Jubilee. (Har. 1896.)
Judge Hinsdale. (Cot. 1904.)
Judith. (Bell 1911.)
Jumbo. (Len. 1893.)
Juno. (Hai. 1904.)
J. W. Wolfeskill. (Hae. 1892.)
J. Y. Markland. (Tho. 1883.)
Kaiser Wilhelm. (1887.)
Karto.
Kate.
Kate Smith. (Wils. 1934.)
Katharyn. (Park 1934.)
Katharyn Elizabeth. (Park 1934.)
Katherin Storrs. (McG. 1893.)
Kathleen Pantlind. (H&L. 1898.)
Kathryn. (Fri. 1897.)
Kenneth. (P&F. 1914.)
Keystone. (Hei. 1900.)
King Albert. (Dut. 1916.)
King Cardinal. (B&St. 1934.)
King Dianthus. (Crei. 1892.)
King of Belgians. (CoE. 1916.)
King of the Crimsons. (Whi. 1876.)
Kitty Clover. (Shel. 1895.)
Kohinoor. (Pen. 1895.)
Labelle. (England 1870.)
Laddy. (Dor. 1918.)
Lady Algy. (Wells. 1912.)
Lady Alington. (Low 1911.)
Lady Bountiful. (Dor. 1904.)
Lady Chattin. (Starr.)
Lady Dainty. (Low 1911.)
Lady Emma. (Starr 1875.)
Lady Fair. (Starr 1890.)
Lady Fuller. (Wall 1911.)
Lady Greenally. (You. 1914.)
Lady Henderson. (You. 1909.)
Lady Martha. (Bri. 1893.)
Lady Maud. (Ed. 1887.)
Lady Meyer. (Gui. 1912.)
Lady Need. (You. 1909.)
Lady Nora. (Good. 1911.)
Lady Northcliffe. (Eng. 1911.)
Lady Nunburnholme. (You. 1914.)
Lady Rachael. (Lar. 1891.)
Laexcellent. (Starr.)
Lafavorite. (France 1884.)
Lafayette. (Dor. 1892.)
Lake City. (Tay. 1895.)
Lamode. (Eng. 1911.)
Lapurite. (DaiZ. 1866.)
Larayonante. (Allw. 1911.)
Lasandria. (Starr 1891.)
Laura. (England.)
Laura Degenhardt. (Rath 1897.)
Laura (*E.*) Doty. (Fri. 1897.)
Laura Hempstead. (Hem. 1892.)
Lavinia. (Starr.)
Lawrence Thompson. (Thom. 1895.)
Lawson Enchantress. (Kno. 1907.)
L'Eclair. (DaiZ. 1866.)
Legion. (Sim 1933.)
Lela Underwood. (Mor. 1899.)
Lena. (Pyle 1901.)
Lena Saling. (May 1894.)
Leon Gambetta. (Hae. 1892.)
Leonie. (DaiZ. 1866.)
Leslie Paul. (Sie. 1899.)
L'Hermine. (DaiZ. 1866.)
Liberty. (Shel. 1899.)
Lieut. Peary. (Cot.)
Light Pink Abundance. (B&St. 1931.)

DIANTHUS, continued
Lillian. (Starr 1878.)
Lillian Pond. (Pond 1903.)
Lily Dean. (May 1897.)
Lincoln. (DaiZ. 1866.)
Lindy Lou. (Sim 1933.)
Little Beauty. (Starr 1880.)
Littlegem. (Chit. 1895.)
Lizzie Gilbert. (WFE. 1895.)
Lizzie McGowan. (McG. 1890.)
Lizzie McKee. (Win. 1905.)
L. L. Lamborn. (SwayW. 1888.)
Lloyd. (JahH. 1908.)
Lochinvar. (Sim 1937.)
Logan. (Grah. 1886.)
Lois Fearnley. (Fear. 1914.)
Lonesa. (Star. 1895.)
Longfellow. (Simm.)
Lord Chancellor. (Woot. 1914.)
Lord Clyde. (Starr 1878.)
Lorna. (Dor. 1901.)
LosAngeles. (Re. 1895.)
Louise Nauman. (Nau. 1903.)
Louise Porsch. (McG. 1891.)
Louis (*J.*) Haettel. (Hae. 1892.)
Louis Lenoir. (Zell. 1868.)
Louvain. (Dut. 1916.)
Lowell. (Simm.)
Lucia. (Tim. 1890.)
Lucifer. (Woot. 1914.)
Lucile. (Hi. 1907.)
Lucy. (Eng. 1912.)
Lucy Brunner. (Rah. 1897.)
Lucy Singler. (1878.)
Lulu. (1885.)
Luminosa. (Sim 1932.)
Luna. (Amer. 1899.)
Luxury. (Sim 1937.)
Lyndhurst Pink. (Sea. 1930.)
Lydia. (Starr 1878.)
Mabel. (Starr 1886.)
Mabel Craw. (Ing. 1895.)
Mackinac. (Cot. 1904.)
Magnet. (Chit. 1895.)
Maharajah. (Law. 1914.)
Maiden Blush. (Wood.)
Maid of Honor. (Bin. 1901.)
Maine Sunshine. (Stro. 1919.)
Majestic. (Allw. 1914.)
Majesty. (Len. 1892.)
Malcolm. (P&F. 1917.)
Mandarin. (Bur. 1910.)
Mangus. (Lake 1901.)
Mapledale. (SmN. 1897.)
Margaret Rath. (Rath 1897.)
Margery.
Marian. (Shel. 1895.)
Marian. (Pass. 1902.)
Marie. (Shup. 1893.)
Marie Starr. (Star. 1895.)
Marion Beauty. (Tei. 1903.)
Marion Wilson. (Allw. 1918.)
Marjorie. (Kir. 1929.)
Marjorie Ward. (Mal. 1934.)
Mark Hannah. (Chr. 1897.)
Marmion. (Bur. 1910.)
Marquise Lorne. (England 1884.)
Mars. (1884.)
Marshall Field. (Chi. 1903.)
Marshall P. Wilder. (Tho. 1884.)
Martha Ellen. (Gran. 1933.)
Martin Wolfskill. (Fed. 1895.)
Marvel. (1892.)
Mary (*A.*) Baker. (Ea. 1899.)
Mary Albert. (DavB. 1904.)
Mary Allwood. (Allw. 1912.)
Mary Anderson. (Simm. 1886.)
Mary Darce.

DIANTHUS, continued
Mary (*E.*) Sim. (Sim 1933.)
Mary Sheppard. (Re. 1895.)
Mary Vilven. (B&L. 1909.)
Mary Wood. (Dor. 1898.)
Mascot. (Mat. 1911.)
Masie. (P&F. 1918.)
Matador. (Law. 1912.)
Matchless. (Cot. 1912.)
Maud Adams. (Niq. 1899.)
Maud Dean. (May 1897.)
Maude. (Starr 1883.)
Maude Granger. (1887.)
May. (B&Sm. 1908.)
Mayflower. (1897.)
Mayor Pingree. (Brei. 1896.)
May Queen. (Tho. 1884.)
May Whitney. Eleanor Ames.
Mchss. of Lithlingow. (Low 1911.)
Meg. (P&F. 1918.)
Melba. (May 1899.)
Melody. (Thor. 1905.)
Melrose. (DavB. 1930.)
Mephisto. (Amer. 1899.)
Mermaid. (Dor. 1901.)
Merry Christmas. (B&St. 1916.)
Merstham Gem. (Wells 1914.)
Meteor. (Dor. 1895.)
Miami Queen. (Mia. 1909.)
Michael Cooper. (Coop. 1930.)
Michigan. (Wa. 1900.)
Mikado. (Pat. 1906.)
Mikado. (Bur. 1910.)
Mildred. (Bol. 1914.)
Millie Gilman. (Harms 1902.)
Miniature. (DaiZ. 1866.)
Minerva Pink. (M&T. 1892.)
Minnie Cook. (Chit. 1895.)
Minuet. (Sim 1938.)
Mirabeau. (DaiZ. 1866.)
Miranda. (Tho.)
Miss (*Blanche*) Payne. (Carr 1897.)
Miss Donelly. (Re. 1895.)
Miss (*Fl.*) Specht. (Spe. 1902.)
Miss Hardcastle. (You. 1912.)
Miss Joliffe. (France 1864.)
Miss (*Louise*) Faber. (F&F. 1901.)
Miss (*Meta*) Behn. (Spe. 1903.)
Miss Moore. (France.)
Miss Theo. (L&W. 1915.)
Mlle. Carle. (France.)
Mlle. Vernay. (DaiZ. 1866.)
Mme. Chapman. (C&H. 1900.)
Mme. (*Chas.*) Page. (Vei. 1915.)
Mme. Chassons. (France.)
Mme. Cobette. (France.)
Mme. (*Diaz*) Albertini. (Dor. 1892.)
Monarch. (Bur. 1913.)
Mons. Gambetta. (Zell.)
Mons. Reveil. (DaiZ. 1866.)
Mon Triomphe. (DaiZ. 1866.)
Montrose. (You. 1917.)
Mont Vesuve. (DaiZ. 1866.)
Moonlight. (Har. 1904.)
Moores Crimson. (Moo. 1899.)
Morello. (H&L. 1896.)
Morningglow. (Wink. 1925.)
Morningray. (Lar. 1890.)
Morningstar. (FisP. 1897.)
Mothers Carnation. (Berta. 1922.)
Motor. (Starr 1890.)
Mrs. (*Ada*) Lenton. (Len. 1893.)
Mrs. (*A. F.*) Dutton. (Dut. 1912.)
Mrs. Agar. (Agar. 1909.)
Mrs. (*A.*) Rolker. (Tho. 1884.)
Mrs. Ayres. (Carro. 1895.)
Mrs. (*B.*) Harrison. (Lar.)
Mrs. (*Bird S.*) Coler. (Mo. 1901.)

DIANTHUS, continued
Mrs. (*Brodie*) Henderson. (You. 1911.)
Mrs. Cassell. (1886.)
Mrs. (*C. B.*) Johnson. (Cond. 1937.)
Mrs. (*C. F.*) Raphael. (Bur. 1911.)
Mrs. (*Charles*) Frick. (Fri. 1897.)
Mrs. (*Chas.*) Duhme. (Dor. 1896.)
Mrs. (*Chas.*) Knopf. (Kno. 1908.)
Mrs. Chas. M. Frick. (Simm.)
Mrs. Childs. (Re. 1895.)
Mrs. Cleveland. (Lons. 1887.)
Mrs. Clode. (Bur. 1910.)
Mrs. (*Constable*) Curtis. (You. 1917.)
Mrs. (*C. W.*) Ward. (Cot. 1909.)
Mrs. Drury. (DaiZ. 1866.)
Mrs. (*Duncan*) McPherson. (Cul. 1916.)
Mrs. (*E. A.*) Nelson. (Nel. 1902.)
Mrs. (*Edw.*) Douty. (Low 1918.)
Mrs. (*E.*) Flagg. (Spi. 1903.)
Mrs. (*E.*) Hippard. (Tho.)
Mrs. (*E.*) Reynolds. (Dor. 1892.)
Mrs. (*E.*) Thalman. (WebC. 1914.)
Mrs. (*E. V.*) Lawson. (Len. 1893.)
Mrs. (*F. C.*) Harwood. (Harw. 1911.)
Mrs. Fisher. (FisS.)
Mrs. (*F. M.*) Crook. (Low 1911.)
Mrs. (*F. R.*) Joost. (Bes. 1898.)
Mrs. Garfield. (1886.)
Mrs. (*Geo. M.*) Bradt. (Dor. 1897.)
Mrs. (*G.*) Williams. (You. 1909.)
Mrs. Harris. (1883.)
Mrs. Harrison. (Dor. 1891.)
Mrs. (*H.*) Burnett. (Bur. 1907.)
Mrs. (*H. C. G.*) Schwarz. (Schw.)
Mrs. (*H. Hallock*) Foote. (Gi. 1897.)
Mrs. (*H. M.*) Stanley. (Shel. 1893.)
Mrs. Inman. (1896.)
Mrs. (*Jas.*) Dean. (Cot. 1898.)
Mrs. (*J. B.*) Perkins. (Simm. 1885.)
Mrs. (*J. C.*) Vaughan. (Rudd 1908.)
Mrs. (*J. E.*) Lowe. (Lowe 1915.)
Mrs. (*J. L.*) Cross. (Dan. 1916.)
Mrs. (*J. P.*) Marsten. (JohC. 1925.)
Mrs. Keene. (Vei.)
Mrs. (*Lemuel*) Fawcett. (Faw. 1890.)
Mrs. (*L.*) Gay. (Len.)
Mrs. (*Lloyd*) Wise. (Wells 1914.)
Mrs. Lonsdale. (Hae. 1892.)
Mrs. (*Louise C.*) Maloy. (Mal. 1934.)
Mrs. (*Lucie*) McKinnon. (Cut. 1916.)
Mrs. (*Mackaye*) Edgar. (Low 1915.)
Mrs. Mailander. (Mai. 1896.)
Mrs. (*M. A.*) Patten. (FisP. 1904.)
Mrs. (*Margaret*) Beuerlein. (Beu. 1933.)
Mrs. (*Marg.*) Behn. (Spe. 1903.)
Mrs. (*Mary*) Fleming. (Fle. 1909.)
Mrs. McBurney. (HillE. 1896.)
Mrs. McKenzie. (Hen. 1875.)
Mrs. (*Nellie C.*) Stimson. (Holl. 1915.)
Mrs. (*Pauline*) Gussman. (Rah. 1897.)
Mrs. Pfeuffer. (Pfe. 1909.)
Mrs. (*Ph.*) Heilig. (Hei. 1901.)
Mrs. (*Potter*) Palmer. (Chi. 1902.)
Mrs. (*Robt.*) Hartshorn. (Tie. 1907.)
Mrs. (*Robt.*) Hitt. (Dor. 1892.)
Mrs. (*S. A.*) Northway. (Simm. 1898.)
Mrs. Skinner. (Simm.)
Mrs. Sprout. (Re. 1895.)
Mrs. Tatton. (Bur. 1910.)
Mrs. (*T. A.*) Western. (Wells 1916.)
Mrs. (*T. B.*) Reed. (1896.)
Mrs. Theodore Roosevelt. (Cot. 1903.)
Mrs. (*Thos. W.*) Lawson. (FisP. 1900.)

DIANTHUS, continued
Mrs. Thwaites. (Will. 1930.)
Mrs. Titus. (Len. 1895.)
Mrs. (*T. M.*) Cook. (Low 1911.)
Mrs. (*V. T.*) Omwake. (Ei. 1908.)
Mrs. (*W.*) Cursham. (Wool. 1915.)
Mrs. (*W. J.*) Hunter. (Bur. 1910.)
Mrs. (*W. L.*) Lewis. (Lew. 1905.)
Mrs. (*W. L.*) Sinclair. (Herm. 1916.)
Mrs. (*Wm.*) McKinley. (1896.)
Mrs. Zeller. (DaiZ. 1866.)
Murphys White. (Murp. 1903.)
My Favorite. (Low 1911.)
My Lady. (Vict. 1931.)
My Love. (Sim 1932.)
My Maryland. (WebH.)
My Rose. (Eng. 1912.)
Myrtle. (Lar. 1892.)
My Welcome. (Hes. 1922.)
Nancy Barnfield. (Hemus 1930.)
Nancy Hanks. (Lew. 1891.)
Nebraska. (Frey 1916.)
Nellie Bly. (Shel. 1891.)
Nellie Lewis.
Nellie Nolan. (How. 1893.)
Nellie St. Clair. (Len. 1893.)
Nelson Fisher. (FisP. 1904.)
Netherwood. (Crei. 1892.)
New Daybreak. (WebH.)
NewJersey. (McG. 1893.)
NewYork. (Cot. 1898.)
Niagara. (HillE. 1910.)
Nicholson. (FisS. 1893.)
Nigella. (See. 1912.)
Nikko. (Bur. 1915.)
Nivea. (Cook 1896.)
Nora West. (West 1915.)
Norma. (Sim 1925.)
Northern Light. (DeW. 1897.)
Northport. (Cock. 1913.)
Norway. (WebH. 1901.)
Novelty. (Ward 1904.)
Nydia. (Chi. 1901.)
Oceanspray. (Sim 1932.)
Octoroon. (Cot. 1902.)
Oddity. (Brin. 1893.)
Ohio. (Simm. 1891.)
O. K. (Mat. 1911.)
Oldglory. (Blake 1906.)
Oldgold. (1889.)
Old Gold. (Dor. 1917.)
Oldrose. (McG. 1893.)
Olivette. (Jab. 1922.)
Olive Whitman. (Sak. 1915.)
Olympia. (May 1900.)
Oneida. (BakC. 1897.)
Oona. (1892.)
Opal. (Knipe 1930.)
O. P. Bassett. (B&W. 1909.)
Orange Blossoms. (Jen. 1892.)
Orange Wonder. (L&W. 1937.)
Orchid Beauty. (L&W. 1934.)
Orient. (FisS. 1886.)
Oriole. (Goe. 1902.)
Orpheus. (Bur. 1910.)
Otello. (Ei. 1924.)
Othello. (Thor. 1884.)
Outcast. (Wit. 1898.)
Pacific. (Len. 1895.)
Pacific. (Die. 1913.)
Painted Lady. (HillE. 1898.)
Paloma. (Re. 1895.)
Panchita. (Re. 1895.)
Panda. (Woot. 1914.)
Paradise. (Len. 1892.)
Paramount. (Schw. 1921.)
Patrician. (B&St. 1930.)
Patrick O'Mara. (1896.)

DIANTHUS, continued
Pattens Pink Eldora. (Pat. 1927.)
Pattens White Eldora. (Pat. 1927.)
Patti. (Shel. 1891.)
Paxton. (Starr 1886.)
Peachblow Coronet. (Crei. 1892.)
Pearl. (Cha. 1892.)
Pearlwhite. (Blau. 1895.)
Peerless. (Hen. 1875.)
Peerlesspink. (Chi. 1914.)
Pelargonium. (Beu. 1934.)
Penelope. (Dor. 1903.)
Pennsylvania. (DeW. 1910.)
Peter Fisher. (JohC. 1936.)
Peter Henderson. (Char. 1880.)
Petunia. (Thor. 1914.)
Pharaoh. (Sim 1938.)
Philadelphia Kirs. (1878.)
Philadelphia Variegated. (Starr.)
Philip Heilig, Jr. (Hei. 1900.)
Phyllis. (Rudd 1903.)
Pikespeak. (Gi. 1897.)
Pilgrim. (1896.)
Pinkabundance. (B&St. 1928.)
Pinkbeauty. (JahB. 1892.)
Pinkdelight. (Dor. 1909.)
Pinkimperial. (Hai. 1906.)
Pinkivory. (Ches. 1936.)
Pinkpatten. (Pat. 1906.)
Pinkpearl. (Mat. 1911.)
Pinksensation. (Dor. 1915.)
Pinktreasure. (B&St. 1938.)
Pioneer. (Eng. 1914.)
Pirate Gold. (Heng. 1934.)
Piru. (Len. 1892.)
Pluto. (Bur. 1911.)
Pocahontas. (B&St. 1910.)
Poe. (Simm.)
Pomona. (Starr 1891.)
Portia. (Tho. 1884.)
Portlands Pride. (Fra. 1917.)
Portola. (Die. 1913.)
Potentate. (B&St.)
Potomac. (Amer. 1899.)
Preciosa. (Re. 1895.)
Premier. (Rath 1914.)
Pres. DeGraw. (DaiZ. 1866.)
Pres. Garfield. (Simm. 1882.)
Pres. McKinley. (Grave 1903.)
Pres. Roosevelt. (Cot. 1902.)
Pres. Seeley. (FieH. 1908.)
Pres. Valentine. (Wit. 1912.)
Pride of Boston.
Pride of Essex. (VR. 1893.)
Pride of Kennett. (SwayW. 1888.)
Pride of Penhurst. (Europe 1884.)
Pride of Wakefield. (Wor. 1911.)
Primrose. (Eng. 1914.)
Prince Edward. (Kni. 1914.)
Prince of Wales. (Low 1915.)
Princess. (Bar. 1897.)
Princess. (Wall. 1911.)
Princess Bonnie. (Shel. 1895.)
Princess Charming. (Ei. 1910.)
Princess Dagmar. (Pat. 1912.)
Princess Henry. (New. 1914.)
Princess Juliana. (Low 1911.)
Princess Louis. (Tai. 1881.)
Progress. (Shel. 1898.)
Prolifica. (Chi. 1901.)
Prosperity. (Mi. 1901.)
Purdue. (Dor. 1893.)
Puritan. (Wood 1892.)
Puritan. (Sor. 1936.)
Purity. (F&F. 1901.)
Purity. (Beu. 1934.)
Purplebeauty.
Purplecrown.

DIANTHUS, continued
Purpleking. (Pen. 1895.)
Purpurea. (Starr 1889.)
Quakercity. (Ban. 1886.)
Queen. (You. 1909.)
Queen Alexandra. (Cla. 1912.)
Queen Louise. (Dil. 1900.)
Queen Mary. (SmA. 1911.)
Queen of Whites. (England.)
Radiance. (B&St. 1913.)
Radiant. (B&St. 1924.)
Radium. (Woot. 1914.)
Rainbow. (Wan. 1911.)
Ramona. (Len. 1892.)
Ramona. (Park 1938.)
Ranston Gem. (BakR. 1909.)
Rapture. (Stei. 1931.)
Rapture. (Beu. 1934.)
R. Diener. (Die. 1917.)
Rebecca. (DaiZ. 1866.)
Redbenora. (Wells 1914.)
Redchief. (Dor. 1907.)
Redcross. (Dor. 1891.)
Redensign. (Low 1912.)
Redhead. (Ei. 1921.)
Redjacket. (BakC. 1897.)
Red Lawson. (Pal. 1905.)
Red Matchless. (Ei. 1921.)
Redmont. (Lowe 1912.)
Red My Love. (Sim 1934.)
Red Ridinghood. (Chi. 1907.)
Red Rosalie. (B&St. 1921.)
Red Sensation. (Wells 1916.)
Redstar. (JohC. 1926.)
Redwave. (H&L. 1896.)
Redwing. (Daw. 1915.)
Regina. (Eng. 1912.)
Reliance. (Chi. 1904.)
Rembrandt. (VdS. 1914.)
Resolute. (Schw.)
Rex. (Eng. 1909.)
R. F. Felton. (Bur. 1910.)
Richmond. (Dor. 1892.)
Rival. (Low 1912.)
Robert Allwood. (Beu. 1934.)
Robert Craig. (Cot. 1906.)
Robin Hood. (HillE. 1895.)
Rob Roy. (Crei. 1892.)
Roideviolets. (France.)
Romance. (Len. 1892.)
Romance. (Dau. 1930.)
Rosa. (Eng. 1912.)
Rosalia. (Dor. 1917.)
Rosalie. (B&St. 1938.)
Rosalind. (Tho. 1884.)
Rosalind. (Allw. 1918.)
Rosalind. (Stro. 1920.)
Rosaline. (DaiZ. 1866.)
Rosa Pizer. (Milno 1896.)
Rose. (Sim 1925.)
Rosecharm. (B&St. 1934.)
Rose d'Or. (Lan. 1909.)
Rose Dubarrie. (Webs. 1912.)
Rosehill. (Dai. 1880.)
Rosemary. (Starr 1889.)
Rosequeen. (Simm. 1895.)
Rosette. (Dor. 1912.)
Rosita. (Park 1938.)
Rosymorn. (Hen. 1883.)
Royal. (Sim 1925.)
Royal Purple. (S&St. 1937.)
R. P. Enchantress. (Schro. 1906.)
R. R. Parker. (Starr 1887.)
Ruby. (1896.)
Ruby. (Kno. 1909.)
Ruth. (Pen. 1893.)
Ruth Baur. (B&St. 1920.)
Ruth Churchill. (VR. 1893.)

DIANTHUS, continued
Ruth Hengstenberg. (Heng. 1938.)
Ruth Marie. (Str. 1930.)
Saffron. (Eng. 1916.)
Sagamore. (Sim. 1936.)
Saginaw. (Hake 1897.)
Saint Nicholas. (B&St. 1912.)
Salmon Beauty. (T&S. 1912.)
Salmon Brittania. (PaW. 1911.)
Salmon Enchantress. (Dow. 1912.)
Salmonking. (Lowe 1914.)
Salmonqueen. (Dor. 1893.)
Salmon Spectrum. (B&St.)
Salome. (Eng. 1912.)
Sambo. (Eis. 1893.)
Samson. (1896.)
Sanchot. (DaiZ. 1866.)
Sandusky. (Hall 1896.)
San Gabriel. (Ing. 1895.)
San Mateo. (Dor. 1891.)
Sanspareil. (DaiZ. 1866.)
Santa Claus. (El. 1926.)
Sarah A. Hill. (BKB. 1908.)
Sarah Nicholson. (Pat. 1909.)
Satellite. (B&St. 1932.)
Satin Robe. (Low 1912.)
Saxon. (FisS. 1900.)
Scallen. (1896.)
Scarlet Carola. (Eng. 1914.)
Scarlet Gem. (Grah. 1886.)
Scarlet Glow. (Dor. 1909.)
Scarlet King. (Starr 1884.)
Scarlet Monarch. (L&W. 1930.)
Scarlet Wonder. (Roh. 1913.)
Sceptre. (Pem. 1925.)
Scribners. (1896.)
Seacaucus. (Hen. 1882.)
Seafoam. (H&T. 1881.)
Seagull. (Dor. 1892.)
Sears. (1896.)
Seawan. (Hen. 1886.)
Secretary Blaine. (Simm. 1886.)
Secretary Hunt. (Simm. 1886.)
Secretary James. (Simm. 1886.)
Secretary Kirkwood. (Simm. 1886.)
Secretary Lincoln. (Simm. 1886.)
Secretary McVeagh. (Simm. 1886.)
Secretary Windom. (Simm. 1886.)
Selec. (FisS. 1897.)
Senator. (Pat. 1926.)
Senator McPherson. (McG. 1892.)
Senior. (Bra. 1933.)
Senorita. (Park 1933.)
Sensation. (Tho. 1866.)
Sentinel. (Dor. 1893.)
Servia. (FisS. 1898.)
Shasta. (B&Sm. 1909.)
Shell Flower. (Hen. 1890.)
Shepherdess. (You. 1916.)
Silverball. (1896.)
Silverglobe. (DaiZ. 1866.)
Silverlake. (FisS. 1884.)
Silvermoon. (Mars. 1932.)
Silverspray. (Simm. 1889.)
Sirin. (Schw. 1914.)
Sirins. (Hae. 1892.)
Sir (*I.*) Pitmann. (Kel. 1914.)
Small. (1896.)
Snowball. (Bur. 1912.)
Snowbird. (Jen. 1891.)
Snowbound. (1886.)
Snowcrest.
Snowden. (Hen. 1880.)
Snowdrift. (Carro. 1897.)
Snowflake. (1884.)
Snowqueen. (Pen. 1893.)
Snowqueen. (Bur. 1912.)
Snowstorm. (Law. 1912.)

DIANTHUS, continued
Snowwhite. (He. 1878.)
Snowwhite. (Kir. 1934.)
Sonny. (Kir. 1932.)
Sonriza. (Re. 1895.)
Sophelia. (Scha. 1924.)
Souvenir. (You. 1916.)
Spanish Dances. (Mars. 1931.)
Spartan. (Dor. 1892.)
Speckles. (Eng. 1918.)
Spectrum. (Dor. 1924.)
Splendor. (Stev. 1907.)
Spotlight. (Vict. 1931.)
S. P. Rees. (Fed. 1895.)
Springfield. (Mu. 1876.)
Spring Glory. (Schw.)
Star. (DaiZ. 1886.)
Starlight. (Han. 1888.)
Star of the West.
Stella. (Dor. 1902.)
Stormking. (Dor. 1895.)
Stormqueen. (Dor. 1897.)
Stourton. (Herm. 1918.)
Striped Unique. (Hae. 1892.)
Stuart. (Dor. 1895.)
Stumpp. (1896.)
Subaltern. (Mas. 1917.)
Success. (Sho. 1903.)
Sultan. (Bur. 1911.)
Sultana. (Wan. 1910.)
Sunbeam. (Chi. 1901.)
Sunflower. (Len. 1892.)
Sunrise. (Kir. 1885.)
Sunset. (DaiZ. 1866.)
Sunset. (1887.)
Sunsetglow. (Sim 1932.)
Sunshine. (Chr. 1895.)
Sunstar. (Eng. 1911.)
Superb. (ThomJ. 1914.)
Superba. (BroA. 1910.)
Superior. (McCo. 1900.)
Super Supreme. (B&St. 1921.)
Sweetbrier. (SwayE. 1893.)
Sybil. (Dor. 1903.)
Syracuse. (Mar. 1900.)
Tamerlane. (Sim 1938.)
T. B. Reed. (1896.)
Tecumseh. (Simm. 1887.)
The B. Eldridge. (Eld. 1902.)
The Belle. (Dor. 1904.)
The Bride. (Tai. 1889.)
The Bride. (May 1904.)
The Challenger. (Hoff. 1901.)
The Commodore. (HillE. 1912.)
The Copley. (Grea. 1900.)
The Crawford. (Grea. 1900.)
The Geisha. (Fai. 1912.)
The Grout. (Gro. 1895.)
The Herald. (Chi. 1912.)
The Maine. (FisP. 1899.)
The Marquis. (Mar. 1900.)
The President. (Cot. 1904.)
The Primate. (PaT. 1912.)
The Princess. (Wi.)
The Queen. (Col. 1903.)
The Royal. (CoE. 1914.)
The Scarlet Dragon. (P&F. 1918.)
The Socialist. (Wor. 1912.)
The Supremewhite. (Mam. 1915.)
The Vicar. (Woot. 1914.)
The Whitehouse. (Dai. 1909.)
Thorley. (1896.)
Thos. Cartledge. (SwayE. 1829.)
T. H. Spaulding. (1896.)
Tidalwave. (Simm. 1887.)
Tidbit. (Woot. 1914.)
Tiger. (Ei. 1903.)
Tokio. (You. 1914.)

DIANTHUS, continued
TOPSY. (Starr 1880.)
Topsy. (HillJ. 1919.)
TOREADOR. (WebH. 1907.)
Toreador. (Allw. 1919.)
TRIUMPH. (Stei. 1934.)
TROJAN. (Rey. 1925.)
TRUTH. (Ei. 1927.)
TWENTIETH CENTURY. (Hoff. 1901.)
UNA WALLACE. (Wal. 1911.)
UNCLE JOHN. (Dor. 1895.)
UNCLE PETER. (No. 1905.)
UNCLE SAM. (Tem. 1886.)
UNIQUE. (DaiZ. 1866.)
Unique. (Dil.)
VAILLANT. (DaiZ. 1866.)
VALENCIA. (Ei. 1927.)
VALENTINE. (Stei. 1922.)
VALERIE. (Wink. 1926.)
VANHOUTTE. (Pi. 1896.)
VANLEURENS. (Blau. 1895.)
VARIEGATED CAROLA. (Eng. 1914.)
VARIEGATED GLORIOSA. (Allw. 1912.)
VARIEGATED LABELLE. (Starr.)
VARIEGATED LAPURITE.
VARIEGATED LAWSON. (Arn. 1905.)
VARIEGATED MY LOVE. (Sim 1934.)
VARIEGATED ROSALIA. (B&St. 1924.)
VASSAR. (Sal. 1911.)
VENUS. (Starr 1878.)
VERA. (ThomJ. 1914.)
VESUVIUS. (Hen. 1877.)
VICEADMIRAL SCHLEY. (F&F. 1899.)
VICEPRESIDENT HOBART. (1897.)
VICTOR. (PaT. 1887.)
Victor. (Grah. 1897.)
VICTORIA. (Cush. 1908.)
VICTORY. (WebH. 1906.)
VILLAGE MAID. (Crei. 1892.)
VILLISCA. (Rah. 1897.)
VIOLA. (Wit. 1929.)
VIOLA ALLEN. (Cot. 1902.)
VIOLET LORD. (You. 1912.)
VIOLET SEELEY. (See. 1912.)
VIOLETTA. (Fair. 1914.)
VIRGINALIS. (Ing.)
VIRGINIA. (Hing. 1934.)
VIRGINIA ROSE. (JohC. 1937.)
VIVIAN. (Wit.)
VIXEN. (Starr 1879.)
VOLUNTEER. (Kirk 1888.)
VULCAN. (1892.)
WABASH. (Dor. 1892.)
WANDERER. (Lar. 1890.)
WANETA. (Cham. 1891.)
WANOKA. (Wan.)
WARRIOR. (Mass 1914.)
WASHINGTON. (Zell. 1865.)
Washington. (Ei. 1912.)
WAVERLY. (Sco.)
W. D. SLOAN. (Pass. 1896.)
WEBERS PINK MATCHLESS. (WebF. 1924.)
WELCOME. (DaiZ. 1866.)
Welcome. (Dai. 1907.)
WELLESLEY. (Rai.)
WESTEND. (Jen. 1885.)
WESTERLEY. (Mun. 1925.)
WESTERN PRIDE. (Dor. 1893.)
W. H. BROWN.
WHEELERS PINK MATCHLESS. (Whee. 1924.)
WHIPPER-IN. (England.)
WHITEBEAUTY. (1893.)
WHITEBRADT. (DaiZ. 1903.)
WHITEBRITTANNIA. (Eng. 1914.)
WHITECAP. (Len. 1892.)
WHITECHIEF. (Bur. 1913.)

DIANTHUS, continued
WHITECLOUD. (Dor. 1898.)
WHITECORONET. (Crei. 1892.)
WHITEDAYBREAK. (Gass. 1897.)
WHITEDELIGHT. (Stro. 1920.)
WHITEDOVE. (Dor. 1892.)
WHITEENCHANTRESS. (Mar. 1905.)
WHITEENSIGN. (PaT. 1918.)
WHITEGEM. (Pil. 1888.)
WHITE GRACE WILDER. (VR. 1888.)
WHITE LAPURITE. (1875.)
WHITE LAWSON. (AlC. 1904.)
WHITE MARJORIE. (Kir. 1934.)
WHITE MY LOVE. (Sim 1934.)
WHITEPEARL. (Eve. 1918.)
WHITEPERFECTION. (Dor. 1906.)
WHITEQUEEN. (Nic. 1888.)
WHITE VARIEGATED. (L&W. 1937.)
WHITEWINGS. (Dor. 1891.)
WHITE WINSOR. (Burn. 1914.)
WHITEWONDER. (Dor. 1910.)
WHITTIER. (Simm.)
WIDEAWAKE. (1892.)
WILLIAM ECCLES. (Sco. 1912.)
WILLIAM (*E.*) ROWLAND. (Pyf. 1886.)
WILLIAM (*F.*) DREER. (Starr 1890.)
WILLIAM (*H.*) TAFT. (S&S. 1909.)
WILLIAM (*I.*) BURKE. (Rath 1897.)
WILLIAM MCKINLEY. (1896.)
WILLIAM PIERCE. (JahB. 1892.)
WILLIAM SCOTT. (Dor. 1893.)
WILLIAM SWAYNE. (SwayW. 1888.)
WINGOLD. (Tu. 1903.)
WINIFRED. (Hall 1896.)
WINONA. (Dor. 1908.)
WINSOME. (H&E. 1924.)
WINSOR. (Murr. 1907.)
WINTERCHEER. (LeC. 1922.)
WINTERGLOW. (Low 1918.)
WINTERS BEAUTY. (Rowe 1927.)
WIVELSFIELD BEAUTY. (Allw. 1919.)
WIVELSFIELD CLARET IMPROVED. (Beu. 1934.)
WIVELSFIELD CRIMSON. (Beu. 1934.)
WIVELSFIELD WHITE. (Allw. 1915.)
WIVELSFIELD WONDER. (Allw. 1912.)
WOBURN. (JohC. 1929.)
WODENETHE. (Whit. 1910.)
WORLDS FAIR. (Hens. 1938.)
W. W. COLES. (Tho. 1889.)
YANKEEGIRL. (Dil. 1925.)
YELLOWGOLD. (B&St. 1937.)
YELLOWJACK. (Len. 1893.)
YELLOWJACKET. (Pass. 1895.)
YELLOWPRINCE. (Dor. 1913.)
YELLOWQUEEN. (Europe.)
YELLOWSTONE. (Dor. 1913.)
YORKBEAUTY. (Scha. 1934.)
YUNEDA PINK. (Kir. 1927.)
ZEBRA. (DaiZ. 1866.)
Zebra. (Ward. 1892.)
ZOE SIMONDS. (Sym. 1913.)
ZORA. (Knipe 1930.)

DIAPEN'SIA |w . . . . . DIAPENSIA
himala'ica . . . . . . HIMALAYA D.
lappon'ica |w . . . . ARCTIC D.

DIARRHE'NA (*DIARINA*) BEAKGRAIN
See **GRASS GENERA.**

DIAS'CIA . . . . TWINSPUR
bar'berae . . . . ROSE T.

DICEN'TRA (*BICUCULLA; BIKUKULLA; DIELYTRA*) BLEEDINGHEART
canaden'sis (*Bikukulla c.*) SQUIRRELCORN

DICENTRA, continued
chrysan'tha (*Bikukulla c.*) GOLDEARDROPS BLEEDINGHEART
cuculla'ria (*Bikukulla c.*) DUTCHMANS-BREECHES
exim'ia (*Bikukulla e.*) . FRINGED B.
—al'ba . . . . WHITE F.B.
formo'sa (*Bikukulla f.*) . PACIFIC B.
ochroleu'ca (*Bikukulla o.*) . CREAM B.
orega'na . . . . OREGON B.
pauciflo'ra . . . . . . CALIFORNIA B.
pusil'la (*Bikukulla p.*) . . . LITTLE B.
spectab'ilis (*Dielytra s.*) . COMMON B.
—al'ba . . . . WHITE C.B.
uniflo'ra (*Bikukulla u.*) . STEERSHEAD B.

DICHELOSTEM'MA . . **BRODIAEA**

DICHON'DRA
carolinen'sis . . . . PONYFOOT

DICHORISAN'DRA
aubletia'na
mosa'ica
—gigan'tea
—unda'ta
thyrsiflo'ra

DICHOTOMAN'THES
tristaniaecar'pa

DICHROME'NA |w . WHITETOP-SEDGE
colora'ta . . . . . STARRUSH W.
floriden'sis . . . . EVERGLADES W.
latifo'lia . . . . . . SANDSWAMP W.

DICHROPHYL'LUM . **EUPHORBIA**
See **SUCCULENTS.**

DICHROSTA'CHYS . . . **CAILLIEA**
nu'tans . . . . **C. glomerata**

DICKSO'NIA . . . . . . DICKSONIA
See **FERN GENERA.**

DICLIP'TERA |w
resupina'ta |w

DICORYN'IA
paraen'sis . . . . PARA ANGELWOOD

DICRANOSTIG'MA
franchetia'num

DICRA'NUM |w . . . . . . FORKMOSS
elonga'tum |w
groenlan'dicum |w . . GREENLAND F.
lae'videns |w
neglec'tum |w
scopa'rium |w . . . . BROOM F.

DICTAM'NUS (*FRAXINELLA*) DITTANY
al'bus (*fraxinella; Fraxinella alba*) GASPLANT D.
GIANT (*caucasicus*) HV.
RUBER (*purpureus*)
tatar'icus . . . . TATAR D.

DICTYOSPER'MA (*LINOMA*) PRINCESSPALM
See **PALM GENERA.**

DICYPEL'LIUM
caryophylla'tum . . CLOVEBARKTREE

DIDELO'TIA . . . . DIDELOTIA
africa'na . . . . BUBINGA D.

DI'DIPLIS |w
dian'dra |w . . . . WATERPURSLANE

DIDIS'CUS . . . . **TRACHYMENE**

DIDYMAO'TUS
lapidifor'mis

DIDYMOPA'NAX
morototo'ni . . . . . . Matchwood

DIDYMOSPER'MA . . . Dryadpalm
See **PALM GENERA.**

DIEFFENBACH'IA . . . . Tuftroot
∞ baus'ei (*picta* × *weiri*) . ∞ Bause T.
The plant in cultivation is probably a clon of this polybrid.

bow'manni (*baumanni*) . Bowmann T.
costa'ta
imperia'lis . . . . Imperial T.
pic'ta (*brasiliensis*) . . . Variable T.
—barraquinia'na
—jen'manni
—magnif'ica (*D. magnifica; D. rex*)
—memo'ria
₵Cars (*carsi*) hv.
se'guine (*verschaffelti*) . . . Seguin T.
₵Noble (*nobilis*) hv.
₵Yellowstripe (*leopoldi; liturata*)
∞ splen'dens (*?leopoldi* × *picta*)
∞ Whitespot T.

DIEL'YTRA . . . . . . **DICENTRA**

DIERA'MA . . . . . . Elfinwands
pen'dula . . . . Nodding E.
pulcher'rima (*Sparaxis p.*)
Australian E.

DIERVIL'LA . . . . Bushhoneysuckle
Some authorities list all species of Weigela under Diervilla; others list all but four species under Weigela. This discrepancy is purely taxonomic. The Committee is following Rehder and Bailey by separating the Weigelas (Asiatic) from the true Diervillas (American). For other species not cited here, see **WEIGELA.**

amab'ilis Carr. . . **Weigela coraeensis**
coraeen'sis . . . . **Weigela c.**
—arbo'rea . . . . . **Weigela c. alba**
floribun'da . . . . **Weigela f.**
flo'rida . . . . **Weigela f.**
grandiflo'ra . . . **Weigela coraeensis**
horten'sis . . . . **Weigela h.**
japon'ica . . . . **Weigela j.**
—al'ba . . . **Weigela hortensis nivea**
—horten'sis . . . . **Weigela h.**
—niv'ea . . . . **Weigela hortensis n.**
lonic'era (*canadensis; diervilla; trifida*)
Dwarf B.
maximowicz'i . . . . . . **Weigela m.**
middendorffia'na . . . . **Weigela m.**
multiflo'ra . . . . **Weigela floribunda**
pauciflo'ra . . . . . . **Weigela florida**
prae'cox . . . . **Weigela p.**
rivula'ris . . . . Georgia B.
sessilifo'lia (*Weigela s.*) Southern B.
∞ splen'dens (*lonicera* × *sessilifolia*)
venus'ta . . . . . **Weigela florida v.**
versic'olor . . . **Weigela floribunda v.**

DIE'TES . . . . **MORAEA**
hut'toni . . . . **M. spathacea**

DIGITA'LIS |w . . . . . Foxglove
ambig'ua (*grandiflora*) . . Yellow F.
₵Isabellina. hv.
bux'baumi Hort.
Hort. name for a yellow-flowered Foxglove.

canarien'sis . . . . . . **Isoplexis c.**
du'bia . . . . Balearic F.
ferrugin'ea . . . . Rusty F.
lacinia'ta . . . . Spanish F.
laeviga'ta . . . . Danube F.
lana'ta . . . . Grecian F.

DIGITALIS, continued
lute'a . . . . . . Straw Foxglove
∞ lutz'i . . . . ∞ Lutz F.
nervo'sa . . . . Oriental F.
purpu'rea |w . . . . . . Common F.
₵Bellbloom (*campanulata*) hv.
₵Double (*monstrosa*)
₵Gloxinia (*gloxiniaeflora*)
₵Leopard (*maculata superba*)
₵Rose (*rosea*)
₵Spotted (*maculata*)
₵White (*alba*)
sibir'ica . . . . Siberian F.

DIGITA'RIA (*SYNTHERISMA*)
Crabgrass; Fingergrass
See **GRASS GENERA.**

DIHOL'COS . . . . **ASTRAGALUS**
scobina'tulus . . . . **A. haydenianus**

Dildoe . Acanthocereus, Barbwire: **Acanthocereus pentagonus**

Dill . . . . . . **Anethum graveolens**

DILLE'NIA . . . . Dillenia
in'dica (*speciosa*) . . . . . India D. (*Hondapara*)
philippinen'sis . . . . . Catmon D.

DILLWYN'IA
preis'si

DIL'SEA
ed'ulis . . . . Dulse
See **RHODYMENIA.**

DIMOCAR'PUS . . . . **EUPHORIA**

DIMORPHAN'DRA . Dimorphandra
latifo'lia . . . . Broadleaf D.
mo'ra . . . . **Mora excelsa**
oleif'era

DIMORPHAN'THUS . . . **ARALIA**

DIMORPHOTHE'CA. Capemarigold
an'nua (*Calendula pluvialis*)
Annual C.
Double (*ligulosa; pongei*) hv.
Ringens
auranti'aca (*Calendula tragus*)
Winter C.
Golden West. hv.
chrysanthemifo'lia
Chrysanthemumleaf C.
cunea'ta . . . . . Scarletorange C.
ecklo'nis . . . . Bedding C.
∞ hy'brida (*annua* × *aurantiaca; Calendula h.*)
pluvia'lis . . . . Rain C.
—rin'gens . . . . Gaping R.C.
sinua'ta . . . . Blueeyed C.
spectab'ilis . . . . Showy C.

Dingleberry **Vaccinium erythrocarpum**

DINTERAN'THUS
puber'ulus

DIOCLE'A . . . . . . Clusterpea
glycinoi'des . . . . . . Scarlet C.
multiflo'ra (*boykini*) . . . Boykin C.
seric'ea

DIO'DIA |w . . . . . . Buttonweed
te'res |w . . . . Rough B.
virginia'na |w . . . . . Virginia B.

DION' (*DIOON*) . . . . Dion
See **CYCAD GENERA.**

DIONAE'A . . . . . . Venusflytrap
muscip'ula . . . . . . Venusflytrap

DIO'ON . . . . **DION**
See **CYCAD GENERA.**

DIOSCORE'A |w . . . . Yam
ala'ta . . . . Winged Y.
bata'tas |w . . . . . Cinnamonvine
bulbif'era . . . . Airpotato Y.
cayenen'sis . . . . Attoto Y.
dis'color . . . . Whiteband Y.
esculen'ta . . . . Chinese Y.
macrou'ra
oppositifo'lia
pilosius'cula (*Rajania pleioneura* Bello, *not* Griseb.)
rotunda'ta . . . . Guinea Y.
sati'va . . . . Common Y.
trif'ida . . . Cushcush Y. (*Yampee*)
villo'sa . . . . Atlantic Y.

DIOS'MA . . . . Diosma
al'ba . . . . **Coleonema album**
capita'ta . . . . **Audouinia c.**
ericoi'des . . . . Buchu D.
purpu'rea . . . . **Agathosma villosa**
reeves'i . . . . Reeves D.

DIOSPY'ROS |w . . . . . Persimmon
arma'ta . . . . Spiny P.
burman'ica . . . Burmese Ebony P.
cargil'lia . . . . . . Illawara E.P.
chinen'sis . . . . **D. kaki**
chlorox'ylon . . . . . . Green E.P.
crassiflo'ra . . . WestAfrican E.P.
den'do . . . . Gaboon E.P.
dis'color (*mabola*) . . . Mabola P.
ebenas'ter . . . . . Indian Ebony.P.
eb'enum . . . . Ebony P.
embryop'teris . . . . Gaub P.
fer'rea (*Maba buxifolia*)
Philippine Ebony P.
insculp'ta . . . . Benin E.P.
ka'ki (*chinensis; D. roxburghi schitse*)
Kaki P.
—silves'tris . . . . . . Wild K.P.
lo'tus . . . . Dateplum P.
mabo'la . . . . **D. discolor**
macas'sar . . . . Macassar Ebony P.
marmora'ta Andaman Marblewood P.
melanox'ylon . Coromandel Ebony P.
mespiliform'is . . . . . Medlar P.
monta'na . . . . Mountain P.
penta'mera . . . Myrtle Ebony P.
pilosan'thera . . . . . Bolongeta P.
piscato'ria . . . . . . Fishermans P.
quaesi'ta . . Calamander Ebony P.
rhombifo'lia . . . . Diamondleaf P.
roxburgh'i schit'se . . . . . . **D. kaki**
sinen'sis . . . . Chinese P.
texa'na |w . . . . Texas P.
tomento'sa . . . . . Nepal Ebony P.
virginia'na |w . . . . . Common P.
—platycar'pa (*D. v. mosieri*)
Oklahoma P.
—pubes'cens . . . . . . Fuzzy C.P.

DIOSTE'A . . . . **BAILLONIA**

DIO'TIS . . . . Cottonweed
candidis'sima . . . . Cottonweed

DIPCA'DI
serot'ina

DIPEL'TA . . . . Dipelta
floribun'da . . . . Rosy D.
ventrico'sa
yunnanen'sis . . . . . . Yunnan D.

DI'PHOLIS . . . . Bustic
salicifo'lia . . . . Willow B.

DIPHYLLE'IA . . . . Umbrellaleaf
cymo'sa . . . . American U.
gray'i . . . . Japan U.

DI'PLACUS . . . . . **MIMULUS**
grandiflo'rus . . . . . **M. leptanthus**

DIPLADE'NIA . . . . . . Dipladenia
bolivien'sis . . . . . . Bolivia D.
splen'dens . . . . Brazil D.
Amabilis. hv. Dipladenia
Amoena
Brearley (*brearleyana*)
The identity of this plant is uncertain. It may be Odontadenia speciosa.
∞ Hybrida
Insignis
Profusa
Rose (*rosea*)

DIPLARRHE'NA
morae'a

DIPLA'ZIUM
See **FERN GENERA.**

DIPLOCY'ATHA
cilia'ta

DIPLOGLOT'TIS
cunningham'i (*Cupania c.*)

DIPLOPAP'PUS . . **APLOPAPPUS; ASTER; CASSINIA**
chrysophyl'lus . . . . . . **C. fulvida**
ericoi'des . . . . . . **Aplopappus e.**
fruticulo'sus . . . . **Aster fruticosus**

DIPLOPEL'TIS
hue'geli

DIPLOSO'MA
retrover'sum

DIPLOTAX'IS . . . . . Wallrocket
erucoi'des . . . . Garden W.
mura'lis . . . . Stinking W.
tenuifo'lia . . . . . . Slimleaf W.

DIPLOTHE'MIUM **ALLAGOPTERA; POLYANDROCOCOS**
See **PALM GENERA.**

DIP'SACUS . . . . Teasel
as'per . . . . Himalaya T.
chinen'sis . . . . China T.
fullo'num . . . . Fullers T.
iner'mis . . . . Spineless T.
lacinia'tus . . . . Cutleaf T.
pilo'sus . . . . Hairy T.
sylves'tris . . . . . . Venuscup T.

DIPTEROCAR'PUS . Gurjunoiltree
cornu'tus . . . . Keruing G.
grandiflo'rus . . . . . . Apitong G.
pilo'sus . . . . Hollong G.
thu'rifer . . . . **Anisoptera thurifera**
tubercula'tus . . . . Eng G.
turbina'tus . . Common G. (*Gurjun*)
zeylan'icus . . . . . . Ceylon G.

DIPTERO'NIA
sinen'sis

DIP'TERYX (*COUMAROUNA*)
Tonkabean
Dipteryx is conserved over the older Coumarouna, under International Rules.
odora'ta (*Coumarouna o.*) . Dutch T.
oppositifo'lia (*Coumarouna o.*)
British T.
panamen'sis . Panama T. (*Almendro*)

DIR'CA . . . . Leatherwood
occidenta'lis . . . . SanFrancisco L.
palus'tris . . . . Atlantic L.

DI'SA
See **ORCHID GENERA.**

DISAN'THUS
cercidifo'lius

DISCA'RIA
serratifo'lia (*Colletia s.*)
tou'matou
triner'vis

DISCOCAC'TUS
See **CACTUS GENERA.**

Dishclothgourd . . Towelgourd: **Luffa**

DISOCAC'TUS
See **CACTUS GENERA.**

DISPHY'MA
MESEMBRYANTHEMUM
See **SUCCULENTS.**

DIS'PORUM (*PROSARTES*)
Fairybells
hook'eri . . . . Hooker F.
lanugino'sum . . . . Hairy F.
macula'tum . . . . Spotted F.
menzies'i . . . . Menzies F.
orega'num . . . . Oregon F.
smith'i . . . . Smiths F.
trachycar'pum . . . . Wartberry F.

DISSANTHE'LIUM
See **GRASS GENERA.**

DISSO'TIS
alpes'tris
grandiflo'ra
inca'na

DISTE'GIA . . . . . . **LONICERA**

DISTEMONAN'THUS
benthamia'nus

DIS'TICHLIS . . . . . . Saltgrass
See **GRASS GENERA.**

DIS'TICTIS . . . . Distictis
gnaphalan'tha
lactiflo'ra (*cinerea*) . . . Vanilla D.

DISTY'LIUM
racemo'sum (*chinense*)
—variega'tum

DITAX'IS . . . . Ditaxis
neomexica'na |w . . NewMexico D.

Ditchsunflower **Bidens trichosperma**

DITHYRAE'A . . . . . Spectaclepod
califor'nica . . . . . . California S.
—marit'ima . . . . . . Seashore C.S.
wislize'ni . . . . . . Wislizenus S.

Dittany . . . . **Dictamnus**
Gasplant D. . . . . **D. albus**
Maryland D. . . Stonemint, Maryland: **Cunila origanoides**
Tatar D. . . . . **D. tataricus**

Dittany of Crete . . . . . Origanum, Crete-dittany: **Origanum dictamnus**

Dividivi . . . . . **Caesalpinia coriaria**

DIZYGOTHE'CA . . . . Falsearalia
elegantis'sima (*Aralia e.*)
Threadleaf F.

DIZYGOTHECA, continued
kerchovea'na (*Aralia k.*)
Kerchov Falsearalia
veitch'i (*Aralia v.*) . . . . Veitch F.
₵Lineleaf (*gracillima*) hv.

Dock . . . . **Rumex**
Alpine D. . . . . **R. alpinus**
Bitter D. . . . . . . **R. obtusifolius**
Canaigre . . . . **R. hymenosepalus**
Clustered D. . . . **R. conglomeratus**
Curly D. . . . . **R. crispus**
Fiddleleaf D. . . . . . . **R. pulcher**
French Sorrel . . . . . **R. scutatus**
Garden Sorrel . . . . . **R. acetosa**
Golden D. . . . . . **R. persicarioides**
Great D. . . . . **R. britannica**
Heartwing Sorrel . **R. hastatulus**
Mexican D. . . . . . . **R. mexicanus**
Mountain Sorrel . . **R. paucifolius**
Patience D. . . . . **R. patientia**
Pond D. . . . . **R. aquaticus**
Rosy D. . . . . **R. roseus**
Sheep Sorrel . . . . . **R. acetosella**
Spinach-rhubarb D. . **R. abyssinicus**
Swamp D. . . . . . . **R. verticillatus**
Veiny D. . . . . **R. venosus**
Water D. . . . . **R. hydrolapathum**
Western D. . . . . . **R. occidentalis**
Willow D. . . . . . . **R. salicifolius**

DOCY'NIA . . . . . . Falsequince
delavay'i (*Pyrus d.*) . . . Delavay F.
docynioi'des

Dodder . . . . **Cuscuta**
Bigseed Alfalfa D. . . . **C. indecora**
Chile D. . . . . **C. suaveolens**
Clover D. . . . . **C. epithymum**
Flax D. . . . . **C. epilinum**
Gronovius D. . . . . **C. gronovi**
Hazel D. . . . . **C. coryli**
Littleseed Alfalfa D. . **C. planiflora**
Lovevine D. . . . . . . **C. americana**
Saltmarsh D. . . . . **C. salina**

DODECA'THEON |w . . Shootingstar
alpi'num . . . . Alpine S.
campes'tre . . . . Plains S.
cleve'landi . . . . Cleveland S.
con'jugens
cu'sicki . . . . Cusick S.
denta'tum . . . . Dentate S.
henderso'ni . . . . . . Henderson S.
hu'geri . . . . Huger S.
jef'freyi . . . . Jeffrey S.
latilo'bum
mead'ia (*integrifolium*) . Common S.
—al'ba . . . . White C.S.
₵Belle Mauve. hv.
₵Brilliant
₵White Swan
—radica'tum
—splen'didum . . . . . Showy C.S.
—viola'ceum . . . . . . Violet C.S.
multiflo'rum . . . . Manyflower S.
pat'ulum . . . . Dwarf S.
pauciflo'rum . . . . Darkthroat S.
poe'ticum . . . . Poets S.
puberulen'tum
radica'tum . . . . Southern S.
sali'num . . . . . Yellowthroat S.
stan'fieldi . . . . Stanfield S.
tetran'drum . . . . . Yellowring S.

DODONAE'A . . . . . Hopseedbush
attenua'ta . . . . Longstem H.
cunea'ta . . . . Wedgeleaf H.
madagascarien'sis . Madagascar H.
microca'rya . . . . Florida H.

DODONAEA, continued
ptarmicaefo'lia . STICKY HOPSEEDBUSH
spathula'ta
Possibly a form of D. viscosa.
thunbergia'na . . . THUNBERG H.
trique'tra . . . . THREECORNER H.
visco'sa . . . . CLAMMY H.
—angustifo'lia . . NARROWLEAF C.H.

DOELLINGE'RIA . . . . . **ASTER**

DOGBANE . . . . **Apocynum**
CLIFF D. . . . . . . **A. scopulorum**
HEMP D. . . . . . . **A. cannabinum**
LOW D. . . . . **A. pumilum**
PRAIRIE D. . . . . . . **A. sibiricum**
SPREADING D. . **A. androsaemifolium**

DOGPARSLEY . . . . . **Cynomarathrum**
NUTTALL D. . . . . **C. nuttalli**

DOGTAIL . . . . **Cynosurus**
CRESTED D. . . . . . . **C. cristatus**
HEDGEHOG D. . . . . . **C. echinatus**

DOGTOOTHGRASS . . . . . . **Cynodon**
GIANT D. . . . . **C. slectostachyus**
KARROOKWEEK D. . . **C. incompletus**
TRANSVAAL D. . . . **C. transvaalensis**

Dogtooth Violet . FAWNLILY: **Erythronium**

DOGWEED . . . . **Dyssodia**
PRAIRIE D. . . . . . . **D. papposa**
PRICKLEAF D. . . . . . **D. acerosa**

DOGWOOD . . . . **Cornus**
∞ARNOLD D. . . . . . ∞**C. arnoldiana**
BAILEY D. . . . . **C. baileyi**
BLACKFRUIT D. . . . . . . **C. sessilis**
BLOODTWIG D. . . . . . **C. sanguinea**
BRETSCHNEIDER D. . **C. bretschneideri**
BROWN D. . . . . **C. glabrata**
BUNCHBERRY D. . . . **C. canadensis**
CALIFORNIA D. . . . . **C. californica**
CHINESE KOUSA D. **C. kousa chinensis**
COLORADO REDOSIER D.
C. stolonifera coloradensis
CORNELIANCHERRY D. . . . **C. mas**
DWARF C. D. . . . . **C. m. nana**
EVERGREEN D. . . . . . **C. capitata**
FLOWERING D. . . . . . . **C. florida**
GIANT D. . . . . . . **C. controversa**
GRAY D. . . . . **C. racemosa**
GREENTWIG REDOSIER D.
C. stolonifera nitida
HEMSLEY CORNEL D. . . **C. hemsleyi**
HESSE D. . . . . **C. hessei**
∞HORSEY D. . . . . . . ∞**C. horseyi**
JAPANESECORNEL D. . . **C. officinalis**
KOREAN D. . . . . **C. coreana**
KOUSA D. . . . . **C. kousa**
LARGELEAF D. . . . . **C. macrophylla**
LITTLELEAF D. . . . . **C. paucinervis**
MONBEIG D. . . . . . . **C. monbeigi**
PACIFIC D. . . . . **C. nuttalli**
PAGODA D. . . . . . . **C. alternifolia**
PALE D. . . . . **C. obliqua**
REDOSIER D. . . . . . **C. stolonifera**
ROUGHLEAF D. . . . . **C. asperifolia**
ROUNDLEAF D. . . . . . . **C. rugosa**
SIBERIAN D. . . . . . **C. alba sibirica**
SILKY D. . . . . **C. amomum**
STIFFCORNEL D. . . . . . **C. foemina**
TATARIAN D. . . . . **C. alba**
WALTER D. . . . . **C. walteri**
WESTERN D. . . . . . **C. occidentalis**
YELLOWBERRY FLOWERING D.
C. florida xanthocarpa
YELLOWTWIG REDOSIER D.
C. stolonifera flaviramea

DOLICHAN'DRA
cynanchoi'des (*Macfadyena c.*)

DOLICH'OLUS . . . **RHYNCHOSIA**
precato'rius . . . . **R. phaseoloides**

DOL'ICHOS . . . . DOLICHOS
biflo'rus . . . . . . TWINFLOWER D.
hose'i . . . . . . SARAWAKBEAN D.
japon'icus . . **Pueraria thunbergiana**
lab'lab . . . . HYACINTH D.
₵GIANT (*giganteus*) HV.
ligno'sus (*jacquini*) AUSTRALIAPEA D.
₵WHITE (*albus*) HV.
sesquipeda'lis . . . . **Vigna s.**

DOLICHOTHE'LE **MAMMILLARIA**
See **CACTUS GENERA.**

Dollarcactus . . . . . . PRICKLYPEAR,
DOLLARJOINT: **Opuntia chlorotica**

DOLLARPLANT . . . . . **Lunaria annua**

DOM'BEYA (*ASSONIA*) . . DOMBEYA
acutan'gula
calan'tha
∞**cayeux'i** (*mastersi × wallichi; Assonia c.*)
gurges'siae
mas'tersi . . . . MASTERS D.
nairoben'sis . . . . NAIROBI D.
natalen'sis (*Assonia n.*)
WEDDINGFLOWER D.
puncta'ta (*Assonia p.*) . . BOURBON D.
spectab'ilis (*Assonia s.*)
wal'lichi (*Assonia w.*) . . SCARLET D.

DON'DIA . . . . **SUAEDA**
Suaeda is conserved under International Rules.

DOO'DIA . . . . HACKSAWFERN
See **FERN GENERA.**

DORE'MA . . . . SUMBUL
ammoni'acum . . . . . BOMBAY S.

DORO'NICUM . . . . LEOPARDBANE
austri'acum . . . . . AUSTRIAN L.
caucas'icum . . . . . CAUCASIAN L.
—magnif'icum (*D. magnificum*)
SUNFLOWER C.L.
MME. MASON. HV. D. caucasicum
clu'si (*Arnica c.*) . . . . . DOWNY L.
corda'tum (*columnae; cordifolium*)
HEARTLEAF L.
macrophyl'lum . . . . . BIGLEAF L.
magnif'icum . . . **D. caucasicum m.**
pardalian'ches
GOLDBUNCH. HV.
plantagin'eum (*excelsum*) PLANTAIN L.
₵SHOWY (*excelsum*) HV.

DOROTHEAN'THUS
MESEMBRYANTHEMUM
See **SUCCULENTS.**

DORSTE'NIA . . . . . . TORUSHERB
contrajer'va . . . . CONTRAYERVA T.

DORYA'LIS . . . . . . **DOVYALIS**

DORYAN'THES . . . . . . SPEARLILY
excel'sa . . . . COMMON S.
₵GIANT (*palmeri*) HV.

DORYC'NIUM . . . CANARYCLOVER
herba'ceum . . . . HERB C.
hirsu'tum . . . . HAIRY C.
rec'tum . . . . UPRIGHT C.
suffrutico'sum . . . . BRANCHING C.

DOUBLE-COCONUT . . **Lodoicea maldivica**

DOUGLASFIR . . . . **Pseudotsuga**
BIGCONE D. . . . . . . **P. macrocarpa**
CHINESE D. . . . . **P. sinensis**
COMMON D. . . . . **P. taxifolia**
JAPANESE D. . . . . **P. japonica**
SHORTBRACT COMMON D.
P. taxifolia brevibracteata

DOUGLAS'IA . . . . DOUGLASIA
laeviga'ta . . . . SMOOTH D.
monta'na . . . . MOUNTAIN D.
vitalia'na (*Androsace v.; Gregoria v.*)

DOUMPALM . . . . **Hyphaene**
CENTRALMADAGASCAR D. . **H. baroni**
EGYPTIAN D. . . . . . . **H. thebaica**
INDIAN D. . . . . **H. indica**
NATAL D. . . . . . . **H. natalensis**
NORTHMADAGASCAR D. . **H. schatan**
SOUTHAFRICAN D. . . . . **H. crinita**
ZAMBESI D. . . . . **H. turbinata**

DOVETREE . . . **Davidia; D. involucrata**
VILMORIN D. . . . **D. i. vilmoriniana**

DOVYA'LIS (*ABERIA; DORYALIS*)
caf'fra (*Aberia c.*) . . . . KEIAPPLE (*Umkokolo*)
hebecar'pa (*Aberia gardneri*)
KITEMBILLA (*Ceylongooseberry*)

DOWNIN'GIA |w . . . . DOWNINGIA
brachyan'tha |w
el'egans (*Clintonia e.*) |w
pulchel'la (*Clintonia p.*) . CALIFORNIA D.

DOWNYBUSH . . **Enchylaena tomentosa**

DOXAN'THA . . . . FUNNELCREEPER
capreola'ta . . . . **Bignonia c.**
unguis-cat'i (*Bignonia tweediana; B. unguis-cati*) . . . . . CATCLAW F.

DRA'BA |w . . . DRABA (*Whitlowwort*)
aizoi'des
ai'zoon . . . . AIZOON D.
alpi'na (*densiflora*) |w . ROCKCRESS D.
altaica . . . . **D. fladnizensis**
androsa'cea **D. fladnizensis; D. lactea**
ara'bisans
arma'ta . . . . **D. longirostra**
atho'a
au'rea . . . . GOLDEN D.
austri'aca . . . . AUSTRIAN D.
bertolo'ni . . **D. longirostra erioscapa**
borea'lis . . . . NORTHERN D.
bruniifo'lia
DIVERSIFOLIA. HV.
carolinia'na . . . . . CAROLINA D.
cascaden'sis . . . . . CASCADES D.
cuspida'ta
dedea'na . . . . DEDE D.
densiflo'ra . . . . **D. alpina**
fladnizen'sis (*altaica; androsacea*)
ARCTIC D.
glacia'lis . . . . GLACIER D.
hir'ta . . . . HAIRY D.
hispan'ica . . . . SPANISH D.
hoppea'na . . . . HOPPEAN D.
inca'na |w . . . . . . TWISTED D.
—a'damsi . . . . . . ADAMS T.D.
incer'ta
kotsch'yi . . . . . . KOTSCHYS D.
lacte'a (*androsacea*) . . . . MILKY D.
lanceola'ta . . . . . LANCEOLATE D.
lonchocar'pa
longiros'tra (*armata*)
—erriosca'pa (*bertoloni*)
nemoro'sa . . . . WOODS D.
ni'tida . . . . SHINY D.
niva'lis . . . . SNOW D.

DRABA, continued
norve'gica (*laxa; scandinavica*) NORWEGIAN DRABA
novolym'pica
olymp'ica . . . . OLYMPIC D.
Often misidentified as D. bruniifolia.
pay'soni . . . . PAYSON D.
pyrena'ica . . . . . . **Petrocallis p.**
ramosis'sima . . . . . BRANCHING D.
rig'ida . . . . RIGID D.
ruax'es . . . . RAINIER D.
rupes'tris . . . . CLIFF D.
scandina'vica . . . . . **D. norvegica**
The name D. scandinavica is, in addition, sometimes misapplied to forms of D. hirta.
sibi'rica (*repens*) . . . . SIBERIAN D.
sonor'ae . . . . SONORA D.
streptocar'pa
subamplexicau'lis . . . TURKESTAN D.
tomento'sa . . . . . . WOOLLY D.
ver'na . . . . SPRING D.
viola'cea . . . . VIOLET D.

DRABA . . . . **Draba**
ADAMS TWISTED D. **D. incana adamsi**
AIZOON D. . . . . **D. aizoon**
ARCTIC D. . . . . . . **D. fladnizensis**
AUSTRIAN D. . . . . . . **D. austriaca**
BRANCHING D. . . . **D. ramosissima**
CAROLINA D. . . . . . **D. caroliniana**
CASCADES D. . . . . . **D. cascadensis**
CLIFF D. . . . . **D. rupestris**
DEDE D. . . . . **D. dedeana**
GLACIER D. . . . . **D. glacialis**
GOLDEN D. . . . . **D. aurea**
HAIRY D. . . . . **D. hirta**
HOPPEAN D. . . . . **D. hoppeana**
KOTSCHYS D. . . . . . . **D. kotschyi**
LANCEOLATE D. . . . . **D. lanceolata**
MILKY D. . . . . **D. lactea**
NORTHERN D. . . . . . . **D. borealis**
NORWEGIAN D. . . . . **D. norvegica**
OLYMPIC D. . . . . . . **D. olympica**
PAYSON D. . . . . **D. paysoni**
RAINIER D. . . . . **D. ruaxes**
RIGID D. . . . . **D. rigida**
ROCKCRESS D. . . . . . . **D. alpina**
SHINY D. . . . . **D. nitida**
SIBERIAN D. . . . . **D. sibirica**
SNOW D. . . . . **D. nivalis**
SONORA D. . . . . **D. sonorae**
SPANISH D. . . . . . . **D. hispanica**
SPRING D. . . . . **D. verna**
TURKESTAN D. . **D. subamplexicaulis**
TWISTED D. . . . . **D. incana**
VIOLET D. . . . . **D. violacea**
WOODS D. . . . . **D. nemorosa**
WOOLLY D. . . . . . . **D. tomentosa**

DRACAE'NA . . . . DRACAENA
See also **CORDYLINE**, DRACENA.
austra'lis . . . . **Cordyline a.**
cinnabar'i . SOCOTRA-DRAGONSBLOOD D. (*Socotra Dragonsblood*)
concin'na
deremen'sis
—al'ba
—war'necki
dra'co . . . . DRAGON D.
ensifo'lia . . . . . . **Dianella e.**
fra'grans . . . . FRAGRANT D.
₵EMERALD (*knerki*) HV.
₵LINDEN (*lindeni*)

DRACAENA fragrans, continued
₵MASSANGE (*massangeana*)
₵ROTH (*rothiana*)
godseffia'na
₵KELLER (*kelleri*) HV.
goldiea'na . . . . GOLDIE DRACAENA
gra'cilis
indivi'sa . . . . **Cordyline i.**
margina'ta
sanderia'na . . . . . . SANDERS D.
termina'lis . . . . **Cordyline t.**

DRACENA . . . . **Cordyline**
AMABILIS D. . . **C. terminalis amabilis**
AUSTRALIAN D. . . . . . . **C. stricta**
BANKS D. . . . . **C. banksi**
BLUE D. . . . . **C. indivisa**
COMMON D. . . . . . **C. terminalis**
GIANT D. . . . . **C. australis**
LILAC D. . . . . **C. rubra**
MANYSTRIPE D. . **₵C. norwoodiensis**
SLIMPANICLE D. . . . . . **C. pumilio**

DRACOCEPH'ALUM (*MOLDAVICA*) DRAGONHEAD
argunen'se . . . . . **D. ruyschianum**
austri'acum . . . . . AUSTRIAN D.
botryoi'des
bulla'tum
for'resti . . . . FORRESTS D.
grandiflo'rum . . . . BIGFLOWER D.
integrifo'lium
isabel'lae . . . . ISABEL D.
japon'icum. . . . **D. ruyschianum j.**
molda'vica (*Moldavica suaveolens*) MOLDAVICA D
nu'tans . . . . NODDING D.
—alpi'num . . . . . ALPINE N.D.
parviflo'rum (*Moldavica parviflora*) AMERICAN D.
peregri'num . . . . . . TRAILING D.
ruyschia'num (*argunense*) RUYSCHIANUM D.
—japon'icum (*D. japonicum*) JAPAN R.D.
specio'sum . . . . . HIMALAYA D.
—imbrica'tum
tangu'ticum . . . . . . TANGUT D.
thymiflo'rum . . . THYMEFLOWER D.
virginia'num . **Physostegia virginiana**
VIVID. HV. Dracocephalum

DRACON'TIUM . . . . DRAGONAROID
as'perum . . . . BRAZIL D.
gi'gas . . . . GIANT D.

DRACONTOME'LUM . DRAGONPLUM
da'o . . . . DAO D.

DRACO'PIS . . . . . **RUDBECKIA**

DRACUN'CULUS . . . STINKDRAGON
canarien'sis . . . . CANARY S.
vulga'ris (*Arum dracunculus*) COMMON S.

DRAGONAROID . . . . . . **Dracontium**
BRAZIL D. . . . . **D. asperum**
GIANT D. . . . . **D. gigas**

DRAGONHEAD . . . . . **Dracocephalum**
ALPINE NODDING D. . **D. nutans alpinum**
AMERICAN D. . . . . **D. parviflorum**
AUSTRIAN D. . . . . . **D. austriacum**
BIGFLOWER D. . . . **D. grandiflorum**
FORRESTS D. . . . . **D. forresti**
HIMALAYA D. . . . . **D. speciosum**
ISABEL D. . . . . **D. isabellae**

DRAGONHEAD, continued
JAPAN RUYSCHIANUM D. . . . **Dracocephalum ruyschianum japonicum**
MOLDAVICA D. . . . . . **D. moldavica**
NODDING D. . . . . **D. nutans**
RUYSCHIANUM D. . . **D. ruyschianum**
TANGUT D. . . . . . . **D. tanguticum**
THYMEFLOWER D. . **D. thymiflorum**
TRAILING D. . . . . . **D. peregrinum**

DRAGONPLUM . . . . **Dracontomelum**
DAO D. . . . . **D. dao**

Dragonsblood, Socotra . . . DRACAENA, SOCOTRA-DRAGONSBLOOD: **Dracaena cinnabari**

Drege'a sinen'sis . . . . **Wattakaka s.**

DRI'MIA
haworthioi'des

DRI'MYS . . . . DRIMYS
aromat'ica . . . . . . AROMATIC D.
axilla'ris
colora'ta
win'teri . . . . . . WINTERSBARK D.

DROPSEED . **Blepharoneuron; Sporobolus**
AFRICAN D. . . . . . . **S. fimbriatus**
BLACK D. . . . . . . **S. interruptus**
BUCKLEY D. . . . . . . **S. buckleyi**
CORAL D. . . . . . **S. domingensis**
CURTISS D. . . . . **S. curtissi**
FLORIDA D. . . . . . . **S. floridanus**
GIANT D. . . . . **S. giganteus**
Hairy D. . . . . PINE D.
HAIRY TALL D. . . **S. asper pilosus**
HIDDEN D. . . . . . **S. clandestinus**
MEADOW TALL D. . **S. asper hookeri**
MESA D. . . . . **S. flexuosus**
MISSISSIPPI D. . . . . . . **S. macrus**
Nealley D. . . . . GYPGRASS
PADREISLAND D. . . . . . . **S. tharpi**
PINE D. **Blepharoneuron tricholepis**
Blepharoneuron is a rather recent segregate from the Dropseed genus, Sporobolus.
PINEYWOODS D. . . . . . **S. gracilis**
POVERTY D. . . . . . **S. vaginiflorus**
PRAIRIE D. . . . . . **S. heterolepis**
PUFFSHEATH D. . . . . **S. neglectus**
PURPLE D. . . . . **S. purpurascens**
RED D. . . . . **S. ramulosus**
SAND D. . . . . . . **S. cryptandrus**
SEASHORE D. . . . . . **S. virginicus**
SIXWEEKS D. . . . **S. microspermus**
SPIKE D. . . . . **S. contractus**
TALL D. . . . . **S. asper**
TEXAS D. . . . . **S. texanus**
WHORLED D. . . . **S. pyramidatus**
WIRELEAF D. . . . . **S. teretifolius**

DROPTONGUE . . . . . **Schismatoglottis**
NEWGUINEA D. . **S. neo-guineensis**
PAINTED D. . . . . **S. picta**
SILVERBLOTCH D. . . . . . **S. pulchra**
WARTYSTEM D. . . . . . **S. asperata**
WHITESPOT W. D. . **S. a. albo-maculata**

DROPWORT . . **Filipendula hexapetala**

DROSAN'THEMUM **MESEMBRYANTHEMUM**
See **SUCCULENTS.**

DRO'SERA . . . . SUNDEW
an'glica . . . . ENGLISH S.
filifor'mis . . . . . THREADLEAF S.
longifo'lia . . . . . NARROWLEAF S.
rotundifo'lia . . . . . ROUNDLEAF S.

Hort. var.; HV. = horticultural variety (or varieties); sp. = species (singular); spp. = species (plural).
₵ = clon; × (as a prefix) = hybrid; × (between scientific plant names) = crossed by; ∞ = polybrid; |w = plant useful to wildlife.
See Glossary for definitions of clon, hybrid, and polybrid.

DRUG PLANT NAMES

This list includes those dye and spice plants which are used for medicinal or pharmaceutical purposes. The list was compiled chiefly from the United States Pharmacopoeia XI, The National Formulary (6th ed.), and the United States Dispensatory (22d ed.), by the Committee on Nomenclature of the American Pharmaceutical Association, H. W. Youngken (Chairman), C. W. Ballard, and E. N. Gathercoal. Great credit is due Dr. Youngken and his Committee for untiring research and for continuous and cordial cooperation with the American Joint Committee on a most difficult and perplexing undertaking. While the results cannot be considered entirely satisfactory nor conclusive, it is a distinct advance in plant nomenclature as related to the drug industry, and it is believed will prove most useful to physicians, druggists and laymen alike.

The Editorial Committee of STANDARDIZED PLANT NAMES wishes to formally and cordially thank Dr. Youngken and his associates for their excellent contributions and cooperation.

Chief synonymous drug names are shown in parenthesized italics following the accepted drug name.

Drug Name	Plant Source *Botanical Name*	 *S.P.N. Common Name*
ABROMA (*Olutkombul*)	**Abroma angusta**	COTTON ABROMA
ABROTANUM (*Southernwood*)	**Artemisia abrotanum**	OLDMAN WORMWOOD
ABRUS (*Jequirity*)	**Abrus praecatorius**	JEQUIRITY ROSARYPEA
ABSINTHIUM (*Common Wormwood*)	**Artemisia absinthium**	COMMON WORMWOOD
Abyssinian Tea. CATHA.		
ACACIA (*Gum Arabic*)	**Acacia senegal**; other African **Acacia** spp.	GUMARABIC ACACIA
ACALYPHA	**Acalypha poireti**	POIRETS COPPERLEAF
ACER SPICATUM (*Mountain Maple Bark*)	**Acer spicatum**	MOUNTAIN MAPLE
ACHILLEA (*Milfoil*)	**Achillea millefolium**	COMMON YARROW
ACOKANTHERA (*Wabayo*)	**Acokanthera** spp., especially **A. abyssinica**	BUSHMANSPOISON ABYSSINIAN B.
ACONITUM (*Monkshood*)	**Aconitum napellus**	ACONITE MONKSHOOD
Acorn Cups. VALONIA		
ACTAEA (*Black Baneberry*)	**Actaea spicata**	BLACK BANEBERRY
ACTINOMERIS (*Gravel Weed*)	**Verbesina helianthoides**	GRAVELWEED CROWNBEARD
ADANSONIA (*Baobab*)	**Adansonia digitata**	BAOBAB
ADHATODA	**Adhatoda vasica** (*Justicia v.*)	MALABARNUT
ADIANTUM (*Maidenhair Fern*)	**Adiantum capillus-veneris** (*fergusoni*)	SOUTHERN MAIDENHAIR
ADIANTUM (*Maidenhair Fern*)	**A. pedatum**	AMERICAN M.
ADIANTUM (*Maidenhair Fern*)	**A. philippense** (*lunulatum*)	WALKING M.
ADONIS (*Pheasants-eye*)	**Adonis vernalis**	SPRING ADONIS
AESCULIN (*Esculin*) The glucoside of the horsechestnut.	**Aesculus hippocastanum**	COMMON HORSECHESTNUT
AESCULUS (*Horsechestnut*)	"	"
AETHUSA (*Fools-parsley*)	**Aethusa cynapium**	FOOLSPARSLEY AETHUSA
African Locust. PARKIA.		
AGAR (*Agar-Agar*) Certain other spp. of red algae are also occasionally sources of Agar.	**Gelidium corneum**	COMMON AGAR
AGARICUS (*Larch Agaric*)	**Fomes officinalis** (*Polyporus o.*)	LARCH FOMES
AGAVE (*Centuryplant*)	**Agave americana**	CENTURYPLANT AGAVE
AGELAEA (*Cephan-Mahi*)	**Agelaea lamarcki**	LAMARCK AGELAEA
Agialida. BALANITES		
AGRIMONIA (*Common Agrimony*)	**Agrimonia eupatoria**	COMMON AGRIMONY
AILANTHUS (*Chinese Sumac*)	**Ailanthus altissima** (*glandulosa*)	TREEOFHEAVEN AILANTHUS
AJOWAN (*Ajava*)	**Trachyspermum ammi** (*Carum copticum*)	AJOWAN-CARAWAY
AJUGA (*Bugle*)	**Ajuga** spp., especially **A. chamaepitys**	BUGLE GROUNDPINE B.
ALANGINA	**Alangium salviifolium** (*lamarcki*)	ANGOLA ALANGIUM
ALCHEMILLA (*Ladysmantle*)	**Alchemilla vulgaris**	COMMON LADYSMANTLE
Alder. ALNUS		
ALETRIS (*Stargrass*)	**Aletris farinosa**	WHITETUBE STARGRASS
ALISMA (*Waterplantain*)	**Alisma plantago-aquatica**	AMERICAN WATER-PLANTAIN
ALKANNA (*Alkanet Root*)	**Alkanna tinctoria**	DYERS ALKANET

Drug Name	Plant Source *Botanical Name*	 *S.P.N. Common Name*
ALLAMANDA	**Allamanda cathartica**	COMMON ALLAMANDA
ALLIARIA (*Hedge-garlic*)	**Sisymbrium alliaria**	GARLICMUSTARD
ALLIUM (*Garlic*)	**Allium sativum**	GARLIC
Allspice. PIMENTA		
ALNUS (*Alder*)	**Alnus glutinosa**	EUROPEAN ALDER
ALOE (*Socotrine Aloes*)	**Aloe perryi**	PERRY ALOE
ALOE (*Curacao Aloes*)	**A. barbadensis**	MEDITERRANEAN A.
ALOE (*Cape Aloes*) "Cape Aloes" also derives from hybrids of A. ferox with A. africana and A. spicata.	**A. ferox**	CAPE A.
ALSTONIA (*Dita Bark*)	**Alstonia constricta**	QUININE ALSTONIA
ALSTONIA	**A. scholaris**	PALIMARA A.
ALTHAEA (*Marshmallow Root*)	**Althaea officinalis**	MARSHMALLOW
ALTHAEAE FOLIA (*Marshmallow Leaves*)	"	"
Alum Root. HEUCHERA		
Ambrette Seed. HIBISCUS		
AMBROSIA (*Roman Wormwood*)	**Ambrosia artemisifolia**	COMMON RAGWEED
AMBROSIA (*Great Ragweed*)	**A. trifida**	GIANT R.
American *Columbo.* FRASERA *Dittany.* CUNILA *Hazelnut.* CORYLUS *Mistletoe.* PHORADENDRON *Pawpaw.* ASIMINA *Saffron.* CARTHAMUS *Sarsaparilla.* ARALIA NUDICAULIS *Senna.* CASSIA MARILANDICA *Spikenard.* ARALIA *Water Hemlock.* CICUTA		
AMMONIACUM (*Gum Ammoniac*)	**Dorema ammoniacum**	BOMBAY SUMBUL
AMPELOPSIS (*Virginia Creeper*)	**Parthenocissus quinquefolia** (*Ampelopsis q.*)	VIRGINIA CREEPER
AMYLUM (*Corn Starch*) *See also* OLEUM MAYDIS and ZEA	**Zea mays**	MAIZE; INDIAN CORN
AMYLUM MANIHOT (*Cassava Starch*)	**Manihot aipi**	AIPI CASSAVA
AMYLUM MANIHOT (*Cassava Starch*)	**M. esculenta** (*utilissima*)	COMMON C.
ANACARDIUM (*West Indian Cashew-nut*)	**Anacardium occidentale**	COMMON CASHEW
ANACARDIUM ORIENTALE (*Oriental Cashew-nut*)	**Semecarpus anacardium**	CASHEW MARKINGNUT
ANAGALLIS (*Scarlet Pimpernel*)	**Anagallis arvensis**	SCARLET PIMPERNEL
ANAGYRIS	**Anagyris foetida**	MEDITERRANEAN STINKBUSH
ANCHIETEA (*Pirageia*)	**Anchietea salutaris**	MERCURY ANCHIETEA
ANCHUSA (*Ox-tongue*)	**Anchusa officinalis**	COMMON BUGLOSS
ANDROGRAPHIS	**Andrographis paniculata**	KARIYAT
ANDROMEDA (*Sourwood*) *See also* OXYDENDRUM	**Oxydendrum arboreum**	SOURWOOD
ANEMONIN *See also* PULSATILLA	**Anemone pulsatilla** (*Pulsatilla vulgaris*)	EUROPEAN PASQUEFLOWER
ANEMOPSIS (*Yerba Mansa*)	**Anemopsis californica**	YERBAMANSA
ANETHI FRUCTUS (*Dill Seed*)	**Anethum graveolens**	DILL
ANGELICAE FRUCTUS (*Angelica Seed*)	**Angelica archangelica** (*Archangelica officinalis*)	GARDEN ANGELICA
ANGELICAE RADIX (*Angelica Root*) Other spp. of Angelica, especially A. atropurpurea, sometimes yield the Angelica root and the seed of drug trade.	"	"
ANGRAECUM (*Bourbon Tea*)	**Angraecum fragrans**	BOURBONTEA ORCHID
ANHALONIUM (*Mescal Buttons*)	**Lophophora williamsi**	MESCALBUTTON PEYOTE
ANISUM (*Anise Seed*) *See also* OLEUM ANISI	**Pimpinella anisum**	ANISE

Drug Name	Plant Source: Botanical Name	S.P.N. Common Name
ANNATTO (*Annotta*)	**Bixa orellana**	ANATTOTREE
Annunciation Lily. LILIUM		
ANONA (*Sugar Apple*)	**Annona squamosa**	SUGARAPPLE
ANTHEMIS (*Roman Chamomile*)	**Anthemis nobilis**	ROMAN CAMOMILE
ANTHRISCUS (*Chervil*)	**Anthriscus cerefolium**	SALADCHERVIL
ANTIARIS (*Upas Antiar*)	**Antiaris toxicaria**	UPASTREE
APII FRUCTUS (*Celery Seed*)	**Apium graveolens dulce**	GARDEN CELERY
APOCYNUM (*Canadian Hemp*)	**Apocynum cannabinum**	HEMP DOGBANE
APOCYNUM ANDROSAEMIFOLIUM (*Dogbane*)	**A. androsaemifolium**	SPREADING D.
AQUILEGIA (*Columbine*)	**Aquilegia vulgaris**	EUROPEAN COLUMBINE
ARACHIS (*Peanut*) *See also* OLEUM ARACHIDIS	**Arachis hypogaea**	PEANUT
ARALIA (*American Spikenard*)	**Aralia racemosa**	AMERICAN SPIKENARD
ARALIA HISPIDA (*Dwarf Elder Root*)	**A. hispida**	BRISTLY ARALIA
ARALIA NUDICAULIS (*American Sarsaparilla*)	**A. nudicaulis**	WILDSARSAPARILLA
ARAROBA (*Goa Powder*) *See also* CHRYSAROBINUM	**Andira araroba** (*Vataireopsis a.; Vouacapoua a.*)	GOA ANGELINTREE
Arbor Vitae. THUJA		
ARECA (*Betel Nut*)	**Areca cathecu**	BETELNUTPALM
ARGEMONE (*Prickly Poppy*)	**Argemone mexicana**	MEXICAN PRICKLEPOPPY
ARMORACIAE RADIX (*Horseradish Root*)	**Armoracia lapathifolia**	HORSERADISH
ARNICA (*Arnica Flowers*)	**Arnica montana**	MOUNTAIN ARNICA
ARNICAE RADIX (*Arnica Root*)	"	"
Arra Diabo. PINI-PINI		
Arrowroot. MARANTA		
ARTABOTRYS (*Fragrant Tailgrape*)	**Artabotrys uncinatus** (*odoratissimus*)	FRAGRANT TAILGRAPE
ARTAR RADIX (*Artar Root*)	**Zanthoxylum senegalense** (*Fagara zanthoxyloides*)	SENEGAL PRICKLYASH
ARTEMISIA DRACUNCULUS (*Tarragon*)	**Artemisia dracunculus**	TARRAGON
ARTEMISIA FRIGIDA (*Colorado Mountain Sage*)	**A. frigida**	FRINGED SAGEBRUSH
ARUM	**Arum maculatum**	LORDSANDLADIES
ARUM (*Indian Turnip*)	**Arisaema atrorubens**	COMMON JACKINTHEPULPIT
ASAFOETIDA (*Gum Asafoetida*)	**Ferula assafoetida**	ASAFETIDA GIANTFENNEL
"	**F. foetida**	DEVILSDUNG G.
ASARABACCA	**Asarum europaeum**	EUROPEAN WILDGINGER
ASARUM (*Wild Ginger*)	**A. canadense**	CANADA W.
ASCLEPIAS (*Pleurisy Root*)	**Asclepias tuberosa**	BUTTERFLY MILKWEED
ASIMINA (*American Pawpaw*)	**Asimina triloba**	COMMON PAWPAW
ASPARAGUS	**Asparagus officinalis**	GARDEN ASPARAGUS
ASPIDIUM (*Male Fern*)	**Dryopteris filixmas** (*Asplenium f.*)	MALEFERN
ASPIDIUM (*American Aspidium*)	**D. marginalis**	LEATHER WOODFERN
ASPIDOSPERMA (*Quebracho Bark*)	**Aspidosperma quebracho-blanco**	COMMON WHITEQUEBRACHO
ASTER	**Aster puniceus**	SWAMP ASTER
ASTERACANTHA	**Hygrophila spinosa** (*Asteracantha longifolia*)	STARTHORN
ATHEROSPERMA (*Australian Sassafras*)	**Atherosperma moschatum**	AUSTRALIAN-SASSAFRAS
ATHYRIUM (*Female Fern*)	**Athyrium filixfemina** (*Asplenium f.*)	LADYFERN
AURANTII AMARI CORTEX (*Bitter Orange Peel*) *See also* OLEUM AURANTII AMARI and OLEUM AURANTII FLORUM	**Citrus aurantium**	SOUR ORANGE (*Seville O.*)
AURANTII DULCIS CORTEX (*Sweet Orange Peel*) *See also* OLEUM AURANTII	**C. sinensis**	SWEET O.

Drug Name	Plant Source: Botanical Name	S.P.N. Common Name
Australian Sassafras. ATHEROSPERMA		
AVENA SATIVA (*Oats*)	**Avena sativa**	COMMON OAT
AZEDARACH (*Pride of India*)	**Melia azedarach**	CHINABERRY
BACCHARIS (*Mio Mio*)	**Baccharis coridifolia**	MIOMIO BACCHARIS
BALANITES (*Agialida*)	**Balanites roxburghi**	ROXBURGH BALANITES
BALATA	**Manilkara bidentata** (*Mimusops balata*)	COMMON BALATA
Balm. MELISSA		
Balm of Gilead Bud. POPULI GEMMA		
Balmony Leaves. CHELONE		
Balsam		
Apple. MOMORDICA		
Copaiba. COPAIBA		
of Fir. TEREBINTHINA CANADENSIS		
Poplar Bud. POPULI GEMMA		
Weed. IMPATIENS		
BALSAMORHIZA	**Balsamorhiza terebinthacea**	TURPENTINE BALSAMROOT
BALSAMUM		
CARPATICUM (*Riga Balsam*)	**Pinus cembra**	SWISS STONE PINE
CEBUR (*Cebur Balsam*) *See also* PARAMERIA	**Parameria vulneraria**	
GILEADENSE (*Balm-of-Gilead*)	**Commiphora opobalsamum**	MECCA MYRRHTREE
PERUVIANUM (*Balsam of Peru*)	**Myroxylon pereirae** (*Toluifera p.*)	PERUBALSAM BALMTREE
TOLUTANUM (*Balsam of Tolu*)	**M. balsamum** (*toluiferum*)	TOLUBALSAM B.
Bamboo Brier Root. SMILAX		
Baobab. ADANSONIA		
BAPTISIA (*Wild Indigo*)	**Baptisia tinctoria**	YELLOW WILDINDIGO
Barbados Nut. JATROPA		
Barley. HORDEUM		
Barley Malt. MALTUM		
BARRINGTONIA	**Barringtonia speciosa**	INDIA BARRINGTONIA
BASSIA (*Illipi Butter Tree*)	**Madhuca indica** (*Bassia latifolia*)	ILLIPE BUTTERTREE
BASSIA (*Mowrah*)	**M. longifolia** (*Bassia l.*)	MOWRA B.
BATIATOR RADIX (*Batiator Root*)	**Vernonia nigritiana**	NIGERIAN IRONWEED
Bayberry Bark. MYRICA		
BAYCURU RADIX (*Baycuru Root*)	**Limonium brasiliense** (*Statice brasiliensis*)	BRAZIL SEA-LAVENDER
Bay Laurel Leaves. LAURUS		
BDELLIUM (*Bissabol*)	**Commiphora africana**	AFRICAN MYRRHTREE
BDELLIUM (*Bissabol*) *See also* OPOPANAX	**C. mukul**	MUKUL M.
Beaked Hazel. CORYLUS		
Bearberry. UVA URSI		
Bears Foot Root. HELLEBORUS FOETIDUS		
Bebeeru. NECTANDRAE CORTEX		
BELLADONNAE FOLIUM (*Deadly Nightshade Leaf*)	**Atropa belladonna**	BELLADONNA
BELLADONNAE RADIX (*Deadly Nightshade Root*)	"	"
Benne Plant. SESAMUM		
BENZOINUM (*Siam Benzoin*)	**Styrax tonkinensis** or other spp. of Styrax	TONKIN SNOWBELL
BENZOINUM (*Sumatra Benzoin*)	**S. benzoin**	SUMATRA S.
BERBERIS (*Oregon Grape Root*)	**Mahonia aquifolium** (*Berberis a.*)	OREGONGRAPE
BERBERIS (*Oregon Grape Root*)	**M. nervosa** (*Berberis n.; Odostemon nervosus*)	CASCADES MAHONIA
BERTHOLLETIA (*Brazil Nut*)	**Bertholletia excelsa**	BRAZILNUT
Betel Nut. ARECA		
Beth Root. TRILLIUM		
BETONICA (*Wood Betony*)	**Stachys officinalis** (*Betonica o.*)	COMMON BETONY

Drug Name	Plant Source: Botanical Name	Plant Source: S.P.N. Common Name
BETULA ALBA (*European White Birch*) *See also* OLEUM BETULAE EMPYREUMATICUM	**Betula pendula** (*alba*)	EUROPEAN WHITE BIRCH
BIDENS (*Spanish Needles*)	**Bidens bipinnata**	SPANISHNEEDLES
Birch Bark. CORTEX BETULAE		
Bissabol. BDELLIUM		
BISTORTA (*Bistort Root*)	**Polygonum bistorta** (*Bistorta officinalis*)	EUROPEAN BISTORT
Biting Stonecrop. SEDUM		
Bitter		
Apple. COLOCYNTHIS		
Bark. PINCKNEYA		
Candytuft. IBERIS		
Herb. CENTAURIUM		
Milkwort. POLYGALA		
Stick. CHIRATA		
Bittersweet. CELASTRUS and DULCAMARA		
Black Alder. PRINOS		
Black Baneberry. ACTAEA		
Blackberry Bark. RUBUS		
Black		
Caraway. NIGELLA		
Cohosh. CIMICIFUGA		
Haw. VIBURNUM PRUNIFOLIUM		
Locust Tree. ROBINIA		
Walnut. JUGLANS NIGRA		
Bladder Senna. COLUTEA		
Bladderwrack. FUCUS		
Blessed Thistle. CNICUS		
Blood Root. SANGUINARIA		
Blueberry. VACCINIUM		
Blue Cohosh. CAULOPHYLLUM		
Blue Flag. IRIS VERSICOLOR		
Blue Gum Leaves. EUCALYPTUS		
Blue Vervain. VERBENA		
BLUMEA	**Blumea lacera** or other spp. of Blumea	MALAY BLUMEA
BOCCONIA	**Bocconia arborea**	TREE BOCCONIA
BOCCONIA	**Macleaya cordata** (*Bocconia c.*)	PINK PLUMEPOPPY
Bog Moss. SPHAGNUM		
Bois Cochon. TETRAGASTRIS		
BOLDUS (*Boldo Leaves*)	**Peumus boldus**	BOLDUTREE
Bonduc Seed. SEMEN BONDUC		
Boneset. EUPATORIUM		
BORAGO (*Borage*)	**Borago officinalis**	COMMON BORAGE
Bottle Gourd. LAGENARIA		
Bourbon Tea. ANGRAECUM		
Bouvardia. TROMPATILA		
BOWDICHIA	**Bowdichia virgilioides**	ALCORNOCO
Bowmans Root. GILLENIA		
BRAGANTIA	**Bragantia wallichi**	ALPAMROOT BRAGANTIA
BRAYERA (*Kousso*)	**Hagenia abyssinica** (*Brayera a.*)	KUSSOTREE
Brazil Nut. BERTHOLLETIA		
Brazilwood. LIGNUM BRAZILIENSE		
Broom Tops. SCOPARIUS		
BRYONIA (*Bryony*)	**Bryonia alba**	WHITE BRYONY
BRYONIA (*Bryony*)	**B. dioica**	REDBERRY B.
BUCHU (*Short Buchu*)	**Barosma betulina**	SHORT BUCHU
BUCHU (*Oval Buchu*)	**B. crenulata**	OVALLEAF B.
BUCHU (*Long Buchu*)	**B. serratifolia**	LONGLEAF B.
Buckbean. MENYANTHES		
Buckthorn Bark. FRANGULA		
Buckthorn Berries. RHAMNUS CATHARTICA		
Buffalo Berry. LEPARGYRAEA		
Bugle. AJUGA		
Bugleweed. LYCOPUS		

Drug Name	Plant Source: Botanical Name	Plant Source: S.P.N. Common Name
Burdock Root. LAPPA		
Burgundy Pitch. PIX BURGUNDICA		
Bush Honeysuckle. DIERVILLA		
Butter and Eggs. LINARIA		
Butternut Bark. JUGLANS		
Butterwort. PINGUICULA		
Button Bush. CEPHALANTHUS		
Button Snakeroot. ERYNGIUM		
BUXUS (*Evergreen Box*)	**Buxus sempervirens**	COMMON BOX
CAAPI	**Banisteriopsis caapi** (*Banisteria c.*)	CAAPI
Cabbage Tree Bark. CORTEX VOUACAPOUAE		
Cacao Butter. OLEUM THEOBROMATIS		
CACAO PRAEPARATUM (*Cacao*) *See also* OLEUM THEOBROMATIS	**Theobroma cacao**	CACAO
CACUR	**Cucumis myriocarpus**	GOOSEBERRYGOURD
Caferana. TACHIA		
Calabar Bean. PHYSOSTIGMA		
CALAMUS (*Sweet Flag*)	**Acorus calamus**	DRUG SWEETFLAG
CALENDULA (*Marigold*)	**Calendula officinalis**	POTMARIGOLD CALENDULA
California		
Fever Bush. GARRYA FREMONTII		
Laurel. UMBELLULARIA		
Poppy. ESCHSCHOLTZIA		
Cali Nuts. SEMEN CALI		
CALOTROPIS (*Mudar*)	**Calotropis gigantea**	AKUND CALOTROPE
CALOTROPIS (*Mudar*)	**C. procera**	FAFTAN C.
CALUMBA (*Colombo*)	**Jateorhiza palmata**	CALUMBAROOT
CALYCANTHUS (*Sweet Shrub*)	**Calycanthus floridus**	COMMON SWEETSHRUB
CALYSTEGIA	**Convolvulus soldanella** (*Calystegia s.*)	SEASHORE GLORYBIND
CAMBOGIA (*Gamboge*)	**Garcinia hanburyi**	SIAM GAMBOGETREE
CAMELLIA	**Camellia japonica**	COMMON CAMELLIA
CAMPHORA (*Camphor*)	**Cinnamomum camphora**	CAMPHORTREE
Cam Wood. LIGNUM BAPHIAE		
Canadian Hemp. APOCYNUM		
Canary Seed. SEMEN CANARIENSE		
CANDELILLA CERA (*Candelilla Wax*)	**Pedilanthus pavonis**	WAX SLIPPERFLOWER
CANELLA (*White Cinnamon*)	**Canella winterana**	CINNAMON CANELLA
CANNABIS (*Indian Hemp*)	**Cannabis sativa**	HEMP
CAPPARIS (*Capers*)	**Capparis spinosa**	COMMON CAPER
CAPSELLA (*Shepherdspurse*)	**Capsella bursa-pastoris**	SHEPHERDSPURSE
CAPSICUM (*Cayenne Pepper*) *See also* PAPRIKA and TABASCO	**Capsicum frutescens** (*annuum*)	BUSH REDPEPPER

The taxonomic authorities of this edition of S.P.N. maintain that Capsicum annuum is indistinguishable from C. frutescens, remanding the former to synonymy. Dr. Youngken maintains that there are definite histological (as well as pharmaceutical) differences between the two.

Drug Name	Plant Source: Botanical Name	Plant Source: S.P.N. Common Name
CAPULINCULLO	**Rhamnus californica**	CALIFORNIA BUCKTHORN
Caraway Seed. CARUM		
CARBO LIGNI (*Charcoal*)	**Acer** spp.	MAPLE
CARBO LIGNI (*Charcoal*)	**Populus** spp.	POPLAR
CARBO LIGNI (*Charcoal*)	**Salix** spp.	WILLOW
CARDAMINE (*Cuckoo Flower*)	**Cardamine pratensis**	CUCKOO BITTERCRESS
CARDAMOMI SEMEN (*Cardamom Seed*)	**Elettaria cardamomum**	CARDAMON
CARDAMOMUM (*Cardamom Fruit*) *See also* OLEUM CARDAMOMI	"	"
CAROTA (*Wild Carrot*)	**Daucus carota sativa**	GARDEN CARROT
CARTHAMUS (*American Saffron*)	**Carthamus tinctorius**	SAFFLOWER

Drug Name	Plant Source: Botanical Name	Plant Source: S.P.N. Common Name
CARUM (*Caraway Seed*) *See also* OLEUM CARI	**Carum carvi**	CARAWAY
CARYA (*Hickory*)	**Carya** spp. (*Hicoria*)	HICKORY
CARYOPHYLLUS (*Clove*) *See also* OLEUM CARYOPHYLLI	**Syzygium aromaticum** (*Caryophyllus aromaticus; Eugenia aromatica; E. caryophyllata*)	CLOVETREE
CASCARA AMARGA (*Honduras Bark*)	**Sweetia panamensis**	BILLYWEBB SWEETIA
CASCARA SAGRADA (*Rhamnus Purshiana*)	**Rhamnus purshiana**	CASCARA BUCKTHORN
CASEARIA	**Casearia esculenta**	
Cashew-nut. ANACARDIUM		
CASIMIROA (*White Sapota*)	**Casimiroa edulis**	WHITESAPOTE
Cassava Starch. AMYLUM MANIHOT		
CASSIA FISTULA (*Purging Cassia*)	**Cassia fistula** (*Cathartocarpus f.*)	GOLDENSHOWER SENNA
CASSIA MARILANDICA (*American Senna*)	**C. marilandica**	WILD S.
Cassumniar. ZERUMBET		
CASTANEA (*Chestnut Leaves*)	**Castanea dentata**	AMERICAN CHESTNUT
CASTELA (*Chaparro Amargosa*)	**Castela texana**	ALLTHORN CASTELA (*Amargosa*)
Castor Oil Bean. RICINUS		
CATALPA (*Indian Bean*)	**Catalpa bignonioides**	SOUTHERN CATALPA
CATARIA (*Catnip*)	**Nepeta cataria**	CATNIP
CATECHU (*Black Catechu*)	**Acacia catechu**	CATECHU ACACIA
CATHA (*Abyssinian Tea*)	**Catha edulis**	ARABIANTEA (*Kat*)
Cativa. RESINA PRIORIA		
CAULOPHYLLUM (*Blue Cohosh*)	**Caulophyllum thalictroides**	BLUE COHOSH
CAYAPONIA (*Silver Manso*)	**Cayaponia globosa**	
Cayenne Pepper. CAPSICUM		
CEANOTHUS (*New Jersey Tea*)	**Ceanothus americanus**	JERSEYTEA CEANOTHUS
CECROPIA (*Cecropia Obtusa*)	**Cecropia obtusa**	MEDICINAL PUMPWOOD
CEDRELA (*Indian Mahogany*) *See also* GUMMI CEDRELAE	**Toona ciliata** (*Cedrela toona*)	BURMA TOON
CEDRON	**Simaba cedron**	CEDRON SIMABA
Celandine Poppy. STYLOPHORUM		
CELASTRUS (*Panicled Bittersweet*)	**Celastrus paniculata**	PANICLED BITTERSWEET
CELASTRUS (*American Bittersweet*)	**C. scandens**	AMERICAN B.
Celery Seed. APII FRUCTUS		
CENTAURIUM (*Bitter Herb*)	**Centaurium umbellatum** (*Erythraea centaurium*)	DRUG CENTAURIUM
Centuryplant. AGAVE		
CEPA (*Onion*)	**Allium cepa**	GARDEN ONION
CEPHALANTHUS (*Button Bush*)	**Cephalanthus occidentalis**	COMMON BUTTONBUSH
Cephan-Mahi. AGELAEA		
CERCIS (*Judas Tree*)	**Cercis canadensis**	EASTERN REDBUD
CEREUS	**Echinocereus reichenbachi** (*Cereus caespitosus*)	LACE ECHINOCEREUS
CETRARIA (*Iceland Moss*)	**Cetraria islandica**	ICELANDMOSS
CHAMPACA	**Michelia champaca**	CHAMPAC MICHELIA
Chaparro Amargosa. CASTELA		
Charcoal. CARBO LIGNI		
CHEIRANTHUS (*Wallflower*)	**Cheiranthus cheiri**	COMMON WALLFLOWER
Cheken. EUGENIA CHEKEN		
CHELIDONIUM (*Great Celandine*)	**Chelidonium majus**	GREATER CELANDINE
CHELONE (*Balmony Leaves*)	**Chelone glabra** (*alba*)	WHITE TURTLEHEAD
Cherry. PRUNUS		
Cherry Laurel Leaves. LAUROCERASUS		
Chervil. ANTHRISCUS		
Chestnut Leaves. CASTANEA		
Chicory. CICHORIUM		

Drug Name	Plant Source: Botanical Name	Plant Source: S.P.N. Common Name
Chilbinj. STRYCHNOS POTATORUM		
CHIMAPHILA (*Pipsissewa*)	**Chimaphila umbellata**	COMMON PIPSISSEWA
China Morada. POGONOPUS		
Chinese Sumac. AILANTHUS		
Chinese Tallow Tree. SAPIUM		
CHIONANTHUS (*Fringe Tree Bark*)	**Chionanthus virginicus**	WHITE FRINGETREE
CHIONE (*Palo Blanco*) *See also* OLEUM CHIONE	**Chione glabra**	SMOOTH CHIONE
CHIRATA (*Bitter Stick*)	**Swertia chirayita** (*chirata*)	CHIRETTA SWERTIA
CHONDRUS (*Irish Moss*)	**Chondrus crispus**	IRISHMOSS
CHONDRUS (*Irish Moss*)	**Gigartina mamillosa**	
CHRYSAROBINUM (*Chrysarobin*) *See also* ARAROBA	**Andira araroba** (*Vataireopsis a.; Vouacapoua a.*)	GOA ANGELINTREE
CICHORIUM (*Chicory*)	**Cichorium intybus**	COMMON CHICORY
CICUTA (*American Water Hemlock*)	**Cicuta maculata**	SPOTTED WATERHEMLOCK
CICUTA (*European Water Hemlock*)	**C. virosa**	EUROPEAN W.
CIMICIFUGA (*Black Cohosh*)	**Cimicifuga racemosa**	COHOSH BUGBANE
CINCHONA (*Yellow Cinchona*)	**Cinchona calisaya**	YELLOWBARK CINCHONA
CINCHONA (*Yellow Cinchona*)	**C. ledgeriana**	LEDGERBARK C.
CINCHONA (*Red Cinchona*) *See also* QUININA	**C. succirubra** and its hybrids	REDBARK C.
CINERARIA (*Dusty Miller*)	**Senecio cineraria** (*Cineraria maritima*)	SILVER GROUNDSEL
CINNAMOMUM (*Saigon Cinnamon*)	**Cinnamomum loureiri**	CASSIAFLOWERTREE
CINNAMOMUM CASSIA (*Cassia Cinnamon*) *See also* OLEUM CINNAMOMI	**C. cassia**	CASSIABARKTREE
CINNAMOMUM BURMANNI (*Fagot Cinnamon*)	**C. burmani**	MALAY CINNAMON
CINNAMOMUM ZEYLANICUM (*Ceylon Cinnamon*)	**C. zeylanicum**	CEYLON C.
Cinquefoil. POTENTILLA		
CITRULLUS (*Water Melon Seed*)	**Citrullus vulgaris**	WATERMELON
Cleavers. GALIUM		
CLEMATIS (*Virgins Bower*) Other spp. of Clematis sometimes enter into the production of this drug.	**Clematis recta** (*erecta*)	GROUND CLEMATIS
Climbing Lily. GLORIOSA		
Clove. CARYOPHYLLUS		
Clove Bark. CORTEX CARYOPHYLLATUS		
Clove Pink. DIANTHUS		
CNICUS (*Blessed Thistle*)	**Cnicus benedictus** (*Carduus b.; Centaurea benedicta*)	BLESSEDTHISTLE
CNIDIUM (*Cnidium Root*)	**Selinum officinale** (*Cnidium o.*)	DRUG SELINUM
COCA (*Coca Leaves*); COCAINA (*Cocaine*)	**Erythroxylum coca**	HUANUCO COCAINETREE
COCA (*Coca Leaves*); COCAINA (*Cocaine*)	**E. novogranatense**	PERUVIAN C.
COCA (*Coca Leaves*); COCAINA (*Cocaine*)	**E. truxillense**	TRUJILLO C.
COCCULUS (*Fish Berry*)	**Anamirta cocculus**	MALAY FISHBERRY
COCHLEARIA (*Common Scurvy Grass*)	**Cochlearia officinalis**	COMMON SCURVYWEED
COCILLANA (*Guapi Bark*)	**Guarea rusbyi**	RUSBY MUSKWOOD
Cocklebur. XANTHIUM		
Cocoa Butter. OLEUM THEOBROMATIS		
COFFEA TOSTA (*Roasted Coffee*)	**Coffea arabica**	ARABIAN COFFEE
COFFEA TOSTA	**C. liberica**	LIBERIAN C.
Cola. KOLA		
COLCHICI CORMUS (*Meadow Saffron Corm*)	**Colchicum autumnale**	COMMON AUTUMNCROCUS
COLCHICI SEMEN (*Meadow Saffron Seed*)	"	"
COLCHICINA (*Colchicine*)	"	"

Drug Name	Plant Source: Botanical Name	Plant Source: S.P.N. Common Name
COLLINSONIA (*Stone Root*)	**Collinsonia canadensis**	CITRONELLA HORSEBALM
COLOCYNTHIS (*Bitter Apple*)	**Citrullus colocynthis**	COLOCYNTH
Colombo. CALUMBA		
Colophony. RESINA		
Colorado Mountain Sage. ARTEMISIA FRIGIDA		
Coltsfoot. FARFARA		
COLUBRINA (*Mabee Bark*)	**Ceanothus reclinatus**	SNAKEROOT CEANOTHUS
Columbine. AQUILEGIA		
COLUTEA (*Bladder Senna*)	**Colutea arborescens**	COMMON BLADDERSENNA
COMBRETUM (*Jungleweed*)	**Combretum sundaicum**	SUNDAI COMBRETUM
Comfrey Root. SYMPHYTUM		
COMMELINA (*Dayflower*)	**Commelina communis**	COMMON DAYFLOWER
COMMELINA (*Dayflower*)	**C. tuberosa**	TUBER D.
COMPTONIA (*Sweet Fern*)	**Comptonia peregrina** (*asplenifolia*)	SWEETFERN
CONDURANGO (*Condurango Bark*)	**Marsdenia cundurango**	CONDORVINE
Cone Flower. ECHINACEA		
CONESSI CORTEX (*Conessi Bark*)	**Holarrhena antidysenterica**	CONESSI HOLARRHENA
CONIUM (*Poison Hemlock*)	**Conium maculatum**	POISONHEMLOCK
CONNARUS	**Connarus guianensis**	GUIANA ZEBRAWOOD
CONTRAYERVA (*Contrayerba*)	**Dorstenia contrajerva**	CONTRAYERVA TORUSHERB
CONVALLARIAE FLORES (*Lily-of-the-valley Flowers*)	**Convallaria majalis**	LILYOFTHEVALLEY
CONVALLARIAE RADIX (*Lily-of-the-valley Root*)	"	"
COPAIBA (*Balsam Copaiba*)	**Copaifera langsdorfi** and other S. Amer. spp. of Copaifera	BALSAM COPALTREE
COPAL (*Inhambane Copal*)	**C. conjugata**	INHAMBANE C.
COPAL (*West African Copal*)	**C. copallifera**	SIERRALEONE C.
COPAL (*South American Copal*)	**Hymenaea courbaril**	COURBARIL
COPAL (*Zanzibar Copal*)	**Trachylobium verrucosum**	
COPTIS (*Goldthread*)	**Coptis groenlandica**	COMMON GOLDTHREAD
Coral Bean. SOPHORA		
CORALLORRHIZA (*Coral Root*)	**Corallorrhiza odontorhiza**	LATE CORALROOT
CORIANDRUM (*Coriander Seed*) *See also* OLEUM CORIANDRI	**Coriandrum sativum**	CORIANDER
CORIARIA (*Tanners Sumac*)	**Coriaria myrtifolia**	MYRTLE CORIARIA
Cork. SUBER		
Corn Silk. ZEA		
Corn Smut. USTILAGO		
Corn Starch. AMYLUM		
CORNUS (*Dogwood Bark*)	**Cornus florida**	FLOWERING DOGWOOD
CORONILLA	**Coronilla scorpioides**	SCORPION CORONILLA
CORTEX		
BETULAE (*Birch Bark*) *See also* METHYLIS SALICYLAS	**Betula lenta**	SWEET BIRCH
CARYOPHYLLATUS (*Clove Bark*)	**Dicypellium caryophyllatum**	CLOVEBARKTREE
CULILIBAN (*Culiliwan*)	**Cinnamomum culilawan**	CULIBAN CINNAMON
VOUACAPOUAE (*Cabbage Tree Bark*)	**Andira inermis** (*jamaicensis; Vouacapoua americana*)	CABBAGE ANGELINTREE
CORYDALIS (*Turkey Corn*)	**Dicentra canadensis** (*Bikukulla c.*)	SQUIRRELCORN BLEEDINGHEART
CORYDALIS (*Dutchmans Breeches*)	**D. cucullaria** (*Bikukulla c.*)	DUTCHMANSBREECHES
CORYLUS (*American Hazelnut*)	**Corylus americana**	AMERICAN FILBERT
CORYLUS (*Filbert*)	**C. avellana**	EUROPEAN F.
CORYLUS (*Beaked Hazel*)	**C. cornuta** (*rostrata*)	BEAKED F. (*Beaked Hazel*)
COSCINIUM (*False Calumba*)	**Coscinium fenestratum**	CALUMBAWOOD
COTO (*True Coto Bark*)	**Aniba coto**	COTOBARK
Cotton. GOSSYPII		
COTULA (*May Weed*)	**Anthemis cotula**	MAYWEED CAMOMILE

Drug Name	Plant Source: Botanical Name	Plant Source: S.P.N. Common Name
COTYLEDON (*Pennywort*)	**Umbilicus pendulinus** (*Cotyledon umbilicus*)	NODDING NAVELWORT.
Couch Grass. TRITICUM		
Cowhage. MUCUNA		
Cowparsnip. HERACLEUM		
Cow Tree. PALO DE VACA		
Cramp Bark. VIBURNUM OPULUS		
Cranesbill. GERANIUM		
CRATAEGUS (*English Hawthorn*)	**Crataegus oxyacantha**	ENGLISH HAWTHORN
CROCUS (*Saffron*)	**Crocus sativus**	SAFFRON CROCUS
Crowfoot. RANUNCULUS		
CRYPTOCARYA	**Cryptocarya australis**	GRAY CRYPTOCARYA
Crystal Tea. LEDUM		
CUBEBA (*Cubebs*)	**Piper cubeba**	CUBEB PEPPER
Cube Root. LONCHOCARPUS		
Cuckoo Flower. CARDAMINE		
Cudbear. PERSIO		
Culiliwan. CORTEX CULILIBAN		
Culvers Root. LEPTANDRA		
CUMINUM (*Cumin Seed*)	**Cuminum cyminum**	CUMIN
CUNILA (*American Dittany*)	**Cunila origanoides** (*mariana*)	MARYLAND STONEMINT
Cup-flower. NIEREMBERGIA		
CURARE (*Upper Amazon Curare*)	**Strychnos castelnaei**	AMAZON POISONNUT
CURARE (*British Guiana Curare; Woorari*) Other spp. of Strychnos enter, but to a lesser extent, in the commercial supply of Curare.	**S. toxifera**	CURARE P.
CURCUMA (*Turmeric*)	**Curcuma longa**	COMMON TURMERIC
Curry Leaves. FOLIA MURRAYAE		
CUSPARIAE CORTEX (*Cusparia Bark*)	**Galipea officinalis**	ANGOSTURA BARKTREE
Cyani Flowers. FLORES CYANI		
CYCLAMEN (*Sowbread*)	**Cyclamen europaeum**	EUROPEAN CYCLAMEN
CYDONIUM (*Quince Seed*)	**Cydonia oblonga**	COMMON QUINCE
CYNARA (*French Artichoke*)	**Cynara scolymus**	ARTICHOKE (*Globe A.*)
CYNOGLOSSUM (*Hounds Tongue*)	**Cynoglossum officinale**	COMMON HOUNDSTONGUE
CYPRIPEDIUM (*Lady Slipper Root*)	**Cypripedium calceolus pubescens**	YELLOW EUROPEAN LADYSLIPPER
CYTISUS (*Golden Chain*)	**Laburnum anagyroides** (*vulgare; Cytisus laburnum*)	GOLDENCHAIN LABURNUM
Daffodil. NARCISSUS		
DAMIANA (*Turnera*)	**Turnera diffusa** (*aphrodisiaca; T. d. aphrodisiaca*)	DAMIANA TURNERA
DAMMARA (*Green Damar*)	**Shorea** spp.	SHOREA
Dandelion. TARAXACUM		
DAPHNANDRA	**Daphnandra micrantha**	SASSAFRAS DAPHNANDRA
Darnel. LOLIUM		
Davids Root. RADIX CAINCAE		
Dayflower. COMMELINA		
Deadly Nightshade. BELLADONNAE		
Deathcamas. ZYGADENUS		
DELPHINIUM (*Larkspur Seed*)	**Delphinium ajacis**	ROCKET LARKSPUR
DERRIS (*Tuba Root*)	**Derris elliptica**	TUBAROOT JEWELVINE
DERRIS (*Tuba Root*)	**D. malaccensis**	MALACCA J.
Devils Club Root. OPLOPANAX		
Devils Shoe Strings. TEPHROSIA		
DIANTHUS (*Clove Pink*)	**Dianthus caryophyllus**	CLOVE PINK; CARNATION
DICENTRA	**Dicentra pusilla**	LITTLE BLEEDINGHEART
DIERVILLA (*Bush Honeysuckle*)	**Diervilla lonicera** (*trifida*)	DWARF BUSHHONEYSUCKLE

Drug Name	Plant Source: Botanical Name	Plant Source: S.P.N. Common Name
DIGITALIS (*Foxglove*)	**Digitalis purpurea**	COMMON FOXGLOVE
DIGITALIS LANATA (*Grecian Foxglove*)	**D. lanata**	GRECIAN F.
Dill Seed. ANETHI FRUCTUS		
DIOSCOREA (*Wild Yam Root*)	**Dioscorea villosa**	ATLANTIC YAM
DIOSPYROS (*Persimmon*)	**Diospyros virginiana**	COMMON PERSIMMON
DIPTERYX (*Dutch Tonka*)	**Dipteryx odorata** (*Coumarouna o.*)	DUTCH TONKABEAN
DIPTERYX (*English Tonka*)	**D. oppositifolia** (*Coumarouna o.*)	BRITISH T.
DIRCA (*Leatherwood*)	**Dirca palustris**	ATLANTIC LEATHERWOOD
Dita Bark. ALSTONIA		
Divi-Divi. FRUCTUS CAESALPINIAE		
Dock. RUMEX		
Dogbane. APOCYNUM ANDROSAEMIFOLIUM		
Dogwood Bark. CORNUS		
DOUNDAKE (*Dundaki*)	**Nauclea esculenta** (*Sarcocephalus esculentus*)	GUINEAPEACH FATHEADTREE
DRACONTIUM (*Skunk Cabbage*)	**Symplocarpus foetidus** (*Spathyema foetida*)	SKUNKCABBAGE
Dragons Blood. SANGUIS DRACONIA		
DRIMYS (*Winters Bark*) *See also* WINTERA	**Drimys winteri**	WINTERSBARK DRIMYS
DROSERA (*Sundew*)	**Drosera anglica**	ENGLISH SUNDEW
DROSERA (*Sundew*)	**D. longifolia**	NARROWLEAF S.
DROSERA (*Sundew*)	**D. rotundifolia**	ROUNDLEAF S.
DUBOISIA	**Duboisia myoporoides**	CORKWOOD DUBOISIA
DULCAMARA (*Bittersweet*)	**Solanum dulcamara**	BITTER NIGHTSHADE
Dundaki. DOUNDAKE		
Dusty Miller. CINERARIA		
Dutchmans Breeches. CORYDALIS		
Dwarf Elder Root. ARALIA HISPIDA		
ECHINACEA (*Cone Flower*)	**Echinacea angustifolia** (*Brauneria a.*)	BLACKSAMSON ECHINACEA
ECHINACEA	**E. pallida** (*Brauneria p.; Rudbeckia p.*)	PALE E.
ELASTICA (*Rubber*)	**Castilla elastica** (*Castilloa e.*)	PANAMA GUMTREE
ELASTICA (*Rubber*)	**Hevea brasiliensis**	PARA RUBBERTREE
ELASTICA (*Rubber*) Other spp. of Castilla, Hevea, and Manihot also enter into the commercial supply of Elastica.	**Manihot glaziovi**	CEARARUBBERPLANT
ELATERIUM (*Squirting Cucumber*)	**Ecballium elaterium** (*Momordica e.*)	SQUIRTINGCUCUMBER
Elder Flowers. SAMBUCUS		
Elecampane Root. INULA		
ELEMI (*Manila Elemi*)	**Canarium luzonicum**	ELEMI CANARYTREE
ELEMI (*Manila Elemi*) Other spp. of Canarium also enter into the production of Manila Elemi.	**C. commune**	JAVAALMOND C.
English Hawthorn. CRATAEGUS		
English Ivy. HEDERA		
ENTADA (*Garbee Bean*)	**Entada phaseoloides** (*scandens*)	CLIMBING ENTADA
EPHEDRA (*Ma Huang*)	**Ephedra distachya**	JOINTFIR EPHEDRA
EPHEDRA (*Ma Huang*)	**E. equisetina**	MONGOLIAN E.
EPHEDRA (*Ma Huang*)	**E. gerardiana**	GERARD E.
EPHEDRA (*Ma Huang*) Certain other spp. of Ephedra containing Ephedrine also enter into the commercial production of this drug.	**E. sinica**	CHINESE E.
EPHEDRINA (*Ephedrine*)	Ephedra spp.	EPHEDRA
EPIFAGUS (*Epiphegus*)	**Epifagus virginiana**	VIRGINIA BEECHDROPS
EPIGEA (*Trailing Arbutus*)	**Epigaea repens**	TRAILING-ARBUTUS
ERECHTITES (*Fireweed*)	**Erechtites hieracifolia**	AMERICAN BURNWEED
ERGOTA (*Ergot of Rye*)	**Claviceps purpurea**	ERGOT CLAVICEPS
ERIGERON (*Fleabane*)	**Erigeron annuus**	ANNUAL FLEABANE
ERIGERON (*Fleabane*)	**E. canadensis** (*Leptilon canadense*)	HORSEWEED F.
ERIGERON (*Fleabane*)	**E. philadelphicus**	PHILADELPHIA F.

Drug Name	Plant Source: Botanical Name	Plant Source: S.P.N. Common Name
ERIOBOTRYA (*Loquat*)	**Eriobotrya japonica**	LOQUAT
ERIODICTYON (*Yerba Santa*)	**Eriodictyon californicum**	CALIFORNIA YERBASANTA
ERODIUM (*Storks Bill*)	**Erodium cicutarium**	ALFILERIA
ERYNGIUM (*Button Snakeroot*)	**Eryngium aquaticum** (*yuccaefolium*)	BUTTONSNAKEROOT ERYNGO
ERYTHRINA Other spp. of this genus enter into the commercial production of Erythrina.	**Erythrina broteroi**	BROTERO CORALBEAN
ERYTHRONIUM (*Yellow Adders Tongue*)	**Erythronium americanum**	COMMON FAWNLILY
ERYTHROPHLEUM (*Sassy Bark*)	**Erythrophleum guineense**	CASCA REDWATERTREE
ESCHSCHOLTZIA (*California Poppy*)	**Eschscholtzia californica**	CALIFORNIAPOPPY
Esculin. AESCULIN		
EUCALYPTUS (*Blue Gum Leaves*) *See also* OLEUM EUCALYPTI	**Eucalyptus globulus**	TASMANIAN BLUE EUCALYPTUS
EUGENIA CHEKEN (*Cheken*)	**Eugenia chequen** (*cheken*)	CHEKEN EUGENIA
EUGENIA JAMBOLANA (*Jambul*)	**Syzygium cumini** (*jambolanum; Eugenia c.; E. jambolana*)	JAMBOLAN
EUONYMUS (*Wahoo Bark*)	**Euonymus atropurpureus**	EASTERN WAHOO
EUPATORIUM (*Boneset*)	**Eupatorium perfoliatum**	BONESET
EUPHORBIA COROLLATA (*Flowering Spurge*)	**Euphorbia corollata**	FLOWERINGSPURGE EUPHORBIA
EUPHORBIA PILULIFERA (*Pill-bearing Spurge*)	**E. pilulifera**	PILLPOD E.
EUPHORBIUM (*Gum Euphorbium*)	**E. resinifera**	GUM E.
EUPHRASIA (*Eyebright*)	**Euphrasia officinalis**	DRUG EYEBRIGHT
European Goats Rue. GALEGA		
European Mistletoe. VISCUM		
European Pennyroyal. MENTHA PULEGIUM		
European Sappan. LIGNUM SAPPAN		
European Water Hemlock. CICUTA		
European White Birch. BETULA ALBA		
Evening Primrose. OENOTHERA		
Evergreen Box. BUXUS		
Eyebright. EUPHRASIA		
FABIANA (*Pichi*)	**Fabiana imbricata**	PERU FALSEHEATH
False Columba. COSCINIUM		
False Unicorn. HELONIAS		
FARFARA (*Coltsfoot*)	**Tussilago farfara**	COMMON COLTSFOOT
Feather Grass. STIPA		
Female Fern. ATHYRIUM		
Fennel Seed. FOENICULUM		
Fenugreek. FOENUM GRAECUM		
Feverfew. PARTHENIUM		
FICUS (*Fig*)	**Ficus carica**	COMMON FIG
Figwort. SCROPHULARIA		
Filbert. CORYLUS		
Fire Pink. SILENE		
Fireweed. ERECHTITES		
Fish Berry. COCCULUS		
Flaxseed. LINUM		
Fleabane. ERIGERON		
FLORES CYANI (*Cyani Flowers*)	**Centaurea cyanus**	CORNFLOWER
FLORES PRUNI	**Prunus spinosa**	BLACKTHORN; SLOE
FOENICULUM (*Fennel Seed*) *See also* OLEUM FOENICULI	**Foeniculum vulgare**	COMMON FENNEL
FOENUM GRAECUM (*Fenugreek*)	**Trigonella foenumgraecum**	FENUGREEK TRIGONELLA
FOLIA MURRAYAE (*Curry Leaves*)	**Murraya koenigi**	CURRYLEAFTREE

Drug Name	Plant Source: Botanical Name	Plant Source: S.P.N. Common Name
FOLIA PLANTAGINIS (*Plantain Leaves*)	**Plantago major**	RIPPLESEED PLANTAIN
Fools-parsley. AETHUSA		
Foxglove. DIGITALIS		
Fragrant Tailgrape. ARTABOTRYS		
FRANGULA (*Buckthorn Bark*)	**Rhamnus frangula**	GLOSSY BUCKTHORN
FRANKENIA (*Yerba Reuma*)	**Frankenia grandifolia**	YERBAREUMA SEAHEATH
Frankincense. OLIBANUM		
FRASERA (*American Columbo*)	**Frasera carolinensis**	CAROLINA FRASERA
French Artichoke. CYNARA		
Fresh Apple Juice. SUCCUS POMORUM		
Fringe Tree Bark. CHIONANTHUS		
FRUCTUS CAESALPINIAE (*Divi-Divi*)	**Caesalpinia coriaria**	DIVIDIVI
FUCUS (*Bladderwrack*)	**Ascophyllum nodosum**	DRUG ROCKWEEP
FUCUS	**Fucus serratus**	CARTWRACK ROCKWEED
FUCUS	**F. vesiculosus**	BLADDERWRACK R.
FUCUS	**Halidrys siliquosa**	DRUG SEAOAK
FUMARIA (*Fumitory*)	**Fumaria officinalis**	DRUG FUMITORY
Furze. ULEX		
FUSTIC (*Old Fustic*)	**Chlorophora tinctoria**	DRUG FUSTICTREE
GALANGA (*Galangal*)	**Alpinia officinarum** (*Languas o.*)	LESSER GALANGAL
GALBANUM	**Ferula galbaniflua**	GALBANUM GIANTFENNEL
GALEGA (*European Goats Rue*)	**Galega officinalis**	COMMON GOATSRUE
GALIUM (*Cleavers*)	**Galium aparine**	CATCHWEED BEDSTRAW
GALLA (*Nutgall*) Galls from other Oriental oaks occasionally enter into the commercial supply of Galla.	**Quercus infectoria**	ALEPPO OAK
GAMBIR (*Pale Catechu*)	**Uncaria gambir** (*Ourouparia g.*)	BENGAL GAMBIR-PLANT
Gamboge. CAMBOGIA		
Garbee Bean. ENTADA		
GARDENIA	**Gardenia jasminoides** (*augusta; florida; grandiflora*)	CAPEJASMINE
Garden Purslane. PORTULACA		
Garlic. ALLIUM		
GARRYA FREMONTII (*California Fever Bush*)	**Garrya fremonti**	FREMONT SILKTASSEL
GAULTHERIA (*Wintergreen*) *See also* METHYLIS SALICYLAS	**Gaultheria procumbens**	CHECKERBERRY WINTERGREEN
GELSEMIUM (*Yellow Jasmine Root*)	**Gelsemium sempervirens**	CAROLINAJESSAMINE
GENTIANA (*Gentian Root*)	**Gentiana lutea**	YELLOW GENTIAN
Georgia or *Bitter Bark.* PINCKNEYA		
GERANIUM (*Cranesbill*)	**Geranium maculatum**	SPOTTED GERANIUM
German Chamaedrys. TEUCRIUM		
German Chamomile. MATRICARIA		
GEUM (*Water Avens*)	**Geum rivale**	WATER AVENS
GILLENIA (*Bowmans Root*)	**Gillenia trifoliata** (*Porteranthus trifoliatus*)	BOWMANSROOT
Ginger. ZINGIBER		
Gingerlily. HEDYCHIUM		
GINSENG (*American Ginseng*)	**Panax quinquefolium** (*Aralia quinquefolia*)	AMERICAN GINSENG
GINSENG (*Chinese Ginseng*)	**P. schinseng** (*ginseng*)	ASIATIC G.
Glandulae Rottlerae. KAMALA		
GLAUCIUM (*Yellow Horned Poppy*)	**Glaucium flavum** (*luteum*)	YELLOW HORNPOPPY
GLECHOMA (*Ground Ivy*)	**Glecoma hederacea** (*Nepeta h.*)	
GLEDITSCHIA (*Honey Locust*)	**Gleditsia triacanthos** (*Gleditschia t.*)	COMMON HONEYLOCUST

Drug Name	Plant Source: Botanical Name	Plant Source: S.P.N. Common Name
GLORIOSA (*Climbing Lily*)	**Gloriosa superba**	MALABAR GLORYLILY
GLYCYRRHIZA (*Spanish Licorice Root*)	**Glycyrrhiza glabra** (typical form)	COMMON LICORICE
GLYCYRRHIZA (*Russian Licorice Root*)	**G. g. glandulifera**	RUSSIAN L.
GLYCYRRHIZA (*Licorice Root, Persian, etc.*)	**G. glabra** var. yielding a yellow and sweet wood	
GNAPHALIUM (*Life-everlasting*)	**Anaphalis margaritacea** (*Antennaria m.*)	COMMON PEARLEVERLASTING
GNAPHALIUM (*Sweet Scented Life-everlasting*)	**Gnaphalium obtusifolium** (*polycephalum*)	FRAGRANT CUDWEED
Goanese Ipecacuanha. NAREGAMIA		
Goa Powder. ARAROBA		
Golden Chain. CYTISUS		
Golden Moss. PENGAWAR DJAMBI		
Golden Seal. HYDRASTIS		
Goldthread. COPTIS		
Gorse. ULEX		
GOSSYPII RADICIS CORTEX (*Cotton Root Bark*)	**Gossypium** spp., cultivated vars. especially of **G. herbaceum** and **G. hirsutum**	COTTON
GOSSYPIUM PURIFICATUM (*Absorbent Cotton*) *See also* OLEUM GOSSYPII SEMINIS	"	"
GRANA PARADISI (*Grains of Paradise*)	**Aframomum melegueta** (*Amomum m.*)	DRUG MELEGUETAPEPPER
GRANATUM (*Pomegranate Bark*)	**Punica granatum**	COMMON POMEGRANATE
GRATIOLA (*Hedgehyssop*)	**Gratiola officinalis**	DRUG HEDGEHYSSOP
Gravel Weed. ACTINOMERIS		
Great Celandine. CHELIDONIUM		
Grecian Foxglove. DIGITALIS LANATA		
GRINDELIA	**Grindelia camporum**	FIELD GUMWEED
GRINDELIA	**G. humilis** (*cuneifolia*)	MARSH G.
GRINDELIA	**G. squarrosa**	CURLYCUP G.
Gromwell. LITHOSPERMUM		
Ground Ivy. GLECHOMA		
Guachamaca. MALOUETIA		
GUAIACUM (*Guaiac Resin*)	**Guajacum officinale**	COMMON LIGNUMVITAE
GUAIACUM (*Guaiac Resin*)	**G. sanctum**	HOLYWOOD L.
Guapi Bark. COCILLANA		
GUARANA (*Guarana Paste*)	**Paullinia cupana**	GUARANA PAULLINIA
Guava. PSIDIUM		
Gulancha. TINOSPORA		
Gum Arabic. ACACIA		
Gum Euphorbium. EUPHORBIUM		
GUMMI		
ALBIZZIAE (*Sassa Gum*)	**Albizzia fastigiata**	FLATCROWN ALBIZZIA
ANOGEISSI (*Indian Gum*)	**Anogeissus latifolia**	BAKLIGUM AXLEWOOD
BASSORA (*Karaya Gum*)	**Cochlospermum religiosum** (*gossypium*)	COTTON SHELLSEED
BREAE (*Brea Gum*)	**Caesalpinia praecox**	BREAGUM CAESALPINIA
CEDRELAE (*Cedar Gum*) *See also* CEDRELA	**Toona ciliata** (*Cedrela toona*)	BURMA TOON
EUCALYPTI (*Red Gum*) This gum in commerce occasionally derives from other spp. of Eucalyptus.	**Eucalyptus camaldulensis** (*rostrata* Schlecht., *not* Cav.)	LONGBEAK EUCALYPTUS
Kuteera. GUMMI STERCULIAE		
MANGIFERAE (*Mango Gum*)	**Mangifera indica**	COMMON MANGO
PIPTADENIA (*Cebil Gum*)	**Piptadenia cebil**	CEBIL PIPTADENIA
PROSOPIS (*Mesquite Gum*)	**Prosopis chilensis** (*juliflora*)	COMMON MESQUITE
SONORAE (*Sonora Gum*)	**Larrea tridentata** (*Covillea t.*)	COVILLE CREOSOTEBUSH
STERCULIAE (*Indian Tragacanth; Gummi Kuteera*)	**Sterculia urens**	KUTEERAGUM STERCULIA

Drug Name	Plant Source: Botanical Name	Plant Source: S.P.N. Common Name
GUTTA PERCHA The Gutta Percha of commerce is also obtained from other species of Palaquium.	**Palaquium gutta**	MALAY GUTTAPERCHA NATOTREE
GUTTA PERCHA	**Payena leeri**	GUTTAPERCHA PAYENA
GYMNEMA	**Gymnema sylvestre**	AUSTRALIAN COWPLANT
GYMNOCLADUS (*Kentucky Coffee Tree*)	**Gymnocladus dioicus**	KENTUCKY COFFEETREE
HAEMATOXYLON (*Logwood*)	**Haematoxylon campechianum**	LOGWOOD
Hair Cap Moss. POLYTRICHUM		
HAMAMELIDIS FOLIUM (*Witch-hazel Leaf*)	**Hamamelis virginiana**	COMMON WITCHHAZEL
Harts Tongue. SCOLOPENDRIUM		
HEDEOMA (*Pennyroyal*)	**Hedeoma pulegioides**	AMERICAN FALSEPENNYROYAL
HEDERA (*English Ivy*)	**Hedera helix**	ENGLISH IVY
Hedge-garlic. ALLIARIA		
Hedge-hyssop. GRATIOLA		
Hedge Mustard. SISYMBRIUM		
HEDYCHIUM (*Gingerlily*)	**Hedychium spicatum**	SPIKED GINGERLILY
HELENIUM (*Sneezeweed*)	**Helenium autumnale**	COMMON SNEEZEWEED
HELIANTHEMUM (*Rockrose*)	**Crocanthemum canadense**	CANADA FROSTWORT
HELIANTHUS (*Common Sunflower*)	**Helianthus annuus**	COMMON SUNFLOWER
Hellebore. VERATRUM		
HELLEBORUS FOETIDUS (*Bears Foot Root*)	**Helleborus foetidus**	BEARSFOOT HELLEBORE
HELLEBORUS NIGER (*Black Hellebore*)	**H. niger**	CHRISTMASROSE (*Black Hellebore*)
HELONIAS (*False Unicorn*)	**Chamaelirium luteum**	FAIRYWAND
HEMIDESMUS (*Indian Sarsaparilla*)	**Hemidesmus indicus**	INDIA-SARSAPARILLA
Hemlock Pitch. PIX CANADENSIS		
Henbane. HYOSCYAMUS		
Henna. LAWSONIA		
HEPATICA (*Liverwort Leaves*)	**Hepatica americana**	ROUNDLOBE HEPATICA
HERACLEUM (*Common Cowparsnip*)	**Heracleum lanatum**	COMMON COWPARSNIP
HERNIARIA (*Herniary*)	**Herniaria glabra**	COMMON BURSTWORT
HETEROMELES	**Photinia arbutifolia** (*salicifolia; Heteromeles a.; H. salicifolia*)	CHRISTMASBERRY
HEUCHERA (*Alum Root*)	**Heuchera americana**	AMERICAN ALUMROOT
HIBISCUS (*Ambrette Seed*)	**Hibiscus abelmoschus**	MUSKMALLOW
Hickory. CARYA		
HIERACIUM (*Rattlesnake Weed*)	**Hieracium venosum**	POORROBINS HAWKWEED
Hoang-Nan. STRYCHNOS MALACCENSIS		
Hoarhound. MARRUBIUM		
Hog Fennel. PEUCEDANUM		
HOLIGARNA	**Holigarna longifolia**	BLACKVARNISHTREE
HOLIGARNA	**Semecarpus longifolius**	LONGLEAF MARKINGNUT
Holly. ILEX		
Holy Herb. SANTOLINA		
Honduras Bark. CASCARA AMARGA		
Honey Locust. GLEDITSCHIA		
Honeysuckle. LONICERA		
Hops. HUMULUS		
HORDEUM (*Barley*)	**Hordeum distichon**	TWOROW BARLEY
HORDEUM (*Barley*) *See also* MALTUM	**H. vulgare**	BARLEY
Horsechestnut. AESCULUS		
Horse Gentian. TRIOSTEUM		
Horsemint. MONARDA		
Horse Nettle Berries. SOLANUM		
Horseradish Root. ARMORACIAE RADIX		

Drug Name	Plant Source: Botanical Name	Plant Source: S.P.N. Common Name
Hounds Tongue. CYNOGLOSSUM		
Houseleek. SEMPERVIVUM		
HUMULUS (*Hops*) *See also* LUPULINUM	**Humulus lupulus**	COMMON HOP
HURA (*Sandbox Tree*)	**Hura crepitans**	SANDBOXTREE
HYDRANGEA (*Seven-barks*)	**Hydrangea arborescens**	SMOOTH HYDRANGEA
HYDRASTIS (*Golden Seal*)	**Hydrastis canadensis**	GOLDENSEAL
Hyena Poison. TOXICODENDRON		
HYOSCYAMUS (*Henbane*)	**Hyoscyamus niger**	BLACK HENBANE
HYPERICUM (*St. Johns Wort*)	**Hypericum perforatum**	COMMON ST. JOHNSWORT
HYSSOPUS (*Hyssop*)	**Hyssopus officinalis**	HYSSOP
IBERIS (*Bitter Candytuft*)	**Iberis amara**	ROCKET CANDYTUFT
Iceland Moss. CETRARIA		
Iceplant. MESEMBRYANTHEMUM		
IGNATIA (*St. Ignatius Bean*)	**Strychnos ignati**	ST. IGNATIUS POISONNUT
ILEX (*Holly*)	**Ilex aquifolium**	ENGLISH HOLLY
ILLICIUM (*Star Anise*) *See also* OLEUM ANISI	**Illicium verum**	TRUESTAR ANISETREE
Illipi Butter Tree. BASSIA		
IMPATIENS (*Balsam Weed*)	**Impatiens biflora**	SPOTTED SNAPWEED
IMPATIENS	**I. pallida**	PALE S.
IMPERATORIA (*Masterwort*)	**Peucedanum ostruthium** (*Imperatoria o.*)	MASTERWORT HOGFENNEL
Indian		
Bean. CATALPA		
Cucumber. MEDEOLA		
Hemp. CANNABIS		
Mahogany. CEDRELA		
Mulberry. MORINDA		
Sarsaparilla. HEMIDESMUS		
Tobacco. LOBELIA		
Tragacanth. GUMMI STERCULIAE		
Turnip. ARUM		
INDICUM (*Indigo*)	**Indigofera suffruticosa**	ANIL INDIGO
INDICUM (*Indigo*) Other spp. of Indigofera also enter into the production of Indigo.	**I. tinctoria**	TRUE I.
Insect Flowers. PYRETHRI FLORES		
INULA (*Elecampane Root*)	**Inula helenium**	ELECAMPANE INULA
IPECACUANHA (*Cartagena Ipecac; Nicaragua I.*)	**Cephaelis acuminata**	
IPECACUANHA (*Rio Ipecac*)	**C. ipecacuanha** (*Psychotria i.*)	
IPOMOEA (*Mexican Scammony*)	**Ipomoea orizabensis**	ORIZABA MORNINGGLORY
IRIS (*Verona Orris Root*)	**Iris germanica** (*vulgaris*)	GERMAN IRIS
IRIS (*Florentine Orris Root*)	**I. g. florentina** (*I. florentina alba*)	ORRISROOT I.
IRIS (*Verona Orris Root*)	**I. pallida**	SWEET I.
IRIS VERSICOLOR (*Blue Flag*)	**I. versicolor**	BLUEFLAG I.
IRIS VERSICOLOR (*Blue Flag*)	**I. virginica**	VIRGINIA I.
Irish Dulse. RHODYMENIA		
Irish Moss. CHONDRUS		
Ironwood. OSTRYA		
ISATIS (*Wood*)	**Isatis tinctoria**	DYERS WOAD
ISOPYRUM	**Isopyrum thalictroides**	MEADOWRUE ISOPYRUM
IWARANCUSA	**Cymbopogon jwarancusa**	IWARANCUSAGRASS
IXORA	**Ixora coccinea**	JUNGLEFLAME IXORA
Jaborandi. PILOCARPUS		
JACARANDA	**Jacaranda** spp.	JACARANDA
JALAPA (*Jalap*)	**Exogonium purga** (*Ipomoea jalapa; I. purga*)	JALAP
Jamaica Dogwood. PISCIDIA		
JAMBOSA (*Jambosa Root*)	**Syzygium jambos** (*Caryophyllus j.; Eugenia j.*)	ROSEAPPLE
JAMBU ASSU	**Piper jaborandi**	JABORANDI PEPPER

Drug Name	Plant Source: Botanical Name	Plant Source: S.P.N. Common Name
Jambul. Eugenia Jambolana		
Japanese Henbane. Scopolia Japonica		
Jatropa (*Barbados Nut*)	**Jatropha curcas**	Barbadosnut
Java Tea. Orthosiphon		
Jeffersonia (*Twinleaf*)	**Jeffersonia diphylla**	American Twinleaf
Jequirity. Abrus		
Jimson Weed. Stramonium		
Judas Tree. Cercis		
Juglans (*Butternut Bark*)	**Juglans cinerea**	Butternut
Juglans Nigra (*Black Walnut*)	**J. nigra**	Eastern Black Walnut
Jujube. Zizyphus		
Jungleweed. Combretum		
Juniperus (*Juniper Berry*) See also Oleum Juniperi	**Juniperus communis**	Common Juniper
Juniperus Virginiana (*Red Cedar*) See also Oleum Juniperi Virginianae	**J. virginiana**	Eastern Redcedar
Kalmia (*Mountain Laurel*)	**Kalmia angustifolia**	Lambkill Kalmia
Kalmia (*Mountain Laurel*)	**K. latifolia**	Mountainlaurel K.
Kamala (*Glandulae Rottlerae*)	**Mallotus philippinensis**	Kamalatree
Kava (*Methysticum*)	**Piper methysticum**	Kava Pepper
Kentucky Coffee Tree. Gymnocladus		
Kidney Bean. Phaseolus		
Kino (*Malabar Kino*)	**Pterocarpus marsupium**	Vengai Padauk
Kola (*Cola*)	**Cola** spp., especially **C. acuminata**	Colanut Sudan C.
Kousso. Brayera		
Krameria (*Brazilian Rhatany*)	**Krameria argentea**	Brazil Krameria
Krameria (*Peruvian Rhatany*)	**K. triandra**	Peruvian K.
Labdanum (*Ladanum*)	**Cistus** spp.	Rockrose
Lacmus (*Litmus*)	**Lecanora** spp.	Lecanora
Lacmus (*Litmus*) And other spp. of Lichens.	**Roccella tinctoria**	Litmus Roccella
Lactucarium (*Wild Lettuce*)	**Lactuca virosa**	Bitter Lettuce
Lady Slipper Root. Cypripedium		
Ladysmantle. Alchemilla		
Lagenaria (*Bottle Gourd*)	**Lagenaria siceraria** (*leucantha*)	Calabash Gourd
Lamium (*White Deadnettle*)	**Lamium album**	White Deadnettle
Lantana (*Yerba Sagrada*)	**Lantana brasiliensis**	Yerbasagrada Lantana
Lappa (*Burdock Root*)	**Arctium lappa** (*Lappa edulis; L. major*)	Great Burdock
Lappa (*Burdock Root*)	**A. minus** (*Lappa minor*)	Smaller B.
Larch Agaric. Agaricus		
Laricis Cortex (*Larch Bark*) See also Terebinthina Laricis	**Larix decidua** (*europaea*)	European Larch
Larkspur Seed. Delphinium		
Lathyrus (*Vetchling*)	**Lathyrus sativus**	Grass Peavine
Laurocerasus (*Cherry Laurel Leaves*)	**Prunus laurocerasus**	Common Laurelcherry
Laurus (*Bay Laurel Leaves*)	**Laurus nobilis**	Grecian Laurel
Lavandula (*Lavender Flowers*) See also Oleum Lavandulae	**Lavandula officinalis** (*spica; vera*)	True Lavender
Lawsonia (*Henna*)	**Lawsonia inermis**	Henna
Leadwort. Plumbago		
Leafcup. Polymnia		
Leatherwood. Dirca		
Ledum (*Crystal Tea*)	**Ledum palustre**	Crystaltea Ledum
Leek. Porrum		

Drug Name	Plant Source: Botanical Name	Plant Source: S.P.N. Common Name
Lemon Peel. Limonis Cortex		
Lemon Verbena. Lippia		
Leonotis (*Lions Ear*)	**Leonotis leonurus**	Drug Lionsear
Leonurus (*Motherwort*)	**Leonurus cardiaca**	Common Motherwort
Lepargyraea (*Buffalo Berry*)	**Shepherdia argentea** (*Lepargyrea a.*)	Silver Buffaloberry
Leptandra (*Culvers Root*)	**Veronicastrum virginicum** (*Leptandra virginica; Veronica v.*)	Culversphysic
Levant Worm Seed. Santonica		
Levisticum (*Lovage*)	**Levisticum officinale** (*Hipposelinum o.*)	Garden Lovage
Lewisia (*Spatlum*)	**Lewisia rediviva**	Bitterroot Lewisia
Liatris (*Spike Gayfeather*)	**Liatris spicata**	Spike Gayfeather
Licorice. Glycyrrhiza		
Life-everlasting. Gnaphalium		
Life Root. Senecio		
Lignum		
Baphiae (*Cam Wood*)	**Baphia nitida**	Shiny Camwood
Braziliense (*Brazilwood*)	**Caesalpinia brasiliensis**	Brazilwood
Caesalpiniae (*Peachwood*)	**C. echinata**	Prickly B.
Rhois Cotini (*Young Fustic*)	**Cotinus coggygria** (*Rhus cotinus*)	Common Smoketree
Sappan (*European Sappan*)	**Caesalpinia sappan** (*Biancaea s.*)	Sappan Caesalpinia
Ligustrum (*Privet*)	**Ligustrum vulgare**	European Privet
Lilac. Syringa		
Lilium (*Annunciation Lily*)	**Lilium candidum**	Madonna Lily
Lily-of-the-valley. Convallaria		
Limonis Cortex (*Lemon Peel*) See also Oleum Limonis	**Citrus limon** (*limonia*)	Lemon
Linaria (*Butter and Eggs*)	**Linaria vulgaris**	Butter-and-eggs Toadflax
Linden Flowers. Tilia		
Linum (*Flaxseed*) See also Oleum Lini	**Linum usitatissimum**	Common Flax
Linum Catharticum (*Purging Flax*)	**L. catharticum**	Purging F.
Lions Ear. Leonotis		
Lippia (*Lemon Verbena*)	**Lippia citriodora**	Lemonverbena Lippia
Liriodendron (*Tulip Tree*)	**Liriodendron tulipifera**	Tuliptree
Lithospermum (*Common Gromwell*)	**Lithospermum officinale**	Common Gromwell
Lithraea	**Lithraea venenosa**	
Litmus. Lacmus		
Liverwort Leaves. Hepatica		
Lizards Tail. Saururus		
Lobelia (*Indian Tobacco*)	**Lobelia inflata**	Indiantobacco Lobelia
Loco (*White Loco*)	**Oxytropis lamberti** (*Astragalus l.*)	Lambert Crazyweed
Loco (*Purple Loco*)	**Astragalus mollissimus**	Woolly Loco
Locust. Robinia		
Logwood. Haematoxylon		
Lolium (*Darnel*)	**Lolium temulentum**	Darnel Ryegrass
Lonchocarpus (*Cube Root*)	**Lonchocarpus** spp., especially **L. nicou**	Lancepod
Lonicera (*Honeysuckle*)	**Lonicera** spp., especially **L. caprifolium**	Honeysuckle Sweet H.
Loquat. Eriobotrya		
Lotus	**Lotus arabicus**	Arabian Deervetch
Lovage. Levisticum		
Luffa (*Vegetable Sponge*)	**Luffa cylindrica**	Suakwa Vegetablesponge
Lungwort. Sticta and Pulmonaria		
Lupinus (*White Lupine*)	**Lupinus albus**	White Lupine
Lupulinum (*Lupulin*) See also Humulus	**Humulus lupulus**	Common Hop
Lycium (*Matrimony Vine*)	**Lycium halimifolium** (*vulgare*)	Matrimonyvine
Lycopodium (*Vegetable Sulphur*)	**Lycopodium clavatum**	Runningpine

Drug Name	Plant Source: Botanical Name	Plant Source: S.P.N. Common Name
LYCOPUS (*Bugleweed*)	**Lycopus virginicus**	VIRGINIA BUGLEWEED
LYCORIS	**Lycoris radiata**	SHORTTUBE LYCORIS
LYTHRUM (*Purple Loosestrife*)	**Lythrum salicaria**	PURPLE LYTHRUM
Mabee Bark. COLUBRINA		
Macassar Nutmeg. MYRISTICA ARGENTEA		
MACIS (*Mace*) *See also* MYRISTICA and OLEUM MYRISTICAE	**Myristica fragrans**	COMMON NUTMEG
Madder. RUBIA		
Ma Huang. EPHEDRA		
Maidenhair Fern. ADIANTUM		
MAJORANA (*Sweet Marjoram*)	**Majorana hortensis** (*Origanum majorana*)	SWEET MARJORAM
Malabar Kino. KINO		
MALAMBO (*Matias Bark*)	**Croton malambo**	MALAMBOBARK CROTON
Male Fern. ASPIDIUM		
MALOUETIA (*Guachamaca*)	**Malouetia nitida**	
MALPIGHIA (*Nance Bark*)	**Malpighia glabra**	BARBADOSCHERRY MALPIGHIA
MALTUM (*Barley Malt*) *See also* HORDEUM	**Hordeum vulgare**	BARLEY
MALVAE FLORES (*Mallow Flowers*)	**Malva neglecta**	
MALVAE FLORES (*Mallow Flowers*)	**M. sylvestris**	HIGH MALLOW
MALVAE FOLIA (*Mallow Leaves*)	**M. neglecta**	
MALVAE FOLIA (*Mallow Leaves*)	**M. sylvestris**	HIGH M.
MANACA (*Vegetable Mercury*)	**Brunfelsia hopeana**	MANACA RAINTREE
Manchineel. MANZANILLO		
MANDRAGORA (*Mandragora Root*)	**Mandragora autumnalis**	AUTUMN MANDRAKE
Mandrake. PODOPHYLLUM		
Mangrove. RHIZOPHORA		
Manila Elemi. ELEMI		
Man-Mu. TANG-KUEI		
MANNA	**Fraxinus ornus**	FLOWERING ASH
MANNA EUCALYPTI (*Australian Manna*)	**Eucalyptus mannifera**	MANNA EUCALYPTUS
Man Root. MICRAMPELIS		
MANZANILLO (*Manchineel*)	**Hippomane mancinella**	MANCHINEEL
MARANTA (*Arrowroot*)	**Maranta arundinacea**	BERMUDA ARROWROOT
Marigold. CALENDULA		
Marjoram. ORIGANUM		
MARRUBIUM (*Hoarhound*)	**Marrubium vulgare**	COMMON HOARHOUND
Marshmallow. ALTHAEA		
MASSOIA (*Massoi Bark*)	**Cinnamomum massoia**	MASSOIA CINNAMON
Masterwort. IMPERATORIA		
MASTICHE (*Mastic*)	**Pistacia lentiscus**	LENTISK PISTACHE
Matias Bark. MALAMBO		
MATICO	**Piper angustifolium**	MATICO PEPPER
MATRICARIA (*German Chamomile*)	**Matricaria chamomilla**	GERMAN-CAMOMILE
Matrimony Vine. LYCIUM		
Maw Seeds. SEMEN PAPAVERIS		
May Weed. COTULA		
Meadow Saffron. COLCHICINA		
MEDEOLA (*Indian Cucumber*)	**Medeola virginiana**	CUCUMBERROOT MEDEOLA
Medlar. MESPILUS		
MELASTOMA	**Melastoma ackermani**	
MELILOTUS (*Yellow Sweet Clover*)	**Melilotus officinalis**	YELLOW SWEETCLOVER
MELISSA (*Common Balm*)	**Melissa officinalis**	COMMON BALM
MENISPERMUM (*Yellow Parilla*)	**Menispermum canadense**	COMMON MOONSEED
MENTHAE PIPERITA (*Peppermint*) *See also* OLEUM MENTHAE PIPERITAE	**Mentha piperita**	PEPPERMINT
MENTHA PULEGIUM (*European Pennyroyal*)	**M. pulegium**	PENNYROYAL MINT
MENTHAE VIRIDIS (*Spearmint*) *See also* OLEUM MENTHAE VIRIDIS	**M. spicata**	SPEARMINT

Drug Name	Plant Source: Botanical Name	Plant Source: S.P.N. Common Name
MENYANTHES (*Buckbean*)	**Menyanthes trifoliata**	COMMON BOGBEAN
Mesbe. SIDA		
Mescal Buttons. ANHALONIUM		
MESEMBRYANTHEMUM (*Iceplant*)	**Mesembryanthemum crystallinum** (*Cryophytum c.*)	ICEPLANT MESEMBRYANTHEMUM
MESENNA (*Musenna*)	**Albizzia anthelmintica**	MUSENNA ALBIZZIA
MESPILUS (*Medlar*)	**Mespilus germanica**	MEDLAR
METHYLIS SALICYLAS (*Methyl Salicylate*) *See also* CORTEX BETULAE	**Betula lenta** (or produced synthetically)	SWEET BIRCH
METHYLIS SALICYLAS *See also* GAULTHERIA	**Gaultheria procumbens**	CHECKERBERRY WINTERGREEN
Methysticum. KAVA		
Mexican Scammony. IPOMOEA		
MEZEREUM (*Mezereon*)	**Daphne gnidium**	SPURGEFLAX DAPHNE
MEZEREUM (*Mezereon*)	**D. laureola**	SPURGELAUREL D.
MEZEREUM (*Mezereon*)	**D. mezereum**	FEBRUARY D.
MICRAMPELIS (*Man Root*)	**Megarrhiza californica** (*fabacea; Echinocystis c.; Marah c.; Micrampelis c.*)	CALIFORNIA BIGROOT
MICROMERIA (*Yerba Buena*)	**Micromeria chamissonis** (*douglasi*)	YERBABUENA
Milfoil. ACHILLEA		
Mio Mio. BACCHARIS		
Miramashikimi. SKIMMIA		
MIRE	**Brunfelsia hydrangeaeformis**	MIRE RAINTREE
MITCHELLA (*Squaw Vine*)	**Mitchella repens**	PARTRIDGEBERRY
MOMORDICA (*Balsam Apple*)	**Momordica balsamina**	BALSAMAPPLE
MONARDA (*Horsemint*)	**Monarda punctata**	SPOTTED BEEBALM
MONARDA DIDYMA (*Oswego Tea*)	**M. didyma**	OSWEGO B.
Monkshood. ACONITUM		
MONSONIA	**Monsonia** spp.	MONSONIA
MORINDA (*Indian Mulberry*)	**Morinda coreia** (*tinctoria*)	DYERS INDIANMULBERRY
MORPHINA (*Morphine*) *See also* OPIUM and PAPAVERIS FRUCTUS	**Papaver somniferum; P. s. album**	OPIUM POPPY; WHITE O. P.
MORUS (*Black Mulberry*)	**Morus nigra**	BLACK MULBERRY
MORUS (*Red Mulberry*)	**M. rubra**	RED M.
Motherwort. LEONURUS		
Mountain Ash Berries. SORBUS		
Mountain Laurel. KALMIA		
Mountain Maple Bark. ACER SPICATUM		
Mowrah. BASSIA		
MUCUNA (*Cowhage*)	**Stizolobium pruritum** (*pruriens; Mucuna p.*)	COWAGE VELVETBEAN
Mudar. CALOTROPIS		
MUIRA-PUAMA	**Liriosma ovata**	
Mulberry. MORUS		
Mullein. VERBASCI		
Musenna. MESENNA		
Musk Root. SUMBUL		
Mustard. SINAPIS		
MUTISIA	**Mutisia viciaefolia**	VETCHLEAF MUTISIA
MYRICA (*Wax Myrtle Bark*)	**Myrica cerifera**	SOUTHERN WAXMYRTLE
MYRICA (*Bayberry Bark*)	**M. pensylvanica** (*caroliniensis*)	NORTHERN BAYBERRY
MYRISTICA (*Nutmeg*) *See also* MACIS and OLEUM MYRISTICAE	**Myristica fragrans**	COMMON NUTMEG
MYRISTICA ARGENTEA (*Macassar Nutmeg*)	**M. argentea**	MACASSAR N.
MYRRHA (*Gum Myrrh*)	**Commiphora abyssinica**	ABYSSINIAN MYRRHTREE
MYRRHA (*Gum Myrrh*) The myrrh of commerce also derives from other spp. of the genus Commiphora.	**C. myrrha**	COMMON M.
MYRTUS (*Myrtle*)	**Myrtus communis**	TRUE MYRTLE
NABALUS (*Rattlesnake Root*)	**Prenanthes alba**	WHITE RATTLESNAKEROOT

Drug Name	Plant Source: Botanical Name	Plant Source: S.P.N. Common Name
Nance Bark. MALPIGHIA		
NARCISSUS (*Daffodil*)	**Narcissus pseudonarcissus**	COMMON DAFFODIL
NARDUS (*Nard*)	**Nardus** spp.	MATGRASS
NAREGAMIA (*Goanese Ipecacuanha*)	**Naregamia alata**	
NECTANDRAE CORTEX (*Bebeeru*)	**Ocotea rodioei** (*Nectandra r.*)	GREENHEART OCOTEA
NERIUM (*Oleander*)	**Nerium oleander**	COMMON OLEANDER
Nettle. URTICA		
New Jersey Tea. CEANOTHUS		
NIEREMBERGIA (*Cupflower*)	**Nierembergia hippomanica**	DWARF CUPFLOWER
NIGELLA (*Black Caraway*)	**Nigella damascena**	LOVEINAMIST
NIGELLA (*Black Caraway*)	**N. sativa**	GARDEN FENNELFLOWER
Nutgall. GALLA		
Nutmeg. MYRISTICA		
NUX VOMICA (*Strychni Semen*) See also STRYCHNINA	**Strychnos nuxvomica**	NUXVOMICA POISONNUT
NYMPHAEA (*Water Lily*)	**Nymphaea odorata** (*Castalia o.*)	AMERICAN WATERLILY
NYSSA (*Sour Gum*)	**Nyssa sylvatica**	BLACK TUPELO
Oak Bark. QUERCUS		
Oats. AVENA SATIVA		
OCIMUM (*Sweet Basil*)	**Ocimum basilicum**	SWEET BASIL
OENANTHE (*Water Hemlock*)	**Oenanthe crocata**	HEMLOCK WATERDROPWORT
OENOTHERA (*Evening Primrose*)	**Oenothera biennis**	COMMON EVENINGPRIMROSE
Oil of Cade. PIX JUNIPERI		
Oleander. NERIUM		
OLEUM		
ALEURITES CORDATA (*Tung Oil*)	**Aleurites cordata**	JAPAN WOODOILTREE
ALEURITES TRILOBAE (*Candlenut Oil*)	**A. moluccana** (*triloba*)	CANDLENUTTREE
AMYGDALAE AMARAE (*Oil of Bitter Almond*) Kernels of other related fruits containing Amygdalin are also commercial sources of this oil.	**Prunus amygdalus amara** (*P. communis a.; Amygdalus c. a.*)	BITTER ALMOND
AMYGDALAE EXPRESSUM (*Sweet Almond Oil*)	**P. amygdalus** (*communis* Arcang., *not* Huds.; *Amygdalus c.*) and vars.	ALMOND
ANDAE (*Oil of Anda*)	**Joannesia princeps**	
ANISI (*Anise Oil*) See also ILLICIUM	**Illicium verum**	TRUESTAR ANISETREE
ANISI (*Anise Oil*) See also ANISUM	**Pimpinella anisum**	ANISE
ANISI CORTICIS (*Oil of Anise Bark*)	**Illicium parviflorum**	YELLOW ANISETREE
ARACHIDIS (*Peanut Oil*) See also ARACHIS	**Arachis hypogaea**	PEANUT
AURANTII (*Oil of Sweet Orange*) See also AURANTII DULCIS CORTEX	**Citrus sinensis**	SWEET ORANGE
AURANTII AMARI (*Oil of Bitter Orange*)	**C. aurantium**	SOUR O. (*Seville O.*)
AURANTII FLORUM (*Oil of Neroli*) See also AURANTII AMARI CORTEX	"	"
BEN (*Behen Oil*)	**Moringa aptera** (*arabica*)	ARABIAN HORSERADISHTREE
BEN (*Behen Oil*)	**M. oleifera** (*pterygosperma*)	HORSERADISHTREE
BERGAMOTTAE (*Oil of Bergamot*)	**Citrus bergamia**	BERGAMOT ORANGE
BETULAE EMPYREUMATICUM (*Oleum Rusci*) See also BETULA ALBA	**Betula pendula** (*alba*)	EUROPEAN WHITE BIRCH
CAJUPUTI (*Oil of Cajeput*)	**Melaleuca** spp., especially **M. leucadendron**	CAJEPUTTREE
CALLITRIS (*Oil of Callitris*)	**Callitris** spp.	CYPRESSPINE
CANANGAE (*Oil of Cananga*)	**Cananga odorata**	YLANGYLANG
OLEUM CARDAMOMI (*Oil of Cardamom*) See also CARDAMOMI SEMEN and CARDAMOMUM	**Elettaria cardamomum**	CARDAMON
CARI (*Caraway Oil*) See also CARUM	**Carum carvi**	CARAWAY
CARYOPHYLLI (*Oil of Clove*)	**Syzygium aromaticum** (*Caryophyllus aromaticus; Eugenia aromatica; E. caryophyllata*)	CLOVETREE
CHAULMOOGRAE (*Chaulmoogra Oil*)	**Hydnocarpus** spp., especially **H. anthelminthicus** and the two species below.	CHAULMOOGRATREE COMMON C.
CHAULMOOGRAE (*Chaulmoogra Oil*)	**H. wightianus**	WIGHT C.
CHAULMOOGRAE (*Chaulmoogra Oil*)	**Taraktogenos kurzi**	
CHENOPODII (*Oil of American Wormseed*)	**Chenopodium ambrosioides anthelminticum**	DRUG WORMSEED GOOSEFOOT
CHIONE (*Oil of Chione*) See also CHIONE	**Chione glabra**	SMOOTH CHIONE
CINNAMOMI (*Oil of Cassia*) See also CINNAMOMUM CASSIA	**Cinnamomum cassia**	CASSIABARKTREE
CITRONELLAE (*Oil of Citronella*)	**Cymbopogon nardus**	CITRONELLAGRASS
CITRONELLAE (*Oil of Citronella*)	**C. winterianus**	MAHAPENGIRI
COCOIS (*Coconut Oil*)	**Cocos nucifera**	COCONUT
COLZAE (*Colza Oil*)	**Brassica campestris oleifera**	OILNAVEW BIRD RAPE
CORIANDRI (*Coriander Oil*) See also CORIANDRUM	**Coriandrum sativum**	CORIANDER
CUPRESSI (*Oil of Cypress*)	**Cupressus sempervirens**	ITALIAN CYPRESS
DIPTEROCARPI (*Oil of Gurjun*)	**Dipterocarpus** spp., especially **D. turbinatus**	GURJUNOILTREE COMMON G.
EUCALYPTI (*Eucalyptus Oil*) Other spp. of Eucalyptus also produce Oleum Eucalypti. See also EUCALYPTUS	**Eucalyptus globulus**	TASMANIAN BLUE EUCALYPTUS
EUPHORBIAE (*Caper Spurge Oil*)	**Euphorbia lathyrus**	CAPER EUPHORBIA
FOENICULI (*Fennel Oil*) See also FOENICULUM	**Foeniculum vulgare**	COMMON FENNEL
GOSSYPII SEMINIS (*Cottonseed Oil*) See also GOSSYPIUM	**Gossypium** spp., especially **G. hirsutum** and **G. herbaceum**	COTTON
GRAMINIS CITRATE (*Oil of Lemon Grass*)	**Cymbopogon citratus**	LEMONGRASS
GRAMINIS CITRATE (*Oil of Lemon Grass*)	**C. flexuosus**	COCHIN L.
JASMINI (*Spanish Jasmine*)	**Jasminum officinale**	COMMON JASMINE
JASMINI (*Spanish Jasmine*)	**J. o. grandiflorum**	
JUNIPERI (*Juniper Oil*) See also JUNIPERUS	**Juniperus communis**	COMMON JUNIPER
JUNIPERI VIRGINIANAE (*Cedarwood Oil*) See also JUNIPERUS VIRGINIANA	**J. virginiana**	EASTERN REDCEDAR
LAVANDULAE (*Oil of Lavender Flowers*) See also LAVANDULA	**Lavandula officinalis** (*spica; vera*)	TRUE LAVENDER
LIMONIS (*Lemon Oil*) See also LIMONIS CORTEX	**Citrus limon** (*limonia*)	LEMON
LINALOE (*Oil of Linaloe*)	**Bursera glabrifolia** (*aloexylon*)	LINALOE BURSERA
LINALOE (*Oil of Linaloe*)	**B. penicillata** (*delpechiana*)	
LINDERAE (*Oil of Kuromoji*)	**Lindera sericea**	SILKY SPICEBUSH
LINDERAE (*Oil of Kuromoji*)	**L. umbellata**	UMBELED S.

Drug Name	Plant Source: Botanical Name	Plant Source: S.P.N. Common Name
OLEUM LINI (*Raw Linseed Oil*) *See also* LINUM	**Linum usitatissimum**	COMMON FLAX
MAYDIS (*Corn Oil*) *See also* AMYLUM and ZEA	**Zea mays**	MAIZE; INDIAN CORN
MENTHAE PIPERITAE (*Peppermint Oil*) *See also* MENTHAE PIPERITA	**Mentha piperita**	PEPPERMINT
MENTHAE VIRIDIS (*Spearmint Oil*) *See also* MENTHAE VIRIDIS	**M. spicata**	SPEARMINT
MYRCIAE (*Oil of Bay*)	**Pimenta racemosa**	BAYRUMTREE
MYRISTICAE (*Oil of Nutmeg*) *See also* MACIS and MYRISTICA	**Myristica fragrans**	COMMON NUTMEG
OLIVAE (*Olive Oil*)	**Olea europaea**	COMMON OLIVE
PALMAE (*Palm Oil*)	**Elaeis guineensis**	AFRICAN OILPALM
PATCHOULI (*Oil of Patchouli*)	**Pogostemon cablin**	CABLIN PATCHOULI
PATCHOULI (*Oil of Patchouli*)	**P. heyneanus**	HEYNE P.
PERILLAE (*Oil of Perilla*)	**Perilla frutescens** (*ocymoides*)	COMMON PERILLA
PIMENTAE (*Oil of Allspice*) *See also* PIMENTA	**Pimenta officinalis**	ALLSPICE PIMENTA
PINI PUMILIONIS (*Dwarf Pine Needle Oil*)	**Pinus mugo** (*montana*)	SWISSMOUNTAIN PINE
RICINI (*Castor Oil*) *See also* RICINUS	**Ricinus communis**	CASTORBEAN
ROSAE (*Otto of Rose*) *See also* ROSA DAMASCENA	**Rosa damascena**	DAMASK ROSE
ROSAE (*Otto of Rose*) *See also* ROSA	**R. gallica** and its vars.	FRENCH R.
ROSMARINI (*Oil of Rosemary*) *See also* ROSMARINUS	**Rosmarinus officinalis**	ROSEMARY
SANTALI (*Oil of Sandalwood*) *See also* SANTALUM ALBUM	**Santalum album**	WHITE SANDALWOOD
SANTALI AUSTRALIENSIS	**Eucarya spicata**	AUSTRALIA-SANDALWOOD
SASSAFRAS (*Sassafras Oil*) *See also* SASSAFRAS	**Sassafras albidum** (*officinale*)	COMMON SASSAFRAS
SESAMI (*Benne Oil*) *See also* SESAMUM	**Sesamum indicum** (*orientale*)	ORIENTAL SESAME
SINAPIS VOLATILE (*Mustard Oil*)	**Brassica juncea** (*rugosa; Sinapis j.*)	INDIA MUSTARD
SINAPIS VOLATILE (*Mustard Oil*) *See also* SINAPIS NIGRA	**B. nigra**	BLACK M.
TEREBINTHINAE (*Turpentine Oil*) Other pines enter into the commercial production of Oleum Terebinthinae. *See also* PIX PINI, RESINA, and TEREBINTHINA	**Pinus palustris**	LONGLEAF PINE
THEAE SEMINIS (*Teaseed Oil of Camellia*) The Theae Seminis of commerce is partially produced also by other spp. of Camellia.	**Camellia drupifera**	HIMALAYAN CAMELLIA
THEOBROMATIS (*Cacao Butter; Cocoa Butter*) *See also* CACAO PRAEPARATUM	**Theobroma cacao**	CACAO
THYMI (*Thyme Oil*) *See also* THYMUS	**Thymus vulgaris**	COMMON THYME
TIGLII (*Croton Oil*)	**Croton tiglium**	PURGING CROTON
OLIBANUM (*Frankincense*) Other spp. of Boswellia produce some of the Olibanum of commerce.	**Boswellia carteri**	BIBLE FRANKINCENSE

Drug Name	Plant Source: Botanical Name	Plant Source: S.P.N. Common Name
Olutkombul. ABROMA		
Onion. CEPA		
ONONIS (*Radix Ononidis*)	**Ononis spinosa**	THORNY ONONIS
OPHIOXYLON (*Radix Musteltoe*)	**Rauwolfia serpentina**	JAVA DEVILPEPPER
OPIUM (*Gum Opium*) *See also* MORPHINA and PAPAVERIS FRUCTUS	**Papaver somniferum; P. s. album**	OPIUM POPPY; WHITE O. P.
OPLOPANAX (*Devils Club Root*)	**Oplopanax horridus** (*Fatsia horrida*)	AMERICAN DEVILS-CLUB
OPOPANAX	**Opopanax chironium**	SURGEONS OPOPANAX
OPOPANAX *See also* BDELLIUM	**Commiphora mukul**	MUKUL MYRRHTREE
OPUNTIA (*Prickly Pear*)	**Opuntia vulgaris**	COMMON PRICKLYPEAR
Orange Peel. AURANTII		
Oregon Grape Root. BERBERIS		
ORIGANUM (*Common Marjoram*)	**Origanum vulgare**	COMMON ORIGANUM
OROXYLON	**Oroxylum indicum**	INDIA TRUMPETFLOWER
Orris Root. IRIS		
ORTHOSIPHON (*Java Tea*)	**Orthosiphon grandiflorus** (*stamineus*)	BIGFLOWER JAVATEA
OSTRYA (*Ironwood*)	**Ostrya virginiana**	AMERICAN HOPHORNBEAM
Oswego Tea. MONARDA DIDYMA		
OUABAINUM	**Acokanthera ouabaio**	OUABAIO BUSHMANSPOISON
OUABAINUM	**Strophanthus glaber** (*gratus*)	
Owala Grains. PENTACLETHRA		
OXALIS (*Wood Sorrel*)	**Oxalis acetosella**	WOODSORREL OXALIS
Ox-tongue. ANCHUSA		
OXYDENDRUM (*Sourwood*) *See also* ANDROMEDA	**Oxydendrum arboreum**	SOURWOOD
PAEONIA (*Peony Root*)	**Paeonia officinalis**	COMMON PEONY
Pale Catechu. GAMBIR		
PALICOUREA	**Palicourea rigida**	
Palo Blanco. CHIONE		
PALO DE VACA (*Cow Tree*)	**Brosimum utile** (*galactodendron*)	COW BREADNUTTREE
PANGIUM	**Pangium edule**	FOOD PANGIUM
PANHOTANO CORTEX (*Panbotano Bark*)	**Calliandra houstoniana** (*houstoni*)	PANBOTANO CALLIANDRA
Pansy Herb. VIOLA TRICOLOR		
PAPAVERIS FRUCTUS (*Poppy Capsules*) *See also* MORPHINA and OPIUM	**Papaver somniferum**	OPIUM POPPY
PAPAVER RHOEAS (*Red Poppy Flowers*)	**P. rhoeas**	CORN P.
PAPAYA (*Paw Paw*)	**Carica papaya**	PAPAYA
PAPRIKA *See also* CAPSICUM	**Capsicum frutescens** and vars.	BUSH REDPEPPER
Para Cress. SPILANTHES		
PARAMERIA *See also* BALSAMUM CEBUR	**Parameria vulneraria**	
PAREIRA (*Pareira Brava*)	**Chondodendron tomentosum**	PAREIRAROOT
PARIETARIA (*Wall Pellitory*)	**Parietaria officinalis**	WALL PELLITORY
PARKIA (*African Locust*)	**Parkia biglandulosa**	MALAYA NITTATREE
Parsley. PETROSELINUM		
PARTHENIUM (*Feverfew*)	**Chrysanthemum parthenium**	FEVERFEW CHRYSANTHEMUM
Pasque Flower. PULSATILLA		
PASSIFLORA (*Passion Vine*)	**Passiflora incarnata**	MAYPOP PASSIONFLOWER
Paw Paw. PAPAYA		
Peach Leaves. PERSICAE FOLIAE		
Peachwood. LIGNUM CAESALPINIAE		
Peanut. ARACHIS		
PEGANUM (*Wild Rue*)	**Peganum harmala**	HARMEL PEGANUM
PELARGONIUM (*Rose Geranium*)	**Pelargonium odoratissimum**	NUTMEG PELARGONIUM
PENGAWAR DJAMBI	**Alsophila lurida**	
PENGAWAR DJAMBI (*Golden Moss*)	**Cibotium barometz**	SCYTHIANLAMB

Drug Name	*Plant Source* *Botanical Name*	*S.P.N.Common Name*
Pengawar Djambi	**Cibotium glaucum**	Underblue Cibotium
Pennyroyal. Hedeoma		
Pennywort. Cotyledon		
Pentaclethra (*Owala Grains*)	**Pentaclethra macrophylla**	Owalaoiltree
Peony. Paeonia		
Pepo (*Pumpkin Seed*)	**Cucurbita pepo**	Pumpkin
Pepper. Piper		
Peppermint. Menthae Piperita		
Perezia (*Perezia Root*)	**Perezia** spp.	Perezia
Periploca (*Silkvine*)	**Periploca graeca**	Grecian Silkvine
Periwinkle. Vinca		
Persicae Foliae (*Peach Leaves*)	**Prunus persica** (*Amygdalus p.*)	Peach
Persimmon. Diospyros		
Persio (*Cudbear*)	**Lecanora** spp.	Lecanora
Persio (*Cudbear*) Other lichens occasionally enter into the production of commercial Persio besides spp. of Lecanora and Roccella.	**Roccella** spp. or other lichens	Roccella
Petiveria (*Pipi Root*)	**Petiveria alliacea**	Garlic Guineahenweed
Petroselini Folia (*Parsley Leaves*)	**Petroselinum crispum latifolium**	Common Garden Parsley
Petroselini Radix (*Parsley Root*)	"	"
Petroselinum (*Parsley Fruit*)	"	"
Peucedanum (*Hog Fennel*)	**Peucedanum officinale**	Common Hogfennel
Phaseolus (*Common Kidney Bean*)	**Phaseolus vulgaris**	Kidney Bean
Pheasants-eye. Adonis		
Phellandrium (*Water Fennel*)	**Oenanthe phellandrium**	Fennelleaf Waterdropwort
Phoradendron (*American Mistletoe*)	**Phoradendron flavescens**	Christmas American-mistletoe
Physalis (*Strawberry Tomato*)	**Physalis alkekengi**	Strawberry Groundcherry
Physostigma (*Calabar Bean*)	**Physostigma venenosum**	Deadly Calabarbean
Phytelephas (*Vegetable Ivory*)	**Phytelephas macrocarpa**	Common Ivorypalm
Phytolacca (*Poke Root*)	**Phytolacca americana** (*decandra*)	Common Pokeberry
Phytolacca Acinosa	**P. acinosa**	India P.
Phytolaccae Fructus (*Poke Berries*)	**P. americana** (*decandra*)	Common P.
Pichi. Fabiana		
Pichurim Beans (*Sassafras Nuts*)	**Ocotea** spp. (*Nectandra*)	Ocotea
Picrasma	**Picrasma quassioides**	India Quassiawood
Pilocarpus (*Pernambuco Jaborandi*)	**Pilocarpus jaborandi**	Jaborandi Pilocarpus
Pilocarpus (*Maranham Jaborandi*)	**P. microphyllus**	Littleleaf P.
Pimenta (*Allspice*) See also Oleum Pimentae	**Pimenta officinalis**	Allspice Pimenta
Pimpinella	**Pimpinella magna**	Greater Pimpinella
Pimpinella (*Pimpernel Root*)	**P. saxifraga**	Saxifrage P.
Pinckneya (*Georgia* or *Bitter Bark*)	**Pinckneya pubens**	Pinckneya
Pinguicula (*Butterwort*)	**Pinguicula alpina**	Mountain Butterwort
Pinguicula (*Butterwort*)	**P. vulgaris**	Common B.
Pini-pini (*Arra Diabo*)	**Cnidoscolus urens** (*Jatropha u.*)	Drug Treadsoftly
Pink Root. Spigelia		
Pinus Alba (*White Pine Bark*)	**Pinus strobus**	Eastern White Pine
Piper (*Black Pepper*)	**Piper nigrum**	Black Pepper
Piper Longum (*Long Pepper*)	**P. longum**	Long P.
Piper Longum	**P. retrofractum** (*officinarum*)	
Pipi Root. Petiveria		
Pipsissewa. Chimaphila		
Pirageia. Anchietea		
Piscidia (*Jamaica Dogwood*)	**Piscidia piscipula** (*erythrina; Ichthyomethia p.*)	Jamaica Fishfuddletree

Drug Name	*Plant Source* *Botanical Name*	*S.P.N.Common Name*
Pitcher Plant. Sarracenia		
Pithecolobium	**Samanea saman** (*Pithecellobium s.*)	Raintree Saman
Pix Burgundica (*Burgundy Pitch*)	**Picea abies** (*excelsa*)	Norway Spruce
Pix Canadensis (*Hemlock Pitch*)	**Tsuga canadensis**	Canada Hemlock; Eastern H. (Forestry)
Pix Juniperi (*Oil of Cade*)	**Juniperus oxycedrus**	Prickly Juniper
Pix Pini (*Pix Liquida*) See also Oleum Terebinthinae, Resina, and Terebinthina	**Pinus** spp., especially **P. palustris**	Pine Longleaf P.
Plantaginis Semen (*French Psyllium Seed*)	**Plantago indica** (*arenaria*)	Whorled Plantain
Plantaginis Semen (*Blonde Psyllium Seed*)	**P. ovata**	Blond P.
Plantaginis Semen (*Psyllium Seed*)	**P. psyllium**	Flaxseed P.
Plantago Lanceolata (*German Psyllium Seed*)	**P. lanceolata**	Buckhorn P.
Plantain Leaves. Folia Plantaginis		
Pleurisy Root. Asclepias		
Plumbago (*Leadwort*)	**Plumbago europaea**	Common Plumbago
Podophyllum (*Mandrake*)	**Podophyllum peltatum**	Common Mayapple
Pogonopus (*China Morada*)	**Pogonopus tubulosus**	
Poison Hemlock. Conium		
Poison Ivy. Rhus Toxicodendron Leaves		
Poison Oak. Rhus Toxicodendron Leaves		
Poison Sumac. Rhus Venenata Leaves		
Poke Berries. Phytolaccae Fructus		
Poke Root. Phytolacca		
Polygala (*Bitter Milkwort*)	**Polygala polygama**	Bitter Polygala
Polygonatum (*Solomons Seal*)	**Polygonatum officinale**	Drug Solomonseal
Polymnia (*Leafcup*)	**Polymnia uvedalia**	Yellow Leafcup
Polypodium (*Polypody*)	**Polypodium vulgare**	Common Polypody
Polytrichum (*Hair Cap Moss*)	**Polytrichum commune**	Common Haircapmoss
Polytrichum (*Hair Cap Moss*)	**P. juniperinum**	Juniper H.
Pomegranate Bark. Granatum		
Pongamia	**Pongamia pinnata**	Poongaoil Pongamia
Poppy. Papaver		
Populi Gemma (*Balm of Gilead Bud*)	**Populus candicans**	Balm-of-Gilead Poplar
Populi Gemma (*Balsam Poplar Bud*)	**P. tacamahaca** (*balsamifera*)	Tacamahac P.
Porrum (*Leek*)	**Allium porrum**	Leek
Portulaca (*Garden Purslane*)	**Portulaca oleracea** (*aurea*)	Common Purslane
Potentilla (*Cinquefoil*)	**Potentilla reptans**	Creeping Cinquefoil
Potentilla Anserina	**P. anserina**	Silverweed C.
Prickly Ash. Xanthoxylum		
Prickly Pear. Opuntia		
Prickly Poppy. Argemone		
Pride of India. Azedarach		
Primula (*Primrose*)	**Primula obconica**	Top Primrose
Prinos (*Black Alder*)	**Ilex verticillata**	Common Winterberry
Privet. Ligustrum		
Prunella (*Self-heal*)	**Prunella vulgaris**	Common Selfheal
Prunum (*Prune*)	**Prunus domestica**	Garden Plum
Prunus Cerasus (*Sour Cherry*)	**P. cerasus**	Sour Cherry
Prunus Virginiana (*Wild Black Cherry Bark*)	**P. serotina**	Black C.
Psidium (*Guava*)	**Psidium** spp., especially **P. guajava**	Guava Common G.

	Plant Source	
Drug Name	*Botanical Name*	*S.P.N. Common Name*
Psyllium Seed. PLANTAGINIS SEMEN		
PTELEA (*Wafer Ash Bark*)	**Ptelea trifoliata**	COMMON HOPTREE
PULMONARIA (*Lungwort*)	**Pulmonaria officinalis** (*maculata*)	COMMON LUNGWORT
PULSATILLA (*Pasque Flower*)	**Anemone patens** (*Pulsatilla p.*)	SPREADING PASQUEFLOWER (*Spreading Anemone*)
PULSATILLA	**A. pratensis** (*Pulsatilla p.*)	MEADOW P.
PULSATILLA *See also* ANEMONIN	**A. pulsatilla** (*Pulsatilla vulgaris*)	EUROPEAN P.
Pumpkin Seed. PEPO		
Purging Flax. LINUM CATHARTICUM		
Purple Loosestrife. LYTHRUM		
PYRETHRI FLORES (*Dalmatian Insect Flowers*)	**Chrysanthemum cinerariaefolium**	DALMATIAN PYRETHRUM
PYRETHRI FLORES (*Persian Insect Flowers*)	**C. marschalli**	CAUCASIAN P.
PYRETHRI FLORES (*Persian Insect Flowers*)	**C. coccineum** (*roseum; Pyrethrum carneum; P. hybridum*)	FLORISTS P.
QUASSIA (*Jamaica Quassia*)	**Picrasma excelsa** (*Picraena e.*)	JAMAICA QUASSIAWOOD
QUASSIA (*Surinam Quassia*)	**Quassia amara**	SURINAM QUASSIA
Quebracho Bark. ASPIDOSPERMA		
Queens Root. STILLINGIA		
QUERCUS (*White Oak Bark*)	**Quercus alba**	WHITE OAK
QUILLAJA (*Soap Bark*)	**Quillaja saponaria**	SOAPBARKTREE
Quince Seed. CYDONIUM		
QUININA (*Quinine*)	**Cinchona calisaya**	YELLOWBARK CINCHONA
QUININA (*Quinine*)	**C. ledgeriana**	LEDGERBARK C.
QUININA (*Quinine*)	**C. pallida**	PALE C.
QUININA (*Quinine*) *See also* CINCHONA	**C. succirubra** and its hybrids	REDBARK C.
QUISQUALIS (*Rangoon Creeper*)	**Quisqualis indica**	RANGOONCREEPER
RADIX CAINCAE (*Davids Root*)	**Chiococca alba** (*racemosa*)	DAVIDS MILKBERRY
Radix Musteltoe. OPHIOXYLON		
Radix Ononidis. ONONIS		
Ragweed. AMBROSIA		
Raisins. UVA PASSA		
RANDIA	**Randia dumetorum**	MALABAR RANDIA
Rangoon Creeper. QUISQUALIS		
RANUNCULUS (*Crowfoot*)	**Ranunculus** spp.	BUTTERCUP
RAPHANUS (*Radish*)	**Raphanus sativus**	GARDEN RADISH
Rattlesnake Root. NABALUS		
Rattlesnake Weed. HIERACIUM		
Red Cedar. JUNIPERUS VIRGINIANA		
Red Clover Blossoms. TRIFOLIUM		
Red Raspberries. RUBUS IDAEUS		
Red Saunders. SANTALUM RUBRUM		
RESINA (*Colophony*) *See also* OLEUM TEREBINTHINAE, PIX PINI, and TEREBINTHINA. Other pines produce some of the Resina of commerce.	**Pinus palustris**	LONGLEAF PINE
RESINA PRIORIA (*Cativa*)	**Prioria copaifera**	CATIVO
RHAMNUS CATHARTICA (*Buckthorn Berries*)	**Rhamnus cathartica**	COMMON BUCKTHORN
Rhamnus Purshiana. CASCARA SAGRADA		
Rhatany. KRAMERIA		
RHEUM (*Rhubarb Root*)	**Rheum officinale**	MEDICINAL RHUBARB
RHEUM The product of other spp. of Rhubarb grown in China and Thibet (excepting **R. rhaponticum**) or hybrids of	**R. palmatum**	SORREL R.

	Plant Source	
Drug Name	*Botanical Name*	*S.P.N. Common Name*
RHEUM, continued **Rheum** also enter into the Rheum of commerce.		
RHIZOPHORA (*Mangrove*)	**Rhizophora mangle**	AMERICAN MANGROVE
RHODODENDRON (*Yellow-flowered Rhododendron*)	**Rhododendron chrysanthum**	GOLDMAT RHODODENDRON
RHODYMENIA (*Irish Dulse*)	**Rhodymenia palmata**	IRISHDULSE SEAKALE
RHUS DIVERSILOBUM LEAVES Extract and antigen.	**Toxicodendron diversilobum** (*Rhus diversiloba*)	PACIFIC POISONOAK
RHUS GLABRA (*Sumac Berries*)	**Rhus glabra**	SMOOTH SUMAC
RHUS TOXICODENDRON LEAVES (*Poison Oak*) Extract and antigen.	**Toxicodendron quercifolium** (*Rhus quercifolia; R. toxicodendron*)	POISONOAK
RHUS TOXICODENDRON LEAVES (*Poison Ivy*) Extract and antigen.	**T. radicans** (*Rhus r.; R. toxicodendron* Auth., *not* L.)	COMMON POISONIVY
RHUS VENENATA LEAVES (*Poison Sumac*) Extract and antigen.	**T. vernix** (*Rhus venenata; R. vernix*)	POISONSUMAC
RICINUS (*Castor Oil Bean*) *See also* OLEUM RICINI	**Ricinus communis**	CASTORBEAN
RIMU (*Rimu Resin*)	**Dacrydium cupressinum**	RIMU DACRYDIUM
ROBINIA (*Black Locust Tree*)	**Robinia pseudoacacia**	BLACK LOCUST
Rockfoil. SAXIFRAGA		
Rock-rose. HELIANTHEMUM		
Rohan Bark. SWIETENIA		
Roman Chamomile. ANTHEMIS		
Roman Wormwood. AMBROSIA		
ROSA (*Red Rose*) *See also* OLEUM ROSAE	**Rosa gallica**	FRENCH ROSE
ROSA CANINA (*Dog Rose*)	**R. canina**	DOG R.
ROSA CENTIFOLIA (*Cabbage Rose*)	**R. centifolia**	CABBAGE R.
ROSA DAMASCENA (*Damask Rose*) *See also* OLEUM ROSAE	**R. damascena**	DAMASK R.
Rose Gentian. SABBATIA		
Rose Geranium. PELARGONIUM		
ROSMARINUS (*Rosemary*) *See also* OLEUM ROSMARINI	**Rosmarinus officinalis**	ROSEMARY
ROUREA	**Rourea oblongifolia**	
Rubber. ELASTICA		
RUBIA (*Madder*)	**Rubia tinctorum**	COMMON MADDER
RUBUS (*Blackberry Bark*)	**Rubus** spp.	BLACKBERRY
RUBUS IDAEUS (*Red Raspberries*)	**R. idaeus**	RED RASPBERRY
RUBUS IDAEUS	**R. i. strigosus** (*R. strigosus*)	AMERICAN R. R.
RUMEX (*Yellow Dock*)	**Rumex crispus**	CURLY DOCK
RUMEX (*European Dock*)	**R. obtusifolius**	BITTER D.
RUTA (*Rue*)	**Ruta graveolens**	COMMON RUE
Rye. SECALE CEREALE		
SABBATIA (*Rose Gentian*)	**Sabatia angularis**	SQUARESTEM ROSEGENTIAN
SABINA (*Savin*)	**Juniperus sabina**	SAVIN JUNIPER
Saffron. CROCUS		
SAGAPENUM	**Ferula persica**	PERSIAN GIANTFENNEL
Sage. SALVIA		
SAGO (*Sago Starch*)	**Cycas revoluta**	SAGO CYCAS
SAGO	**Metroxylon sagu** (*laeve; Sagus laevis*)	SMOOTH SAGOPALM
SALEP (*Salep Tubers*)	**Orchis latifolia**	MARSH ORCHIS
SALEP (*Salep Tubers*)	**O. maculata**	SPOTLEAF O.
SALIX (*Willow Bark*) Other spp. of Willow occasionally enter into the production of commercial Salix.	**Salix alba**	WHITE WILLOW
SALIX NIGRA (*Black Willow Bark*)	**S. nigra**	BLACK W.
SALVIA (*Sage*)	**Salvia officinalis**	GARDEN SAGE
SALVIA TRILOBA (*Greek Sage*)	**S. triloba**	GREEK S.
SAMADERA (*Samadera Bark*)	**Samadera indica**	NIEPABARKTREE
SAMBUCUS (*Elder Flowers*)	**Sambucus canadensis**	AMERICAN ELDER

Drug Name	*Plant Source*	
	Botanical Name	*S.P.N. Common Name*
SAMBUCUS	**Sambucus nigra**	EUROPEAN ELDER
SANDARACA (*Sandarac*)	**Tetraclinis articulata** (*Callitris quadrivalvis*)	ARARTREE
Sandbox Tree. HURA		
SANGUINARIA (*Blood Root*)	**Sanguinaria canadensis**	BLOODROOT
SANGUIS DRACONIA (*Dragons Blood*)	**Pterocarpus draco**	DRAGONSBLOOD PADAUK
SANICULA	**Sanicula marilandica**	BLACK SANICLE
SANTALUM ALBUM (*White Sandalwood*) *See also* OLEUM SANTALI	**Santalum album**	WHITE SANDALWOOD
SANTALUM RUBRUM (*Red Saunders*)	**Pterocarpus santalinus**	SANDALWOOD PADAUK
SANTOLINA (*Holy Herb*)	**Santolina chamaecyparissus**	CYPRESS LAVENDER-COTTON
SANTONICA (*Levant Worm Seed*)	**Artemisia cina**	LEVANT WORMWOOD
SAPINDUS (*Sapind*)	**Sapindus** spp.	SOAPBERRY
SAPIUM (*Chinese Tallow Tree*)	**Sapium sebiferum** (*Stillingia sebifera*)	CHINESE TALLOW-TREE
SARCOCOLLA	**Astragalus sarcocolla**	
SARRACENIA (*Pitcher Plant*)	**Sarracenia flava**	TRUMPET PITCHER-PLANT
SARRACENIA	**S. purpurea**	COMMON P.
SARSAPARILLA (*Mexican Sarsaparilla*)	**Smilax aristolochiifolia** (*medica*)	MEXICAN SARSAPARILLA
SARSAPARILLA	**S. regeli**	JAMAICA S. (*Honduras S.*)
SARSAPARILLA (*Central American or Jamaican Sarsaparilla; Honduras S.*)	**S.,** unknown sp.	
SARSAPARILLA (*Ecuadorian Sarsaparilla*)	**S.,** unknown spp.	
SASSAFRAS (*Sassafras Bark*)	**Sassafras albidum** (*officinale*)	COMMON SASSAFRAS
SASSAFRAS MEDULLA (*Sassafras Pith*) *See also* OLEUM SASSAFRAS	"	"
Sassafras Nuts. PICHURIM BEANS		
Sassy Bark. ERYTHROPHLEUM		
SATUREJA (*Summer Savory*)	**Satureia hortensis**	SUMMER SAVORY
SAURURUS (*Lizards Tail*)	**Saururus cernuus**	COMMON LIZARDTAIL
Savannah Flower. URECHITES		
Savin. SABINA		
Saw Palmetto Berries. SERENOA		
SAXIFRAGA (*Rockfoil*)	**Bergenia crassifolia** (*Saxifraga c.*)	LEATHER BERGENIA
Scarlet Pimpernel. ANAGALLIS		
SCILLA (*White Squill*)	**Urginea maritima** (*Scilla m.*) (White variety)	SHORE DRUGSQUILL
SCILLA INDICA (*Indian Squill*)	**U. indica**	INDIA D.
SCILLA RUBRA (*Red Squill*)	**U. maritima** (*Scilla m.*) (Red variety)	SHORE D.
SCOLOPENDRIUM (*Harts Tongue*)	**Phyllitis scolopendrium** (*Scolopendrium vulgare*)	HARTSTONGUE
SCOPARIUS (*Broom Tops*)	**Cytisus scoparius**	SCOTCH BROOM
SCOPOLIA (*Scopola*)	**Scopolia carniolica**	EUROPEAN SCOPOLIA
SCOPOLIA JAPONICA (*Japanese Henbane*)	**S. japonica**	JAPANESE S.
SCROPHULARIA (*Figwort*)	**Scrophularia marilandica**	MARYLAND FIGWORT
Scurvy Grass. COCHLEARIA		
SCUTELLARIA (*Skullcap*)	**Scutellaria lateriflora**	SIDEFLOWERING SKULLCAP
SECALE CEREALE (*Rye*)	**Secale cereale**	RYE
SEDUM (*Biting Stonecrop*)	**Sedum acre**	GOLDMOSS STONECROP
Self-heal. PRUNELLA		
SEMECARPUS (*Tschongott Tree*)	**Semecarpus venosus**	VEINY MARKINGNUT
SEMEN		
BONDUC (*Bonduc Seed*)	**Caesalpinia crista** (*bonducella; Guilandina c.*)	NICKERNUT CAESALPINIA
CALI (*Cali Nuts*)	**Dioclea** spp.	CLUSTERPEA
SEMEN CALI (*Cali Nuts*)	**Mucuna** spp.	MUCUNA
CANARIENSE (*Canary Seed*)	**Phalaris canariensis**	CANARYGRASS
PAPAVERIS (*Maw Seeds*)	**Papaver somniferum nigrum**	BLACK OPIUM POPPY
SEMPERVIVUM (*Common Houseleek*)	**Sempervivum tectorum** (*robustum*)	ROOF HOUSELEEK
SENECIO (*Life Root*)	**Senecio aureus**	GOLDEN GROUNDSEL
SENEGA (*Senega Snakeroot*)	**Polygala senega**	SENECA-SNAKEROOT POLYGALA
SENNA (*Alexandrian Senna Leaves*)	**Cassia acutifolia** (*senna*)	ALEXANDRIA SENNA
SENNA (*Tinnevelly Senna Leaves*)	**C. angustifolia**	CONGO S.
SENNAE FRUCTUS (*Senna Pods*)	**C. acutifolia** (*senna*)	ALEXANDRIA S.
SENNAE FRUCTUS (*Senna Pods*)	**C. angustifolia**	CONGO S.
SERENOA (*Saw Palmetto Berries*)	**Serenoa repens** (*serrulata*)	SAWPALMETTO
SERPENTARIA (*Texas Snakeroot*)	**Aristolochia reticulata**	TEXAS SNAKEROOT DUTCHMANSPIPE
SERPENTARIA (*Virginia Snakeroot*)	**A. serpentaria**	VIRGINIA S. D.
SESAMUM (*Benne Plant*) *See also* OLEUM SESAMI	**Sesamum indicum** (*orientale*)	ORIENTAL SESAME
Seven-barks. HYDRANGEA		
Shepherds-purse. CAPSELLA		
SIDA (*Mesbe*)	**Sida rhombifolia**	BROOMJUTE SIDA
SIEGESBECKIA	**Siegesbeckia orientalis**	COMMON ST.PAULSWORT
SILENE (*Fire Pink*)	**Silene virginica**	FIREPINK SILENE
Silkvine. PERIPLOCA		
Silver Manso. CAYAPONIA		
SIMARUBA (*Orinoco Simaruba*)	**Simaruba amara**	ORINOCO SIMARUBA
SIMULO	**Capparis coriacea**	SIMULO CAPER
SINAPIS ALBA (*White Mustard*)	**Brassica hirta** (*alba; Sinapis a.*)	WHITE MUSTARD
SINAPIS NIGRA	**B. juncea** (*rugosa; Sinapis j.*)	INDIA M.
SINAPIS NIGRA (*Brown Mustard*) *See also* OLEUM SINAPIS VOLATILE	**B. nigra** or vars. of these spp.	BLACK M.
SISYMBRIUM (*Hedge Mustard*)	**Sisymbrium officinale**	
SIUM (*Water Parsnip*)	**Sium suave** (*cicutaefolium*)	HEMLOCK WATER-PARSNIP
SKIMMIA (*Miramashikimi*)	**Skimmia japonica**	JAPANESE SKIMMIA
Skullcap. SCUTELLARIA		
Skunk Cabbage. DRACONTIUM		
Slippery Elm. ULMUS		
SMILAX (*Bamboo Brier Root*)	**Smilax tamnoides**	BAMBOO GREENBRIER
Snakeroot. SERPENTARIA and SENEGA		
Sneezeweed. HELENIUM		
Soap Bark. QUILLAJA		
SOJA (*Soybean*)	**Glycine soja** (*hispida; max; Soja m.*)	SOYBEAN
SOLANUM (*Horse Nettle Berries*)	**Solanum carolinense**	CAROLINA HORSENETTLE
SOLIDAGO (*Sweet Goldenrod*)	**Solidago odora**	FRAGRANT GOLDENROD
Solomons Seal. POLYGONATUM		
SONCHUS (*Sow Thistle*)	**Sonchus oleraceus**	COMMON SOWTHISTLE
SOPHORA (*Coral Bean*)	**Sophora speciosa**	CORALBEAN SOPHORA
SORBUS (*Mountain Ash Berries*)	**Sorbus aucuparia**	EUROPEAN MOUNTAINASH
SORGHUM	**Sorghum vulgare** (*Andropogon sorghum; Holcus s.*)	SORGHUM
Sour Cherry. PRUNUS CERASUS		
Sour Gum. NYSSA		
Sourwood. OXYDENDRUM and ANDROMEDA		
Southernwood. ABROTANUM		
Sowbread. CYCLAMEN		
Sow Thistle. SONCHUS		
Soybean. SOJA		

Drug Name	Plant Source: Botanical Name	Plant Source: S.P.N. Common Name
Spanish Jasmine. OLEUM JASMINI		
Spanish Needles. BIDENS		
SPARTIUM (*Spanish Broom*)	**Spartium junceum**	WEAVERSBROOM
Spatlum. LEWISIA		
Spearmint. MENTHAE VIRIDIS		
Speedwell. VERONICA		
SPHAGNUM (*Bog Moss*)	**Sphagnum** spp.	SPHAGNUM
SPIGELIA (*Pink Root*)	**Spigelia marilandica**	PINKROOT SPIGELIA
Spike Gayfeather. LIATRIS		
SPILANTHES (*Para Cress*)	**Spilanthes oleracea**	PARACRESS SPOTFLOWER
SPIREA	**Spiraea** spp.	SPIREA
Spurge. EUPHORBIA		
Squaw Vine. MITCHELLA		
Squill. SCILLA		
Squirting Cucumber. ELATERIUM		
Star Anise. ILLICIUM		
Stargrass. ALETRIS		
STICTA (*Lungwort*)	**Sticta pulmonaria** (*Lobaria p.*)	LUNGWORT STICTA
St. Ignatius Bean. IGNATIA		
STILLINGIA (*Queens Root*)	**Stillingia sylvatica**	QUEENSDELIGHT STILLINGIA
STIPA (*Feather Grass*)	**Stipa** spp.	NEEDLEGRASS; FEATHERGRASS
St. Johns Wort. HYPERICUM		
Stone Root. COLLINSONIA		
Storax. STYRAX		
Storks Bill. ERODIUM		
STRAMONIUM (*Jimson Weed*)	**Datura stramonium**	JIMSONWEED DATURA
Strawberry Tomato. PHYSALIS		
STROPHANTHINUM (*Strophanthin*)	**Strophanthus kombe**	KOMBE STROPHANTHUS
STROPHANTHUS (*Brown Strophanthus Seed*)	**S. hispidus**	TRANSVAAL S.
STROPHANTHUS (*Green Strophanthus Seed*)	**S. kombe**	KOMBE S.
STRYCHNINA (*Strychnine*) *See also* NUX VOMICA	**Strychnos nuxvomica**	NUXVOMICA POISONNUT
Strychni Semen. NUX VOMICA		
STRYCHNOS MALACCENSIS (*Hoang-Nan*)	**S. malaccensis** (*gautheriana*)	MALACCA P.
STRYCHNOS POTATORUM (*Chilbinj*)	**S. potatorum**	CLEARING P.
STYLOPHORUM (*Celandine Poppy*)	**Stylophorum diphyllum**	CELANDINE-POPPY
STYRAX (*Liquid Storax*)	**Liquidambar orientalis**	ORIENTAL SWEETGUM
STYRAX (*Liquid Storax*)	**L. styraciflua**	AMERICAN S.
SUBER (*Cork*)	**Quercus suber**	CORK OAK
SUBER (*Cork*)	**Q. s. occidentalis**	BIENNIAL C. O.
SUCCUS POMORUM (*Fresh Apple Juice*)	**Malus pumila** (*sylvestris*)	COMMON APPLE
SUCROSUM (*Beet Sugar*)	**Beta vulgaris**	COMMON BEET
SUCROSUM (*Cane Sugar*)	**Saccharum officinarum**	SUGARCANE
Sugar Apple. ANONA		
Sumac Berries. RHUS GLABRA		
SUMBUL (*Musk Root*)	**Ferula sumbul** And other **Ferula** spp. possessing a musk-like odor.	MUSKROOT GIANTFENNEL
Summer Savory. SATUREJA		
Sundew. DROSERA		
Sunflower. HELIANTHUS		
Sweet		
Basil. OCIMUM		
Flag. CALAMUS		
Fern. COMPTONIA		
Goldenrod. SOLIDAGO		
Pellitory. TANACETUM UMBELLIFERUM		
Shrub. CALYCANTHUS		
SWIETENIA (*Rohan Bark*)	**Soymida febrifuga** (*Swietenia f.*)	ROHAN SOYMIDA
SYMPHYTUM (*Comfrey Root*)	**Symphytum officinale**	COMMON COMFREY

Drug Name	Plant Source: Botanical Name	Plant Source: S.P.N. Common Name
SYMPLOCOS (*Sweet Leaf*)	**Symplocos racemosa**	LODEBARK SWEETLEAF
SYRINGA (*Common Lilac*)	**Syringa vulgaris**	COMMON LILAC
TABACUM (*Tobacco*)	**Nicotiana tabacum**	COMMON TOBACCO
TABASCO (*Tabasco Pepper*)	**Capsicum frutescens conoides**	TABASCO REDPEPPER
TACHIA (*Caferana*)	**Tachia guianensis**	GUIANA TACHIA
TAMARINDUS (*Tamarind*)	**Tamarindus indica**	TAMARIND
TANACETUM (*Tansy*)	**Tanacetum vulgare**	COMMON TANSY
TANACETUM UMBELLIFERUM (*Sweet Pellitory*)	**T. umbelliferum**	UMBEL T.
TANGHINIA (*Tanguin*)	**Tanghinia venenifera**	MADAGASCAR TANGHIN
TANG-KUEI (*Man-Mu*)	**Angelica anomala chinensis**	CHINESE EUMENOL ANGELICA
Tanners Sumac. CORIARIA		
TARAXACUM (*Dandelion*)	**Taraxacum officinale**	COMMON DANDELION
Tarragon. ARTEMISIA DRACUNCULUS		
TAXUS (*Yew*)	**Taxus baccata**	ENGLISH YEW
TAYUYA	**Dermophylla pendulina** (*Cayaponia p.*)	TAYUYA SKINLEAF
Tea. THEA		
TECTONA (*Teakwood*)	**Tectona grandis**	COMMON TEAK
TELFAIRIA	**Telfairia pedata**	ZANZIBAR OILVINE
TEPHROSIA (*Devils Shoe Strings*)	**Tephrosia virginiana** (*Cracca v.*)	VIRGINIA TEPHROSIA
TEREBINTHINA (*Crude Turpentine*) *See also* OLEUM TEREBINTHINAE, PIX PINI, and RESINA	**Pinus palustris** Also other spp.	LONGLEAF PINE
TEREBINTHINA CANADENSIS (*Balsam of Fir*)	**Abies balsamea**	BALSAM FIR
TEREBINTHINA LARICIS (*Venice Turpentine*) *See also* LARICIS CORTEX	**Larix decidua** (*europaea*)	EUROPEAN LARCH
TETRAGASTRIS (*Bois Cochon*)	**Tetragastris panamensis**	
TEUCRIUM (*German Chamaedrys*)	**Teucrium chamaedrys**	CHAMAEDRYS GERMANDER
THALICTRUM	**Thalictrum flavum**	YELLOW MEADOWRUE
THALICTRUM	**T. macrocarpum** Also other spp.	BIGFRUIT M.
THAPSIA (*Thapsie*)	**Thapsia garganica**	GARGAN DEATHCARROT
THEA (*Tea*)	**Camellia sinensis** (*thea; Thea s.*) and vars.	COMMON TEA
THEVETIA (*Yccotli*)	**Thevetia yccotli**	JOYOTE THEVETIA
THUJA (*Arbor Vitae*)	**Thuja occidentalis**	EASTERN ARBORVITAE; NORTHERN WHITECEDAR (Forestry)
THYMUS (*Thyme*) *See also* OLEUM THYMI	**Thymus vulgaris**	COMMON THYME
THYMUS SERPYLLUM (*Wild Thyme*)	**T. serpyllum**	MOTHER-OF-THYME
TILIA (*Linden Flowers*)	**Tilia** spp., especially **T. europaea**	LINDEN EUROPEAN L.
TILIA (*Linden Flowers*)	**T. platyphyllos** (*grandifolia*)	BIGLEAF L.
TIMBO	**Serjania curassavica**	CURACAO SERJANIA
TINOSPORA (*Gulancha*)	**Tinospora cordifolia**	GULANCHA TINOSPORA
TISSA	**Spergularia rubra** (*Tissa r.*)	RED SANDSPURRY
Tobacco. TABACUM		
TODDALIA	**Toddalia asiatica** (*aculeata*)	ASIAN TODDALIA
TONGA	**Epipremnum pinnatum**	CENTIPEDE TONGAVINE
TONGA	**Premna taitensis**	TAHITI PREMNA
Tonka. DIPTERYX		
TORMENTILLA (*Tormentilla Rhizome*)	**Potentilla erecta** (*tormentilla*)	TORMENTILLA CINQUEFOIL
TOXICODENDRON (*Hyena Poison*)	**Hyaenanche capensis** (*Toxicodendron capense*)	HYENABANE
TRADESCANTIA	**Tinantia fugax** (*erecta; Tradescantia e.*)	
TRAGACANTH (*Gum Tragacanth*)	**Astragalus gummifer** Also other Asiatic Astragalus spp.	TRAGACANTH MILKVETCH

Drug Name	Plant Source: Botanical Name	Plant Source: S.P.N. Common Name
Trailing Arbutus. EPIGEA		
TRIFOLIUM (*Red Clover Blossoms*)	**Trifolium pratense**	RED CLOVER
TRILLIUM (*Beth Root*)	**Trillium erectum** Also other spp.	PURPLE TRILLIUM
TRIOSTEUM (*Horse Gentian*)	**Triosteum perfoliatum**	COMMON HORSEGENTIAN
TRITICUM (*Couch Grass*)	**Agropyron repens**	QUACKGRASS
TROMPATILA (*Bouvardia*)	**Bouvardia ternifolia** (*triphylla*)	SCARLET BOUVARDIA
Tschongott Tree. SEMECARPUS		
Tuba Root. DERRIS		
Tulip Tree. LIRIODENDRON		
Turkey Corn. CORYDALIS		
Turmeric. CURCUMA		
Turnera. DAMIANA		
Turpentine. TEREBINTHINA		
Twinleaf. JEFFERSONIA		
TYLOPHORAE FOLIA (*Tylophora*)	**Tylophora indica** (*asthmatica*)	IPECAC TYLOPHORA
ULEX (*Common Furze* or *Gorse*)	**Ulex europaeus**	COMMON GORSE
ULMUS (*Slippery Elm*)	**Ulmus fulva**	SLIPPERY ELM
UMBELLULARIA (*California Laurel*)	**Umbellularia californica**	CALIFORNIALAUREL (*Oregon-myrtle*)
Upas Antiar. ANTIARIS		
URECHITES (*Savannah Flower*)	**Urechites suberecta**	DOMINICAN VIPERTAIL
URTICA (*Nettle*)	**Urtica** spp.	NETTLE
USTILAGO (*Corn Smut*)	**Ustilago zeae** (*maydis*)	CORNSMUT
UVA PASSA (*Raisins*)	**Vitis vinifera**	EUROPEAN GRAPE
UVA URSI (*Bearberry*)	**Arctostaphylos uva-ursi**	BEARBERRY
UZARA (*Uzaron*)	**Asclepiadaceae,** undet. spp.	
VACCINIUM (*Blueberry*)	**Vaccinium crassifolium** (*Herpothamnus crassifolius*)	CREEPING BLUEBERRY
VALERIANA (*Valerian Root*)	**Valeriana officinalis**	COMMON VALERIAN
VALONIA (*Acorn Cups*)	**Quercus macrolepis** (*aegilops; graeca*)	VALONIA OAK
VANILLA (*Vanilla Bean*)	**Vanilla planifolia**	MEXICAN VANILLA
VANILLA, TAHITI	**V. tahitensis**	TAHITI V.
Vegetable		
Ivory. PHYTELEPHAS		
Mercury. MANACA		
Rennet. WITHANIA		
Sponge. LUFFA		
Sulphur. LYCOPODIUM		
VERATRINA	**Schoenocaulon officinale**	DRUG SABADILLA
VERATRUM ALBUM (*European Hellebore*)	**Veratrum album**	WHITE FALSEHELLEBORE
VERATRUM VIRIDE (*American Hellebore*)	**V. viride**	AMERICAN F.
VERBASCI FLORES (*Mullein Flowers*)	**Verbascum phlomoides**	CLASPING MULLEIN
VERBASCI FLORES (*Mullein Flowers*)	**V. thapsiforme** (*densiflorum*)	WOOL M.
VERBASCI FOLIA (*Mullein Leaves*)	**V. thapsus**	FLANNEL M.
VERBENA (*Blue Vervain*)	**Verbena hastata**	BLUE VERBENA
VERNONIA	**Vernonia anthelmintica**	KINKAOIL IRONWEED
VERONICA (*Speedwell*)	**Veronica officinalis**	DRUG SPEEDWELL
Vetchling. LATHYRUS		
VIBURNUM CASSINOIDES (*Withe Rod Bark*)	**Viburnum cassinoides**	WITHEROD VIBURNUM
VIBURNUM OPULUS (*Cramp Bark*)	**V. trilobum** (*V. opulus americanum*)	AMERICAN CRANBERRYBUSH V.
VIBURNUM PRUNIFOLIUM (*Black Haw*)	**V. prunifolium**	BLACKHAW V.
VILCAE CORTEX (*Vilca Bark*)	**Piptadenia macrocarpa**	LONGPOD PIPTADENIA
VINCA (*Greater Periwinkle*)	**Vinca major**	BIGLEAF PERIWINKLE
VINCA (*Lesser Periwinkle*)	**V. minor**	COMMON P.
VINCETOXICUM (*White Swallowwort*)	**Cynanchum vincetoxicum** (*Vincetoxicum officinale*)	WHITE SWALLOWWORT
VIOLA (*Sweet Violet*)	**Viola odorata**	SWEET VIOLET
VIOLA TRICOLOR (*Pansy Herb*)	**V. tricolor**	WILD PANSY

Drug Name	Plant Source: Botanical Name	Plant Source: S.P.N. Common Name
Virginia Creeper. AMPELOPSIS		
Virgins Bower. CLEMATIS		
VISCUM (*European Mistletoe*)	**Viscum album**	EUROPEAN MISTLETOE
Wabayo. ACOKANTHERA		
Wafer Ash Bark. PTELEA		
Wahoo Bark. EUONYMUS		
Wallflower. CHEIRANTHUS		
Wall Pellitory. PARIETARIA		
Waras. WURRUS		
Water		
Avens. GEUM		
Fennel. PHELLANDRIUM		
Hemlock. OENANTHE and CICUTA		
Lily. NYMPHAEA		
Melon Seed. CITRULLUS		
Parsnip. SIUM		
Waterplantain. ALISMA		
Wax Myrtle Bark. MYRICA		
White		
Cinnamon. CANELLA		
Deadnettle. LAMIUM		
Pine Bark. PINUS ALBA		
Sandalwood. SANTALUM ALBUM		
Sapota. CASIMIROA		
Swallowwort. VINCETOXICUM		
Wild		
Black Cherry Bark. PRUNUS VIRGINIANA		
Carrot. CAROTA		
Indigo. BAPTISIA		
Ginger. ASARUM		
Lettuce. LACTUCARIUM		
Rue. PEGANUM		
Yam Root. DIOSCOREA		
Willow Bark. SALIX		
WINTERA (*Winters Bark*) *See also* DRIMYS	**Drimys winteri**	WINTERSBARK DRIMYS
Wintergreen. GAULTHERIA		
WISTARIA	**Wistaria sinensis**	CHINESE WISTARIA
Witch-hazel Leaves. HAMAMELIDIS FOLIUM		
WITHANIA (*Vegetable Rennet*)	**Withania coagulans**	AFGHAN WITHANIA
Withe Rod Bark. VIBURNUM CASSINOIDES		
Woad. ISATIS		
Wood Betony. BETONICA		
Wood Sorrel. OXALIS		
Woorari. CURARE		
Wormwood. ABSINTHIUM		
WURRUS (*Waras*)	**Flemingia macrophylla** (*congesta*)	LONGLEAF WURRUS
XANTHIUM (*Cocklebur*)	**Xanthium** spp.	COCKLEBUR
XANTHORRHIZA (*Yellowroot*)	**Xanthorhiza simplicissima** (*Zanthorhiza apiifolia*)	YELLOWROOT
XANTHOXYLI FRUCTUS (*Northern Prickly Ash Berries*)	**Zanthoxylum americanum**	COMMON PRICKLYASH
XANTHOXYLI FRUCTUS (*Southern Prickly Ash Berries*)	**Z. clavaherculis**	HERCULESCLUB P.
XANTHOXYLUM (*Northern Prickly Ash Bark*)	**Z. americanum**	COMMON P.
XANTHOXYLUM (*Southern Prickly Ash Bark*)	**Z. clavaherculis**	HERCULESCLUB P.
Yccotli. THEVETIA		
Yellow		
Adders Tongue. ERYTHRONIUM		
Horned Poppy. GLAUCIUM		
Jasmine. GELSEMIUM		
Parilla. MENISPERMUM		
Yellowroot. XANTHORRHIZA		

Drug Name	Plant Source: Botanical Name	Plant Source: S.P.N. Common Name
Yellow Sweet Clover. MELILOTUS		
Yerba		
Buena. MICROMERIA		
Mansa. ANEMOPSIS		
Reuma. FRANKENIA		
Sagrada. LANTANA		
Santa. ERIODICTYON		
Yew. TAXUS		
YOHIMBE (*Yohimbe Bark*)	**Corynanthe johimbe**	YOHIMBE CORYNANTHE

Drug Name	Plant Source: Botanical Name	Plant Source: S.P.N. Common Name
Young Fustic. LIGNUM RHOIS COTINI		
ZEA (*Corn Silk*) *See also* AMYLUM and OLEUM MAYDIS	**Zea mays**	MAIZE; INDIAN CORN
ZEDOARIA (*Zedoary*)	**Curcuma zedoaria**	ZEDOARY TURMERIC
ZERUMBET (*Cassumniar*)	**Zingiber zerumbet**	ZERUMBET GINGER
ZINGIBER (*Ginger*)	**Z. officinale**	COMMON G.
ZIZYPHUS (*Common Jujube*)	**Zizyphus jujuba** (*sativa*)	COMMON JUJUBE
ZYGADENUS (*Deathcamas*)	**Zigadenus venenosus**	MEADOW DEATHCAMAS

Plant Source: Botanical Name	Plant Source: S.P.N. Common Name	Drug Name
Abies balsamea	BALSAM FIR	TEREBINTHINA CANADENSIS (*Balsam of Fir*)
Abroma angusta	COTTON ABROMA	ABROMA (*Olutkombul*)
Abrus praecatorius	JEQUIRITY ROSARYPEA	ABRUS (*Jequirity*)
Acacia catechu	CATECHU ACACIA	CATECHU (*Black Catechu*)
A. senegal; other African **Acacia** spp.	GUMARABIC A.	ACACIA (*Gum Arabic*)
Acalypha poireti	POIRETS COPPERLEAF	ACALYPHA
Acer spp.	MAPLE	CARBO LIGNI (*Charcoal*)
A. spicatum	MOUNTAIN M.	ACER SPICATUM (*Mountain Maple Bark*)
Achillea millefolium	COMMON YARROW	ACHILLEA (*Milfoil*)
Acokanthera abyssinica	ABYSSINIAN BUSHMANSPOISON	ACOKANTHERA (*Wabayo*)
A. ouabaio	OUABAIO B.	OUABAINUM
Aconitum napellus	ACONITE MONKSHOOD	ACONITUM (*Monkshood*)
Acorus calamus	DRUG SWEETFLAG	CALAMUS (*Sweet Flag*)
Actaea spicata	BLACK BANEBERRY	ACTAEA (*Black Baneberry*)
Adansonia digitata	BAOBAB	ADANSONIA (*Baobab*)
Adhatoda vasica (*Justicia v.*)	MALABARNUT	ADHATODA
Adiantum capillus-veneris (*fergusoni*)	SOUTHERN MAIDENHAIR	ADIANTUM (*Maidenhair Fern*)
A. pedatum	AMERICAN M.	ADIANTUM (*Maidenhair Fern*)
A. philippense (*lunulatum*)	WALKING M.	ADIANTUM (*Maidenhair Fern*)
Adonis vernalis	SPRING ADONIS	ADONIS (*Pheasants-eye*)
Aesculus hippocastanum	COMMON HORSECHESTNUT	AESCULUS (*Horsechestnut*)
"	"	AESCULIN (*Horsechestnut*)
Aethusa cynapium	FOOLSPARSLEY AETHUSA	AETHUSA (*Fools-parsley*)
Aframomum melegueta (*Amomum m.*)	DRUG MELEGUETAPEPPER	GRANA PARADISI (*Grains of Paradise*)
Agave americana	CENTURYPLANT AGAVE	AGAVE (*Centuryplant*)
Agelaea lamarcki	LAMARCK AGELAEA	AGELAEA (*Cephan-Mahi*)
Agrimonia eupatoria	COMMON AGRIMONY	AGRIMONIA (*Common Agrimony*)
Agropyron repens	QUACKGRASS	TRITICUM (*Couch Grass*)
Ailanthus altissima (*glandulosa*)	TREEOFHEAVEN AILANTHUS	AILANTHUS (*Chinese Sumac*)
Ajuga chamaepitys	GROUNDPINE BUGLE	AJUGA (*Bugle*)
Alangium salviifolium (*lamarcki*)	ANGOLA ALANGIUM	ALANGINA
Albizzia anthelmintica	MUSENNA ALBIZZIA	MESENNA (*Musenna*)
A. fastigiata	FLATCROWN A.	GUMMI ALBIZZIAE (*Sassa Gum*)
Alchemilla vulgaris	COMMON LADYSMANTLE	ALCHEMILLA (*Ladysmantle*)
Aletris farinosa	WHITETUBE STARGRASS	ALETRIS (*Stargrass*)
Aleurites cordata	JAPAN WOODOILTREE	OLEUM ALEURITES CORDATA (*Tung Oil*)
A. moluccana (*triloba*)	CANDLENUTTREE	OLEUM ALEURITES TRILOBAE (*Candlenut Oil*)
Alisma plantago-aquatica	AMERICAN WATERPLANTAIN	ALISMA (*Waterplantain*)
Alkanna tinctoria	DYERS ALKANET	ALKANNA (*Alkanet Root*)
Allamanda cathartica	COMMON ALLAMANDA	ALLAMANDA
Allium cepa	GARDEN ONION	CEPA (*Onion*)
A. porrum	LEEK	PORRUM (*Leek*)
A. sativum	GARLIC	ALLIUM (*Garlic*)
Alnus glutinosa	EUROPEAN ALDER	ALNUS (*Alder*)
Aloe barbadensis	MEDITERRANEAN ALOE	ALOE (*Curacao Aloes*)
A. ferox	CAPE A.	ALOE (*Cape Aloes*)
A. perryi	PERRY A.	ALOE (*Socotrine Aloes*)
Alpinia officinarum (*Languas o.*)	LESSER GALANGAL	GALANGA (*Galangal*)
Alsophila lurida		PENGAWAR DJAMBI

Plant Source: Botanical Name	Plant Source: S.P.N. Common Name	Drug Name
Alstonia constricta	QUININE ALSTONIA	ALSTONIA (*Dita Bark*)
A. scholaris	PALIMARA A.	ALSTONIA
Althaea officinalis	MARSHMALLOW	ALTHAEA (*Marshmallow Root*)
"	"	ALTHAEAE FOLIA (*Marshmallow Leaves*)
Ambrosia artemisifolia	COMMON RAGWEED	AMBROSIA (*Roman Wormwood*)
A. trifida	GIANT R.	AMBROSIA (*Great Ragweed*)
Anacardium occidentale	COMMON CASHEW	ANACARDIUM (*West Indian Cashew-nut*)
Anagallis arvensis	SCARLET PIMPERNEL	ANAGALLIS (*Scarlet Pimpernel*)
Anagyris foetida	MEDITERRANEAN STINKBUSH	ANAGYRIS
Anamirta cocculus	MALAY FISHBERRY	COCCULUS (*Fish Berry*)
Anaphalis margaritacea (*Antennaria m.*)	COMMON PEARLEVERLASTING	GNAPHALIUM (*Life-everlasting*)
Anchietea salutaris	MERCURY ANCHIETEA	ANCHIETEA (*Pirageia*)
Anchusa officinalis	COMMON BUGLOSS	ANCHUSA (*Ox-tongue*)
Andira araroba (*Vataireopsis a.; Vouacapoua a.*)	GOA ANGELINTREE	ARAROBA (*Goa Powder*)
"	"	CHRYSAROBINUM (*Chrysarobin*)
A. inermis (*jamaicensis; Vouacapoua americana*)	CABBAGE A.	CORTEX VOUACAPOUAE (*Cabbage Tree Bark*)
Andrographis paniculata	KARIYAT	ANDROGRAPHIS
Anemone patens (*Pulsatilla p.*)	SPREADING PASQUEFLOWER (*Spreading Anemone*)	PULSATILLA (*Pasque Flower*)
A. pratensis (*Pulsatilla p.*)	MEADOW P.	PULSATILLA
A. pulsatilla (*Pulsatilla vulgaris*)	EUROPEAN P.	ANEMONIN
"	"	PULSATILLA (*Pasque Flower*)
Anemopsis californica	YERBAMANSA	ANEMOPSIS (*Yerba Mansa*)
Anethum graveolens	DILL	ANETHI FRUCTUS (*Dill Seed*)
Angelica anomala chinensis	CHINESE EUMENOL ANGELICA	TANG-KUEI (*Man-Mu*)
A. archangelica (*Archangelica officinalis*)	GARDEN ANGELICA	ANGELICAE RADIX (*Angelica Root*)
"	"	ANGELICAE FRUCTUS (*Angelica Seed*)
Angraecum fragrans	BOURBONTEA ORCHID	ANGRAECUM (*Bourbon Tea*)
Aniba coto	COTOBARK	COTO (*True Coto Bark*)
Annona squamosa	SUGARAPPLE	ANONA (*Sugar Apple*)
Anogeissus latifolia	BAKLIGUM AXLEWOOD	GUMMI ANOGEISSI (*Indian Gum*)
Anthemis cotula	MAYWEED CAMOMILE	COTULA (*May Weed*)
A. nobilis	ROMAN C.	ANTHEMIS (*Roman Chamomile*)
Anthriscus cerefolium	SALADCHERVIL	ANTHRISCUS (*Chervil*)
Antiaris toxicaria	UPASTREE	ANTIARIS (*Upas Antiar*)
Apium graveolens dulce	GARDEN CELERY	APII FRUCTUS (*Celery Seed*)
Apocynum androsaemifolium	SPREADING DOGBANE	APOCYNUM ANDROSAEMIFOLIUM (*Dogbane*)
A. cannabinum	HEMP D.	APOCYNUM (*Canadian Hemp*)
Aquilegia vulgaris	EUROPEAN COLUMBINE	AQUILEGIA (*Columbine*)
Arachis hypogaea	PEANUT	ARACHIS (*Peanut*)
"	"	OLEUM ARACHIDIS (*Peanut Oil*)

Plant Source: Botanical Name	Plant Source: S.P.N. Common Name	Drug Name
Aralia hispida	Bristly Aralia	Aralia Hispida (*Dwarf Elder Root*)
A. nudicaulis	Wildsarsaparilla	Aralia Nudicaulis (*American Sarsaparilla*)
A. racemosa	American Spikenard	Aralia (*American Spikenard*)
Arctium lappa (*Lappa edulis; L. major*)	Great Burdock	Lappa (*Burdock Root*)
A. minus (*Lappa minor*)	Smaller B.	Lappa (*Burdock Root*)
Arctostaphylos uvaursi	Bearberry	Uva Ursi (*Bearberry*)
Areca cathecu	Betelnutpalm	Areca (*Betel Nut*)
Argemone mexicana	Mexican Pricklepoppy	Argemone (*Prickly Poppy*)
Arisaema atrorubens	Common Jackinthepulpit	Arum (*Indian Turnip*)
Aristolochia reticulata	Texas Snakeroot Dutchmanspipe	Serpentaria (*Texas Snakeroot*)
A. serpentaria	Virginia S. D.	Serpentaria (*Virginia Snakeroot*)
Armoracia lapathifolia	Horseradish	Armoraciae Radix (*Horseradish Root*)
Arnica montana	Mountain Arnica	Arnica (*Arnica Flowers*)
"	"	Arnicae Radix (*Arnica Root*)
Artabotrys uncinatus (*odoratissimus*)	Fragrant Tailgrape	Artabotrys (*Fragrant Tailgrape*)
Artemisia abrotanum	Oldman Wormwood	Abrotanum (*Southernwood*)
A. absinthium	Common W.	Absinthium (*Common Wormwood*)
A. cina	Levant W.	Santonica (*Levant Worm Seed*)
A. dracunculus	Tarragon	Artemisia Dracunculus (*Tarragon*)
A. frigida	Fringed Sagebrush	Artemisia Frigida (*Colorado Mountain Sage*)
Arum maculatum	Lordsandladies	Arum
Asarum canadense	Canada Wildginger	Asarum (*Wild Ginger*)
A. europaeum	European W.	Asarabacca
Asclepias tuberosa	Butterfly Milkweed	Asclepias (*Pleurisy Root*)
Ascophyllum nodosum	Drug Rockweep	Fucus (*Bladderwrack*)
Asimina triloba	Common Pawpaw	Asimina (*American Pawpaw*)
Asparagus officinalis	Garden Asparagus	Asparagus
Aspidosperma quebracho-blanco	Common White-quebracho	Aspidosperma (*Quebracho Bark*)
Aster puniceus	Swamp Aster	Aster
Astragalus gummifer	Tragacanth Milkvetch	Tragacanth (*Gum Tragacanth*)
A. mollissimus	Woolly Loco	Loco (*Purple Loco*)
A. sarcocolla		Sarcocolla
Atherosperma moschatum	Australian-sassafras	Atherosperma (*Australian Sassafras*)
Athyrium filixfemina (*Asplenium f.*)	Ladyfern	Athyrium (*Female Fern*)
Atropa belladonna	Belladonna	Belladonnae Folium (*Deadly Nightshade Leaf*)
"	"	Belladonnae Radix (*Deadly Nightshade Root*)
Avena sativa	Common Oat	Avena Sativa (*Oats*)
Baccharis coridifolia	Miomio Baccharis	Baccharis (*Mio Mio*)
Balanites roxburghi	Roxburgh Balanites	Balanites (*Agialida*)
Balsamorhiza terebinthacea	Turpentine Balsamroot	Balsamorhiza
Banisteriopsis caapi (*Banisteria c.*)	Caapi	Caapi
Baphia nitida	Shiny Camwood	Lignum Baphiae (*Cam Wood*)
Baptisia tinctoria	Yellow Wildindigo	Baptisia (*Wild Indigo*)
Barosma betulina	Short Buchu	Buchu (*Short Buchu*)
B. crenulata	Ovalleaf B.	Buchu (*Oval Buchu*)
B. serratifolia	Longleaf B.	Buchu (*Long Buchu*)
Barringtonia speciosa	India Barringtonia	Barringtonia
Bergenia crassifolia (*Saxifraga c.*)	Leather Bergenia	Saxifraga (*Rockfoil*)
Bertholletia excelsa	Brazilnut	Bertholletia (*Brazil Nut*)
Beta vulgaris	Common Beet	Sucrosum (*Beet Sugar*)
Betula lenta	Sweet Birch	Cortex Betulae (*Birch Bark*)
"	"	Methylis Salicylas (*Methyl Salicylate*)
Betula pendula (*alba*)	European White Birch	Betula Alba (*European White Birch*)
"	"	Oleum Betulae Empyreumaticum (*Oleum Rusci*)
Bidens bipinnata	Spanishneedles	Bidens (*Spanish Needles*)
Bixa orellana	Anattotree	Annatto (*Annotta*)
Blumea lacera	Malay Blumea	Blumea
Bocconia arborea	Tree Bocconia	Bocconia
Borago officinalis	Common Borage	Borago (*Borage*)
Boswellia carteri	Bible Frankincense	Olibanum (*Frankincense*)
Bouvardia ternifolia (*triphylla*)	Scarlet Bouvardia	Trompatila (*Bouvardia*)
Bowdichia virgilioides	Alcornoco	Bowdichia
Bragantia wallichi	Alpamroot Bragantia	Bragantia
Brassica campestris oleifera	Oilnavew Bird Rape	Oleum Colzae (*Colza Oil*)
B. hirta (*alba; Sinapis a.*)	White Mustard	Sinapis Alba (*White Mustard*)
B. juncea (*rugosa; Sinapis j.*)	India M.	Sinapis Nigra
"	"	Oleum Sinapis Volatile (*Mustard Oil*)
B. nigra or vars. of these spp.	Black M.	Sinapis Nigra (*Brown Mustard*)
"	"	Oleum Sinapis Volatile (*Mustard Oil*)
Brosimum utile (*galactodendron*)	Cow Breadnuttree	Palo de Vaca (*Cow Tree*)
Brunfelsia hopeana	Manaca Raintree	Manaca (*Vegetable Mercury*)
B. hydrangeaeformis	Mire R.	Mire
Bryonia alba	White Bryony	Bryonia (*Bryony*)
B. dioica	Redberry B.	Bryonia (*Bryony*)
Bursera glabrifolia (*aloexylon*)	Linaloe Bursera	Oleum Linaloe (*Oil of Linaloe*)
B. penicillata (*delpechiana*)		Oleum Linaloe (*Oil of Linaloe*)
Buxus sempervirens	Common Box	Buxus (*Evergreen Box*)
Caesalpinia brasiliensis	Brazilwood	Lignum Braziliense (*Brazilwood*)
C. coriaria	Dividivi	Fructus Caesalpiniae (*Divi-Divi*)
C. crista (*bonducella; Guilandina c.*)	Nickernut Caesalpinia	Semen Bonduc (*Bonduc Seed*)
C. echinata	Prickly Brazilwood	Lignum Caesalpiniae (*Peachwood*)
C. praecox	Breagum Caesalpinia	Gummi Breae (*Brea Gum*)
C. sappan (*Biancaea s.*)	Sappan C.	Lignum Sappan (*European Sappan*)
Calendula officinalis	Potmarigold Calendula	Calendula (*Marigold*)
Calliandra houstoniana (*houstoni*)	Panbotano Calliandra	Panhotano Cortex (*Panbotano Bark*)
Callitris spp.	Cypresspine	Oleum Callitris (*Oil of Callitris*)
Calotropis gigantea	Akund Calotrope	Calotropis (*Mudar*)
C. procera	Faftan C.	Calotropis (*Mudar*)
Calycanthus floridus	Common Sweetshrub	Calycanthus (*Sweet Shrub*)
Camellia drupifera	Himalayan Camellia	Oleum Theae Seminis (*Tea-seed Oil of Camellia*)
C. japonica	Common C.	Camellia
C. sinensis (*thea; Thea s.*)	Common Tea	Thea (*Tea*)
Cananga odorata	Ylangylang	Oleum Canangae (*Oil of Cananga*)
Canarium commune	Javaalmond Canarytree	Elemi (*Manila Elemi*)
C. luzonicum	Elemi C.	Elemi (*Manila Elemi*)
Canella winterana	Cinnamon Canella	Canella (*White Cinnamon*)
Cannabis sativa	Hemp	Cannabis (*Indian Hemp*)
Capparis coriacea	Simulo Caper	Simulo
C. spinosa	Common C.	Capparis (*Capers*)
Capsella bursa-pastoris	Shepherdspurse	Capsella (*Shepherds-purse*)
Capsicum frutescens (*annuum*)	Bush Redpepper	Capsicum (*Cayenne Pepper*)
"	"	Paprika
C. f. conoides	Tabasco R.	Tabasco (*Tobasco Pepper*) See note under Capsicum in the first half of this list.

Plant Source		
Botanical Name	S.P.N. Common Name	Drug Name
Cardamine pratensis	Cuckoo Bittercress	Cardamine (*Cuckoo Flower*)
Carica papaya	Papaya	Papaya (*Paw Paw*)
Carthamus tinctorius	Safflower	Carthamus (*American Saffron*)
Carum carvi	Caraway	Carum (*Caraway Seed*)
"	"	Oleum Cari (*Caraway Oil*)
Carya spp. (*Hicoria*)	Hickory	Carya (*Hickory*)
Casearia esculenta		Casearia
Casimiroa edulis	Whitesapote	Casimiroa (*White Sapota*)
Cassia acutifolia (*senna*)	Alexandria Senna	Senna (*Alexandrian Senna Leaves*)
"	"	Sennae Fructus (*Senna Pods*)
C. angustifolia	Congo S.	Senna (*Tinnevelly Senna Leaves*)
"	"	Sennae Fructus (*Senna Pods*)
C. fistula (*Cathartocarpus f.*)	Goldenshower S.	Cassia Fistula (*Purging Cassia*)
C. marilandica	Wild S.	Cassia Marilandica (*American Senna*)
Castanea dentata	American Chestnut	Castanea (*Chestnut Leaves*)
Castela texana	Allthorn Castela (*Amargosa*)	Castela (*Chaparro Amargosa*)
Castilla elastica (*Castilloa e.*)	Panama Gumtree	Elastica (*Rubber*)
Catalpa bignonioides	Southern Catalpa	Catalpa (*Indian Bean*)
Catha edulis	Arabiantea (*Kat*)	Catha (*Abyssinian Tea*)
Caulophyllum thalictroides	Blue Cohosh	Caulophyllum (*Blue Cohosh*)
Cayaponia globosa		Cayaponia (*Silver Manso*)
Ceanothus americanus	Jerseytea Ceanothus	Ceanothus (*New Jersey Tea*)
C. reclinatus	Snakeroot C.	Colubrina (*Mabee Bark*)
Cecropia obtusa	Medicinal Pumpwood	Cecropia (*Cecropia Obtusa*)
Celastrus paniculata	Panicled Bittersweet	Celastrus (*Panicled Bittersweet*)
C. scandens	American B.	Celastrus (*American Bittersweet*)
Centaurea cyanus	Cornflower	Flores Cyani (*Cyani Flowers*)
Centaurium umbellatum (*Erythraea centaurium*)	Drug Centaurium	Centaurium (*Bitter Herb*)
Cephaelis acuminata		Ipecacuanha (*Cartagena Ipecac; Nicaragua I.*)
C. ipecacuanha (*Psychotria i.*)		Ipecacuanha (*Rio Ipecac*)
Cephalanthus occidentalis	Common Buttonbush	Cephalanthus (*Button Bush*)
Cercis canadensis	Eastern Redbud	Cercis (*Judas Tree*)
Cetraria islandica	Icelandmoss	Cetraria (*Iceland Moss*)
Chamaelirium luteum	Fairywand	Helonias (*False Unicorn*)
Cheiranthus cheiri	Common Wallflower	Cheiranthus (*Wallflower*)
Chelidonium majus	Greater Celandine	Chelidonium (*Great Celandine*)
Chelone glabra (*alba*)	White Turtlehead	Chelone (*Balmony Leaves*)
Chenopodium ambrosioides anthelminticum	Drug Wormseed Goosefoot	Oleum Chenopodii (*Oil of American Wormseed*)
Chimaphila umbellata	Common Pipsissewa	Chimaphila (*Pipsissewa*)
Chiococca alba (*racemosa*)	Davids Milkberry	Radix Caincae (*Davids Root*)
Chionanthus virginicus	White Fringetree	Chionanthus (*Fringe Tree Bark*)
Chione glabra	Smooth Chione	Chione (*Palo Blanco*)
"	"	Oleum Chione (*Oil of Chione*)
Chlorophora tinctoria	Drug Fustictree	Fustic (*Old Fustic*)
Chondodendron tomentosum	Pareiraroot	Pareira (*Pareira Brava*)
Chondrus crispus	Irishmoss	Chondrus (*Irish Moss*)
Chrysanthemum cinerariaefolium	Dalmatian Pyrethrum	Pyrethri Flores (*Dalmatian Insect Flowers*)
C. coccineum (*roseum; Pyrethrum carneum; P. hybridum*)	Florists P.	Pyrethri Flores (*Persian Insect Flowers*)
Chrysanthemum marschalli	Caucasian Pyrethrum	Pyrethri Flores (*Persian Insect Flowers*)
C. parthenium	Feverfew Chrysanthemum	Parthenium (*Feverfew*)
Cibotium barometz	Scythianlamb	Pengawar Djambi (*Golden Moss*)
C. glaucum	Underblue Cibotium	Pengawar Djambi
Cichorium intybus	Common Chicory	Cichorium (*Chicory*)
Cicuta maculata	Spotted Waterhemlock	Cicuta (*American Water Hemlock*)
C. virosa	European W.	Cicuta (*European Water Hemlock*)
Cimicifuga racemosa	Cohosh Bugbane	Cimicifuga (*Black Cohosh*)
Cinchona calisaya	Yellowbark Cinchona	Quinina (*Quinine*)
"	"	Cinchona (*Yellow Cinchona*)
C. ledgeriana	Ledgerbark C.	Quinina (*Quinine*)
"	"	Cinchona (*Yellow Cinchona*)
C. pallida	Pale C.	Quinina (*Quinine*)
C. succirubra and its hybrids	Redbark C.	Quinina (*Quinine*)
"	"	Cinchona (*Red Cinchona*)
Cinnamomum burmani	Malay Cinnamon	Cinnamomum Burmanni (*Fagot Cinnamon*)
C. camphora	Camphortree	Camphora (*Camphor*)
C. cassia	Cassiabarktree	Cinnamomum Cassia (*Cassia Cinnamon*)
"	"	Oleum Cinnamomi (*Oil of Cassia*)
C. culilawan	Culiban Cinnamon	Cortex Culiliban (*Culiliwan*)
C. loureiri	Cassiaflowertree	Cinnamomum (*Saigon Cinnamon*)
C. massoia	Massoia Cinnamon	Massoia (*Massoi Bark*)
C. zeylanicum	Ceylon C.	Cinnamomum Zeylanicum (*Ceylon Cinnamon*)
Cistus spp.	Rockrose	Labdanum (*Ladanum*)
Citrullus colocynthis	Colocynth	Colocynthis (*Bitter Apple*)
C. vulgaris	Watermelon	Citrullus (*Water Melon Seed*)
Citrus aurantium	Sour Orange (*Seville O.*)	Aurantii Amari Cortex (*Bitter Orange Peel*)
"	"	Aurantii Florum (*Oil of Neroli*)
"	"	Oleum Aurantii Amari (*Oil of Bitter Orange*)
C. bergamia	Bergamot O.	Oleum Bergamottae (*Oil of Bergamot*)
C. limon (*limonia*)	Lemon	Limonis Cortex (*Lemon Peel*)
"	"	Oleum Limonis (*Lemon Oil*)
C. sinensis	Sweet Orange	Aurantii Dulcis Cortex (*Sweet Orange Peel*)
"	"	Oleum Aurantii (*Oil of Sweet Orange*)
Claviceps purpurea	Ergot Claviceps	Ergota (*Ergot of Rye*)
Clematis recta (*erecta*)	Ground Clematis	Clematis (*Virgins Bower*)
Cnicus benedictus (*Carduus b.; Centaurea benedicta*)	Blessedthistle	Cnicus (*Blessed Thistle*)
Cnidoscolus urens (*Jatropha u.*)	Drug Treadsoftly	Pini-pini (*Arra Diabo*)
Cochlearia officinalis	Common Scurvyweed	Cochlearia (*Common Scurvy Grass*)
Cochlospermum religiosum (*gossypium*)	Cotton Shellseed	Gummi Bassora (*Karaya Gum*)
Cocos nucifera	Coconut	Oleum Cocois (*Coconut Oil*)
Coffea arabica	Arabian Coffee	Coffea Tosta (*Roasted Coffee*)
C. liberica	Liberian C.	Coffea Tosta
Cola acuminata	Sudan Colanut	Kola (*Cola*)
Colchicum autumnale	Common Autumncrocus	Colchicina (*Colchicine*)
"	"	Colchici Cormus (*Meadow Saffron Corm*)
"	"	Colchici Semen (*Meadow Saffron Seed*)

Plant Source		
Botanical Name	*S.P.N. Common Name*	*Drug Name*
Collinsonia canadensis	Citronella Horsebalm	Collinsonia (*Stone Root*)
Colutea arborescens	Common Bladdersenna	Colutea (*Bladder Senna*)
Combretum sundaicum	Sundai Combretum	Combretum (*Jungleweed*)
Commelina communis	Common Dayflower	Commelina (*Dayflower*)
C. tuberosa	Tuber D.	Commelina (*Dayflower*)
Commiphora abyssinica	Abyssinian Myrrhtree	Myrrha (*Gum Myrrh*)
C. africana	African M.	Bdellium (*Bissabol*)
C. mukul	Mukul M.	Bdellium (*Bissabol*)
"	"	Opopanax
C. myrrha	Common M.	Myrrha (*Gum Myrrh*)
C. opobalsamum	Mecca M.	Balsamum Gileadense (*Balm-of-Gilead*)
Comptonia peregrina (*asplenifolia*)	Sweetfern	Comptonia (*Sweet Fern*)
Conium maculatum	Poisonhemlock	Conium (*Poison Hemlock*)
Connarus guianensis	Guiana Zebrawood	Connarus
Convallaria majalis	Lilyofthevalley	Convallariae Flores (*Lily-of-the-valley Flowers*)
"	"	Convallariae Radix (*Lily-of-the-valley Root*)
Convolvulus soldanella (*Calystegia s.*)	Seashore Glorybind	Calystegia
Copaifera conjugata	Inhambane Copaltree	Copal (*Inhambane Copal*)
C. copallifera	SierraLeone C.	Copal (*West African Copal*)
C. langsdorfi	Balsam C.	Copaiba (*Balsam Copaiba*)
Coptis groenlandica	Common Goldthread	Coptis (*Goldthread*)
Corallorrhiza odontorhiza	Late Coralroot	Corallorrhiza (*Coral Root*)
Coriandrum sativum	Coriander	Coriandrum (*Coriander Seed*)
"	"	Oleum Coriandri (*Coriander Oil*)
Coriaria myrtifolia	Myrtle Coriaria	Coriaria (*Tanners Sumac*)
Cornus florida	Flowering Dogwood	Cornus (*Dogwood Bark*)
Coronilla scorpioides	Scorpion Coronilla	Coronilla
Corylus americana	American Filbert	Corylus (*American Hazelnut*)
C. avellana	European F.	Corylus (*Filbert*)
C. cornuta (*rostrata*)	Beaked F. (*Beaked Hazel*)	Corylus (*Beaked Hazel*)
Corynanthe johimbe	Yohimbe Corynanthe	Yohimbe (*Yohimbe Bark*)
Coscinium fenestratum	Calumbawood	Coscinium (*False Calumba*)
Cotinus coggygria (*Rhus cotinus*)	Common Smoketree	Lignum Rhois Cotini (*Young Fustic*)
Crataegus oxyacantha	English Hawthorn	Crataegus (*English Hawthorn*)
Crocanthemum canadense	Canada Frostwort	Helianthemum (*Rockrose*)
Crocus sativus	Saffron Crocus	Crocus (*Saffron*)
Croton malambo	Malambobark Croton	Malambo (*Matias Bark*)
C. tiglium	Purging C.	Oleum Tiglii (*Croton Oil*)
Cryptocarya australis	Gray Cryptocarya	Cryptocarya
Cucumis myriocarpus	Gooseberrygourd	Cacur
Cucurbita pepo	Pumpkin	Pepo (*Pumpkin Seed*)
Cuminum cyminum	Cumin	Cuminum (*Cumin Seed*)
Cunila origanoides (*mariana*)	Maryland Stonemint	Cunila (*American Dittany*)
Cupressus sempervirens	Italian Cypress	Oleum Cupressi (*Oil of Cypress*)
Curcuma longa	Common Turmeric	Curcuma (*Turmeric*)
C. zedoaria	Zedoary T.	Zedoaria (*Zedoary*)
Cycas revoluta	Sago Cycas	Sago (*Sago Starch*)
Cyclamen europaeum	European Cyclamen	Cyclamen (*Sowbread*)
Cydonia oblonga	Common Quince	Cydonium (*Quince Seed*)
Cymbopogon citratus	Lemongrass	Oleum Graminis Citrate (*Oil of Lemon Grass*)
C. flexuosus	Cochin L.	Oleum Graminis Citrate (*Oil of Lemon Grass*)
C. jwarancusa	Iwarancusagrass	Iwarancusa
C. nardus	Citronellagrass	Oleum Citronellae (*Oil of Citronella*)
Cymbopogon winterianus	Mahapengiri	Oleum Citronellae (*Oil of Citronella*)
Cynanchum vincetoxicum (*Vincetoxicum officinale*)	White Swallowwort	Vincetoxicum (*White Swallowwort*)
Cynara scolymus	Artichoke (*Globe A.*)	Cynara (*French Artichoke*)
Cynoglossum officinale	Common Houndstongue	Cynoglossum (*Hounds Tongue*)
Cypripedium calceolus pubescens	Yellow European Ladyslipper	Cypripedium (*Lady Slipper Root*)
Cytisus scoparius	Scotch Broom	Scoparius (*Broom Tops*)
Dacrydium cupressinum	Rimu Dacrydium	Rimu (*Rimu Resin*)
Daphnandra micrantha	Sassafras Daphnandra	Daphnandra
Daphne gnidium	Spurgeflax Daphne	Mezereum (*Mezereon*)
D. laureola	Spurgelaurel D.	Mezereum (*Mezereon*)
D. mezereum	February D.	Mezereum (*Mezereon*)
Datura stramonium	Jimsonweed Datura	Stramonium (*Jimson Weed*)
Daucus carota sativa	Garden Carrot	Carota (*Wild Carrot*)
Delphinium ajacis	Rocket Larkspur	Delphinium (*Larkspur Seed*)
Dermophylla pendulina (*Cayaponia p.*)	Tayuya Skinleaf	Tayuya
Derris elliptica	Tubaroot Jewelvine	Derris (*Tuba Root*)
D. malaccensis	Malacca J.	Derris (*Tuba Root*)
Dianthus caryophyllus	Carnation; Clove Pink	Dianthus (*Clove Pink*)
Dicentra canadensis (*Bikukulla c.*)	Squirrelcorn Bleedingheart	Corydalis (*Turkey Corn*)
D. cucullaria (*Bikukulla c.*)	Dutchmans-breeches	Corydalis (*Dutchmans Breeches*)
D. pusilla	Little Bleedingheart	Dicentra
Dicypellium caryophyllatum	Clovebarktree	Cortex Caryophyllatus (*Clove Bark*)
Diervilla lonicera (*trifida*)	Dwarf Bushhoneysuckle	Diervilla (*Bush Honeysuckle*)
Digitalis lanata	Grecian Foxglove	Digitalis Lanata (*Grecian Foxglove*)
D. purpurea	Common F.	Digitalis (*Foxglove*)
Dioclea spp.	Clusterpea	Semen Cali (*Cali Nuts*)
Dioscorea villosa	Atlantic Yam	Dioscorea (*Wild Yam Root*)
Diospyros virginiana	Common Persimmon	Diospyros (*Persimmon*)
Dipterocarpus turbinatus	Common Gurjunoiltree	Oleum Dipterocarpi (*Oil of Gurjun*)
Dipteryx odorata (*Coumarouna o.*)	Dutch Tonkabean	Dipteryx (*Dutch Tonka*)
D. oppositifolia (*Coumarouna o.*)	British T.	Dipteryx (*English Tonka*)
Dirca palustris	Atlantic Leatherwood	Dirca (*Leatherwood*)
Dorema ammoniacum	Bombay Sumbul	Ammoniacum (*Gum Ammoniac*)
Dorstenia contrajerva	Contrayerva Torusherb	Contrayerva (*Contrayerba*)
Drimys winteri	Wintersbark Drimys	Drimys (*Winters Bark*)
"	"	Wintera (*Winters Bark*)
Drosera anglica	English Sundew	Drosera (*Sundew*)
D. longifolia	Narrowleaf S.	Drosera (*Sundew*)
D. rotundifolia	Roundleaf S.	Drosera (*Sundew*)
Dryopteris filixmas (*Asplenium f.*)	Malefern	Aspidium (*Male Fern*)
D. marginalis	Leather Woodfern	Aspidium (*American Aspidium*)
Duboisia myoporoides	Corkwood Duboisia	Duboisia
Ecballium elaterium (*Momordica e.*)	Squirtingcucumber	Elaterium (*Squirting Cucumber*)
Echinacea angustifolia (*Brauneria a.*)	Blacksamson Echinacea	Echinacea (*Cone Flower*)
E. pallida (*Brauneria p.; Rudbeckia p.*)	Pale E.	Echinacea
Echinocereus reichenbachi (*Cereus caespitosus*)	Lace Echinocereus	Cereus
Elaeis guineensis	African Oilpalm	Oleum Palmae (*Palm Oil*)
Elettaria cardamomum	Cardamon	Cardamomum (*Cardamom Fruit*)
"	"	Cardamomi Semen (*Cardamom Seed*)
"	"	Oleum Cardamomi (*Oil of Cardamom*)

Plant Source		
Botanical Name	*S.P.N. Common Name*	*Drug Name*
Entada phaseoloides (*scandens*)	Climbing Entada	Entada (*Garbee Bean*)
Ephedra spp.	Ephedra	Ephedrina (*Ephedrine*)
E. distachya	Jointfir E.	Ephedra (*Ma Huang*)
E. equisetina	Mongolian E.	Ephedra (*Ma Huang*)
E. gerardiana	Gerard E.	Ephedra (*Ma Huang*)
E. sinica	Chinese E.	Ephedra (*Ma Huang*)
Epifagus virginiana	Virginia Beechdrops	Epifagus (*Epiphegus*)
Epigaea repens	Trailing-arbutus	Epigea (*Trailing Arbutus*)
Epipremnum pinnatum	Centipede Tongavine	Tonga
Erechtites hieracifolia	American Burnweed	Erechtites (*Fireweed*)
Erigeron annuus	Annual Fleabane	Erigeron (*Fleabane*)
E. canadensis (*Leptilon canadense*)	Horseweed F.	Erigeron (*Fleabane*)
E. philadelphicus	Philadelphia F.	Erigeron (*Fleabane*)
Eriobotrya japonica	Loquat	Eriobotrya (*Loquat*)
Eriodictyon californicum	California Yerbasanta	Eriodictyon (*Yerba Santa*)
Erodium cicutarium	Alfileria	Erodium (*Storks Bill*)
Eryngium aquaticum (*yuccaefolium*)	Buttonsnakeroot Eryngo	Eryngium (*Button Snakeroot*)
Erythrina broteroi	Brotero Coralbean	Erythrina
Erythronium americanum	Common Fawnlily	Erythronium (*Yellow Adders Tongue*)
Erythrophleum guineense	Casca Redwatertree	Erythrophleum (*Sassy Bark*)
Erythroxylum coca	Huanuco Cocainetree	Coca; Cocaina
E. novogranatense	Peruvian C.	Coca; Cocaina
E. truxillense	Trujillo C.	Coca; Cocaine
Eschscholtzia californica	Californiapoppy	Eschscholtzia (*California Poppy*)
Eucalyptus camaldulensis (*rostrata* Schlecht., *not* Cav.)	Longbeak Eucalyptus	Gummi Eucalypti (*Red Gum*)
E. globulus	Tasmanian Blue E.	Eucalyptus (*Blue Gum Leaves*)
"	"	Oleum Eucalypti (*Oil of Eucalyptus*)
E. mannifera	Manna E.	Manna Eucalypti (*Australian Manna*)
Eucarya spicata	Australia-sandalwood	Oleum Santali Australiensis
Eugenia chequen (*cheken*)	Cheken Eugenia	Eugenia Cheken (*Cheken*)
Euonymus atropurpureus	Eastern Wahoo	Euonymus (*Wahoo Bark*)
Eupatorium perfoliatum	Boneset	Eupatorium (*Boneset*)
Euphorbia corollata	Floweringspurge Euphorbia	Euphorbia Corollata (*Flowering Spurge*)
E. lathyrus	Caper E.	Oleum Euphorbiae (*Caper Spurge Oil*)
E. pilulifera	Pillpod E.	Euphorbia Pilulifera (*Pill-bearing Spurge*)
E. resinifera	Gum E.	Euphorbium (*Gum Euphorbium*)
Euphrasia officinalis	Drug Eyebright	Euphrasia (*Eyebright*)
Exogonium purga (*Ipomoea jalapa; I. purga*)	Jalap	Jalapa (*Jalap*)
Fabiana imbricata	Peru Falseheath	Fabiana (*Pichi*)
Ferula assafoetida	Asafetida Giantfennel	Asafoetida (*Gum Asafoetida*)
F. foetida	Devilsdung G.	Asafoetida (*Gum Asafoetida*)
F. galbaniflua	Galbanum G.	Galbanum
F. persica	Persian G.	Sagapenum
F. sumbul	Muskroot G.	Sumbul (*Musk Root*)
Ficus carica	Common Fig	Ficus (*Fig*)
Flemingia macrophylla (*congesta*)	Longleaf Wurrus	Wurrus (*Waras*)
Foeniculum vulgare	Common Fennel	Foeniculum (*Fennel Seed*)
"	"	Oleum Foeniculi (*Fennel Oil*)
Fomes officinalis (*Polyporus o.*)	Larch Fomes	Agaricus (*Larch Agaric*)
Frankenia grandifolia	Yerbareuma Seaheath	Frankenia (*Yerba Reuma*)
Frasera carolinensis	Carolina Frasera	Frasera (*American Columbo*)
Fraxinus ornus	Flowering Ash	Manna
Fucus serratus	Cartwrack Rockweed	Fucus
Fucus vesiculosus	Bladderwrack Rockweed	Fucus
Fumaria officinalis	Drug Fumitory	Fumaria (*Fumitory*)
Galega officinalis	Common Goatsrue	Galega (*European Goats Rue*)
Galipea officinalis	Angostura Barktree	Cuspariae Cortex (*Cusparia Bark*)
Galium aparine	Catchweed Bedstraw	Galium (*Cleavers*)
Garcinia hanburyi	Siam Gambogetree	Cambogia (*Gamboge*)
Gardenia jasminoides (*augusta; florida; grandiflora*)	Capejasmine	Gardenia
Garrya fremonti	Fremont Silktassel	Garrya Fremontii (*California Fever Bush*)
Gaultheria procumbens	Checkerberry Wintergreen	Gaultheria (*Wintergreen*)
"	"	Methylis Salicylas (*Methyl Salicylate*)
Gelidium corneum	Common Agar	Agar (*Agar-Agar*)
Gelsemium sempervirens	Carolinajessamine	Gelsemium (*Yellow Jasmine Root*)
Gentiana lutea	Yellow Gentian	Gentiana (*Gentian Root*)
Geranium maculatum	Spotted Geranium	Geranium (*Cranesbill*)
Geum rivale	Water Avens	Geum (*Water Avens*)
Gigartina mamillosa		Chondrus (*Irish Moss*)
Gillenia trifoliata (*Porteranthus trifoliatus*)	Bowmansroot	Gillenia (*Bowmans Root*)
Glaucium flavum (*luteum*)	Yellow Hornpoppy	Glaucium (*Yellow Horned Poppy*)
Glecoma hederacea (*Nepeta h.*)		Glechoma (*Ground Ivy*)
Gleditsia triacanthos (*Gleditschia t.*)	Common Honeylocust	Gleditschia (*Honey Locust*)
Gloriosa superba	Malabar Glorylily	Gloriosa (*Climbing Lily*)
Glycine soja (*hispida; max; Soja m.*)	Soybean	Soja (*Soybean*)
Glycyrrhiza glabra	Common Licorice	Glycyrrhiza (*Spanish Licorice Root*)
G. glabra var.		Glycyrrhiza (*Licorice Root, Persian, etc.*)
G. g. glandulifera	Russian L.	Glycyrrhiza (*Russian Licorice Root*)
Gnaphalium obtusifolium (*polycephalum*)	Fragrant Cudweed	Gnaphalium (*Sweet Scented Life-everlasting*)
Gossypium herbaceum	Levant Cotton	Gossypii Radicis Cortex (*Cotton Root Bark*)
"	"	Oleum Gossypii Seminis (*Cottonseed Oil*)
"	"	Gossypium Purificatum (*Absorbent Cotton*)
G. hirsutum	Upland C.	Gossypii Radicis Cortex (*Cotton Root Bark*)
"	"	Gossypium Purificatum (*Absorbent Cotton*)
Gratiola officinalis	Drug Hedgehyssop	Gratiola (*Hedge-hyssop*)
Grindelia camporum	Field Gumweed	Grindelia
G. humilis (*cuneifolia*)	Marsh G.	Grindelia
G. squarrosa	Curlycup G.	Grindelia
Guajacum officinale	Common Lignumvitae	Guaiacum (*Guaiac Resin*)
G. sanctum	Holywood L.	Guaiacum (*Guaiac Resin*)
Guarea rusbyi	Rusby Muskwood	Cocillana (*Guapi Bark*)
Gymnema sylvestre	Australian Cowplant	Gymnema
Gymnocladus dioicus	Kentucky Coffeetree	Gymnocladus (*Kentucky Coffee Tree*)
Haematoxylon campechianum	Logwood	Haematoxylon (*Logwood*)
Hagenia abyssinica (*Brayera a.*)	Kussotree	Brayera (*Kousso*)
Halidrys siliquosa	Drug Seaoak	Fucus
Hamamelis virginiana	Common Witchhazel	Hamamelidis Folium (*Witch-hazel Leaf*)
Hedeoma pulegioides	American Falsepennyroyal	Hedeoma (*Pennyroyal*)
Hedera helix	English Ivy	Hedera (*English Ivy*)
Hedychium spicatum	Spiked Gingerlily	Hedychium (*Gingerlily*)
Helenium autumnale	Common Sneezeweed	Helenium (*Sneezeweed*)
Helianthus annuus	Common Sunflower	Helianthus (*Common Sunflower*)
Helleborus foetidus	Bearsfoot Hellebore	Helleborus Foetidus (*Bears Foot Root*)

Plant Source		
Botanical Name	*S.P.N. Common Name*	*Drug Name*
Helleborus niger	Christmasrose (*Black Hellebore*)	Helleborus Niger (*Black Hellebore*)
Hemidesmus indicus	India-sarsaparilla	Hemidesmus (*Indian Sarsaparilla*)
Hepatica americana	Roundlobe Hepatica	Hepatica (*Liverwort Leaves*)
Heracleum lanatum	Common Cowparsnip	Heracleum (*Common Cowparsnip*)
Herniaria glabra	Common Burstwort	Herniaria (*Herniary*)
Heuchera americana	American Alumroot	Heuchera (*Alum Root*)
Hevea brasiliensis	Para Rubbertree	Elastica (*Rubber*)
Hibiscus abelmoschus	Muskmallow	Hibiscus (*Ambrette Seed*)
Hieracium venosum	Poorrobins Hawkweed	Hieracium (*Rattlesnake Weed*)
Hippomane mancinella	Manchineel	Manzanillo (*Manchineel*)
Holarrhena antidysenterica	Conessi Holarrhena	Conessi Cortex (*Conessi Bark*)
Holigarna longifolia	Blackvarnishtree	Holigarna
Hordeum distichon	Tworow Barley	Hordeum (*Barley*)
H. vulgare	Barley	Hordeum (*Barley*)
"	"	Maltum (*Barley Malt*)
Humulus lupulus	Common Hop	Humulus (*Hops*)
"	"	Lupulinum (*Lupulin*)
Hura crepitans	Sandboxtree	Hura (*Sandbox Tree*)
Hyaenanche capensis (*Toxicodendron capense*)	Hyenabane	Toxicodendron (*Hyena Poison*)
Hydnocarpus spp.	Chaulmoogratree	Oleum Chaulmoograe (*Chaulmoogra Oil*)
H. anthelminthicus	Common C.	Oleum Chaulmoograe (*Chaulmoogra Oil*)
H. wightianus	Wight C.	Oleum Chaulmoograe (*Chaulmoogra Oil*)
Hydrangea arborescens	Smooth Hydrangea	Hydrangea (*Seven-barks*)
Hydrastis canadensis	Goldenseal	Hydrastis (*Golden Seal*)
Hygrophila spinosa (*Asteracantha longifolia*)	Starthorn	Asteracantha
Hymenaea courbaril	Courbaril	Copal (*South American Copal*)
Hyoscyamus niger	Black Henbane	Hyoscyamus (*Henbane*)
Hypericum perforatum	Common St. Johnswort	Hypericum (*St. Johns Wort*)
Hyssopus officinalis	Hyssop	Hyssopus (*Hyssop*)
Iberis amara	Rocket Candytuft	Iberis (*Bitter Candytuft*)
Ilex aquifolium	English Holly	Ilex (*Holly*)
I. verticillata	Common Winterberry	Prinos (*Black Alder*)
Illicium parviflorum	Yellow Anisetree	Oleum Anisi Corticis (*Oil of Anise Bark*)
I. verum	Truestar A.	Illicium (*Star Anise*)
"	"	Oleum Anisi (*Anise Oil*)
Impatiens biflora	Spotted Snapweed	Impatiens (*Balsam Weed*)
I. pallida	Pale S.	Impatiens
Indigofera suffruticosa	Anil Indigo	Indicum (*Indigo*)
I. tinctoria	True I.	Indicum (*Indigo*)
Inula helenium	Elecampane Inula	Inula (*Elecampane Root*)
Ipomoea orizabensis	Orizaba Morningglory	Ipomoea (*Mexican Scammony*)
Iris germanica (*vulgaris*)	German Iris	Iris (*Verona Orris Root*)
I. g. florentina (*I. florentina alba*)	Orrisroot I.	Iris (*Florentine Orris Root*)
I. pallida	Sweet I.	Iris (*Verona Orris Root*)
I. versicolor	Blueflag I.	Iris Versicolor (*Blue Flag*)
I. virginica	Virginia I.	Iris Versicolor (*Blue Flag*)
Isatis tinctoria	Dyers Woad	Isatis (*Woad*)
Isopyrum thalictroides	Meadowrue Isopyrum	Isopyrum
Ixora coccinea	Jungleflame Ixora	Ixora
Jacaranda spp.	Jacaranda	Jacaranda
Jasminum officinale	Common Jasmine	Oleum Jasmini (*Spanish Jasmine*)
J. o. grandiflorum		Oleum Jasmini (*Spanish Jasmine*)
Jateorhiza palmata	Calumbaroot	Calumba (*Colombo*)
Jatropha curcas	Barbadosnut	Jatropa (*Barbados Nut*)
Jeffersonia diphylla	American Twinleaf	Jeffersonia (*Twinleaf*)
Joannesia princeps		Oleum Andae (*Oil of Anda*)
Juglans cinerea	Butternut	Juglans (*Butternut Bark*)
Juglans nigra	Eastern Black Walnut	Juglans Nigra (*Black Walnut*)
Juniperus communis	Common Juniper	Juniperus (*Juniper Berry*)
"	"	Oleum Juniperi (*Juniper Oil*)
J. oxycedrus	Prickly J.	Pix Juniperi (*Oil of Cade*)
J. sabina	Savin J.	Sabina (*Savin*)
J. virginiana	Eastern Redcedar	Juniperus Virginiana (*Red Cedar*)
"	"	Oleum Juniperi Virginianae (*Cedarwood Oil*)
Kalmia angustifolia	Lambkill Kalmia	Kalmia (*Mountain Laurel*)
K. latifolia	Mountainlaurel K.	Kalmia (*Mountain Laurel*)
Krameria argentea	Brazil Krameria	Krameria (*Brazilian Rhatany*)
K. triandra	Peruvian K.	Krameria (*Peruvian Rhatany*)
Laburnum anagyroides (*vulgare; Cytisus laburnum*)	Goldenchain Laburnum	Cytisus (*Golden Chain*)
Lactuca virosa	Bitter Lettuce	Lactucarium (*Wild Lettuce*)
Lagenaria siceraria (*leucantha*)	Calabash Gourd	Lagenaria (*Bottle Gourd*)
Lamium album	White Deadnettle	Lamium (*White Deadnettle*)
Lantana brasiliensis	Yerbasagrada Lantana	Lantana (*Yerba Sagrada*)
Larix decidua (*europaea*)	European Larch	Laricis Cortex (*Larch Bark*)
"	"	Terebinthina Laricis (*Venice Turpentine*)
Larrea tridentata (*Covillea t.*)	Coville Creosotebush	Gummi Sonorae (*Sonora Gum*)
Lathyrus sativus	Grass Peavine	Lathyrus (*Vetchling*)
Laurus nobilis	Grecian Laurel	Laurus (*Bay Laurel Leaves*)
Lavandula officinalis (*spica; vera*)	True Lavender	Lavandula (*Lavender Flowers*)
"	"	Oleum Lavandulae (*Oil of Lavender Flowers*)
Lawsonia inermis	Henna	Lawsonia (*Henna*)
Lecanora spp.	Lecanora	Persio (*Cudbear*)
"	"	Lacmus (*Litmus*)
Ledum palustre	Crystaltea Ledum	Ledum (*Crystal Tea*)
Leonotis leonurus	Drug Lionsear	Leonotis (*Lions Ear*)
Leonurus cardiaca	Common Motherwort	Leonurus (*Motherwort*)
Levisticum officinale (*Hipposelinum o.*)	Garden Lovage	Levisticum (*Lovage*)
Lewisia rediviva	Bitterroot Lewisia	Lewisia (*Spatlum*)
Liatris spicata	Spike Gayfeather	Liatris (*Spike Gayfeather*)
Ligustrum vulgare	European Privet	Ligustrum (*Privet*)
Lilium candidum	Madonna Lily	Lilium (*Annunciation Lily*)
Limonium brasiliense (*Statice brasiliensis*)	Brazil Sea-lavender	Baycuru Radix (*Baycuru Root*)
Linaria vulgaris	Butter-and-eggs Toadflax	Linaria (*Butter and Eggs*)
Lindera sericea	Silky Spicebush	Oleum Linderae (*Oil of Kuromoji*)
L. umbellata	Umbeled S.	Oleum Linderae (*Oil of Kuromoji*)
Linum catharticum	Purging Flax	Linum Catharticum (*Purging Flax*)
L. usitatissimum	Common F.	Linum (*Flaxseed*)
"	"	Oleum Lini (*Linseed Oil*)
Lippia citriodora	Lemonverbena Lippia	Lippia (*Lemon Verbena*)
Liquidambar orientalis	Oriental Sweetgum	Styrax (*Liquid Storax*)
L. styraciflua	American S.	Styrax (*Liquid Storax*)
Liriodendron tulipifera	Tuliptree	Liriodendron (*Tulip Tree*)
Liriosma ovata		Muira-Puama
Lithospermum officinale	Common Gromwell	Lithospermum (*Common Gromwell*)
Lithraea venenosa		Lithraea
Lobelia inflata	Indiantobacco Lobelia	Lobelia (*Indian Tobacco*)
Lolium temulentum	Darnel Ryegrass	Lolium (*Darnel*)

Plant Source *Botanical Name*	Plant Source *S.P.N. Common Name*	*Drug Name*
Lonchocarpus spp.	LANCEPOD	LONCHOCARPUS (*Cube Root*)
L. nicou		LONCHOCARPUS (*Cube Root*)
Lonicera caprifolium	SWEET HONEYSUCKLE	LONICERA (*Honeysuckle*)
Lophophora williamsi	MESCALBUTTON PEYOTE	ANHALONIUM (*Mescal Buttons*)
Lotus arabicus	ARABIAN DEERVETCH	LOTUS
Luffa cylindrica	SUAKWA VEGETABLE-SPONGE	LUFFA (*Vegetable Sponge*)
Lupinus albus	WHITE LUPINE	LUPINUS (*White Lupine*)
Lycium halimifolium (*vulgare*)	MATRIMONYVINE	LYCIUM (*Matrimony Vine*)
Lycopodium clavatum	RUNNINGPINE	LYCOPODIUM (*Vegetable Sulphur*)
Lycopus virginicus	VIRGINIA BUGLE-WEED	LYCOPUS (*Bugleweed*)
Lycoris radiata	SHORTTUBE LYCORIS	LYCORIS
Lythrum salicaria	PURPLE LYTHRUM	LYTHRUM (*Purple Loose-strife*)
Macleaya cordata (*Bocconia c.*)	PINK PLUMEPOPPY	BOCCONIA
Madhuca indica (*Bassia latifolia*)	ILLIPE BUTTERTREE	BASSIA (*Illipi Butter Tree*)
M. longifolia (*Bassia l.*)	MOWRA B.	BASSIA (*Mowrah*)
Mahonia aquifolium (*Berberis a.*)	OREGONGRAPE	BERBERIS (*Oregon Grape Root*)
M. nervosa (*Berberis n.; Odostemon nervosus*)	CASCADES MAHONIA	BERBERIS (*Oregon Grape Root*)
Majorana hortensis (*Origanum majorana*)	SWEET MARJORAM	MAJORANA (*Sweet Marjoram*)
Mallotus philippinensis	KAMALATREE	KAMALA (*Glandulae Rottlerae*)
Malouetia nitida		MALOUETIA (*Guachamaca*)
Malpighia glabra	BARBADOSCHERRY MALPIGHIA	MALPIGHIA (*Nance Bark*)
Malus pumila (*sylvestris* Hort., *not* Mill.; *Pyrus malus*)	COMMON APPLE	SUCCUS POMORUM (*Fresh Apple Juice*)
Malva neglecta		MALVAE FLORES (*Mallow Flowers*)
"		MALVAE FOLIA (*Mallow Leaves*)
M. sylvestris	HIGH MALLOW	MALVAE FLORES (*Mallow Flowers*)
"	"	MALVAE FOLIA (*Mallow Leaves*)
Mandragora autumnalis	AUTUMN MANDRAKE	MANDRAGORA (*Mandragora Root*)
Mangifera indica	COMMON MANGO	GUMMI MANGIFERAE (*Mango Gum*)
Manihot aipi	AIPI CASSAVA	AMYLUM MANIHOT (*Cassava Starch*)
M. esculenta (*utilissima*)	COMMON C.	AMYLUM MANIHOT (*Cassava Starch*)
M. glaziovi	CEARARUBBERPLANT	ELASTICA (*Rubber*)
Manilkara bidentata (*Mimusops balata*)	COMMON BALATA	BALATA
Maranta arundinacea	BERMUDA ARROWROOT	MARANTA (*Arrowroot*)
Marrubium vulgare	COMMON HOARHOUND	MARRUBIUM (*Hoarhound*)
Marsdenia cundurango	CONDORVINE	CONDURANGO (*Condurango Bark*)
Matricaria chamomilla	GERMAN-CAMOMILE	MATRICARIA (*German Chamomile*)
Medeola virginiana	CUCUMBERROOT MEDEOLA	MEDEOLA (*Indian Cucumber*)
Megarrhiza californica (*fabacea; Echinocystis c.; Marah c.; Micrampelis c.*)	CALIFORNIA BIGROOT	MICRAMPELIS (*Man Root*)
Melaleuca leucadendron	CAJEPUTTREE	OLEUM CAJUPUTI (*Oil of Cajeput*)
Melastoma ackermani		MELASTOMA
Melia azedarach	CHINABERRY	AZEDARACH (*Pride of India*)
Melilotus officinalis	YELLOW SWEET-CLOVER	MELILOTUS (*Yellow Sweet Clover*)
Melissa officinalis	COMMON BALM	MELISSA (*Common Balm*)
Menispermum canadense	COMMON MOONSEED	MENISPERMUM (*Yellow Parilla*)
Mentha piperita	PEPPERMINT	MENTHAE PIPERITA (*Peppermint*)
"	"	OLEUM MENTHAE PIPERITAE (*Peppermint Oil*)
Mentha pulegium	PENNYROYAL MINT	MENTHA PULEGIUM (*European Pennyroyal*)
M. spicata	SPEARMINT	MENTHAE VIRIDIS (*Spearmint*)
"	"	OLEUM MENTHAE VIRIDIS (*Spearmint Oil*)
Menyanthes trifoliata	COMMON BOGBEAN	MENYANTHES (*Buckbean*)
Mesembryanthemum crystallinum (*Cryophytum c.*)	ICEPLANT MESEMBRY-ANTHEMUM	MESEMBRYANTHEMUM (*Iceplant*)
Mespilus germanica	MEDLAR	MESPILUS (*Medlar*)
Metroxylon sagu (*laeve; Sagus laevis*)	SMOOTH SAGOPALM	SAGO
Michelia champaca	CHAMPAC MICHELIA	CHAMPACA
Micromeria chamissonis (*douglasi*)	YERBABUENA	MICROMERIA (*Yerba Buena*)
Mitchella repens	PARTRIDGEBERRY	MITCHELLA (*Squaw Vine*)
Momordica balsamina	BALSAMAPPLE	MOMORDICA (*Balsam Apple*)
Monarda didyma	OSWEGO BEEBALM	MONARDA DIDYMA (*Oswego Tea*)
M. punctata	SPOTTED B.	MONARDA (*Horsemint*)
Monsonia spp.	MONSONIA	MONSONIA
Morinda coreia (*tinctoria*)	DYERS INDIANMUL-BERRY	MORINDA (*Indian Mulberry*)
Moringa aptera (*arabica*)	ARABIAN HORSERAD-ISHTREE	OLEUM BEN (*Behen Oil*)
M. oleifera (*pterygosperma*)	HORSERADISHTREE	OLEUM BEN (*Behen Oil*)
Morus nigra	BLACK MULBERRY	MORUS (*Black Mulberry*)
M. rubra	RED M.	MORUS (*Red Mulberry*)
Mucuna spp.	MUCUNA	SEMEN CALI (*Cali Nuts*)
Murraya koenigi	CURRYLEAFTREE	FOLIA MURRAYAE (*Curry Leaves*)
Mutisia viciaefolia	VETCHLEAF MUTISIA	MUTISIA
Myrica cerifera	SOUTHERN WAX-MYRTLE	MYRICA (*Wax Myrtle Bark*)
M. pensylvanica (*caroliniensis*)	NORTHERN BAYBERRY	MYRICA (*Bayberry Bark*)
Myristica argentea	MACASSAR NUTMEG	MYRISTICA ARGENTEA (*Macassar Nutmeg*)
M. fragrans	COMMON N.	MACIS (*Mace*)
"	"	MYRISTICA (*Nutmeg*)
"	"	OLEUM MYRISTICAE (*Oil of Nutmeg*)
Myroxylon balsamum (*toluiferum*)	TOLUBALSAM BALM-TREE	BALSAMUM TOLUTANUM (*Balsam of Tolu*)
M. pereirae (*Toluifera p.*)	PERUBALSAM B.	BALSAMUM PERUVIANUM (*Balsam of Peru*)
Myrtus communis	TRUE MYRTLE	MYRTUS (*Myrtle*)
Narcissus pseudonarcissus	COMMON DAFFODIL	NARCISSUS (*Daffodil*)
Nardus spp.	MATGRASS	NARDUS (*Nard*)
Naregamia alata		NAREGAMIA (*Goanese Ipecacuanha*)
Nauclea esculenta (*Sarcocephalus esculentus*)	GUINEAPEACH FAT-HEADTREE	DOUNDAKE (*Dundaki*)
Nepeta cataria	CATNIP	CATARIA (*Catnip*)
Nerium oleander	COMMON OLEANDER	NERIUM (*Oleander*)
Nicotiana tabacum	COMMON TOBACCO	TABACUM (*Tobacco*)
Nierembergia hippomanica	DWARF CUPFLOWER	NIEREMBERGIA (*Cupflower*)
Nigella damascena	LOVEINAMIST	NIGELLA (*Black Caraway*)
N. sativa	GARDEN FENNEL-FLOWER	NIGELLA (*Black Caraway*)
Nymphaea odorata (*Castalia o.*)	AMERICAN WATERLILY	NYMPHAEA (*Water Lily*)
Nyssa sylvatica	BLACK TUPELO	NYSSA (*Sour Gum*)
Ocimum basilicum	SWEET BASIL	OCIMUM (*Sweet Basil*)
Ocotea spp. (*Nectandra*)	OCOTEA	PICHURIM BEANS (*Sassafras Nuts*)
O. rodioei (*Nectandra r.*)	GREENHEART O.	NECTANDRAE CORTEX (*Bebeeru*)
Oenanthe crocata	HEMLOCK WATER-DROPWORT	OENANTHE (*Water Hemlock*)
O. phellandrium	FENNELLEAF W.	PHELLANDRIUM (*Water Fennel*)
Oenothera biennis	COMMON EVENING-PRIMROSE	OENOTHERA (*Evening Primrose*)
Olea europaea	COMMON OLIVE	OLEUM OLIVAE (*Olive Oil*)
Ononis spinosa	THORNY ONONIS	ONONIS (*Radix Ononidis*)
Oplopanax horridus (*Fatsia horrida*)	AMERICAN DEVILS-CLUB	OPLOPANAX (*Devils Club Root*)
Opopanax chironium	SURGEONS OPOPANAX	OPOPANAX

Plant Source Botanical Name	S.P.N. Common Name	Drug Name
Opuntia vulgaris	Common Prickly-pear	Opuntia (*Prickly Pear*)
Orchis latifolia	Marsh Orchis	Salep (*Salep Tubers*)
O. maculata	Spotleaf O.	Salep (*Salep Tubers*)
Origanum vulgare	Common Origanum	Origanum (*Common Marjoram*)
Oroxylum indicum	India Trumpet-flower	Oroxylon
Orthosiphon grandiflorus (*stamineus*)	Bigflower Javatea	Orthosiphon (*Java Tea*)
Ostrya virginiana	American Hophornbeam	Ostrya (*Ironwood*)
Oxalis acetosella	Woodsorrel Oxalis	Oxalis (*Wood Sorrel*)
Oxydendrum arboreum	Sourwood	Andromeda (*Sourwood*)
"	"	Oxydendrum (*Sourwood*)
Oxytropis lamberti (*Astragalus l.*)	Lambert Crazyweed	Loco (*White Loco*)
Paeonia officinalis	Common Peony	Paeonia (*Peony Root*)
Palaquium gutta	Malay Gutta-percha Natotree	Gutta Percha
Palicourea rigida		Palicourea
Panax quinquefolium (*Aralia quinquefolia*)	American Ginseng	Ginseng (*American Ginseng*)
P. schinseng (*ginseng*)	Asiatic G.	Ginseng (*Chinese Ginseng*)
Pangium edule	Food Pangium	Pangium
Papaver rhoeas	Corn Poppy	Papaver Rhoeas (*Red Poppy Flowers*)
P. somniferum (including the variety album and possibly other varieties). Note that many different drug products are produced from different parts of the Poppy plant.	Opium P.	Opium (*Gum Opium*)
"	"	Morphina (*Morphine*)
"	"	Papaveris Fructus (*Poppy Capsules*)
P. s. nigrum	Black O. P.	Semen Papaveris (*Maw Seeds*)
Parameria vulneraria		Parameria
"		Balsamum Cebur (*Cebur Balsam*)
Parietaria officinalis	Wall Pellitory	Parietaria (*Wall Pellitory*)
Parkia biglandulosa	Malaya Nittatree	Parkia (*African Locust*)
Parthenocissus quinquefolia (*Ampelopsis q.*)	Virginia Creeper	Ampelopsis (*Virginia Creeper*)
Passiflora incarnata	Maypop Passion-flower	Passiflora (*Passion Vine*)
Paullinia cupana	Guarana Paullinia	Guarana (*Guarana Paste*)
Payena leeri	Guttapercha Payena	Gutta Percha
Pedilanthus pavonis	Wax Slipperflower	Candelilla Cera (*Candelilla Wax*)
Peganum harmala	Harmel Peganum	Peganum (*Wild Rue*)
Pelargonium odoratissimum	Nutmeg Pelargonium	Pelargonium (*Rose Geranium*)
Pentaclethra macrophylla	Owalaoiltree	Pentaclethra (*Owala Grains*)
Perezia spp.	Perezia	Perezia (*Perezia Root*)
Perilla frutescens (*ocymoides*)	Common Perilla	Oleum Perillae (*Oil of Perilla*)
Periploca graeca	Grecian Silkvine	Periploca (*Silkvine*)
Petiveria alliacea	Garlic Guineahenweed	Petiveria (*Pipi Root*)
Petroselinum crispum latifolium	Common Garden Parsley	Petroselinum (*Parsley Fruit*)
"	"	Petroselini Folia (*Parsley Leaves*)
"	"	Petroselini Radix (*Parsley Root*)
Peucedanum officinale	Common Hogfennel	Peucedanum (*Hog Fennel*)
P. ostruthium (*Imperatoria o.*)	Masterwort H.	Imperatoria (*Masterwort*)
Peumus boldus	Boldutree	Boldus (*Boldo Leaves*)
Phalaris canariensis	Canarygrass	Semen Canariense (*Canary Seed*)
Phaseolus vulgaris	Kidney Bean	Phaseolus (*Common Kidney Bean*)
Phoradendron flavescens	Christmas American-mistletoe	Phoradendron (*American Mistletoe*)

Plant Source Botanical Name	S.P.N. Common Name	Drug Name
Photinia arbutifolia (*salicifolia; Heteromeles a.; H. salicifolia*)	Christmasberry	Heteromeles
Phyllitis scolopendrium (*Scolopendrium vulgare*)	Hartstongue	Scolopendrium (*Harts Tongue*)
Physalis alkekengi	Strawberry Ground-cherry	Physalis (*Strawberry Tomato*)
Physostigma venenosum	Deadly Calabar-bean	Physostigma (*Calabar Bean*)
Phytelephas macrocarpa	Common Ivorypalm	Phytelephas (*Vegetable Ivory*)
Phytolacca acinosa	India Pokeberry	Phytolacca Acinosa
P. americana (*decandra*)	Common P.	Phytolacca (*Poke Root*)
"	"	Phytolaccae Fructus (*Poke Berries*)
Picea abies (*excelsa*)	Norway Spruce	Pix Burgundica (*Burgundy Pitch*)
Picrasma excelsa (*Picraena e.*)	Jamaica Quassia-wood	Quassia (*Jamaica Quassia*)
P. quassioides	India Q.	Picrasma
Pilocarpus jaborandi	Jaborandi Pilocarpus	Pilocarpus (*Pernambuco Jaborandi*)
P. microphyllus	Littleleaf P.	Pilocarpus (*Maranham Jaborandi*)
Pimenta officinalis	Allspice Pimenta	Pimenta (*Allspice*)
"	"	Oleum Pimentae (*Oil of Allspice*)
P. racemosa (*acris*)	Bayrumtree	Oleum Myrciae (*Oil of Bay*)
Pimpinella anisum	Anise	Anisum (*Anise Seed*)
"	"	Oleum Anisi (*Anise Oil*)
P. magna	Greater Pimpinella	Pimpinella
P. saxifraga	Saxifrage P.	Pimpinella (*Pimpernel Root*)
Pinckneya pubens	Pinckneya	Pinckneya (*Georgia* or *Bitter Bark*)
Pinguicula alpina	Mountain Butterwort	Pinguicula (*Butterwort*)
P. vulgaris	Common B.	Pinguicula (*Butterwort*)
Pinus spp.	Pine	Pix Pini (*Pix Liquida*)
P. cembra	Swiss Stone P.	Balsamum Carpaticum (*Riga Balsam*)
P. mugo (*montana*)	SwissMountain P.	Oleum Pini Pumilionis (*Dwarf Pine Needle Oil*)
P. palustris	Longleaf P.	Terebinthina (*Crude Turpentine*)
"	"	Oleum Terebinthinae (*Turpentine Oil*)
"	"	Pix Pini (*Pix Liquida*)
"	"	Resina (*Colophony*)
P. strobus	Eastern White P.	Pinus Alba (*White Pine Bark*)
Piper angustifolium	Matico Pepper	Matico
P. cubeba	Cubeb P.	Cubeba (*Cubebs*)
P. jaborandi	Jaborandi P.	Jambu Assu
P. longum	Long P.	Piper Longum (*Long Pepper*)
P. methysticum	Kava P.	Kava (*Methysticum*)
P. nigrum	Black P.	Piper (*Black Pepper*)
P. retrofractum (*officinarum*)		Piper Longum
Piptadenia cebil	Cebil Piptadenia	Gummi Piptadenia (*Cebil Gum*)
P. macrocarpa	Longpod P.	Vilcae Cortex (*Vilca Bark*)
Piscidia piscipula (*erythrina; Ichthyomethia p.*)	Jamaica Fishfuddle-tree	Piscidia (*Jamaica Dogwood*)
Pistacia lentiscus	Lentisk Pistache	Mastiche (*Mastic*)
Plantago indica (*arenaria*)	Whorled Plantain	Plantaginis Semen (*French Psyllium Seed*)
P. lanceolata	Buckhorn P.	Plantago Lanceolata (*German Psyllium Seed*)
P. major	Rippleseed P.	Folia Plantaginis (*Plantain Leaves*)
P. ovata	Blond P.	Plantaginis Semen (*Blonde Psyllium Seed*)
P. psyllium	Flaxseed P.	Plantaginis Semen (*Psyllium Seed*)
Plumbago europaea	Common Plumbago	Plumbago (*Leadwort*)
Podophyllum peltatum	Common Mayapple	Podophyllum (*Mandrake*)
Pogonopus tubulosus		Pogonopus (*China Morada*)

Plant Source		
Botanical Name	*S.P.N. Common Name*	*Drug Name*
Pogostemon cablin	Cablin Patchouli	Oleum Patchouli (*Oil of Patchouli*)
P. heyneanus	Heyne P.	Oleum Patchouli (*Oil of Patchouli*)
Polygala polygama	Bitter Polygala	Polygala (*Bitter Milkwort*)
P. senega	Seneca-snakeroot P.	Senega (*Senega Snakeroot*)
Polygonatum officinale	Drug Solomonseal	Polygonatum (*Solomons Seal*)
Polygonum bistorta (*Bistorta officinalis*)	European Bistort	Bistorta (*Bistort Root*)
Polymnia uvedalia	Yellow Leafcup	Polymnia (*Leafcup*)
Polypodium vulgare	Common Polypody	Polypodium (*Polypody*)
Polytrichum commune	Common Haircap-moss	Polytrichum (*Hair Cap Moss*)
P. juniperinum	Juniper H.	Polytrichum (*Hair Cap Moss*)
Pongamia pinnata	Poongaoil Pongamia	Pongamia
Populus spp.	Poplar	Carbo Ligni (*Charcoal*)
P. candicans	Balm-of-Gilead P.	Populi Gemma (*Balm of Gilead Bud*)
P. tacamahaca (*balsamifera*)	Tacamahac P.	Populi Gemma (*Balsam Poplar Bud*)
Portulaca oleracea (*aurea*)	Common Purslane	Portulaca (*Garden Purslane*)
Potentilla anserina	Silverweed Cinquefoil	Potentilla Anserina
P. erecta (*tormentilla*)	Tormentilla C.	Tormentilla (*Tormentilla Rhizome*)
P. reptans	Creeping C.	Potentilla (*Cinquefoil*)
Premna taitensis	Tahiti Premna	Tonga
Prenanthes alba	White Rattlesnakeroot	Nabalus (*Rattlesnake Root*)
Primula obconica	Top Primrose	Primula (*Primrose*)
Prioria copaifera	Cativo	Resina Prioria (*Cativa*)
Prosopis chilensis (*juliflora*)	Common Mesquite	Gummi Prosopis (*Mesquite Gum*)
Prunella vulgaris	Common Selfheal	Prunella (*Self-heal*)
Prunus amygdalus (*communis* Arcang., *not* Huds.; *Amygdalus c.*) and vars.	Almond	Oleum Amygdalae Expressum (*Sweet Almond Oil*)
P. a. amara (*P. communis a.; Amygdalus c. a.*)	Bitter A.	Oleum Amygdalae Amarae (*Oil of Bitter Almond*)
P. cerasus	Sour Cherry	Prunus Cerasus (*Sour Cherry*)
P. domestica	Garden Plum	Prunum (*Prune*)
P. laurocerasus	Common Laurelcherry	Laurocerasus (*Cherry Laurel Leaves*)
P. persica (*Amygdalus p.*)	Peach	Persicae Foliae (*Peach Leaves*)
P. serotina	Black Cherry	Prunus Virginiana (*Wild Black Cherry Bark*)
P. spinosa	Blackthorn; Sloe	Flores Pruni
Psidium guajava	Common Guava	Psidium (*Guava*)
Ptelea trifoliata	Common Hoptree	Ptelea (*Wafer Ash Bark*)
Pterocarpus draco	Dragonsblood Padauk	Sanguis Draconia (*Dragons Blood*)
P. marsupium	Vengai P.	Kino (*Malabar Kino*)
P. santalinus	Sandalwood P.	Santalum Rubrum (*Red Saunders*)
Pulmonaria officinalis (*maculata*)	Common Lungwort	Pulmonaria (*Lungwort*)
Punica granatum	Common Pomegranate	Granatum (*Pomegranate Bark*)
Quassia amara	Surinam Quassia	Quassia (*Surinam Q.*)
Quercus alba	White Oak	Quercus (*White Oak Bark*)
Q. infectoria	Aleppo O.	Galla (*Nutgall*)
Q. macrolepis (*aegilops; graeca*)	Valonia O.	Valonia (*Acorn Cups*)
Q. suber	Cork O.	Suber (*Cork*)
Q. s. occidentalis	Biennial C. O.	Suber (*Cork*)
Quillaja saponaria	Soapbarktree	Quillaja (*Soap Bark*)
Quisqualis indica	Rangooncreeper	Quisqualis (*Rangoon Creeper*)
Randia dumetorum	Malabar Randia	Randia
Ranunculus spp.	Buttercup	Ranunculus (*Crowfoot*)
Raphanus sativus	Garden Radish	Raphanus (*Radish*)
Rauwolfia serpentina	Java Devilpepper	Ophioxylon (*Radix Musteltoe*)
Rhamnus californica	California Buckthorn	Capulincullo
R. cathartica	Common B.	Rhamnus Cathartica (*Buckthorn Berries*)

Plant Source		
Botanical Name	*S.P.N. Common Name*	*Drug Name*
Rhamnus frangula	Glossy Buckthorn	Frangula (*Buckthorn Bark*)
R. purshiana	Cascara B.	Cascara Sagrada (*Rhamnus Purshiana*)
Rheum officinale	Medicinal Rhubarb	Rheum (*Rhubarb Root*)
R. palmatum, spp. (excepting **R. rhaponticum**) or hybrids of **Rheum** grown in China and Thibet.	Sorrel R.	Rheum
Rhizophora mangle	American Mangrove	Rhizophora (*Mangrove*)
Rhododendron chrysanthum	Goldmat Rhododendron	Rhododendron (*Yellow-flowered Rhododendron*)
Rhodymenia palmata	Irishdulse Seakale	Rhodymenia (*Irish Dulse*)
Rhus glabra	Smooth Sumac	Rhus Glabra (*Sumac Berries*)
Ricinus communis	Castorbean	Ricinus (*Castor Oil Bean*)
"	"	Oleum Ricini (*Castor Oil*)
Robinia pseudoacacia	Black Locust	Robinia (*Black Locust Tree*)
Roccella spp.	Roccella	Persio (*Cudbear*)
R. tinctoria	Litmus R.	Lacmus (*Litmus*)
Rosa canina	Dog Rose	Rosa Canina (*Dog Rose*)
R. centifolia	Cabbage R.	Rosa Centifolia (*Cabbage Rose*)
R. damascena	Damask R.	Rosa Damascena (*Damask Rose*)
"	"	Oleum Rosae (*Otto of Rose*)
R. gallica	French R.	Rosa (*Red Rose*)
"	"	Oleum Rosae (*Otto of Rose*)
Rosmarinus officinalis	Rosemary	Rosmarinus (*Rosemary*)
"	"	Oleum Rosmarini (*Oil of Rosemary*)
Rourea oblongifolia		Rourea
Rubia tinctorum	Common Madder	Rubia (*Madder*)
Rubus spp.	Blackberry	Rubus (*Blackberry Bark*)
R. idaeus	Red Raspberry	Rubus Idaeus (*Red Raspberries*)
R. i. strigosus (**R.** *strigosus*)	American R. R.	Rubus Idaeus
Rumex crispus	Curly Dock	Rumex (*Yellow Dock*)
R. obtusifolius	Bitter D.	Rumex (*European Dock*)
Ruta graveolens	Common Rue	Ruta (*Rue*)
Sabatia angularis	Squarestem Rosegentian	Sabbatia (*Rose Gentian*)
Saccharum officinarum	Sugarcane	Sucrosum (*Cane Sugar*)
Salix spp.	Willow	Carbo Ligni (*Charcoal*)
S. alba	White W.	Salix (*Willow Bark*)
S. nigra	Black W.	Salix Nigra (*Black Willow Bark*)
Salvia officinalis	Garden Sage	Salvia (*Sage*)
S. triloba	Greek S.	Salvia Triloba (*Greek Sage*)
Samadera indica	Niepabarktree	Samadera (*Samadera Bark*)
Samanea saman (*Pithecellobium s.*)	Raintree Saman	Pithecolobium
Sambucus canadensis	American Elder	Sambucus (*Elder Flowers*)
S. nigra	European E.	Sambucus
Sanguinaria canadensis	Bloodroot	Sanguinaria (*Blood Root*)
Sanicula marilandica	Black Sanicle	Sanicula
Santalum album	White Sandalwood	Santalum Album (*White Sandalwood*)
"	"	Oleum Santali (*Oil of Sandalwood*)
Santolina chamaecyparissus	Cypress Lavender-cotton	Santolina (*Holy Herb*)
Sapindus spp.	Soapberry	Sapindus (*Sapind*)
Sapium sebiferum (*Stillingia sebifera*)	Chinese Tallow-tree	Sapium (*Chinese Tallow Tree*)
Sarracenia flava	Trumpet Pitcher-plant	Sarracenia (*Pitcher Plant*)
S. purpurea	Common P.	Sarracenia
Sassafras albidum (*officinale*)	Common Sassafras	Sassafras (*Sassafras Bark*)
"	"	Sassafras Medulla (*Sassafras Pith*)
"	"	Oleum Sassafras (*Sassafras Oil*)
Satureia hortensis	Summer Savory	Satureja (*Summer Savory*)

Plant Source		
Botanical Name	S.P.N. Common Name	Drug Name
Saururus cernuus	Common Lizardtail	Saururus (*Lizards Tail*)
Schoenocaulon officinale	Drug Sabadilla	Veratrina
Scopolia carniolica	European Scopolia	Scopolia (*Scopola*)
S. japonica	Japanese S.	Scopolia Japonica (*Japanese Henbane*)
Scrophularia marilandica	Maryland Figwort	Scrophularia (*Figwort*)
Scutellaria lateriflora	Sideflowering Skullcap	Scutellaria (*Skullcap*)
Secale cereale	Rye	Secale Cereale (*Rye*)
Sedum acre	Goldmoss Stonecrop	Sedum (*Biting Stonecrop*)
Selinum officinale (*Cnidium o.*)	Drug Selinum	Cnidium (*Cnidium Root*)
Semecarpus anacardium	Cashew Marking-nut	Anacardium Orientale (*Oriental Cashew-nut*)
S. longifolius	Longleaf M.	Holigarna
S. venosus	Veiny M.	Semecarpus (*Tschongott Tree*)
Sempervivum tectorum (*robustum*)	Roof Houseleek	Sempervivum (*Common Houseleek*)
Senecio aureus	Golden Groundsel	Senecio (*Life Root*)
S. cineraria (*Cineraria maritima*)	Silver G.	Cineraria (*Dusty Miller*)
Serenoa repens (*serrulata*)	Sawpalmetto	Serenoa (*Saw Palmetto Berries*)
Serjania curassavica	Curacao Serjania	Timbo
Sesamum indicum (*orientale*)	Oriental Sesame	Sesamum (*Benne Plant*)
"	"	Oleum Sesami (*Benne Oil*)
Shepherdia argentea (*Lepargyrea a.*)	Silver Buffaloberry	Lepargyraea (*Buffalo Berry*)
Shorea spp.	Shorea	Dammara (*Green Damar*)
Sida rhombifolia	Broomjute Sida	Sida (*Mesbe*)
Siegesbeckia orientalis	Common St.Paulswort	Siegesbeckia
Silene virginica	Firepink Silene	Silene (*Fire Pink*)
Simaba cedron	Cedron Simaba	Cedron
Simaruba amara	Orinoco Simaruba	Simaruba (*Orinoco Simaruba*)
Sisymbrium alliaria	Garlicmustard	Alliaria (*Hedge-garlic*)
S. officinale		Sisymbrium (*Hedge Mustard*)
Sium suave (*cicutaefolium*)	Hemlock Waterparsnip	Sium (*Water Parsnip*)
Skimmia japonica	Japanese Skimmia	Skimmia (*Miramashikimi*)
Smilax aristolochiifolia	Mexican Sarsaparilla	Sarsaparilla (*Mexican Sarsaparilla*)
S. regeli	Jamaica S. (*Honduras S.*)	Sarsaparilla
S., unknown sp.		Sarsaparilla (*Central American or Jamaican Sarsaparilla; Honduras S.*)
S. tamnoides	Bamboo Greenbrier	Smilax (*Bamboo Brier Root*)
S., unknown spp.		Sarsaparilla (*Ecuadorian Sarsaparilla*)
Solanum carolinense	Carolina Horsenettle	Solanum (*Horse Nettle Berries*)
S. dulcamara	Bitter Nightshade	Dulcamara (*Bittersweet*)
Solidago odora	Fragrant Goldenrod	Solidago (*Sweet Goldenrod*)
Sonchus oleraceus	Common Sowthistle	Sonchus (*Sow Thistle*)
Sophora speciosa	Coralbean Sophora	Sophora (*Coral Bean*)
Sorbus aucuparia	European Mountainash	Sorbus (*Mountain Ash Berries*)
Sorghum vulgare (*Andropogon sorghum; Holcus s.*)	Sorghum	Sorghum
Soymida febrifuga (*Swietenia f.*)	Rohan Soymida	Swietenia (*Rohan Bark*)
Spartium junceum	Weaversbroom	Spartium (*Spanish Broom*)
Spergularia rubra (*Tissa r.*)	Red Sandspurry	Tissa
Sphagnum spp.	Sphagnum	Sphagnum (*Bog Moss*)
Spigelia marilandica	Pinkroot Spigelia	Spigelia (*Pink Root*)
Spilanthes oleracea	Paracress Spotflower	Spilanthes (*Para Cress*)
Spiraea spp.	Spirea	Spirea
Stachys officinalis	Common Betony	Betonica (*Wood Betony*)
Sterculia urens	Kuteeragum Sterculia	Gummi Sterculiae (*Indian Tragacanth; Gummi Kuteera*)
Sticta pulmonaria	Lungwort Sticta	Sticta (*Lungwort*)
Stillingia sylvatica	Queensdelight Stillingia	Stillingia (*Queens Root*)
Stipa spp.	Needlegrass; Feathergrass	Stipa (*Feather Grass*)
Stizolobium pruritum (*pruriens; Mucuna p.*)	Cowage Velvetbean	Mucuna (*Cowhage*)
Strophanthus glaber (*gratus*)		Ouabainum
S. hispidus	Transvaal Strophanthus	Strophanthus (*Brown Strophanthus Seed*)
S. kombe	Kombe S.	Strophanthus (*Green Strophanthus Seed*)
"	"	Strophanthinum (*Strophanthin*)
Strychnos castelnaei	Amazon Poisonnut	Curare (*Upper Amazon Curare*)
S. ignati	St. Ignatius P.	Ignatia (*St. Ignatius Bean*)
S. malaccensis (*gautheriana*)	Malacca P.	Strychnos Malaccensis (*Hoang-Nan*)
S. nuxvomica	Nuxvomica P.	Strychnina (*Strychnine*)
"	"	Nux Vomica (*Strychni Semen*)
S. potatorum	Clearing P.	Strychnos Potatorum (*Chilbinj*)
S. toxifera	Curare P.	Curare (*British Guiana Curare; Woorari*)
Stylophorum diphyllum	Celandine-poppy	Stylophorum (*Celandine Poppy*)
Styrax benzoin	Sumatra Snowbell	Benzoinum (*Sumatra Benzoin*)
S. tonkinensis	Tonkin S.	Benzoinum (*Siam Benzoin*)
Sweetia panamensis	Billywebb Sweetia	Cascara Amarga (*Honduras Bark*)
Swertia chirayita (*chirata*)	Chiretta Swertia	Chirata (*Bitter Stick*)
Symphytum officinale	Common Comfrey	Symphytum (*Comfrey Root*)
Symplocarpus foetidus (*Spathyema foetida*)	Skunkcabbage	Dracontium (*Skunk Cabbage*)
Symplocos racemosa	Lodebark Sweetleaf	Symplocos (*Sweet Leaf*)
Syringa vulgaris	Common Lilac	Syringa (*Common Lilac*)
Syzygium aromaticum (*Caryophyllus aromaticus; Eugenia aromatica; E. caryophyllata*)	Clovetree	Caryophyllus (*Clove*)
"	"	Oleum Caryophylli (*Oil of Clove*)
S. cumini (*jambolanum; Eugenia c.; E. jambolana*)	Jambolan	Eugenia Jambolana (*Jambul*)
S. jambos (*Caryophyllus j.; Eugenia j.*)	Roseapple	Jambosa (*Jamosa Root*)
Tachia guianensis	Guiana Tachia	Tachia (*Caferana*)
Tamarindus indica	Tamarind	Tamarindus (*Tamarind*)
Tanacetum umbelliferum	Umbel Tansy	Tanacetum Umbelliferum (*Sweet Pellitory*)
T. vulgare	Common T.	Tanacetum (*Tansy*)
Tanghinia venenifera	Madagascar Tanghin	Tanghinia (*Tanguin*)
Taraktogenos kurzi		Oleum Chaulmoograe (*Chaulmoogra Oil*)
Taraxacum officinale	Common Dandelion	Taraxacum (*Dandelion*)
Taxus baccata	English Yew	Taxus (*Yew*)
Tectona grandis	Common Teak	Tectona (*Teakwood*)
Telfairia pedata	Zanzibar Oilvine	Telfairia
Tephrosia virginiana (*Cracca v.*)	Virginia Tephrosia	Tephrosia (*Devils Shoe Strings*)
Tetraclinis articulata (*Callitris quadrivalvis*)	Arartree	Sandaraca (*Sandarac*)
Tetragastris panamensis		Tetragastris (*Bois Cochon*)
Teucrium chamaedrys	Chamaedrys Germander	Teucrium (*German Chamaedrys*)
Thalictrum flavum	Yellow Meadowrue	Thalictrum
T. macrocarpum	Bigfruit M.	Thalictrum
Thapsia garganica	Gargan Deathcarrot	Thapsia (*Thapsie*)
Theobroma cacao	Cacao	Cacao Praeparatum (*Cacao*)
"	"	Oleum Theobromatis (*Cocoa Butter*)
Thevetia yccotli	Joyote Thevetia	Thevetia (*Yccotli*)
Thuja occidentalis	Eastern Arborvitae; Northern Whitecedar (Forestry)	Thuja (*Arbor Vitae*)

Plant Source Botanical Name	S.P.N. Common Name	Drug Name
Thymus serpyllum	MOTHER-OF-THYME	THYMUS SERPYLLUM (*Wild Thyme*)
T. vulgaris	COMMON THYME	THYMUS (*Thyme*)
"	"	OLEUM THYMI (*Thyme Oil*)
Tilia spp.	LINDEN	TILIA (*Linden Flowers*)
"	"	CARBO LIGNI (*Charcoal*)
T. europaea	EUROPEAN L.	TILIA (*Linden Flowers*)
T. platyphyllos (*grandifolia*)	BIGLEAF L.	TILIA (*Linden Flowers*)
Tinantia fugax (*erecta; Tradescantia e.*)		TRADESCANTIA
Tinospora cordifolia	GULANCHA TINOSPORA	TINOSPORA (*Gulancha*)
Toddalia asiatica (*aculeata*)	ASIAN TODDALIA	TODDALIA
Toona ciliata (*Cedrela toona*)	BURMA TOON	CEDRELA (*Indian Mahogany*)
"	"	GUMMI CEDRELAE (*Cedar Gum*)
Toxicodendron diversilobum (*Rhus diversiloba*)	PACIFIC POISONOAK	RHUS DIVERSILOBUM LEAVES
T. quercifolium (*Rhus quercifolia*)	POISONOAK	RHUS TOXICODENDRON LEAVES (*Poison Oak*)
T. radicans (*Rhus r.; R. toxicodendron* Auth., *not* L.)	COMMON POISONIVY	RHUS TOXICODENDRON LEAVES (*Poison Ivy*)
T. vernix (*Rhus venenata; R. vernix*)	POISONSUMAC	RHUS VENENATA LEAVES (*Poison Sumac*)
Trachylobium verrucosum		COPAL (*Zanzibar Copal*)
Trachyspermum ammi (*Carum copticum*)	AJOWAN-CARAWAY	AJOWAN (*Ajava*)
Trifolium pratense	RED CLOVER	TRIFOLIUM (*Red Clover Blossoms*)
Trigonella foenum-graecum	FENUGREEK TRIGONELLA	FOENUM GRAECUM (*Fenugreek*)
Trillium erectum	PURPLE TRILLIUM	TRILLIUM (*Beth Root*)
Triosteum perfoliatum	COMMON HORSEGENTIAN	TRIOSTEUM (*Horse Gentian*)
Tsuga canadensis	CANADA HEMLOCK; EASTERN H. (Forestry)	PIX CANADENSIS (*Hemlock Pitch*)
Turnera diffusa (*aphrodisiaca; T. d. aphrodisiaca*)	DAMIANA TURNERA	DAMIANA (*Turnera*)
Tussilago farfara	COMMON COLTSFOOT	FARFARA (*Coltsfoot*)
Tylophora indica (*asthmatica*)	IPECAC TYLOPHORA	TYLOPHORAE FOLIA (*Tylophora*)
Ulex europaeus	COMMON GORSE	ULEX (*Common Furze* or *Gorse*)
Ulmus fulva	SLIPPERY ELM	ULMUS (*Slippery Elm*)
Umbellularia californica	CALIFORNIALAUREL (*Oregon-myrtle*)	UMBELLULARIA (*California Laurel*)
Umbilicus pendulinus (*Cotyledon umbilicus*)	NODDING NAVELWORT	COTYLEDON (*Pennywort*)
Uncaria gambir (*Ourouparia g.*)	BENGAL GAMBIRPLANT	GAMBIR (*Pale Catechu*)
Urechites suberecta	DOMINICAN VIPERTAIL	URECHITES (*Savannah Flower*)
Urginea indica	INDIA DRUGSQUILL	SCILLA INDICA (*Indian Squill*)
U. maritima (*Scilla m.*). (White variety)	SHORE D.	SCILLA (*White Squill*)
U. m. (*Scilla m.*) (Red variety)	SHORE D.	SCILLA RUBRA (*Red Squill*)
Urtica spp.	NETTLE	URTICA (*Nettle*)
Ustilago zeae (*maydis*)	CORNSMUT	USTILAGO (*Corn Smut*)
Vaccinium crassifolium (*Herpothamnus crassifolius*)	CREEPING BLUEBERRY	VACCINIUM (*Blueberry*)

Plant Source Botanical Name	S.P.N. Common Name	Drug Name
Valeriana officinalis	COMMON VALERIAN	VALERIANA (*Valerian Root*)
Vanilla planifolia	MEXICAN VANILLA	VANILLA (*Vanilla Bean*)
V. tahitensis	TAHITI V.	TAHITI VANILLA
Veratrum album	WHITE FALSEHELLEBORE	VERATRUM ALBUM (*European Hellebore*)
V. viride	AMERICAN F.	VERATRUM VIRIDE (*American Hellebore*)
Verbascum phlomoides	CLASPING MULLEIN	VERBASCI FLORES (*Mullein Flowers*)
V. thapsiforme (*densiflorum*)	WOOL M.	VERBASCI FLORES (*Mullein Flowers*)
V. thapsus	FLANNEL M.	VERBASCI FOLIA (*Mullein Leaves*)
Verbena hastata	BLUE VERBENA	VERBENA (*Blue Vervain*)
Verbesina helianthoides	GRAVELWEED CROWNBEARD	ACTINOMERIS (*Gravel Weed*)
Vernonia anthelmintica	KINKAOIL IRONWEED	VERNONIA
V. nigritiana	NIGERIAN I.	BATIATOR RADIX (*Batiator Root*)
Veronica officinalis	DRUG SPEEDWELL	VERONICA (*Speedwell*)
Veronicastrum virginicum (*Leptandra virginica; Veronica v.*)	CULVERSPHYSIC	LEPTANDRA (*Culvers Root*)
Viburnum cassinoides	WITHEROD VIBURNUM	VIBURNUM CASSINOIDES (*Withe Rod Bark*)
V. prunifolium	BLACKHAW V.	VIBURNUM PRUNIFOLIUM (*Black Haw*)
V. trilobum (*V. opulus americanum*)	AMERICAN CRANBERRYBUSH VIBURNUM	VIBURNUM OPULUS (*Cramp Bark*)
Vinca major	BIGLEAF PERIWINKLE	VINCA (*Greater Periwinkle*)
V. minor	COMMON P.	VINCA (*Lesser Periwinkle*)
Viola odorata	SWEET VIOLET	VIOLA (*Sweet Violet*)
V. tricolor	WILD PANSY	VIOLA TRICOLOR (*Pansy Herb*)
Viscum album	EUROPEAN MISTLETOE	VISCUM (*European Mistletoe*)
Vitis vinifera	EUROPEAN GRAPE	UVA PASSA (*Raisins*)
Wistaria sinensis	CHINESE WISTARIA	WISTARIA
Withania coagulans	AFGHAN WITHANIA	WITHANIA (*Vegetable Rennet*)
Xanthium spp.	COCKLEBUR	XANTHIUM (*Cocklebur*)
Xanthorhiza simplicissima (*Zanthorhiza apiifolia*)	YELLOWROOT	XANTHORRHIZA (*Yellowroot*)
Zanthoxylum americanum	COMMON PRICKLYASH	XANTHOXYLUM (*Northern Prickly Ash Bark*)
"	"	XANTHOXYLI FRUCTUS (*Northern Prickly Ash Berries*)
Z. clavaherculis	HERCULESCLUB P.	XANTHOXYLUM (*Southern Prickly Ash Bark*)
"	"	XANTHOXYLI FRUCTUS (*Southern Prickly Ash Berries*)
Z. senegalense (*Fagara zanthoxyloides*)	SENEGAL P.	ARTAR RADIX (*Artar Root*)
Zea mays	MAIZE; INDIAN CORN	AMYLUM (*Corn Starch*)
"	"	OLEUM MAYDIS (*Corn Oil*)
"	"	ZEA (*Corn Silk*)
Zigadenus venenosus	MEADOW DEATHCAMAS	ZYGADENUS (*Deathcamas*)
Zingiber officinale	COMMON GINGER	ZINGIBER (*Ginger*)
Z. zerumbet	ZERUMBET G.	ZERUMBET (*Cassumniar*)
Zizyphus jujuba	COMMON JUJUBE	ZIZYPHUS (*Common Jujube*)

DRUGSQUILL
- INDIA D. . . . . **Urginea indica**
- SHORE D. . . . . **U. maritima**

DRYAD . . . . **Dryas**
- ASIAN D. . . . **D. octopetala asiatica**
- DRUMMOND D. . . . . **D. drummondi**
- MT. WASHINGTON D. . **D. octopetala**
- ∞SUENDERMANN D. ∞**D. suendermanni**

DRYADPALM . . . . **Didymosperma**
- LITTLE D. . . . . **D. nanum**

DRYAN'DRA . . . . . . DRYANDRA
- **floribun'da** . . . . MANYFLOWER D.

DRYANDRA, continued
- **formo'sa** . . . . SHOWY DRYANDRA
- **fra'seri** . . . . FRASER D.
- **pteridifo'lia**
- **seneciifo'lia**
- **specio'sa**

DRY'AS |w . . . . DRYAD
- **drum'mondi** . . . . DRUMMOND D.
- **octopet'ala** |w . . MT. WASHINGTON D.
- **—asiat'ica** . . . . ASIAN D.
- **—integrifo'lia**
- **—lana'ta**

DRYAS, continued
- ∞**suendermann'i** (*drummondi × octopetala*) . ∞SUENDERMANN DRYAD
  The plant in cultivation is probably a clon of this polybrid.

DRYMA'RIA . DRYMARY (*Seccomaria*)
- **holosteoi'des** (*pachyphylla*) THICKLEAF D.

DRYMOCAL'LIS . . . **POTENTILLA**
- *agrimonioi'des* . . . . . . **P. arguta**

DRYMOPHLOE'US
- See **PALM GENERA.**

DRYNA'RIA . . . . Drynaria
See **FERN GENERA.**

DRYOBAL'ANOPS . . Borneocamphor
aromat'ica . . . . Common B.

DRYOP'TERIS (*LASTREA; NEPHRODIUM; PHEGOPTERIS; THELYPTERIS*) . . . . . Woodfern
See **FERN GENERA.**

DRYPET'ES . Drypetes (*Guianaplum*)
diversifo'lia . . . . . Milkbark D.
laterifo'ra . . . . . Whitewood D.

DUABAN'GA
sonneratioi'des

DUBOI'SIA . . . . Duboisia
hop'woodi . . . . Pituri
myoporoi'des . . . . Corkwood D.

DUCHES'NEA |w . Mockstrawberry
in'dica (*Fragaria i.*) |w . . India M.

Ducksmeat . . . . **Spirodela**
Common D. . . . . **S. polyrhiza**

Duckweed . . . . **Lemna**
Common D. . . . . **L. minor**
Least D. . . . . **L. minima**
Minute D. . . . . . . **L. perpusilla**
Star D. . . . . **L. trisulca**
Swollen D. . . . . **L. gibba**

DUD'LEYA . . . . . . **ECHEVERIA**
See **SUCCULENTS.**

DUGAL'DIA . . . . . **HELENIUM**

DUGGE'NIA
hirsu'ta (*spicata*)

Duhat . . . Jambolan: **Syzygium cumini**

DULI'CHIUM |w
arundina'ceum |w

Dulse . . . . **Dilsea edulis**

Dunebroom . . . . . **Parryella filifolia**

Dunegrass . . Wildrye, Common Dune: **Elymus mollis**

DURAN'TA . . . . Skyflower
lorentz'i . . . . Lorentz S.
re'pens (*plumieri*) . . . Creeping S.
—al'ba . . . . White C.S.
—variega'ta . . . Variegated C.S.
stenosta'chya . . . . Brazil S.

Durian . . . . **Durio**
Civet D. . . . . **D. zibethinus**
Malacca D. . . . . . **D. malaccensis**
Wild D. . . . . Malacca D.

DU'RIO . . . . Durian
malaccen'sis . Malacca D. (*Wild D.*)
zibethi'nus (*D. malaccensis z.*) Civet D.

Durra . . . . **Sorghum vulgare durra**
Sudan D. . . Feterita: Hort. race of **Sorghum vulgare durra**

Dustymiller . . **Centaurea cineraria**

Dustymiller . . . Wormwood, Beach: **Artemisia stelleriana**

Dutchmans-breeches **Dicentra cucullaria**

Dutchmanspipe . . . . . **Aristolochia**
Argentine D. . . . . . **A. fimbriata**
Birthwort D. . . . . . **A. clematitis**
Brazil D. . . . . . . **A. brasiliensis**

Dutchmanspipe, continued
Broadblade D. . **Aristolochia galeata**
Calico D. . . . . **A. elegans**
California D. . . . . . **A. californica**
Common D. . . . . **A. durior**
Evergreen D. . . . **A. sempervirens**
Fragrant D. . . . . . **A. odoratissima**
Gaping D. . . . . **A. ringens**
Herb D. . . . . **A. hastata**
Hookers Pelican D. **A. grandiflora hookeri**
Kaempfer D. . . . . . . **A. kaempferi**
Largeleaf Brazil D. **A. brasiliensis macrophylla**
Longtail Pelican D. **A. grandiflora sturtevanti**
Manchurian D. . . **A. manshuriensis**
Mexican D. . . . . **A. galeotti**
Moupin D. . . . . . **A. moupinensis**
Pelican D. . . . . . . **A. grandiflora**
Roundroot D. . . . . **A. rotunda**
Tall D. . . . . **A. altissima**
Texas Snakeroot D. . . **A. reticulata**
Virginia S. D. . . . . **A. serpentaria**
Watson D. . . . . **A. watsoni**
Yellowmouth D. . . **A. heterophylla**

DUVA'LIA . . . . Duvalia
angustilo'ba
corderoy'i . . . . Corderoy D.
el'egans . . . . . ×**Stapelia radiata**
hirtel'la
poli'ta
pubes'cens

DUVAU'A . . . . **SCHINUS**

Dwarfdandelion . . . . **Krigia**
Mountain D. . . . . . . **K. montana**
Virginia D. . . . . . . **K. virginica**
Western D. . . . . . **K. occidentalis**

Dwarfmistletoe . . . **Arceuthobium**
Small D. . . . . **A. pusillum**

DYCK'IA . . . . Dyckia
fri'gida
rariflo'ra
sulphu'rea . . . . Sulfur D.

DY'ERA . . . . Dyera
costula'ta . . . . . . Jelutong D.

DYP'SIS . . . . Dypsis
See **PALM GENERA.**

DYSCHORIS'TE
linea'ris

DYSOX'YLUM . . . . . Pencilwood
frasera'num . . . . Fraser P.
spectab'ile . . . . Showy P.

DYSSO'DIA (*BOEBERA*) |w Dogweed
acero'sa . . . . Prickleaf D.
pappo'sa (*Boebera p.*) |w . Prairie D.

Eaglewood . . . . **Aquilaria**
Agalloch E. . . . . **A. agallocha**

Earpodtree . . . . . . **Enterolobium**
Guanacaste E. . . . **E. cyclocarpum**
Pacara E. . . . . **E. contortisiliquum**
Timbouva E. . . . . . . **E. timbouva**

Earthnut . . . **Carum bulbocastanum**

Earthstar, Barometer **Geaster hygrometricus**

Eastercactus **Schlumbergera gaertneri**

EASTWOOD'IA . . . . . Mockaster
el'egans . . . . Yellow M.

EATONEL'LA (*ACTINOLEPIS* in part) Eatonella
cong'doni . . . . . . SanJoaquin E.
niv'ea . . . . Sierra E.

E'BENUS
cre'tica
natalen'sis . . . . **Maba n.**
sandwicen'sis . . . . **Maba s.**

EBRACTE'OLA
derenbergia'na
montis-molt'kei

EBUROPHY'TON **CEPHALANTHERA**
See **ORCHID GENERA, HARDY TERRESTRIAL GROUP.**

ECBAL'LIUM . . Squirtingcucumber
elate'rium (*Momordica e.*) Squirtingcucumber

ECCREMOCAC'TUS
See **CACTUS GENERA.**

ECCREMOCAR'PUS (*CALAMPELIS*) Gloryflower
sca'ber (*Calampelis scabra*) Chilean G.
₵Carmine (*carmineus*) hv.
₵Golden (*aureus*)
₵Redpurple (*punicea*)
₵Scarlet (*coccineus*)

ECDYSAN'THERA
u'tilis

ECHEVE'RIA (*COURANTIA; DUDLEYA; OLIVERANTHUS; STYLOPHYLLUM; URBINIA*) Echeveria
See **SUCCULENTS.**

Echeveria . . . . **Echeveria**
Abrams E. . . . . **E. abramsi**
Bronze E. . . **E. gibbiflora metallica**
Carpet E. . . . . **E. agavoides**
Chalky E. . . . . **E. farinosa**
Fringed E. . . . . **E. fimbriata**
Green Lanceleaf E. **E. lanceolata aloides**
Lanceleaf E. . . . . . **E. lanceolata**
Lozan E. . . . . **E. lozani**
Lurid Lanceleaf E. **E. lanceolata lurida**
Maxon E. . . . . **E. maxoni**
Mountain E. . . . . **E. montana**
Nevada E. . . . . **E. nevadensis**
Northern E. . . **E. septentrionalis**
Palmer E. . . . . **E. palmeri**
Peacock E. . . . . **E. peacocki**
Pinewoods E. . . . . . . **E. pinetorum**
Pittier E. . . . . **E. pittieri**
Platt E. . . . . **E. plattiana**
Powdered E. . . . . **E. pulverulenta**
Pringle E. . . . . **E. pringlei**
Purpus E. . . . . **E. purpusi**
Redrim E. . . . . **E. rubromarginata**
Runyon E. . . . . **E. runyoni**
SanFrancisco E. . . . **E. caespitosa**
Scarlet E. . . . . **E. coccinea**
Setchell E. . . . . **E. setchelli**
Sheldon E. . . . . **E. sheldoni**
Southern E. . . . . **E. australis**
Spotted E. . . . . **E. maculata**
Spruces E. . . . . **E. sprucei**
Tighttuft E. . . . . **E. compacta**
Toluca E. . . . . **E. tolucensis**
Tongueleaf E. . . . **E. linguaefolia**

ECHEVERIA, continued
- VENEZUELA E. **Echeveria venezuelensis**
- WALPOLE E. . . . . . . **E. walpoleana**
- WHITES E. . . . . **E. whitei**
- XANTUS E. . . . . **E. xanti**

ECHIDIOCA'RYA ⌊w
- **arizo'nica** ⌊w

ECHIDNOP'SIS
See **SUCCULENTS.**

ECHINA'CEA (*BRAUNERIA*) . . . ECHINACEA
- **angustifo'lia** (*Brauneria a.*) . . . BLACKSAMSON E.
- **pal'lida** (*Brauneria p.; Rudbeckia p.*) . . . PALE E.
- **purpu'rea** (*Rudbeckia p.*) . PURPLE E.
- —**serot'ina** (*E. intermedia*)
  - BRIGHTLING. HV. E. purpurea
  - GOLDEN QUEEN
  - LEUCHSTERN
  - MASTERPIECE
  - ROSEQUEEN
  - SCARLETTA
  - THE KING
  - THE PILOT
  - WINCHMORE HILL

ECHINOCAC'TUS (*DENMOZA; HOMALOCEPHALA*) ECHINOCACTUS
See **CACTUS GENERA.**

ECHINOCE'REUS . . . ECHINOCEREUS
See **CACTUS GENERA.**

ECHINOCEREUS . . . . . **Echinocereus**
- ALICOCHE E. . . . . . . **E. papillosus**
- ARIZONA E. . . . . . **E. arizonicus**
- BAILEY E. . . . . **E. baileyi**
- BRANDEGEE E. . . . . **E. brandegeei**
- BROWNPITAYA E. . . . **E. chloranthus**
- CLARETCUP E. . . . **E. triglochidiatus**
- EHRENBERG E. . . . . **E. ehrenbergi**

ECHINOCEREUS, continued
- ENGELMANN E. . . . **Echinocereus engelmanni**
- FENDLER E. . . . . . . **E. fendleri**
- FITCH E. . . . . **E. fitchi**
- GREENPITAYA E. . . . **E. viridiflorus**
- LACE E. . . . . . . **E. reichenbachi**
- LLOYD E. . . . . **E. lloydi**
- MERKER E . . . . **E. merkeri**
- MOHAVE E. . . . . . . **E. mojavensis**
- OKLAHOMA E. . . . . **E. oklahomensis**
- PACIFIC E. . . . . . . **E. pacificus**
- PALMER E. . . . . . . **E. palmeri**
- RAINBOW E. . . . . **E. rigidissimus**
- ROETTER E. . . . . . . **E. roetteri**
- ROSE E. . . . . **E. rosei**
- SCHEER E. . . . . **E. scheeri**
- SQUIRREL E. . . . . . . **E. sciurus**
- VIERECK E. . . . . . . **E. vierecki**
- WHITESPINE E. . . . . **E. albispinus**
- YELLOWPITAYA E. . **E. dasyacanthus**

ECHINOCH'LOA . . . . COCKSPUR
See **GRASS GENERA.**

ECHINOCYS'TIS (*MICRAMPELIS*) ⌊w . . . . MOCKCUCUMBER
Echinocystis, a later name, is conserved under International Rules.
- *califor'nica* . . . . . . **Megarrhiza c.**
- **loba'ta** (*Micrampelis l.*) ⌊w . WILD M.
- **macrocar'pa** . . . . CHILICOTHE M.
- *orega'na* . . . . . . **Megarrhiza o.**

ECHINODO'RUS ⌊w . . . . BURHEAD
- **cordifo'lius** ⌊w
- **rad'icans** ⌊w
- **tenel'lus** ⌊w

ECHINOFOSSULOCAC'TUS . . . **STENOCACTUS**
See **CACTUS GENERA.**

ECHINOMAS'TUS . **THELOCACTUS**
See **CACTUS GENERA.**

ECHINOPAN'AX . . **OPLOPANAX**

E'CHINOPS . . . . . . GLOBETHISTLE
- **banna'ticus** . . . . . YUGOSLAV G.
- **dahu'ricus**
- **exalta'tus** . . . . RUSSIAN G.
- **gigan'teus** . . . . GIANT G.
- **hor'ridus**
- **hu'milis** . . . . SIBERIAN G.
- —**cya'neus** . . . . DARKBLUE S.G.
- **ri'tro** . . . . SMALL G.
- **sphaeroce'phalus** . . . . COMMON G.
- **visco'sus**

ECHINOP'SIS . . . HEDGEHOGCACTUS
See **CACTUS GENERA.**

ECHINOSPER'MUM . . **LAPPULA**

ECHI'NUS
- **maximilia'num**

ECHI'TES . . . . . SAVANNAFLOWER
- *andrew'si* . . . . . **Urechites lutea**
- **tomento'sa** . . . . . . WOOLLY S.
- **umbella'ta** (*echites*) . . DEVILSPOTATO

E'CHIUM ⌊w . . . . . VIPERSBUGLOSS
- **bourgaea'num**
- **can'dicans** . . . . MADEIRA V.
- **cre'ticum** . . . . CRETAN V.
- **fastuo'sum** . . . PRIDE-OF-MADEIRA
- **gigan'teum** . . . . . TENERIFFE V.
- **pinina'na** . . . . PININANA V.
- **plantagin'eum**
- **rose'um** . . . . . TOWER-OF-JEWELS
- **sim'plex**
- **vulga're** ⌊w . COMMON V. (*Blueweed*)
- **wildpret'ti** . . . . . . HONEYBELL V.

ECLIP'TA ⌊w
- **al'ba** ⌊w . . . . YERBADETAJO

ECONOMIC CRYPTOGAMS
See **CRYPTOGAMS, ECONOMIC.**

ECONOMIC PLANTS

STANDARDIZED PLANT NAMES presents this listing of Economic Plants as one of the most important contributions to this edition. This material was prepared in chief part by Albert F. Hill, Botanical Museum, Harvard University, Cambridge, Mass., who has specialized in this field and is the author of a textbook on the subject entitled "Economic Botany."

The following groups of Economic Plants in Dr. Hill's original manuscript are treated elsewhere in a somewhat more exhaustive way by specialists in each particular category, viz.: Cereals, Fibers (Textile and Other), Fruits, Legumes, Medicinal Plants (Drugs), Nuts.

The Editorial Committee acknowledges with sincere thanks Dr. Hill's fine cooperation and valuable contribution.

BEVERAGES

Economic Name	Plant Source: Botanical Name	Plant Source: S.P.N. Common Name
CASSIA	**Cassia occidentalis**	COFFEE SENNA
This is a coffee substitute—not to be confused with **Cinnamomum cassia.**		
CASSINE	**Ilex cassine**	DAHOON
CASSINE	**I. vomitoria**	YAUPON
CHICORY	**Cichorium intybus**	COMMON CHICORY
CHOCOLATE; COCOA	**Theobroma cacao**	CACAO
COFFEE		
ARABIAN C.	**Coffea arabica**	ARABIAN COFFEE
CONGO C.	**C. robusta**	ROBUST C.
LIBERIAN C.	**C. liberica**	LIBERIAN C.
COLA	**Cola acuminata**	SUDAN COLANUT
GINGER	**Zingiber officinale**	COMMON GINGER
GUARANA	**Paullinia cupana**	GUARANA PAULLINIA
KHAT	**Catha edulis**	ARABIANTEA (*Kat*)
MATÉ	**Ilex paraguariensis**	PARAGUAYTEA
MESCAL	**Agave atrovirens**	PULQUE AGAVE
This species is the principal source of mescal and pulque, though other Agaves enter into the supply.		
OKRA	**Hibiscus esculentus**	OKRA
PULQUE	**Agave atrovirens**	PULQUE AGAVE
SAKE	**Oryza sativa**	RICE
TEA	**Camellia sinensis** (*Thea s.*)	COMMON TEA

ESSENTIAL OILS

Economic Name	Plant Source: Botanical Name	Plant Source: S.P.N. Common Name
ANISE	**Pimpinella anisum**	ANISE PIMPINELLA
Attar-of-roses. OTTO-OF-ROSES		
BALSAM-OF-PERU	**Myroxylon pereirae**	PERUBALSAM BALMTREE
BAY	**Pimenta racemosa**	BAYRUMTREE
BERGAMOT	**Citrus bergamia**	BERGAMOT ORANGE
CALAMUS	**Acorus calamus**	DRUG SWEETFLAG
CAMPHOR	**Cinnamomum camphora**	CAMPHORTREE
BORNEO C.	**Dryobalanops aromatica**	COMMON BORNEO-CAMPHOR
CANISTEL	**Lucuma nervosa**	CANISTEL LUCUMA
CARAWAY	**Carum carvi**	CARAWAY
CARNATION	**Dianthus caryophyllus**	CARNATION; CLOVE PINK
CASSIA	**Cinnamomum cassia**	CASSIABARKTREE
CASSIE	**Acacia farnesiana**	SWEET ACACIA
CEDAR WOOD	**Juniperus virginiana**	EASTERN REDCEDAR
CHAMPACA	**Michelia champaca**	CHAMPAC MICHELIA
CINNAMON	**Cinnamomum zeylanicum**	CEYLON CINNAMON
CITRONELLA	**Cymbopogon nardus**	CITRONELLAGRASS
CLOVE	**Syzygium aromaticum** (*Eugenia caryophyllata*)	CLOVETREE
COUMAROUNA	**Dipteryx odorata**	DUTCH TONKABEAN
DILL	**Anethum graveolens**	DILL
EUCALYPTUS	**Eucalyptus dives**	BROADLEAF PEPPERMINT EUCALYPTUS
GERANIUM	**Pelargonium graveolens**	ROSE PELARGONIUM
GERANIUM	**P. odoratissimum**	NUTMEG P.
GINGER-GRASS	**Cymbopogon martini**	ROSHAGRASS
HELIOTROPE	**Heliotropium arborescens**	COMMON HELIOTROPE
HIBISCUS	**Hibiscus** spp.	HIBISCUS
HOP	**Humulus lupulus**	COMMON HOP
HYACINTH	**Hyacinthus orientalis**	COMMON HYACINTH
JASMINE	**Jasminum officinale grandiflorum**	
JONQUIL	**Narcissus jonquilla**	JONQUIL

ESSENTIAL OILS, continued

Economic Name	Botanical Name (Plant Source)	S.P.N. Common Name (Plant Source)
Lavender	**Lavandula officinalis**	True Lavender
Lemon	**Citrus limon**	Lemon
Lemon-grass	**Cymbopogon citratus**	Lemongrass
Lignaloe	**Bursera glabrifolia** (*aloexylon*)	Linaloe Bursera
Lignaloe	**B. penicillata** (*delpechiana*)	
Lily-of-the-valley	**Convallaria majalis**	Lilyofthevalley
Limeberry	**Triphasia trifolia**	Limeberry
Mignonette	**Reseda odorata**	Common Mignonette
Narcissus	**Narcissus tazetta**	Polyanthus Narcissus
Neroli		
Bigarade N.	**Citrus aurantium**	Sour Orange (*Seville O.*)
Portugal N.	**C. sinensis**	Sweet O.
Orange	**Citrus aurantium**	Sour Orange (*Seville O.*)
Orange	**C. sinensis**	Sweet O.
Orris	**Iris germanica florentina** Hort.	Orrisroot Iris
Otto-of-roses	**Rosa centifolia**	Cabbage Rose
Otto-of-roses	**R. damascena**	Damask R.
Palmarosa	**Cymbopogon martini**	Roshagrass
Patchouli	**Pogostemon cablin**	Cablin Patchouli
India P.	**P. heyneanus**	Heyne P.
Pennyroyal	**Hedeoma pulegioides**	American False-pennyroyal
Peppermint	**Mentha piperita**	Peppermint
Rosemary	**Rosmarinus officinalis**	Rosemary
Sandalwood	**Santalum album**	White Sandalwood
Sassafras	**Sassafras albidum**	Common Sassafras
Spearmint	**Mentha spicata**	Spearmint
Spike Lavender	**Lavandula latifolia**	Broadleaf Lavender
Tansy	**Tanacetum vulgare**	Common Tansy
Thyme	**Thymus vulgaris**	Common Thyme
Tuberose	**Polianthes tuberosa**	Tuberose
Turpentine	**Pinus palustris**	Longleaf Pine
Turpentine	**Pinus** spp.	Pine
Vetiver	**Vetiveria zizanioides**	Khuskhus Vetiver
Violet	**Viola odorata**	Sweet Violet
Wintergreen	**Gaultheria procumbens**	Checkerberry Wintergreen
Wormseed	**Chenopodium ambrosioides anthelminticum**	Drug Wormseed Goosefoot
Wormwood	**Artemisia absinthium**	Common Wormwood
Ylang-ylang	**Cananga odorata**	Ylangylang
Zedoary	**Curcuma zedoaria**	Zedoary Turmeric

FATTY OILS

Economic Name	Botanical Name (Plant Source)	S.P.N. Common Name (Plant Source)
Ben	**Moringa oleifera**	Horseradishtree
Borneo Tallow	**Shorea aptera**	Borneo Shorea
Camelina	**Camelina sativa**	Bigseed Falseflax
Candlenut	**Aleurites moluccana**	Candlenuttree
Carapa Fat	**Carapa guianensis**	Guiana Crabwood
Carapa Fat	**C. moluccensis**	Molucca C.
Castor	**Ricinus communis**	Castorbean
Chaulmoogra	**Taraktogenos kurzi**	
Chia	**Salvia hispanica**	Mexican Chia
Chinawood	**Aleurites montana**	Mu-oiltree
Chinawood	**A. fordi**	Tungoiltree
Chinese Vegetable Tallow	**Sapium sebiferum**	Chinese Tallowtree
Cocoa Butter	**Theobroma cacao**	Cacao
Coconut	**Cocos nucifera**	Coconut
Cohune	**Orbignya cohune**	Cohune Palm
Colza	**Brassica campestris**	Bird Rape
Corn	**Zea mays**	Maize; Indian Corn
Cottonseed	**Gossypium** spp.	Cotton
Croton	**Croton tiglium**	Purging Croton
Hempseed	**Cannabis sativa**	Hemp
Illipe Butter	**Madhuca indica** (*latifolia*)	Illipe Buttertree
Kapok	**Ceiba pentandra**	Kapok Ceiba
Linseed	**Linum usitatissimum**	Common Flax
Lumbang, Soft	**Aleurites trisperma**	Soft Lumbang
Macassar	**Schleichera oleosa**	Malay Lactree
Mowra Fat	**Madhuca longifolia**	Mowra Buttertree
Nigerseed	**Guizotia abyssinica**	Ethiopian Nigerseed
Nutmegbutter	**Myristica fragrans**	Common Nutmeg
Oiticica	**Licania rigida**	
Olive	**Olea europaea**	Common Olive
Ongokea	**Ongokea klaineana**	
Palm; Palmkernel	**Elaeis guineensis**	African Oilpalm

FATTY OILS, continued

Economic Name	Botanical Name (Plant Source)	S.P.N. Common Name (Plant Source)
Peanut	**Arachis hypogaea**	Peanut
Perilla	**Perilla frutescens**	Common Perilla
Pistachio-nut	**Pistacia vera**	Common Pistache
Pongam	**Pongamia pinnata**	Poongaoil Pongamia
Poppy	**Papaver somniferum**	Opium Poppy
Po-Yoak	**Afrolicania eleosperma**	Nikkonuttree
Rapeseed	**Brassica napus**	Winter Rape
Rice	**Oryza sativa**	Rice
Safflower	**Carthamus tinctorius**	Safflower
Sesame	**Sesamum indicum** (*orientale*)	Oriental Sesame
Shea Butter	**Butyrospermum parki**	Shea Butterseed
Soybean	**Glycine soja** (*Soja max*)	Soybean
Sunflower	**Helianthus annuus**	Common Sunflower
Teaseed	**Camellia sasanqua**	Sasanqua Camellia
Telfairia	**Telfairia occidentalis**	Common Oysternut-tree
Tung	**Aleurites fordi**	Tungoiltree
Walnut	**Juglans regia**	Persian Walnut

FUMITORIES AND MASTICATORIES

Economic Name	Botanical Name (Plant Source)	S.P.N. Common Name (Plant Source)
Betel	**Areca cathecu**	Betelnutpalm
Caapi	**Banisteriopsis caapi**	Caapi
Cannabis	**Cannabis sativa**	Hemp
Chicle	**Achras zapota**	Sapodilla
Coca	**Erythroxylum coca**	Huanuco Cocainetree
Cola	**Cola nitida**	Sudan Colanut
Fly Agaric	**Amanita muscaria**	Caesars Amanita
Henbane	**Hyoscyamus niger**	Black Henbane
Henbane	**H. muticus**	
Jimsonweed	**Datura stramonium**	Jimsonweed Datura
Kavakava	**Piper methysticum**	Kava Pepper
Maikoa	**Datura arborea**	Floripondio Datura
Marijuana	**Cannabis sativa**	Hemp
Opium	**Papaver somniferum**	Opium Poppy
Peyote	**Lophophora williamsi**	Mescalbutton Peyote
Pituri	**Duboisia hopwoodi**	Pituri
Spruce Gum	**Picea rubens**	Red Spruce
Tobacco	**Nicotiana tabacum**	Common Tobacco
Tobacco	**N. rustica**	Aztec T.

GUMS AND RESINS

Economic Name	Botanical Name (Plant Source)	S.P.N. Common Name (Plant Source)
Acaroid Resins		
Red A.	**Xanthorrhoea australis**	Australian Grasstree
Yellow A.	**X. hastilis**	Spearleaf G.
Amber	**Pinus succinifera** (extinct)	
Ammoniacum	**Dorema ammoniacum**	Bombay Sumbul
Asafetida	**Ferula assafoetida**	Asafetida Giantfennel
Balsam		
Canada B.	**Abies balsamea**	Balsam Fir
Copaiba B.	**Copaifera officinalis**	Copaiba Copaltree
Copaiba B.	**C. langsdorfi**	Balsam C.
Gurgun B.	**Dipterocarpus turbinatus**	Common Gurjunoiltree
Illurin B.	**Daniella oliveri**	Illurin-balsam Daniella
Mecca B.	**Commiphora opobalsamum**	Mecca Myrrhtree
Oregon B.	**Pseudotsuga taxifolia** (*mucronata*)	Common Douglasfir
Balsam of Peru	**Myroxylon pereirae**	Perubalsam Balmtree
Balsam of Tolu	**M. balsamum**	Tolubalsam B.
Bdellium	**Commiphora africana**	African Myrrhtree
Benzoin		
Siam B.	**Styrax tonkinensis**	Tonkin Snowbell
Siam B.	**S. benzoides**	Siam S.
Sumatra B.	**S. benzoin**	Sumatra S.
Copal		
Accra C.	**Daniella ogea**	Ogeagum Daniella
Congo C.	**Copaifera demeusi**	Congo Copaltree
Congo C.	**C. mopane**	Mopane C.
Inhambane C.	**C. conjugata** (*gorskiana*)	Inhambane C.
Kauri C.	**Agathis australis**	Kauri Dammarpine
Manila C.	**A. alba**	White D.
Sierra Leone C.	**Copaifera copallifera** (*guibortiana*)	SierraLeone Copaltree
South American C.	**Hymenaea courbaril**	Courbaril

GUMS AND RESINS, continued

Economic Name	Plant Source: Botanical Name	S.P.N. Common Name
Copal, West African	**Daniella thurifera**	SierraLeone-frankincense
Zanzibar C.	**Trachylobium verrucosum**	
Damar		
Batavian D.	**Shorea wiesneri**	Batavian Shorea
Black D.	**Canarium strictum**	Blackdamar Canarytree
Sal D.	**Shorea robusta**	Sal Shorea
White D.	**Vateria indica**	
Damar Mata Kuching	**Hopea micrantha**	
Damar Penak	**Balanocarpus heimi**	
Damar Temak	**Shorea hypochra** (*crassifolia*)	Temak Shorea
Dragon's Blood		
Socotra D.	**Dracaena cinnabari**	Socotra-dragonsblood Dracena
Sumatra D.	**Daemonorops draco**	Sumatra-dragonsblood
Elemi		
African E.	**Boswellia frereana**	Elemi Frankincense
American E.	**Amyris elemifera**	Sea Amyris
American E.	**A. balsamifera**	Balsam A.
Brazilian E.	**Protium heptaphyllum**	Brazil Resintree
Manila E.	**Canarium luzonicum**	Elemi Canarytree
Frankincense (*Olibanum*)	**Boswellia carteri**	Bible Frankincense
Galbanum	**Ferula galbaniflua**	Galbanum Giantfennel
Gamboge	**Garcinia hanburyi**	Siam Gambogetree
Guaiacum	**Guajacum officinale**	Common Lignumvitae
Guaiacum	**G. sanctum**	Holywood L.
Gum		
Cherry G.	**Prunus** spp.	
Cycas G.	**Cycas circinalis**	Crozier Cycas
Feronia G.	**Feronia limonia**	Woodapple
Kadaya G.	**Sterculia urens**	Kuteeragum Sterculia
Kadaya G.	**Cochlospermum religiosum**	Cotton Shellseed
Mesquite G.	**Prosopis** spp.	Mesquite
Spruce G.	**Picea rubens** (*rubra* Link, *not* A. Dietr.)	Red Spruce
Gum Arabic	**Acacia senegal**	Gumarabic Acacia
Gum Ghatti	**Anogeissus latifolia**	Bakligum Axlewood
Gum Tragacanth	**Astragalus gummifer**	Tragacanth Milkvetch
Kino		
American K.	**Dipteryx odorata**	Dutch Tonkabean
American K.	**Coccolobis uvifera**	Common Seagrape
Australian K.	**Eucalyptus camaldulensis**	Longbeak Eucalyptus
Australian K.	**Eucalyptus** spp.	Eucalyptus
Bengal K.	**Butea monosperma**	Bengal Kino
Malabar K.	**Pterocarpus marsupium**	Vengai Padauk
West African K.	**P. erinaceus**	WestAfrican P.
Lacquer		
Burmese L.	**Melanorrhoea usitata**	
Chinese L.	**Toxicodendron vernicifluum** (*Rhus verniciflua*)	Japanese Lacquertree
Mastic		
Bombay M.	**Pistacia cabulica**	Afghan Pistache
Chios M.	**P. lentiscus**	Lentisk P.
Myrrh		
Bisabol M.	**Commiphora erythraea**	Bisabol Myrrhtree
Herabol M.	**C. myrrha**	Common M.
Olibanum. Frankincense		
Opopanax	**Commiphora kataf**	Opopanax Myrrhtree
Opopanax	**Opopanax chironium**	Surgeons Opopanax
Rosin	**Pinus** spp.	Pine
Rosin	**P. palustris**	Longleaf P.
Sandarac	**Tetraclinis articulata**	Arartree
Styrax		
American S.	**Liquidambar styraciflua**	American Sweetgum
Levant S.	**L. orientalis**	Oriental S.
Tragasol	**Ceratonia siliqua**	Carob
Turpentine		
American T.	**Pinus palustris**	Longleaf Pine
American T.	**Pinus** spp.	Pine
Bordeaux T.	**P. pinaster**	Cluster P.
Jura T.	**Picea abies**	Norway Spruce
Strasbourg T.	**Abies alba**	Silver Fir
Venetian T.	**Larix decidua**	European Larch

INSECTICIDES

Economic Name	Plant Source: Botanical Name	S.P.N. Common Name
Cube	**Lonchocarpus nicou**	
Derris	**Derris elliptica**	Tubaroot Jewelvine
Derris	**D. trifoliata**	Trifoliate J.
Pyrethrum	**Chrysanthemum cinerariaefolium**	Dalmatian Pyrethrum
Pyrethrum	**C. coccineum**	Florists P.
Pyrethrum	**C. marschalli**	Caucasian P.

LATEX PRODUCTS, INCLUDING RUBBER

Economic Name	Plant Source: Botanical Name	S.P.N. Common Name
Balata	**Manilkara bidentata** (*Mimusops balata*)	Common Balata
Chicle	**Achras zapota**	Sapodilla
Goldenrod	**Solidago leavenworthi**	Leavenworth Goldenrod
Guayule	**Parthenium argentatum**	Guayule Parthenium
Gutta-percha	**Palaquium gutta**	Malay Guttapercha
Indian Hemp	**Apocynum cannabinum**	Hemp Dogbane
Intisy	**Euphorbia intisy**	Intisy Euphorbia
Jelutong	**Dyera costulata**	Jelutong Dyera
Milkweed	**Asclepias subulata**	Skeleton Milkweed
Rubber		
Assam R.	**Ficus elastica**	Indiarubber Fig
Cryptostegia R.	**Cryptostegia** spp.	Rubbervine
Ceara R.	**Manihot glaziovi**	Ceararubberplant
India R.	**Ficus elastica**	Indiarubber Fig
Lagos Silk R.	**Funtumia elastica**	Lagos Silkrubber
Landolphia R.	**Landolphia** spp.	Gumvine
Panama R.	**Castilla elastica**	Panama Gumtree
Para R.	**Hevea brasiliensis**	Para Rubbertree

SOAP SUBSTITUTES

Economic Name	Plant Source: Botanical Name	S.P.N. Common Name
Soapbark	**Quillaja saponaria**	Soapbarktree
Soapberries	**Sapindus saponaria**	Southern Soapberry
Soaproot	**Chlorogalum pomeridianum**	Amole Soapplant
Soapweed	**Yucca** spp.	Yucca
Soapwort	**Saponaria officinalis**	Bouncingbet

SPICES AND OTHER FLAVORING MATERIALS

Economic Name	Plant Source: Botanical Name	S.P.N. Common Name
Allspice	**Pimenta officinalis**	Allspice Pimenta
Almond	**Prunus amygdalus** (*communis* Arcang, *not* Huds.; *Amygdalus c.*)	Almond
Angelica	**Angelica archangelica** (*Archangelica officinalis*)	Garden Angelica
Anise	**Pimpinella anisum**	Anise
Star A.	**Illicium verum**	Truestar Anisetree
Balm	**Melissa officinalis**	Common Balm
Basil		
Bush B.	**Ocimum minimum**	Least Basil
Sweet B.	**O. basilicum**	Sweet B.
Bay	**Laurus nobilis**	Grecian Laurel
Borage	**Borago officinalis**	Common Borage
Calamus	**Acorus calamus**	Drug Sweetflag
Canella	**Canella winterana**	Cinnamon Canella
Canistel	**Lucuma nervosa**	Canistel Lucuma
Capers	**Capparis spinosa**	Common Caper
Capsicum	**Capsicum frutescens longum**	Long Redpepper
Caraway	**Carum carvi**	Caraway
Cardamon	**Elettaria cardamomum**	Cardamon
Cassava	**Manihot esculenta**	Common Cassava
Cassia	**Cinnamomum cassia**	Cassiabarktree
India C.	**C. tamala**	Himalaya Cinnamon
Padang C.	**C. burmani**	Malay C.
Catnip	**Nepeta cataria**	Catnip
Cayenne Pepper	**Capsicum frutescens longum**	Long Redpepper
Celery	**Apium graveolens dulce**	Garden Celery
Checkerberry	**Gaultheria procumbens**	Wintergreen
Chervil	**Anthriscus cerefolium**	Saladchervil
Chilis	**Capsicum frutescens longum**	Long Redpepper
Chives	**Allium schoenoprasum**	Chive

SPICES, ETC., continued

Economic Name	Plant Source: Botanical Name	Plant Source: S.P.N. Common Name
CINNAMON		
CEYLON C.	Cinnamomum zeylanicum	CEYLON CINNAMON
CHINESE C.	C. cassia	CASSIABARKTREE
SAIGON C.	C. loureiri	CASSIAFLOWERTREE
CITRON	Citrus medica	CITRON
CLARY	Salvia sclarea	CLARY SAGE
CLOVES	Syzygium aromaticum (*Eugenia caryophyllata*)	CLOVETREE
CORIANDER	Coriandrum sativum	CORIANDER
CUMIN	Cuminum cyminum	CUMIN
DILL	Anethum graveolens	DILL
FENNEL	Foeniculum vulgare	COMMON FENNEL
FENUGREEK	Trigonella foenum-graecum	FENUGREEK TRIGONELLA
GALANGAL	Alpina galanga	
GALANGAL	A. officinarum	LESSER GALANGAL
GINGER	Zingiber officinale	COMMON GINGER
GRAINS OF PARADISE	Amomum melegueta	DRUG MELEGUETA-PEPPER
HOARHOUND	Marrubium vulgare	COMMON HOARHOUND
HORSERADISH	Armoracia lapathifolia	HORSERADISH
HORSERADISHTREE	Moringa oleifera (*pterygosperma*)	HORSERADISHTREE
HYSSOP	Hyssopus officinalis	HYSSOP
JUNIPER	Juniperus communis	COMMON JUNIPER
LEMON	Citrus limon	LEMON
LICORICE	Glycyrrhiza glabra	COMMON LICORICE
LIME	Citrus aurantifolia	LIME
LOVAGE	Levisticum officinale	GARDEN LOVAGE
MACE	Myristica fragrans	COMMON NUTMEG
MARJORAM		
POT M.	Origanum vulgare	COMMON ORIGANUM
SWEET M.	Majorana hortensis (*Origanum majorana*)	SWEET MARJORAM
MASSOIA BARK	Cinnamomum massoia	MASSOIA CINNAMON
MINT		
JAPANESE FIELD M.	Mentha arvensis piperascens	JAPANESE FIELD MINT
MUSTARD		
BLACK M.	Brassica nigra	BLACK MUSTARD
INDIA M.	B. juncea (*rugosa; Sinapis j.*)	INDIA M.
WHITE M.	B. hirta (*alba; Sinapis a.*)	WHITE M.
NUTMEG	Myristica fragrans	COMMON NUTMEG
ORANGE	Citrus sinensis	SWEET ORANGE
SEVILLE O.	C. aurantium	SOUR O. (*Seville O.*)
PAPRIKA	Capsicum frutescens	BUSH REDPEPPER
PARSLEY	Petroselinum crispum latifolium	COMMON GARDEN PARSLEY
PENNYROYAL	Mentha pulegium	PENNYROYAL MINT
PEPPER		
BLACK P.	Piper nigrum	BLACK PEPPER
CAYENNE P.	Capsicum frutescens longum	LONG REDPEPPER
LONG P.	Piper longum	LONG PEPPER
LONG P.	P. retrofractum	
RED P.	Capsicum frutescens longum	LONG REDPEPPER
PEPPERMINT	Mentha piperita	PEPPERMINT
JAPANESE FIELD MINT	M. arvensis piperascens	JAPANESE FIELD MINT
PIMIENTO	Capsicum frutescens	BUSH REDPEPPER
PISTACHIO	Pistacia vera	COMMON PISTACHE
POPPY	Papaver somniferum	OPIUM POPPY
POT MARIGOLD	Calendula officinalis	POTMARIGOLD CALENDULA
ROSEMARY	Rosmarinus officinalis	ROSEMARY
RUE	Ruta graveolens	COMMON RUE
SAFFRON	Crocus sativus	SAFFRON CROCUS
SAGE	Salvia officinalis	GARDEN SAGE
SARSAPARILLA	Smilax aristolochiifolia	MEXICAN SARSAPARILLA
SARSAPARILLA	S. officinalis	
SARSAPARILLA	S. regeli	JAMAICA S.
SASSAFRAS	Sassafras albidum (*officinale*)	COMMON SASSAFRAS
SAVORY		
SUMMER S.	Satureia hortensis	SUMMER SAVORY
WINTER S.	S. montana	WINTER S.
SPEARMINT	Mentha spicata	SPEARMINT
STAR ANISE	Illicium verum	TRUESTAR ANISETREE
TANSY	Tanacetum vulgare	COMMON TANSY
TARRAGON	Artemisia dracunculus	TARRAGON
THYME	Thymus vulgaris	COMMON THYME
TONKA BEANS	Dipteryx odorata	DUTCH TONKABEAN
TONKA BEANS	D. oppositifolia	BRITISH T.
TURMERIC	Curcuma longa	COMMON TURMERIC
VANILLA	Vanilla planifolia	MEXICAN VANILLA
WINTERGREEN	Gaultheria procumbens	WINTERGREEN
ZEDOARY	Curcuma zedoaria	ZEDOARY TURMERIC

STARCHES

Economic Name	Plant Source: Botanical Name	Plant Source: S.P.N. Common Name
ARROWROOT		
EAST INDIAN A.	Curcuma angustifolia	
FLORIDA A.	Zamia floridana	
GUINEA A.	Calathea allouia	EDIBLE CALATHEA
QUEENSLAND A.	Canna edulis	EDIBLE CANNA
WEST INDIAN A.	Maranta arundinacea	BERMUDA ARROWROOT
CASSAVA	Manihot esculenta	COMMON CASSAVA
CORN	Zea mays	MAIZE; INDIAN CORN
POTATO	Solanum tuberosum	POTATO
SWEET P.	Ipomoea batatas	SWEETPOTATO
RICE	Oryza sativa	RICE
SAGO	Metroxylon sagu	SMOOTH SAGOPALM
WHEAT	Triticum aestivum	WHEAT
YAUTIA	Xanthosoma sagittifolium	YAUTIA MALANGA

SUGARS

Economic Name	Plant Source: Botanical Name	Plant Source: S.P.N. Common Name
DAHLIA	Dahlia pinnata	AZTEC DAHLIA
JERUSALEM ARTICHOKE	Helianthus tuberosus	JERUSALEMARTICHOKE SUNFLOWER
MANNA ASH	Fraxinus ornus	FLOWERING ASH
PALM		
COCONUT P.	Cocos nucifera	COCONUT
GOMUTI P.	Arenga pinnata	GOMUTI SUGARPALM
PALMYRA P.	Borassus flabellifer	PALMYRAPALM
TODDY P.	Caryota urens	TODDY FISHTAILPALM (*Kittoolpalm*)
WILD DATE P.	Phoenix sylvestris	SUGAR DATE (*India D.*)
SORGO	Sorghum vulgare saccharatum	SORGHO
SUGAR BEET	Beta vulgaris	COMMON BEET
SUGARCANE	Saccharum officinarum	SUGARCANE
SUGAR MAPLE	Acer saccharum	SUGAR MAPLE

TANNING MATERIALS

Economic Name	Plant Source: Botanical Name	Plant Source: S.P.N. Common Name
AVARAM BARK	Cassia auriculata	AVARAM SENNA
BABUL BARK	Acacia arabica	BABUL ACACIA
CANAIGRE	Rumex hymenosepalus	CANAIGRE
CHESTNUT		
AMERICAN C.	Castanea dentata	AMERICAN CHESTNUT
EUROPEAN C.	C. sativa	SPANISH C.
DIVI-DIVI	Caesalpinia coriaria	DIVIDIVI
GALLS		
ALEPPO OAK G.	Quercus infectoria	ALEPPO OAK
SUMAC G.	Rhus chinensis	CHINESE SUMAC
GAMBIR	Uncaria gambir	BENGAL GAMBIRPLANT
HEMLOCK		
EASTERN H.	Tsuga canadensis	CANADA HEMLOCK
WESTERN H.	T. heterophylla	PACIFIC H.
MALLET BARK	Eucalyptus occidentalis	FLATTOP YATE EUCALYPTUS
MANGROVE	Rhizophora mangle	AMERICAN MANGROVE
MYROBALAN	Terminalia chebula	CHEBULA TERMINALIA
MYROBALAN	T. bellerica	BELLERIC T.
OAK	Quercus	
BLACK O.	Q. velutina	BLACK OAK
CALIFORNIA TANBARK O.	Lithocarpus densiflorus	TANOAK
CHESTNUT O.	Quercus montana	CHESTNUT OAK
WHITE O.	Q. alba	WHITE O.
PALMETTO	Sabal palmetto	CABBAGE PALMETTO
QUEBRACHO	Schinopsis lorentzi	LORENTZ REDQUEBRACHO
QUEBRACHO	S. balansae	WILLOWLEAF R.
SUMAC		
DWARF S.	Rhus copallina	FLAMELEAF SUMAC
SICILIAN S.	R. coriaria	SICILIAN S.
SMOOTH S.	R. glabra	SMOOTH S.
STAGHORN S.	R. typhina	STAGHORN S.
TANEKAHA BARK	Phyllocladus trichomanoides	TANEKAHA CELERYPINE
VALONIA	Quercus macrolepis	VALONIA OAK
WATTLE	Acacia spp.	

VEGETABLE DYES

Bla.	Black	G.	Green	R.	Red
Blu.	Blue	O.	Orange	Y.	Yellow
Br.	Brown	P.	Purple		

Economic Name	Plant Source: Botanical Name	Plant Source: S.P.N. Common Name
Agrimony. Y.	**Agrimonia eupatoria**	Common Agrimony
Alder. Br.Bla.	**Alnus glutinosa**	European Alder
Alkanna. R.	**Alkanna tinctoria**	Dyers Alkanet
Annatto. Y.	**Bixa orellana**	Anattotree
Apple. Y.	**Malus pumila**	Common Apple
Ash. Y.	**Fraxinus excelsior**	European Ash
Barberry. Y.	**Berberis vulgaris**	European Barberry
Barwood. R.	**Pterocarpus** spp.	Padauk
Bearberry. Blu.	**Arctostaphylos uva-ursi**	Bearberry
Bedstraw		
Ladies B.	**Galium verum**	Yellow Bedstraw
Stiffmarsh B. R.	**G. tinctorium**	Dye B.
Belladonna	**Atropa belladonna**	Belladonna
Birch. Br.R.Y.	**Betula pendula** (*alba*)	European White Birch
Blackberry. Bla.Y.	**Rubus fruticosus**	European Blackberry
Bog Asphodel. Y.	**Narthecium ossifragum**	
Bracken. Y.	**Pteridium aquilinum**	
Bramble. Y.	**Rubus fruticosus**	European Blackberry
Brazilette. R.	**Haematoxylon brasiletto**	Brazil Bloodwoodtree
Brazilwood. R.	**Caesalpinia echinata**	Prickly Brazilwood
Broom. Y.	**Cytisus scoparius**	Scotch Broom
Bryony. P.	**Bryonia dioica**	Redberry Bryony
Buckthorn. G.Y.	**Rhamnus cathartica**	Common Buckthorn
Buckthorn	**R. frangula**	Glossy B.
Camwood. R.	**Baphia nitida**	Shiny Camwood
Currant. Br.	**Ribes** spp.	Currant; Gooseberry
Cutch. Br.	**Acacia catechu**	Catechu Acacia
Dandelion. P.	**Taraxacum officinale**	Common Dandelion
Danewort. P.	**Sambucus ebulus**	Mediterranean Herb Elder
Devilsbit. Blu.	**Succisa pratensis**	Meadow Succisa
Dock	**Rumex obtusifolius**	Bitter Dock
Dogs Mercury. Blu.	**Mercurialis perennis**	
Dyers Greenwood. Y.	**Genista tinctoria**	Common Woadwaxen
Dyers Woodruff. R.	**Asperula tinctoria**	Dyers Woodruff
Elder. Bla.Blu.G.P.	**Sambucus nigra**	European Elder
Flowering Reed. G.	**Phragmites communis**	Common Reed
Fustic. Br.Y.		
Old F.	Chlorophora tinctoria	Drug Fustictree
Young F.	**Cotinus coggygria**	Common Smoketree
Gamboge. Y.	**Garcinia hanburyi**	Siam Gambogetree
Gooseberry. *See* Currant		
Gorse. Y.	**Ulex europaeus**	Common Gorse
Gromwell. R.	**Lithospermum arvense**	Corn Gromwell
Heather. Y.	**Calluna vulgaris**	Scotch Heather
Hedge Stachys. Y.	**Stachys palustris**	Marsh Betony
Henna. O.	**Lawsonia inermis**	Henna
Hop. Br.Y.	**Humulus lupulus**	Common Hop
Hornbeam. Y.	**Carpinus betulus**	European Hornbeam
Indigo. Blu.	**Indigofera tinctoria**	True Indigo
Indigo. Blu.	**I. suffruticosa** (*anil*)	Anil I.
Iris. Bla.Blu.	**Iris pseudacorus**	Yellowflag Iris
Kidney Vetch. Y.	**Anthyllis vulneraria**	Kidneyvetch Anthyllis
Larch. Br.G.	**Larix** spp.	Larch
Lichen		
Borrera. Br.	**Borrera flavicans**	Yellow Borrera
Chutcheleera. R.P.O.	**B. ashneyi**	Chutcheleera B.
Corkir. R.P.O.	**Urceolaria calcarea**	Limestone Urceolaria
Cornicularia. R.P.O.	**Cornicularia aculeata spadicea**	Brown Prickly Cornicularia
Crottle		
Black C. R.P.O.Br.	**Parmelia omphalodes**	Blackcrottle Parmelia
Coral C. R.P.O.	**Isidium corallinum**	Coralcrottle Isidium
Dark C. Y. Br.	**Parmelia ceratophylla**	Horny Parmelia
Dark C. Br.	**P. physodes**	Darkcrottle P.
Light C. R.P.O.	**Lecanora parella**	Crabseye Lecanora
Stone C. R.P.O.	**Parmelia caperata**	Wrinkled Parmelia

VEGETABLE DYES, continued

Economic Name	Plant Source: Botanical Name	Plant Source: S.P.N. Common Name
Lichen, Stone Crottle R.P.O.	**Lecanora tatarea**	Litmus Lecanora
Stone C. R.P.O.	**Parmelia saxatilis**	Stonecrottle Parmelia
En-mossa. Br.	**Cetraria juniperina**	Junipermoss
Evernia		
Staghorn E. R.P.O.	**Evernia prunastri**	Staghorn Evernia
Wolfbane E. Br.	**E. flavicans**	Yellowbrown E.
Wolfbane E. Y.	**E. vulpina**	Wolfbane E.
Gyrophora. Br.G.	**Gyrophora pustulata**	Blister Gyrophora
Cylindrical G. Br.	**G. cylindrica**	Cylinder G.
Scorched G. Br.	**G. deusta**	Scorched G.
Iceland Moss. Br.	**Cetraria islandica**	Icelandmoss
Lecanora		
Bloodyspot L. R.P.O.	**Lecanora haematoma**	Bloodspot Lecanora
Pale L. P.	**L. pallescens**	Pale L.
Lecidea. R.P.O.	**Lecidea sanguinaria**	Bloodred Lecidea
Lepraria	**Lepraria chlorina**	Brimstone Lepraria
Ljus Massa. Br.	**Lecanora candelaria**	Candelaria Lecanora
Lungwort. Br.R.P.O.	**Sticta pulmonaria**	Lungwort Sticta
Map Lichen. Br.	**Lecidea atrovirens**	Map Lecidea
Nephroma. R.P.O.	**Nephroma parilis**	Chocolate Nephroma
Oakrag. Br.	**Sticta scrobiculata**	Pitted Sticta
Orseille (*Cudbear*). R.P.O.	**Roccella tinctoria**	Litmus Roccella
Parmelia		
Sprinkled P. R.P.O.	**Parmelia conspersa**	Sprinkled Parmelia
Sprinkled P. P.	**P. perlata**	
Ramalina		
Ivory R. R.P.O.	**Ramalina scopulorum**	Ivory Ramalina
Mealy R. R.P.O.	**R. farinacea**	Mealy R.
Rockhair. Br.	**Alectoria jubata**	Rockhair Alectoria
Solorina. R.P.O.	**Solorina crocea**	Saffron Solorina
Sticta		
Yellow S. Br.	**Sticta crocata**	Yellow Sticta
Umbilicaria		
Blistered U. R.P.O.	**Umbilicaria pustulata**	Blister Umbilicaria
Fleecy U. P.	**U. vellea**	Fleecy U.
Urceolaria		
Greyish U. R.P.O.	**Urceolaria cinerea**	Ashy Urceolaria
Rock U. R.P.O.	**U. scruposa**	Jagged U.
Usnea		
Bearded U. R.P.O.	**Usnea barbata**	Bearded Usnea
Flowering U. R.P.O.	**U. florida**	Florida U.
Pleated U. R.P.O.	**U. plicata**	Pleated U.
Viol Massa. Br.	**Lepraria iolithus**	Violet Lepraria
Wall Lichen. Br.	**Parmelia parietina**	Wall Parmelia
Westrings Isidium. R.P.O.	**Isidium westringi**	Westrings Isidium
Lily-of-the-valley. G.	**Convallaria majalis**	Lilyofthevalley
Logwood. P.	**Haematoxylon campechianum**	Logwood
Lokao (*Chinese green*). G.	**Rhamnus globosa**	Lokao Buckthorn
Lokao (*Chinese green*). G.	**R. utilis**	Chinese B.
Madder. R.	**Rubia tinctorum**	Common Madder
Wild M. R.	**R. peregrina**	Levant M.
Marshmarigold. Y.	**Caltha palustris**	Common Marshmarigold
Meadowrue. Y.	**Thalictrum flavum**	Yellow Meadowrue
Meadowsweet. Bla.	**Filipendula ulmaria** (*Spiraea u.*)	European Meadowsweet
Nettle. G.Y.	**Urtica dioica**	Bigsting Nettle
Nettle. G.Y.	**U. urens**	Dog N.
Oak. Blu.Br.	**Quercus robur**	English Oak
Onion. Br.	**Allium cepa**	Garden Onion
Osageorange. O.	**Maclura pomifera**	Osageorange
Pear. Y.	**Pyrus** spp.	Pear
Persian Berries. G.Y.	**Rhamnus infectoria**	Persianberry Buckthorn
Plum. P.Y.	**Prunus** spp.	Plum
Poplar. Y.	**Populus** spp.	Poplar
Potentilla. R.	**Potentilla erecta**	Tormentilla Cinquefoil
Marsh P. R.Y.	**P. palustris**	Marsh C.
Privet	**Ligustrum vulgare**	European Privet
Quercitron. Y.	**Quercus velutina** (*tinctoria*)	Black Oak
Ragweed. Y.	**Senecio jacobaea**	Ragwort Groundsel
Safflower. R.Y.	**Carthamus tinctorius**	Safflower
Saffron. Y.	**Crocus sativus**	Saffron Crocus
Sanderswood. R.	**Pterocarpus santalinus**	Sandalwood Padauk

VEGETABLE DYES, continued

Economic Name	Plant Source: Botanical Name	S.P.N. Common Name
Sappanwood. R.	**Caesalpinia sappan**	Sappan Caesalpinia
Sawwort	**Serratula tinctoria**	Dyers Sawwort
Sloe. Blu.	**Prunus spinosa**	Blackthorn; Sloe
Sorrel. Bla.	**Rumex** spp.	Dock
Common S. R.	**R. acetosa**	Garden Sorrel
Spindletree. Y.	**Euonymus europaeus**	European Euonymus
St. Johns Wort. Y.	**Hypericum perforatum**	Common St.Johnswort
Sumac. Y.	**Rhus coriaria**	Sicilian Sumac
Sundew. P.	**Drosera** spp.	Sundew
Sweet Gale. Y.	**Myrica gale**	Sweetgale
Teasel. Y.	**Dipsacus sylvestris**	Venuscup Teasel
Turmeric. Y.	**Curcuma longa**	Common Turmeric
Walnut. Br.	**Juglans** spp.	Walnut
Waterlily. Br.	**Nymphaea alba**	European White Waterlily
Wayfaringtree. Y.	**Viburnum lantana**	Wayfaringtree Viburnum
Weld. Y.	**Reseda luteola**	Weld Mignonette
Whortleberry. Blu.Br.P.	**Vaccinium myrtillus**	European Whortleberry
Willow. Y.	**Salix** spp.	Willow
Woad. Blu.	**Isatis tinctoria**	Dyers Woad
Yellow Camomile. Y.	**Anthemis tinctoria**	Golden Camomile
Yellow Centaury. Y.	**Chlora perfoliata**	Common Yellowwort
Yellow Corydal. Y.	**Corydalis lutea**	Yellow Corydalis

VEGETABLE IVORY

Economic Name	Plant Source: Botanical Name	S.P.N. Common Name
Ivorynut (*Taguanut*)	**Phytelephas macrocarpa**	Common Ivorypalm

VEGETABLES

Economic Name	Plant Source: Botanical Name	S.P.N. Common Name
Akee Fruit	**Blighia sapida**	Akee
Alligator-pear. Avocado		
Apio	**Arracacia xanthorrhiza** (*esculenta*)	Apio Arracacia
Artichoke	**Cynara scolymus**	Artichoke (*Globe A.*)
Jerusalem A.	**Helianthus tuberosus**	Jerusalemartichoke Sunflower
Asparagus	**Asparagus officinalis**	Garden Asparagus
Avocado (*Alligator-pear*)	**Persea americana**	American Avocado
Bean	**Phaseolus**	Bean
Kidney B.	**P. vulgaris**	Kidney B.
Lima B.	**P. limensis**	Lima B.
Beet	**Beta vulgaris**	Common Beet
Breadfruit	**Artocarpus altilis**	Breadfruit
Broccoli	**Brassica oleracea botrytis**	Cauliflower
Brussels Sprouts	**B. o. gemmifera**	Brussels Sprouts
Cabbage	**B. o. capitata**	Cabbage
Chinese C.	**B. chinensis**	Pakchoi
Peking C.	**B. pekinensis**	Petsai
Carrot	**Daucus carota sativa**	Garden Carrot
Cassava	**Manihot esculenta**	Common Cassava
Cauliflower	**Brassica oleracea botrytis**	Cauliflower
Celeriac	**Apium graveolens rapaceum**	Celeriac
Celery	**A. g. dulce**	Garden Celery
Ceylon-spinach	**Basella rubra**	Red Vinespinach
Chard	**Beta cicla**	Leaf Beet
Chayote	**Sechium edule**	Chayote

VEGETABLES, continued

Economic Name	Plant Source: Botanical Name	S.P.N. Common Name
Chicory	**Cichorium intybus**	Common Chicory
Chives	**Allium schoenoprasum**	Chive
Collards	**Brassica oleracea acephala**	Kale
Corn	**Zea mays**	Indian Corn; Maize
Cucumber	**Cucumis sativus**	Cucumber
Dandelion	**Taraxacum officinale**	Common Dandelion
Dasheen	**Colocasia esculenta**	Dasheen
Eggplant	**Solanum melongena**	Garden Eggplant
Endive	**Cichorium endivia**	Endive
Fennel	**Foeniculum vulgare**	Common Fennel
Finnochio	**F. v. dulce**	Florence F.
Garlic	**Allium sativum**	Garlic
Gherkin	**Cucumis anguria**	WestIndian Gherkin
Jakfruit	**Artocarpus heterophyllus**	Jakfruit
Kale	**Brassica oleracea acephala**	Kale
Kohlrabi	**B. o. gongylodes**	Kohlrabi
Lablab	**Dolichos lablab**	Hyacinth Dolichos
Leek	**Allium porrum**	Leek
Lentil	**Lens culinaris** (*esculenta*)	Common Lentil
Lettuce	**Lactuca sativa**	Garden Lettuce
Malanga	**Xanthosoma** spp.	Malanga
Mangels	**Beta vulgaris**	Common Beet
Okra	**Hibiscus esculentus**	Okra
Onion	**Allium cepa**	Garden Onion
Oysterplant	**Tragopogon porrifolius**	Vegetable-oyster Salsify
Parsnip	**Pastinaca sativa**	Garden Parsnip
Pea	**Pisum sativum**	Garden Pea
Peanut	**Arachis hypogaea**	Peanut
Pepper	**Capsicum frutescens**	Bush Redpepper
Plantain	**Musa paradisiaca**	Plantain Banana
Potato	**Solanum tuberosum**	Potato
Sweet P.	**Ipomoea batatas**	Sweetpotato
Potatobean	**Pachyrhizus angulatus**	Wayaka Yambean
Potatobean	**P. tuberosus**	WestIndies Y.
Pumpkin	**Cucurbita pepo**	Pumpkin
Radish	**Raphanus sativus**	Garden Radish
Rhubarb	**Rheum rhaponticum**	Garden Rhubarb
Rice	**Oryza sativa**	Rice
Rutabaga	**Brassica napobrassica**	Rutabaga
Shallots	**Allium ascalonicum**	Shallot
Snakegourd	**Trichosanthes anguina**	Edible Snakegourd
Spinach	**Spinacia oleracea**	Pricklyseed Spinach
Squash	**Cucurbita maxima**	Winter Squash
Sweetheart	**Talinum triangulare**	Potherb Fameflower
Sweetpotato	**Ipomoea batatas**	Sweetpotato
Taro	**Colocasia antiquorum**	Taro
Tomato	**Lycopersicon esculentum**	Common Tomato
Turnip	**Brassica rapa**	Turnip
Watercress	**Rorippa nasturtium-aquaticum**	Watercress
Yam	**Dioscorea alata**	Winged Yam
Yautia	**Xanthosoma sagittifolium**	Yautia Malanga

WAXES

Economic Name	Plant Source: Botanical Name	S.P.N. Common Name
Candelilla	**Pedilanthus pavonis**	Wax Slipperflower
Candelilla	**Euphorbia antisyphilitica**	Wax Euphorbia
Carnauba	**Copernicia cerifera**	Carnauba Copernicia
Japanese Wax	**Toxicodendron succedaneum**	Waxtree
Myrtle	**Myrica cerifera**	Southern Waxmyrtle
Myrtle	**M. pensylvanica**	Northern Bayberry
Palm Wax	**Ceroxylon andicola**	
Uricury	**Syagrus coronata** (*Cocos c.*)	Uricury Syagrus

EDAN'THE (*CHAMAEDOREA* in part) . . . . Pacaya
See **PALM GENERA.**

Edelweiss . . . . . . **Leontopodium**
Common E. . . . . **L. alpinum**
Siberian E. . . . . . . **L. sibiricum**

EDGEWORTH'IA . . . . Paperbush
tomento'sa (*chrysantha; gardneri; papyrifera*) . . . . Oriental P.

EDRAIAN'THUS
dalma'ticus (*caudatus*)
kitaibel'i (*graminifolius*)
pumil'io

EDRAIANTHUS, continued
serpyllifo'lius
tenuifo'lius

Edward'sia grandiflo'ra **Sophora tetraptera**

EDWIN'IA . . . . **JAMESIA**

Eelgrass . . . . **Zostera**
Common E. . . . . **Z. marina**

Eggfruit . . . . . Lucuma, Canistel: **Lucuma nervosa**

Eggplant
Ethiopian E. **Solanum integrifolium**
False E. . . . **S. pseudo-melongena**
Garden E. . . . . **S. melongena**

Egyptianlotus, Blue **Nymphaea caerulea**
White E. . . . . **N. lotus**

EHRE'TIA |w . . . . Ehretia
ana'cua (*elliptica*) |w . . Anaqua E.
buxifo'lia . . . . . . **E. microphylla**
dick'soni . . . . Dickson E.
formosa'na . . . . . . Formosa E.
lae'vis . . . . Smooth E.
macrophyl'la . . . . . Largeleaf E.
microphyl'la (*buxifolia*) . Falsetea E.
thyrsiflo'ra . . . . . Heliotrope E.
tinifo'lia . . . . Cherry E.

EICHHORN'IA (*PIAROPUS*) |w WATERHYACINTH
azu'rea (*Piaropus azureus*) SAWPETAL W.
cras'sipes (*Piaropus c.*) |w COMMON W.
—ma'jor . . . . ROSY W.
martia'na
specio'sa . . . . SHOWY W.

EINKORN . . . **Triticum monococcum**

Ekhimi . . . . PIPTADENIA, AFRICAN: **Piptadenia africana**

ELAEAG'NUS |w . . . . . ELAEAGNUS
angustifo'lia |w . . . . RUSSIANOLIVE
—orienta'lis
—spino'sa
commuta'ta (*argentea*) |w SILVERBERRY
gla'bra . . . . SMOOTH E.
latifo'lia . . . . BROADLEAF E.
macrophyl'la . . . . . LONGLEAF E.
multiflo'ra (*edulis; longipes*) CHERRY E.
—cris'pa
—ova'ta
philippen'sis (*perrotteti*) . LINGARO E.
pun'gens . . . . THORNY E.
—reflex'a (*E. reflexa*)
The identity of this plant is uncertain; it may be a hybrid between E. glabra and E. pungens.
—si'moni (*E. simoni*) . . SIMON T.E.
¢COMPACT (*compacta*) HV. E. pungens
¢DWARF (*nana*)
¢FREDERICK (*aureopicta; frederici*)
¢FRUITLAND (*fruitlandi*)
¢ROUNDLEAF (*rotundifolia*)
¢SILVEREDGE (*marginata*)
¢TRICOLOR
¢VARIEGATED (*variegata*)
¢YELLOWEDGE (*aurea*)
¢YELLOWSPOT (*aureo-maculata; aureo-variegata; maculata*)
reflex'a . . . . **E. pungens r.**
si'moni . . . . **E. pungens s.**
umbella'ta . . . . . . AUTUMN E.
—parvifo'lia (*E. parvifolia*)

ELAE'IS . . . . OILPALM
See **PALM GENERA.**

ELAEOCAR'PUS . . . . ELAEOCARPUS
cya'neus
denta'tus . . . . HINAU E.
hookeria'nus . . . . . . HOOKER E.
serra'tus . . . . . . CEYLON E.

ELAEODEN'DRON (*ELAEODENDRUM*) . . . . FALSEOLIVE
capen'se . . . . CAPE F.
lanea'num . . . . . . BERMUDA F.
orienta'le (*Aralia chabrieri*) ORIENTAL F.
quadrangula'tum
xylocar'pum . . . . . COCORRON E.

ELAEOPHOR'BIA
drupif'era

Elaphoglos'sum crini'tum **Hymenodium c.**

ELA'PHRIUM . . . . . **BURSERA**

ELATI'NE |w . . . . . . WATERWORT
america'na |w . . . . . AMERICAN W.
brachysper'ma |w . . . SHORTSEED W.
min'ima |w . . . . LEAST W.
In the past this has been confused with E. americana.
trian'dra |w
wil'liamsi |w . . . . . WILLIAMS W.

ELDER . . . . **Sambucus**
AMERICAN E. . . . . **S. canadensis**
ARIZONA BLUEBERRY E. **S. cerulea arizonica**
BLACKBEAD E. . . . **S. melanocarpa**
BLUEBERRY E. . . . . . **S. cerulea**
BUNCHBERRY E. . . . **S. microbotrys**
CANYON E. . . . . **S. vestita**
EUROPEAN E. . . . . **S. nigra**
EUROPEAN RED E. . . . **S. racemosa**
FLORIDA E. . . . . . . **S. simpsoni**
∞FONTENAYS E. . . . . ∞**S. fontenaysi**
GREENBERRY AMERICAN E. **S. canadensis chlorocarpa**
GREENBERRY EUROPEAN E. **S. nigra viridis**
KAMCHATKA E. . . . **S. kamtschatica**
MEDITERRANEAN HERB E. . **S. ebulus**
MEXICAN E. . . . . . . **S. mexicana**
NEWMEXICAN BLUEBERRY E. **S. cerulea neomexicana**
PACIFIC RED E. . . . . . **S. callicarpa**
REDBERRY AMERICAN E. **S. canadensis rubra**
ROUNDLEAF EUROPEAN E. **S. nigra rotundifolia**
SCARLET E. . . . . **S. pubens**
SIEBOLD E. . . . . . . **S. sieboldiana**
TREE SCARLET E. **S. pubens arborescens**
WESTERN RED E. . . . **S. leiosperma**
WILLIAMS E. . . . . . . **S. williamsi**

ELEO'CHARIS |w . . . . SPIKESEDGE
acicula'ris |w . . . . . . NEEDLE S.
al'bida |w
arenic'ola |w
atropurpu'rea |w
canaden'sis . . . . CANADA S.
capita'ta |w
caribae'a |w
cellulo'sa |w . . . . . GULFCOAST S.
compres'sa |w . . . . . FLATSTEM S.
dian'dra |w
elonga'ta |w
engelmann'i |w . . . ENGELMANN S.
equisetoi'des (*interstincta* Auth.) |w JOINTED S.
flac'cida |w
interme'dia |w . . . . . MATTED S.
macrosta'chya |w
This has often been confused with E. palustris.
melanocar'pa |w . . . BLACKFRUIT S.
microcar'pa |w
obtu'sa |w . . . . BLUNT S.
oliva'cea |w . . . . BRIGHTGREEN S.
ova'ta |w . . . . OVOID S.
palus'tris |w . . . . . . COMMON S.
par'ishi |w
par'vula |w . . . . DWARF S.
pauciflo'ra |w . . FEWFLOWERED S.
prolif'era |w
quadrangula'ta |w . SQUARESTEM S.
rob'binsi |w . . . . ROBBINS S.
rostella'ta |w . . . . . . BEAKED S.
sim'plex |w
ten'uis . . . . SLENDER S.
torreya'na |w . . . . . . TORREY S.
tricosta'ta |w
tuberculo'sa |w
tubero'sa . . . . WATERNUT
vivip'ara |w
wolf'i |w . . . . WOLFS S.

ELEPHANTEAR FERN **Hymenodium crinitum**

ELEPHANTGRASS . . **Typha elephantina**
This is not a true grass.

Elephantgrass . . . . . NAPIERGRASS: **Pennisetum purpureum**

ELEPHANTSEAR . . . . **Colocasia**
DASHEEN . . . . **C. esculenta**
FONTAINE TARO **C. antiquorum fontanesi**
GREEN T. . . . . **C. indica**
IMPERIAL T. . **C. antiquorum illustris**
TARO . . . . **C. antiquorum**

ELETTA'RIA . . . . . . CARDAMON
cardamo'mum . . . . . CARDAMON

ELEUSI'NE
See **GRASS GENERA.**

ELEUTHERI'NE
plica'ta

ELEUTHEROPET'ALUM (*CHAMAEDOREA* in part)
See **PALM GENERA.**

ELFINWANDS . . . . **Dierama**
AUSTRALIAN E. . . . . **D. pulcherrima**
NODDING E. . . . . . . **D. pendula**

ELICHRY'SUM . . **HELICHRYSUM**

ELISE'NA . . . . ELISENA
longipet'ala . . . . LONGPETAL E.
rin'gens . . . . SMILING E.
subli'ma . . . . SUBLIME E.

Elkweed . . . . . . FRASERA: **Frasera**

ELLEAN'THUS
See **ORCHID GENERA.**

ELLIOT'TIA . . . . . SOUTHERNPLUME
racemo'sa . . . . . SOUTHERNPLUME

ELLIS'IA (*NYCTELEA*) |w . . ELLISIA
chrysanthemifo'lia
nycte'lea (*Nyctelea ambigua*) |w

ELM . . . . **Ulmus**
AMERICAN E. . . . . **U. americana**
ARMENIAN E. . . . . . . **U. elliptica**
BERGMANN E. . . . **U. bergmanniana**
BIGFRUIT E. . . . . . **U. macrocarpa**
BRANDIS E. . . . . . **U. brandisiana**
CEDAR E. . . . . . . **U. crassifolia**
CHINESE E. . . . . . . **U. parvifolia**
CORKBARK SMOOTHLEAF E. **U. carpinifolia suberosa**
CORNISH S. E. . . **U. c. cornubiensis**
DAVID E. . . . . **U. davidiana**
∞DUTCH E. . . . . . ∞**U. hollandica**
ENGLISH E. . . . . **U. procera**
HAIRYLEAF BERGMANN E. **U. bergmanniana lasiophylla**
HILLIER E. . . . . **U. hillieri**
HIMALAYAN E. . . . . . . **U. wallichi**
ITALIAN SMOOTHLEAF E. **U. carpinifolia italica**
JAPANESE E. . . . . . . **U. japonica**
MANCHURIAN E. . . . . . **U. laciniata**
MEXICAN E. . . . . . . **U. mexicana**
NARROW SIBERIAN E. **U. pumila arborea**
NIKKO MANCHURIAN E. **U. laciniata nikkoensis**
PLOTS E. . . . . **U. ploti**
ROCK E. . . . . **U. thomasi**
RUSSIAN E. . . . . **U. laevis**
SARNIA SMOOTHLEAF E. **U. carpinifolia sarniensis**
SCOTCH E. . . . . **U. glabra**
SEPTEMBER E. . . . . . **U. serotina**
SIBERIAN E. . . . . **U. pumila**
SLIPPERY E. . . . . **U. fulva**
SMOOTHLEAF E. . . . . **U. carpinifolia**

Elm, continued
Southern English E. **Ulmus procera australis**
Wilson E. . . . . **U. wilsoniana**
Winged E. . . . . **U. alata**

ELODE'A . . . . Elodea
canaden'sis . . . . . . **Anacharis c.**
den'sa . . . . . . Denseleaved E.
occidenta'lis . . . . . . **Anacharis o.**

ELSHOLT'ZIA . . . . . . Elsholtzia
crista'ta . . . . Crested E.
staun'toni . . . . . . Staunton E.

E'LYMUS . . . . Wildrye
See **GRASS GENERA.**

ELYONU'RUS . . . . . Balsamscale
See **GRASS GENERA.**

EMBE'LIA
floribun'da

Emblic (*Myrobalan* in part) **Phyllanthus emblica**

EMBO'THRIUM
coccin'eum . . . Chilean Firebush

EMI'LIA . . . . Tasselflower
sagitta'ta (*Cacalia coccinea*) Earleaf T.
sonchifo'lia . . . . Sowthistle T.

EMMENAN'THE . Whisperingbells
parviflo'ra . . . . . . Sagebrush W.
penduliflo'ra . . . . . . Yellow W.
—rose'a . . . . Pink W.

EMMENOP'TERYS
hen'ryi

Emmer . . . . . . **Triticum dicoccum**

EMPE'TRUM |w . . . . . Crowberry
atropurpu'reum (*E. nigrum tomentosum*) Purple C.
ni'grum (*E. n. scoticum*) |w Black C. (*Wineberry*)
—purpu'reum

EMPLECTOCLA'DUS . . **PRUNUS**
glandulo'sus . . . . **P. texana**

EMPLEU'RUM
serrula'tum

Emuplum . . . . **Owenia**
Cherry E. . . . . . . **O. cerasifera**
Crowsapple E. . . . . . **O. venosa**
Mooley E. . . . . **O. acidula**
Onionwood E. . . . . . **O. cepiodora**

ENALLAG'MA . . . . Blackcalabash
cucurbiti'na . . . . Blackcalabash

Enantiospar'ton radia'tum **Genista radiata**

ENCE'LIA . . . . Encelia
adeno'phora . . . . . **Simsia foetida**
califor'nica . . . . . . California E.
erioce'phala . . . **Geraea canescens**
farino'sa . . . White Brittlebush
frutes'cens . . . . Bush E.
—ac'toni (*E. actoni*) . . . Acton E.
—virginen'sis (*E. virginensis*) VirginRiver E.

ENCELIOP'SIS . . . . . Enceliopsis
argophyl'la . . . . . Silverleaf E.
nudicau'lis . . . . . . Barestem E.

ENCEPHALAR'TOS . . . Kafirbread
See **CYCAD GENERA.**

ENCEPHALOCAR'PUS **ARIOCARPUS**
See **CACTUS GENERA.**

Enchanters-nightshade . Circaea: **Circaea**
Encholir'ion saun'dersi . . . **Vriesia s.**

ENCHYLAE'NA
tomento'sa . . . . . . Downybush

ENDIAN'DRA (*SILVIA* Allem., *not* Benth. *nor* Vell.)
ita-u'ba (*Silvia i.*) . . . . . Ita-uba
palmersto'ni . . . . . Orientalwood

Endive . . . . **Cichorium endivia**

ENDO'THIA . . . . Endothia
parasit'ica . . . . Chestnutblight E.

Engelmanndaisy . . . . **Engelmannia**

ENGELMAN'NIA . Engelmanndaisy
pinnatif'ida

ENGLEROPHOE'NIX **MAXIMILIANA**
See **PALM GENERA.**

ENKIAN'THUS . . . . Enkianthus
campanula'tus (*E. c. recurvus*) Redvein E.
—albiflo'rus . . . . . . White R.E.
—palibi'ni . . . . . . Palibin R.E.
cer'nuus
—nippon'icus (*E. nipponicus*)
—ru'bens
chinen'sis . . . . Chinese E.
deflex'us (*himalaicus; sulcatus*)
perula'tus (*japonicus*) . . . White E.
quinqueflo'rus . . . . Evergreen E.
serrula'tus
subses'silis . . . . Nikko E.

ENNEAPO'GON
See **GRASS GENERA.**

ENTA'DA . . . . Entada
phaseoloi'des (*scandens*) . Climbing E.
sudan'ica . . . . Sudan E.

ENTANDROPHRAG'MA . . . Sapele
candol'lei . . . . Heavy S.
cylin'dricum

ENTELE'A
arbores'cens
palma'ta . . . . **Sparmannia p.**

ENTEROLO'BIUM . . . . Earpodtree
contortisili'quum . . . . Pacara E.
cyclocar'pum . . . . Guanacaste E.
timbou'va . . . . . Timbouva E.

ENTEROMOR'PHA |w
prolif'era |w

EOME'CON . . . . Snowpoppy
chionan'tha . . . . . . Snowpoppy

EO'RA . . . . . **RHOPALOSTYLIS**
See **PALM GENERA.**

E'PACRIS . . . . . . Australiaheath
impres'sa . . . . Common A.

Epaulettetree . . . . . **Pterostyrax**
Fragrant E. . . . . **P. hispida**
Little E. . . . . . . **P. corymbosa**

EPER'UA . . . . Wallabatree
falca'ta . . . . Soft W.
jen'mani . . . . Ituri W.
schomburgkia'na . . . . . Bimiti W.

E'PHEDRA |w . . . Ephedra (*Jointfir*)
altis'sima . . . . Highclimbing E.
america'na . . . . . . American E.
antisyphilit'ica (*pedunculata*) . Vine E.
as'pera . . . . Rough E.
califor'nica . . . . . . California E.

EPHEDRA, continued
dista'chya . . . . Jointfir Ephedra
equiseti'na . . . . . . Mongolian E.
folia'ta . . . . Persian E.
fra'gilis . . . . . Mediterranean E.
fune'rea . . . . . . DeathValley E.
gerardia'na . . . . . . Gerard E.
interme'dia
ma'jor
nevaden'sis . . . . . . Nevada E.
pachycla'da
peduncula'ta . . . . **E. antisyphilitica**
przewal'ski
si'nica . . . . Chinese E.
torreya'na . . . . Torrey E.
trifur'ca |w . . . . . . Longleaf E.
vir'idis |w . . . . Green E.

Ephedra . . . . **Ephedra**
American E. . . . . **E. americana**
California E. . . . . **E. californica**
Chinese E. . . . . **E. sinica**
DeathValley E. . . . . . **E. funerea**
Gerard E. . . . . . . **E. gerardiana**
Green E. . . . . **E. viridis**
Highclimbing E. . . . . **E. altissima**
Jointfir E. . . . . . . **E. distachya**
Longleaf E. . . . . **E. trifurca**
Mediterranean E. . . . **E. fragilis**
Mongolian E. . . . . **E. equisetina**
Nevada E. . . . . . **E. nevadensis**
Persian E. . . . . **E. foliata**
Rough E. . . . . **E. aspera**
Torrey E. . . . . **E. torreyana**
Vine E. . . . . . . **E. antisyphilitica**

EPIBATE'RIUM . . . **COCCULUS**

EPICAM'PES . . **MUHLENBERGIA**
See **GRASS GENERA.**

EPICATT'LEYA
See **ORCHID GENERA.**

EPIDEN'DRUM (*EPIDENDRON*)
See **ORCHID GENERA.**

EPIFA'GUS |w . . . . . . Beechdrops
virginia'na |w . . . . . Virginia B.

EPIGAE'A |w . . . Trailing-arbutus
asiat'ica . . . . Asiatic T.
re'pens |w . . . . Trailing-arbutus
—glabrifo'lia . . . . . Smoothleaf T.
—ple'na . . . . Double T.

EPILO'BIUM (*CHAMAENERION*) |w Willowweed
adenocau'lon . . . . Sticky W.
adna'tum
alpi'num . . . . Alpine W.
amplec'tens
angustifo'lium (*spicatum; Chamaenerion a.*) . . . . Fireweed
—al'bum
borea'le . . . . Northern W.
brevisty'lum . . . . . . Sierra W.
chloraefo'lium
colora'tum . . . . . Purpleleaf W.
den'sum |w . . . . . Canescent W.
Perhaps the same as the older E. lineare, a "name of doubtful application."
dodonae'i
flei'scheri . . . . Fleischer W.
francisca'num . . . . Francisco W.
glandulo'sum . . . . Glandular W.
hec'tori . . . . Hector W.
hirsu'tum . . . . Hairy W.
hornemann'i . . . . Hornemann W.
la'myi . . . . Lamy W.
latifo'lium |w . . . . Red W.

EPILOBIUM, continued
lute'um . . . YELLOW WILLOWWEED
macro'pus
mol'le ⌊w
nummularifo'lium
obcorda'tum
obscur'um . . . . DWARF W.
panicula'tum . . . . . . AUTUMN W.
parviflo'rum
rose'um
rubes'cens
spica'tum . . . . . **E. angustifolium**

EPIME'DIUM . . . . . . EPIMEDIUM
alpi'num . . . . ALPINE E.
—ru'brum . . . . RED A.E.
coccin'eum . . . . . . SCARLET E.
col'chicum . . . . . . **E. pinnatum c.**
diphyl'lum . . . **Aceranthus diphyllus**
lilaci'num
macran'thum . . . . LONGSPUR E.
—niv'eum . . . . SNOWY E.
—rose'um . . . . . BISHOPSHAT E.
—viola'ceum (*E. violaceum*) VIOLET E.
musschia'num . . . . . JAPANESE E.
pinna'tum . . . . PERSIAN E.
—col'chicum (*E. colchicum*)
GOLDENFLEECE E.
—el'egans . . . . SHOWY G.E.
—sulphu'reum . . . . . YELLOW E.
viola'ceum . . . . **E. macranthum v.**

EPIPAC'TIS (*SERAPIAS*) EPIPACTIS
See **ORCHID GENERA, HARDY TERRESTRIAL GROUP.**

EPIPHRONI'TIS
See **ORCHID GENERA.**

EPIPHYLLAN'THUS . . . **CEREUS**
See **CACTUS GENERA.**

EPIPHYLLOP'SIS
SCHLUMBERGERA
See **CACTUS GENERA.**

EPIPHYL'LUM (*CHIAPASIA; NOPALXOCHIA; PHYLLOCACTUS*) . . EPIPHYLLUM (*Leafcactus*)
See **CACTUS GENERA.**

EPIPREM'NUM
pinna'tum . . CENTIPEDE TONGAVINE

EPI'SCIA
chontalen'sis
cuprea'ta
—viridifo'lia
ful'gida
tessella'ta

EPITHELAN'THA
See **CACTUS GENERA.**

EPPAW . . . . . . **Perideridia oregana**

EQUISE'TUM ⌊w . . . . HORSETAIL
arven'se ⌊w . . . . FIELD H.
fluviat'ile ⌊w . . . . WATER H.
hyema'le ⌊w . . . . . SCOURINGRUSH
—califor'nicum . . . . . WESTERN S.
laeviga'tum ⌊w . . . . SMOOTH H.
limo'sum . . . . SWAMP H.
littora'le . . . . SHORE H.
palus'tre . . . . MARSH H.
praeal'tum (*robustum*)
STOUT SCOURINGRUSH
praten'se . . . . MEADOW H.
scirpoi'des . . . . . . SEDGELIKE H.
sylvat'icum . . . . SYLVAN H.
telmatei'a ⌊w . . . . GIANT H.
variega'tum . . . . . VARIEGATED H.

ERAGROS'TIS . . . . . . LOVEGRASS
See **GRASS GENERA.**

ERAN'THEMUM (*DAEDALACANTHUS*)
al'bum
atropurpu'reum . **Pseuderanthemum a.**
bi'color . . . . **Pseuderanthemum b.**
nervo'sum
reticula'tum . . **Pseuderanthemum r.**
tri'color
tubercula'tum . . **Pseuderanthemum t.**
variega'tum

ERAN'THIS . . . . . . WINTERACONITE
hyema'lis . . . . . WINTERACONITE
—cilic'ica . . . . CILICIAN W.
pinnatif'ida
sibir'ica . . . . DWARF W.
×tubergen'i . . . . . . TUBERGEN W.

ERCIL'LA . . . . ERCILLA
spica'ta . . . . SPIKED E.
volu'bilis . . . . COMMON E.

ERDIS'IA . . . . **CEREUS**
See **CACTUS GENERA.**

ERECHTI'TES ⌊w . . . . BURNWEED
argu'ta . . . . BUSHMANS B.
hieracifo'lia ⌊w . . . AMERICAN B.
prenanthoi'des . . . AUSTRALIAN B.

EREMAE'A . . . . EREMAEA
ebractea'ta
fimbria'ta . . . . SWANRIVER E.
viola'cea . . . . VIOLET E.

EREMAL'CHE . . . **MALVASTRUM**

EREMOCAR'PUS (*PISCARIA*) ⌊w
TURKEYMULLEIN
setig'erus (*Piscaria setigera*) ⌊w
TURKEYMULLEIN

EREMOCA'RYA . . . . . . DESERTNUT
micran'tha

EREMOCH'LOA
See **GRASS GENERA.**

EREMOCIT'RUS
glau'ca . . . . DESERTLIME
∞ EREMOLEMON . . . **Citrus limon × Eremocitrus glauca**
∞ EREMORADIA . . **Citrus aurantium × Eremocitrus glauca**
∞ EREMORANGE . . **Citrus sinensis × Eremocitrus glauca**

EREMOSTA'CHYS
lacinia'ta

EREMU'RUS . . . . . DESERTCANDLE
auranti'acus . . . . ORANGE D.
bun'gei . . . . BUNGE D.
—perfec'tus
chinen'sis . . . . CHINESE D.
el'wesi . . . . ELWES D.
himala'icus . . . . . . HIMALAYAN D.
kauf'manni . . . . . . KAUFMANN D.
ol'gae . . . . OLGA D.
—al'bus . . . . WHITE O.D.
robus'tus . . . . GIANT D.
shel'fordi . . . . SHELFORD D.
tau'ricus . . . . TAURUS D.
∞ **tubergen'i** (*bungei × himalaicus*)
∞ TUBERGEN D.
turkestan'icus . . . . TURKESTAN D.

EREP'SIA **MESEMBRYANTHEMUM**
See **SUCCULENTS.**

E'RIA
See **ORCHID GENERA.**

ERIAN'THUS . . . . PLUMEGRASS
See **GRASS GENERA.**

ERI'CA . . . . HEATH
arbo'rea . . . . TREE H.
The plant from which briar pipe bowls are made.
—alpi'na . . . . ALPINE T.H.
austra'lis . . . . SOUTHERN H.
₵MR. ROBERT. HV.
bac'cans
bergeria'na . . . . BERGER H.
blan'da . . . . EVERBLOOMING H.
bowiea'na (*bowiena*) . . . . BOWIE H.
caf'fra
canalicula'ta
capita'ta . . . . WOOLLYLEAF H.
car'nea (*herbacea*) . . . . SPRING H.
—al'ba . . . . WHITE S.H.
₵CARMINE (*vivella*) HV. E. carnea
₵JAMES BACKHOUSE
₵KING GEORGE
₵MRS. (*Samuel*) DONCASTER
PALE (*pallida*)
PURPLE (*purpurascens*)
₵QUEEN MARY
₵QUEEN OF SPAIN
ROSYPINK (*rosea*)
₵RUBYGLOW
SCARLET (*coccinea*)
₵SLENDER (*gracilis*)
₵SNOWQUEEN
₵SPRINGWOOD
₵THOMAS KINGSCOTE
₵WHITEMOOR
₵WINTER BEAUTY
∞ **cavendishia'na** (*depressa × patersoni*)
∞ CAVENDISH H.
cerinthoi'des
cilia'ris . . . . FRINGED H.
—al'ba . . . . WHITE F.H.
—mawea'na . . . . . MAWEANA F.H.
₵MRS. C. H. GILL. HV. E. ciliaris
₵STOBOROUGH
cine'rea . . . . TWISTED H.
—al'ba . . . . WHITE T.H.
₵ATRORUBENS. HV. E. cinerea
₵C. D. EASON
₵DOMINO
₵GRAY (*atropurpurea*)
₵LILAC (*lilacina*)
₵PALE (*pallida*)
₵ROSY (*rosea*)
₵SCARLET (*coccinea*)
₵SHINY (*fulgida*)
cruen'ta
cupressi'na . . . . CYPRESS H.
cylin'drica
∞ **darleyen'sis** (*carnea × mediterranea; E. mediterranea hybrida*)
∞ DARLEY H.
depres'sa
dis'color
doliifor'mis
glandulo'sa
globo'sa
grac'ilis
grandiflo'ra . . . . . . BIGFLOWER H.
herba'cea . . . . **E. carnea**
hirtiflo'ra
hyema'lis . . . . WINTER H.
A plant of unknown origin.

linnaeoi'des
Perhaps a hybrid.

ERICA, continued
lusitan'ica . . . . . SPANISH HEATH
∞**macka'i** (*ciliaris × tetralix; mackaiana; E. tetralix mackaiana*)
∞ MACKAY H.
₵DOUBLE (*plena*) HV.
₵WATSON (*watsoni*)
mammo'sa
mediterra'nea . . . . . . BISCAY H.
—**al'ba** . . . . WHITE B.H.
—**hiber'nica** . . . . . . IRISH B.H.
—*hyb'rida* . . . . . ∞**E. darleyensis**
₵BRIGHTNESS. HV. E. mediterranea
₵DAWN
₵DWARF (*nana*)
₵SUPERBA
melanthe'ra . . . . . BLACKEYED H.
₵PURPUREA. HV.
₵RUBRA
multiflo'ra . . . . . DENSESPIKE H.
—*grandiflo'ra* . . . **E. ventricosa g.**
ova'ta
paterso'ni
persolu'ta . . . . . **E. subdivaricata**
polifo'lia
reger'minans
—**ova'ta**
—**ru'bra**
ru'bens
scario'sa
scopa'ria . . . . BESOM H.
₵DWARF (*pumila*) HV.
₵LEAST (*minima*)
sessiliflo'ra
spiculifo'lia . . . . **Bruckenthalia s.**
stric'ta . . . . CORSICAN H.
subdivarica'ta (*persoluta*). GARLAND H.
₵ROSY (*rosea*) HV.
termina'lis
tetra'lix . . . . CROSSLEAF H.
—**al'ba** . . . . WHITE C.H.
—*mackaia'na* . . . . . ∞**E. mackai**
—**martine'si** . . . . . WOOLLY C.H.
₵LAWSON (*lawsoniana*) HV. E. tetralix
₵MOLLIS
₵PRAEGER
₵RUBY (*rubra*)
∞**translu'cens** (*tubiflora × ventricosa*)
umbella'ta
va'gans . . . . CORNISH H.
—**al'ba** . . . . WHITE C.H.
₵CERISE. HV. E. vagans
₵LYONESSE
₵MRS. (*D. F.*) MAXWELL
₵RED (*rubra*)
₵SHOWY (*grandiflora*)
₵ST. KEVERNE
∞**veitch'i** (*arborea × lusitanica*)
∞ VEITCH H.
ventrico'sa . . . . . . PORCELAIN H.
—**grandiflo'ra** (*E. multiflora g.*)
LARGEFLOWER P.H.
verticilla'ta
viridipurpu'rea
vulga'ris . . . . **Calluna v.**
∞**wil'liamsi** (*tetralix × vagans*)
wil'morei . . . . WILMORE H.
₵CHARLES (*charlesiana*) HV. Erica
₵CHARLESWORTH (*charlesworthiana*)
₵TREHAN (*trehani*)

ERICAME'RIA . . **APLOPAPPUS**

ERIGE'NIA . . HARBINGER-OF-SPRING
bulbo'sa . . . HARBINGER-OF-SPRING

ERIG'ERON (*LEPTILON; STENACTIS*) |w . . . . . . FLEABANE
a'cris (*umbellatus*) . . . . BITTER F.
al'gidus
ali'ceae
alpi'nus . . . . ALPINE F.
an'nuus . . . . ANNUAL F.
argenta'tus
armerifo'lius . . . . **E. lonchophyllus**
auranti'acus . . . . ORANGE F.
au'reus . . . . GOLD F.
bellidifo'lius . . . . . **E. pulchellus**
bloom'eri . . . . BLOOMER F.
caespito'sus . . . . TUFTED F.
canaden'sis (*Leptilon canadense*)
HORSEWEED F.
ca'nus . . . . HOARY F.
caucas'icus . . . . . CAUCASIAN F.
chrysop'sidis
compos'itus . . . . . FERNLEAF F.
—**incer'tus** (*E. discoideus*)
concin'nus . . . . HAIRY F.
—**aphanac'tis**
corymbo'sus . . . . PURPLEDAISY F.
coul'teri . . . . COULTER F.
diver'gens (*wootoni*) . SPREADING F.
ea'toni . . . . EATON F.
ela'tior . . . . TALL F.
engelmann'i . . . . ENGELMANN F.
filifo'lius . . . . . . THREADLEAF F.
flagella'ris . . . . TRAILING F.
folio'sus . . . . LEAFY F.
glabel'lus . . . . SMOOTH F.
glabra'tus
—**rose'us**
glandulo'sus . . . . **E. porteri**
glau'cus . . . . BEACH F.
how'elli . . . . HOWELL F.
hyssopifo'lius . . . . HYSSOPLEAF F.
interme'dius . . . . . . **E. speciosus**
karvinskia'nus (*mucronatus*)
BONYTIP F.

This Mexican plant is often misidentified as the Australian Vittadinia australis (triloba).

lei'bergi . . . . LEIBERG F.
linea'ris
lonchophyl'lus (*armerifolius; minor; racemosus*) . . . . . SPEARLEAF F.
macran'thus . . . . ASPEN F.
multiradia'tus . . . . HIMALAYAN F.
—**rose'us** . . . . PINK H.F.
na'nus . . . . DWARF F.
nudiflo'rus . . . . . . SPRAWLING F.
peregri'nus . . . . . . PEREGRINE F.
philadel'phicus . . . PHILADELPHIA F.
pinnatisec'tus . . . . . . PINNATE F.
por'teri (*glandulosus*) . . . PORTER F.
pulchel'lus (*bellidifolius*)
POORROBINS-PLANTAIN
pu'milus |w . . . . LOW F.
racemo'sus . . . . . **E. lonchophyllus**
radica'tus
ramo'sus Raf.

The identity of this species is uncertain. Some botanists regard it as a synonym of E. divaricatus. The existence of the name E. ramosus Raf. preoccupies and renders untenable the later E. ramosus (Walt.) B. S. P.

ramo'sus (Walt.) B. S. P. **E. strigosus**
re'pens . . . . CREEPING F.
salsugino'sus . . . . ASTER F.
—**angustifo'lius** . . NARROWLEAF A.F.
sen'ilis
sim'plex
specio'sus (*intermedius; Stenactis speciosa*) . . . . OREGON F.

ERIGERON speciosus, continued
LILAC (*roseus*) HV.
MAJOR
MESA GRANDE
PURPLE (*grandiflorus*)
SEMIPLENUS
SUPERBUS
strigo'sus (*ramosus* (Walt.) B. S. P., *not* Raf.)
subtriner'vis . THREENERVE FLEABANE
thomp'soni . . . . . THOMPSON F.
ton'sus . . . . SHORN F.
trif'idus . . . . TRIFID F.
umbella'tus . . . . **E. acris**
uniflo'rus . . . . ARCTIC F.
ursi'nus . . . . BEARRIVER F.
ver'nus . . . . EARLY WHITETOP F.
vis'cidus . . . . VISCID F.
woot'oni . . . . **E. divergens**
FONTAINEBLEU. HV. Erigeron
QUAKERESS

ERINA'CEA
pun'gens

ERI'NUS . . . . LIVERBALSAM
alpi'nus . . . . ALPINE L.
—**hirsu'tus**
CARMINEUS. HV. E. alpinus
ROSEUS
WALL (*albus*)

ERIOBO'TRYA . . . . LOQUAT
japon'ica (*Photinia j.*) . . . . LOQUAT
(*Japanesemedlar*)

For cultivated varieties see **FRUIT AND EDIBLE NUT NAMES.**

VARIEGATA. HV.
prinoi'des

ERIOCAR'PUM . . . **APLOPAPPUS**

ERIOCAU'LON |w . . . . . PIPEWORT
compres'sum |w
decangula're |w . . . TENANGLE P.
par'keri |w . . . . PARKER P.
septangula're |w

ERIOCEPH'ALUS
africa'nus

ERIOCE'REUS
See **CACTUS GENERA.**

ERIOCH'LOA . . . . CUPGRASS
See **GRASS GENERA.**

ERIODEN'DRON . . . . . . **CEIBA**
anfractuo'sum . . . . **C. pentandra**

ERIODIC'TYON |w . . . YERBASANTA
angustifo'lium . . . NARROWLEAF Y.
califor'nicum |w . . . CALIFORNIA Y.
capita'tum . . . . LOMPOC Y.
crassifo'lium . . . . . THICKLEAF Y.
glutino'sum
lana'tum . . . . SANDIEGO Y.
par'ryi . . . . **Nama p.**
tomento'sum . . . . WOOLLY Y.
trask'iae . . . . TRASK Y.
trichoca'lyx . . . . HAIRY Y.

ERIOG'ONUM |w . . . . . ERIOGONUM
ala'tum |w . . . . WING E.
alpi'num . . . . ALPINE E.
an'nuum . . . . ANNUAL E.
arbores'cens . . . . ISLAND E.
ar'idum . . . . DRYLAND E.
caespito'sum |w . . . . . . MAT E.
cer'nuum . . . . NODDING E.
chrysoceph'alum . . . . GOLDBALL E.
cine'reum . . . . ASHYLEAF E.

ERIOGONUM, continued
compos'itum . Northern Eriogonum
corymbo'sum |w . . . Corymbed E.
depres'sum
desertic'ola . . . . . . Desert E.
doug'lasi . . . . Douglas E.
ela'tum . . . . Rush E.
elonga'tum . . . . Silver E.
fascicula'tum . . . . . Flattop E.
—folio'sum . . . . . . Leafy F.E.
fla'vum . . . . Yellow E.
gigan'teum . . . . Giant E.

Sold in nurseries under the name of St. Catherines Lace.

heer'manni . . . . . . Mohave E.
heracleoi'des |w . . . . . Wyeth E.
inca'num . . . . Sierra E.
infla'tum . . . Deserttrumpet E.
james'i . . . . James E.
kel'loggi . . . . Mendocino E.
ken'nedyi . . . . Kennedy E.
la'tens . . . . Inyo E.
latifo'lium . . . . Coast E.
lobb'i . . . . Granite E.
lonchophyl'lum . . . . Spearleaf E.
marifo'lium . . . . . Mountain E.
microthe'cum . . . Slenderbush E.
neglec'tum
niv'eum . . . . Snow E.
nodo'sum . . . . Sonoran E.
nu'dum . . . . Barestem E.
ochroceph'alum . . . . Woolly E.
ovalifo'lium . . . . . . Cushion E.
parvifo'lium . . . . . . Seacliff E.
pharnaceoi'des . . . . Wirestem E.
pi'peri . . . . Piper E.
plumatel'la . . . . Yucca E.
polifo'lium . . . . . . Rosemary E.
polycla'don . . . . Sorrel E.
pyrolaefo'lium . . . . . Oarleaf E.
racemo'sum |w . . . . . Redroot E.
rubes'cens . . . . Red E.
saxat'ile . . . . Hoary E.
siskiyouen'se . . . . . . Siskiyou E.
sphaeroceph'alum . . . . Rock E.
stella'tum . . . . Longray E.
subalpi'num . . . . . . Subalpine E.
taxifo'lium . . . . Pine E.
thymoi'des . . . . Thyme E.
torreya'num . . . . Donner E.
trip'odum . . . . Lake E.
umbella'tum . . . . Sulfur E.
ursi'num . . . . Bear E.
vimin'eum . . . . Broom E.
wright'i . . . . Wright E.

Eriogonum . . . . **Eriogonum**
Alpine E. . . . . **E. alpinum**
Annual E. . . . . **E. annuum**
Ashyleaf E. . . . . . **E. cinereum**
Barestem E. . . . . **E. nudum**
Bear E. . . . . **E. ursinum**
Broom E. . . . . . . **E. vimineum**
Coast E. . . . . **E. latifolium**
Corymbed E. . . . **E. corymbosum**
Cushion E. . . . . . **E. ovalifolium**
Desert E. . . . . . . **E. deserticola**
Deserttrumpet E. . . . **E. inflatum**
Donner E. . . . . . **E. torreyanum**
Douglas E. . . . . . . **E. douglasi**
Dryland E. . . . . **E. aridum**
Flattop E. . . . . . **E. fasciculatum**
Giant E. . . . . **E. giganteum**
Goldball E. . . . **E. chrysocephalum**
Granite E. . . . . **E. lobbi**
Hoary E. . . . . **E. saxatile**
Inyo E. . . . . **E. latens**
Island E. . . . . . . **E. arborescens**

Eriogonum, continued
James E. . . . . **Eriogonum jamesi**
Kennedy E. . . . . **E. kennedyi**
Lake E. . . . . **E. tripodum**
Leafy Flattop E.
E. fasciculatum foliolosum
Longray E. . . . . **E. stellatum**
Mat E. . . . . **E. caespitosum**
Mendocino E. . . . . . . **E. kelloggi**
Mohave E. . . . . . . **E. heermanni**
Mountain E. . . . . . **E. marifolium**
Nodding E. . . . . **E. cernuum**
Northern E. . . . . **E. compositum**
Oarleaf E. . . . . **E. pyrolaefolium**
Pine E. . . . . **E. taxifolium**
Piper E. . . . . **E. piperi**
Red E. . . . . **E. rubescens**
Redroot E. . . . . . **E. racemosum**
Rock E. . . . . **E. sphaerocephalum**
Rosemary E. . . . . . . **E. polifolium**
Rush E. . . . . **E. elatum**
Seacliff E. . . . . . **E. parvifolium**
Sierra E. . . . . **E. incanum**
Silver E. . . . . **E. elongatum**
Siskiyou E. . . . . . **E. siskiyouense**
Slenderbush E. . . **E. microthecum**
Snow E. . . . . **E. niveum**
Sonoran E. . . . . **E. nodosum**
Sorrel E. . . . . **E. polycladon**
Spearleaf E. . . . **E. lonchophyllum**
Subalpine E. . . . . . **E. subalpinum**
Sulfur E. . . . . . . **E. umbellatum**
Thyme E. . . . . **E. thymoides**
Wing E. . . . . **E. alatum**
Wirestem E. . . **E. pharnaceoides**
Woolly E. . . . **E. ochrocephalum**
Wright E. . . . . **E. wrighti**
Wyeth E. . . . . . . **E. heracleoides**
Yellow E. . . . . **E. flavum**
Yucca E. . . . . **E. plumatella**

ERIOPH'ORUM . . . . Cottonsedge
angustifo'lium . . . Narrowleaf C.
cal'lithrix
latifo'lium . . . . . . Broadleaf C.
vagina'tum . . . . . . Sheathed C.
virgin'icum . . . . . . Virginia C.
viridicarina'tum

ERIOPHYL'LUM (*ACTINOLEPIS* in part) . . . . Eriophyllum
caespito'sum . . . . . . Oregon E.
confertiflo'rum . . Goldenyarrow E.
integrifo'lium
jep'soni . . . . Jepson E.
lana'tum . . . . Woolly E.
—integrifo'lium
leucophyl'lum
multiflo'rum
ne'vini . . . . Nevin E.
peduncula'tum
staechadifo'lium . . . Lizardtail E.
walla'cei . . . . Wallace E.

ERIOP'SIS
See **ORCHID GENERA.**

ERIOSE'MA
viola'cea

ERIOSTE'MON . . . . Eriostemon
myoporoi'des
salicifo'lius . . . Willowleaved E.
spica'tus

ERIOSY'CE . . . . **TRICHOCEREUS**
See **CACTUS GENERA.**

ERI'TRICHUM (*ERITRICHIUM*)
argen'teum
na'num

ERLAN'GEA
cordifo'lia
tomento'sa

ERO'DIUM |w . . . . . . Heronbill
absinthoi'des
—ama'num
—sibthorpia'num
bo'trys . . . . Big H.
chamaedryoi'des
cheilanthifo'lium
chrysan'thum
cico'nium . . . . Stork H.
cicuta'rium |w . . . . . . Alfileria
cor'sicum . . . . Corsican H.
daucoi'des . . . . Carrot H.
grui'num . . . . Crane H.
∞ **kolbia'num** (*macradenum* × *supracanum*) . . . . ∞ Kolb H.
macrade'num
—rose'um
macrophyl'lum . . . . California H.
manesca'vi . . . . Pyrenees H.
moscha'tum |w . . . . . . Musk H.
petrae'um . . . . Cliff H.
roma'num . . . . Roman H.
supraca'num
texa'num |w . . . . Texas H.
trichomanefo'lium
∞ **willkommia'num** (*cheilanthifolium* × *macradenum*) . . . ∞ Willkomm H.

Erpe'tion renifor'me . . **Viola hederacea**

ERU'CA
sati'va . . . . Rocketsalad

ERUCAS'TRUM
gal'licum (*pollichi*) . . Rocketweed

ERVATA'MIA
corona'ria (*Tabernaemontana c.*) Crapejasmine
Florepleno. hv.

Er'vum lens' . . . . . . **Lens culinaris**

ERYN'GIUM |w . . . . Eryngo
agavifo'lium
alpi'num . . . . Bluetop E.
amethys'tinum (*coelestinum*) Amethyst E.
aqua'ticum (*yuccaefolium*) |w Buttonsnakeroot E.
articula'tum |w . . . . Beethistle E.
bourga'ti . . . Mediterranean E.
caeru'leum
campes'tre . . . . . . Snakeroot E.
florida'num |w . . . . . . Florida E.
gigan'teum . . . . Stout E.
leavenworth'i . . Leavenworth E.
marit'imum . . . . Seaholly E.
oliveria'num . . . . Oliver E.
pandanifo'lium
pla'num
prostra'tum . . . . Creeping E.
ser'ra . . . . Brazil E.
spinal'ba . . . . . Whitespine E.
triparti'tum
virginia'num . . . . . . Virginia E.
yuccaefo'lium . . . . . . **E. aquaticum**
∞ **za'beli** (*alpinum* × *bourgati*) ∞ Zabel E.

Eryngo . . . . **Eryngium**
Amethyst E. . . . . **E. amethystinum**
Beethistle E. . . . . . **E. articulatum**
Bluetop E. . . . . **E. alpinum**
Brazil E. . . . . **E. serra**
Buttonsnakeroot E. . . **E. aquaticum**
Creeping E. . . . . . . **E. prostratum**
Florida E. . . . . **E. floridanum**

ERYNGO, continued
LEAVENWORTH E. Eryngium leavenworthi
MEDITERRANEAN E. . . . E. bourgati
OLIVER E. . . . E. oliverianum
SEAHOLLY E. . . . E. maritimum
SNAKEROOT E. . . . E. campestre
STOUT E. . . . E. giganteum
VIRGINIA E. . . . E. virginianum
WHITESPINE E. . . . E. spinalba
∞ ZABEL E. . . . ∞ E. zabeli

ERYS'IMUM (*CHEIRINIA*) |w . . . ERYSIMUM
as'perum (*arkansanum; Cheiranthus allioni; Cheirinia aspera*) PLAINS E.
—arkansa'num . . . ARKANSAS E.
aurantia'cum . . . ORANGE E.
canes'cens . . . HOARY E.
capita'tum (*grandiflorum*) . COAST E.
cheiranthoi'des (*parviflorum* Pers., *not* Nutt.; *Cheirinia c.*) . . TREACLE E.
cuspida'tum
ela'tum |w . . . TALL E.
inconspic'uum . . . **E. parviflorum**
insula're . . . ISLAND E.
kotschya'num . . . KOTSCHY E.
linifo'lium (*Cheiranthus linifolius*) FLAXLEAF E.
mura'le . . . WALL E.
niva'le . . . SNOWY E.
ochroleu'cum (*helveticum*) . TURF E.
officina'le . . . **Sisymbrium o.**
pachycar'pum
parviflo'rum (*inconspicuum; Cheirinia inconspicua*) . . . SMALLFLOWER E.
parviflo'rum Pers., *not* Nutt. E. cheiranthoides
perofskia'num . . . AFGHAN E.
pulchel'lum . . . ROCKERY E.
pu'milum . . . LOW E.
purpu'reum . . . PURPLE E.
repan'dum . . . SPREADING E.
rupes'tre . . . ASIATIC E.
suffrutes'cens . . . BEACH E.
torulo'sum . . . NECKLACE E.

ERYSIMUM . . . **Erysimum**
AFGHAN E. . . . **E. perofskianum**
ARKANSAS E. **E. asperum arkansanum**
ASIATIC E. . . . **E. rupestre**
BEACH E. . . . **E. suffrutescens**
COAST E. . . . **E. capitatum**
FLAXLEAF E. . . . **E. linifolium**
HOARY E. . . . **E. canescens**
ISLAND E. . . . **E. insulare**
KOTSCHY E. . . . **E. kotschyanum**
LOW E. . . . **E. pumilum**
NECKLACE E. . . . **E. torulosum**
ORANGE E. . . . **E. aurantiacum**
PLAINS E. . . . **E. asperum**
PRAIRIE E. . . . **E. inconspicuum**
PURPLE E. . . . **E. purpureum**
ROCKERY E. . . . **E. pulchellum**
SMALLFLOWER E. . . . **E. parviflorum**
SNOWY E. . . . **E. nivale**
SPREADING E. . . . **E. repandum**
TALL E. . . . **E. elatum**
TREACLE E. . . . **E. cheiranthoides**
TURF E. . . . **E. ochroleucum**
WALL E. . . . **E. murale**

ERYTHE'A (*GLAUCOTHEA*) ERYTHEA
See **PALM GENERA.**

ERYTHRAE'A . . . **CENTAURIUM**
centau'rium . . . **C. umbellatum**
diffu'sa . . . **C. massoni**
ramosis'sima . . . **C. pulchellum**

ERYTHRI'NA . . . CORALBEAN
arbo'rea . . . **E. herbacea**
arbores'cens . . . HIMALAYAN C.
brotero'i . . . BROTERO C.
caf'fra
coralloden'drum . . . COMMON C.
coralloi'des . . . CORALLINE C.
crista-gal'li . . . COCKSPUR C.
flabellifor'mis . . . WESTERN C.
fus'ca
glau'ca
gold'mani . . . GOLDMAN C.
herba'cea (*arborea; E. herbacea a.*) EASTERN C.
humea'na . . . HUME C.
in'dica . . . INDIA C.
—pic'ta
microp'teryx
pal'lida
poeppigia'na . . . BUCARE C.
poian'thes
senegalen'sis . . . SENEGAL C.
specio'sa
tomento'sa
variega'ta . . . VARIEGATED C.
velu'tina
Erythrochae'te palmatif'ida **Ligularia japonica**

ERYTHRO'NIUM |w . . . FAWNLILY
Members of this genus are also known as Adderstongue, Dogtooth Violet, and Troutlily.
al'bidum . . . WHITE F.
america'num . . . COMMON F.
califor'nicum . . . CALIFORNIA F.
WHITE BEAUTY. HV.
citri'num . . . LEMON F.
dens-ca'nis . . . DOGTOOTH F.
gigan'teum . . . OREGON F.
grandiflo'rum |w . . LAMBSTONGUE F.
—al'bum . . . WHITE L.F.
—pal'lidum (*E. parviflorum*)
—robus'tum
henderso'ni . . . HENDERSON F.
how'elli . . . HOWELL F.
klamathen'se
monta'num . . . AVALANCHE F.
multiscapoi'deum (*hartwegi; purdyi*)
obtusa'tum
parviflo'rum . **E. grandiflorum pallidum**
purpuras'cens . . . SIERRA F.
revolu'tum . . . MAHOGANY F.
₵JOHNSON (*johnsoni*) HV.
₵OREGON (*oreganum; praecox*)
₵PINKBEAUTY
₵ROSEBEAUTY
₵WATSON (*albiflorum; watsoni*)
tuolumnen'se . . . TUOLUMNE F.

ERYTHROPHLE'UM
guineen'se . . CASCA REDWATERTREE

ERYTHRORHIP'SALIS
See **CACTUS GENERA.**

ERYTHROX'YLUM (*ERYTHROXYLON*) . . . COCAINETREE
There is controversy among botanists as to the proper spelling of the Latin generic name. Erythroxylum is the original spelling, but there is some question as to the validity of that publication under the Rules. The next oldest (and admittedly properly published) spelling is Erythroxylon.
co'ca . . . HUANUCO C.
novogranaten'se . . . PERUVIAN C.
ova'tum
truxillen'se . . . TRUJILLO C.

ESCALLO'NIA . . . ESCALLONIA
berteria'na . . . **E. pulverulenta**
∞ **edinen'sis** (*rubra × virgata*)
∞ **exonien'sis** (*pterocladon × rubra*)
floribun'da
fonk'i
∞ **francisca'na** (*?illinita × macrantha*) ∞ SLIPPERY-ELM E.
glutino'sa . . . GUMMY E.
grahamia'na . . . GRAHAM E.
illini'ta
∞ **in'grami** (*?macrantha × punctata*) ∞ INGRAM E.
i'veyi . . . IVEY E.
∞ **langleyen'sis** (*punctata × virgata*) ∞ LANGLEY E.
leucan'tha . . . WHITE E.
macran'tha
monta'na
monteviden'sis . . . MONTEVIDEO E.
organen'sis . . . ORGAN E.
philippia'na . . . **E. virgata**
pterocla'don
pulverulen'ta (*berteriana*)
—gla'bra
puncta'ta
revolu'ta
∞ **rock'i** (*macrantha × montevidensis*) ∞ ROCKS E.
rose'a Hort.
Apparently loosely used for various rosy-flowered forms.
ru'bra . . . RED E.
—glabrius'cula
—pyg'maea
—uniflo'ra
∞ **rubrica'lyx** (*?grahamiana × rubra*)
virga'ta (*philippiana*)
visco'sa . . . STICKYSTEM E.
₵APPLEBLOSSOM (*glasneviensis*) HV. Escallonia
₵C. F. BALL
₵DONARD BEAUTY
₵DONARD BRILLIANCE
₵DONARD GEM
₵SLIEVE DONARD
₵WILLIAM WATSON

ESCALLONIA . . . **Escallonia**
GRAHAM E. . . . **E. grahamiana**
GUMMY E. . . . **E. glutinosa**
∞ INGRAM E. . . . ∞ **E. ingrami**
IVEY E. . . . **E. iveyi**
∞ LANGLEY E. . . . ∞ **E. langleyensis**
MONTEVIDEO E. . . . **E. montevidensis**
ORGAN E. . . . **E. organensis**
RED E. . . . **E. rubra**
∞ ROCKS E. . . . ∞ **E. rocki**
∞ SLIPPERY-ELM E. . . . ∞ **E. franciscana**
STICKYSTEM E. . . . **E. viscosa**
WHITE E. . . . **E. leucantha**

ESCHENBACH'IA . . RAYLESS-ASTER
coul'teri . . . COULTER R.

ESCHSCHOLTZ'IA |w . . GOLDPOPPY
caespito'sa
califor'nica |w . . . CALIFORNIAPOPPY
—cro'cea (*E. crocea*)
—doug'lasi (*E. douglasi*). DOUGLAS C.
CARMINE KING. HV. E. californica
GOLDEN WEST
MANDARIN
MIKADO
ORANGE FLAME (*aurantiaca*)
SCARLET BEAUTY
TANGO

ESCHSCHOLTZIA californica, continued
THE GEISHA
VESUVIUS
WHITE (*alba*)
glyptosper'ma . DESERT GOLDPOPPY
marit'ima . . . . SEA G.
mexica'na . . . . MEXICAN G.
minutiflo'ra . . . . . . LITTLE G.
tenuifo'lia . . . . . THREADLEAF G.

There are said to be over 100 natural forms and garden varieties of California-poppy and other Goldpoppies, the names of which will remain in confusion until careful field and cultural studies are made.

ESCHWEI'LERA
corruga'ta . . . . . . MANBARKLAK

ESCOBA'RIA . . **CORYPHANTHA**
See **CACTUS GENERA.**

ESCOBE'DIA (*SILVIA* Vell., *not* Allem. *nor* Benth.)
lae'vis
scabrifo'lia

ESCON'TRIA . . . . . . **CEREUS**
See **CACTUS GENERA.**

ESENBECK'IA
leiocar'pa . . GUARANTAN GASPARILLO

Esparto . . . . ESPARTOGRASS: **Lygeum spartium**; NEEDLEGRASS, ESPARTO: **Stipa tenacissima**

ESPARTOGRASS . . . . **Lygeum spartium**

ESPOSTO'A . . . . . **PILOCEREUS**
See **CACTUS GENERA.**

ESSENTIAL OILS (Plant Sources of)
See **ECONOMIC PLANTS, ESSENTIAL OILS.**

EUAN'THE
See **ORCHID GENERA.**

EUBO'TRYS . . . . . **LEUCOTHOE**

EUCALYP'TUS . . . . . EUCALYPTUS

So far as possible the Editorial Committee has endeavored to reconcile the Latin nomenclature of this list with that of W. F. Blakely's "A Key to the Eucalypts" (1934), perhaps the latest and most authoritative taxonomic work on this difficult genus. Our thanks are extended to Eric Walther of the San Francisco Park Commission for valuable advice and suggestions.

Popularly (in Australia) as well as in the Lumber Trade, species of Eucalyptus are differentiated as various kinds of Bloodwood, Box, Gum, Ironbark, Mahogany, Mallee, Manna, Peppermint, Stringybark, Tallowwood, Tuart, Wando, Woollybutt, Yate, etc. See **LUMBER TRADE NAMES.**

acce'dens . . . . . POWDERBARK E.
acer'vula Hook. f., *not* Sieb. **E. gunni a.**
acmenioi'des . . . . . . **E. triantha**
agglomera'ta . . GRAY STRINGYBARK E.
al'ba . . . . POPLAR E. (*Poplargum*)
al'bens (*E. hemiphloia a.*)
WHITEBOX E.
×**algerien'sis** . . . . . ALGERIAN E.

Blakely lists this as a "supposed exotic hybrid" and states that, morphologically, "it does not appear to differ from E. camaldulensis."

alpi'na . . . . GRAMPIAN E.
amplifo'lia . . . . . . CUMBORA E.
amygdali'na . . . . . . **E. salicifolia**
—angustifo'lia . . . . . . **E. linearis**
—di'ves . . . . **E. dives**
—nit'ida . . . . **E. nitida**

EUCALYPTUS, continued
amygdali'na numero'sa . **E. lindleyana**
—radia'ta . . . . **E. radiata**
—reg'nans . . . . **E. regnans**
andrews'i
ANDREWS PEPPERMINT EUCALYPTUS
angulo'sa (*E. incrassata a.*)
ANGLEPOD MALLEE E.
annula'ta . . . . RING E.
argophloi'a SILVERBARK E. (*Whitegum*)
astrin'gens . . . . ALUM E.
australia'na . . . . . . **E. radiata a.**
baileya'na . . BLACK STRINGYBARK E.
baueria'na . . . . BLUEBOX E.
bey'eri BEYER IRONBARK E. (*Mogargro*)
bi'color . . . . COOBURN E.
bicosta'ta . . . . EURABBIE E.
blax'landi BLAXLAND STRINGYBARK E.
bosistoa'na . . BOSISTO GRAYBOX E.
botryoi'des . . . . . . BANGALAY E.
bridgesia'na . . . . . . **E. stuartiana**
cae'sia . . . . GUNGURRU E.
cajuput'ea . . . . **E. odorata**
ca'leyi . . . . . CALEY IRONBARK E.

This tree is sometimes mislabeled E. sideroxylon pallens.

calophyl'la . . . . MARRI E.
—**guilfoyle'i** (*E. c. rosea*) PINK M.E.
camaldulen'sis (*longirostris; rostrata* Schlecht., *not* Cav.) . LONGBEAK E.
cambagea'na (*cambagei*) CAMBAGE E. (*Coowarrabox*)
campanula'ta
STRINGYBARK PEPPERMINT E.
camph'ora . . . . CAMPHOR E.
capitella'ta . . BROWN STRINGYBARK E.
cephalocar'pa (*E. cinerea multiflora*)
SILVERLEAF S.E.

This tree is sometimes mislabeled E. pulverulenta lanceolata.

cine'rea . . . . MEALY S.E.
citriodo'ra (*E. maculata c.*) LEMON E. (*Lemongum*)
cladoca'lyx (*corynocalyx*) . . SUGAR E. (*Sugargum*)
coccif'era . . . . RIDGETOP E.
considenia'na . . . . YERTCHUK E.
coolabah' . . . . COOLABAH E.
corda'ta . . . . HEARTLEAF E.
coria'cea . . . . **E. pauciflora**
cornu'ta . . . . YATE E.
corymbo'sa . . . . **E. gummifera**
corynoca'lyx . . . . . . **E. cladocalyx**
cosmophyl'la . . . . . . KANGAROO E.
cre'bra . NARROWLEAF IRONBARK E.
cru'cis . . . . . SOUTHERNCROSS E.
dalrymplea'na . . . . DALRYMPLE E.
daw'soni . . . . DAWSON E.
dealba'ta . . . . . . TUMBLEDOWN E.
dean'ei . . . . DEANE E.
de-beuzevil'lei JOUNAMA E. (*Whitegum*)
decip'iens . . . . COASTLINE E.
delegaten'sis . . . . . . **E. gigantea**
desmonden'sis . . . . . DESMOND E.
diversicol'or . . . . KARRI E.
di'ves (*E. amygdalina d.*)
BROADLEAF PEPPERMINT E.
drum'mondi . . . . . . DRUMMOND E.
dumo'sa . . . . CONGOO MALLEE E.
dun'dasi . . . . DUNDAS E.
elaeoph'ora . . . . BUNDY E.
eremoph'ila . . . . DESERTMALLEE E.
erythroco'rys . . . . . . ILLYARIE E.
erythrone'ma . . . . . REDTHREAD E.
eugenioi'des WHITE STRINGYBARK E.
exim'ia . . . YELLOW BLOODWOOD E.
exser'ta . . . . BENDO E.
fastiga'ta . . . . CUTTAIL E.

EUCALYPTUS, continued
ferguso'ni . . FERGUSON EUCALYPTUS
ficifo'lia . . . . SCARLET E.
flockton'iae . . FLOCKTON E. (*Merrit*)
foecun'da . . FREMANTLE MALLEE E.
—loxophle'ba . . . . . **E. loxophleba**
forrestia'na . . . . FORREST E.
fraxinoi'des . . . . ASH E.
gard'neri . . . . . BLUEMALLET E.
gigan'tea (*delegatensis; obliqua* Deca., *not* L'Her.) . . . . DELEGATE E.
glob'ulus . . . TASMANIAN BLUE E. (*Tasmanian Bluegum*)
—**compac'ta** . . . . . DWARF T.B.E.
gomphoceph'ala . TUART E. (*Tooart*)
gonioca'lyx . . . . BIGLEAF E.
grac'ilis . . . . YORRELL E.
gran'dis . . . . TOOLUR E.
gros'sa . . . . . PHILLIPS RIVER E.
guilfoyl'ei . YELLOW TINGLETINGLE E.
gummif'era (*corymbosa*)
DARK BLOODWOOD E.
gunn'i . . . . CIDER E.
—**acer'vula** (*E. acervula* Hook. f., *not* Sieb.) . . . . . . TASMANIAN C.E.
—**monta'na** . . . . . . MOUNTAIN C.E.
haemasto'ma . . . . . SCRIBBLY E. (*Scribblygum*)
—**capita'ta** . . . . . . CAPITATE S.E.
—micran'tha . . . . . **E. m. signata**

This name is also often misapplied to E. haemastoma var. sclerophylla, to E. micrantha, and to E. rossi.

—**sclerophyl'la** (*E. h. micrantha* Auth. in part) . . . . . HARDLEAF S.E.
hemiphloi'a . . . . GRAYBOX E.
—al'bens . . . . **E. albens**
incrassa'ta . . . . . LERP MALLEE E.
—angulo'sa . . . . . . **E. angulosa**
interme'dia . . PINK BLOODWOOD E.
jack'soni . . . . . . REDTINGLE E.
laevopi'nea SILVERTOP STRINGYBARK E.
—**mi'nor**
leh'manni . . . . LEHMANN E.
leucox'ylon . . . . WHITE IRONBARK E.

The varietal names erythrostema, purpurea, and rosea—applied to forms with colored stamens—are doubtfully valid.

lindleya'na (*E. amygdalina numerosa*)
KAYERRO E.
linea'ris (*E. amygdalina angustifolia*)
NARROWLEAF E.
longicor'nis . . . . RED MORRELL E.
longifo'lia . LONGLEAF WOOLLYBUTT E.
longiros'tris . . . . **E. camaldulensis**
loxophle'ba (*E. foecunda l.*) . YORK E. (*Yorkgum*)
macar'thuri . . . . MACARTHUR E.
macran'dra . . . . . LONGSTAMEN E.
macrocar'pa . . . . . . SILVERLEAF E.
macrorhyn'cha . RED STRINGYBARK E.
macula'ta . SPOTTED E. (*Spottedgum*)
—citriodo'ra . . . . **E. citriodora**
maculo'sa . . . SPOTTED BRITTLE E.
mai'deni . . . . MAIDENS E.
mannif'era . . MANNA E. (*Mannagum*)
margina'ta . . . . JARRAH E.
megacar'pa . . . BIGPOD E. (*Bullich*)
melliodo'ra . . . . . YELLOWBOX E.
micran'tha (*E. haemastoma m.* Auth. in part) . . . . SNAPPYGUM E.
—**signa'ta** (*E. haemastoma micrantha* Auth. in part) . PEPPERMINT S.E.
microcar'pa . . . . . . LITTLEPOD E.
microco'rys . . . . TALLOWWOOD E.
microthe'ca . . . . . FLOODEDBOX E.
minia'ta . . . . PAINTED E.

EUCALYPTUS, continued
muelleria'na . MUELLER EUCALYPTUS
multiflo'ra (*robusta; rostrata* Cav., *not* Schlecht.) . . . . . . BEAKPOD E. (*Browngum; Swampmahogany*)
murph'yi . . . . MURPHY E.
nan'glei . . . . **E. paniculata**
niphoph'ila . . . . . SNOWLAND E.
nit'ida (*E. amygdalina n.*) SHINYLEAF E.
nu'tans . . . . NODDING E.
obli'qua . MESSMATE STRINGYBARK E.
obli'qua Deca., *not* L'Her. **E. gigantea**
obtusiflo'ra
occidenta'lis . . . FLATTOP YATE E.
odora'ta (*cajuputea*) . PEPPERMINT E. (*Peppermintgum*)
old'fieldi . . . . . . OLDFIELDS E.
oleo'sa . . . . . . OIL MALLEE E.
ova'ta . . . . OVALLEAF E.
panicula'ta (*nanglei*) GRAY IRONBARK E.
parvifo'lia . . . . . NIMITYBELLE E.
pa'tens . . . . . . SWANRIVER E.
pauciflo'ra (*coriacea*) . . . SNOW E. (*Snowgum*)
pelli'ta . . . . SLATEYHIDE E.
This tree is sometimes mislabeled E. punctata grandiflora.
phellan'dra WILLOWLEAF PEPPERMINT E.
pilula'ris . . . . . . BLACKBUTT E.
piperi'ta . . . SYDNEY PEPPERMINT E.
planchonia'na PLANCHON TALLOWWOOD E.
platyphyl'la . . . . . WONGOOLA E.
pla'typus . . . . MAALOK E.
polyan'themos . . . . . . REDBOX E.
populifo'lia POPLARLEAF E. (*Bimblebox*)
preissia'na . . . . PREISS E.
propin'qua . . . . GRAY E.
pulverulen'ta . . . . DOLLARLEAF E.
puncta'ta . . . . LEATHERJACKET E.
pyrifor'mis . . . PEARPOD MALLEE E.
radia'ta (*E. amygdalina r.*) GRAY PEPPERMINT E.
—australia'na (*E. australiana*)
rariflo'ra . . . . BLACKBOX E.
raveretia'na . . . IRON E. (*Irongum*)
redun'ca . . . . BLACKMARLOCK E.
—ela'ta . . . . **E. wandoo**
reg'nans (*E. amygdalina r.*) GIANT E. (*Giantgum*)
resinif'era . . . . KINO E. (*Kinogum; Redmahogany*)
ris'doni . . . . RISDON E.
—ela'ta . . . . **E. tasmanica**
robus'ta . . . . **E. multiflora**
ross'i . . . . . ROSS E. (*Whitegum*)
rostra'ta Cav., *not* Schlecht. **E. multiflora**
rostra'ta Schlecht., *not* Cav. **E. camaldulensis**
ru'bida . . . . . . CANDLEBARK E.
rud'deri . . . . . . RUDDERBOX E.
ru'dis . . . . MOITCH E.
salicifo'lia (*amygdalina*) . . WILLOWLEAF E. (*Black Peppermint*)
salig'na . . . . . . SYDNEY BLUE E. (*Sydney Bluegum*)
salmonophloi'a . . . SALMONBARK E.
salu'bris . . . . GIMLET E.
sepulcra'lis . . . . . . SEPULCRAL E.
siderophloi'a BROADLEAF IRONBARK E.
siderox'ylon . . . . . . MULGA I.E.
sieberia'na . . . . SIEBER E.
smith'i . . . . SMITH E.
spathula'ta . . . . SWAMPMALLET E.
stellula'ta . . . . . . BLACKSALLY E.

EUCALYPTUS, continued
strick'landi . STRICKLAND EUCALYPTUS
stuartia'na (*bridgesiana*) . BUTBUT E.
tasman'ica (*E. risdoni elata*) TASMANIAN PEPPERMINT E.
tereticor'nis . . . . . **E. umbellata**
termina'lis . . KUTCHA BLOODWOOD E.
tessela'ris (*viminalis* Hook., *not* Benth. *nor* Labill.) . . . . . CARBEEN E.
tetrag'ona . . . . . . FIREHAZARD E.
tetrap'tera . . . . . . FOURWING E.
torqua'ta . . . . COOLGARDIE CORAL E.
trachyphloi'a . . WHITE BLOODWOOD E.
transcontinenta'lis . . . MORRELL E.
trian'tha (*acmenioides*)
umbella'ta (*tereticornis*) . HORNCAP E.
um'bra . . . . SHADOW E.
uncina'ta . . HOOKLEAF MALLEE E.
urnig'era . . . . URNPOD E.
vimina'lis . . RIBBON E. (*Ribbongum*)
vimina'lis Benth., *not* Hook. *nor* Labill. **E. rubida** (in part)
vimina'lis Hook., *not* Benth. *nor* Labill. **E. tesselaris**
virga'ta . . . . ANGLETWIG E. (*Twiggygum; Yellowtop*)
vir'idis . . . . . GREEN MALLEE E.
wan'doo (*E. redunca elata*) WANDOO E.

EUCALYPTUS . . . . **Eucalyptus**
ALGERIAN E. . . . . . ×**E. algeriensis**
ALUM E. . . . . **E. astringens**
ANDREWS PEPPERMINT E. **E. andrewsi**
ANGLEPOD MALLEE E. . . **E. angulosa**
ANGLETWIG E. . . . . . . **E. virgata**
ASH E. . . . . **E. fraxinoides**
BANGALAY E. . . . . . **E. botryoides**
BEAKPOD E. . . . . . **E. multiflora**
BENDO E. . . . . **E. exserta**
BEYER IRONBARK E. . . . . **E. beyeri**
BIGLEAF E. . . . . . **E. goniocalyx**
BIGPOD E. . . . . . **E. megacarpa**
BLACKBOX E. . . . . . . **E. rariflora**
BLACKBUTT E. . . . . . **E. pilularis**
BLACKMARLOCK E. . . . **R. redunca**
BLACKSALLY E. . . . . . **E. stellulata**
BLACK STRINGYBARK E. **E. baileyana**
BLAXLAND S. E. . . . . . **E. blaxlandi**
BLUEBOX E. . . . . . . **E. baueriana**
BLUEMALLET E. . . . . **E. gardneri**
BOSISTO GRAYBOX E. **E. bosistoana**
BROADLEAF IRONBARK E. **E. siderophloia**
BROADLEAF PEPPERMINT E. . **E. dives**
BROWN STRINGYBARK E. . **E. capitellata**
BUNDY E. . . . . **E. elaeophora**
BUTBUT E. . . . . **E. stuartiana**
CALEY IRONBARK E. . . . . **E. caleyi**
CAMBAGE E. . . . . . **E. cambageana**
CAMPHOR E. . . . . . . **E. camphora**
CANDLEBARK E. . . . . . . **E. rubida**
CAPITATE SCRIBBLYGUM E. **E. haemastoma capitata**
CARBEEN E. . . . . . . **E. tesselaris**
CIDER E. . . . . **E. gunni**
COASTLINE E. . . . . . **E. decipiens**
CONGOO MALLEE E. . . . . **E. dumosa**
COOBURN E. . . . . **E. bicolor**
COOLABAH E. . . . . . . **E. coolabah**
COOLGARDIE CORAL E. . . **E. torquata**
CUMBORA E. . . . . . . **E. amplifolia**
CUTTAIL E. . . . . **E. fastigata**
DALRYMPLE E. . . . . **E. dalrympleana**
DARK BLOODWOOD E. . **E. gummifera**
DAWSON E. . . . . **E. dawsoni**
DEANE E. . . . . **E. deanei**
DELEGATE E. . . . . **E. gigantea**
DESERTMALLEE E. . . **E. eremophila**

EUCALYPTUS, continued
DESMOND E. **Eucalyptus desmondensis**
DOLLARLEAF E. . . . **E. pulverulenta**
DRUMMOND E. . . . . . **E. drummondi**
DUNDAS E. . . . . **E. dundasi**
DWARF TASMANIAN BLUE E. **E. globulus compacta**
EURABBIE E. . . . . **E. bicostata**
FERGUSON E. . . . . . . **E. fergusoni**
FIREHAZARD E. . . . . . **E. tetragona**
FLATTOP YATE E. . . . **E. occidentalis**
FLOCKTON E. . . . . . **E. flocktoniae**
FLOODEDBOX E. . . . . **E. microtheca**
FORREST E. . . . . . . **E. forrestiana**
FOURWING E. . . . . . **E. tetraptera**
FREMANTLE MALLEE E. . **E. foecunda**
GIANT E. . . . . **E. regnans**
GIMLET E. . . . . **E. salubris**
GRAMPIAN E. . . . . **E. alpina**
GRAYBOX E. . . . . . **E. hemiphloia**
GRAY E. . . . . **E. propinqua**
GRAY IRONBARK E. . . **E. paniculata**
GRAY PEPPERMINT E. . . . **E. radiata**
GRAY STRINGYBARK E. **E. agglomerata**
GREEN MALLEE E. . . . . **E. viridis**
GUNGURRU E. . . . . . . **E. caesia**
HARDLEAF SCRIBBLYGUM E. **E. haemastoma sclerophylla**
HEARTLEAF E. . . . . . . **E. cordata**
HOOKLEAF MALLEE E. . . **E. uncinata**
HORNCAP E. . . . . . . **E. umbellata**
ILLYARIE E. . . . . **E. erythrocorys**
IRON E. . . . . **E. raveretiana**
JARRAH E. . . . . **E. marginata**
JOUNAMA E. . . . . **E. de-beuzevillei**
KANGAROO E. . . . . **E. cosmophylla**
KARRI E. . . . . **E. diversicolor**
KAYERRO E. . . . . . . **E. lindleyana**
KINO E. . . . . **E. resinifera**
KUTCHA BLOODWOOD E. **E. terminalis**
LEATHERJACKET E. . . . **E. punctata**
LEHMANN E. . . . . **E. lehmanni**
LEMON E. . . . . **E. citriodora**
LERP MALLEE E. . . . . **E. incrassata**
LITTLEPOD E. . . . . . **E. microcarpa**
LONGBEAK E. . . . **E. camaldulensis**
LONGLEAF WOOLLYBUTT E. **E. longifolia**
LONGSTAMEN E. . . . . **E. macrandra**
MAALOK E. . . . . **E. platypus**
MACARTHUR E. . . . . . **E. macarthuri**
MAIDENS E. . . . . **E. maideni**
MANNA E. . . . . **E. mannifera**
MARRI E. . . . . **E. calophylla**
MEALY STRINGYBARK E. . . **E. cinerea**
MESSMATE STRINGYBARK E. **E. obliqua**
MOITCH E. . . . . **E. rudis**
MORRELL E. . . **E. transcontinentalis**
MOUNTAIN CIDER E. . **E. gunni montana**
MUELLER E. . . . . . . **E. muelleriana**
MULGA IRONBARK E. . **E. sideroxylon**
MURPHY E. . . . . **E. murphyi**
NARROWLEAF E. . . . . . . **E. linearis**
NARROWLEAF IRONBARK E. . **E. crebra**
NIMITYBELLE E. . . . . . **E. parvifolia**
NODDING E. . . . . **E. nutans**
OIL MALLEE E. . . . . **E. oleosa**
OLDFIELDS E. . . . . . . **E. oldfieldi**
OVALLEAF E. . . . . **E. ovata**
PAINTED E. . . . . **E. miniata**
PEARPOD MALLEE E. . **E. pyriformis**
PEPPERMINT E. . . . . . . **E. odorata**
PEPPERMINT SNAPPYGUM E. **E. micrantha signata**
PHILLIPS RIVER E. . . . . **E. grossa**
PINK BLOODWOOD E. . **E. intermedia**
PINK MARRI E. **E. calophylla guilfoylei**
PLANCHON TALLOWWOOD E. **E. planchoniana**

EUCALYPTUS, continued
POPLAR E. . . . . . **Eucalyptus alba**
POPLARLEAF E. . . . . **E. populifolia**
POWDERBARK E. . . . . **E. accedens**
PREISS E. . . . . . **E. preissiana**
REDBOX E. . . . . . **E. polyanthemos**
RED MORRELL E. . . . **E. longicornis**
RED STRINGYBARK E. . **E. macrorhyncha**
REDTHREAD E. . . . **E. erythronema**
REDTINGLE E. . . . . . **E. jacksoni**
RIBBON E. . . . . . . **E. viminalis**
RIDGETOP E. . . . . . **E. coccifera**
RING E. . . . . **E. annulata**
RISDON E. . . . . . . **E. risdoni**
ROSS E. . . . . **E. rossi**
RUDDERBOX E. . . . . . **E. rudderi**
SALMONBARK E. . . **E. salmonophloia**
SCARLET E. . . . . . . **E. ficifolia**
SCRIBBLY E. . . . . **E. haemastoma**
SEPULCRAL E. . . . . **E. sepulcralis**
SHADOW E. . . . . . . **E. umbra**
SHINYLEAF E. . . . . . . **E. nitida**
SIEBER E. . . . . . . **E. sieberiana**
SILVERBARK E. . . . . **E. argophloia**
SILVERLEAF E. . . . . **E. macrocarpa**
SILVERLEAF STRINGYBARK E.
E. cephalocarpa
SILVERTOP S. E. . . . **E. laevopinea**
SLATEYHIDE E. . . . . . . **E. pellita**
SMITH E. . . . . **E. smithi**
SNAPPYGUM E. . . . . **E. micrantha**
SNOW E. . . . . **E. pauciflora**
SNOWLAND E. . . . . **E. niphophila**
SOUTHERNCROSS E. . . . . **E. crucis**
SPOTTED BRITTLE E. . . **E. maculosa**
SPOTTED E. . . . . . . **E. maculata**
STRICKLAND E. . . . . **E. stricklandi**
STRINGYBARK PEPPERMINT E.
E. campanulata
SUGAR E. . . . . . . **E. cladocalyx**
SWAMPMALLET E. . . . **E. spathulata**
SWANRIVER E. . . . . . . **E. patens**
SYDNEY BLUE E. . . . . . **E. saligna**
SYDNEY PEPPERMINT E. . . **E. piperita**
TALLOWWOOD E. . . . **E. microcorys**
TASMANIAN BLUE E. . . **E. globulus**
TASMANIAN CIDER E.
E. gunni acervula
TASMANIAN PEPPERMINT E.
E. tasmanica
TOOLUR E. . . . . **E. grandis**
TUART E. . . . . **E. gomphocephala**
TUMBLEDOWN E. . . . . **E. dealbata**
URNPOD E. . . . . . . **E. urnigera**
WANDOO E. . . . . **E. wandoo**
WHITE BLOODWOOD E. **E. trachyphloia**
WHITEBOX E. . . . . . . **E. albens**
WHITE IRONBARK E. . **E. leucoxylon**
WHITE STRINGYBARK E. **E. eugenioides**
WILLOWLEAF E. . . . . **E. salicifolia**
WILLOWLEAF PEPPERMINT E.
E. phellandra
WONGOOLA E. . . . . **E. platyphylla**
YATE E. . . . . **E. cornuta**
YELLOW BLOODWOOD E. . . **E. eximia**
YELLOWBOX E. . . . . **E. melliodora**
YELLOW TINGLETINGLE E. **E. guilfoylei**
YERTCHUK E. . . . **E. consideniana**
YORK E. . . . . **E. loxophleba**
YORRELL E. . . . . **E. gracilis**

EUCA'RYA (*FUSANUS* R. Br., *not* Murr.)
spica'ta (*Fusanus spicatus*)
AUSTRALIA-SANDALWOOD

EUCEPH'ALUS . . . . . . **ASTER**
el'egans . . . . . . **A. perelegans**
glau'cus . . . . **A. glaucodes**

EUCHARID'IUM . . . . **CLARKIA**
grandiflo'rum . . . . . . **C. concinna**

EU'CHARIS . . . . EUCHARIS
can'dida . . . . . . GILTSTAMEN E.
grandiflo'ra (*amazonica*) AMAZONLILY E.
—moor'ei . . . . . YELLOWCUP A. E.
mas'tersi . . . . MASTERS E.
Possibly a hybrid of grandiflora × sanderi.
multiflo'ra . . . . . GREENSTRIPE E.
san'deri . . . . SANDERS E.
Possibly a hybrid of candida × grandiflora.
subedenta'ta . . . LITTLEFLOWER E.

EUCHEU'MA . . . . JELLYALGA
gelati'nae . . . . GELATINE J.
specio'sum . . . . . AUSTRALIAN J.
spino'sum . . . . MACASSAR-AGAR J.

EUCHLAE'NA . . . . TEOSINTE
See **GRASS GENERA**.

EUCLE'A . . . . EUCLEA
pseudeb'enus . . . . CAPEEBONY E.

EUCNI'DE
u'rens (*Loasa u.*) . . . . STINGBUSH

EUCO'MIS
puncta'ta . . . . PINEAPPLEFLOWER
undula'ta

EUCOM'MIA
ulmoi'des

EUCRY'PHIA . . . . . . EUCRYPHIA
The lumber of the larger species is known as Leatherwood and Pinkwood.
billardier'i . . . . . . TASMANIAN E.
cordifo'lia . . . . . . HEARTLEAF E.
glutino'sa (*pinnatifolia*)
×interme'dia
moor'ei . . . . MOORE E.
×nymansen'sis

EUGE'NIA (*ANAMOMIS; CARYOPHYLLUS; PHYLLOCALYX; STENOCALYX*) . . . . EUGENIA
apicula'ta (*luma; Myrtus l.*)
SHORTLEAF E.
a'quea . . . . . . **Syzygium aqueum**
aromat'ica . . **Syzygium aromaticum**
austra'lis . . . . . **E. paniculata a.**
axilla'ris . . . . WHITESTOPPER E.
bahamen'sis . . . . . . BAHAMA E.
brasilien'sis (*Stenocalyx b.*). BRAZIL E.
This name, unfortunately, is frequently misapplied to E. dombeyi.
buxifo'lia . . . . BOXLEAF E.
caryophylla'ta **Syzygium aromaticum**
cauliflo'ra . . . . **Myrciaria c.**
che'quen (*cheken*) . . . . CHEKEN E.
confu'sa . . . . REDBERRY E.
corona'ta
cu'mini . . . . **Syzygium c.**
cur'rani . . . . LIPOTE E.
cyanocar'pa
dicra'na . . . . . . TWINBERRY E.
dom'beyi . . . . . . GRUMICHAMA
This species is frequently misidentified as E. brasiliensis. It bears numerous vernacular names, including Brazilian-cherry and Grumixameiratree.
eucalyptoi'des
floribun'da . . . . . . RUMBERRY E.
(*Guavaberrytree*)
gran'dis
hook'eri; hookeria'na Hort.
E. paniculata

EUGENIA, continued
jambola'na . . . . **Syzygium cumini**
jam'bos . . . . **Syzygium j.**
klotzschia'na . . . . . PERADOCAMPO
linea'ta . . . . . **Syzygium lineatum**
lon'gipes (*Anamomis l.*)
TRAILING EUGENIA
lu'ma . . . . **E. apiculata**
luschnathia'na (*Phyllocalyx luschnathianus*) . . . . PITOMBA
malaccen'sis . . **Syzygium malaccense**
ma'to
michel'i . . . . **E. uniflora**
montic'ola
myriophyl'la (*microphylla*)
myrtifo'lia . . **E. paniculata australis**
opercula'ta . . **Syzygium operculatum**
owarien'sis . . . **Syzygium owariense**
panicula'ta (*hookeri; hookeriana* Hort.)
BRUSHCHERRY E.
—austra'lis (*E. australis; E. myrtifolia*)
AUSTRALIAN B.E.
¢VARIEGATED (*variegata*) HV.
pitan'ga
Not to be confused with the Pitanga of commerce, E. uniflora, considered the finest of the fruits borne by this genus.
pun'gens
rhom'bea . . . . . . SPICEBERRY E.
simp'soni (*Anamomis s.*) . SIMPSON E.
sinemarien'sis
smith'i . . . . **Acmena s.**
supraaxilla'ris . . . REDRODWOOD E.
tomento'sa . . . . . . CABELLUDA
umbellulif'era . . . . MONOSPLUM
uniflo'ra (*micheli; Stenocalyx brasiliensis; S. micheli*) . . . . PITANGA
This species bears numerous vernacular names, including Brazilcherry, Cayennecherry, Floridacherry, and Surinamcherry.
uval'ha . . . . UVALHA E.

EUGENIA . . . . **Eugenia**
AUSTRALIAN BRUSHCHERRY E.
E. paniculata australis
BAHAMA E. . . . . . **E. bahamensis**
BOXLEAF E. . . . . . . **E. buxifolia**
BRAZIL E. . . . . . **E. brasiliensis**
BRUSHCHERRY E. . . . **E. paniculata**
CABELLUDA . . . . . . **E. tomentosa**
CHEKEN E. . . . . . . **E. chequen**
GRUMICHAMA . . . . . . **E. dombeyi**
LIPOTE E. . . . . **E. currani**
MONOSPLUM . . . . **E. umbellulifera**
PERADOCAMPO . . . **E. klotzschiana**
PITANGA . . . . **E. uniflora**
PITOMBA . . . . . **E. luschnathiana**
REDBERRY E. . . . . . . **E. confusa**
REDRODWOOD E. . . **E. supraaxillaris**
RUMBERRY E. . . . . **E. floribunda**
SHORTLEAF E. . . . . . **E. apiculata**
SIMPSON E. . . . . . . **E. simpsoni**
SPICEBERRY E. . . . . . **E. rhombea**
TRAILING E. . . . . . . **E. longipes**
TWINBERRY E. . . . . . . **E. dicrana**
UVALHA E. . . . . **E. uvalha**
WHITESTOPPER E. . . . **E. axillaris**

EULA'LIA . . . . EULALIA
See **GRASS GENERA**.

Eulalia . . . . SILVERGRASS, CHINESE:
Miscanthus sinensis

EULO'BUS . . . . . . **OENOTHERA**

EULO'PHUS . . . . . **PERIDERIDIA**

EULY'CHNIA . . . . . . **CEREUS**
See **CACTUS GENERA**.

EUON'YMUS (*EVONYMUS*) |w
EUONYMUS

There is controversy both as to the spelling of this name and its gender. Linnaeus published this as masculine and in the form Evonymus. The spelling Eu- and feminine gender better conform to classic usage. The spelling Euonymus is now generally accepted and agrees with customary pronunciation. As International Rules now stand, Euonymus seems to be masculine.

acu'tus . . . . **E. fortunei**
ala'tus . . . . WINGED E.
—aper'tus . . . . . BLACKSEED W.E.
—ap'terus
¢DWARF (*compactus*) HV. E. alatus
america'nus |w . . . . . . BROOK E.
—angustifo'lius . NARROWLEAF B.E.
aquifo'lium . . . . . HOLLYLEAF E.
atropurpu'reus |w . . EASTERN WAHOO (*Eastern Burningbush*)

The name E. atropurpureus is sometimes misapplied to E. europaeus a.

bulga'ricus . . . . . BULGARIAN E.
bungea'nus . . . . WINTERBERRY E.
¢MIDWINTER (*semipersistens*) HV.
¢WEEPING (*pendulus*)
echina'tus
europae'us . . . . . . EUROPEAN E.
¢ALDENHAMENSIS. HV.
¢BRILLIANT
¢CRIMSONFRUIT (*atrorubens*)
¢DWARF (*nanus*)
¢INTERMEDIUS
¢PURPLELEAF (*atropurpureus*)
¢WHITEFRUIT (*albus; leucocarpus*)
fimbria'tus
fortun'ei (*acutus; E. radicans a.*) WINTERCREEPER E.
—rad'icans (*E. radicans*) COMMON W.E.
—veg'etus (*E. vegetus; E. radicans v.*) BIGLEAF W.E.
BABY (*minimus*). Form of E. fortunei
GLOSSY (*carrierei*). HV. E. fortunei
KEW (*kewensis*). Form of E. fortunei
¢PURPLELEAF (*coloratus*)
¢SILVEREDGE (*argenteo-marginatus; gracilis*)
¢SILVERGEM
¢SILVERQUEEN
¢WHITEVEIN (*reticulatus*)
grandiflo'rus . . . . . HIMALAYAN E.
—salicifo'lius
hamiltonia'nus . . . . HAMILTON E.
hi'ans
ilicifo'lius . . . . . . SPINYLEAF E.
japon'icus . . . . . . EVERGREEN E.
BOXLEAF (*microphyllus*) HV.
COLUMN (*fastigiatus*)
DUC D'ANJOU (*viridi-variegatus*)
GILTEDGE (*aureo-marginatus*)
GOLDENKING
GOLDLEAF (*aureus*)
GOLDSPOT (*aureo-variegatus*)
LARGELEAF (*macrophyllus; robustus*)
MOSSYGREEN (*compactus viridis*)
PEARLEDGE (*albo-marginatus*)
PRESIDENT GAUTHIER
PULCHELLUS
PYRAMID (*pyramidatus*)
SILVERQUEEN
SILVERSPOT (*albo-variegatus*)

EUONYMUS japonicus, continued
SILVER VARIEGATED (*argenteo-variegatus*)
YELLOWEYE (*medio-pictus*)
kiautscho'vicus (*patens*) SPREADING EUONYMUS
lanceifo'lius . . . . . LANCELEAF E.
latifo'lius . . . . . . BROADLEAF E.
maack'i . . . . MAACK E.
—lanceola'ta
macrop'terus (*ussuriensis*)
nanoi'des . . . . LOW E.
na'nus . . . . DWARF E.
—turkestan'icus (*E. n. koopmanni*)
nikoen'sis . . . . NIKKO E.
nippon'icus . . . . NIPPON E.
obova'tus . . . . RUNNING E.
occidenta'lis |w . . WESTERN WAHOO (*Western Burningbush*)
—par'ishi
ores'bius
oxyphyl'lus
pa'tens . . . . . . **E. kiautschovicus**
pauciflo'rus
pen'dulus
phello'manus
pla'nipes . . . . . **E. sachalinensis**
pyg'maeus
rad'icans . . . . **E. fortunei r.**
—acu'tus . . . . **E. fortunei**
—veg'etus . . . . **E. fortunei v.**
sachalinen'sis (*planipes*) . SAKHALIN E.
sanguin'eus
—brevipeduncula'tus
—camptoneu'rus
sargentia'nus . . . . . SARGENT E.
semeno'vi
semiexser'tus
sieboldia'nus . . . . . . SIEBOLD E.

True E. sieboldianus is not in the trade. The plants cultivated under this name are E. bungeanus, and its HV. Midwinter, or else E. kiautschovicus or E. yedoensis.

tin'gens
ussurien'sis . . . . **E. macropterus**
veg'etus . . . . **E. fortunei v.**
verruco'sus . . . . . WARTYBARK E.
wil'soni . . . . WILSON E.
yedoen'sis . . . . YEDDO E.
—koehnea'nus
CRIMSON (*calocarpus*) HV. E. yedoensis

EUONYMUS . . . . **Euonymus**
BIGLEAF WINTERCREEPER E. **E. fortunei vegetus**
BLACKSEED WINGED E. **E. alatus apertus**
BROADLEAF E. . . . . . **E. latifolius**
BROOK E. . . . . . . **E. americanus**
BULGARIAN E. . . . . **E. bulgaricus**
COMMON WINTERCREEPER E. **E. fortunei radicans**
DWARF E. . . . . **E. nanus**
EASTERN WAHOO . . **E. atropurpureus**
EUROPEAN E. . . . . **E. europaeus**
EVERGREEN E. . . . . **E. japonicus**
HAMILTON E. . . . **E. hamiltonianus**
HIMALAYAN E. . . . . **E. grandiflorus**
HOLLYLEAF E. . . . . **E. aquifolium**
LANCELEAF E. . . . . **E. lanceifolius**
LOW E. . . . . **E. nanoides**
MAACK E. . . . . **E. maacki**
NARROWLEAF BROOK E. **E. americanus angustifolius**
NIKKO E. . . . . **E. nikoensis**
NIPPON E. . . . . . . **E. nipponicus**
RUNNING E. . . . . . . **E. obovatus**
SAKHALIN E. . . . . **E. sachalinensis**

EUONYMUS, continued
SARGENT E. . **Euonymus sargentianus**
SIEBOLD E. . . . . . **E. sieboldianus**
SPINYLEAF E. . . . . . **E. ilicifolius**
SPREADING E. . . . **E. kiautschovicus**
WARTYBARK E. . . . . **E. verrucosus**
WESTERN WAHOO . . . **E. occidentalis**
WILSON E. . . . . **E. wilsoni**
WINGED E. . . . . **E. alatus**
WINTERBERRY E. . . . **E. bungeanus**
WINTERCREEPER E. . . . **E. fortunei**
YEDDO E. . . . . . . **E. yedoensis**

EUPATO'RIUM (*CONOCLINIUM*) |w
EUPATORIUM

ageratoi'des . . . . . . **E. rugosum**
al'bum
altis'simum . . . . TALL E.
araliaefo'lium
aromat'icum |w
—melissoi'des . . . . . MELISSA E.
aromat'isans . . . HAVANA-CIGAR E.
atroru'bens
bru'neri . . . BRUNER JOEPYEWEED
cannabi'num . . . . HEMP E.
—ple'num
capillifo'lium . . . . . DOGFENNEL E.
cine'reum
coelesti'num (*Conoclinium c.*) MISTFLOWER E.
conspic'uum
du'bium (*verticillatum*) COASTALPLAIN JOEPYEWEED
fistulo'sum . . . . . PURPLESTEM J.
fra'seri . . . . **E. rugosum**
glabra'tum
glandulo'sum
glechonophyl'lum (*Ageratum conspicuum*) . . . . CHILE E.
ianthi'num . . . . **E. sordidum**
incarna'tum |w . . . . PINK E.
lasseaux'i (*Ageratum l.; A. roseum*)
ligustri'num (*micranthum; weinmannianum*) . . . . MEXICAN E.
macrophyl'lum . . . . . BIGLEAF E.
macula'tum (*E. purpureum m.*) SPOTTED JOEPYEWEED
occidenta'le . . . . . . WESTERN E.
odora'tum . . . . CHRISTMASBUSH E.
perfolia'tum |w . . . . . . BONESET
purpu'reum . BLUESTEM JOEPYEWEED
—macula'tum . . . . **E. maculatum**
ripa'rium . . . . RIVER E.
rugo'sum (*ageratoides; fraseri; urticaefolium*) . . . . WHITE SNAKEROOT (*Richweed*)
serot'inum . . . . LATE E.
serrula'tum
sessilifo'lium
sor'didum (*ianthinum*)
torreya'num . . . . . . TORREY E.
urticaefo'lium . . . . . **E. rugosum**
verna'le . . . . SPRING E.
verticilla'tum . . . . . . **E. dubium**
weinmannia'num . . . **E. ligustrinum**

EUPATORIUM . . . . **Eupatorium**
BIGLEAF E. . . . . **E. macrophyllum**
BLUESTEM JOEPYEWEED **E. purpureum**
BONESET . . . . . . **E. perfoliatum**
BRUNER JOEPYEWEED . **E. bruneri**
CHILE E. . . . **E. glechonophyllum**
CHRISTMASBUSH E. . . . **E. odoratum**
COASTALPLAIN JOEPYEWEED **E. dubium**
DOGFENNEL E. . . . **E. capillifolium**
HAVANA-CIGAR E. . . **E. aromatisans**
HEMP E. . . . . . . **E. cannabinum**
LATE E. . . . . **E. serotinum**

EUPATORIUM, continued
MELISSA E.
Eupatorium aromaticum melissoides
MEXICAN E. . . . . . **E. ligustrinum**
MISTFLOWER E. . . **E. coelestinum**
PINK E. . . . . . . **E. incarnatum**
PURPLESTEM JOEPYEWEED
E. fistulosum
RIVER E. . . . . **E. riparium**
SPOTTED JOEPYEWEED . **E. maculatum**
SPRING E. . . . . . . **E. vernale**
TALL E. . . . . **E. altissimum**
TORREY E. . . . . . **E. torreyanum**
WESTERN E. . . . . . **E. occidentale**
WHITE SNAKEROOT . . . **E. rugosum**

EUPHOR'BIA (*Chamaesyce; Dichrophyllum; Poinsettia; Tithymalopsis; Tithymalus; Trichosterigma; Zygophyllidium*) . . . . . . EUPHORBIA
See **SUCCULENTS.**

EUPHORBIA . . . . **Euphorbia**
ALLTHORN E. . . . . . . **E. horrida**
AMMAK E. . . . . **E. ammak**
ANCIENTS E. . . . . . **E. antiquorum**
APOTHECARIES E. . . . **E. officinarum**
AUSTRALIAN E. . . . . **E. australis**
BALSAM E. . . . . . . **E. balsamifera**
BARNHART E. . . . . . **E. barnharti**
BEETLE E. . . . . . . **E. crenulata**
BIGHORN E. . . . . **E. grandicornis**
BIGTOOTH E. . . . . . **E. grandidens**
BIRDSFOOT E. . . . . **E. ornithopus**
BRAZIL E. . . . . . **E. brasiliensis**
CALIFORNIA E. . . . . **E. californica**
CANARY E. . . . . . **E. canariensis**
CANDELABRA E. . . . **E. candelabrum**
CAPER E. . . . . **E. lathyrus**
CEREUS E. . . . . . **E. cereiformis**
COMMON POINSETTIA . **E. pulcherrima**
COOPER E. . . . . **E. cooperi**
CORNCOB E. . . . **E. submammillaris**
CRESTED MILKSTRIPE E.
E. lactea cristata
CROWNOFTHORNS E. . . . . . **E. mili**
CUSHION E. . . . . **E. epithymoides**
CYPRESS E. . . . . **E. cyparissias**
DINTER E. . . . . **E. dinteri**
EDIBLE E. . . . . . . **E. esculenta**
ELKHORN E. . . . . . . **E. alcicornis**
ETHIOPIAN E. . . . . . **E. abyssinica**
FENDLER E. . . . . . . **E. fendleri**
FISHERMENS E. . . . . **E. piscatoria**
FIVERIDGE E. . . . . **E. pentagona**
FLATSTEM E. . . . . **E. xylophylloides**
FLOWERINGSPURGE E. . . **E. corollata**
FOURANGLE E. . . . **E. quadrangularis**
FOURRIDGE E. . . . . . **E. tetragona**
FRANCKS E. . . . . . **E. franckiana**
FRINGED E. . . . . . . **E. fimbriata**
GEYER E. . . . . **E. geyeri**
GLOBE E. . . . . **E. globosa**
GORGO E. . . . . . . **E. gorgonis**
GRANTS E. . . . . **E. granti**
GUM E. . . . . **E. resinifera**
HEAD E. . . . . **E. capitellata**
HEDGE E. . . . . **E. neriifolia**
HEDGEHOG E. . . . . . . **E. echinus**
HOARY E. . . . . **E. lata**
HOTTENTOT E. . . . . **E. hottentotae**
INTISY E. . . . . **E. intisy**
IPECAC E. . . . . . **E. ipecacuanhae**
JYCHEE-OIL E. . . . **E. dracunculoides**
KING-JUBA E. . . . . **E. regis-jubae**
LEAFLESS E. . . . . **E. aphylla**
LEAFY E. . . . . **E. esula**
LEDIEN E. . . . . **E. ledieni**
LYTTON E. . . . . . . **E. lyttoniana**

EUPHORBIA, continued
MALABARTREE E. . **Euphorbia tirucalli**
MAURITANIA E. . . . **E. mauritanica**
MEDUSAHEAD E. . **E. caput-medusae**
MELON E. . . . . . . **E. meloformis**
MEXICAN E. . . . . . . **E. mexicana**
MILKSTRIPE E. . . . . . . **E. lactea**
MORIN E. . . . . **E. morini**
MUIR E. . . . . **E. muiri**
MYRTLE E. . . . . . . **E. myrsinites**
NATAL E. . . . . **E. natalensis**
NICENE E. . . . . . . **E. nicaeensis**
NUBIAN E. . . . . **E. nubica**
PAINTED E. . . . . . **E. heterophylla**
PALMER E. . . . . **E. palmeri**
PETTY E. . . . . **E. peplus**
PILLPOD E. . . . . . . **E. pilulifera**
POLYGON E. . . . . . . **E. polygona**
REINHARDT E. . . . . . **E. reinhardti**
RIDGESEED E. . . . **E. glyptosperma**
ROBUST E. . . . . **E. robusta**
ROYLES E. . . . . **E. royleana**
SCARLETPLUME E. . . . . **E. fulgens**
SCHINZ E. . . . . **E. schinzi**
SERPENT E. . . . . **E. serpens**
SEVENRIDGE E. . . . . **E. heptagona**
SHINING E. . . . . **E. lucida**
SICKLE E. . . . . **E. falcata**
SIKKIM E. . . . . . . **E. sikkimensis**
SIPOLIS E. . . . . **E. sipolisi**
SIXANGLE E. . . . . . . **E. hexagona**
SLIMBRANCH E. . . . . . **E. tenuirama**
SNOW-ON-THE-MOUNTAIN E.
E. marginata
SPOTTED E. . . . . . . **E. maculata**
STARSPINE E. . . . . **E. stellaespina**
SUN E. . . . . **E. helioscopia**
TENERIFFE E. . . . **E. atropurpurea**
THREERIB E. . . . . **E. trigona**
THYMELEAF E. . . . . **E. serpyllifolia**
TOOTHED E. . . . . **E. dentata**
TRAILING E. . . . . . **E. procumbens**
WAX E. . . . . . . **E. antisyphilitica**
WHITEMARGIN E. . . **E. albomarginata**
WINGRIB E. . . . . . . **E. pteroneura**
YELLOW-U E. . . . . **E. pseudocactus**
YUMA E. . . . . **E. setiloba**

EUPHO'RIA (*DIMOCARPUS*)
lon'gan (*longana; Dimocarpus longan; Nephelium longana*) . . . LONGAN

EUPHRA'SIA . . . . . . EYEBRIGHT
arc'tica . . . . GLANDULAR E.
canaden'sis . . . . . . CANADIAN E.
officina'lis . . . . DRUG E.
purpu'rea . . . . PURPLE E.

EUPLO'CA . . . . EUPLOCA
This genus perhaps is hardly more than a subgenus of Heliotropium.
convolvula'cea (*Heliotropium convolvulaceum*) ⊾w . . . . . BINDWEED E.

EUPRITCHARD'IA (*PRITCHARDIA; STYLOMA*) . . PRITCHARDIAPALM
See **PALM GENERA.**

EUPTE'LEA . . . . EUPTELEA
franchet'i . . . . FRANCHET E.
pleiosper'ma
polyan'dra . . . . JAPANESE E.

EURO'TIA ⊾w . . . . . . WINTERFAT
ceratoi'des . . . . . . OLDWORLD W.
lana'ta ⊾w . . . . COMMON W.
subspino'sa . . . . BUSH W.

EU'RYA
acumina'ta
chinen'sis
emargina'ta
japon'ica (*latifolia*)
—variega'ta
ochna'cea . . . . . **Cleyera japonica**

EURY'ALE . . . . EURYALE
fe'rox . . . . GORDON E.

EURY'CLES . . . . EURYCLES
cunningham'i . . . MORETONBAY E.
nu'da . . . . JAVA E.
sylves'tris . . . . BRISBANE E.

EURY'OPS
abrotanifo'lius
athana'siae
pectina'tus
spatha'ceus

EU'SCAPHIS
japon'ica

EUSIDEROX'YLON . . . . . BILLIAN
zwa'geri . . . . BORNEO B.

EU'STOMA . . . . . PRAIRIEGENTIAN
andrews'i . . . . ANDREWS P.
russellia'num (*Lisianthus russellianus*) RUSSELL P.
silenifo'lium

EU'STREPHUS
latifo'lius

EU'STYLIS
purpu'rea

EUTAX'IA
empetrifo'lia

EUTER'PE (*ACRISTA; CATIS*) EUTERPEPALM
See **PALM GENERA.**

Eutha'mia tenuifo'lia . . . . **Solidago t.**

EUTO'CA . . . . **PHACELIA**
multiflo'ra . . . . **P. linearis**

EUXYLO'PHORA
paraen'sis . . . BRAZILIAN-SATINWOOD

EVENINGPRIMROSE . . . . **Oenothera**
See also SUNDROPS.
ALYSSUM E. . . . . . . **O. alyssoides**
BEACH E. . . . . **O. spiralis**
BROWNEYED E. . . . **O. clavaeformis**
CLUTES E. . . . . **O. clutei**
COCKERELLS E. . . . . . **O. cockerelli**
COMMON E. . . . . **O. biennis**
CROSSFLOWER E. . . . . . **O. cruciata**
CUTLEAF E. . . . . **O. laciniata**
DESERT E. . . . . . . **O. californica**
DRUMMOND E. . . . . **O. drummondi**
FOURWING E. . . . . . . **O. tetraptera**
GOLDEN E. . . . . **O. brevipes**
HEARTLEAF E. . . . . **O. cardiophylla**
HOOKER E. . . . . **O. hookeri**
JOHNSON E. . . . . . . **O. johnsoni**
LAMARCK E. . . . . . **O. lamarckiana**
LAVENDERLEAF E. . **O. lavandulaefolia**
PALE E. . . . . **O. pallida**
SMALLFLOWER E. . . . . **O. parviflora**
TANSYLEAF E. . . . . **O. tanacetifolia**
TUFTED E. . . . . **O. caespitosa**
UTAH E. . . . . **O. utahensis**
WHITE E. . . . . **O. eximia**
YELLOW E. . . . . **O. flava**

Evergreen, Chinese . . . Chinagreen: **Aglaonema simplex**

Evergreenchinkapin . . **Castanopsis**
Chinese E. . . . . . . **C. caudata**
Giant E. . . . . . . **C. chrysophylla**
Golden E. . . . . . . **C. c. minor**
Japanese E. . . . . . . **C. cuspidata**
Sierra E. . . . . . **C. sempervirens**

Everlasting . . . . . . **Helichrysum**
Cudweed E. . . . . . **H. petiolatum**
Diosmaleaf E. . . **H. diosmaefolium**
Heath D. E. . . . . **H. d. ericifolium**
Purple D. E. . . **H. d. purpurascens**
Strawflower . . . **H. bracteatum**
Whiteleaf E. . . . **H. angustifolium**

Everlastinggrass . Cupgrass, Louisiana: **Eriochloa punctata**

EVER'NIA . . . . Evernia
fla'vicans . . . Yellowbrown E.
prunas'tri . . . . . . Staghorn E.
vulpi'na . . . . Wolfbane E.

EVO'DIA . . . . Evodia
bodinier'i . . . . Bodinier E.
daniel'li (*Zanthoxylum d.*) . Korean E.
fraxinifo'lia
glau'ca . . . . Japanese E.
hen'ryi . . . . Henry E.
hupehen'sis . . . . . . Hupeh E.
meliaefo'lia . . . . . . Dyebark E.
officina'lis
velu'tina . . . . . Velvet-twig E.

EVOL'VULUS lw . . . . . Evolvulus
arizo'nicus lw . . . . . Arizona E.
mol'lis lw
nuttallia'nus . . . . . . Nuttall E.
pilo'sus lw
ten'uis (*bocasanus*) . . . Birdseye E.
wilcoxia'nus lw . . . . . Wilcox E.

EVON'YMUS . . . . . **EUONYMUS**

EX'ACUM
affi'ne
—atrocaeru'leum
macran'thum
te'res
zeylan'icum

EXCOECA'RIA
bi'color

EXOCHOR'DA . . . . . . Pearlbush
girald'i . . . . Redbud P.
—wil'soni (*E. wilsoni*) . Wilson R.P.
korolkow'i (*alberti*) . . Turkestan P.
×macran'tha (*korolkowi × racemosa*)
racemo'sa (*grandiflora*) . Common P.
serratifo'lia

EXOGO'NIUM
pur'ga (*Ipomoea jalapa; I. purga*) Jalap

EXOSTEM'MA
caribae'um . Caribbean Princewood
longiflo'rum

EXOTHE'A
panicula'ta . . . . . Butterbough

Eyebright . . . . **Euphrasia**
Canadian E. . . . . . . **E. canadensis**
Drug E. . . . . **E. officinalis**
Glandular E. . . . . **E. arctica**
Purple E. . . . . **E. purpurea**

EYSENHARDT'IA (*VIBORQUIA*)
polysta'chya (*orthocarpa; Viborquia p.*) Kidneywood

FABIA'NA
imbrica'ta . . . . Peru Falseheath

FACHEIRO'A . . . . **PILOCEREUS**
See **CACTUS GENERA.**

FAGA'RA . . . . **ZANTHOXYLUM**
zanthoxyloi'des . . . . **Z. senegalense**

FAGE'LIA . . . . . **CALCEOLARIA**

FAGO'NIA . . . . Fagonia
califor'nica . . . . . California F.

FAGOPY'RUM lw . . . . Buckwheat
Some botanists unite this genus with Polygonum.
sagitta'tum (*esculentum; Polygonum fagopyrum*) lw . . . . Common B.
tatar'icum . . . . Tartary B.

FAGRAE'A . . . . Fagraea
fra'grans . . . . Sweet F.

FA'GUS lw . . . . Beech
antarc'tica . . . . . . **Nothofagus a.**
engleria'na . . . . Engler B.
fus'ca . . . . **Nothofagus f.**
grandifo'lia (*americana; ferruginea*) lw American B.
—carolinia'na . . . . . Carolina B.
japon'ica . . . . Japanese B.
longipetiola'ta
obli'qua . . . . **Nothofagus o.**
orienta'lis . . . . Oriental B.
sie'boldi (*F. sylvatica s.*) . Siebold B.
sylvat'ica . . . . . . European B.
Probably most of the below are clons.
Albovariegata. hv.
Bigleaf European (*latifolia*)
Conglomerata
Cristata
Cutleaf (*heterophylla; incisa; laciniata*)
Fernleaf (*asplenifolia*)
Golden (*zlatia*)
Milton (*miltonensis*)
Oakleaf (*quercifolia*)
Purple (*atropunicea; purpurea*)
Pyramidal (*fastigiata*)
Rivers (*riversi*)
Rosepink (*roseo-marginata*)
Roundleaf (*rotundifolia*)
Sawtooth (*grandidentata*)
Tortuosa
Tricolor
Variegated (*variegata*)
Weeping (*pendula*)
Weeping Purple (*purpureo-pendula*)
Yellowspot (*luteo-variegata*)

Fairybells . . . . **Disporum**
Hairy F. . . . . **D. lanuginosum**
Hooker F. . . . . **D. hookeri**
Menzies F. . . . . . . **D. menziesi**
Oregon F. . . . . **D. oreganum**
Smiths F. . . . . **D. smithi**
Spotted F. . . . . . . **D. maculatum**
Wartberry F. . . . **D. trachycarpum**

Fairylantern
Golden F. . . . . Mariposa, Lovely: **Calochortus amabilis**
Mt. Diablo F. . Goldenlantern M.: **C. pulchellus**

Fairylantern, continued
Purple F. . . . . Mariposa, Purple: **Calochortus amoenus**
White F. . . . . White M.: **C. albus**

Fairywand . . . **Chamaelirium luteum**

FALCA'TA . . . . **AMPHICARPA**
como'sa . . . . **A. bracteata**

Falldaffodil . . . **Sternbergia lutea**

FALLU'GIA . . . . . . Apacheplume
paradox'a . . . . Apacheplume

Falseabutilon . . . . . **Pseudabutilon**
Lozano F. . . . . **P. lozani**

Falsealyssum . . . . **Berteroa**
Hoary F. . . . . **B. incana**

Falsearalia . . . . **Dizygotheca**
Kerchov F. . . . . . **D. kerchoveana**
Threadleaf F. . . . **D. elegantissima**
Veitch F. . . . . **D. veitchi**

Falsearborvitae . . . . . . **Thujopsis**
Hiba F. . . . . **T. dolabrata**
Honda H. F. . . . . **T. d. hondai**

Falsebeech . . . . **Nothofagus**
Antarctic F. . . . . . . **N. antarctica**
Black F. . . . . **N. fusca**
Clinker F. . . . . **N. truncata**
Mountain F. . . . . **N. cliffortioides**
Negrohead F. . . . . **N. moorei**
Silver F. . . . . **N. menziesi**
Southern F. . . . . . . **N. dombeyi**
Tasmanian F. . . . **N. cunninghami**

Falsebox . . . . **Gyminda**
WestIndies F. . . . . . **G. latifolia**

Falsebrome . . . . . . **Brachypodium**
Japanese F. . . . . . . **B. pinnatum**
Purple F. . . . . . . **B. distachyon**
Slender F. . . . . . . **B. sylvaticum**

Falsecarrot . . **Caucalis microcarpa**

Falsecypress . . . . . **Chamaecyparis**
Erect Lawson F. **C. lawsoniana erecta**
Formosa Hinoki F. **C. obtusa formosana**
Hinoki F. . . . . **C. obtusa**
Lawson F. . . . . . . **C. lawsoniana**
Nootka F. . . . . . . **C. nootkatensis**
Sawara F. . . . . **C. pisifera**
Whitecedar F. . . . . . **C. thyoides**

Falseflag . . . . **Neomarica**
Longleaf F. . . . . . . **N. longifolia**
Norths F. . . . . **N. northiana**
Slender F. . . . . **N. gracilis**

Falseflax . . . . **Camelina**
Bigseed F. . . . . **C. sativa**
Flatseed F. . . . . **C. dentata**
Littlepod F. . . . . . **C. microcarpa**

Falsefreesia . . . . **Lapeirousia**
Red F. . . . . **L. cruenta**
Sedge F. . . . . **L. juncea**

Falsegarlic . . . . . . **Nothoscordum**
Fragrant F. . . . . **N. fragrans**
Yellow F. . . . . **N. bivalve**

Falsegrama . . . **Cathestecum erectum**

Falseheath, Peru . **Fabiana imbricata**

Falsehellebore . . . . **Veratrum**
American F. . . . . **V. viride**
Black F. . . . . **V. nigrum**
California F. . . . **V. californicum**
Colorado F. . . . . **V. tenuipetalum**
Eschscholtz F. . . . **V. eschscholtzi**

Hort. var.; hv. = horticultural variety (or varieties); sp. = species (singular); spp. = species (plural).
¢ = clon; × (as a prefix) = hybrid; × (between scientific plant names) = crossed by; ∞ = polybrid; lw = plant useful to wildlife.
See Glossary for definitions of clon, hybrid, and polybrid.

FALSEHELLEBORE, continued
FRINGED F. . . **Veratrum fimbriatum**
WHITE F. . . . . **V. album**

FALSEHOUSELEEK **Sedum sempervivoides**

FALSEMALLOW . . . . . . **Malvastrum**
FREMONT F. . . . . . . **M. fremonti**
INDIAN F. . . . . . . **M. aboriginum**
JONES F. . . . . **M. jonesi**
MESA F. . . . . . . **M. fasciculatum**
NUTTALL F. . . . . . . **M. nuttalli**
PALMER F. . . . . **M. palmeri**
SALINAS F. . . . . **M. abbotti**
SANCLEMENTE F. . . **M. clementinum**
SAND F. . . . . **M. davidsoni**
SANTACRUZ F. . . . . **M. nesioticum**
SLENDER F. . . . . **M. gracile**
SOUTHERN F. . . . . **M. marrubioides**

FALSEMANGROVE
Laguncularia; L. racemosa

FALSEMELIC . **Schizachne purpurascens**

FALSEMERMAID
Floerkea; F. proserpinacoides

FALSENETTLE . . . . . . **Boehmeria**
AFRICAN F. . . . . . **B. platyphylla**
BIGLEAF F. . . . . . **B. macrophylla**
SILVERSPOT F. . . . . . **B. argentea**
SMALLSPIKE F. . . . . . **B. cylindrica**

FALSEOLIVE . . . . . . **Elaeodendron**
BERMUDA F. . . . . . . **E. laneanum**
CAPE F. . . . . **E. capense**
COCORRON E. . . . . **E. xylocarpum**
ORIENTAL F. . . . . . . **E. orientale**

Falseorange . . OXANTHERA, NEW CALEDONIA: **Oxanthera neocaledonica**

FALSEPANAX . . . . **Nothopanax**
DAVID F. . . . . **N. davidi**
TREE F. . . . . **N. arboreus**

FALSEPENNYROYAL . . . . **Hedeoma**
AMERICAN F. . . . . **H. pulegioides**
DRUMMOND F. . . . **H. drummondi**
ROUGH F. . . . . **H. hispida**

Falsepennyroyal . . FLUXWEED: **Isanthus**

FALSEPIMPERNEL . . . . . . **Lindernia**

FALSEPISTACHE . . . . **Tapiscia**
CHINESE F. . . . . . . **T. sinensis**

FALSEQUINCE . . . . **Docynia**
DELAVAY F. . . . . . . **D. delavayi**

FALSESPIREA . . . . **Sorbaria**
KASHMIR F. . . . . . . **S. aitchisoni**
LINDLEY F. . . . . . . **S. tomentosa**
SHOWY F. . . . . . . **S. grandiflora**
SMOOTH TREE F. . **S. arborea glabrata**
STARRY URAL F.
S. sorbifolia stellipila
TREE F. . . . . **S. arborea**
URAL F. . . . . **S. sorbifolia**

FALSESUNROSE . . . . . . **Halimium**
AFRICAN F. . . . . **H. halimifolium**
GOLDEN F. . . . . . **H. alyssoides**
LINELEAF F. . . . . **H. umbellatum**
LISBON F. . . . . . **H. lasianthum**
MOROCCO F.
H. halimifolium multiflorum
PORTUGAL F. . . . **H. cheiranthoides**
PURPLESPOT F. . . . . **H. ocymoides**
ROSEMARY F. . . . . . . **H. libanotis**

FALSETAMARIX . . . . **Myricaria**
DAHURIAN F. . . . . . **M. dahurica**
GERMAN F. . . . . . **M. germanica**

Falsetoadflax . . COMANDRA: **Comandra**

FALSEVALERIAN . . . . . **Stachytarpheta**
JAMAICA F. . . . . . . **S. jamaicensis**
SCARLET F. . . . . . . **S. coccinea**
VARIABLE F. . . . . . . **S. mutabilis**

Falseyarrow . . CHAENACTIS: **Chaenactis**

FAMEFLOWER . . . . **Talinum**
COWSTONGUE F. . . . . **T. crenatum**
ORANGE F. . . . . . **T. aurantiacum**
PANICLED F. . . . . **T. paniculatum**
POTHERB F. . . . . . **T. triangulare**
PRAIRIE F. . . . . . **T. parviflorum**
QUILL F. . . . . . . **T. teretifolium**
ROCKPINK F. . . . . . **T. calycinum**
SPINY F. . . . . **T. spinescens**
WRINKLESEED F. . . **T. rugospermum**

Fancyfern . . . . WOODFERN, COMMON: **Dryopteris intermedia**

FANPALM . . . . **Livistona**
ASSAM F. . . . . . . **L. jenkinsiana**
AUSTRALIAN F. . . . . . **L. australis**
BELEMBUNA F. . . . . . **L. muelleri**
BRONZE F. . . . . **L. mariae**
BUSH F. . . . . **L. humilis**
CHINESE F. . . . . . . **L. chinensis**
JAVA F. . . . . **L. rotundifolia**
LUZON F. . . . . . . **L. r. luzonensis**
MALAYAN F. . . . **L. cochinchinensis**
WEEPING F. . . . . **L. decipiens**

FANWORT . . . . **Cabomba**
CAROLINA F. . . . . . **C. caroliniana**
PURPLE C. F. . . . **C. c. pulcherrima**
ROSE C. F. . . . . . **C. c. rosaefolia**
TROPICAL F. . . . . . . **C. aquatica**

FARFU'GIUM . . . . . **LIGULARIA**
argen'teum **L. kaempferi** ¢SILVEREDGE
gran'de; macula'tum
L. kaempferi ¢LEOPARD

FARKLEBERRY . . **Vaccinium arboreum**
MISSOURI F. . . . . **V. a. glaucescens**

FASCICULA'RIA
pitcairniaefo'lia

FATHEADTREE . . . . **Nauclea**
BILINGA F. . . . . **N. trillesi**
GUINEAPEACH F. . . . . **N. esculenta**
OPEPE F. . . . . **N. diderichi**

∞**FATSHED'ERA** (*FATSIA* × *HEDERA*) . . . . . ∞FATSHEDERA
∞**liz'ei** (*F. japonica* × *H. helix*)

FAT'SIA . . . . FATSIA
hor'rida . . . **Oplopanax horridus**
japon'ica (*Aralia j.; A. sieboldi*)
JAPAN F.
¢MOSER (*moseri*) HV.
¢VARIEGATED (*variegata; Aralia japonica v.*)
papyrif'era . . **Tetrapanax papyriferus**

FATTY OILS (Plant Sources of)
See **ECONOMIC PLANTS, FATTY OILS.**

FAUCA'RIA
MESEMBRYANTHEMUM
See **SUCCULENTS.**

∞FAUSTRIMEDIN . . ∞KUMANDARIN × ∞**Microcitrus australasica**

FAVEIRO . . . . **Pterodon**
FUZZY F. . . . . **P. pubescens**

FAWNLILY . . . . **Erythronium**
AVALANCHE F. . . . . . **E. montanum**
CALIFORNIA F. . . . **E. californicum**
COMMON F. . . . . . **E. americanum**
DOGTOOTH F. . . . . . **E. dens-canis**
HENDERSON F. . . . . **E. hendersoni**

FAWNLILY, continued
HOWELL F. . . **Erythronium howelli**
LAMBSTONGUE F. . . **E. grandiflorum**
LEMON F. . . . . **E. citrinum**
MAHOGANY F. . . . . **E. revolutum**
OREGON F. . . . . . . **E. giganteum**
SIERRA F. . . . . . **E. purpurascens**
TUOLUMNE F. . . . **E. tuolumnense**
WHITE F. . . . . **E. albidum**
WHITE LAMBSTONGUE F.
E. grandiflorum album

FEATHERFOIL . . . . **Hottonia**
AMERICAN F. . . . . **H. inflata**
EUROPEAN F. . . . . . **H. palustris**

FEATHERGRASS . . . . **Stipa**

Feathergrass is applied to the species with conspicuously plumose (feather-like) awns. See also NEEDLEGRASS and PORCUPINEGRASS.

AUSTRALIAN F. . . . **S. elegantissima**
ARGENTINE F. . . . . . **S. argentea**
EUROPEAN F. . . . . . **S. pennata**
NEWMEXICO F. . . . **S. neomexicana**
PHEASANTS-TAIL F. . . **S. arundinacea**

FEATHERTOP . . . **Pennisetum villosum**

FEATHERWOOD . **Polyosma cunninghami**

FED'IA . . . . . . AFRICANVALERIAN
cornuco'piae

FEIJO'A . . . . FEIJOA
sellowia'na . . . . FEIJOA

FELIC'IA (*AGATHAEA*) . FELICIA
amelloi'des (*Agathaea a.; A. coelestis*)
BLUE F.
bergeria'na (*Aster bergerianus*)
KINGFISHER F.
echina'ta . . . . . . HEDGEHOG F.
—para'lia
petiola'ta
tenel'la

FELTFERN . . . . **Cyclophorus**
CRESTED F. . . . . . **C. lingua** HV.
JAPANESE F. . . . . **C. lingua**
VARIEGATED F. . . . . **C. lingua** HV.

FELWORT . . . . **Pleurogyna**
MARSH F. . . . . **P. rotata**

FEND'LERA . . . . FENDLERBUSH
rupic'ola . . . . CLIFF F.
—falca'ta . . . . . SICKLELEAF C.F.
wright'i . . . . WRIGHTS F.

FENDLEREL'LA [W] . . FENDLERELLA
cymo'sa
lasiopet'ala
mexica'na . . . . MEXICAN F.
utahen'sis (*Whipplea u.*) [W] . UTAH F.

FENESTRA'RIA
MESEMBRYANTHEMUM
See **SUCCULENTS.**

FENNEL . . . . **Foeniculum**
COMMON F. . . . . **F. vulgare**

FENNELFLOWER . . . . **Nigella**
GARDEN F. . . . . **N. sativa**
LOVEINAMIST . . . . . **N. damascena**
SPANISH F. . . . . . . **N. hispanica**

Fenugreek . . TRIGONELLA, FENUGREEK: **Trigonella foenum-graecum**

Fenz'lia dianthiflo'ra . **Gilia dianthoides**

Ferdinan'da em'inens . **Podachaenium e.**

FERNCYCAD . . . . **Stangeria**
STRANGE F. . . . . **S. eriopus**

FERN GENERA

For convenience of reference the genera, species, and varieties of Ferns are here brought together in one consolidated list.

For the Fern Genera, with the exception of Nephrolepis, we are indebted to a committee composed of William R. Maxon, Curator, U. S. National Herbarium, C. A. Weatherby, Research Associate, Gray Herbarium of Harvard University, and C. V. Morton, Asst. Curator, U. S. National Herbarium. Ralph C. Benedict, Resident Investigator (Ferns), Brooklyn Botanic Garden, has supplied the material for the genus Nephrolepis. To these specialists the Editorial Committee extends warm appreciation and thanks.

ADIAN'TUM . . . . MAIDENHAIR
ae'mulum . . . . **A. cuneatum**
affi'ne (*cunninghami*) NEWZEALAND M.
an'ceps (*peruvianum* Auth.)
bel'lum . . . . BERMUDA M.
capillus-ven'eris (*fergusoni*) SOUTHERN M.
cauda'tum . . . . . . TRAILING M.
concin'num . . . . . . BRITTLE M.
cunea'tum (*aemulum; hybridum; mundulum; versaillense*) . . DELTA M.
See also hort. var. list below.
cunningham'i . . . . **A. affine**
deco'rum . . . . **A. wagneri**
dia'phanum . . . . FILMY M.
exci'sum . . . . CHILEAN M.
ferguso'ni . . . . **A. capillus-veneris**
formo'sum . . . . . AUSTRALIAN M.
hispid'ulum . . . . . . ROUGH M.
hy'bridum . . . . **A. cuneatum**
jor'dani . . . . . . CALIFORNIA M.
macrophyl'lum . . . . TWINLEAF M.
moore'i . . . . MOORE M.
mun'dulum . . . . **A. cuneatum**
peda'tum . . . . . . AMERICAN M.
peruvia'num Auth. . . . . . **A. anceps**
philippen'se (*lunulatum*). WALKING M.
polyphyl'lum . . . . GIANT M.
ten'erum (*princeps; scutum; victoriae*) FAN M.
See also hort. var. list below.
trapezifor'me . . . . DIAMOND M.
See also hort. var. list below.
versaillen'se . . . . . . **A. cuneatum**
victo'riae . . . . **A. tenerum**
wag'neri (*decorum; weigandi*) PERUVIAN M.
wil'liamsi . . . . . . WILLIAMS M.
BARBADOS (*farleyense*, incl. *gloriosum lemkesii*). HV. A. tenerum.
BAUSE (*bausei*). HV. A. tenerum.
CROWE (*cuneatum croweanum*).
FRAGRANT (*fragrantissimum*). HV. A. cuneatum.
LATHOM (*lathomii*). HV. A. tenerum.
MIST (*gracillimum*). HV. A. cuneatum.
ROSY (*rhodophyllum*). HV. A. tenerum.
ST. CATHARINE (*sanctae-catharinae*). HV. A. trapeziforme.
TASSEL (*cuneatum grandiceps*)

ALCICOR'NIUM **PLATYCERIUM**

ALSO'PHILA . . . . TREEFERN
austra'lis . . . . . AUSTRALIAN T.
coo'peri . . . . COOPER T.
glau'ca (*dealbata*)
iu'rida

ANCHIS'TEA . **WOODWARDIA**

ANE'MIA
adiantifo'lia . . . . PINEFERN

ANGIOP'TERIS . . . VESSELFERN
evec'ta . . . . ORIENTAL V.

FERN GENERA, continued

ANOP'TERIS
hexag'ona (*Pteris heterophylla*)
MOORES BRAKE (*heterophylla internata*) HV.

ASPI'DIUM
acrostichoi'des . . . . **Polystichum a.**
boott'i . . . . **Dryopteris b.**
braun'i . . . . **Polystichum b.**
crista'tum . . . . **Dryopteris cristata**
filixmas' . . . . **D. filixmas**
goldia'num . . . . **D. goldiana**
margina'le . . . . . . **D. marginalis**
muni'tum . . . . . **Polystichum m.**
noveboracen'se **Dryopteris noveboracensis**
spinulo'sum . . . . . . **D. spinulosa**
thelyp'teris . . . . . . **D. thelypteris**
tsussimen'se . . . . . **Polystichum t.**

ASPLE'NIUM . . . SPLEENWORT
acrostichoi'des. **Athyrium thelypteroides**
angustifo'lium . **Athyrium pycnocarpon**
belan'geri . . . . . . BELANGER S.
bulbif'erum . . . . . . MOTHER S.
ebe'neum . . . **Asplenium platyneuron**
filixfem'ina . . . . **Athyrium f.**
gemmif'erum . . . . BUD S.
goeringia'num . . . . . **Athyrium g.**
longis'simum . . . . . LONGLEAF S.
lu'cidum . . . . GLOSSY S.
monta'num . . . . . . MOUNTAIN S.
ni'dus (*nidus-avis*) . . BIRDSNESTFERN
palma'tum (*hemionitis* Auth.). STAR S.
platyneu'ron (*ebeneum*) . . EBONY S.
pycnocar'pon . . . . . . **Athyrium p.**
resil'iens (*parvulum*) . BLACKSTEM S.
thelypteroi'des . . . . . . **Athyrium t.**
trichom'anes . . . . MAIDENHAIR S.
vir'ide . . . . GREEN S.
vivip'arum . . . . . . MAURITIUS S.

ATHY'RIUM
filixfem'ina (*Asplenium f.*) . LADYFERN
goeringia'num (*Asplenium g.*) GOERING SPLEENWORT
pycnocar'pon (*Asplenium angustifolium; A. pycnocarpon*) NARROWLEAF S.
thelypteroi'des (*Asplenium acrostichoides; A. thelypteroides*) . SILVERY S.

AZOL'LA W . . . . AZOLLA
carolinia'na W . . . MOSQUITOFERN (*Atlantic A.*)
filiculoi'des W . . . . . PACIFIC A.

BLECH'NUM (*LOMARIA*) BLECHNUM
brasilien'se . . . . . BRAZILIAN B.
elonga'tum
fluvia'tile (*Lomaria fluviatilis*)
gib'bum (*Lomaria gibba*)
moore'i (*Lomaria ciliata*) . MOORES B.
occidenta'le . . . . OCCIDENTAL B.
orienta'le . . . . ORIENTAL B.
serrula'tum . . . . SAWFERN
spi'cant (*Lomaria s.*) . . DEERFERN

BOTRY'CHIUM W . . GRAPEFERN
alabamen'se . . . . . . ALABAMA G.
dissec'tum . . . . CUTLEAF G.
luna'ria . . . . MOONWORT
matricariaefo'lium . . MATRICARY G.
multif'idum . . . . . BROADLEAF G.
obli'quum W . . . . . COMMON G.
virginia'num . . . RATTLESNAKEFERN

CAMPTOSO'RUS . WALKINGFERN
rhizophyl'lus

FERN GENERA, continued

CERATOP'TERIS W . WATERFERN
deltoi'dea W . . . . . DELTOID W.
pteridoi'des W . . . . AMERICAN W.
thalictroi'des . . . . . ORIENTAL W.

CEROP'TERIS **PITYROGRAMMA**

CHEILAN'THES . . . . LIPFERN
alabamen'sis . . . . . . ALABAMA L.
califor'nica . . . . . CALIFORNIA L.
covil'lei . . . . COVILLE L.
eat'oni . . . . EATON L.
fee'i . . . . FEE L.
fend'leri . . . . FENDLER L.
gracil'lima . . . . LACE L.
lano'sa . . . . HAIRY L.
lindheim'eri . . . . LINDHEIMER L.
microphyl'la . . . . . SOUTHERN L.
siliquo'sa (*Pellaea densa*) . PODFERN
tomento'sa . . . . WOOLLY L.
villo'sa . . . . SHAGGY L.
wright'i . . . . WRIGHT L.

CIBO'TIUM . . . . . . CIBOTIUM
bar'ometz . . . . . . SCYTHIANLAMB
glau'cum . . . . . . UNDERBLUE C.
rega'le . . . . ROYAL C.
schied'ei . . . . MEXICAN C.

CONIOGRAM'ME
japon'ica . . . . . . BAMBOOFERN

CRYPTOGRAM'MA . ROCKBRAKE
acrostichoi'des . . . . . AMERICAN R.
stel'leri (*Pellaea gracilis*). SLENDER R.

CYA'THEA . . . . . . TREEFERN
medulla'ris . . . . SAGOFERN

CYCLO'PHORUS (*NIPHOBOLUS*) . . . . FELTFERN
lin'gua (*Niphobolus l.*). . JAPANESE F.
CRESTED (*corymbiferus*) HV.
VARIEGATED (*variegatus*)

CYRTO'MIUM
caryotid'eum
falca'tum . . . . HOUSE-HOLLYFERN
BUTTERFIELDFERN (*butterfieldi*) HV.
DWARF ROCHFORDFERN (*rochfordianum compactum*)
ROCHFORDFERN (*rochfordianum*)
fortun'ei

CYSTOP'TERIS (*FILIX*) BLADDERFERN
bulbif'era (*Filix b.*) . . . . BERRY B.
frag'ilis (*Filix f.*) . . . . BRITTLE B.

DAVAL'LIA . . . . . . DAVALLIA
bulla'ta . . . . BALLFERN
canarien'sis . . . . CANARY D.
denticula'ta (*elegans*) . TOOTHED D.
dissec'ta . . . . . **D. trichomanoides**
fijien'sis . . . . FIJI D.
griffithia'na . . . . **Humata g.**
pal'lida (*mooreana*) . . . BORNEO D.
pentaphyl'la . . . . . FIVEBLADE D.
pyxida'ta . . . . . . AUSTRALIA D.
sol'ida . . . . . . POLYNESIAN D.
tenuifo'lia . . **Sphenomeris chinensis**
trichomanoi'des (*dissecta*)
PLUME (*fijiensis plumosa*) HV. Davallia

DENNSTAED'TIA . . . CUPFERN
adiantoi'des . . . . . . GLOSSY C.
punctilob'ula . . . HAYSCENTEDFERN

DICKSO'NIA . . . . DICKSONIA
antarc'tica . . . . . TASMANIAN D.
fibro'sa . . . . FIBROUS D.
squarro'sa . . . . NEWZEALAND D.

FERN GENERA, continued
DIPLA'ZIUM
lan'ceum

DOO'DIA . . . . Hacksawfern
as'pera
cauda'ta

DRYNA'RIA . . . . . . Drynaria
quercifo'lia (*Polypodium quercifolium*)
Oakleaf D.

DRYOP'TERIS (*LASTREA; NEPHRODIUM; PHEGOPTERIS; THELYPTERIS*) |w
Woodfern
acrostichoi'des . . . . **Polystichum a.**
am'pla . . . . . . Cinnamon W.
argu'ta . . . . Coast W.
boott'i (*Aspidium b.*) . . . Boott W.
chrysolo'ba . . . . **D. falciculata**
clintonia'na . . . . . . Clinton W.
crista'ta (*Aspidium cristatum; Thelypteris cristata*) . . . . Crested W.
decompos'ita
denta'ta (*mollis; Nephrodium molle*)
Downy W.
dilata'ta |w . . . . . . Mountain W.
disjunc'ta (*dryopteris; linnaeana; Phegopteris dryopteris*) . . Oakfern
erythroso'ra
falcicula'ta (*chrysoloba*)
filixmas' (*Aspidium f.*) . Malefern
florida'na . . . . . . **D. ludoviciana**
goldia'na (*Aspidium goldianum; Thelypteris goldiana*) . . . . Goldie W.
gongylo'des . . . . Everglade W.
hexagonop'tera (*Phegopteris h.*)
Broad Beechfern
hir'tipes (*Nephrodium h.*). Shaggy W.
interme'dia . . . . . . Common W.
The fronds of this species are commonly sold by florists under the name Fancyfern.
linnaea'na . . . . **D. disjuncta**
ludovicia'na (*floridana*). Louisiana W.
margina'lis (*Aspidium marginale; Thelypteris marginalis*) |w
Leather W.
mol'lis . . . . **D. dentata**
nevaden'sis (*oregana*) . . Sierra W.
norma'lis
noveboracen'sis (*Aspidium noveboracense; Thelypteris noveboracensis*)
NewYork Fern
orega'na . . . . **D. nevadensis**
oreop'teris . . . . . Northern W.
palus'tris . . . . . . **D. thelypteris**
pennig'era
phegop'teris (*Phegopteris polypodioides; Thelypteris phegopteris*)
Narrow Beechfern
rep'tans . . . . Creeping W.
setig'era Auth. . . . . . **D. uliginosa**
spinulo'sa (*Aspidium spinulosum; Thelypteris spinulosa*) |w Toothed W.
thelyp'teris (*palustris; Aspidium t.*) |w
Marshfern
uligino'sa (*setigera* Auth.) Oviedo W.
virides'cens . . . . . . Glossy W.

FI'LIX . . . . . **CYSTOPTERIS**

GONIOPHLE'BIUM
POLYPODIUM

GYMNOGRAM'MA
PITYROGRAMMA

HEMIONI'TIS
palma'ta . . . . . Strawberryfern

FERN GENERA, continued
HUMA'TA
griffithia'na (*Davallia g.*)
tyermann'i . . . . . Bearsfootfern

HYMENO'DIUM
crini'tum (*Elaphoglossum c.*)
Elephantear Fern

HYPOLE'PIS
re'pens
tenuifo'lia

LAS'TREA . . . **DRYOPTERIS**

LEPTOP'TERIS
hymenophylloi'des
super'ba . . . . Crapefern

LOMA'RIA . . . . **BLECHNUM**
cilia'ta . . . . **B. moorei**

LORINSE'RIA . **WOODWARDIA**

LYGO'DIUM . . . Climbingfern
circina'tum . . . . Malay C.
japon'icum . . . . Japanese C.
palma'tum . . . . . . Hartfordfern
scan'dens . . . . . . Feathery C.
volu'bile

MARAT'TIA . . . . . . Marattia
attenua'ta
doug'lasi . . . . Hawaii M.
fraxin'ea . . . . Ashleaf M.

MARSIL'EA |w . . . Pepperwort
drum'mondi . . . . . Drummond P.
macrop'oda |w
quadrifo'lia |w
tenuifo'lia |w
uncina'ta |w . . . . . . Hooked P.
vesti'ta (*oligospora*) |w

MATTEUC'CIA . . **PTERETIS**
struthiop'teris . . . . . **P. nodulosa**

MICROLE'PIA
platyphyl'la

NEPHRO'DIUM . **DRYOPTERIS**
mol'le . . . . **D. dentata**

NEPHROLE'PIS . . . Swordfern
acumina'ta . . . . Java S.
Forked. hv.
biserra'ta (*acuta*) . . Purplestalk S.
—fur'cans
cordifo'lia (*cordata* Hort.; *tuberosa*)
Tuber S.
—compac'ta
—duff'i (*N. duffi*) . . . . Duffs S.
—pectina'ta
—tessella'ta
exalta'ta . . . . Common S.
—bostonien'sis . . . . . Bostonfern
₵Amerpohl (*amerpohli*). hv.
₵Anna Foster (*fosteriana*)
₵Barrows (*barrowsi*)
₵Big Four (*splendida*)
₵Childs (*childsi*)
₵Cockatoo (*elegantissima compacta cristata*)
₵Compact (*compacta*)
₵Curly (*superbissima*)
₵Double Feather (*elegantissima*)
₵Elmsford (*elmsfordi*)
₵Emerald Fleece (*goodi*)
₵Galveston (*galvestoni*)
₵Giatras (*giatrasi*)
₵Golden Plume (*plumosa aurea*)
₵Good (*goodi*)
₵Gretna (*gretnai*)
₵Harris (*harrisi*)

FERN GENERA (NEPHROLEPIS exaltata bostoniensis), continued
₵King Constantine
₵Lace (*smithi*)
₵Mills (*millsi*)
₵Minerva (*robusta*)
₵New Jersey
₵New York
₵Norwood (*norwoodi*)
₵Ostrich Plume (*elegantissima compacta*)
₵Parrot Feather (*magnifica*)
₵Philippine (*philippinensis*)
₵Pierson (*piersoni*)
₵Plume (*whitmani compacta*)
₵Queen Sophie
₵Randolph (*randolphi*)
₵Roosevelt (*rooseveltì*)
₵Scholzel (*scholzeli*)
₵Schubert (*schuberti*)
₵Scott (*scotti*)
₵Shingle (*muscosa*)
₵Sickle (*falcata*)
₵Superior
₵Teddy Junior
₵Trailing
₵Verona
₵Victoria
₵Virago (*viridissima*)
₵Wanamaker (*wanamakeri*)
₵Whitman (*whitmani*)
₵Wicher (*wicheri*)
hirsut'ula . . . . Scurfy S.
Mayi. hv.
Superba
Tripinnatifida
Westoni
pectina'ta . . . . Basketfern
tubero'sa . . . . **N. cordifolia**

NIPHOB'OLUS **CYCLOPHORUS**

NOTHOLAE'NA . . . Cloakfern
au'rea (*bonariensis*) . . Slender C.
fend'leri . . . . Zigzag C.
sinua'ta . . . . Bulb C.
—crena'ta . . . . . . Little B.C.
stand'leyi . . . . Star C.

ODONTOSO'RIA in part
SPHENOMERIS

ONOCLE'A
sensib'ilis . . . . . . Sensitivefern

ONY'CHIUM . . . . Clawfern
japon'icum . . . . . Japanese C.

OPHIOGLOS'SUM. Adderstongue
engelmann'i . . . . Engelmann A.
vulga'tum . . . . . . Common A.

OSMUN'DA
cinnamo'mea . . . Cinnamonfern
claytonia'na . . . Interrupted-fern
rega'lis . . . . Royalfern
Slender R. (*gracilis*) hv.

PELLAE'A . . . . . Cliffbrake
andromedaefo'lia . . . . Coffeefern
atropurpu'rea . . . . . . Purple C.
brachyp'tera . . . . Sierra C.
brew'eri . . . . Brewers C.
brid'gesi . . . . Bridges C.
den'sa . . . . . **Cheilanthes siliquosa**
falca'ta . . . . Australian C.
grac'ilis . . . **Cryptogramma stelleri**
mucrona'ta (*ornithopus*). Birdsfoot C.
pu'mila (*occidentalis*) . . . Dwarf C.
rotundifo'lia . . . NewZealand C.
vir'idis (*Pteris adiantoides*). Green C.

FERN GENERA, continued

PHEGOP'TERIS . **DRYOPTERIS**
dryop'teris . . . . **D. disjuncta**
polypodioi'des . . . **D. phegopteris**

PHLEBO'DIUM. **POLYPODIUM**

PHYLLI'TIS (*SCOLOPENDRIUM*)
scolopen'drium (*Scolopendrium vulgare*) HARTSTONGUE

PHYMATO'DES. **POLYPODIUM**
glau'cum . . . **P. glauco-pruinatum**

PITYROGRAM'MA (*CEROPTERIS; GYMNOGRAMMA*)
calomel'anos . . . . . . SILVERFERN
chrysophyl'la (*P. calomelanos aureoflava*) . . . . GOLDFERN
lauchea'na Hort. . . . . LAUCHE G.
Hort. var. of P. chrysophylla.
sulphu'rea (*Ceropteris s.; Gymnogramma s.*) . . . . JAMAICA G.
tarta'rea (*Ceropteris t.*) MOUNTAIN SILVERFERN
triangula'ris (*Ceropteris t.*) CALIFORNIA G.

PLATYCE'RIUM (*ALCICORNIUM*) . . . . STAGHORNFERN
aethio'picum . . . . . . **P. stemaria**
angolen'se . . . . ANGOLA S.
bifurca'tum (*alcicorne*) . COMMON S.
—ma'jus
corona'rium (*biforme*) . . . . DISK S.
gran'de . . . . GIANT S.
hill'i . . . . GREEN S.
—ma'jus . . . . . GREATER G. S.
stema'ria (*aethiopicum*) . TRIANGLE S.
veitch'i . . . . AUSTRALIAN S.
wal'lichi . . . . INDIA S.
willinck'i . . . . JAVA S.

POLYPO'DIUM (*GONIOPHLEBIUM; PHLEBODIUM; PHYMATODES*) . . . . POLYPODY
au'reum (*Phlebodium a.*). . GOLDEN P.
LOWS (*lowi*) HV.
¢MANDA (*mandianum*)
califor'nicum . . . . . CALIFORNIA P.
diversifo'lium . . . . VARIFORM P.
falca'tum . . . . . . **P. glycyrrhiza**
fraxinifo'lium . . . . ASHLEAF P.
glauco-pruina'tum (*glaucum; Phymatodes glaucum*)
glycyrrhi'za (*falcatum*). LICORICEFERN
hesper'ium . . . . . WESTERN P.
inca'num . . . . . **P. polypodioides**
irioi'des . . . . **P. polycarpon**
pal'meri . . . . PALMER P.
pectina'tum . . . . COMB P.
percus'sum . . . . NIPPLE P.
phyllit'idis . . . . STRAP P.
phymato'des . . . . EAST INDIAN P.
plu'mula . . . . ELASTIC P.
polycar'pon (*irioides; punctatum*) POLYNESIAN P.
polypodioi'des (*incanum*) RESURRECTIONFERN
pustula'tum . . . . FRAGRANT P.
quercifo'lium . . **Drynaria quercifolia**
scou'leri . . . . COAST P.
subauricula'tum (*Goniophlebium s.*) JOINTED P.
¢KNIGHT (*knightiae*) HV.
¢REINWARDT
vulga're . . . . COMMON P.

POLYS'TICHUM |w . HOLLYFERN
acrostichoi'des (*Aspidium a.; Dryopteris a.*) |w . . . . CHRISTMASFERN

FERN GENERA (POLYSTICHUM), con.
aculea'tum (*lobatum*) LOBE HOLLYFERN
adiantifor'me (*capense; coriaceum*) LEATHER H.
anderso'ni . . . . . . ANDERSON H.
angula're . . . . **P. setiferum**
arista'tum . . . . . EAST INDIAN H.
¢VARIEGATED (*variegatum*) HV.
braun'i (*Aspidium b.*) . . . . BRAUN H.
califor'nicum . . . . CALIFORNIA H.
capen'se . . . . . . **P. adiantiforme**
coria'ceum . . . . . **P. adiantiforme**
lem'moni . . . . LEMMON H.
loba'tum . . . . **P. aculeatum**
lonchi'tis . . . . . . MOUNTAIN H.
muni'tum (*Aspidium m.*) |w WESTERN SWORDFERN
scopuli'num . . . . EATON H.
setif'erum (*angulare*) . . BRISTLE H.
¢PROLIFEROUS (*proliferum*) HV.
tsussimen'se (*Aspidium t.*) TSUSSIMA H.
va'rium . . . . JAPANESE H.
vivip'arum . . . . . VIVIPAROUS H.

PTERE'TIS (*MATTEUCCIA; STRUTHIOPTERIS* Willd., *not* Weis)
nodulo'sa (*Matteuccia struthiopteris*) OSTRICHFERN

PTERID'IUM |w . . . . BRACKEN
aquili'num |w
—pubes'cens (*Pteris aquilina p.*) WESTERN B.
cauda'tum . . . . TAILED B.
latius'culum |w . . . . . EASTERN B.

PTER'IS . . . . BRAKE
adiantoi'des . . . . . **Pellaea viridis**
aquili'na pubes'cens **Pteridium aquilinum p.**
crena'ta . . . . **P. ensiformis**
cre'tica . . . . CRETAN B.
See also hort. var. list below.
ensifor'mis (*crenata*) . . . SWORD B.
See also hort. var. list below.
heterophyl'la . . **Anopteris hexagona**
—interna'ta . . . . . . MOORES B.
Hort. var. of Anopteris hexagona.
longifo'lia . . . . RUSTY B.
margina'ta . . . . **P. tripartita**
multif'ida (*serrulata*) . . . SPIDER B.
See also hort. var. list below.
quadriauri'ta
See also hort. var. list below.
serrula'ta . . . . **P. multifida**
trem'ula . . . . . . AUSTRALIAN B.
triparti'ta (*marginata*) . . TRISECT B.
umbro'sa . . . . FOREST B.
vitta'ta . . . . CHINESE B.
ALEXANDRA BRAKE (*alexandrae*). HV. P. cretica.
CHARLESWORTH B. (*charlesworthi*). HV. P. multifida.
CHILDS B. (*childsi*). HV. P. cretica.
CRESTED SPIDER B. (*cristata*). HV. P. multifida.
DRINKWATER B. (*drinkwateri*). HV. P. cretica.
DUTRE B. (*dutrei*). HV. P. cretica.
GAUTHER B. (*gautheri*). HV. P. cretica.
MAYS B. (*mayi*). HV. P. cretica.
OUVRARD B. (*ouvrardi*). HV. P. multifida.
RIBBON B. (*albolineata*). HV. P. cretica.

FERN GENERA (PTERIS), continued
RIVERTON B. (*rivertoniana*). HV. P. cretica.
SIEBOLD B. (*sieboldi*). HV. P. ensiformis.
STRIPED B. (*argyraea*). HV. P. quadriaurita.
TALL CRETAN B. (*nobilis*). HV. P. cretica.
VICTORIA B. (*victoriae*). HV. P. ensiformis.
WILSON B. (*wilsoni*). HV. P. cretica.
WIMSETT B. (*wimsetti*). HV. P. cretica.

SALVIN'IA |w . . . . . SALVINIA
rotundifo'lia
Florida material of S. rotundifolia is frequently misidentified as S. auriculata.

SCHIZAE'A
pusil'la . . . . CURLYGRASS

SCOLOPEN'DRIUM **PHYLLITIS**
vulga're . . . . . . **P. scolopendrium**

SPHENOM'ERIS (*ODONTOSORIA* in part)
chinen'sis (*Davallia tenuifolia; Odontosoria c.*)

STENOCHLAE'NA . STENOCHLAENA
palus'tris (*scandens*)
tenuifo'lia

STRUTHIOP'TERIS Willd., *not* Weis . . . . **PTERETIS**

TECTA'RIA
heracleifo'lia . . . . . HALBERDFERN

THELYP'TERIS. **DRYOPTERIS**

TRICHOM'ANES . . . FILMYFERN
boschia'num . . . . . BRISTLEFERN
kraus'i . . . . TREEMOSS F.
lineola'tum
prieur'i . . . . PRIEUR F.
puncta'tum

VITTA'RIA
linea'ta . . . . . . SHOESTRINGFERN

WOODS'IA . . . . . . WOODSIA
glabel'la . . . . SMOOTH W.
ilven'sis . . . . RUSTY W.
mexica'na . . . . . . MEXICAN W.
obtu'sa . . . . COMMON W.
orega'na . . . . OREGON W.
scopuli'na . . . ROCKYMOUNTAIN W.

WOODWARD'IA (*ANCHISTEA; LORINSERIA*) . . CHAINFERN
areola'ta (*angustifolia; Lorinseria areolata*) . . . . NETVEIN C.
fimbria'ta (*chamissoi*) . . . GIANT C.
rad'icans . . . . . . EUROPEAN C.
spinulo'sa . . . . . . MEXICAN C.
virgin'ica (*Anchistea v.*). . VIRGINIA C.

FEROCAC'TUS . . . . BARRELCACTUS
See **CACTUS GENERA.**

FERO'NIA . . . . WOODAPPLE
limo'nia (*Limonia acidissima*) WOODAPPLE (*Feronia*)

FERONIEL'LA . . . . . FERONIELLA
lu'cida . . . . JAVA F.
obla'ta . . . . INDOCHINA F.

FER'ULA . . . . GIANTFENNEL
assafoe'tida . . . . . ASAFETIDA G.
commu'nis . . . . COMMON G.
foe'tida . . . . DEVILSDUNG G.
galbanif'lua . . . . . GALBANUM G.

FERULA, continued
karata'vica
link'i
per'sica . . . Persian Giantfennel
sum'bul . . . . . . Muskroot G.
tingita'na

Fescue . . . . **Festuca**
Alpine F. . . **F. ovina brachyphylla**
Amethyst F. . . . **F. amethystina**
Arizona F. . . . . . **F. arizonica**
Bearded F. . . . . . **F. subulata**
Big Rough F. . . **F. scabrella major**
Bluebunch F. . . . . Idaho F.
Blue F. . . . . **F. ovina glauca**
Brome F. . . . . . **F. dertonensis**
California F. . . . . **F. californica**
Chewings F. . **F. rubra commutata**
Cluster F. . . . . . . **F. paradoxa**
Coastrange F. . . . . . **F. elmeri**
Crinkleawn F. . . . . **F. subuliflora**
Desert F. . . . . **F. arida**
Eastwood F. . . . . **F. eastwoodae**
Foxtail F. . . . . . **F. megalura**
Giant F. . . . . **F. gigantea**
Grays F. . . . . **F. grayi**
Green F. . . . . **F. viridula**
Greenleaf F. . . . . Green F.

Fescue, continued
Guadalupe F. . . . **Festuca ligulata**
Hair F. . . . . **F. capillata**
Hairyscale Red F.
F. rubra lanuginosa
Hairy Sixweeks F.
F. octoflora hirtella
Hard F. . . . **F. ovina duriuscula**
Idaho F. . . . . . . **F. idahoensis**
Klickitat F. . . . . . **F. confusa**
Maires F. . . . . **F. mairei**
Meadow F. . . . . **F. elatior**
Nodding F. . . . . **F. obtusa**
Pacific F. . . . . . . **F. pacifica**
Portuguese F. . . . **F. geniculata**
Rattail F. . . . . . . **F. myuros**
Ravine F. . . . . **F. sororia**
Red F. . . . . **F. rubra**
Reed F. . . . **F. elatior arundinacea**
Rough F. . . . . **F. scabrella**
Sea F. . . . . **F. maritima**
Shade F. . . . **F. rubra heterophylla**
Sheep F. . . . . **F. ovina**
Sixweeks F. . . . . . **F. octoflora**
Small F. . . . . . **F. microstachys**
Squirrel F. . . . . **F. sciurea**
Tall F. . . . . Meadow F.

Fescue, continued
Tall Coastrange F.
Festuca elmeri conferta
Texas F. . . . . **F. versuta**
Thurber F. . . . . . . **F. thurberi**
Tracy F. . . . . **F. tracyi**
Twoflower F. . . . . . **F. reflexa**
Utah F. . . . . . . **F. dasyclada**
Western F. . . . . . **F. occidentalis**

FESTU'CA . . . . Fescue
See **GRASS GENERA.**

Feterita
Hort. race of **Sorghum vulgare durra**

Feverplant, Jamaica **Tribulus cistoides**

Fevervine . . . . **Paederia**
Chinese F. . . . . . . **P. scandens**

Feverwort . . Horsegentian, Common:
Triosteum perfoliatum

Fiberlily . . . . **Phormium**
Alpine NewZealand F.
P. tenax alpinum
Green F. . . . . **P. colensoi**
Hookers F. . . . . **P. hookeri**
NewZealand F. . . . . . **P. tenax**

FIBER PLANTS

This list includes textile, cordage, brush, basket, hat, matting, upholstery, pillow, and insulating fibrous material. Nearly two thousand species of plants have been listed as yielding fibers, but most of these fibers have never entered commerce and even their limited native uses are replaced by commercial fibers when available.

Grateful acknowledgment is made to Mr. H. T. Edwards, Dr. Brittain B. Robinson, Mr. C. B. Doyle, and Dr. T. H. Kearney of the Division of Cotton and Other Fiber Crops and Diseases, Bureau of Plant Industry, U. S. Department of Agriculture, for valuable criticism and suggestions.

Synonyms are in italics and in parentheses.

Lyster H. Dewey
Formerly Botanist in charge Fiber Plants,
Bureau of Plant Industry, U. S. Department of Agriculture

Fiber Name	Plant Source: *Botanical Name*	Plant Source: *S.P.N. Common Name*
Abaca (*Manila-hemp*)	**Musa textilis**	Abaca Banana
Some of the geographic types of Abaca, recognized in the trade, are as follows, those indicated by the letter (P) being from the Philippine Islands:		
Albay A. (P)		
Borneo A.		
Cebu A. (P)		
Davao A. (P)		
Sumatra A.		
African Fiber. Crin Vegetal		
Akund (*Madar*)	**Calotropis gigantea**	Akund Calotrope
Akund. Faftan		
Alfa. Esparto		
Aloe Fiber. Piteira		
Ambari. Kenaf		
Aramina. Cadillo		
Aren Fiber (*Ejoo; Gomuti*)	**Arenga pinnata** (*saccharifera*)	Gomuti Sugarpalm
Bamboo		
See Bamboo Genera. Many bamboos yield fibers used in hats, mats and baskets.		
Barreta (*Palma-istle; Samandoca*)	**Samuela carnerosana**	Barreta Samuela
Bimlipitam Jute. Kenaf		
Broomcorn	**Sorghum vulgare technicum**	Broomcorn
Broomroot (*Riceroot*)	**Muhlenbergia macroura** (*Epicampes m.*)	Whiskgrass Muhly (*Zacaton, Mex.*)
Cabuya (*Cabulla*)	**Furcraea cabuya**	Cabuya Furcrea
Cadillo (*Aramina; Bun Ochra; Guaxima; Malva Blanca; Paka*)	**Urena lobata**	Cadillo
Cantala (*Kantala; Manila Maguey*)	**Agave cantala**	Cantala Maguey
Caroa	**Neoglaziovia variegata**	Caroa
China Grass. Ramie		
Chingma (*Tientsin Jute*)	**Abutilon theophrasti** (*avicennae*)	Chingma Abutilon
Chiqui Chiqui (*Monkey Bass; Para Piassava*)	**Leopoldinia piassaba**	Para Piassava
Chuchao	**Furcraea andina**	Chuchao Furcrea
Cocuiza	**F. humboldtiana**	Humboldt F. (*Cocuiza Brava*)
Coir (*Coconut Fiber*)	**Cocos nucifera**	Coconut
Some of the geographical types of Coir, recognized in the trade are as follows:		
Ceylon C.; Cochin C.		
Corojo (*Pita de Corojo*)	**Acrocomia armentalis** (*crispa*)	Cuban Acrocomia (*Corojo*)
Cotton	**Gossypium** species	Cotton
The botanical names for Cotton follow the classification of S. C. Harland in The Genetics of Gossypium. 1932.		
American Long-staple C.	**G. hirsutum** Hort. var.	American Long-staple C.
American Upland C.	**G. hirsutum**	Upland C.
Some of the geographical types of upland cotton outside of the United States, recognized in the trade, are the following: Argentina; Belgian Congo; Brazil (southern); China; East Africa; Punjab; Russia; Sind; Sudan (rain grown); West Africa.		
Asiatic Tree C.	**G. arboreum**	Asiatic Tree C.
China C.	**G. a. nanking**	China C.
India C.	**G. a. assamicum**	India Largeboll C.
India C.	**G. a. soudanense**	India Smallboll C.
Bourbon C.	**G. purpurascens**	Bourbon C.
American Tree C.	**G. purpurascens** Hort. var.	American Tree C.
Moco C.	**G. purpurascens** Hort. var.	Moco C.
Brazilian C.	**G. barbadense** Hort. var.	Brazilian C.
Egyptian C.	**G. barbadense** Hort. var.	Egyptian C.
American E. C.	**G. barbadense** Hort. var.	American E. C.
Russian E. C.	**G. barbadense** Hort. var.	Russian E. C.
Ishan C.	**G. barbadense** Hort. var.	Ishan C.

Fiber Name	Plant Source: Botanical Name	Plant Source: S.P.N. Common Name
COTTON, LEVANT	**Gossypium herbaceum**	LEVANT COTTON
PERUVIAN C.	**G. barbadense** Hort. var. PERUVIANUM (*G. peruvianum*)	PERUVIAN C.
TANGUIS C. (*Ecuador C.; Peru C.*)	**G. barbadense** Hort. var.	TANGUIS C.
SEAISLAND C.	**G. barbadense** (*brasiliense; microcarpon; mustelinum; vitifolium*)	SEAISLAND C.
CRIN VEGETAL (*African Fiber*)	**Chamaerops humilis**	MEDITERRANEAN-PALM (*Hairpalm*)
CUBA-BAST	**Hibiscus tiliaceus elatus** (*H. elatus; Paritium elatum*)	JAMAICA LINDEN HIBISCUS
Da or *Dha*. KENAF		
DATEPALM FIBER	**Phoenix dactylifera**	DATE
Deccan-hemp. KENAF		
EELGRASS	**Zostera marina**	COMMON EELGRASS
Ejoo. AREN FIBER		
Emajagua. MAJAGUA		
ESPARTO (*Alfa*)	**Stipa tenacissima**	ESPARTO NEEDLEGRASS
FAFTAN (*Akund; Madar*)	**Calotropis procera**	FAFTAN CALOTROPE
FIQUE	**Furcraea macrophylla**	FIQUE FURCREA
FLAX Some of the geographical and commercial types of flax fiber recognized in the trade, are as follows: BELGIAN F.; IRISH F.; OREGON F.; RUSSIAN F.	**Linum usitatissimum**	COMMON FLAX Flax grown for fiber belongs to the race known as Fiber Flax. Seed Flax, grown much more extensively than Fiber F., is a distinctly different race.
Florida Moss. TREEBEARD		
Formio. PHORMIUM		
Gombo. KENAF		
Gomuti. AREN FIBER		
Guaxima. CADILLO		
Gumbo. OKRA FIBER		
Haitian Pita. PITRE		
HEMP Some of the geographical types of Hemp recognized in the trade are as follows: CHINA H.; HUNGARIAN H.; ITALIAN H.; KENTUCKY H.; RUSSIAN H.; WISCONSIN H.	**Cannabis sativa**	HEMP
HENEQUEN (*Mexican Sisal*) Some of the geographical types of Henequen recognized in the trade, are as follows: CUBAN H.; MEXICAN H.; YUCATAN H.	**Agave fourcroydes**	HENEQUEN AGAVE
IFE (*Ifi*)	**Sansevieria cylindrica**	IFE SANSEVIERIA
ISTLE (*Ixtle; Tampico; Tula Istle*)	**Agave lophantha poselgeri** (*A. lecheguilla*)	LECHUGUILLA AGAVE
Palma-istle. BARRETA		
JAUMAVE (*Jaumave Istle*)	**A. funkiana**	JAUMAVE LECHUGUILLA
Jipajapa. TOQUILLA		
JUTE	**Corchorus**	JUTE
DESI J. (*Daisee J.; Nolita J.; Tossa J.*)	**C. olitorius**	POTHERB J.
WHITE J. (*India J.*)	**C. capsularis**	ROUNDPOD J.
Kantala. CANTALA		
KAPOK (*Silkcotton*)	**Ceiba pentandra**	KAPOK CEIBA
Kappa. TAPPA		
KENAF (*Ambari; Bimlipitam Jute; Da* or *Dha; Deccan-hemp; Gombo*)	**Hibiscus cannabinus**	KENAF HIBISCUS
KITTOOL (*Kittul*)	**Caryota urens**	TODDY FISHTAILPALM (*Kittoolpalm*)
LACEBARK	**Lagetta lintearia**	LINT LACEBARKTREE
LETONA (*Salvador Henequen*)	**Agave letonae**	LETONA AGAVE
Liberian Piassava. WEST AFRICAN PIASSAVA		
Louisiana Moss. TREEBEARD		
Madagascar Piassava. VONITRA PIASSAVA		
Madar. AKUND; FAFTAN		
MAGUEY	**Agave** species; **Furcraea** species	
Manila M. CANTALA		
Mescal M. MESCAL FIBER		
MAJAGUA (*Emajagua; Mahoe*)	**Hibiscus tiliaceus**	LINDEN HIBISCUS
Malva Blanca. CADILLO		
Manila-hemp. ABACA		
Manila Maguey. CANTALA		
Mauritius-hemp. PITEIRA		
MESCAL FIBER (*Mescal Maguey*)	**Agave pseudotequilana**	MESCALFIBER AGAVE
MEXICAN HAT FIBER	**Sabal mexicana** (*Inodes m.*)	OAXACA PALMETTO
Mexican Sisal. HENEQUEN		
MILKWEED	**Asclepias** species	MILKWEED
Monkey Bass. CHIQUI CHIQUI		
MOORVA	**Sansevieria roxburghiana**	INDIA SANSEVIERIA
Newzealand-flax. PHORMIUM		
Newzealand-hemp. PHORMIUM		
OCHROMA WOOL (*Rabbitfoot-cotton*)	**Ochroma pyramidale** (*lagopus*)	WESTINDIES BALSA
OKRA FIBER (*Gumbo*)	**Hibiscus esculentus** (*Abelmoschus e.*)	OKRA
OLONA	**Touchardia latifolia**	OLONA
OSIER	**Salix** species	WILLOW
Ox-fiber. PALMETTO FIBER		
Paka. CADILLO		
Palma-istle. BARRETA		
PALMETTO FIBER (*Ox-fiber*)	**Sabal palmetto** (*jamesiana; schwarzi; Inodes p.; I. schwarzi*)	CABBAGE PALMETTO
PALMYRA FIBER (*Palmyra Bass*)	**Borassus flabellifer**	PALMYRAPALM
Panama Hatfiber. TOQUILLA		
PANDAN (*Sabotan*)	**Pandanus** species	SCREWPINE
Papermulberry. TAPPA		
Para Piassava. CHIQUI CHIQUI		
PHORMIUM (*Formio; Newzealand-flax; Newzealand-hemp*)	**Phormium tenax**	NEWZEALAND FIBERLILY
PIASSAVA (*Piassaba*) A type of brush fiber from various palms.		
BAHIA P. (*Piassaba*)	**Attalea funifera**	PIASSAVA ATTALEA (*Bahia-Piassava*)
IVORYCOAST P.	**Raphia hookeri**	IVORYCOAST RAFFIAPALM (*Ivorycoast-Piassava*)
Liberian P. WEST AFRICAN P.		
Madagascar P. VONITRA P.		
Para P. CHIQUI CHIQUI		
VONITRA P. (*Madagascar P.*)	**Vonitra fibrosa** (*thouarsiana; Dictyosperma fibrosum; Dypsis t.*)	PIASSAVA VONITRAPALM (*Madagascar-Piassava*)
WEST AFRICAN P.	**Raphia gigantea** (*hookeri* Chev., *not* Mann & Wendl.; *R. hookeri mancipiorum*)	GIANT RAFFIAPALM
WEST AFRICAN P. (*Liberian P.; West African Bass*)	**R. vinifera**	WINE R. (*West-African-Piassava*)
PINA (*Pineapple Fiber*)	**Ananas comosus**	PINEAPPLE
Pita de Corojo. COROJO		
PITAFLOJA	**Aechmea magdalenae** (*Ananas m.*)	PITAFLOJA
PITEIRA (*Aloe Fiber; Mauritius-hemp*)	**Furcraea gigantea**	PITEIRA FURCREA
PITRE (*Haitian Pita*)	**F. hexapetala** (*cubensis*)	PITRE F.
POCHOTE	**Ceiba aesculifolia**	POCHOTE CEIBA
Puerto Rican Hat-fiber. YARAY		
Rabbitfoot-cotton. OCHROMA WOOL		

Fiber Name	Plant Source: Botanical Name	Plant Source: S.P.N. Common Name
RAFFIA A type of surface fiber from various palms.		
BURI R.	**Corypha utan** (*elata; gebanga* Blume, *not* Hort.)	BURIPALM
IVORYCOAST R.	**Raphia hookeri**	IVORYCOAST RAFFIAPALM
MADAGASCAR R.	**R. pedunculata** (*ruffia*)	MADAGASCAR R.
WEST AFRICAN R.	**R. gigantea**	GIANT R.
RAMIE (*China Grass*)	**Boehmeria nivea**	RAMIE
RATTAN (*Reed*)	**Calamus** species	RATTANPALM
Riceroot. BROOMROOT		
ROSELLE FIBER	**Hibiscus sabdariffa altissima**	TALL ROSELLE
Sabotan. PANDAN		
Salvador Henequen. LETONA		
Samandoca. BARRETA		
SAMOHU Other species of this genus produce Samohu fiber but this species is the most important.	**Chorisia insignis**	SAMOHU CHORISIA
SELEB	**Sansevieria ehrenbergi**	SELEB SANSEVIERIA
Silkcotton. KAPOK		
SIMAL	**Salmalia malabarica** (*Bombax malabaricum*)	MALABAR SIMALTREE

Fiber Name	Plant Source: Botanical Name	Plant Source: S.P.N. Common Name
SISAL Some of the geographical types of Sisal recognized in the trade are as follows: AFRICAN S.; BAHAMA S.; HAITIAN S.; JAVA S.	**Agave sisalana**	SISAL AGAVE
Southern Moss. TREEBEARD		
Spanish Moss. TREEBEARD		
SUNN (*Sunn-hemp*)	**Crotalaria juncea**	SUNN CROTALARIA
SWEETGRASS	**Hierochloe odorata**	SWEETGRASS
Tampico. ISTLE		
TAPPA (*Kappa; Papermulberry*)	**Broussonetia papyrifera**	COMMON PAPERMULBERRY
Tientsin Jute. CHINGMA		
TOQUILLA (*Jipajapa; Panama Hatfiber*)	**Carludovica palmata**	HAT CARLUDOVICA (*Panama Hatpalm*)
TREEBEARD (*Florida Moss; Louisiana Moss; Southern Moss; Spanish Moss*)	**Tillandsia usneoides** (*Dendropogon u.*)	TREEBEARD TILLANDSIA (*Spanishmoss*)
Tula Istle. ISTLE		
VEGETABLESPONGE	**Luffa cylindrica**	SUAKWA VEGETABLESPONGE
West African Bass. WEST AFRICAN PIASSAVA		
YARAY (*Puerto Rican Hatfiber*)	**Sabal causiarum** (*Inodes c.*)	PUERTORICO PALMETTO (*Yaray*)
ZAMANDOQUE	**Hesperaloe funifera**	ZAMANDOQUE HESPERALOE

Fica'ria ver'na . . . **Ranunculus ficaria**

FI'CUS |w . . . FIG
afze'li . . . **F. eriobotryoides**
altis'sima . . . LOFTY F.
angustifo'lia . . . SLIMLEAF F.
asper'rima
au'rea . . . FLORIDA STRANGLER F.
auricula'ta . . . EARED S.F.
austra'lis . . . **F. rubiginosa**
bar'teri . . . BARTER F.
bellin'geri . . . BELLINGER F.
benghalen'sis . BANYAN F. (*Banyan*)
benjami'na . . . BENJAMIN F.
—como'sa . . . YELLOW B.F.
brevifo'lia (*populnea*) . SHORTLEAF F.
can'noni (*Artocarpus c.*) . CANNONS F.
capen'sis . . . CAPE F.
cari'ca |w . . . COMMON F.
—sylves'tris . . . CAPRI F.
For hort. var. of F. carica see **FRUIT AND EDIBLE NUT NAMES.**
clava'ta . . . CLUBBY F.
coop'eri . . . COOPER F.
cum'ingi . . . CUMING F.
cunningham'i . . . CUNNINGHAM F.
diversifo'lia (*lutescens*) . MISTLETOE F.
ebur'nea . . . IVORY F.
elas'tica . . . INDIARUBBER F.
—variega'ta . . . VARIEGATED I.F.
¢CHAUVIERI. HV. F. elastica
eriobotryoi'des (*afzeli*) . AFZELIUS F.
eugenioi'des . . . EUGENIA F.
falca'ta . . . SICKLE F.
ful'va . . . TAWNY F.
glabel'la . . . SMOOTH F.
glomera'ta . . . CLUSTER F.
hennea'na
his'pida (*oppositifolia*) OPPOSITELEAF F.
hook'eri . . . HOOKER F.
in'dica . . . INDIA F.
infecto'ria (*lucescens*) . . . DOTTED F.
jacquiniaefo'lia . . . JACQUINIA F.
krish'nae . . . KRISHNABOR F.
lutes'cens . . . **F. diversifolia**
lyra'ta . . . **F. pandurata**

FICUS, continued
macroph'ora
macrophyl'la . . . MORETONBAY FIG
magnolioi'des . . . MAGNOLIA F.
mariannen'sis . . . MARIANNE F.
microphyl'la . . . LITTLELEAF F.
min'ima Hort. . . . **F. pumila m.**
mitroph'ora
mysoren'sis . . . MYSORE F.
—subrepan'da
nekbu'du (*utilis*) . . . ZULU F.
nit'ida . . . **F. retusa**
no'ta
oppositifo'lia . . . **F. hispida**
padifo'lia . . . PLUMLEAF F.
palma'ta . . . PUNJAB F.
pal'meri . . . PALMER F.
pandura'ta (*lyrata*) . FIDDLELEAF F.
parcel'li . . . MOSAIC F.
philippinen'sis . . . PHILIPPINE F.
platyphyl'la . . . BROADLEAF F.
popul'nea . . . **F. brevifolia**
prin'ceps . . . PRINCELY F.
pseudocar'ica . . . ABYSSINIAN F.
pseudopal'ma
pu'mila (*repens; stipulata*) CLIMBING F.
—min'ima (*F. minima* Hort.) DWARF C.F.
quercifo'lia . . . OAKLEAF F.
rad'icans . . . ROOTING F.
—variega'ta . . . VARIEGATED R.F.
religio'sa . . . BOTREE F. (*Botree*)
re'pens . . . **F. pumila**
retu'sa (*nitida*) . . . INDIALAUREL F.
ri'go
roxburgh'i . . . ROXBURGH F.
rubigino'sa (*australis*) . . . RUSTY F.
ru'bra . . . RED F.
salicifo'lia . . . WILLOWLEAF F.
sap'ida . . . GOOSEBERRY F.
sca'bra . . . ROUGH F.
spraguea'na . . . SPRAGUE F.
stipula'ta . . . **F. pumila**
suringar'i . . . SURINGAR F.
sycomo'rus . SYCOMORE F. (*Sycomore*)
tincto'ria . . . DYE F.
triangula'ris

FICUS, continued
ulmifo'lia . . . ELMLEAF FIG
u'tilis . . . **F. nekbudu**
veluti'na . . . VELVET F.
villo'sa . . . SHAGGY F.
vo'geli . . . VOGEL F.

FIDDLENECK . . . **Amsinckia**
COAST F. . . . **A. spectabilis**
DOUGLAS F. . . . **A. douglasiana**
FIREWEED F. . . . **A. intermedia**
MENZIES F. . . . **A. menziesi**
TARWEED F. . . . **A. lycopsoides**

FIDDLEWOOD . . . **Citharexylum**
BERLANDIER F. . . . **C. berlandieri**
FLORIDA F. . . . **C. fruticosum**
HOLLYLEAF F. . . . **C. ilicifolium**
SPINY F. . . . **C. spinosum**
THREESPIKE F. . . . **C. tristachyum**

FIELDCRESS
AUSTRIAN F. . . . **Rorippa austriaca**
OBTUSE F. . . . **R. obtusa**
YELLOW F. . . . **R. sylvestris**

FIELDMADDER . **Sherardia; S. arvensis**

FIG . . . **Ficus**
ABYSSINIAN F. . . . **F. pseudocarica**
AFZELIUS F. . . . **F. eriobotryoides**
BANYAN F. . . . **F. benghalensis**
BARTER F. . . . **F. barteri**
BELLINGER F. . . . **F. bellingeri**
BENJAMIN F. . . . **F. benjamina**
BOTREE F. . . . **F. religiosa**
BROADLEAF F. . . . **F. platyphylla**
CANNONS F. . . . **F. cannoni**
CAPE F. . . . **F. capensis**
CAPRI F. . . . **F. carica sylvestris**
CLIMBING F. . . . **F. pumila**
CLUBBY F. . . . **F. clavata**
CLUSTER F. . . . **F. glomerata**
COMMON F. . . . **F. carica**
COOPER F. . . . **F. cooperi**
CUMING F. . . . **F. cumingi**
CUNNINGHAM F. . . . **F. cunninghami**
DOTTED F. . . . **F. infectoria**
DWARF CLIMBING F. **F. pumila minima**
DYE F. . . . **F. tinctoria**

Fig, continued
Eared Strangler F. **Ficus auriculata**
Elmleaf F. . . . . . . **F. ulmifolia**
Eugenia F. . . . . . **F. eugenioides**
Fiddleleaf F. . . . . . **F. pandurata**
Florida Strangler F. . . . **F. aurea**
Gooseberry F. . . . . . . **F. sapida**
Hooker F. . . . . **F. hookeri**
India F. . . . . **F. indica**
Indialaurel F. . . . . . **F. retusa**
Indiarubber F. . . . . **F. elastica**
Ivory F. . . . . **F. eburnea**
Jacquinia F. . . . **F. jacquiniaefolia**
Krishnabor F. . . . . . **F. krishnae**
Littleleaf F. . . . . **F. microphylla**
Lofty F. . . . . **F. altissima**
Magnolia F. . . . . **F. magnolioides**
Marianne F. . . . . **F. mariannensis**
Mistletoe F. . . . . **F. diversifolia**
Moretonbay F. . . . **F. macrophylla**
Mosaic F. . . . . **F. parcelli**
Mysore F. . . . . . . **F. mysorensis**
Oakleaf F. . . . . . **F. quercifolia**
Oppositeleaf F. . . . . . **F. hispida**
Palmer F. . . . . **F. palmeri**
Philippine F. . . . **F. philippinensis**
Plumleaf F. . . . . . . **F. padifolia**
Princely F. . . . . . . **F. princeps**
Punjab F. . . . . **F. palmata**
Red F. . . . . **F. rubra**
Rooting F. . . . . . . **F. radicans**
Rough F. . . . . **F. scabra**
Roxburgh F. . . . . . **F. roxburghi**
Rusty F. . . . . . . **F. rubiginosa**
Shaggy F. . . . . **F. villosa**
Shortleaf F. . . . . . **F. brevifolia**
Sickle F. . . . . **F. falcata**
Slimleaf F. . . . . **F. angustifolia**
Smooth F. . . . . **F. glabella**
Sprague F. . . . . . **F. spragueana**
Suringar F. . . . . . . **F. suringari**
Sycomore F. . . . . . **F. sycomorus**
Tawny F. . . . . **F. fulva**
Variegated Indiarubber F. **F. elastica variegata**
Variegated Rooting F. . **F. radicans v.**
Velvet F. . . . . **F. velutina**
Vogel F. . . . . **F. vogeli**
Willowleaf F. . . . . **F. salicifolia**
Yellow Benjamin F. **F. benjamina comosa**
Zulu F. . . . . **F. nekbudu**

Fighazel . . . . **Sycopsis**
Chinese F. . . . . . . **S. sinensis**

Figmarigold . . Mesembryanthemum: **Mesembryanthemum**

Figwort . . . . **Scrophularia**
California F. . . . . **S. californica**
Caucasian F. . . . . . **S. lateriflora**
Lanceleaf F. . . . . **S. lanceolata**
Lange F. . . . . . . **S. langeana**
Maryland F. . . . . **S. marilandica**
Mediterranean F. . . . **S. peregrina**
Smith F. . . . . **S. smithi**
Spring F. . . . . **S. vernalis**
Water F. . . . . **S. aquatica**
Western F. . . . . **S. occidentalis**
Wood F. . . . . **S. nodosa**

FILA'GO . . . . Fluffweed
califor'nica . . . . California F.

Filaree . . . . Alfileria; Heronbill: **Erodium** species

FILA'RIA . . . . . **PHILLYREA**

Filbert . . . . **Corylus**
∞Amax F. ∞**C. americana × C. maxima**
American F. . . . . . . **C. americana**
Beaked F. . . . . **C. cornuta**
California F. . . . . . **C. californica**
Caucasian F. . . **C. avellana pontica**
Chinese F. . . . . **C. chinensis**
Cob F. . . . . . **C. avellana grandis**
∞Colurnoid F. . . . . ∞**C. colurnoides**
European F. . . . . . . **C. avellana**
Giant F. . . . . **C. maxima**
Himalaya F. . . . . **C. ferox**
Japanese F. . . . . . **C. sieboldiana**
Manchu F. . . . . **C. s. mandshurica**
∞Mildred F. . . . ∞**C. mildredensis**
Siberian F. . . . . . **C. heterophylla**
∞Spiny F. . . . . . . ∞**C. spinescens**
Szechwan F. **C. heterophylla sutchuenensis**
Tibetan F. . . . . **C. tibetica**
Turkish F. . . . . **C. colurna**
∞Vilmorin F. . . . . . . ∞**C. vilmorini**
Yunnan F. **C. heterophylla yunnanensis**

FILIPEN'DULA (*ULMARIA*) Meadowsweet
camtschat'ica (*Spiraea c.; S. gigantea; S. kamtschatica*) . Kamchatka M.
Rosea (*rosea; Spiraea camtschatica r.*) hv.
hexapet'ala (*Spiraea filipendula; Ulmaria f.*) . . . . . . Dropwort
Double (*florepleno*) hv.
Grandiflora
purpu'rea (*palmata; Spiraea p.*) Japanese M.
Showy (*elegans*) hv.
White (*alba*)
ru'bra (*Spiraea lobata; Ulmaria r.*) Prairie M.
Carmine (*venusta; Spiraea v.*) hv.
ulma'ria (*Spiraea u.*) . European M.
Aureovariegata. hv.
Double (*plena*)

FI'LIX . . . . **CYSTOPTERIS**
See **FERN GENERA.**

Filmyfern . . . . **Trichomanes**
Prieur F. . . . . **T. prieuri**
Treemoss F. . . . . **T. krausi**

FIMBRISTY'LIS |w
autumna'lis |w
casta'nea |w
diphyl'la (*flaxa*) |w
milia'cea |w
puber'ula |w
therma'lis |w
vahl'i |w

Fingergrass . . **Digitaria** (erect spp.)
This name is applied to the erect species. See also Crabgrass.

Blue F. . . . . **D. didactyla**
Dune F. . . . . **D. runyoni**
Fundi F. . . . . **D. exilis**
Isle-of-pines F. . . . **D. simpsoni**
Longleaf F. . . . . **D. gracillima**
Millet F. . . . . . . **D. panicea**
Pentz F. . . . . **D. pentzi**
Plant City F. . . . . **D. subcalva**
Shaggy F. . . . . **D. villosa**
Slender F. . . . . . **D. filiformis**
Swaziland F. . . . **D. swazilandensis**
Texas F. . . . . **D. texana**
Twospike F. . . . . **D. pauciflora**
Woolly F. . . . . . . **D. eriantha**

Fingergrass . . . . . Chloris: **Chloris**

Fingerlime . . . . **Microcitrus**
See also Wildlime.
∞Australian F. . . . ∞**M. australasica**
Redpulp A. F. . . . **M. a. sanguinea**

Fingermillet . . . . . . Ragimillet: **Eleusine coracana**

Fiorin (English) . Bentgrass, Creeping: **Agrostis palustris**

Fir . . . . **Abies**
Algerian F. . . . . **A. numidica**
Alpine F. . . . . **A. lasiocarpa**
Apollo F. . . **A. cephalonica apollinis**
Azure Red F. . **A. magnifica glauca**
Balsam F. . . . . **A. balsamea**
Beissner Nordish F. ×**A. insignis beissneriana**
Bigcone Balsam F. **A. balsamea macrocarpa**
Blue Algerian F. . **A. numidica glauca**
Blueleaf Noble F. . **A. procera g.**
Blue Spanish F. . . . . **A. pinsapo g.**
Bornmueller F. . **A. bornmuelleriana**
Bracted Balsam F. **A. balsamea phanerolepis**
Bristlecone F. . . . . . . **A. venusta**
California Red F. . . . **A. magnifica**
Cascades F. . . . . **A. amabilis**
Cilician F. . . . . **A. cilicica**
Columnar Silver F. **A. alba columnaris**
Conical White F. **A. concolor conica**
Corkbark F. **A. lasiocarpa arizonica**
Dimplecone Nikko F. **A. homolepis umbellata**
Dwarf Alpine F. **A. lasiocarpa compacta**
Dwarf Balsam F. . **A. balsamea nana**
Dwarf Nikko F. . **A. homolepis scottae**
Dwarf Silver F. . . **A. alba compacta**
Ernest F. . . . . **A. ernesti**
Faber F. . . . . **A. fabri**
Farges F. . . . . **A. fargesi**
Faxon F. . . . . **A. faxoniana**
Flaky F. . . . . **A. squamata**
Forrest F. . . . . **A. forresti**
Fraser Balsam F. . . . . . **A. fraseri**
Georges F. . . . . **A. georgei**
Globe White F. . **A. concolor globosa**
Golden Nordmann F. **A. nordmanniana aurea**
Golden White F. . . **A. concolor a.**
Grand F. . . . . **A. grandis**
Greek F. . . . . . . **A. cephalonica**
Himalayan F. . . . . . **A. spectabilis**
Hoary White F. **A. concolor candicans**
Hudson Balsam F. **A. balsamea hudsonia**
Kawakami F. . . . . . **A. kawakami**
Khingan F. . . . . . **A. nephrolepis**
KingBoris F. . . . . . **A. borisiregis**
Korean F. . . . . **A. koreana**
Littlecone Veitch F. **A. veitchi nikkoensis**
Manchurian F. . . . . **A. holophylla**
Maries F. . . . . **A. mariesi**
Min F. . . . . **A. recurvata**
Momi F. . . . . **A. firma**
Nikko F. . . . . **A. homolepis**
Noble F. . . . . **A. procera**
Nordish F. . . . . ×**A. insignis**
Nordmann F. . . . **A. nordmanniana**
OliveconeVeitch F. **A. veitchi olivacea**
Pacific Silver F. . . . . **A. amabilis**
Pacific White F. **A. concolor lowiana**
Pindrow F. . . . . **A. pindrow**
Prostrate Fraser Balsam F. **A. fraseri prostrata**

FIR, continued
Purplecone White F. Abies concolor violacea
Red F. . . . . A. magnifica
Sacred F. . . . . A. religiosa
Sakhalin F. . . . . A. sachalinensis
Sentinel Silver F. A. alba pyramidalis
Shasta Red F. A. magnifica shastensis
Shensi F. . . . . . . A. chensiensis
Shortleaf Pindrow F. A. pindrow brevifolia
Shortleaf White F. . A. concolor b.
Siberian F. . . . . A. sibirica
Silver F. . . . . A. alba
Silverleaf Red F. A. magnifica argentea
Silver Noble F. . . . A. procera a.
Smoothbark Himalayan F. A. spectabilis brevifolia
Spanish F. . . . . A. pinsapo
Szechwan F. . . . A. sutchuenensis
Tomomi Nikko F. A. homolepis tomomi
Trojan Silver F. A. alba equi-trojani
Twisted Silver F. . . A. a. tortuosa
Twistleaf Nordmann F. A. nordmanniana tortifolia
Veitch F. . . . . A. veitchi
Vilmorin F. . . . . . ×A. vilmorini
Wattez White F. A. concolor wattezi
Weeping Silver F. . A. alba pendula
Weeping Spanish F. . A. pinsapo p.
Weeping White F. . . A. concolor p.
White F. . . . . A. concolor
Wilson Sakhalin F. A. sachalinensis nemorensis

Firebush, Chilean Embothrium coccineum

Firechalice . . . . Zauschneria
Arizona F. . . . . . . Z. arizonica
Broadleaf F. . . . . . . Z. latifolia
California F. . . . . Z. californica
Garrett F. . . . . Z. garretti
Gray California F. Z. californica microphylla
Thickleaf F. . . . . . Z. crassifolia

Firecracker-cactus Cleistocactus baumanni

Firespike . . . . Odontonema
Colombia F. . . O. schomburgkianum
Tall F. . . . . . O. callistachyum

Firethorn . . . . Pyracantha
Formosa F. . . . . P. koidzumi
Kansu F. . . P. crenulata kansuensis
Laland F. . . . P. coccinea lalandi
Narrowleaf F. . . . P. angustifolia
Nepal F. . . . . P. crenulata
Rogers F. . . . . . P. c. rogersiana
Scarlet F. . . . . . . P. coccinea
Sparse F. . . . . . P. c. pauciflora
Yellow Nepal F. . P. crenulata flava

Firetree . . . . Nuytsia
Australian F. . . . . N. floribunda

Fireweed . . Epilobium angustifolium

Firewheeltree . . . . . Stenocarpus
Cunningham F. . . S. cunninghami
Tall F. . . . . S. sinuatus
Willow F. . . . . . . S. salignus

FIRMIA'NA
sim'plex (*Sterculia platanifolia*) Chinese Parasoltree
Variegata. hv.

Fishberry . . . . Anamirta
Malay F. . . . . A. cocculus

Fishfuddletree . . . . Piscidia
Florida F. . . . . . P. communis
Jamaica F. . . . . . . P. piscipula

Fishhookcactus . . . . Ancistrocactus
Bigroot F. . . . . . . A. megarhizus
Scheer F. . . . . A. scheeri

Fishtailpalm . . . . Caryota
Philippine F. . . . . . C. cumingi
Rumph F. . . . . . C. rumphiana
Toddy F. . . . . C. urens
Tufted F. . . . . C. mitis

FIS'SIPES . . . . **CYPRIPEDIUM**
See **ORCHID GENERA, HARDY TERRESTRIAL GROUP.**

FISTULI'NA . . . . Fistulina
hepat'ica . . . . Beefsteak F.

FITTO'NIA . . . . Fittonia
gigan'tea . . . . Tall F.
verschaffel'ti
Pearce (*pearcei*) hv.
Silvernerve (*argyroneura*)

FITZROY'A . . . . Fitzroya
cupressoi'des (*patagonica*) Patagonian F.

FLACOUR'TIA
euphle'bia
in'dica (*ramontchi*) . . . Ramontchi (*Governorsplum*)
iner'mis . . . . Louvi (*Batokoplum*)
jan'gomas (*cataphracta*) . . Paniala
ru'kam . . . . Rukam
sepia'ria

Flambeautree . . . . Spathodea
Bell F. . . . . . . S. campanulata

Flamboyanttree . . . . Delonix regia

Flameacanthus . . . . Phlogacanthus

Flamebean . . . . Brownea
Broadleaf F. . . . . . B. latifolia
Glory F. . . . . . . B. grandiceps
Great F. . . . . . . B. macrophylla
Mountainrose F. B. rosa-de-monte
Orange F. . . . . B. capitella
Scarlet F. . . . . B. coccinea

Flamelily . . . . Pyrolirion
Golden F. . . . . P. aureum

Flamepea . . . . Chorizema
Bush F. . . . . C. varium
Heartleaf F. . . . . . C. cordatum
Holly F. . . . . C. ilicifolium
Showy Bush F. C. varium grandiflorum

Flametree . . . Bottletree, Flame: Brachychiton acerifolius

Flamingpoppy. Meconopsis heterophylla

Flatpod . . . . Adenocarpus
Canaryislands F. . . . A. foliolosus
Sticky F. . . . . A. viscosus

Flatsedge . . . . Cyperus
Bearded F. . . . . . . C. aristatus
Brazilian F. . . . C. adenophorus
Brook F. . . . . C. rivularis
Chinesemat F. . . . C. tegetiformis
Chufa F. . . . . . . C. esculentus
Cylinder F. . . . . . C. cylindricus
Engelmann F. . . . . C. engelmanni
Fendler F. . . . . . C. fendlerianus
Fern F. . . . . C. filicinus
Galingale F. . . . . . . C. longus
Gates F. . . . . C. gatesi
Green F. . . . . C. virens
Hochstetter F. . . . C. hochstetteri
Jointed F. . . . . . . C. articulatus
Longspike F. . . . C. longispicatus

Flatsedge, continued
Natal F. . . . . Cyperus natalensis
Nutgrass F. . . . . . . C. rotundus
Oneflower F. . . . . . . C. uniflorus
Papyrus . . . . C. papyrus
Pollard F. . . . . C. pollardi
Schweinitz F. . . . . . C. schweinitzi
Slender Umbrella F. C. alternifolius gracilis
Taperleaf F. . . . . C. acuminatus
Toothleaf F. . . . . . . C. dentatus
Umbrella F. . . . . C. alternifolius

Flax . . . . Linum
African F. . . . . . . L. africanum
Alpine F. . . . . L. alpinum
Austrian F. . . . . . L. austriacum
Berlandier Yellow F. L. berlandieri
Bush F. . . . . L. arboreum
Common F. . . . . L. usitatissimum
Dehiscent C. F. . . . L. u. crepitans
Dwarf Russianthistle F. L. salsoloides nanum
Flowering F. . . . L. grandiflorum
French F. . . . . L. gallicum
Golden F. . . . . L. flavum
Grooved F. . . . . . . L. sulcatum
Hairy F. . . . . L. hirsutum
Harebell F. . . . L. campanulatum
Hill F. . . . . L. collinum
Lewis F. . . . . L. lewisi
Low F. . . . . L. humile
Narbonne F. . . . . L. narbonnense
Narrowleaf F. . . L. angustifolium
NewMexico F. . L. neomexicanum
NewZealand F. . . . L. monogynum
Perennial F. . . . . . . L. perenne
Purging F. . . . . . L. catharticum
Rigid F. . . . . L. striatum
Russianthistle F. . . L. salsoloides
Slimleaf F. . . . . . L. tenuifolium
Sticky F. . . . . . . L. viscosum
Stiffstem F. . . . . . . L. rigidum
Woodland F. . . . . L. virginianum

Fleabane . . . . Erigeron
Alpine F. . . . . E. alpinus
Annual F. . . . . E. annuus
Arctic F. . . . . . . E. uniflorus
Aspen F. . . . . . E. macranthus
Aster F. . . . . . E. salsuginosus
Beach F. . . . . E. glaucus
BearRiver F. . . . . . . E. ursinus
Bitter F. . . . . E. acris
Bloomer F. . . . . . . E. bloomeri
Bonytip F. . . . . E. karvinskianus
Caucasian F. . . . . E. caucasicus
Coulter F. . . . . E. coulteri
Creeping F. . . . . E. repens
Dwarf F. . . . . E. nanus
Early Whitetop F. . . . E. vernus
Eaton F. . . . . E. eatoni
Engelmann F. . . . . E. engelmanni
Fernleaf F. . . . . . E. compositus
Gold F. . . . . E. aureus
Hairy F. . . . . E. concinnus
Himalayan F. . . . E. multiradiatus
Hoary F. . . . . E. canus
Horseweed F. . . . . E. canadensis
Howell F. . . . . E. howelli
Hyssopleaf F. . . . E. hyssopifolius
Leafy F. . . . . E. foliosus
Leiberg F. . . . . E. leibergi
Low F. . . . . E. pumilus
Narrowleaf Aster F. E. salsuginosus angustifolius
Orange F. . . . . . . E. aurantiacus
Oregon F. . . . . E. speciosus
Peregrine F. . . . . E. peregrinus

FLEABANE, continued
PHILADELPHIA F. Erigeron philadelphicus
PINK HIMALAYAN F. E. multiradiatus roseus
PINNATE F. . . . . E. pinnatisectus
POORROBINS-PLANTAIN . E. pulchellus
PORTER F. . . . . E. porteri
PURPLEDAISY F. . . . E. corymbosus
SHORN F. . . . . E. tonsus
SMOOTH F. . . . . E. glabellus
SPEARLEAF F. . . . E. lonchophyllus
SPRAWLING F. . . . . E. nudiflorus
SPREADING F. . . . . . E. divergens
TALL F. . . . . E. elatior
THOMPSON F. . . . . E. thompsoni
THREADLEAF F. . . . . . E. filifolius
THREENERVE F. . . . E. subtrinervis
TRAILING F. . . . . . . E. flagellaris
TRIFID F. . . . . E. trifidus
TUFTED F. . . . . . . E. caespitosus
VISCID F. . . . . E. viscidus

FLEECEFLOWER . . . . . Polygonum
See also BISTORT, CORNBIND, KNOTWEED, LADYSTHUMB, SMARTWEED.
ALPINE F. . . . . P. alpinum
BOKARAVINE F. . . P. baldschuanicum
HIMALAYAN F. . . . . P. affine
JAPANESE F. . . . . . P. cuspidatum
LOW J. F. . . . . . P. c. compactum
MOUNTAIN F. . . . P. amplexicaule
NEWBERRY F. . . . . P. newberryi
POKEWEED F. . P. phytolaccaefolium
SILKY F. . . . . P. sericeum
SILVERVINE F. . . . . . . P. auberti
TUBER F. . . . . . . P. multiflorum

FLEMIN'GIA
macrophyl'la (*congesta*) LONGLEAF WURRUS
strobilif'era

FLEU'RYA
aes'tuans

FLINDER'SIA . . . . . . FLINDERSIA
austra'lis . . . . . . BALLROOM F.
bennettia'na . . . . . . BENNETT F.
brayleya'na . . . . . . BRAYLEY F.
chatawaia'na . . . . . . CHATAWAY F.
colli'na . . . . HILL F.
ifflaia'na . . . . IFFLA F.
maculo'sa . . . . LEOPARD F.
oxleya'na . . . . LONGJACK F.
pimentelia'na . . . . . . PIMENTEL F.
schottia'na . . . . CUDGERIE F.

FLOATINGHEART . . . . . Nymphoides
INDIA F. . . . . N. indicum

FLOER'KEA |w . . . FALSEMERMAID
doug'lasi . . . . Limnanthes d.
proserpinacoi'des |w . FALSEMERMAID

FLORALFIRECRACKER Brevoortia; B. ida-maia

FLORIDA-BOXWOOD . Schaefferia frutescens

Floridacherry PITANGA: Eugenia uniflora

FLOSS-SILKTREE . . . Chorisia speciosa

FLOUREN'SIA . . . . . . TARBUSH
cer'nua . . . . AMERICAN T.

FLOWERINGQUINCE . . . Chaenomeles
ALPINE JAPANESE F. . C. japonica alpina
CHINESE F. . . . . C. sinensis
COMMON F. . . . . . . C. lagenaria
JAPANESE F. . . . . . . C. japonica

FLOWERINGRUSH . Butomus umbellatus

FLOWEROFANHOUR . Hibiscus trionum

FLOWEROFJOVE . . . . Lychnis flosjovis

FLUEG'GEA
microcar'pa
suffrutico'sa . . . . . Securinega s.

FLUFFGRASS . . . . . Triodia pulchella

FLUFFWEED . . . . Filago
CALIFORNIA F. . . . . F. californica

FLUMIN'EA (*SCOLOCHLOA*) RIVERGRASS
See GRASS GENERA.

FLUVELLIN . . . . Kickxia
ROUNDLEAF F. . . . . . . K. spuria
SHARPPOINT F. . . . . . . K. elatine

FLUXWEED . . Isanthus; I. brachiatus

FOAMFLOWER . . . . Tiarella
ALLEGANY F. . . . . . . T. cordifolia
COOLWORT F. . . . . . T. unifoliata
HIMALAYA F. . . . . . T. polyphylla
TREFOIL F. . . . . T. trifoliata

FOENIC'ULUM . . . . . . FENNEL
vulga're (*officinale*) . . . COMMON F.
FLORENCE (*dulce*) HV.
ITALIAN (*piperitum*)

FOKIEN'IA
hod'ginsi

FO'MES . . . . FOMES
applana'tus . . . . SHELF F.
lu'cidus . . . . LACQUERED F.
officina'lis (*Polyporus o.*) . LARCH F.

FONTANE'SIA . . . . . FONTANESIA
fortun'ei . . . . FORTUNE F.
phillyreoi'des . . . SYRIANPRIVET F.

FONTINA'LIS |w . . . . WATERMOSS
antipyret'ica . . . . FEVER W.

FORESTIER'A (*ADELIA* Michx., *not* L.) |w . . . . FORESTIERA
acumina'ta (*Adelia a.*) |w . TEXAS F.
—vesti'ta . . . . . . ARKANSAS F.
ligustri'na (*Adelia l.*) . . . PRIVET F.
neomexica'na (*F. acuminata parvifolia; Adelia p.*) . . . . NEWMEXICAN F.
pubes'cens . . . . DOWNY F.
rhamnifo'lia . . . . . BUCKTHORN F.

FORGETMENOT . . . . Myosotis
ALPINE F. . . . . M. alpestris
AZORES F. . . . . M. azorica
BAY F. . . . . M. laxa
FIELD F. . . . . M. arvensis
SWISS F. . . . . M. dissitiflora
TRUE F. . . . . M. scorpioides
TUFTED F. . . . . M. cespitosa
WOODLAND F. . . . . . M. sylvatica

FORKMOSS . . . . Dicranum
BROOM F. . . . . . . D. scoparium
GREENLAND F. . . D. groenlandicum

FORSELLE'SIA (*GLOSSOPETALON*) GREASEBUSH
meionan'dra (*Glossopetalon meionandrum*)
pun'gens (*Glossopetalon p.*) DWARF G.
spines'cens (*Glossopetalon s.*) SPINY G.

FORSY'THIA . . . . FORSYTHIA
europae'a . . . . ALBANIAN F.
fortun'ei . . . . F. suspensa f.
giraldia'na . . . . GIRALDI F.
∞**interme'dia** (*suspensa* × *viridissima*) ∞BORDER F.
₵CLUSTERED (*densiflora*) HV.
₵PRIMROSE (*primulina*)
₵SHOWY (*spectabilis*)
₵VITELLINA

FORSYTHIA, continued
japon'ica . . . JAPANESE FORSYTHIA
ova'ta . . . . EARLY F.
suspen'sa . . . . WEEPING F.
—fortun'ei (*F. fortunei*) . FORTUNE W.F.
—sie'boldi . . . . SIEBOLD W.F.
The type of the species.
DECIPIENS. HV. F. suspensa
₵GOLDBLOTCH (*variegata*)
₵PALE (*pallida*)
₵PURPLESTEM (*atrocaulis*)
viridis'sima . . . . . GREENSTEM F.
—korea'na . . . . . . KOREAN G.F.

Fortunae'a chinen'sis Platycarya strobilacea

FORTUNEA'RIA
sinen'sis

FORTUNEL'LA . . . . . . KUMQUAT
crassifo'lia . . . . MEIWA K.
hind'si . . . . HONGKONG K.
—chin'tou . . . . GOLDENBEAN H.K.
japon'ica (*Citrus j.*) . . . MARUMI K. (*Round K.*)
margari'ta (*Citrus m.*) . . NAGAMI K. (*Oval K.*)
polyan'dra . . . . MALAY K.

FOTHERGIL'LA . . . . FOTHERGILLA
gar'deni (*carolina*) . . . . DWARF F.
ma'jor . . . . LARGE F.
montic'ola . . . . ALABAMA F.
parvifo'lia

FOUNTAINGRASS . . Pennisetum ruppeli
CRIMSON F. . . P. r. atrosanguineum
PURPLE F. . . . . P. r. cupreum

FOUNTAINPLANT . . . Russelia lemoinei

FOUQUIER'IA
See SUCCULENTS.

FOUR-O'CLOCK . . . . Mirabilis
CALIFORNIA F. . . . . M. californica
COLORADO F. . . . . M. multiflora
COMMON F. . . . . M. jalapa
SLENDER F. . . . . . M. tenuiloba
SWEET F. . . . . . . M. longiflora
WISHBONEPLANT. M. bigelovi retrorsa

FOURPODSPURGE . . . . . Tetracoccus
CALIFORNIA F. . . . . . . T. dioicus
HALL F. . . . . T. halli
HOLLYLEAF F. . . . . . T. ilicifolius

FOXGLOVE . . . . Digitalis
BALEARIC F. . . . . D. dubia
COMMON F. . . . . D. purpurea
DANUBE F. . . . . D. laevigata
GRECIAN F. . . . . D. lanata
∞LUTZ F. . . . . ∞D. lutzi
ORIENTAL F. . . . . D. nervosa
RUSTY F. . . . . D. ferruginea
SIBERIAN F. . . . . D. sibirica
SPANISH F. . . . . F. laciniata
STRAW F. . . . . D. lutea
YELLOW F. . . . . D. ambigua

FOXTAIL . . . . Alopecurus
ALPINE F. . . . . A. alpinus
CAROLINA F. . . . . A. carolinianus
CREEPING F. . . . . . A. ventricosus
CRETE F. . . . . A. creticus
HOWELL F. . . . . A. howelli
MEADOW F. . . . . A. pratensis
MOUSE F. . . . . . . A. myosuroides
PACIFIC F. . . . . A. saccatus
SHORTAWN F. . . . . A. aequalis
WASHINGTON F. . . . . A. pallescens
WATER F. . . . . . . A. geniculatus

Foxtail . . . . . . Barley, Foxtail: **Hordeum jubatum**; Squirreltail, Bottlebrush: **Sitanion hystrix**

FRAGA'RIA |w . . . . Strawberry
america'na . . . . **F. vesca a.**
ananas'sa . . . . Pine S.
bractea'ta . . . . Bracted S.
califor'nica . . . . . California S.
chiloen'sis |w . . . . . . Chiloe S.
glau'ca |w . . . . Blueleaf S.
in'dica . . . . **Duchesnea i.**
mexica'na . . . . Mexican S.
The name Mexican Strawberry is sometimes misapplied to the Alpine Strawberry.
moscha'ta . . . . Hautbois S.
platypet'ala . . . . . Broadpetal S.
semperflo'rens . . . . . . Alpine S.
ves'ca |w . . . . . . European S.
—america'na (*F. americana*) American S.
virginia'na |w . . . . . Virginia S.
—illinoen'sis . . . . . . Illinois S.

FRAIL'EA . . . . Frailea
See **CACTUS GENERA.**

Franchetvine . . . . . **Sinofranchetia**
China F. . . . . **S. chinensis**

FRANCIS'CEA . . . . **BRUNFELSIA**
floribun'da . . . . . . **B. calycina f.**

FRANCO'A . . . . Francoa
appendicula'ta
ramo'sa . . . . Branching F.
—hy'brida
sonchifo'lia

Frangipani . . . . **Plumeria**
Bluntlobe F. . . . . . . **P. obtusa**
Cuban F. . . . . . . **P. emarginata**
Mexican F. . . . . . **P. acuminata**
Nosegay F. . . . . **P. rubra**
White F. . . . . **P. alba**

Fran'gula rupes'tris . . . . **Rhamnus r.**

FRANKE'NIA |w . . . . . Frankenia
grandifo'lia |w Yerbareuma Seaheath
pal'meri . . . . Palmer F.
pulverulen'ta

Frankincense . . . . **Boswellia**
Bible F. . . . . **B. carteri**
Elemi F. . . . . **B. frereana**
India F. . . . . **B. serrata**

FRANKLI'NIA . . . . . . Franklinia
alatama'ha (*Gordonia a.; G. pubescens*) Franklinia

FRANSE'RIA (*GAERTNERIA*) |w Bursage
Franseria, a later name, is conserved under International Rules.
acanthicar'pa
ambrosioi'des . . . . . Ambrosia B.
bipinnatif'ida
chamisso'nis
chenopodiifo'lia . . . . SanDiego B.
deltoi'dea . . . . Triangle B.
dis'color (*Gaertneria d.*) Skeletonleaf B.
dumo'sa |w . . . . White B.
eriocen'tra . . . . Woolly B.
ilicifo'lia . . . . Hollyleaf B.
tenuifo'lia . . . . Slimleaf B.
tomento'sa . . . . . . Woollyleaf B.

FRA'SERA . . . . Frasera (*Elkweed*)
albomargina'ta . . . Whitemargin F.
carolinen'sis . . . . . . Carolina F.
monta'na . . . . Small F.

FRASERA, continued
nit'ida . . . . Shiny Frasera
par'ryi . . . . Parry F.
specio'sa . . . . Showy F.

FRAXINEL'LA . . . . **DICTAMNUS**

FRAX'INUS |w . . . . Ash
america'na (*acuminata; alba; novaeangliae*) |w . . . . White A.
—ascidia'ta
—juglandifo'lia . . Walnutleaf W.A.
—microcar'pa . . . . Smallseed W.A.
—subcoria'cea . . . Thickleaf W.A.
angustifo'lia . . . . Narrowleaf A.
—austra'lis (*F. tamariscifolia*)
—lentiscifo'lia
anom'ala . . . . . . Singleleaf A.
attenua'ta . . . . **F. velutina toumeyi**
au'rea . . . . **F. excelsior**
berlandieria'na . . . . Berlandier A.
biltmorea'na . . . . . Biltmore A.
bungea'na . . . . Bunge A.
califor'nica . . . . . . **F. oregona**
carolinia'na (*platycarpa*) . Carolina A.
—rehderia'na . . . . . . Rehder A.
chinen'sis . . . . Chinese A.
—acumina'ta
—rhynchophyl'la . . . . Korean A.
coria'cea . . . . **F. velutina c.**
cuspida'ta . . . . Fragrant A.
—macropet'ala (*F. macropetala*)
dimor'pha . . . . Algerian A.
dipet'ala . . . . Twopetal A.
elon'za
excel'sior (*aurea*) . . . European A.
₵Argenteo-variegata. hv.
₵Aureo-variegata
₵Curlyleaf (*atrovirens; crispa; cucullata*)
₵Cutleaf (*asplenifolia*)
₵Dwarf (*globosa; nana; polemonifolia*)
₵Erosa
₵Golden (*aurea*)
₵Golden Weeping (*aurea pendula*)
₵Hesse (*hessei*)
₵Spectabilis
₵Verrucosa
₵Verticillata
₵Weeping (*pendula; wentworthi*)
floribun'da . . . . . . Himalayan A.
florida'na . . . . **F. pauciflora**
gregg'i . . . . Gregg A.
grif'fithi . . . . Griffith A.
holot'richa
hook'eri . . . . Hooker A.
lanceola'ta . . . . **F. pennsylvanica l.**
lentiscifo'lia . . . . . **F. rotundifolia**
longicus'pis . . . . . . Japanese A.
—sieboldia'na (*E. sieboldiana*) Siebold J.A.
low'elli . . . . Lowell A.
macropet'ala . . . . **F. cuspidata m.**
mandshur'ica . . . . Manchurian A.
This is sometimes mislabeled F. sieboldiana.
maries'i . . . . Maries A.
ni'gra (*sambucifolia*) . . . Black A.
novaean'gliae . . . . . **F. americana**
numid'ica . . . . Numidian A.
orego'na (*californica*) . . Oregon A.
—gla'bra . . . . . . Smooth O.A.
or'nus (*Ornus europaea*) Flowering A.
—rotundifo'lia . . . Roundleaf F.A.
oxyacanthifo'lia . . **F. xanthoxyloides**
oxycar'pa
pal'lisae

FRAXINUS, continued
parvifo'lia . . . . **F. rotundifolia**
pauciflo'ra (*floridana*) . Florida Ash
paxia'na . . . . Pax A.
pennsylvan'ica (*pubescens*) . . Red A.
—aucubaefo'lia . . Aucubaleaf A.
—lanceola'ta (*F. lanceolata; F. viridis*) Green A.
platycar'pa . . . . **F. caroliniana**
platypo'da
potamo'phila . . . . . Turkestan A.
profun'da . . . . **F. tomentosa**
pubiner'vis
quadrangula'ta . . . . Blue A.
raibocar'pa
retu'sa
—henrya'na
rotundifo'lia (*lentiscifolia; parvifolia*) Roundleaf A.
₵Weeping (*pendula*) hv.
sambucifo'lia . . . . **F. nigra**
sieboldia'na . . . . **F. longicuspis s.**
sogdia'na
spaethia'na (*stenocarpa*) . . Spaeth A.
syri'aca . . . . Syrian A.
tamariscifo'lia **F. angustifolia australis**
texen'sis . . . . Texas A.
tomento'sa (*profunda*) . . Pumpkin A.
uh'dei . . . . Shamel A.
veluti'na (*standleyi*) . . . Velvet A.
—coria'cea (*F. coriacea*) Leatherleaf A.
—gla'bra . . . . Smooth A.
—tou'meyi (*F. attenuata; F. toumeyi*) Toumey A.
vir'idis . . **F. pennsylvanica lanceolata**
xanthoxyloi'des (*oxyacanthifolia*) Afghan A.
—dumo'sa

FREE'SIA . . . . Freesia
arm'strongi . . . . . Armstrong F.
refrac'ta . . . . Common F.
Leichtlin (*leichtlini*) hv. F. refracta
White (*alba*)
Xanthospila
Yellow (*odorata*)

Fardel. hv. Freesia
Fischer (*fischeri*)
General Pershing
Hybrida
Purity
Rainbow
Sunset
Veronica (*splendens*)
Victory
Viola

FREMONT'IA (*FREMONTODENDRON*) . . . . Fremontia
califor'nica (*Fremontodendron californicum*) . . . . California F.
crassifo'lia . . . . Thickleaf F.
mexica'na . . . . SanDiego F.

FREMONTODEN'DRON **FREMONTIA**

Frenel'a rhomboi'dea **Callitris cupressiformis**

FREYCINE'TIA
banks'i

FREYLIN'IA
cestroi'des

Fringebell **Schizocodon; S. soldanelloides**
Alpine F. . . . . **S. s. alpinus**
Bigflower F. . . . **S. s. grandiflorus**
Hollyleaf F. . . . . **S. s. ilicifolius**

Fringecup . . . **Tellima**
Alaska F. . . . **T. grandiflora**
Fragrant F. . . . **T. odorata**

Fringelily . . . **Thysanotus**
Bauers F. . . . **T. baueri**
Forked F. . . . **T. dichotomus**
Manyflowered F. . . **T. multiflorus**
Rushleaf F. . . . **T. junceus**
Tuber F. . . . **T. tuberosus**
White T. F. . . . **T. t. albus**

Fringemyrtle . . . **Calytrix**
Haircup F. . . . **C. tetragona**
Shortleaf F. . . . **C. tenuifolia**
Sullivan F. . . . **C. sullivani**

Fringeorchid . . . **Habenaria**
Andrews F. . . . **×H. andrewsi**
Bigflower F. . . . **H. grandiflora**
Canby F. . . . **×H. canbyi**
Largepurple F. . . . **H. fimbriata**
Prairie F. . . . **H. leucophaea**
Smallpurple F. . . . **H. psycodes**
White F. . . . **H. blephariglottis**
Yellow F. . . . **H. ciliaris**

Fringetree . . . **Chionanthus**
Chinese F. . . . **C. retusus**
White F. . . . **C. virginicus**

FRITILLA'RIA . . . Fritillary
agres'tis . . . Illscented F.
atropurpu'rea . . . Purplespot F.
biflo'ra . . . Black F.
camtschatcen'sis . . . Kamchatka F.
cirrho'sa . . . Tendrilleaf F.
coccin'ea . . . **F. recurva**
delphinen'sis . . . **F. tubaeformis**
glau'ca . . . Siskiyou F.
imperia'lis . . . Imperial F.
japon'ica . . . Japanese F.
lanceola'ta . . . Riceroot F.
—grac'ilis . . . Frail R.F.
lilia'cea . . . White F.
meleag'ris . . . Checkered F.
—al'ba . . . White C.F.
—purpu'rea . . . Purple C.F.
pallidiflo'ra . . . Siberian F.
parviflo'ra . . . Smallflower F.
pluriflo'ra . . . Pink F.
pu'dica . . . Yellow F.
pur'dyi . . . Purdy F.
pyrena'ica . . . Pyrenees F.
recur'va (*coccinea*) . . . Scarlet F.
tenel'la . . . Slender F.
tubaefor'mis (*delphinensis*) . Alpine F.

Fritillary . . . **Fritillaria**
Alpine F. . . . **F. tubaeformis**
Black F. . . . **F. biflora**
Checkered F. . . . **F. meleagris**
Frail Riceroot F. **F. lanceolata gracilis**
Illscented F. . . . **F. agrestis**
Imperial F. . . . **F. imperialis**
Japanese F. . . . **F. japonica**
Kamchatka F. . . **F. camtschatcensis**
Pink F. . . . **F. pluriflora**
Purdy F. . . . **F. purdyi**
Purple Checkered F. **F. meleagris purpurea**
Purplespot F. . . . **F. atropurpurea**
Pyrenees F. . . . **F. pyrenaica**
Riceroot F. . . . **F. lanceolata**
Scarlet F. . . . **F. recurva**
Siberian F. . . . **F. pallidiflora**
Siskiyou F. . . . **F. glauca**
Slender F. . . . **F. tenella**
Smallflower F. . . . **F. parviflora**

Fritillary, continued
Tendrilleaf F. . **Fritillaria cirrhosa**
White Checkered F. **F. meleagris alba**
White F. . . . **F. liliacea**
Yellow F. . . . **F. pudica**

Frogbit . **Hydrocharis; H. morsus-ranae**

Frostwort . . . **Crocanthemum**
Amador F. . . . **C. suffrutescens**
Bush F. . . . **C. scoparium**
Canada F. . . . **C. canadense**
Greenes F. . . . **C. greenei**

FRUIT AND EDIBLE NUT NAMES

See also **CITRUS GENERA AND CITRUS HYBRIDS, FRUIT GROUP COMMON NAMES,** and **NUT GROUP COMMON NAMES.**

For the following lists of Fruit and Nut Names the Editorial Committee is mainly indebted to M. J. Dorsey, Chairman of the Committee on Nomenclature of the American Pomological Society; to H. P. Gould, formerly Chief of the Division of Fruit and Vegetable Crops and Diseases, Bureau of Plant Industry, U. S. Department of Agriculture, and to his associates Dr. G. M. Darrow, C. A. Reed (Nuts), W. W. Aldrich, Charles F. Kinman, C. S. Pomeroy, and H. P. Traub; to H. S. Wolfe, Head Professor of Horticulture, Florida College of Agriculture, and to I. J. Condit, W. P. Tufts, and Herbert J. Webber, California College of Agriculture and Agricultural Experiment Station. Walter T. Swingle, well-known authority on Citrus, has given invaluable assistance with that group, and the late G. A. Zimmerman, of Harrisburg, Pa., with Pawpaw and Persimmon. To all of these collaborators the Committee wishes to extend cordial thanks.

Presumably most, if not all, of the hort. var. listed here are clons.

Abbreviations of Originators and Introducers of Fruits and Nuts

Ada., G.	Gerald Adams, Moorhead, Iowa.
Ada., H.	Henry Adams, Scotts, Mich.
Adams	Adams Bros., Springfield, Mass.
Adlum	J. Adlum, District of Columbia.
Akin	W. J. Akin.
Alb.	Albright, Placerville, Calif.
Alba.	B. F. Albaugh, Covington, Ohio.
Ale.	O. A. Alexander, Mt. Pulaski, Ill.
Alios	A. Alios.
All.	S. Allinson.
Allen, G.	Glenn W. Allen, Middleville, Mich.
Allen, W.	W. F. Allen, Salisbury, Md.
Alley	Mrs. C. H. Alley, Pascagoula, Miss.
Alt.	H. E. Altman, Nooksack, Wash.
Alv.	M. E. Alverson, R. 1, Howard City, Mich.
And.	W. C. Anderson, Calif.
Andr.	F. P. Andrus, Almont, Mich.
Ani.	Anita Plantation, Saint James Parish, La.
Ant.	A. B. Anthony, R. 3, Sterling, Ill.
App.	W. I. Appleby Ranch, Esparto, Calif.
Arm.	Armstrong Bros., Ontario, Calif.
Arn.	C. Arnold, Paris Nurseries, Paris, Ont., Canada.
Arndt	J. H. Arndt, Arlington, Md.
Arris	J. Arris.
Atki.	Ralph P. Atkinson, Setauket, L. I., N. Y.
Aur.	Geo. D. Aurand, Lewistown, Pa.

FRUITS AND EDIBLE NUTS, continued

Aus.	Frank B. Austin, Milford, Del.
Ayer	O. H. Ayer.
Bac.	J. Backman, Altus, Ark.
Bacon	G. M. Bacon, DeWitt, Ga.
Baker	Mrs. Caroline Baker.
Bal.	S. J. Baldwin, Seneca, Kan.
Ball	J. Ball.
Balla.	L. A. Ballard, Pennington, Calif.
Bals.	W. G. Balsey, Greensboro, N. C.
Balt.	Baltet Bros., Troyes, Aube, France.
Banks	C. E. Banks.
Bar.	D. H. Barnes, Poughkeepsie, N. Y.
Barc.	Walter Barclay, Knightsen, Calif.
Bar., H.	Howard G. Barnes, Fayetteville, Ohio.
Barnh.	Harmon Barnhart, Rt. 6, Mt. Vernon, Ohio.
Barr	C. C. Barr, Esparto, Calif.
Bar., T.	Theo. Barnes, Washington, D. C.
Bart.	F. H. Bartlett, Stamford, Conn.
Bartr.	J. Hibbard Bartram, Milltown, Pa.
Bass	J. B. Bass, Bass, Texas.
Bat.	C. F. Batham Ranch, Chico, Calif.
Bates	R. Bates, Jackson, S. C.
Baum	J. G. Baum, Los Gatos, Calif.
Bea.	J. F. Beaver, Dayton, Ohio.
Beam	Mrs. Beam.
Beam, E.	E. C. Beam, Mt. Oreb, Ohio.
Bec.	Theo. Bechtel, Ocean Springs, Miss.
Beck	Daniel Beck, Rt. 2, Hamilton, Mich.
Beem.	H. W. Beeman, New Preston, Conn.
Belt	W. Belt, Williamsburg, Ohio.
Bent.	W. A. Benton, Wassaic, N. Y.
Benth.	John Benthien, Rt. 1, Wheatland, Iowa.
Bents	W. A. Bents, Cresco, Iowa.
Beq.	Benjamin Bequette, Visalia, Calif.
Ber.	Russell Berger, Cove Gap, Pa.
Ber., L.	L. E. Berckmans, Rome, Ga.
Ber., P.	P. J. Berckmans, Fruitland Nurseries, Augusta, Ga.
Bert.	M. Bertin, Versailles, France.
Best	Best.
Bid.	A. I. Bidwell, Arlington, Fla.
Bidw.	Bidwell Ranch, Chico, Calif.
Big.	M. J. Bigelow Ranch, Oakley, Calif.
Bil.	Bilyeu, Caroline County, Md.
Biles	H. A. Biles.
Bin.	C. D. Bingham.
Bis.	Bishop Ranch, Goleta, Calif.
Black	M. Black.
Bla., J.	J. H. Black & Son Co., Hightstown, N. J.
Blan.	L. Blanchard, Abington, Mass.
Ble.	Mrs. Bleeker.
Bliss	Miss Abbie C. Bliss, Bradford, Vt.
Blo.	H. W. Blowers, Westfield, N. Y.
Blue	G. W. Blue, Indianapolis, Ind.
Boell.	L. B. Boellner, Roswell, N. Mex.
Bon.	M. Bonnet.
Boon	J. Boon.
Bou.	Bourgeois.
Bour.	Fred Bourne, Milford, Mich.
Bow.	Elgin Bowers, Lockhart, Texas.
Bradt	W. J. Bradt.
Brake	Wm. H. Brake, Rocky Mount, N. C.
Bre.	Dr. Bretonneau, Bourgueil, Indre-et-Loire, France.
Brew.	C. H. Brewer, Rahway, N. J.
Bri.	J. G. Briggs, near Yuba City, Calif.
Brier	B. B. Brier.

FRUITS AND EDIBLE NUTS, continued

Brier, W.	W. W. Brier, Centerville, Calif.
Brin.	C. T. Briney, McMinnville, Ore.
Brit.	A. H. Briton.
Brix.	C. T. Brixey, Gervais, Ore.
Bro.	Lord Brooks, Twickenham, Middlesex, England.
Brod.	R. Brodie.
Bro., F.	Fred Brooks, French Creek, W. Va.
Br., W.	Mrs. Williard Brown, Rock Bridge, Ohio.
Bub.	J. G. Bubach, Princeton, Ill.
Buc.	Parke Buckley, Edgewood, Iowa.
Buck.	Benjamin Buckman, Farmingdale, Ill.
Budd	Budd.
Budd, J.	J. L. Budd, Ames, Iowa.
Bue.	H. A. Buehring, Oshkosh, Wis.
Buel	Jessie Buel, Albany, N. Y.
Buel, J.	Judge Buel.
Buf.	D. Buffum.
Bul.	J. Bullock.
Bull	E. W. Bull, Concord, Mass.
Bun.	D. Bundy, Belmont County, Ohio.
Buny.	E. A. Bunyard, Allington, Maidstone, England.
Bur.	John Burkhardt, Fayette County, Texas.
Burb.	Luther Burbank, Santa Rosa, Calif.
Burk.	J. H. Burkett, Clyde, Texas.
Burr	J. Burr, Leavenworth, Kan.
Burs.	E. H. Burson Nursery, Clifton, N. Y.
Burt.	E. L. Burton, Grayson County, Texas.
Burt., E.	Emmit Burton, Rt. 3, Utica, Ky.
Bush	C. D. Bush, Eagle Creek, Ore.
Camp.	James Campbell, Pensacola, Fla.
Campb.	Judge G. W. Campbell, Delaware, Ohio.
Campv.	Campville Nurseries, Campville, Fla.
Capps	Capps Brothers, Mt. Pulaski, Ill.
Car.	S. P. Carpenter, New Rochelle, N. Y.
Card.	Robert Cardinell, East Lansing, Mich.
Carm.	John Carmichael, Harwood, Texas.
Carr.	R. D. Carr, Magnolia, N. C.
Cas.	Mr. Casser.
Cay.	A. J. Caywood, Marlboro, N. Y.
C.C.S.	California Citrus Experiment Station.
C.E.F.	Central Experimental Farm, Ottawa, Canada.
Cel.	George B. Cellon, Miami, Fla.
Cerre	G. Cerre.
Cha.	Franklin Chairs, Anne Arundel County, Md.
Chab.	Mr. Chabot.
Chap.	H. Chapin.
Chapm.	H. Chapman.
Chapm., M.	M. Chapman.
Chase	Chase Place, Whittier, Calif.
Chi.	Mr. Chipman.
Chip.	Chipola Nursery, Appalachicola, Fla.
Chis.	L. C. Chisholm, Springhill, Tenn.
Clai.	P. Clairgeau.
Cla., L.	L. Clapp.
Clark	Fred E. Clark, Portland, Ore.
Clark, C.	Miss Clara Clark, McCutcheonville, Ohio.
Clark, E.	Eugene J. Clark, Ludlow, Mass.
Cla., T.	T. Clapp.
Cle.	A. Clement, Dracut, Mass.
Cl., F.	Frank Clark, Lamoille, Minn.
Cli.	May Cline, Phillipsburg, N. J.
Clo.	J. M. Clough, Stamford, Conn.
Cloud	R. L. Cloud, Independence, La.
C.N.C.	California Nursery Co., Niles, Calif.
Coa.	Leonard Coates, Morgan Hill, Calif.
Coc.	E. H. Cocklin, Shepherdstown, Pa.
Coe	J. Coe.
Coe, A.	A. J. Coe, Meriden, Conn.
Coe, F.	Fred Coe, Rt. 5, Fulton, N. Y.
Coit	J. Eliot Coit, Encinitas, Calif.
Col.	J. B. Collamer.
Cole.	Mrs. Theo. Coleman, Saltsburg, Pa.
Coll.	John Collison, Bridgeville, Del.
Colt.	Colton.
Colu.	Columbia & Okanagan Nursery Co., Wenatchee, Wash.
Com.	H. W. Comfort, Fallsington, Pa.
Con.	A. Connett, McLeansville, N. C.
Cons.	T. Constant.
Coo.	D. W. Coolidge, Pasadena, Calif.
Cook	O. C. Cook, Milford, Mass.
Coombs	Mr. Coombs, Nestor, Calif.
Coop.	S. Cooper.
Coop., M.	M. L. Cooper, Summers, Ark.
Cor.	M. Corsaint.
Cors.	G. H. Corsan, Islington, Ont., Canada.
Cors., W.	Walter H. Corson, Plymouth Meeting, Pa.
Cov.	Frederick V. Coville, U. S. D. A.
Cover	J. A. Cover Ranch, Modesto, Calif.
Cowen	R. Cowen.
Cowle	B. A. Cowle, Rt. 8, Defiance, Ohio.
Cox	U. T. Cox.
Cra.	Wm. Crawford, Middletown, N. J.
Crai.	W. H. Craighead, Brigham, Utah.
Cran.	Dr. J. R. Crandell.
Cran., R.	R. W. Crandall, Newton, Kan.
Cranz	E. F. Cranz, Ira, Ohio.
Crath	Rev. P. C. Crath, Toronto, Ont., Canada.
Cre.	Diana Crehore, Milton, Mass.
Crei.	W. A. Creitz, Cambridge City, Ind.
Cro.	Crosby, Billerica, Mass.
Croo.	Crooks.
Crot.	Crothers, Neosho Falls, Kan.
Cruse	E. W. Cruse.
Cun.	Goldman Cundiff, Rt. 1, East View, Ky.
Cur.	Joseph Curtis, Grand Prairie, Ill.
Cur., J.	J. B. Curtis, Orange Heights, Fla.
Cut.	T. Cuthbert.
Dager	H. M. Dager, Camden, Del.
Dan.	E. W. Daniels.
Dana	F. Dana.
Dar.	G. M. Darrow, U. S. D. A.
Dard.	O. K. Darden, Lone Grove, Okla.
Darl.	Thos. Darlington, West Chester, Pa.
Davis	G. W. Davis.
Davis, J.	John Davis, Banks, Ore.
DeC.	Count DeColoma.
DeJ.	M. DeJonghe, Brussels, Belgium.
Del.	R. Delamatter.
Delm.	A. G. Delmas, Pascagoula, Miss.
DeLo.	M. DeLongueval.
Dem.	W. C. Deming, Litchfield, Conn.
Dep.	Will. Dependahl, Delhi, Ill.
Dery	A. Dery.
DeV.	F. E. DeVan, Rock Creek, Ohio.
DeW.	DeWitt Ranch, Sutter, Calif.
Dic.	O. Dickinson, Salem, Ore.
Dic., A.	A. J. Dickinson, Los Angeles, Calif.
Dike	A. C. Dike.
Din.	L. F. Dintleman, Belleville, Ill.
Dish.	D. C. Disher, Garden Grove, Calif.
Dixon	F. Dixon.
Dodd	W. Dodd.
Dor.	J. F. Dorman.
Dou.	J. Dougall, Amherstburgh, Canada.
Dough.	L. D. Dougherty, Crane, Mo.
Dow.	Charles Downing, Newburgh, N. Y.
Down.	S. Downer, Dorchester, Mass.
Drake, H.	H. C. Drake, Suisun, Calif.
Drake, N.	N. F. Drake, Fayetteville, Ark.
Drep.	Mrs. Blake Dreppert, Roanoke, W. Va.
Duane	J. Duane.
Dud.	J. W. Dudley.
Duis	J. G. Duis, Shattuc, Ill.
Duley	John Duley, New Haven, Ill.
Dun.	W. A. Dunnett, Dedham, England.
Dunb.	John Dunbar, Dept. of Parks, Rochester, N. Y.
Dunba.	John Dunbar, Oshtemo, Mich.
Dunn	J. Dunn.
Duq.	Abbe Duquesne.
Dur.	Miss Durham.
Dut.	E. C. Dutton, Otto Keup Pl., Anaheim, Calif.
Dye.	Dyehouse, Lincoln County, Ky.
Eaton	U. Eaton, Cambridge City, Ind.
Eaton, C.	C. Eaton, Concord, N. H.
E.&B.	Ellwanger & Barry, Rochester, N. Y.
Ede	Henry Ede, Cobden, Ill.
Edm.	Lewis Edmunds, Rt. 1, Glasgow, Ky.
Ehr.	V. E. Ehrhardt, Santa Ana, Calif.
Ell.	Wyman Elliot, Minneapolis, Minn.
Ely	S. Ely.
Emer.	Miss Etta Emerick, West Camp, N. Y.
End.	G. W. Endicott, Villa Ridge, Ill.
Eng.	Harold English, Chatham, Ont., Canada.
Engle	C. C. Engle, Paw Paw, Mich.
Engle, H.	H. M. Engle, Marietta, Pa.
Eri.	P. A. Erickson, Oakley, Calif.
Ers.	G. A. Ersenberger, Bloomington, Ill.
Esh.	J. K. Eshelman.
Esp.	Maj. Esperen.
Etter	A. F. Etter, Ettersburg, Calif.
Evans	J. A. Evans, Arlington, Texas.
Evers	A. H. Evers, Petoskey, Mich.
Ewell	M. F. Ewell, Accomac Co., Va.
Fal.	C. Falkner, Waco, Texas.
Far.	L. J. Farmer, Pulaski, N. Y.
Fay	L. Fay, Portland, N. Y.
Fel.	O. F. Felton, Camden, N. J.
F.G.N.	Felix Gillet Nursery, Nevada City, Calif.
Fil.	G. Filler, Milton, N. Y.
Fit.	Fitzgerald Nurseries, Stephenville, Texas.
Fitz.	Dell Fitzgerald, Washougal, Wash.
Fle.	Mrs. Maria Fleming.
Flo.	Wm. Flowers, Lamberton, N. C.
Flory	D. Flory.
Folts	Mrs. C. Folts, Locke, N. Y.
For.	C. Forkert, Ocean Springs, Miss.
Fos.	J. T. Foster, Medford, Mass.
Fox	B. S. Fox.

FRUITS AND EDIBLE NUTS, continued

Fox, R.	Roland D. Fox, Eonda, N. Y.
Fre.	H. F. Freeny.
Fre., A.	A. F. Freeny, Wicomico Co., Md.
Free.	Mr. Freeman.
Freel	Mrs. E. W. Freel, Pleasantville, Iowa.
F.&S.	Fish & Sons, Stillwater, Calif.
Ful.	Andrew S. Fuller, Ridgewood, N. J.
Gal.	Wm. H. Galloway, Blue Ash, Ohio.
Gandy	W. S. Gandy, Newport, N. J.
Gar.	C. W. Garfield, Grand Rapids, Mich.
Garb.	J. B. Garber.
Gard.	Gardner Nurseries, Osage, Iowa.
Garr.	Mr. Garriel.
Garw.	W. S. Garwood, Oakley, Calif.
Gau.	W. T. Gaulden, Quitman, Ga.
Gaume	L. Gaume.
Gei.	C. C. Geissler, Sharon, Mass.
Gel.	J. U. Gellatly, Westbank, B.C., Canada.
Ger.	Jos. Gerardi, O'Fallon, Ill.
Ger. N.	Gerardi Nurseries, O'Fallon, Ill.
Gib.	W. Gibbons.
Gid., P. M.	Peter M. Gideon, Excelsior, Minn.
Gif.	N. Gifford.
Giles	A. E. Giles, Peoria, Ill.
Gil., F.	Felix Gillet, Nevada City, Calif.
Gil., H.	H. N. Gillet.
Gill	Mr. Gill, Broad St., New York, N. Y.
Gir.	L. H. Girton, Bristol, Ind.
Glass	A. Glass.
Gle.	S. Gleason.
Glen	Glen St. Mary Nurseries Co., Glen St. Mary, Fla.
G.N.C.	Green Nursery Co.
God.	T. K. Godbey, Waldo, Fla.
Gof.	Bert Goforth, New Haven, Ill.
Goh.	Mrs. Martha Goheen, Pa. Furnace, Pa.
Gohn	N. Gohn, Deep Creek, Va.
Got.	Edward Gottfried, Key Largo, Fla.
Gou.	M. Goubault.
Gov.	R. C. Govett, Sequin, Texas.
Gow., G.	G. W. Gowing.
Gow., J.	J. D. Gowing, North Reading, Mass.
Gra.	Mr. Granville, Brewington, Md.
Grah.	S. H. Graham, Bostwick Rd., Ithaca, N. Y.
Grant	C. W. Grant, Iowa Is., Westchester Co., N. Y.
Grat.	L. Graton, Whitman, Mass.
Gray	A. M. Gray, Milwaukie, Ore.
Gre.	Greening Bros., Monroe, Mich.
Green	C. A. Green, Rochester, N. Y.
Green, W.	W. Green, Vergennea, Vt.
Gregg	R. & P. Gregg, Ohio Co., Ind.
Grein	N. Grein, Hermann, Mo.
Gre., S.	S. Greenfield, Ottawa, Ont., Canada.
Gri.	G. W. Griffin, Casco, Mich.
Grie.	A. H. Griesa, Lawrence, Kan.
Grif.	Griffing Bros., MacClenny, Fla.
Gro.	Russell Grover.
Groot	S. C. Groot.
Guild	Dr. Guild, Atlanta, Ga.
Gut.	C. Guthrie.
Had.	Geo. G. Hadley, Leominster, Mass.
Hage	Chas. Hage, Vandalia, Ill.
Hal.	Nicholas Hallock, Milton, N. Y.
Halb.	H. A. Halbert, Coleman, Texas.
Hale	J. H. Hale, South Glastonbury, Conn.
Hales	Henry Hales, Ridgewood, N. J.
Hale, W.	W. L. Hale, Fullerton, Calif.

FRUITS AND EDIBLE NUTS, continued

Hall, L.	Miss Lena Hall, Pascagoula, Miss.
Hall, L. C.	L. C. Hall, Fairview, Pa.
Ham.	E. H. Hamblin, Pittsville, Md.
Hamb.	T. M. Hamback, Warrenton, Va.
Hamp.	J. M. Hampton Ranch, Live Oak, Calif.
Han.	Thomas Hancock, Burlington, N. J.
Hand	Gen. Hand.
Hann	George Hann, Bridgman, Mich.
Hanna.	A. J. Hannah, Whigville, Conn.
Hans.	N. E. Hansen, S. Dak. Agr. Exp. Station, Brookings, S. Dak.
Har.	John S. Harris, La Crescent, Wis.
Hard., A.	Abbe Hardenpont.
Hardi.	Ralph Harding.
Hard., M.	M. Hardenpont.
Hardo.	P. L. Hardow.
Hare	P. T. Hare.
Harr.	Howard Harris, Allegan, Mich.
Hart.	John Hartley, Napa, Calif.
Hass	Rudolph G. Hass, La Habra Hts., Calif.
Hat.	E. C. Hatheway.
Hatch	A. T. Hatch, Suisun, Calif.
Hath.	W. Hathaway, Madison, Ohio.
Hath., B.	B. Hathaway, Marcellus, Mich.
Hau.	Hauseman Bros., Hilton, N. Y.
Haupt.	Col. W. W. Haupt, Kyle, Texas.
Hav.	B. H. Haverland.
Hav., R.	R. E. Havice, Rt. 1, Bellevue, Ohio.
Haw.	M. Hawley.
Hay.	A. O. Haymaker, Earlville, Ohio.
Hayn.	J. H. Haynes, Delphi, Ind.
Haz.	D. C. Hazelton.
Hazz.	A. G. Hazzard, Vista, Calif.
Heath	General Heath, Roxbury, Mass.
H.&C.	C. L. Hoag & B. W. Clark, Lockport, N. Y.
Heep	T. Heep, Austin, Texas.
Hefty	Thos. C. Hefty, Evansville, Wis.
Hei.	C. W. H. Heideman.
Heib.	Harry A. Heibner, Danville, Iowa.
Hel.	Andrew Helmuth, Rt. 3, Napanee, Ind.
Helm.	Jas. K. Helmick, Columbus Junction, Iowa.
Hen.	H. A. Henneman, Portland, Ore.
Hep.	G. Y. Hepler, Rt. 5, South Bend, Ind.
Her.	J. E. Heritage, Marlton, N. J.
Herb.	N. H. Herbemont, Columbia, S. C.
Herg.	John Hergert, Saint Peter, Minn.
Hers.	John W. Hershey, Downingtown, Pa.
Hiatt	J. Hiatt, Peru, Madison, Iowa.
High	A. H. High, Jordon, Ont., Canada.
Hil.	W. W. Hilborn, Leamington, Ont., Canada.
Hiley	Eugene Hiley, Marshallville, Ga.
Hilt.	Mrs. R. H. Hilton, Pulaski, N. Y.
Hind	Geo. Hind & Co., Fullerton, Calif.
Hob.	Jas. R. Hobson, Jasper, Ga.
Hod.	J. C. Hodges, Eastern Tenn.
Hodge	H. G. Hodge, York, Ill.
Hof.	O. J. Hoffman, Henderson, Ky.
Hol.	E. B. Holden, Hilton, N. Y.
Hoo.	Hoogen Dyke, Boskoop, Holland.
Hook.	C. G. Hooker, Rochester, N. Y.
Hoop.	Wilmer P. Hoopes, Forest Hill, Md.

FRUITS AND EDIBLE NUTS, continued

Hoov.	Kermit C. Hoover, Glenford, Ohio.
Hor.	B. Hornsby.
Hos.	T. H. Hoskins.
Host.	L. K. Hostetter, Rt. 3, Lancaster, Pa.
Hou.	A. Houghton, Lynn, Mass.
How., A.	A. B. Howard & Son, Belchertown, Mass.
How., E.	Everett C. Howard.
Howe., T.	T. Howell.
How., S.	S. S. Howard.
H.S.V.	Hort. Exp. Sta., Vineland, Ont., Canada.
Hub.	I. G. Hubbard, Nokomis, Ill.
Huba.	Louis Hubach, Judsonia, Ark.
Huen	E. F. Huen, Eldora, Iowa.
Huff	L. S. Huff, White Pigeon, Mich.
Huls.	D. H. Hulseman, Lakeside, Wash.
Hulse	John Hulse, Burlington, N. J.
Hunt	C. Hunt.
Hunt, J.	J. T. Hunt.
Hus.	J. D. Husted, Vineyard, Ga.
Hut.	W. J. Hutchinson Estate, Caspiana, Fla.
Hynes	E. F. Hynes, West Plains, Mo,
Hys.	David Hyslop, Brookline, Mass.
I.A.S.	Iowa Agr. Exp. Sta.
I.H.S.	Iowa State Horticultural Society.
Imlay	J. Imlay, Muskingum Co., Ohio.
Ing., E.	E. C. Ingram, Frogmore, England.
Ing., J.	J. A. Ingram, East Bradford, Pa.
Ing., M.	M. Ingram.
Irv.	L. K. Irvine, Rt. 8, Menomonee, Wis.
Ives	J. M. Ives, Salem, Mass.
Ives, H.	H. Ives, Cincinnati, Ohio.
Jab.	M. Jaboulay, Ouillins, near Lyons, France.
Jac.	Homer L. Jacobs, Kent, Ohio.
James	S. H. James, Mound, La.
Jan.	W. W. Janson, Jefferson, Ohio.
J.&D.	Jamin & Durand.
Jef.	I. Jefferis.
Jeff.	G. Jeffry.
J.H.R.	John Henle Ranch, Davis, Calif.
Joc.	I. L. Jockett, Hart, Mich.
Joh.	Johnson.
Joh., A.	A. S. Johnson, Washington, D. C.
Joho	Brother Joseph Joho, Mt. Angel College, St. Benedict, Ore.
Johs.	J. E. Johnson, Pottawattamie Co., Iowa.
Joh., W.	W. H. Johnson, Northboro, Mass.
Jol.	Geo. C. Jolliffe, Uffington, W. Va.
Jones	J. F. Jones Nursery, Lancaster, Pa.
Jon., J.	Jessie L. Jones, near Escondido, Calif.
Joy	Henry Joy, Woodstock, Conn.
J.&P.	Jackson & Perkins, Newark, N. Y.
K.A.S.	Knoxville Agr. Exp. Sta., Knoxville, Tenn.
Kat.	A. B. Katkamier, Macedon, N. Y.
K.B.N.	Keith Bros. Nurseries.
Kees.	H. G. Keesling, San Jose, Calif.
Kelly	F. J. Kelly, San Saba, Texas.
Ken.	Mrs. F. Kendall, Dundee, N. Y.
Kenw.	John F. Kenworthy, Rockton, Wis.
Kerr	Jonathan W. Kerr, Denton. Md.
Ket.	J. J. Kettle, Corfe Castle, Dorset, England.
Kett.	Fred J. Kettler, Plotteville, Wis.

FRUITS AND EDIBLE NUTS, continued

Kie.	P. Kieffer.
Kil.	Barney Kilgore, near Clearwater, Fla.
Kill.	J. W. Killen, Felton, Del.
Kir.	E. W. Kirpatrick, McKinney, Texas.
Kirk	Mrs. W. R. Kirk, Brownsville, Ore.
Kirt.	Jared P. Kirtland, Cleveland, Ohio.
Kirt., H.	Mrs. H. S. Kirtland, Yalesville, Conn.
Kle.	G. F. Kleinsteiber, Winfield, Kan.
Kni.	T. A. Knight, Downton Castle, England.
Kni., G.	George Knight, Knightsen, Calif.
Knu.	H. Knudson.
Korn	G. J. Korn, Berrien Springs, Mich.
Kra.	E. W. Krause, Waco, Texas.
Kre.	J. Kready, Mt. Joy, Pa.
Kroh	P. H. Kroh.
Kru.	Krummel.
Krum.	Krumeries or Krumrei, St. Joseph, Mo.
Kruse	H. A. Kruse, Sherwood, Ore.
Kuhns	J. Kuhns, Cliffwood, N. J.
LaFay	M. LaFay, Portland, N. Y.
Lamb	Geo. W. Lamb, 75 East Wacker Drive, Chicago, Ill.
Lan.	Otto Lander.
Lane	Miles P. Lane, Santa Barbara, Calif.
Lang.	L. B. Langwell, New York.
Lar.	Larose.
Lars.	Mrs. Mary Larson, Ionia, Mich.
Laur.	J. W. Laurendine, Bayou Labatre, Ala.
Law.	Mr. Lawson.
Lawr.	L. V. Lawrence.
Laws.	Donald Lawson, Dorloo, N. Y.
Lax.	T. Laxton, Bedford, England.
Lea.	C. Learnes.
Learn	Buford Learn, Aylmer, Ont., Canada.
LeC.	Major LeConte.
Lee.	M. D. Leepton.
Leek	Rube Leek.
Lee, T.	T. Lee, Clevedon, Somerset, England.
Leib	F. A. Leib, San Jose, Calif.
Leon.	S. R. Leonard, Middletown, N. Y.
LeRoy	M. A. LeRoy.
Lew.	S. Lewelling, Milwaukie, Ore.
Lew., D.	Dwight B. Lewis, Vasser, Mich.
Lewe.	Mrs. Martin Lewerenz, 251 Queenston St., St. Catharines, Ont., Canada.
Lewis	N. W. Lewis, Allegan Co., Mich.
Lew., J.	John Lewelling, Oakley, Calif.
Lews., F.	F. H. Lewis, Pascagoula, Miss.
Lin.	Jessie B. Lingenfelter, McKeesport, Pa.
Ling.	Mrs. E. J. Lingle, Pittsfield, Pa.
Lion.	John W. Lionberger, Rt. 2, Table Rock, Neb.
Lit.	J. Little, Granton, Ont., Canada.
Litt.	T. P. Littlepage, Bowie, Md.
L.N.C.	Lovett Nursery Co., Little Silver, N. J.
Loc.	Otto Locke, New Braunfels, Texas.
Locke	W. H. Locke, Bonham, Texas.
Logan	J. H. Logan, Santa Cruz, Calif.
Lon.	R. F. Lonnen, Mayville, N. Y.
Loo.	F. D. Loomis, Bloomingburg, N. Y.
Lord	Orville Morell Lord, Rollingstone Valley, Minn.
Lou.	F. W. Loudon, Jonesville, Wis.

FRUITS AND EDIBLE NUTS, continued

Lov.	J. T. Lovett, Little Silver, N. J.
Luc.	Mr. Lucomb.
Lup.	M. D. Lupton, Newport, N. J.
Luth.	F. Luther, Fairgrove, Mich.
Lyman	S. Lyman.
Lyon	Mr. Lyon, 7276 Sunset Blvd., Hollywood, Calif.
Mac.	E. Macomber.
MacD.	L. H. MacDaniels, Cornell University, Ithaca, N. Y.
M.A.E.S.	Minn. Agriculture Exp. Sta.
Mag.	W. J. Magoon, Portland, Ore.
Mahan	F. A. Mahan, Monticello, Fla.
Major	Mrs. L. M. B. Major, Henderson, Ky.
Mall	F. A. Mall, Lamoni, Ia.
Man.	Geo. W. Manahan, Sabillasville, Md.
Mann	Mrs. Rae D. Mann, Rt. 3, Davison, Mich.
Mar.	Dr. Marvin, Morristown, N. J.
Mark.	C. H. Markey, Beallsville, Ohio.
Mat.	J. C. Matthews, Cuthbert, Ga.
Mats.	B. T. Matsler, Bend, Texas.
Maut.	Jacob Mautner, Yuba City, Calif.
Mayes	John Mayes, Pilot Point, Texas.
M.B.F.	Minn. State Fruit Breeding Farm, Excelsior, Minn.
McC.	McClung, Tyler, Texas.
McCa.	M. E. McCance.
McCal.	O. L. McCallister, Mt. Vernon, Ind.
McCo.	H. L. McConnell & Son, Port Burwell, Ont., Canada.
McCu.	W. D. McCulley, Brownwood, Texas.
McD.	N. McDevitt, Placer Co., Calif.
McDer.	Peter McDermid, St. Catharines, Ont., Canada.
McH.	R. McHinds.
McI.	A. McIntosh.
McI., J.	J. J. McIntosh, Vernal, Miss.
McK.	A. McKevitt, Vaca Valley, Calif.
McL.	J. McLaughlin.
McLa.	Elizabeth McLaughlin, Middletown Springs, Vt.
McM.	Lowell McMillen, Buchanan, Mich.
McN.&G.	McNary & Gaines.
McP.	H. G. McPike, Alton, Ill.
McPh.	A. McPherson, Jr., Caledonia, N. Y.
Meech	W. W. Meech.
M.E.F.	Minn. Exp. Farm, St. Paul, Minn.
Mem.	T. S. Memory, Whiteville, N. C.
Men.	G. Mendenhall.
Mer.	J. M. Mersereau, New York.
Meu.	M. Meuris.
Meuli	Martin Meuli, Tuolumne Co., Calif.
Mi.	Wm. J. Millican, Bend, Texas.
Mic.	G. Michel, Judsonia, Ark.
Mie.	Jacob Miehl, Atlantic Co., N. J.
Mil.	Mr. Miller, Brandywine Creek, near Wilmington, Del.
Mil., D.	D. P. Miller, North Branch, Mich.
Mill.	J. G. Miller.
Mill., C.	C. Miller.
Miller	Herbert Miller, Richfield, Pa.
Mill., S.	S. Miller, Hamilton, Ont., Canada.
Mills	Z. Mills, Springbrook, Ore.
Mil., S.	Samuel B. Miller, Bluffton, Mo.
Min.	P. C. Minnich, Waldo, Fla.
Mina.	J. A. Minassian, Orose, Calif.
Mink.	S. G. Minkler.
Mint.	J. R. Mintle, Glenwood, Iowa.
Mish	W. W. Mish, Washington, N. C.

FRUITS AND EDIBLE NUTS, continued

Mitch.	Claude Mitchell, Scotland, Ont., Canada.
Moas	Randolph Moas, Portage Co., Ohio.
M.O.C.	Miller Orchard Co., Edgemont, Md.
Mon.	W. H. Monroe, Beverly, Mass.
Moo.	Judge Mooney.
Moody	F. Moody.
Moon	Samuel C. Moon, Morrisville, Pa.
Moor.	A. T. Moore.
Moore	John B. Moore, Concord, Mass.
Moore, J.	J. Moore, Brighton, N. Y.
Mor.	J. A. Morgan, Scottsville, N. Y.
Morel	F. Morel, Lyon-Vaise, France.
Morr.	Robt. T. Morris, Stamford, Conn.
Mos.	Noah Mosier, Dayton, Ore.
Muir	J. Muir, Silveyville, Calif.
Mul.	A. H. Mullins.
Mulk.	Mrs. Mulkey.
Mumma	Z. T. Mumma.
Mun.	T. V. Munson, Dennison, Texas.
Mung.	T. Munger, Western, Ohio.
Muns.	W. K. Munson, Grand Rapids, Mich.
Mur.	F. C. Murphy, Sunbury, Ohio.
Myer	Myer & Son, Bridgeville, Del.
Myers	Elmer Myers, Rt. 2, Bellefontaine, Ohio.
Myott	Mr. Myott, Dexford, England.
N.C.S.	North Carolina Sta., Raleigh, N. C.
N.D.S.	North Dakota Sta., Fargo, N. Dak.
Neer	F. L. Neer, Pennington, Calif.
Neff	J. B. Neff, Anaheim, Calif.
Neff, J.	J. C. Neff, Duncan Falls, Ohio.
Nel.	Wm. Nelson, New Orleans, La.
Nelis	J. C. Nelis.
Ness	H. Ness, Texas Agr. Exp. Sta.
Net.	Walter Netking, Rt. 1, Ravenna, Ohio.
New.	S. Newhall.
Newl.	A. M. Newland Ranch, Colusa, Calif.
Newm.	C. P. Newman, Veille LaSalle, Quebec, Canada.
Nib.	Mason J. Niblack, Vincennes, Ind.
Nic.	Joseph Nichols, Niles, Calif.
Nimon	James Nimon, Denison, Texas.
N.J.S.	New Jersey Agr. Exp. Sta., New Brunswick, N. J.
Nor.	E. J. Norman, near Lee, Mass.
Nor., A.	A. L. Norton, Clarkesville, Mo.
Nort.	D. N. Norton, Richmond, Va.
N.Y.S.	New York Exp. Sta., Geneva, N. Y.
Oakes	Royal Oakes, Bluff, Ill.
O'Connor	P. A. O'Connor, Bowie, Md.
Odom	R. L. Odom, Toledo, Texas.
O.H.S.	Ont. Hort. Exp. Sta.
Old.	J. Oldmixon.
Older	Mr. Older, Independence, Iowa.
Oli.	M. Olivier.
Ond.	G. Onderdonk, Nursery, Texas.
Oren	J. K. Oren.
Orr	C. P. Orr, Arp, Texas.
O.S.S.	Oregon State Sta., Corvallis, Ore.
Pabst	C. E. Pabst, Ocean Springs, Miss.
Page	Victor Page, Elmsford, N. Y.
Par.	J. Parker, near San Diego, Calif.
Park.	W. Russell Parker, Little Silver, N. J.
Parke.	S. J. Parker, Ithaca, N. Y.
Parks	J. W. Parks, Nanticoke, Md.
Parm.	Wm. Parmalee, New Haven, Conn.
Parry	Parry Bros., Parry, N. J.
Parry, J.	John R. Parry, Parry, N. J.
Pars.	R. G. Parsons, Parsonburg, Md.

FRUITS AND EDIBLE NUTS, continued

Pat.	C. G. Patten, Charles City, Iowa.
Patt.	Mrs. Wm. Patterson, Wever, Iowa.
Payne	Geo. C. Payne, Campbell, Calif.
Pea.	Knight Pearcy, Salem, Ore.
Ped.	Elwood Pedrick, Cumberland Co., Md.
Pef.	G. P. Peffer, Pewaukee, Wis.
Pen.	J. Pennock.
Penn.	M. Penning.
Per.	F. I. Perkins.
Perk.	John Perkins, Bridgewater, Mass.
Phi.	Joseph Phillips, Sutter Co., Calif.
Pho.	F. K. Phoenix.
Pic.	A. Picquet, Belair, Ga.
Pie.	L. B. Pierce.
Pier.	J. P. Pierce, Santa Clara, Calif.
Plat.	Mrs. Robert Platman, Penn Yan, N. Y.
Platt	Judge Platt.
Pleas	E. Pleas, Collinsville, Okla.
Plumb	Mr. Plumb.
Poc.	I. Pocklington, Sandy Hill, N. Y.
Poe	Oscar Poe, Scotts Valley, Calif.
Pol.	H. S. Pollock, Miami, Fla.
Pom.	Norman Pomeroy, Lockport, N. Y.
Pop.	F. W. Popence, Tela, Honduras.
Por.	S. Porter.
Pow.	E. P. Powell, Clinton, N. Y.
Pre.	P. Prettyman.
Pri.	Prince Nursery, Flushing, L. I., N. Y.
Price	E. M. Price, Westpoint, Calif.
Pri., T.	Thos. Prince, Dundee, Ore.
Pri., W.	William Prince, Prince Nursery, Flushing, L. I., N. Y.
Pro.	Prochaska.
Put.	J. A. Putnam, Fredonia, N. Y.
Pyne	G. Pyne, Topsham, Devon, England.
Quarn.	A. A. Quarnberg, Vancouver, Wash.
Qui.	C. Quillen, Monrovia, Ind.
Ralls	C. Ralls.
Ram.	F. T. Ramsey & Son, Austin, Texas.
Rams.	H. M. Ramsdell.
Ray	D. Ray, Tyler, Texas.
Rea	John Rea.
Read	W. H. Read, Port Dalhousie, Ont., Canada.
Reams	J. W. Reams, Suisun, Calif.
Reas.	J. R. Reasoner, Urbana, Ill.
Red.	Adam Redcay, R. 3, Lititz, Pa.
Ree.	S. Reeves.
Reed.	H. Reeder.
Reed, C.	C. P. Reed, R. 2, Howell, Mich.
Reed, W.	W. C. Reed & Son, Vincennes, Ind.
Reek	W. R. Reek, Ridgetown, Ont., Canada.
Reuss	G. B. Reuss, Hohen Solms, La.
R.F.N.	E. A. Riehl Farm & Nursery, Godfrey, Ill.
R.H.S.	Royal Horticultural Society, England.
Ric.	E. M. Richards.
Rich.	Richard Ranch, El Monte, Calif.
Rick	P. Rick.
Ricke.	J. H. Ricketts, Newburgh, N. Y.
Rid.	A. R. Rideout, Whittier, Calif.
Rie.	E. A. Riehl, Godfrey, Ill.
Riehl, E.	Edwin Riehl, Alton, Ill.
Ris.	E. E. Risien & Son, San Saba, Texas.
Rit.	John R. Ritchie, Flemington, N. J.
Riv.	Rivers, Sawbridgeworth, England.
Rob.	W. P. Robinson, Atlanta, Ga.
Robe.	Horace Roberts, Flushing, L. I., N. Y.

FRUITS AND EDIBLE NUTS, continued

Roc.	H. Rockhill, Conrad, Iowa.
Rog.	Daniel E. Rogers, Scottsville, N. Y.
Roh.	John W. Rohwer, Grundy Center, Iowa.
Rol.	J. W. Rollins.
Rom.	J. Rommel, Morrison, Mo.
Rome	Sebastian Rome, Convent, La.
Ross	A. J. Ross, Dallas, Texas.
Roth	Albert Roth, Cuero, Texas.
Rou.	Routier Ranch, Mills, Calif.
Ruedy	G. Ruedy.
Ruf	O. Ruf, Baldwin Park, Calif.
Rum., L.	L. A. Rumph, Marshallvilie, Ga.
Rum., S.	Samuel H. Rumph, Marshallville, Ga.
Run.	Sol Runyon, Sacramento County, Calif.
Run., O.	O. R. Runyon, Sacramento County, Calif.
Rus.	F. Russell, Greenfield, N. H.
Rus., H.	H. F. Russell, Ocean Springs, Miss.
Rush	J. G. Rush, West Willow, Pa.
Rusk	Lewis Rusk, Pershing, Ind.
Rut.	J. Rutter.
Rya.	Edward L. Ryan, Rideout Beach, Whittier, Calif.
Sal.	Col. Salwey.
Sali.	Mrs. F. A. Salisbury, Phelps, N. Y.
Salt.	John Salter, Hammersmith, England.
San.	L. T. Sanders, London, Ont., Canada.
Sande	Elmer T. Sande, Story City, Iowa.
Sau.	Wm. Saunders, Ottawa, Ont., Canada.
Sch.	Schmidt.
Sch., C.	Carl Schmidt, West India Gardens, Altadena, Calif.
Sche.	M. Scheidweiler.
Scher.	A. B. Scherf, Newberg, Ore.
Schu.	P. Schuckhardt, North Lake, Wis.
Sco.	Judge Scott, Burlington, N. J.
S.D.S.	S. Dak. Exp. Sta., Brookings, S. Dak.
Sea.	Lewis A. Seacor, New Rochelle, N. Y.
Sel.	S. A. Sellers, Contra Costa Co., Calif.
Sel., A.	George Sellers, Oakley, Calif.
Sha.	G. Shaffer, Scottsville, N. Y.
Shar.	J. K. Sharpless, Catawissa, Pa.
Shaul	J. D. Shaul, Ladora, Iowa.
She.	J. Sheriff.
Shed.	Thos. H. Sheddon, Monrovia, Calif.
Shel.	Major Sheldon.
Shi.	Shipley.
S.H.S.	So. Haven Exp. Sta., South Haven, Mich.
Shull	C. Shull, Sarcoxie, Mo.
Siers	I. T. Siers, Lawrenceburg, Ky.
Sif.	C. L. Sifford, Buchanan, Va.
Sim.	Dr. Simmons, Sacramento, Calif.
Sim., M.	Simpson Bros., Monticello, Ga.
Simo.	Mrs. A. B. Simonson, Mondovi, Wis.
Sim., U.	J. A. Simpson, Uvalde, Texas.
Sim., V.	Simpson Bros., Vincennes, Ind.
Sir.	John Sirocka, Lagrange, Texas.
Smi.	W. & T. Smith Nursery.
Smi., G. L.	Gilbert L. Smith, Wasaic, N. Y.
Smi., G. W.	George W. Smith, Brentwood, Calif.
Smi., H.	Helen M. Smith, Linden Lodge, Stamford, Conn.
Smi., J.	J. Russell Smith, Swarthmore, Pa.
Smi., T.	Thos. R. Smith, Westport, Calif.
Smith	Dr. Smith, Windsor, Vt.
Smo.	Mr. Smock, Middletown, N. J.

FRUITS AND EDIBLE NUTS, continued

S.N.B.	Sunnyslope Nursery, Bangor, Calif.
Sneed	J. L. T. Sneed, Nashville, Tenn.
Snow	S. Snow, Wrest Park, Bedfordshire, England.
Sny.	Henry Snyder, Laporte, Ind.
Snyd.	Snyder Bros. Inc., Center Point, Iowa.
Sooy	E. Sooy, Browns Mills, N. J.
Spar.	Harvey C. Sparrow, R. 1, Lomax, Ill.
Speer	Geo. L. Speer, Alba, Texas.
Spr.	W. A. Springer.
Sta.	Dr. Joseph Stayman, Leavenworth, Kan.
Stad.	Leo A. Stadelbacker, R. 1, Cobden, Ill.
Stair	Stair.
Stam.	H. M. Stambaugh, Galesburg, Ill.
Stan.	L. L. Stanley, Griffin, Ga.
Ste.	J. N. Stearns, Kalamazoo, Mich.
Ste., J.	J. Steckler Seed Co., New Orleans, La.
Steel.	P. W. Steele, West Hartford, Conn.
Stein	F. T. Stein, Sherwood, Ore.
Stein, C.	C. V. Stein, Manheim, Pa.
Step.	Wm. Stephens, Montebello, Calif.
Stev.	B. Stevens, Morristown, N. J.
Stev., A.	A. Stevens, Wellesley, Mass.
Sto.	Ezra Stokes, Berlin, N. J.
Sto., E.	Eugene Stocking, Owosso, Mich.
Stoke	H. F. Stoke, Roanoke, Va.
Str.	I. F. Street, West Middleton, Ind.
Stro.	Geo. Stromer.
Stu.	J. W. Stubenrauch, Mexia, Texas.
Stua., J.	J. F. Stuart, Ripon, Calif.
Stua., W.	W. R. Stuart, Ocean Springs, Miss.
Stuc.	Mrs. B. M. Stuckey.
Sue.	L. Suelter, Carver, Minn.
Sum.	C. H. Summer, Sterling, Ill.
Swa.	Warren C. Swayne, West Grove, Pa.
Swaim	H. H. Swaim, R. 1, South Bend, Ind.
Tabor	G. L. Tabor, Glen St. Mary, Fla.
Taf.	C. P. Taft, Orange, Calif.
Tan.	M. Y. Tanner, Slaterville Springs, N. Y.
Tay.	S. W. Taylor, Stamford, Conn.
Teas	E. Y. Teas, Covington, Ind.
Ten.	J. Tennant.
Ten., E.	E. M. Ten Eyck, S. Plainfield, N. J.
Ter.	H. A. Terry, Crescent, Ia.
Tha.	E. S. Thacher, Ojai, Calif.
Thi.	G. W. Thissell, Winters, Calif.
Thill	H. J. Thill, R. 1, Bloomer, Wis.
Tho.	J. T. Thompson, Oneida, N. Y.
Thom.	T. Thompson.
Thom., A.	Adelbert Thomson, East Avon, N. Y.
Thoma.	Drury Thomas, Marion, S. C.
Thomas	J. W. Thomas & Son, King of Prussia, Pa.
Thomp.	D. A. Thompson, Mt. Olive, N. C.
Thomp., A.	A. Thompson, Delaware, Ohio.
Thor.	Mr. Thorne, Fishkill Landing, N. Y.
Throp	Ralph Throp, Rt. 8, Greensburg, Ind.
Til.	J. E. Tilton.
Tin.	J. H. Tinsley.
Titus	Titus Nursery Co., Waynesboro, Va.
T.N.C.	Texas Nursery Co., Sherman, Texas.
Todd	Albert Todd, Wakeman, Ohio.
Todd, J.	J. H. Todd, Dover, Del.

FRUITS AND EDIBLE NUTS, continued

Toole	R. Toole.
Town.	E. W. Townsend, Salisbury, Md.
T.P.C.	Texas Pecan Co., Tyler, Texas.
Tra.	H. R. Trapp, Coconut Grove, Fla.
Treat	Webster Treat, Davis, Calif.
Trem.	John Trembath, Antioch, Calif.
Trib.	Tribble Bros., Elk Grove, Calif.
Trip.	E. E. Trippels, Mesa, Ariz.
Trit.	Sam Tritten, Lisbon, Ohio.
Tro.	L. Trollope, Bath, England.
Tru.	B. Truesdell.
Tuck.	E. O. Tucker, Ventura, Calif.
Tup.	Mr. Tupper.
Tyler	N. Tyler, Auburn, N. Y.
Tyson	J. Tyson.
Und.	S. W. Underhill, Croton Point, N. Y.
U.S.D.A.	United States Dept. of Agri.
U.S.P.I.G.	U. S. Pl. Intro. Gard., Miami, Fla.
U.S.P.S.	United States Plant Field Sta.
Uve.	Dr. Uvedale.
Valk	Wm. Valk, Flushing, L. I., N. Y.
Van.	Arthur Vandenbark, New Haven, Ill.
VanD.	H. VanDusen, Palmyra, N. Y.
VanF.	W. Van Fleet, U. S. D. A.
VanH.	H. E. Van Deman, Washington, D. C.
VanL.	Van Lindley, Pitt Co., N. C.
VanM.	Dr. Van Mons.
VanW.	E. L. Van Wormer, Canandaigua, N. Y.
V.D.P.	Everett E. Van Der Poppen, Hamilton, Mich.
Vest	L. W. Vest, Blacksburg, Va.
Voer	G. Voer.
Voll.	Conrad Vollertson, Rochester, N. Y.
VonL.	H. Von Luttichau.
Wad.	Wm. Waddell, Griffin, Ga.
Wads.	H. O. Wadsworth, Wolcott, N. Y.
Wager	Benjamin Wager, West Bloomfield, N. Y.
Wagner	J. B. Wagner, Pasadena, Calif.
Wal.	Wallen, Rochester, N. Y.
Wald.	B. A. Waldin, Homestead, Fla.
Walds.	L. O. Waldsmith, Hartsell, Ala.
Walk.	S. Walker, Roxbury, Mass.
Walk., B.	Ben. T. Walker, Rt. 3, Siloam Springs, Ark.
Wall.	H. Wallis, Welliston, Mo.
Walt.	John Walton Ranch, Oakley, Calif.
War.	L. E. Wardell, Marlboro, N. Y.
Ward	A. Ward, Athens, Ga.
Ward, T.	T. Ward, Manalapan, N. J.
Ward, W. F.	W. F. Ward, Avon Park, Fla.
Ward, W. H.	W. H. Ward, Morgan Hill, Calif.
Ware	E. G. Ware, and D. C. Disher, Garden Grove, Calif.
Warf.	C. B. Warfield, Sandoval, Ill.
Warr.	W. Warren.
Warre.	Mrs. J. P. Warren, Burlington, Wis.
Was.	Wasson Ranch, Saticoy, Calif.
Wass.	O. Wasserzieher, Nauvoo, Ill.
Watts	R. L. Watts, State College, Pa.
Way.	H. B. Wayland.
Way., L.	Dr. Wayland.
Wea.	Weaver.
Webb	Richard Webb, Calcat, near Reading, England.
Weber	H. R. Weber, Cincinnati, Ohio.
Wel.	Frank J. Wellman, Mason, Texas.
Welty	Mrs. M. J. Welty, Gordon, Texas.
Wes.	Carl Weschcke, St. Paul, Minn.
Wetz.	Annie M. Wetzel, New Berlin, Pa.

FRUITS AND EDIBLE NUTS, continued

Whe.	G. W. Wheller.
Whee.	G. F. Wheeler, Concord, Mass.
Whit.	A. R. Whitney, Franklin Grove, Ill.
Whit., W.	W. O. Whitney, Rt. 1, Berea, Ohio.
White	J. J. White.
White, N.	N. B. White, Norwood, Mass.
Whyte	R. B. Whyte, Ottawa, Ont., Canada.
Wiard	Everett Wiard, Ypsilanti, Mich.
Wight	Wight.
Wil.	P. Wilcox, Chili, N. Y.
Wild	Henry W. Wild, Sarcoxie, Mo.
Wilk.	O. Wilkins, Bridgeburg, Ont., Canada.
Wilki.	J. F. Wilkinson, Rockport, Ind.
Will.	Mr. Williams.
Willa.	S. D. Willard, Geneva, N. Y.
Will., J.	J. Williams, Pitmaston, near Worcester, England.
Will., M.	M. N. Williamson, Mill Creek, Okla.
Wills.	F. C. Willson, Sunnyvale, Calif.
Will., T.	T. Williams.
Wil., P.	P. E. Wilcox, Geneva, Ohio.
Wils.	J. Wilson, Burlington, N. J.
Wiltz	R. Wiltz, San Jose, Calif.
Wis.	J. H. Wismer.
Wolf	D. B. Wolf.
Wolf, R.	Ross R. Wolf, Stephenville, Texas.
Wolfs.	Wolfskill Ranch, Suisun, Calif.
Woo.	W. Woodbury.
Wood	Beder Wood, Moline, Ill.
Wooda.	B. F. Woodall, Milford, Del.
Woodf.	E. W. Woodford, Forest Grove, Ore.
Wood, J.	J. Wood
Woodl.	Woodlawn Nurseries, Rochester, N. Y.
Woodr.	C. H. Woodruff, Ann Arbor, Mich.
Woodw.	A. Woodward, Rockford, Ill.
Woot.	Mrs. Anna Wooten, Waukeenah, Fla.
Wor.	S. Worden, Minetta, N. Y.
W.P.N.	Wolfe's Pecan Nursery, Stephenville, Texas.
Wray	H. Wray, White Salmon, Wash.
Wri.	Herman Wright, Rt. 2, Wolcott, N. Y.
Wright	Douglas N. Wright, Colchester, Vt.
Wright, R.	Ross Pier Wright, Westfield, N. Y.
Wyant	J. B. Wyant.
Wylie	A. P. Wylie, Chester, S. C.
Wyn.	Wyndham.
Young	B. M. Young, Morgan City, La.
Zim., G.	G. A. Zimmerman, Linglestown, Pa.
Zim., N.	Noah Zimmerman, Linglestown, Pa.
Zim., W.	Wells Zimmerman, Linglestown, Pa.
Zink	J. W. Zink, Pascagoula, Miss.

Fruit or Nut Name	*Botanical Name*
ABIU	**Pouteria caimito** (*Lucuma c.*)
ACORN (Edible)	**Quercus** spp.
ACTINIDIA	**Actinidia** spp.
AEGLOPSIS (*Dwarf Powderflaskfruit*)	**Aeglopsis**
IVORYCOAST A.	**A. chevalieri**
UGANDA A.	**A. egglingi**
AFRAEGLE (*Powderflaskfruit*)	**Afraegle**
GABON A.	**A. gabonensis**
NIGERIA A.	**A. paniculata**
AKEE	**Blighia sapida**
Alligator Apple	PONDAPPLE
Alligator Pear	AVOCADO
ALMOND	**Prunus amygdalus**

Aust. Australia Eu. Europe

ACAMPO. *Acampo Texas.*
ALGERIA. Eu. (U.S.D.A. 1910.)
ALICANTE. Eu.
ALMENDRO DE LA P. Eu. (U.S.D.A. 1912.)
Almendro del Desmayo. DESMAYO.
Almendrone. CATAMERA.
ARIZONA. (Trip. about 1900.) *Arizona Prolific.*
ASTACHAN. (U.S.D.A. 1911.) *Astachan Badam.*
Bakers Seedling. TREMBATH.
BALLARD. (Balla. 1897.)
BARCLAY. (Barc. 1895.)
BARI. Eu.
BATHAM. (Bat. 1894.) *Bathams Everbearing.*
BIDWELL. (Bidw. 1881.)
BIGELOW. (Big. 1896.) *Bigelows Seedling.*
BLANCAL. Eu.
BONITA. Eu.
BRANDIS. Aust. *Brandis Jordan.*
BRIER. (W. Brier) *Briers Languedoc.*
BROWN. (J.H.R.) *Brown XX.*
BURBANK. (Burb.)
CALIFORNIA. (Before 1900.) *California Paper Shell.*
CALIFORNIA JORDAN. (Newl. about 1890.)
CARTAGENA. Eu. *French Languedoc.*
CASTILLET. Eu.
CATAMERA. Eu. (U.S.D.A. 1901.) *Almendrone.*
CHELLASTON. Aust.
COMMERCIAL. (Newl. before 1890.)
Commercial. HARRIOTT.
CONCORD. Calif.
COPE. Calif.
CORRIENTE. Eu.
COVER. (Cover 1915.)
Crescent. EUREKA.
CROWN. (Cover about 1910.)
DAYTON. Washington.
DESMAYO. Eu. (U.S.D.A.) *Almendro del Desmayo.*
DEWITT. (DeW. 1906.)
DICKENSON. Calif.
DIXIE. Utah.
DRAKE. (H.Drake about 1875.) *Drake Seedling.*
EL SUPREMO. (Wolfs early 80's.)
ESPARTO. (Barr)
ESPERANZA. Eu. (U.S.D.A. 1912.)
EUREKA. (Newl. 1886.) *Crescent; Little Jordan.*
FABRICA. Eu.
FAIR. Calif.
FAIROAKS. (About 1910.)
FAVORITE. (G.Kni. 1887.)
FLINT. Type name. Calif.
French Languedoc. CARTAGENA.
GAPIN. Calif.
GARWOOD. (Garw. 1907.)
GILTEDGE. Calif.
GOLDEN NUGGET. (App. about 1900.)
GOLDEN STATE. (Treat before 1890.)
GORDON. Calif.
GRAY. Utah.
GROSSE TENDRE. Eu. (F. Gil. 1888.) *Improved Languedoc.*

ALMOND, continued
HAMPTON. (Hamp. 1908.)
HARPAREIL. (U.S.D.A. and Calif. Exp. Sta. 1939.)
HARPUT. Eu.
HARRIOTT. (About 1873.) *Commercial.*
HAWTHORNE. Aust.
HENLE. (J.H.R. 1909.) *Henles Doubleshell.*
HUDSON. Calif.
IMPERIAL. Calif.
Improved Languedoc. GROSSE TENDRE.
IVICA. Eu.
I. X. L. (Hatch. early 80's.)
JORDAN. Eu.
JORDANOLO. (U.S.D.A. and Calif. Exp. Sta. 1939.)
KIMBALL.
KING. (Before 1893.) *Kings Soft Shell.*
KLONDIKE. (G. Kni. 1894.)
LA FRANCE. Calif.
LANGUEDOC. Eu. (W. Pri. 1843.)
LAPRIMA. (Hatch. early 80's.)
LASSEN. (Newl. 1888.)
LEWELLING. (J. Lew. early 90's.)
Little Jordan. EUREKA.
MARIE DUPREY. Eu. (F. Gil. 80's.)
McCOY. Calif.
MEDINA. Texas.
MOLLAR. Eu.
NEER. (Neer.)
NE PLUS ULTRA. (Hatch early 80's.)
NEVERFAIL. (G.W. Smi.)
NEW BRANDIS. Aust.
NEWHALL. Calif.
NONPAREIL. (Hatch. early 80's.)
O'NEIL. (Barr. 1894.)
PALATINE. (Burb.)
PEERLESS. Calif. (Before 1895.)
PISTACHE. Eu. (About 1840.)
PLANEJA. Eu.
PLANETA. Eu.
POLLACKS. Aust.
PRIDE. (F.&S.)
PRINCESS. Eu. (W. Pri. 1847.)
PROCTOR. Calif.
PROVENCE. Eu. (F. Gil.)
QUEEN. Calif.
RAMELL. Eu. *Ramellet.*
REAMS. (Reams before 1910.)
RICE. Calif. (Before 1891.)
RIDENHOWER. (W. Reed 1914.)
RIO BONITO. Calif.
RIO VIRGIN.
RIVERSIDE PEERLESS. Aust.
ROUTIER. (Rou.)
SARDINA. Eu.
SELLERS. (G. Sel. before 1890.)
SILVERSHELL. Calif. (About 1890.)
SIMMONS. (Sim.)
SMITH. (G. W. Smi. about 1890.) *Smiths X.L.*
SPAGON. Eu.
STANDARD. (Eri. 1906.)
STUART. (J. Stua.)
SULTANA. Eu. (1843.)
TARRAGONA. Eu. (Before 1890.)
TEXAS. Texas. *Texas Prolific.*
TREMBATH. (Trem. 1906.) *Bakers Seedling.*
VICTORY. Calif. (About 1920.)
WALTON. (Walt. about 1890.)
WASHINGTON. Utah.

Amatungula . . . . CARISSA

AMBARELLA (*Otaheiteapple* in part; *Viapple*) . . **Spondias cytherea**

Antidesma . . . . BIGNAY

APPLE . . . . **Malus** spp.

Professor Rehder reports that Malus pumila "is the parent of most of our cultivated apples, though some probably are the offspring of hybrids with M. sylvestris, M. prunifolia, and also M. baccata." For Crabapple varieties, see CRABAPPLE.

ADNO.
AKIN. (Akin 1868.)
Albemarle Pippin. YELLOW NEWTOWN.
ALEXANDER.
AMBO.
ANIS.
ANISIM.
ANIS ROSE.
ANOKA. (S.D.S. 1920.)
ANTONOVKA.
ARKANSAS. *Mammoth Black Twig.*
ARKANSAS BLACK.
ATLAS.
AUTUMN STRAWBERRY.
BAILEY SWEET.
BAILLIE. *Baillie Red Rome.*
BALDWIN. (Ball 1740.)
Banana. WINTER BANANA.
BANKS GRAVENSTEIN. (Banks 1880.)
BATTLE.
BAXTER.
BEACH.
BEACON. (M.A.E.S. 1936.)
BEAUTIFUL ARCADE.
BEAUTY OF BATH.
BECKER.
BELMONT. (Beam 1800.)
BEN DAVIS.
BENONI. (Ric. 1852.)
BENTLEY. *Bentley Sweet.*
BETHEL.
BIETIGHEIMER.
BIRDMAN DELICIOUS.
BISMARCK.
BLACK ANNETTE.
BLACKBEN. (Black 1880.) *Black Ben Davis.*
BLACK GILLIFLOWER.
BLACK JONATHAN.
BLACKJON JONATHAN.
BLACKMACK McINTOSH.
Black Mickey. ROGERS McINTOSH.
BLAXTAYMAN.
BLEDSOE.
BLENHEIM. *Blenheim Orange.*
BLUE PEARMAIN.
BLUSHED CALVILLE.
BODE.
BOIKEN.
BONUM.
BOROVINKA.
BOSKOOP. (Lan. 1856.)
BRAMLEY.
BREAKEY.
BRILLIANT.
BROCK.
BUCKINGHAM.
BULLOCK.
CALVILLE BLANCHE.
CANADA BALDWIN. (Dery 1855.)
CAPITOLA.
CARLTON. (N.Y.S. 1923.)
Carolina Red June. RED JUNE.
CASE RED WEALTHY.
CELLINI.

APPLE, continued
Champion. COLLINS.
CHANCE. (S.D.S. 1919.)
CHARLAMOFF.
CHARLES ROSS.
CHELAN.
CHENANGO.
CHICAGO.
CLAYTON.
COLLAMER TWENTYOUNCE. (Col. 1895.)
COLLINS. *Champion.*
COLORA YORK. *Colora Red York.*
COLTON. (Colt. 1840.)
CORNELL. *Cornell Fancy.*
CORTLAND. (N.Y.S. 1915.)
COXORANGE.
COX REDROME.
CRANBERRY PIPPIN.
CRIMSON BEAUTY. *Early Red Bird.*
CRIMSON COXORANGE.
CRIMSON GRAVENSTEIN.
CRIMSON SPY.
CRUSOE.
Daniels Red Duchess. RED DUCHESS.
Delaware Red Winter. LAWVER.
DELICIOUS. (Hiatt 1881.)
DELUXE.
Devonshire Quarrindon. QUARRINDON.
DICKINSON.
DOMINE.
DONALD.
DUCHESS. *Duchess of Oldenburg; Oldenburg.*
DUDLEY. (Dud. 1891.) *Dudley Winter.*
DYER.
EARLY COOPER.
EARLY HARVEST.
EARLY JOE. (Chap. 1800.)
EARLY McINTOSH. (N.Y.S. 1923.)
EARLY MELON.
EARLY PENNOCK.
Early Red Bird. CRIMSON BEAUTY.
EARLY RIPE.
EARLY STRAWBERRY.
EASTMAN.
EDGAR.
EDGEMONT.
ELMER.
ENGLISH RUSSET.
ENSEE. (Cox 1900.)
ERICKSON.
ESOPUS SPITZENBURG.
EVELYN.
FALLAWATER.
FALL CHEESE.
FALLPIPPIN.
FALL WINE. (Buel 1832.)
FALL WINESAP.
FAMEUSE. *Snow.*
FANNY. (Esh. 1869.)
FLORY.
FLUSHING SPITZENBURG.
FOLWELL. (M.A.E.S. 1922.)
Fourth of July. JULY.
FULTON.
GALETTA.
GALLIA BEAUTY.
GANO.
GARDEN ROYAL.
GARDNER DELICIOUS.
Geneton. RALLS.
GIDEON. (P. Gid. 1880.)
GILBERT.
GILPIN.
GLORIA MUNDI. (Croo. 1804.)

APPLE, continued
GOAL.
GODFREY.
GOLDEN DELICIOUS. (Mul. 1892.) *Yellow Delicious.*
GOLDEN RUSSET.
GOLDEN SWEET.
GOLDEN WHITE. (Hos. 1888.)
GOLDO.
GRAVENSTEIN.
Green Newtown. YELLOW NEWTOWN.
GREEN SWEET.
GRIMES GOLDEN. *Grimes.*
HACKWORTH.
HARALSON. (M.B.F. 1923.)
HAWKEYE GREENING. (I.A.S. 1921.)
HAWLEY. (Haw. 1750.)
HELM.
HENRY CLAY.
HERALD.
HIBERNAL.
HILAIRE. (Dery 1875.)
HOADLEY.
HOLLAND WINTER.
HOOVER.
HORACE.
HORSE. (Cerre 1875.)
HUBBARDSTON.
HUBBS ROME.
HUME.
HUNTSMAN.
HURLBUT.
HYDE KING.
INDIANA FAVORITE.
INGRAM. (M. Ing. 1850.)
IOWA BEAUTY. (Pat. 1898.)
IOWA BLUSH.
ISHAM. (Pho. 1864.)
JACOBS SWEET.
JEFFERIS. (Jef. 1848.)
JERSEY SWEET.
JETHRO.
JEWELL. *Jewell Winter.*
JEWETT RED. *Nodhead.*
JOAN. (I.A.S. 1932.)
JONARED JONATHAN.
JONATHAN. (Rick 1800.)
JOYCE.
JULY. *Fourth of July.*
KEETOSH.
KENDALL. (N.Y.S. 1932.)
KESWICK. *Keswick Codlin.*
King. TOMPKINS KING.
KING DAVID.
KINNARD. *Kinnard Choice.*
KIRBY DELICIOUS.
LADY.
LADYSWEET.
LANGFORD BEAUTY.
LANKFORD.
LANSINGBURG.
LASALLE.
LATE STRAWBERRY.
LAWFAM.
LAWSEED.
LAWVER. *Delaware Red Winter.*
LEHIGH GREENING.
LIMBERTWIG.
LINDA.
LINTON.
Livland Raspberry. LOWLAND RASPBERRY.
LOBO.
LODI. (N.Y.S. 1924.)
LONGFIELD.
LORD SUFFIELD.
LOWELL.

APPLE, continued
LOWLAND RASPBERRY. *Livland Raspberry.*
LOWRY.
LUBSK QUEEN.
MACOUN. (N.Y.S. 1923.)
MACROSS.
MAGOG. (Warr. 1870.)
MAIDEN BLUSH. (All. 1817.)
MALINDA. (Rol. 1858.)
Mammoth Black Twig. ARKANSAS.
MANAN.
MANITOBA.
MANITOBA SPY.
MANN. (Moo. 1870.)
MANRED.
MANTET.
MANTON.
MCAFEE.
MCINTOSH. (McI. 1870.)
MCMAHON. *McMahon White.*
MCSWEET.
MEDINA. (N.Y.S. 1923.)
MELBA.
MELVIN.
MENDEL.
MILAM.
MILDEN.
MILLS REDROME.
MILTON. (N.Y.S. 1923.)
MILWAUKEE. (Jeff. 1899.)
MINKLER. (Mink. 1865.)
MINNEHAHA. (M.A.E.S. 1920.)
MISSOURI PIPPIN. (Hor. 1840.)
MONMOUTH.
MORDEN RUSSET.
MORRIS.
MORTOF.
MOSCOW PEAR.
MOSEBAR WINESAP. *Mosebar Black Winesap.*
MOTHER.
MUNSON. *Munson Sweet.*
NERO.
NEWFANE. (N.Y.S. 1928.)
Newtown; Newtown Pippin. YELLOW NEWTOWN.
NEWTOWN SPITZENBURG.
NICKAJACK.
NIOBE.
Nodhead. JEWETT RED.
NORTHERN SPY. (Chap. 1800.)
NORTHWESTERN GREENING. (Dan. 1872.)
OAKLAND. (Gar. 1883.)
OGDEN. (N.Y.S. 1928.)
OHIO NONPAREIL.
OKABENA.
Oldenburg. DUCHESS.
OLIVER RED. *Senator.*
ONTARIO. (Arn. 1874.)
OPALESCENT. (McN.&G. 1899.)
ORENCO.
ORLEANS. (N.Y.S. 1924.)
ORTLEY.
OSTEM.
OSTRAKOFF.
OSWEGO.
OXBO. (S.D.S. 1922.)
PALOUSE. (Ruedy 1892.)
PARAGON. (Toole 1830.)
PARRY WHITE.
PATRICIA.
PATTEN. (Pat. 1885.) *Patten Greening.*
PAYNE. *Payne Keeper.*
PEACH OF MONTREAL. *Peach.*
PEASGOOD.

APPLE, continued
PECK PLEASANT.
PEDRO.
PEERLESS. (Mill. 1867.)
PENNOCK. (Pen. 1800.)
PERKINS. (Per. 1902.)
PERRY RUSSET.
PETER. (P. M. Gid. 1886.)
PETREL.
PEWAUKEE. (Pef. 1870.)
PINE GROVE RED.
PINTO.
PLUMB CIDER. (Plumb 1844.)
POMME GRISE.
PORTER. (Por. 1800.)
Pound Sweet. PUMPKIN SWEET.
Pride of Texas. TEXAS.
PRIMATE. (Bin. 1840.)
PRYOR.
PUMPKIN SWEET. (Lyman 1834.) *Pound Sweet.*
QUARRINDON. *Devonshire Quarrindon.*
RAINIER.
RALLS. (Ralls 1800.) *Rawles Genet; Geneton.*
RAMBO.
RAMSDELL SWEET. (Rams. 1838.)
Rawles Genet. RALLS.
REDANT.
RED ASTRACHAN.
REDCANADA. *Steele Red.*
RED DUCHESS. *Daniels Red Duchess.*
RED GRAVENSTEIN.
RED JUNE. *Carolina Red June.*
REDKING.
RED MCINTOSH.
REDRIBSTON.
REDROME.
REDSAUCE. (N.Y.S. 1926.)
REDSPY.
REDSTARK.
REDSTAYMAN.
RED TRANSPARENT.
RED TWENTYOUNCE.
REDWEALTHY.
REDWING.
RED YORKING.
RHODE ISLAND GREENING.
RIBSTON.
RICHARD GRAFT. (Del. 1860.)
RICHARED DELICIOUS.
ROGERS MCINTOSH. *Black Mickey.*
ROLFE.
ROMANSTEM.
ROME BEAUTY. (Gil. 1848.)
ROXBURY RUSSET.
ROYAL LIMBERTWIG.
RUBY RED WINESAP.
RUPERT.
SALOME. (Hat. 1853.)
SANDOW.
SANDY GLASS.
SAN JACINTO.
SCARLET PIPPIN.
SCOTT WINTER. (Hos. 1864.)
SECOR. (I.A.S. 1921.)
SEEANDO REDROME.
SEEANDO WINESAP.
Senator. OLIVER RED.
SHACKLEFORD.
SHARON. (I.A.S. 1921.)
SHARP.
SHERIFF. (She. 1880.)
SHIAWASSEE. (Tru. 1850.)
SHOCKLEY.
SHOTWELL DELICIOUS.
SIMBIRSK No. 1.
SIMBIRSK No. 9.

APPLE, continued
SMITH CIDER.
SMOKEHOUSE. (Gib. 1837.)
Snow. FAMEUSE.
SOPS OF WINE.
SPANGELO.
SPOKANE BEAUTY.
STARKING DELICIOUS.
STARK REDROME.
STARR.
STAYMAN WINESAP. (Sta. 1866.)
STAYMARED STAYMAN.
Steele Red. REDCANADA.
STEVENSON.
ST. LAWRENCE.
STREAKED PIPPIN.
SUGARLOAF.
SUMMER HAGLOE.
SUMMER PEARMAIN.
SUMMER QUEEN.
SUMMER RAMBO.
SUMMER ROSE.
SUTTON.
SWAAR.
SWAZIE. *Swazie Pomme Grise.*
SWEETBOUGH.
SWEET DELICIOUS. (N.Y.S. 1923.)
SWEET MCINTOSH. (N.Y.S. 1923.)
SWEET WINESAP.
TERRY.
TETOFSKI.
TEXAS. (Buc. 1889.) *Pride of Texas.*
TEXASRED.
THALER.
TITOVKA.
TITUS.
TOLMAN SWEET.
TOMPKINS KING. *King.*
TOPPENISH GRAVENSTEIN.
TOSHKEE.
TURLEY.
TWENTY OUNCE.
UNIVERSITY. (Pat. 1882.)
UTTER.
VANBUREN DUCHESS.
VANCE DELICIOUS.
VANDERPOOL.
VANDEVERE.
VANHOY.
VARGULEK.
VICTORIA SWEET.
VIRGINIA BEAUTY.
VOLGA ANIS.
WAGENER.
WALBRIDGE. (Cur. 1818.)
WASHINGTON ROYAL.
WASHINGTON STRAWBERRY. (Whi. 1849.)
WATTS.
WAUKON.
WEALTHY. (P. Gid. 1860.)
WEDGE. (M.A.E.S. 1922.)
WELLINGTON.
WESTFIELD. *Westfield Seek-no-further.*
WHITE ASTRACHAN.
WHITE PEARMAIN. *White Winter Pearmain.*
WHITE PIPPIN.
WILLIAMS. *Williams Early Red; Williams Favorite.*
WILLOWTWIG.
WILSON REDJUNE.
WINDSOR.

APPLE, continued
WINE.
WINESAP.
WINTER BANANA. (Flory 1876.) *Banana.*
WINTER PARADISE.
WINTERSTEIN. (Burb. 1898.)
WISMER. (Wis. 1897.)
WOLFRIVER. (Spr. 1881.)
YATES.
YELLOW BELLFLOWER.
Yellow Delicious. GOLDEN DELICIOUS.
YELLOW NEWTOWN. *Albemarle Pippin; Green Newtown; Newtown; Newtown Pippin.*
YELLOW TRANSPARENT.
YORKARED YORK.
YORK IMPERIAL. (Joh. 1830.)
YORKING YORK.

APRICOT . . . . . **Prunus armeniaca**
See also APRICOT, p. 19.
Acme. SHENSE.
ALBERGE.
ALEXANDER.
ALEXIS.
AMBER.
BARRY.
BLENHEIM. (Shi.)
BREDA.
BUDD. (J. Budd 1870.)
CATHARINE.
CLUSTER.
DERBY ROYAL.
EARLY GOLDEN.
EARLY MAY.
EARLY MOORPARK.
GENEVA.
GIBB.
HARRIS.
HEMSKIRKE.
HENDERSON.
KALEDEN.
LITTLE SAM.
LUIZET.
MANCHU.
MOORPARK.
NEWCASTLE.
NOBLE.
PEACH.
RILAND.
ROUTIER.
ROUTIER PEACH.
ROYAL.
SCOUT.
SHENSE. *Acme; Yakimene.*
ST. AMBROISE.
STELLA.
STEWART.
SUPERB.
TILTON. (Til. 1885.)
TOYAHVALE. (Gri. 1899.)
WENATCHEE MOORPARK.
WIGGIN.
WILSON.
Yakimene. SHENSE.

Araca . . . . GUAVA

ARAUCNUT (*Araucarian Pinenut*) **Araucaria araucana**

ATALANTIA . . . . **Atalantia**
BOMBAY A. . . . . . **A. racemosa**
CEYLON A. . . . . . **A. ceylonica**

ATALANTIA, continued
Dwarf C. A. . . . . ROUNDLEAF A.
GIANT A. (*Giant India A.*) **Atalantia macrophylla**
HENRY BOMBAY A. (*Henry A.*) **A. racemosa henryi**
INDIA A. . . . . . . **A. monophylla**
ROUNDLEAF A. (*Dwarf Ceylon A.*) **A. rotundifolia**

∞ATEMOYA . ∞**Annona cherimola** × **A. squamosa**

AVOCADO (*Alligator Pear*) **Persea americana**

The commercial Avocado is P. americana, but the name is applicable also to any species of the subgenus Eupersea with an edible fruit.

Cal. California.
Fla. Florida.
Hyb. Hybrid or Mixed Race.
Guat. Guatemala or Guatemalan Race (winter and spring-ripening; rind thick and woody).
Mex. Mexico or Mexican Race (P. americana drymifolia).
P.I. U. S. Dept. Agr. Plant Intro. No.
W.I. West Indian Race (summer and fall-ripening; rind leathery but thinner than in Guatemalan Race).

Ables. BEARDSLEE.
ACE. Guat. *Simpson.*
ACKERMAN. W.I.
Acme. BOOTH 2.
ACOSTA. W.I.
AJAX. Guat. × W.I. (Fla. 1920.)
AKBAL. Guat. P.I. 45505.
ALEGRE.
ALEXANDRIA. Guat.
ALPINE. Mex.
ALTO. Guat.
AMBASSADOR. Guat.
AMECA. Guat. *Furnival.*
AMERICA. Guat.
AMERICAN A. **P. americana.**
AMIGO. Guat.
ANAHEIM. Guat. (Dut. 1910.)
ANTIGUA No. 1. Guat. P.I. 38587 and 38549.
ANTIGUA No. 2. Guat. P.I. 38583.
ANTIGUA No. 3. Guat. P.I. 38578.
ARANGO. *Cor. Raul Arango.*
ARCTIC. Guat.
ATHERTON. W.I.
ATKINS. Mex. × Guat.
ATLIXCO. Guat.
AUBREY. W.I.; Hyb. ?
AUBURNDALE. W.I.
AVILA. W.I.
AVON. Guat. × W.I. (Ward 1923.)
AZUSA. Mex.
BAIRD. Guat. (Registered 1933.)
BAKER. W.I.
BALDWIN. W.I. P.I. 12933 and 13729.
BANNER.
BANNERTON.
BARKER. W.I.
BARTLETT. W.I. P.I. 40978.
BARTLEY. Guat.
BASKERVILLE. W.I.
BATAB. Guat. P.I. 43487.
BATANGAS. W.I. *Cardinal No. 2.*
BEACHS CHOICE. W.I.
BEARDSLEE. Guat. *Ables.*
BEAUTY. Guat.
BENEDICT. Mex. (S.N.B. 1912.)

Hort. var.; HV. = horticultural variety (or varieties); sp. = species (singular); spp. = species (plural).
₵ = clon; × (as a prefix) = hybrid; × (between scientific plant names) = crossed by; ∞ = polybrid; |w = plant useful to wildlife.
See Glossary for definitions of clon, hybrid, and polybrid.

AVOCADO, continued
BENIK. Guat. (Pop. 1917.) P.I. 44626.
BENLEE. W.I.
BERGER. W.I.
BICKNELL. Hyb.
BILLINGSLEY. Guat.
BITTE. W.I.
BLACKBIRD, Mex.
BLACKGANTER. Mex.
BLACKMAN. W.I. P.I. 26701.
BLAIR. Guat.
BLAKE. Mex.
BLAKEMAN. Guat. (Col. 1912.) P.I. 39373. *Dickey No. 2.*
BLUEBIRD. Mex.
BON. Guat.
BONITA. Guat. × W.I.
BOOTH 1. Guat. × W.I.
BOOTH 2. Guat. × W.I. *Acme.*
BOOTH 3. Guat. × W.I.
BOOTH 7. Guat. × W.I. (Fla. 1920.)
BOOTH 8. Guat. × W.I. (Fla. 1920.)
BOUNTIFUL. Guat. × W.I.
BRADBURY. Guat.
BRIGHAM. W.I.
BRODIA. Guat.
BROMLEY. W.I.
BUDDINGTON. Guat.
BUFFANDAU. W.I.
BUTLER. W.I. P.I. 26690.
BUTTERCUP. Guat.
BUTTERNUT. Guat.
CABNAL. Guat. P.I. 44782.
CADY. Guat.
CALABASH. Guat. × W.I. (Mex. 1912.)
CALIENTE. Mex.
California. WAGNER.
California Trapp. VERDE.
CAMEL. Guat.
CAMPBELL. W.I.
CANTEL. Guat. P.I. 44783.
CANTO. Guat.
CANYADA. Mex.
CAPAC. Mex. P.I. 53895 and 54276.
CARABAS. Guat.
CARCHI. Mex. P.I. 53185.
CARDINAL. W.I.
Cardinal No. 2. BATANGAS.
CARIBOU. Guat.
CARLSBAD. Guat. (Rid. and Ste. 1912.) *Stephens No. 2 at Montebello.*
CARMEN. Mex.
CARTON. Mex.
CASE. Guat.
CHABIL. Guat. P.I. 45564.
CHALLENGE. Guat. (Cal. 1898.)
CHAMPION. Guat.
CHAPPELOW. Mex. P.I. 12934.
CHILAN. Guat. P.I. 43933.
CHILE. Guat.
CHISOY. Guat. P.I. 43935.
CHOICE. Guat. (Ste. 1912.) *Stephens Choice.*
CHOTA. Mex. P.I. 53184 and 54272.
CHRISTIE. Guat.
CHRISTMAS GRAND. W.I.
CHRISTMAS RED. W.I. (Fla. 1910.)
CLOWER. Guat.
COBAN. Guat. P.I. 43932.
COCKETT. Guat.
COLIMA. Guat. *Johnston No. 5.*
COLLA. Guat. P.I. 19058.
COLLASON. Guat. × W.I.
COLLINRED. Guat. × W.I. P.I. 62376.

AVOCADO, continued
COLLINRED SEEDLING B. Guat. × W.I. P.I. 106941. *Fairchild.*
COLLINS. Guat. P.I. 19080.
COLLINSON. Guat. × W.I. (Fla. 1915.)
COLOMBIA. P.I. 51105.
COLON.
COLORADO. Guat. *Purple Murrieta.*
COLORADOS. Guat. P.I. 43603.
COMMODORE.
CONDON. Mex.
COOK. Guat.
COOPER. W.I.
Cor. Raul Arango. ARANGO.
COWANE. Mex.
COYO A. **P. schiedeana.**
Cuban Early. EARLY.
CUMMINS.
CYRUS. W.I. P.I. 26699. *St. Petersburg.*
DADE. W.I. P.I. 50968.
DANDELYON. Guat.
DAVIS. Nos. 4, 6, 7.
DEFIANCE. Guat.
DELICIOUS. Guat.
DELROSA. Guat.
DICKEY. Guat.
Dickey No. 2. BLAKEMAN.
DICKINSON. Guat. (Dic. 1899.) P.I. 39370.
DIESELDORFF No. 1. Guat. P.I. 38477.
DIESELDORFF No. 2. Guat. P.I. 38401.
DIESELDORFF No. 3. Guat. P.I. 38402.
DILLINGHAM. W.I.
DODEN.
DON. Guat. (Registered 1935.)
DON CARLOS. W.I. P.I. 40979.
DOROTHEA. Guat. × Mex.
DOUGLAS.
Dr. Weldon. WELDON.
DUKE. Mex. (S.N.B. 1912.)
DUNEDIN. Guat. × W.I. *Skinner.*
DUTTON. Guat. (Cal. 1912.)
Eagle Rock. GALLOUPE.
EARLY. W.I. *Cuban Early.*
EDDY. Mex.
EDRANOL. Guat. (Rid. 1927; registered 1932.)
Eells. NORTHROP.
E. Garcia. GARCIARICO.
EGAS. Mex. P.I. 53183 and 54271.
EGBERTO. Guat. × Mex.
ENOI. W.I.
ESBANK. W.I.
ESTELLE. W.I. (Truitt 1899.)
Fairchild. COLLINRED SEEDLING B.
FAIRHEAD. Guat.
FAMILY. W.I. P.I. 12935. (Fla. 1897.)
FARNSWORTH.
FERRY. Guat.
FIFTEEN. Guat. *Stephens No. 15.*
FOWLER. Mex.
FRANCES. Guat.
FREY. Guat. (Ruf. 1915.)
FUCHSIA. W.I. (Fla. 1910.) *Fuchs; Fuchs Early.*
FUERTE. Guat. × Mex. (Sch. 1911.)
FULFORD. W.I. P.I. 26707.
Furnival. AMECA.
GAGE. Guat.
GALLOUPE. Guat. *Eagle Rock.*
GALVANA.
GALVANA GREEN.
GANO. Plant Patent 100.

AVOCADO, continued
GANTER. Mex. (Rid. 1905.) P.I. 39374.
Ganter, Black. BLACKGANTER.
GARCIA (of Calif.). Guat.
GARCIARICO (of Puerto Rico). *E. Garcia.*
Generalissimo Maximo Gomez. GOMEZ.
GERTZ. W.I.
GLORIA. Guat.
GOERING.
GOLDIE.
GOMEZ. *Generalissimo Maximo Gomez.*
GORDO. Guat.
GOTTFRIED. Mex. (Got. 1906.) P.I. 19094 and 46337.
GOVERNMENT HOUSE.
GRANDE. Guat.
GRANT. W.I. P.I. 18731.
GUADALUPE. W.I. P.I. 40980.
GUAMEX. Guat. × Mex.
GUATEMALA. Guat.
GULICK. W.I.
GURREY. W.I.
HABERSHAM. Guat., possibly W.I. hyb. *Sherman.*
HADEN. W.I. P.I. 13730.
HALEY. Guat.
HALL. Guat. × W.I.
HARDEE. W.I. (Fla. 1900.)
HARDY. Mex. *Taft Hardy.*
HARMAN. Mex. (Mex. 1899.) P.I. 39375-A.
HART.
HARTRUSSET. Guat.
HASS. Guat. (Hass 1926; Plant Patent 139.)
HATHAWAY. Mex.
HAWAII. Hyb. ? Largely W.I.
HAYES.
HAYMAN. W.I.
HAZZARD. Guat. (Haz. 1928.)
HELIX. Mex.
HENRYS SELECT. Mex. Plant Patent 234.
Henrys Select. (Jon. 1925.)
HERMAN. Guat. × W.I.
HERNANDEZ. W.I. *Manuel.*
HICKSON. Guat. × W.I.
HIMEBAUGH.
HOFF. Guat.
HOLLENBECK. Mex.
HOLT. Guat.
Holts No. 1. INEZHOLT.
HONOLULU GREEN. W.I.
HORN. Mex.
HUIRA. Mex. P.I. 54278.
HULUMANU. W.I.
HUNAPUH. Guat. P.I. 44628.
IDEAL. Guat.
ILIALU. Guat. × W.I.
IMBABURA. Mex. P.I. 54275.
INCA. Mex. Possibly a W.I. hyb. P.I. 54277.
INDIAN RIVER. Mex. × W.I. (Fla. 1927.)
INEZHOLT. W.I. *Holts No. 1.*
INGERSOLL. Mex.
IRUMINA. Mex. P.I. 54274.
ISABELLA. Guat. × Mex.
ISHIM. Guat. Possibly a hyb. P.I. 45562.
ISHKAL. Guat. P.I. 43602.
ITZAMNA. Guat. (Pop. 1916.) P.I. 43486 and 55736.

AVOCADO, continued

Itzia. VOLCAN by error for *Iztaccihuatl*.
I.X.L. Guat.
Iztaccihuatl. VOLCAN.
JALNA. Mex. (Coit 1928.)
JERSEY CREAM. W.I.
JESSIE. Guat.
JOHNSTON. Guat. *Johnston No. 6*.
JOHNSTONE. W.I. P.I. 18729.
Johnston No. 5. COLIMA.
JUMBO. W.I.
KAGUAH. Guat. P.I. 45561.
KALUA. Guat.
KANAN. Guat. P.I. 45563.
KANOLA. Guat. P.I. 43560.
KASHLAN. Guat. P.I. 43834.
KATUN. Guat. P.I. 44781.
KAY. W.I. (Fla. 1923.)
KAYAB. Guat. P.I. 44681.
KEKCHI. Guat. P.I. 44679.
KEYLARGO. Guat. Probably synonymous with COLLINS.
KILGORE SPECIAL. Guat. × Mex. × W.I.? (Kil. 1927.)
KINAU. Guat. × W.I.
KIST. Guat.
KNIGHT. Guat. (Kni. 1914.) *Verde*.
KNOWLES. Mex.
KOBIE. Guat.
LADA. Hyb.
LAHAINA PRIZE. W.I.
LAHAINA PURPLE. W.I.
LAHI. Guat. × W.I.
LAMAT. Guat. P.I. 43476.
LAMBERT. Guat.
LANDO. W.I.
LANDON.
LANGE. Guat.
LARGO. W.I. P.I. 18730.
LAUREL. Guat.
LEADER. Guat.
LEE. Guat.
LEHUA. Guat. × W.I.
LENEGAN.
LEONA. Guat.
LEONARD. Guat. × Mex. (Leo. 1917.)
LEUCADIA. Mex. (Cal. 1927; registered 1932.)
LEWIS. W.I.
LINBETH. Guat. × Mex. (registered 1932.)
LINDA. Guat. (Kni. 1914.)
LINDGREN. Guat. × W.I.
LINSCOTT. Guat.
LOPENA. W.I.
LORD. *R. C. Lord*.
LOSANGELES. Mex.
LOUGHER. W.I.
LUISA. W.I. P.I. 40912.
LUKINI. W.I.
LULA. Guat. × Mex. (Cel. 1915.)
LYCETT.
LYMAN.
LYON OF CALIF. Guat. (Lyon 1908.)
LYON OF PHILIPPINES. Guat.
MAAG. Guat.
MACARTHUR. Guat. (She. 1922.)
MACDONALD. Guat. P.I. 36603.
MACEO. *Mayor Gral Antonio Maceo*.
MAGOON.
MAGUERIPE.
MAHAKA. I and II.
MAKAI. Hyb.
MANIK. Guat. P.I. 45560.
Manuel. HERNANDEZ.
MANZ. Guat.

AVOCADO, continued

MARION. Guat.
MARQUES. W.I.
MARTIN-SPERRY.
MARY GARDEN. Guat.
MATAMOROS. W.I. P.I.G. 14292.
MATNEY. Guat.
MATTERN. Mex.
MAXIMILIAN. Mex.
MAYAPAN. Guat. (Pop. 1917.) P.I. 44680.
Mayor Gral Antonio Maceo. MACEO.
MCCANN. W.I.
MCCARTNEY. Guat.
MCCLURE. W.I.
MCCONAGLE. W.I.
MCINERNY. Guat.
MERCED. W.I. P.I. 40981.
MERITO. Guat.
MESERVE. Guat. P.I. 39371.
METCALF. Guat.
MEXICAN A. **P. americana drymifolia.**
MEXICOLA. Mex. (C.R.P.G. 1910.)
MEYEN PERSEA. **P. meyeniana.**
MEYERS. Guat.
MILES. Guat.
MILLER. Guat.
MILLIE. C. Guat. (Coombs.)
MISSION. Mex.
MISSION BELL. Guat. × Mex.
MITCHELL. W.I. P.I. 18120. (Fla. 1906.)
Mitchell. W.I. (Fla. 1920.)
MOANALUA. P.I. 44104.
MODESTO. Guat.
MONGE.
MONROE OF CALIF. Guat.
MONROE OF FLA. W.I. × Guat. (Plant Patent 261.)
MONROVIA. Mex. *Valadenia*.
MONTEBELLO.
MONTEZUMA. Guat.
MOORE. W.I.
MORENO. Guat. P.I. 43604.
MORNE.
MUNIS.
MURRIETA. Guat. P.I. 38888. *Murrieta Green*.
MURRIETA TWOPOUND. Guat.
MYATT. W.I.
NABAL. Guat. (Pop. 1917.) P.I. 44439.
NEGROS. Guat. P.I. 43605.
NEHRLING. Guat. × W.I.
NELSON. Guat. Hyb.? (Fla. 1920.)
NEWBERRY. Guat.
NIMAH. Guat. P.I. 45078.
NIMLIOH. Guat. (Pop. 1917.) P.I. 44440.
NIRODY. Guat. × W.I. (Nirody 1922.)
NORTHROP. Mex. (Cal. 1900.) *Eells*.
NUTMEG. Guat. P.I. 36604.
OAKLEY No. 1, 2, 3, 5, 7, 10. Guat.
OAXACA A. **P. floccosa.**
OBISPO. Guat.
ORO. Guat.
OSBORN. Guat.
PALTA No. 1. P.I. 31478.
PALTITA.
PANCHOY. Guat. P.I. 44625. (Pop. 1917.)
PANKAY. Guat. P.I. 44785.
PATENT 100. Guat. (Gano; Plant Patent 100.)
PEACH. W.I.

AVOCADO, continued

PEACOCK. W.I. P.I. 26720.
Peacock. Guat. × W.I. (Fla. 1924.)
PEERLESS. Guat.
PENGUIN. Mex.
PERFECTION.
PERFECTO. Guat. (Sch. 1911.)
PETERSON. W.I.
PICO. Mex.
PINELLI. W.I.
PLATA. Mex.
POLLOCK. W.I. (Pol. 1894.) P.I. 12936.
POMONA. Mex.
POPOCATEPETL. Guat.
PRATT. Guat. × W.I.
PREMIER. Guat.
PRESIDENTE. Guat.
PRESTON. W.I.
PRINCE. Guat.
PRINCESS. Guat.
PRONTO. Mex.
PUEBLA. Mex. (Sch. 1911.)
PURDY. Mex.
PURPLE BEAUTY. Mex.
Purple Murrieta. COLORADO.
PURPLE PROLIFIC. Guat.
QUAKER. Guat.
QUALITY. W.I.
QUEEN. Guat. (Kni. 1914.)
QUERETARO. Mex. (Sch. 1911.)
RADER. W.I.
RAINEY. Mex.
R. C. Lord. LORD.
REASONER. W.I.
REDO. W.I.
REDONDO. Guat.
REY. Guat. (Kni. 1914.)
RHOAD. Guat.
RICHARDSON.
RICO. W.I. P.I. 13731.
RITA. Guat.
RIVER. W.I.
ROBERTS. Mex.
ROBINSON. W.I.
RODOLPH. Mex.
Rolfs. WINSLOWSON.
ROOP. W.I. P.I. 32426.
ROTUND. Guat. × Mex.
ROY. Guat. (Hawaii 1926.)
ROYAL. Guat.
ROYALPURPLE.
RUDDER.
RUF. Guat.
RYAN. Guat. × Mex. (Rya. 1927.)
SAMOAN. W.I.
SANRAFAEL. Mex.
SANSEBASTIAN. Mex. (Sch. 1911.)
SANTA ANNA. W.I.
Santa Barbara Early. WHITE.
SCHMIDT. Guat. (Sch. 1911.)
SEEDLESS. P.I. 14889.
SEEDLESS BUTTER. P.I. 14890.
SENOR. Guat.
SEXTON (of Hawaii). Mex.
Sexton (of Fla.). WALDO.
SEYDE. W.I.
SHARPLESS. Guat. (Cal. 1913.)
Sherman. HABERSHAM.
SHIPMAN. W.I.
SILVA. W.I.
SIMMONDS. W.I. (Fla. 1908.) P.I. 36270.
SIMPSON (of Fla.). Guat. × W.I. (Fla. 1918.)
Simpson. ACE.
SINALOA. Guat.

AVOCADO, continued
SKINNER. Mex.
Skinner. DUNEDIN.
SMITH. Mex.
SMITH-CLARK. Guat.
SNELL. Mex.
SOLANO. Guat. (Cal. 1912.) P.I. 39372.
SOUTH KONA. W.I
SPINKS. Guat. (Cal. 1915.)
ST. ANNS.
ST. CLAIR.
STEFFANI. Guat. × W.I. (Fla. 1921.)
STEPHENS. W.I. P.I. 26691.
Stephens Choice. CHOICE.
Stephens No. 2 at Montebello. CARLSBAD.
Stephens No. 15. FIFTEEN.
STERLING. W.I. P.I. 26697.
ST. JOSEPH.
ST. JUST.
STOREY. W.I.
STORLARG. W.I.
St. Petersburg. CYRUS.
SUAREZ. W.I.
SURPRISE. Guat.
TAFT. Guat. (Taf. 1899.) P.I. 39369.
Taft Hardy. HARDY.
TAHITI.
TAMAYO. Mex. P.I. 53182 and 54270.
TANTALUS. W.I.
TAYLOR. Guat. (U.S.P.I.G. 1908.) P.I. 26710.
Taylor. W.I.
TAYLORSON. Guat. × W.I.
TERTOH. Guat. P.I. 44856.
THEVENIN. W.I.
THOMPSON. Guat.
TIGER. Guat.
TINGLEY. Mex.
TONNAGE. Guat.
TOPATOPA. Mex. (Tha. 1907.)
TOWSE. Guat.
TRAPP A. W.I. P.I. 12937, 16871 and 26689. (Tra. 1894.) **P. americana leiogyna.**
TRAPPSON. W.I. × Guat. × W.I. P.I. 61740.
TUMIN. Guat. P.I. 44627.
TWOPOUND GREEN. Guat.
ULTIMATE. Guat.
Valadenia. MONROVIA.
VALDEFLOR. Mex.
VANNIE. Guat. (Fla. 1930.)
VEGA.
VENZUELA.
VERDE. Guat. *California Trapp.*
Verde. KNIGHT.
VERDES. Guat. P.I. 43606.
VERIBEST. Guat.
VERNAERO. W.I. P.I. 35121.
VERO. Mex. × W.I. (Fla. 1927.)
VICTORY. Guat.
VILLA. M.H. (Fla. 1920.)
VIRGINIA. Guat.
VOLCAN. Guat. *Iztaccihuatl* and erroneously *Itzia.*
WAGNER. Guat. (Cal. 1908.) *California.*
WALDIN. W.I. (Wal. 1909.)
WALDO. Mex. × W.I. (Fla. 1927.) *Sexton* (*of Fla.*).
WALKER. Guat. *Walker Prolific.*
WALL. W.I.
WARD. Guat. × Mex.
WEIGHT. W.I. × Guat.

AVOCADO, continued
WELDON. *Dr. Weldon.*
WESTER. W.I. P.I. 19297. (Fla. 1871.)
WHITE. Mex. P.I. 30080. *Santa Barbara Early.*
WHITTIER. Guat.
WHITTIERMEX. Mex.
W.I.G.
WILDER. Guat. P.I. 55625 and 61084.
WILSHIRE. Guat.
WILSON. W.I. P.I. 40982.
WINSLOW. Guat. P.I. 10978.
WINSLOWSON. Guat. × W.I. (Fla. 1911.) P.I. 58444. *Rolfs.*
WINTER MEXICAN. Guat. × Mex. (Fla. 1916.)
WORSHAM. Guat. × Mex.
YAS A. **P. pittieri.**
YON. Guat. × W.I. (Fla. 1926.)
YOUNG.
ZAK. Guat.

BAELFRUIT . . . . **Aegle marmelos**

BAKUPARI . . . . **Rheedia brasiliensis**
See WILDLEMON.

BAKURI . . . . . . **Platonia insignis**

BALSAMOCITRUS **Balsamocitrus dawei**

BANANA . . . . **Musa** spp.
Com. Common Banana.
CHAMALUCO. Com.
Chinese B. CAVENDISH B.
CLARET. *Red Banana.*
COMMON B. **M. paradisiaca sapientum.**
DWARF B. **M. nana** (*cavendishi; chinensis*).
GROS MICHEL. Com.
HART. Com.
LADYFINGER. Com.
MANZANO. Com.
ORINOCO. Com.
PLANTAIN B. **M. paradisiaca.**

BARBADOSCHERRY . . **Malpighia glabra**

BARBERRY . . . . . . **Berberis** spp.

Batokoplum . . . . LOUVI

BEECHNUT . . . . **Fagus** spp.
AMERICAN B. . . . **F. grandifolia**
EUROPEAN B. . . . . **F. sylvatica**
SIEBOLD B.. . . . . . . **F. sieboldi**

BETELNUT . . . . . . **Areca cathecu**

BIGNAY (*Antidesma*) **Antidesma bunius**

BILIMBI . . . . . . **Averrhoa bilimbi**

BIRIBA . . . . . . **Rollinia deliciosa**

BLACKBERRY . . . . . . **Rubus** spp.

ABBREVIATIONS OF TYPES OF BLACKBERRIES
Er. Erect Blackberries.
Se. Semi-erect Blackberries.
Str. Semi-trailing Blackberries.
Tr. Trailing Blackberries or Dewberries.
Dr. Darrow reports that the vars. prefixed by an asterisk (*) are no longer in cultivation.

ADVANCE. Str.
AGAWAM. Er. (Perk. 1865?)
ALFRED. Er. (Stro. 1917.)
ANCIENT BRITON. Er. (Brit. 1875?)
AUSTIN THORNLESS. Tr. (Par. 1918?)
Black Diamond. EVERGREEN.
BLOWERS. Er. (Blo. 1888.)
BOYSEN. Tr. (1935.)
BRAINERD. Se. (Dar. 1919.)
BREWER. Er. (Brew. 1909.)

BLACKBERRY, continued
BURBANK THORNLESS. Se. (Burb. 1904.)
CASCADE. (Darrow 1932.)
CORY THORNLESS. Str. (Meuli 1909.)
Crandall. TEXAS EARLY.
DALLAS. Se. (1880?)
*DORCHESTER.
EARLY HARVEST. Er. (Men. 1880?)
EARLY WONDER. Er. (Fit. 1902.)
ELDORADO. Er. (1880.) *Stuart; Texas.*
ERIE. Er. (Pie. 1876.)
EVERGREEN. Se. *Black Diamond.*
HAUPT. Se. (Haupt. 1898?)
HIMALAYA. Se. (Burb. 1889.)
ICEBERG. Er. (J.&P. 1897.)
IDEAL WILD. Tr.
JORDAN. Er. (Nimon. 1895.)
JOY. Er. (Miehl. 1914.?)
KING. Er.
*KITTATINNY.
KOSMO. Str.
LAWTON. Er. (Sea. 1834.)
LAXTON.
LOGAN. Str. (Logan 1881.)
LUCRETIA. Tr. (Alba. 1875.)
Macatawa. TEXAS EARLY.
MAHDI.
MAMMOTH. Str. (Logan 1909.)
MAYES. Tr. (Mayes 1880.)
McDONALD. Str. (T.N.C.)
MERSEREAU. Er. (Mer. 1890?)
MINNEWASKA.
NANTICOKE. Er. (Allen 1912.)
NECTAR.
NESS. Str. (Ness 1913.)
*OHMER.
PACIFIC. (Darrow 1932.)
PHENOMENAL. Str. (Burb. 1897?)
POCONO.
PREMO. Tr. (1905?)
RATHBUN.
ROBINSON.
RUSSELL. Er.
SNYDER. Er. (Sny. 1851.)
SORSBY.
STONE.
Stuart. ELDORADO.
TAYLOR.
Texas. ELDORADO.
TEXAS EARLY. Er. (Cran. 1885.) *Crandall; Macatawa.*
THORNLESS EVERGREEN. Se.
THORNLESS LOGAN. Str.
THORNLESS YOUNG.
*WACHUSETT.
WARD. Er. (T. Ward.)
WILSON.
WILSON EARLY.
YOUNG. Str. (Young 1905.)
ZIELINSKI. Tr.

BLACKSAPOTE . . **Diospyros ebenaster**

BLUEBERRY . . . . . **Vaccinium** spp.
ADAMS. (White.)
ATLANTIC. (Cov. 1925.)
BROOKS. (Bro. 1908.)
BURLINGTON. (Cov. 1916.)
CABOT. (Cov. 1913.)
CATAWBA. (Cov. 1913.)
CHATSWORTH.
CONCORD. (Cov. 1917.)
DIXI. (Cov. 1930.)
DUNFEE.
GREENFIELD. (Cov. 1913.)
GROVER. (Gro.)
HARDING. (Hardi.)

BLUEBERRY, continued
JERSEY. (Cov. 1916.)
JUNE. (Cov. 1919.)
KATHARINE. (Cov. 1913.)
PEMBERTON. (Cov. 1921.)
PIONEER. (Cov. 1912.)
RALPH.
RANCOCAS. (Cov. 1915.)
REDSKIN. (Cov. 1913.)
RUBEL. (Leek.)
RUSSELL. (Rus. 1909.)
SAM. (White.)
SCAMMELL. (Cov. 1915.)
SOOY. (Sooy 1911.)
STANLEY. (Cov. 1921.)
WAREHAM. (Cov. 1915.)
WEYMOUTH. (Cov. 1928.)

BOXORANGE . . . . . **Severinia spp.**
BOUQUET B. . . . . **S. paniculata**
CHINESE B. . . . . **S. buxifolia**
DWARF C. B. . . **S. b. subinermis**
NARROWLEAF B. . . . . **S. linearis**
PHILIPPINE B. . . . . . **S. disticha**

Brazilcherry . . . . PITANGA

Braziliancherry . . . . GRUMICHAMA

BRAZILNUT (*Castanha; Niggertoe*) **Bertholletia excelsa**

BREADFRUIT . . . . **Artocarpus altilis**
HAWAIIAN
SAMOAN

BREADNUT, RAMON **Brosimum alicastrum**

BRUSHCHERRY, AUSTRALIAN **Eugenia paniculata australis**

∞ BUARTNUT (*Bixby Walnut*) ∞ **Juglans bixbyi**
LANCASTER B. . ×**J. lancastriensis**

BUCKBERRY . . . **Gaylussacia ursina**

BUFFALOBERRY, SILVER **Shepherdia argentea**

BUFFALONUT . . . . **Pyrularia pubera**

Bullocks Heart . . . . CUSTARDAPPLE

BURDEKINPLUM **Pleiogynium solandri**

BUTTERNUT (*White Walnut*) **Juglans cinerea**
AIKEN. (Jones 1918.)
ALVERSON. (Alv. 1932.)
BAKER. (G. Zim. 1934.)
BLISS. (Bliss 1929.)
BUCKLEY. (Buc. 1924.)
DEMING. (Dem. 1920.)
DE VAN. (DeV. 1929.)
HERGERT. (Herg. 1929.)
IRVINE. (Irv. 1929.)
KENWORTHY. (Kenw. 1929.)
LINGLE. (Ling. 1929.)
LOVE. (C. Reed 1930.)
LUTHER. (Luth. 1932.)
SAUGATUCK. (Dem. 1926.)
SHERWOOD. (Snyd. 1924.)
SIMONSON. (Simo. 1929.)
THILL. (Thill 1929.)
UTTERBACK. (Snyd. 1927.)
VAN DER POPPEN. (VDP. 1929.)
VINCAMP. (Jac. 1936.)
WATTS. (Watts 1936.)
WRIGHT. (R. Wright 1932.)
ZIMMERMAN. (N. Zim. 1932.)

CABELLUDA . . . **Eugenia tomentosa**

CACAO . . . . . . **Theobroma cacao**

Cainito . . . . STARAPPLE

CANDLENUT . . **Aleurites moluccana**

CANISTEL (*Eggfruit*) . **Lucuma nervosa**

CANTALOUP (*Cantaloupe*) **Cucumis melo cantalupensis**
The name is generally (but loosely and incorrectly) applied to other varieties and races of Muskmelon.

Capulasan . . . . PULASAN

CAPULIN . **Prunus serotina salicifolia**

CARAMBOLA . . **Averrhoa carambola**

CARISSA (*Amatungula; Natalplum*) **Carissa grandiflora**
ALLES. GIFFORD.
CHESLEY. SERENA.
FRANK.

CAROB (*St. Johnsbread*) **Ceratonia siliqua**
Now grown in the United States almost exclusively as an ornamental and propagated as seedlings. Varieties named below are all selections made in California.
BOLSER. SANTA FE.
FAIRMONT.

CASHEW (*Cashewapple; Cashewnut*) **Anacardium occidentale**

Casimiroa . . . . . . WHITESAPOTE

Castanha . . . . BRAZILNUT

Cayennecherry . . . . . . PITANGA

CERIMAN . . . . **Monstera deliciosa**

Ceylongooseberry . . . . KITEMBILLA

CHERIMOYA . . . **Annona cherimola**
∞ ATEMOYA (*cherimola × squamosa*).
BAYS. MCPHERSON.
BENSONA. ROY.
BOOTH. RYERSON.
CARTER. SMOOTH.
DALTOL. SUAVISSIMA.
DELICIOSA. TUBERCULATE.
FINGERPRINT. UMBONATE.
GOLDEN RUSSET. WHALEY.
LOMA. WHITE.
MAMMILLATE. WILD C. **A. longiflora.**

CHERRY . . . . . . **Prunus cerasus;** also **P. avium; P. mahaleb** (as stock)
See also CHERRY, p. 109.
D. Duke.
S. Sour.
Sw. Sweet.

ABESSE D'OIGNIES. D.
ABUNDANCE. Sw. (Burb. 1911.)
ADVANCE. Sw. *California Advance.*
ARCHDUKE. D.
BALDWIN. S. (Bal. 1891.)
BEDFORD PROLIFIC. Sw. *Bedford.*
Belle Magnifique. MAGNIFIQUE.
BESSARABIAN. S.
BIGARREAU PELISSIER. Sw.
BING. Sw. (Lew. 1875.)
BLACK GUIGNE. Sw.
BLACKHEART. Sw.
Black Oregon; Black Republican. REPUBLICAN.
BLACK TARTARIAN. Sw.
BOURGUEIL. S. (Bre. 1844.)
BRUSSELER BRAUNE. S.
BUNTE AMARELLE. S.
BURBANK. Sw. (Burb. 1911.)
California Advance. ADVANCE.
CARNATION. S.
CARNIVAL. D.
CENTENNIAL. Sw. (Chapm. 1876.)
CHAPMAN. Sw.
CHOICY. D.
CLUSTER. S.

CHERRY, continued
COE. Sw. *Coes Transparent.*
DEACON. Sw.
DIKEMAN. Sw.
DOUBLE NATTE. S.
DOWNER. Sw. (Down. 1832.)
∞ DUKE C. **P. avium × P. cerasus.**
DYEHOUSE. S. (Dye. 1860.)
EAGLE. Sw. (Kni. 1806.)
EARLY HONEYHEART. Sw.
EARLY PURPLE. Sw. *Early Purple Guigne; Purple Guigne.*
EARLY RICHMOND. S.
EARLY RIVERS. Sw. (Riv. 1869.)
ELKHORN. Sw.
ELTON. Sw. (Kni. 1806.)
EMPEROR FRANCIS. Sw.
EMPRESS EUGENIE. D.
ENGLISH MORELLO. S.
GIANT. Sw. (Burb. 1900.)
GIL PECK. Sw.
GOLD. Sw.
GOV. WOOD. Sw. *Wood.*
HEDELFINGEN. Sw.
HONEYHEART. Sw.
IDA. Sw. (Coc. 1909.)
KING AMARELLE.
KIRTLAND. Sw.
KNIGHT EARLY BLACK. Sw. (Kni. 1810.) *Knight.*
LAMBERT. Sw. (Lew. 1848.)
LARGE MONTMORENCY. S.
LATEDUKE. D.
LATE KENTISH. S.
Lewelling. REPUBLICAN.
LOUIS PHILIPPE. D. *Philippe.*
LUTOVKA. S.
LYONS. Sw. (Jab. 1822.)
MAGNIFIQUE. D. *Belle Magnifique.*
MAHALEB C. **P. mahaleb.**
MANCHU C. **P. tomentosa.**
MAYDUKE. D.
MAZZARD C. (*Sweet C.*). **P. avium.**
MONTEARLY MONTMORENCY.
MONTLATE MONTMORENCY.
MONTMORENCY. S.
Nanking C. MANCHU C.
NAPOLEON. Sw. *Royal Ann.*
NOUVELLE ROYAL. D.
OLIVET. D.
OSTHEIM. S.
Philippe. LOUIS PHILIPPE.
Purple Guigne. EARLY PURPLE.
RAINBOW STRIPE. Sw.
REINE HORTENSE. D. (Lar. 1826.)
REPUBLICAN. Sw. (Lew. 1860). *Black Oregon; Black Republican; Lewelling.*
ROCKPORT. Sw. (Kirt. 1842.)
Royal Ann. NAPOLEON.
ROYAL DUKE. D.
SCHMIDT. Sw. (Sch. 1841.)
SENECA. Sw.
SKLANKA. S.
SOUR C. **P. cerasus.**
Spanish. YELLOW SPANISH.
SPARHAWK. Sw.
Sweet C. MAZZARD C.
VICTOR. Sw.
VLADIMIR. S.
WINDSOR. Sw. (Dou. 1881.)
Wood. GOV. WOOD.
WRAGG. S.
YELLOW SPANISH. Sw. (Pri. 1802.) *Spanish.*

CHERRYORANGE . . . . . **Citropsis**
ANGOLA C.. . . . . **C. angolensis**

CHERRYORANGE, continued
CAMEROON C. . . **Citropsis zenkeni**
EASTAFRICAN C. . **C. schweinfurthi**
GABON C. . . . . . **C. gabonensis**
GILLET C. . . . . . . **C. gilletiana**
IKONGU C. . . . . . . **C. latialata**
IVORYCOAST C. . . . . **C. mirabilis**
KASAI C. **C. gabonensis lacourtiana**
LETESTU C. . . . . . . **C. letestui**
WESTAFRICAN C. . . . **C. articulata**

CHESTNUT . . . . . . **Castanea spp.**

The hort. var. in the list below are clons. Common names of species (to which the initial letter C. is appended) are also included as a matter of convenient reference.
Eu. European.

ADVANCE. (Parry 1890.)
ALPHA. (Parry 1892.)
AMERICAN C. **C. dentata.**
ANDERSON. (Robe. about 1895.)
ATKINSON. (Atki. 1930.)
AUSTIN. (Aus. 1930.)
AVANT. Eu. (F. Gil. 1890–91.) *Avant Chataigne; Early Marron.*
BARNEY. (Parry 1890.)
BARTLETT. (Bart. 1934.)
BARTRAM. (Bartr. 1890 or before.)
BERTRAND. Eu. (F. Gil. 1890.) *Marron Bertrand.*
BETA. (Parry 1892.)
BIDDLE. (Kerr 1893.)
BIGBOY. (Bush 1931.)
BLACK. (Kerr 1893.) *Dr. Black.*
∞ BLARINGHEM C. ∞ **C. blaringhemi.**
BLUEGREEN. (Mor. 1929.)
BOONE. (End. 1902.)
BOWMAN. (Bush 1930.)
∞ BURBANK C. ∞ **C. burbanki.**
Burbank. COE.
CARR. (Carr 1930.) *Carrissima.*
CASTIVA. (F.G.N. 1929.)
CHALON. Eu. (F. Gil. 1890.) *Chalan; Chelan; Marron Chalon.*
CHAMPION. (Riehl 1920 or before.)
CHATAENE. Eu. (F. Gil. early 90's.)
CHINESE C. (*Hairy C.*). **C. mollissima.**
CLINE. (Cline 1930.)
COE. (Hale 1898.) *Burbank.*
Coes Early. McFARLAND.
Col. Martin. MARTIN.
COLOSSAL. (F.G.N. 1925.)
COMBALE. Eu. (F. Gil. 1870.) *Marron Combale.*
COMFORT. (Comf. 1890 or before.)
Concord. STYER.
Connecticut Yankee. YANKEE.
COOPER. (Early 90's.)
CORSON. (W. Cors. before 1896.)
∞ COUDERC C. ∞ **C. couderci.**
CREVERLING. (G. Zim. 1935.)
DAGER. (Dager 1893.)
DANPATCH. (Riehl 1925.)
DARLINGTON. (Dar. about 1850.)
DECKER. (G. Zim. 1938.)
DELAWARE. (Kill. 1900.)
DE LYON. (F. Gil. 1890 or before.) *Marron de Lyon.*
Deming. VIBBERT.
DENTON. (Kerr 1910 or before.)
DEVONSHIRE PROLIFIC. Eu. (Before 1892.)
DOWNTON. Eu. (1845.) *Knights Prolific.*
Dr. Black. BLACK.
DRESCHER. (G. Zim. 1929.)

CHESTNUT, continued
DUNBAR. (Dunba. 1933.)
DU PONT. Group name. (Before 1896.)
Early Marron. AVANT.
Early Prolific. PROLIFIC.
EDDY. (Bush 1928.)
EDWIN. (E. Riehl 1925.)
Eighteen-Months. HALE.
∞ ENDICOTT C. ∞ **C. endicotti.**
EUREKA. (Parry 1887.)
EUROPEAN C. (*Spanish C.*). **C. sativa.**
EXALADE. Eu. (Before 1892.)
Extra Early. KENT.
FELTON. (Kill. 1893.)
FOUNTAIN. (F.G.N. 1930.)
FULLER. (R.F.N. 1916.)
GIANT. (90's.)
Giant Japan. PARRY.
Giant Superb. SUPERB.
GIBBENS. (R.F.N. 1923.)
Great American. PARAGON.
GROSSE PRECOSE. Eu. (F. Gil. 1890.) *Marron Precose,* in part.
HALE. (Hale 1895.) *Eighteen-Months.*
Hannum. STYER.
HATHAWAY. (Hath. 1896.)
HENLOPEN. (Kill. 1900.)
HOBSON. (Hob. 1930.)
HORACE. (Kerr before 1911.)
INGRAHAM. (1890.)
JAPANESE C. **C. crenata.**
Japan Giant. PARRY.
JOCKETT. (Jock. 1933.)
KENT. (Kill. about 1895.) *Extra Early.*
KERR. (Kerr 1893.)
KILLEN. (Kill. 1894.)
Knights Prolific. DOWNTON.
LARGE AMERICAN SWEET. (F.G.N. 1923.)
LOVETT. (Lov. 1905.)
Marron Bertrand. BERTRAND.
Marron Chalon. CHALON.
Marron Combale. COMBALE.
Marron de Lyon. DE LYON.
Marron Merle. MERLE.
Marron Nauzillard. NAUZILLARD.
Marron Precose. GROSSE PRECOSE; PRECOSE.
Marron Precose-Prolifique. PRECOSE.
Marron Quercy. QUERCY.
MARTIN. (Kerr 1893.) *Col. Martin.*
MATHER. (J. Parry 1899.)
MAYSEPTJAN. (F.G.N. 1932.)
McFARLAND. (Hale 1898.) *Coes Early.*
MERLE. Eu. (F. Gil. 1891.) *Marron Merle.*
MERRIBROOKE. (Morr. about 1915.)
MILFORD. (Aus. 1934.)
MILLER. (1890.) *Millers du Pont.*
MIRACLE. (Burb. 1915.)
MONCUR. (Todd 1895.)
∞ MORRIS C. ∞ **C. morrisi.**
MORRIS. (J. Smith 1937.)
MURDEN. (Stoke 1936.)
MYERS. (G. Zim.)
NAUZILLARD. Eu. (F. Gil. about 1880.) *Marron Nauzillard.*
NUMBO. (Moon 1882 or 1883.)
PAGE. (Page 1930.)
PARAGON. (H. Engle about 1875.) *Great American.*
PARKER. (W. Park. 1930.)
PARRY. (Parry 1898.) *Giant Japan; Japan Giant; Parrys Giant.*

CHESTNUT, continued
Parry. (Riehl 1918.)
Parrys Giant. PARRY.
Parrys Superb. SUPERB.
PEARL. China. (U.S.D.A. 1934.)
PEMEL. (U.S. 1890.)
PHILLIPI. (J. Parry 1889 or before.)
PRECOSE. Eu. (F. Gil. 1890.) *Marron Precose; Marron Precose-Prolifique.*
PROGRESS. (Riehl 1916.)
PROLIFIC. (Parry 1887.) *Early Prolific.*
∞ PULCHELLA C. ∞ **C. pulchella.**
QUERCY. Eu. (F. Gil. 1883.) *Marron Quercy.*
REEK. (Reek 1933.)
RELIABLE. (Stoke 1938.)
RELIANCE. (Parry 1890.)
RIDGELY. (Van De. 1890.)
ROCHESTER. (Riehl about 1905.)
RUSH. (Rush 1896.)
SCOTT. (Scott early 90's.)
S-8. (U.S.D.A. 1921.)
SHIBAGURI. Japan.
SIEBERT. (G. Zim. 193–.)
SMITH. (H. Smi. 1929.)
SOLEBURY. (1891.)
Spanish C. EUROPEAN C.
STEIN. (C. Stein 1930.)
STOKE. (Stoke 1936.) *Stoke Hybrid.*
STYER. (Styer 1890.) *Concord; Hannum.*
SUCCESS. (Parry 1890.)
SUPERB. (Parry 1892.) *Giant Superb; Parrys Superb.*
SWAYNE. (Swa. 1930.)
TAMBAGURI. (Gri. 1923.)
TATE. (Hers. 1935.)
∞ VANFLEET C. ∞ **C. fleeti.**
VAN FLEET. (R.F.N. 1926.)
VIBBERT. (Dem. 1930.) *Deming.*
WALTERS. (Glen. 1916.)
YANKEE. (J. Smith 1935.) *Connecticut Yankee.*
ZIMMERMAN. (G. Zim. 1930.)

CHILENUT (*Chilehazel*) **Gevuina avellana**

Chinese-date . . . . JUJUBE

CHINKAPIN (*Chinquapin*) **Castanea spp.**

See also EVERGREENCHINKAPIN.

ALABAMA C. . . . **C. alabamensis**
ALLEGANY C. . . . . . **C. pumila**
ASHE C. . . . . **C. ashei**
FLORIDA C. . . . . . **C. floridana**
GOLDEN C. **Castanopsis chrysophylla**
HENRY C. (*Chinese Tree C.*) **Castanea henryi**
JAPANESE C. . **Castanopsis cuspidata**
MARGARET FLORIDA C. **Castanea floridana margaretta**
OZARK C. . . . . . **C. ozarkensis**
SEGUIN C. (*Chinese Dwarf C.*) **Castanea seguini**
SIERRA C. **Castanopsis sempervirens**
TRAILING C. . . . . . **C. alnifolia**
WATERCHINKAPIN **Nelumbium pentapetalum**

∞ CHINKNUT . . . ∞ **Castanea neglecta**
₵RUSH. HV.

Chinquapin . . . . CHINKAPIN

CHOKEBERRY . . . . . . **Aronia spp.**

CHOKECHERRY . . **Prunus virginiana**

∞CICITRANGE . . . . ∞CITRANGE × **Poncirus trifoliata**

∞CITRADIA . . . **Citrus aurantium** × **Poncirus trifoliata**

₵BROWNELL

∞CITRANDIRIN . . . **Citrus reticulata** × **Poncirus trifoliata**

∞CITRANGE . . . . **Citrus sinensis** × **Poncirus trifoliata**

₵COLEMAN.
₵CORRIZO.
₵CUNNINGHAM.
₵ETONIA.
₵MORTON.
₵PHELPS.
₵RUSK.
₵RUSTIC.
₵SANFORD.
₵SAUNDERS.
₵SAVAGE.
₵TROYER.
₵WILLITS.

∞CITRANGEDIN
∞CITRANGE × ∞KUMANDARIN

₵ALTAMAHA. *Glen.*

∞CITRANGEQUAT
∞CITRANGE × **Fortunella** spp.

₵SINTON.
₵TELFAIR.
₵THOMASVILLE.

∞CITRANGEREMO . . . ∞CITRANGE × **Eremocitrus glauca**

∞CITREMON . . . . **Citrus reticulata** × **Poncirus trifoliata**

CITRON . . . . **Citrus medica**

A. Acid. S. Sweet.

₵CEDRESSA. A.
₵CHINA C. *The China Lemon.*
₵CORSICAN. S.
₵DIAMANTE. A.
₵EARLE. A.
₵ETHROG C. **C. medica ethrog.** A. *Adams; Atrog; Paradise Apple.*
₵FINGERED C. **C. medica sarcodactylis.** A.

CITRONMELON
Citrullus vulgaris citroides

∞CITRUMELO . . . **Citrus paradisi** × **Poncirus trifoliata**

₵SACATON

∞CITRUMQUAT . . . **Fortunella** spp. × **Poncirus trifoliata**

CLYMENIA . . . **Clymenia polyandra**

Cobnut . . . . COB FILBERT

COCONUT . . . . . . **Cocos nucifera**

COMMON. DWARF GOLDEN.

COCOPLUM (*Icaco*) **Chrysobalanus icaco**

COHUNENUT . . . . **Orbignya cohune** (*Attalea c.*)

COLANUT, SUDAN . . **Cola acuminata**

Corkwood . . . . PONDAPPLE

CORNELIANCHERRY . . . **Cornus mas**

CRABAPPLE . . . . **Malus** spp.

See also CRABAPPLE, p. 141. For ornamental vars. ("Flowering Crabapples"), see **MALUS**.

ADAM.
ALBERTA.
ALEXIS.
AMUR.
ANAROS.
BEAUTY.
BEDFORD.
BRIER. (Brier 1870.)
CALROS.
CHARLES.
CHERRY.
COLUMBIA.
CORAL.
CURRANT.

CRABAPPLE, continued

DARTT.
DAUPHIN.
DOLGO.
ELKHORN.
EXCELSIOR. (P. Gid. 1885.)
FLAME.
FLORENCE. (P. Gid. 1886.)
GARNETCRAB.
GENERAL GRANT.
GERTRUDE.
GIBB. (Pef. 1884.)
GRETNA.
HOPA.
HYSLOP.
IVAN.
JEWEL.
LINDA SWEET.
LYMAN.
MAGNUS.
MARTHA. (P. Gid. 1839.)
MARTIN.
MECCA.
MERCER.
MINNESOTA.
MONTREAL BEAUTY.
OLGA.
ORANGE.
OSMAN.
PAUL IMPERIAL.
PHILLIPS.
PIONEER.
PIOTASH.
PRINCE.
PRINTOSH.
REDMAN.
REDSIBERIAN.
REDTIP.
ROBIN.
ROSILDA.
SCUGOG.
SEPTEMBER. (P. Gid. 1888.)
SILVIA.
SUGAR.
TOBA.
TRAIL.
TRANSCENDENT.
VAN WYCK.
VIRGINIA.
WAPELLA.
WHITNEY. (Whit. 1869.) *Whitney No. 20.*
YELLOW SIBERIAN.
YOUNG AMERICA.

CRANBERRY . . . . **Vaccinium** spp.

₵AVIATOR.
₵BENNETT.
₵BUGLE.
₵CENTENNIAL.
₵CENTERVILLE.
₵CHAMPION.
₵EARLY BLACK.
₵HOLLISTON.
₵HOWES.
₵MATTHEWS.
₵McFARLIN.
₵PROLIFIC.
₵SEARL.

CRANBERRYBUSH, AMERICAN
Viburnum trilobum

₵ANDREWS.
₵HAHS.
₵WENTWORTH.

CURRANT . . . . **Ribes** spp.

See also CURRANT, p. 148.

Bl. Black (R. nigrum).
Gold. Golden (R. aureum).
Red Red (R. sativum).
Wh. White (R. sativum, form or race).

ADMIRABLE. Red.
ALBERT. Red.
BALDWIN. Bl.

CURRANT, continued

BEAUTY. Bl. (Sau. 1887.)
BLACK NAPLES. Bl. *Naples.*
BLACK VICTORIA. Bl.
BOSKOOP GIANT. Bl. (Hoo. 1868.)
BUDDENBORG. Bl.
CHAMPION. Bl. (Dun. 1858.)
CHAUTAUQUA. Red. (Lon. 1893.)
CHERRY. Red. (Valk. 1846.)
CLIMAX. Wh. (Sau.)
CLIPPER. Bl. (Sau. 1887.)
COLLINS PROLIFIC. Bl.
CRANDALL. Bl. (R. Cran. 1888.)
DIPLOMA. Red. (Moore. 1885.)
EAGLE. Bl. (Sau. 1887.)
ECLIPSE. Bl. (Sau. 1887.)
EVERYBODY. Red. (Lov. 1897.)
FAY. Red. (Fay 1868.) *Prolific.*
FILLER. Red. (Fil. 1892.)
GIANT RED. Red. (Pow. 1912.)
GOLDEN PROLIFIC. Gold.
GREENFIELD. Red. (S. Gre. 1868.)
KERRY. Bl. (Sau. 1887.)
KNIGHT. Red. (Kni. 1835.)
LALENDE. Red.
LARGERED. Red.
LARGEWHITE. Wh.
LEE. Bl. (G. Lee 1860.) *Lee Prolific.*
LONDON MARKET. Red.
LONG BUNCH HOLLAND. Red. (Fay 1871.)
MAGNUS. Bl. (Sau. 1887.)
MARGESON. Wh.
MERVEILLE DE LA GIRONDE. Red.
Naples. BLACK NAPLES.
NORTH STAR. Red. (Adams 1865.)
ONTARIO. Bl. (Sau. 1887.)
PERFECTION. Red. (Hook. 1887.)
POMONA. Red. (Blue 1873.)
PRINCE ALBERT. Red.
Prolific. FAY.
RANKIN RED. Red.
RED CROSS. Red. (Moore 1885.)
RED DUTCH. Red.
RED GRAPE. Red.
RED LAKE. Red. (M.B.F. 1924.)
REDPATH RUBY. Red.
RIVERS. Red.
SAUNDERS. Bl. (Sau. 1887.)
STEPHENS No. 9. Red. (A. Stev.)
STEWART. Bl. (Sau. 1887.)
TOPSY. Bl. (Sau. 1890.)
VERSAILLES. Red. (Bert. 1835.)
VICTORIA. Red.
VIKING. Red. (U.S.D.A. 1930.)
WHITE CHERRY. Wh.
WHITE DUTCH. Wh.
WHITE GRAPE. Wh.
WHITE IMPERIAL. Wh.
WILDER. Red. (Teas 1877.)

CURUBA (*Kuruba*) **Passiflora maliformis**

CUSTARDAPPLE . . **Annona reticulata**

See also PONDAPPLE; SUGARAPPLE.

HARDSHELL C. (*Poshte*) **A. scleroderma**

DATE . . . . . . **Phoenix dactylifera**

AMRI.
ASHRASI. *Ascharasi; Asharasi.*
Azadi. ZAHIDI.
BARHEE.
Birkawi; Birket Al Hajji. HAYANY.
DAYRI. *Dairi.*
DEGLET NOOR. *Deglet Nur; Deglet En-Nour.*
FARD. *Fardh.*

DATE, continued
HALAWY. *Halawi.*
HAYANY. *Birkawi; Birket Al Hajji; Hayani.*
HORRA.
ITEEMA.
KASBEH. *Kesba; Kessebi.*
KHADRAWY. *Khadrawi.*
KHALASA. *Khalas; Khalasi.*
KUSTAWY. *Khustawi; Kustawi.*
MAKTOOM. *Makdum.*
MEDJHOOL. *Majhul; Medjool.*
MENAKHER. *Manakhir.*
RHARS.
SAIDY. *Sewi; Siwah; Wahi.*
SAYER.
Sewi; Siwah. SAIDY.
TABIRZAL.
TAZIZOOT.
THOORY. *Thuri; Tsuri.*
Wahi. SAIDY.
ZAHIDI. *Azadi; Zadie; Zehedi.*

DESERTLIME . . . **Eremocitrus glauca**

DEWBERRY . . . . . . **Rubus** spp.
For varieties see BLACKBERRY, TRAILING.

Duhat . . . . JAMBOLAN

DURIAN . . . . **Durio zibethinus**
JOLO. *Lake Lanad; Mindanao.*
MALACCA D. **D. malaccensis.**

Eggfruit . . . . CANISTEL

ELAEAGNUS . . . . . **Elaeagnus** spp.
CHERRY E. . . . . . . **E. multiflora**
LINGARO . . . . . . **E. philippensis**

ELDERBERRY . . . . . **Sambucus** spp.
ADAMS.

EMBLIC (*Myrobalan* in part) **Phyllanthus emblica**

∞EREMOLEMON . . . . **Citrus limon** × **Eremocitrus glauca**

∞EREMORADIA . . **Citrus aurantium** × **Eremocitrus glauca**

∞EREMORANGE . . **Citrus sinensis** × **Eremocitrus glauca**

EVERGREENCHINKAPIN **Castanopsis** spp.

∞FAUSTRIMEDIN . . ∞KUMANDARIN × **Microcitrus australasica**

FEIJOA . . . . . . **Feijoa sellowiana**
ANDRE.
BESSON.
CHOICEANA. *Choice.*
COOLIDGE.
HEHRE.
PINEAPPLE.
SUPERBA.

FERONIELLA . . . . **Feroniella**
INDOCHINA F. . . . . . **F. oblata**
JAVA F. . . . . **F. lucida**

FIG . . . . **Ficus carica**
See also **FICUS.**

ADRIATIC.
Black Douro. TURKEY.
BLACK ISCHIA.
Brown Turkey. TURKEY.
BRUNSWICK. *Magnolia.*
Calimyrna.

This is not a variety name, though frequently so used. It is a trademarked term for Smyrna-type Figs grown in California. Since Lob Ingir is the only one of this type grown there, the name Calimyrna is commonly, though incorrectly, applied to that variety.

FIG, continued
CELESTE. *Celestial.*
CROISIC. *Cordelia.*
DAUPHINE. *Ronde Violette Hative.*
DOREE.
Dottato. KADOTA.
Endich. KADOTA.
GENOA. *Genoa White.*
GREEN ISCHIA.
ISCHIA. *White Ischia.*
KADOTA. *Dottato; Endich.*
LEMON. *Marseilles White.*
LEON.
LOB INGIR. *Lob Injir; Lop Injur; Sari Lob.*
Magnolia. BRUNSWICK.
Markarian 1. SAMSON.
Marseilles White. LEMON.
MILCO. (Caprifig var.)
MISSION.
OSBORN. *Osbornes Prolific; Ronde Noire.*
PANACHE.
RAMSEY.
ROEDING No. 1. (Caprifig var.)
ROEDING No. 2. (Caprifig var.)
ROEDING No. 3. (Caprifig var.)
ROEDING No. 4. (Caprifig var.)
Ronde Noire. OSBORN.
Ronde Violette Hative. DAUPHINE.
SAMSON. (Caprifig var.) *Markarian 1.*
San Pedro Black. TURKEY.
SAN PEDRO WHITE.
Sari Lob. LOB INGIR.
STANFORD. (Caprifig var.)
TURKEY. *Black Douro; Brown Turkey; San Pedro Black.*
VERDAL LONGUE.
WHITE GENOA.
White Ischia. ISCHIA.

FILBERT (*Hazelnut*) . . . **Corylus** spp.
All these hort. var. are either seed or hybrid clons. Most vars. are of C. avellana; some are of C. maxima; all American vars. are of C. americana; Bixby and Buchanan are C. americana × avellana.
Am. American. G. Giant.
Eu. European.

A'COQUE TENDRE. Eu.
A'Grappes. CLUSTER.
A'Grappes Precose. BURNS.
ALBA. Eu. *Avelinier Blanche; White Filbert; Wrotham Park.*
Algiers. BARCELONA.
Almondnut. BADEM FUNDUK.
ALMOND ZELLERNUSS. Eu. *Cracknut; Mandelnuss.*
ALPHA. (Quarn. 1925.)
ALTHALDENSLEBENER LAMBERTSNUSS. Eu.
∞AMAX F. ∞ **C. americana** × **C. maxima.**
AMERICAN F. (*American Hazelnut*). **C. americana.**
ANGULAR BARCELLONER. Eu. (Goes.) *Barcelone de Loddiges; Loddiges Barcelona.*
APOLDANUSS. Eu.
ATLAS. Eu. (Hogg.) *Downton; Downton Large Square.*
Atlas. ENGLISCHE ZELLERNUSS.
Aveline Blanche. WHITE AVELINE.
AVELINE DE PIEMONT. Eu.
AVELINE DE PROVENCE. Eu.
Aveline Grosse Longue. GROSSE LONGUE D'ESPAGNE.
AVELINE GROSSE RONDE. Eu.
Aveline Rouge. RED AVELINE.

FILBERT, continued
Avelinier Blanche. ALBA.
BADEM FUNDUK. Eu. *Almondnut; Badiem Fundug; Korasan Funduk; Lambertsnuss.*
BANDNUSS. Eu. *Bandartige Nuss; Bondnut; Grosse Lambertsnuss; Ribbonnut.*
Barcellonanut. (Goes.) CATALONIAN ZELLERNUSS.
BARCELONA. Eu. (F. Gil. about 1880.) *Algiers; D'Algiers; Grosse Blanche; Grosse Blanche d'Angleterre.*
Barcelona Zellernuss. CATALONIAN ZELLERNUSS; LARGE MOTLEY ZELLERNUSS.
Barcelone de Loddiges. ANGULAR BARCELLONER.
BARD ESPAGNOL. Eu.
BARRS ZELLERNUSS. Eu. (Goes.) *Barrs Spanish.*
BAWDEN. (Gell. 1938.)
BEAKED F. (*Beaked Hazelnut*). **C. cornuta.**
Beardnut. RED AVELINE.
BEARN. Eu.
BEETHE. Eu. *Beethes Zellernuss.*
BELLE DE GUILBILINE. Eu.
BERGER. Eu. (1860–70.) *Bergers Zellernuss; Bergeri; La Bergeri; Louis Berger.*
BERNE. Eu.
BIXBY. (Jones 1937.)
BIZANE. Eu.
Bloodnut. RED AVELINE.
BLUESHELL. Eu.
BLUMBERGER ZELLERNUSS. Eu.
BOLWYLLER. Eu. (1854.) *Bollweiller; Bollwiller; Halls Giant; Merveille de Bollwiller; Wunder von Bollwyller.*
Bondnut. BANDNUSS.
BONYBUSH. (Morris. 1906.)
BOOTH. Eu. *Booths.*
BRAG. (Gell. 1938.)
BRAUNSCHWEIGISCHE. Eu.
BRIXNUT. (Brixey 1919.)
Brunswick; Brunswick Aveline. DU CHILLY.
BUCHANAN. (Jones 1933.)
Bulletnut. LARGE GLOBE.
BULLNOSE. (D. Gell. 1928.)
BURCHARDTS ZELLERNUSS. Eu.
BURNS. Eu. (Hogg.) *A'Grappes Precose; Burns Nut.*
BUTTNER. Eu. *Buttners Zellernuss.*
CALDWELL. (Huen. 1934.)
CALIFORNIA F. (*California Hazelnut*). **C. californica.**
CANNONBALL. Eu. (Hogg.)
Cape Nut. FRIZZLEDNUT.
CAREY. (Gell. 1938.)
CATALONIAN ZELLERNUSS. Eu. (Goes.) *Barcellonanut; Barcelona Zellernuss; Large Spanish Nut; Spanish Zellernuss.*
Catalonian Zellernuss. LARGE MOTLEY ZELLERNUSS.
CAUCASIAN F. **C. avellana pontica.**
CHAPERONE. (Brixey 1915.)
CHINESE F. (*Chinese Tree Hazelnut*). **C. chinensis.**
CLACKAMAS. (Kruse 1917.)
Clarke County Cob. DU PROVENCE.
Close Filbert. WHITE AVELINE.
CLUSTER. Eu. (Hogg.) *A'Grappes.*

FILBERT, continued
COB F. (*Cobnut*). **C. avellana grandis.**
Cobnut. ENGLISCHE ZELLERNUSS; SPANISH LAMBERT.
COLCHIS F. (*Alboff F.*). **C. colchica.**
∞ COLWINOID F. ∞ **C. colurnoides.**
COMET. (Gell. 1938.)
CORRUCONIC. (F.G.N. about 1915.)
COSFORD. Eu. (1916. RHS 1920.) *Miss Youngs Thinshell; Thinshell.*
Coutard; Coutards Fertile. FERTILE.
Cracknut. ALMOND ZELLERNUSS.
CRAIG. (Gell. 1938.)
Creswell. DU PROVENCE.
Crispa. FRIZZLED.
Cup Filbert. FRIZZLEDNUT.
Curly. FRIZZLED.
D'Algiers. BARCELONA.
DAVIANA. Eu. (Hogg.) *Duchess of Edinburgh; Eugenie.*
DAVIS. (J. Davis 1918.)
DE BEARY. Eu.
DE BEYNE. Eu.
DE METZ. Eu.
DES ANGLAIS. Eu.
D'INGHILTERRA. Eu.
Downton in part. ATLAS; GRANDIS.
Downton Large Square. ATLAS.
Downtons Large Nut. ENGLISCHE ZELLERNUSS.
DREADNAUGHT. Eu.
DU BEARN. Eu.
Duchess of Edinburgh. DAVIANA.
DU CHILLY. Eu. (1830.) *Brunswick; Brunswick Aveline; Kent Cob; Kentish Cob.*
DUKE OF EDINBURGH. (Hogg 1883.) *Princess Royal.*
DU PROVENCE. Eu. *Clarke County Cob; Creswell; Du Provenz; Norelins; Norelius.*
DUTTON. (Jones 1916.)
Dwarf Prolific in part. ENGLISCHE ZELLERNUSS; GRANDIS; NORTHAMPTONSHIRE; PEARSONS PROLIFIC.
Dysenterynut. RED AVELINE.
EARLY GLOBE. (Voll. 1915.)
Early Long Zellernuss. FRUHE LANGE ZELLERNUSS.
EARLY PROLIFIC. (Buny. 1900.)
ECKIGE BARCELONA. Eu. *Eckige Barcelonaer.*
EINZELTRAGENDE KEGELFORMIGE. Eu.
EMPEROR. Eu. (Webb.) *Prize Emperor.*
Empress Eugenie. KAISERIN EUGENIE.
Englische Lambertsnuss. Eu. (Goes.) NORTHAMPTONSHIRE.
ENGLISCHE ZELLERNUSS. Eu. (Goes.) *Atlas; Cobnut; Downtons Large Nut; Dwarf Prolific; Glasgow Prolific; Great Cobnut; Pearsons Prolific; Prolific; Spanish Cob; St. Grisier.*
Eugenie in part. DAVIANA; KAISERIN EUGENIE.
EUROPEAN F. **C. avellana.**
FERTILE. Eu. *Coutard; Coutards Fertile; Fertile de Coutard.*
Fertile de Nottingham. NORTHAMPTONSHIRE.
FICHTWERDERESCHE ZELLERNUSS. Eu.
Filbert Cob. LAMBERT FILBERT.
FITZGERALD. (Fitz. 1936.)
FRISCHE LANGE. Eu.

FILBERT, continued
FRIZZLED. *Crispa; Curly.*
FRIZZLEDNUT. Eu. (Goes.) *Cape Nut; Cup Filbert; Gekrauselte.*
FRUCHTBARRE. Eu.
FRUHE LANGE ZELLERNUSS. Eu. *Early Long Zellernuss.*
FRUHE VON FRAUENDORF. Eu.
FULL ZELLERNUSS. *Italian Long.*
GARIBALDI. *Webbs Garibaldi.*
GASAWAY. (Bush 1926.)
Geantes de Halle. HALLER.
Gekrauselte. FRIZZLEDNUT.
GELLATLY. (Gell. 1928.) *Gellatlys Triumph.*
GIANT F. **C. maxima.**
Giant Nut of Halle. HALLER.
Glasgow Prolific. ENGLISCHE ZELLERNUSS.
GOLDEN F. **C. aurea.**
GORDONS THINSHELL. Eu.
GRANDIS. Eu. (Nich.) *Downton; Dwarf Prolific; Great Cobnut; Pearsons Prolific; Round Cob.*
Great Cobnut in part. ENGLISCHE ZELLERNUSS; GRANDIS.
Grosse Blanche; Grosse Blanche d' Angleterre. BARCELONA.
GROSSE BUNTE ZELLERNUSS. Eu.
Grosse Kugelnuss. LARGE GLOBE.
Grosse Lambertsnuss. BANDNUSS.
GROSSE LONGUE D'ESPAGNE. Eu. *Aveline Grosse Longue.*
GROSSE RONDE. Eu.
Grosse Zellernuss. HALLER.
GUBENER BARCELLONER. Eu.
GUBENER ZELLERNUSS. Eu.
GUNZELEBENER ZELLERNUSS. Eu. (About 1765.)
GUSTAVS ZELLERNUSS. Eu. (About 1840.) *Italian Red.*
Halle; Halle'esche Riessennuss; Halle Giant. HALLER.
HALLER. Eu. (1788.) *Geantes de Halle; Giant Nut of Halle; Grosse Zellernuss; Halle; Halle'esche Riessennuss; Halle Giant; Halls Giant; Market Giantnut; Pfundnuss.*
Halls Giant. BOLWYLLER; HALLER.
HARDIN. (Huen. 1924.)
HARTINGTON PROLIFIC. Eu.
HEMPBELS LAMBERTSNUSS. Eu. (About 1840.) *Hempels Zellernuss.*
HENNEMAN. (Henn. 1926.)
HEYNICKS ZELLERNUSS. Eu. *Heynichs Zellernuss.*
HIMALAYA F. **C. ferox.**
HOLDER. (Gell. 1938.)
HUEN. (Huen. 1934.) Am.
IMPERIAL. Eu. *Imperiale Detrebizonde; Imperiale de Trebizont; Trapezunter Kaiserhazel.*
Italian Long. FULL ZELLERNUSS.
Italian Red. GUSTAVS ZELLERNUSS.
Italian Zellernuss. LARGE MOTLEY ZELLERNUSS.
Ivess. JEEVES.
JAHNS ZELLERNUSS. Eu.
JAPANESE F. **C. sieboldiana.**
JEEVES. Eu. (Goes.) *Ivess; Jeeves Long Seedling; Jeeves Samling; Yvess.*
Jeeves Seedling. LIEGELS.
JONES. (Kill. 1893.)
KADETTEN ZELLERNUSS. Eu.
KAISERIN EUGENIE. Eu. *Empress Eugenie; Eugenie.*

FILBERT, continued
KENT COB. *Lamberts Filbert.*
Kent Cob; Kentish Cob in part. Used in England for DU CHILLY.
Kentish Cob. LAMBERT FILBERT.
KENTISH FILBERT. Eu.
KNIGHTS LARGE COB. Eu.
Knights Small. WHITE AVELINE.
KOCKS LAMBERT. Eu.
KONIGLISCHE. Eu.
Korasan Funduk. BADEM FUNDUK.
KRUSE. (Kruse 1917.)
KUNZEMULLER ZELLERNUSS. Eu.
KÜRZHULLIGE ZELLERNUSS. Eu. *Shorthusked Zellernuss.*
La Bergeri. BERGER.
LAMBERT FILBERT. (Hogg.) *Filbert Cob; Kentish Cob; Webbs Prize Cob.*
Lamberts Filbert. KENT COB.
Lamberts Large. SPANISH LAMBERT.
Lambertsnuss. BADEM FUNDUK.
LANGE LANDSBERGER. Eu. (About 1840.)
LANGELISCHE RIESENNUSS. Eu.
Large Bondnut; Large Cob. SPANISH LAMBERT.
Large Dutch Nut. LARGE MOTLEY ZELLERNUSS.
LARGE GLOBE. Eu. *Bulletnut; Grosse Kugelnuss; Large Round Nut.*
LARGE MOTLEY ZELLERNUSS. Eu. (Goes.) *Barcelona Zellernuss; Catalonian Zellernuss; Italian Zellernuss; Large Dutch Nut; Motley Zellernuss; Piemontese Zellernuss.*
Large Round Nut. LARGE GLOBE.
Large Spanish Nut. CATALONIAN ZELLERNUSS.
LIEGELS. Eu. (Hogg.) *Jeeves Seedling; Sicklers Zellernuss.*
LITTLEPAGE. (Litt. 1912.)
Loddiges Barcelona. ANGULAR BARCELLONER.
Lombardnut; Lombardy. WHITE AVELINE.
LONGFELLOW. (Noah Mosier 1925.)
LONGISH GIANT. Eu.
LONGUE POINTEE. Eu.
Louis Berger. BERGER.
LOUISEN ZELLERNUSS. (Eu. 1887.) *Luisens Zellernuss.*
LUCAS ZELLERNUSS. Eu.
LUDOLPHS ZELLERNUSS. Eu.
Luisens Zellernuss. LOUISEN ZELLERNUS.
MACROCARPA. Eu.
MAJESTIC. (Pearcy 1936.)
MANCHU F. **C. sieboldiana mandshurica.**
Mandelnuss. ALMOND ZELLERNUSS.
MANITOBA. (S. D. Coll. 1927.)
Market Giantnut. HALLER.
MEDIUM LONG. (Voll. 1914.)
MERRIBROOKE. (Morris. 1915.) Am.
Merveille de Bollwiller. BOLWYLLER.
MESSMERS ZELLERNUSS. Eu.
∞ MILDRED F. ∞ **C. mildredensis.**
MINNAS ZELLERNUSS. Eu.
Miss Youngs Thinshell. COSFORD.
MOGULNUSS. Eu. (About 1840.)
MONTEBELLO. Eu.
MORNINGSIDE. (Grah. 1939.)
MOSIER. (Mos. 1932.)
Motley Zellernuss. LARGE MOTLEY ZELLERNUSS.
NEGRETTA. Eu.

FILBERT, continued

NEUE RIESENNUSS. Eu. (About 1875.)
NEVIS. (S. D. Coll. 1927.)
NIBLER. (Gray 1926.)
NOCE LUNGHE. Eu.
NOOKSACK. (Alt. 1928.)
Norelins; Norelius. DU PROVENCE.
NORTHAMPTONSHIRE. Eu. (Goes.) *Dwarf Prolific; Englische Lambertsnuss; Fertile de Nottingham; Nottingham Prolific; Pearsons Prolific.*
NORWICH PROLIFIC. Eu.
NOTTINGHAM. Eu.
Nottingham Prolific in part. NORTHAMPTONSHIRE; PEARSONS PROLIFIC.
OGDEN. (Gray 1926.)
OTTOS ZELLERNUSS. Eu.
PEARSONS PROLIFIC. (Hogg, Buny.) *Dwarf Prolific; Nottingham Prolific.*
Pearsons Prolific in part. ENGLISCHE ZELLERNUSS; GRANDIS; NORTHAMPTONSHIRE.
Pfundnuss. HALLER.
PIEMONT. Eu. *Piedmont.*
Piemontese Zellernuss. LARGE MOTLEY ZELLERNUSS.
PIGNATALE. Eu.
PLEASANT GROVE. (I.H.S. 1924.)
PRECOSE DE FRAUENDORF. Eu.
PRECOSE DE GRUGLIASCO. Eu.
PRIMLEY. Eu.
Princess Royal. DUKE OF EDINBURGH.
PRINCIPESSA REALE. Eu.
Prize Emperor. EMPEROR.
Prolific. ENGLISCHE ZELLERNUSS.
PROLIFIC CLOSEHEAD. Eu.
PROLIFIC FILBERT. Eu.
PROLIFIQUE A'COQUE SERREE. Eu.
PROVENCE. Eu.
PURPLE AVELINE. Eu.
RADIX. (Quarn. 1926.) *Turkish.*
RED AVELINE. Eu. (Before 1650.) *Aveline Rouge; Beardnut; Bloodnut; Dysenterynut; Red Filbert; Red Lambert.*
Red Filbert; Red Lambert. RED AVELINE.
Remy. WHITE AVELINE.
Ribbonnut. BANDNUSS.
RIEKCHENS ZELLERNUSS. Eu.
ROBERTA. (Kruse 1915.)
ROMISCHENUSS. Eu.
ROUGE RONDE. Eu.
Round Cob. GRANDIS.
ROYAL. (Pearcy 1934.)
RUDOLPHS LAMBERTSNUSS. Eu. (Muss.) *Rudolphinuss.*
RUSH. (Rush 1900.)
RUSS. (Bush 1928.)
SCHERF. (Scher. 1936.)
SCHLESIERIN. Eu. (1885.)
SCHMIDTS LAMBERT. Eu.
SHAH. Eu.
Shorthusked Zellernuss. KURZHULLIGE ZELLERNUSS.
SIBERIAN F. **C. heterophylla.**
SICILISCHE. Eu.
SICILY. (Kruse 1915.)
Sicklers Zellernuss. LIEGELS.
SILKLIKE ZELLERNUSS. Eu.
Spanish Cob. ENGLISCHE ZELLERNUSS.
SPANISH GREATH. Eu.

FILBERT, continued

SPANISH LAMBERT. Eu. (Goes.) *Cobnut; Lamberts Large; Large Bondnut; Large Cob; Spanish Nut.*
Spanish Nut. SPANISH LAMBERT.
Spanish Zellernuss. CATALONIAN ZELLERNUSS.
∞ *Spiny F.* ∞ **C. spinescens.**
St. Grisier. ENGLISCHE ZELLERNUSS.
SZECHWAN F. **C. heterophylla sutchuenensis.**
Thinshell. COSFORD; ZARTSCHALIGE.
TIBETAN F. **C. tibetica.**
Trapezunter Kaiserhazel. IMPERIAL.
TRUCHSESS ZELLERNUSS. Eu.
TURKISH F. (*Tree Hazelnut*). **C. colurna.**
Turkish. RADIX.
∞ VILMORIN F. ∞ **C. vilmorini.**
VOLLE ZELLERNUSS. Eu.
VOLLKUGEL. Eu. (1887.)
VON MEHL. Eu.
WALKERS ZELLERNUSS. Eu.
WALLYS GROSSE ZELLERNUSS. Eu. (About 1860.)
WATERLOO. Eu.
Webbs Garibaldi. GARIBALDI.
Webbs Prize Cob. LAMBERT FILBERT.
Weisse Lambertsnuss. WHITE AVELINE.
WHITE AVELINE. Eu. (Before 1650.) *Aveline Blanche; Close Filbert; Knights Small; Lombardnut; Lombardy; Remy; Weisse Lambertsnuss; White Filbert; White Hazel; White Kent; Whiteskinned Lambert.*
White Filbert. ALBA; WHITE AVELINE.
White Hazel; White Kent. WHITE AVELINE.
WHITE LAMBERT. Eu.
WILLAMETTE. (Stein 1915.)
WINKLER. (Snyder 1918.) Am.
WOODFORD. (Woodf. 1936.)
Wrotham Park. ALBA.
Wunder von Bollwyller. BOLWYLLER.
Yvess. JEEVES.
ZARTSCHALIGE. Eu. *Thinshell.*

FINGERLIME . . . . **Microcitrus** spp.
See also WILDLIME.

AUSTRALIAN F. . . **M. australasica**
REDPULP A. F. . . **M. a. sanguinea**

Floridacherry . . . . . . PITANGA

GENIP (*Marmaladebox*) **Genipa americana**

GHOSTLIME. **Burkillanthus malaccensis**

GINKGONUT . . . . . **Ginkgo biloba**

GLYCOSMIS. . . . . **Glycosmis**
CHINESE G. . . . . **G. citrifolia**
MALAY G. . . . . . **G. pentaphylla**

GOOSEBERRY . . . . **Ribes** spp.
See also GOOSEBERRY, p. 277.

Am. American spp. (R. hirtellum, or hybrids of it).
Eng. English spp. (R. uva-crispa, or hybrids of it).

ABUNDANCE. (N.D.S. 1932.)
CARELESS.
CARRIE. Am. (Ell.)
CHAMPION. Am. (Dic.)
CHARLES. Eng. (C.E.F.)
CHAUTAUQUA. Eng.
CLARKE. Am.
COLUMBUS. Eng.

GOOSEBERRY, continued

COMO. Am. (M.A.E.S. 1922.)
CROWN BOB. Eng.
DOWNING. Am. (Dow. 1855.)
EARLY SULPHUR.
FREDONIA. Eng. (N.Y.S. 1926.)
GLENDALE. (VanF. 1905.)
GREENKING.
HOENING EARLIEST. Eng.
HOUGHTON. Am. (Hou. 1833.)
INDUSTRY. Eng. (Wyn.)
Josselyn. REDJACKET.
KAPOZA. (S.D.S. 1925.)
KATAGA. (S.D.S. 1925.)
KEEPSAKE. Eng.
KOPA. (S.D.S. 1925.)
LANCASHIRE LAD.
MABEL. Am. (C.E.F. 1927.)
MAY DUKE.
OREGON. Am. (Pre. 1860.) *Oregon Champion.*
PEARL. Am. (Sau. 1885.)
PERKINS. Eng.
PERRY. Am. (N.D.S. 1932.)
PIXWELL. Am. (N.D.S. 1932.)
POORMAN. Am. (Crai. 1890.)
QUEEN ANNE.
REDJACKET. Eng. *Josselyn.*
REDJACKET IMPROVED. (Sau. 1876.)
REDWARRINGTON. Eng.
ROSS.
SMITH. Am. (Smith 1868.)
SMITH IMPROVED.
SPINEFREE. (C.E.F. 1927.)
SUNSET. (S.D.S. 1924.)
SYLVIA. (C.E.F.)
VICTORIA.
WELLINGTON GLORY.
WHITE EAGLE.
WHITESMITH.

Governorsplum . . . . . RAMONTCHI

Granada . . . . POMEGRANATE

GRANADILLA (*Passionfruit*) . **Passiflora**
The name Granadilla is used in STANDARDIZED PLANT NAMES for the plants of the Passionflower (Passiflora) genus which produce the Granadilla fruits.

CURUBA G. . . . . . **P. maliformis**
GIANT G. . . . **P. quadrangularis**
MAYPOP G. . . . . . **P. incarnata**
PURPLE G. (*Passionfruit*). **P. edulis**
SWEET G. . . . . . . **P. ligularis**
WATERLEMON (*Yellow G.*) **P. laurifolia**

GRAPE . . . . **Vitis** spp.
See also GRAPE, p. 278.

This list of American varieties of Grape has been prepared from "American Grape Varieties" (U. S. Department of Agriculture Circular 437, 1937), supplemented by the American Pomological Society's list dated August 17, 1938.

ABBREVIATIONS OF NAMES OF SPECIES FROM WHICH THE FOLLOWING HORT. VAR. WERE DERIVED

Aes. V. aestivalis.
Bou. V. aestivalis bourquiniana (*V. bourquiniana*).
Can. V. candicans.
Cha. V. champini.
Cin. V. cinerea.
Lab. V. labrusca.
Lin. V. lincecumi.
Rip. V. riparia.
Rot. V. rotundifolia.
Rup. V. rupestris.
Vin. V. vinifera.
Vul. V. vulpina.

GRAPE, continued
ADAM. Lab.
AGAWAM. Lab. Vin. (Roge. 1852.)
AGLIANICO. Vin.
ALEATICO. Vin.
ALEXANDER WINTER. Lab. Vin.
ALICANTE BOUSCHET. Vin.
ALICANTE GANZIN. Vin.
ALICE. Aes. Lab. ?Vin.
Almeria. OHANEZ.
ALPHA. Vul.
ALPHONSE LAVALLEE. Vin. *Ribier.*
ALVEY. Aes. Vin.
AMBER QUEEN. Lab. Vin. Vul. (N. White 1870.)
AMBROSIA. Lab. Vin.
AMERBONTE. Bou. Lin. Rup.
AMERICA. Lin. Rup. (Mun. 1885.)
AMINIA. Lab. Vin. (Roge. 1852.)
ARAMON. Vin.
ARKANSAW. Lab.
ARMALAGA. Lab. Lin. Vin.
ATOKA. Bou. Lab. Lin. Rup. Vin.
AUGUST GIANT. Lab. Vin. (N. White 1861.)
Austrian Seedless. ROUND SEEDLESS.
BACCHUS. Lab. Vul. (Ricke. 1879.)
BAILEY. Lab. Lin. Vin. (Mun. 1886.)
BANNER. Bou. Lab. Vin. (Bac. 1898.)
BARBERA. Vin.
BARRY. Lab. Vin. (Roge. 1852.)
BASTARDO. Vin.
BEACON. Lab. Lin. (Mun. 1886.)
BECLAN. Vin.
BELL. Bou. Lab. Vin. Vul. (Mun. 1883.)
BELLINO. Vin.
BERCKMANS. Bou. Lab. ?Rip. ?Vul. (Wylie 1871.)
BETA. Lab. ?Rip. ?Vul. (Sue. 1881.)
BICANE. Vin. *Chasselas Napoleon.*
BIG HOPE. Lab. Lin. Vin.
BLACK CORINTH. Vin. *Panariti; Zante Currant.*
BLACK DAMASCUS.
BLACK EAGLE. Lab. Vin.
BLACK FERRARA. Vin.
BLACK HAMBURG. Vin.
Black Malvoisie. CINSAUT.
Black Monukka. MONUKKA.
BLACK MOROCCO. Vin.
BLACK PEARL. Lab. Vul.
Black Prince. ROSE OF PERU.
BLAUER PORTUGIESER. *Early Burgundy.*
BLONDIN. Aes. Bou. Lin.
BONARDA. Vin.
BRANT. Lab. Vin. Vul. (Arn. 1860.)
BRIDE. Bou. Lab. Vin.
BRIGHTON. Lab. Vin. (Moore 1870.)
BRILLIANT. Bou. Lab. Vin. (Mun. 1883.)
BRILLIANT SEEDLING. Bou. Lab. Vin.
BROCTON. Aes. Lab. Vin. (N.Y.S. 1919.)
BRONX. Lab. Vin.
BROWN. Lab. Vin.
BURGER. Vin.
CABERNET FRANC. Vin.
CABERNET SAUVIGNON. Vin.
CACO. Lab. Vin. (Lov. 1901.)
California Concord. PIERCE.

GRAPE, continued
CAMPBELL EARLY. Lab. Vin. (Campb. 1892.)
CANADA. Lab. Vin. Vul. (Arn. 1860.)
CANANDAIGUA. Lab. Vin. (VanW. 1897.)
CAPTAIN. Lab. Lin. Rup. Vin. (Mun. 1896.)
CAPTIVATOR. Bou. Lab. Vin. (Mun. 1902.)
CARIGNANE. Vin.
CARMAN. Lab. Lin. Vin. (Mun. 1883.)
CASTIZA. Vin. *Maraville de Malaga.*
CATARRATTO. Vin.
CATAWBA. Lab. Vin. (Adlum 1893.)
CAYUGA. Lab. Vin.
CAYWOOD. Lab. Vin.
CENZO.
CHALLENGE. Lab. Vin.
CHAMPANEL. Cha. Lab. ?Vin. (Mun. 1893.)
CHAMPION. Lab.
CHARBONO. Vin.
CHARLES (*A.*) GREEN. Lab.
CHASSELAS DORE. Vin. *Golden Chasselas; Gutedel; Sweet Water.*
Chasselas Napoleon. BICANE.
CHASSELAS ROSE. Vin.
CHAUCH GRIS. Vin.
CHENIN BLANC. Vin.
CHICAGO. Lab.
CHRISTINE. Aes. Lab.
CINSAUT. Vin. *Black Malvoisie; Malvoisie.*
CLAIRETTE BLANCHE. Vin.
CLEVENER. Aes. Lab. Rip.
CLINTON. Lab. Rip. Vul. (Lang. 1835.)
CLOETA. Lab. Lin. Rup. Vin. (Mun. 1902.)
COCHEE. Bou. Lab.
COLERAIN. Lab. (Bundy 1880.)
COLOMBARD. Vin. *Sauvignon Vert.*
COLUMBIAN IMPERIAL. Lab. ?Vul.
CONCORD. Lab. Vin. (Bull 1849.)
CONCORD SEEDLESS. Lab.
CORNICHON. Vin.
COTTAGE. Lab. (Bull 1867.)
Crabb Burgundy. REFOSCO.
CRAIG. ?Vul.
CREVELING. Lab. ?Vin.
CROTON. Bou. Lab. Vin. (Und. 1865.)
CUNNINGHAM. Bou.
CYNTHIANA. Aes. ?Lab. (W. Pri. 1850.)
DAISY. Lab. Vin. (Sta.)
DAKOTA. Lab. Vul.
DAMAS ROSE. Vin.
DANUGUE. Vin. *Gros Guillaume.*
DATTIER. Vin.
DELAWARE. Bou. Lab. Vin. (A Thomp. 1849.)
DELAWBA. Bou. Lab. Vin.
DIAMOND. Lab. Vin. (Moore 1870.)
DIANA. Lab. Vin. (Cre. 1834.)
DIOGENES. Lab. Rip. *Ironclad.*
DIZMAR. Vin.
DOWNING. Lab. Vin. (Ricke. 1865.)
DRACUT AMBER. Lab. (Cle. 1855.)
DUNKIRK. Lab. Vin. (N.Y.S. 1920.)
Durif. PETITE SYRAH.
DUTCHESS. ?Aes. Bou. Lab. Vin. (Cay. 1868.)
Early Burgundy. BLAUER PORTUGIESER.

GRAPE, continued
EARLY CONCORD. Lab.
EARLY DAISY. Lab. (Kre. 1874.)
EARLY DAWN. ?Aes. Lab. Vin.
EARLY GIANT.
EARLY VICTOR. Bou. Lab. Vin. (Burr 1871.)
EATON. Lab. (Eaton 1868.)
ECLIPSE. Lab. (Riehl 1890.)
EDEN. Rot. (Guild.)
EDNA. Lab. Lin. Vin. (Mun.)
ELDORADO. Lab. Vin.
ELLEN SCOTT. Lab. Lin. Vin. (Mun. 1902.)
ELVIBACH. Lab. Vul.
ELVICAND. Can. Lab. Vul. (Mun. 1885.)
ELVIRA. Lab. Rip. ?Vin. Vul. (Rom. 1863.)
EMERALD. Bou. Lab. Vin. (Sau. 1886.)
EMPEROR. Vin.
EMPIRE STATE. Lab. Vin. Vul. (Ricke. 1879.)
EONA.
ERICKSON. Lab.
ERIE. Aes. Lab. Vin.
ESSEX. Lab. Vin.
ETTA. Lab. Vul.
EUMELAN. Aes. Lab. Vin. (Thor. 1847.)
EXTRA. Lab. Lin. Vin. (Mun. 1886.)
EZERJO. Vin.
FAITH. Lab. Vul.
FEHER SZAGOS. Vin.
FERN MUNSON. Lab. Lin. Vin. (Mun. 1885.)
FLAME MUSCAT. Vin. *Muscat of Alexandria Rose.*
FLAME TOKAY. Vin. *Tokay.*
FLOWERS. Rot. (Flo. 1819.)
FOLLE BLANCHE. Vin.
FOSTER. Vin.
Franken Riesling. SYLVANER.
FRANKLIN. Vul.
FREDONIA. Lab. (N.Y.S. 1915.)
FRESIA. Vin.
Fresno Beauty. GROS COLMAN.
FURMINT. Vin. *White Tokay.*
GAERTNER. Lab. Vin. (Roge. 1852.)
GAMAY BEAUJOLAIS. Vin.
GENEVA. Lab. Vin.
GEWURZ TRAMINER. Vin.
GLENFIELD. Lab.
GOETHE. Lab. Vin. (Roge. 1852.)
GOFF. ?Aes. Lab. Vin. (N.Y.S. 1898.)
GOLD COIN. Aes. Lab. (Mun. 1885.)
GOLD DUST. Bou. Lab. Vin.
GOLDEN CHAMPION. Vin.
Golden Chasselas. CHASSELAS DORE.
GOLDEN DROP. Bou. Lab. Vin.
GOLDEN GRAIN. Bou. Lab. Vin.
GOLDEN MUSCAT. Lab. Vin. (N.Y.S. 1916.)
GOVERNOR ROSS. Lab. Vin.
GRADISKA. Vin.
GRAND NOIR. Vin.
GREEN EARLY. Lab.
GREEN HUNGARIAN. Vin.
GREIN GOLDEN. Lab. Vul. (Grein 1875.)
GRENACHE. Vin.
GRIGNOLINO. Vin.
GROS COLMAN. Vin. *Fresno Beauty.*
Gros Guillaume. DANUGUE.

GRAPE, continued
GROS MANZENC. Vin.
GROS VERDOT. Vin.
Gutedel. CHASSELAS DORE.
HARTFORD. Lab. ?Vin. (Steel 1849.)
HAYES. Lab. (Moore 1872.)
HAYNES. Lab. Vin.
HEADLIGHT. Bou. Lab. Vin. (Mun. 1896.)
HECTOR. Lab. Vin.
HERBEMONT. Bou. (Herb. 1800.)
HERBERT. Lab. Vin. (Roge. 1852.)
HERCULES. Lab. Vin. (Ens. 1890.)
HERMANN. Aes. ?Lab.
HERNITO. Lab. Vin. (Mun. 1900.)
HICKS. Lab. (Wall. 1898.)
HIDALGO. Bou. Lab. Vin.
HIGHLAND. Lab. Vin. (Ricke 1866.)
HUBBARD. Lab. Vin.
HUNGARIAN. Vul.
HUNISA. Vin.
INZOLIA. Vin.
IONA. Lab. Vin. (Grant 1855.)
Ironclad. DIOGENES.
ISABELLA. Lab. Vin.
Isabella Regia. PIERCE.
IVES. ?Aes. Lab. (Ives 1841.)
Jacques. LENOIR.
JAEGER. Bou. Lin.
JAMES. Rot.
JANESVILLE. Lab. Vul. (Lou. 1859.)
JEFFERSON. Lab. Vin. (Ricke 1874.)
JESSICA. Lab. Vin.
JEWEL. Bou. Lab. Vin. (Burr 1874.)
Johannisberger Riesling. WHITE RIESLING.
JUDGE MILLER. Bou. Lab.
JURA MUSCAT. Vin.
KADARKA. Vin.
KAHALLILLEE. Vin.
KANDHAR. Vin.
KENSINGTON. Lab. Vin. Vul.
KENTUCKY. Aes. Lab.
KEUKA. Lab. Vin. (N.Y.S. 1923.)
KING. ?Lab. (Muns. 1892.)
KING PHILIP. Lab. Vin. Vul.
KIOWA. Bou. Lin.
KLINE.
KRAUSE. Bou. Lab. Vin. (Kra. 1893.)
KURTELASKA. Vin.
LADANO. Bou. Cha. Lab. Vin. (Mun. 1902.)
LADY. Lab. (Imlay 1863.)
LADY WASHINGTON. Lab. Vin.
LAST ROSE. Lab. Lin. Vin.
LENOIR. Bou. *Jacques.*
LIGHTFOOT. Lab. Vin.
LIGNAN BLANC. Vin. *Luglienga.*
LIMBERGER. Vin.
LINDLEY. Lab. Vin.
LINDMAR. Lab. Vin.
LINN. Lab.
LITTLE BLUE. Aes. Lab. Vin.
LIVINGSTON. Lab. Vin.
LOMANTO. Bou. Cha. Lab. Vin.
LORETTO. ?Lab. Lin.
LOUISIANA. Bou.
LUCILE. Lab.
Luglienga. LIGNAN BLANC.
LUKFATA. Cha. Lab.
LUTIE. Lab.
MABEL. Bou. Lab. Vin.
MADELEINE ANGEVINE. Vin.
MALAGA. Vin.
MALBEC. Vin.
MALVASIA BIANCA. Vin.

GRAPE, continued
Malvoisie. CINSAUT.
MAMMOLO TOSCANO. Vin.
MANITO. Bou. Lab. Lin. Rup. Vin.
Maraville de Malaga. CASTIZA.
MARGUERITE. Bou. Lin. (Mun. 1886.)
MARIE LOUISE. Lab. ?Vin.
MARION. Lab. Rip.
MARSANNE. Vin.
MARTHA. Lab. ?Vin. (S. Mill. 1864.)
MARY FAVORITE. ?Bou. Lab. Vin.
MARZEMINO. Vin.
MASSASOIT. Lab. Vin. (Roge. 1852.)
MATARO. Vin.
MAXATAWNEY. Lab. Vin.
MCPIKE. Lab.
MELTON. Aes. Lab. Vin. (N.Y.S. 1923.)
MEMORY. Rot. (Mem. 1868.)
MERICADEL. Bou. Lab. Lin. Rup. Vin. (Mun. 1893.)
MERRIMAC. Lab. Vin. (Roge. 1852.)
MEUNIER. Vin.
MILLS. Lab. Vin. (Mills 1870.)
MISH. Rot. (Mish 1846.)
MISSION. Vin.
MISSOURI RIESLING. Lab. Vul. (Grien 1870.)
MOLINERA. Vin.
MONDEUSE. Vin.
MONTEFIORE. Lab. Vul.
MONUKKA. Vin. *Black Monukka.*
MOORE EARLY. Lab.
MORETO. Vin.
Moscatello Fino. MUSCAT HAMBURG.
MOURISCO BIANCO. Vin.
MOURISCO PRETO. Vin.
MOYER. Bou. Lab. Vin.
MUENCH. Bou. Lin.
MUSCADELLE. Vin.
MUSCAT ALBARDIENS.
MUSCAT CANELLI. Vin.
MUSCAT DE FRONTIGNAN. Vin.
MUSCAT HAMBURG. Vin. *Moscatello Fino.*
MUSCAT OF ALEXANDRIA. Vin.
Muscat of Alexandria Rose. FLAME MUSCAT.
MUSCAT OTTONEL.
NEBBIOLO. Vin.
NECTAR. Bou. Lab. Vin.
NEVA MUNSON. Bou. Lin.
NIAGARA. Lab. Vin. (H. & C. 1868.)
NITODAL. Bou. Cha. Lab. Vin. (Mun. 1902.)
NOAH. Lab. Vul. (Wass. 1870.)
NORFOLK. Lab. Vin.
NORTON. Aes. ?Lab. (Nort. 1830.)
NORWOOD. Lab. Vin.
OHANEZ. Vin. *Almeria.*
OLD GOLD. Lab. Vin. Vul.
OLITA. Bou. Lab. Vin.
OLITATOO. Lab. Lin. Vin.
OLIVETTE BLANCHE. Vin.
OLIVETTE DE VENDEMAIN. Vin.
ONEIDA. Lab. Vin.
ONTARIO. Aes. Lab. Vin. (N.Y.S. 1908.)
ORIENTAL. Lab. Vin.
OTHELLO. Lab. Vin. Vul.
PAGADEBITO. Vin.
PALMYRA. Lab. ?Vin.
PALOMINO. Vin.
Panariti. BLACK CORINTH.
PARADOX. Lab. Vin.

GRAPE, continued
PARAGON. Lab.
PATRICIA. Lab. Vin.
PAYKANEE. Vin.
PEABODY. ?Lab. Vin. ?Vul. (Ricke. 1870.)
PEARL. Lab. Vul.
PEARL OF CSABA. Vin. *Perle de Csaba.*
PEDRO XIMINES. Vin.
PERKINS. Lab. ?Vin. (Per. 1830.)
PETIT BOUSCHET. Vin.
PETITE SYRAH. Vin. *Durif.*
PIERCE. Lab. Vin. (Pie. 1882.) *California Concord; Isabella Regia.*
PINOT BLANC. Vin.
PINOT DE CHARDONNAY. Vin.
PINOT DE BERNAND. Vin.
PINOT NOIR. Vin.
PIZZUTELLO. Vin.
POCKLINGTON. Lab. (Poc. 1870.)
PONTIAC. Lab. Vin.
PORTLAND. Lab.
PORTUGUESE BLUE. Vin.
POUGHKEEPSIE. Bou. Lab. Vin.
PRESIDENT. Lab. Vin.
PRESLY. Lab. Vul.
PRUNE DE CAZOULS. Vin.
REBECCA. Lab. Vin.
RED EAGLE. Lab. Vin.
REFOSCO. Vin. *Crabb Burgundy.*
REGAL. Lab. Vin.
REQUA. Lab. Vin.
Ribier. ALPHONSE LAVALLEE.
RIPLEY. Aes. Lab. Vin. (N.Y.S. 1912.)
RISH BABA. Vin.
ROBIN NOIR. Vin.
ROCHESTER. Lab. Vin.
ROCKWOOD. Lab.
ROMMEL. Lab. Vin. Vul. (Mun. 1883.)
RONALDO. Lab. Lin. Vin. (Mun.)
ROSE OF PERU. Vin. *Black Prince.*
ROUND SEEDLESS. Vin. *Austrian Seedless; Seedless Sultana; Sultana.*
RUBY. Lab. Vin. Vul.
RUPERT. Bou. Lab. Lin. Rup. Vin.
RUSTLER. Lab. Vin.
R. W. MUNSON. Lab. Lin. Vin.
SAINT EMILION. Vin. *Trebbiano; Ugni Blanc.*
SAINT MACAIRE. Vin.
SALEM. Lab. Vin. (Roge. 1852.)
SALVADOR. Rup. Vin.
SANGIOVETO. Vin.
SAUVIGNON. Vin.
Sauvignon Vert. COLOMBARD.
SCHULTZE.
SCUPPERNONG. Rot.
SECRETARY. ?Lab. Vin. Vul.
Seedless Sultana. ROUND SEEDLESS.
SEMILLON. Vin.
SENECA. Aes. Lab. Vin. (N.Y.S. 1930.)
SERINE. Vin.
SERVANT. Vin.
SHAUMAN. Lab. ?Vin.
SHELBY. Lab. Vul.
SHELTER. Lab. Rip.
SHERIDAN. Lab. Vin. (N.Y.S. 1921.)
STARK DELICIOUS. Lab. Vin.
ST.JOHN. Bou. Lab. Vin.
STOUT SEEDLESS. Lab. Vin. (N.Y.S. 1930.)
Sultana. ROUND SEEDLESS.
SULTANINA. Vin. *Thompson Seedless.*

Grape, continued
Sultanina Rose. Vin.
Sungari.
Sunrise. Bou. Lab. Vin.
Sweet Water. Chasselas Dore.
Sylvaner. Vin. *Franken Riesling.*
Tannat. Vin.
Taylor. Lab. Vul.
Thomas. Rot. (Thoma. 1855.)
Thompson Seedless. Sultanina.
Tinta Amarella. Vin.
Tinta Madeira. Vin.
Tokay. Flame Tokay.
Tonkawa. Bou. Lab. Vin.
Traminer. Vin.
Trebbiano. Saint Emilion.
Triumph. Lab. Vin.
Trousseau. Vin.
Ugni Blanc. Saint Emilion.
Uhland. Lab. Rip.
Ulster. ?Aes. Lab. Vin. (Cay. 1885.)
Urbana. Lab. Vin. (N.Y.S. 1912.)
Valdepenas. Vin.
Valhallah. Bou. Can. Lab. Vin. Vul.
Verdelho. Vin.
Vergennes. Lab. (W. Green 1874.)
Vernaccia Bianca. Vin.
Vesta. Lab. Vin.
Waddel. Lab.
Walsh Riesling. Vin.
Wapanuka. Bou. Lab. Vin. Vul. (Mun. 1893.)
Watkins. Lab. Vin.
Wayne. Lab. Vin. (N.Y.S. 1901.)
Wetumka. Aes. Bou. Lab. Vin.
White Riesling. Vin. *Johannisberger Riesling.*
White Tokay. Furmint.
Wilder. Lab. Vin. (Roge. 1852.)
Wilding. Lab. Rip.
Wilkins. Lab. (Wilk. 1895.)
Winchell. Aes. Lab. Vin. (Clo. 1885.)
Wine King. Aes. Lin. Rup.
Woodruff Red. Lab. ?Vin. (Woodr. 1874.)
Worden. Lab. ?Vin. (Wor. 1863.)
Wyoming. Lab. (Park. 1861.)
Xlnta. Lab. Lin. Rup. Vin. (Mun. 1893.)
Yates. Lab. Vin.
Zabalkanski. Vin.
Zante Currant. Black Corinth.
Zinfandel. Vin.

Grapefruit . . . . . **Citrus paradisi**
Imp. Improved. Unc. Uncolored.
RC. Redcolored.

₵Aurantium. Unc. *Orange.*
₵Cecily. Unc.
₵Clayson. Unc.
₵Conner.
₵Davis.
₵Desota. Unc.
Duarte Seedling. ₵Nectar.
₵Duncan. Unc.
₵Excelsior. Unc.
₵Foster. RC. *Foster Pink-Flesh.*
₵Hall. Unc. *Halls Silver Cluster.*
₵Henninger. RC. *Henningers Ruby.*
₵Imperial. Unc.
Indian Pomelo. ₵Poorman.
₵Indian River. Unc. *Standard. Indian River.* ₵McCarty.
₵Jordan. Unc.

Grapefruit, continued
₵Josselyn. Unc.
₵Leonardy. Unc.
₵Manville. Unc. *Manville Imp.*
₵Marsh. Unc.
₵May. Unc. *Mays.*
₵McCarty. Unc. *Indian River.*
₵McKinley. Unc.
₵Nectar. Unc. *Duarte Seedling.*
New Zealand Grapefruit. ₵Poorman. *Orange.* ₵Aurantium.
₵Pernambuco. Unc.
Pink Marsh. ₵Thompson.
₵Poorman. Unc. *Indian Pomelo; New Zealand Grapefruit; Poormans Orange.*
₵Royal. Unc.
Standard. ₵Indian River.
₵Thompson. RC. *Pink Marsh.*
₵Triumph. Unc.
₵Walters. Unc.
₵Webb. RC. *Webbs Redblush Seedless.*

Groundnut . . . . . . Potatobean

Grumichama (*Braziliancherry; Grumixam[ier]a*) . . . **Eugenia dombeyi**
This plant is frequently misidentified as E. brasiliensis.
Red. White.
Vermilion.

Guabiroba . . **Abbevillea fenzliana** (*Campomanesia f.*)

Guanabana . . . . Soursop

Guava . . . . **Psidium** spp.
Apple (*pomiferum*)
A group name, referring to fruit shape.
Brazilian G. (*Araca*). **P. guineense.**
Cattley G. **P. littorale** (*cattleianum*).
Common G. **P. guajava.**
CostaRican G. **P. friedrichsthalianum.**
Guisaro G. **P. molle.**
Lemon (*acre*). *Sour.*
A group name.
Paraguava. **Britoa acida** (*P. araca*).
Pear (*pyriferum*).
A group name, referring to fruit shape.
₵Redland.
Strawberry G. Cattley G.

Guisaro . . . . **Psidium molle**

Hardyorange . . Trifoliate-orange

Hawthorn . . . . . **Crataegus** spp.
Ecuador H. (*Manzanilla*) **C. stipulosa**
Mexican H. (*Tejocote*) **C. pubescens**

Hazelnut . . . . Filbert

Heartnut (*Flat Siebold Walnut; Flat W.*). **Juglans sieboldiana cordiformis**

Hedgethorn . . . **Carissa arduina**

Hesperethusa **Hesperethusa crenulata**

Hickorynut . . . . . . **Carya** spp.
B. Bitternut. R. Red Hickory.
Car. Carolina. Shag. Shagbark.
M. Mockernut. Shell. Shellbark.
P. Pecan.

₵Adelhurst. Shag. (Beem. 1935.)
₵Anthony. Shag. (Ant. 1932.)
Ashleaf Shagbark H. **C. ovata fraxinifolia.**
₵Barnes. M. × Shag. (H. Bar. 1919.)
₵Beam. Shag. (E. Beam 1919.)

Hickorynut, continued
₵Beaver. B. × Shag. (Jones 1916.)
₵Beecher. Shag. × Shell. (Zim. 1933.)
₵Beeman. Shag. (Beem. 1931.)
₵Benthien. Shag. (Benth. 1929.)
₵Benton. Shag. (Bent. 1934.)
₵Berger. M. × Shell. (Ber. 1934.)
Bitter H. **C. cordiformis.**
Black H. **C. texana.**
₵Bridgewater. Shag. (Beem. 1936.)
Broadleaf Bitter H. **C. cordiformis latifolia.**
₵Brocktondale. Shag. (Grah. 1924.)
₵Brooks. Shag. (F. Bro. 1924.)
∞Browns H. ∞**C. browni.**
₵Buehring. Shag. (Bue. 1934.)
₵Burlington. P. × Shell. (Jones 1915.)
₵Burton. P. × Shag. (E. Burt. 1880.)
Carolina H. **C. carolinae-septentrionalis.**
Cathay H. **C. cathayensis.**
₵Cedar Rapids. Shag. (Snyd. 1915.)
₵Clark. Shag. (E. Clark 1918.)
₵Coe. Shag. (A. Coe 1892.)
₵Coleman. Shag. (Cole 1934.)
₵Cranz. Shag. (Cranz 1934.)
₵Creager. B. × Shag. (Snyd. 1925.)
₵Davis. Shag. (G. L. Smi. 1934.)
₵Dennis. Shag. (Snyd. 1915.)
₵Des Moines. P. × Shell. (Snyd. 1924.)
₵Dintleman. P. × Shell. (Din. 1922.)
₵Drepperd. Shell. (Drep. 1934.)
Dunbar H. ×**C. dunbari.**
₵Emerick. Shag. (Emer. 1932.)
₵Enfield. Shag. (MacD. 1934.)
₵Eversman. Shell. (Snyd. 1920.)
₵Fairbanks. B. × Shag. (Jones 1916.)
Florida H. Scrub H.
₵Folts. Shag. (Folts 1934.)
₵Fox. Shag. (R. Fox 1934.)
₵Galloway. B. × P. (Gal. 1894.)
₵Gerardi. P. × Shell. (Ger. 1930.)
₵Glover. Shag. from Conn. (Jones 1918.)
₵Goheen. Shag. (Goh. 1926.)
₵Grainger. Car. (Hers. 1935.)
₵Hadley. Shag. (Had. 1934.)
₵Hage. Shell. (Hage 1926.)
₵Hagen. Shag. (Snyd. 1924.)
₵Hales. Shag. (Hales 1879.)
₵Hand. Shag. (Snyd. 1920.)
₵Hasbrouck. Shag. (G. L. Smi. 1935.)
₵Hefty. Shag. (Hefty 1934.)
₵Heibner. Shag. (Heib. 1932.)
₵Helmuth. Shag. (Hel. 1929.)
₵Hilton. Shag. (Hilt. 1934.)
₵Huff. R. (Huff 1929.)
₵Jolliffe. Shag. (Jol. 1933.)
₵Joy. Shag × Shell. (Joy 1934.)
₵Kendall. Shag. (Ken. 1934.)
₵Kentucky. Shag. (Cun. 1916.)
₵Kirtland. Shag. (H. Kirt. 1897.)
₵Landis. Shell. (Red. 1934.)

HICKORYNUT, continued
¢LANEY. B. × Shag. (Dunb. 1916.)
LANEY H. ×**C. laneyi.**
¢LAST. Shag. (Huen. 1934.)
¢LAWSON. Shag. (Laws. 1934.)
¢LEONARD. Shag. (Leon. 1908.)
¢LINGENFELTER. Shag. (Lin. 1925.)
¢LOOMIS. Shag. (Loo. 1934.)
¢MALL. B. × P. (Mall 1934.)
¢MANAHAN. Shag. (Man. 1906.)
¢MANN. Shag. (Mann 1932.)
¢MCCALLISTER. P. × Shell. (McCal. 1890.)
¢MCLAUGHLIN. Shag. (McLa. 1934.)
¢MILFORD. Shag. (Cook 1891.)
¢MILLER. Shag. (D. Mil. 1932.)
¢MINNIE. Shag. (Snyd. 1920.)
MOCKERNUT H. **C. tomentosa.**
¢MURDOCK. Shag. (G. L. Smi. 1935.)
NARROWLEAF WATER H. **C. aquatica australis.**
¢NEILSON. Shag. (Cors. 1930.)
¢NETKING. Shag. (Net. 1934.)
¢NUSSBAUMER. P. × Shell. (S. Mil. 1888.)
NUSSBAUMER H. ×**C. nussbaumeri.**
NUTMEG H. **C. myristicaeformis.**
¢PECK. B. × Shag. (G. L. Smi. 1934.)
PIGNUT H. **C. glabra.**
¢PLATMAN. Shag. (Plat. 1934.)
¢PLEAS. B. × P. (Pleas 1916.)
RED H. **C. ovalis.**
¢ROCKVILLE. P. × Shell. (From Mo.) (Jones 1900.)
¢ROMIG. Shag. (Hers. 1927.)
¢SALISBURY. Shag. (Sali. 1934.)
¢SANDE. Shag × Shell. (Sande 1925.)
SAND H. **C. pallida.**
¢SCHINNERLING. Shag. (Snyd. 1920.)
SCHNECK H. ×**C. schnecki.**
SCRUB H. **C. floridana.**
SHAGBARK H. **C. ovata.**
SHELLBARK H. **C. laciniosa.**
¢SIERS. B. × M. (Siers 1916.)
¢STADELBACKER. Shag. (Stad. 1934.)
¢STANLEY. Shell. (From Ind.) (Jones 1916.)
¢STOCKING. B. × Shag. (E. Sto. 1932.)
¢STRATFORD. Shag. (Snyd. 1920.)
¢SWAIM. Shag. (Swaim 1912.)
¢TAMA QUEEN. Shell. (Snyd. 1920.)
¢TAYLOR. Shag. (Tay. 1914.)
¢VEST. Shag. (Vest 1906.)
¢WARREN. Shag. (Warre. 1934.)
WATER H. **C. aquatica.**
¢WEIKER. Shag × Shell. (Jones 1903.)
¢WESCHCKE. Shag. (Wes. 1926.)
¢WHITNEY. Shag. (W. Whit. 1934.)
¢WILCOX. Shag. (P. Wil. 1934.)
¢WOODS. Shag × Shell. (Zim. 1927.)

Hogplum . . . . YELLOW MOMBIN

HONDAPARA . . . . . **Dillenia indica**

HONEYBERRY **Melicocca** (*Melicoccus*) spp.
See also MAMONCILLO.

HUCKLEBERRY . . . **Gaylussacia** spp.

Icaco . . . . COCOPLUM

∞ ICHANDARIN . . **Citrus ichangensis × C. reticulata**
¢YUZU

∞ ICHANGELO . . . . **Citrus grandis × C. ichangensis**
¢ICHANGLEMON (*Shangyuan*)

ILAMA . . . . . . **Annona diversifolia**

IMBE . . . . . **Garcinia livingstonei**

IMBU . . . . . . **Spondias tuberosa**

India-almond . . TROPICAL-ALMOND

INDIANFIG . . . **Opuntia ficus-indica**

IVORYNUT . . **Phytelephas seemanni**

JABOTICABA . . . . . **Myrciaria** spp.
BRANCA. PINTADA.
BRONZCADA. RAJADA.
COROA. ROXA.
MURTA. SABARA.

JAKFRUIT (*Jackfruit*) . . . **Artocarpus heterophyllus** (*integrifolius*)
JOHOREJAK.
KURUWARAKA.
PENIWARAKA (*Honey Jack*).
VELA.
WARAKA.

JAMBOLAN (*Duhat; Jambolanplum*) **Syzygium cumini** (*jambolanum; Eugenia c.; E. jambolana*)

Jamrosade . . . . ROSEAPPLE

Japanesemedlar . . . . . . LOQUAT

JASMINORANGE . . . . **Murraya** spp.

Javaalmond . . . . PILINUT

Jobo . . . . YELLOW MOMBIN

JUJUBE (*Chinese-date*) **Zizyphus jujuba**
INDIA J. **Z. mauritiana.**
LANG. SUIMEN.
LI. YU.
MUSHINGHONG.

Juneberry . . . . . . SERVICEBERRY

KAFIRORANGE . . . **Strychnos spinosa**

KAFIRPLUM . **Harpephyllum caffrum**

Kapoelasan . . . . PULASAN

KARANDA . . . . . **Carissa carandas**

KEIAPPLE (*Umkokolo*) **Dovyalis caffra** (*Aberia c.*)

KITEMBILLA (*Ceylongooseberry*) **Dovyalis hebecarpa** (*Aberia gardneri*)

∞ KUMANDARIN . . **Citrus reticulata × Fortunella** spp.
¢CALAMONDIN (*To-kumquat*)

KUMQUAT . . . . . . **Fortunella** spp.
GOLDENBEAN HONGKONG K. **F. hindsi chinton.**
HONGKONG K. **F. hindsi.**
MARUMI K. **F. japonica** (*Round Kumquat*).
MEIWA K. **F. crassifolia.**
NAGAMI K. **F. margarita** (*Oval Kumquat*).
¢NIPPON

Kuruba . . . . CURUBA

LANGSAT . . . **Lansium domesticum**
DUKU (*Doekoe*). LANGSAT.

Leechee . . . . LYCHEE

∞ LEMANDARIN . . . . **Citrus limon × C. reticulata**
¢OTAHEITE.

LEMON . . . **Citrus limon** (*limonia*)
AG. Anomalus Group.
EG. Eureka Group.
H. Hybrid.
LG. Lisbon Group.
SL. Sweet Lemon.

Presumably the hort. var. listed below are clons.

AMERFO. EG.
American Wonder Lemon. PONDEROSA.
BELAIR. EG.
BONNIE BRAE. LG.
CUBAN. AG. *Cuban Shaddock.*
DORSHAPO. SL. *Sweet Lemon.*
EUREKA. EG.
EVERBEARING. EG.
Florida Rough. ROUGH.
French. ROUGH.
GENOA. EG.
KENNEDY. LG.
LISBON. LG.
MARSEILLES. *White.*
Mazoe. ROUGH.
MESSER. LG.
MESSINA. LG.
MEYER. AG.
MILLSWEET. SL. *Sweet Lemon.*
PERRINE. H. (*Mexican lime × Genoa lemon*).
PONDEROSA. AG. *American Wonder Lemon; Wonder Lemon.*
ROUGH. AG. *Florida Rough; French; Mazoe.*
SICILY. LG.
Sweet Lemon. DORSHAPO; MILLSWEET.
VILLAFRANCA. EG.
WHEATLEY. EG.
White. MARSEILLES.
Wonder Lemon. PONDEROSA.

∞ LEMONIME **Citrus aurantifolia × C. limon**
PERRINE.

LIME . . . . . . **Citrus aurantifolia**
A. Acid. S. Sweet.
M. Mandarin. T. Tahiti.
Mex. Mexican.

Bearss; Bearss Persian; Bearss Seedless. ¢TAHITI.
¢EVERGLADE. Mex.
¢IDEMORE. T.
¢KUSAIE. M.
¢MEXICAN. A. *Key; West Indian.*
¢OTAHEITE. S. *Otaite Orange.*
¢PALESTINE. S. *Palestine Sweet Lemon.*
¢PALMETTO. Mex.
Persian. ¢TAHITI.
¢POND. T.
¢RANGPUR. M. *Rungpur.*
¢SWEET. S.
¢TAHITI. T. *Bearss; Bearss Persian; Bearss Seedless; Persian.*
West Indian. ¢MEXICAN.
¢YOUNG. Mex. *Thornless.*

LIMEBERRY . . . . **Triphasia trifolia**

∞ LIMEQUAT . . . **Citrus aurantifolia × Fortunella** spp.
¢EUSTIS. ¢TAVARES.
¢LAKELAND.

LINGARO . . . **Elaeagnus philippensis**

LIPOTE . . . . . . **Eugenia currani**

Litchi . . . . LYCHEE

LONGAN . . **Euphoria longan** (*longana; Dimocarpus longan; Nephelium longana*)

LOQUAT (*Japanese-medlar*) **Eriobotrya japonica**
- ADVANCE.
- CHAMPAGNE.
- EARLY RED.
- GOLDEN YELLOW.
- KANRO.
- MOGI.
- OLIVER.
- PINEAPPLE.
- PREMIER.
- TANAKA.
- TAZA.
- THALES (*Gold Nugget; Placentia Giant*).
- VICTOR.
- WHITE.

LOUVI (*Batokoplum*) **Flacourtia inermis**

LUCUMA (*Lucumo*) . . . **Lucuma** spp.
See also CANISTEL; YELLOWSAPOTE.

LUVUNGA (*Lavanga*) . . **Luvunga** spp.

LYCHEE (*Leechee; Litchi*) . . . **Litchi chinensis** (*Nephelium litchi*)
- BEDANA.
- BREWSTER.
- CHUIMACHI.
- CHUNFUNG.
- *Cinnamon.* KWAIMEI.
- FEITSZESIU.
- HARKYIP. *Haak Ip.*
- HEUNGLAI.
- HOMSHIUCHI.
- KATJATKWO.
- KWAIMEI. *Cinnamon.*
- KWALUK.
- LOHMAICHI.
- MCLEAN.
- MOUNTAIN.
- NOMAI. *Nomaichi.*
- SHANCHI.
- SHEUNGSHUWAI.
- SWEETCLIFF.
- TONGPOK.
- WAAICHI. *Waichi.*
- YUKHOPO.

MABOLA (*Mabolo*). **Diospyros discolor**

MACADAMIA (*Queenslandnut*) **Macadamia ternifolia**

MAHONIA, CASCADES **Mahonia nervosa**
See also OREGONGRAPE.

Malayapple . . . . OHIA

MAMEY (*Mamey de Santo Domingo; Mameeapple*) **Mammea americana**

Mamey Colorado; Mammee Sapota SAPOTE

MAMONCILLO (*Spanishlime*) **Melicocca bijuga**

MANGO . . . . . . **Mangifera** spp.

I Indian subspecies of Common Mango.
S. Saigon (*Philippine*) subspecies of Common Mango.
SR. Seedling race.

- ALPHONSE. I.
- ₵AMEERI. I.
- ₵AMINI. I.
- APPLE. I.; SR. *Bombay; Manga Blanca.*
- BACHANG M. (*Ambatjang M.*). **M. foetida.**
- BAUNO M. **M. verticillata.**

MANGO, continued
- ₵BENNETT. I. *Douglas Bennetts Alphonse.*
- BINJAI M. **Mangifera caesia.**
- BLANCO. I.; SR.
- *Bombay.* APPLE.
- ₵BORSHA. I.
- ₵BROOKS. I.
- ₵CAMBODIANA. S.
- CARABAO. S.; SR.
- ₵CECIL. S.
- CEYLON M. **M. zeylanica.**
- COMMON M. **M. indica.**
- D'OR. I.
- *Douglas Bennetts Alphonse.* ₵BENNETT.
- ESPADA. I.; SR.
- ₵FAIZANSON. I.
- ₵FASCELL. I.
- ₵FERNANDEZ. I.
- ₵FRAGRANCE. I.
- ₵GOLA. I.
- ₵GOLEK. S.
- *Gordon.* ₵TOTOFARI.
- ₵HADEN. I.
- ₵ITAMARACA. I.
- ₵JULIE. I.
- KUWINI M. (*Bumbum M.*). **M. odorata.**
- ₵LANGRA BENARSI. I.
- LARGO. I.; SR.
- *Manga Amarilla.* PEACH.
- *Manga Blanca.* APPLE.
- MANGA DA ROSA. I.; SR. *Rose Mango.*
- MANGOTINA. I.; SR.
- MONJET M. (*Manga Monjet; Manga Pari*). **M. laurina.**
- ₵MULGOBA. I.
- NEPAL M. **M. sylvatica.**
- NUMBER 11. I.; SR.
- *Padero.* PICO.
- ₵PAHERI. I. *Pairi; Pirie; Pyrie.*
- PAHUTAN M. **M. altissima.**
- *Pairi.* ₵PAHERI.
- PEACH. I.; SR. *Manga Amarilla; Turpentine.*
- PICO. S.; SR. *Padero.*
- PINA. I.; SR.
- *Pirie; Pyrie.* ₵PAHERI.
- ₵RAJPURI. I. *Rajabury; Rajapur(r)i; Rajpur; Rajpury.*
  Perhaps not distinct from ₵Paheri.
- REDONDO. I.; SR.
- *Rose Mango.* MANGA DA ROSA.
- SAIGON (*Philippine*).
  A subspecific name.
- ₵SANDERSHA. I. *Sandershaw; Soondershaw; Sundersha.*
- ₵SINGAPUR. I.
- *Soondershaw.* ₵SANDERSHA.
- ₵SPRINGFELS. I.
- *Sundersha.* ₵SANDERSHA.
- ₵TOTOFARI. I. *Gordon; Totopari.*
- *Turpentine.* PEACH.

MANGOSTEEN . **Garcinia mangostana**

Mangrove Annona . . . PONDAPPLE

MARANG . . **Artocarpus odoratissimus**

Marmaladefruit; Marmaladeplum SAPOTE

Matasano . . . . . . WHITESAPOTE

Mayhaw . . . . HAWTHORN

MEDLAR . . . . **Mespilus germanica**

MEROPE . . . . . . **Merope angulata**

MERRILLIA . . . **Merrillia caloxylon**

Mexican Apple . . . . WHITESAPOTE

MICROMELUM . . . . **Micromelum**
- PHILIPPINE M. . . **M. compressum**

MOMBIN . . . . **Spondias** spp.
- RED M. (*Spanishplum*). **S. purpurea**
- YELLOW M. (*Hogplum; Jobo*) **S. mombin** (*lutea*)

MONANTHOCITRUS (*Spotseed Falsewenzelia*) . . . **Monanthocitrus** spp.

MORETONBAYCHESTNUT **Castanospermum australe**

MOUNTAINASH, EUROPEAN (*Rowantree*) **Sorbus aucuparia**

MULBERRY . . . . **Morus** spp.

MUSKMELON . . . . . **Cucumis melo**

Myrobalan . . . . EMBLIC

Natalplum . . . . CARISSA

NECTARINE. **Prunus persica nectarina** (*Amygdalus p. n.; Persica nucipersica*)
- ADVANCE.
- ANSENNE.
- BLOOD.
- BOSTON.
- BRECK.
- CARDINAL.
- DAVIS.
- DIAMOND JUBILEE.
- DIXIE.
- DOWNTON.
- DRYDEN.
- EARLY NEWINGTON.
- EARLY RIVERS.
- EARLY VIOLET.
- ELRUGE.
- FISHER YELLOW.
- FLAMINGGOLD.
- GARDEN.
- GAYLORD.
- GOLD MINE.
- GOWER.
- GRIFFITH.
- HARDWICKE.
- HUMBOLDT.
- HUNTER.
- *J. C. Wees.* WEES.
- JOHN RIVERS.
- KATHRYN.
- *Large White.* NEW WHITE.
- LIPPIATT. *Lippiatt Late Orange.*
- LITTLE YELLOW.
- LORD NAPIER.
- MEXICAN.
- MILTON.
- MUIR.
- NETTARINA GILLA D'PADOVA.
- NEWBOY.
- NEWTON.
- NEWWHITE. *Large White.*
- NIGH.
- OZARK.
- PINEAPPLE.
- PITMASTON ORANGE.
- QUETTA.
- RED CLING.
- RED ROMAN.
- RIVERS ORANGE.
- ROBINSON.
- SMITH.
- SPANISH.
- SPENCER.
- STANWICK.

NECTARINE, continued
STANWICK ELRUDGE.
SURECROP.
TOGATCH MONECK.
TRAVELLER.
VICTORIA.
WEES. *J. C. Wees.*
WILKINSON.
YENNAN.

Niggertoe . . . . BRAZILNUT

OHIA (*Malayapple; Otaheiteapple* in part; *Pomerack*) **Syzygium malaccense** (*Caryophyllus malaccensis; Eugenia m.; Jambosa m.*)

OLIVE . . . . **Olea europaea**
ASCOLANO. NEVADILLO.
BAROUNI. PICHOLINE.
MANZANILLO. RUBRA.
MISSION. SEVILLANO.

ORANGE . . . . **Citrus** spp.

ABBREVIATIONS OF ORANGE CLASSIFICATIONS

Berg. BERGAMOT O. **C. bergamia.**
Bit. BITTERSWEET O. **C. aurantium** HV.
BO. BLOOD ORANGE. **C. sinensis** HV.
Cal. CALAMONDIN O. **C. mitis.**
King. KING O. **C. nobilis.**
Man. MANDARIN O. (including Tangerine). **C. reticulata** (*C. nobilis reticulata*).
Myr. MYRTLELEAF SOUR O. **C. aurantium myrtifolia.**
NO. NAVEL O. **C. sinensis** ₵NAVEL.
Sat. SATSUMA O. **C. nobilis unshiu.**
SO. SOUR O. (*Seville O.; Bigarade O.*) **C. aurantium.**
Sw. SWEET O. **C. sinensis.**

Presumably all hort. var. listed below are clons.

ACME. Sw. *Beachs Acme.*
AFRICAN. SO.
Algerian. CLEMENTINE.
ARCADIA. Sw.
AUSTRALIAN. NO.
Bahia. WASHINGTON NAVEL.
Beachs Acme. ACME.
BEAUTY. Man. *Beauty of Glen Retreat.*
BERGAMOT O. **C. bergamia.**
BESSIE. Sw.
Bigarade O. SOUR O.
Bijou. DANCY.
BITTERSWEET O. **C. aurantium** HV.
BLOOD O. **C. sinensis** HV.
BOONE. Sw.
BOUQUET. Berg. *Bouquet Defleurs.*
BRAZILIANSOUR. SO. *Brazilian.*
BRAZILIANSWEET. Sw. *Brazilian.*
BUCKEYE. NO. *Golden Buckeye.*
CALAMONDIN O. **C. mitis.**
Carlton. CONNOR.
CARTER. NO.
CENTENNIAL. Sw.
Chinese Honey Orange. PONKAN.
CHINOTTO. Myr.
CIRCASSIAN. Sw.
CLEMENTINE. Man. *Algerian.*
CLEOPATRA. Man. *Ponki; Spice Tangerine.*
CONNOR. Sw. *Carlton; Connors Seedless.*
DAIDAI. Berg.
DANCY. Man. *Bijou; Moragnes Tangerine.*
DILLAR. Sw.
DOUBLE IMPERIAL. NO.
DRAKE STAR. Sw. *Star Calyx.*
DUMMITT. Sw.

ORANGE, continued
DUROI. Sw.
EARLY OBLONG. Sw. *St. Michael; St. Michaels Egg.*
EGYPTIAN. NO.
EGYPTIAN BLOOD. BO.
EMPEROR. Man.
ENTERPRISE. Sw. *Seedless.*
EXQUISITE. Sw.
FOSTER. Sw.
Garcys Mediterranean Sweet. MALTESEOVAL.
Golden Buckeye. BUCKEYE.
GOLDEN RING.
GOLD NUGGET. BO.
GOLETA. Berg.
HAMLIN. Sw. *Norris.*
HICKS. Sw. *Hicks Sweet Seville.*
HOMOSASSA. Sw.
IKEDA. Sat.
INDIAN RIVER. Sw.
JAFFA. Sw.
JOPPA. Sw. *Joppa Late.*
KING O. **C. nobilis.** *King of Siam; Kunembo.*
KINNELOA. Man.
KINOKUNI. Man.
KOETHEN. Sw.
Kunembo. KING O.
LAMB SUMMER. Sw.
LUE GIM GONG. Sw. *Lue.*
MADAM VINOUS. Sw.
MAGNUM BONUM. Sw.
MAJORCA. Sw.
MALTESE. BO.
MALTESEOVAL. Sw. *Garcys Mediterranean Sweet.*
MANDARIN O. **C. reticulata.**
MARQUIS. Sw.
MAY. Sw.
MEDITERRANEAN SWEET. Sw. *Sanfords Mediterranean Sweet.*
MIKADO. Sat.
MILITENSIS. NO.
Moragnes Tangerine. DANCY.
MYRTLELEAF O. **C. aurantium myrtifolia.**
Naranja Apepu. PARAGUAY.
NAVELENCIA. NO.
NAVEL O. **C. sinensis ₵.**
NONPAREIL. SW.
Norris. HAMLIN.
OLD VINI. Sw.
ONECO. Man.
OSCELA. Sw.
OWARI. Sat.
PAPERRIND. Sw. *Paperrind St. Michael; St. Michael.*
PARAGUAY. Bit. *Naranja Apepu.*
PARSON. NO.
PARSON BROWN. Sw.
PINEAPPLE. Sw.
PONKAN. Man. *Chinese Honey Orange; Wanurco.*
Ponki. CLEOPATRA.
PRATA. Sw. *Silver.*
Riverside Navel. WASHINGTON NAVEL.
ROBERTSON. NO.
RUBIDOUX. SO.
RUBY. BO.
SANFORD. BO. *Sanfords Sweet Blood.*
Sanfords Mediterranean Sweet. MEDITERRANEAN SWEET.
Sanfords Sweet Seville. SWEET SEVILLE.
SATSUMA O. **C. nobilis unshiu.**
SAUL. BO. *Sauls Blood.*

ORANGE, continued
Seedless. ENTERPRISE.
SELECTA. Sw.
Seville O. SOUR O.
SHAMOUTI. Sw. *Shamooti Chamondi.*
Silver. PRATA.
SOUR O. **C. aurantium.** *Bigarade O.; Seville O.*
Spice Tangerine. CLEOPATRA.
STANDARD. SO.
Star Calyx. DRAKE STAR.
STARK. Sw. *Starks Favorite.*
ST. MICHAEL. BO. *St. Michaels Blood.*
St. Michael in part. EARLY OBLONG; PAPERRIND.
St. Michaels Egg. EARLY OBLONG.
SURPRISE. NO.
SUSTAIN. NO.
SWEET O. **C. sinensis.**
SWEET SEVILLE. Sw. *Sanfords Sweet Seville.*
TEXAS. NO.
THOMSON. NO. *Thomson Navel.*
TRIMBLE. Man.
TROVITA. Sw.
VALENCIA. Sw.
Wanurco. PONKAN.
WASHINGTON NAVEL. NO. *Bahia; Riverside Navel.*
WASI. Sat.
WELDON. Sw.
WESHART. Man.
WHITE. Sw.
WHITTAKER. Sw.
WILLOWLEAF. Man.
ZAIRAI. Sat.

ORANGEASTER . . . . **Pleiospermium**
BORNEO O. . . . . **P. latialatum**
CEYLON O. . . . . **P. alatum**
JAVA O. . . . . **P. dubium**
LONGSEPAL O. . . **P. longisepalum**
SUMATRA O. . . . **P. sumatranum**

∞ ORANGEQUAT . **Citrus nobilis unshiu** × **Fortunella** spp.

OREGONGRAPE . . **Mahonia aquifolium**
See also CASCADES MAHONIA.

Otaheiteapple . . . AMBARELLA; OHIA

OTAHEITE-GOOSEBERRY **Phyllanthus acidus**

OXANTHERA . . . . . . **Oxanthera**
FRAGRANT O. . . . . **O. fragrans**
NEWCALEDONIA O. (*Bigleaf O.; Falseorange*) . . . . **O. neocaledonica**

OYSTERNUT . . . . **Telfairia pedata**

PAMBURUS . . . **Pamburus missionis**

PANIALA . . . . **Flacourtia jangomas**

Papaw . . . . PAWPAW

PAPAYA . . . . **Carica papaya**
BETTY.
BLUESTEM.
FAIRCHILD.
GOLDENNUGGET.
KISSIMMEE.
MOUNTAIN P. **C. candamarcensis.**
SOLO.
STANDARD BLUESTEM.

Paradisenut . . . . . SAPUCAIANUT

PARAGUAVA . . . . . . **Britoa acida**

PARAMIGNYA (*Vinelime*) . **Paramignya**
ONELEAF P. . . . . **P. monophylla**
PHILIPPINE P. . **P. longipedunculata**

Passionfruit . . . . . . GRANADILLA

PAWPAW (*Papaw*) . . **Asimina** spp.

The Editorial Committee is indebted to the late Dr. G. A. Zimmerman, Harrisburg, Pa., for the list of Pawpaw hort. var. below. All of these are of Common Pawpaw origin (A. triloba) unless otherwise indicated. Dr. Zimmerman also assisted with the list of Persimmon varieties.

Bu. Benjamin Buckman.
Ga. Jos. Gable, Stewartstown, Pa.
Ke. Mrs. Frank Ketter, Ironton, Ohio.
Os. Arthur Osborne, Spiceland, Ill.
Zi. Dr. G. A. Zimmerman, Harrisburg, Pa.

BIGFLOWER P. **A. obovata.**
₵BUCKMAN.
COMMON P. **A. triloba.**
₵DR. POTTER.
₵DUCK.
₵EARLYGOLD (Zi. 1924.)
₵FAIRCHILD. (Fa. 1917.)
₵GABLE. (Ga.)
₵HOLTWOOD. (W. Hoopes.)
₵HOPES AUGUST. (Bu.)
₵KETTER. (Ke. 1917.)
₵LONGJOHN. (Bu.)
₵MARTIN.
₵OSBORNE. (Os.)
₵REESE.
RUGEL P. **A. rugeli.**
₵SCHICKER.
SEMINOLETEA P. **A. reticulata.**
₵SHANNONDALE. (Febrey.)
SLIMLEAF P. **A. angustifolia.**
SLIMPETAL P. **A. pulchella.**
SMALLFLOWER P. **A. parviflora.**
SPRAWLING P. **A. pygmaea.**
ST. LUCIE P. **A. tetramera.**
₵TAYLOR.
₵TIEDKE.
₵TRIGUSTIFOLIA (*angustifolia* × *triloba*).
₵TRILOBOVATA (*obovata* × *triloba*).
WOOLLY P. **A. incana.**

PEACH. **Prunus persica** (*Amygdalus p.; Persica vulgaris*)

See also PEACH, p. 468.

A-1.
ADMIRAL DEWEY. (Hus. 1899.) *Dewey.*
ALBRIGHT CLING. (Alb. 1897.)
ALEXANDER. (Ale. 1870.)
ALTON. (Mun. 1890.)
AMBERGEM. (N.J.S. 1934.)
AMSDEN.
ANDERSON COUNTY BEAUTY.
ANGEL. (Min. 1880.)
ANITA.
ANNA.
ANNABEL.
ARP. (Orr 1897.)
AUGBERT. (Boon 1897.)
AUSTRALIAN SAUCER.
BABCOCK. (C.C.S. 1933.)
BAILEY.
BANNER.
BARBARA.
BARNARD.
BEAUTY.
BECKER.
BEERS SMOCK.
BELLE. (L. Rum. 1870.) *Belle of Georgia.*
BEQUETTE FREE. (Beq. 1860.)
BERENICE. (L. Ber. 1890.)

PEACH, continued

BERK FAVORITE.
BEST JUNE. (Bur. 1894.)
BESTMAY.
BIDWELL EARLY. (Bid.1886.)
BIDWELL LATE. (Bid. 1891.)
BILYEU. (Bil. 1880.)
BLEDSOE.
BLISS EVERBEARING.
BLOOD CLING. *Indian Blood Cling.*
BLOOD FREE. (Ives 1873.)
BOKHARA. (Budd 1890.)
BRACKETT. (P. Ber. 1912.)
BRIGDON.
BRIGGS. (Bri. 1870.) *Briggs May; Briggs Red May.*
BRONSON.
BURBANK GIANT. *Burbank Giant Freestone.*
BUTTERCUP. (N.J.S. 1925.)
CABLER. *Cobler.*
CANADA. (High 1890.)
CANADIAN QUEEN.
CANDOKA. (Plant Patent No. 51, 1932.)
CAPTAIN EDE. (Ede 1870.) *Ede.*
CARMAN. (Stu. 1889.)
CARPENTER.
CARRIE.
CHAFFEY.
CHAIRS. (Cha. 1880.)
CHAMPION. (Hub. 1880.)
CHILI. (Wil. 1856.) *Hill Chili.*
CHILOW.
CHINESE CLING. (Dow. 1850.)
CHINESE FREE. (Rob. 1880.)
CHRISTABEL.
CLIMAX. (Taber 1886.)
Cobler. CABLER.
COLON. (Taber 1892.)
COLORA.
CONNET. (Con. 1880.)
C. O. SMITH.
CROSBY. (Cro. 1876.)
CROTHERS. (Crot. 1893.)
CUMBERLAND. (N.J.S. 1925.)
CURRIE. (Tuft.) *Currie Free; Currie Seedling.*
CURRY. (Dorsey.) *Curry Seedling.*
DECKER.
DELICIOUS. (N.J.S. 1925.)
Dewey. ADMIRAL DEWEY.
DR. BURTON. (Burt. 1905.)
DUKE HALE.
DUKE OF YORK.
EARLY CRAWFORD. (Cra. 1832.)
EARLY ELBERTA. (Gle. 1908.)
Early Hale. HALE EARLY.
EARLY HILEY.
EARLY IMPERIAL.
EARLY MAY.
EARLY ROSE.
EARLY WHEELER. (Kir. 1900.) *Red Bird.*
ECLIPSE. (N.J.S. 1925.)
Ede. CAPTAIN EDE.
EDGEMONT. (M.O.C. 1902.)
ELBERTA. (S. Rum. 1870.)
ELLIS. (U.S.D.A. 1935.)
ENGLE. (Engle 1875.) *Engle Mammoth.*
EUREKA.
FAIR BEAUTY.
FAIRHAVEN.
FAMILY FAVORITE. (Locke 1909.)
FAY ELBERTA.
FEI.

PEACH, continued

FERIDA.
FERTILE HALE. *Laduke.* (Plant Patent No. 175, 1936.)
FISHER. *Howard Fisher.* (Plant Patent, 1936.)
FITZGERALD.
FLORENCE.
FLORIDA GEM. (Taber 1896.)
FONTANA.
FOSTER. (Fos. 1857.)
FOX.
FRANCES. (San. 1900.)
FRANK. (Stu. 1903.)
FREDERICKA.
GAGE. *Gage Elberta.*
GAUME. (Gaume 1913.)
GEARY.
GENERAL LEE. (Gam. 1860.)
GEORGE IV. (Gill 1821.)
GEORGE LATE.
GEORGIA HALE.
GIANT SNOWBALL.
GLOBE.
GLOBE ELBERTA.
GOLDDROP.
GOLDEN BEAUTY.
GOLDEN EARLY CLING.
GOLDENEAST.
GOLDENGEM.
GOLDENGLOBE.
GOLDENHEATH.
GOLDEN JUBILEE. (N.J.S. 1925.)
GOLDEN STATE.
GOLDENSWEET.
GOLDFINCH.
GOVERNOR HOGG. (McP. 1892.)
GOVERNOR LANHAM. (Ram. 1909.)
GRADY.
GREENSBORO. (Bals. 1891.)
HALATE.
HALBERTA GIANT. (Plant Patent No. 7, 1932.)
HALE EARLY. (Moas 1850.) *Early Hale.*
HALEHAVEN. (S.H.S. 1932.)
HALFORD No. 1.
HALFORD No. 2.
HALFORD No. 3.
HALLS YELLOW.
HARTCLING.
HAUSS.
HEATH CLING. *White Heath.*
HEATH FREE.
Henrietta. LEVY.
HERMOSA.
HILEY. (Hiley 1886.) *Hiley Belle.*
Hill Chili. CHILI.
HOBSON. (Kir. 1901.)
HONEY. (Dow. 1846.)
HOOSIER.
HOPEFARM.
HORTON RIVER.
Howard Fisher. FISHER.
HYNES. (Hynes 1877.)
HYSLOP. (Hys. 1810.) *Hyslop Cling.*
ICECREAM.
IDEAL.
ILLINOIS. (Riehl 1910.)
IMPERIAL. (Taber 1890.)
IMPROVED ELBERTA.
IMPROVED LATE CRAWFORD.
Indian Blood Cling. BLOOD CLING.
INDIAN CLING.
INDIAN FREE.
IRON MOUNTAIN.
JAPAN DWARF.

PEACH, continued
JAPAN GIANT. *Japan Giant Cling.*
JEWEL. (God. 1892.)
J. H. HALE. (Hale 1912.)
J. M. MACK.
JOHN RIVERS.
JOHNSON.
JULY ELBERTA.
JULYGOLD.
June Elberta. MIKADO.
KALAMAZOO. (Ste. 1869.)
KATIE.
KETTE.
KING SOLOMON.
KRUMMEL. (Kru. 1900.)
Laduke. FERTILE HALE.
LA GRANGE. (Hulse 1840.)
LATE ARP.
LATE CHAMPION.
LATE CRAWFORD. (Cra. 1822.)
LATE ELBERTA.
LATE STUMP.
LEETON. (U.S.D.A. 1935.)
LEMON CLING.
LEMON FREE.
LEVY. *Henrietta; Levi.*
LEWIS. (Lewis 1882.)
LIBBEE.
LIBERTY. (of N.J.)
LINWORTH.
LIZZIE. (Stu. 1913.)
LOLA. (Stu. 1876.)
LOVELL. (Thi. 1882.)
LOVING.
LUKENS. *Lukens Honey.*
LUTTICHAU. (VonL. 1908.)
MAMIE ROSS. (Ross 1881.)
MANLY.
MARIGOLD. (N.J.S. 1925.)
MARK.
MARQUETTE.
MARTHA FERN.
MARYJANE.
MASSASOIT. (N.J.S. 1925.)
MATHEWS. (Mat. 1898.)
MAXINE. (U.S.D.A. 1935.)
MAYFLOWER.
MCCOLLISTER.
MCDEVITT CLING. (McD.)
MCKEVITT CLING. (McK. 1882.)
METEOR. (N.J.S. 1925.)
MIKADO. (Capps 1908.) *June Elberta.*
MILLARD.
MILLERS LATE.
MINNIE STANFORD.
MONEYMAKER.
MORRIS WHITE.
MOUNTAIN ROSE. (Mar. 1851.)
MUIR. (Muir 1880.)
MUNSON FREE. (Mun. 1904.)
NECTAR. (Plant Patent, 1933.)
NESTOR. (Wight 1939.)
NEWCOMB.
NEWHALL. (New. 1889.)
NEW PROLIFIC.
NIAGARA. (Har. 1890.)
NICHOLS. (Nic. 1889.)
OCTOBERTA. (Heep 1909.)
OLDMIXON CLING. (Old. 1730.)
OLDMIXON FREE.
ONDERDONK. (Ond. 1900.)
ONTARIO.
OPULENT. (Burb.)
ORANGE CLING.
ORIOLE. (N.J.S. 1925.)
PALLAS. (L. Ber. 1878.)

PEACH, continued
PALORO. (Dixon 1912.)
PARAGON.
PEACHARINE.
PEAK.
PEENTO. (W. Pri. 1828.)
PENRYN. (Wight 1939.)
PHILLIPS CLING. (Phi. 1898.)
PICKETT.
PICQUET LATE. (Pic. 1869.)
PIONEER. (N.J.S. 1925.)
POLLY. (I.A.S. 1932.)
PRATT LOW.
PRIMROSE. (N.J.S. 1925.)
PRINCE ALBERT.
PROLIFIC. (Gre. 1890.)
RADIANCE. (N.J.S. 1925.)
RAMONA.
RARITAN ROSE.
RAY. (Ray 1890.)
Red Bird. EARLY WHEELER.
RED CEYLON. (Bos. 1880.)
REDELBERTA. (Plant Patent No. 232, 1937.)
REDINDIAN.
REEVES. (Ree. 1840.)
RIO OSO GEM. (Plant Patent No. 84, 1933.)
RIVERDALE.
ROBERTA.
ROCHESTER. (Wal. 1900.)
ROSEBUD. (N.J.S. 1925.)
ROSY.
RUNYON ORANGE CLING. (Run. 1889.)
SALBERTA.
SALWEY. (Sal. 1844.) *Salway.*
SELLERS CLING. (Sel. 1889.)
SELMA. *Selmacling.*
SEPTEMBER ELBERTA.
SEPTEMBER MAMMOTH.
SHALIL.
SHERMAN.
SIMS.
SLAPPEY.
SMITH.
SMITH INDIAN.
SMOCK. (Smo. 1850.)
SNEED. (Sneed 1885.)
SOUTHHAVEN. *Sun Glo.*
STANFORD. (U.S.D.A. 1935.)
STEVENS. (Stev. 1858.)
STINSON.
ST. JOHN. *Yellow St. John.*
STRAWBERRY. (Han. 1841.)
STRAWBERRY CLING.
STRAWBERRY FREE.
STUART.
STUMP.
SULLIVAN CLING. (Plant Patent No. 186, 1936.)
SUMMERSNOW.
SUNBEAM. (N.J.S. 1925.)
Sun Glo. SOUTHHAVEN.
SUNGLOW.
SUNGOLD.
SURESHOT CLING.
SURESHOT FREE.
SUSQUEHANNA.
TABER.
TENA.
TEXAN.
TEXAS. *Texas King.*
THURBER. (L. Ber. 1870.)
TOGO.
TOUGHINA. (Stu. 1915.)
TRIANA. (G.S.M. 1888.)
TRIUMPH. (Hus. 1895.)

PEACH, continued
TROTH.
TUSKENA. *Tuscan.*
UNEEDA.
UP-TO-DATE.
VALIANT. (O.H.S. 1925.)
VANBUREN DWARF.
VAUGHAN. (O.H.S. 1925.)
VEDETTE. (O.H.S. 1925.)
VETERAN. (O.H.S. 1928.)
VICEROY. (O.H.S. 1930.)
VICTOR. (Bass 1901.)
WADDELL. (Wad. 1890.)
WAGER. (Wager 1870.)
WALDO. (God. 1886.)
WALKER.
WALTON.
WARD LATE. (Ward 1862.)
WATERLOO.
WEEMHALE.
WELCOME.
WELDON.
WEST LATE.
WESTLATEFREE.
WHEATLAND. (Rog. 1870.)
WHITE HALE. (N.J.S.) (Plant Patent No. 31, 1932.)
White Heath. HEATH CLING.
WILLOWLEAF.
WILMA.
WINTERCHEEK.
WONDERFUL.
WOODLANDCLING.
YELLOW INDIAN.
Yellow St. John. ST. JOHN.
YELLOW SWAN.
YUNNAN.

PEANUT . . . . . **Arachis hypogaea**

PEAR . . . . **Pyrus** spp.
ANDRE DESPORTES. (LeRoy 1854.)
Angouleme. DUCHESSE D'ANGOULEME.
ANJOU.
ANSAULT. (LeRoy 1863.)
BARSECK. (Moore 1890.)
BARTLETT. (Stair 1845.) *Williams Bon Chretien.*
BEIRSCHMITT.
BELLE LUCRATIVE. *Lucrative.*
BESSEMIANKA.
BEURRE BOSC. (VanM. 1807.) *Bosc.*
BEURRE CLAIRGEAU. (Clai. 1830.) *Clairgeau.*
BEURRE D'ARENBERG.
BEURRE DEJONGHE. (DeJ. 1852.)
BEURRE DIEL. (Meu. 1805.)
BEURRE GIFFARD. (Gif. 1825.) *Giffard.*
BEURRE HARDY. (Bon. 1820.) *Hardy.*
BEURRE SUPERFIN. (Gou. 1837.) *Superfin.*
BLOODGOOD.
BORDEAUX.
Bosc. BEURRE BOSC.
BRANDYWINE. (Harv. 1820.)
BUFFUM. (Buf. 1828.)
CAYUGA. (N.Y.S. 1920.)
Clairgeau. BEURRE CLAIRGEAU.
CLAPP FAVORITE. (T. Cla. 1860.)
CLYDE. (N.Y.S. 1932.)
COLONEL WILDER. (Fox 1870.)
COLUMBIA. (Cas. 1813.)
Comet. LAWSON.
Comice. DOYENNE DU COMICE.
CONFERENCE. (Riv. 1894.)
COVERT. (N.Y.S. 1935.)
DANA HOVEY. (Dana 1854.)

PEAR, continued
DEARBORN.
DORSET. (L. Cla. 1895.)
DOUGLAS. (Ayer 1897.)
DOYENNE BOUSSOCK. (VanM. 1819.)
DOYENNE DU COMICE. *Comice.*
DR. (*Jules*) GUYOT.
Drouard. PRESIDENT DROUARD.
DUCHESSE D'ANGOULEME. *Angouleme; Duchess.*
EARLY ELY. (Ely 1906.)
EARLY HARVEST.
EARLY SECKEL. (N.Y.S. 1935.)
EASTER BEURRE. (VanM. 1823.)
ELIZABETH. (VanM. 1836.)
ENIE.
EWART.
FAME.
FEAGAN.
FLEMISH BEAUTY. (VanM. 1810.)
FORELLE.
FOX. (Fox 1875.)
FREDERICK CLAPP. (L. Cla. 1870.)
GARBER. (Garb. 1880.)
Giffard. BEURRE GIFFARD.
GLOU MORCEAU. (M. Hard. 1750.)
GORHAM. (N.Y.S. 1923.)
GUYOT. (Balt. 1870.)
Hardy. BEURRE HARDY.
HENDERSON SPECIAL.
HOOD. (Hood 1911.)
HOWELL. (T. Howe. 1829.)
IDAHO. (Mulk 1867.)
JARGONNELLE.
JOSEPHINE DE MALINES. (Esp. 1830.)
KIEFFER. (Kie. 1863.)
KOONCE.
LAWRENCE.
LAWSON. (Law. 1800.) *Comet.*
LE CONTE. (LeC. 1850.)
LINCOLN. (Fle. 1835.)
LINCOLN CORELESS.
LOUISE BONNE DE JERSEY. (DeLo. 1780.)
Lucrative. BELLE LUCRATIVE.
MADELEINE.
MAGNOLIA.
MARGUERITE.
MARIE LOUISE. (Duq. 1809.)
MENDEL.
MENIE.
MING.
MINIE.
MOE.
MOUNT VERNON. (Walk. 1868.)
ONONDAGA.
ONTARIO. (Smi. 1856.)
OSBAND.
OVID. (N.Y.S. 1931.)
PARKER.
PASSE COLMAR. (A. Hard. 1758.)
PATTEN.
P. BARRY. (Fox 1873.)
PHILESON.
PINEAPPLE. (Stuc.)
PITMASTON. (J. Will. 1841.)
POUND. (Uve. 1690.)
PRESIDENT DROUARD. (Oli. 1886.) *Drouard.*
PULTENEY. (N.Y.S. 1925.)
PUSHKIN. (Hans. 1919.)
REEDER. (Reed. 1855.)
REIDINGER BARTLETT.
RIEHL BEST. (Riehl 1870.)
ROOSEVELT.
ROSSNEY. (Woo. 1881.)
RUSSET BARTLETT. (Rut. 1893.)

PEAR, continued
RUTTER. (Rut. 1860.)
SECKEL.
SHELDON. (Shel. 1815.)
SOUVENIR D'ESPEREN.
SOUVENIR DU CONGRESS. (Morel 1852.)
SUDDUTH. (Cons. 1820.)
SUMMER DOYENNE. (VanM. 1800.)
Superfin. BEURRE SUPERFIN.
SWANEGG.
TAIT DROPMORE.
TAIT No. 1.
TAIT No. 2.
TYSON. (Tyson 1794.)
URBANISTE. (DeC. 1786.)
VERMONT BEAUTY. (Mac. 1880.)
VICAR OF WAKEFIELD.
WHITE DOYENNE.
WILDER EARLY. (Green 1884.)
WILLARD. (N.Y.S. 1931.)
Williams Bon Chretien. BARTLETT.
WINTER BARTLETT.
WINTER NELIS. (Nelis 1830.)
WORDEN SECKEL. (Wor. 1881.)

PECAN . . . **Carya illinoensis** (*pecan*)
All these hort. var. are clons.

ACME. (Campv. 1924.)
ALLEY. (Alley 1896.)
BACON. (Bacon 1903.)
BANQUET. (Ris. 1913.)
Big Z. ZINK.
BILOXI. (W. Stua. 1893.) *Bass; Bass Papershell; Mexican Papershell.*
BITTER **P. × C. lecontei.**
BOWERS. (Bow. 1925.)
BRADLEY. (Grif. 1896.)
BRAKE. (Brake 1932.)
BROOKS. (Gau. 1903.)
BURKETT. (Burk. 1903.)
BUSSERON. (V. Sim. 1907.)
Calora. GOVETT.
CANDY. (Bec. 1913.)
CARMAN. (James 1898.)
CARMICHAEL. (Carm. 1930.)
CASPIANA. (Hut. 1909.)
CENTENNIAL. (Ani. 1846.)
CLARK. (Evans 1917.)
CLARKSVILLE. (A. Nor. 1930.)
CLINE. (Evans 1917.)
COLORADO. (Ris. 1905.)
COMMONWEALTH. (Ris. 1927.)
CURTIS. (J. Cur. 1896.)
DAISY. (Loc. 1900.)
DELMAS. (Delm. 1890.)
DESIRABLE. (For. 1915.)
DUIS. (Duis 1933.)
DULEY. (Duley 1934.)
ELGIN. (Ram. 1907.)
EVANS. (Evans 1917.)
FARLEY. (Chip. 1916.)
FISHER. (Ger. 1935.)
FROTSCHER. (Nel. 1882.)
GALLATIN. (Van. 1934.)
GARNER. (R. Wolf 1932.)
GEORGIA. (Bacon 1902.)
GILES. (Giles 1930.)
GOFORTH. (Gof. 1934.)
GOLDEN. (Evans 1917.)
GOVETT. (Gov. 1932.) *Calora.*
GREENRIVER. (Major 1911.)
HALBERT. (Halb. 1901.)
HALL. (L. Hall 1906.)
HALSEY. (Wel. 1930.)
HODGE. (Hodge 1908.)
HOFFMANN. (Hof. 1934.)

PECAN, continued
HOLLIS. (Fal. 1900.)
HUMBLE. (U. Sim. 1931.)
IDEAL. (Evans 1929.)
INDIANA. (V. Sim. 1909.)
JAMES. (James 1906.)
JERSEY. (Ris. 1923.)
KELLY. (Kelly 1930.)
KENNEDY.
KENTUCKY. (Wilki. 1912.)
KINCAID. (Ris. 1900.)
LEWIS. (Lewis 1906.)
LIBERTY BOND. (Ris. 1917.)
LONGFELLOW. (Ris. 1894.)
MAHAN. (Mahan 1924.)
MAJOR. (Major 1908.)
MATSLER. (Mats. 1910.)
MCCULLEY. (McCu. 1920.)
MCINTOSH. (McI. 1921.)
Mexican Papershell. BILOXI.
MEYERS. (Ram. 1917.)
MILLICAN. (Mi. 1917.)
MOBILE. (Laur. 1900.)
MONEYMAKER. (James 1898.)
MOORE. (Woot. 1900.)
NELLIS. (Arm. 1932.)
NELSON. (Nel. 1901.)
NIBLACK. (Nib. 1913.)
NORTON. (A. Nor. 1912.)
NUGGET. (Evans 1917.)
ODOM. (Odom 1920.)
OKLAHOMA. (Dard. 1914.)
OLIVER. (Ram. 1907.)
ONLIWON. (Ris. 1915.)
PABST. (Pabst 1890.)
POSEY. (Litt. 1911.)
PRESIDENT. (Grif. 1902.)
REUSS. (Reuss 1910.)
RIVERSIDE. (Ris. 1913.)
ROME. (Rome 1883.)
ROTH. (Roth 1925.)
RUSSELL. (H. Rus. 1894.)
SABINE. (Odom 1920.)
SAN SABA. (Ris. 1893.)
SAN SABA IMPROVED. (Ris. 1915.)
SCHLEY. (Delm. 1900.)
SEMINOLE. (M. Sim. 1923.)
SEPTEMBER. (Litt. 1910.)
SIROCKA. (Sir. 1917.)
SLOAN. (Ris. 1893.)
SOVEREIGN. (Ris. 1897.) *Texas Prolific.*
SQUIRREL. (Ris. 1913.) *Squirrels Delight.*
STECKLER. (J. Ste. 1900.)
STUART. (W. Stu. 1886.)
SUCCESS. (Bec. 1902.)
SUPREME. (Ris. 1923.)
TECHE. (Nel. 1885.)
Texas Prolific. SOVEREIGN.
VAN DEMAN. (W. Stu. 1890.)
VENUS. (Ris. 1913.)
WAUKEENAH. (Woot. 1900.)
WELTY. (Welty 1917.)
WESTERN. (Ris. 1915.) *Western Schley.*
WILLIAMSON. (M. Will. 1910.)
WILSON. (T.P.C. 1927.)
YOUNG. (Young 1904.)
ZENITH. (Evans 1927.)
ZINK. (Zink 1909.) *Big Z.*

Pekeanut . . . . . . SAWARRINUT

PEKOLA . . . . . . **Manilkara kauki**

PEPINO . . . . **Solanum muricatum**

PERADOCAMPO . **Eugenia klotzschiana**

PERSIMMON . . . . . **Diospyros** spp.

See also PERSIMMON, p. 474.

The Editorial Committee is in debt to the late Dr. G. A. Zimmerman, Harrisburg, Pa., for the names of American hort. var. included in this list.

Am. American (**D. virginiana** parentage).
Or. Oriental (**D. kaki** parentage).

BLACKSAPOTE. **D. ebenaster.**
COMMON P. **D. virginiana.**
COSTATA. Or.
DELMAS. Am.
EARLY GOLDEN. Am.
EUREKA. Or.
FORD. Am.
FUYU. Or. *Fuyugaki.*
GAILEY. Or.
GARRETSON. Am.
GLENWOOD. Am.
GLIDEWELL. Am.
GOLDENGEM. Am.
GOSHO. Or.
HACHIYA. Or.
HARRIS. Am.
HICKS. Am.
HYAKUME. Or.
IDA. Am.
JOSEPHINE. Am.
JUMBU. Or.
KAKI P. **D. kaki** (*chinensis; roxburghi; schitse*).
KANOKA. Or.
KAWAKAMI. Or.-Am.
LAMBERT. Am.
LONESTAR. Or.
MABOLA. **D. discolor.**
MILLER. Am.
OKAME. Or.
ORMOND. Or.
RUBY. Am.
SILKYFINE. Am.
STOUT. Am.
TABER 23. Or.
TABER 129. Or.
TAMOPAN. Or.
TANENASHI. Or.
TRIUMPH. Or.
TSURU. Or.
WOODWARD. Am.
YEDDO ICHI. Or.
YEMON. Or.
ZENGI. Or.

Peruvianalmond . . . . SAWARRINUT

PHALSA . . . . . . **Grewia asiatica**

Pignolia

Trade name used in eastern U. S. for shelled seeds of any edible Pine. See PINENUT.

PILINUT (*Javaalmond* in part) **Canarium ovatum**

PINEAPPLE . **Ananas comosus** (*sativus*)
ABACHI. *Abakka; Golden.*
CABEZONA.
CAYENNE. *Smooth Cayenne.*
CLEOPATRA. *Natal.*
SPANISH. *Red Spanish.*

Pineappleguava . . . . FEIJOA

PINENUT . . . . **Pinus**
ALEPPO P. . . . . . . **P. halepensis**
Bigcone P. . . . . . . COULTER P.
CHILGHOZA P. . . . **P. gerardiana**
COLORADO PINYON P. **P. cembroides edulis** (*P. edulis*)

PINENUT, continued
COULTER P. . . . . **Pinus coulteri**
DIGGER P. . . . . . . **P. sabiniana**
Grayleaf P. . . . . . . DIGGER P.
ITALIAN STONE P. . . . . . **P. pinea**
JEFFREY P. . . . . . . **P. jeffreyi**
KOREAN P. . . . . **P. koraiensis**
LACEBARK P. . . . . . **P. bungeana**
LIMBER P. . . . . **P. flexilis**
MEXICAN PINYON P. . **P. cembroides**
Mountain White P. WESTERN WHITE P.
Nut P. . . . MEXICAN PINYON P.
PARRY PINYON P. . **P. cembroides parryana** (*P. parryana*)
PONDEROSA P. . . . . **P. ponderosa**
Singleleaf P. SINGLELEAF PINYON P.
SINGLELEAF PINYON P. **P. cembroides monophylla** (*P. monophylla*)
SUGAR P. . . . . . **P. lambertiana**
SWISS STONE P. . . . . . **P. cembra**
TORREY P. . . . . . . **P. torreyana**
WESTERN WHITE P. . **P. monticola**
Western Yellow P. . . PONDEROSA P.
WHITEBARK P. . . . . **P. albicaulis**

PISTACHIONUT . . . . . **Pistacia** spp.

The Pistachionuts of commerce are derived from Common Pistache (P. vera) and Himalayan P. (P. integerrima).

All the below hort. var. are seed or other type clons.

AINTAB. (U.S.D.A. 1902.)
ALEMI. (U.S.D.A. 1902.)
ASHOORI. (U.S.D.A. 1902.)
BRONTE. (U.S.D.A. 1905.)
BUENZLE.
FULLER. (1906.)
KAZ. (1902.)
KOZ. (U.S.D.A. 1902.) *Walnut.*
MINASSIAN. (Minassian.)
PETERS. (Peters.)
RED ALEPPO. (U.S.D.A. selection. 1906.)
SFAX. (From Algeria U.S.D.A. 1901.)
SICILIAN. (From Italy U.S.D.A. 1903.)
TRABONELLA. (From Sicily U.S.D.A. 1905.)
Walnut. KOZ.

PITANGA (*Brazilcherry; Cayennecherry; Floridacherry; Surinamcherry*) **Eugenia uniflora** (*micheli; Stenocalyx brasiliensis; S. micheli*)

PITAYA (*Pitahaya; Pitajaya; Pitajuia; Pitalla; Pithaya*)

A group name for certain cactus fruits, especially of Acanthocereus pentagonus, Hylocereus trigonus, H. undatus, Lemaireocereus eburneus, and L. thurberi.

PITOMBA . . . **Eugenia luschnathiana** (*Phyllocalyx luschnathianus*)

PLUM . . . . **Prunus** spp.

See also PLUM, p. 488.

ABBREVIATIONS OF BOTANICAL NAMES AND CLASSIFICATIONS

Am.	**P. americana.**
Am.S.	**P. americana × P. salicina.**
Ang.	**P. angustifolia.**
Bes.	**P. besseyi.**
Cer.	**P. cerasifera.**
Dom.	**P. domestica.**
H.	Hybrid.
Hort.	**P. hortulana.**
Insit.	**P. insititia.**
M.H.	Mixed hybrid

PLUM, continued

Mun.	**Prunus munsoniana.**
Nig.	**P. nigra.**
Pr.	Prune.
Sal.	**P. salicina.**
Sim.	**P. simoni.**
Spi.	**P. spinosa.**
Subc.	**P. subcordata.**

ABUNDANCE. Sal.-Jap.
AGEN. Dom. Pr. *French; Petite.*
AITKIN. Am. (Haz. 1896.)
ALASKA.
ALBION. Dom.
ALTHANN. Dom. (Pro. 1869.)
AMERICA. Am.S. (Burb. 1898.)
ANITA. Dom.
APEX. Sal.
APPLE. Sal.-Am. (Burb. 1898.)
APRICOT. Dom.
ARCHDUKE. Dom. (Riv. 1883.)
ARCTIC. Dom. (Moor. 1881.) *Moore Arctic.*
ARKANSAS. Am.
ASSINIBOIN. Nig.
AUTUMN COMPOTE. Dom. (Riv. 1840.)
BARTLETT. Sal. Am.
BAVAY. Dom. (Esp. 1832.)
BEAUTY.
Beauty. ELPASO.
BECKY SMITH. Sal.
BEJONNIERES. Dom. (LeRoy 1827.)
BELGIAN PURPLE. Dom.
BELLE. Dom.
BERCKMANS. Sal.
BERGER. Sal.
BILONA. Sal. H. (Biles 1910.)
BLACK BULLACE. Insit.
Black Diamond. DIAMOND.
BLEEKER. Dom. (Ble. 1810.)
BLUE PERDRIGON. Dom.
BODDAERT. Dom.
Bonne St. Anne. SAINT ANNE.
Botan. OGON.
BRACKETT. Am. (Terry 1900.)
BRADSHAW. Don.
BRITTLEWOOD. Am. (T. Will. 1897.)
BRODIE. Dom. (Brod. 1903.)
BRUCE. Sal. H.
BRYANSTON. Dom.
BURBANK. Sal. (Burb. 1883.)
BURTON. Dom. Pr.
CALIFORNIA BLUE. Dom. *Vacaville Blue.*
CHABOT. Sal. (Chab. 1886.)
CHALCO. Sal. (Burb. 1898.)
CHAMBOURCY. Dom. (Bou. 1840.)
CHAMPA. Bes.
CHAMPION. Dom. (Bul. 1876.)
CHENEY. Am.
CHERESOTO. HH.
Clairac Mommoth. IMPERIAL EPINEUSE.
CLIMAX. Am.S.
CLYMAN. Dom. (Cly. 1866.)
COATES 1418. Dom. Pr. *Cox; Date Prune; Saratoga; Smith; XX.*
Coe Golden Drop. GOLDEN DROP.
COLUMBIA. Dom. (Lawr. 1842.)
COMBINATION. Sal. H.
COMPASS. M.H. (Knu. 1894.)
COOPER. H.
COPPER. Dom.
Cox. COATES 1418.
CREE. Nig. Sal.
CRITTENDEN.
CULLIN. Dom.

PLUM, continued
CZAR. Dom. (Riv. 1874.)
DAMSON.
See note under **Prunus domestica,** p. 502.
DANDY. Nig.
DATE. Dom. Pr.
Date Prune. COATES 1418.
DECAISNE. Dom. (J.&D. 1846.)
DEMONTFORT. Dom.
DESOTO. Am. (Tup. 1853.)
DIAMOND. Dom. *Black Diamond.*
DOWNING. Am. (Ter. 1882.)
DRAP D'OR. Insit.
DROPMORE BLUE.
DROPMORE GOLD.
DUANE. Dom. (Duane 1820.) *Duane Purple.*
DUARTE. Sal. H. *Indian Blood.*
EAGLE.
EARLIANA. Dom.
EARLY FUNK.
EARLY LAXTON. Dom.
EARLY RED. Dom. *Early Red Russian.*
EARLY RIVERS. Dom. (Riv. 1834.)
EARLY ROYAL. Dom. *Royale Hative.*
EARLY TOURS. Dom.
EARLY YELLOW. Dom.
ELDORADO. Sal. H.
ELEPHANT HEART. Sal. H.
ELLIOT. Am. S.
ELPASO. Ang. Mun. *Beauty.*
EMBER. M.H.
EMERALD. Am. S.
EMILIE. Dom. Eu.
EMPIRE. Dom.
ENGLEBERT. Dom. (Sche. 1855.)
ENGLISH DAMSON. Insit.
ENGRE. Sal.
ESPEREN. Dom. (Esp. 1830.)
ETOPA. Bes. × Sal.
EXCELSIOR. Am. S. (Tabor 1887.)
EZAPTAN. Bes. × Sal.
Fellenberg. ITALIAN PRUNE.
FIEBING. M.H.
FIELD. Dom. (Willa. 1889.)
FIRST. M.H.
FLAMING DELICIOUS. Sal. H.
FLICKINGER. Am. S.
FOREST GARDEN. Am. (Hare 1862.)
FOREST ROSE. Am.
FORMOSA. Sal. H.
FRANCES.
FREEMAN. Dom. (Free. 1890.)
FREESTONE. Insit.
FRENCH. Insit. Damson Group.
French. AGEN.
FROGMORE. Insit.
FROST GAGE. Dom.
FURST. Dom.
GAVIOTA. Am. S.
GEORGESON. Sal.
GERMAN PRUNE. Dom. Pr.
GIANT. Dom. (Burb. 1893.)
GLASS. Dom. (Glass 1881.)
GLOUCESTER.
GOLDEN. Am. S. (Burb. 1887.)
GOLDEN BEAUTY. Am. S.
GOLDEN DROP. Dom. (Coe 1809.) *Coe Golden Drop; Silver Prune.*
GOLIATH. Dom.
GONZALES. Am. S.
GRAND DUKE. Dom. (Riv. 1876.)
GREAT YELLOW. Sal. H.
Green Gage. REINE CLAUDE.
GRENVILLE.
Gros. POND.

PLUM, continued
GUEII. Eu.
GUTHRIE LATE. Dom. (Gut. 1855.)
HALE. Sal. (Burb. 1893.)
HALL. Dom.
HAMMER. Am. (Ter. 1888.)
HAND. Dom. (Hand 1790.)
HANSKA. Am. Sim.
HAPPINESS. Sal. H.
HARRIET. Dom. (Riv. 1870.)
HAWKEYE. Am. (Terry 1882.)
HENNEPIN. H.
HONEYMOON. Sal. H.
HUDSON. Dom. *Purple Egg.*
HULINGS. Dom. (Key. 1828.)
HUNGARIAN. Dom. Pr.
ICKWORTH. Dom. (Kni. 1841.)
IMPERATRICE. Dom.
IMPERIAL EPINEUSE. Dom. Pr. *Clairac Mommoth; Imperial.*
IMPERIAL GAGE. Dom. (Pri. 1790.)
INCA. M.H.
Indian Blood. DUARTE.
INKPA. Am. × Sim.
IRBY. Hort.
ITALIAN PRUNE. Dom. Pr. *Fellenberg.*
JAPEX. Sal. H. (Burb. 1893.)
JEFFERSON. Dom. (J. Buel 1825.)
JUICY. Am. S. (Burb. 1893.)
JUNE BLOOD. Sal. H.
JUNE REDSKIN. Sal. H.
JUNIOR BRUCE. Ang. Sal.
KAGA. Am. Sim.
KAHINTA. Am. S.
KELSEY. Sal.
KERR. Sal.
KING DAMSON. Insit.
KIRKE. Dom.
LACRESCENT. M.H.
LAFAYETTE. Dom.
LAIRE. Am.
LARGE ENGLISH. Dom.
LATCHFORD. Dom.
LATE DUARTE. M.H.
LATE MIRABELLE. Insit.
LATE MUSCATELL. Dom.
LATE ORLEANS. Dom.
LATE SANTA ROSA.
LAWRENCE. Dom. (Lawr. 1843.)
LEEDS. Nig. Sal.
LINCOLN. Dom.
LOMBARD. Dom. (Platt 1830.)
LUCOMBE. Dom. (Luc. 1825.)
LUNN. Dom.
MALLARD. Dom.
MAMMOTH. Nig.
MAMMOTH CARDINAL. Sal. H.
MANKATO. Am.
MANSAN.
MAQUOKETA. Hort.
MARIPOSA. M.H.
MARU. Sal. (Burb. 1885.)
MAYNARD. Sal. H. (Burb. 1897.)
MCCARTNEY.
MCLAUGHLIN. Dom. (McL. 1840.)
MCRAE. Sal.
MCROBERT. Nig.
MENDOTA. H.
METHLEY. Sal.
MICHELSON.
MIDDLEBURG. Dom.
MILLER SUPERB. Dom. (C. Mill. 1889.)
MILTON. Am. (Ter. 1885.)
MINA. Am.
MINER. Am. (Dodd 1814.)

PLUM, continued
MIRABELLE. Dom. Insit.
MIRACLE. Insit. × Dom. (Burb. 1899.)
MONARCH. Dom. (Riv. 1885.)
MONITOR. Am. S.
MONROE. Dom. (Dur. 1850.)
MONTMORENCY. Dom.
Moore Arctic. ARCTIC.
MORDEL. Nig.
MORDENA. Bes. H.
MOREMAN. Am. (Wayl. 1881.)
MOROCCO. Dom.
MOUND. Am. S.
MOUNT ROYAL. Dom.
MUNSON. Ang.
NECTARINE. Dom.
NEVERFAIL. Am.
NEWARK. Dom.
NEWMAN. Mun.
NEW ULM. Am. (Hei. 1890.)
NICHOLAS. Dom. *White Nicholas.*
NICOLLET. H.
NONA. Sal. × Mun.
OCCIDENT. Sal. (Burb. 1899.)
OCHEEDA. Am. (Hardo. 1872.)
OCTOBER. Sal. (Burb. 1892.)
ODEGARD. Nig.
OGON. Sal. *Botan.*
OJIBWAY.
OKA. Bes. H.
OLSON. Nig.
OMAHA. Am. S.
OPATA. HH.
ORANGE. Dom.
OREN. Am. (Oren 1878.)
ORLEANS. Dom.
OSAGE. Mun.
OULLINS. Dom. (Cor. 1866.)
PACIFIC. Dom. Eu. (Bul. 1875.)
PADRE. Sal. H. (U.S.D.A. 1939.)
PALATINE. Dom. (Best 1760.)
PAPAGONE. Dom. Pr.
PEACH. Dom.
PEARL. Dom. (Burb. 1898.)
PEMBINA. H.
PERAL.
PETERS. Dom.
Petite. AGEN.
POND. Dom. *Gros.*
POOLE PRIDE. Am. (Kroh 1885.)
POTTAWATTAMIE. Am.
PRESIDENT. Dom.
Pride. SHELDRAKE.
Prince of Wales. WALES.
PRINLEW. Dom.
Purple Egg. HUDSON.
PURPLE FLAME.
PURPLE GAGE. Dom.
QUACKENBOSS. Dom. (Groot 1828.)
QUEENMAY. Dom.
RADISSON. Am. S.
RAYNES. Dom.
REAGAN. Hort. × Am.
RED ACE. Sal. H.
RED APRICOT. Dom.
RED CANNONBALL. Sal. H.
RED DIAPER. Dom.
RED JUNE. Sal.
RED MAGNUMBONUM. Dom.
RED ROSA. Sal.
REDWING. Am. S.
REEVES.
REINE CLAUDE. Dom. *Green Gage.*
RICHLAND. Dom.
Robe; Robe de Sergeant. SERGEANT.
ROLLINGSTONE. Am.

PLUM, continued
ROWLEY. Dom. (Lord 1852.)
Royale Hative. EARLY ROYAL.
ROYAL TOURS. Dom.
SAINT ANNE. Dom. *Bonne St. Anne.*
SAINT ANTHONY. Sal. H.
SAINT CATHERINE. Dom.
SAINT JULIEN. Insit.
SAINT MARTIN. Dom.
SANNOIS. Dom.
SANSOTO. Bes. × Am.
SANTA ROSA. Jap.
SAPA. HH.
Saratoga. COATES 1418.
SATSUMA. Sal. (Burb. 1889.)
SAUNDERS. Dom. (Arris 1883.)
SCHLEY. Mun.
SERGEANT. Dom. Pr. *Robe; Robe de Sergeant.*
SHARKEY. Sal.
SHELDRAKE. Dom. (J. Hunt 1895.) *Pride.*
SHIPPER. Dom.
SHIRO. Am.S. M.H. Eu. (Burb. 1899.)
SHROPSHIRE. Insit. Damson Group.
Silver Prune. GOLDEN DROP.
SIMON. Sal.-Sim.
SIMPSON. Dom.
SIX WEEKS. Sal.-Am.
Smith. COATES 1418.
SMITH ORLEANS. Dom. Eu. (Smith 1825.)
SOPHIE. Mun. (Kerr 1892.)
SPAULDING. Dom. (Garr. 1888.)
SPLENDOR. Dom. Eu.
STANDARD. Dom. Eu. Pr.
STANLEY.
STANTON. Dom.
STEVENS. Am.
STODDARD. Am. (Baker 1875.)
STONELESS. Insit.
STRANG.
STUART. Dom. Eu. Pr.
SUGAR. Dom. Eu. Pr. (Burb. 1899.)
SUPERIOR. Sal. H.
SURPRISE. Am. H. (Penn. 1882.)
TAWENA. Sal. Am.
TECUMSEH. H.
TENNANT. Dom. Eu. (Ten. 1893.)
TERRELL. Jap.-A. (Ter. 1895.)
TERRY. Am.
TOKA. Sim. Am.
TOKATA. Am. Sim.
TOMTHUMB. Bes. H.
TONKA. Sal. × Am.
TRAGEDY. Dom. Eu. Pr. (O. Run. 1880.)
TRANSPARENT. Dom. (Lafay 1836.)
UNDERWOOD. M.H.
UNGARISH. Dom.
UTAH. Bes. H. (Johs. 1870.)
UTILITY. Dom.
Vacaville Blue. CALIFORNIA BLUE.
VALLEY RIVER. Am.
VICTORIA. Dom.
VORONESH. Dom. Eu.
WACHAMPA. H.
WALES. Dom. (M. Chapm. 1830.) *Prince of Wales.*
WANETA. Sal. × Am.
WANGENHEIM. Dom.
WASHINGTON. Dom. Eu.
WAYLAND. Am. (Way. 1875.)

PLUM, continued
WEAVER. Am. (Wea. 1873.)
WHITAKER. Am.
WHITE BULLACE. Insit.
WHITE DAMSON. Insit.
WHITE IMPERATRICE. Dom.
White Nicholas. NICHOLAS.
WHITE PERDRIGON. Dom.
WICKSON. Sal. H. Jap. (Burb. 1895.)
WILDGOOSE. Mun. Am. (McCa. 1820.)
WILLARD. Sal.
WILSON. Am.
WINNESBORO. Am.
WINNIPEG. Nig.
WINONA. Sal. × Am.
WOLF. Am. (Wolf 1852.)
WOOD. Am. (J. Wood 1894.)
WORLD BEATER. Hort. (Tin. 1838.)
WYANT. Am. (Wyant 1866.)
XX. COATES 1418.
YAKIMA. Dom. Eu.
YELLOW EGG. Dom. Eu.
YELLOW GAGE. Dom. (W. Pri. 1783.)
ZUMBRA. M.H.

∞ PLUMCOT . . . **Prunus armeniaca × P. salicina**
RUTLAND.
SHARPE.
STANFORD.

∞ PLUMPEACH . . . **Prunus persica × P. salicina**

POMEGRANATE (*Granada*) **Punica granatum**
AMLASI.
ASWAD.
HALU.
PAPER-SHELL.
PURPLESEED.
RAGAWI.
RHODA.
SALIMI.
SPANISH RUBY. *Purple.*
SWEET.
WONDERFUL.

Pomerack . . . . OHIA

PONDAPPLE (*Alligator Apple; Corkwood; Custardapple; Mangrove Annona*) . . . . . . **Annona glabra**

Poshte . HARDSHELL CUSTARDAPPLE

POTATOBEAN (*Groundnut*) **Apios americana** (*tuberosa*)

Powderflaskfruit . . . . . AFRAEGLE

PRICKLYPEAR . . . . . **Opuntia** spp.
See also INDIANFIG; TUNA.

∞ PROCIMEQUAT **Fortunella hindsi** × ∞ LIMEQUAT

PRUNE
A name applied to varieties of Garden Plum (Prunus domestica), whose fruit will dry without fermentation and is usually cooked before eating.

PULASAN (*Capulasan; Kapoelasan; Pulassan*) . **Nephelium mutabile**

PUMMELO (*Pomelo; Pompelmous; Shaddock*) . **Citrus grandis** (*maxima*)
₵AMOY.
₵BAHAMA.
₵BLOOD.

PUMMELO, continued
₵HORTON.
₵KAO PANNE. *White Flat.*
₵KAO PHUANG. *White Tassel.*
₵MAMMOTH.
₵MOANALUA.
₵PANDAN BENER.
₵PANDAN WANGI.
₵PINK.
₵SIAM.
₵SOUR SHADDOCK.
₵THONGDEE.
₵TRESCA.
White Flat. ₵KAO PANNE.
White Tassel. ₵KAO PHUANG.

QUANDONGNUT . **Fusanus acuminatus**

Queenslandnut . . . . . MACADAMIA

QUINCE . . . . . . **Cydonia oblonga**
ANGERS.
Apple. ORANGE.
Bourgeat. DE BOURGEAT.
CHAMPION.
CHAMPION ORANGE.
DE BOURGEAT. *Bourgeat.*
FULLER. (Ful. 1868.)
MEECH. (Meech 1883.)
MISSOURI.
ORANGE. *Apple.*
PINEAPPLE. (Burb. 1899.)
REA. (Rea.) *Reas Mammoth.*
SMYRNA.
VAN DEMAN. (Burb.)

RAISIN . . . . **Vitis** spp.
A name applied to dried grapes, especially of a high sugar content.

RAMBUTAN (*Ramboetan; Rambotang; Rambustan*) **Nephelium lappaceum**

RAMONTCHI (*Governorsplum*) **Flacourtia indica** (*ramontchi*)

RASPBERRY . . . . . . **Rubus** spp.
See also RASPBERRY, p. 524.

Bl. Black. Red Red.
Pur. Purple.

Dr. Darrow reports that the vars. prefixed by an asterisk (*) are no longer in cultivation.

ADAMS 87. Red.
ADAMS 101. Red.
ANTWERP. Red. (Bri. 1817.)
BLACKBEAUTY. Bl. (Cowen 1924.)
BLACKPEARL. Bl. (Krum. 1905.) *Pearl.*
BRANT. Pur. (N.Y.S. 1913.)
BRIGHTON. Red. (Sau. 1887.)
BRILLIANT. Red. (Coll. 1900.)
BRISTOL. Bl. (N.Y.S. 1934.)
CALIFORNIA SURPRISE.
CARDINAL. Pur. (Grie. 1888.)
CAROLINE. Red. (Gar. 1877.) Yellow fruit.
CAYUGA. Red. (N.Y.S. 1911.)
CHIEF. Red. (M.E.F. 1930.)
COLOSSUS. Red. (Str. 1892.)
COLUMBIAN. Pur. (Tho. 1888.)
COUNT. Red. (Sau. 1887.)
CUMBERLAND. Bl. (Mil. 1896.)
CUTHBERT. Red. (Cut. 1865.)
DIKE. Red. (Dike 1933.)
DIXIE. Red. (N.C.S. 1936–37.)
DUNDEE. Bl. (N.Y.S. 1927.)

RASPBERRY, continued
EATON. Red. (Eaton 1885.)
*EMPIRE. Red. (War. 1904.)
ERSKINE. Red. (Nor. 1903.)
EVANS. Bl. (N.Y.S. 1935.)
GOLDEN QUEEN. Red. (Sto. 1882.) Yellow fruit.
GREGG. Bl. (Gregg 1866.)
*HAYMAKER. Pur. (Hay. 1893.)
HERBERT. Red. (Whyte 1887.)
*HILBORN. Bl. (Hil. 1878.)
*HIRAM. Red. (Bradt 1891.)
HONEYSWEET. Bl. (Kat. 1912.)
HOOSIER. Bl. (Dunn 1895.)
INDIANSUMMER. Red. (N.Y.S. 1936.)
JUNE. Red. (N.Y.S. 1897.)
KANSAS. Bl. (Grie. 1884.)
KING. Red. (Thom. 1892.)
LAFRANCE. Red. (Alius 1912.)
LATHAM. Red. (M.B.F. 1908.) *Redpath.*
LLOYD GEORGE. Red. (Ket.)
LOGAN. Bl.
*LOUDON. Red. (Lou. 1884.)
MAHOOD. Bl.
MARCY. Red. (N.Y.S. 1936.)
MARLBORO. Red. (Cay. 1880.)
*MILLER. Red. (Mil. 1885.)
MONROE. Red. (N.Y.S. 1932.)
MUNGER. Bl. (Mung. 1890.)
NAPLES. Bl. (N.Y.S. 1921.)
NEWBURGH. Red. (N.Y.S. 1929.)
NEWMAN. Red.
*NEWMAN No. 20. Red. (Newm. 1907.)
*NEWMAN No. 23. Red. (Newm.)
*OHIO. Bl. (VanD. 1865.)
OHTA. Red. (S.D.S. 1906.)
OLDER. Bl. (Older 1872.)
ONTARIO. Red. (N.Y.S. 1909.)
OTTAWA. Red.
Pearl. BLACKPEARL.
*PERFECTION. Red. (Lou.)
PLUM FARMER. Bl. (Far. 1890.)
POTOMAC. Pur. (U.S.D.A. 1932.)
PYNEROYAL. Red. (Pyne 1913.)
QUILLEN. Bl. (Qui. 1917.)
RANERE. Red. (L.N.C. 1912.) *St. Regis.*
Redpath. LATHAM.
RIDEAU. Red.
ROYAL PURPLE. (Gir. 1898.) *Royal.*
RUBY. Red. (War. 1896.)
SARAH. Red. (Sau. 1893.)
SENECA. Red. (N.Y.S. 1911.)
*SHAFFER. Pur. (Sha. 1871.)
SHUTTLEWORTH. Bl.
SODUS. Pur. (N.Y.S. 1935.)
SOUVENIR DE DESIRE BRUNEAU. Red.
STARLIGHT. Red. (S.D.S. 1922.)
St. Regis. RANERE.
SUNBEAM. Red. (S.D.S. 1906.)
SUNRISE. Red. (U.S.D.A. 1940.)
*SUPERLATIVE. Red. (E.&B. 1892.)
SURPRISE. Red. (Coo. 1901.)
*SYRACUSE. Red. (G.N.C. 1900.)
TAHOMA. Red.
TAYLOR. Red. (N.Y.S. 1935.)
TENNESSEE AUTUMN. (Drain 1935.)
*TYLER. Bl. (Tyler 1876.)
ULSTER. Red. (N.Y.S. 1933.)
VAN FLEET. Red. (VanF. 1911.)
VIKING. Red. (H.S.V. 1914.)
WASHINGTON. Red.
WEBSTER. Pur. (N.Y.S. 1926.)
*WELCH. Red.
WINFIELD. Bl. (Kle. 1902.)

Rattlenut . . . . WATERCHINKAPIN

∞ REGRANUT (*Intermediate Walnut*) ∞ **Juglans intermedia**

∞ ROFAUSTRIME **Microcitrus australasica × M. australis**

¢SYDNEY

ROSEAPPLE (*Jamrosade*) . . **Syzygium jambos** (*Caryophyllus j.; Eugenia j.*)

ROSEMYRTLE, DOWNY . **Rhodomyrtus tomentosa** (*Myrtus t.*)

Rowantree . EUROPEAN MOUNTAINASH

RUKAM . . . . . . **Flacourtia rukam**

SANSAPOTE . . . . . **Licania platypus**

SANTOL **Sandoricum koetjape** (*indicum*)

SAPODILLA . . . . . . **Achras zapota** (*Sapota achras; S. zapotilla*)

SAPOTE (*Mamey Colorado; Mammee Sapota; Marmaladefruit; Marmaladeplum*) **Calocarpum** spp.; **C. sapota** (*mammosum; Lucuma mammosa*)
BLACKSAPOTE . **Diospyros ebenaster**
GREEN S. . . . **Calocarpum viride**
WHITESAPOTE . . **Casimiroa edulis**
WOOLLYLEAF WHITESAPOTE **Casimiroa tetrameria**
YELLOWSAPOTE . **Lucuma salicifolia**

SAPUCAIANUT (*Paradisenut*) **Lecythis zabucajo**

SAWARRINUT (*Pekeanut; Peruvian-almond; Souarinut*) **Caryocar nuciferum**

SERVICEBERRY (*Juneberry*) **Amelanchier** spp.

Shaddock . . . . PUMMELO

SINGHARANUT . . . **Trapa bispinosa**

Snakewood Tree . . . TRUMPETTREE

SOAPBERRY, SOUTHERN (*Wingleaf S.*) **Sapindus saponaria**

SONCOYA . . . . . . **Annona purpurea**

Souarinut . . . . SAWARRINUT

SOURSOP (*Guanabana*) **Annona muricata**
MOUNTAIN S. . . . . **A. montana**

SPANISHCHERRY . . **Mimusops elengi**

Spanishlime . . . . . MAMONCILLO

Spanishplum . . . . . RED MOMBIN

STARAPPLE (*Cainito*) **Chrysophyllum cainito**
GREEN. PURPLE.

St. Johnsbread . . . . CAROB

STRAWBERRY . . . . . **Fragaria** spp.
See also STRAWBERRY, p. 600.

Dr. Darrow reports that the vars. prefixed by an asterisk (*) are no longer in cultivation.

ABERDEEN. (Kuhns 1923.)
*ABINGTON. (Blan. 1895.)
*ALDRICH.
*AMANDA. (Mumma 1904.)
*AMERICUS. (Roc. 1905.)
*ARIZONA.
AROMA. (Cruse 1889.)
*AUGUSTA. (Moore 1870.)
BEACON. (N.Y.S. 1911.)
BEAUTY. (Hayn. 1892.)
BEAVER. (Bea. 1925.)
BEDERWOOD. (Wood 1881.)
BELLMAR. (U.S.P.S. 1923.)

STRAWBERRY, continued
BELT. (Belt 1888.) ***William Belt.***
*BEST. (Far. 1918.)
BIGLATE. (Davis 1913.)
BLAKEMORE. (U.S.P.S. 1923.)
BLISS. (N.Y.S. 1911.)
BOUQUET. (N.Y.S. 1911.)
BORDEN.
BRANDYWINE. (E. Ing. 1889.)
BRITISH QUEEN. (Myott 1841.)
BRITISH SOVEREIGN.
*BUBACH. (Bub. 1882.)
*BURRILL. (Reas. 1909.)
*CALEDONIA. (N.Y.S. 1929.)
CAMDEN. (N.Y.S. 1931.)
*CAMPBELL. (Camp. 1910.)
*CASSANDRA. (C.E.F. 1906.)
CATO. (N.Y.S. 1929.)
CATSKILL. (N.Y.S. 1924.)
*CHAMPION. (Neff 1860.)
*CHARLES. (Hann. 1905.)
CHASKA.
CHESAPEAKE. (Parks 1903.)
*CHIPMAN. (Chi. 1901.)
*CLARA. (Kuhns 1903.)
*CLARIBEL.
CLARK. (Clark 1875.)
CLERMONT. (N.Y.S. 1925.)
*COLUMBIA. (Wild 1900.)
*COMMONWEALTH. (Mon. 1900.)
*CONFEDERATION.
CORVALLIS. (O.S.S. 1930.)
*CRESCENT. (Parm. 1870.)
CULVER. (N.Y.S.)
DAKOTA. (S.D.S.)
DAYBREAK. (U.S.D.A. 1931.)
*DELICIOUS. (Mor. 1914.)
*DESDEMONIA. (C.E.F. 1913.)
*DICK. (G. Gow. 1908.)
*DOLLAR. (Fel. 1885.)
DORSETT. (U.S.D.A. 1923.)
DRYWEATHER. (N.D.S. 1925.)
*DUCHESS OF YORK. (Bar. 1875.)
*DUFFIN.
DULUTH. (M.E.F. 1909.)
DUNLAP. (Reas. 1890.)
*EARLYBIRD. (Riehl 1906.)
*EARLY HATHAWAY. (Huba. 1892.)
*EARLY JERSEYGIANT. (VanF. 1907.)
*EARLY PROLIFIC.
EASYPICKER. (M.E.F. 1921.)
*ECHO. (Woodl. 1901.)
ELEANOR ROOSEVELT. (U.S.D.A. 1931.)
*EMPIRE ALLRED.
*EMPIRESTATE.
ETTERSBURG 121. (Etter 1905.)
EXCELSIOR. (Huba. 1890.)
FAIRFAX. (U.S.P.S. 1923.)
FAIRMORE. (U.S.D.A. 1933.)
*FIRSTQUALITY. (J. Gow. 1910.)
*FORD. (Gra. 1913.)
FRUITLAND.
GANDY. (Gandy 1885.)
GEM. (Fre. 1911.)
Gibson. PARSONS.
GLENMARY. (J. Ing. 1890.)
*GOLDDOLLAR. (Mills 1906.)
*GOLDEN PALACE.
*GOODLUCK. (Ped. 1904.)
*GOVERNOR FORT.
GRAND CHAMPION.
*GRANDPRIZE. (McCo. 1915.)
GREEN MOUNTAIN.
HARVEST KING.
HAVERLAND. (Hav. 1882.)
HEFLIN.

STRAWBERRY, continued
*HENRY. (Wads.)
HOWARD 17. (A. How. 1909.) *Premier*.
HOWARD SUPREME. (E. How. 1929.)
HEBRON. (C.S.)
*HERITAGE. (Her. 1902.)
*HOWELL. (T. Howe. 1880.)
*IMPROVED DUNLAP.
*JESSIE. (Lou. 1880.)
JOE. (J. Bla. 1899.)
*JOHN.
*JOSSELYN.
JOYCE.
JUCUNDA. (Salt. 1859.)
KANNER KING. (K.B.N. 1932.)
KING GEORGE. (Lax. 1916.)
*KITTIE RICE. (Bea. 1890.) *Rice*.
KLONDIKE. (Cloud 1890.)
LATE STEVENS. (A. Stev. 1897.) *Stevens Late*.
*LAVERGNE.
*LOUISE. (Hal. 1886.)
LUCKY STRIKE. (Tow. 1915.)
LUPTON. (Lup. 1905.)
*MACGOWAN.
MAGOON. (Mag. 1890.)
MARSHALL. (Ewell 1890.) *Oregon*.
*MARVEL. (Schu. 1922.)
*MASCOT. (Hanb. 1908.)
MASSEY. (U.S.D.A. 1934.)
MASTODON. (Voer 1917.)
MAYTIME. (U.S.D.A. 1931.)
MCALPINE. (Hau. 1909.)
*MCCABE.
*MCCLINTOCK. (K.A.S. 1923.)
*MCKENSIE.
*METEOR. (Hunt. 1907.)
MICHEL EARLY. (Mic. 1886.)
MINNEHAHA.
MINNESOTA. (M.B.F. 1909.)
*MINUTEMAN. (Whe. 1895.)
MISSIONARY. (Gohn 1900.)
*MONEYMAKER. (Hath. 1897.)
*MORSE. (Moody 1911.)
*MYER. (Myer 1906.)
NARCISSA. (U.S.P.S. 1923.)
*NEW EVERBEARING.
*NEWHOPE.
NEWYORK. (Tan. 1890.)
*NIAGARA.
NICK OHMER. (Bea. 1898.)
NORTH STAR. (U.S.D.A. 1938.)
*O.A.C. EARLY.
Oregon. MARSHALL.
*OREM. (Arndt 1908.)
*OSHKOSH.
OZARK. (Shull 1902.)
*PANAMERICAN. (Coop. 1898.)
PARSONS. (Pars. 1890.) *Gibson; Parsons Beauty*.
PATHFINDER. (N.J.S. 1936.)
PAUL JONES. (W. Joh. 1898.)
PAXTON.
*PEERLESS. (Coop. 1906.)
*POCOMOKE. (Ham. 1902.)
PORTIA. (C.E.F. 1906.)
Premier. HOWARD 17.
PROGRESSIVE. (Roc. 1908.)
*PROLIFIC. (N.Y.S. 1899.)
REDGOLD. (Gard. 1925.)
*REDHART. (U.S.P.S. 1923.)
REDHEART. (U.S.D.A. 1931.)
Rice. KITTIE RICE.
RIDGELEY.
*ROBERT.
ROCKHILL. (Roc. 1918.) *Wayzata*.

STRAWBERRY, continued
*ROUGHRIDER. (Lea. 1893.)
ROYAL SOVEREIGN. (Lax. 1891.)
SAMPLE. (G. Gow. 1894.)
*SHARPLESS. (Shar. 1872.)
SHELTON.
*SHROPSHIRE.
SIMCOE.
SOUTHLAND. (U.S.P.S. 1920.)
*SPLENDID. (Sum. 1892.)
*STANLEY. (Stan. 1896.)
STARBRIGHT. (U.S.D.A. 1931.)
Stevens Late. LATE STEVENS.
*ST. MARTIN. (Grat. 1908.)
*SUCCESS. (Hanna. 1897.)
*SUPERB. (Coop. 1908.)
*SUPERGIANT.
*SUPERIOR. (Tow. 1888.)
*TENNESSEE. (Hod. 1892.)
TENNESSEE SUPREME.
THOMPSON. (Thomp. 1894.)
*TRIOMPH. (DeJ. 1855.) *Triomph Degand*.
ULRICH.
*UNCLE JIM. (Dor. 1898.)
*VALERIA. (C.E.F. 1906.)
VANGUARD. (H.S.V. 1913.)
*VICTORIA. (Tro. 1849.)
WARFIELD. (Warf. 1882.)
Wayzata. (Roc. 1918.) ROCKHILL.
*WHATAFLAVOUR.
William Belt. BELT.
*WILLIAMS. (Will. 1890.)
WILSON. (Wils. 1851.)
*WOOLVERTON. (Lit. 1891.)
*WORLDWONDER. (Pars. 1906.)
WRAY RED. (Wray 1894.)
*WRIGHT SEEDLING.
WYONA. (A. Joh. 1922.)

SUGARAPPLE (*Custardapple; Sweetsop*) **Annona squamosa**

Surinamcherry . . . . . . PITANGA

SWAMPORANGE **Limnocitrus; L. littoralis**

TABOG (*Swinglea*). **Swinglea glutinosa**

TAMARIND . . . . **Tamarindus indica**
Races of Tamarind are sometimes distinguished as "East Indian" and "West Indian," but the validity of that terminology is very questionable.

∞ TANGELO **Citrus paradisi × C. reticulata**
₵CLEMENT.
₵LAKE. *Orlando*.
₵MINNEOLA.
₵NACOTEE.
Orlando. ₵LAKE.
Pink Tangelo. ₵WEKIWA.
₵SAMPSON.
₵SANJACINTO.
₵SEMINOLE.
₵THORNTON.
UMATILIA.
₵WEKIWA. *Pink Tangelo*.
₵WILLIAMS.
₵YALAHA.

∞ TANGERINE . . **Citrus reticulata** HV.

∞ TANGOR **Citrus reticulata × C. sinensis**
KING.
₵TANGERONA.
₵TEMPLE.
₵UMATILLA.

TREETOMATO . . **Cyphomandra betacea**
PINKFRUIT.
REDFRUIT.

TRIFOLIATE-ORANGE (*Hardyorange*) **Poncirus trifoliata**

TROPICAL-ALMOND (*India-almond*) **Terminalia catappa**

TRUMPETTREE (*Snakewood Tree*) **Cecropia palmata**

TUNA . . . . **Opuntia** spp.
A name applied to the edible fruit of certain large-fruited Opuntia spp. of Mexico and the Southwest belonging to O. tuna and allied spp.

TUNGNUT . . . . . . **Aleurites fordi**

Umkokolo . . . . KEIAPPLE

UVALHA . . . . . . **Eugenia uvalha**

Viapple . . . . AMBARELLA

Vinelime . . . . PARAMIGNYA

VOAVANGA . . . . . **Vangueria** spp., especially **V. madagascarensis**

WALNUT. . . . . **Juglans** spp.

WALNUT, EASTERN BLACK **Juglans nigra**
All these hort. var. are clons, probably for the most part selected seedlings.

ADAMS. (H. Ad. 1923.)
ALLEN. (G. Allen 1923.)
BARNHART. (Barnh. 1933.)
BECK. (Harr. 1928.)
BENGE. (Kir. 1910.)
BENTON. (Bent. 1936.)
BOELLNER. (Boell. 1932.)
BROWN. (W. Br. 1933.)
CLARK. (F. Cl. 1934.)
COE. (F. Coe 1934.)
COOPER. (M. Coop. 1929.)
COWLE. (Cowle 1933.)
CREITZ. (Creitz 1926.)
CRESCO. (Bents 1930.)
DOUGHERTY. (Dough. 1930.)
EDGEWOOD. (B. Walk. 1930.)
EDMUNDS. (Edm. 1934.)
EDRAS. (G. Ad. 1926.)
FREEL. (Freel 1929.)
GRUNDY. (Roh. 1927.)
HAVICE. (R. Havice 1933.)
HEPLER. (Hep. 1931.)
HOOVER. (Hoov. 1933.)
HOWELL. (Drake 1928.)
IMPIT. (Gel. 1929.)
JANSON. (Jan. 1933.)
KALAMAZOO. (Korn 1937.)
KETTLER. (Kett. 1934.)
KORN. (Korn 1928.)
LAMB. (Lamb 1926.)
LEARN. (Learn 1934.)
LIONBERGER. (Lion. 1931.)
MARION. (Freel 1929.)
MARKEY. (Mark. 1933.)
MCMILLAN. (McM. 1932.)
MCPHERSON. (McPh. 1934.)
METCALF. (Freel 1929.)
MICHIGAN. (Korn 1939.)
MINTLE. (Mint. 1929.)
MONTEREY. (Host. 1931.)
MURPHEY. (Murph. 1933.)
MYERS. (Myers 1926.)
OAKES. (Oakes 1932.)
OHIO. (C. Clark 1915.)
PACE. (N. Drake 1937.)
PATTERSON. (Patt. 1926.)
PINECREST. (Miller 1931.)
ROHWER. (Roh. 1926.)
SIFFORD. (Sif. 1934.)
SNYDER. (Grah. 1934.)
SPARROW. (Spar. 1935.)
SPEER. (Speer 1931.)

WALNUT, EASTERN BLACK, continued
STABLER. (Litt. 1916.)
STAMBAUGH. (Stam. 1926.)
STERLING. (Korn. 1932.)
TASTERITE. (Grah. 1927.)
TEN EYCK. (Ten E. 1915.)
THOMAS. (Thomas 1881.)
THROP. (Throp 1926.)
TODD. (Todd 1934.)
TRITTEN. (Trit. 1933.)
WALDSMITH. (Walds. 1929.)
WANDA. (G. Ad. 1932.)
WEBER. (Weber 1932.)
WETZEL. (Wetz. 1929.)
WIARD. (Wiard 1926.)
WOODALL. (Wooda. 1907.)
WORTHINGTON. (Freel 1928.)
WRIGHT. (Wri. 1934.)

WALNUT, PERSIAN (*English Walnut*) **Juglans regia**
ACME. (Wills. 1910.)
ALPINE. Eu. (F. Gil. about 1890.) *Wonder of the Alps.*
Alpine. LANCASTER.
ANDREW. (Gel. 1938.)
ANDRUS. (Andr. 1911.)
AURAND. (Aur. 1912.)
AVON. (A. Thom. 1916.)
BARNES. (Bar. 1911.)
BARTHERE. Eu. (F. Gil. 1871.) *Barthera.*
BAUM. (Baum about 1920.) *Baum Franquette.*
BECK. (Beck 1932.)
BEDFORD. (Stoke 1936.)
Bijou. GANT.
BISHOP. (Bis. 1906.)
BLACKMER. (Maut. about 1915.) *Colusa; Leib; Leib Special; Mautner; Meridian; Moneymaker; Sutter County; Vaughn; Vaughns Pride; Westfall; Woodland Perfection.*
BOSTON. (Jones 1913.)
BRESLAU. (Bush about 1935.) *Russ.*
BROADVIEW. (Gel. 1930.)
Burbank. SANTA ROSA.
BURLINGTON. (Jones 1914.)
BURSON. (Burs. 1933.)
CALAVETTE. (Price before 1910.)
CALOMA. (W. Reed 1915.)
CAMMACK. (Colu. 1937.)
CARPATHIAN. Eu. (Crath about 1923.)

Group name.

CHABERTE. Eu. (F. Gil. 1871.)
CHAMBERS. (Bush about 1935.)
CHANGLI. China. (U.S.D.A. 1908.)
CHASE. (Chase about 1895.)
CHELAN. (Huls. 1910.)
CHICOETTE. (Bidw. 1910.)
CLUSTER. Eu. (F. Gil. 1875.)
CLUSTER PRAEPARTURIENS. Eu. (F. Gil. 1875.)
COLUMBIA. (F. Gil. 1893.) *Columbus.*
Colusa. BLACKMER.
CONCORD. (Coa. 1908.)
CRATH. Eu. (Crath about 1923.)
Cutleaf. LACINIATED.
DEPENDAHL. (Dep. 1930.)
EHRHARDT. (Ehr. 1906.)
EL MONTE. (Rich. about 1908.)
EUREKA. (Ware about 1903.)
FAVORITE. (T. Smi. before 1910.)
Fernleaved. LACINIATED.
Fertile. PRAEPARTURIENS.
FRANMAY. (Trib. 1912.)

WALNUT, PERSIAN, continued
FRANQUETTE. Eu. (F. Gil. 1871.)
GANT. Eu. (F. Gil. 1871.) *Bijou.*
GEISSLER. (Gei. 1926.)
GLADY. Oregon. (Before 1919.)
GRANDE. (W.P.N. 1934.)
GRENOBLE.

Type name for walnuts from France, especially from Grenoble district.

GROVE. (And. about 1912.)
HALE. (W. Hale 1903.) *Hales.*
HALL. (L. C. Hall 1910.)
HARTLEY. (Hart. 1923.)
HENNEMAN. (Hen. 1918.)
HIGHFLYER. Eng.
HOLDEN. (Hol. 1911.)
HONEYDEW. (Leib. 1910.)
HULSEMAN. (Huls. 1913.)
JOCKETT. (Jock. 1932.)
JOURNEAY. (Price 1910.)
KAGHAZI. Eu. (About 1870.) *Persian.*
KEESLING. (Kees. about 1912.)
KING. (Bush 1926.)
KIRK. (Kirk 1911.)
KLONDYKE.

Group term in southern California for very large walnuts of Bijou type.

LACINIATED. Eu. (F. Gil. before 1900.) *Cutleaf; Fernleaved.*
LANCASTER. (Rush 1913.) *Alpine.*
LANE. (Lane about 1910.)
LANFRAY. Eu. (F. Gil. about 1895.)
LARSEN. (Lars. 1933.)
Leib; Leib Special. BLACKMER.
LEWIS. (D. Lew. 1933.)
LINDY. (Gel. 1934.)
MACKENZIE. (Gel. about 1935.)
Mautner. BLACKMER.
MAYETTE. Eu. (F. Gil. 1871.) *Mayette Blanche.*
MAYQUETTE. (Trib. about 1905.)
McDERMID. (McDer. 1933.)
Meridian. BLACKMER.
MESANGE. Eu. (F. Gil. 1871.)
MEYER. (U.S.D.A. 1927.)
MEYLAN. Eu. (F. Gil. 1891.)
MISSION.

Type name, southern California.

Moneymaker. BLACKMER.
MONSTREUSE. (C.N.C. before 1910.)
NEBO. (Rush 1910.)
NEFF. (Neff about 1905.)
ONTARIO. (Lewe. 1914.)
Ornamental. WEEPING.
PARISIENNE. Eu. (F. Gil. 1875.)
PARRY. Eu. (F. Gil. probably 1875.)
PAYNE. (Payne about 1898.)
PAYOU. (Payne about 1904.)
Persian. KAGHAZI.
PLACENTIA. (Hind about 1893.)
POE. (Poe 1883.)
POMEROY. (Pom. about 1900.)

Type name.

POORMAN. Calif. (Before 1898.)
PRAEPARTURIENS. Eu. (F. Gil. 1871.) *Fertile.*
PRIDE OF VENTURA. (Tuck. about 1910.)
PRINCE. (T. Pri. about 1905.)
PROLIFIC. (Dish 1899.)
RAPIER. (Gel. 1934.)
RITCHIE. (Gel. 1926.)
ROBERTS. (N. Ger. 1938.)
RUSH. (Rush 1903.)
Russ. BRESLAU.

WALNUT, PERSIAN, continued
SAN JOSE. (Wiltz about 1907.) *San Jose Mayette; Wiltz.*
SANTA BARBARA SOFTSHELL.

Group term.

SANTA ROSA. (Burb. 1882.) *Burbank.*
SEEANDO. (Colu. 1930.)
SEROTINA. Eu. (F. Gil. 1871.)
SHEFFIELD. (Hoop. 1912.)
SINCLAIR. (Hoop. 1911.)
SORRENTO. Eu. (F. Gil.) *St. John.*
SPENCER. (Gel. 1926.)
St. John. SORENTO.
Sutter County. BLACKMER.
SWISS. (Joho 1910.) *Swiss Mayette.*
TEAGUE. (About 1900.)
TREYVE. Eu. (F. Gil. about 1900.)
Triple X Mayette. XXX MAYETTE.
UNCLE JOE. (Hers. 1930.)
Vaughn; Vaughns Pride. BLACKMER.
VIRGINIA. (Titus 1928.) *Virginia Favorite.*
VOLGA. (J. Budd 1903.)
VOUREY. Eu. (F. Gil. before 1890.)
WARD. (W. H. Ward about 1897.)
WARE. (Ware before 1914.) *Wares Prolific.*
WASHINGTON. (Huls. 1924.)
WASSON. (Was. about 1932.)
WATT. (Gel. 1934.)
WEEPING. Eu. (F. Gil. 1895.) *Ornamental.*
Westfall. BLACKMER.
WILLSON. (Wills. 1909.) *Willson Wonder.*
Wiltz. SAN JOSE.
Wonder of the Alps. ALPINE.
Woodland Perfection. BLACKMER.
XXX MAYETTE. (Cover about 1935.) *Triple X Mayette.*
ZIMMERMAN. (W. Zim. 1933.)

WALNUT, SIEBOLD . **Juglans sieboldiana** and HEARTNUT, **J. s. cordiformis**
H. Heartnut. S. Siebold Walnut.

All these hort. var. are either seedling selections or hybrids.

BATES. H. (Bates 1919.)
BOURNE. H. (Bourne 1932.)
CALENDAR. H. (Gel. 1928.)
CANOKA. H. (Gel. 1938.)
CARDINELL. S. (Card. 1932.)
ENGLISH. S. (Eng. 1932.)
EVERS. S. (Evers 1932.)
FAUST. H. (Jones 1918.)
FODERMAIER. H. (G. Smi. 1936.)
GELLATLY. H. (Gell. 1932.)
IONA. H. (Gel. 1932.)
KING. H. (Hers. 1928.)
KORNI. H. (Gel. 1932.)
LANCASTER. H. (Jones 1916.)
MACKENZIE. H. (Gel. 1932.)
RITCHIE. H. (Rit. 1918.)
STRANGER. H. (Bates 1919.)
WALTERS. H. (Gel. 1926.)
WRIGHT. H. (Wri. 1932.)

WALNUT HYBRIDS, MISCELLANEOUS **Juglans spp.**

JUGLANS
∞ **bixbyi** (*cinerea* × *sieboldiana*) ∞ BUARTNUT (*Bixby Walnut; Butterjap; Ignotum*)
₵BARNEY. (Gel. 1938.)
₵CREITZ. (Rusk 1929.)
₵CROFTER. (Gel. 1938.)

WALNUT HYBRIDS, MISC., continued
¢FISH. (Gel. 1938.)
¢HELLAM. (Gel. 1936.)
¢HELMICK. (Helm. 1929.)
¢KINGSBURY. (Gel. 1936.)
¢LESLIE. (Gel. 1938.)
¢MITCHELL. (Mitch. 1930.)
¢OKANDA. (Gel. 1936.)
∞**californica** × **nigra** . ∞NIGORNICA
∞**californica** × **regia** ∞REGIFORNICA (*Paradox* in part)
¢ROYAL. (Burb. 1897.)
¢WAGNER. (Wagner 1907.)
∞**hindsi** × **nigra**
∞**hindsi** × **regia** . . . . ∞REGINDSI (*Paradox* in part)
∞**intermedia** (*nigra* × *regia*) ∞INTERMEDIATE (*Paradox* in part)
¢O'CONNOR. (O'Connor 1921.)
¢VILMORIN. Eu. (F. Gil. 1877.)
∞**nigra** × **sieboldiana** ∞NIGROLDIANA
¢CORDIBLACK. (Bates 1920.)
∞**notha** (*regia* × *sieboldiana*) ∞PERBOLD WALNUT
¢CORDING. (Bates 1920.)
¢SIEBOSIAN. (Bates 1920.)

WAMPEE . . . . **Clausena**
ANISE-OIL W. . . . **C. anisum-olens**
CHINESE W. . . . . . **C. lansium**
INDIA W. . . . . . **C. dentata dulcis**

WATERCHESTNUT . . . **Trapa natans**

WATERCHINKAPIN (*Rattlenut*) . **Nelumbium pentapetalum** (*luteum*)

WATERLEMON (*Yellow Granadilla*) **Passiflora laurifolia**

WATERMELON . . . **Citrullus vulgaris**

WATERNUT . . **Eleocharis tuberosa**

WENZELIA . . . . **Wenzelia**
ARCHBOLDS W. . . **W. archboldiana**
FIJI W. . . . . . . **W. kambarae**
PHILIPPINE W. . . . . **W. brevipes**

WHITESAPOTE (*Casimiroa; Matasano; Mexican Apple*) . **Casimiroa** spp. especially **C. edulis**
COLMAN.
FLOURNOY.
JOHNSON GOLDEN (*C. edulis*).
MALTBY (*C. edulis*).
MAX GOLDEN.
PIKE (*C. edulis*).
SUEBELLE (*C. edulis*).
WILSON (*C. edulis*).
WOOLLYLEAF W. **C. tetrameria.**

White Walnut . . . . . BUTTERNUT

WILDLEMON . . . . . **Rheedia edulis**
See BAKUPARI.

WILDLIME . . . . . **Microcitrus** spp.
See also FINGERLIME.
AUSTRALIAN ROUND W. **M. australis**
QUEENSLAND W. . . . **M. inodora**

WINTERGREEN **Gaultheria procumbens**

WOODAPPLE . . . . **Feronia limonia**

YELLOWSAPOTE . . **Lucuma salicifolia**

FRUIT GROUP COMMON NAMES

Cit. Citrus Fruits
Dec. Deciduous Fruits
Sm. Small Fruits
Sub. Subtropical (or Tropical) Fruits

ABIU. Sub. **Pouteria caimito** (*Lucuma c.*)
ACTINIDIA. Sm. . **ACTINIDIA** species
AEGLOPSIS. Cit. . **AEGLOPSIS** species
AFRAEGLE (*Powderflaskfruit*). Cit. **AFRAEGLE** species

FRUIT GROUP COMMON NAMES, continued

AKEE. Sub. . . . . . **Blighia sapida**
Alligator Apple . . . . . PONDAPPLE
Alligator Pear . . . . . . AVOCADO
Amatungula . . . . CARISSA
AMBARELLA (*Otaheiteapple* in part; *Viapple*). Sub. . . **Spondias cytherea**
Antidesma . . . . BIGNAY
APPLE. Dec. . . . . **MALUS** species, especially **M. pumila**
APRICOT. Dec. . . **Prunus armeniaca**
ATALANTIA. Cit. **ATALANTIA** species
∞ATEMOYA. Sub. ∞**Annona cherimola** × **A. squamosa**
AVOCADO (*Alligator Pear*). Sub. **Persea americana**
BAELFRUIT. Cit. . . **Aegle marmelos**
BAKUPARI. Sub. **Rheedia brasiliensis**
BAKURI. Sub. . . . **Platonia insignis**
BALSAMOCITRUS. Cit. **Balsamocitrus dawei**
BANANA. Sub. . . . . **MUSA** species, especially **M. paradisiaca** and var. **sapientum**
BARBADOSCHERRY. Sub. **Malpighia glabra**
BARBERRY. Sm. . **BERBERIS** species
Batokoplum . . . . LOUVI
BIGNAY (*Antidesma*). Sub. **Antidesma bunius**
BILIMBI. Sub. . . . **Averrhoa bilimbi**
BIRIBA. Sub. . . . **Rollinia deliciosa**
BLACKBERRY. Sm. . **RUBUS** species
BLACKSAPOTE. Sub. **Diospyros ebenaster**
BLUEBERRY. Sm. **VACCINIUM** species
Brazilcherry . . . . PITANGA
Braziliancherry . . . . GRUMICHAMA
BREADFRUIT. Sub. . **Artocarpus altilis** (*communis; incisus*)
BRUSHCHERRY, AUSTRALIAN. Sub. **Eugenia paniculata australis**
BUCKBERRY . . . **Gaylussacia ursina**
BUFFALOBERRY. Sm. **Shepherdia argentea**
Bullocks Heart . . . . CUSTARDAPPLE
BURDEKINPLUM. Sub. **Pleiogynium solandri**
CABELLUDA. Sub. . **Eugenia tomentosa**
Cainito . . . . STARAPPLE
CANISTEL (*Eggfruit*). Sub. **Lucuma nervosa**
CANTALOUP (*Cantaloupe*) **Cucumis melo cantalupensis**
CAPULIN . **Prunus serotina salicifolia**
CARAMBOLA. Sub. **Averrhoa carambola**
CARISSA (*Amatungula; Natalplum*). Sub. . . . . **Carissa grandiflora**
CAROB (*St. Johnsbread*). Sub. **Ceratonia siliqua**
Casimiroa . . . . . . WHITESAPOTE
Cayennecherry . . . . . . PITANGA
CERIMAN. Sub. **Monstera deliciosa**
Ceylongooseberry . . . . KITEMBILLA
CHERIMOYA. Sub. **Annona cherimola**
CHERRY. Dec. . . . **PRUNUS** species
CHERRYORANGE. Cit. **CITROPSIS** species
Chinese-date . . . . JUJUBE
CHOKEBERRY. Dec. . **ARONIA** species
CHOKECHERRY. Dec. **Prunus virginiana**
∞CICITRANGE. Cit. ∞CITRANGE × **Poncirus trifoliata**
∞CITRADIA Cit. **Citrus aurantium** × **P. trifoliata**
∞CITRANDIRIN. Cit. **C. reticulata** × **P. trifoliata**

FRUIT GROUP COMMON NAMES, continued

∞CITRANGE. Cit. **Citrus sinensis** × **P. trifoliata**
∞CITRANGEDIN. Cit. ∞CITRANGE × ∞KUMANDARIN
∞CITRANGEQUAT. Cit. ∞CITRANGE × **Fortunella** spp.
∞CITRANGEREMO. Cit. ∞CITRANGE × **Eremocitrus glauca**
∞CITREMON. Cit. **Citrus reticulata** × **Poncirus trifoliata**
CITRON. Cit. . . . . **Citrus medica**
CITRONMELON **Citrullus vulgaris citroides**
∞CITRUMELO. Cit. **C. paradisi** × **Poncirus trifoliata**
∞CITRUMQUAT. Cit. **Fortunella** spp. × **P. trifoliata**
CITRUS. Cit.. . . . . **CITRUS** species
Here belong Citron, Grapefruit, Lemon, Lime, Orange, Pummelo, etc.
CLYMENIA. Cit. . **Clymenia polyandra**
COCOPLUM (*Icaco*). Sub. **Chrysobalanus icaco**
Corkwood . . . . PONDAPPLE
CORNELIANCHERRY. Sm. . **Cornus mas**
CRABAPPLE. Dec. . . **MALUS** species
CRANBERRY. Sm. **VACCINIUM** species
CRANBERRYBUSH, AMERICAN. Sm. **Viburnum trilobum**
CURRANT. Sm. . . . . **RIBES** species
CURUBA. Sub. . **Passiflora maliformis**
CUSTARDAPPLE (*Bullocks Heart*). Sub. **Annona reticulata**
This species is the Custardapple of commerce.
CUSTARDAPPLE, HARDSHELL (*Poshte*). Sub. . . . . **Annona scleroderma**
Custardapple. PONDAPPLE; SUGARAPPLE
DATE. Sub. . . . **Phoenix dactylifera**
DESERTLIME. Cit. **EREMOCITRUS** species
DEWBERRY. Sm. . . **RUBUS** species
Duhat . . . . JAMBOLAN
DURIAN. Sub. . . . **Durio zibethinus**
Eggfruit . . . . CANISTEL
ELAEAGNUS. Sm. **ELAEAGNUS** species
ELDERBERRY. Sm. **SAMBUCUS** species
EMBLIC (*Myrobalan* in part). Sub. **Phyllanthus emblica**
∞EREMOLEMON. Cit. **Citrus limon** × **Eremocitrus glauca**
∞EREMORADIA. Cit. **C. aurantium** × **E. glauca**
∞EREMORANGE. Cit. **C. sinensis** × **E. glauca**
∞FAUSTRIMEDIN. Cit. . ∞KUMANDARIN × **Microcitrus australasica**
FEIJOA (*Pineappleguava*). Sub. **Feijoa sellowiana**
FERONIELLA. Cit. . **FERONIELLA** spp.
FIG. Dec. . . . . **Ficus carica**
FINGERLIME. **MICROCITRUS** (in part)
See also WILDLIME.
Floridacherry . . . . . . PITANGA
GENIP (*Marmaladebox*). Sub. **Genipa americana**
GHOSTLIME. Cit. . **BURKILLANTHUS**
GLYCOSMIS. Cit. **GLYCOSMIS** species
GOOSEBERRY. Sm. . . **RIBES** species
Governorsplum . . . . RAMONTCHI
Granada . . . . POMEGRANATE
GRANADILLA. Sub. **PASSIFLORA** species

FRUIT GROUP COMMON NAMES, continued

Grape. Sm. . . . . . **VITIS** species
Grapefruit. Cit. . . . **Citrus paradisi**
Grumichama (*Braziliancherry; Grumixam[ier]a*). Sub. . **Eugenia dombeyi**
This plant is frequently misidentified as E. brasiliensis (*Stenocalyx b.*).
Guabiroba. Sub. **Abbevillea fenzliana** (*Campomanesia f.*)
Guanabana . . . . Soursop
Guava. Sub. . . . **PSIDIUM** species
Guisaro. Sub. . . . . **Psidium molle**
Hardyorange . . . Trifoliate-orange
Hawthorn (*Mayhaw*). Dec. **CRATAEGUS** species
Hedgethorn . . . **Carissa arduina**
Hesperethusa. Cit. **HESPERETHUSA** species
Hondapara. Sub. . . . **Dillenia indica**
Honeyberry. Sub. . . **MELICOCCA** (*Melicoccus*)
Huckleberry. Sm. **GAYLUSSACIA** species
Icaco . . . . Cocoplum
∞ Ichandarin. Cit. **Citrus ichangensis × C. reticulata**
∞ Ichangelo. Cit. **C. grandis × C. ichangensis**
Ilama. Sub. . . . **Annona diversifolia**
Imbe. Sub. . . **Garcinia livingstonei**
Imbu. Sub. . . . **Spondias tuberosa**
Indianfig. Sub. **Opuntia ficus-indica**
Jaboticaba. Sub. **MYRCIARIA** species
Jakfruit (*Jackfruit; Jak*). Sub. **Artocarpus heterophyllus** (*integrifolius*)
Jambolan (*Duhat; Jambolanplum*). Sub. **Syzygium cumini** (*jambolanum; Eugenia c.; E. jambolana*)
Jamrosade . . . . Roseapple
Japanesemedlar . . . . . . Loquat
Jujube (*Chinese-date*). Sub. **Zizyphus jujuba**
Juneberry . . . . . . Serviceberry
Kafirorange. Sub. **Strychnos spinosa**
Kafirplum. . **Harpephyllum caffrum**
Kaki . . . . Oriental Persimmon
Karanda. Sub. . . . **Carissa carandas**
Keiapple (*Umkokolo*). Sub. **Dovyalis caffra** (*Aberia c.*)
Kitembilla (*Ceylongooseberry*). Sub. **Dovyalis hebecarpa** (*Aberia gardneri*)
∞ Kumandarin. Cit. **Citrus reticulata × Fortunella spp.**
Kumquat. Cit. **FORTUNELLA** species
Langsat. Sub. **Lansium domesticum**
∞ Lemandarin. Cit. **Citrus limon × C. reticulata**
Lemon. Cit. . **Citrus limon** (*limonia*)
∞ Lemonime. Cit. **C. aurantifolia × C. limon**
Lime. Cit. . . . **Citrus aurantifolia**
Limeberry. Cit. . . **Triphasia trifolia**
∞ Limequat. Cit. . . **Citrus aurantifolia × Fortunella species**
Lingaro. Sub. **Elaeagnus philippensis**
Lipote . . . . . . **Eugenia currani**
Longan. Sub. . . . **Euphoria longan** (*Dimocarpus l.; Nephelium longana*)
Loquat (*Japanese-medlar*). Sub. **Eriobotrya japonica** (*Photinia j.*)
Louvi (*Batokoplum*). Sub. **Flacourtia inermis**
Lychee (*Litchi*). Sub. **Litchi chinensis**
Mabola (*Mabolo*). Sub. **Diospyros discolor**
Mahonia. Sm. . . **MAHONIA** species
Malayapple . . . . Ohia

FRUIT GROUP COMMON NAMES, continued

Mamey (*Mamey de Santo Domingo; Mammeeapple*). Sub. **Mammea americana**
Mamey Colorado . . . . . . Sapote
Mamey de Santo Domingo . . Mamey
Mammee Sapota . . . . . . Sapote
Mamoncillo (*Spanishlime*). Sub. **Melicocca bijuga**
Mango. Sub. . . . **Mangifera indica**
Mangosteen. Sub. **Garcinia mangostana**
Mangrove Annona . . . Pondapple
Manzanilla. Sub. **Crataegus mexicana**
Marang. Sub. **Artocarpus odoratissimus**
Marmaladefruit; Marmaladeplum Sapote
Matasano . . . . . . Whitesapote
Mayhaw . . . . Hawthorn
Medlar. Dec. . **Mespilus germanica**
Merope. Cit. . . **Merope angulata**
Merrillia. Cit. **Merrillia caloxylon**
Mexican Apple . . . . Whitesapote
Micromelum. Cit. **MICROMELUM** species
Mombin
Red M. (*Spanishplum*) **Spondias purpurea**
Yellow M. (*Hogplum; Jobo*) **S. mombin** (*lutea*)
Monanthocitrus. Cit. **MONANTHOCITRUS** species
Mountainash, European (*Rowantree*). Dec. . . . . . . **Sorbus aucuparia**
Mulberry. Dec. . . **MORUS** species
Muskmelon . . . . . **Cucumis melo**
Myrobalan . . . . Emblic
Not to be confused with Myrobalan Plum (Prunus cerasifera) nor with the commercial nut Tropical-almond (also called Myrobalan) derived from Tropical-almond Terminalia (Terminalia catappa).
Natalplum . . . . Carissa
Nectarine. Dec. . . **Prunus persica nectarina** (*Amygdalus p. n.; Persica nucipersica*)
Ohia (*Malayapple; Otaheiteapple* in part; *Pomerack*). Sub. **Syzygium malaccense** (*Caryophyllus malaccensis; Eugenia m.; Jambosa m.*)
Olive. Sub. . . . . . **Olea europaea**
Orange. Cit. . . . **CITRUS** species
Orangeaster. Cit. **PLEIOSPERMIUM** species
∞ Orangequat. Cit. **Citrus nobilis unshiu × Fortunella** species
Oregongrape. Dec. **Mahonia aquifolium**
Otaheiteapple . . . Ambarella; Ohia
Otaheite-gooseberry. Sub. **Phyllanthus acidus**
Oxanthera. Cit. **OXANTHERA** species
Pamburus. Cit. **Pamburus missionis**
Paniala. Sub. . **Flacourtia jangomas**
Papaw . . . . Pawpaw
Papaya. Sub. . . . . **Carica papaya**
Paraguava . . . . . . **Britoa acida**
Paramignya (*Vinelime*) **PARAMIGNYA** species
Passionfruit . . Purple Granadilla
Pawpaw (*Papaw*). Dec. **ASIMINA** species
Peach. Dec. . . . . **Prunus persica**
Pear. Dec. . . . . . **PYRUS** species

FRUIT GROUP COMMON NAMES, continued

Pekola. Sub. . . . **Manilkara kauki**
Pepino. Sub. . **Solanum muricatum**
Peradocampo. Sub. **Eugenia klotzschiana**
Persimmon. Dec. **DIOSPYROS** species
Phalsa. Sub. . . . **Grewia asiatica**
Pineapple. Sub. **Ananas comosus** (*sativus*)
Pineappleguava . . . . Feijoa
Pitanga (*Brazilcherry; Cayennecherry; Floridacherry; Surinamcherry*). Sub. **Eugenia uniflora** (*micheli; Stenocalyx brasiliensis; S. micheli*)
Pitaya (*Pitahaya; Pitajaya; Pitajuia; Pitalla; Pithaya*). Sub.
A group name for certain cactus fruits, especially of Acanthocereus pentagonus, Hylocereus trigonus, H. undatus, Lemaireocereus griseus, and L. thurberi.
Pitomba. Sub. **Eugenia luschnathiana** (*Phyllocalyx luschnathianus*)
Plum. Dec. . . . . **PRUNUS** species
∞ Plumcot. Dec. **Prunus armeniaca × P. salicina**
Pomegranate (*Granada*). Dec. **Punica granatum**
Pomerack . . . . Ohia
Pondapple (*Alligator Apple; Corkwood; Custardapple* in part; *Mangrove Annona*). Sub. . **Annona glabra** (*laurifolia; palustris*)
Poshte . Hardshell Custardapple
Powderflaskfruit . . . . . Afraegle
Pricklypear. Dec. . **OPUNTIA** species
∞ Procimequat. Cit. **Fortunella hindsi** × ∞ Limequat
Prune . . . **Prunus domestica vars.**
See note in **FRUIT AND EDIBLE NUT NAMES.**
Pulasan (*Pulassan*). Sub. **Nephelium mutabile**
Pummelo (*Shaddock*). Cit. **Citrus grandis** (*maxima*)
Quince. Dec. . . . **Cydonia oblonga**
Raisin . . . . **VITIS** species
See note in **FRUIT AND EDIBLE NUT NAMES.**
Rambutan (*Ramboetan; Rambotang; Rambustan*). Sub. **Nephelium lappaceum**
Ramontchi (*Governorsplum*). Sub. **Flacourtia indica** (*ramontchi*)
Raspberry. Sm. . . . **RUBUS** species
∞ Rofaustrime. Cit. . . . **Microcitrus australasica × M. australis**
Roseapple (*Jamrosade*). Sub. **Syzygium jambos** (*Caryophyllus j.; Eugenia j.*)
Rosemyrtle, Downy. Sub. **Rhodomyrtus tomentosa** (*Myrtus t.*)
Rowantree . European Mountainash
Rukam. Sub. . . . **Flacourtia rukam**
Sansapote. Sub. . . **Licania platypus**
Santol. Sub. **Sandoricum koetjape** (*indicum*)
Sapodilla. Sub. . . . **Achras zapota** (*sapota; Sapota achras; S. zapotilla*)
Sapote (*Mamey Colorado; Mammee Sapota; Marmaladefruit; Marmaladeplum*). Sub. **CALOCARPUM** spp.; **C. sapota** (*mammosum; Lucuma mammosa*)
See also Blacksapote, Whitesapote, and Yellowsapote. Green Sapote is C. viride.

FRUIT GROUP COMMON NAMES, continued
Serviceberry (*Juneberry*). Sm. **AMELANCHIER** species
Shaddock . . . . Pummelo
Snakewood Tree . . . Trumpettree
Soapberry, Southern (*Wingleaf S.*). Sub. . . . . . **Sapindus saponaria**
Soncoya. Sub. . . . **Annona purpurea**
Soursop (*Guanabana*) . **Annona muricata**
Mountain S. Sub. . . **A. montana**
Spanishcherry. Sub. **Mimusops elengi**
Spanishlime . . . . . Mamoncillo
Spanishplum . . . . . Red Mombin
Starapple (*Cainito*). Sub. **Chrysophyllum cainito**
St. Johnsbread . . . . Carob
Strawberry. Sm. **FRAGARIA** species
Sugarapple (*Custardapple* in part; *Sweetsop*). Sub. . **Annona squamosa**
Surinamcherry . . . . . . Pitanga
Swamporange. Cit. **LIMNOCITRUS** species
Sweetsop . . . . Sugarapple
Tabog. Cit. . . **SWINGLEA** species
Tamarind. Sub. . **Tamarindus indica**
∞ Tangelo. Cit. **Citrus paradisi × C. reticulata**
∞ Tangerine. Cit. **Citrus reticulata** hv.
∞ Tangor. Cit. **Citrus reticulata × C. sinensis**
Treetomato. Sub. **Cyphomandra betacea**
Trifoliate-orange (*Hardyorange*). Cit. **Poncirus trifoliata**
Trumpettree (*Snakewood Tree*). Sub. **Cecropia palmata**
Tuna. Sub. . . . **OPUNTIA** species
Umkokolo . . . . Keiapple
Uvalha. Sub. . . . **Eugenia uvalha**
Viapple . . . . Ambarella
Vinelime . . . . . . Paramignya
Voavanga. Sub. . **VANGUERIA** species
Wampee. Cit. . . **Clausena lansium**
Waterlemon (*Yellow Granadilla*). Sub. **Passiflora laurifolia**
Watermelon . . . **Citrullus vulgaris**
Wenzelia. Cit. . **WENZELIA** species
Whitesapote (*Casimiroa; Matasano; Mexican Apple*). Sub. **CASIMIROA** spp., especially **C. edulis**
Wildlemon. Sub. . . **Rheedia edulis**
Wildlime. Cit. **MICROCITRUS** species
See also Fingerlime.
Wintergreen. Sm. **Gaultheria procumbens**
Woodapple. Cit. . . **Feronia limonia**
Yellowsapote. Sub. **Lucuma salicifolia**

Ft. Thompsongrass . . . . Knotgrass: **Paspalum distichum**

FUCHS'IA . . . . Fuchsia
alpes'tris . . . . Amazon F.
arbores'cens (*syringaeflora*) Lilac F.
bacilla'ris . . . . Babyrose F.
bolivia'na (*braziliensis*) . . Bolivia F.
coccin'ea . . . . Scarlet F.
colenso'i . . . . Colenso F.
con'ica . . . . . . **F. magellanica c.**
coralli'na . . . . . . **F. exoniensis**
cordifo'lia . . . . . . Guatemala F.
corymbiflo'ra . . . . Vine F.
—al'ba . . . . White V.F.
dis'color . . . . . . **F. magellanica d.**
excortica'ta . NewZealand Tree F.

FUCHSIA, continued
exonien'sis (*corallina*) Coral Fuchsia
ful'gens . . . . Flame F.
globo'sa . . . . . . **F. magellanica g.**
grac'ilis . . . . . . **F. magellanica g.**
∞ **hy'brida** Hort. (*?fulgens × ?magellanica*; ∞ *speciosa* Hort.) . . ∞ Common F.
lycioi'des . . . . **F. rosea**
magellan'ica . . . . . Magellan F.
—con'ica (*F. conica*) . . . . Cone F.
—dis'color (*F. discolor*) . Falkland F.
—globo'sa (*F. globosa*) Roundbud F.
—grac'ilis (*F. gracilis*) . . Naiad F.
—riccarto'ni (*F. riccartoni*) Riccarton F.
microphyl'la . . . . . Littleleaf F.
parviflo'ra . . . . Littleflower F.
procum'bens . . . . . . Trailing F.
rose'a (*lycioides*) . . . . . . Rose F.
serratifo'lia . . . . . . Peruvian F.
∞ *specio'sa* Hort. . . ∞ **F. hybrida Hort.**
splen'dens . . . . Candy F.
syringaeflo'ra . . . . . **F. arborescens**
thymifo'lia . . . . . . Thymeleaf F.
triphyl'la . . . . . . Threeleaf F.
venus'ta . . . . Colombia F.
virga'ta
The identity of this plant is obscure.

Common names and hort. var. (clons) of **Fuchsia:**

DF. Doubleflowered.
Ref. Reflexed.
SD. Semidouble.
SF. Singleflowered.
TH. Triphylla Hybrids.
Tra. Trailers.

Abbey Farges. DF.
Alfred Rambeau. DF.
Alice Eastwood. SD.
Alice Hoffman. SF.
Alsace. DF.
Amazon F. **F. alpestris.**
Amelia Auban. SF.
Amy Lye. SF.
Andre Lenotre. DF.
Annie Earle. SF.
Antigone. SF.
April. SF.
Arabella. SF.
Aurora Borealis. SF. *Speciosa.*
Aurora Superba. SF.
Autumnale. SF. *Meteor.*
Avalanche. DF.
Aviator. SF. *Deiner.*
Babyrose F. **F. bacillaris.**
Balkon. SF.; Tra.
Ballet Girl. DF.
Baron Vonketteler. DF.
Beauty of Exmouth. DF.
Beauty of Swanley. SF. *Villa Hebe.*
Beauty of Trowbridge. SF.
Bella Forbes. DF.
Beranger. DF.
Berliner Kind. DF.
Bertrade. DF.
Betty. SD.
Beverly Hills. SF.
Blue Gown. DF.
Bolivia F. **F. boliviana.**
Brentwood. DF.
Brilliant. SF.
Brutus. SF.
Buffon. DF.
Burningbush. SF.
Caledonia. SF.
California. SF.
Camellia. DF.

FUCHSIA, continued
Candy F. **F. splendens.**
Carmencita. SF.
Carminequeen. SF.
Carnea. SF.
Cascade. SF.; Tra.
Charming. SF.
Christmas Gem. TH.
Cinderella. SF.
Clair Delune. SF.
Claretcup. SF.; Tra.
Clio. DF.
Clipper. SF.
Coccinea Florean. SF.
Colenso F. **F. colensoi.**
Colombia F. **F. venusta.**
∞ Common F. ∞ **F. hybrida.**
Cone F. **F. magellanica conica.**
Constance. DF.
Coral F. **F. exoniensis.**
Coralle. TH.
Corallina.
Countess of Aberdeen. SF. *Schneewitschen.*
Covent Garden. SF.
Crystal. DF.
Cupid. SF.
Cupidon. SF.
Dainty Lady. DF.
Dalliance. SF.
Daniel Lambert. SF.
Danube Blue. DF.
Decherville. DF.
Deiner. Aviator.
Diament. DF.
Diane. SF.
Display. SF. *Karl Blanc; Prince Charming; Prince Noir.*
Dollar Princes. DF.
Don Pedro. SF.
Dr. Behring. DF.
Dr. (*John*) Gallwey. DF.
Dr. Vance. DF.
Duchess of Albany. SF.
Duchess of Edinburgh. DF.
Durango. SF.
Earl of Beaconsfield. SF.
Elaine. SF.
Elegance. SF.
Elm City. DF.
Elsa. DF.
Elysee. SF.
Emile Zola. SF.
Eppsi. SF.
Erecta Novelty. SF.
Ernest Renain. SF.
Evelyn Little. SF.
Falkland F. **F. magellanica discolor.**
Fascination. DF. *Irwins Giant Pink.*
Firefall. SF.
Fireflush. SF.
Flame F. **F. fulgens.**
Flocon Deneige. DF.
Formosissima. SF.
Fra Elbertus. DF.
Gartenmeister Bonstedt. TH.
General Roberts. DF.
George Barr. SF.
George Portesi. DF.
Gerbert. DF.
Geroldstein. SF.
Gladiator. DF.
Glendale. SF.
Gloire Demarchi. DF.
G. Monk. DF.
Graffe Witte. SF.
Grenadier. DF.

FUCHSIA, continued
GUATEMALA F. **F. cordifolia.**
GUY DAUPHINE. DF.
GYPSY QUEEN. DF.
H. A. GREENE. TH.
HALLOWE'EN. SF.; Tra.
HAPHAZARD. DF.
HARLEQUIN. SF.
H. DUTTERAIL. DF.
HENRI POINCARE. SF.
HERON. SF.
Irwins Giant Pink. FASCINATION.
ISTAR. SF.
IVOIRE. DF.
JANE EVANS. SF.
JULES DALOGES. DF.
JULIETTE ADAMS. DF.
JULIUS. SF.
JUNE CAROLYN. SF.
Karl Blanc. DISPLAY.
KATE HAYES. SF.
KITTY O'DAY. DF.
KYANOS. DF.
LACEDEMONE. DF.
LADY CLAIRE. TH.
LADY HEYTESBURY. SF.
LA FRANCE. DF.
LAVENDER BEAUTY. DF.
LEEANNA BELL. SF.
LENA. DF.
L'ENFANT PRODIGUE. SF.
LEO DELIBES. SF.
LEROBUSTE. DF.
LEVERKUSEN. TH.
LIBUSE. SF.
LILAC F. **F. arborescens.**
LILAC QUEEN. DF.
LITTLE BEAUTY. SF.
LITTLEFLOWER F. **F. parviflora.**
LITTLELEAF F. **F. microphylla.**
LONGIPEDUNCULATA. SF.
LORD BYRON. SF.
LOS ANGELES. SF.
LOVELINESS. SF.
LUCIENNE BREVAL. SF.
LUSTRE IMPROVED. SF.
LYES EXCELSIOR. SF.
MAGELLAN F. **F. magellanica.**
MARINKA. SF.
MARJORIE HILGERS. SF.
MARVEL. DF.
MARY. TH.
MARY LOU. DF.
MASTERPIECE. SF.
MAUVE BEAUTY. DF.
Meteor. AUTUMNALE.
MICHELANGELO. DF.
MINNESOTA. SF.
MISS B. HESSE. DF.
MISS JACQUELINE. SF.
MISS JOAN HADDOCK. SF.
MME. AUBIN. SF.
MME. BRUANT. DF.
MME. CORNELISSEN. SF.
MME. DANJOUX. DF.
MME. J. FEUILLET. DF.
MME. JULES CHRETIEN. DF.
MME. LANTELMA. DF.
MME. THIBAUD. SF.
MME. VANDERSTRASS. SF.
MOLESWORTH. DF.
MONSIEUR MORLIERE. DF.
MONTEREY. SF.
MORNING MIST. SF.
MR. GLADSTONE. DF.
MRS. DESMOND. DF.
MRS. JOHN D. FREDERICK. SF.

FUCHSIA, continued
MRS. MARSHALL. SF.
MRS. POPPLE. SF.
MRS. RUNDLE. SF.
MRS. VICTOR REITER. SF.; Tra.
MRS. W. H. WARE. SF.
MURIEL. SF.
MURIEL EVANS. SF.
NAIAD F. **F. magellanica gracilis.**
NESTOR. SF.
NEWZEALAND TREE F. **F. excorticata.**
NULAN. SF.
OLYMPIA. SF.
PASTEUR. DF.
PATRICIA. SF.
PATTY EVANS. DF.
PAUL CAMBON. DF.
PERKY. SF.
PERLE MAUVE. DF.
Perle Rose. PINK PEARL.
PERUVIAN F. **F. serratifolia.**
PHENOMENAL. DF.
PINK PEARL. DF. *Perle Rose.*
PRESIDENT. SF.
PRESIDENT FELIX FAURE. DF.
PRIDE OF EXETER. DF.
PRIDE OF ORION. DF.
Prince Charming. DISPLAY.
Prince Noir. DISPLAY.
PRINCE OF MAY. DF.
PRINCE OF ORANGE. SF.
PUMILA. SF.
PURPLE GEM. DF.
PYTHAGORE. DF.
QUEEN OF BEAUTIES. SF.
QUERY. SF.
RACINE. DF.
RHOMBIFOLIUM. SF.
RICCARTON F. **F. magellanica riccartoni.**
ROBERT BLATRY.
ROLLA. DF.
RONSARD. DF.
ROSE F. **F. rosea.**
ROSE OF CASTILE. SF.
ROSE OF CASTILE IMP. SF.
ROSE OF DENMARK. SF.
ROSE PHENOMENAL. DF.
ROSE PILLAR. SF.
ROUNDBUD F. **F. magellanica globosa.**
ROYAL PURPLE. DF.
SANTA BARBARA. SF. *Triumph of Frankford.*
SANTA MONICA. DF.
SCABIEUSE. DF.
SCARLET BEAUTY.
SCARLET F. **F. coccinea.**
Schneewitschen. COUNTESS OF ABERDEEN.
SCINTILLATION. SD.
SOUVENIR DE HENRY HENKEL. TH.
Speciosa. AURORA BOREALIS.
STANFORD. SF.
STARLIGHT. SF.
STORM KING. DF.
SUNRAY. SF.
SUZANNE PASQUIER. DF.
SUZETTE. Ref.
SWANLEY GEM. SF.
SWANLEY YELLOW. SF.
TAUDESCHEN BONSTEDT. TH.
TENOR. DF.
THALIA. TH.
THE DOCTOR. SF.
THOMASINA. SF.
THOMPSON (*thompsoni*).
THREELEAF F. **F. triphylla.**

FUCHSIA, continued
THYMELEAF F. **F. thymifolia.**
TORPILLEUR. DF.
TRAILING F. **F. procumbens.**
TRAILING KING. SF.
TRAILING QUEEN. SF.
TREASURE ISLAND.
Triumph of Frankford. SANTA BARBARA.
VALIANT. SF.
VANDERSTRAUSS. DF.
VENUS VICTRIX. SF.
VICTORIEN SARDOU. SF.
Villa Hebe. BEAUTY OF SWANLEY.
VINCENT D'INDIE. DF.
VINE F. **F. corymbiflora.**
VOLTAIRE. SF.
WAVE OF LIFE. SF.
WHITE BEAUTY. SF.
WHITE PHENOMENAL. DF.
WHITE VINE F. **F. corymbiflora alba.**
YERBA BUENA. SD.

FU'CUS |w . . . . ROCKWEED
serra'tus . . . . . CARTWRACK R.
vesiculo'sus . . . BLADDERWRACK R.

FUGO'SIA . . . . . . **CIENFUGOSIA**

FUIRE'NA |w
his'pida |w
scirpoi'dea |w
squarro'sa |w

FUMA'NA
nudiflo'ra (*Helianthemum fumana*)
nudifo'lia (*Helianthemum procumbens*)

FUMA'RIA . . . . FUMITORY
officina'lis . . . . DRUG F.

FUMITORIES AND MASTICATORIES
(Plant Sources of)
See **ECONOMIC PLANTS, FUMITORIES AND MASTICATORIES.**

FUMITORY . . . . **Fumaria**
DRUG F. . . . . **F. officinalis**

FUNAS'TRUM . . . . **PHILIBERTIA**

FUNK'IA . . . . **HOSTA**
al'ba . . . . **H. plantaginea**
lanceola'ta . . . . **H. caerulea**
lancifo'lia . . . . **H. japonica**
ova'ta . . . . **H. caerulea**
subcorda'ta . . . . . **H. plantaginea**

FUNNELCREEPER . . . . . . **Doxantha**
CATCLAW F. . . . . . **D. unguis-cati**

FUNNELLILY . . . . . **Androstephium**
BLUE F. . . . . **A. caeruleum**

FUNNELVINE . . . . **Arrabidaea**
TRINIDAD F. . . . . **A. mollis**

Funori . . . . GLUE-ALGA: **Gloiopeltis**

FUNTU'MIA . . . . . . SILKRUBBER
africa'na
elas'tica . . . . LAGOS S.

FURCRAE'A . . . . FURCREA
See **SUCCULENTS.**

Furze . . . . GORSE: **Ulex**

FUSA'NUS (*MIDA*) . . SPINDLETREE
acumina'tus (*Mida acuminata*)
QUANDONGNUT S. (*Quandongnut*)
persica'rius . . . . . . TANGBER S.

FUSA'NUS R. Br., *not* Murr . **EUCARYA**

FUSTICTREE . . . . **Chlorophora**
DRUG F. . . . . **C. tinctoria**
IROKO F. . . . . **C. excelsa**

GAERTNE'RIA . . . **FRANSERIA**

GAILLAR'DIA ⌊w . . . . Gaillardia
amblyo'don . . . . . . Maroon G.
arista'ta (*grandiflora; G. g. maxima; maxima*) . Common Perennial G.
Barnes Ruby. hv.
Bush (*compacta*)
Carmine Gem
Goldseam (*sanguinea*)
John Harkness
La Mastodonte
Mr. Sherbrook
Mrs. McKellar
Neudort
¢Portola Hybrids
Salmon (*salmonea*)
Tangerine
The King
Yellow (*maxima*)
Yellow Prince
lanceola'ta
pinnatif'ida
pulchel'la (*drummondi*) ⌊w Rosering G.
—pic'ta (*G. picta*) . . . . Painted G.
Double Sunset (*lorenziana*) hv.
The Bride

GALAC'TIA ⌊w . . . . Milkpea
erec'ta ⌊w . . . . Erect M.
mol'lis ⌊w . . . . Hoary M.
regula'ris . . . . Shapely M.
stria'ta
veluti'na
volu'bilis ⌊w . . . . Downy M.
wright'i ⌊w . . . . Wright M.

Galangal . . . . **Alpinia**
Banded G. . . . . **A. sanderae**
Formosa G. . . . . . . **A. formosana**
India G. . . . . **A. calcarata**
Lesser G. . . . . . . **A. officinarum**
Malacca G. . . . . **A. vitellina**
Malay G. . . . . **A. mutica**
Shellflower G. . . . . **A. speciosa**
Tricolor G. . . . . **A. tricolor**

GALAN'THUS . . . . Snowdrop
al'leni . . . . Allen S.
byzanti'nus . . . . . Byzantine S.
cilic'icus . . . . Cilician S.
elwes'i . . . . Giant S.
Cassaba. hv.
Clawpetal (*unguiculatus*)
Erithrae
Globe (*globosus*)
Ochrospilus
Snowcup (*poculiformis*)
ika'riae . . . . Nikarian S.
niv'alis . . . . Common S.
—corcyren'sis . . . November C.S.
—flaves'cens . . . . Yellow C.S.
—max'imus . . . . Big C.S.
—octobren'sis . . . . October C.S.
—reflex'us . . . . Reflexed C.S.
—viridi-a'pice . . . . Greentip C.S.
Double (*florepleno*) hv. G. nivalis
ol'gae . . . . Greek S.
plica'tus . . . . Crimean S.

GALATEL'LA . . . . **ASTER**

GA'LAX ⌊w . . . . Galax
aphyl'la ⌊w . . . . Galax

GALEAN'DRA
See **ORCHID GENERA.**

GALE'GA ⌊w . . . . Goatsrue
officina'lis ⌊w . . . . . . Common G.

GALEGA officinalis, continued
Albino (*alba*) hv.
Duchess of Bedford
Hartland (*hartlandi*)
Sunset (*carnea*)
orienta'lis . . . Caucasus Goatsrue

GALEOP'SIS . . . . . Hempnettle
landa'num . . . . Red H.
ochroleu'ca
tetra'hit . . . . Bristlestem H.

Galeor'chis spectab'ilis . . . . **Orchis s.**

GA'LERA . . . . Galera
tener'a . . . . Lawn G.

GALINSO'GA . . . . . . Quickweed
cilia'ta . . . . Fringed Q.
parviflo'ra . . . . Littleflower Q.

GALI'PEA
officina'lis . . Angostura Barktree

GA'LIUM ⌊w . . . . Bedstraw
an'drewsi . . . . Needle B.
angustifo'lium . . . Narrowleaf B.
apari'ne ⌊w . . . . . . Catchweed B.
asper'rimum
asprel'lum . . . . Rough B.
bifo'lium . . . . Twinleaf B.
bolan'deri . . . . Bolander B.
borea'le ⌊w . . . . . . Northern B.
catalinen'se . . . . . Catalina B.
cir'caezans
clay'toni ⌊w . . . . Claytons B.
hall'i . . . . Hall B.
hispid'ulum ⌊w . . . . Coast B.
kamtschat'icum
Northern Wildlicorice
labrado'ricum . . . . Bog B.
lanceola'tum
Lanceleaf Wildlicorice
matth'ewsi . . . . . . Matthews B.
mollu'go ⌊w . . . . White B.
multiflo'rum . . . . Shrubby B.
munz'i . . . . Munz B.
nutt'alli . . . . Nuttall B.
palus'tris ⌊w . . . . Marsh B.
par'ishi . . . . Parish B.
pilo'sum ⌊w . . . . Hairy B.
pu'bens . . . . Downy B.
roth'rocki . . . . Rothrock B.
tincto'rium . . . . Dye B.
trif'idum ⌊w . . . . Small B.
triflo'rum ⌊w . . . . Sweetscented B.
ve'rum . . . . Yellow B.

Galleta . . . . **Hilaria jamesi**
Big G. . . . . **H. rigida**
Bush G. . . . . Big G.

GALPHIM'IA . . . . **THRYALLIS**

GALPIN'SIA . . . . . **OENOTHERA**

GALTO'NIA . . . . Summerhyacinth
can'dicans (*Hyacinthus c.*) . Giant S.

GALVE'ZIA
specio'sa (*Antirrhinum speciosum*)

Gamagrass . . . . **Tripsacum**
Eastern G. . . . . . . **T. dactyloides**
Florida G. . . . . **T. floridanum**
Guatemala G. . . . . **T. laxum**
Mexican G. . . . . . . **T. lanceolatum**

Gambirplant . . . . **Uncaria**
Bengal G. . . . . **U. gambir**

Gambogetree, Siam . **Garcinia hanburyi**

GAMO'LEPIS
tage'tes

Garambullo **Myrtillocactus geometrizans**

GARBER'IA . . . . Garberia
frutico'sa . . . . Garberia

GARCIN'IA . . . . Garcinia
atrovir'idis
banca'na
cambo'gia
dul'cis
—pyrifor'me
forbes'i . . . . Forbes G.
grif'fithi . . . . Griffith G.
hanbury'i . . . Siam Gambogetree
hombronea'na
ky'dia
livingston'ei . . . . Imbe
mangosta'na . . . . . Mangosteen
morel'la
nigrolinea'ta
spica'ta
zanthochy'mus

Gardeners Garters . . . . Ribbongrass:
Phalaris arundinacea picta

GARDE'NIA (*WARNERIA*) Gardenia
jasminoi'des (*augusta; florida; grandiflora*) . . . . Capejasmine

Gardenia augusta, perhaps the name in most common usage for this species, is untenable. Prof. Rehder states that it is based on a "nomen nudum" (*i. e.,* a mere name, without description—hence unallowable), Varneria augusta L.

—fortunia'na (*G. fortunei*)
Fortunes C.
Belmont. hv. G. jasminoides
Mystery
Veitch (*veitchi*)
latifo'lia . . . . Boxwood G.

Garlandflower . . . . **Calocephalus**
Browns G. . . . . **C. browni**

Garlic . . . . **Allium sativum**
Canada G. . . . . **A. canadense**
Crow G. . . . . Field G.
Field G. . . . . **A. vineale**
Giant G. . . . . . **A. scorodoprasum**
Streakleaf G. . . . . **A. strictum**
Twistedleaf G. . . . . . **A. obliquum**

Garlicmustard . **Sisymbrium alliaria**

GAR'RYA ⌊w . . . . Silktassel
buxifo'lia . . . . . . **G. flavescens b.**
cong'doni . . . . Interior S.
ellip'tica . . . . Tree S.
fad'yeni . . . . Fadyen S.
flaves'cens (*G. veitchi f.*)
Yellowleaf S.
—buxifo'lia (*G. buxifolia*) Boxleaf S.
fre'monti . . . . Fremont S.
(*Skunkbush; Squawbush*)
gold'mani ⌊w . . . . Goldman S.
laurifo'lia (*macrophylla*)
Laurelleaf S.
ova'ta
—salicifo'lia
∞ **thuret'i** (*elliptica* × *fadyeni*)
∞ Thuret S.

The cultivated plant is presumably a clon of this.

veitch'i . . . . Veitch S.
—flaves'cens . . . . . . **G. flavescens**
wright'i . . . . Wrights S.

Gasparillo, Guarantan
Esenbeckia leiocarpa

GASTE'RIA . . . . Gasteria
See **SUCCULENTS.**

Gasto'nia palma'ta . . . . **Trevesia p.**

GASTRI'DIUM . . . . NITGRASS
See **GRASS GENERA.**

GASTROLO'BIUM
calyci'num
spino'sum

GAULTHE'RIA [W] . . . WINTERGREEN
adeno'thrix
antip'oda
cunea'ta (*G. pyroloides c.*)
depres'sa
fagifo'lia
for'resti . . . . FORRESTS W.
fragrantis'sima . . . . FRAGRANT W.
fur'iens . . . . **Arbutus f.**
his'pida
hook'eri . . . . HOOKER W.
humifu'sa (*myrsinites*) . WESTERN W.
lanceola'ta
microphyl'la . . . . LITTLELEAF W.
min'ima
miquelia'na . . . . . . MIQUEL W.
nummularioi'des
—mi'nor
oppositifo'lia . . . OPPOSITELEAF W.
ovatifo'lia . . . . OREGON W.
parviflo'ra
perplex'a
procum'bens [W] . CHECKERBERRY W.
pyroloi'des
—cunea'ta . . . . **G. cuneata**
rupes'tris . . . . ROCK W.
shal'lon [W] . . . . SALAL
trichophyl'la
veitchia'na . . . . VEITCH W.
ward'i . . . . WARD W.

∞ **GAULTHET'TYA** (*Gaultheria* × *Pernettya*)
∞ **wisleyen'sis** (*Gaultheria shallon* × *Pernettya mucronata*)

GAU'RA [W] . . . . GAURA
bien'nis [W] . . . . . . BIENNIAL G.
coccin'ea [W] . . . . . . SCARLET G.
lindheim'eri . . . . WHITE G.
lyall'i . . . . LACEBARK G.

GAUS'SIA (*AERIA*) . . . LLUMEPALM
See **PALM GENERA.**

GA'YA . . . . GAYA
calyptra'ta (*disticha; hermannioides*)
MEXICAN G.
lyall'i . . . . **Hoheria l.**
occidenta'lis (*affinis*) . WESTINDIES G.

GAYFEATHER . . . . **Liatris**
CHAPMAN G. . . . . **L. chapmani**
DOTTED G. . . . . **L. punctata**
DWARF SPIKE G. . **L. spicata montana**
GRASSLEAF G. . . . . **L. graminifolia**
HELLER G. . . . . **L. helleri**
KANSAS G. . . . . . . **L. pycnostachya**
ONTARIO G. . . . . . . **L. cylindracea**
PINKSCALE G. . . . . **L. elegans**
ROCKYMOUNTAIN G. . . **L. ligulistylis**
SHAGGY G. . . . . **L. pilosa**
SHORTLEAF G. . . . . . **L. tenuifolia**
SLENDER G. . . . . **L. gracilis**
SPIKE G. . . . . **L. spicata**
TALL G. . . . . **L. scariosa**
WHITE SPIKE G. . . . **L. spicata alba**
WHITE TALL G. . . . . **L. scariosa a.**

GAYLUSSA'CIA [W] . . . HUCKLEBERRY
bacca'ta (*resinosa*) [W] . . . BLACK H.
—glaucocar'pa
—leucocar'pa
brachy'cera . . . . BOX H.

GAYLUSSACIA, continued
dumo'sa . . . DWARF HUCKLEBERRY
—bigelovia'na
frondo'sa [W] . . . . . . DANGLEBERRY
na'na [W] . . . . LITTLE H.
resino'sa . . . . **G. baccata**
ursi'na . . . . BUCKBERRY

GAYOPHY'TUM [W] . GROUNDSMOKE
cae'sium . . . . KITCHENWEED G.
diffu'sum . . . . . . BIGFLOWER G.
ramosis'simum [W]

GAZA'NIA (*MERIDIANA*) . GAZANIA
longisca'pa
monta'na
oxylo'ba
pavo'nia . . . . PAVON G.
potts'i
ri'gens . . . TREASUREFLOWER G.
splen'dens . . . . PIED G.
Possibly a hybrid.
GRANDIFLORA. HV. G. splendens
AURANTIACA. HV. Gazania

GEAS'TER
hygromet'ricus BAROMETER EARTHSTAR

Geb'lera suffrutico'sa . . . **Securinega s.**

GELID'IUM AGAR (*Agar-Agar; Tongusa*)
cor'neum . . . . COMMON A.

GELSE'MIUM [W]
sempervi'rens [W]. CAROLINAJESSAMINE (*Yellow Jessamine*)
DOUBLE. HV.

GEMMIN'GIA . . . **BELAMCANDA**

GENIOS'TOMA
ligustrifo'lium

GENI'PA . . . . GENIP
america'na . . . MARMALADEBOX G.
clusiifo'lia . . . SEVENYEARAPPLE G.

GENIS'TA . . . . WOADWAXEN
aethnen'sis . . . . AETNA W.
an'glica . . . . NEEDLE W.
—subiner'mis . . . SPINELESS N.W.
Originally published by Koch as a subvariety.
anxan'tica . . . . . . **G. tinctoria a.**
ardoi'ni . . . . **Cytisus a.**
canarien'sis . . . . **Cytisus c.**
cine'rea . . . . ASHY W.
dalma'tica . . . . **G. silvestris pungens**
decum'bens . . . . **Cytisus d.**
ela'ta . . . . **G. tinctoria virgata**
ephedroi'des
falca'ta
fe'rox
flor'ida
fra'grans . . . . **Cytisus f.**
german'ica . . . . GERMAN W.
—iner'mis
hal'leri . . . . . **Cytisus decumbens**
hispan'ica (*Cytisus hispanicus*)
SPANISH W.
COMPACTA. HV.
DWARF (*nana*)
hor'rida . . . . CUSHION W.
januen'sis . . . . GENOA W.
man'tica . . . . **G. tinctoria humilior**
monosper'ma . . . BRIDALVEIL W.
ALBA. HV.
PENDULA
nyssa'na . . . . NISH W.
occidenta'lis
ova'ta
pilo'sa . . . . SILKYLEAF W.

GENISTA, continued
prae'cox . . . . **Cytisus p.**
pubes'cens . . . . **G. tinctoria hirsuta**
racemo'sa . . . . **Cytisus racemosus**
radia'ta (*Cytisus radiatus; Enantiospar-ton radiatum*)
sagitta'lis (*Cytisus s.*)
scopa'ria . . . . . **Cytisus scoparius**
seric'ea
silves'tris
—pun'gens (*G. dalmatica*)
tincto'ria . . COMMON WOADWAXEN (*Dyers Greenweed*)
—alpes'tris . . . . . . ALPINE C.W.
—anxan'tica (*G. anxantica*)
—hirsu'ta (*G. pubescens*) DOWNY C.W.
—humil'ior (*G. mantica*)
—virga'ta (*G. elata; G. virgata*)
TALL C.W.
DOUBLE (*plena*) HV. G. tinctoria
villars'i . . . . VILLARS W.

GENTIAN . . . . **Gentiana**
ALPINE G. . . . . . . **G. angustifolia**
ALTAI G. . . . . **G. altaica**
ANDREWS G. . . . . **G. andrewsi**
ANNUAL G. . . . . **G. amarella**
BAVARIAN G. . . . . **G. bavarica**
BIGELOW G. . . . . **G. bigelovi**
BLUEGREEN G. . . . . **G. glauca**
BOTTLE G. . . . . **G. saponaria**
CHINESE G. . . . . . . **G. sino-ornata**
CLUSIUS STEMLESS G. **G. acaulis clusii**
CROSS G. . . . . **G. cruciata**
DANUBE G. . . . . **G. pannonica**
DOWNY G. . . . . **G. puberula**
ELWES G. . . . . **G. elwesi**
FARRER G. . . . . **G. farreri**
FIVELEAF G. . . . . . **G. quinquefolia**
FRINGED G. . . . . **G. crinita**
GERMAN G. . . . . **G. germanica**
∞ HASCOMB G. . . . ∞ **G. hascombensis**
HIMALAYAN G. . . . . **G. tibetica**
INGRAM G. . . . . **G. ingrami**
KASHMIR G. . . . . . **G. cachemirica**
KESSELRING G. . . . . **G. kesselringi**
LARGELEAF G. . . . . **G. macrophylla**
MAKINO G. . . . . **G. makinoi**
MEADOW G. . . . . **G. campestris**
MENZIES G. . . . . **G. menziesi**
MILKWEED G. . . . . . **G. asclepiadea**
NARROWLEAF G. . . . . . . **G. linearis**
NEWBERRY G. . . . . . . **G. newberryi**
NEWWORLD ANNUAL G. . . **G. plebeia**
NORTHERN G. . . . . **G. acuta**
OLIVIER G. . . . . **G. olivieri**
OREGON G. . . . . **G. oregana**
PACIFIC G. . . . . **G. sceptrum**
PARRY G. . . . . **G. parryi**
PINEBARREN G. . . . . . **G. porphyrio**
PURDOM G. . . . . **G. purdomi**
PURPLE G. . . . . **G. purpurea**
PYRENEES G. . . . . **G. pyrenaica**
RAINIER PLEATED G. . . . **G. calycosa**
ROCKYMOUNTAIN FRINGED G.
G. thermalis
ROCKYMOUNTAIN G. . . **G. scopulorum**
ROCKYMOUNTAIN PLEATED G. **G. affinis**
ROMANZOFF G. . . . . . **G. romanzovi**
ROUGH G. . . . . **G. scabra**
SIKKIM G. . . . . **G. sikkimensis**
SNOW G. . . . . **G. nivalis**
SPRING G. . . . . **G. verna**
STEMLESS G. . . . . **G. acaulis**
VICTORIN G. . . . . **G. victorini**
WESTERN FRINGED G. . . . **G. elegans**
WHITE ANDREWS G.. **G. andrewsi alba**
WHITE MILKWEED G. **G. asclepiadea a.**
YELLOW G. . . . . **G. lutea**

GENTIA'NA (*AMARELLA; ANTHOPOGON; DASYSTEPHANA*) |w
GENTIAN

acau'lis (*excisa*) . . . STEMLESS G.
—clu'sii (*G. clusii*) . . CLUSIUS S.G.
COELESTINA. HV. G. acaulis
GIANT (*gigantea*)
NARROWLEAF (*angustifolia*)
acu'ta (*G. amarella a.*) . NORTHERN G.
affi'nis (*Dasystephana a.*)
ROCKYMOUNTAIN PLEATED G.
al'gida
—sibir'ica
alta'ica . . . . ALTAI G.
amarel'la . . . . ANNUAL G.
an'drewsi (*Dasystephana a.*)
ANDREWS G.
—al'ba . . . . WHITE A.G.
angustifo'lia . . . . ALPINE G.
asclepiade'a . . . . . MILKWEED G.
—al'ba . . . . WHITE M.G.
bava'rica . . . . BAVARIAN G.
bigelo'vi . . . . BIGELOW G.
bisetae'a
brev'idens
bur'seri
cachemi'rica . . . . . . KASHMIR G.
calyco'sa (*Dasystephana c.*)
RAINIER PLEATED G.
campes'tris . . . . . . MEADOW G.
clu'sii . . . . **G. acaulis c.**
crini'ta . . . . FRINGED G.
crucia'ta . . . . CROSS G.
dahur'ica . . . . **G. olivieri**
deco'ra
decum'bens
depres'sa
deton'sa
el'egans . . . . **G. thermalis**
elwes'i . . . . ELWES G.
exci'sa . . . . **G. acaulis**
far'reri . . . . FARRER G.
fetiso'wi
fla'vida (*Dasystephana f.*)
frig'ida
gel'ida
german'ica . . . . . . GERMAN G.
gigan'tea
glau'ca . . . . . . BLUEGREEN G.
gracil'ipes
∞ **hascomben'sis** (*septemfida lagodechiana* × *septemfida* var.) ∞ HASCOMB G.
heterosep'ala (*Amarella h.*)
in'grami Hort. . . . . . INGRAM G.
kesselring'i . . . . KESSELRING G.
kurroo'
lagodechia'na . . . . **G. septemfida l.**
linea'ris . . . . . . NARROWLEAF G.
lute'a . . . . YELLOW G.
macrophyl'la . . . . . LARGELEAF G.
makino'i . . . . MAKINO G.
menzies'i . . . . MENZIES G.
newber'ryi . . . . . . NEWBERRY G.
niva'lis . . . . SNOW G.
olivier'i (*dahurica*) . . . OLIVIER G.
orega'na . . . . OREGON G.
or'fordi . . . . **G. sceptrum**
panno'nica . . . . DANUBE G.
par'ryi (*Dasystephana p.*) . PARRY G.
phlogifo'lia
plebei'a (*Amarella p.*)
NEWWORLD ANNUAL G.
Perhaps not (at least specifically) distinct from the Old World G. amarella.
pneumonan'the
porphy'rio . . . . PINEBARREN G.
prola'ta
przewal'ski

GENTIANA, continued
pteroca'lyx
puber'ula (*Dasystephana p.*)
DOWNY GENTIAN
pur'domi . . . . PURDOM G.
purpu'rea . . . . PURPLE G.
pyrena'ica . . . . . . PYRENEES G.
quinquefo'lia . . . . . FIVELEAF G.
rochel'i
romanzo'vi (*Dasystephana r.*)
ROMANZOFF G.
sapona'ria . . . . BOTTLE G.
sca'bra . . . . ROUGH G.
BUERGER (*buergeri*) HV.
scep'trum (*orfordi*) . . . PACIFIC G.
scopulo'rum (*Amarella s.*)
ROCKYMOUNTAIN G.
septem'fida
—lagodechia'na (*G. lagodechiana*)
—procum'bens
FREYNIANA. HV. G. septemfida
seto'sa Hort.
sikkimen'sis . . . . SIKKIM G.
sino-orna'ta . . . . . . CHINESE G.
stramin'ea
styloph'ora
therma'lis (*elegans; Anthopogon e.*)
ROCKYMOUNTAIN FRINGED G.
tibet'ica . . . . HIMALAYAN G.
ver'na . . . . SPRING G.
—ala'ta (*G. v. angulosa*)
victori'ni . . . . VICTORIN G.
walujew'i

GEONO'MA . . . . . SHADOWPALM
See **PALM GENERA.**

GEOPRUM'NON . . . **ASTRAGALUS**
crassicar'pum . . . . **A. mexicanus**

GERAE'A . . . . DESERTGOLD
canes'cens (*Encelia eriocephala*)

GERA'NIUM |w . GERANIUM (*Crowfoot*)
STANDARDIZED PLANT NAMES restricts the common name Geranium to the genus Geranium, and uses Pelargonium for the genus Pelargonium.

aconitifo'lium
alba'num
albiflo'rum
anemonifo'lium
argen'teum . . . . . SILVERLEAF G.
LISSADELL PURPLE. HV.
arme'num . . . . . . **G. psilostemon**
asphodelioi'des
atropurpu'reum
bick'nelli . . . . . . BICKNELL G.
carolinia'num |w . . . CAROLINA G.
cine'reum
colli'num (*londesi*) . . . UPLAND G.
columbi'num . . . . . LONGSTALK G.
dissec'tum |w . . . . CUTLEAF G.
endres'si
E. J. JOHNSON. HV.
erioste'mon
—rein'i
far'reri . . . . FARRER G.
fre'monti . . . . FREMONT G.
grandiflo'rum . . . . . . LILAC G.
grevillea'num
gymnocau'lon
hel'dreichi
ibe'ricum . . . . CAUCASUS G.
—platypet'alum . . . **G. platypetalum**
WHITE (*album*) HV. G. ibericum
inci'sum . . . . CLEFTLEAF G.
japon'icum
londes'i . . . . **G. collinum**
macrorrhi'zum . . . . . BIGROOT G.

GERANIUM, continued
macula'tum . . . SPOTTED GERANIUM
WHITE (*album*) HV.
mol'le . . . . DOVEFOOT G.
napulig'erum
nepalen'se . . . . NEPAL G.
nervo'sum
nodo'sum
orega'num . . . . OREGON G.
par'ryi . . . . PARRY G.
phae'um
platypet'alum (*G. ibericum p.*)
praten'se . . . . MEADOW G.
DOUBLE (*plenum*) HV.
STRIPED (*striatum*)
WHITE (*album*)
psiloste'mon (*armenum*). ARMENIAN G.
pusil'lum . . . . SMALL G.
pylzowia'num
pyrena'icum . . . . . PYRENEES G.
richardso'ni . . . . RICHARDSON G.
robertia'num . . . . HERBROBERT G.
sanguin'eum . . . . . BLOODRED G.
DWARF (*lancastriense; prostratum*) HV.
TRAVERS (*traversi*)
WHITE (*album*)
subcaules'cens
tubero'sum
viscosis'simum |w . . . . STICKY G.
wallichia'num . . . . . WALLICH G.
BUXTON. HV.
wil'fordi

GERANIUM . . . . **Geranium**
For hort. var. of Pelargonium (often called Geranium) see **PELARGONIUM.**

ARMENIAN G. . . . . **G. psilostemon**
BICKNELL G. . . . . . . **G. bicknelli**
BIGROOT G. . . . **G. macrorrhizum**
BLOODRED G. . . . . **G. sanguineum**
CAROLINA G. . . . . **G. carolinianum**
CAUCASUS G. . . . . . . **G. ibericum**
CLEFTLEAF G. . . . . . . **G. incisum**
CUTLEAF G. . . . . . . **G. dissectum**
DOVEFOOT G. . . . . **G. molle**
FARRER G. . . . . **G. farreri**
FREMONT G. . . . . **G. fremonti**
HERBROBERT G. . . . **G. robertianum**
LILAC G. . . . . . . **G. grandiflorum**
LONGSTALK G. . . . . **G. columbinum**
MEADOW G. . . . . **G. pratense**
NEPAL G. . . . . **G. nepalense**
OREGON G. . . . . **G. oreganum**
PARRY G. . . . . **G. parryi**
PYRENEES G. . . . . . **G. pyrenaicum**
RICHARDSON G. . . . . **G. richardsoni**
SILVERLEAF G. . . . . . **G. argenteum**
SMALL G. . . . . **G. pusillum**
SPOTTED G. . . . . . . **G. maculatum**
STICKY G. . . . . . **G. viscosissimum**
UPLAND G. . . . . **G. collinum**
WALLICH G. . . . . . **G. wallichianum**

GERAR'DIA (*AGALINIS*) |w GERARDIA
marit'ima |w . . . . SEASIDE G.
pauper'cula (*Agalinis p.*) |w
SMALLFLOWER G.
pedicula'ria . . . . . **Aureolaria p.**
purpu'rea (*Agalinis p.*) . . PURPLE G.
tenuifo'lia (*Agalinis t.*)
trif'ida |w

GER'BERA (*GERBERIA; PERDICIUM*) . . . . GERBERA
anan'dria . . . . CHINESE G.
jameso'ni . . . . FLAMERAY G.
kunzea'na . . . . KUNZE G.

GERMAN-CAMOMILE
Matricaria chamomilla

GERMANDER . . . . **Teucrium**
AMERICAN G. . . . . . **T. canadense**
BUSH G. . . . . **T. fruticans**
CAT-THYME G. . . . . . **T. marum**
CHAMAEDRYS G. . . . **T. chamaedrys**
GOLDEN G. . . . . **T. polium**
HAIRY G. . . . . . **T. occidentale**
MOUNTAIN G. . . . . **T. montanum**
ORIENTAL G. . . . . . . **T. orientale**
PYRENEES G. . . . . . **T. pyrenaicum**
ROSE G. . . . . . . **T. massiliense**
WOOD G. . . . . . . **T. scorodonia**
YELLOW G. . . . . **T. flavum**

GESNE'RIA
CORYTHOLOMA; NAEGELIA
amab'ilis . . . . . . **N. multiflora**
cardina'lis . . . . . . **C. cardinalis**
cinnabari'na . . . . . **N. cinnabarina**
macran'tha . . . . . . **C. cardinalis**
zebri'na . . . . **N. zebrina**

GE'UM |w . . . . AVENS
alep'picum . . . . ALEPPO A.
×**bo'risi** (*bulgaricum* × *reptans*)
bulgar'icum . . . . . BULGARIAN A.
campanula'tum. **Sieversia campanulata**
canaden'se (*album*) . . . . WHITE A.
chiloen'se . . . . CHILE A.
DOLLY NORTH. HV.
DOUBLE CRIMSON (*atrosanguineum*)
FIREOPAL
LADY STRATHEDEN
MRS. BRADSHAW
PRINCE OF ORANGE
PRINCESS JULIANA
VERMILION (*miniatum*)
cilia'tum . . . . . . **Sieversia ciliata**
coccin'eum
A name often misapplied to G. chiloense. The true G. coccineum of botanists is probably not in the trade.

ew'eni Hort. . . . . EWEN A.
×**jan'kae** (*coccineum* × *rivale*) JANKA A.
japon'icum . . . . . . JAPANESE A.
macrophyl'lum . . . . LARGELEAF A.
magellan'icum . . . . MAGELLAN A.
monta'num . . . . **Sieversia montana**
oregonen'se . . . . OREGON A.
peck'i . . . . **Sieversia p.**
pyrena'icum . . . . . PYRENEES A.
rep'tans . . . . **Sieversia r.**
riva'le . . . . WATER A.
ross'i . . . . **Sieversia r.**
stric'tum . . . . YELLOW A.
turbina'tum (*Acomastylis turbinata*)
urba'num
SIBERIAN (*sibiricum*) HV. Geum

GEVUI'NA
avella'na . . . . CHILEHAZEL
This is the source of the Chilenuts of commerce.

GHERKIN, WESTINDIAN **Cucumis anguria**

GHOSTLIME . . . . . . **Burkillanthus**
MALAY G. . . . . . **B. malaccensis**

GHOSTPIPE . . . . **Thalesia; T. uniflora**

GIANTARUM . . . . . **Amorphophallus**
GREAT G. . . . . **A. giganteus**
TITAN G. . . . . **A. titanum**
WHITESPOT G. . . . **A. campanulatus**

GIANTBELL . **Ostrowskia; O. magnifica**

Giantcactus . SAGUARO: **Cereus giganteus**

GIANTDAISY **Chrysanthemum uliginosum**

GIANTFENNEL . . . . **Ferula**
ASAFETIDA G. . . . . . **F. assafoetida**
COMMON G. . . . . . **F. communis**
DEVILSDUNG G. . . . . . . **F. foetida**
GALBANUM G. . . . . **F. galbaniflua**
MUSKROOT G. . . . . . . **F. sumbul**
PERSIAN G. . . . . **F. persica**

GIANTGRASS . . . . . . **Gigantochloa**
ROUGH G. . . . . **G. aspera**

Giantgum . . . . EUCALYPTUS, GIANT: **Eucalyptus regnans**

GIANTHYSSOP . . . . **Agastache**
CATNIP G. . . . . . . **A. nepetoides**
FENNEL G. . . . . . . **A. foeniculum**
MEXICAN G. . . . . **A. mexicana**
MOSQUITOPLANT . . . . . . **A. cana**
NETTLELEAF G. . . . . **A. urticifolia**
WRINKLED G. . . . . **A. rugosa**

GIANTKELP . **Macrocystis; M. pyrifera**

GIANTREED . . . . **Arundo; A. donax**
WHITESTRIPE G. . . **A. d. versicolor**

GIBBAE'UM
MESEMBRYANTHEMUM
See **SUCCULENTS.**

GI'FOLA
german'ica . . . . COTTONROSE

GIGANTOCHLO'A . . . . GIANTGRASS
See **BAMBOO GENERA.**

GIGARTI'NA
mamillo'sa

GIL'IA (*COLLOMIA; IPOMOPSIS; LEPTODACTYLON; LEPTOSIPHON; LINANTHUS; NAVARRETIA; WELWITSCHIA* Reichb., *not* Hook. f.) |w . . GILIA
There is much difference of botanical opinion as to the generic limits of Gilia.

abrotanifo'lia . . . SANTABARBARA G.
achilleaefo'lia . . . . . YARROW G.
aggrega'ta . . . . . . SKYROCKET G.
androsa'cea (*Leptosiphon androsaceus; Linanthus a.*) . . . . TRUMPET G.
au'rea (*Linanthus aureus*) YELLOW G.
brew'eri (*Navarretia b.*) . BREWER G.
calca'rea . . . . STICKY G.
califor'nica (*Leptodactylon californicum*) CALIFORNIA G.
capilla'ris (*leptalea*) . . HAIRSTEM G.
capita'ta . . . . GLOBE G.
chamisso'nis . . . . BLUE G.
conges'ta . . . . BALLHEAD G.
coronopifo'lia . . . . **G. rubra**
densiflo'ra (*Leptosiphon densiflorus; Linanthus densiflorus; L. grandiflorus*) . . . . TUBE G.
dianthoi'des (*Fenzlia dianthiflora; Linanthus dianthiflorus*) . TUFTED G.
dichot'oma (*Linanthus dichotomus*) EVENINGSNOW G.
floribun'da . . . . **G. nuttalli**
grac'ilis |w
grandiflo'ra (*Collomia g.; Linanthus grandiflorus*) . . . . BIGFLOWER G.
greenea'na . . . . . GREENES G.
harkness'i (*Linanthus h.*) HARKNESS G.
hutchinsifo'lia
iberidifo'lia . . . . . . CANDYTUFT G.
inconspic'ua . . . . SHY G.
intertex'ta (*Navarretia i.*) WOOLLY G.
lacinia'ta . . . . CUTLEAF G.
lar'seni
leptale'a . . . . **G. capillaris**
leucophyl'la (*Navarretia l.*) WHITEHEAD G.

GILIA, continued
linea'ris (*Collomia l.*) SLENDERLEAF GILIA
liniflo'ra (*Linanthus liniflorus*) FLAXFLOWER G.
lute'a (*micrantha* Steud., *not* (Kell.) A. Nels.; *Leptosiphon parviflorus; Linanthus p.*)
micran'tha (Kell.) A. Nels. **Microsteris m.**
micran'tha Steud. . . . . **G. lutea**
multicau'lis
nutt'alli (*floribunda; Leptodactylon n.*) NUTTALL G.
pharnaceoi'des (*Linanthus p.*) THREADPLANT G.
pinnatif'ida |w
pulchel'la . . . . TINPIUTE G.
pun'gens (*Leptodactylon p.*) GRANITE G.
rigid'ula
ru'bra (*coronopifolia; Ipomopsis elegans*) . . . . TEXASPLUME
spica'ta . . . . SPIKE G.
squarro'sa (*Navarretia s.*) SKUNKWEED G.
tri'color |w . . . . BIRDSEYE G.
ROSY (*rosea*) HV.
WHITE (*nivalis*)
twee'dyi . . . . TWEEDY G.

GILIA . . . . **Gilia**
BALLHEAD G. . . . . . . **G. congesta**
BIGFLOWER G. . . . . **G. grandiflora**
BIRDSEYE G. . . . . **G. tricolor**
BLUE G. . . . . . . **G. chamissonis**
BREWER G. . . . . **G. breweri**
CALIFORNIA G. . . . . **G. californica**
CANDYTUFT G. . . . . **G. iberidifolia**
CUTLEAF G. . . . . **G. laciniata**
EVENINGSNOW G. . . . . **G. dichotoma**
FLAXFLOWER G. . . . . . **G. liniflora**
GLOBE G. . . . . **G. capitata**
GRANITE G. . . . . **G. pungens**
GREENES G. . . . . . . **G. greeneana**
HAIRSTEM G. . . . . . . **G. capillaris**
HARKNESS G. . . . . . **G. harknessi**
NUTTALL G. . . . . **G. nuttalli**
SANTABARBARA G. . . **G. abrotanifolia**
SHY G. . . . . **G. inconspicua**
SKUNKWEED G. . . . . **G. squarrosa**
SKYROCKET G. . . . . **G. aggregata**
SLENDERLEAF G. . . . . . **G. linearis**
SPIKE G. . . . . **G. spicata**
STICKY G. . . . . **G. calcarea**
TEXASPLUME . . . . **G. rubra**
THREADPLANT G. . . **G. pharnaceoides**
TINPIUTE G. . . . . **G. pulchella**
TRUMPET G. . . . . . **G. androsacea**
TUBE G. . . . . **G. densiflora**
TUFTED G. . . . . **G. dianthoides**
TWEEDY G. . . . . **G. tweedyi**
WHITEHEAD G. . . . . **G. leucophylla**
WOOLLY G. . . . . **G. intertexta**
YARROW G. . . . . **G. achilleaefolia**
YELLOW G. . . . . **G. aurea**

GILLE'NIA (*PORTERANTHUS*)
stipula'ta (*stipulacea; Porteranthus stipulatus*) . . . . . . INDIANPHYSIC
trifolia'ta (*Porteranthus trifoliatus*) BOWMANSROOT

GILMA'NIA (*PHYLLOGONUM*) GOLDCARPET
luteo'la (*Phyllogonum luteolum*) DEATHVALLEY G.

GINGER . . . . **Zingiber**
CASSUMUNAR G. . . . **Z. cassumunar**
CATTAIL G. . . . . . **Z. cylindricum**

GINGER, continued
COMMON G. . . . Zingiber officinale
HARLEQUIN G. . . . . . . Z. darceyi
MIOGA G. . . . . Z. mioga
REDBRACT G. . . . . . . Z. spectabile
ZERUMBET G. . . . . . Z. zerumbet

GINGERLILY . . . . Hedychium
COMMON G. . . . . . H. coronarium
GREAT G. . . . . . . H. maximum
GREENES G. . . . . . . H. greenei
INDIA G. . . . . . . H. gardnerianum
NARROWLEAF SCARLET G.
H. coccineum angustifolium
ORANGE G. . . . . H. aurantiacum
SCARLET G. . . . . . H. coccineum
SLENDER G. . . . . H. gracile
SMOOTH G. . . . . H. glaucum
SPIKED G. . . . . H. spicatum
TALL G. . . . . H. elatum
YELLOW G. . . . . H. flavum

GINK'GO (*SALISBURIA*) . . GINKGO
bilo'ba (*Salisburia adiantifolia*) GINKGO
¢CUTLEAF (*laciniata*) HV.
¢LARGELEAF (*macrophylla*)
¢SENTRY (*fastigiata*)
¢VARIEGATED (*variegata*)
¢WEEPING (*pendula*)
¢YELLOWLEAF (*aurea*)

GINSENG . . . . Panax
AMERICAN G. . . . P. quinquefolium
ASIATIC G. . . . . P. schinseng
DWARF G. . . . . P. trifolium

GINSENGTREE . . . . Tieghemopanax
ELDERLEAF G. . . . T. sambucifolius
PENCILWOOD G. . . . . T. murrayi
UMBRELLA G. . . . . . . T. elegans

GLADEMALLOW . . . . Napaea

GLADI'OLUS |w . . . . . GLADIOLUS
ala'tus . . . . SMALL G.
—namaquen'sis (*G. namaquensis*)
NAMAQUALAND G.
Ronald Bamford, Professor of Botany, University of Maryland, is studying the relationship of namaquensis to the species alatus. He says "It certainly is vastly different in the seedling stage."
alep'picus . . . . ALEPPO G.
angus'tus . . . . SLIMLEAF G.
atroviola'ceus
blan'dus . . . . SNOWPINK G.
¢FLORIBUNDUS. HV.
brevifo'lius . . . . . SHORTLEAF G.
byzanti'nus . . . . . BYZANTINE G.
callis'tus . . . . . CAPEGLORY G.
cardina'lis . . . . . . CARDINAL G.
ELEGANS. HV.
carmin'eus . . . . . . CARMINE G.
car'neus . . . . FLESH G.
coccin'eus . . . . . . CRIMSON G.
cochlea'tus
colvil'lei . . . . . . COLVILLE G.
¢THE BRIDE (*albus; G. c. albus*) HV.
commu'nis . . . . COMMON G.
coop'eri . . . . COOPER G.
crassifo'lius . . . . THICKLEAF G.
cruen'tus . . . . . . BLOODRED G.
cuspida'tus
daviso'niae . . . . . DAVISON G.
deb'ilis . . . . SLIMSTEM G.
dracoceph'alus . . . DRAGONHEAD G.
formo'sus
∞ **gandaven'sis** Hort. (*?oppositifolius* × *?psittacinus*) . . . ∞ BREEDERS G.
Some authorities prefer to regard cardinalis, rather than oppositifolius, as one of the parents of this polybrid.

GLADIOLUS, continued
grac'ilis . . . SLIMSWEET GLADIOLUS
gran'dis (*versicolor*)
LARGEBROWN AFRIKANDER G.
hirsu'tus . . . PINKAFRIKANDER G.
∞ **hortula'nus**
∞ COMMON HORTICULTURAL G.
ignes'cens . . . . . MADAGASCAR G.
illyr'icus (*reuteri*) . . . . GRECIAN G.
imbrica'tus
infla'tus (*ringens* Eckl., *not* Thunb.)
∞ **leicht'lini** (*? ∞ gandavensis* × *?saundersi*)
∞ LEICHTLIN G.
The commonly cultivated plant is presumably a clon of this polybrid.
mil'leri . . . . MILLER G.
mart'leyi . . . . MARTLEY G.
muriel'ae Hort. (*Acidanthera m.* Hort.)
James H. Odell, President of the New England Gladiolus Society, reports that this cultivated plant, reputed native to Ethiopia, "is not generally considered a gladiolus species."
namaquen'sis . . . . . . G. alatus n.
∞ **odora'tus** (*hirsutus* × *spofforthianus*)
oppositiflo'rus . . . . TWOSIDED G.
orchidiflo'rus . . ORCHIDFLOWER G.
palus'ter (*triphyllus*). THREEFLOWER G.
papil'io . . . . . . GOLDBLOTCH G.
permeab'ilis
primuli'nus . . . . . . PRIMROSE G.
psittaci'nus . . . . PARROT G.
purpureo-aura'tus . . GOLDORCHID G.
quadrangula'ris
quartinia'nus
—angolen'sis
recur'vus (*ringens* Andr., *not* Thunb.)
MAUVEAFRIKANDER G.
reu'teri . . . . G. illyricus
riges'cens
rin'gens Andr., *not* Thunb. **G. recurvus**
rin'gens Eckl., *not* Thunb.. **G. inflatus**
rin'gens Thunb. (1794) . **Babiana mucronata; B. stricta sulphurea**
saun'dersi . . . . . . SAUNDERS G.
sege'tum . . . . CORNFLAG G.
sericeo-villo'sus
spofforthia'nus . . . . SPOFFORTH G.
stanford'iae . . . . . . STANFORD G.
trichonemifo'lius . . . . HAIRLEAF G.
triphyl'lus . . . . G. paluster
tris'tis . . . . EVENINGFLOWER G.
undula'tus . . . . BABY G.
versicol'or . . . . G. grandis
villo'sus . . . . . . HAIRYSHEATH G.
watermey'eri. . . . WATERMEYER G.
watso'nius . . . . WATSON G.
The Editorial Committee greatly regrets that space limitations have prevented inclusion of a list of hort. var. of Gladiolus. In the former (1923) edition of this work appeared a list of Gladiolus hort. var. prepared by A. C. Beal, Registrar of the American Gladiolus Society. For the present edition we had combined two lists furnished us by A. M. S. Pridham, revised by James H. Odell, Chairman of the Board of Trustees of the New England Gladiolus Society, together with the list published by that Society in "The Gladiolus" in 1940. Our cordial thanks are extended to the two experts mentioned for their assistance and advice, which, to our chagrin, cannot take tangible form here in a published list.

GLADIOLUS . . . . Gladiolus
ALEPPO G. . . . . G. aleppicus
BABY G. . . . . G. undulatus
BLOODRED G. . . . . . . G. cruentus

GLADIOLUS, continued
∞ BREEDERS G. ∞ Gladiolus gandavensis
BYZANTINE G. . . . . G. byzantinus
CAPEGLORY G. . . . . . G. callistus
CARDINAL G. . . . . . . G. cardinalis
CARMINE G. . . . . . G. carmineus
COLVILLE G. . . . . . . G. colvillei
COMMON G. . . . . . . G. communis
∞ COMMON HORTICULTURAL G.
∞ G. hortulanus
COOPER G. . . . . G. cooperi
CORNFLAG G. . . . . . . G. segetum
CRIMSON G. . . . . . . G. coccineus
DAVISON G. . . . . . G. davisoniae
DRAGONHEAD G. . . G. dracocephalus
EVENINGFLOWER G. . . . . G. tristis
FLESH G. . . . . G. carneus
GOLDBLOTCH G. . . . . . . G. papilio
GOLDORCHID G. . G. purpureo-auratus
GRECIAN G. . . . . . . G. illyricus
HAIRLEAF G. . . . G. trichonemifolius
HAIRYSHEATH G. . . . . G. villosus
LARGEBROWN AFRIKANDER G. G. grandis
∞ LEICHTLIN G. . . . . ∞ G. leichtlini
MADAGASCAR G. . . . . G. ignescens
MARTLEY G. . . . . . . G. martleyi
MAUVEAFRIKANDER G. . . G. recurvus
MILLER G. . . . . G. milleri
NAMAQUALAND G.
G. alatus namaquensis
ORCHIDFLOWER G. . G. orchidiflorus
PARROT G. . . . . . . G. psittacinus
PINKAFRIKANDER G. . . . G. hirsutus
PRIMROSE G. . . . . . G. primulinus
SAUNDERS G. . . . . . G. saundersi
SHORTLEAF G. . . . . G. brevifolius
SLIMLEAF G. . . . . . . G. angustus
SLIMSTEM G. . . . . G. debilis
SLIMSWEET G. . . . . . . G. gracilis
SMALL G. . . . . G. alatus
SNOWPINK G. . . . . . . G. blandus
SPOFFORTH G. . . . G. spofforthianus
STANFORD G. . . . . . G. stanfordiae
THICKLEAF G. . . . . G. crassifolius
THREEFLOWER G. . . . . G. paluster
TWOSIDED G. . . . . G. oppositiflorus
WATERMEYER G. . . . G. watermeyeri
WATSON G. . . . . . . G. watsonius

GLADIXIA . . . . Acidanthera
DARKEYE G. . . . . A. bicolor

GLASSWORT . . . . Salicornia
BIGELOW G. . . . . S. bigelovi
LEADBUSH G. . . . . . . S. fruticosa
MARSHFIRE G. . . . . . S. europaea
ROCKYMOUNTAIN G. . . . . S. rubra
UTAH G. . . . . S. utahensis
WOODY G. . . . . S. perennis

GLAUCID'IUM . . . . GLAUCIDIUM
palma'tum . . . . . . MAPLELEAF G.

GLAU'CIUM . . . . . . HORNPOPPY
cornicula'tum . . . . BLACKSPOT H.
fla'vum (*luteum*) . . . . YELLOW H.
—tri'color
leiocar'pum . . MEDITERRANEAN H.
serpier'i

GLAUCOTHE'A . . . . . **ERYTHEA**
See **PALM GENERA.**

GLAUX' |w . . . . . . SEAMILKWORT
marit'ima |w . . . . . SEAMILKWORT

GLAZIO'VA . . . . . . **SYAGRUS**
See **PALM GENERA.**

GLECO'MA (*GLECHOMA*)
hedera'cea (*Nepeta h.*)

GLEDIT'SIA (*GLEDITSCHIA*) |w . . . Honeylocust
amorphoi'des . . . . Amorpha H.
aqua'tica . . . . . . Waterlocust
cas'pica . . . . Caspian H.
delavay'i . . . . . . Delavay H.
fe'rox . . . . Cockspur H.
heterophyl'la . . . . . Fernleaf H.
japon'ica (*horrida* Mak., *not* Willd.) . . . Japanese H.
macran'tha . . . . . Bigspine H.
sinen'sis . . . . Chinese H.
×**texa'na** (*aquatica* × *triacanthos*) . . . Texas H.
triacan'thos (*Gleditschia t.*) |w . . . Common H.
₵Bujot (*bujoti*) hv.
₵Bushy (*elegantissima*)
₵Calhoun
₵Dwarf (*nana*)
₵Millwood
₵Smith
₵Thornless (*inermis*)

GLIRICID'IA
se'pium (*maculata*)

Globeamaranth . . . . . **Gomphrena**
Common G. . . . . **G. globosa**
Haage G. . . . . **G. haageana**
Prostrate G. . . . . **G. decumbens**

Globedaisy . . . . **Globularia**
Common G. . . . . . . **G. vulgaris**
Ground G. . . . . . . **G. nudicaulis**
Heartleaf G. . . . . **G. cordifolia**
Hoary G. . . . . . **G. incanescens**
Majorca G. . . . . . **G. majorcensis**
Prostrate G. . . . . **G. nana**
Syrian G. . . . . . . **G. trichosantha**
White Heartleaf G. **G. cordifolia alba**

Globeflower . . . . **Trollius**
Altai G. . . . . **T. altaicus**
American G. . . . . **T. laxus**
Caucasian G. . . . . **T. caucasicus**
Chinese G. . . . . . . **T. chinensis**
Common G. . . . . . . **T. europaeus**
Dwarf G. . . . . **T. pumilus**
Himalaya G. . . . . **T. acaulis**
Japanese G. . . . . . . **T. japonicus**
Ledebour G. . . . . . . **T. ledebouri**
Persian G. . . . . **T. patulus**
Siberian G. . . . . . . **T. asiaticus**
Turkestan G. . . . **T. dshungaricus**
White G. . . . . **T. albiflorus**
Yunnan G. **T. pumilus yunnanensis**

Globemallow . . . . . . **Sphaeralcea**
Brick G. . . . . **S. cisplatina**
Desert G. . . . . . . **S. ambigua**
Fremont G. . . . . . . **S. fremonti**
Gooseberryleaf G. **S. grossulariaefolia**
Lobed G. . . . . **S. lobata**
Mexican G. . . . . . . **S. umbellata**
Munro G. . . . . . . **S. munroana**
Narrowleaf G. . . . **S. angustifolia**
Rosy G. . . . . **S. rosea**
Scarlet G. . . . . . . **S. coccinea**
Stream G. . . . . **S. rivularis**
Tufted G. . . . . . . **S. caespitosa**

Globepea . . . . **Sphaerophysa**
Salt G. . . . . **S. salsula**

Globethistle . . . . **Echinops**
Common G. . . . **E. sphaerocephalus**
Darkblue Siberian G. **E. humilis cyaneus**

Globethistle, continued
Giant G. . . . . **Echinops giganteus**
Russian G. . . . . **E. exaltatus**
Siberian G. . . . . **E. humilis**
Small G. . . . . **E. ritro**
Yugoslav G. . . . . . **E. bannaticus**

Globetulip
Obispo G. . . . . . Mariposa, Obispo: *Calochortus obispoensis*
Plummer G. . . . . . . Plummer M.: **C. plummerae**
Weeds G. . . . . . Weeds M.: **C. weedi**

GLOBULA'RIA . . . . . Globedaisy
aly'pum
cordifo'lia . . . . Heartleaf G.
—al'ba . . . . White H.G.
incanes'cens . . . . Hoary G.
majorcen'sis . . . . . . Majorca G.
na'na (*bellidifolia*) . . Prostrate G.
nudicau'lis . . . . Ground G.
trichosan'tha . . . . Syrian G.
vulga'ris . . . . Common G.

GLOIOPEL'TIS . Glue-alga (*Funori*)
coliform'is . . . . Sieve G.

GLORIO'SA . . . . Glorylily
roehrsia'na . . . . . . Roehrs G.
rothschildia'na . . . . Rothschild G.
superb'a . . . . Malabar G.
—grandiflo'ra . . . . . Showy M.G.
vires'cens (*simplex*) . . . . Green G.

Glorybind . . . . **Convolvulus**
Baby G. . . . . **C. siculus**
California G. . . . **C. macrostegius**
Canary G. . . . . **C. floridus**
Cantabrian G. . . . . **C. cantabrica**
Crawling G. . . **C. pentapetaloides**
Dwarf G. . . . . **C. tricolor**
European G. . . . . **C. arvensis**
Golden G. . . . . **C. aureus**
Hedge G. . . . . **C. sepium**
Ivy G. . . . . **C. hederaceus**
Mediterranean G. . . **C. althaeoides**
Morocco G. . . . . **C. mauritanicus**
Nebraska G. . . . . **C. incanus**
Pacific G. . . . . . . **C. purpuratus**
Rose G. . . . . **C. japonicus**
Scammony G. . . . . . **C. scammonia**
Seashore G. . . . . . . **C. soldanella**
Solitary G. . . . . . . **C. elongatus**
Variable G. . . . . . **C. polymorphus**

Glorybower . . . . . **Clerodendron**
Bleedingheart G. . . . **C. thomsonae**
Colebrook G. . . **C. colebrookianum**
Commerson G. . . . **C. commersoni**
Double Fragrant G. **C. fragrans pleniflorum**
Farges Bleedingheart G. **C. thomsonae fargesi**
Fragrant G. . . . . . . **C. fragrans**
Harlequin G. . . . **C. trichotomum**
Japanese G. . . . . . . **C. japonicum**
Java G. . . . . . **C. speciosissimum**
Mayflower G. . . **C. cyrtophyllum**
Natal G. . . . . **C. glabrum**
Rose G. . . . . **C. bungei**
Sunshine Bleedingheart G. **C. thomsonae delectum**
Variegated B. G. . . **C. t. variegatum**

Glorybush . . . . **Tibouchina**
Brazilian G. . . . **T. semidecandra**
Bristlecup G. . . . . . **T. elegans**

Gloryflower . . . . **Eccremocarpus**
Chilean G. . . . . **E. scaber**

Glorylily . . . . **Gloriosa**
Green G. . . . . **G. virescens**
Malabar G. . . . . **G. superba**
Roehrs G. . . . . . **G. roehrsiana**
Rothschild G. . . **G. rothschildiana**
Showy Malabar G. **G. superba grandiflora**

Gloryofthesnow **Chionodoxa; C. luciliae**

GLOSSOPET'ALON . **FORSELLESIA**

GLOTTID'IUM |w . . . . . . Bagpod
vesica'rium (*Sesbania vesicaria*) |w . . . Bagpod

GLOTTIPHYL'LUM **MESEMBRYANTHEMUM**
See **SUCCULENTS.**

GLOXIN'IA
The Gloxinia of florists is Sinningia speciosa. Gloxinia crassifolia and G. gigantea are names loosely and incorrectly applied in the trade to some of the varieties of that species. The genus Gloxinia, of botanists, is not in cultivation.

Gloxinia . . . . **Sinningia**
Bigleaf Common G. **S. speciosa macrophylla**
Common G. . . . . . . **S. speciosa**

Glue-alga . . . . **Gloiopeltis**
Sieve G. . . . . . . **G. coliformis**

GLU'TA . . . . Gluta
beng'has (*renghas*) . . . Renghas G.
el'egans . . . . . . Tenasserim G.
tavoya'na . Tavoy G. (*Tavoy Redwood*)
travancor'ica . . . . Travancore G.

GLYCE'RIA (*PANICULARIA*) . . . Mannagrass
See **GRASS GENERA.**

GLYCI'NE (*SOJA*) |w . . Groundnut
a'pios . . . . **Apios americana**
floribun'da . . . . **Wistaria f.**
grac'ilis . . . . Slender G.
sinen'sis . . . . **Wistaria s.**
so'ja (*hispida; max; Soja m.*) |w . . . Soybean

GLYCOS'MIS . . . . . . Glycosmis
citrifo'lia . . . . Chinese G.
pentaphyl'la . . . . Malay G.

GLYCYRRHI'ZA |w . . . . Licorice
gla'bra (typical form) . . Common L.
—glandulif'era . . . . . Russian L.
lepido'ta |w . . . . . American L.
triphyl'la

GLYPTOSTRO'BUS . . Chinacypress
pen'silis (*heterophyllus; sinensis*) . . . Chinacypress

GMELI'NA . . . . Bushbeech
arbo'rea (*Premna a.*) . . . Malay B.
hys'trix . . . . Bristly B.
leichhard'ti . . . . . Leichhardt B. (*Whitebeech*)

GNAPHA'LIUM |w . . . . . Cudweed
chilen'se (*sprengeli*) Cottonbatting C.
decur'rens . . . . Clammy C.
lana'tum . . . **Helichrysum petiolatum**
leontopo'dium . **Leontopodium alpinum**

Hort. var.; hv.=horticultural variety (or varieties); sp.=species (singular); spp.=species (plural).
₵=clon; × (as a prefix)=hybrid; × (between scientific plant names)=crossed by; ∞=polybrid; |w=plant useful to wildlife.
See Glossary for definitions of clon, hybrid, and polybrid.

GNAPHALIUM, continued
obtusifo'lium (*polycephalum*) FRAGRANT CUDWEED
purpu'reum |w . . . . . PURPLE C.
ramosis'simum
sylvat'icum . . . . WOOD C.
uligino'sum . . . . LOW C.

GNE'TUM . . . . JOINTFIR
gne'mon . . . . SPINACH J.
scan'dens . . . . . SWEETBERRY J.

GOABEAN . . . . **Psophocarpus**
INDIES G. . . . . **P. tetragonolobus**

GOATGRASS . . . . **Aegilops**
BARB G. . . . . **A. triuncialis**
JOINTED G. . . . . . . **A. cylindrica**

GOATSBEARD . . . . **Aruncus**
ALLEGANY G. . . . **A. allegheniensis**
HAIRY A. G. . . . . **A. a. pubescens**
SYLVAN G. . . . . **A. sylvester**

GOATSRUE . . . . **Galega**
CAUCASUS G. . . . . . . **G. orientalis**
COMMON G. . . . . **G. officinalis**

GODE'TIA . . . . GODETIA
amoe'na . . FAREWELL-TO-SPRING G.
bot'tae . . . . BOTTS G.
densiflo'ra . . . . **Boisduvalia d.**
grandiflo'ra (*whitneyi; Oenothera w.*) WHITNEY G.
lep'ida
parviflo'ra . . . . . SMALLFLOWER G.
quadrivul'nera
vimin'ea . . . . ORCHID G.
APPLEBLOSSOM. HV. Godetia
BRILLIANT
CRIMSONGLOW
CRIMSONKING
DUCHESS OF ALBANY
GLORIOSA
LADY ALBEMARLE
LADY SATINROSE
LINDLEY
MARCHIONESS OF SALISBURY
ROSAMOND
ROSYMORN
THE BRIDE
WHITEPEARL
YELLOWQUEEN

GOLDASTER . . . . **Chrysopsis**
BREWER G. . . . . **C. breweri**
COTTONY G. . . . . . . **C. gossypina**
GRASSLEAF G. . . . . **C. graminifolia**
HAIRY G. . . . . **C. villosa**
LEAFY G. . . . . **C. foliosa**
MARYLAND G. . . . . **C. mariana**
NARROWLEAF G. . . . . **C. stenophylla**
OREGON G. . . . . **C. oregona**
ROUGH G. . . . . **C. hispida**
RUTTERS HAIRY G. . **C. villosa rutteri**
SICKLELEAF G. . . . . . . **C. falcata**

GOLDBALLCACTUS . **Echinocactus grusoni**

GOLDCARPET . . . . **Gilmania**
DEATHVALLEY G. . . . . . **G. luteola**

Goldenball . . . . . GOLDBALLCACTUS: **Echinocactus grusoni**

GOLDENCLUB . **Orontium; O. aquaticum**

GOLDENCUP
Hunnemannia; H. fumariaefolia

GOLDENEYE . . . . **Viguiera**
ANNUAL G. . . . . **V. annua**
CUTLEAF G. . . . . . . **V. laciniata**
DEATHVALLEY G. . . . . **V. reticulata**
HAIRY G. . . . . **V. ciliata**
HEARTLEAF G. . . . . . **V. cordifolia**

GOLDENEYE, continued
LONGLEAF G. . . . **Viguiera longifolia**
NEVADA SHOWY G.
V. multiflora nevadensis
OVALLEAF G. . . . . **V. ovalis**
PARISH G. . . . . **V. deltoidea parishi**
PORTER G. . . . . **V. porteri**
SHOWY G. . . . . **V. multiflora**
SKELETONLEAF G. . . . **V. stenoloba**
SLIMLEAF G. . . . . **V. tenuifolia**

GOLDENHEAD . . . . . **Acamptopappus**
RAYLESS G. . . . **A. sphaerocephalus**
SHOCKLEY G. . . . . **A. shockleyi**

GOLDENLARCH . . . . . . **Pseudolarix**
DWARF G. . . . . . **P. amabilis nana**
LOVELY G. . . . . **P. amabilis**

GOLDENRAY . . . . **Ligularia**
BIGLEAF G. . . . . **L. clivorum**
GREATLEAF G. . . . . **L. macrophylla**
JAPAN G. . . . . **L. japonica**
KAEMPFER G. . . . . . . **L. kaempferi**
SIBERIAN G. . . . . **L. sibirica**
VEITCH G. . . . . **L. veitchiana**
WILSON G. . . . . **L. wilsoniana**

GOLDENROD . . . . **Solidago**
ALPINE G. . . . . **S. algida**
ARIZONA G. . . . . **S. arizonica**
ATLANTIC G. . . . . **S. arguta**
BABY G. . . . . **S. nana**
BOG G. . . . . **S. uliginosa**
BOOTT G. . . . . **S. bootti**
BUCKLEY G. . . . . **S. buckleyi**
CALIFORNIA G. . . . . **S. californica**
CANADA G. . . . . **S. canadensis**
CAPULIN G. . . . . **S. capulinsis**
CLUSTER G. . . . . **S. glomerata**
COAST G. . . . . **S. spathulata**
CREEK G. . . . . **S. elongata**
CUTLER G. . . . . **S. cutleri**
DECUMBENT G. . . . . . **S. decumbens**
DOWNY G. . . . . **S. puberula**
DYERSWEED G. . . . . . **S. nemoralis**
ELEGANT G. . . . . **S. lepida**
EUROPEAN G. . . . . **S. virgaurea**
FRAGRANT D. . . . . **S. odora**
FURRY G. . . . . **S. pubens**
GIANT G. . . . . **S. gigantea**
GRASSLEAF G. . . . . . **S. graminifolia**
HAIRY G. . . . . **S. hispida**
LEAVENWORTH G. . . **S. leavenworthi**
LINDHEIMER G. . . **S. lindheimeriana**
MISSOURI G. . . . . **S. missouriensis**
NELSON G. . . . . **S. concinna**
NEVADA G. . . . . **S. spectabilis**
NOBLE G. . . . . **S. speciosa**
NOVEMBER G. . **S. gigantea leiophylla**
NUTTALL GRASSLEAF G.
S. graminifolia nuttalli
OHIO G. . . . . **S. ohioensis**
PALELEAF G. . . . . **S. pallida**
PARRY D. . . . . **S. parryi**
PINEBARREN G. . . . . . . **S. fistulosa**
PLUME G. . . . . **S. juncea**
RAND G. . . . . **S. randi**
RIDDELL G. . . . . **S. riddelli**
ROCK G. . . . . **S. petradoria**
ROUGHLEAF G. . . . . **S. patula**
RUGGED G. . . . . **S. squarrosa**
SEASIDE G. . . . . . . **S. sempervirens**
SCEPTER G. . . . . **S. erecta**
SHORTS G. . . . . **S. shorti**
SHOWYWAND G. . . . . **S. rigidiuscula**
SILVER G. . . . . **S. bicolor**
STIFF G. . . . . **S. rigida**
SWAMP G. . . . . **S. neglecta**

GOLDENROD, continued
TALL G. . . . . . . **Solidago altissima**
THREENERVE G. . . . . . **S. trinervata**
WARD G. . . . . **S. wardi**
WESTERN G. . . . . . . **S. occidentalis**
WILLOWLEAF G. . . . . **S. stricta**
WREATH G. . . . . **S. caesia**
WRINKLED G. . . . . **S. rugosa**
ZIGZAG G. . . . . **S. flexicaulis**

GOLDENSEAL . **Hydrastis; H. canadensis**

GOLDENSTAR
Chrysogonum; C. virginianum

Goldenthistle . OYSTERPLANT: **Scolymus**

GOLDENTOP . . . **Lamarckia; L. aurea**

GOLDENTRUMPET
Anemopaegma chamberlayni

GOLDENWEED . . . . **Aplopappus**
BRICKELL G. . . . . **A. brickellioides**
BURROWEED . . . . **A. fruticosus**
CHAPARRAL G. . . . . . . **A. propinquus**
COAST G. . . **A. venetus vernonioides**
COOPER G. . . . . **A. cooperi**
DAMIANA G. . . . . **A. venetus**
DESERT G. . **A. linearifolius interior**
DWARF G. . . . . **A. nanus**
FLEECE G. . . . . **A. arborescens**
FREMONT G. . . . . **A. fremonti**
GREENES G. . . . . **A. greenei**
HEATHER G. . . . . **A. ericoides**
HOARY G. . . . . **A. canus**
IRONPLANT G. . . . . . . **A. spinulosus**
JIMMYWEED . . . . **A. heterophyllus**
LANCELEAF G. . . . . . **A. lanceolatus**
LARCHLEAF G. . . . . . . **A. laricifolius**
MONTEREY G. . . . . . **A. eastwoodae**
NARROWLEAF G. . . . . **A. linearifolius**
NUTTALL G. . . . . **A. nuttalli**
PALELEAF G. . . . . **A. acradenius**
PALMER G. . . . . **A. palmeri**
PARISH G. . . . . **A. parishi**
PINE G. . . . . **A. pinifolius**
PLANTAIN G. . . . . **A. uniflorus**
RABBITBRUSH G. . . . . . **A. bloomeri**
RUSH G. . . . . **A. junceus**
SAWTOOTH G. . . . . . . **A. squarrosus**
SINGLEHEAD G. . . . **A. suffruticosus**
STEMLESS G. . . . . **A. acaulis**
TUFTED G. . . . . **A. falcatus**
WEDGELEAF G. . . . . **A. cuneatus**
WHITESTEM G. . . . . . **A. macronema**
WHOLELEAF G. . . . . . **A. integrifolius**

GOLDFERN . **Pityrogramma chrysophylla**
CALIFORNIA G. . . . . . **P. triangularis**
JAMAICA G. . . . . **P. sulphurea**
LAUCHE G. . . . **P. chrysophylla** HV.

GOLDFIELDS . . . . **Baeria**
BRANCHY G. . . . . . **B. chrysostoma**
BROADFRUIT G. . . . . . **B. platycarpa**
EVERLASTING G. . . . . **B. aristata**
MARITIME G. . . . . **B. maritima**
TUBER G. . . . . **B. macrantha**

GOLDHAIR-PLANT
Chrysocoma coma-aurea

GOLDILOCKS, EUROPEAN **Linosyris vulgaris**

GOLDPOPPY . . . . **Eschscholtzia**
CALIFORNIAPOPPY . . . **E. californica**
DESERT G. . . . . . **E. glyptosperma**
DOUGLAS CALIFORNIAPOPPY
E. californica douglasi
LITTLE G. . . . . **E. minutiflora**
MEXICAN G. . . . . **E. mexicana**
SEA G. . . . . **E. maritima**
THREADLEAF G. . . . . . **E. tenuifolia**

GOLDRAINTREE . . . . . . Koelreuteria
BOUGAINVILLEA G. . . K. bipinnata
FLAME G. . . . . . . K. formosana
PANICLED G. . . . . . K. paniculata
PYRAMID P. G. . . . . K. p. fastigiata

GOLDSAXIFRAGE . . . Chrysosplenium
ALTERNATELEAF G. . C. alternifolium
AMERICAN G. . . . C. americanum
BERING G. . . . . . C. beringianum
OPPOSITELEAF G. . . C. oppositifolium

Goldspanglewood . . . . . LACEWOOD: Cardwellia sublimis

GOLDSTARGRASS . . . . . . Hypoxis
BAROMETER G. . . . H. hygrometrica
CAPE G. . . . . H. stellata
COMMON G. . . . . H. hirsuta

Goldstem . . . . INDIANGRASS, YELLOW: Sorghastrum nutans

GOLDTHREAD . . . . Coptis
ALASKA G. . . . . C. trifolia
COMMON G. . . . . . C. groenlandica
CUTLEAF G. . . . . . . C. laciniata
FERNY G. . . . . . . C. asplenifolia
WESTERN G. . . . . . C. occidentalis

GOLDWAND . . Wachendorfia thyrsiflora

GOME'SA (*GOMEZA*)
See **ORCHID GENERA.**

GOMPHOCAR'PUS
cordifo'lius (*Asclepias cordifolia*)
frutico'sus
purpuras'cens . . . . . **Solanoa p.**
tex'tilis
tomento'sus

GOMPHOLO'BIUM . GOMPHOLOBIUM
latifo'lium . . . . . BROADLEAF G.
polymor'phum

GOMPHRE'NA . . . GLOBEAMARANTH
decum'bens . . . . . PROSTRATE G.
globo'sa . . . . COMMON G.
GOLDEN (*aurea*) HV.
haagea'na . . . . HAAGE G.
nit'ida

GONGO'RA
See **ORCHID GENERA.**

GONIOLI'MON . . . . . **LIMONIUM**

GONIO'MA
kamas'si . . . . . . KAMASSIWOOD

GONIOPHLE'BIUM . **POLYPODIUM**
See **FERN GENERA.**

Gonolo'bus macrophyl'lus **Vincetoxicum gonocarpos**

GONOSPER'MUM
canarien'se

GONZALAGU'NIA
spica'ta

GOOBER . . . . Voandzeia
CONGO G. . . . . . . V. subterranea

GOOBERGRASS . . . . . Amphicarpum
ANNUAL G. . . . . A. purshi
PERENNIAL G. . A. muhlenbergianum

GOOD'IA . . . . GOODIA
lotifo'lia . . . . CLOVER G.

GOOD'YERA (*PERAMIUM*) RATTLESNAKEPLANTAIN
See **ORCHID GENERA, HARDY TERRESTRIAL GROUP.**

GOOSEBERRY . . . . Ribes
See also CURRANT.
BAY G. . . . . R. leptosmum
BIG HEDGE G. . R. alpestre giganteum
BITTER G. . . . . R. amarum
BLOOD SIERRA G. . R. roezli cruentum
BUREJA G. . . . . R. burejense
CALIFORNIA G. . . . R. californicum
CANADA G. . . . . R. oxyacanthoides
∞ CULVERWELL G. . . ∞ R. culverwelli
DESERT G. . . . . . . R. velutinum
EUROPEAN G. . . . . R. uva-crispa
FLORIDA G. . . . . . R. echinellum
FUCHSIA G. . . . . . R. speciosum
∞ GARDEN G. . . . . . ∞ R. rusticum
GEORGIA G. . . . . . . R. curvatum
∞ GOTHOBURG G. . ∞ R. gothoburgense
Gummy G. . . . . LOBBS G.
HAIRYSTEM G. . . . . . R. hirtellum
∞ HALFBLOOD G. . . . . . . ∞ R. utile
∞ HAWTHORN G. . . . ∞ R. robustum
HEDGE G. . . . . R. alpestre
HUPA G. . . . . R. marshalli
IDAHO G. . . . . R. irriguum
∞ INNOMINATE G. . . ∞ R. innominatum
KANSU G. . . . . . R. stenocarpum
KLAMATH G. . . . . R. klamathensis
KNIGHTS G. . . . . ×R. knighti
LOBBS G. . . . . R. lobbi
MENZIES G. . . . . R. menziesi
MISSOURI G. . . . . R. missouriense
Mt. Adams G. . . . . . . WATSON G.
OAKWOODS G. . . . . R. quercetorum
ORANGE G. . . . . . . R. pinetorum
PARISH G. . . . . R. parishi
PASTURE G. . . . . . . R. cynosbati
PURPUS G. . . . . R. purpusi
REDSHOOT G. . . . . R. setosum
ROUNDLEAF G. . . . R. rotundifolium
SANGABRIEL G. . . . . R. hesperium
SIERRA G. . . . . R. roezli
SILKY G. . . . . R. sericeum
SISKIYOU G. . . . . R. binominatum
SMOOTH PASTURE G. R. cynosbati inerme
SNOW G. . . . . R. niveum
STICKY MENZIES G. R. menziesi ixoderme
STRAGGLY G. . . . . . R. divaricatum
TRUMPET G. . . . . . R. leptanthum
TULARE G. . . . . . . R. tularense
UMATILLA G. . . . . . . R. cognatum
∞ VAN FLEET G. . ∞ R. vanfleetianum
VICTORS G. . . . . R. victoris
WATSON G. . . . . R. watsonianum
WHITESTEM G. . . . . R. inerme
WOOLLYFLOWER G. . . R. lasianthum

GOOSEBERRYGOURD Cucumis myriocarpus

GOOSEFOOT . . . . . . Chenopodium
BLITE G. . . . . C. capitatum
CITY G. . . . . C. urbicum
DRUG WORMSEED G. C. ambrosioides anthelminticum
FREMONT G. . . . . C. fremonti
GOODKINGHENRY G. C. bonus-henricus
JERUSALEMOAK G. . . . . . C. botrys
LAMBSQUARTERS G. . . . . C. album
MAPLELEAF G. . . . . . C. hybridum
NETTLELEAF G. . . . . . . C. murale
OAKLEAF G. . . . . C. glaucum
PIGWEED G. . . . . . . C. paganum
PITSEED G. . . . . . C. berlandieri
QUINOA . . . . C. quinoa
RAGLEAF G. . . . . C. incisum
RED G. . . . . C. rubrum
SLIMLEAF G. . . . . C. leptophyllum
WORMSEED G. . . . C. ambrosioides

GOOSEGRASS . . . . . Eleusine indica
THREESPIKE G. . . . E. tristachya

GORDO'NIA . . . . GORDONIA
alatama'ha . . . . **Franklinia a.**
axilla'ris
chrysan'dra
lasian'thus . . . . . LOBLOLLYBAY G.
pubes'cens . . . **Franklinia alatamaha**

GORGA'SIA . . . . . . **ROYSTONEA**
See **PALM GENERA.**

GORMA'NIA . . . . **SEDUM**
See **SUCCULENTS.**

GORSE . . . . Ulex
COMMON G. . . . . . . U. europaeus
DWARF G. . . . . U. nanus
SLENDER SMALLFLOWER G. U. parviflorus provincialis
SMALLFLOWER G. . . . U. parviflorus

Gor'skia conjuga'ta . . . . **Copaifera c.**

GOSSWEILERODEN'DRON GOSSWEILERTREE
balsamif'erum . . . . . . AGBA G.

GOSSYPIOSPER'MUM
prae'cox

GOSSYP'IUM (*INGENHOUZIA; THURBERIA*) |w . . . COTTON
See also Cotton in **FIBER PLANTS.**

arbo'reum . . . . . ASIATIC TREE C.
—assam'icum . INDIA LARGEBOLL C.
—nan'king . . . . CHINA C.
—soudanen'se . INDIA SMALLBOLL C.
armouria'num
barbaden'se (*brasiliense; microcarpon; mustelinum; vitifolium*) SEAISLAND C.
AMERICAN EGYPTIAN. HV.
BRAZILIAN
EGYPTIAN
ISHAN
PERUVIAN (*peruvianum*)
RUSSIAN EGYPTIAN
TANGUIS (*Ecuador; Peru*)
davidso'ni . . . . DAVIDSON C.
herba'ceum . . . . LEVANT C.
hirsu'tum . . . . UPLAND C.
—religio'sum
AMERICAN LONGSTAPLE. HV. G. hirsutum
kirk'i . . . . KIRKS C.
microcar'pum; musteli'num **G. barbadense**
obtusifo'lium
purpuras'cens . . . . . BOURBON C.
AMERICAN TREE. HV.
MOCO
stocks'i . . . . ARABIAN C.
sturt'i . . . . AUSTRALIAN C.
taiten'se . . . . FIJI C.
thur'beri (*Thurberia thespesioides*) THURBER C.
tomento'sum . . . . . HAWAIIAN C.
trilo'bum (*Ingenhouzia triloba*)
vitifo'lium . . . . . . **G. barbadense**

GOUA'NIA
lupuloi'des . . . . CHAWSTICK

GOUP'IA
gla'bra . . . . KOPIE

GOURD . . . . Lagenaria
BUFFALOGOURD Cucurbita foetidissima
CALABASH G. . . . . . . L. siceraria
MALABARGOURD . . Cucurbita ficifolia
YELLOWFLOWERGOURD. C. pepo ovifera

GOURLIE'A
spino'sa

GOUTWEED . . . . **Aegopodium**
BISHOPS G. . . . . . **A. podograria**
SILVEREDGE B. G. . . **A. p. variegatum**

Governorsplum . . . . . RAMONTCHI: **Flacourtia indica**

GRABOW'SKIA
boerhaaviaefo'lia (*glauca*)

GRACILA'RIA . . . . . CEYLONMOSS
lichenoi'des . . . . AGAR C.

Gram, Black . . . . . . BEAN, MUNGO: **Phaseolus mungo**

GRAMA . . . . **Bouteloua**
AMAZON G. . . . **B. megapotamica**
BLACK G. . . . . **B. eriopoda**
BLUE G. . . . . **B. gracilis**
FIVESPIKE B. G. . . . . **B. g. stricta**
GYP G. . . . . **B. breviseta**
HAIRY G. . . . . **B. hirsuta**
MAT G. . . . . **B. simplex**
NEALLEY G. . . . . **B. uniflora**
NEEDLE G. . . . . . **B. aristidoides**
PARRY G. . . . . **B. parryi**
PURPLE G. . . . . . . **B. radicosa**
RED G. . . . . **B. trifida**
ROTHROCK G. . . . . . **B. rothrocki**
SANTARITA G. . . . . . **B. eludens**
SIDEOATS G. . . . . **B. curtipendula**
SIXWEEKS G. . . . . . **B. barbata**
SLENDER G. . . . . . . **B. filiformis**
SPRUCETOP G. . . **B. chondrosioides**
TEXAS G. . . . . **B. rigidiseta**
Woollyfoot G. . . . . BLACK G.

GRAMMAN'GIS **GRAMMATOPHYLLUM**
See **ORCHID GENERA.**

GRAMMAN'THES . . **VAUANTHES**
See **SUCCULENTS.**

GRAMMATOPHYL'LUM(*GRAMMANGIS*)
See **ORCHID GENERA.**

Granada . . . POMEGRANATE, COMMON: **Punica granatum**

GRANADILLA
GIANT G. . **Passiflora quadrangularis**
PURPLE G. . . . . **P. edulis**
SWEET G. . . . . **P. ligularis**
Yellow G. . WATERLEMON: **P. laurifolia**

GRAPE . . . . **Vitis**
AMUR G. . . . . . . **V. amurensis**
∞ ANDERSON G. . . . . ∞ **V. andersoni**
AUTUMNGLOW THUNBERG G. **V. thunbergi sinuata**
BIRCH G. . . . . . . **V. betulifolia**
BIRD G. . . . . . . **V. munsoniana**
BLUE BRIER G. . **V. davidi cyanocarpa**
BLUELEAF G. . . . . **V. argentifolia**
BOURQUIN G. **V. aestivalis bourquiniana**
BRIER G. . . . . **V. davidi**
BRONZELEAF G. . . . . . **V. pulchra**
CALIFORNIA G. . . . . **V. californica**
CALLOOSE G. . . . **V. shuttleworthi**
CANYON G. . . . . . . **V. arizonica**
CAT G. . . . . **V. palmata**
CHAMPIN G. . . . . . . **V. champini**
CHINAWOOL G. . . . . **V. pentagona**
CLARETLEAF EUROPEAN G. **V. vinifera purpurea**
CURTISS G. . . . . **V. sola**
DOAN G. . . . . **V. doaniana**
DOWNY G. . . . . **V. lanata**
EUROPEAN G. . . . . . **V. vinifera**

GRAPE, continued
FIGLEAF G. . . . . . **Vitis smalliana**
FLORIDA BLUE G. . . . . . . **V. gigas**
FOX G. . . . . **V. labrusca**
FROST G. . . . . **V. vulpina**
GLORYVINE G. . . . . **V. coignetiae**
JUNE RIVERBANK G.. **V. riparia praecox**
LITTLELEAF CHINAWOOL G. **V. pentagona bellula**
LITTLELEAF ORIENTAL G. **V. flexuosa parvifolia**
LONGS G. . . . . **V. longi**
MUSCADINE G. . . . . **V. rotundifolia**
MUSTANG G. . . . . . . **V. candicans**
NEWENGLAND G. . . **V. novae-angliae**
ORIENTAL G. . . . . . . **V. flexuosa**
PAGNUCCI G. . . **V. piasezki pagnucci**
PARSLEYLEAF EUROPEAN G. **V. vinifera apiifolia**
PIASEZKY G. . . . . **V. piasezki**
PINEWOODS G. . . . . . **V. lincecumi**
POSSUM G. . . . . **V. baileyana**
QUICKSAND RIVERBANK G. **V. riparia syrticola**
REDSHANK G. . . . **V. rufotomentosa**
RIVERBANK G. . . . . **V. riparia**
ROMANET G. . . . . . . **V. romaneti**
SAND G. . . . . **V. rupestris**
SIMPSON G. . . . . **V. simpsoni**
∞ SLAVIN G. . . . . ∞ **V. slavini**
SUMMER G. . . . . . . **V. aestivalis**
SWEET MOUNTAIN G. . . **V. monticola**
SWEET WINTER G. . . . . **V. cinerea**
THUNBERG G. . . . . . . **V. thunbergi**
TOTOLOCHE G. . . . . . **V. popenoei**
TRELEASE G. . . . . **V. treleasei**
VALLEY G. . . . . **V. girdiana**
WHITE FOX G. . . . **V. labrusca alba**
WILSON G. . . . . **V. wilsonae**
WINTER G. . . . . . . **V. berlandieri**
WOODLAND EUROPEAN G. **V. vinifera sylvestris**

GRAPEFERN . . . . **Botrychium**
ALABAMA G. . . . . . **B. alabamense**
BROADLEAF G. . . . . **B. multifidum**
COMMON G. . . . . **B. obliquum**
CUTLEAF G. . . . . . . **B. dissectum**
MATRICARY G. . . **B. matricariaefolius**
MOONWORT . . . . **B. lunaria**

GRAPEFRUIT . . . . . . **Citrus paradisi**

GRAPEHYACINTH . . . . **Muscari**
ARMENIAN G. . . . **M. armeniacum**
CAUCASUS G. . . . . **M. paradoxum**
COMMON G. . . . . . **M. botryoides**
FLESHPINK C. G. . . . **M. b. carneum**
HELDREICH G. . . . . **M. heldreichi**
MUSK G. . . . . . . **M. moschatum**
STARCH G. . . . . . **M. racemosum**
TASSEL G. . . . . **M. comosum**
WHITE COMMON G. **M. botryoides album**
YELLOW MUSK G. **M. moschatum flavum**

GRAPTOPET'ALUM (*BYRNESIA*) LETTERPETAL
See **SUCCULENTS.**

GRAPTOPHYL'LUM
pic'tum (*hortense*)

GRASS GENERA

This list of grasses includes those native to, naturalized in, or more commonly cultivated in the United States. Bamboos, however, are omitted, as they are covered in a separate list. See also the Cereals list. This Grass Genera list has been based chiefly on the late Dr. A. S. Hitchcock's "Manual of the Grasses of the United States" (U. S. Department of Agriculture Misc. Pub. 200. 1935), the common names of which were prepared by the late Dr. F. V. Coville (see p. 14, *op. cit.*). Preliminary to that work Dr. Coville asked me to furnish him with a list of grass names and, for that purpose, my 45-p. mss. "Alphabetical List of U. S. Grass Names," dated September 20, 1932, was prepared and a copy sent to Dr. Coville. I have drawn freely on that for this list, as well as on 30 years of range research records in the U. S. Forest Service.

Prior to publication, this list of Grass Genera was mimeographed and about 200 copies were sent out to agronomists, agrostologists, range and wildlife specialists, and other persons actively interested in this subject. Replies, which run the gamut from warm commendation to severe denunciation, have been received from about 60 of these people. Sincere effort has been made to weigh all this criticism carefully and, we hope, with some success. Obviously it is impossible to please everybody. I am especially indebted to Jason R. Swallen of the Bureau of Plant Industry for his full and careful review, for answering innumerable questions, and making many valuable and helpful suggestions. Others who have given material aid include: T. M. Stevenson, Dominion of Canada Agrostologist; O. A. Stevens and Warren C. Whitman of the North Dakota Agricultural Experiment Station; L. C. Snyder of the South Dakota Agricultural Experiment Station; O. S. Aamodt, E. Marion Brown, L. A. Clark, M. A. Hein, Wesley Keller, John H. Martin, John Monteith, Jr., Laurence C. Newell, George E. Ritchey, George A. Rogler, J. T. Sarvis, D. A. Savage, and D. C. Smith of the Bureau of Plant Industry, U. S. Department of Agriculture; F. J. Crider, H. A. Gunning, A. L. Hafenrichter, M. M. Hoover, C. G. Marshall, Gale Monson (now with the Interior Department), H. D. Stoesz, Paul Tabor, W. R. Van Dersal, and G. L. Weber of the Soil Conservation Service, and Lincoln E. Ellison and L. J. Pessin of the Forest Service, U. S. Department of Agriculture.

Some criticism has been voiced as to the number of entries in this list, both of scientific and common names. It is important to remember that the Grass family is economically the most important family of plants, including as it does cereals, bamboos, and a host of pasture, forage, hay, and silage plants; sugarcane, and numerous ornamentals, dye, drug, and fiber species, etc. The significance of grasses is not confined to agriculture but vitally extends into the realms of horticulture, forestry, range management, soil conservation, wildlife management, and other fields. The value of hundreds of grass species in all these fields yet remains to be explored, a prodigious task, yet vitally necessary considering the enormous potential value of grasses in the economy of man. For this reason the Editorial Committee believes that the inclusion of the fullest possible list of grasses in this book will serve a useful purpose.

W. A. DAYTON, Forest Service,
U. S. Department of Agriculture

ACHYRO'DES . . **LAMARCKIA**

AE'GILOPS . . . . . GOATGRASS
cylin'drica . . . . JOINTED G.
ova'ta
triuncia'lis . . . . BARB G.

AEGOPO'GON
tenel'lus

GRASS GENERA, continued

AELURO'PUS ·
litora'lis

AGROPY'RON ⌊w . . Wheatgrass
al'bicans . . . . . . Montana W.
arenic'ola . . . . Dune W.
arizo'nicum . . . . . . Arizona W.
ba'keri . . . . Baker W.
crista'tum . . . . . . Crested W.
Hort. *strain* of A. cristatum: Fairway
dasystach'yum . . . Thickspike W.
el'meri . . . . Elmer W.
elonga'tum . . . . Tall W.
grif'fithsi . . . . . . Griffiths W.
iner'me (*A. spicatum i.*)
Beardless Bluebunch W.
latiglu'me
par'ishi . . . . Parish W.
—lae've
pauciflo'rum (*tenerum*) ⌊w . Slender W.
pring'lei . . . . Pringle W.
pseudore'pens . . False Quackgrass
pun'gens . . . . . . Stiffleaf Q.
re'pens ⌊w . . . . Quackgrass
richardso'ni . . . . **A. subsecundum**
ripa'rium . . . . . Streambank W.
saun'dersi (*Elymus s.*) Saunders W.
saxic'ola . . . . Foxtail W.
scrib'neri . . . . . . Scribner W.
semicosta'tum . . . . Drooping W.
sibir'icum . . . . . . Siberian W.
smith'i ⌊w . . . . . . Bluestem W.
(*Colorado Bluestem; Western W.*)

This important, widely distributed, and now cultivated species is often called by the trite name Western Wheatgrass, which appears to be a translation of the synonymous Latin name, A. occidentale. The species has been uniformly known by the U. S. Forest Service as Bluestem Wheatgrass (or "Bluestem") for more than 35 years, and the Editorial Committee deems that name preferable.

spica'tum ⌊w . Bearded Bluebunch W.
—iner'me . . . . **A. inerme**
—pubes'cens . . . . Hairy B.W.
subsecun'dum (*richardsoni*)
Bearded W.
—andi'num . . . . . Alpine B.W.
te'nerum . . . . **A. pauciflorum**
tricho'phorum . . . . Stiffhair W.
tritice'um . . . . Annual W.
ugam'icum . . . . Ugam W.
viola'ceum . . . . Violet W.

This Old World species is listed here, because a short, stocky subalpine form of A. pauciflorum, with thick purplish heads, is often mistaken for it and appears under the name in American botanical works.

vulpi'num . . . . Swale W.

AGROS'TIS ⌊w . . . . Bentgrass
aequival'vis ⌊w . . . . . Alaska B.
affi'nis
al'ba ⌊w . . . . Redtop
am'pla . . . . **A. exarata a.**
asperifo'lia . . . . **A. exarata**
ba'keri . . . . Baker B.
blasdal'ei . . . . . . Blasdale B.
borea'lis . . . . Arctic B.
califor'nica . . . . California B.
cani'na . . . . Velvet B.
capilla'ris Auth., *not* L. . . **A. tenuis**
diegoen'sis (*foliosa* Auth., *not* R. & S.)
Thin B. (*Thingrass*)
elliottia'na . . . . . . Elliott B.
(*Annual Ticklegrass*)
exara'ta (*asperifolia; scouleri*). Spike B.

GRASS GENERA (AGROSTIS), continued

exara'ta am'pla (*A. ampla*)
Big Spike Bentgrass
—monole'pis (*A. microphylla*)
Awned S.B.
exi'gua . . . . Sixweeks B.
folio'sa Auth., *not* R. & S.
A. diegoensis
hall'i . . . . Halls B.
—pringle'i . . . . . . Pringle B.
henderso'ni . . . . Henderson B.
hiema'lis ⌊w . . . . . . Winter B.

One of the numerous grass species commonly called Ticklegrass.

—gemina'ta . . . . . Arctic W.B.
(*Arctic Ticklegrass*)
how'elli . . . . Howell B.
hu'milis . . . . Alpine B.
idahoen'sis . . . . Idaho B.
interrup'ta . . . . Italian B.
(*Italian Windgrass*)
le'pida . . . . Sequoia B.
longilig'ula ⌊w . . . Longtongue B.
marit'ima . . . . **A. palustris**
microphyl'la . . **A. exarata monolepis**
nebulo'sa . . . . Cloud B.
ni'gra . . . . Black B.
oregonen'sis ⌊w . . . . . Oregon B.
pal'lens . . . . Dune B.
palus'tris (*maritima*) ⌊w . Creeping B.
(*Carpet B.; Fiorin*)

Cocoos, Coos Bay, Metropolitan, Seaside, Seashore, and Washington Bentgrasses are *strains* of A. palustris used for lawns and golf greens.

peren'nans (*schiedeana*) . Autumn B.
—ela'ta ⌊w
retrofrac'ta . . . . . . Pacific B.
ross'ae . . . . Ross B.
scoul'eri . . . . **A. exarata**
spica-vent'i . Wind B. (*Windgrass*)
stolonif'era

This species has been confused in literature with A. palustris.

ten'uis (*capillaris* Auth., *not* L.; *vulgaris; A. v. alba*) . . . Colonial B.
—arista'ta . . . . Awned C.B.

RhodeIsland Bent is a noncreeping strain of A. tenuis.

—astoria'na . . . . Astoriana C.B.
thurberia'na . . . . . Thurber B.
verticilla'ta ⌊w . . . . . Water B.
vulga'ris . . . . **A. tenuis**
—al'ba . . . . **A. tenuis**

AI'RA (*ASPRIS*) ⌊w . . Hairgrass
capilla'ris . . . . Annual H.
caryophylle'a ⌊w . . . . . Silver H.
prae'cox . . . . Early H.

AI'RA Auth., *not* L.
DESCHAMPSIA

ALOPECU'RUS ⌊w . . . Foxtail
aequa'lis (*aristulatus*) ⌊w Shortawn F.
alpi'nus ⌊w . . . . Alpine F.
arundina'ceus
carolinia'nus (*macouni; ramosus*) ⌊w
Carolina F.
cre'ticus . . . . Crete F.
genicula'tus ⌊w . . . . . . Water F.
how'elli (*californicus*) ⌊w . Howell F.
macoun'i . . . . . . **A. carolinianus**
myosuroi'des . . . . Mouse F.
palles'cens ⌊w . . . . Washington F.
praten'sis . . . . Meadow F.
ramo'sus . . . . **A. carolinianus**
sacca'tus ⌊w . . . . Pacific F.
ventrico'sus . . . . . Creeping F.

GRASS GENERA, continued

AMMO'PHILA ⌊w . . Beachgrass
arena'ria . . . . . . European B.
breviligula'ta ⌊w . . . . American B.

AMPHICAR'PUM (*AMPHICARPON*) . . . . . Goobergrass
muhlenbergia'num (*floridanum*)
Perennial G.
pursh'i . . . . Annual G.

ANATH'ERUM . . **VETIVERIA**

ANDROPO'GON ⌊w . Bluestem
(*Broomsedge*)
annula'ris . . . . . . Angleton B.
arcta'tus
argen'teus . . . . . **A. saccharoides**
barbino'dis . . . . Cane B.
brachystach'yus . . . Shortspike B.
cabanis'i . . . . Cabanis B.
campylora'cheus
capil'lipes
carrico'sus . . . . India B.
cirra'tus . . . . Texas B.
diver'gens
elliott'i . . . . Elliott B.
emer'sus . . . . **A. perforatus**
exarista'tus . . . . Awnless B.
florida'nus . . . . Florida B.
foveola'tus . . . . Delhi B.
furca'tus ⌊w . . . . Big B.
glomera'tus ⌊w . . . . . . Bushy B.
grac'ilis . . . . Wiry B.
halepen'sis . . . . **Sorghum halepense**
hall'i . . . . Sand B.
(*Sandhill B.; Turkeyfoot*)
hirtiflo'rus
—feen'sis . . . . SantaFe B.
hir'tus . . . . . **Vetiveria zizanioides**
interme'dius . . . . Australian B.
ischae'mum . . . . . EastIndies B.
iwarancu'sa . **Cymbopogon jwarancusa**
laguroi'des . . . . . **A. saccharoides**
littora'lis . . . . . . Seacoast B.
longiber'bis
marit'imus . . . . Gulf B.
mohr'i . . . . Mohrs B.
nodo'sus
perangusta'tus . . . . . . Slim B.
perfora'tus (*emersus*) . . Pinhole B.
pertu'sus . . . . Pitted B.
pu'milus . . . . Low B.
saccharoi'des (*argenteus; laguroides; torreyanus*) ⌊w . . . . Silver B.
scopa'rius ⌊w . . . . Little B.
—neomexica'nus . . NewMexico B.
semiber'bis
seric'eus . . . . Silky B.
sor'ghum . . . . . **Sorghum vulgare**
—sudanen'sis . . . **S. v. sudanense**
stolo'nifer . . . . . . Creeping B.
subten'uis
te'ner . . . . Slender B.
terna'rius
torreya'nus . . . . . **A. saccharoides**
tra'cyi . . . . Tracy B.
virgin'icus ⌊w . . . Yellowsedge B.
—glaucop'sis
—hirsu'tior . . . . Gulf Y.B.
wright'i . . . . Wrights B.

ANTHAENAN'TIA ⌊w . Silkyscale
ru'fa ⌊w . . . . Purple S.
villo'sa ⌊w . . . . Green S.

ANTHEPHO'RA
hermaphrodi'ta

ANTHOCH'LOA
colusa'na . . . . . . Colusagrass

GRASS GENERA, continued

ANTHOXAN'THUM |w VERNALGRASS
arista'tum . . . . ANNUAL V.
grac'ile . . . . ITALIAN V.
odora'tum |w . . . . . . SWEET V.

ARIS'TIDA |w . . . . THREEAWN
adscensio'nis . . . SIXWEEKS T.
affi'nis (*palustris*) . . . LONGLEAF T.
arizo'nica . . . . . . ARIZONA T.
barba'ta (*havardi*) . . . HAVARD T.
basira'mea . . . . . . FORKTIP T.
califor'nica . . . . . MOHAVE T.
condensa'ta . . . . BIG T.
curtiss'i . . . . CURTISS T.
desman'tha . . . . CURLY T.
dichot'oma . . . CHURCHMOUSE T.
divarica'ta (*palmeri*) . . POVERTY T.
diver'gens . . . . **A. ternipes minor**
fendleria'na |w . . . . FENDLER T.
florida'na . . . . . . KEYWEST T.
glabra'ta . . . . . SANTARITA T.
glau'ca (*reverchoni*) . . . . BLUE T.
gy'rans . . . . . CORKSCREW T.
hamulo'sa
ha'vardi . . . . **A. barbata**
interme'dia . . . . . KEARNEY T.
lano'sa . . . . WOOLLYSHEATH T.
longespi'ca . . . . SLIMSPIKE T.
longise'ta |w . . . . RED T.
—rariflo'ra
—robus'ta
mohr'i . . . . MOHRS T.
oligan'tha . . . . PRAIRIE T.
orcuttia'na (*schiediana* Auth.) SINGLE T.
pal'meri . . . . **A. divaricata**
palus'tris . . . . **A. affinis**
pan'sa . . . . WOOTON T.
par'ishi . . . . PARISH T.
pat'ula . . . . TALL T.
purpuras'cens |w . ARROWFEATHER T.
purpu'rea . . . . PURPLE T.
—laxiflo'ra
ramosis'sima . . . . . . S-CURVE T.
revercho'ni . . . . **A. glauca**
rhizomoph'ora . . . . . FLORIDA T.
roemeria'na . . . . . . ROEMER T.
sca'bra . . . . **A. ternipes**
schiedia'na Auth., *not* Trin. & Rupr. **A. orcuttiana**
simpliciflo'ra . . . . . CHAPMAN T.
spicifor'mis . . . . BOTTLEBRUSH T.
stric'ta . . . . PINELAND T.
tenuispi'ca . . . . . . HILLSBORO T.
ter'nipes (*scabra*) . . . . SPIDERGRASS
—mi'nor (*A. divergens*)
tuberculo'sa . . . . BEACHWOODS T.
virga'ta . . . . TRINIUS T.
wright'i . . . . WRIGHT T.

ARRHENA'THERUM . OATGRASS
ela'tius . . . . TALL O.
—bulbo'sum . . . . TUBER O.

ARTHRAX'ON
his'pidus
—crypta'therus

ARUNDINA'RIA . . . . . . CANE
gigan'tea (*macrosperma*) . . GIANT C.
tec'ta . . . . SWITCH C.

ARUN'DO . . . . GIANTREED
do'nax . . . . GIANTREED
—versicol'or . . . . WHITESTRIPE G.
qui'la . . . . **Chusquea q.**

AS'PRIS . . . . **AIRA**

GRASS GENERA, continued

ASTRE'BLA . . . MITCHELLGRASS
elymoi'des . . . . HOOP M.
lappa'cea . . . . CURLY M.
pectina'ta . . . . BULL M.

AVE'NA |w . . . . OAT
barba'ta . . . . SLENDER O.
brev'is . . . . LITTLE O.
byzanti'na . . . . RED O.
fa'tua |w . . . . WILD O.
flaves'cens . . . . **Trisetum f.**
hook'eri . . . . SPIKE O.
mortonia'na . . . . ALPINE O.
nu'da . . . . NAKED O.
pubes'cens . . . . HAIRY O.
sati'va |w . . . . COMMON O.
—diffu'sa . . . . . TREEPANICLE O.
—orienta'lis . . . . SIDE O.
ster'ilis . . . . ANIMATED O.
strigo'sa . . . . LOPSIDED O.

AXON'OPUS |w . . CARPETGRASS
affi'nis . . . . COMMON C.
compres'sus |w . . . . TROPICAL C.
furca'tus |w . . . . BIG C.

BECKMAN'NIA |w . SLOUGHGRASS
syzigach'ne (*erucaeformis* Auth., *not* (L.) Hort.) |w . . . AMERICAN S.

BLEPHARIDACH'NE DESERTGRASS
bigelo'vi . . . . BIGELOW D.
king'i . . . . KING D.

BLEPHARONEU'RON |w
trichol'epis |w . . . PINE DROPSEED

BOUTELOU'A |w . . . . . GRAMA
aristidoi'des |w . . . . . NEEDLE G.
barba'ta |w . . . . . . SIXWEEKS G.
brevise'ta . . . GYP G. (*Chinograss*)
chondrosioi'des . . . . SPRUCETOP G.
curtipen'dula . . . . . . SIDEOATS G.
elu'dens . . . . SANTARITA G.
erio'poda |w . . . . BLACK G. (*Woollyfoot G.*)
filifor'mis . . . . SLENDER G.
grac'ilis (*oligostachya*) |w . . BLUE G.
—stric'ta . . . . . FIVESPIKE B.G.

This is perhaps of doubtful validity.

hirsu'ta . . . . HAIRY G.
megapota'mica . . . . . AMAZON G.
par'ryi . . . . PARRY G.
radico'sa . . . . PURPLE G.
rigidise'ta (*texana*) . . . . TEXAS G.
rothrock'i . . . . ROTHROCK G.
sim'plex . . . . MAT G.
trif'ida |w . . . . RED G.
uniflo'ra . . . . NEALLY G.

BRACHIA'RIA |w . . SIGNALGRASS
brizan'tha . . . . PALISADE S.
ciliatis'sima |w
erucaefor'mis
exten'sa |w
plantagin'ea

BRACHYELY'TRUM . SHORTHUSK
erec'tum . . . . BEARDED S.

BRACHYPO'DIUM . FALSEBROME
dista'chyon . . . . PURPLE F.
pinna'tum . . . . . . JAPANESE F.
sylvat'icum . . . . SLENDER F.

BRI'ZA . . . . QUAKINGGRASS
max'ima . . . . BIG Q.
me'dia . . . . PERENNIAL Q.
mi'nor . . . . LITTLE Q.

GRASS GENERA, continued

BRO'MUS |w . . . . BROME (*Bromegrass; Cheat; Chess*)
aleuten'sis . . . . . . ALEUTIAN B.
anom'alus (*porteri*) |w . . NODDING B. (*Porter B.*)
—lana'tipes . . . . . WOOLLY N.B.
arena'rius . . . . . AUSTRALIAN B.
arven'sis . . . . FIELD B.
breviarista'tus (*subvelutinus*) SLIMLEAF B.
brizaefor'mis . . . . RATTLE B.
carina'tus (*californicus; marginatus; maritimus; polyanthus*) |w MOUNTAIN B.
cathar'ticus (*unioloides*) |w RESCUE B. (*Rescuegrass*)
cilia'tus (*richardsoni*) . . FRINGED B. (*Richardson B.*)
—laeviglu'mis (*B. laeviglumis*)
commuta'tus . . . . HAIRY B.
—aprico'rum . . . . . SUNSHINE B.
erec'tus . . . . MEADOW B.
frondo'sus |w . . . . . WEEPING B.
gran'dis . . . . TALL B.
inerm'is . . . . SMOOTH B.
japon'icus . . . . JAPANESE B.
kalm'i . . . . KALM B.
lacinia'tus
laeviglu'mis . . . . . . **B. ciliatus l.**
laev'ipes . . . . CHINOOK B.
latiglu'mis . . . . EARLEAF B.
macrosta'chys . MEDITERRANEAN B.
madriten'sis . . . . SPANISH B.
margina'tus . . . . . . **B. carinatus**
marit'imus . . . . **B. carinatus**
mollifor'mis . . . . PYGMY B.
mol'lis . . . . SOFT B.

This species is often mistaken for the European B. hordeaceus.

orcuttia'nus . . . . ORCUTT B.
—hall'i . . . . HALL O.B.
pacif'icus . . . . PACIFIC B.
polyan'thus . . . . . . **B. carinatus**
por'teri . . . . **B. anomalus**
pumpellia'nus . . . . . PUMPELLY B.
—tweed'yi . . . . TWEEDY B.
pur'gans . . . . CANADA B.
racemo'sus |w . . . . BALD B.
richardso'ni . . . . **B. ciliatus**
rig'idus (*villosus* Forsk., *not* Scop.) |w RIPGUT B.
—gusson'ei . . . . . LONGARM R.B.
ru'bens . . . . FOXTAIL B. (*Red B.*)
scopa'rius . . . . BROOM B.
secali'nus |w . . . . CHESS B.
—veluti'nus
sitchen'sis . . . . ALASKA B.
ster'ilis . . . . POVERTY B.
subveluti'nus . . . . **B. breviaristatus**
suksdorf'i . . . . . . SUKSDORF B.
tecto'rum |w . . . . CHEATGRASS B. (*Downy B.*)
texen'sis . . . . TEXAS B.
trin'ii . . . . CHILEAN B.
—excel'sus . . . . . . PANAMINT B.
unioloi'des . . . . **B. catharticus**
villo'sus Forsk., *not* Scop. . **B. rigidus**
vulga'ris . . . . COLUMBIA B.

BU'CHLOE (*BULBILIS*) |w
dactyloi'des |w . . . . BUFFALOGRASS

BUL'BILIS . . . . **BUCHLOE**

CALAMAGROS'TIS |w . REEDGRASS
bolan'deri . . . . REDWOODS R.
brew'eri . . . . SHORTHAIR R.
cain'i . . . . CAINS R.
califor'nica . . . . SIERRA R.

GRASS GENERA (CALAMAGROSTIS), con.
canaden'sis |w Bluejoint Reedgrass*
—macounia'na . . . . Macoun B.R.
—sca'bra (*C. langsdorfi* Auth.) Rough B.R.
cinnoi'des . . . . . . Hairyseed R.
crassiglu'mis
den'sa . . . . Cuyamaca R.
epigei'os . . . . Chee R.
folio'sa . . . . . . Humboldt R.
how'elli . . . . . Riverbluff R.
inexpan'sa (*hyperborea*) |w Northern R.
—barbula'ta . . . . Washington R.
—novae-an'gliae . . NewEngland R.
koelerioi'des . . . . Fire R.
lac'tea . . . . Knotroot R.
langsdorf'i Auth., *not* (Link) Trin. **C. canadensis scabra**
montanen'sis . . . . . Plains R.
neglec'ta |w . . . . . Slimstem R.
nutkaen'sis . . . . . . Pacific R.
perplex'a . . . . Dudley R.
pick'eringi |w . . . . . Pickering R.
por'teri . . . . Porter R.
purpuras'cens . Purple Pinegrass
rubes'cens . . . . Pinegrass
scopulo'rum . . . . Jones R.
scrib'neri . . . . . . Scribner R.
twee'dyi . . . . Cascades R.

CALAMOVIL'FA |w . . . Sandreed
brevi'pilis |w . . . . . Riverbank S.
cur'tissi . . . . Florida S.
gigan'tea . . . . Big S.
longifo'lia . . . . Prairie S.
—mag'na . . . . . . GreatLakes S.

CAMPULO'SUS . . . **CTENIUM**

CAPRIO'LA . . . . **CYNODON**

CATABRO'SA |w
aquat'ica (*Glyceria a.*) |w . Brookgrass

CATAPO'DIUM
tuberculo'sum

CATHES'TECUM
erec'tum . . . . . . Falsegrama

CEN'CHRUS |w . . . . Sandbur
barba'tus . . . . Guinea S.
biflo'rus . . . . India S.
brown'i (*viridis*) . . Slimbristle S.
echina'tus . . . . . . Southern S.
gracil'limus . . . . . . Slender S.
incer'tus . . . . Coast S.
myosuroi'des . . . . Big S.
pauciflo'rus |w . . . . Mat S.
tribuloi'des |w . . . . Dune S.

CHAETOCH'LOA . **SETARIA**

CHLO'RIS |w
Chloris; Windmillgrass

The species with stiff spreading-radiating spikes are called Windmillgrass.

andropogonoi'des . . . Slimspike W.
barba'ta Nash, *not* Swartz **C. polydactyla**
berro'i . . . . Argentine C.
chlori'dea . . . . Buryseed C.
cilia'ta . . . . Fringed C.
cuculla'ta . . . . Hooded W.
distichophyl'la . . . . Weeping C.
el'egans . . . . **C. virgata**
florida'na . . . . . . Twospike C.
gaya'na . . . . Rhodesgrass
glau'ca |w . . . . . . Saltmarsh C.
latisqua'mea . . . . Nash W.
neglec'ta . . . . . . Fourspike C.

GRASS GENERA (CHLORIS), continued
pet'raea . . . . Stiffleaf Chloris
polydac'tyla (*barbata*) Manyspiked C.
prieur'i . . . . Moroccan C.
radia'ta . . . . Annual C.
subdolichosta'chya Shortspike Windmillgrass
texen'sis . . . . Texas W.
trunca'ta . . . . Creeping W.
ventrico'sa . . . . . Australian W.
verticilla'ta . . . . . . Tumble W.
virga'ta (*elegans*) |w . . . . Showy C.

CHRYSOPO'GON
pauciflo'rus . . . . **Rhaphis p.**

CHUSQUE'A
qui'la (*Arundo q.*) . . . . . Quila

CIN'NA . . . . Woodreed
arundina'cea . . . . Stout W.
latifo'lia . . . . Drooping W.

CLEISTOG'ENES
serot'ina

CO'IX . . . . Jobstears
lacryma-job'i . . . . Jobstears

COLEAN'THUS |w . . Mudgrass
sub'tilis |w . . . . Mudgrass

CORIDOCH'LOA . Bugseedgrass
cimici'na (*Panicum cimicinum*) Bugseedgrass

CORTADE'RIA . . Pampasgrass
rudius'cula (*quila*) . . . Quila P.
selloa'na (*argentea; Gynerium argenteum*) . . . . Selloa P.

CORYNE'PHORUS Clubawngrass
canes'cens (*Weingaertneria c.*)

COT'TEA . . . . . Cottagrass
pappophoroi'des . . . . Cottagrass

CRYP'SIS |w . . . . Pricklegrass
aculea'ta |w . . . . . Pricklegrass

CTE'NIUM (*CAMPULOSUS*) Combgrass
aromat'icum . . . . Toothachegrass
florida'num . . . . . . Florida C.

CUTAN'DIA
memphit'ica . . . . Memphisgrass

CYMBOPO'GON
citra'tus . . . . Lemongrass
flexuo'sus . . . . Cochin L.
jwarancu'sa (*Andropogon iwarancusa*) Iwarancusagrass
martin'i . . . . Roshagrass
nar'dus Citronellagrass (*Nardgrass*)
winteria'nus . . . . . Mahapengiri
The validity of this species has been questioned.

CY'NODON (*CAPRIOLA*) |w Dogtoothgrass
dac'tylon |w . . . . Bermudagrass
incomple'tus . . . Karrookweek D.
slectostach'yus . . . . . . Giant D.
transvaalen'sis . . . . Transvaal D.

CYNOSU'RUS . . . . . Dogtail
crista'tus . . . . Crested D.
echina'tus . . . . . . Hedgehog D.

DAC'TYLIS |w . . . Orchardgrass (*Cocksfoot*)
glomera'ta |w . . . . Orchardgrass

DACTYLOCTE'NIUM |w Crowfootgrass
aegyp'tium |w . . . . . . Durban C.

GRASS GENERA, continued
DANTHO'NIA |w . . . Danthonia
califor'nica . . . . . California D.
—america'na (*D. americana*) Hairy C.D.
compres'sa |w . . . . Flatstem D.
elephanti'na . . . . . . Elephant D.
flaves'cens . . . . Yellow D.
interme'dia . . . . Timber D.
par'ryi . . . . Parry D.
penicilla'ta . . . . Wallaby D.
pilo'sa . . . . Hairy D.
purpu'rea . . . . . . Haaschare D.
robus'ta . . . . Bandicoot D.
semiannula'ris . . . Australian D.
seric'ea . . . . Downy D.
spica'ta |w . . . . Poverty D.
unispica'ta . . . . . . Onespike D.

DEMAZE'RIA . **DESMAZERIA**

DESCHAMP'SIA (*AIRA* Auth., *not* L.) |w . . . . Hairgrass
atropurpu'rea |w . . . Mountain H.
caespito'sa |w . . . . . . Tufted H.
danthonioi'des . . . . . . Annual H.
elonga'ta . . . . Slender H.
flexuo'sa . . . . Wavy H.
holcifor'mis |w . . . . . . Pacific H.

DESMAZE'RIA (*DEMAZERIA*) Demazeria
sic'ula . . . . Demazeria

DIARRHE'NA (*DIARINA*) Beakgrain
america'na (*Korycarpus diandrus*) American B.

DIGITA'RIA (*SYNTHERISMA*) |w
Crabgrass; Fingergrass

Crabgrass is applied to the creeping species and Fingergrass to the erect species.

albico'ma
decum'bens . . . . . Spreading C.
didac'tyla . . . . Blue F.
erian'tha . . . . Woolly F.
—stolonif'era
ex'ilis . . . . Fundi F.
filifor'mis |w . . . . . . Slender F.
florida'na . . . . Florida C.
gracil'lima . . . . Longleaf F.
horizonta'lis . . . . Jamaica C.
ischae'mum |w . . . . . Smooth C.
—mississippien'sis . . . . Big S.C.
littora'lis . . . . Shore C.
pani'cea . . . . Millet F.
pauciflo'ra . . . . Twospike F.
pentz'i . . . . Pentz F.
run'yoni . . . . Dune F.
sanguina'lis |w . . . . . . Hairy C.
serot'ina . . . . Blanket C.
simp'soni . . . . Isle-of-pines F.
subcal'va . . . . . Plant City F.
swazilanden'sis . . . Swaziland F.
texa'na . . . . Texas F.
villo'sa |w . . . . Shaggy F.
violas'cens . . . . Violet C.

DISSANTHE'LIUM
califor'nicum . . . . Catalinagrass

DIS'TICHLIS |w . . . Saltgrass
denta'ta |w . . . . Little S.
spica'ta |w . . . . . . Seashore S.
stric'ta |w . . . . Inland S.
texa'na . . . . Texas S.

ECHINOCH'LOA |w . Cockspur
colo'num |w . . . . Junglerice (*Shanwamillet*)

GRASS GENERA (ECHINOCHLOA), con.
crusgal'li |w . . . . Barnyardgrass
—frumenta'cea (*E. c. edulis; E. frumentacea*) . . . . Japanesemillet
—mi'tis . Beardless Barnyardgrass
—zelayen'sis |w . . . . Alkali B.
crus-pavo'nis |w . . Gulf Cockspur
paludig'ena |w . . . . . Florida C.
wal'teri |w . . . . Coast C.

ELEUSI'NE |w
coraca'na . . . . Ragimillet
in'dica |w . . . . Goosegrass
trista'chya . . . . . Threespike G.

E'LYMUS |w . . . . Wildrye
ambig'uus . . . . Colorado W.
—strigo'sus (*E. strigosus*) Hairyscale C.W.
arena'rius . . European Dune W.
arenico'la . . . . Sand W.
arista'tus . . . . Purple W.
borea'lis . . . . **E. hirsutus**
canaden'sis . . . . Canada W.
—brachystach'ys Smoothscale C.W.
—robus'tus (*E. robustus*) Robust C.W.
caput-medu'sae . . . Medusahead W.
chinen'sis (*pseudoagropyron*) Chinese W.
condensa'tus . . . . . . Giant W.
—pu'bens . . . . . . Pacific G.W.
dahu'ricus . . . . . . Dahurian W.
dasystach'ys . . . . Thickspike W.
flaves'cens . . . . Yellow W.
gigan'teus . . . . . . Mammoth W.
glau'cus |w . . . . Blue W.
—jep'soni . . . . Jepson W.
—ten'uis . . . . Vancouver W.
hirsu'tus (*borealis*) . . . Alaska W.
hirtiflo'rus . . . . . . Wyoming W.
innova'tus . . . . . Fuzzyspike W.
interrup'tus . . . . Texas W.
jun'ceus . . . . Russian W.
leckenby'i . . . . . **Sitanion hanseni**
macoun'i . . . . Macoun W.
mol'lis |w . . . Common Dune W.
pseudoagropy'ron . . . . **E. chinensis**
ripa'rius . . . . Riverbank W.
robus'tus . . . . . . **E. canadensis r.**
sabulo'sus
sali'na . . . . Salina W.
saun'dersi . . . . **Agropyron s.**
sibir'icus . . . . Siberian W.
stria'tus . . . . **E. virginicus**
strigo'sus . . . . . **E. ambiguus s.**
triticoi'des . . . . . Creeping W.
—pubes'cens . . Hairyleaf C.W.
—sim'plex (*E. simplex*) . Low C.W.
vancouveren'sis Vancouver Dune W.
villo'sus . . . . Hairy W.
vires'cens . . . . Pacific W.
virgin'icus (*striatus*) |w . Virginia W.
—austra'lis . . . . . . Prairie W.
—glabriflo'rus . . . Longawn V.W.
—haloph'ilus . . . Saltmarsh V.W.
—interme'dius . . Hairyscale V.W.
—submu'ticus . . . Beardless V.W.

ELYONU'RUS . . . Balsamscale
barbicul'mis . . . . . Woolspike B.
tripsacoi'des . . . PanAmerican B.

ENNEAPO'GON
brachystach'yus

EPICAM'PES **MUHLENBERGIA**
ligula'ta . . . . **M. longiligula**
subpa'tens . . . . . . **M. emersleyi**

GRASS GENERA, continued
ERAGROS'TIS |w . . . Lovegrass
abyssin'ica . . . . Teff
acu'ta . . . . Florida L.
amab'ilis (*plumosa*) . . . Feather L.
ar'ida . . . . Desert L.
bahien'sis . . . . Bahia L.
barrelier'i . . . Mediterranean L.
bey'richi . . . . Wichita L.
brizan'thes . . . . . Kimberly L.
capilla'ris . . . . Lacegrass
carolinia'na . . . . . **E. pectinacea**
cha'riis . . . . . Thalia Lovegrass
chlorome'las . . . . Boer L.
cilianen'sis (*major; megastachya*) |w Stinkgrass
cilia'ris . . . . . . Gophertail L.
curtipedicella'ta . . . . Gummy L.
cur'vula . . . . Weeping L.
cyperoi'des . . . . Bristly L.
diffu'sa . . . . Spreading L.
elliott'i |w . . . . Elliott L.
eragros'tis . . . . . . **E. poaeoides**
ero'sa . . . . Chihuahua L.
ferrugin'ea . . . . Korean L.
frank'i |w . . . . Sandbar L.
—brev'ipes . . . . . Glenhaven S.L.
glomera'ta |w . . . . Pond L.
hirsu'ta |w . . . . Bigtop L.
hypnoi'des |w . . . . Teal L.
interme'dia . . . . Plains L.
japon'ica . . . . **E. tenella**
lehmannia'na . . . . . Lehmann L.
lu'gens . . . . Mourning L.
lutes'cens . . . . Sixweeks L.
ma'jor; megasta'chya . **E. cilianensis**
mexica'na . . . . Mexican L.
mi'nor . . . . **E. poaeoides**
neo-mexica'na . . . NewMexico L.
obtu'sa . . . . Flarescale L.
obtusiflo'ra . . . . Alkali L.
orcuttia'na . . . . Orcutt L.
pal'meri . . . . RioGrande L.
pectina'cea (*caroliniana*) |w Carolina L.
peregri'na . . . . . . Peregrine L.
pilif'era . . . . Sandhill L.

Perhaps not more than a variety of E. trichodes.

pilo'sa . . . . India L.
plumo'sa . . . . **E. amabilis**
poaeoi'des (*eragrostis; minor*) Little L.
refrac'ta . . . . Coastal L.
rep'tans |w . . . . Creeping L.
secundiflo'ra . . . . Red L.
sessilispi'ca . . . . Tumble L.
silvea'na . . . . Silveus L.
sim'plex . . . . Fortyflower L.
spectab'ilis . . . . Purple L.
spica'ta . . . . Spike L.
stenophyl'la . . . . . Slimflower L.
suave'olens . . . . Candy L.
swal'leni . . . . Swallen L.
tenel'la (*japonica*) . . . Japanese L.
tephrosan'thos . . . . Gulf L.
tra'cyi . . . . SanibelIsland L.
trem'ula
trichoco'lea . . . . . Hairysheath L.
tricho'des . . . . Sand L.
unioloi'des . . . . Chinese L.
vires'cens . . . . Chilean L.

EREMOCH'LOA
cilia'ris
ophiuroi'des . . . . Centipedegrass

ERIAN'THUS |w . . Plumegrass
alopecuroi'des (*divaricatus*) |w Silver P.

GRASS GENERA (ERIANTHUS), continued
alopecuroi'des hirsu'tus Florida Silver Plumegrass
brevibar'bis . . . . Brown P.
contor'tus |w . . . . . Bent-awn P.
divarica'tus . . . . . **E. alopecuroides**
gigan'teus (*saccharoides*) . Sugarcane P.
raven'nae . . . . . . Ravennagrass
stric'tus |w . . . . Narrow P.

ERIOCH'LOA |w . . . Cupgrass
arista'ta . . . . Bearded C.
contrac'ta |w . . . . Prairie C.
distach'ys
grac'ilis |w . . . . Southwestern C.
—mi'nor . . . . Small S.C.
lem'moni . . . . Canyon C.
michaux'i (*longifolia; mollis*) |w Longleaf C.
—simp'soni . . . . Everglades C.
nel'soni . . . . Nelson C.
polystach'ya |w
proc'era . . . . Tropical C.
puncta'ta |w . . . . . . Louisiana C. (*Everlastinggrass*)
seric'ea . . . . Texas C.
villo'sa . . . . Hairy C.

EUCHLAE'NA . . . . . Teosinte
mexica'na . . . . Mexican T.
peren'nis . . . . Perennial T.

EULA'LIA . . . . Eulalia
vimin'ea . . . . Nepal E.

FESTU'CA |w . . . . . . Fescue
amethysti'na . . . . . Amethyst F.
ar'ida . . . . Desert F.
arizo'nica |w . . . . Arizona F.
arundina'cea . . . . **F. elatior a.**
brachyphyl'la . . . . **F. ovina b.**
bromoi'des Auth., *not* L. **F. dertonensis**
califor'nica . . . . . . California F.
callig'era . . . . **F. ovina**
capilla'ta (*tenuifolia*) . . . . Hair F.
confin'is . . . . . **Hesperochloa kingi**
—rabio'sa . . . . **H. k. rabiosa**
confu'sa . . . . Klickitat F.
dasycla'da . . . . Utah F.
dertonen'sis (*bromoides* Auth., *not* L.) Brome F.
durius'cula . . . . **F. ovina d.**
eastwood'ae . . . . . . Eastwood F.
ela'tior (*pratensis*) |w . . Meadow F.
—arundina'cea (*F. arundinacea*) Reed F.
el'meri . . . . Coastrange F.
—confer'ta . . . . Tall C.F.
genicula'ta . . . . . Portuguese F.
gigan'tea . . . . Giant F.
glau'ca . . . . **F. ovina g.**
gray'i . . . . Grays F.
hall'i . . . . **F. scabrella**
heterophyl'la . . . . **F. rubra h.**
idahoen'sis (*ingrata; F. ovina i.*) Idaho F.
king'i . . . . **Hesperochloa k.**
—rabio'sa . . . . **H. k. rabiosa**
ligula'ta . . . . Guadalupe F.
maire'i . . . . Maires F.
marit'ima . . . . Sea F.
megalu'ra . . . . Foxtail F.
microsta'chys . . . . Small F.
myu'ros . . . . Rattail F.
obtu'sa (*nutans*) . . . . . Nodding F.
occidenta'lis . . . . Western F.
octoflo'ra |w . . . . . . Sixweeks F.
—hirtel'la . . . . Hairy S.F.
ovi'na (*calligera; F. o. calligera; F. o. pseudovina; F. o. sciaphila; saximontana*) |w . . . . . . Sheep F.

GRASS GENERA (FESTUCA), continued
ovi'na brachyphyl'la (*F. brachyphylla; F. o. supina*) . . . . ALPINE FESCUE
—durius'cula (*F. duriuscula*) HARD F.
—glau'ca (*F. glauca*) . . . BLUE F.
—ingra'ta . . . . **F. idahoensis**
—supi'na . . **F. ovina brachyphylla**
pacif'ica . . . . PACIFIC F.
paradox'a (*shorti*) . . . . CLUSTER F.
praten'sis . . . . **F. elatior**
reflex'a . . . . . TWOFLOWER F.
ru'bra lw . . . . RED F.
—commuta'ta . . . . CHEWINGS F.
—fal'lax
—heterophyl'la (*F. heterophylla*) SHADE F.
—lanugino'sa . HAIRYSCALE RED F.
saximonta'na . . . . **F. ovina**
scabrel'la (*halli*) . . . . ROUGH F.
—ma'jor . . . . BIG R.F.
sciu'rea . . . . SQUIRREL F.
short'i . . . . **F. paradoxa**
soro'ria . . . . RAVINE F.
spadic'ea
subula'ta . . . . BEARDED F.
subuliflo'ra . . . . CRINKLEAWN F.
tenuifo'lia . . . . **F. capillata**
texa'na Vasey, *not* Steud. . **F. versuta**
F. texana Steud. is not a Fescue!
thur'beri . . . . THURBER F.
tra'cyi . . . . TRACY F.
va'ria
—alpes'tris
—scopa'ria
versu'ta (*texana* Vasey, *not* Steud.) TEXAS F.
virid'ula . . . . GREEN F.

FLUMIN'EA (*SCOLOCHLOA*) lw RIVERGRASS
festuca'cea lw

GASTRI'DIUM . . . . NITGRASS
ventrico'sum (*lendigerum*) . NITGRASS

GLYCE'RIA (*PANICULARIA*) lw MANNAGRASS
acutiflo'ra lw . . . . . CREEPING M.
america'na . . . . **G. grandis**
aquat'ica . . . . . . **Catabrosa a.**
arkansa'na lw . . . . ARKANSAS M.
borea'lis lw . . . . NORTHERN M.
canaden'sis lw . . . RATTLESNAKE M.
—lax'a . . . . TALL R.M.
ela'ta (*G. nervata e.*) lw . . TALL M.
erec'ta . . . . SPIKE M.
fernald'i (*neogaea* Auth., *not* Steud.) lw FERNALD M.
flu'itans lw . . . . . . WATER M.
gran'dis (*americana*) lw AMERICAN M.
leptosta'chya lw . . . SLIMHEAD M.
melica'ria (*torreyana*) . . MELIC M.
neogae'a . . . . **G. striata**
neogae'a Auth., *not* Steud. **G. fernaldi**
nerva'ta . . . . **G. striata**
—ela'ta . . . . **G. elata**
nubig'ena . . SMOKYMOUNTAINS M.
obtu'sa lw . . . . . . ATLANTIC M.
occidenta'lis lw . NORTHWESTERN M.
otis'i . . . . . . WASHINGTON M.
pal'lida lw . . . . PALE M.
pauciflo'ra lw . . . . . . WEAK M.
septentriona'lis lw . . EASTERN M.
stria'ta (*neogaea; nervata*) lw FOWL M.
torreya'na . . . . . . **G. melicaria**

GRASS GENERA, continued
GYMNOPO'GON lw SKELETONGRASS
ambig'uus lw . . . . . . BEARDED S.
brevifo'lius . . . . SLIM S.
chapmania'nus . . . . CHAPMAN S.
florida'nus . . . . FLORIDA S.

GYNE'RIUM
argen'teum . . . **Cortaderia selloana**
sagitta'tum (*saccharoides*) . UVAGRASS

HACKELOCH'LOA (*RYTILIX*) lw PITSCALEGRASS
granula'ris lw

HELEOCH'LOA . . HELEOCHLOA
alopecuroi'des . . . . . FOXTAIL H.
schoenoi'des . . . . SWAMPTIMOTHY

HESPEROCH'LOA . SPIKEFESCUE
king'i (*Festuca confinis; F. kingi*) SPIKEFESCUE
—rabio'sa (*Festuca confinis r.; F. kingi r.*) . . . . SHORTAWN S.

HETEROPO'GON lw
contor'tus lw . . . . . TANGLEHEAD
melanocar'pus . . . . . SWEET T.

HIEROCH'LOE (*SAVASTANA; TORRESIA*) lw . . SWEETGRASS
alpi'na . . . . ALPINE S.
occidenta'lis (*macrophylla*) lw CALIFORNIA S.
odora'ta lw . . . . . . SWEETGRASS

HILA'RIA lw . . . . . . HILARIA
belan'geri . . . . CURLYMESQUITE
—longifo'lia
james'i lw . . . . GALLETA
mu'tica lw . . . . TOBOSA
rig'ida . . . . BIG G.

HOL'CUS (*NOTHOLCUS*) lw VELVETGRASS
halepen'sis . . . **Sorghum halepense**
lana'tus (*Notholcus l.*) lw . COMMON V.
mol'lis . . . . GERMAN V.
sor'ghum . . . . . **Sorghum vulgare**
—sudanen'se . . . . **S. v. sudanense**
sudanen'sis . . . . **S. v. sudanense**

HOMALOCEN'CHRUS **LEERSIA**

HOR'DEUM lw . . . . . BARLEY
adscen'dens . . . . . . MEXICAN B.
borea'le . . . . . . **H. nodosum b.**
bulbo'sum . . . . BULBOUS B.
dis'tichon . . . . TWOROW B.
gussonia'num . MEDITERRANEAN B.
hexas'tichon . . . . . . SIXROW B.
juba'tum lw . . . . FOXTAIL B.
—caespito'sum . . . . . BOBTAIL B.
mari'num . . . . SEASIDE B.
montanen'se (*pammeli*) MONTANA B.
muri'num lw . . . . MOUSE B.
nodo'sum . . . . MEADOW B.
—borea'le (*H. b.*) . . NORTHERN M.B.
pusil'lum lw . . . . LITTLE B.
—pu'bens
sponta'neum . ANCESTRAL TWOROW B.
vulga're lw . . . . BARLEY
—trifurca'tum . . . . BEARDLESS B.

HYDROCH'LOA lw . WATERGRASS
carolinien'sis lw . . . . WATERGRASS

HYPARRHE'NIA
hir'ta
ru'fa . . . . JARAGUA

HYS'TRIX . BOTTLEBRUSHGRASS
califor'nica . . . . CALIFORNIA B.
pat'ula (*hystrix*) . BOTTLEBRUSHGRASS

GRASS GENERA, continued
IMPERA'TA . . . . . . SATINTAIL
brasilien'sis . BRAZIL S. (*Sapegrass*)
cylin'drica . . COGON S. (*Cogongrass*)
hook'eri . . . . CALIFORNIA S.

KOELE'RIA lw . . . . KOELERIA
crista'ta lw . . PRAIRIE JUNEGRASS
hirsu'ta . . . . HAIRY K.
phleoi'des . . . . ANNUAL K.
seta'cea . . . . . BRISTLELEAF K.

Korycar'pus dian'drus **Diarrhena americana**

LAGU'RUS . . . . . HARESTAIL
ova'tus . . . . HARESTAIL

LAMARCK'IA (*ACHYRODES*) GOLDENTOP
au'rea . . . . GOLDENTOP

LASIA'CIS . . . TIBISEE (*Tibisi*)
divarica'ta . . . . FLORIDA T.

LEER'SIA (*HOMALOCENCHRUS*) lw . . . . . CUTGRASS
hexan'dra lw . . . . . CLUBHEAD C.
lenticula'ris lw . . . CATCHFLYGRASS
monan'dra . . . . BUNCH CUTGRASS
oryzoi'des lw . . . . RICE C.
virgin'ica lw . . . . . WHITEGRASS

LEPTOCH'LOA lw . SPRANGLETOP
chloridifor'mis . . . . ARGENTINE S.
domingen'sis . . . . . DOMINICAN S.
du'bia . . . . GREEN S.
fascicula'ris lw . . . . . BEARDED S.
filifor'mis . . . . RED S.
neal'leyi lw . . . . NEALLEY S.
panicoi'des (*floribunda*) lw . AMAZON S.
sca'bra lw . . . . ROUGH S.
uniner'via (*imbricata*) lw . MEXICAN S.
virga'ta . . . . TROPICS S.
vis'cida . . . . STICKY S.

LEPTOLO'MA
cogna'tum (*Panicum c.*) FALL WITCHGRASS

LEPTU'RUS lw
cylin'dricus lw . . . . . . THINTAIL

LIMNO'DEA
arkansa'na . . . . . . OZARKGRASS

LO'LIUM lw . . . . RYEGRASS
multiflo'rum (*italicum*) lw ITALIAN R.
peren'ne . . . . . PERENNIAL R.
—crista'tum . . . . . . CRESTED R.
remo'tum . . . . HARDY R.
rig'idum . . . . SWISS R.
stric'tum . . . . SICILIAN R.
subula'tum . . . . . DALMATIAN R.
temulen'tum lw . DARNEL R. (*Darnel*)
—leptochae'ton . . BEARDLESS D.R.

LUZI'OLA lw . . . . . LUZIOLA
bahien'sis (*alabamensis*) lw BRAZILIAN L.
peruvia'na lw . . . . . PERUVIAN L.

LYCU'RUS . . . . . . WOLFTAIL
phleoi'des . . . . WOLFTAIL

LY'GEUM
spar'tium . . . . . . ESPARTOGRASS

MANISU'RIS lw . . . . JOINTTAIL
altis'sima lw . . . . . . AFRICAN J.
cylin'drica . . . . . . CAROLINA J.
exalta'ta . . . . **Rottboellia e.**
rugo'sa lw . . . . . . WRINKLED J.
tessella'ta . . . . LATTICE J.
tuberculo'sa . . . . . . FLORIDA J.

GRASS GENERA, continued

ME'LICA |w . MELIC; ONIONGRASS

The species of Melica with bulblike stem-bases are known as ONIONGRASS.

altis'sima (*sibirica*) . . SIBERIAN M.
arista'ta . . . . BEARDED M.
bulbo'sa (*bella*) |w . . . ONIONGRASS
califor'nica . . . . CALIFORNIA M.
cilia'ta . . . . . . SILKYSPIKE M.
frutes'cens . . . . . WOODY M.
fu'gax . . . . LITTLE O.
gey'eri . . . . GEYER O.
har'fordi . . . . HARFORD M.
imperfec'ta . . . . COASTRANGE M.
—flexuo'sa
—mi'nor
—refrac'ta
infla'ta . . . . YOSEMITE O.
mu'tica . . . . . TWOFLOWER M.
ni'tens . . . . . THREEFLOWER M.
por'teri . . . . PORTER M.
purpuras'cens . . . . . **Schizachne p.**
sibir'ica . . . . **M. altissima**
smith'i . . . . SMITH M.
spectab'ilis |w . . . . . SHOWY O.
stric'ta . . . . ROCK M.
subula'ta . . . . ALASKA O.
torreya'na . . . . TORREY M.
transsilva'nica . . TRANSYLVANIA M.

MELI'NIS
minutiflo'ra . . . . MOLASSESGRASS

MIBO'RA . . . . MIBORA
min'ima

MIL'IUM . . . . . MILLETGRASS
effu'sum . . . . . . AMERICAN M.

MISCAN'THUS (*XIPHAGROSTIS*) . SILVERGRASS (*Swordgrass*)
capen'sis . . . . CAPE S.
japon'icus . . . . JAPANESE S.
luzonen'sis . . . . LUZON S.
nepalen'sis . . . . NEPAL S.
saccha'rifer . . . . AMUR S.
sinen'sis . . . . CHINESE S.

The name Eulalia is sometimes, unfortunately, misapplied to this grass.

¢GOLDEN ZEBRAGRASS (*japonica zebrina stricta*) HV.
¢MAIDENGRASS (*gracillimus*)
¢STRIPED (*variegatus*). *Japan Rush.*
¢ZEBRAGRASS (*zebrinus*)

MOLI'NIA
caeru'lea . . . . MOORGRASS
¢STRIPED (*variegata*) HV.

MONANTHOCH'LOE |w
SHOREGRASS (*Saltcedar*)
littora'lis |w . . . . . . SHOREGRASS

MUHLENBER'GIA (*EPICAMPES*) |w . . . . MUHLY
acumina'ta . . . . **M. dubia**
andi'na (*comata*) . . . . FOXTAIL M.
arena'cea (*Sporobolus arenaceus; S. auriculatus*) . . . . . . EAR M.
arenic'ola . . . . SAND M.
arizo'nica . . . . ARIZONA M.
arsen'ei . . . . NAVAHO M.
asperifo'lia |w . . . . . . ALKALI M.
berlandier'i . . . . **M. rigida**
brachyphyl'la . . . . NODDING M.
califor'nica . . . . CALIFORNIA M.
capilla'ris . . . . HAIRAWN M.
—fi'lipes . . . . GULF H.M.
coma'ta . . . . **M. andina**
curtifo'lia . . . . UTAH M.

GRASS GENERA (MUHLENBERGIA), con.

curtiseto'sa . ILLINOIS NIMBLEWILL
cuspida'ta . . . STONYHILLS MUHLY
depaupera'ta . . . . . SIXWEEKS M.
du'bia (*acuminata*) . . . . PINE M.
dumo'sa . . . . BAMBOO M.
emersley'i (*Epicampes e.; E. subpatens*) BULLGRASS
expan'sa . . . . CUTOVER M.
filicul'mis . . . . . . SLIMSTEM M.
filiform'is |w . . . . PULLUP M.
folio'sa . . . . LEAFY M.
—setiglu'mis (*M. f. ambigua*) BEARDED L.M.
glabriflo'ra . . . . INLAND M.
glau'ca . . . . DESERT M.
grac'ilis Auth., *not* Kunth **M. montana**
gracil'lima . . . . **M. torreyi**
involu'ta . . . . CANYON M.
jones'i . . . . MODOC M.
lindheim'eri . . . . LINDHEIMER M.
longili'gula (*Epicampes ligulata*) LONGTONGUE M.
macrou'ra (*Epicampes m.*) WHISKGRASS M. (*Zacaton*, Mex.)
metcalf'ei . . . . . . METCALFE M.
mexica'na . . . . WIRESTEM M.
—commuta'ta . . . BEARDED W.M.
microsper'ma . . . LITTLESEED M.
monta'na (*gracilis* Auth., *not* Kunth; *trifida*) . . . . . . MOUNTAIN M.
montic'ola . . . . MESA M.
parviglu'mis . . . . . LONGAWN M.
pauciflo'ra (*neomexicana*) NEWMEXICO M.
polycau'lis . . . . CLIFF M.
por'teri . . . . BUSH M. (*Hoegrass*)
pun'gens . . . . SANDHILL M.
racemo'sa . . . . GREEN M.
re'pens . . . . RED M.
revercho'ni . . . . SEEP M.
richardso'nis . . . . . **M. squarrosa**
rig'ens (*Epicampes r.*) . . DEERGRASS
rig'ida (*berlandieri*) . . . PURPLE M.
schre'beri |w . . . . . NIMBLEWILL
—palus'tris . . . . WASHINGTON N.
setifo'lia . . . . . . CURLYLEAF M.
sobolif'era . . . . ROCK M.
—setig'era . . . . . BEARDED R.M.
squarro'sa (*richardsonis*) . . MAT M.
sylvat'ica . . . . FOREST M.
tenuiflo'ra . . . . . SLIMFLOWER M.
texa'na . . . . TEXAS M.
thur'beri . . . . THURBER M.
torreya'na . . . . . NEWJERSEY M.
tor'reyi (*gracillima*) . . . . RING M. (*Ringgrass*)
trif'ida . . . . **M. montana**
uniflo'ra . . . . BOG M.
u'tilis |w . . . . . . APAREJOGRASS
vires'cens . . . . . SCREWLEAF M.
wright'i . . . . SPIKE M.

MUNRO'A |w
squarro'sa |w . FALSE BUFFALOGRASS

NAR'DUS . . . . . . MATGRASS
stric'ta

NASSEL'LA
ma'jor

NA'ZIA . . . . **TRAGUS**
occidenta'lis . . . . **T. berteronianus**

NEYRAUD'IA
madagascarien'sis MADAGASCARGRASS
reynaudia'na . . . . . . BURMAREED

NOTHOL'CUS . . . . **HOLCUS**

GRASS GENERA, continued

OLY'RA . . . . OLYRA
latifo'lia . . . . CARRICILLO

OPIZ'IA
stolonif'era . . . . ACAPULCOGRASS

OPLISME'NUS |w
hirtel'lus . . . . BASKETGRASS
seta'rius |w

ORCUT'TIA . . . . ORCUTTIA
califor'nica
green'ei . . . . BEARDLESS O.
ten'uis

ORY'ZA |w . . . . RICE
latifo'lia . . . . BROADLEAF R.
sati'va |w . . . . RICE

ORYZOP'SIS |w . . . RICEGRASS
asperifo'lia |w . . . ROUGHLEAF R.
bloom'eri . . . . . . BLOOMERS R.
canaden'sis . . . . . . CANADA R.
exig'ua . . . . LITTLE R.
fimbria'ta . **Piptochaetium fimbriatum**
henderso'ni . . . . HENDERSON R.
hymenoi'des |w . . . . . INDIAN R.
king'i . . . . SIERRA R.
micran'tha |w . . . LITTLESEED R.
milia'cea . . . . SMILOGRASS
pun'gens . . . . . . SHORTHORN R.
racemo'sa . . . . . BLACKSEED R.
webb'eri . . . . WEBBER R.

OSTERDA'MIA . . . **ZOYSIA**

PANICULA'RIA . . **GLYCERIA**

PAN'ICUM |w
PANICUM; WITCHGRASS
abscis'sum
acicula're . . . . . NEEDLELEAF P.

This enormous genus, much the largest of American grass genera, is highly critical and the species often difficult of determination. It seems neither desirable nor feasible to attempt to standardize English names for more than a relatively few species.

aculea'tum
addiso'ni . . . . ADDISON P.
adsper'sum . . . . . DOMINICAN P.
agrostoi'des |w . . . . . REDTOP P.
albemarlen'se
albomargina'tum
ama'rulum
ama'rum . . . . BITTER P.
an'ceps |w . . . . BEAKED P.
angustifo'lium
an'nulum
antidota'le . . . . BLUE P.
arenicoloi'des . . . . SAND P.
arizo'nicum |w . . . . . . ARIZONA P.
ashe'i |w . . . . ASHE P.
aubur'ne
barbino'de . . . . . . **P. purpurascens**
barbipulvina'tum **P. capillare occidentale**
barbula'tum |w
bartowen'se |w . . . . . . BARTOW P.
berg'i . . . . BERG P.
bicknell'i |w . . . . . BICKNELL P.
borea'le
bosc'i
—mol'le
brachyan'thum
brev'e
bulbo'sum . . . . BULB P.
—mi'nus (*P. b. sciaphilum*) LITTLE B.P.

GRASS GENERA (PANICUM), continued
caerules'cens |w
calliphyl'lum
capilla're |w . . COMMON WITCHGRASS
—occidenta'le (*P. barbipulvinatum*) CUSHION W.
capillarioi'des
chamaelon'che
chap'mani . . . . . CORAL PANICUM
chrysopsidifo'lium
cilia'tum
cimici'num . . . **Coridochloa cimicina**
clandesti'num |w
clu'tei . . . . CLUTE P.
cogna'tum . . . . **Leptoloma c.**
columbia'num
—thi'nium
combs'i . . . . COMBS P.
commonsia'num
commuta'tum |w
concin'nius
conden'sum |w
consanguin'eum
cryptan'thum
curtifo'lium
deam'i . . . . DEAM P.
depaupera'tum
dichotomiflo'rum |w . . . . FALL P. (*Knucklegrass*)
—puritano'rum
dichot'omum
ensifo'lium
equilatera'le
erectifo'lium
fascicula'tum |w . . . BROWNTOP P.
—reticula'tum
fil'ipes
firm'ulum
flavovi'rens
flex'ile |w
fusifor'me
gat'tingeri . . . . . GATTINGER W.
gemina'tum |w . . . . EGYPTIAN P.
ghiesbreght'i
glabrifo'lium
goui'ni . . . . GOUIN P.
gymnocar'pon |w . . . . SAVANNAH P.
hall'i |w . . . . HALLS P.
hav'ardi . . . . HAVARD P.
hel'leri . . . . HELLER P.
hemito'mon |w . . . . MAIDENCANE
hi'ans . . . . GAPING P.
hill'mani |w . . . . . . HILLMAN P.
hirsu'tum
hirticau'le |w . . . . ROUGHSTALK W.
huachu'cae . . . . . HUACHUCA P.
—fascicula'tum
implica'tum |w
joor'i
lancea'rium
lan'guidum
lanugino'sum |w . . . . WOOLLY P.
latifo'lium
laxiflo'rum
leiberg'i . . . . LEIBERG P.
lepid'ulum
leu'cothrix
lindheim'eri |w . . . LINDHEIMER P.
linearifo'lium |w . . . SLIMLEAF P.
longifo'lium |w . . . . LONGLEAF P.
longiligula'tum
lu'cidum
ma'lacon
malacophyl'lum . . . . SOFTLEAF P.
mattamuskeeten'se
max'imum . . . . . . GUINEAGRASS

GRASS GENERA (PANICUM), continued
meridiona'le
microcar'pon
milia'ceum |w . . . . PROSO (*Broomcorn Millet*)
mutab'ile
neuran'thum |w
nit'idum
noda'tum
nudicau'le
obtu'sum |w . . . . VINE-MESQUITE
occidenta'le
oligosan'thes |w
oric'ola
ova'le
ovi'num . . . . . . SHEEP PANICUM
pacif'icum . . . . PACIFIC P.
paludiva'gum |w . . . . . WATER P.
pampino'sum . ARIZONA WITCHGRASS
patentifo'lium
pa'tulum
pedicella'tum
perlon'gum
philadelph'icum . PHILADELPHIA W.
ple'num
polyan'thes |w
polycau'lon . . . . LITTLE P.
portoricen'se
praeco'cius
pseudopubes'cens
purpuras'cens (*barbinode*) |w PARAGRASS
ramise'tum |w
ramo'sum |w . . . BROWNTOPMILLET
ravenel'i
re'pens |w TORPEDO P. (*Torpedograss*)
rep'tans . . . . SPRAWLING P.
revercho'ni |w
rhizoma'tum
roanoken'se
scabrius'culum |w
scoparioi'des
scopa'rium |w . . . . . VELVET P.
scribneria'num |w . . . SCRIBNER P.
shasten'se . . . . SHASTA P.
sphaerocar'pon |w . . ROUNDSEED P.
—infla'tum
sphagnic'ola . . . . . . CYPRESS P.
spre'tum
stipita'tum . . . . PURPLE P.
stramin'eum |w . . . SONORA W.
strigo'sum
subvillo'sum
ten'erum
tennesseen'se |w . . . TENNESSEE P.
ten'ue
texa'num . . . . TEXAS P.
therma'le |w
thuro'wi
trifo'lium
tsugeto'rum . . . . . HEMLOCK P.
tuckerman'i . . . . TUCKERMAN W.
urvillea'num . . . . DESERT P.
verna'le . . . . BOG P.
verruco'sum . . . . WARTY P.
villosis'simum |w
virga'tum |w . . . . . SWITCHGRASS
—cuben'se
—spis'sum
webberia'num . . . . . WEBBER P.
wer'neri . . . . WERNER P.
wilcoxia'num |w . . . . . WILCOX P.
wilmingtonen'se . . WILMINGTON P.
wrightia'num |w . . . . . WRIGHT P.
xalapen'se . . . . JALAPA P.
—strictira'meum
xanthophy'sum
yadkinen'se

GRASS GENERA, continued

PAPPO'PHORUM |w PAPPUSGRASS
bi'color . . . . PINK P.
mucronula'tum . . . . WHIPLASH P.
wright'i |w . . . . FEATHER P.

PAS'PALUM |w . . . . PASPALUM
acumina'tum |w . . . . . . BROOK P.
al'mum . . . . COMBS P.
bi'fidum |w . . . . . . PITCHFORK P.
blodget'ti . . . . CORAL P.
boscia'num |w . . . . BULL P.
caespito'sum . . . . BLUE P.
ciliatifo'lium |w . . . FRINGELEAF P.
circula're . . . . . ROUNDSEED P.
conjuga'tum . . . . SOUR P.
de'bile . . . . GOLDHAIR P.
diffor'me . . THICKSPIKE KNOTGRASS
dilata'tum |w . . . . . . DALLISGRASS
dissec'tum |w . . . . . MUDBANK P.
dis'tichum |w . . . . . . KNOTGRASS (*Ft. Thompsongrass*)
florida'num |w . . . . . FLORIDA P.
—glabra'tum . . . . . SMOOTH F.P.
gigan'teum |w . . . . GIANT P.
hartwegia'num |w . . . HARTWEG P.
lae've |w . . . . FIELD P.
lang'ei . . . . RUSTYSEED P.
lax'um . . . . COCONUT P.
lentif'erum |w . . . . . CYPRESS P.
li'vidum |w . . . . LONGTOM
longepeduncula'tum . BARESTEM P.
longip'ilum . . . . . HAIRYLEAF P.
malacophyl'lum . . . . RIBBED P.
mi'nus . . . . MAT P.
monosta'chyum . . . GULFDUNE P.
nota'tum . . . . BAHIAGRASS
paucispica'tum
plica'tulum |w . . . BROWNSEED P.
prae'cox . . . . EARLY P.
propin'quum . . . . LITTLESEED P.
psammoph'ilum . . . . . DUNE P.
pubes'cens |w . . . . HURRAHGRASS
pubiflo'rum |w . . . HAIRYSEED P.
—gla'brum
racemo'sum . . . . . PERUVIAN P.
re'pens |w . . . . . . HORSETAIL P.
rigidifo'lium . . . . STIFF P.
scrobicula'tum . . . . . . INDIA P.
seta'ceum |w . . . . THIN P.
stramin'eum |w . . . . . . SAND P.
supi'num |w . . . . . LONGLEAF P.
unispica'tum . . . . . ONESPIKE P.
urvil'lei . . . . VASEYGRASS
vagina'tum |w . . . . SEASHORE P.
virga'tum . . . . TALQUEZAL

PENNISE'TUM (*GYMNOTHRIX*) |w . . . . PENNISETUM
alopecuroi'des . . . . . CHINESE P.
cilia're
clandesti'num . . . . KIKUYUGRASS
glau'cum (*spicatum; typhoideum*) PEARLMILLET (*Cattailmillet*)
latifo'lium . URUGUAY PENNISETUM
macrosta'chyum . . . EASTINDIES P.
—atropurpu'reum . . PURPLE E.P.
nervo'sum . . . . . . BENTSPIKE P.
orienta'le . . . . ORIENTAL P.
purpu'reum . . . . . NAPIERGRASS
ruppel'i . . . . . . FOUNTAINGRASS
¢CRIMSON (*atrosanguineum*) HV.
¢PURPLE (*cupreum*)
seto'sum . . . . WESTINDIES P.
spica'tum; typhoid'eum . **P. glaucum**
villo'sum . . . . FEATHERTOP

PHAL'ARIS . . . . CANARYGRASS
angus'ta |w . . . . TIMOTHY C.

GRASS GENERA (**PHALARIS**), continued
arundina'cea |w REED CANARYGRASS
—pic'ta . . . . . . RIBBONGRASS
brachysta'chys . . . SHORTSPIKE C.
califor'nica . . . . CALIFORNIA C.
canarien'sis |w . . . . CANARYGRASS
carolinia'na |w . . . . CAROLINA C.
lem'moni . . . . LEMMON C.
mi'nor . . . . LITTLESEED C.
paradox'a |w . . . . . . HOOD C.
—praemor'sa . . . . CUTSCALE C.
tubero'sa . . . . BULB C.
—stenop'tera . . . . HARDINGGRASS

PHA'RUS . . . . LEAFSTALKGRASS
parvifo'lius . . . . . CREEPING L.

PHIPPS'IA
al'gida . . . . ICEGRASS

PHLE'UM |w . . . . . TIMOTHY
alpi'num |w . . . . . . ALPINE T.
arena'rium . . . . . . SAND T.
panicula'tum . . . . . . BRITISH T.
praten'se |w . . . . . . TIMOTHY
subula'tum . . . . . . ITALIAN T.

PHOLIU'RUS |w . . . SICKLEGRASS
incur'vus |w . . . . . . SICKLEGRASS

PHRAGMI'TES |w . . . . . REED
commu'nis |w . . . . . COMMON R.

PIPTOCHAE'TIUM (*ORYZOPSIS* in part) |w . . . . . RICEGRASS

This genus, segregated from Oryzopsis on technical characters, has recently been restored.

fimbria'tum (*Oryzopsis fimbriata*) |w PINYON R.

PLEUROPO'GON |w SEMAPHOREGRASS
califor'nicus |w . . . . . ANNUAL S.
refrac'tus |w . . . . . . NODDING S.

PO'A |w . . . . BLUEGRASS
al'cea . . . . **P. gracillima**
alpi'na . . . . ALPINE B.
also'des . . . . GROVE B.
amab'ilis Hort.

A name sometimes misapplied in the hort. trade to Eragrostis unioloides.

am'pla (*confusa*) . . . . . . BIG B.
an'nua |w . . . . ANNUAL B.
arachnif'era . . . . TEXAS B.
arc'tica (*alpicola; aperta; grayana; longipila*) . . . . ARCTIC B.
ar'ida (*praтericola; pseudopratensis; sheldoni*) . . . . PLAINS B.
atropurpu'rea . . SANBERNARDINO B.
autumna'lis . . . . . . AUTUMN B.
baden'sis
bigelo'vi . . . . BIGELOW B.
bolan'deri . . . . . . BOLANDER B.
brevipanicula'ta . . . . **P. fendleriana**
buckleya'na . . . . . . **P. scabrella**
bulbo'sa . . . . BULBOUS B.
can'byi (*laevigata; lucida*) |w CANBY B.
chapmania'na . . . . . CHAPMAN B.
compres'sa . . . . CANADA B.
confin'is . . . . DUNE B.
confu'sa . . . . **P. ampla**
croca'ta . . . . **P. palustris**
cur'ta . . . . WASATCH B.
curtifo'lia . . . . . . MT.STUART B.
cusick'i (*idahoensis; nematophylla*) CUSICK B.
cuspida'ta . . . . EARLY B.
debil'is Torr., *not* Thuill. . **P. languida**

GRASS GENERA (**POA**), continued
doug'lasi . . . DOUGLAS BLUEGRASS
ep'ilis (*paddensis*) . . . SKYLINE B.
fendleria'na (*brevipaniculata; longepedunculata*) |w . . . . MUTTON B. (*Fendler B.; Muttongrass*)
fibra'ta
glau'ca . . . . GREENLAND B.
glaucifo'lia
gracil'lima (*alcea; invaginata; saxatilis*) SLENDER B.
graya'na . . . . **P. arctica**
han'seni . . . . **P. leibergi**
how'elli . . . . HOWELL B.
idahoen'sis . . . . **P. cusicki**
inte'rior |w . . . . INLAND B.
involu'ta . . . . CHISOS B.
juncifo'lia |w . . . . . . ALKALI B.
kellogg'i . . . . KELLOGG B.
laeviga'ta . . . . **P. canbyi**
lan'guida (*debilis* Torr., *not* Thuill.) TORREY B.
lax'a . . . . . MT.WASHINGTON B.
laxiflo'ra . . . . . HOTSPRINGS B.
leiberg'i (*hanseni*) . . . LEIBERG B.
leptoco'ma . . . . BOG B.
letterman'i . . . . LETTERMAN B.
longepeduncula'ta . . . **P. fendleriana**
longili'gula LONGTONGUE MUTTON B.
longip'ila . . . . **P. arctica**
lu'cida . . . . **P. canbyi**
macran'tha . . . . . SEASHORE B.
macrocla'da
mar'cida
nematophyl'la . . . . **P. cusicki**
nemora'lis . . . . WOOD B.
nervo'sa (*olneyae; vaseyana; wheeleri*) WHEELER B.
nevaden'sis |w . . . . . NEVADA B.
occidenta'lis . . . . NEWMEXICO B.
padden'sis . . . . **P. epilis**
paludig'ena
palus'tris (*crocata; triflora*) |w FOWL B.
patterso'ni . . . . . . PATTERSON B.
paucispic'ula . . . . ALASKA B.
praten'sis |w . . . . . KENTUCKY B.
prateric'ola . . . . **P. arida**
pringle'i . . . . PRINGLE B.
pseudopraten'sis . . . . . . **P. arida**
reflex'a . . . . NODDING B.
rhizo'mata (*piperi*) . . . SISKIYOU B.
rupic'ola . . . . . . TIMBERLINE B.
saltuen'sis
saxat'ilis . . . . **P. gracillima**
scabrel'la (*buckleyana*) . . PINE B.
secun'da (*sandbergi*) |w . SANDBERG B.
shel'doni . . . . **P. arida**
stenan'tha . . . . TRINIUS B.
sudet'ica . . . . SUDETIC B.
sylves'tris . . . . . . WOODLAND B.
tatar'ica . . . . TARTAR B.
tra'cyi . . . . TRACY B.
triflo'ra . . . . **P. palustris**
trivia'lis . . . . . . ROUGHSTALK B.
unilatera'lis . . . . SEACLIFF B.
vaseya'na . . . . **P. nervosa**
vaseyo'chloa . . . . . . OREGON B.
wheel'eri . . . . **P. nervosa**
wolf'i . . . . WOLFS B.

POLYPO'GON |w . . POLYPOGON
austra'lis . . . . CHILEAN P.
luto'sus (*littoralis*) . . . . DITCH P.
marit'imus . . . MEDITERRANEAN P.
monspelien'sis |w . . RABBITFOOT P.

POLYT'RIAS
praemor'sa . . . . . . JAVAGRASS

GRASS GENERA, continued
PUCCINEL'LIA |w . . ALKALIGRASS
dis'tans |w . . . . . . WEEPING A.
fascicula'ta |w . . . . . TORREY A.
lem'moni |w . . . . . . LEMMON A.
marit'ima |w . . . . . . SEASHORE A.
nutkaen'sis |w . . . . . . NOOTKA A.
nuttallia'na |w . . . . . . NUTTALL A.

ZAWADKE A. is a cultivated form of this.

par'ishi . . . . PARISH A.
pu'mila |w . . . . ARCTIC A.
rupes'tris . . . . BRITISH A.
sim'plex . . . . CALIFORNIA A.

REDFIELD'IA . . BLOWOUTGRASS
flexuo'sa . . . . . BLOWOUTGRASS

REIMAROCH'LOA |w REIMARGRASS
oligostach'ya |w . . . . FLORIDA R.

RHA'PHIS |w . . . . . RHAPHIS
gryl'tus . . . . CRICKET R.
pauciflo'rus (*Chrysopogon p.*) |w FLORIDA R.

ROTTBOEL'LIA . . . ITCHGRASS
exalta'ta (*Manisuris e.*) . ITCHGRASS (*Guineafowlgrass*)

RY'TILIX . **HACKELOCHLOA**

SAC'CHARUM . . . SWEETCANE
cilia're . . . . **S. sarc**
officina'rum . . . . . . SUGARCANE
sarc' (*ciliare; munja*) MUNJ SWEETCANE (*Munj*)
sponta'neum

SACCIO'LEPIS |w . . . CUPSCALE
in'dica . . . . INDIA C.
stria'ta |w . . . . . . AMERICAN C.

SAVASTA'NA . **HIEROCHLOE**

SCHEDONNAR'DUS TUMBLEGRASS
panicula'tus . . . . . TUMBLEGRASS

SCHIS'MUS

HAASGRASS, of Africa, is of this genus.

barba'tus . . MEDITERRANEANGRASS

SCHIZACH'NE |w
purpuras'cens (*Melica p.*) |w FALSEMELIC

SCLEROCH'LOA . . HARDGRASS
du'ra . . . . HARDGRASS

SCLERO'POA . . . . STIFFGRASS
rig'ida . . . . STIFFGRASS

SCLEROPO'GON . . BURROGRASS
brevifo'lius . . . . . BURROGRASS

SCOLOCH'LOA . . . **FLUMINEA**

SCRIBNE'RIA . . . . SCRIBNERIA
bolan'deri . . . . SCRIBNERIA

SECA'LE |w . . . . RYE
cerea'le |w . . . . RYE
monta'num . . . . . MOUNTAIN R.

SESLE'RIA
coeru'lea
rig'ida

SETA'RIA (*CHAETOCHLOA*) |w BRISTLEGRASS; MILLET (*Pigeongrass*)
barba'ta . . . . EASTINDIES B.
corruga'ta . . . . COAST B.
genicula'ta |w . . . . . KNOTROOT B.
globulif'era (*Chaetochloa g.*)
grisebach'i |w. . . . . GRISEBACH B.
ital'ica |w . . . . FOXTAIL M.

GRASS GENERA (SETARIA italica), con.
German. hv.
Golden (*stramineo-fructa*)
Hungarian (*nigro-fructa*)
Kursk
Siberian (*rubro-fructa*)
liebmann'i ⌊w
Liebmann Bristlegrass
lutes'cens ⌊w . . . . . . Yellow B.
macrosper'ma . . . . . . Coral B.
macrostach'ya ⌊w . . . . . Plains B.
mag'na ⌊w . . . . Giant B.
nigriros'tris . . . . . . Black B.
palmifo'lia . . . . Palmgrass
plica'ta
poiretia'na . . . . Poiret P.
rariflo'ra . . . . Brazil B.
scheele'i . . . . Southwestern B.
seto'sa . . . . . WestIndies B.
sulca'ta
verticilla'ta . . . . . . Hooked B.
—ambig'ua . . . . Sicilian H.B.
villosis'sima . . . . . Hairyleaf B.
vir'idis ⌊w . . . . Green B.

SITA'NION ⌊w . . . Squirreltail
han'seni (*Elymus leckenbyi*) Hansen S.
hys'trix ⌊w . . . . . Bottlebrush S.
juba'tum . . . . Big S.

SORGHAS'TRUM . . Indiangrass
elliott'i . . . . Slender I.
nu'tans . . . . Yellow I.
secun'dum . . . . Lopside I.

SOR'GHUM ⌊w . . . . Sorghum
halepen'se (*Andropogon halepensis; Holcus h.*) ⌊w . . . Johnsongrass
virga'tum . . . . Tunisgrass
vulga're (*Andropogon sorghum; Holcus s.*) ⌊w . . . . Sorghum
—bi'color . . . Gooseneck Sorgho
—caffro'rum . . . . Kafir
—drum'mondi . . . . Chickencorn
—dur'ra . . . Durra (*Brown Durra*)
Feterita (*caudatum*) hv.
White (*cernum*)
—nervo'sum . . . . Kaoliang
—ni'gricans . . . . Sumac Sorgho
—roxburgh'i . . . . Shallu
—sacchara'tum . . . . . . Sorgho
—subglabres'cens . . . . . . Milo
—sudanen'se (*Andropogon sorghum sudanensis; Holcus sorghum sudanensis; H. sudanensis*) . . . . Sudangrass
—tech'nicum . . . . . . Broomcorn

SPARTI'NA ⌊w . . . . Cordgrass
alterniflo'ra (*glabra*) ⌊w . Smooth C.
ba'keri . . . . Sand C.
cynosuroi'des ⌊w . . . . . . Big C.
grac'ilis ⌊w . . . . Alkali C.
leian'tha ⌊w . . . . . California C.
pa'tens ⌊w . . . . . . Marshhay C.
—caespito'sa . . . . . Tufted M.C.
pectina'ta (*michauxiana*) ⌊w
Prairie C.
sparti'nae ⌊w . . . . Gulf C.
town'sendi . . . . . . Townsend C.

SPHENOPH'OLIS . Wedgescale
filifor'mis . . . . . Longleaf W.
interme'dia . . . . . Slender W.
longiflo'ra . . . . Texas W.
nit'ida . . . . Shiny W.
obtusa'ta . . . . Prairie W.
pal'lens . . . . Pale W.

SPORO'BOLUS ⌊w . . . Dropseed
airoi'des ⌊w . . . . Alkali Sacaton
arena'ceus . . **Muhlenbergia arenacea**

GRASS GENERA (SPOROBOLUS), con.
argu'tus . . . . . . **S. pyramidatus**
as'per ⌊w . . . . . Tall Dropseed
—hook'eri . . . . . . Meadow T.D.
—pilo'sus . . . . Hairy T.D.
auricula'tus . **Muhlenbergia arenacea**
berteroa'nus . . . . **S. poireti**
buck'leyi . . . . Buckley D.
clandesti'nus ⌊w . . . . Hidden D.
confu'sus . . . . . **S. microspermus**
contrac'tus . . . . Spike D.
cryptan'drus ⌊w . . . . . Sand D.
curtiss'i ⌊w . . . . Curtiss D.
domingen'sis . . . . Coral D.
elonga'tus . Australian Smutgrass
fimbria'tus . . . . African D.
flexuo'sus . . . . Mesa D.
florida'nus . . . . Florida D.
gigan'teus . . . . Giant D.
grac'ilis ⌊w . . . . . Pineywoods D.
hetero'lepis . . . . Prairie D.
in'dicus . . . WestIndies Smutgrass
interrup'tus . . . . Black D.
ma'crus . . . . Mississippi D.
microsper'mus (*confusus*) Sixweeks D.
neal'leyi . . . . Gypgrass
neglec'tus ⌊w . . . . Puffsheath D.
poiret'i (*berteroanus*) ⌊w
Rattail Smutgrass
purpuras'cens . . . . . . Purple D.
pyramida'tus (*argutus*) Whorled D.
ramulo'sus . . . . Red D.
teretifo'lius . . . . . Wireleaf D.
texa'nus ⌊w . . . . Texas D.
tharp'i . . . . Padre Island D.
vaginiflo'rus ⌊w . . . . . Poverty D.
virgin'icus ⌊w . . . . . Seashore D.
wright'i . . . . Sacaton

STENOTA'PHRUM
secunda'tum . . St. Augustinegrass

STI'PA ⌊w
Needlegrass; Feathergrass
Species of Stipa with conspicuously feathery ("plumose") awns are known as Feathergrass.

argen'tea . . . . Argentine F.
ar'ida (*mormonum*) . . . Mormon N.
arundina'cea (*Apera a.*)
Pheasants-tail F.
avena'cea . . . . . . Blackseed N.
avenacioi'des . . . . . . Florida N.
brachychae'ta . . . . Araucanian N.
califor'nica . . . . Pacific N.
capilla'ta
columbia'na (*minor*) . Subalpine N.
—nelso'ni (*S. nelsoni*) . . . Big S.N.
coma'ta ⌊w . . . . Needleandthread
—interme'dia (*S. tweedyi*) Tweedy N.
corona'ta . . Crested Needlegrass
—depaupera'ta . . . . . Small C.N.
curvifo'lia . . . . . Guadalupe N.
diegoen'sis
elegantis'sima . . . Australian F.
el'meri . . . . Elmer N.
em'inens . . . . . Southwestern N.
latiglu'mis . . . . . . Yosemite N.
lem'moni . . . . Lemmon N.
lep'ida . . . . Foothill N.
—anderso'ni . . . . Slim N.
let'termani . . . . . Letterman N.
leuco'tricha . . . . Texas N.
loba'ta . . . . Littleawn N.
mi'nor . . . . **S. columbiana**
mormo'num . . . . **S. arida**
neesia'na . . . . Uruguay N.
nel'soni . . . . . . **S. columbiana n.**

GRASS GENERA (STIPA), continued
neomexica'na
NewMexico Feathergrass
occidenta'lis . Western Needlegrass
penna'ta . . . . European F.
pineto'rum . . . . . . Pinewoods N.
por'teri . . . . Colorado N.
pringle'i ⌊w . . . . Pringle N.
pul'chra . . . . California N.
richardso'ni . . . . Richardson N.
robus'ta (*vaseyi*) ⌊w . . Sleepygrass
scrib'neri . . . . Scribner N.
spar'tea ⌊w . . . . . Porcupinegrass
—curtise'ta . . . . . . Shortawn P.
specio'sa . . . . Desert N.
splen'dens . . . . Cheegrass
still'mani . . . . Sierra N.
tenacis'sima . . . . Esparto N.
tenuis'sima . . . . Finestem N.
thurberia'na . . . . Thurber N.
twee'dyi . . . . **S. comata intermedia**
va'seyi . . . . **S. robusta**
virid'ula ⌊w . . . . Green N.
will'iamsi ⌊w . . . . . . Williams N.

SYNTHERIS'MA . . **DIGITARIA**

THYSANOLAE'NA . . Tigergrass
max'ima (*agrostis*) . . . Tigergrass

TORRES'IA . . . **HIEROCHLOE**

TRACHYPO'GON
montufa'ri . . . . . . Crinkleawn

TRA'GUS (*NAZIA*) . . Burgrass
berteronia'nus (*Nazia occidentalis*)
Spike B.
racemo'sus (*Nazia racemosa*)
Stalked B.

TRICHACH'NE (*VALOTA*) ⌊w
Cottontop
califor'nica (*saccharata; Valota s.*) ⌊w
Arizona C.
hitch'cocki . . . . . . Shortleaf C.
insula'ris . . . . Sourgrass
pa'tens ⌊w . . . . Texas C.

TRICHLO'RIS ⌊w . . Trichloris
mendoci'na ⌊w . . . Twoflower T.
pluriflo'ra . . . . . Fourflower T.

TRICHOLAE'NA
re'pens (*rosea*) . . . . . Natalgrass

TRICHONEU'RA
el'egans . . . . Silveusgrass

TRI'DENS . . . . **TRIODIA**

TRIO'DIA (*TRIDENS*) ⌊w
Triodia
albes'cens . . . . White T.
buckleya'na . . . . Buckley T.
carolinia'na (*drummondi*) Carolina T.
conges'ta . . . . Pink T.
elonga'ta . . . . Rough T.
eragrostoi'des . . . . . Lovegrass T.
fla'va ⌊w . . . . Purpletop
grandiflo'ra . . . . . . Shortleaf T.
langlois'i . . . . . . Pinebarren T.
mu'tica ⌊w . . . . Slim T.
pilo'sa . . . . Hairy T.
pulchel'la ⌊w . . . . . . Fluffgrass
stric'ta . . . . Longspike T.
texa'na . . . . Texas T.

TRIP'LASIS ⌊w . . . Sandgrass
america'na . . . . . . Perennial S.
purpu'rea ⌊w . . . . Purple S.

TRIPO'GON . . . . . Tripogon
spica'tus . . . . American T.

GRASS GENERA, continued

TRIP'SACUM ⊮ . . . GAMAGRASS
dactyloi'des ⊮ . . . . . EASTERN G.
florida'num . . . . . FLORIDA G.
lanceola'tum . . . . MEXICAN G.
lax'um . . . . . GUATEMALA G.

TRIRA'PHIS
fleck'i

TRISE'TUM ⊮ . . . . TRISETUM
au'reum . . . . GOLDEN T.
canes'cens . . . . TALL T.
cer'nuum . . . . NODDING T.
flaves'cens (*Avena f.*) . . YELLOW T.
interrup'tum . . . . . . PRAIRIE T.
melicoi'des . . . . . . MELIC T.
monta'num . . ROCKYMOUNTAIN T.
orthochae'tum . . . BITTERROOT T.
pennsylva'nicum . . . . . SWAMP T.
spica'tum ⊮ . . . . SPIKE T.
wolf'i . . . . WOLFS T.

TRI'TICUM ⊮ . . . . . WHEAT
aes'tivum (*sativum; vulgare*) ⊮ . WHEAT
compac'tum Hort. . . . . CLUB W.
dicoccoi'des . . . . WILD W.
dicoc'cum (*T. aestivum d.*) . . EMMER
du'rum . . . . DURUM W.
monococ'cum (*T. aestivum m.*) EINKORN
polon'icum (*T. aestivum p.*) POLISH W.
sati'vum . . . . **T. aestivum**
spel'ta (*T. aestivum s.*) . . . SPELT
timopheer'i . . . . TIMOPHEERI W.
tur'gidum . . . . POULARD W.

ALASKA W. (*Egyptian W.; Mummy W.*) is a hort. strain of this.

vulga're . . . . **T. aestivum**

UNI'OLA ⊮ . . . . UNIOLA
latifo'lia . . . . BROADLEAF U.
lax'a ⊮ . . . . SPIKE U.
nit'ida . . . . SHINY U.
ornithorhyn'ca . . . . BIRDBILL U.
panicula'ta . . . . SEAOATS
sessiliflo'ra (*longifolia*) ⊮ LONGLEAF U.

VALO'TA . . . **TRICHACHNE**
sacchara'ta . . . . . . **T. californica**

VASEYOCH'LOA ⊮
multinervo'sa ⊮ . . . . TEXASGRASS

VETIVE'RIA (*ANATHERUM*) VETIVER
zizanioi'des (*Anatherum z.; Andropogon hirtus*) . . . . . . KHUSKHUS V.

WEINGAERTNE'RIA
canes'cens . . . . . **Corynephorus c.**

WILLKOM'MIA . . WILLKOMMIA
texa'na . . . . TEXAS W.

XIPHAGROS'TIS **MISCANTHUS**

ZE'A ⊮ . . . MAIZE; INDIAN CORN
mays' ⊮ . . . . MAIZE; INDIAN CORN
—ever'ta
—japon'ica . . . . STRIPED M.
—tunica'ta . . . . POD C.

ZIZA'NIA ⊮ . . . . . . WILDRICE
aquat'ica ⊮ . . . . ANNUAL W.
—angustifo'lia (*Z. palustris*) NORTHERN W.
milia'cea . . . . . . **Zizaniopsis m.**
texa'na ⊮ . . . . TEXAS W.

GRASS GENERA, continued

ZIZANIOP'SIS ⊮ . . . WILDRICE
milia'cea (*Zizania m.*) ⊮ SOUTHERN W.

ZOY'SIA (*OSTERDAMIA*)
japon'ica . . JAPANESE LAWNGRASS (*Korean L.*)
matrel'la (*pungens*) . . MANILAGRASS
tenuifo'lia . . . . MASCARENEGRASS (*Korean Velvetgrass*)

GRASSTREE . . . . . . **Xanthorrhoea**
AUSTRALIAN G. . . . . . **X. australis**
DACKOWAR G. . . . . . **X. arborea**
PREISS G. . . . . **X. preissi**
SPEARLEAF G. . . . . . **X. hastilis**

GRATIO'LA ⊮ . . . . HEDGEHYSSOP
lute'a (*aurea*) ⊮ . . . . GOLDEN H.

This species has been confused with G. neglecta.

neglec'ta ⊮
officina'lis . . . . DRUG H.
pilo'sa ⊮ . . . . SHAGGY H.
virginia'na ⊮ . . . . VIRGINIA H.
viscid'ula ⊮ . . . . . . CLAMMY H.

GRAY'IA . . . . HOPSAGE
brandeg'ei . . . . . . SPINELESS H.
spino'sa . . . . SPINY H.

GRAYTWIG . . . . **Schoepfia**
GULF G. . . . . **S. chrysophylloides**

GREASEBUSH . . . . **Forsellesia**
DWARF G. . . . . **F. pungens**
SPINY G. . . . . **F. spinescens**

GREASEWOOD . . . . **Sarcobatus**
BAILEY G. . . . . **S. baileyi**
BLACK G. . . . . . **S. vermiculatus**

GREENBRIER . . . . **Smilax**
See also SARSAPARILLA.

BAMBOO G. . . . . . **S. tamnoides**
BLUEBEAD G. . . **S. menispermoides**
BRISTLY G. . . . . **S. hispida**
CALIFORNIA G. . . . . **S. californica**
CANTAB G. . . . . **×S. cantab**
CARRIONFLOWER G. . . . **S. herbacea**
CAT G. . . . . **S. glauca**
CHINAROOT G. . . . . **S. china**
COMMON G. . . . . . **S. rotundifolia**
CORALBEAD G. . . . . **S. megalantha**
EURASIAN G. . . . . **S. aspera**
LANCELEAF G. . . . . . **S. lanceolata**
LAUREL G. . . . . **S. laurifolia**
LITTLELEAF G. . . . . **S. microphylla**
NIPPON G. . . . . **S. biflora**
REDBEAD G. . . . . **S. walteri**
SAW G. . . . . **S. bonanox**
SIEBOLD G. . . . . . . **S. sieboldi**
SPOTTED EURASIAN G. **S. aspera maculata**
SQUARETWIG COMMON G. **S. rotundifolia quadrangulata**
STURDY G. . . . . **S. excelsa**

GREENFELT . . . . **Vaucheria**
LAND G. . . . . **V. terrestris**
TWINEGG G. . . . . . . **V. geminata**

Greenlaver . . . . . SEALETTUCE: **Ulva**

GREENO'VIA
See **SUCCULENTS**.

Green-sapote . . . . LUCUMA, GREEN: **Lucuma viride**

GREENSTAR . . . . **Polyalthia**
INDIA G. . . . . **P. longifolia**

GREENTHREAD . . . . . **Thelesperma**
BURRIDGE G. . . . **T. burridgeanum**
COLORADO G. . . . . . . **T. ambiguum**
GEBANGA G. . . . . **T. elatum**

Greenweed, Dyers WOADWAXEN, COMMON: **Genista tinctoria**

Grego'ria vitalia'na . . . . **Douglasia v.**

GREIG'IA
sphacela'ta
vulcan'ica

GREVIL'LEA . . . . . . GREVILLEA
alpi'na . . . . ALPINE G.
banks'i . . . . BANKS G.
—al'ba . . . . WHITE B.G.
—for'steri . . . . FORSTERS G.
bipinnatif'ida . . . . STIFFLEAF G.
buxifo'lia . . . . BOXLEAF G.
crithmifo'lia . . . SAMPHIRELEAF G.
endlicheria'na . . . . ENDLICHER G.
eriosta'chya
glabra'ta
hillia'na . . . . YIELYIEL G.
juniperi'na . . . . JUNIPER G.
—sulphu'rea . . . . . . YELLOW J.G.
leucop'teris . . . . WHITEPLUME G.
macrosty'lis
monta'na . . . . MOUNTAIN G.
obtusifo'lia . . . . . BLUNTLEAF G.
oleoi'des . . . . OLIVELEAF G.
—dimor'pha
ornithop'oda
panicula'ta
petrophiloi'des
polybot'rya
punic'ea
quercifo'lia . . . . OAKLEAF G.
robus'ta . . . . SILKOAK G.
rosmarinifo'lia . . . . ROSEMARY G.
thelemannia'na . . . . SPIDERNET G.
vesti'ta
wil'soni . . . . WILSONS G.

GREVILLEA . . . . **Grevillea**
ALPINE G. . . . . **G. alpina**
BANKS G. . . . . **G. banksi**
BLUNTLEAF G. . . . . . **G. obtusifolia**
BOXLEAF G. . . . . . . **G. buxifolia**
ENDLICHER G. . . . **G. endlicheriana**
FORSTERS G. . . . **G. banksi forsteri**
JUNIPER G. . . . . . . **G. juniperina**
MOUNTAIN G. . . . . . . **G. montana**
OAKLEAF G. . . . . . . **G. quercifolia**
OLIVELEAF G. . . . . . . **G. oleoides**
ROSEMARY G. . . . **G. rosmarinifolia**
SAMPHIRELEAF G. . . . **G. crithmifolia**
SILKOAK G. . . . . **G. robusta**
SPIDERNET G. . . . **G. thelemanniana**
STIFFLEAF G. . . . . **G. bipinnatifida**
WHITE BANKS G. . . . **G. banksi alba**
WHITEPLUME G. . . . . **G. leucopteris**
WILSONS G. . . . . **G. wilsoni**
YELLOW JUNIPER G. **G. juniperina sulphurea**
YIELYIEL G. . . . . **G. hilliana**

GREW'IA . . . . GREWIA
asiat'ica . . . . PHALSA
bilo'ba
—parviflo'ra (*G. parviflora*)
caf'fra

GREWIA, continued
occidenta'lis . . Starflower Grewia
oppositifo'lia
populifo'lia . . . . Poplarleaf G.
tiliaefo'lia . . . . Lindenleaf G.

GREY'IA
sutherland'i

GRI'AS
loreten'sis

GRIFFIN'IA . . . . Griffinia
hyacin'thina . . . . Hyacinth G.

GRINDE'LIA |w . . . . . Gumweed
campo'rum . . . . . . Field G.
hirsut'ula
hu'milis (*cuneifolia*) |w . . Marsh G.
integrifo'lia
na'na . . . . Low G.
orega'na . . . . Oregon G.
robus'ta . . . . Shore G.
—latifo'lia . . . . Broadleaf S.G.
squarro'sa |w . . . . Curlycup G.
—serrula'ta (*G. serrulata*)

GRISELIN'IA
littora'lis . . . . . . Kupukatree
—variega'ta
lu'cida
—variega'ta

Gris'lea coccin'ea **Combretum coccineum**

Gromwell . . . . . . **Lithospermum**
American G. . . . . . **L. latifolium**
Carolina G. . . . . . **L. carolinense**
Common G. . . . . . **L. officinale**
Corn G. . . . . **L. arvense**
Hoary G. . . . . . . **L. canescens**
Manyflower G. . . . **L. multiflorum**
Narrowleaf G. . . **L. angustifolium**
Wayside G. . . . . . **L. ruderale**
Wyoming G. . . . . . **L. asperum**

GROSSULA'RIA . . . . . **RIBES**
reclina'ta . . . . . . **R. uva-crispa**

Groundcedar . . . . **Lycopodium complanatum flabelliforme**
Slender G. . . . . . **L. tristachyum**

Groundcherry . . . . **Physalis**
Clammy G. . . . . **P. heterophylla**
Cutleaf G. . . . . . . **P. angulata**
Downy G. . . . . . . **P. pubescens**
Hairy G. . . . . **P. pruinosa**
Peruvian G. . . . . . **P. peruviana**
Prairie G. . . . . **P. pumila**
Roundleaf G. . . . . . **P. rotundata**
Strawberry G. . . . . **P. alkekengi**
Taperleaf G. . . . . **P. subglabrata**
Tomatillo G. . . . . . . **P. ixocarpa**
Virginia G. . . . . . . **P. virginiana**

Groundnut . . . . **Glycine**
Slender G. . . . . **G. gracilis**
Soybean . . . . **G. soja**

Groundnut . . . . . Earthnut: **Carum bulbocastanum**; Goober: **Voandzeia**; Peanut: **Arachis hypogaea**; Potatobean: **Apios**

Groundpine . . **Lycopodium obscurum**

Groundsel . . . . **Senecio**
Aconiteleaf G. . . . **S. aconitifolius**
Adonisleaf G. . . . **S. adonidifolius**
Argentine G. . . . . **S. leucostachys**
Arrowleaf G. . . . . **S. triangularis**
Balsam G. . . . . . **S. pauperculus**
Bidwill G. . . . . **S. bidwilli**
Bigbloom G. . . . . . **S. grandiflorus**
Bigleaf G. . . . . . **S. grandifolius**

Groundsel, continued
Black G. . . . . **Senecio atratus**
Blochman G. . . . . **S. blochmanae**
Broom G. . . . . **S. spartioides**
Butterweed G. . . . . **S. serra**
Candleplant G. . . . **S. articulatus**
Catalina G. . . . . **S. lyoni**
Chinese G. . . . . . **S. tanguticus**
Cleftleaf G. . . **S. cymbalarioides**
Climbing G. . . . . . . **S. scandens**
Colorado Nodding G. . . **S. accedens**
Columbia G. . . . . **S. columbianus**
Common Cineraria . . . **S. cruentus**
Common G. . . . . **S. vulgaris**
Cressleaf G. . . . . . . **S. lobatus**
Desert G. . . . . . **S. eremophilus**
Douglas G. . . . . . . **S. douglasi**
Elaeagnus G. . . **S. elaeagnifolius**
Elmer G. . . . . **S. elmeri**
Fendler G. . . . . **S. fendleri**
Fig G. . . . . **S. ficoides**
Fleshy G. . . . . . . **S. succulentus**
Flett G. . . . . **S. fletti**
Flodman G. . . . . **S. glaucescens**
Fremont G. . . . . **S. fremonti**
Fuchs G. . . . . **S. fuchsi**
Gaspe G. . . . . **S. gaspensis**
Golden G. . . . . **S. aureus**
Graygreen G. . . . . . **S. canovirens**
Greys G. . . . . **S. greyi**
Harford G. . . . . **S. harfordi**
Hunts G. . . . . **S. hunti**
Ivy G. . . . . **S. mikanioides**
Kirk G. . . . . **S. kirki**
Lambstongue G. . . **S. integerrimus**
Leopardsbane G. . . **S. doronicum**
Lobeleaf G. . . . . **S. multilobatus**
Lyall G. . . . . **S. lyalli**
Monro G. . . . . **S. monroi**
Montenegrin G. . . . . **S. visianus**
Nasturtium G. . **S. tropaeolifolius**
NewMexico G. . . **S. neomexicanus**
Orange-glowvine . . . **S. confusus**
Prairie G. . . . . . . **S. plattensis**
Purple G. . . . . **S. elegans**
Pursh G. . . . . . . **S. purshianus**
Ragweed G. . . . **S. ambrosioides**
Ragwort G. . . . . . . **S. jacobaea**
Rayless G. . . . . **S. aronicoides**
Riddell G. . . . . **S. riddelli**
Robbins G. . . . . . . **S. robbinsi**
Roundleaf G. . . **S. rotundifolius**
Saffron G. . . . . **S. crocatus**
Seabeach G. . . **S. pseudo-arnica**
Showy Alpine G. . . **S. amplectens**
Silver G. . . . . **S. cineraria**
Small Elaeagnus G. **S. elaeagnifolius buchanani**
Smith G. . . . . **S. smithi**
Sticky G. . . . . **S. viscosus**
Teneriffe G. . . . . . . **S. heritieri**
Thickleaf G. . . . . . . **S. crassulus**
Threadleaf G. . . . . **S. longilobus**
Uinta G. . . . . . . **S. uintahensis**
Uruguay G. . . . . **S. pulcher**
Velvet G. . . . . **S. petasitis**
Water G. . . . . . . **S. hydrophilus**
Webster G. . . . . **S. websteri**
Wholeleaf Butterweed G. **S. serra integriuscula**
Willow G. . . . . **S. salignus**
Wingstalk G. . . . . **S. alatus**
Woodland G. . . . . . . **S. sylvaticus**
Woolly G. . . . . **S. canus**

Groundsmoke . . . . . **Gayophytum**
Bigflower G. . . . . . . **G. diffusum**
Kitchenweed G. . . . . **G. caesium**

Grumichama . . . **Eugenia dombeyi**
Grumixameiratree . . . . Grumichama: **Eugenia dombeyi**

GRUSO'NIA . . . . Grusonia
See **CACTUS GENERA.**

Gruynixeria . . . . . . Grumichama: **Eugenia dombeyi**

Guabiroba . . . **Abbevillea fenzliana**
Guacima . . . **Robinsonella divergens**

GUAJ'ACUM (*GUAIACUM*) Lignumvitae
The first syllable of this generic name is pronounced Gwy.

guatemalen'se . . . . Guatemala L.
officina'le . . . . Common L.
sanc'tum . . . . . . Holywood L.

Guanabana . Soursop: **Annona muricata**

GUARE'A . . . . Muskwood
cedra'ta . . . . Pink M.
gla'bra . . . . Jamaica M.
rus'byi . . . . Rusby M.
thomp'soni . . . . Black M.
trichilioi'des . . . . American M.

Guava . . . . **Psidium**
Brazilian G. . . . . . **P. guineense**
Cattley G. . . . . **P. littorale**
Common G. . . . . **P. guajava**
CostaRican G. **P. friedrichsthalianum**
Dwarf G. . . . . **P. cujavillum**
Guisaro G. . . . . **P. molle**
Yellow Cattley G. **P. littorale lucidum**

Guavaberrytree . Eugenia, Rumberry: **Eugenia floribunda**

Guayule . . . Parthenium, Guayule: **Parthenium argentatum**

GUAZU'MA
ulmifo'lia

GUETTAR'DA . . . . . . Velvetseed
ellip'tica . . . . . . Everglades V.
sca'bra . . . . Roughleaf V.

Gugertree . . . . **Schima**
Burma G. . . . . **S. noronhae**
Darjeeling G. . . . . . **S. wallichi**

Guianaorange . . . . **Platonia**
Bakuri G. . . . . **P. insignis**

Guianaplum . . . Drypetes: **Drypetes**

Guijo . . Shorea, Guijo: **Shorea guiso**

GUILANDI'NA . . . . . Guilandina
bon'duc . . . . Nickernut G.
cris'ta . . . . **Caesalpinia c.**

GUILIEL'MA (*BACTRIS* in part)
See **PALM GENERA.**

Guineafowlgrass . . . . . Itchgrass: **Rottboellia exaltata**

Guineagrass . . **Panicum maximum**

Guineahenweed . . . . . . **Petiveria**
Garlic G. . . . . **P. alliacea**

GUIZO'TIA . . . . Nigerseed
abyssin'ica . . . . . . Ethiopian N.

GULU'BIA . . . . . . Gulubiapalm
See **PALM GENERA.**

Gumbolimbo . . . . **Bursera simaruba**

Gummyrtle . . . . **Angophora**
Kino G. . . . . **A. intermedia**
Rusty G. . . . . **A. lanceolata**

GUMS AND RESINS (Plant Sources of)
See **ECONOMIC PLANTS, GUMS AND RESINS.**

GUMTREE . . . . **Castilla**
PANAMA G. . . . . **C. elastica**

GUMVINE . . . . **Landolphia**
GUINEA G. . . . . . . **L. heudelotti**
MOZAMBIQUE G. . . . . . . **L. kirki**
WESTAFRICAN G. . . . **L. owariensis**

GUMWEED . . . . **Grindelia**
BROADLEAF SHORE G.
G. robusta latifolia
CURLYCUP G. . . . . **G. squarrosa**
FIELD G. . . . . . . **G. camporum**
LOW G. . . . . **G. nana**
MARSH G. . . . . **G. humilis**
OREGON G. . . . . . . **G. oregana**
SHORE G. . . . . **G. robusta**

GUN'NERA . . . . GUNNERA
chilen'sis (*scabra*) . . . CHILEAN G.
magellan'ica . . . . . MAGELLAN G.
manica'ta . . . . GREAT G.

Gurjun . . GURJUNOILTREE, COMMON: **Dipterocarpus turbinatus**

GURJUNOILTREE . . . . **Dipterocarpus**
APITONG G. . . . . **D. grandiflorus**
CEYLON G. . . . . . . **D. zeylanicus**
COMMON G. . . . . . **D. turbinatus**
ENG G. . . . . . . **D. tuberculatus**
HOLLONG G. . . . . **D. pilosus**
KERUING G. . . . . **D. cornutus**

GUSTA'VIA
augus'ta

GUTIERRE'ZIA lw . . . . SNAKEWEED
califor'nica . . . . . CALIFORNIA S.
dracunculoi'des (*Amphiachyris d.*) lw
TARRAGON S. (*Broomweed*)
lu'cida . . . . STICKY S.
microceph'ala (*filifolia*). THREADLEAF S.
saro'thrae . . . . BROOM S.
texa'na lw . . . . TEXAS S.

GUZMA'NIA . . . . GUZMANIA
lingula'ta . . . . . . DROOPHEAD G.
—cardina'lis . . . BURNINGHEART G.
musa'ica . . . . . . COLOMBIAN G.

GYMIN'DA . . . . FALSEBOX
latifo'lia . . . . . . WESTINDIES F.

GYMNAN'THES . . . . OYSTERWOOD
lu'cida . . . . SHINY O.

GYMNE'MA
sylves'tre . . AUSTRALIAN COWPLANT

GYMNOCALYC'IUM . . . AWLCACTUS
See **CACTUS GENERA.**

GYMNO'CLADUS . . . . COFFEETREE
chinen'sis . . . . CHINESE C.
dioi'cus (*canadensis*) . KENTUCKY C.
₵VARIEGATED (*variegata*) HV.

GYMNOGRAM'MA
PITYROGRAMMA
See **FERN GENERA.**

GYMNOLO'MIA . . . . **VIGUIERA**
linea'ris; nevaden'sis
V. multiflora nevadensis

GYMNOPO'GON . . SKELETONGRASS
See **GRASS GENERA.**

GYMNO'THRIX . . . **PENNISETUM**
See **GRASS GENERA.**

GYNANDROP'SIS . . . . SPIDERHERB
grac'ilis . . . . SLENDER S.
pentaphyl'la . . . . . . AFRICAN S.
specio'sa . . . . SHOWY S.

GYNE'RIUM
See **GRASS GENERA.**

GYNU'RA (*CRASSOCEPHALUM*)
VELVETPLANT
angulo'sa . . . . ANGLED V.
auranti'aca (*Crassocephalum aurantiacum*) . . . . JAVA V.

GYPGRASS . . . . **Sporobolus nealleyi**

GYPSOPH'ILA . . . . . GYPSOPHILA
acutifo'lia . . . . BIG G.
altis'sima . . . . TALL G.
cerastioi'des . . . . . MOUSEEAR G.
colli'na . . . . HILLTOP G.
el'egans . . . . COMMON G.
BLOODRED (*atrosanguinea*) HV.
CARMINE (*carminea*)
LARGE WHITE (*alba grandiflora*)
ROSY (*rosea*)
libanot'ica
man'gini . . . . MANGINS G.
mura'lis . . . . CUSHION G.
oldhamia'na . . . . . . OLDHAM G.
pacif'ica . . . . PACIFIC G.
panicula'ta . . . . . . BABYSBREATH
₵DOUBLE (*florepleno*) HV.
₵EHRLE (*ehrlei*)
perfolia'ta . . . . . . CLASPING G.
re'pens (*prostrata*) . . CREEPING G.
₵BODGER (*bodgersi*) HV.
₵LARGE (*monstrosa*)
₵ROSY (*rosea*)
₵WHITE (*alba*)
rokeje'ka
ste'veni . . . . STEVEN G.
stru'thium
tianscha'nica
transsylvan'ica . . TRANSYLVANIA G.
trichot'oma . . . . . THREEFORK G.
visco'sa (*rosea* Hort.) . . . STICKY G.
₵ALPIGENA. HV. Gypsophila
₵BRISTOLFAIRY
FRATENSIS
₵MATPINK (*glabrata*)
₵SILENIFOLIA
₵SUNDERMANN (*sundermanni*)

GYPSOPHILA . . . . **Gypsophila**
BABYSBREATH . . . . **G. paniculata**
BIG G. . . . . **G. acutifolia**
CLASPING G. . . . . . **G. perfoliata**
COMMON G. . . . . **G. elegans**
CREEPING G. . . . . **G. repens**
CUSHION G. . . . . . . **G. muralis**
HILLTOP G. . . . . **G. collina**
MANGINS G. . . . . **G. mangini**
MOUSEEAR G. . . . . **G. cerastioides**
OLDHAM G. . . . . . . **G. oldhamiana**
PACIFIC G. . . . . **G. pacifica**
STEVEN G. . . . . **G. steveni**
STICKY G. . . . . **G. viscosa**
TALL G. . . . . **G. altissima**
THREEFORK G. . . . . **G. trichotoma**
TRANSYLVANIA G. . . **G. transsylvanica**

GYROPH'ORA . . . . . GYROPHORA
cylin'drica . . . . . . CYLINDER G.
deus'ta . . . . SCORCHED G.
pustula'ta . . . . BLISTER G.

GYROTHE'CA . . **LACHNANTHES**

HAAGEOCE'REUS . . **BINGHAMIA**
See **CACTUS GENERA.**

HABENA'RIA (*BLEPHARIGLOTTIS; LIMNORCHIS*) . . . HABENARIA
See **ORCHID GENERA, HARDY TERRESTRIAL GROUP.**

HABENARIA . . . . **Habenaria**
ALASKA H. . . . . **H. unalascensis**
BIGLEAF H. . . . . **H. macrophylla**
CALIFORNIA HILLSIDE H. . **H. elegans**
CANYON H. . . . . . **H. sparsiflora**
CRESTED H. . . . . **H. cristata**
HOOKER H. . . . . **H. hookeri**
MICHAEL H. . . . . . . **H. michaeli**
MILKWHITE H. . . **H. leucostachys**
MODOC H. . . . . **H. saccata**
NORTHERN GREEN H. . . **H. hyperborea**
SATYR H. . . . . **H. viridis bracteata**
SEACLIFF H. . . . . . . **H. maritima**
SHIELD H. . . . . **H. scutellata**
SNOWY H. . . . . **H. nivea**
TUBERCLE H. . . . . **H. flava**

HABER'LEA
ferdinandi-co'burgi
rhodopen'sis
—virgina'lis

HABRACAN'THUS
sanguin'eus (*Justicia sanguinea*)

HABRAN'THUS . . . . HABRANTHUS

Regarded by some botanists as a synonym of Amaryllis (*Hippeastrum*).

andersonia'nus (*Zephyranthes andersoni; Z. andersoniana*) ANDERSON H.
brachyan'drus
cardina'lis . . . . CARDINAL H.
robus'tus (*Zephyranthes robusta*)
texa'nus (*Zephyranthes texana*)
TEXAS H.

HABROTHAM'NUS . . **CESTRUM**

HACKBERRY . . . . **Celtis**
ARIZONA SUGAR H.
C. laevigata brevipes
BIGLEAF H. **C. occidentalis crassifolia**
BUNGE H. . . . . **C. bungeana**
CAUCASIAN H. . . . . . **C. caucasica**
CHINESE H. . . . . **C. sinensis**
COMMON H. . . . . . **C. occidentalis**
DOG H. . . . . **C. o. canina**
DOUGLAS H. . . . . **C. douglasi**
EUROPEAN H. . . . . . . **C. australis**
GEORGIA H. . . . **C. pumila georgiana**
KENTUCKY SUGAR H.
C. laevigata apposita
KOREAN H. . . . . . . **C. koraiensis**
LINDHEIMER H. . . . **C. lindheimeri**
NETLEAF H. . . . . **C. reticulata**
NIGERIAN H. . . . . **C. soyauxi**
OKLAHOMA H. . . **C. reticulata vestita**
ORIENTAL H. . . . . . . **C. tournefortii**
SMALL H. . . . . **C. pumila**
SMALLS SUGAR H. . **C. laevigata smalli**
SPINY H. . . . . **C. pallida**
SUGAR H. . . . . **C. laevigata**
TEXAS S. H. . . . . **C. l. texana**
UVALDE S. H. . . . . **C. l. brachyphylla**

HACKE'LIA

Biennial and perennial species with nutlets attached to a pyramidal base formerly referred to the genus Lappula are now transferred to Hackelia.

deflex'a (*Lappula d.*)
diffu'sa (*Lappula d.*)
floribun'da (*Lappula f.*)
virginia'na (*Lappula v.*)

HACKELOCH'LOA (*RYTILIX*)
PITSCALEGRASS
See **GRASS GENERA.**

HACKSAWFERN . . . . **Doodia**

HACQUE'TIA
epipac'tis

HAEMAN'THUS . . . . . . Bloodlily
al'biflos (*albiflor*) . . . . . White B.
—pubes'cens . . . . . Hairy W.B.
can'didus . . . . Snow B.
coccin'eus . . . . . . Scarlet B.
—coarcta'tus . . . . Littleleaf S.B.
kathari'nae . . . . . Katharine B.
lin'deni . . . . Lindens B.
¢Fascinator. hv.
¢Imperialis
¢Lawrence (*laurenti*)
¢Marvel (*mirabilis*)
¢Queen Alexandra
magnif'icus . . . . . . Leafy B.
—insig'nis . . . . Greenbract L.B.
multiflo'rus (*tenuiflorus*) . Salmon B.
¢Superbus. hv.
natalen'sis . . . . Natal B.
punic'eus . . . . Baseball B.
tigri'nus . . . . Tiger B.
¢Andromeda (*katharinae* × *magnificus*) hv. Haemanthus
¢Clark (*albiflos* × *coccineus*)
¢King Albert. *Koenig Albert.*

HAEMA'RIA . . . . **GOODYERA**
See **ORCHID GENERA.**

HAEMATOX'YLON (*HAEMATOXYLUM; HEMATOXYLON*)
Bloodwoodtree
brasilet'to . . . . Brazil B.
campechia'num . . . . . Logwood

HAGE'NIA (*BRAYERA*)
abyssin'ica (*Brayera a.; B. anthelmintica*) . . . . Kussotree

Hairbrushcactus
Pachycereus pecten-aboriginum

Haircapmoss . . . . **Polytrichum**
Alpine H. . . . . **P. alpinum**
Common H. . . . . **P. commune**
Juniper H. . . . . . **P. juniperinum**
Yukon H. . . . . . . **P. yukonense**

Hairgrass
Aira; A. capillaris; Deschampsia
Deschampsia is a segregate of Aira.

Annual H. . . . . **D. danthonioides**
Early H. . . . . **A. praecox**
Mountain H. . . . **D. atropurpurea**
Pacific H. . . . . . **D. holciformis**
Silver H. . . . . . **A. caryophyllea**
Slender H. . . . . . . **D. elongata**
Tufted H. . . . . . . **D. caespitosa**
Wavy H. . . . . **D. flexuosa**

Hairpalm . . . Mediterraneanpalm: **Chamaerops humilis**

HA'KEA . . . . Hakea
acicula'ris . . . . . Needleleaf H.
auricula'ta . . . . Earleaf H.
—spathula'ta
cine'rea . . . . Ashyleaf H.
crassifo'lia . . . . . . Thickleaf H.
crista'ta . . . . Crested H.
cuculla'ta . . . . Hooded H.
cyclocar'pa . . . . Roughfruit H.
dactyloi'des . . . . Finger H.
ellip'tica . . . . . . Ovalfruit H.
erina'cea . . . . . . Hedgehog H.
gibbo'sa . . . . Rock H.
glabel'la . . . . Smooth H.
hookeria'na . . . . . . Hookers H.
incrassa'ta . . . . . . SwanRiver H.
lauri'na Seaurchin H. (*Pincushiontree*)

HAKEA, continued
margina'ta
multilinea'ta . . . Grassleaf Hakea
myrtioi'des
oleifo'lia . . . . Oliveleaf H.
petiola'ris
platysper'ma
propin'qua . . . . . . Sandbank H.
pugionifor'mis . . . Daggerfruit H.
ruscifo'lia
salig'na . . . . Willow H.
stenocar'pa
suave'olens . . . . Sweet H.
trifurca'ta . . . . . . Threefork H.
undula'ta . . . . Wavyleaf H.
va'ria . . . . Variedleaf H.

Hakea . . . . **Hakea**
Ashyleaf H. . . . . **H. cinerea**
Crested H. . . . . **H. cristata**
Daggerfruit H. . . . **H. pugioniformis**
Earleaf H. . . . . . . **H. auriculata**
Finger H. . . . . . . **H. dactyloides**
Grassleaf H. . . . . **H. multilineata**
Hedgehog H. . . . . . . **H. erinacea**
Hooded H. . . . . **H. cucullata**
Hookers H. . . . . . . **H. hookeriana**
Needleleaf H. . . . . . **H. acicularis**
Oliveleaf H. . . . . . . **H. oleifolia**
Ovalfruit H. . . . . . . **H. elliptica**
Rock H. . . . . **H. gibbosa**
Roughfruit H. . . . . **H. cyclocarpa**
Sandbank H. . . . . . **H. propinqua**
Seaurchin H. . . . . **H. laurina**
Smooth H. . . . . **H. glabella**
SwanRiver H. . . . . . **H. incrassata**
Sweet H. . . . . **H. suaveolens**
Thickleaf H. . . . . . **H. crassifolia**
Threefork H. . . . . . . **H. trifurcata**
Variedleaf H. . . . . **H. varia**
Wavyleaf H. . . . . **H. undulata**
Willow H. . . . . **H. saligna**

Halberdfern . . **Tectaria heracleifolia**

HALE'NIA . . . . . . Spurgentian
deflex'a . . . . American S.

HALERPES'TES . . **RANUNCULUS**

HALE'SIA . . . . Silverbell
caroli'na (*tetraptera*) . . Carolina S.
—mol'lis . . . . Suwanee C.S.
¢Meehan (*meehani*) hv. H. carolina
dip'tera . . . . Twowing S.
fortun'ei . . . . **Alniphyllum f.**
montic'ola . . . . Mountain S.
—rose'a . . . . Pink M.S.
—vesti'ta . . . . . . Fuzzyleaf M.S.
parviflo'ra . . . . Florida S.

HALI'DRYS
siliquo'sa . . . . . . Drug Seaoak

HALI'MIUM . . . . Falsesunrose
alyssoi'des (*Helianthemum a.*)
Golden F.
cheiranthoi'des (*Helianthemum c.*)
Portugal F.
halimifo'lium (*Helianthemum h.*)
African F.
—multiflo'rum (*Helianthemum h. m.*)
Morocco F.
lasian'thum (*Helianthemum formosum; H. lasianthum*) . . . . . Lisbon F.
libano'tis (*Helianthemum l.; H. rosmarinifolium*) . . . . . Rosemary F.
ocymoi'des (*Cistus algarvensis; Helianthemum o.; H. umbellatum*)
Purplespot F.
umbella'tum (*Helianthemum u.*)
Lineleaf F.

HALIMODEN'DRON . . . Salttree
haloden'dron (*argenteum*) Siberian S.
—purpu'reum . . . . . Purple S.S.

HALLIOPHY'TUM Chuckawallabush
hall'i . . . . Halls C.

HALO'DULE |w . . . . . Shoalweed
wright'i |w . . . . Cuban S.

HALO'PHILA |w . . . . . Halophila
baillo'nis |w . . . . . . Baillon H.
engelmann'i |w . . . Engelmann H.

HALORA'GIS . . . . Seaberry
erec'ta . . . . Erect S.

HAMAME'LIS |w . . . . Witchhazel
japon'ica . . . . Japanese W.
—arbo'rea . . . . Tree J.W.
—flavo-purpuras'cens (*H. incarnata*)
Red J.W.
—zuccarinia'na . . . . . Lemon J.W.
macrophyl'la . . . . . . Southern W.
mol'lis . . . . Chinese W.
verna'lis . . . . Vernal W.
—car'nea . . . . . Redpetal V.W.
—tomentel'la . . Woollyleaf V.W.
virginia'na |w . . . . . Common W.
—rubes'cens . . . . Pink C.W.

HAMATOCAC'TUS
See **CACTUS GENERA.**

HAME'LIA . . . . Hamelia
erec'ta (*patens*) . . . . . Scarlet H.
sphaerocar'pa . . . . Peru H.

HAMO'SA . . . . . **ASTRAGALUS**

HAPLOPAP'PUS . **APLOPAPPUS**

Harbinger-of-spring
Erigenia; E. bulbosa

HARBOUR'IA
trachypleu'ra

HARDENBER'GIA . . . . Vinelilac
bimacula'ta
comptonia'na (*Kennedia c.; K. caerulea*) . . . . Compton V.
—al'ba . . . . White C.V.
macula'ta (*H. monophylla bimaculata*)
Spotted V.
monophyl'la (*Kennedia m.; K. ovata*)
Singleleaf V.
¢Lilac (*lilacina*) hv.
¢Pink (*rosea*)
¢Whiteflower (*alba*)

Hardgrass . . . **Sclerochloa; S. dura**

Hardinggrass
Phalaris tuberosa stenoptera

Hardyorange . . . Trifoliate-orange: **Poncirus trifoliata**

Harebell, American
Campanula petiolata

Haresear . . . . **Conringia**
Treacle H. . . . . . . **C. orientalis**

Harestail . . . . . **Lagurus; L. ovatus**

HARPEPHYL'LUM
caf'frum . . . . Kafirplum

HARPEREL'LA |w
nodo'sa |w

HARPUL'LIA
cupanioi'des
pen'dula . . . . Tulipwood

HARRIMANEL'LA
stelleria'na

HARRIS'IA . . . . . . Applecactus (*Pricklyapple*)
See **CACTUS GENERA.**

HARRISO'NIA abyssin'ica

Hartfordfern. . . **Lygodium palmatum**

HARTMAN'NIA . . **OENOTHERA**

HARTO'GIA . . . . **AGATHOSMA**

Hartstongue . **Phyllitis scolopendrium**

HARTWE'GIA
See **ORCHID GENERA.**

Hatchetvetch **Securigera; S. coronilla**

HATIO'RA . . . . . **RHIPSALIS**
See **CACTUS GENERA.**

Hatpalm, Panama. . Carludovica, Hat: **Carludovica palmata**

Hawkbit . . . . **Leontodon**
Fall H. . . . . **L. autumnalis**
Rough H. . . . . . . **L. nudicaulis**

Hawksbeard . . . . **Crepis**
Dandelion H. . . . . . **C. runcinata**
Gray H. . . . . . . **C. intermedia**
Narrowleaf H. . . . . . **C. tectorum**
Red H. . . . . **C. rubra**
Rough H. . . . . **C. biennis**
Siskiyou H. . . . . . **C. monticola**
Smooth H. . . . . . . **C. capillaris**
Tapertip H. . . . . . **C. acuminata**
Tiny H. . . . . **C. nana**
Western H. . . . . . **C. occidentalis**
Yellowstone H. . . . **C. scopulorum**

Hawkweed . . . . **Hieracium**
Branching H. . . . . **H. ciadanthum**
Canada H. . . . . . . **H. canadense**
Field H. . . . . **H. pratense**
Houndstongue H.. **H. cynoglossoides**
Kingdevil H. . . . . **H. florentinum**
Mouseear H. . . . . . **H. pilosella**
Narrowleaf H. . . **H. umbellatum**
Orange H. . . . . **H. aurantiacum**
Panicled H. . . . . **H. paniculatum**
Poorrobins H. . . . . **H. venosum**
Rough H. . . . . . . **H. scabrum**
Shaggy H. . . . . . . **H. villosum**
Slender H. . . . . **H. gracile**
White H. . . . . . . **H. albiflorum**
Woollyweed . . . . . **H. scouleri**
Yellowdevil H. . . . **H. floribundum**

∞ Hawmedlar . . . ∞ **Crataegomespilus**
Asnieres H. . ×**C. dardari asnieresi**
∞ Bigflower H. . . . ∞ **C. grandiflora**
Bronvaux H. . . . . ×**C. dardari**
∞ Gillot H. . . . . . . ∞ **C. gilloti**

HAWORTH'IA
See **SUCCULENTS.**

Hawthorn . . . . **Crataegus**
Albany H. . . **C. punctata canescens**
Altai H. . . . . **C. altaica**
Arkansas H. . . . . . **C. arkansana**
Arnold H. . . . . . **C. arnoldiana**
Ashe H. . . . . **C. ashei**
Augustine H. . . . . **C. sublobulata**
Azarole H. . . . . . . **C. azarolus**
Baby H. . . . . **C. modesta**
Barberryleaf H. . . . **C. berberifolia**
Barry H. . . . . **C. barryana**
Beadle H. . . . . **C. aprica**
Berlandier H. . . . **C. berlandieri**
Bissell Delaware H. **C. apposita bisselli**
Blackfruit H. . . . . **C. chlorosarca**
Blueberry H. . . **C. brachyacantha**

Hawthorn, continued
Bottom H. . . . . **Crataegus erecta**
Boynton H. . . . . . . **C. boyntoni**
Brazos H. . . . . **C. brazoria**
Britton H. . . . . **C. brittoni**
Bronzy H. . . . . **C. cuprea**
Buckley H. . . . . . . **C. buckleyi**
Bunch H. . . . . **C. delosi**
Buncombe H. . . . . . . **C. algens**
Bushes H. . . . . **C. bushi**
Canada H. . . . . . **C. canadensis**
Canby H. . . . . **C. canbyi**
Cerro H. . . . . **C. cerronis**
Champlain H. . . **C. champlainensis**
Cherokee H. . . . **C. cherokeensis**
Chicago H. . . . . . **C. arduennae**
Chinese H. . . . . . **C. pinnatifida**
Chippewa H. . . . **C. chippewaensis**
Christmas H. . . . **C. durobrivensis**
Cocks H. . . . . **C. cocksi**
Cockspur H. . . . . . . **C. crusgalli**
Colorado H. . . . . **C. coloradensis**
Dallas H. . . . . . . **C. dallasiana**
Dawson H. . . . . . **C. dawsoniana**
Delaware H. . . . . . . **C. apposita**
Dewey H. . . . . . . **C. deweyana**
Dotted H. . . . . **C. punctata**
Douglas H. . . . . . . **C. douglasi**
Downy H. . . . . **C. mollis**
Dunbar H. . . . . **C. dunbari**
Eames H. . . . . **C. eamesi**
Eastern Fireberry H. **C. chrysocarpa phoenicea**
Ecuador H. . . . . . . **C. stipulosa**
Egans H. . . . . **C. egani**
Ellwanger H. . . . **C. ellwangeriana**
Engelmann H. . . . . **C. engelmanni**
English H. . . . . . **C. oxyacantha**
Eureka Springs H. . . **C. subpilosa**
European Black H. . . . **C. nigra**
Fanleaf H. . . . . . . **C. flabellata**
Fireberry H. . . . . **C. chrysocarpa**
Fleshy H. . . . . . . **C. succulenta**
Franklin H. . . . . **C. lauta**
Frosted H. . . . . . . **C. pruinosa**
Gault H. . . . . **C. gaulti**
Georgia H. . . . . . . **C. georgiana**
Glossy H. . . . . **C. nitida**
Green H. . . . . **C. viridis**
Gregg H. . . . . **C. greggi**
Hannibal H. . . . . . **C. intermixta**
Harbison H. . . . . . **C. harbisoni**
Hawcreek H. **C. aestivalis maloides**
Heldreich H. . . . . . **C. heldreichi**
Hills H. . . . . **C. hilli**
Holmes H. . . . . . **C. holmesiana**
Hudson H. . . . . . . **C. hudsonica**
Illinois H. . . . . . **C. illinoiensis**
Inkberry H. . . . . . . **C. multiflora**
Jacksonville H. . . . **C. floridana**
JeffDavis H. . . . . . **C. montivaga**
Kansas H. . . . . . **C. coccinioides**
Kansu H. . . . . . . **C. kansuensis**
Kellogg H. . . . . . . **C. kelloggi**
Kingston H. . . . **C. kingstonensis**
∞ Lambert H. . . . . ∞ **C. lambertiana**
Laney H. . . . . **C. laneyi**
Large Chinese H. **C. pinnatifida major**
∞ Lavalle H. . . . . ∞ **C. lavallei**
LawrenceCounty H. . **C. lawrencensis**
Letterman H. . . . . . **C. lettermani**
Littlehip H. . . . . . **C. spathulata**
Lowhedge H. . . . . . . **C. fruticosa**
Mansfield H. . . . **C. mansfieldensis**
Margaret H. . . . . . **C. margaretta**
Marietta H. . . . . . **C. mariettensis**
Maximowicz H. . . . **C. maximowiczi**
May H. . . . . **C. aestivalis**

Hawthorn, continued
Mississippi H. . . **Crataegus denaria**
Missouri H. . . . . **C. fecunda**
Mohrs H. . . . . **C. mohri**
Mongol H. . . . . . . **C. dsungarica**
Montgomery H. . . . . . **C. arborea**
Niagara H. . . . . . . **C. asperifolia**
Nippon H. . . . . **C. cuneata**
October H. . . . . **C. infera**
Ohio H. . . . . **C. ohioensis**
Oneflower H. . . . . . . **C. uniflora**
Ontario H. . . . . . . **C. pedicellata**
Opelousas H. . . . . **C. tersa**
Palmer H. . . . . **C. palmeri**
Parsley H. . . . . **C. marshalli**
Pear H. . . . . . . **C. calpodendron**
Pennsylvania Cockspur H. **C. crusgalli oblongata**
Pennsylvania H. . . **C. pennsylvanica**
Pensacola H. . . . . . . **C. lacrimata**
Peoria H. . . . . **C. peoriensis**
∞ Peregrina H. . . . . ∞ **C. peregrina**
Piedmont H. . . . . **C. regalis**
PikeCounty H. . . **C. phaneroneura**
Pineland H. . . . . **C. signata**
Plumleaf H. . . . . . . **C. prunifolia**
Pond H. . . . . **C. rufula**
Prairie H. . . . . **C. pratensis**
Pringle H. . . . . **C. pringlei**
Quebec H. . . . . **C. submollis**
Ravenel H. . . . . **C. raveneli**
Redhaw H. . . . . . . **C. sanguinea**
Redhip Cockspur H. **C. crusgalli pyracanthifolia**
Riverflat H. . . . . **C. opaca**
River H. . . . . **C. rivularis**
Robeson H. . . . . . **C. robesoniana**
Russet H. . . . . **C. foetida**
Russian H. . . . . **C. ambigua**
Sabine H. . . . . **C. edita**
Sandhill H. . . . . **C. collina**
Sargent H. . . . . **C. sargenti**
Showy Cockspur H. **C. crusgalli splendens**
Silver H. . . . . **C. orientalis**
Singleseed H. . . . . . **C. monogyna**
Smith H. . . . . **C. smithi**
Sorbus H. . . . . **C. sorbifolia**
Spike H. . . . . . . **C. macracantha**
St.Louis H. . . . . **C. acutifolia**
Sutherland H. . . **C. sutherlandensis**
Swan H. . . . . **C. swanensis**
Tansyleaf H. . . . . . **C. tanacetifolia**
Texas H. . . . . **C. texana**
Thicket H. . . . . **C. intricata**
Threeflower H. . . . . . . **C. triflora**
Trelease H. . . . . **C. treleasei**
Turkeyapple H. . . . . . . **C. induta**
Wakulla H. . . . . . . **C. limnophila**
Warner H. . . . . **C. warneri**
Washington H. . . . **C. phaenopyrum**
Watts H. . . . . **C. wattiana**
Westchester H. . . . . . **C. fructuosa**
Willow H. . . . . **C. saligna**
Wilmington Cockspur H. **C. crusgalli capillata**
Wilson H. . . . . **C. wilsoni**
Wood H. . . . . **C. nemoralis**
Yellow Dotted H. . **C. punctata aurea**
Yellow H. . . . . **C. flava**
Youngs H. . . . . **C. youngi**

Hayscentedfern **Dennstaedtia punctilobula**

Hazar'dia ca'na . . **Aplopappus canus**

Hazel . . . . Filbert: **Corylus**
See note under **CORYLUS.**

Heartnut . . . Walnut, Flat Siebold: **Juglans sieboldiana cordiformis**

Heartseed . . . . . **Cardiospermum**
Balloonvine H. . . **C. halicacabum**
Hairy H. . . . . . . **C. hirsutum**
Showy H. . . . . **C. grandiflorum**

Heath . . . . **Erica**
Alpine Tree H. . **E. arborea alpina**
Berger H. . . . . . **E. bergeriana**
Besom H. . . . . . . **E. scoparia**
Bigflower H. . . . **E. grandiflora**
Biscay H. . . . . **E. mediterranea**
Blackeyed H. . . . **E. melanthera**
Bowie H. . . . . . . **E. bowieana**
∞ Cavendish H. . . ∞ **E. cavendishiana**
Cornish H. . . . . . **E. vagans**
Corsican H. . . . . . . **E. stricta**
Crossleaf H. . . . . . **E. tetralix**
Cypress H. . . . . **E. cupressina**
∞ Darley H. . . . ∞ **E. darleyensis**
Densespike H. . . . **E. multiflora**
Everblooming H. . . . **E. blanda**
Fringed H. . . . . . . **E. ciliaris**
Garland H. . . . . **E. subdivaricata**
Irish Biscay H. **E. mediterranea hibernica**
Largeflower Porcelain H. **E. ventricosa grandiflora**
∞ Mackay H. . . . . . ∞ **E. mackai**
Maweana Fringed H. **E. ciliaris maweana**
Porcelain H. . . . . **E. ventricosa**
Southern H. . . . . . **E. australis**
Spanish H. . . . . . **E. lusitanica**
Spring H. . . . . **E. carnea**
Tree H. . . . . **E. arborea**
Twisted H. . . . . **E. cinerea**
∞ Veitch H. . . . . . . ∞ **E. veitchi**
White Biscay H. **E. mediterranea alba**
White Cornish H. . . . **E. vagans a.**
White Crossleaf H. . . **E. tetralix a.**
White Fringed H. . . . **E. ciliaris a.**
White Spring H. . . . **E. carnea a.**
White Twisted H. . . . **E. cinerea a.**
Wilmore H. . . . . . . **E. wilmorei**
Winter H. . . . . . . **E. hyemalis**
Woolly Crossleaf H. **E. tetralix martinesi**
Woollyleaf H. . . . . **E. capitata**

Heather . . . . **Calluna**
Scotch H. . . . . **C. vulgaris**
White S. H. . . . . . . **C. v. alba**

Heathmyrtle . . . . . . **Verticordia**
Fontanes H. . . . . . **V. fontanesi**
Fringe H. . . . . . . **V. densiflora**

HE'BE . . . . Hebe
al'bicans (*Veronica a.*) . . White H.
amab'ilis (*Veronica a.*) . . Lovely H.
—blan'da (*Veronica a. b.*)
amplexicau'lis (*Veronica a.*)
anderso'ni (*Veronica a.*) Anderson H.
—variega'ta (*Veronica a. v.*)
angustifo'lia (*Veronica a.*)
anom'ala (*Veronica a.*)
baileya'na (*Veronica b.*)
balfouria'na (*Veronica b.*)
bar'keri (*Veronica b.*) . . Barker H.
bid'willi (*Veronica b.*)
bol'lonsi (*Veronica b.*)
buchan'ani (*Veronica b.*)
buxifo'lia (*Veronica b.*) . Boxleaf H.
carne'a (*Veronica c.*) . . Crimson H.
carno'sula (*Veronica c.*)
car'sei (*Veronica c.*)
catarrac'tae (*Veronica c.*)

HEBE, continued
catarrac'tae diffu'sa (*Veronica c. d.*)
chatham'ica (*Veronica c.*) Chatham Hebe
—erec'ta (*Veronica c. e.*) Erect C.H.
colenso'i (*Veronica c.*)
cookia'na (*Veronica c.*)
cupressoi'des (*Veronica c.*)
darwinia'na (*Veronica d.*) Darwin H.
decum'bens (*Veronica d.*) Ground H.
dieffenbach'i (*Veronica d.*) Dieffenbach H.
diosmaefo'lia (*Veronica d.*)
dorrien-smith'i (*Veronica d.*)
ellip'tica (*Veronica e.*)
₵Autumnglory. hv.
₵Bluegem
epacrid'ea (*Veronica e.*)
eveno'sa (*Veronica e.*)
formo'sa (*Veronica f.*) . Tasmanian H.
gigan'tea (*Veronica g.*)
glaucophyl'la (*Veronica g.*)
gracil'lima (*Veronica g.*) Graceful H.
guthriea'na (*Veronica g.*)
haas'ti (*Veronica h.*)
hec'tori (*Veronica h.*)
hulkea'na (*Veronica h.*) . Hulkes H.
insula'ris (*Veronica i.*)
kirk'i (*Veronica k.; V. salicifolia k.*)
lae'vis (*Veronica l.*) . . . Smooth H.
lavaudia'na (*Veronica l.*)
leiophyl'la (*Veronica l.*)
lew'isi (*Veronica l.*) . . . . Lewis H.
ligustrifo'lia (*Veronica l.*)
linifo'lia (*Veronica l.*)
loganioi'des (*Veronica l.*)
ly'alli (*Veronica l.*)
macran'tha (*Veronica m.*)
macrocar'pa (*Veronica m.*) Bigfruit H.
—latisep'ala (*Veronica l.*)
macrou'ra (*Veronica m.*)
matthews'i (*Veronica m.*)
obova'ta (*Veronica o.*)
obtusa'ta (*Veronica o.*)
ol'seni (*Veronica o.*)
parviflo'ra (*Veronica p.*) Littleflower H.
pimeleoi'des (*Veronica p.*)
pinguifo'lia (*Veronica p.*)
propin'qua (*Veronica p.*)
pubes'cens (*Veronica p.*)
rigid'ula (*Veronica r.*)
rotunda'ta (*Veronica r.*)
rupic'ola (*Veronica r.*) . . . Cliff H.
salicifo'lia (*Veronica s.*) Willowleaf H.
salicornioi'des (*Veronica s.*)
specio'sa (*Veronica imperialis; V. speciosa*) . . . . Showy H.
₵Alicia Amherst (*veitchi*). *Royal Purple*. hv.
₵Autumnglory
₵Gloriosa. *Pink Pearl.*
₵La Seduisante
₵Purplequeen
₵Silverbeauty
₵Simon Deleaux
town'soni (*Veronica t.*) Townsons H.
tra'versi (*Veronica t.*) . . Travers H.
vernico'sa (*Veronica v.*)

Hebe . . . . **Hebe**
Anderson H. . . . . **H. andersoni**
Barker H. . . . . **H. barkeri**
Bigfruit H. . . . . **H. macrocarpa**
Boxleaf H. . . . . . . **H. buxifolia**
Chatham H. . . . . . **H. chathamica**
Cliff H. . . . . **H. rupicola**
Crimson H. . . . . **H. carnea**

Hebe, continued
Darwin H. . . . . **Hebe darwiniana**
Dieffenbach H. . . **H. dieffenbachi**
Erect Chatham H. **H. chathamica erecta**
Graceful H. . . . . **H. gracillima**
Ground H. . . . . . **H. decumbens**
Hulkes H. . . . . . . **H. hulkeana**
Lewis H. . . . . **H. lewisi**
Littleflower H. . . . **H. parviflora**
Lovely H. . . . . **H. amabilis**
Showy H. . . . . **H. speciosa**
Smooth H. . . . . **H. laevis**
Tasmanian H. . . . . . **H. formosa**
Townsons H. . . . . . **H. townsoni**
Travers H. . . . . . . **H. traversi**
White H. . . . . **H. albicans**
Willowleaf H. . . . . **H. salicifolia**

HEBENSTREIT'IA
como'sa
denta'ta

HEDEO'MA |w . . Falsepennyroyal
drum'mondi . . . . . Drummond F.
his'pida . . . . Rough F.
pulegioi'des |w . . . . American F.

HED'ERA . . . . Ivy
canarien'sis (*algeriensis; azorica* Hort.; *H. helix c.; H. h. maderensis; maderensis*) . . . . Algerian I.
Gloire Demarengo. hv.
Yellowedge (*variegata*)
col'chica (*coriacea; roegneriana* Hort.) Colchis I.
Goldleaf (*aurea*) hv.
Shrub (*arborescens*)
Thinleaf (*dentata*)
Variegated (*variegata*)
he'lix . . . . English I.
—hiber'nica (*H. hibernica*) . Irish I.
—poet'ica (*H. chrysocarpa; H. poetarum*) . . . . Poets I.
—taur'ica . . . . Crimean I.
All the hort. var. below are clons.
Albany. hv. H. helix
Arrowleaf (*sagittifolia*)
Baltic (*baltica*)
Bunchleaf (*conglomerata*)
Bush (*arborescens*)
Caenwood (*caenwoodiana*)
Cavendish (*cavendishi*)
Darkleaf (*nigra*)
Emerald Gem
Fingerleaf (*digitata*)
Footleaf (*pedata*)
Goldfruit (*chrysocarpa*)
Goldleaf (*aureo-variegata*)
Grayleaf (*canescens*)
Handleaf (*palmata*)
Heartleaf (*deltoidea; hastata*)
Leatherleaf (*coreacea*)
Lees Silver
Leopard (*maculata*)
Lexington
Marbled (*marmorata*)
Miniature (*gracilis*)
Mrs. Pollock
Niagara
Pittsburgh
Purpleleaf (*purpurea*)
Scallopleaf (*crenata*)
Silverleaf (*argenteo-variegata*)
Small-leaf (*minima*)
Spotted Giant (*dentata variegata*)
Stripeleaf (*marginata*)
Tricolor (*elegantissima*)
Twisted (*tortuosa*)
Twocolor (*discolor*)

HEDERA helix, continued
Upright (*stricta*)
Variegated (*variegata*)
maderen'sis . . . . . **H. canariensis**
nepalen'sis (*himalaica; H. helix cinerea*) Nepal Ivy
poeta'rum . . . . . **H. helix poetica**
rhom'bea (*japonica* Tobl., *not* Jungh.) Tallclimbing I.
roegneria'na . . . . . . **H. colchica**

Hedgehogcactus . . . . . **Echinopsis**
Black H. . . . . **E. nigra**
Bridges H. . . . . **E. bridgesi**
Cordova H. . . . . . **E. cordobensis**
Silvestri H. . . . . . . **E. silvestri**

Hedgehyssop . . . . **Gratiola**
Clammy H. . . . . . . **G. viscidula**
Drug H. . . . . . . **G. officinalis**
Golden H. . . . . **G. lutea**
Shaggy H. . . . . **G. pilosa**
Virginia H. . . . . . **G. virginiana**

Hedgeparsley . . . . **Torilis**
Knotted H. . . . . **T. nodosa**

HEDY'CHIUM . . . . Gingerlily
auranti'acum . . . . . . Orange G.
chrysoleu'cum
coccin'eum . . . . . . Scarlet G.
—angustifo'lium Narrowleaf S.G.
corona'rium . . . . . . Common G.
ela'tum . . . . Tall G.
ellip'ticum
flaves'cens
fla'vum . . . . Yellow G.
gardneria'num . . . . . . India G.
glau'cum . . . . Smooth G.
grac'ile . . . . Slender G.
green'ei . . . . Greene G.
max'imum . . . . Great G.
spica'tum . . . . Spiked G.
—acumina'tum
thyrsifor'me
villo'sum

HEDYS'ARUM . . . Sweetvetch
borea'le (*mackenzi; pabulare*) Northern S.
corona'rium . . . . Sulla S. (*Sulla*)
hedysaroi'des
multiju'gum . . . . . Mongolian S.
—apicula'tum
obscu'rum
occidenta'le . . . . . . Western S.
pabula're . . . . **H. boreale**
polymor'phum
songar'icum
sulphures'cens . . . . . . Sulfur S.
utahen'se . . . . Utah S.

HEDYSCE'PE . . . . Umbrellapalm
See **PALM GENERA.**

He-huckleberry . . **Lyonia ligustrina**
Bracted H. . . . . **L. l. foliosiflora**
Downy H. . . . . **L. l. pubescens**

HEIM'IA . . . . Heimia
myrtifo'lia . . . . . Myrtleleaf H.
salicifo'lia . . . . Willowleaf H.

HELE'NIUM (*DUGALDIA*) ⌊w Sneezeweed
aromat'icum . . . . . Aromatic S.
autumna'le ⌊w . . . . . Common S.
¢Bronzequeen. hv.
¢Chipperfield Orange
¢Dwarf (*pumilum*)
¢Gartensonne
¢Golden Jugend
¢Great (*superbum*)

HELENIUM autumnale, continued
¢Julisonne
¢Red (*rubrum*)
¢Ruby Thornley
¢Windley
bigelo'vi . . . Bigelow Sneezeweed
hoopes'i (*Dugaldia h.*) . . Orange S.
monta'num (*autumnale* D. C. Eaton, *not* L.) . . . . . . Mountain S.
nudiflo'rum . . . . . Purplehead S.
¢Georgia (*grandicephalum striatum*) hv.
puber'ulum
tenuifo'lium . Bitter S. (*Bitterweed*)
¢Riverton Beauty. hv. Helenium
¢Riverton Gem

HELEOCH'LOA . . . . Heleochloa
See **GRASS GENERA.**

HELIAM'PHORA . . . . Sunpitcher
nu'tans . . . . Nodding S.

HELIANTHEL'LA ⌊w . . Helianthella
arizo'nica . . . . Arizona H.
califor'nica . . . . . California H.
doug'lasi . . . . Douglas H.
par'ryi . . . . Parry H.
quinquener'vis . . . . Fivenerve H.
uniflo'ra . . . . Oneflower H.

HELIAN'THEMUM ⌊w . . . Sunrose
alpes'tre . . . . Alpine S.
alyssoi'des . . . . . . **Halimium a.**
apenni'num . . . . . . Apennine S.
¢Rosy (*rhodanthum; roseum*) hv.
¢Versicolor
canaden'se . . . . **Crocanthemum c.**
ca'num . . . . Hoary S.
chamaecis'tus . . . **H. nummularium**
cheiranthoi'des . . . . . **Halimium c.**
formo'sum . . **Halimium lasianthum**
fuma'na . . . . . **Fumana nudiflora**
glau'cum . . . . Smooth S.
—cro'ceum
grandiflo'rum (*H. nummularium g.*)
¢Copper (*cupreum*) hv.
¢Double (*multiplex*)
green'ei . . . . . **Crocanthemum g.**
gutta'tum
halimifo'lium . . . . . . **Halimium h.**
—multiflo'rum . . . . **Halimium h. m.**
lasian'thum . . . . . **Halimium l.**
libano'tis . . . . **Halimium l.**
lunula'tum
ma'jus ⌊w . . . . . . Frostweed S.
nummula'rium (*chamaecistus; variabile; vulgare*)
—grandiflo'rum . . . **H. grandiflorum**
¢Afflick. hv. H. nummularium
¢Apricot
¢Attraction
¢Ball of Gold
¢Beauty
¢Bendledi
¢Benheckler
¢Benmare
¢Bennevis
¢Benvenue
¢Bouledefeu
¢Bronze
¢Bronzebeauty
¢Bronzequeen
¢Burntorange
¢Dazzler
¢Deep Yellow (*aureum*)
¢Diversifolium
¢Double White (*albo-plenum*)
¢Fickle (*mutabile*)

HELIANTHEMUM nummularium, continued
¢Fireball
¢Firedragon
¢Fireflame
¢Jack Scott
¢Jubilee
¢Lemonqueen
¢Miss Lake
¢Mrs. Earle
¢Multiplex
¢Pilot
¢Rhodanthe
¢Rhodanthe Carnea
¢Rosemary (*tomentosa*)
¢Roseoplenum
¢Rose Perfection
¢Roseum
¢Rosygem
¢Rubroplenum
¢Salmonqueen
¢Scopoli
¢Snowdrift
¢Somerville Copper
¢Stramineum
¢Sudburygem
¢The Bride
¢Venustum
¢Wesley (*Primrose*)
ocymoi'des . . . . **Halimium o.**
oelan'dicum
pilo'sum
prae'cox
procum'bens . . . **Fumana nudifolia**
rosmarinifo'lium . **Halimium libanotis**
scopa'rium . . . . **Crocanthemum s.**
suffrutes'cens . . . **Crocanthemum s.**
×**sulphu'reum** (*apenninum × nummularium*)
¢Copper (*cupreum*) hv.
¢Pink (*roseum*)
tubera'ria . . . . **Tuberaria vulgaris**
umbella'tum . **Halimium ocymoides; H. umbellatum**
variab'ile; vulga're **H. nummularium**

HELIAN'THUS ⌊w . . . . Sunflower
angustifo'lius . . . . . . Swamp S.
an'nuus ⌊w . . . . Common S.
¢Double Dwarf (*nanus*) hv.
¢Doubleray (*californicus*)
¢Globe (*globosus*)
argophyl'lus (*argyrophyllus*) Silverleaf S.
atroru'bens (*sparsifolius*) Darkeye S.
califor'nicus . . . . . California S.
The name H. californicus is often misapplied to the Doubleray Sunflower, hort. var. of H. annuus.
cilia'ris
deb'ilis (*cucumerifolius*) Cucumberleaf S.
¢Copperred (*cupreatus*)
¢Purple (*purpureus*)
decapet'alus . . . . . . Thinleaf S.
¢Bouquet d'Or. hv.
¢Double (*florepleno*)
¢Giant (*maximum*)
¢Golden (*multiflorus*)
¢Meteore
¢Meteore Plenus
¢Soleil d'Or
divarica'tus . . . . . Divaricate S.
doronicoi'des . . . . Oblongleaf S.
dowellia'nus . . . . . . Dowell S.
gigan'teus . . . . Giant S.
gracilen'tus . . . . Slender S.
grosseserra'tus . . . . Sawtooth S.
laetiflo'rus . . . . Showy S.

HELIANTHUS, continued
macrophyl'lus . . . . **H. strumosus m.**
maximilia'ni (*maximilianus*) |w
MAXIMILIAN SUNFLOWER
microceph'alus . . . . SMALLHEAD S.
mol'lis . . . . ASHY S.
—grandiflo'rus
occidenta'lis . . . . . . FEWLEAF S.
petiola'ris |w . . . . PRAIRIE S.
rig'idus (*scaberrimus*) . . . STIFF S.
¢MISS MELLISH. HV.
¢WOOLEYDOD
salicifo'lius (*orgyalis*) WILLOWLEAF S.
scaber'rimus |w . . . BLACKHEAD S.
sparsifo'lius . . . . . **H. atrorubens**
strumo'sus . . . . . WOODLAND S.
—macrophyl'lus (*H. macrophyllus*)
BIGLEAF W.S.
subrhomboi'deus . . RHOMBICLEAF S.
tomento'sus . . . . . . WOOLLY S.
trachelifo'lius |w . . THROATWORT S.
tubero'sus . JERUSALEMARTICHOKE S.
(*Jerusalemartichoke*)

HELICHRY'SUM (*ELICHRYSUM*)
EVERLASTING
anato'licum . . . . . . **H. plicatum**
angustifo'lium . . . . WHITELEAF E.
antenna'rium . **Ozothamnus antennaria**
bellidioi'des
bractea'tum . . . . . STRAWFLOWER
DOUBLE (*monstrosum*) HV.
DWARF (*nanum*)
FIREBALL (*roseum*)
PURPLE (*purpureum*)
TWOCOLOR (*bicolor*)
WHITE (*album*)
YELLOW (*luteum*)
diosmaefo'lium (*rosmarinifolium; Ozothamnus rosmarinifolius*)
DIOSMALEAF E.
—ericifo'lium . . . . HEATH D.E.
—purpuras'cens . . . PURPLE D.E.
glomera'tum
lana'tum
ledifo'lium . . **Ozothamnus ledifolius**
petiola'tum (*Gnaphalium lanatum*)
CUDWEED E.
plica'tum (*anatolicum*)
rosmarinifo'lium . . **H. diosmaefolium**
sela'go
stoe'chas

HELICODIC'EROS (*MEGOTIGEA*)
TWISTARUM
musciv'orus (*Arum crinitum*)
TWISTARUM

HELICO'NIA (*BIHAI*) . HELICONIA
aureostria'ta (*aurea*) . GOLDSTRIPE H.
biha'i . . . . CARIB H.
illus'tris
REDSTEM (*rubricaulis*) HV.
psittaco'rum . . . . . . PARROTS H.
san'deri . . . . SANDERS H.

HELICTE'RES . . . . . SCREWTREE
jamaicen'sis . . . . . . JAMAICA S.

HELIET'TA
parvifo'lia . . . . BARETTA

HELIOCAR'PUS
austra'lis

HELIOCE'REUS
See **CACTUS GENERA.**

HELIOP'SIS |w . . . . . . HELIOPSIS
helianthoi'des (*laevis*) . SUNFLOWER H.
PITCHER (*pitcheriana*) HV.

HELIOPSIS, continued
sca'bra . . . . . ROUGH HELIOPSIS
DWARF GOLD (*imbricata*) HV.
FORMOSA
HERCULES (*major*)
INCOMPARABILIS
LEMON (*gratissima*)
ORANGE (*excelsa*)
ZINNIA (*zinniaeflora*)

Heliosper'ma alpes'tris . . . **Silene a.**

HELIOTRO'PIUM |w . . HELIOTROPE
amplexicau'le
arbores'cens (*peruvianum*) COMMON H.
convolvula'ceum **Euploca convolvulacea**
corymbo'sum . . . . BIG H.
curassa'vicum |w . . . . . . SALT H.
europae'um
in'dicum |w
spathula'tum . . . . WILD H.
BUISSON FLEURI. HV. Heliotropium
CENTEFLEUR
CHIEFTAIN
FLORENCE NIGHTINGALE
JERSEY BEAUTY
LA DUSE
LEMOINE GIANT
LORD ROBERTS
LORNE
LUEUR D'OPALE
MIDNIGHT
MME. BRUANT
MME. DELAUX
MME. LEDERLE
PRINCE CHARMANT
REGAL
SNOWBALL
SNOW WREATH
TALL DARK
WHITE LADY

HELIP'TERUM (*ACROCLINIUM; RHODANTHE*) . . . . SUNRAY
anthemoi'des
corymbiflo'rum . . . . . CLUSTER S.
humboldtia'num (*sanfordi*)
HUMBOLDT S.
mangles'i (*Rhodanthe m.*) MANGLES S.
—macula'tum (*Rhodanthe maculata*)
SPOTTED M.S.
rose'um (*Acroclinium r.*) . . ROSE S.
WHITE. HV.

HELLE'BORUS . . . . . HELLEBORE
caucas'icus . . . . . CAUCASUS H.
cyclophyl'lus
foe'tidus . . . . . . BEARSFOOT H.
gutta'tus
liv'idus
ni'ger . . CHRISTMASROSE (*Black H.*)
LITTLELEAF (*praecox*) HV.
NARROWLEAF (*angustifolius*)
olym'picus
orienta'lis . . . . . . LENTENROSE
Very commonly grown and sold as the true Christmasrose; a handsome and interesting plant.

vir'idis . . . . GREEN H.
ARCHIE HIND. HV. Helleborus
COMMANDANT BENARY
CORDELIA
DORA FROEBEL
FRIAR TUCK
GERTRUDE FROEBEL
MORNING MIST
MRS. LAMBERT
POURPRE ROYAL
PRIMROSE DAME

HELLEBORUS, continued
PRINCE RUPERT
QUEEN CHRISTINA
ROBERT BURNS
ROBIN HOOD
ROSAMUNDE
ROSE AIRY
ROSY MORN
SEAGULL
SNOWSPRITE
SOPHIA FROEBEL
SULPHUR GEM
UNIQUE
W. E. GLADSTONE
WHITECUP

HELO'NIAS . . . . SWAMPPINK
bulla'ta . . . . SWAMPPINK

HELWIN'GIA . . . . . . HELWINGIA
himala'ica . . . . . . HIMALAYAN H.
japon'ica . . . . JAPAN H.

HELXI'NE . . . . BABYSTEARS
soleiro'li . . . . BABYSTEARS

HEMATOX'YLON **HAEMATOXYLON**

HEMEROCAL'LIS . . . . . DAYLILY
D. Subgenus Dihemera.
E. Subgenus Euhemera.
auranti'aca. E. . . . . . . ORANGE D.
—littor'ea
¢MAJOR. HV. H. aurantiaca
citri'na. E. . . . . CITRON D.
corea'na . . . . KOREAN D.
dis'ticha . . . . **H. fulva**
dumortier'i (*rutilans; sieboldi*)
EARLY D.
—flore-ple'no. D. . . DOUBLE E.D.
esculen'ta
exalta'ta. E. . . . . STOUT D.
fla'va (*lilio-asphodelus; H. l. flava*). E.
LEMON D.
for'resti. E. . . . . . . FORRESTS D.
ful'va (*disticha*). E. . . . TAWNY D.
—longitu'ba. E. . . LONGTUBE T.D.
—rose'a. E. . . . . ROSETAWNY D.
¢CYPRIANA. HV. H. fulva
¢FLOREPLENO
¢HUPEHENSIS
¢MACULATA
gramin'ea . . . . **H. minor**
graminifo'lia . . . . **H. minor**
lilio-asphod'elus . . . . . . **H. flava**
—fla'va . . . . **H. flava**
longitu'ba. E. . . . . LONGTUBE D.
middendorff'i. D. . MIDDENDORFF D.
—ma'jor. D. . . . . . . GREAT M.D.
mi'nor (*graminea; graminifolia*)
GRASSLEAF D.
multiflo'ra. E. . . . MANYFLOWER D.
na'na. E. . . . . DWARF D.
pedicella'ta
plica'ta. E. . . . . . . FOLDLEAF D.
ru'tilans . . . . **H. dumortieri**
siebold'i . . . . **H. dumortieri**
sulphu'rea
thunberg'i (*serotina*). E. THUNBERG D.

Hort. var. (clons) of **Hemerocallis**, DAYLILY:
This list of horticultural varieties (all clons), prepared from the publications of A. B. Stout, includes hybrids and a few distinctive individuals of certain species. The Editorial Committee wishes to acknowledge with sincere thanks this important contribution of Dr. Stout.

HEMEROCALLIS, continued

Abbreviations of Classification of Daylily

Aur. Clon of H. aurantiaca.
Ful. Clon of H. fulva.

Abbreviations of Names of Originators and Introducers

All. Mrs. Mary G. Alley, Pine Grove, W. Va.
Ash. R. V. Ashley, Battle Creek, Mich.
Barr Barr & Sons, Taplow, England.
Bet. Carl Betscher, Dover, Ohio.
Bri. Bristol Nurseries, Bristol, Conn.
Bur. Luther Burbank.
C. G. Craemore Garden, Merrimac, Mass.
Chi. John Lewis Childs, Inc., Flowerfield, L. I., N. Y.
Chr. H. Christ.
Clev. Mrs. Frances E. Cleveland, Sunnybrook Iris Gardens, Eatontown, N. J.
Cook Paul H. Cook, Bluffton, Ind.
Denn. C. N. Dennett, Amesburg, Mass.
D. G. Duncan Gardens, Greenville, S. C.
Don. T. F. Donahue, Newton Lower Falls, N. Y.
Dre. H. A. Dreer, Inc., Riverton, N. J.
El. H. J. Elwes.
FAES. Florida Agri. Exp. Sta., College of Agri., Univ. of Florida, Gainesville, Fla.
Farr Bertrand H. Farr, Wyomissing, Pa.
Few. Arthur Fewkes, Newton Highlands, Mass.
F. G. Floravista Gardens, Olympia, Wash.
FIG. Fairmont Iris Gardens, Lowell, Mass.
Fish.,W. Wm. E. Fisher, Seneca Falls, N.Y.
Foer. Karl Foerster, Potsdam-Bornum, Germany.
G. C. Gardeners Chronicle, London, England.
G.&C. Gray & Cole, Ward Hill, Mass.
Hay. Wyndham Hayward, Lakemont Gardens, Winter Park, Fla.
Hen. W. H. Henderson, Fresno, Calif.
Her. A. Herrington, Madison, N. Y.
H. G. Hillside Gardens, Amesbury, Mass.
Hild. Hildemar Gardens, Wawa, Pa.
Hort Sir Arthur Hort, Fenton, Bart., England.
Hume H. Harold Hume, Asst. Dir. of Research, Agri. Exp. Sta., Gainesville, Fla.
KHN. Kelsey-Highlands Nursery, East Boxford, Mass.
KIG. Kenwood Iris Gardens.
Kun. A. E. Kunderd, Inc., Goshen, Ind.
Lem. V. Lemoine & Son, Nancy, France.
Lord R. P. & E. L. Lord, Orlando, Fla.
Lov. Lovett's Nursery, Inc., Little Silver, N. J.
Mee. Thomas Meehan Sons.
Me.,F. Franklin B. Mead, Fort Wayne, Ind.
Me.,T. Theodore L. Mead, Oviedo, Fla.
M. G. Midwest Gardens, Elkhorn, Neb.
Mor. B. Y. Morrison, Dept. of Agriculture, Washington, D. C.
MSC. Mass. State College of Agri. Exp. Sta., Field Sta., Cedar Hill, Waltham, Mass.
Mul. Wily Muller, Hortus Nucerensis, Naples, Italy.
Nes. Mrs. Thomas Nesmith, Fairmont Iris Gardens, Lowell, Mass.
NYBG. New York Botanical Garden, Bronx Park, New York, N. Y.
Per. Amos Perry, Enfield, England.
PNC. Parker Nursery Co., Newark, N. Y.

HEMEROCALLIS, continued

PRG. Port Rose Garden, Freeport, Ill.
Pur. Carl Purdy, Ukiah, Calif.
Q. G. Quality Gardens, Freeport, Ill.
R. G. Roadside Gardens, East Arlington, Vt.
RHSL. Royal Horticultural Society, London, England.
Russ. H. M. Russell, Route 6, Houston, Texas.
Sass H. P. Sass, Midwest Gardens, Washington, Neb.
Sch. John Scheepers, Paradou, Brookville, N. Y.
Sche. Mrs. Elizabeth Scheffey, West Mansfield, Mass.
Sh. J. Marion Shull, Chevy Chase, Md.
SIG. Sunnybrook Iris Gardens, Eatontown, N. J.
Spr. Karl Ludwig Sprenger, Naples, Italy.
Sto. A. B. Stout, New York Botanical Garden, Bronx Park, New York, N. Y.
Tra. Dr. Hamilton P. Traub, Beltsville, Md.
V. T. C. G. Van Tubergen, Haarlem, Holland.
Wal. Messrs. Wallace, Colchester, England.
Wal.,R. R. Wallace & Co., Ltd., Old Gardens, Tunbridge Wells, England.
Wh. R.W. Wheeler, Winter Park, Fla.
Yeld George Yeld, Gerrards' Cross, England.

As all the horticultural varieties listed below are clons, it is deemed needless to here place the clon sign ₵ before each name. The clon sign should be used, however, in all publications.

A. E. Kunderd. (Kun. 1934.)
Afterglow. (NYBG. 1941.)
Ajax. (Mul. 1908.)
Aladdin. (NYBG. 1941.)
Alba Striata. (Per. 1934.)
Algeria. (Hay. 1938.)
Aloma. (Hay. 1937.)
Amarillo. (Hay.)
Amaryllis. (Bet. 1932.)
Amber. (Yeld 1930.)
Amos Perry. (Per. 1905.)
Anitra. (Sh. 1940.)
Anna Betscher; or A. Betscher. (Bet. 1929.)
Antares. (Hay.)
Apricot. (Yeld 1892.)
Araby. (Hay.)
Aristocrat. (Wh. 1940.)
Audrey Blaser. (Tra. 1939.)
August Pioneer. (Sto. 1939.)
Auranthe. (G. C. 1934.)
Aurantiaca Major. (Wal. 1895.)
Aurelia. (Yeld 1930.)
Aureole. (1903.)
Aurillo. (Hay.)
Autumnhaze. (Nes. 1937.)
Autumn Prince. (NYBG. 1941.)
Aztecgold. (F. G.)
Bagdad. (Sto. 1935.)
Bali. (Wh. 1940.)
Balsara. (G. C. 1937.)
Barbara Lord. (Lord 1938.)
Bardeley. (Per. 1932.)
Baronet. (NYBG. 1941.)
Baroni. (Spr. 1903.)
Baystate. (Bet. 1929.)
Beacon. (Bet.)
Beauty. Sovereign.
Beauty of Kent. (R.Wal. 1937.)
Beloit. (MSC.)
Berenice. (Per. 1936.)

HEMEROCALLIS, continued

Bernstein. (Foer. 1929.)
Bertrand Farr. (NYBG. 1941.)
Bicolor. (NYBG. 1941.)
Bijou. (Sto. 1933.)
B. Ladhams.
Bobette. (R. G.)
Boutonniere. (Sto. 1938.)
Bretwalda. (Yeld.)
Brunette. (NYBG. 1941.)
Buckeye. (NYBG. 1941.)
Burbank. (Bur.)
Burgundy. (Nes. 1936.)
Burma. (Nes. 1937.)
Buttercup. (1908.)
Byng of Vimy. (Per. 1931.)
Cadmus. (Wh. 1940.)
Calypso. (Pur. 1929.)
Canarybird.
Carmen. (Hay. 1938.)
Carnival. (Tra. 1939.)
Caroline Vernon. (Wh. 1940.)
Cecil Houdyshel. (Tra. 1939.)
Ceres. (R.Wal.)
Charlotte Traub. (Tra. 1938.)
Charmaine. (Sto. 1934.)
Chengtu. (Sto. 1935.)
Chipsea. *Chisca.*
Chloe. (F. G.)
Chocolate Soldier. Giuseppe.
Christi. (1908.)
Chrome-orange. (T.Me. 1933.)
Chrysantha. (H. G.)
Chrysolite. (Yeld 1906.)
Chrysolora. (Per. 1925.)
Cimarron. (Lord 1938.)
Cinnabar. (Sto. 1930.)
Circe. (Sto. 1937.)
Cissy. Giuseppe.
Citronella. (Farr 1926.)
Cleo. (Hay. 1938.)
Columbine. (Lord 1938.)
Copper Lustre. (Lord 1938.)
Coralie. (Lord 1938.)
Corinne Robinson. (Tra. 1939.)
Corona. (Yeld 1906.)
Craemore Ruby. (C. G.)
Crepe. (D. G.)
Cressida. (Bet. 1929.)
Crinkles. (Hay.)
Crown of Gold. (Nes. 1933.)
Crown Prince. (Hay.)
C. Russell. (Russ.)
Crystal Pink. (F. G.)
Curiosity. (G. C. 1931.)
Curlypate. (Sche. 1935.)
Cygnet. (Bur. 1924.)
Cyprea. (RHSL.)
Possibly H. fulva clon Cypriana.
Cypriana. Ful.
Dainty. (Bet. 1937.)
Dauntless. (Sto. 1935.)
Dawn. (Per. 1932.)
Dawnplay. (F. G.)
Dazzler. (Dre. 1937.)
Delovely. (Hay.)
Domestico. (FAES.)
Dominion. (NYBG. 1941.)
Donald Wyman. (Bet. 1929.)
Dora Wyman. (F.Me. 1934.)
Dorothy McDade. (M. G.)
Dover. (Bet. 1932–33.)
Dr. Hughes. (Tra. 1938.)
Dr. Regel. (1904.)
Dr. Stout. (Tra. 1938.)
Duchess of Windsor. (Tra.-Hay. 1937.)
Dustystars. (Russ.)
Dwarf Yellow. (Bri. 1930.)

HEMEROCALLIS, continued
E. A. Bowles. (Per. 1931.)
Earliana. (Bet.)
Earliest. (KHN.)
Earliest Lemon. (Bet. 1936.)
Elaine. (Tra. 1938.)
Eldorado. (Per. 1926.)
Elemense. (Spr. 1903.)
Elizabeth Pyke. (Per. 1934.)
Elizabeth Wheeler. (Wh. 1940.)
Emberglow. (Tra. 1940.)
Emily Hume. (Hume 1933.)
Emperor Jones. (Hay.)
Enchantress. (Bri.)
Erica. (Per. 1925.)
Estelle Friend. (Tra. 1939.)
Estmere. (Yeld 1906.)
Europa. (Sto. 1929.)
Everblooming. (All. 1935.)
E. W. Yandre. (Hay.)
Festival. (Sto. 1939.)
Fire Red. (Tra. 1940.)
Fisher Variegated. (W.Fish.; PNC.)
Flamante. (Hay.)
Flame. (Yeld 1906.)
Flamid.
Flammea. (1906.)
Flamula. (R. G.)
Flavamajor. (1908; Farr 1925.)
Flavia. (Per. 1936.)
Flavina. (Few. 1934.)
Flavocitrina. (Chr. 1898.)
Florepleno. Ful. (Spr. 1903.)
Florham. (Her. 1899.)
Floribunda. (R. G.)
Florida. (Hay. 1938.)
Framingham. (Bet. 1930.)
Francis. (Yeld 1895.)
Frank Russell. (Russ.)
Fred Howard. (Tra. 1939.)
Fulcitrina. (Mul. 1907.)
Fulvacypriana. (Spr. 1903.)
Fulvala. (Bet.)
Fulvaspeciosa. (R.Wal. 1937.)
Fulvax. (FIG. 1931.)
Fulvola. (Bet.)
Gaiety. (Bet. 1932.)
Gardengold. (Clev. 1936.)
Gayday. (Nes. 1933.)
Gelasma. (Yeld 1937.)
George Kelso. (Tra. 1940.)
George Yeld. (Per. 1926.)
Giantess. (Bet. 1937.)
Giant Orange. (Hen. 1934.)
Ginger. (Hay.)
Gipsy Lass. (Sh. 1940.)
Gitana. (Lord 1938.)
Giuseppe. (Per. 1932.) *Chocolate Soldier; Cissy.*
Gladys Perry. (Per. 1931.)
Gloaming. (Cook 1936.)
Globe d'Or. (Mor. 1928.)
Gloriana. (Bet. 1936.)
Gloriosa. (Tra. 1938.)
Glow. (R.Wal.)
Goblin. Goldeni.
Golconda. (Farr 1824.)
Goldball. (Mul. 1907.)
Golddust. (Yeld 1906.) *Golden Dust.*
Goldenbell. (Wal. 1915.)
Golden Byng of Vimy. (Per.; Q. G.; C.G.)
Goldendawn. (F. G.)
Goldendream. (Bet. 1929.)
Golden Dust. Golddust.
Goldenempress. (Denn. 1936.)
Goldenfleece. (F. G.)

HEMEROCALLIS, continued
Goldenfulva. (Bet. 1936.)
Goldenglow. (Tra. 1938.)
Goldeni. (Bet. 1929.) *Goblin.*
Goldenmammy. (Don.)
Goldenmantle. (FAES.)
Goldenshadows. (Russ.)
Goldenwest. (Sass. 1932.)
Goldimperial. (1925.)
Goldstandard. (Per. 1925.)
Gorgio. (Sh. 1940.)
Gracilis.
Graminea Crocea. (Mul. 1910.)
Granada. (Tra. 1938.)
Gypsy. (Bet. 1929.)
Halo. (Yeld 1906.)
Hankow. (Sto. 1939.)
Happiness. (Tra. 1938.)
Harlequin. (Lord 1938.)
Harlequin. (NYBG. 1941.)
Harriet Moore. (Pur.)
Harvestmoon. (Bet. 1929.)
Harvey Russell. (Russ.)
Heatherrose. (F. G.)
Hector. (Lord 1938.)
Helen Campbell. Hermes.
Helen Wheeler. (Tra. 1940.)
Herbert Spencer. (F.Me.)
Herkimer Johnson. (Wh. 1940.)
Hermes. (Per. 1936.) *Helen Campbell.*
Hesperus. (M. G.)
Hiawatha. (NYBG. 1941.)
Highboy. (G.&C. 1934.)
Hindoo Girl. (Wh. 1940.)
Hippeastroides. (Spr. 1903.)
Hippeastrum. (1925.)
H. M. S. Revenge. (Per. 1931.)
Howard Russell. (Russ.)
Hupehensis. Ful.
Hyperion. (F.Me. 1925.)
Imperator. (Per. 1931.)
Indian Chief. (Tra. 1938.)
Indian Squaw. (Wh. 1940.)
J. A. Crawford. (Bet. 1929.)
Japanese Fall. (PRG.)
Japanese Spring. (PRG.)
Japanese Summer. (Q. G.)
Jennie Lee. (Russ.)
John Blaser. (Tra. 1939.)
J. R. Mann. (Nes. 1932.)
J. S. Gaynor. (Yeld 1928.)
J. T. Russell. (Russ.)
Jubilee. (Sto. 1934.)
June Boissier. (Per. 1934.)
Keston. (Per. 1929.)
Kublai Khan. (Lord 1938.)
Kwanso. *H. fulva kwanso* Hort.
Kwanso Floreplena. *H. kwanso floreplena* Hort.
Kwanso Virginica.
Lady Franklin. (Wh. 1940.)
Lady (*Fermoy*) Hesketh. (Per. 1924.)
Lamar Russell. (Russ.)
Large Gold. (Ash. 1936.)
Latest. Mrs. W. H. Wyman.
Latulipe. (Tra. 1939.)
Lemona. (Bet. 1928.)
Lemone. (Dre.)
Lemonetta. (Bet.)
Lemonking. (Bet. 1932.)
Lemonqueen. (Farr 1926.)
Lena Hughes. (Tra. 1938.)
Lenore. (Hay.)
Lila White. (FAES.)
Linda. (Sto. 1936.)
Louise. (Hay.)
Lovetts Lemon. (Lov. 1916.)
Lovetts Orange. (Lov. 1916.)

HEMEROCALLIS, continued
Lowgrowing. (Bur. 1917.)
Luteola. (Spr. prior to 1902.)
Luteola Grandiflora. (Lem. 1908.)
Luteola Major. (V. T.)
Luteola Pallens. (Lem. 1907.)
Maculata. Ful. (Spr. 1903.)
Madcap. (Nes. 1935.)
Maggie Perry. Margaret Perry.
Magnifica. (Yeld 1935.)
Majestic. (Sto. 1934.)
Major. Aur. (Wal. 1895.)
Mandarin. (Farr 1924.)
Marcus Perry. (Per. 1932.)
Margaret Perry. (Per. 1925.) *Maggie Perry.*
Marigold. (Yeld 1931.)
Mars. (Per. 1936.)
Mary Florence. (Bet. 1934.)
Mary Stoker. (Per. 1932.)
Mauve Rose. (Tra. 1938.)
Maymorn. (Nes. 1937.)
Mayor Starzynski. (Tra. 1939.)
Mayqueen. (1924.)
May Sadler. (Per. 1934.)
Medusa. (R. G.)
Meehan. (Mee. 1915.)
Meg. (Yeld 1930.)
Mercia. (Per. 1936.)
Midas. (Sto. 1935.)
Middendorffiana. (V. T. 1898.)
Mignon. (NYBG. 1941.)
Mikado. (Sto. 1929.)
Mildred Orpet. (Tra. 1939.)
Minikem. (Yeld 1933.)
Minnie. (Hay.)
Miranda. (Yeld 1929.)
Miss Annis. (Russ.)
Miss Ianni Russell. (Russ.)
Modesty. (Bet. 1929.)
Moidore. (Yeld 1930.)
Mona. (Per. 1936.)
Monarch. (NYBG. 1941.)
Moonbeam.
Moonglow. (Lord 1938.)
Moonlight. (Yeld 1937.)
Moonshine. (Per. 1932.)
Moonstone. (Per. 1932.)
Mrs. A. H. Austin. (Bet. 1929.)
Mrs. Carl Holmes. (1931.)
Mrs. C. L. Seith. (Bet.)
Mrs. Garlock. (PNC.)
Mrs. Herbert H. Dewey. (Hay. '38.)
Mrs. James R. Mann. (Chi. 1930.)
Mrs. Perry. (Per. 1925.)
Mrs. Seith.
Mrs. Viesseaux. (Per. 1936.)
Mrs.W.H.Wyman. (Bet. 1929.) *Latest.*
Mulleri. (Spr. 1903.) *Muelleri.*
Multiflora. (Farr 1939.)
Multiflora Hybrid. (Russ.)

Possibly this is one of the Summer Multiflora Hybrids.

Multiflora Isis. (Per. 1936.)
Multiflora Luna. (Per. 1936.)
Multiflora Perry. (Per.)
Musette. (Sh. 1940.)
Mutabilis. (Mul. 1908.)
Mystery Star. (MSC.)
Nebraska. (M. G.)
Nilbio. (Mul. 1908.)
Nocerensis. Nucerensis.
Nubiana. (Hay. 1938.)
Nucerensis. (R.Wal. 1929.) *Nocerensis.*
Ochroleuca. (Spr. 1903.)
Oldrose. (R. G.)
Olif. (Chi. before 1934.)
Olive. (PRG.)

HEMEROCALLIS, continued
OMPHALE. (C. G.; Yeld)
OPHIR. (Farr 1924.)
ORANGE. (Mul. 1907.)
ORANGEGEM. (Per. 1925.)
ORANGEGLOW. (Barr 1927.)
ORANGEKING. (FIG. 1934.)
ORANGEMAN. (1906.)
ORANGEQUEEN. (R.Wal.)
ORANGEVASE. (Barr 1932.)
ORB. (RHSL.)
ORIOLE. (Nes. 1936.)
OTHELLO. (Hay.)
PALEMOON. (Clev. 1934.)
PANDORA. (Per. 1936.)
PARSON BROWN.
PARTHENOPE. (Spr. 1903.)
PASTELROSE. (C. G.)
PATRICIA. (Sto. 1935.)
PEACHBLOW. (Nes. 1936.)
PEACHGLOW.
PEONYRED. (Tra. 1939.)
PERFECTION. (Per. 1936.)
PERRYS PIGMY. (Per. 1932.)
PERSIAN PRINCESS. (F. G.)
PINKLASS. (F. G.)
PINKLUSTRE. (Nes. 1937.)
PIONEER. (1899.)
POLLY. (Per. 1930.)
POLLYANNA. (Nes.)
PORT. (NYBG. 1941.)
PRINCESS. (Sto. 1934.)
PRINCESS ELIZABETH. (Per. 1936.)
PROFESSOR JOST. (Mul. 1907.)
PROFESSOR KIRCHLEDGE. (Mul. 1907.)
PROFESSOR KRAUSE. (Mul. 1907.)
PROFESSOR STAHL. (Mul. 1907.)
Pyrrha. SIRIUS.
QUAKER LADY. (Wh. 1940.)
QUANSO.
QUANSO VARIEGATED.
QUEEN MARY. (Per. 1925.)
QUEEN OF MAY. (V. T. 1925.)
QUEEN WILHELMINA. (Tra. 1940.)
RADIANT. (Yeld. 1925.)
RAJAH. (Sto. 1935.)
RALPH SCHREIVE. (Don.)
RALPH WHEELER. (Hay.)
RAMONA. (Hay.; R. G.)
RAYON D'OR. (Per. 1936.)
REBA COOPER. (Tra. 1939.)
REBA ELGAR. (Wh. 1940.)
RED BIRD. (NYBG. 1941.)
REDMAN. (R. G.)
REGGIE PERRY. (Per. 1931.)
RHODOS. (Per. 1936.)
R. I. LEMON. (KIG. 1939.)
RITA. (Yeld)
ROBIN REDBREAST. (Nes. 1936.)
ROMANY. (Lord 1938.)
ROSA KELL. (Sch.)
ROSALIND. (Farr; Sto. 1938–40.)
ROSE QUEEN. (Per. 1931.)
ROSITA. (R. G.)
ROUGE VERMILION. (Tra. 1940.)
ROYAL. (F.Me. 1925.)
RUBY SUPREME. (Wh. 1940.)
RUSSELL WOLFE. (Tra. 1939.)
SACHEM. (NYBG. 1941.)
SALEM. (FIG. 1834.)
SAMOSET. (F. G.)
SANJUAN. (Tra. 1938.)
SASS No. 10–33. (M. G.)
SATURN. (Sto. 1934.)
SAYDA. (Yeld 1937.)
SEMERAMUS. (Per. 1937.)
SEMPERFLORENS. (V. T. 1925.)
SENATOR ANDREWS. (Hay.)

HEMEROCALLIS, continued
SEQUOIA. (Russ.)
SERENA.
SERENADE. (Sto. 1935.)
SHANGRI. (Wh. 1940.)
SHARON. (Cook 1937.)
SHAURI. (Wh. 1940.)
SHEKINAH. (Per. 1932.)
SHIRLEY. (Per. 1926.)
SICA. (Yeld 1934.)
SIPPAN. (El. 1929.)
SIRIUS. (Yeld 1930.) *Pyrrha.*
SIR MICHAEL FOSTER. (Mul. 1904.)
SIR WILLIAM. (Per. 1932.)
SONIA. (Vas.)
SONNY. (Sto. 1925.)
SOUDAN. (Sto. 1932.)
SOVEREIGN. (Yeld 1906.) *Beauty.*
SPARTAN. (Russ.)
SPECIOSA. (R.Wal.)
SPRENGERI. (FIG. 1932.)
SPRINGTIME. (Mes. 1935.)
STALWART. (Cook 1935.)
STARLIGHT. (Nes. 1936.)
STAR OF GOLD. (Sass 1934.)
STELLA ROSE. (Lord 1938.)
ST. JOAN. (Tra. 1939.)
STORMCLOUD. (Russ.)
SUMMEREVE. (Nes. 1934.)
SUMMER MULTIFLORA HYBRIDS. (Sto. 1935.)
SUNBEAM. (Lord 1938.)
SUNGOLD. (Dre. 1937.)
SUNKIST. (Nes. 1932.)
SUNNYWEST. (Sass)
SUNRISE. (F. G.)
SUNSET. (Per. 1932.)
SUNSHINE. (D. G.)
SWEETBRIAR. (F. G.)
SYLPHIDE. (Per. 1936.)
SYMPHONY. (NYBG. 1941.)
TANGERINE. (Yeld 1906.)
TAPLOW ORANGE. (Barr 1932.)
TAPLOW YELLOW. (Barr 1930.)
TARUGA. (Sto. 1933.)
THE GEM. (Bet. 1929.)
THELMA PERRY. (Per. 1925.)
THE MILLERS DAUGHTER. (Russ.)
THEODORE MEAD. (Tra. 1940.)
THERON. (Sto. 1934.)
THE SARACEN. (V. T. 1916.)
TITANIA. (Wh. 1940.)
TODMORDEN. (Hild. 1934.)
TRIUMPH. (NYBG. 1941.)
TURY. (Lord 1938.)
URMIENSIS. (Hort. 1929.)
U. RUSSELL. (Yeld; Russ.)
VARIEGATED. Ful.
VESTA. (Sto. 1929.)
VESUVIUS. (Lord 1938.)
VICTOR LORD. (Lord 1938.)
VICTORY MONTEVIDEO. (Tra. 1940.)
VICTORY SUOMUSSALMI. (Tra. 1940.)
VICTORY TAIERHCHWANG. (Tra. 1938.)
VIRGINICA.
VISCOUNTESS BYNG. (Per. 1931.)
VOMERENSE. (Spr. 1903.)
VULCAN. (Sto. 1934.)
WAUBUN. (Sto. 1929.)
WEKIWA. (Tra. 1938.)
WHITE LADY. (Sass)
WILLIAM DEAN. (Yeld 1906.)
WINNIE NIGHTINGALE. (Per. 1932.)
WINSOME. (Yeld 1925.)
WOLOF. (Sto. 1936.)
WONDERGOLD. (Bet. 1937.)
WOODLOT GOLD. (SIG. 1934.)
YELDRIN. (NYBG. 1941.)

HEMEROCALLIS, continued
YELLOWHAMMER. (Per. 1925.)
YELLOWTULIP. (Wh. 1940.)
YELLOWWONDER. (Kun. 1937.)
ZARA. (Per. 1936.)
ZOUAVE. (NYBG. 1941.)

HEMIAN'DRA
pun'gens

HEMICAR'PHA |w
micran'tha |w

HEMICY'CLIA
australa'sica

HEMIDES'MUS
in'dicus . . . . INDIA-SARSAPARILLA

HEMIE'VA
ranunculifo'lia (*Saxifraga r.*)

HEMI'GRAPHIS
colora'ta

HEMIONI'TIS
See **FERN GENERA.**

HEMIPTE'LEA . . . . . HEMIPTELEA
da'vidi (*Zelkova d.*) . . . . DAVID H.

HEMIZONEL'LA |w
min'ima |w

HEMIZO'NIA |w . . . . . HEMIZONIA
clementi'na . . . . ISLAND H.
fascicula'ta |w
luzulaefo'lia

HEMLOCK . . . . **Tsuga**
The name Hemlock for this genus is actually a misnomer, fixed by the tyranny of usage. See note under **CONIUM.**
CANADA H. . . . . . . **T. canadensis**
CAROLINA H. . . . . . **T. caroliniana**
CHINESE H. . . . . . . **T. chinensis**
FORMOSA H. . . . . . **T. formosana**
HIMALAYAN H. . . . . **T. dumosa**
JAPANESE H. . . . . **T. diversifolia**
JEFFREY H. . . . . . ×**T. jeffreyi**
LOWDENSE CAROLINA H. **T. caroliniana compacta**
MOUNTAIN H. . . . **T. mertensiana**
PACIFIC H. . . . . . . **T. heterophylla**
SIEBOLD H. . . . . . . **T. sieboldi**
SILVER H. . **T. mertensiana argentea**
WEEPING PACIFIC H. **T. heterophylla flaccida**
YUNNAN H. . . . . **T. yunnanensis**

HEMLOCKPARSLEY . . . **Conioselinum**
APPALACHIAN H. . . . . **C. chinense**

HEMP . . . . **Cannabis; C. sativa**

HEMPNETTLE . . . . **Galeopsis**
BRISTLESTEM H. . . . . . **G. tetrahit**
RED H. . . . . **G. landanum**

HEMPWEED, CLIMBING **Mikania scandens**

HEN-AND-CHICKENS **Sempervivum tectorum**

HENBANE . . . . **Hyoscyamus**
BLACK H. . . . . **H. niger**
ROUNDLEAF H. . . . . . . **H. albus**
YELLOW H. . . . . **H. aureus**

HENNA . . . . . **Lawsonia; L. inermis**

HEPAT'ICA |w . . . . . . HEPATICA
acutilo'ba . . . . . . SHARPLOBE H.
america'na |w . . . . ROUNDLOBE H.
angulo'sa (*Anemone a.*) HUNGARIAN H.
ROSY (*rosea*) HV.
WHITE (*alba*)
no'bilis

HERACLE'UM |w . . . . COWPARSNIP
lana'tum . . . . COMMON C.
mantegazzia'num . . . . BIGLEAF C.
nepalen'se
pubes'cens (*wilhelmi*) . CAUCASIAN C.
sphondyl'ium . . . . HOGWEED C.
villo'sum (*giganteum*) . . . GIANT C.
wal'lichi

HERALDTRUMPET . . . . . **Beaumontia**
EASTER H. . . . . . . **B. grandiflora**

HERBGARDEN PLANTS

This list, prepared by the Herbarium Committee of the Herb Society of America (Helen Noyes Webster, Chairman), includes herbs and simples, as well as certain woody plants of interest to American herbgardens.

Mrs. Webster is the author of one of the most recent, interesting and authoritative works on this subject entitled "Herbs," one of "The Gardener's Library" series of the Massachusetts Horticultural Society. With her permission, the Committee feels it is pertinent to print here Mrs. Webster's foreword "Dedication" of this book:

"Since the first printing of a bulletin on herbs by the Massachusetts Horticultural Society, and nearly coincident with it, a small group of New England women with reverence for herbal wisdom of the past and belief in the present revival of herbgardens founded the Herb Society of America. To this Society, in recognition of its high standards, its ideals, its sincerity of purpose, and its untiring efforts to establish authoritative data concerning herbs, this book is dedicated."

EXPLANATION OF SYMBOLS

I. Culinary herbs and simples.
II. Herbs for fragrance, of historic, ornamental or legendary value and interest in old-fashioned gardens.
III. Woody plants of herbgarden interest.
IV. Other old-fashioned plants, chiefly medicinal, especially adapted to wildflower gardens.

ACHILLE'A . . . . . . YARROW
ageratifo'lia II . . . . . . GREEK Y.
—**ai'zoon** (*Anthemis aizoon*) II
AIZOON Y.
agera'tum I; II . . . . . SWEET Y.
alpi'na IV . . . . . . ALPINE Y.
argen'tea II . . . . . . SILVER Y.
filipenduli'na (*eupatorium*) I; II
FERNLEAF Y.
ligus'tica I . . . . . . LOVAGE Y.
millefo'lium I . . . . . COMMON Y.
—**rose'um** I . . . . . . PINK C.Y.
—**ru'brum** II . . . . . . RED C.Y.
moscha'ta I . . . . MUSK Y.
na'na II . . . . . . DWARF Y.
ptar'mica I . . . . SNEEZEWORT Y.
santolinoi'des II . . . SANTOLIN Y.
sibir'ica (*mongolica*) II . SIBERIAN Y.
tomento'sa I . . . . . . WOOLLY Y.
umbella'ta II . . . . UMBEL Y.

ACONI'TUM napel'lus II
ACONITE MONKSHOOD

AC'ORUS cal'amus IV
DRUG SWEETFLAG

ACTAE'A . . . . . . BANEBERRY
al'ba (*pachypoda; A. spicata a.*) IV
WHITE B.
ru'bra (*A. spicata r.*) IV . . RED B.

ADIAN'TUM peda'tum IV
AMERICAN MAIDENHAIR

AEGOPO'DIUM podogra'ria I
BISHOPS GOUTWEED

HERBGARDEN PLANTS, continued

AGAS'TACHE . . . GIANTHYSSOP
ca'na (*Brittonastrum canum; Cedronella cana*) I . . . . . MOSQUITOPLANT
foenic'ulum (*anethiodora*) I FENNEL G.

AGRIMO'NIA eupato'ria IV
COMMON AGRIMONY

AJU'GA I . . . . BUGLE
chamaepi'tys I . . . GROUNDPINE B.
geneven'sis I . . . . . GENEVA B.
rep'tans I . . . . CARPET B.

ALCHEMIL'LA ma'jor II
LARGE LADYSMANTLE

ALE'TRIS farino'sa IV
WHITETUBE STARGRASS

AL'LIUM . . . . ONION
ascalon'icum I . . . . . . SHALLOT
ce'pa I . . . . GARDEN O.
—**vivip'arum** (*A. c. bulbelliferum*) I
TOP O.
fla'vum I . . . . YELLOW O.
karatavien'se I . . TURKESTAN O.
mo'ly I . . . . LILY LEEK
neapolita'num I . . . . NAPLES O.
por'rum I . . . . LEEK
pyrena'icum I . . . . PYRENEES O.
sati'vum I; IV . . . . GARLIC
schoeno'prasum I . . . . . . CHIVE
scorodo'prasum I . GIANT GARLIC
sphaeroceph'alum II . BALLHEAD O.

AL'NUS inca'na I; III
SPECKLED ALDER

ALTHAE'A
officina'lis I; IV . . MARSHMALLOW
rose'a II; IV . . . . HOLLYHOCK

AMBRO'SIA artemisifo'lia
COMMON RAGWEED

ANAGAL'LIS arven'sis I; IV
SCARLET PIMPERNEL

ANAPH'ALIS margarita'cea II; IV
COMMON PEARLEVERLASTING

ANCHU'SA . . . . . . BUGLOSS
azu'rea (*italica*) IV . . . ITALIAN B.
barrelier'i IV . . . . . . EARLY B.
capen'sis IV . . . . CAPE B.
myosotidiflo'ra **Brunnera macrophylla**
officina'lis I; II . . . . COMMON B.

ANE'THUM grave'olens I; II DILL

ANGEL'ICA . . . . . . ANGELICA
archangel'ica I . . . . . GARDEN A.
atropurpu'rea I . . PURPLESTEM A.
cur'tisi I . . . . FILMY A.
rosaefo'lia II . . . . . . ROSE A.
sylves'tris . . . . . WOODLAND A.

AN'THEMIS . . . . . CAMOMILE
ai'zoon . . . **Achillea ageratifolia a.**
cine'rea I . . . . GRAY C.
macedon'ica II . . . MACEDONIAN C.
monta'na II . . . . . . RIVIERA C.
no'bilis I . . . . ROMAN C.
tincto'ria I . . . . . . GOLDEN C.

ANTHRIS'CUS cerefo'lium I
SALADCHERVIL

ANTIRRHI'NUM ma'jus II
COMMON SNAPDRAGON

A'PIOS america'na I; IV
AMERICAN POTATOBEAN

A'PIUM grave'olens dul'ce I; IV
GARDEN CELERY

HERBGARDEN PLANTS, continued

AQUILE'GIA vulga'ris II
EUROPEAN COLUMBINE

ARA'LIA nudicau'lis III; IV
WILDSARSAPARILLA

ARCTOSTAPH'YLOS uva-ur'si IV
BEARBERRY

ARISAE'MA triphyl'lum II; IV
INDIAN JACKINTHEPULPIT

ARME'RIA marit'ima IV
COMMON THRIFT

ARMORA'CIA lapathifo'lia (*Rorippa armoracia*) I . . . HORSERADISH

AR'NICA monta'na IV
MOUNTAIN ARNICA

ARTEMIS'IA . . . . WORMWOOD
abrota'num I . . . . . OLDMAN W.
(*Southernwood*)
absin'thium I . . . . COMMON W.
al'bula I . . . SILVERKING SAGEBRUSH
an'nua I SWEET W. (*Sweet Mugwort*)
arbores'cens III . . . SHRUBBY W.
austri'aca III . . . . AUSTRIAN W.
camphora'ta . . . . . CAMPHOR W.
dracun'culus I . . . . . TARRAGON
frig'ida I . . . FRINGED SAGEBRUSH
glacia'lis II . . . . . . GLACIER W.
lactiflo'ra (*A. vulgaris l.*) I
GHOSTPLANT W.
longifo'lia I . LONGLEAF SAGEBRUSH
mutelli'na I . . . . . SILVERALP W.
pon'tica I . . . . ROMAN W.
sacro'rum I . . . . . RUSSIAN W.
—**vir'idis** I . . . SUMMERFIR R.W.
stelleria'na I BEACH W. (*Dustymiller*)
vulga'ris I . . . . . . MUGWORT W.
—*lactiflo'ra* . . . . . . **A. lactiflora**

AS'ARUM canaden'se I; IV
CANADA WILDGINGER

ASCLE'PIAS . . . . MILKWEED
incarna'ta II; IV . . . SWAMP M.
tubero'sa IV . . . . BUTTERFLY M.

ASPER'ULA . . . . . WOODRUFF
hexaphyl'la I . . . . . MISTY W.
longiflo'ra . . . . LONGFLOWER W.
odora'ta I; II . . . . . SWEET W.
orienta'lis (*azurea*) I . ORIENTAL W.
tincto'ria I . . . . . . DYERS W.

A'TRIPLEX . . . . . . SALTBUSH
The Old World annuals are known as Orach.
horten'sis I . . . . . GARDEN ORACH
—**atrosanguin'ea** I . . . . RED G.O.

BARBARE'A . . . . WINTERCRESS
ver'na I . . . . EARLY W.
vulga'ris I . . . . BITTER W.

BEL'LIS peren'nis I; II
ENGLISH DAISY

BEN'ZOIN . . . . . **LINDERA**

BER'BERIS vulga'ris I; IV
EUROPEAN BARBERRY

Bocco'nia corda'ta . . . **Macleaya c.**

BORA'GO . . . . BORAGE
laxiflo'ra IV . . . . . CORSICAN B.
officina'lis I . . . . . . COMMON B.

BRAS'SICA
hir'ta I . . . . . WHITE MUSTARD
jun'cea I; IV . . . . . . INDIA M.
—**crispifo'lia** (*japonica* Hort., *not* Sieb.)
I . . . . POTHERB M.
ni'gra I . . . . BLACK M.

HERBGARDEN PLANTS, continued

BRITTONAS'TRUM **AGASTACHE**

BRUN'NERA macrophyl'la (*Anchusa myosotidiflora*) II . . HEARTLEAF BRUNNERA (*Siberian Bugloss*)

BRYO'NIA dio'ica III REDBERRY BRYONY

BUX'US sempervi'rens III COMMON BOX

CALEN'DULA officina'lis I; IV POTMARIGOLD CALENDULA

CAL'THA palus'tris I; IV COMMON MARSHMARIGOLD

CALYCAN'THUS flor'idus I; III COMMON SWEETSHRUB

CAMAS'SIA qua'mash I; IV COMMON CAMAS

CAMPAN'ULA . . . BELLFLOWER
rapunculoi'des I; II . CREEPING B.
rapun'culus I . . . . . . RAMPION B.

CAMP'SIS rad'icans III COMMON TRUMPETCREEPER

CAP'SICUM frutes'cens I BUSH REDPEPPER

CARDAM'INE praten'sis I; IV CUCKOO BITTERCRESS

CARTHA'MUS tincto'rius I; IV SAFFLOWER

CA'RUM car'vi I . . . . CARAWAY

CAS'SIA marilan'dica IV WILD SENNA

CEANO'THUS america'nus I; IV JERSEYTEA CEANOTHUS

CEDRONEL'LA . . . CEDRONELLA
ca'na . . . . **Agastache c.**
triphyl'la (*canariensis*) . . CANARY C.

CELAS'TRUS scan'dens III AMERICAN BITTERSWEET

CENTAU'REA . . . . CENTAUREA
cinera'ria II . . . . . DUSTYMILLER
cya'nus II . . . . . . CORNFLOWER
ni'gra II . . . BLACK CENTAUREA

CENTAU'RIUM umbella'tum IV DRUG CENTAURIUM

CENTRAN'THUS ru'ber I JUPITERSBEARD CENTRANTHUS

CERIN'THE retor'ta II GREEK HONEYWORT

Chamomil'la matrica'ria **Matricaria chamomilla**

CHEIRAN'THUS cheir'i II COMMON WALLFLOWER

CHELIDO'NIUM ma'jus IV GREATER CELANDINE

CHELO'NE . . . . TURTLEHEAD
gla'bra IV . . . . WHITE T.
ly'oni IV . . . . PINK T.

CHENOPO'DIUM . . GOOSEFOOT
bonus-hen'ricus I GOOD KING HENRY G.
bo'trys II . . . . JERUSALEMOAK G.
capita'tum I . . . . BLITE G.

CHIMA'PHILA . . . PIPSISSEWA
macula'ta IV . . . . . STRIPED P.
umbella'ta IV . . . . . COMMON P.

HERBGARDEN PLANTS, continued

CHIONAN'THUS virgin'icus III WHITE FRINGETREE

CHRYSAN'THEMUM CHRYSANTHEMUM
cinerariaefo'lium DALMATIAN PYRETHRUM
ma'jus (*balsamita*) II . COSTMARY C.
—**tanacetoi'des** . . . . RAYLESS C.C.
parthe'nium (*Matricaria eximia*) II; IV FEVERFEW C.

CICHO'RIUM . . . . . CHICORY
endiv'ia I . . . . ENDIVE
in'tybus I; II; IV . . . COMMON C.

CIMICIF'UGA racemo'sa I; IV COHOSH BUGBANE

CINERA'RIA . . . . **SENECIO**

CIT'RUS berga'mia III BERGAMOT ORANGE

CLEM'ATIS virginia'na III VIRGINSBOWER

CLE'THRA alnifo'lia I; III SUMMERSWEET CLETHRA

CLINTO'NIA borea'lis IV YELLOW BEADLILY

CNI'CUS benedic'tus II; IV BLESSEDTHISTLE

COCHLEA'RIA . . SCURVYWEED
officina'lis I; IV . . . . COMMON S.

COL'CHICUM autumna'le II; IV COMMON AUTUMNCROCUS

CO'LEUS . . . . COLEUS
amboin'icus (*aromaticus*) IV SPANISHTHYME C.
pu'milus IV . . . . DWARF C.

COMPTO'NIA peregri'na (*aspleni-folia*) III . . . . . SWEETFERN

CONVALLA'RIA maja'lis II; IV LILYOFTHEVALLEY

COP'TIS trifo'lia IV ALASKA GOLDTHREAD

CORIAN'DRUM sati'vum I; II; IV CORIANDER

COR'NUS flor'ida III FLOWERING DOGWOOD

COTI'NUS coggyg'ria (*Rhus cotinus*) III . . . . COMMON SMOKETREE

CRATAE'GUS phaenopy'rum (*cor-data*) III WASHINGTON HAWTHORN

CRITH'MUM marit'imum I SAMPHIRE

CRO'CUS sati'vus I; IV SAFFRON CROCUS

CU'MINUM cy'minum I . CUMIN

CUNI'LA origanoi'des (*mariana*) II MARYLAND STONEMINT (*Maryland Dittany*)

CYPRIPE'DIUM parviflo'rum pu-bes'cens (*C. pubescens*) IV LARGEYELLOW LADYSLIPPER

CY'TISUS spp. I . . . . . BROOM

DATU'RA stramo'nium IV JIMSONWEED DATURA

HERBGARDEN PLANTS, continued

DAU'CUS caro'ta IV WILD CARROT
The Garden Carrot is Daucus carota sativa.

DELPHIN'IUM formo'sum II HARDY LARKSPUR

DENTA'RIA diphyl'la IV CRINKLEROOT TOOTHWORT

DIAN'THUS
barba'tus II . . . . SWEETWILLIAM
caryophyl'lus II CARNATION; CLOVE PINK

DICEN'TRA . . . BLEEDINGHEART
canaden'sis IV . . . SQUIRRELCORN
exim'ia . . . . FRINGED B.

DICTAM'NUS al'bus II GASPLANT DITTANY

DIGITA'LIS purpu'rea I; II; IV COMMON FOXGLOVE

DIP'SACUS . . . . TEASEL
fullo'num IV . . . . . FULLERS T.
sylves'tris II . . . . VENUSCUP T.

DIR'CA palus'tris III ATLANTIC LEATHERWOOD

DRO'SERA spp. IV . . SUNDEW

DRYOP'TERIS filixmas' IV MALEFERN

E'CHIUM vulga're IV COMMON VIPERSBUGLOSS

ELSHOLT'ZIA staun'toni III STAUNTON ELSHOLTZIA

EPIGAE'A re'pens IV TRAILING-ARBUTUS

EQUISE'TUM hyema'le I; IV SCOURINGRUSH

ERU'CA sati'va I . ROCKETSALAD

ERYN'GIUM marit'imum I SEAHOLLY ERYNGO

ERYTHRO'NIUM america'num IV COMMON FAWNLILY

EUON'YMUS atropurpu'reus III EASTERN WAHOO

EUPATO'RIUM . . EUPATORIUM
perfolia'tum IV . . . . . BONESET
purpu'reum IV BLUESTEM JOEPYEWEED
rugo'sum (*ageratoides*) IV WHITE SNAKEROOT

EUPHOR'BIA spp. I; IV EUPHORBIA

FILIPEN'DULA . MEADOWSWEET
hexapet'ala I . . . . . . DROPWORT
ulma'ria IV . . . . . EUROPEAN M.

FOENIC'ULUM . . . . FENNEL
vulga're I; IV . . . . . . COMMON F.
FLORENCE (*dulce; Finocchio*) HV.
ITALIAN (*piperitum; Carosella*)

FRAGA'RIA virginia'na IV VIRGINIA STRAWBERRY

FRITILLA'RIA . . . . FRITILLARY
imperia'lis . . . . . . IMPERIAL F.
meleag'ris II . . . . CHECKERED F.

GALAN'THUS niv'alis I; II COMMON SNOWDROP

Hort. var.; HV. = horticultural variety (or varieties); sp. = species (singular); spp. = species (plural).
₵ = clon; × (as a prefix) = hybrid; × (between scientific plant names) = crossed by; ∞ = polybrid; |w = plant useful to wildlife.
See Glossary for definitions of clon, hybrid, and polybrid.

HERBGARDEN PLANTS, continued

GALE'GA officina'lis IV
COMMON GOATSRUE

GA'LIUM . . . . . . BEDSTRAW
mollu'go IV . . . . WHITE B.
ve'rum I . . . . YELLOW B.

GAULTHE'RIA procum'bens I; IV
CHECKERBERRY WINTERGREEN

GENIS'TA tincto'ria I; II; IV
COMMON WOADWAXEN

GENTIA'NA an'drewsi IV
ANDREWS GENTIAN

GERA'NIUM robertia'num IV
HERBROBERT GERANIUM

GILLE'NIA trifolia'ta IV
BOWMANSROOT

GLECO'MA hedera'cea (*Nepeta h.*) I; IV

GLYCYRRHI'ZA gla'bra I; IV
COMMON LICORICE

HAMAME'LIS virginia'na I; III; IV
COMMON WITCHHAZEL

HEDEO'MA pulegioi'des IV
AMERICAN FALSEPENNYROYAL

HED'ERA he'lix III ENGLISH IVY

HELE'NIUM spp. . SNEEZEWEED

HELIAN'THUS an'nuus I
COMMON SUNFLOWER

HELIOTRO'PIUM arbores'cens (*peruvianum*) II; IV
COMMON HELIOTROPE

HELLE'BORUS ni'ger IV
CHRISTMASROSE

HEMEROCAL'LIS . . . DAYLILY
fla'va I; II . . . . . . LEMON D.
ful'va II; IV . . . . . . TAWNY D.

HEPAT'ICA america'na IV
ROUNDLOBE HEPATICA

HES'PERIS matrona'lis II
DAMES ROCKET

HEU'CHERA america'na IV
AMERICAN ALUMROOT

HU'MULUS lu'pulus I; IV; III
COMMON HOP

HYPER'ICUM spp. IV
ST. JOHNSWORT

HYSSO'PUS . . . . . . HYSSOP
arista'tus III
officina'lis I; IV . . . . . . HYSSOP
BIGFLOWER (*grandiflorus*) **HV.**
RED (*ruber*)
WHITE (*albus*)

IBE'RIS ama'ra II
ROCKET CANDYTUFT

I'LEX opa'ca III AMERICAN HOLLY

IN'ULA hele'nium IV
ELECAMPANE INULA

I'RIS . . . . IRIS
german'ica II; IV . . . GERMAN I.
—florenti'na II . . . ORRISROOT I.
pal'lida IV . . . . SWEET I.
pseudac'orus I; IV . YELLOWFLAG I.
versicol'or II; IV . . . BLUEFLAG I.

ISA'TIS tincto'ria II; IV
DYERS WOAD

JUNIP'ERUS . . . . JUNIPER
commu'nis I; III . . . . COMMON J.
virginia'na III . EASTERN REDCEDAR

HERBGARDEN PLANTS, continued

LA'MIUM . . . . . DEADNETTLE
amplexicau'le II . . . . HENBIT D.
galeob'dolon II . . . ARCHANGEL D.
macula'tum II . . . . . SPOTTED D.
—al'bum II . . . . . . WHITE S.D.
purpu'reum I; II . . . . PURPLE D.

LAU'RUS no'bilis I; III
GRECIAN LAUREL (*True Bay*)

LAVAN'DULA II; III LAVENDER
denta'ta II . . . . . . TOOTHED L.
officina'lis (*spica; vera*) I; II TRUE L.
¢WHITE (*alba*) HV.
pinna'ta II . . . . . . FRINGED L.
stoech'as II . . . . . . FRENCH L.

LE'DUM groenland'icum I
LABRADORTEA LEDUM

LEONU'RUS cardi'aca IV
COMMON MOTHERWORT

LEPID'IUM sati'vum I; II
GARDENCRESS PEPPERWEED

LEUCO'JUM spp. II . SNOWFLAKE

LEVIS'TICUM officina'le I; IV
GARDEN LOVAGE

LIA'TRIS spica'ta IV
SPIKE GAYFEATHER

LIGUS'TRUM vulga're III
EUROPEAN PRIVET

LIL'IUM . . . . LILY
canaden'se I; IV . . . . CANADA L.
can'didum IV . . . . . MADONNA L.
mar'tagon I; II . . . MARTAGON L.

LIMO'NIUM carolinia'num IV
CAROLINA SEA-LAVENDER

LINA'RIA vulga'ris IV
BUTTER-AND-EGGS TOADFLAX

LIN'DERA ben'zoin (*Benzoin aestivale*) I; III ATLANTIC SPICEBUSH

LI'NUM peren'ne I; II
PERENNIAL FLAX

LIP'PIA citriodo'ra I; II
LEMONVERBENA LIPPIA

LOBE'LIA . . . . . . LOBELIA
cardina'lis IV . . . CARDINALFLOWER
infla'ta IV . . . . INDIANTOBACCO L.
siphilit'ica II; IV . . . . BIGBLUE L.

LONIC'ERA . . . . HONEYSUCKLE
caprifo'lium II; III . . . . SWEET H.
pericly'menum II; III . WOODBINE H.

LUNA'RIA an'nua I; II
DOLLARPLANT

LUPI'NUS peren'nis I; IV
SUNDIAL LUPINE

LYCH'NIS . . . . . . CAMPION
chalcedon'ica IV . MALTESECROSS C.
floscu'culi IV . . . . . RAGGEDROBIN

LYCOPO'DIUM spp. IV CLUBMOSS

LYSIMACH'IA . . . LOOSESTRIFE
nummula'ria IV . . . . MONEYWORT
terres'tris IV . . . SWAMPCANDLE L.
vulga'ris IV . . . . GOLDEN L.

LY'THRUM salica'ria IV
PURPLE LYTHRUM

MACLEAY'A corda'ta (*Bocconia c.*) II . . . . . PINK PLUMEPOPPY

MAGNO'LIA . . . . . MAGNOLIA
acumina'ta III . . CUCUMBERTREE M.
virginia'na (*glauca*) III . SWEETBAY M.

HERBGARDEN PLANTS, continued

MAHO'NIA aquifo'lium III
OREGONGRAPE

MAJORA'NA . . . . MARJORAM
horten'sis (*Origanum majorana*) I; II
SWEET M.
oni'tes I; II . . . . POT M.

MAL'VA . . . . MALLOW
moscha'ta II . . . . MUSK M.
rotundifo'lia I; IV . . RUNNING M.

MARRU'BIUM I; IV . HOARHOUND
candidis'simum
catariaefo'lium
leonuroi'des (*astracanicum*)
MOTHERWORT H.
vulga're I; IV . . . . . COMMON H.

MATHI'OLA . . . . . . STOCK
bicor'nis II . . . . . . GRECIAN S.
inca'na I . . . . COMMON S.

MATRICA'RIA . . . . . MAYWEED
chamomil'la (*Chamomilla matricaria*) IV . . . . . GERMAN-CAMOMILE
exim'ia . **Chrysanthemum parthenium**
inodo'ra II . . . . . SCENTLESS M.
tchihat'chewi II . . . TURFINGDAISY

MEDICA'GO spp. I . . . MEDIC

MELILO'TUS spp. I . SWEETCLOVER

MELIS'SA . . . . BALM
officina'lis I . . . . . . COMMON B.
—au'rea I . . . . . . GOLDEN C.B.

MEN'THA I; IV . . . . . MINT
aquat'ica . . . . WATER M.
arven'sis . . . . FIELD M.
—piperas'cens . . . JAPANESE F.M.
canaden'sis I . . . . . CANADA M.
citra'ta . . . . BERGAMOT M.
gen'tilis . . . . RED M.
longifo'lia . . . . HORSE M.
nilia'ca . . . . EGYPTIAN M.
piperi'ta I; II . . . . . PEPPERMINT
—citra'ta II . . . . . . ORANGE P.
pule'gium I; IV . . PENNYROYAL M.
requien'i II . . . . . REQUIEN M.
rotundifo'lia II . . . . . . APPLE M.
—variega'ta Hort. . . PINEAPPLE M.
spica'ta I . . . . SPEARMINT

MERTEN'SIA spp. IV BLUEBELLS

MICROME'RIA chamisso'nis I
YERBABUENA

MIM'ULUS moscha'tus IV
MUSKPLANT MONKEYFLOWER

MITCHEL'LA re'pens IV
PARTRIDGEBERRY

MONAR'DA . . . . . . BEEBALM
did'yma I; II; IV . . . OSWEGO B.
WHITE (*alba*) II
fistulo'sa II . . . WILDBERGAMOT B.
—al'ba II . . . . . . WHITE W.B.

MO'RUS ni'gra I; III
BLACK MULBERRY

MUSCA'RI botryoi'des I
COMMON GRAPEHYACINTH

MYOSO'TIS spp. IV FORGETMENOT

MYR'ICA . . . . . BAYBERRY
cerif'era (*caroliniensis*) III
SOUTHERN WAXMYRTLE
ga'le III . . . . SWEETGALE
pensylvan'ica III . . . NORTHERN B.

HERBGARDEN PLANTS, continued
MYR'RHIS odora'ta I; II SWEETCICELY
MYR'TUS commu'nis III TRUE MYRTLE
NARCIS'SUS . . . . NARCISSUS
poet'icus II . . . . POETS N.
pseudonarcis'sus II COMMON DAFFODIL
NEP'ETA . . . . NEPETA
cata'ria I; IV . . . . CATNIP
hedera'cea . . . . **Glecoma h.**
macran'tha IV . . . . . ENGLISH N.
mussi'ni II . . . . . . PERSIAN N.
nervo'sa IV
—al'ba IV
nu'da IV
wil'soni IV . . . . . . WILSON N.
NIGEL'LA . . . FENNELFLOWER
damasce'na I . . . . LOVEINAMIST
sati'va I . . . . GARDEN F.
NYMPH'AEA odora'ta IV AMERICAN WATERLILY
OC'IMUM . . . . BASIL
basil'icum I; II; IV . . SWEET B.
—purpu'reum II . . . PURPLE S.B.
ca'num I . . . . HOARY B.
cris'pum I . . . . . . JAPANESE B.
gratis'simum I . . . EASTINDIES B.
min'imum I . . . . LEAST B.
—purpu'reum II . . . PURPLE L.B.
sanc'tum I . . . . HOLY B.
vir'ide I. . . . . FEVER B.
ORIG'ANUM . . . . ORIGANUM
dictam'nus II . . CRETE-DITTANY O. (*Dittany of Crete*)
heracleot'icum I . . . . WINTER O. (*Winter Marjoram*)
sipyle'um I; II . . MOUNTSIPYLOS O.
vulga're I; II . . . . . COMMON O.
₵GOLDLEAF (*aureum*) I; II
ORNITHOG'ALUM umbella'tum I COMMON STAR-OF-BETHLEHEM
OSMORHI'ZA clay'toni IV CLAYTON SWEETROOT
OSMUN'DA cinnamo'mea IV CINNAMONFERN
PAEO'NIA officina'lis IV COMMON PEONY
PAN'AX . . . . GINSENG
quinquefo'lium IV . . AMERICAN G.
schin'seng (*ginseng*) IV . ASIATIC G.
trifo'lium IV . . . . . . DWARF G.
PAPA'VER somnif'erum IV OPIUM POPPY
PARTHENOCIS'SUS quinquefo'lia III . . . . VIRGINIA CREEPER
PEDICULA'RIS canaden'sis I; IV EARLY PEDICULARIS
PELARGO'NIUM . PELARGONIUM
cris'pum II . . . . FINGERBOWL P.
denticula'tum II . SKELETONLEAF P.
∞fra'grans II . . . . ∞FRAGRANT P.
grave'olens II . . . . ROSE P.
∞melis'sinum II . . . . ∞BALM P.
odoratis'simum II . . . NUTMEG P.
quercifo'lium II . . . . OAKLEAF P.
PERIL'LA . . . . . . PERILLA
frutes'cens IV . . . . COMMON P.
—cris'pa IV . . . . . PURPLE C.P.
PETASI'TES fra'grans II SWEET BUTTERBUR

HERBGARDEN PLANTS, continued
PETROSELI'NUM . . . PARSLEY
cris'pum I; II . . CURLY GARDEN P.
—filici'num II . . . FERNLEAF G.P.
—radico'sum I . . . . TURNIP G.P.
PHILADEL'PHUS corona'rius III SWEET MOCKORANGE
PHYTOLAC'CA america'na (*decandra*) IV . . COMMON POKEBERRY
PIMPINEL'LA ani'sum I . . ANISE
PODOPHYL'LUM pelta'tum IV COMMON MAYAPPLE
POLEMO'NIUM . . POLEMONIUM
caeru'leum IV . GREEKVALERIAN P.
rep'tans II . . . . . CREEPING P.
POLIAN'THES tubero'sa II TUBEROSE
POLYGONA'TUM . SOLOMONSEAL
biflo'rum IV . . . . SMALL S.
commuta'tum IV . . . . . GREAT S.
POLYPO'DIUM vulga're IV COMMON POLYPODY
POTE'RIUM spino'sum (*Sanguisorba spinosa*) III SPINY BURNET
PRIM'ULA . . . . . . PRIMROSE
ela'tior I . . . . OXLIP P.
ve'ris IV . . . . COWSLIP P.
vulga'ris (*acaulis*) I . . . ENGLISH P.
PRUNEL'LA vulga'ris IV COMMON SELFHEAL
PTERID'IUM aquili'num IV
PULMONA'RIA officina'lis I; IV COMMON LUNGWORT
PYCNAN'THEMUM inca'num IV ATLANTIC MOUNTAINMINT
PYRACAN'THA spp. III FIRETHORN
PYRO'LA . . . . PYROLA
ellip'tica IV . . . . WAXFLOWER P.
rotundifo'lia IV . . . EUROPEAN P.
RANUN'CULUS fica'ria I; IV FIGROOT BUTTERCUP
RESE'DA odora'ta II COMMON MIGNONETTE
RHAM'NUS cathar'tica III COMMON BUCKTHORN
RHUS' . . . . SUMAC
aromat'ica III . . . . FRAGRANT S.
cot'inus . . . . . **Cotinus coggygria**
typhi'na III . . . . . STAGHORN S.
RI'BES . . . . CURRANT
au'reum I; III . . . . . GOLDEN C.
odora'tum III . . . . . . CLOVE C.
RICI'NUS commu'nis IV CASTORBEAN
ROBIN'IA his'pida III ROSEACACIA LOCUST (*Rose-acacia*)
RORIP'PA
armora'cia . . **Armoracia lapathifolia**
nasturtium-aquat'icum I WATERCRESS
RO'SA . . . . ROSE
∞al'ba III . . . . . ∞COTTAGE R.
centifo'lia II; III . . . CABBAGE R.
cinnamo'mea I. . . . CINNAMON R.
damasce'na I; III . . . . DAMASK R.
eglante'ria (*rubiginosa*) I; II SWEETBRIER R.
gal'lica II; IV . . . . . FRENCH R.
moscha'ta II . . . . MUSK R.

HERBGARDEN PLANTS, continued
ROSMARI'NUS . . . ROSEMARY
officina'lis I; II; IV . . . ROSEMARY
₵PROSTRATE. II
RU'BUS odora'tus III FRAGRANT THIMBLEBERRY
RU'MEX
aceto'sa I . . . . . GARDEN SORREL
scuta'tus I . . . . . . FRENCH S.
RU'TA . . . . RUE
chalepen'sis I . . . . . FRINGED R.
grave'olens I; III; IV . COMMON R. (*Herb of Grace*)
patavi'na I . . . . . . DWARF R.
SABA'TIA stella'ris II; IV SALTMARSH ROSEGENTIAN
SALICOR'NIA europae'a I MARSHFIRE GLASSWORT
SA'LIX . . . . WILLOW
ca'prea III . . . . GOAT W.
lu'cida III. . . . . . . SHINING W.
SAL'VIA . . . . SAGE
argen'tea II . . . . SILVER S.
azu'rea II. . . . . AZURE S.
columba'riae I . . CALIFORNIA CHIA
farina'cea II . . . . . MEALYCUP S.
hor'minum I. . . . . . . JOSEPH S.
officina'lis I; II; III . . GARDEN S.
—albiflo'ra III . . . . . WHITE G.S.
ru'tilans II . . . . . . PINEAPPLE S.
scla'rea I; II . . . . CLARY S.
splen'dens II . . . . . SCARLET S.
SAMBU'CUS . . . . . . ELDER
canaden'sis I; III . . AMERICAN E.
ni'gra I; III . . . . . EUROPEAN E.
SANGUINA'RIA canaden'sis IV BLOODROOT
SANGUISOR'BA . . . . BURNET
canaden'sis . . . . . AMERICAN B.
mi'nor IV . . . . SMALL B.
obtu'sa II . . . . . . JAPANESE B.
officina'lis I . . . . . . GARDEN B.
spino'sa . . . . . **Poterium spinosum**
tenuifo'lia II . . . . . SIBERIAN B.
SANTOLI'NA . . LAVENDERCOTTON
chamaecyparis'sus II; IV CYPRESS L.
pinna'ta II; IV. . . . . PINNATE L.
vi'rens II; IV . . . . . . GREEN L.
SAPONA'RIA officina'lis IV BOUNCINGBET
SARRACE'NIA purpu'rea IV COMMON PITCHERPLANT
SAS'SAFRAS al'bidum I; III COMMON SASSAFRAS
SATUREI'A . . . . . . SAVORY
alpi'na I . . . . ALPINE S.
calamin'tha II . . . . CALAMINT S.
catalon'ica II . . . . . CATALONIA S.
glabra'ta II . . . . OZARK S.
horten'sis I; IV . . . . SUMMER S.
monta'na I; III; IV . . WINTER S.
nep'eta I . . . . CATNIP S.
vulga'ris I . . . . . . WILDBASIL S.
—al'ba I . . . . WHITE W.S.
SCIL'LA nonscrip'ta IV COMMON BLUE SQUILL
SCUTELLA'RIA lateriflo'ra IV SIDEFLOWERING SKULLCAP
SE'DUM a'cre I; II GOLDMOSS STONECROP

HERBGARDEN PLANTS, continued
SEMPERVI'VUM . . HOUSELEEK
sobolif'erum II . HEN-AND-CHICKENS
tecto'rum II . . . . ROOF H.

SENE'CIO . . . . . GROUNDSEL
cinera'ria (*Cineraria maritima*) II SILVER G.
leucosta'chys II . . . ARGENTINE G.

SES'AMUM in'dicum (*orientale*) I; IV . . . . . ORIENTAL SESAME

SI'UM sisa'rum II SKIRRET WATERPARSNIP

SOLIDA'GO odo'ra (*suaveolens*) I; IV . . . FRAGRANT GOLDENROD

SOR'BUS america'na III AMERICAN MOUNTAINASH

SPHAG'NUM spp. IV . SPHAGNUM

SPIRAE'A . . . . SPIREA
latifo'lia III; IV BROADLEAF MEADOWSWEET S.
salicifo'lia I; III . . WILLOWLEAF S.
tomento'sa II; III; IV HARDHACK S.

STA'CHYS . . . . BETONY
lana'ta II . . . . WOOLLY B.
officina'lis IV . . . . . COMMON B.

STYLOPH'ORUM diphyl'lum IV CELANDINE-POPPY

SYM'PHYTUM . . . . COMFREY
as'perum IV . . . . . . PRICKLY C.
officina'le I; IV . . . . COMMON C.

SYRIN'GA vulga'ris III COMMON LILAC

TANACE'TUM . . . . . TANSY
huronen'se IV . . . . . HURON T.
vulga're I; IV . . . . . COMMON T.
¢CURLYLEAF. I

TAX'US spp. III . . . . . . YEW

TEPHRO'SIA virginia'na III; IV VIRGINIA TEPHROSIA

TEU'CRIUM . . . . GERMANDER
canaden'se II . . . . AMERICAN G.
chamae'drys III; IV CHAMAEDRYS G.
ma'rum II; III . . CAT-THYME G.
massilien'se II . . . . . ROSE G.
po'lium (*aureum*) II; III GOLDEN G.
pyrena'icum II . . . PYRENEES G.

THU'JA occidenta'lis III EASTERN ARBORVITAE

THY'MUS . . . . THYME
britan'nicus I; II . . . . BRITISH T.
carno'sus I; II . . . PORTUGUESE T.
cimici'nus I; II . . . . REDSTEM T.
cineras'cens I; II . . . . ASHY T.
herba-baro'na I; II . . . CARAWAY T.
hirsu'tus I; II . . . . . . HAIRY T.
hyema'lis I; II . . . . WINTER T.
lanicau'lis I; II . . WOOLLYSTEM T.
membrana'ceus I; II . . . PAPER T.
nit'idus I; II . . . . . . SICILY T.
przewal'ski I; II . . . CARPET T.
serpyl'lum (*azoricus*) I; II; III MOTHER-OF-THYME
—lanugino'sus I; II; III WOOLLY M. (*Woolly T.*)
¢CRIMSON (*coccineus*). I; II
¢DOWNY (*villosus*). I; II
¢FIREFLY (*splendens*). I; II
¢GOLDEN (*aureus*). I; II
¢LEMON (*vulgaris*). I; II
¢SILVER (*argenteus*). I; II

HERBGARDEN PLANTS (THYMUS serpyllum lanuginosus), continued
¢WHITE (*albus*). I; II
¢WHITESPOT (*variegatus*). I; II
vulga'ris I; II; III . COMMON THYME
—*fragrantis'simus* Hort.
zy'gis I; II . . . . ZYGIS T.

TIAREL'LA cordifo'lia IV ALLEGANY FOAMFLOWER

TRADESCAN'TIA spp. II SPIDERWORT

TRIFO'LIUM spp. IV . . CLOVER

TRIGONEL'LA foenum-grae'cum I FENUGREEK TRIGONELLA

TRIL'LIUM . . . . . . TRILLIUM
erec'tum IV . . . . . . PURPLE T.
grandiflo'rum IV . . . . . SNOW T.

TROPAE'OLUM spp. I NASTURTIUM

TUSSILA'GO far'fara IV COMMON COLTSFOOT

URGIN'EA marit'ima (*Scilla m.*) II SHORE DRUGSQUILL

VACCIN'IUM . . . . BLUEBERRY
corymbo'sum I; III . . HIGHBUSH B.
vitis-idae'a I; III . . . . COWBERRY

VALERIA'NA officina'lis II; IV COMMON VALERIAN

VERBAS'CUM thap'sus IV FLANNEL MULLEIN

VERBE'NA . . . . . . VERBENA
hasta'ta IV . . . . BLUE V.
officina'lis II; IV . . . EUROPEAN V.

VERON'ICA officina'lis II; IV DRUG SPEEDWELL

VERONICAS'TRUM virgin'icum IV CULVERSPHYSIC

VETIVE'RIA zizanioi'des II KHUSKHUS VETIVER

VIBUR'NUM trilo'bum (*americanum*) III . . . . AMERICAN CRANBERRYBUSH VIBURNUM

VIN'CA . . . . . . PERIWINKLE
ma'jor III . . . . BIGLEAF P.
mi'nor III . . . . COMMON P.

VIO'LA . . . . VIOLET
odora'ta I; II . . . . . . SWEET V.
tri'color II . . . . . WILD PANSY
—horten'sis II . . . . . . GARDEN P.

VI'TEX agnuscas'tus III LILAC CHASTETREE

VI'TIS . . . . GRAPE
aestiva'lis I; III . . . . SUMMER G.
labrus'ca III . . . . FOX G.

XANTHORHI'ZA simplicis'sima III YELLOWROOT

ZANTHOX'YLUM america'num III COMMON PRICKLYASH

HERBMERCURY . . . **Mercurialis annua**

Herb of Grace . . . . . RUE, COMMON: **Ruta graveolens**

Hercules-allheal . OPOPANAX, SURGEONS: **Opopanax chironium**

Herculesclub . . DEVILS-WALKINGSTICK: **Aralia spinosa**; PRICKLYASH, HERCULESCLUB: **Zanthoxylum clavaherculis**

HERERO'A **MESEMBRYANTHEMUM**
See **SUCCULENTS**.

HERMODAC'TYLUS
tubero'sus (*Iris tuberosa*)

HERNAN'DIA
ovig'era
pelta'ta
sono'ra

HERNIA'RIA . . . . . . BURSTWORT
cine'rea . . . . GRAY B.
gla'bra . . . . COMMON B.
hirsu'ta . . . . HAIRY B.
inca'na . . . . SYRIAN B.
latifo'lia . . . . VELVETY B.

HERONBILL . . . . **Erodium**
ALFILERIA . . . . . . **E. cicutarium**
BIG H. . . . . **E. botrys**
CALIFORNIA H. . . . **E. macrophyllum**
CARROT H. . . . . **E. daucoides**
CLIFF H. . . . . **E. petraeum**
CORSICAN H. . . . . . . **E. corsicum**
CRANE H. . . . . **E. gruinum**
∞KOLB H. . . . . . . ∞**E. kolbianum**
MUSK H. . . . . . . **E. moschatum**
PYRENEES H. . . . . . **E. manescavi**
ROMAN H. . . . . **E. romanum**
STORK H. . . . . **E. ciconium**
TEXAS H. . . . . **E. texanum**
∞WILLKOMM H. . ∞**E. willkommianum**

Herpes'tis rotundifo'lia . . . **Bacopa r.**

Herpet'ica ala'ta . . . . **Cassia a.**

Herpotham'nus crassifo'lius **Vaccinium crassifolium**

HESPERA'LOE . . . . . HESPERALOE
funif'era . . . . . . ZAMANDOQUE H.
parviflo'ra . . . . RED H.
—engelmann'i

HESPERETHU'SA . . HESPERETHUSA
crenula'ta

HES'PERIS . . . . ROCKET
fra'grans
matrona'lis . . . . DAMES R.
—niv'ea . . . . WHITE D.R.
PURPLE (*purpurea*) HV. H. matronalis
WHITE (*alba*)
niva'lis . . . . PERSIANSNOW R.
This name is sometimes misapplied to H. matronalis nivea.
tris'tis

HESPEROCAL'LIS . . . DESERTLILY
undula'ta . . . . DESERTLILY

HESPEROCHI'RON
califor'nicus

HESPEROCH'LOA . . SPIKEFESCUE
See **GRASS GENERA**.

HESPERO'NIA . . . . **MIRABILIS**
lae'vis retror'sa . . . . . **M. retrorsa**

HESPEROSCOR'DUM. . **BRODIAEA**

HESPEROYUC'CA . . . . . **YUCCA**

HES'SEA . . . . HESSEA
zey'heri . . . . ZEYHER H.

HETERAN'THERA |w . MUDPLANTAIN
du'bia |w
limo'sa |w
peduncula'ris |w
renifor'mis |w

HETEROCEN'TRON
rose'um (*mexicanum*)
—al'bum

HETEROME'LES . . . **PHOTINIA**
salicifo'lia . . . . . . **P. arbutifolia**

HETEROPAP'PUS
his'pidus

HETEROPHRAG'MA
adenophyl'lum

HETEROPO'GON
See **GRASS GENERA.**

HETEROP'TERIS (*BANISTERIA* in part)
argen'tea (*Banisteria a.; Banisteriopsis a.*)

HETEROSPA'THE(-A) . . Sagisipalm
See **PALM GENERA.**

HETEROSPER'MUM
pinna'tum

HETEROTHE'CA
lamarck'i
subaxilla'ris

HEU'CHERA ⌊w . . . . . Alumroot
america'na ⌊w . . . . American A.
bractea'ta
brizoi'des . . . . **H. lithophila**
chloran'tha
convalla'ria
cylin'drica . . . . . . Roundleaf A.
glabel'la
gla'bra
hall'i
his'pida . . . . Rough A.
lithoph'ila (*brizoides*) . . Pinkbells
micran'tha
ovalifo'lia . . . . Ovalleaf A.
parvifo'lia . . . . . . Littleleaf A.
pilosis'sima
pubes'cens (*rubifolia*) . . Marbled A.
rubes'cens . . . . Red A.
sanguin'ea . . . . Coralbells
Flambeau. hv.
Grassleaf (*gracillima*)
Huntsman
Mary Rose
Maxima
Nebulance
Petworth
Pluie de Feu
Rose Queen
Shirley
Snowdrop (*alba*)
Splendens
Virginal
Walker
villo'sa . . . . Hairy A.

HEUR'NIA (*HUERNIA*)
See **SUCCULENTS.**

HEURNIOP'SIS (*HUERNIOPSIS*)
See **SUCCULENTS.**

HEVE'A . . . . Rubbertree
brasilien'sis . . . . Para R.
O. F. Cook (Journ. Wash. Acad. Sci. 31: 46–65, 1941) indicates that the correct name of this extremely important tree is Siphonia ridleyana. Louis C. Wheeler, expert in Euphorbiaceae, however, is not willing to accept this change, which is in violation of the International Rules of Botanical Nomenclature, but indicates that Dr. Cook may be correct in his contention that Hevea brasiliensis is not correctly applicable to the plant commonly called by that name.
confu'sa

HEXAGLOT'TIS
longifo'lia
virga'ta

HEXALEC'TRIS
See **ORCHID GENERA, HARDY TERRESTRIAL GROUP.**

HEXASTY'LIS . . . . . **ASARUM**

HEXOPE'TION (*ASTROCARYUM*)
See **PALM GENERA.**

HIBBER'TIA . . . . Buttonflower
amplexicau'lis
cuneifor'mis . . . . . . **Candollea c.**
denta'ta . . . . Toothleaf B.
perfolia'ta
volu'bilis . . . . Twining B.

HIBIS'CUS (*ABELMOSCHUS; PARITIUM*) ⌊w Hibiscus; Rosemallow
The subtropical-tropical species of this genus, often small trees or shrubs, are referred to as Hibiscus. The native American, chiefly herbaceous, species are called Rosemallow. It seems desirable not to attempt to interfere with that practice in Standardized Plant Names.

abelmos'chus . . . . Muskmallow
aculea'tus ⌊w . . . . Rough R.
africa'nus . . . . **H. trionum**
arnottia'nus . . . . . . Arnott H.
bifurca'tus . . . . Forkleaf H.
califor'nicus ⌊w . . . . California R.
calyphyl'lus (*calycinus*) Lemonyellow H.
canna'binus . . . . Kenaf H.
coccin'eus (*militaris*) ⌊w . Scarlet R.
colli'nus . . . . Hill H.
coul'teri . . . . Desert R.
deniso'ni . . . . Denison H.
denuda'tus . . . . . Paleface R.
ela'tus . . . . **H. tiliaceus e.**
esculen'tus (*Abelmoschus e.*) . . Okra
gossyp'inus . . . . **H. platanifolius**
grandiflo'rus ⌊w . . . . . Great R.
hama'bo . . . . Hamabo H.
heterophyl'lus . . . . . Batham H.
hue'geli . . . . Huegel H.
—glabres'cens . . . . Smooth H.H.
—grossulariaefo'lia Gooseberryleaf H.H.
lambertia'nus . . . . . Lambert H.
lasiocar'pos (*incanus*) ⌊w . Woolly R.
man'ihot (*Abelmoschus m.*) Sunset H.
Bigflower (*grandiflorus*) hv.
milita'ris . . . . **H. coccineus**
mutab'ilis . . . . . Cottonrose H.
palus'tris (*moscheutos*) ⌊w . Common R.
—oculirose'us (*H. oculiroseus*) ⌊w Crimsoneye C.R.
platanifo'lius (*gossypinus*) Sycamoreleaf H.
rosa-sinen'sis (*miniatus; sinensis*) Chinese H.
Agnes Gault. hv.
Aloha
Apricot
Bali
Bonnie Clare
Brilliante
California Gold
Caller (*calleri*)
Cecile
Chala
Coopers (*cooperi*)
Coral Reefs
Dark Red
Doublepink
Doublered
Doublered Peachblow
Doubleyellow
Fair Jeannette

HIBISCUS rosa-sinensis, continued
Flaming Dawn
Fleuron
Hawaiian Moon
Honolulu
Hula
Hula Dancer
Kilauea
Largeflower (*grandiflorus*)
Mauna Loa
Mauve
Miniatus
Mrs. (*Muriel*) Evans
Mrs. Wilder
Multicolor (*versicolor*)
Oahu
Orange (*aurantiaca*)
Peachblow
Prince Sakamoto
Princess der Ling
Psyche
Shellpink
Single Salmon
Single Scarlet
Single Surf
Vanhoutte (*vanhouttei*)
Whirligig
White
Whitewings
sabdarif'fa . . . . Roselle
—altis'sima . . . . . Tall Roselle
schizopet'alus . . Fringed Hibiscus
syria'cus . . . . Shrubalthea
The common name Shrubalthea is not to be confused with the genus Althaea, which includes the Hollyhock and the true Marshmallow.
Admiral Dewey. hv.
Amaranthus
Amplest (*amplissimus*)
Anemone (*anemonaeflorus*)
Ardens
Banner
Bicolor
Boule de Feu
Coelestis
Comte de Hainault
Comte des Flandres
Double Precoce
Doublewhite (*albus plenus*)
Duc de Brabant
Duchesse de Brabant
Flesh (*carneus plenus; incarnatus*)
Granville
Jeanne d'Arc
Lady Stanley
Leopardleaf (*variegatus*)
Meehan (*meehani*)
Peony (*paeoniflorus*)
Pulcherrimus
Purity
Purple (*purpureus semiplenus*)
Rosy (*roseus*)
Showy (*speciosus*)
Snowdrift
Snowstorm (*totus albus*)
Souv. Charles Breton
Spotleaf (*foliovariegatus*)
W. R. Smith
tilia'ceus . . . . Linden H.
—ela'tus (*H. elatus; Paritium elatum*) Jamaica L.H.
By some authors this is regarded as a distinct species; by others as a synonym of the older and more widespread H. tiliaceus.
trio'num (*africanus*) ⌊w Flowerofanhour

HIBISCUS . . . . **Hibiscus**
See also ROSEMALLOW.

ARNOTT H. . . . . . **H. arnottianus**
BATHAM H. . . . . **H. heterophyllus**
CHINESE H. . . . . **H. rosa-sinensis**
COTTONROSE H. . . . **H. mutabilis**
DENISON H. . . . . . **H. denisoni**
FLOWEROFANHOUR . . . **H. trionum**
FORKLEAF H. . . . . **H. bifurcatus**
FRINGED H. . . . . **H. schizopetalus**
GOOSEBERRYLEAF HUEGEL H.
H. huegeli grossulariaefolia
HAMABO H. . . . . . . **H. hamabo**
HILL H. . . . . **H. collinus**
HUEGEL H. . . . . . . **H. huegeli**
JAMAICA LINDEN H.
H. tiliaceus elatus
KENAF H. . . . . . . **H. cannabinus**
LAMBERT H. . . . . **H. lambertianus**
LEMONYELLOW H. . . **H. calyphyllus**
LINDEN H. . . . . . . **H. tiliaceus**
MUSKMALLOW . . . **H. abelmoschus**
OKRA . . . . **H. esculentus**
ROSELLE . . . . . . **H. sabdariffa**
SHRUBALTHEA . . . . . **H. syriacus**
SMOOTH HUEGEL H.
H. huegeli glabrescens
SUNSET H. . . . . . . **H. manihot**
SYCAMORELEAF H.. . . **H. platanifolius**
TALL ROSELLE
H. sabdariffa altissima

HICKE'NIA . . . . . **PARODIA**
See **CACTUS GENERA.**

HICKORY . . . . **Carya**
ARKANSAS BLACK H.
C. texana arkansana
ASHE BITTERNUT H.
C. cordiformis elongata
ASHLEAF SHAGBARK H.
C. ovata fraxinifolia
BITTERNUT H. . . . . **C. cordiformis**
BITTER PECAN . . . . **×C. lecontei**
BLACK H. . . . . **C. texana**
BROADLEAF BITTERNUT H.
C. cordiformis latifolia
BROWNS H. . . . . **×C. browni**
CANADA H.
× C. laneyi chateaugayensis
CAROLINA H.
C. carolinae-septentrionalis
CAROLINA RED H. . **C. ovalis hirsuta**
CATHAY H. . . . . . **C. cathayensis**
CHINESE H. . . . . . . **C. sinensis**
COASTAL CAROLINA H.
C. carolinae-septentrionalis australis
COAST PIGNUT H. **C. glabra megacarpa**
DEMAREE H. . . . . . **×C. demareei**
DUNBAR H. . . . . . **×C. dunbari**
FERNOW H. . . . . . **C. fernowiana**
FIG MOCKERNUT H.
C. tomentosa ficoides
GULF M. H. . . . . **C. t. subcoriacea**
HAMMOCK H. . . . . **C. ashei**
LANEY H. . . . . **×C. laneyi**
LITTLENUT SHAGBARK H.
C. ovata nuttalli
Louisiana H. . . . . SWAMP H.
MICHIGAN RED H. . **C. ovalis borealis**
MISSISSIPPI SWAMP H.
C. leiodermis mollissima
MISSOURI SHAGBARK H.
C. ovata ellipsoidalis
MOCKERNUT H. . . . **C. tomentosa**
MOUNTHOPE SHAGBARK H.
C. ovata complanata

HICKORY, continued
NARROWLEAF WATER H.
Carya aquatica australis
NORTHERN RED H. **C. ovalis obcordata**
NUSSBAUMER H. . **×C. nussbaumeri**
NUTMEG H. . . . **C. myristicaeformis**
OHIO RED H. . . . . **C. ovalis mollis**
PEARNUT R. H. . . . **C. o. obovalis**
PECAN . . . . **C. illinoensis**
PIGNUT H. . . . . **C. glabra**
RED H. . . . . **C. ovalis**
ROUNDNUT R. H. . . . **C. o. odorata**
RUDDY SWAMP H.
C. leiodermis callicoma
SAND H. . . . . **C. pallida**
SCHNECK H. . . . . . **×C. schnecki**
SCRUB H. . . . . **C. floridana**
SEARS CREEK H. ₵*C. browni varians*
SHAGBARK H. . . . . . . **C. ovata**
SHELLBARK H. . . . . . **C. laciniosa**
SOUTHERN SHAGBARK H.
C. ovata pubescens
SWAMP H. . . . . . . **C. leiodermis**
VALLEY H. . . . . . **C. texana villosa**
WATER H. . . . . **C. aquatica**

HICKSBEACH'IA
pinnatifo'lia

HICO'RIA . . . . **CARYA**
al'ba . . . . **C. tomentosa**
buck'leyi . . . . **C. texana**
—arkansa'na . . . . **C. t. arkansana**
—villo'sa . . . . **C. t. villosa**
microcar'pa **C. ovalis; C. ovata nuttalli**
min'ima . . . . **C. cordiformis**
mollis'sima . . . . **C. leiodermis m.**
pecan' . . . . **C. illinoensis**

HIDAL'GOA
werck'lei . . . . . CLIMBINGDAHLIA

HIERA'CIUM |w . . . . . HAWKWEED
albiflo'rum . . . . WHITE H.
amplexicau'le
auranti'acum |w . . . . ORANGE H.
bombyci'num
canaden'se |w . . . . . CANADA H.
cladan'thum . . . . . BRANCHING H.
cynoglossoi'des . . HOUNDSTONGUE H.
florenti'num . . . . . KINGDEVIL H.
floribun'dum . . . YELLOWDEVIL H.
grac'ile . . . . SLENDER H.
grono'vi
gymnoceph'alum
lana'tum
marmo'reum
panicula'tum . . . . PANICLED H.
pilosel'la . . . . . . MOUSEEAR H.
praeal'tum
—decip'iens
praten'se . . . . FIELD H.
ru'brum
sca'brum . . . . ROUGH H.
scou'leri . . . . WOOLLYWEED
tridenta'tum
umbella'tum . . . . NARROWLEAF H.
veno'sum |w . . . . . POORROBINS H.
villo'sum . . . . SHAGGY H.
vulga'tum

HIEROCH'LOE (*SAVASTANA; TORRESIA*) . . . . SWEETGRASS
See **GRASS GENERA.**

HIERON'YMA
alchorneoi'des
car'ibae

HILA'RIA . . . . HILARIA
See **GRASS GENERA.**

HIMALAYAHONEYSUCKLE . . **Leycesteria**
SHOWY H. . . . . **L. formosa**

HINAHINA . . . **Melicytus ramiflorus**

HIPPEAS'TRUM . . . **AMARYLLIS**
punic'eum . . . . **A. belladonna**

HIPPOCRE'PIS
como'sa
multisiliquo'sa

HIPPOMA'NE
mancinel'la . . . . . . MANCHINEEL

HIPPO'PHAE . . . . SEABUCKTHORN
rhamnoi'des . . . . . . COMMON S.
—angustifo'lia
—proc'era
salicifo'lia . . . . . WILLOWLEAF S.
Hipposeli'num officina'le . **Levisticum o.**

HIPPU'RIS |w . . . . MARESTAIL
vulga'ris |w . . . . MARESTAIL

HOARHOUND . . . . **Marrubium**
COMMON H. . . . . **M. vulgare**
MOTHERWORT H. . . **M. leonuroides**

HOCQUART'IA . . **ARISTOLOCHIA**

Hoegrass . . . . MUHLY, BUSH:
Muhlenbergia porteri

HOFFMAN'NIA
dis'color
ghiesbreght'i
VARIEGATA. HV.
reful'gens
rega'lis

HOFFMANNSEG'GIA |w . . RUSHPEA
densiflo'ra . . . . INDIAN R.
drepanocar'pa |w . . . SICKLEPOD R.
james'i |w
microphyl'la . . . . . LITTLELEAF R.

HOFMEISTE'RIA
pleurise'ta . . . . BUSH ARROWLEAF

HOGFENNEL . . . . . . **Peucedanum**
COMMON H. . . . . . . **P. officinale**
MASTERWORT H. . . . **P. ostruthium**

HOGPEANUT . . . . **Amphicarpa**
PITCHERS H. . . . . **A. pitcheri**
SOUTHERN H. . . . . . **A. bracteata**

HOHE'RIA . . . . RIBBONWOOD
angustifo'lia
glabra'ta (*H. lyalli g.*) . . HARDY R.
ly'alli (*Gaya l.; Plagianthus l.*)
LACEBARK R.
popul'nea . . . . OTAGO R.
sexstylo'sa

HOLACAN'THA
emo'ryi . . . . CRUCIFIXION THORN

HOLARRHE'NA . . . . HOLARRHENA
antidysenter'ica . . . . CONESSI H.

HOLBOEL'LIA
chinen'sis . . . . . **Sinofranchetia c.**
coria'cea
cunea'ta . . . . . . **Sargentodoxa c.**
far'gesi
grandiflo'ra
latifo'lia (*Stauntonia l.*)

HOL'CUS (*NOTHOLCUS*) VELVETGRASS
See **GRASS GENERA.**

HOLIGAR'NA
longifo'lia . . . BLACKVARNISHTREE

Holly . . . . Ilex
Alabama Dahoon I. cassine angustifolia
∞ Altaclara H. . . . ∞ I. altaclarensis
American H. . . . . I. opaca
Azores H. . . . . I. perado
∞ Beans H. . . . . ∞ I. beani
Bigfruit H. . . . . . I. macrocarpa
Buswell Possumhaw . I. buswelli
CanaryIslands H. I. perado platyphylla
Chinese H. . . . . I. cornuta
Common Winterberry . I. verticillata
Coral H. . . . . I. corallina
Curtiss Possumhaw I. decidua curtissi
Dahoon . . . . I. cassine
Droopbead H. . . . . . I. geniculata
English H. . . . . . . I. aquifolium
Farges H. . . . . I. fargesi
Finetooth H. . . . . . . I. serrata
Franchet H. . . . . I. franchetiana
Georgia H. . . . . I. longipes
Himalaya H. . . . . . . I. dipyrena
Hummuck H. . . . . I. cumulicola
Inkberry . . . . I. glabra
Japanese H. . . . . I. crenata
∞ Koehne H. . . . . . ∞ I. koehneana
Longstalk H. . . . . I. pedunculosa
Lusterleaf H. . . . . . . I. latifolia
Mountain Winterberry I. montana
Myrtle Dahoon . I. cassine myrtifolia
Nepal H. . . . . I. intricata
Paraguaytea . . . I. paraguariensis
Perny H. . . . . I. pernyi
Plumleaf Common Winterberry
I. verticillata padifolia
Possumhaw . . . . I. decidua
Sikkim H. . . . . . . I. sikkimensis
Smoothleaf Yunnan H.
I. yunnanensis gentilis
Smooth Winterberry . I. laevigata
Sugeroki H. . . . . I. sugeroki
Szechwan H. . . . I. szechwanensis
Tawnyberry H. . . . . I. krugiana
Topel H. . . . . . . ×I. attenuata
Veitch H. . . . . . . I. pernyi veitchi
Wholeleaf American H.
I. opaca subintegra
Yaupon . . . . I. vomitoria
Yellow Winterberry
I. laevigata herveyi
Yunnan H. . . . . . I. yunnanensis

Hollyfern . . . . Polystichum
Anderson H. . . . . . . P. andersoni
Braun H. . . . . P. brauni
Bristle H. . . . . P. setiferum
California H. . . . P. californicum
East Indian H. . . . P. aristatum
Eaton H. . . . . . . P. scopulinum
Japanese H. . . . . P. varium
Leather H. . . . . P. adiantiforme
Lemmon H. . . . . P. lemmoni
Lobe H. . . . . P. aculeatum
Mountain H. . . . . . P. lonchitis
Tsussima H. . . . . P. tsussimense
Viviparous H. . . . . P. viviparum

Hollyhock . . . . . . Althaea rosea
Figleaf H. . . . . A. ficifolia

HOLMSKIOLD'IA
sanguin'ea

HOLODIS'CUS (*SCHIZONOTUS* Raf., *not* Lindl.; *SERICOTHECA*)
Rockspirea
boursier'i
dis'color (*Schizonotus d.; Spiraea d.; Sericotheca d.*) . . . Creambush R.
—ariaefo'lius (*Sericotheca d. ariaefolia; Spiraea ariaefolia*) Oceanspray R.

HOLODISCUS, continued
dumo'sus (*H. discolor d.; Sericotheca dumosa*) . . . . Bush Rockspirea
microphyl'lus

HOLOPTE'LEA
gran'dis . . . . Ayo Indiaelm
integrifo'lia . . . . Indiaelm

Holyghostflower . . Peristeria elata

Holygrass . . . . Sweetgrass: Hierochloe odorata

HOMALAN'THUS
populifo'lius

HOMA'LIUM
dolichophyl'lum

HOMALO'BUS . . . **ASTRAGALUS**

HOMALOCEN'CHRUS . . **LEERSIA**
See GRASS GENERA.

HOMALOCEPH'ALA **ECHINOCACTUS**
See CACTUS GENERA.

HOMALOCLA'DIUM . . Ribbonbush (*Centipedeplant*)
platycla'dum (*Muehlenbeckia platyclados*) . . . . Ribbonbush

HOMALOME'NA (*CURMERIA*)
pictura'ta
wal'lisi (*Curmeria w.*)

HOMER'IA
colli'na
Yellow (*aurantiaca*) hv.
el'egans
lilaci'na
pal'lida

HOMOG'YNE
alpi'na

Homoiocel'tis as'pera . . Aphananthe a.

HONCKEN'YA
ficifo'lia

Hondapara . . . . Dillenia, Indian: Dillenia indica

Honesty . . . . Lunaria
Dollarplant . . . . L. annua
Perennial H. . . . . . L. rediviva

Honeyberry . . . . Melicocca

Honeybush . . . . Melianthus
Bigleaf H. . . . . M. major

Honeylocust . . . . Gleditsia
Amorpha H. . . . . G. amorphoides
Bigspine H. . . . . . G. macrantha
Caspian H. . . . . G. caspica
Chinese H. . . . . . . G. sinensis
Cockspur H. . . . . G. ferox
Common H. . . . . G. triacanthos
Delavay H. . . . . . . G. delavayi
Fernleaf H. . . . G. heterophylla
Japanese H. . . . . . . G. japonica
Texas H. . . . . ×G. texana
Waterlocust . . . . . . G. aquatica

Honeysuckle . . . . Lonicera
Albert Thorn H. . L. spinosa alberti
Alps H. . . . . L. alpigena
Altmann H. . . . . . . L. altmanni
American Fly H. . . L. canadensis
Amur H. . . . . L. maacki
Arizona H. . . . . . . L. arizonica
Bearberry H. . . . . L. involucrata
∞ Belle H. . . . . ∞ L. bella

Honeysuckle, continued
Blueleaf H. . . Lonicera korolkowi
Blush H. . . . . L. tangutica
Box H. . . . . L. nitida
∞ Browns H. . . . . ∞ L. browni
Buckthorn H. . . . . . L. orientalis
∞ Bunchberry H. . . ∞ L. minutiflora
California H. . L. hispidula vacillans
Chaparral H. . . . . . L. interrupta
Chinese H. . . . . . L. tragophylla
Coralline H. . . . . L. chrysantha
Creeping H. . . . . . . L. prostrata
Delavay H. . . . L. similis delavayi
Donald H. . . . . . L. glaucescens
Etruscan H. . . . . L. etrusca
European Fly H. . . . L. xylosteum
∞ Everblooming H. . . ∞ L. heckrotti
Ferdinand H. . . . . . L. ferdinandi
Fuchsia H. . . . . . L. fuchsioides
Giant H. . . . . L. hildebrandiana
Girald H. . . . . L. giraldi
∞ Gotha H. . . . . ∞ L. amoena
Grape H. . . . . L. prolifera
Griffith H. . . . . L. griffithi
Hairy H. . . . . L. hirsuta
Halls Japanese H. L. japonica halliana
Henry H. . . . . L. henryi
Iberian H. . . . . L. iberica
Japanese H. . . . . L. japonica
Johnston H. . . . . . . L. johnstoni
Koehne H. . . . . . . L. koehneana
Ledebour H. . . . . . . L. ledebouri
Lilac H. . . . . . . L. syringantha
Limber H. . . . . L. dioica
Manchurian H. . . L. ruprechtiana
Mistletoe H. . . L. quinquelocularis
Moronel H. . . . . . . L. subspicata
Morrow H. . . . . L. morrowi
∞ Muenden H. . . ∞ L. muendeniensis
∞ Muscovy H. . . . ∞ L. muscaviensis
Olga H. . . . . L. olgae
Privet H. . . . . L. pileata
Purpleflower H. . . . L. conjugialis
Purple Japanese H.
L. japonica chinensis
∞ Purplestem H. . . . ∞ L. americana
∞ Purpus H. . . . . ∞ L. purpusi
Pyrenees H. . . . . . . L. pyrenaica
Regels Coralline H.
L. chrysantha regeliana
∞ Rutarian H. . . . . ∞ L. notha
Sakhalin H.
L. maximowiczi sachalinensis
∞ Sargent H. . . . . ∞ L. sargenti
Slender H. . . . . . L. trichosantha
Spangle H. . . . . L. gracilipes
Standish H. . . . . . . L. standishi
Swamp Fly H. . . . L. oblongifolia
Sweetberry H. . . . . . L. coerulea
Sweet H. . . . . . . L. caprifolium
Tatarian H. . . . . L. tatarica
∞ Tellmann H. . . . ∞ L. tellmanniana
Thorn H. . . . . L. spinosa
Tibet H. . . . . L. thibetica
Trumpet H. . . . . . L. sempervirens
Turkestan Coralline H.
L. chrysantha latifolia
Utah H. . . . . L. utahensis
∞ Vienna H. . . . . . ∞ L. xylosteoides
∞ Vilmorin H. . . . . . . ∞ L. vilmorini
Webb H. . . . . L. webbiana
Western Trumpet H. . . . L. ciliosa
∞ Willowleaf H. . . . . ∞ L. salicifolia
Winter H. . . . . L. fragrantissima
Wolfs Lilac H. . L. syringantha wolfi
Woodbine H. . . . . L. periclymenum
Yellow H. . . . . L. flava
Yunnan H. . . . . . . L. yunnanensis

Honeywort . . . . **Cerinthe**
Greek H. . . . . **C. retorta**

HOOD'IA
See **SUCCULENTS.**

HOOK'ERA . . . . . . **BRODIAEA**

Hop . . . . **Humulus**
Common H. . . . . **H. lupulus**
Japanese H. . . . . . . **H. japonicus**
NewMexican H.
H. lupulus neomexicanus

HO'PEA . . . . Merawan
Some botanists unite Hopea with the Sweetleaf genus, Symplocos.

acumina'ta
low'i . . . . Lows M.
maran'ti
micran'tha
nu'tans . . . . Nodding M.
odora'ta . . . . Thingan M.
plaga'ta

Hophornbeam . . . . **Ostrya**
American H. . . . . . **O. virginiana**
European H. . . . . **O. carpinifolia**
Guatemala H. . . . **O. guatemalensis**
Japanese H. . . . . . . **O. japonica**
Knowlton H. . . . . . **O. knowltoni**
Northern American H.
O. virginiana glandulosa
Woolly A. H. . . . . **O. v. lasia**

Hopsage . . . . **Grayia**
Spineless H. . . . . . **G. brandegei**
Spiny H. . . . . **G. spinosa**

Hopseedbush . . . . **Dodonaea**
Clammy H. . . . . **D. viscosa**
Florida H. . . . . . **D. microcarya**
Longstem H. . . . . . . **D. attenuata**
Madagascar H.. **D. madagascariensis**
Narrowleaf Clammy H.
D. viscosa angustifolia
Sticky H. . . . . **D. ptarmicaefolia**
Threecorner H. . . . . **D. triquetra**
Thunberg H. . . . **D. thunbergiana**
Wedgeleaf H. . . . . . **D. cuneata**

Hoptree . . . . **Ptelea**
Baldwin H. . . . . . . **P. baldwini**
Common H. . . . . **P. trifoliata**
Fiveleaf C. H. . . . **P. t. pentaphylla**
Shiny H. . . . . **P. nitens**
Woolly Common H. **P. trifoliata mollis**
Yellow H. . . . . **P. lutescens**

HOR'DEUM . . . . Barley
See **CEREALS** and **GRASS GENERA.**

Horehound . . Hoarhound: **Marrubium**

HORKE'LIA . . . . Horkelia
fus'ca . . . . Tawny H.
gor'doni . . . . **Ivesia g.**

HORMI'NUM
pyrena'icum

Hornbeam . . . . **Carpinus**
American H. . . . . . **C. caroliniana**
Carpinizza European H.
C. betulus carpinizza
Davids Looseflower H.
C. laxiflora davidi
European H. . . . . **C. betulus**
Farges H. . . . . . . **C. fargesiana**
Heartleaf H. . . . . . . **C. cordata**
Henry H. . . . . **C. henryana**
Japanese H. . . . . . . **C. japonica**
Korean H. . . . . **C. eximia**
Looseflower H. . . . . **C. laxiflora**
Oriental H. . . . . . **C. orientalis**
Yeddo H. . . . . . . **C. tschonoski**

Horncone . . . . **Ceratozamia**
Blue H. . . . . **C. miqueliana**
Broadleaf H. . . . . . . **C. latifolia**
Kuster H. . . . . . . **C. kusteriana**
Mexico H. . . . . **C. mexicana**
Purpus H. . . . . **C. purpusi**

Hornpoppy . . . . **Glaucium**
Blackspot H. . . . **G. corniculatum**
Mediterranean H. . . **G. leiocarpum**
Yellow H. . . . . **G. flavum**

Hornwort . **Ceratophyllum demersum**

Horsebalm . . . . **Collinsonia**
Citronella H. . . . . **C. canadensis**

Horsebean . . . . . **Vicia faba equina**
Small H. . . . . **V. f. minor**

Horsebrush . . . . **Tetradymia**
Cottonthorn H. . . . . . **T. spinosa**
Gray H. . . . . **T. canescens**
Hairy H. . . . . **T. comosa**
Littleleaf H. . . . . . . **T. glabrata**
Longspine H. . . . . . . **T. axillaris**
Mohave H. . . . . . . **T. stenolepis**
Nuttall H. . . . . **T. nuttalli**
Spineless Gray H.
T. canescens inermis

Horsechestnut . . . . **Aesculus**
See also Buckeye.

Chinese H. . . . . **A. chinensis**
Common H. . . . **A. hippocastanum**
Indies H. . . . . **A. indica**
Japanese H. . . . . . . **A. turbinata**
∞ Red H. . . . . ∞ **A. carnea**
Wilson H. . . . . **A. wilsoni**

Horsegentian . . . . **Triosteum**
Common H. . . . . . **T. perfoliatum**
Narrowleaf H. . . **T. angustifolium**
Orange H. . . . . . **T. aurantiacum**

Horsemint . . . . Mint, Horse:
Mentha longifolia

Horsenettle, Carolina
Solanum carolinense

Horse-purslane . . . . . **Trianthema**
Desert H. . . . **T. portulacastrum**

Horseradish . **Armoracia lapathifolia**

Horseradishtree. . . **Moringa oleifera**
Arabian H. . . . . **M. aptera**

Horsetail . . . . **Equisetum**
Field H. . . . . **E. arvense**
Giant H. . . . . **E. telmateia**
Marsh H. . . . . **E. palustre**
Meadow H. . . . . . . **E. pratense**
Scouringrush . . . . . . **E. hyemale**
Sedgelike H. . . . . . **E. scirpoides**
Shore H. . . . . **E. littorale**
Smooth H. . . . . . **E. laevigatum**
Stout Scouringrush . **E. praealtum**
Swamp H. . . . . **E. limosum**
Sylvan H. . . . . . . **E. sylvaticum**
Variegated H. . . . . **E. variegatum**
Water H. . . . . **E. fluviatile**
Western Scouringrush
E. hyemale californicum

HORSFORD'IA . . . . . . Horsfordia
ala'ta . . . . Tall H.
newber'ryi . . . . Newberry H.

HOSACK'IA . . . . **LOTUS**
gla'bra . . . . **L. scoparius**
grac'ilis . . . . . . **L. formosissimus**
purshia'na . . . . **L. americanus**
tor'reyi . . . . . . **L. oblongifolius t.**

HOS'TA (*FUNKIA; NIOBE*)
Plantainlily
caeru'lea (*Funkia c.; F. lanceolata; F. ovata; Niobe c.*) . . . . . Blue P.
Aurea. hv.
decora'ta . . . . Blunt P.
errome'na . . . . . . Midsummer P.
fortun'ei (*Funkia f.; Niobe f.*)
Fortunes P.
Giant (*gigantea*) hv.
Wavy Lanceleaf (*lancifolia undulata*)
japon'ica (*lancifolia; Funkia l.; Niobe j.*) . . . . . . Japanese P.
Autumn (*tardiflora*) hv.
Bigjap (*fortis*)
Wavyleaf (*undulata*)
Whiterim (*albomarginata*)
plantagin'ea (*H. p. grandiflora; Funkia alba; F. subcordata; Niobe p.*)
Fragrant P.
sieboldia'na (*Funkia s.; Niobe s.*)
Siebold P.
undula'ta . . . . Wavyleaf P.
Media. hv.
Mediapicta
Variegata

Hottentotfig
Mesembryanthemum edule

Hottentot-tobacco
Tarchonanthus camphoratus

HOTTO'NIA |w . . . . . Featherfoil
infla'ta |w . . . . . . American F.
palus'tris . . . . European F.

HOULLE'TIA
See **ORCHID GENERA.**

Houndstongue . . . . . **Cynoglossum**
Ceylon H. . . . . . . **C. zeylanicum**
Chinese H. . . . . **C. amabile**
Common H. . . . . **C. officinale**
Great H. . . . . **C. nervosum**
Pacific H. . . . . **C. grande**
Wallich H. . . . . **C. wallichi**
Western H. . . . . . **C. occidentale**
White Chinese H. **C. amabile album**
Wildcomfrey H. . . . . **C. virginicum**

House-hollyfern. **Cyrtomium falcatum**

Houseleek . . . . **Sempervivum**
Albert H. . . . . **S. alberti**
Atlantic H. . . . . . . **S. atlanticum**
Brauns H. . . . . **S. brauni**
Dolomite H. . . . . . **S. dolomiticum**
Hen-and-chickens . . . **S. tectorum**
Italian H. . . . . **S. hirtum**
Laharpe H. . . . . **S. laharpei**
Lamotte H. . . . . **S. lamottei**
Pitton H. . . . . **S. pittoni**
Roof H. . . . . . . Hen-and-chickens
Sand H. . . . . **S. arenarium**
∞ Schott H. . . . . ∞ **S. schotti**
Spiderweb H. . . . . **S. arachnoideum**

HOUSTO'NIA |w . . . . Bluets
angustifo'lia
caeru'lea . . . . Common B.
florida'na . . . . Florida B.
longifo'lia . . . . Longleaf B.
min'ima . . . . Tiny B.
monta'na
purpu'rea . . . . Purple B.
rotundifo'lia |w
serpyllifo'lia . . . . . . Creeping B.
tenuifo'lia
wright'i |w . . . . Wrights B.

HOUTTUY'NIA
corda'ta

HO'VEA
cel'si
pun'gens
trisper'ma

HOVE'NIA . . . . RAISINTREE
dul'cis . . . . JAPANESE R.

HOW'EA (*DENEA; HOWEIA; HOWIEA; KENTIA* in part)
SENTRYPALM
See **PALM GENERA.**

HOWEL'LIA |w
aquat'ilis |w

HOY'A . . . . WAXPLANT
carno'sa . . . . COMMON W.
VARIEGATA. HV.
dalrymplea'na
lasian'tha
metos'kei

HUCKLEBERRY . . . . . . **Gaylussacia**
BLACK H. . . . . **G. baccata**
BOX H. . . . . **G. brachycera**
BUCKBERRY . . . . **G. ursina**
DANGLEBERRY . . . . . **G. frondosa**
DWARF H. . . . . **G. dumosa**
Hairy H. . WHORTLEBERRY, HAIRY: **Vaccinium hirsutum**
LITTLE H. . . . . **G. nana**

HUDSO'NIA . . . . BEACHHEATHER
ericoi'des
monta'na . . . . . . MOUNTAIN B.
tomento'sa . . . . . . WOOLLY B.

HUER'NIA . . . . **HEURNIA**
See **SUCCULENTS.**

HUERNIOP'SIS . . **HEURNIOPSIS**
See **SUCCULENTS.**

HUFELAND'IA
a'nay

HUGE'LIA
densifo'lia
virga'ta

HUL'SEA
al'gida
na'na

HUMA'TA
See **FERN GENERA.**

HU'MEA . . . . HUMEA
el'egans . . . . FOUNTAIN H.

HU'MULUS . . . . HOP
america'nus
japon'icus . . . . JAPANESE H.
lu'pulus . . . . COMMON H.
—neomexica'nus . NEWMEXICAN H.
GOLDEN (*aureus*) HV. **H. lupulus**

HUNNEMAN'NIA . . . . GOLDENCUP
fumariaefo'lia . . . . . GOLDENCUP

HUNT'LEYA . . **ZYGOPETALUM**
See **ORCHID GENERA.**

HU'RA
cre'pitans . . . . . . SANDBOXTREE

HURRAHGRASS . . **Paspalum pubescens**

HUTCHIN'SIA
alpi'na . . . . ALPENCRESS
brevicau'lis
stylo'sa

HYACIN'THUS . . . . HYACINTH
amethys'tinus
azu'reus (*Muscari a.*)
can'dicans . . . . **Galtonia c.**
orienta'lis . . . . COMMON H.

HYAENAN'CHE
capen'sis (*Toxicodendron capense*)
HYENABANE

HYA'LIS . . . . **IXIA**

HYBAN'THUS (*CALCEOLARIA* Loefl., *not* L.; *IONIDIUM*)
linearifo'lius (*Ionidium linearifolium; Viola linearifolia*)
verticilla'tus (*Calceolaria verticillata; Ionidium lineare*)

Hydat'ica petiola'ris **Saxifraga leucanthemifolia**

HYDNOCAR'PUS . CHAULMOOGRATREE
anthelmin'thicus . . . . COMMON C.
ilicifo'lius
kurz'i . . . . **Taraktogenos k.**
venena'tus
wightia'nus . . . . WIGHT C.

HYD'NUM . . . . HYDNUM
caput-ur'si . . . . . . BEARSHEAD H.
coralloi'des . . . . CORAL H.
erina'ceum . . . . SATYRSBEARD H.

HYDRAN'GEA . . . . . HYDRANGEA
anom'ala . . . . TIBETAN H.
arbores'cens (*H. a. cordata*)
SMOOTH H.
—austra'lis (*H. a. urticifolia* Hort.)
WESTVIRGINIA S.H.
—grandiflo'ra . . . . . SNOWHILL H.
—oblon'ga . OBLONGLEAF SMOOTH H.
—ster'ilis

This name is sometimes misapplied to the Snowhill Hydrangea, a natural var. of H. arborescens. The true H. a. sterilis is not in the trade.

as'pera
bretschnei'deri . . . . . . SHAGGY H.
∞ **canes'cens** (*arborescens* × *radiata*)

The cultivated shrub is presumably a clon of this cross.

chinen'sis . . . . CHINESE H.
cine'rea . . . . ASHY H.
₵STERILE (*sterilis*) HV.
da'vidi . . . . DAVID H.
dumic'ola
grandiflo'ra Hort.

A name used indiscriminately for the Peegee Hydrangea, HV. of H. paniculata, and for the Snowhill Hydrangea, a natural var. of H. arborescens.

heteromal'la . . . . . HIMALAYAN H.
hypoglau'ca
integer'rima . . . . WHOLELEAF H.
involucra'ta
lon'gipes
macrophyl'la (*hortensis; opuloides*)
BIGLEAF H.

Presumably all the HV. listed below are clons.

ALTOONA. HV.
AMI PASQUAAR
BLUE PRINCE
CENDRILLION
CHAUTARD
COERULEA
DEUTSCHLAND
DOMOTOI
EUROPA

HYDRANGEA macrophylla, continued
F. MATTHES
FREYA
FRUEHLINGSERWACHEN
GERT GLAHN
GISELHERR
GOLIATH
HAMBURG
HELGE
HOLLANDIA
KUNERT
LA MARNE
LORELEI
LOUIS SAVAGE
MACROSEPALA
MACULATA
MANDSHURICA
MARECHAL FOCH
MARIESI
M. BAARDSE
MEIN LIEBLING
MERVEILLE
MME. E. MOULLIERE
NIEDERSACHSEN
NIKKO BLUE
NIXE
NORMALIS
OTAKSA
PARSIFAL. *Parcival.*
PRESIDENT DOUMIER
RENE GAILLARD
RHEINGOLD
ROCHAMBEAU
ROSABELL
ROSEA
RUBIS
SCHOENE DRESDNERIN
SCH. PERLE
(*Souv. de*) MME. CHAUTARD
SPLENDENS
VEITCHI
VIBRAYE
VULCAN
WILLKOMMEN

panicula'ta . . . PANICLE HYDRANGEA
₵EARLY (*praecox*) HV.
₵LATE (*tardiva*)
₵MANYFLOWER (*floribunda*)
₵PEEGEE (*grandiflora*)
petiola'ris (*scandens*) . CLIMBING H.
quercifo'lia . . . . . . OAKLEAF H.
radia'ta (*nivea*) . . . SILVERLEAF H.
sargentia'na . . . . . . SARGENT H.
serra'ta
₵ACUMINATA. HV.
₵PROLIFERA
₵PUBESCENS
₵ROSALBA
strigo'sa . . . . BRISTLY H.
₵BIGLEAF (*macrophylla*) HV.
villo'sa
xanthoneu'ra . . . . YELLOWVEIN H.
—setchuenen'sis . . SZECHWAN Y.H.
—wil'soni . . . . WILSON Y.H.

Presumably all the HV. listed below are clons.

AGNES BARILLET. HV. Hydrangea
AVALANCHE
BABY BIMBENET
Botaniste Poltereau. **POLTEREAU.**
BOUQUET ROSE
ECLAIREUR
E. G. HILL
EMILE MOUILLERE
ETINCELANT
FRAICHEUR
GENERAL DE VIBRAYE

HYDRANGEA, continued
GRACIEUX
G. RENAULT. *Monsieur G. Renault.*
HENRI DAVID. *Senateur Henri David.*
INNOCENCE
LA LORRAINE
LIEUTENANT CHAURE. *Souvenir de Lieutenant Chaure.*
LILIE MOUILLERE
L'ISLETTE
LOUIS FOUCARD
MME. AUGUSTE NONIN
MME. E. CHAUTARD. *Souvenir de Mme. E. Chautard.*
MME. E. MOUILLERE
MME. FOUCARD
MME. LEGOU
MME. MAURICE HAMAR
MME. RAYMOND
MME. RENE JACQUET
MME. TRUFFAUT
MME. VICTOR RAOULT. *Souvenir de Mme. Victor Raoult.*
Monsieur G. Renault. G. RENAULT.
MONTROSE
MOUSSELINE
OPALE
ORNAMENT
POLTEREAU. *Botaniste Poltereau.*
PROFESSOR D. BOIS
PURPLESTEM (*opuloides cyanoclada*)
RADIANT
Senateur Henri David. HENRI DAVID.
Souvenir de Lieutenant Chaure. LIEUTENANT CHAURE.
Souvenir de Mme. E. Chautard. MME. E. CHAUTARD.
Souvenir de Mme. Victor Raoult. MME. VICTOR RAOULT.
THOMAS HOGG
TROPHEE
VIEUX CHATEAU
VISCOMTESSE DE VIBRAYE

HYDRANGEA . . . . **Hydrangea**
ASHY H. . . . . **H. cinerea**
BIGLEAF H. . . . . **H. macrophylla**
BRISTLY H. . . . . . . **H. strigosa**
CHINESE H. . . . . . **H. chinensis**
CLIMBING H. . . . . . **H. petiolaris**
DAVID H. . . . . **H. davidi**
HIMALAYAN H. . . . . **H. heteromalla**
OAKLEAF H. . . . . . **H. quercifolia**
OBLONGLEAF SMOOTH H. **H. arborescens oblonga**
PANICLE H. . . . . . **H. paniculata**
SARGENT H. . . . . **H. sargentiana**
SHAGGY H. . . . . **H. bretschneideri**
SILVERLEAF H. . . . . . . **H. radiata**
SMOOTH H. . . . . **H. arborescens**
SNOWHILL H. . . . . **H. a. grandiflora**
SZECHWAN YELLOWVEIN H. **H. xanthoneura setchuenensis**
TIBETAN H. . . . . . . **H. anomala**
WESTVIRGINIA SMOOTH H. **H. arborescens australis**
WHOLELEAF H. . . . . **H. integerrima**
WILSON YELLOWVEIN H. **H. xanthoneura wilsoni**
YELLOWVEIN H. . . . **H. xanthoneura**

HYDRANGEAVINE . . . **Schizophragma**
CHINESE H. . . . . **S. integrifolium**
JAPANESE H. . . . . **S. hydrangeoides**
WOOLLY CHINESE H. **S. integrifolium molle**

HYDRAS'TIS . . . . . . GOLDENSEAL
canaden'sis . GOLDENSEAL (*Puccoon*)

HYDRIASTE'LE . . . . HYDRIASTELE
See **PALM GENERA.**

HYDROCH'ARIS . . . . . FROGBIT
morsus-ra'nae . . . . . . FROGBIT
spon'gia . . . . **Limnobium s.**

HYDROCH'LOA . . . . WATERGRASS
See **GRASS GENERA.**

HYDRO'CLEIS . . . . WATERPOPPY
nymphoi'des (*Limnocharis humboldti*) WATERPOPPY

HYDROCOT'YLE |w . . . PENNYWORT
america'na . . . . MARSH P.
bonarien'sis |w . . . . LARGELEAF P.
peduncula'ris . . . . TASMANIAN P.
prolif'era |w
ranunculoi'des |w . . . . FLOATING P.
rotundifo'lia . . . . SHINY P.
umbella'ta |w
verticilla'ta |w . . . . . WHORLED P.
—cunea'ta
vulga'ris . . . . COMMON P.

HYDRO'LEA |w . . . . . . HYDROLEA
affi'nis |w
ova'ta |w
quadrival'vis |w
spino'sa

HYDROPHYL'LUM . . . WATERLEAF
appendicula'tum
canaden'se . . . . CANADA W.
capita'tum . . . . BALLHEAD W.
fend'leri . . . . FENDLER W.
—al'bifrons (*H. albifrons*) WHITEFACE F.W.
occidenta'le . . . . . WESTERN W.
virginia'num . . . . . VIRGINIA W.

HYDROS'ME
rivier'i (*Amorphophallus r.*) DEVILSTONGUE

HYDRO'TRIDA
carolinia'na . . CAROLINA BOGHYSSOP

HYENABANE . . **Hyaenanche capensis**

HYGROPH'ILA |w
lacus'tris |w
spino'sa (*Asteracantha longifolia*) STARTHORN

HYGROPH'ORUS . . . HYGROPHORUS
chrys'odon . . . . . . GOLDTOOTH H.
coccin'eus . . . . SCARLET H.
con'icus . . . . CONIC H.
hypothe'jus

HYGRORY'ZA (*HYGRORHIZA*) WATERRICE
arista'ta . . . . AWNED W.

HYLOCE'REUS NIGHTBLOOMING-CEREUS
See **CACTUS GENERA.**

HYMENAE'A
courbaril' . . . . COURBARIL

HYMENAN'THERA
angustifo'lia
chatham'ica
crassifo'lia
denta'ta
novae-zeland'iae
obova'ta
tra'versi

HYMENOCAL'LIS |w . . HYMENOCALLIS

The term Spiderlily is often used for some species of this genus, but Hamilton P. Traub informs the Editorial Committee that the name has been rejected by the American Amaryllis Society, which sponsors the generic name as a common one, because Spiderlily is also used for Lycoris radiata in the South.

aman'caes . . . . YELLOW H.
america'na . . . . . AMERICAN H.
calathi'na . . . . BASKETFLOWER H.
caribae'a (*Pancratium declinatum*) CARIBBEAN H.
caymanen'sis . . . . . CAYMAN H.
crassifo'lia |w . . . . . GEORGIA H.
florida'na . . . . FLORIDA H.
galvestonen'sis . . . . GALVESTON H.
harrisia'na . . . . HARRIS H.
keyen'sis . . . . KEYS H.
kimbal'liae . . . . . . TEAROSE H.
littora'lis . . . TROPICAMERICAN H.
maclea'na . . . . MACLEAN H.
×**macrosteph'ana** (*?calathina × speciosa*) GREATCUP H.
moritzia'na . . . . . VENEZUELA H.
occidenta'lis |w . . . . . INLAND H.
ova'ta . . . . WESTINDIES H.
pal'meri . . . . ALLIGATOR H.
rota'ta . . . . CAROLINA H.
schizosteph'ana . . FRINGECUP H.
senegam'bica . . . SENEGAMBIA H.
specio'sa . . . . . . WINTERSPICE H.
—angustifo'lia . . . STIFFLEAF W.H.
tenuiflo'ra . . . . . SLIMFLOWER H.
tridenta'ta |w
tubiflo'ra . . . . . . FOUNTAIN H.
₵ADVANCE. HV. Hymenocallis
₵DAPHNE
₵FESTAL (*festalis*)
₵SULFURBEAUTY
₵SULFURGEM
₵SULFURQUEEN

HYMENOCALLIS . . . . . **Hymenocallis**
ALLIGATOR H. . . . . . **H. palmeri**
AMERICAN H. . . . . **H. americana**
BASKETFLOWER H. . . . **H. calathina**
CARIBBEAN H. . . . . . **H. caribaea**
CAROLINA H. . . . . **H. rotata**
CAYMAN H. . . . . **H. caymanensis**
FLORIDA H. . . . . . . **H. floridana**
FOUNTAIN H. . . . . . . **H. tubiflora**
FRINGECUP H. . . **H. schizostephana**
GALVESTON H. . . **H. galvestonensis**
GEORGIA H. . . . . . . **H. crassifolia**
GREATCUP H. . ×**H. macrostephana**
HARRIS H. . . . . . . **H. harrisiana**
INLAND H. . . . . . . **H. occidentalis**
KEYS H. . . . . **H. keyensis**
MACLEAN H. . . . . . . **H. macleana**
SENEGAMBIA H. . . **H. senegambica**
SLIMFLOWER H. . . . **H. tenuiflora**
STIFFLEAF WINTERSPICE H. **H. speciosa angustifolia**
TEAROSE H. . . . . . . **H. kimballiae**
TROPICAMERICAN H. . . **H. littoralis**
VENEZUELA H. . . . . **H. moritziana**
WESTINDIES H. . . . . . . **H. ovata**
WINTERSPICE H. . . . . **H. speciosa**
YELLOW H. . . . . . **H. amancaes**

HYMENOCLE'A |w . . BURROBRUSH
monogy'ra . . . . . SINGLEWHORL B.
sal'sola |w . . . . WHITE B.

HYMENOCY'CLUS **MESEMBRYANTHEMUM**
See **SUCCULENTS.**

HYMENO'DIUM
See **FERN GENERA.**

HYMENOPAP'PUS |w . HYMENOPAPPUS
carolinen'sis (*scabiosaeus*) WHITEBRACT H.
eriop'odus . . . . . WOOLLYFOOT H.
filifo'lius . . . . . . FINELEAF H.
mexica'nus |w . . . . . MEXICAN H.

HYMENOPHY'SA . . . . **CARDARIA**

HYMENOS'PORUM . . SWEETSHADE
fla'vum . . . . SWEETSHADE

HYMENOX'YS . . . . . . **ACTINEA**
cockerel'li . . . . **A. odorata**
floribun'da . . . . . . **A. richardsoni**
multiflo'ra . . . . **A. odorata**

Hymentostem'ma fontane'si **Chrysanthemum f.**

HYOPHOR'BE
See **PALM GENERA.**

HYOSCY'AMUS |w . . . . HENBANE
al'bus . . . . ROUNDLEAF H.
au'reus . . . . YELLOW H.
mu'ticus
ni'ger |w . . . . BLACK H.

HYOSPA'THE
See **PALM GENERA.**

HYPARRHE'NIA
See **GRASS GENERA.**

HYPELA'TE
trifolia'ta . . . . INKWOOD

HYPERAN'THERA . . **MORINGA**

HYPER'ICUM |w . . . ST.JOHNSWORT
adpres'sum . . . . SHORE S.
aegypt'icum . . . . . . EGYPTIAN S.
anagalloi'des . . . . . TRAILING S.
androsae'mum . . . . . . TUTSAN S.
∞**arnoldia'num** (*galioides* × *lobocarpum*) ∞ARNOLD S.
as'cyron . . . . GIANT S.
aspalathoi'des
au'reum Bartr., *not* Lour. **H. frondosum**
austra'le . . . . MEDITERRANEAN S.
balear'icum . . . . . . BALEARIC S.
buck'leyi (*bucklei*) . . BLUERIDGE S.
calyc'inum . . . . . AARONSBEARD S. (*Aaronsbeard*)
canaden'se . . . . CANADA S.
—**borea'le** (*H. boreale*). NORTHERN S.
—**ma'jus** (*H. majus*) |w
canarien'se . . . CANARYISLANDS S.
chinen'se . . . . CHINESE S.
cistifo'lium
concin'num . . . . . CALIFORNIA S.
co'ris
∞**dawsonia'num** (*lobocarpum* × *prolificum*) . . . . ∞DAWSON S.
de'geni
densiflo'rum . . . . DENSE H.
ela'tum
el'egans . . . . SIBERIAN S.
ellip'ticum |w . . . . PALE S.
empetrifo'lium
fascicula'tum . . . . . SANDBUSH S.
floribun'dum
formo'sum . . . . SOUTHWESTERN S.
frag'ile . . . . GREEK S.
frondo'sum (*aureum* Bartr., *not* Lour.) GOLDEN S.
galioi'des . . . . . . BEDSTRAW S.
gentianoi'des (*Sarothra g.*) PINEWEED S.

HYPERICUM, continued
glomera'tum . CLUSTER ST.JOHNSWORT
hir'cinum . . . . GOAT S.
hirsu'tum
hookeria'num . . . . . . HOOKERS S.
—**leschenault'i**
—**rog'ersi**
hyssopifo'lium
inodo'rum
japon'icum . . . . . . JAPANESE S.
kalmia'num . . . . KALM S.
kotschya'num
lanceola'tum
lanugino'sum
linearifo'lium
lobocar'pum
lysimachioi'des
macula'tum Walt., *not* Crantz **H. punctatum**
ma'jus . . . . . . **H. canadense m.**
monta'num
×**moseria'num**
VARIEGATED (*tricolor*) HV.
mu'tilum |w
∞**no'thum** (*densiflorum* × *kalmianum*)
nudiflo'rum
nummula'rium . . . . PYRENEES S.
oblongifo'lium
olymp'icum . . . . . . OLYMPIC S.
orienta'le . . . . SYRIAN S.
pat'ulum . . . . . . GOLDENCUP S.
—**for'resti**
—**hen'ryi** . . . . HENRY S.
—**oblongifo'lium**
—**ura'lum** (*H. uralum*) . . . URAL S.
perfora'tum |w . . . . . COMMON S.
See note under *Klamathweed.*
petiola'tum |w
polyphyl'lum
prolif'icum . . . . SHRUBBY S.
pul'chrum
puncta'tum (*maculatum* Walt., *not* Crantz) . . . . SPOTTED S.
quadran'gulum
quartinia'num
re'pens . . . . CREEPING S.
rep'tans
rhodope'um . . . . RHODOPE S.
rich'eri
scou'leri . . . . SCOULER S.
splen'dens
tomento'sum . . . . WOOLLY S.
tur'gidum
ura'lum . . . . **H. patulum u.**
×**vanfleet'i** . . . . . . VANFLEET S.
virga'tum
virgin'icum |w . . . . MARSH S.

HYPHAE'NE . . . . DOUMPALM
See **PALM GENERA.**

HYPHOLO'MA . . . . . HYPHOLOMA
appendicula'tum
perplex'um . . . . PERPLEXING H.
sublaterit'ium . . . . BRICKTOP H.

HYPOCALYM'MA . . . PEACHMYRTLE
robus'tum . . . . . . SWANRIVER P.

HYPOCHOER'IS (*HYPOCHAERIS*) |w . . . . CATSEAR
gla'bra . . . . SMOOTH C.
radica'ta |w . . . . SPOTTED C.
uniflo'ra

HYPOLE'PIS
See **FERN GENERA.**

HYPOP'ITYS
latisqua'ma . . . . PINESAP

HYPOX'IS |w . . . . GOLDSTARGRASS
hirsu'ta (*erecta*) |w . . . COMMON G.
hygromet'rica . . . . BAROMETER G.
jun'cea |w
stella'ta . . . . CAPE G.
¢CANOPUS (*elegans*) HV.

HYP'TIS . . . . BUSHMINT
emo'ryi . . . . EMORY B.

HYSSO'PUS . . . . HYSSOP
arista'tus
officina'lis . . . . HYSSOP
BIGFLOWER (*grandiflorus*) HV.
RED (*ruber*)
ROSE (*roseus*)
WHITE (*albus*)

HYS'TRIX . . . . BOTTLEBRUSH
See **GRASS GENERA.**

Iberidel'la triner'via **Aethionema trinervium**

IBE'RIS . . . . CANDYTUFT
affi'nis
Plants cultivated under this name may also be I. lagascana, odorata, pandurae-formis, pectinata.
ama'ra (*coronaria*) . . . . ROCKET C.
EMPRESS. HV.
HESPERIDIFLORA
HYACINTH
WHITE SPIRAL
corifo'lia (*I. saxatilis c.*)
garrexia'na . . . **I. sempervirens g.**
gibraltar'ica . . . . . . GIBRALTAR C.
jor'dani . . . . JORDAN C.
jucun'da . **Aethionema coridifolium**
lagasca'na
Plants cultivated under this name may be I. affinis.
odora'ta . . . . SWEET C.
Plants cultivated under this name may be I. affinis.
panduraefor'mis
Plants cultivated under this name may be I. affinis.
pectina'ta . . . . . . COMBLEAF C.
Plants cultivated under this name may be I. affinis.
pru'iti . . . . PRUIT C.
saxat'ilis . . . . ROCK C.
—*corifo'lia* . . . . **I. corifolia**
semperflo'rens . . . . . SICILIAN C.
sempervi'rens . . . . EVERGREEN C.
—**garrexia'na** (*I. garrexiana*)
COMPACT (*compacta*) HV. I. sempervirens
DWARF (*nana*)
LITTLE GEM
SNOWFLAKE
SUPERBA
tau'rica . . . . TAURUS C.
tenorea'na . . . . TENORE C.
—**petrae'a** . . . . . REDFLUSH T.C.
umbella'ta . . . . GLOBE C.
ATROPURPUREA. HV.
CARDINAL
DUNNETT (*dunnetti*)
LAVENDER
LILAC (*liliacea*)
ROSE (*rosa*)

IBERVIL'LEA |w
tenuisec'ta |w

IBICEL'LA (*MARTYNIA* in part) UNICORNPLANT
lute'a (*Martynia l.*) . . . YELLOW U.

IBID'IUM . . . . . **SPIRANTHES**
See **ORCHID GENERA, HARDY TERRESTRIAL GROUP.**

IBO'ZA
ripa'ria (*Moschosma riparium*)

ICACO'REA . . . . **ARDISIA**

Icegrass . . . . . . **Phippsia algida**

Icelandmoss . . . . **Cetraria islandica**

∞Ichandarin . . **Citrus ichangensis × C. reticulata**

∞Ichangelo
Citrus grandis × C. ichangensis

ICHTHYOME'THIA . . **PISCIDIA**

ICI'CA Engl., *not* Aubl. . **PROTIUM**
The older Icica of Aublet proves to be a synonym of the related genus Bursera.

IDES'IA
polycar'pa
—vesti'ta

ID'RIA . . . . . Boojamtree (*Cirio*)
See **SUCCULENTS.**

IGNA'TIA . . . . . . **STRYCHNOS**
ama'ra . . . . **S. ignati**

Ilama . . . . . . **Annona diversifolia**

I'LEX |w . . . . Holly
∞**altaclaren'sis** (*aquifolium × perado*)
∞Altaclara H.
₵Belgian (*belgica*) hv.
₵Camellia (*camelliaefolia*)
₵Henderson (*hendersoni*)
₵Hodgins (*hodginsi*)
₵Lawson (*lawsoniana*)
₵Mundy (*mundyi*)
₵Noble (*nobilis*)
₵Shepherd (*shepherdi*)
₵Wilson (*wilsoni* Henry, *not* Loes.)
aquifo'lium . . . . . . English H.
—chinen'sis
₵Balearic (*balearica*) hv. I. aquifolium
₵Cutleaf (*heterophylla*)
₵Donnington (*donningtonensis*)
₵Golden Beauty
₵Golden King
₵Golden Milkmaid (*aurea medio-picta*)
₵Golden Queen (*aureo-regina*)
₵Goldspot (*aureo-maculata*)
₵Halberdleaf (*hastata*)
₵Handsworth
₵Hedgehog (*ferox*)
₵Laurel (*laurifolia*)
₵Mme. Briot
₵Moonlight (*flavescens*)
₵Myrtifolia
₵Narrowleaf (*angustifolia*)
₵Ovata
₵Planifolia
₵Polycarpa
₵Princeps
₵Pyramid (*pyramidalis*)
₵Recurva
₵Sawtooth (*serratifolia*)
₵Scotch (*scotica*)
₵Silverqueen
₵Silver Variegated
₵Small-leaf (*microphylla*)
₵Vantol
₵Variegated (*variegata*)
₵Waterer (*watereriana*)
₵Weeping (*pendula*)
₵Whitemargin (*albo-marginata*)

ILEX aquifolium, continued
₵Yellowedge (*aureo-marginata*)
₵Yellowfruit (*bacciflava*)
arenic'ola . . . . **I. cumulicola**
×**attenua'ta** (*cassine × opaca; topeli* Hort.) . . . . . . Topel Holly
Apparently a natural hybrid.
bead'lei . . . . **I. montana b.**
∞**bean'i** (*aquifolium × dipyrena*)
∞Beans H.
The cultivated plant presumably is a clon of this.
bronxen'sis . . **I. verticillata tenuifolia**
bus'welli . . Buswell Possumhaw
carolinia'na Loes., *not* Mill. **I. vomitoria**
cassi'ne (*dahoon*) |w . . . . . Dahoon
—angustifo'lia . . . . . Alabama D.
—myrtifo'lia (*I. myrtifolia*) . Myrtle D.
cassi'ne Walt., *not* L. . . . **I. vomitoria**
ciliospino'sa
coralli'na . . . . Coral H.
cornu'ta . . . . Chinese H.
₵Burford (*burfordi*) hv.
crena'ta (*fortunei*) . . . Japanese H.
₵Bigleaf (*elliptica; latifolia; major*) hv.
₵Boxleaf (*mariesi; nummularia*)
₵Convexleaf (*bullata; convexa*)
₵Heller (*helleri*)
₵Kingsville
₵Littleleaf (*microphylla*)
₵Longleaf (*longifolia*)
₵Variegated (*luteo-variegata*)
cumulic'ola (*arenicola*) . Hummock H.
cur'tissi . . . . Curtiss Possumhaw
dahoon' . . . . **I. cassine**
decid'ua |w . . . . . . Possumhaw
dipyre'na . . . . . Himalaya H.
—paucispino'sa
du'bia
—macrop'oda . . . . **I. montana m.**
—montic'ola . . . . . . **I. montana**
far'gesi . . . . Farges H.
fortun'ei . . . . **I. crenata**
frag'ilis
franchetia'na . . . . . Franchet H.
genicula'ta . . . . . . Droopbead H.
gla'bra |w . . . . Inkberry
integ'ra
—leucocla'da
intrica'ta . . . . Nepal H.
∞**koehnea'na** (*aquifolium × latifolia*)
∞Koehne H.
The cultivated plant is presumably a clon of this.
krugia'na . . . . Tawnyberry H.
laeviga'ta . . Smooth Winterberry
Yellowfruit (*herveyi*) hv.
latifo'lia . . . . . . Lusterleaf H.
lon'gipes . . . . Georgia H.
macrocar'pa . . . . . . Bigfruit H.
micrococ'ca
monta'na (*I. dubia monticola; monticola*) |w . Mountain Winterberry
—bead'lei (*I. beadlei*)
—hupehen'sis
See note under var. macropoda.
—macrop'oda (*I. dubia m.; I. macropoda*)
I. montana is native to eastern United States. The Sino-Japanese vars. hupehensis and macropoda are recognized by American botanists, but the enormous physical gap between the natural ranges of the American type and the Asiatic forms suggests the need of further field and laboratory study.

ILEX, continued
myrtifo'lia . . . . **I. cassine m.**
opa'ca |w . . . . American Holly
—subinteg'ra . . . Wholeleaf A.H.
₵Howard. hv. I. opaca
₵Yellowfruit (*xanthocarpa*)
paraguarien'sis . . . . Paraguaytea
pedunculo'sa . . . . . Longstalk H.
—continenta'lis
pera'do . . . . Azores H.
—platyphyl'la (*I. platyphylla*)
CanaryIslands H.
₵Balearic (*balearica*) hv. I. perado
₵Black (*nigrescens*)
₵Madeira (*maderensis*)
₵Variegated (*variegata*)
per'nyi . . . . Perny H.
—manipuren'sis (*I. wilsoni* Loes., *not* Henry)
—veitch'i . . . . Veitch H.
platyphyl'la . . . . **I. perado p.**
pubes'cens
purpu'rea
—old'hami
rotun'da
rugo'sa
serra'ta (*sieboldi*) . . . Finetooth H.
—argu'tidens
₵Whitefruit (*leucocarpa*) hv. I. serrata
₵Yellowfruit (*xanthocarpa*)
sikkimen'sis . . . . Sikkim H.
sugero'ki . . . . . . Sugeroki H.
₵Longipedunculata. hv.
szechwanen'sis . . . . Szechwan H.
tope'li Hort. . . . . . . ×**I. attenuata**
venulo'sa
verticilla'ta |w Common Winterberry
—fastigia'ta
—padifo'lia . . . . Plumleaf C.W.
—tenuifo'lia (*I. bronxensis*)
Prolific (*polycarpa*) hv. I. verticillata
₵Roundleaf (*cyclophylla*)
₵Yellowfruit (*chrysocarpa*)
vomito'ria (*caroliniana* Loes., *not* Mill.; *cassine* Walt., *not* L.) |w . . Yaupon
wil'soni Henry
∞**I. altaclarensis** ₵ Wilson
wil'soni Loes. . **I. pernyi manipurensis**
yunnanen'sis . . . . . . Yunnan H.
—gen'tilis . . . . Smoothleaf Y.H.

ILLE'CEBRUM
verticilla'tum . . . . Whitlowwort

ILLI'CIUM . . . . Anisetree
anisa'tum . . . . Japanese A.
—variega'tum . . . Variegated J.A.
cambodia'num . . . . Cambodia A.
florida'num . . . . . . Florida A.
grif'fithi . . . . . . Himalaya A.
hen'ryi . . . . Henry A.
ma'jus . . . . Burma A.
parviflo'rum . . . . . . Yellow A.
ve'rum . . . . Truestar A.

ILLI'PE . . . . **MADHUCA**
latifo'lia . . . . **M. indica**

Illurin-balsam . . . . Daniella,
Illurin-balsam: **Daniella oliveri**

ILYSAN'THES . . . **LINDERNIA**

Imantophyl'lum cyrtanthiflo'rum
×**Clivia cyrtanthiflora**

Imbe . . . . . **Garcinia livingstonei**

Immortelle . . . . . . **Xeranthemum**
Common I. . . . . **X. annuum**
Cylinder I. . . . . . **X. cylindraceum**

IMMORTELLE, continued
DOUBLE I. Xeranthemum annuum perligulosum
SEMIDOUBLE I. . . . X. a. ligulosum

IMPA'TIENS |w . . . . . . SNAPWEED
bal'fouri . . . . BALFOUR S.
balsam'ina . . . . GARDEN BALSAM
biflo'ra (*fulva*) |w . . . . SPOTTED S.
holst'i . . . . HOLSTS S.
oliver'i . . . . OLIVER S.
pal'lida |w . . . . PALE S.
petersia'na . . . . PETERS S.
platypet'ala . . . . JAVA S.
royl'ei (*glanduligera*) . . . ROYLE S.
sca'brida
sul'tani . . . . SULTAN S.
urticifo'lia

IMPERA'TA . . . . SATINTAIL
See **GRASS GENERA.**

IMPERATO'RIA . . **PEUCEDANUM**

INCARVIL'LEA . . . . . INCARVILLEA
compac'ta
delavay'i . . . . DELAVAY I.
grandiflo'ra . . . . . BIGFLOWER I.
—brev'ipes
lute'a . . . . YELLOW I.
ol'gae . . . . OLGA I.
variab'ilis . . . . . . PINKSHRUB I.

INCENSECEDAR . . . . . . **Libocedrus**
BLUE CALIFORNIA I. **L. decurrens glauca**
CALIFORNIA I. . . . . . . **L. decurrens**
CHILEAN I. . . . . **L. chilensis**
FORMOSA I. . . . . . . **L. macrolepis**
PAHAUTEA I. . . . . **L. bidwilli**
PLUME I. . . . . **L. plumosa**

INDIAELM . . . **Holoptelea integrifolia**
AYO I. . . . . **H. grandis**

INDIALOTUS, BLUE . **Nymphaea stellata**

INDIANFIG . . . . **Opuntia ficus-indica**
Not to be confused with India Fig: Ficus indica.

INDIANGRASS . . . . **Sorghastrum**
LOPSIDE I. . . . . . . **S. secundum**
SLENDER I. . . . . **S. elliotti**
YELLOW I. . . . . **S. nutans**

INDIANLETTUCE . . . . **Montia**

INDIANMULBERRY . . . . . . **Morinda**
DYERS I. . . . . **M. coreia**
ROYOC I. . . . . **M. royoc**

INDIANPHYSIC . . . . **Gillenia stipulata**

INDIANPIPE . . **Monotropa; M. uniflora**

INDIANPOTATO . . **Orogenia linearifolia**

INDIANWHEAT
BOTTLEBRUSH I. . . **Plantago aristata**
DESERT I. . . . . **P. fastigiata**
FOOTHILL I. . . . . **P. ignota**
PATAGONIA I. . . . . . **P. patagonica**
WOOLLY I. . . . . **P. purshi**

INDIA-SARSAPARILLA **Hemidesmus indicus**

INDIGO . . . . **Indigofera**
ANIL I. . . . . **I. suffruticosa**
AUSTRALIAN I. . . . . . . **I. australis**
CAROLINA I. . . . . . **I. caroliniana**
CHINESE I. . . . . **I. incarnata**
FORTUNES I. . . . . **I. fortunei**
HAIRY I. . . . . **I. hirsuta**
HIMALAYAN I. . . . . . **I. gerardiana**
KIRILOW I. . . . . **I. kirilowi**
LOVELY I. . . . . **I. pulchella**
PINK I. . . . . **I. amblyantha**
POTANIN I. . . . . **I. potanini**
SONORA I. . . . . . . **I. sphaerocarpa**
TRUE I. . . . . **I. tinctoria**

INDIGO, continued
WEEPING I. . . . **Indigofera pendula**
WESTERN I. . . . . . **I. leptosepala**
WHITE CHINESE I. . **I. incarnata alba**
ZOLLINGER I. . . . . . **I. zollingeriana**

INDIGOF'ERA |w . . . . . . INDIGO
amblyan'tha . . . . PINK I.
an'il . . . . **I. suffruticosa**
austra'lis . . . . . . AUSTRALIAN I.
carolinia'na |w . . . . . CAROLINA I.
cylindra'cea
fortun'ei . . . . FORTUNES I.
gerardia'na (*floribunda*). HIMALAYAN I.
hebepet'ala
hirsu'ta . . . . HAIRY I.
incarna'ta (*decora*) . . . CHINESE I.
—al'ba (*I. decora a.*) . . WHITE C.I.
kirilow'i . . . . KIRILOW I.
langebergen'sis
leptosep'ala . . . . . . WESTERN I.
leptosta'chya
lespedezioi'des
pen'dula . . . . WEEPING I.
potani'ni . . . . POTANIN I.
pulchel'la . . . . LOVELY I.
sphaerocar'pa . . . . . . SONORA I.
stachyo'des
suffrutico'sa (*anil*) . . . . . ANIL I.
tincto'ria . . . . TRUE I.
zollingeria'na . . . . ZOLLINGER I.

INDOCAL'AMUS
See **BAMBOO GENERA.**

IN'GA . . . . INGA
ed'ulis . . . . FOOD I.
feuil'lei
lauri'na . . . . SACKYSAC I.
pulcher'rima . . . **Calliandra tweedi**
ve'ra . . . . GUABA I.

INGENHOUZ'IA . . . **GOSSYPIUM**

INKBERRY . . . . **Ilex glabra**

INKWOOD . . . . . **Hypelate trifoliata**

INOCAR'PUS
fagif'erus (*edulis*) . . TAHITI-CHESTNUT

INO'DES . . . . **SABAL**
See **PALM GENERA.**

INSECTICIDES (Plant Sources of)
See **ECONOMIC PLANTS, INSECTICIDES.**

INTERRUPTED-FERN **Osmunda claytoniana**

INT'SIA . . . . IPIL
ba'keri . . . . MERBAU I.
biju'ga . . . . COMMON I.

IN'ULA |w . . . . INULA
acau'lis . . . . STEMLESS I.
bi'frons
britan'nica . . . . BRITISH I.
cony'za . . . . . . CINNAMONROOT I.
dysenter'ica . . . . . . **Pulicaria d.**
ensifo'lia . . . . . . SWORDLEAF I.
glandulo'sa . . . . . . CAUCASIAN I.
grandiflo'ra . . . . . SUNFLOWER I.
—floribun'da
hele'nium |w . . . . ELECAMPANE I.
hir'ta
hook'eri . . . . HOOKER I.
limonifo'lia . . . . GREEK I.
monta'na . . . . MOUNTAIN I.
oculus-chris'ti . . . . . CHRISTEYE I.
odo'ra . . . . **Pulicaria o.**
rhizoceph'ala
roylea'na (*macrocephala*). BLACKBUD I.
salici'na . . . . . . WILLOWLEAF I.

INULA . . . . **Inula**
BLACKBUD I. . . . . **I. royleana**
BRITISH I. . . . . **I. britannica**
CAUCASIAN I. . . . . **I. glandulosa**
CHRISTEYE I. . . . . **I. oculus-christi**
CINNAMONROOT I. . . . . . . **I. conyza**
ELECAMPANE I. . . . . . . **I. helenium**
GREEK I. . . . . **I. limonifolia**
HOOKER I. . . . . **I. hookeri**
MOUNTAIN I. . . . . **I. montana**
STEMLESS I. . . . . **I. acaulis**
SUNFLOWER I. . . . . . **I. grandiflora**
SWORDLEAF I. . . . . **I. ensifolia**
WILLOWLEAF I. . . . . **I. salicina**

IOCHRO'MA . . . . VIOLETBUSH
coccin'eum . . . . SCARLET V.
fuchsioi'des . . . . . . ORANGE V.
lanceola'tum . . . . . . PURPLE V.
×**purpu'reum** Hort. . PURPLE TOBACCO V.
tubulo'sum . . . . . COLOMBIAN V.

IONAC'TIS . . . . **ASTER**
alpi'na . . . . **A. scopulorum**

IONID'IUM . . . . . **HYBANTHUS**
linea're . . . . **H. verticillatus**

IONOPSID'IUM . . . DIAMONDFLOWER
acau'le . . . . PORTUGAL D.

IONOX'ALIS . . . . **OXALIS**

IPIL . . . . **Intsia**
COMMON I. . . . . **I. bijuga**
MERBAU I. . . . . **I. bakeri**

IPOMOE'A |w . . . . . MORNINGGLORY
arbores'cens . . . . TREE M.
barbig'era |w
bata'tas . . . . SWEETPOTATO
bona-nox' . . **Calonyction aculeatum**
cair'ica . . . . CAIRO M.
cardiophyl'la |w
coccin'ea . . . . **Quamoclit c.**
costella'ta |w
digita'ta (*paniculata*) FINGERLEAF M.
dissec'ta
grandiflo'ra . **Calonyction aculeatum**
hedera'cea . . . . IVYLEAF M.
¢BIGBLUE (*grandiflora*) HV.
¢WHITEEDGE (*limbata*)
hederifo'lia . . **Quamoclit coccinea h.**
hirsu'tula (*mexicana*) . MEXICAN M.
horsfal'liae . . . . . HORSFALL M.
—briggs'i . . . . . . MAGENTA H.M.
jala'pa . . . . . . **Exogonium purga**
lear'i . . . . DAWNFLOWER M.
leptophyl'la |w . . . . . . BUSH M.
leptoto'ma |w
mexica'na . . . . **I. hirsutula**
monta'na . . . . . **Jacquemontia m.**
mutab'ilis . . . . . . WHITETUBE M.
nil' . . . . WHITEEDGE M.
—limba'ta (*I. limbata*)
noctiflo'ra . . **Calonyction aculeatum**
orizaben'sis . . . . ORIZABA M.
palma'ta . . . . HANDLEAF M.
pandura'ta . . . . BIGROOT M.
panicula'ta . . . . **I. digitata**
pes-ca'prae . . . . SOILBIND M.
ptero'des . . . . TOBAGO M.
pur'ga . . . . **Exogonium p.**
purpu'rea (*Convolvulus major; C. purpureus*) . . . . COMMON M.
—al'ba . . . . WHITE C.M.
quam'oclit . . . . **Quamoclit pennata**
seto'sa . . . . BRAZILIAN M.
sidaefo'lia . . . . **Rivea corymbosa**
sinua'ta . . . . TRINIDAD M.

IPOMOEA, continued
tilia'cea
tri'color (*rubrocaerulea*) TRICOLOR MORNINGGLORY
tu'ba . . . . **Calonyction t.**
tuxtlen'sis . . . . TUXTLAS M.
₵HEAVENLYBLUE. HV. Ipomoea
IPOMOP'SIS . . . . **GILIA**
el'egans . . . . **G. rubra**
IRESI'NE . . . . BLOODLEAF
celo'sia (*paniculata*) . JUBASBUSH B.
herbst'i (*Achyranthes verschaffelti; A. herbsti*) . . . . HERBST B.
—aureoreticula'ta
lin'deni (*Achyranthes acuminata*) LINDEN B.
₵EMERSON (*emersoni*) HV.
IRIPILBARKTREE **Pentaclethra filamentosa**
I'RIS ⊻ . . . . IRIS

The Editorial Committee expresses great regret that, owing to limited space, it has been found necessary to omit the list of Iris horticultural varieties prepared for this book by Ethel Anson S. Peckham and John C. Wister, of the American Iris Society, to whom its sincere thanks are extended. Those seeking information on Iris horticultural varieties should consult "Alphabetical Iris Check List," edited and compiled in 1939 for the American Iris Society, 821 Washington Loan & Trust Building, Washington, D. C. This 582-page lexicon of 19,000 Iris names is a fine example of American horticultural literature and indispensable to anyone who wishes to know this important plant group. Apparently the nomenclature of Iris is in far better order than that of many other ornamental plants, but even here there is need for closer attention to priority rule in the case of homonyms.

acutilo'ba
aequilo'ba . . . . **I. pumila**
aitchiso'ni . . . . . . AITCHISON I.
ala'ta (*scorpioides*) . . . SCORPION I.
al'berti . . . . ALBERT I.
al'bicans . . . . YEMEN I.

The name I. florentina is often misapplied to this species.

albopurpu'rea . . . . **I. laevigata a.**
an'glica . . . . **I. xiphioides**
antilibanot'ica . . . . . BLUDAN I.
aphyl'la (*biflora* L. in part; *bifurca; bohemica; breviscapa; clusiana* Tausch., *not* Reichb.; *extrafoliacea; falcata; fieberi; furcata; hungarica; nudicaulis; reflexa; rigida; schmidti; subtriflora*) STOOL I.
arena'ria . . . . **I. flavissima**
arizo'nica . . . . ARIZONA I.
ascherso'ni . . . . . ASCHERSON I.
atrofus'ca (*haynei*) . . . . BLACK I.
atropurpu'rea (*eggeri*). BLACKPURPLE I.

The name I. atropurpurea is sometimes misapplied to color forms of I. pumila and I. germanica.

auranit'ica . . . . LAVA I.
bakerka'na . . . . BAKER I.
balka'na . . . . **I. reichenbachi**
bar'numae . . . . BARNUM I.
—mari'ae (*I. helenae; I. m.*) . MARY I.
—urmien'sis (*I. chrysantha; I. urmiensis*) . . . . URMIA I.
bar'toni . . . . **I. kashmiriana**
biflo'ra . . . **I. aphylla; I. subbiflora**

IRIS, continued
bifur'ca . . . . **I. aphylla**
biglu'mis . . . . **I. ensata**
biliot'ti . . . . PHRYGIAN IRIS
bismarckia'na (*I. sari nazarensis*) BISMARCK I.
bloudow'i (*I. flavissima b.*) TURKESTAN I.
bohe'mica . . . . **I. aphylla**
boissier'i (*heterophylla*) YELLOWBEARD I.
bornmuel'leri . . . . . **I. danfordiae**
bosni'aca . . . . . . **I. reichenbachi**
bractea'ta . . . . BRACTED I.
brevisca'pa . . . . **I. aphylla**
buchar'ica . . . . BOKHARA I.
bulleya'na . . . . . HOLLOWSTEM I.
bung'ei . . . . BUNGE I.
caroli'na . . . . **I. virginica**
carolinia'na . . . . . **I. virginica** form
caucas'ica . . . . CAUCASIAN I.
cengial'ti . . . . TYROLEAN I.
chamaei'ris (*lutescens; olbiensis; virescens*) . . . . CRIMEAN I.
—ital'ica (*I. italica*)
chinen'sis . . . . **I. japonica**
chrysan'tha . . **I. barnumae urmiensis**
chrysog'raphes . . . . GOLDVEIN I.
chrysophyl'la . . **I. macrosiphon** form
clark'ei (*himalaica*) . . . CLARKE I.
clusia'na Reichb . . . . . . **I. pumila**
clusia'na Tausch . . . . . **I. aphylla**
coeru'lea . . . . WHITEEDGE I.
collet'ti . . . . COLLETT I.
cory'gei
creten'sis . . . . **I. unguicularis** form
crista'ta . . . . CRESTED I.
—al'ba Hort. . . . . . . WHITE C.I.
—lacus'tris . . . . **I. lacustris**
cu'prea . . . . **I. fulva**
cypria'na . . . . CYPRIAN I.

In the trade this species is often confused with I. mesopotamica and I. trojana.

daenaen'sis
dahur'ica . . . . **I. flavissima**
danford'iae (*bornmuelleri*) DANFORD I.
darwa'sica . . . . DARWAS I.
delavay'i . . . . DELAVAY I.
demawend'ica

Perhaps a form of I. iberica.

dichot'oma . . . . VESPER I.
douglasia'na . . . . . . DOUGLAS I.
drepanophyl'la
dykes'i . . . . DYKES I.
eg'geri . . . . **I. atropurpurea**
elonga'ta . . . . **I. scariosa**
ensa'ta (*biglumis*) . . . RUSSIAN I.
—pabula'ria (*I. pabularia*)
eulefeld'i . . . . **I. scariosa**
ewbankia'na . . . . EWBANK I.
extrafolia'cea; falca'ta . . . **I. aphylla**
falcifo'lia
far'reri . . . . FARRER I.
fie'beri . . . . **I. aphylla**
filifo'lia . . . . GIBRALTAR I.
fimbria'ta Klatt., *not* Vent . **I. tectorum**
fimbria'ta Vent . . . . . . **I. japonica**
flavis'sima (*arenaria; dahurica*) GOLDBEARD I.
—bloudow'i . . . . **I. bloudowi**
florenti'na Hort.
—al'ba . **I. germanica florentina** Hort.
foetidis'sima . . . . . . GLADWIN I.

IRIS, continued
folio'sa . . . . LAMANCE IRIS
fontanes'i . . . . **I. tingitana**
for'resti . . . . YUNNAN I.
fosteria'na . . . . FOSTER I.
ful'va (*cuprea*) ⊻ . . . . . COPPER I.
∞**fulva'la** (*foliosa* × *fulva*)
furca'ta . . . . **I. aphylla**
gates'i . . . . MONARCH I.
german'ica (*vulgaris*) . . . GERMAN I.

To the true I. germanica have also been applied the following common names, which are to be treated as synonyms: *Bluebird, Florentina Blue, Purple Queen.* I. germanica, especially in the forms known in the drug trade as vars. florentina Hort. and pallida, produces the drug Iris, or Orris Root. See **DRUG PLANT NAMES.**

—florenti'na Hort. (*I. f. alba*) ORRISROOT I.
—nepalen'sis (*I. g. atropurpurea; I. nepalensis* Wall., *not* D. Don) PURPLEKING I.
giganticaeru'lea
glauces'cens . . . . **I. scariosa**
goniocar'pa
gor'mani . . . . GORMAN I.
gracil'ipes . . . . SLENDER I.
grac'ilis . . . . **I. prismatica**
gramin'ea . . . . GRASS I.
grantduff'i . . . . JAFFA I.
grif'fithi . . . . GRIFFITH I.
grijs'i . . . . GRIJS I.
grossheim'i . . . . . . GROSSHEIM I.
halo'phila . . . . **I. spuria h.**
hart'wegi . . . . FOOTHILL I.
hauranen'sis . . . . HAURAN I.
hayn'ei . . . . **I. atrofusca** form
hele'nae . . . . . **I. barnumae mariae**
hen'ryi . . . . HENRY I.
heterophyl'la . . . . **I. boissieri**
hexag'ona . . . . DIXIE I.
himala'ica . . . . **I. clarkei**
hispan'ica . . . . **I. xiphium**
hissar'ica
his'trio . . . . SYRIAN I.
histrioi'des . . . . HARPUT I.
hoogia'na . . . . REDBEARD I.
hook'eri
hookeria'na . . . . HOOKER I.
hu'milis . . . . LOWLY I.
hunga'rica . . . . **I. aphylla**
hyrca'na
ibe'rica . . . . IBERIAN I.
imbrica'ta (*sulphurea*)
innomina'ta
ital'ica . . . . **I. chamaeiris i.**
japon'ica (*chinensis; fimbriata* Vent., *not* Klatt.) . . . . FRINGED I.
jun'cea . . . . RUSH I.
juno'nia . . . . JUNONIA I.
kaemp'feri (*I. laevigata k.*) JAPANESE I.
kashmiria'na (*bartoni*) . . KASHMIR I.
kerneria'na . . . . KERNER I.
kimbal'liae . . . **I. savannarum** form
koch'i . . . . KOCH I.
kolpakowskia'na
korolkow'i . . . . REDVEIN I.
kumaonen'sis . . . . KUMAON I.
lacus'tris (*I. cristata l.*) DWARF LAKE I.
laeviga'ta . . . . RABBITEAR I.
—albopurpu'rea (*I. albopurpurea*)

Hort. var.; HV. = horticultural variety (or varieties); sp. = species (singular); spp. = species (plural).
₵ = clon; × (as a prefix) = hybrid; × (between scientific plant names) = crossed by; ∞ = polybrid; ⊻ = plant useful to wildlife.
See Glossary for definitions of clon, hybrid, and polybrid.

IRIS, continued

laeviga'ta kaemp'feri . . . **I. kaempferi**
leicht'lini . . . **I. stolonifera l.**
linifo'lia
lisbonen'sis . . . **I. subbiflora**
longiflo'ra . . . **I. scariosa**
longipet'ala . . . Coast Iris
—monta'na . . . **I. missouriensis**
lortet'i . . . Lebanon I.
lupi'na . . . **I. sari**
lur'ida
lusita'nica . . . **I. xiphium**
lute'a . . . **I. pseudacorus**
lutes'cens . . . **I. chamaeiris**
lyco'tis
macedo'nica . . . **I. reichenbachi**
macrosi'phon (*chrysophylla*) . Tube I.
mandshur'ica . . . Manchurian I.
manissadjia'ni . . . **I. sari**
mari'ae . . . **I. barnumae m.**
me'da . . . Karaghan I.
mel'lita . . . Troad I.
mesopota'mica . . . Mardin I.

In the trade this is often confused with I. cypriana and with HV. Ricardi.

miles'i (*watti*) . . . Himalayan I.
minu'ta . . . Little Jap I.
mississippien'sis . . . Mississippi I.
missourien'sis (*I. longipetala montana; tolmieana*) |w . RockyMountain I.
monnier'i . . . Monnier I.
monta'na
naryen'sis
∞**neglec'ta** (*?sambucina* × *variegata*)
nepalen'sis
nepalen'sis Wall., *not* D. Don
I. germanica n.
nudicau'lis . . . **I. aphylla**
ochroleu'ca (*orientalis* Auth. in part, *not* Thunb.) . . . Yellowband I.
odoratis'sima . . . **I. pallida** form
olbien'sis . . . **I. chamaeiris** form
orchioi'des . . . Orchid I.
orienta'lis Mill. (1768)

This name is rejected under International Rules (Art. 62) as ambiguous and a cause of confusion. See I. ochroleuca.

orienta'lis Thunb. (1794)
I. sibirica sanguinea
pabula'ria . . . **I. ensata p.**
palesti'na . . . Palestine I.
pal'lida . . . Sweet I.
panormita'na . . . **I. pseudo-pumila**
paradox'a . . . Velvet I.
pavo'nia . . . **Moraea p.**
per'sica (*praecox*) . . . Persian I.

The varieties issica, purpurea, sieheana, stenophylla, and tauri appear to be doubtfully distinct from the typical form of the species.

potani'ni . . . Potanin I.
prae'cox . . . **I. persica**
prismat'ica (*gracilis*) |w . Cubeseed I.
pseudac'orus (*lutea*) |w Yellowflag I.
pseudo-pu'mila (*panormitana*) Tineo I.
pu'mila (*aequiloba; clusiana* Reichb., *not* Tausch.; *stenoloba; taurica; transsilvanica; tristis*) . . . Dwarf I.
pur'dyi . . . Purdy I.
redoutea'na . . . **I. lurida** HV.
reflex'a . . . **I. aphylla**
re'geli . . . **I. tenuifolia**
reichenbach'i (*balkana; bosniaca; macedonica; serbica; suaveolens*)
Balkan I.
reticula'ta . . . Netted I.
—krela'gei . . . Krelage N.I.

IRIS, continued

ricar'di . . . **I. mesopotamica** HV.
rig'ida . . . **I. aphylla**
rivula'ris . . . **I. hexagona** form
rosenbachia'na . . . Spinster Iris
ross'i . . . Ross I.
rubromargina'ta . . . **I. mellita** HV.
ruthe'nica . . . Pilgrim I.
sa'ri (*lupina; manissadjiani*) . Saar I.
—nazaren'sis . . . **I. bismarckiana**
savanna'rum (*kimballiae*) . Prairie I.
scario'sa (*elongata; eulefeldi; glaucescens; longiflora*)
schmidt'i . . . **I. aphylla**
scorpioi'des . . . **I. alata**
ser'bica . . . **I. reichenbachi**
seto'sa . . . Arctic I.
shrev'ei . . . Interior I.
sibir'ica . . . Siberian I.
—al'ba . . . White S.I.
—sanguin'ea (*orientalis* Thunb., *not* Mill.)
sikkimen'sis . . . Sikkim I.
sindjaren'sis . . . Aleppo I.
sinteni'si
sisyrin'chium (*Moraea s.*) . Moraea I.
sofara'na . . . **I. susiana** form
songar'ica
spectab'ilis . . . **I. xiphium**
specula'trix
spu'ria . . . Seashore I.
—halo'phila (*I. halophila*)
stenolo'ba . . . **I. pumila**
stocks'i . . . Stocks I.
stolonif'era . . . Runner I.
—leicht'lini (*I. leichtlini*)
—va'ga (*I. vaga*)
stylo'sa . . . **I. unguicularis**
suave'olens . . . **I. reichenbachi**
subbiflo'ra (*biflora* in part; *lisbonensis*)
Portugal I.
subtriflo'ra . . . **I. aphylla**
sulphu'rea . . . **I. imbricata**
susia'na (*sofarana*) . . . Mourning I.
tai'ti . . . **I. xiphium**

I. taiti, "a slender form of I. xiphium," is recognized by some as a distinct species.

tau'rica . . . **I. pumila**
tecto'rum (*fimbriata* Klatt., *not* Vent.; *tomiolopha*) . . . Roof I.
ten'ax . . . Oregon I.
tenuifo'lia (*regeli*)
ten'uis
tenuis'sima
thomp'soni . . . Thompson I.
tigrid'ia
tingita'na (*fontanesi*) . Tangiers I.
tolmiea'na . . . **I. missouriensis**
tomiolo'pha . . . **I. tectorum**
transsilva'nica . . . **I. pumila**
tricus'pis . . . **Moraea t.**
tripet'ala . . . Bay I.
tris'tis . . . **I. pumila**
troja'na . . . Trojan I.
tubergenia'na . . . Tashkent I.
tubero'sa . . **Hermodactylus tuberosus**
unguicula'ris (*cretensis; cretica; stylosa*)
Algerian I.
urmien'sis . . . **I. barnumae u.**
va'ga . . . **I. stolonifera v.**
variega'ta . . . Hungarian I.
varta'ni . . . Christmas I.
ventrico'sa . . . Inflated I.
ver'na . . . Vernal I.
versicol'or |w . . . Blueflag I.
vires'cens . . . **I. chamaeiris**

IRIS, continued

virgin'ica (*carolina; caroliniana*) |w
Virginia Iris
vulga'ris . . . **I. germanica**
warleyen'sis . . . Warley I.
watt'i . . . **I. milesi** form
willmottia'na . . . Willmott I.
wil'soni . . . Wilson I.
wink'leri . . . Winkler I.
winogradow'i
xiphioi'des (*anglica*) . . English I.
xiph'ium (*hispanica; lusitanica; spectabilis; taiti*) . . . Spanish I.

Iris . . . **Iris**
Aitchison I. . . . **I. aitchisoni**
Albert I. . . . **I. alberti**
Aleppo I. . . . **I. sindjarensis**
Algerian I. . . . **I. unguicularis**
Arctic I. . . . **I. setosa**
Arizona I. . . . **I. arizonica**
Ascherson I. . . . **I. aschersoni**
Baker I. . . . **I. bakeriana**
Balkan I. . . . **I. reichenbachi**
Barnum I. . . . **I. barnumae**
Bay I. . . . **I. tripetala**
Bismarck I. . . . **I. bismarckiana**
Black I. . . . **I. atrofusca**
Blackpurple I. . . . **I. atropurpurea**
Bludan I. . . . **I. antilibanotica**
Blueflag I. . . . **I. versicolor**
Bokhara I. . . . **I. bucharica**
Bracted I. . . . **I. bracteata**
Bunge I. . . . **I. bungei**
Caucasian I. . . . **I. caucasica**
Christmas I. . . . **I. vartani**
Clarke I. . . . **I. clarkei**
Coast I. . . . **I. longipetala**
Collett I. . . . **I. colletti**
Copper I. . . . **I. fulva**
Crested I. . . . **I. cristata**
Crimean I. . . . **I. chamaeiris**
Cubeseed I. . . . **I. prismatica**
Cyprian I. . . . **I. cypriana**
Danford I. . . . **I. danfordiae**
Darwas I. . . . **I. darwasica**
Delavay I. . . . **I. delavayi**
Dixie I. . . . **I. hexagona**
Douglas I. . . . **I. douglasiana**
Dwarf I. . . . **I. pumila**
Dwarf Lake I. . . . **I. lacustris**
Dykes I. . . . **I. dykesi**
English I. . . . **I. xiphioides**
Ewbank I. . . . **I. ewbankiana**
Farrer I. . . . **I. farreri**
Foothill I. . . . **I. hartwegi**
Foster I. . . . **I. fosteriana**
Fringed I. . . . **I. japonica**
German I. . . . **I. germanica**
Gibraltar I. . . . **I. filifolia**
Gladwin I. . . . **I. foetidissima**
Goldbeard I. . . . **I. flavissima**
Goldvein I. . . . **I. chrysographes**
Gorman I. . . . **I. gormani**
Grass I. . . . **I. graminea**
Griffith I. . . . **I. griffithi**
Grijs I. . . . **I. grijsi**
Grossheim I. . . . **I. grossheimi**
Harput I. . . . **I. histrioides**
Hauran I. . . . **I. hauranensis**
Henry I. . . . **I. henryi**
Himalayan I. . . . **I. milesi**
Hollowstem I. . . . **I. bulleyana**
Hooker I. . . . **I. hookeriana**
Hungarian I. . . . **I. variegata**
Iberian I. . . . **I. iberica**
Inflated I. . . . **I. ventricosa**
Interior I. . . . **I. shrevei**
Jaffa I. . . . **I. grantduffi**

IRIS, continued
JAPANESE I. . . . . . . Iris kaempferi
JUNONIA I. . . . . I. junonia
KARAGHAN I. . . . . I. meda
KASHMIR I. . . . . . . I. kashmiriana
KERNER I. . . . . I. kerneriana
KOCH I. . . . . I. kochi
KRELAGE NETTED I.
I. reticulata krelagei
KUMAON I. . . . . . I. kumaonensis
LAMANCE I. . . . . I. foliosa
LAVA I. . . . . I. auranitica
LEBANON I. . . . . I. lorteti
LITTLE JAP I. . . . . I. minuta
LOWLY I. . . . . I. humilis
MANCHURIAN I. . . . I. mandshurica
MARDIN I. . . . . . . I. mesopotamica
MARY I. . . . . . I. barnumae mariae
MISSISSIPPI I. . . . I. mississippiensis
MONARCH I. . . . . I. gatesi
MONNIER I. . . . . I. monnieri
MORAEA I. . . . . I. sisyrinchium
MOURNING I. . . . . I. susiana
NETTED I. . . . . I. reticulata
ORCHID I. . . . . I. orchioides
OREGON I. . . . . I. tenax
ORRISROOT I. . I. germanica florentina
PALESTINE I. . . . . I. palestina
PERSIAN I. . . . . I. persica
PHRYGIAN I. . . . . I. biliotti
PILGRIM I. . . . . I. ruthenica
PORTUGAL I. . . . . I. subbiflora
POTANIN I. . . . . I. potanini
PRAIRIE I. . . . . I. savannarum
PURDY I. . . . . I. purdyi
PURPLEKING I. I. germanica nepalensis
RABBITEAR I. . . . . I. laevigata
REDBEARD I. . . . . I. hoogiana
REDVEIN I. . . . . I. korolkowi
ROCKYMOUNTAIN I. . I. missouriensis
ROOF I. . . . . I. tectorum
ROSS I. . . . . I. rossi
RUNNER I. . . . . I. stolonifera
RUSH I. . . . . I. juncea
RUSSIAN I. . . . . I. ensata
SAAR I. . . . . I. sari
SCORPION I. . . . . I. alata
SEASHORE I. . . . . I. spuria
SIBERIAN I. . . . . I. sibirica
SIKKIM I. . . . . I. sikkimensis
SLENDER I. . . . . I. gracilipes
SPANISH I. . . . . I. xiphium
SPINSTER I. . . . . . I. rosenbachiana
STOCKS I. . . . . I. stocksi
STOOL I. . . . . I. aphylla
SWEET I. . . . . I. pallida
SYRIAN I. . . . . I. histrio
TANGIERS I. . . . . I. tingitana
TASHKENT I. . . . . . . I. tubergeniana
THOMPSON I. . . . . I. thompsoni
TINEO I. . . . . I. pseudo-pumila
TROAD I. . . . . I. mellita
TROJAN I. . . . . I. trojana
TUBE I. . . . . I. macrosiphon
TURKESTAN I. . . . . I. bloudowi
TYROLEAN I. . . . . I. cengialti
URMIA I. . . . I. barnumae urmiensis
VELVET I. . . . . I. paradoxa
VERNAL I. . . . . I. verna
VESPER I. . . . . I. dichotoma
VIRGINIA I. . . . . I. virginica
WARLEY I. . . . . I. warleyensis
WHITE CRESTED I. . . . I. cristata alba
WHITEEDGE I. . . . . I. coerulea
WHITE SIBERIAN I. . . . I. sibirica alba
WILLMOTT I. . . . . I. willmottiana
WILSON I. . . . . I. wilsoni
WINKLER I. . . . . I. winkleri

IRIS, continued
YELLOWBAND I. . . . Iris ochroleuca
YELLOWBEARD I. . . . . . I. boissieri
YELLOWFLAG I. . . . . . I. pseudacorus
YEMEN I. . . . . I. albicans
YUNNAN I. . . . . I. forresti

IRISHHEATH . . . . Daboecia
BELL I. . . . . D. cantabrica

IRISHMOSS . . . . Chondrus; C. crispus

Irongum . . . . . . EUCALYPTUS, IRON:
Eucalyptus raveretiana

IRONTREE . . . . Metrosideros

IRONWEED . . . . Vernonia
BALDWIN I. . . . . V. baldwini
BUR I. . . . . V. crinita
KINKAOIL I. . . . . V. anthelmintica
NEWYORK I. . . . V. noveboracensis
NIGERIAN I. . . . . V. nigritiana
TALL I. . . . . V. altissima
WESTERN I. . . . . V. fasciculata

IRONWOUNDWORT . . . . Sideritis
EUBOEAN I. . . . . S. euboea
HYSSOP I. . . . . S. hyssopifolia
LEBANON I. . . . . S. libanotica
LONGSPIKE I. . . . . S. macrostachya
MADEIRA I. . . . . S. candicans
ROMAN I. . . . . S. romana
SYRIAN I. . . . . S. syriaca

ISAN'THUS . . . . . FLUXWEED
(*Falsepennyroyal*)
brachia'tus . . . . . . FLUXWEED

ISA'TIS . . . . WOAD
boissieria'na . . . . . BOISSIERS W.
glau'ca . . . . SMOOTH W.
tincto'ria . . . . DYERS W.

ISCHNOSI'PHON . . . . . TIRITE
arou'ma . . . . BASKET T.

ISER'TIA . . . . WILDIXORA
parviflo'ra . . . . TRINIDAD W.

ISID'IUM . . . . ISIDIUM
coralli'num . . . . CORALCROTTLE I.
west'ringi . . . . WESTRINGS I.

ISME'LIA . . **CHRYSANTHEMUM**

ISME'NE . . . . . PERUVIANDAFFODIL
amanca'es
calathi'na
¢ADVANCE. HV. Ismene
¢DAPHNE
¢FESTALIS
¢SULFUR BEAUTY
¢SULFUR GEM
¢SULFUR QUEEN

ISNAR'DIA

This genus is perhaps not sufficiently distinct from Ludwigia to be maintained.

palus'tris (*Ludwigia p.*) |w
MARSHPURSLANE

ISOCO'MA . . . . . **APLOPAPPUS**
coronopifo'lia . . . . . . A. fruticosus
wright'i . . . . . . A. heterophyllus

ISO'ETES |w . . . . QUILLWORT
bolan'deri |w . . . . . . BOLANDER Q.
braun'i |w . . . . BRAUNS Q.
ea'toni |w . . . . EATONS Q.
engelmann'i |w . . . . ENGELMANN Q.
flac'cida |w
flett'i |w . . . . FLETT Q.
foveola'ta |w
how'elli |w . . . . HOWELL Q.
macros'pora |w

ISOETES, continued
melanop'oda |w
nutt'alli |w . . . NUTTALL QUILLWORT
occidenta'lis |w
pi'peri |w . . . . PIPER Q.
ripa'ria |w
sacchara'ta |w
trunca'ta |w
tuckerman'i |w . . . TUCKERMAN Q.

ISO'LEPIS . . . . **SCIRPUS**
grac'ilis . . . . S. cernuus

ISOLO'MA . . . . ISOLOMA
amab'ile . . . . SHOWY I.
bogoten'se (*tydaea*) . . . . BOGOTA I.
hirsu'tum . . . . TRINIDAD I.
honden'se . . . . HONDA I.

ISOM'ERIS . . . . BURROFAT
arbo'rea . . . . TREE B.

Isonan'dra gut'ta . . . . Palaquium g.

ISOPLEX'IS
canarien'sis (*Digitalis c.*)
scep'trum

ISOPO'GON . . . . CONEBUSH
anemonifo'lius . . . ANEMONELEAF C.
anethifo'lius . . . . . . ANETHUM C.
diver'gens
rose'us . . . . HORNY C.
sphaerocephʹalus . . . ROUNDHEAD C.

ISOPY'RUM . . . . ISOPYRUM
biterna'tum . . . . ATLANTIC I.
fumarioi'des . . . . . Leptopyrum f.
hall'i . . . . HALLS I.
occidenta'le
stipita'tum
thalictroi'des . . . . . MEADOWRUE I.

ISOT'OMA . . . . . . SHRUBHAREBELL
longiflo'ra . . . . . . LONGFLOWER S.
petrae'a . . . . CLIFF S.
—al'ba . . . . WHITE C.S.

Isotre'ma chry'sops . . . Aristolochia c.
heterophyl'la . . . . . Aristolochia h.

ISO'TRIA . . . . **POGONIA**
See **ORCHID GENERA, HARDY TERRESTRIAL GROUP.**

ITA-UBA . . . . . . Endiandra ita-uba

ITCHGRASS . . . Rottboellia; R. exaltata

I'TEA . . . . SWEETSPIRE
chinen'sis . . . . CHINESE S.
ilicifo'lia . . . . HOLLYLEAF S.
virgin'ica . . . . VIRGINIA S.
yunnanen'sis . . . . YUNNAN S.

ITHYPHAL'LUS . . . . . ITHYPHALLUS
impu'dicus . . . . STINKHORN I.

I'VA |w . . . . SUMPWEED
angustifo'lia |w . . . NARROWLEAF S.
axilla'ris |w . . . . POVERTY S.
cilia'ta |w . . . . SEACOAST S.
frutes'cens |w . . . . BIGLEAF S.
hayesia'na . . . . HAYES S.
ora'ria (*I. frutescens o.*) NORTHERN S.
xanthifo'lia |w . . . . RAG S.

IVES'IA . . . . IVESIA
gor'doni (*Horkelia g.*) . . . GORDON I.
utahen'sis . . . . UTAH I.

Ivorycoast-piassava . . . RAFFIAPALM,
IVORYCOAST: Raphia hookeri

IVORYNUTPALM . . . . . . Metroxylon
POLYNESIAN I. . . . . M. amicarum
SOLOMON I. . . . . . M. salomense

IVORYPALM . . . . **Phytelephas**
Common I. . . . . . . **P. macrocarpa**
Seemann I. . . . . . . **P. seemanni**

IVORYWOOD . . . . **Siphonodon**
Australian I. . . . . . . **S. australe**

IVY . . . . **Hedera**
Algerian I. . . . . . **H. canariensis**
Boston I. . . . Creeper, Japanese: **Parthenocissus tricuspidata**
Colchis I. . . . . **H. colchica**
Crimean I. . . . . **H. helix taurica**
English I. . . . . **H. helix**
Irish I. . . . . **H. h. hibernica**
Nepal I. . . . . **H. nepalensis**
Poets I. . . . . . . **H. helix poetica**
Tallclimbing I. . . . . **H. rhombea**

IVYARUM . . . . **Scindapsus**
Drug I. . . . . **S. officinalis**
Painted I. . . . . **S. pictus**
Poisondart I. . . . . . **S. cuscuaria**
Silver Painted I. **S. pictus argyraeus**
SolomonIslands I. . . . **S. aureus**
Wilcox S. I. . . . . . . **S. a. wilcoxi**

IVYGOURD . . . . **Coccinia**
India I. . . . . **C. cordifolia**

IWARANCUSAGRASS
Cymbopogon jwarancusa

IX'IA (*HYALIS*) . . . . . . Ixia
columella'ris . . . . Pillar I.
leucan'tha
lute'a (*aurantiaca*) . . . Yellow I.
macula'ta . . . . African I.
—ochroleu'ca
—orna'ta
panicula'ta (*nelsoni*) . . Panicled I.
scario'sa
specio'sa (*crateroides*) . Crimsoncup I.
viridiflo'ra . . . . Green I.

IXIOLIR'ION . . . . . . Ixiolirion
monta'num . . . . Syria I.
—tatar'icum (*I. tataricum; I. ledebouri*) Tartary I.
pal'lasi . . . . Pallas I.

IXO'RA . . . . Ixora
acumina'ta . . . . . Sharpleaf I.
amboin'ica . . . . . . Moluccan I.
barba'ta
chinen'sis . . . . Chinese I.
coccin'ea (*incarnata*). Jungleflame I.
conges'ta
duff'i . . . . **I. macrothyrsa**
finlaysonia'na Hort.
Probably indistinguishable from I. thwaitesi.
fra'grans . . . . Fragrant I.
ful'gens
javan'ica . . . . Coral I.
laxiflo'ra
macrothyr'sa (*duffi*) . . . Malay I.
odora'ta . . . . Sweet I.
parviflo'ra . . . . . . Torchwood I.
polyan'tha
thwaites'i . . . . Thwaites I.
wil'liamsi . . . . Williams I.
₵Amabilis. hv. Ixora
₵Chelson (*chelsoni*)
₵Coles (*colei*)
₵Dixiana
₵Flore-luteo
₵Lutea
₵Orange (*aurantiaca*)
₵Wests (*westi*)
₵Williams (*williamsi*)

JABORO'SA
integrifo'lia

JABOTICABA . . . . **Myrciaria**

JACARAN'DA . . . . . . Jacaranda
acutifo'lia (*mimosaefolia; ovalifolia*) Sharpleaf J.
brasilien'sis . . . . Brazil J.
caeru'lea . . . . Ferntree J.
cauca'na
copai'a . . . . Copaia J.
cuspidifo'lia . . . . . Toothleaf J.
mimosaefo'lia; ovalifo'lia . **J. acutifolia**
sagraea'na

JACKBEAN . . . . **Canavalia**
Climbing J. . . . . **C. plagiosperma**
Common J. . . . . . . **C. ensiformis**
Ground J. . . . . . **C. obtusifolia**
Sword J. . . . . **C. gladiata**
Jackfruit . . . . Jakfruit: **Artocarpus heterophyllus**

JACKINTHEPULPIT . . . . . . **Arisaema**
Blumes Japan J. . **A. serratum blumei**
Common J. . . . . . **A. atrorubens**
Dragonroot J. . . . . **A. dracontium**
Griffith J. . . . . **A. griffithi**
Indian J. . . . . . . **A. triphyllum**
Japan J. . . . . **A. serratum**
Plumecalla J. . . . . **A. fimbriatum**
Showy J. . . . . . . **A. speciosum**
Wallichian J. . . . **A. wallichianum**

JACKTREE . . . . **Sinojackia**
Rehder J. . . . . . . **S. rehderiana**

JACOBAE'A . . . . **SENECIO**

Jacobeanlily . . . Azteclily: **Sprekelia**

JACOBIN'IA (*LIBONIA*) . Jacobinia
au'rea . . . . **J. umbrosa**
car'nea (*Justicia c.; J. magnifica*)
coccin'ea . . . . . . **Pachystachys c.**
ghiesbreghtia'na (*Justicia g.*)
obtus'ior
pauciflo'ra (*Libonia floribunda*)
∞ **penrhozien'sis** (*ghiesbreghtiana* × *pauciflora*)
pohlia'na
spicig'era (*mohintli; Justicia m.; J. spicigera*)
umbro'sa (*aurea*)
veluti'na

JACOBSROD . . . . **Asphodeline**
Common J. . . . . **A. lutea**

JACQUEMON'TIA |w
caeru'lea
Perhaps synonymous with Ipomoea hederacea.
eastwoodia'na
monta'na (*Ipomoea m.*)
pentan'tha (*violacea*)
pringle'i |w
tamnifo'lia |w

JACQUIN'IA . . . . Jacquinia
armilla'ris . . . . Armed J.
keyen'sis . . . . Joewood J.
pun'gens . . . . Pungent J.

Jajoba . . . . . Jojoba: **Simmondsia**

JAKFRUIT . . **Artocarpus heterophyllus**

JALAP . . . . **Exogonium purga**

JAMAICACHERRY . . **Muntingia calabura**

JAMBOLAN . . . . . . **Syzygium cumini**

JAMBO'SA . . . . **SYZYGIUM**

JAMES'IA (*EDWINIA*) . . . Jamesia
america'na (*Edwinia a.*) . . . Cliff J.
—califor'nica . . . California C.J.
—rose'a . . . . Rose C.J.

JANU'SIA |w . . . . Janusia
califor'nica |w . . . California J.
grac'ilis . . . . Slender J.

Japanclover . . . Lespedeza, Common: **Lespedeza striata**

Japanesemedlar . . . . . . Loquat: **Eriobotrya japonica**

JAPANESEMILLET
Echinochloa crusgalli frumentacea

JARAGUA . . . . **Hyparrhenia rufa**

JASIO'NE . . . . Jasione
hu'milis . . . . Dwarf J.
jan'kae
monta'na . . . . . . Sheepsbit J.
peren'nis . . . . Scabious J.

JASMINE . . . . **Jasminum**
Arabian J. . . . . **J. sambac**
Arborescent J. . . . **J. arborescens**
Australian J. . . . . **J. gracile**
Azores J. . . . . **J. azoricum**
Bahia J. . . . . **J. bahiense**
Bees J. . . . . **J. beesianum**
Common J. . . . . **J. officinale**
Farrer J. . . . . **J. farreri**
Furry J. . . . . **J. multiflorum**
Girald J. . . . . **J. giraldi**
Goldcoast J. . . . . **J. dichotomum**
Golden Winter J. **J. nudiflorum aureum**
Italian J. . . . . **J. humile**
Parker J. . . . . **J. parkeri**
Pinwheel J. . . . . . **J. gracillimum**
Primrose J. . . . . **J. mesnyi**
Privet J. . . . . **J. rigidum**
Showy J. . . . . **J. floridum**
SouthSea J. . . . . **J. simplicifolium**
∞ Stephan J. . . . . ∞ **J. stephanense**
Sweet J. . . . . . **J. odoratissimum**
Winter J. . . . . **J. nudiflorum**

JASMINOCE'REUS
See **CACTUS GENERA.**

JASMINORANGE . . . . **Murraya**
Chinabox J. . . . . **M. exotica**
Common J. . . . . . . **M. paniculata**
Curryleaftree . . . . . **M. koenigi**

JAS'MINUM . . Jasmine (*Jessamine*)
amplexicau'le (*undulatum*)
arbores'cens (*montanum*) Arborescent J.
azor'icum . . . . Azores J.
bahien'se . . . . Bahia J.
beesia'num . . . . Bees J.
dichot'omum . . . . . Goldcoast J.
diversifo'lium (*heterophyllum*)
—glabricymo'sum
far'reri . . . . Farrer J.
flor'idum . . . . Showy J.
fru'ticans
gir'aldi . . . . Girald J.
grac'ile (*?lucidum*) . . Australian J.
gracil'limum . . . . . Pinwheel J.
grandiflo'rum . . . . . **J. officinale g.**
heterophyl'lum . . . **J. diversifolium**
hu'mile . . . . Italian J.
—gla'brum
—kansuen'se
—revolu'tum
—siderophyl'lum

JASMINUM, continued
ligustrifo'lium . . . . . . **J. rigidum**
lu'cidum
Probably identical with J. gracile.
mes'nyi (*primulinum*) PRIMROSE JASMINE
monta'num . . . . . **J. arborescens**
multiflo'rum (*pubescens*) . . FURRY J.
nit'idum
nudiflo'rum . . . . . . WINTER J.
—au'reum . . . . . . GOLDEN W.J.
odoratis'simum . . . . . . SWEET J.
officina'le COMMON J. (*Poets Jessamine*)
—affi'ne
—grandiflo'rum (*J. grandiflorum*)
¢YELLOWSPOT (*aureovariegatum*) HV. J. officinale
par'keri . . . . PARKER J.
polyan'thum
primuli'num . . . . **J. mesnyi**
pubes'cens . . . . . . **J. multiflorum**
rig'idum (*ligustrifolium*) . . PRIVET J.
sam'bac . . . . ARABIAN J.
¢GRAND DUKE. HV.
¢MAID OF ORLEANS
simplicifo'lium . . . . . SOUTHSEA J.
The plant in cultivation in the U. S. under this name is J. gracile.
∞ **stephanen'se** (*beesianum* × *officinale grandiflorum*) . . . ∞ STEPHAN J.
tortuo'sum
triner've
undula'tum . . . . **J. amplexicaule**

JASO'NIA
tubero'sa

JATEORHI'ZA
palma'ta . . . . CALUMBAROOT

JAT'ROPHA (*ADENOROPIUM*) |w NETTLESPURGE
berlandier'i . . . . BERLANDIER N.
chil'te
cur'cas . . . . . . BARBADOSNUT
gossypifo'lia . . . . . BELLYACHE N.
hasta'ta (*Adenoropium hastatum*) PEREGRINA N.
macrorhi'za |w
man'ihot . . . . . **Manihot esculenta**
multif'ida . . . . . CORALPLANT N.
podag'rica . . . . . . TARTOGO N.
stimulo'sa . . **Cnidoscolus stimulosus**
texa'na . . . . **Cnidoscolus texanus**
u'rens . . . . **Cnidoscolus u.**

JAU'MEA |w
carno'sa |w
Javaalmond . . . . PILINUT: **Canarium ovatum**
JAVAGRASS . . . . **Polytrias praemorsa**
JAVATEA . . . . **Orthosiphon**
BIGFLOWER J. . . . **O. grandiflorus**

JEFFERSO'NIA |w . . . . . TWINLEAF
diphyl'la |w . . . . . AMERICAN T.
du'bia . . . . CHINESE T.

JELLYALGA . . . . **Eucheuma**
AUSTRALIAN J. . . . . **E. speciosum**
GELATINE J. . . . . . **E. gelatinae**
MACASSAR-AGAR J. . . . **E. spinosum**
Jerusalemartichoke . . . . SUNFLOWER, JERUSALEMARTICHOKE: **Helianthus tuberosus**
JERUSALEMCHERRY **Solanum pseudocapsicum**
CHRISTMAS J. . . . **S. p. clevelandi**
FALSE J. . . . . . . **S. capsicastrum**
HENDERSON J. . . . . **S. hendersoni**

JERUSALEMSAGE . . . . . . **Phlomis**
ALPINE J. . . . . **P. alpina**
COMMON J. . . . . . . **P. fruticosa**
GREEK J. . . . . **P. samia**
KASHMIR J. . . . . **P. cashmeriana**
LAMPWICK J. . . . . . . **P. lychnitis**
PRICKLY J. . . . . **P. pungens**
SHOWY J. . . . . . . **P. spectabilis**
STICKY J. . . . . **P. viscosa**
TUBER J. . . . . **P. tuberosa**
WOOLLY J. . . . . **P. lanata**
JERUSALEMTHORN . **Parkinsonia aculeata**
Jessamine . . . . CESTRUM: **Cestrum;** JASMINE: **Jasminum**
Carolina J. (*Yellow J.*) CAROLINAJESSAMINE: **Gelsemium sempervirens**
Poets J. . . . . . JASMINE, COMMON: **Jasminum officinale**
JETBEAD . . . . **Rhodotypos**
BLACK J. . . . . **R. scandens**
Jewbush . . . SLIPPERFLOWER, REDBIRD: **Pedilanthus tithymaloides**
JEWELVINE . . . . **Derris**
MALACCA J. . . . . . **D. malaccensis**
MALAY J. . . . . **D. scandens**
TIMOR J. . . . . . . **D. timoriensis**
TRIFOLIATE J. . . . . . **D. trifoliata**
TUBAROOT J. . . . . . . **D. elliptica**
Jews-mallow . . . . . JUTE, POTHERB: **Corchorus olitorius**
JICAMA . . . **Calopogonium caeruleum**
JIGGERWOOD . . . **Bravaisia floribunda**
Jimgrass. SKELETONGRASS: **Gymnopogon**

JOANNE'SIA
prin'ceps

JOBSTEARS . . . . **Coix; C. lacryma-jobi**
JOEPYEWEED
BLUESTEM J. . **Eupatorium purpureum**
BRUNER J. . . . . **E. bruneri**
COASTALPLAIN J. . . . . . **E. dubium**
PURPLESTEM J. . . . . **E. fistulosum**
SPOTTED J. . . . . . . **E. maculatum**
JOHNNYJUMPUP **Viola kitaibeliana rafinesqui**
JOHNSONGRASS . . . **Sorghum halepense**
JOINTFIR . . . . **Gnetum**
SPINACH J. . . . . **G. gnemon**
SWEETBERRY J. . . . . . **G. scandens**
Jointfir . . . . . . EPHEDRA: **Ephedra**
JOINTTAIL . . . . **Manisuris**
AFRICAN J. . . . . . . **M. altissima**
CAROLINA J. . . . . . **M. cylindrica**
FLORIDA J. . . . . **M. tuberculosa**
LATTICE J. . . . . . **M. tessellata**
WRINKLED J. . . . . **M. rugosa**
JOINTVETCH . . . . . . **Aeschynomene**
AMERICAN J. . . . . . **A. americana**
SENSITIVE J. . . . . . . **A. virginica**
STICKY J. . . . . **A. viscidula**
JOINTWEED . . . . **Polygonella**
COAST J. . . . . **P. articulata**
SOUTHERN J. . . . . . **P. americana**
JOJOBA . . . . **Simmondsia**
CALIFORNIA J. . . . . . **S. chinensis**
Jones'ia aso'ca . . . . . **Saraca indica**
JONQUIL . . . . . . **Narcissus jonquilla**
AUTUMN J. . . . . **N. serotinus**
CAMPERNELLE J. . . . . . **N. odorus**
GREEN AUTUMN J. . . . **N. viridiflorus**

JONQUIL, continued
QUEEN ANNES J. **Narcissus jonquilla florepleno**
RUSHLEAF J. . . . . **N. gracilis**
SILVER R. J. . . . . . . **N. g. tenuior**
JOSSWOOD . . . . . . **Mitragyna africana**

JOVELLA'NA
sin'clairi
viola'cea (*Calceolaria v.*)

JUAN'IA . . . . JUANPALM
See **PALM GENERA.**

JUBAE'A . . . . JUBAEA
See **PALM GENERA.**

JUDASTREE . . . . . **Cercis siliquastrum**

JU'GLANS |w . . . . WALNUT
For hort. var. of Juglans cultivated for their nuts see **FRUIT AND EDIBLE NUT NAMES.**
ailanthifo'lia . . . . . **J. sieboldiana**
austra'lis . . ARGENTINE BLACK W.
∞ **bix'byi** (*cinerea* × *sieboldiana*) ∞ BIXBY W.
bolivia'na . . . BOLIVIAN BLACK W.
califor'nica . . . . CALIFORNIA B.W.
—querci'na (*Juglans q.*) THREELEAF C.B.W.
cathayen'sis . . . . CATHAY W.
cine'rea . . . . BUTTERNUT
columbien'sis COLOMBIAN BLACK W.
cordifor'mis . . . . **J. sieboldiana c.**
fal'lax . . . . **J. regia f.**
hinds'i . . . . HINDS BLACK W.
—quercinifo'lia
honor'ei . . . . ECUADOR W.
insula'ris . . . . CUBAN W.
∞ **interme'dia** (*nigra* × *regia*) ∞ REGINIGRA W.
—pyrifor'mis
—vilmorea'na (*J. vilmoriniana*)
∞ **lancastrien'sis** . . . ∞ LANCASTER W.
ma'jor (*J. rupestris m.*) ARIZONA BLACK W.
mandshur'ica . . . . . . MANCHU W.
mol'lis . . . . . . GUATEMALAN W.
ni'gra . . . . . . EASTERN BLACK W.
∞ **no'tha** (*regia* × *sieboldiana*) NOTHA W. (*Perbold W.*)
∞ **quadrangula'ta** (*cinerea* × *regia*) ∞ PERBUT W.
querci'na . . . . . **J. californica q.**
re'gia |w . . . . PERSIAN W.
—fal'lax (*J. fallax*) THICKSHELL P.W.
—kamao'nia . . . . HIMALAYAN P.W.
—turcoman'ica . . . TURKESTAN P.W.
¢BIG (*maxima*) HV. J. regia
¢BUSH (*praeparturiens; J. r. fertilis*)
¢CARPATHIAN
¢FERNLEAF (*laciniata*)
¢SIMPLELEAF (*monophylla*)
¢WEEPING (*pendula*)
rupes'tris . . . . . TEXAS BLACK W.
—ma'jor . . . . **J. major**
sieboldia'na (*ailanthifolia*). SIEBOLD W.
—cordifor'mis (*J. cordiformis*) FLAT S.W. (*Heartnut*)
∞ **sinen'sis** (*mandshurica* × *regia*) ∞ CHINESE W.
stenocar'pa
vilmorinia'na **J. intermedia vilmoreana**
JUJUBE . . . . **Zizyphus**
ARGENTINE J. . . . . **Z. mistol**
COGWOOD J. . . . . . **Z. chloroxylon**
COMMON J. . . . . **Z. jujuba**

JUJUBE, continued
India J. . . . . . Zizyphus mauritiana
Spineless Common J.
Z. jujuba inermis
Jump-up-and-kiss-me . . . Portulaca,
Shaggy: Portulaca pilosa

JUNCOI'DES . . . . . . LUZULA
pi'peri . . . . L. wahlenbergi

JUN'CUS |w . . . . Rush
aborti'vus |w
acumina'tus |w
acu'tus |w
alpi'nus |w . . . . Alpine R.
articula'tus |w
bal'ticus |w . . . . Baltic R.
brachyceph'alus |w
brevicauda'tus |w
brunnes'cens . . . . . . Button R.
bufo'nius |w . . . . Toad R.
bulbo'sus |w . . . . . . Bulbous R.
canaden'sis |w . . . . . . Canada R.
confu'sus
coo'peri |w . . . . Cooper R.
covil'lei |w . . . . Coville R.
dichot'omus . . . . J. tenuis
effu'sus |w . . . . Common R.
filifor'mis |w
gerard'i |w . . . . . Saltmeadow R.
inte'rior . . . . Inland R.
les'curi |w . . . . Pacific R.
ma'cer (*tenuis* Auth., *not* Willd.)
Soft R.
milita'ris |w . . . . . . Soldier R.
nodo'sus |w . . . . . . Jointed R.
pa'tens |w . . . . . . Spreading R.
pelocar'pus |w
polyceph'alus |w
re'pens |w . . . . Creeping R.
roemeria'nus |w . . . Needlegrass R.
rugulo'sus |w
saximonta'nus . RockyMountain R.
seta'ceus |w . . . . Bristly R.
sub'tilis |w
supinifor'mis |w
ten'uis (*dichotomus*) . . . Poverty R.
ten'uis Auth., *not* Willd. . . J. macer
tor'reyi |w . . . . Torrey R.
xiphioi'des |w

Juneberry . Serviceberry: Amelanchier

Jungleplum . . . . Sideroxylon
Capiri J. . . . . S. capiri
Mastic J. . . . . S. mastichodendron
NewZealand J. . S. novo-zelandicum
Pohlman J. . . . . . S. pohlmanianum
Tempisque J. . . . . . S. tempisque
Trinidad J. . . . . S. quadriloculare

Junglerice . . . Echinochloa colonum

Juniper . . . . Juniperus
African J. . . . . J. procera
Alligator J. . . . . . J. pachyphloea
Alpine Creeping J.
J. horizontalis alpina
Andorra C. J. . . . . . J. h. plumosa
Bermuda Redcedar . J. bermudiana
Bigberry Utah J.
J. utahensis megalocarpa
Blackseed J. . . . . . . J. saltuaria
California J. . . . . . J. californica
CanaryIslands J. . . . . . J. cedrus
Common J. . . . . J. communis
Cox J. . . . . J. coxi
Creeping J. . . . . . J. horizontalis
Eastern Redcedar . . . J. virginiana
Farges Singleseed J.
J. squamata fargesi

Juniper, continued
Flat Creeping J.
Juniperus horizontalis glomerata
Formosa J. . . . . . . J. formosana
Fortunes J. . . . . J. sphaerica
Greek J. . . . . J. excelsa
Himalayan J. . . . . J. recurva
Incense J. . . . . J. thurifera
Irish J. . . . . J. communis hibernica
Jack Common J. . . . . . . J. c. jacki
Japanese J. . . . J. chinensis japonica
Japgarden J. . . . . . J. procumbens
Mexican Drooping J. . . J. flaccida
Mexican J. . . . . J. mexicana
Meyer Singleseed J.
J. squamata meyeri
Mountain Common J.
J. communis saxatilis
Needle J. . . . . J. rigida
Nippon Common J.
J. communis nipponica
North Eastern Redcedar
J. virginiana crebra
Oldfield Common J.
J. communis depressa
Oneseed J. . . . . . J. monosperma
Phoenicean J. . . . . . J. phoenicea
Plum J. . . . . J. macrocarpa
Portuguese Savin J.
J. sabina lusitanica
Prickly J. . . . . J. oxycedrus
Prostrate Singleseed J.
J. squamata prostrata
Pyramid Chinese J. . . J. chinensis
Redberry J. . . . . J. pinchoti
RockyMountain J. . . . J. scopulorum
Sargent Chinese J.
J. chinensis sargenti
Savin J. . . . . J. sabina
Shore J. . . . . J. conferta
Sierra J. . . . . J. occidentalis
Singleseed J. . . . . . . J. squamata
Southern Redcedar . . J. silicicola
Swedish J. . . J. communis suecica
Syrian J. . . . . J. drupacea
Tibet J. . . . . J. tibetica
Turkestan J. . . . . J. pseudosabina
Upright Common J.
J. communis erecta
Utah J. . . . . J. utahensis
Wallichs J. . . . . . . J. wallichiana
Waukegan Creeping J.
J. horizontalis douglasi
WestIndies J. . . . . . . J. lucayana
Wilson Singleseed J.
J. squamata wilsoni

Junipermoss . . . Cetraria juniperina

JUNIP'ERUS |w . . . . . . Juniper
bermudia'na (*barbadensis*)
Bermuda Redcedar
califor'nica . . . . . California J.
—*utahen'sis* . . . . . . J. utahensis
canaden'sis . . J. communis depressa
ce'drus . . . . . CanaryIslands J.
chinen'sis (*pyramidalis*)
Pyramid Chinese J.
—japon'ica (*J. japonica*) Japanese J.
—*recur'va* . . . . J. recurva
—sar'genti . . . . . Sargent C.J.
₵Armstrong (*armstrongi*) hv. J. chinensis
₵Blue Columnar (*columnaris*)
₵Blueleaf (*glauca*)
₵Compact Pfitzer (*pfitzeriana compacta*)
₵Conical (*neaboriensis*)
₵Drummond (*drummondi*)

JUNIPERUS chinensis, continued
₵Fortunes (*fortunei*)
₵Globe (*globosa*)
₵Golden (*aurea*)
₵Goldenglobe (*aureoglobosa*)
₵Golden Pfitzer (*pfitzeriana aurea*)
₵Golden Variegated (*aureo-variegata*)
₵Green Columnar (*columnaris viridis*)
₵Oblong (*oblonga*)
₵Pfitzer (*pfitzeriana*)
₵Plume (*plumosa*)
₵Reeves (*femina*)
₵Sheppard (*sheppardi*)
₵Smith (*smithi*)
₵Twisted (*torulosa*)
₵Whiteleaf (*alba; procumbens albovariegata*)
₵White Variegated Japan (*japonica albovariegata*)
₵Yellow Variegated (*japonica aureovariegata*)
commu'nis |w . . Common Juniper
—depres'sa (*J. canadensis*)
Oldfield C.J.
Aureo-spica. hv.
—erec'ta . . . . Upright C.J.
—glauces'cens
—hiber'nica (*J. hibernica*) . . Irish J.
₵Blue (*glauca*) hv.
₵Dwarf (*nana compacta*)
₵Kiyonoi (*kiyonoi*)
₵Pyramidal (*excelsa pyramidalis*)
—jack'i . . . . Jack C.J.
—nippon'ica . . . . Nippon C.J.
—saxat'ilis (*J. montana; J. nana; J. sibirica*) . . . . . Mountain C.J.
—sue'cica (*J. suecica*) . . Swedish J.
₵Dwarf (*nana*) hv. J. c. suecica
₵Ashford (*ashfordi*) hv. J. communis
₵Broad Weeping (*oblongopendula*)
₵Days Columnar (*dayi*)
₵Denseball (*hemisphaerica*)
₵Dwarf (*compressa*)
₵Golden (*aurea*)
₵Goldenflat (*prostrata aurea*)
₵Grays (*grayi*)
₵Hedgehog (*echiniformis*)
₵Polish (*cracovia*)
₵Upright (*columnaris*)
₵Weeping (*pendula*)
confer'ta (*litoralis*) . . . . Shore J.
cox'i . . . . Cox J.
depres'sa plumo'sa . J. horizontalis p.
drupa'cea . . . . Syrian J.
excel'sa . . . . Greek J.
₵Spiny (*stricta*) hv.
₵Variegated (*variegata*)
flac'cida . . . Mexican Drooping J.
formosa'na . . . . Formosa J.
fortun'ei . . . . J. sphaerica
hiber'nica . . . . . J. communis h.
horizonta'lis (*prostrata; J. sabina h.*) |w
Creeping J.
—alpi'na (*J. sabina a.*) Alpine C.J.
—doug'lasi . . . . Waukegan C.J.
—glomera'ta . . . . Flat C.J.
—plumo'sa (*J. depressa p.*)
Andorra C.J.
₵Bar Harbor. hv. J. horizontalis
₵Blue (*glauca*)
₵Golden (*aurea*)
₵Variegated (*variegata*)
japon'ica . . . . . . J. chinensis j.
litora'lis . . . . J. conferta
lucaya'na . . . . . WestIndies J.

JUNIPERUS, continued
macrocar'pa . . . . . Plum Juniper
megalocar'pa . . . . . **J. utahensis m.**
mexica'na . . . . Mexican J.
monosper'ma |w . . . . Oneseed J.
monta'na; na'na **J. communis saxatilis**
occidenta'lis . . . . Sierra J.
oxyce'drus . . . . . . Prickly J.
pachyphloe'a . . . . . Alligator J.
phoenic'ea . . . . . . Phoenicean J.
pin'choti . . . . Redberry J.
pro'cera . . . . African J.
procum'bens . . . . . Japgarden J.
prostra'ta . . . . . . **J. horizontalis**
pseudosabi'na . . . . Turkestan J.
pyramida'lis . . . . **J. chinensis**
recur'va (*J. chinensis r.*) Himalayan J.
rig'ida . . . . Needle J.
sabi'na . . . . Savin J.
—*alpi'na* . . . . . **J. horizontalis a.**
—*horizonta'lis* . . . . **J. horizontalis**
—**lusitan'ica** . . . . Portuguese S.J.
¢Column (*fastigiata*) hv. J. sabina
¢Cypress (*cupressifolia*)
¢Hoarfrost (*variegata*)
¢Knaphill
¢Tamarix (*tamariscifolia; J. tamarisicifolia*)
¢Vonehron
saltua'ria . . . . Blackseed J.
scopulo'rum |w . . RockyMountain J.
¢Chandler Blue. hv.
¢Columnar (*columnaris*)
¢Green Pyramid (*viridifolia*)
¢Horizontal (*horizontalis*)
¢Marshall
¢Moonlight
¢Silver Column (*argentea*)
sibir'ica . . . . **J. communis saxatilis**
silicic'ola . . . Southern Redcedar
sinen'sis . . . . **J. chinensis**
sphae'rica (*fortunei*) . . Fortunes J.
squama'ta . . . . . . Singleseed J.
—**far'gesi** . . . . Farges S.J.
—**mey'eri** . . . . Meyer S.J.
—**prostra'ta** . . . . . Prostrate S.J.
—**wil'soni** . . . . Wilson S.J.
¢Variegated (*variegata*) hv. J. squamata
sue'cica . . . . **J. communis s.**
thurif'era . . . . Incense J.
tibet'ica . . . . Tibet J.
utahen'sis (*J. californica u.*) |w Utah J.
—**megalocar'pa** (*J. megalocarpa*) Bigberry U.J.
virginia'na |w . . Eastern Redcedar
—**cre'bra** . . . . North E.R.
¢Burk (*burki*) hv. J. virginiana
¢Canaert (*canaerti*)
¢Chamberlayn (*chamberlayni*)
¢Column (*cylindrica*)
¢Creeping (*horizontalis; reptans*)
¢Cypress (*cupressifolia*)
¢Elegans
¢Featherwhite (*plumosa alba*)
¢Fountain (*tripartita*)
¢Globe (*globosa*)
¢Goldtip (*elegantissima*)
¢Green Pyramid (*venusta*)
¢Hill Dundee (*hilli*)
¢Keteleer (*keteleeri*)
¢Koster (*kosteri; kosteriana*)
¢Lebreton (*lebretoni*)
¢Maccabe (*maccabei*)
¢Purple Pyramid (*pyramidiformis*)
¢Pyramidal (*pyramidalis*)
¢Reeves (*reevesiana*)
¢Schott (*schotti*)

JUNIPERUS virginiana, continued
¢Silver (*glauca*)
¢Smith (*smithi*)
¢Threadleaf (*filifera*)
¢Triomphe d'Angers
¢Upright (*fastigiata*)
¢Variegated (*albo-variegata; variegata*)
¢Weeping (*pendula*)
¢Whitetip (*albo-spica*)
wallichia'na . . . Wallichs Juniper

JURIN'EA
ala'ta

JUSSIAE'A |w . . . . Waterprimrose
califor'nica |w . . . California W.
decur'rens |w
diffu'sa . . . . Floating W.
grandiflo'ra |w . . . . . Large W.
leptocar'pa |w
longifo'lia . . . . . . Brazilian W.
peruvia'na |w . . . . . . Peru W.
re'pens . . . . Creeping W.

JUSTIC'IA . . . . Justicia
adhato'da . . . . . . Malabarnut J.
car'nea . . . . **Jacobinia c.**
ghiesbreghtia'na . . . . **Jacobinia g.**
magnif'ica . . . . . **Jacobinia carnea**
mohint'li . . . . . **Jacobinia spicigera**
sanguin'ea **Habracanthus sanguineus**
secun'da . . . . Red J.
spicig'era . . . . **Jacobinia s.**
va'sica . . . . **Adhatoda v.**

Jute . . . . **Corchorus**
Potherb J. . . . . **C. olitorius**
Roundpod J. . . . . . . **C. capsularis**

JUTTADINTE'RIA
alba'ta
prox'ima
rhe'olens
simp'soni

KADSU'RA . . . . Kadsura
japon'ica . . . . Scarlet K.
¢Variegated (*variegata*) hv.
peltig'era

KAEMPFER'IA . . Resurrectionlily
ovalifo'lia . . . . Ovalleaf R.
rotun'da . . . . Roundleaf R.

Kafir . . . **Sorghum vulgare caffrorum**
Kafirbeantree . . . . **Schotia**
Elephant-hedge K. . . . **S. latifolia**
Hottentot K. . . . . . . **S. speciosa**
Kafirbread . . . . **Encephalartos**
Altenstein K. . . . . . **E. altensteini**
Broadleaf K. . . . . . . **E. latifrons**
Congo K. . . . . . . **E. laurentianus**
Globe K. . . . . **E. cycadifolius**
Hilldebrandt K. . . **E. hilldebrandti**
Hooker Longleaf K. **E. longifolius hookeri**
Kosibay K. . . . . **E. kosiensis**
Lehmann K. . . . . **E. lehmanni**
Longleaf K. . . . . . . **E. longifolius**
Narrow L. K. . . . **E. l. angustifolius**
Northern K. . . . **E. septentrionalis**
Pinleaf K. . . . . **E. ghellincki**
Rolled Longleaf K. **E. longifolius revolutus**
Sharpleaf K. . . . . . . **E. pungens**
Spiny K. . . . . **E. horridus**
Woolly K. . . . . **E. villosus**
Zulu K. . . . . . . **E. brachyphyllus**
Kafirlily . . . . **Clivia**
Greentip K. . . . . **C. nobilis**
Scarlet K. . . . . **C. miniata**

Kafirplum . . **Harpephyllum caffrum**
Kafirpotato . **Plectranthus esculentus**

KAGENECK'IA
oblon'ga

Kaki . . . . . Persimmon, Oriental: **Diospyros kaki**

Kalamansanai . . **Neonauclea calycina**

KALANCHO'E (*BRYOPHYLLUM; KITCHINGIA*) . . Kalanchoe
See **SUCCULENTS.**

Kale . . . **Brassica oleracea acephala**
Portuguese K. . . **B. o. tronchuda**

KALLSTROE'MIA |w . . . . Caltrop
hirsutis'sima |w . . . . . Hairy C.

KAL'MIA |w . . . . Kalmia
angustifo'lia |w . . . . Lambkill K.
—**can'dida** . . . . . . White L.K.
—**ova'ta** . . . . . . Ovateleaf L.K.
—**ru'bra** . . . . Red L.K.
caroli'na . . . . Carolina K.
cunea'ta . . . . Whitewicky K.
hirsu'ta . . . . Sandhill K.
latifo'lia |w . . Mountainlaurel K. (*Mountainlaurel*)
—**lae'vipes** . . . . Southern M.K.
¢Banded (*fuscata*) hv. K. latifolia
¢Featherpetal (*polypetala*)
¢Hedge (*obtusata*)
¢Myrtleleaf (*myrtifolia*)
¢Red (*rubra*)
¢White (*alba*)
polifo'lia (*glauca; occidentalis*) Bog K.
—**microphyl'la** (*K. microphylla*) Alpine B.K.
—**rosmarinifo'lia** Rosemaryleaf B.K.

Kalmia . . . . **Kalmia**
Alpine Bog K. **K. polifolia microphylla**
Bog K. . . . . **K. polifolia**
Carolina K. . . . . **K. carolina**
Lambkill K. . . . . . **K. angustifolia**
Mountainlaurel K. . . . **K. latifolia**
Ovateleaf Lambkill K. **K. angustifolia ovata**
Red L. K. . . . . **K. a. rubra**
Rosemaryleaf Bog K. **K. polifolia rosmarinifolia**
Sandhill K. . . . . **K. hirsuta**
Southern Mountainlaurel K. **K. latifolia laevipes**
White Lambkill K. **K. angustifolia candida**
Whitewicky K. . . . . . **K. cuneata**

KALMIOP'SIS . . . . . Kalmiopsis
leachia'na . . . . Oregon K.

KALOPAN'AX
pic'tus (*ricinifolius; Acanthopanax septemlobus*)
—**magnif'icus** (*Acanthopanax acerifolius*)
—**maximowicz'i** (*Acanthopanax ricinifolius m.; A. septemlobus m.; Aralia m.*)

Kalunti . . . . . . Shorea, Kalunti: **Shorea kalunti**

Kamahi . . . . **Weinmannia racemosa**
Kamalatree . . **Mallotus philippinensis**
Kamassiwood . . . **Gonioma kamassi**
Kamea . . . . Terfas: **Terfezia**
Kangaroopaw . **Anigozanthos manglesi**
Kaoliang . . . **Sorghum vulgare** form

Kapoelasan . . . . PULASAN: **Nephelium mutabile**

KARAKANUT . . . . . . **Corynocarpus**
NEWZEALAND K. . . . . . **C. laevigata**

KARIYAT . . . . **Andrographis paniculata**

KARWIN'SKIA ⩊ . . . . . COYOTILLO
caldero'ni . . . . CALDERON C.
humboldtia'na . . . . HUMBOLDT C.

Kat . . . . ARABIANTEA: **Catha edulis**

KATSURATREE . . . . . **Cercidiphyllum; C. japonicum**
CHINESE K. . . . . **C. j. sinense**

Kaulfus'sia amelloi'des **Charieis heterophylla**

Kauri(pine) . . . DAMMARPINE, KAURI: **Agathis australis**

KEIAPPLE . . . . **Dovyalis caffra**

KEL'SEYA . . . . KELSEYA
uniflo'ra . . . . . . LONEFLOWER K.

KENILWORTHIVY . . **Cymbalaria muralis**

KENNE'DIA (*KENNEDYA*) KENNEDIA
caeru'lea . **Hardenbergia comptoniana**
comptonia'na . . . . **Hardenbergia c.**
monophyl'la . . . . **Hardenbergia m.**
ni'gricans (*Lotus n.*) . . . . BLACK K.
ova'ta . . . **Hardenbergia monophylla**
prostra'ta . . . . PROSTRATE K.
—**ma'jor** (*K. marryattae*) . LARGE P.K.
rubicun'da . . . . RED K.

KENT'IA . . . . KENTIA
See **PALM GENERA.**

KENTIOP'SIS
See **PALM GENERA.**

KENTROPHY'TA . . **ASTRAGALUS**

KER'NERA
saxat'ilis (*Cochlearia s.*)

KER'RIA . . . . KERRIA
japon'ica (*Corchorus japonicus*) JAPANESE K.
¢DOUBLE (*pleniflora*) HV.
¢STRIPED (*aureovittata*)
¢WHITEEDGE (*picta*)
¢YELLOWEDGE (*aureovariegata*)

KETELEER'IA . . . . . KETELEERIA
davidia'na . . . . DAVID K.
fortun'ei . . . . FORTUNE K.

KHA'YA . . . . KHAYA
anthothe'ca . . . . WHITE K.
grandifolio'la . . . . . . BIGLEAF K.
ivoren'sis . . . . . . IVORYCOAST K.
nyas'ica . . . . NYASSA K.
senegalen'sis . . . . . SENEGAL K.

KICKX'IA . . . . FLUVELLIN
elati'ne (*Linaria e.*) . . SHARPPOINT F.
spu'ria (*Linaria s.*) . . ROUNDLEAF F.

KIDNEYWOOD . **Eysenhardtia polystachya**

KIGE'LIA . . . . SAUSAGETREE
africa'na . . . . AFRICAN S.
madagascarien'sis . MADAGASCAR S.
pinna'ta . . . . COMMON S.

KIKUYUGRASS. **Pennisetum clandestinum**

KINETOSTIG'MA . **CHAMAEDOREA**
See **PALM GENERA.**

KING'IA . . . . BROOMTREE
austra'lis . . . . . . AUSTRALIAN B.

KINGIODEN'DRON . . . KINGSTREE
alternifo'lium . . . . PHILIPPINE K.

KINGPALM . . . . **Archontophoenix**
ALEXANDRA K. . . . . **A. alexandrae**
PICCABEEN K. . . **A. cunninghamiana**
STEP K. . . . **A. alexandrae beatricae**

KINGSTREE . . . . . . **Kingiodendron**
PHILIPPINE K. . . . **K. alternifolium**

Kinnikinnick . . . . . . BEARBERRY: **Arctostaphylos uva-ursi**

KINO, BENGAL . . . **Butea monosperma**

Kinogum . . . . . EUCALYPTUS, KINO: **Eucalyptus resinifera**

KIRENGESHO'MA
palma'ta

KITAIBE'LIA
vitifo'lia

KITCHING'IA . . . . **KALANCHOE**
See **SUCCULENTS.**

KITEMBILLA . . . . **Dovyalis hebecarpa**

KITTENTAILS . . . . **Synthyris**
ALPINE K. . . . . **S. alpina**
CUTLEAF K. . . . . **S. dissecta**
FEATHERLEAF K. . . . **S. pinnatifida**
FRINGEPETAL K. . . . **S. schizantha**
HEARTLEAF K. . . . . . . **S. cordata**
KIDNEYLEAF K. . . . **S. reniformis**
MAJOR K. . . . . **S. major**
PLANTAINLEAF K. . . . **S. plantaginea**
RED K. . . . . **S. rubra**
RITTER K. . . . . **S. ritteriana**
ROUNDLEAF K. . . . . **S. rotundifolia**
SWEETZER R. K. . . . **S. r. sweetzeri**
WOOLLY FEATHERLEAF K. **S. pinnatifida lanuginosa**
WYOMING K. . . . . **S. wyomingensis**

Kittoolpalm . . FISHTAILPALM, TODDY: **Caryota urens**

Klamathweed . ST. JOHNSWORT, COMMON: **Hypericum perforatum**
Klamathweed, unfortunately, is extensively used on the Pacific Coast of the U. S. for this common, widely distributed Old World weed.

KLEINHO'VIA
hos'pita

KLEIN'IA . . . . KLEINIA
This genus of African succulents is somewhat doubtfully separable, botanically, from Senecio. See **SUCCULENTS.**

KNAUT'IA
This genus is referred by some botanists to Scabiosa.
arven'sis . . . . **Scabiosa a.**
sylvat'ica (*Scabiosa s.*)

KNAWEL . . . . **Scleranthus**
ANNUAL K. . . . . **S. annuus**
PERENNIAL K. . . . . . **S. perennis**

KNEIF'FIA . . . . . **OENOTHERA**

KNIGHT'IA
excel'sa . . . . REWAREWA

KNIPHOF'IA (*TRITOMA*) . TORCHLILY (*Pokerplant; Redhotpoker*)
aloi'des; alooi'des . . . . . **K. uvaria**
caules'cens
∞**coralli'na** (*macowani* × *uvaria; Tritoma c.*) . . . . ∞CORAL T.
¢SCARLET. HV.

KNIPHOFIA, continued
el'egans . . . . HOTPOKER TORCHLILY
ensifo'lia . . . . . . SWORDLEAF T.
erec'ta
folio'sa (*quartiniana*) . . . SWORD T.
gal'pini . . . . GALPIN T.
grac'ilis . . . . . . CORALQUEEN T.
¢EMPEROR. HV.
¢GOLDELSE
¢LEMONQUEEN
macow'ani (*Tritoma m.*). MACOWAN T.
nel'soni . . . . NELSON T.
north'iae . . . . NORTHS T.
quartinia'na . . . . **K. foliosa**
ru'fa . . . . EARLY T.
sarmento'sa . . . . . TRAVELING T.
sulphu'rea (*Tritoma s.*) . . SULFUR T.
tuck'i . . . . TUCK T.
uva'ria (*aloides; alooides*). COMMON T.
¢DAYGLOW (*grandiflora*) HV. K. uvaria
¢EARLY (*floribunda*)
¢ERECTA
¢GIANT (*nobilis*)
¢GOLDTOWER (*grandis; pfitzeri; pfitzeriana; Bonfire*)
¢SAUNDERS (*saundersi*)
This name is sometimes misapplied to the species K. foliosa.
¢SUMMER (*praecox*)
All the following are clons.
C. M. PRICHARD. HV. Kniphofia
EVERBLOOM (*semperflorens*)
EXPRESS
(*H. G.*) MILLS
IPSWICH GEM
JUNEGLORY
LORD ROBERTS
MARVEL (*mirabilis*)
MRS. SMITH
MT. ETNA
NATHALINA (*nathalinae*)
ORANGEBEAUTY
OSIRIS
ROYALSTANDARD
RUFUS
RUSSELLS GOLD
(*R.*) WILSON KER
SIR (*C. K.*) BUTLER
SNOWDEN (*snowdeni*)
(*Star of*) BADENBADEN
SULPHURSPIRE
SUNSET
TRICOLOR

KNOTGRASS . . . **Paspalum distichum**
THICKSPIKE K. . . . . . **P. difforme**

KNOTWEED . . . . **Polygonum**
See also BISTORT, CORNBIND, FLEECEFLOWER, LADYSTHUMB, SMARTWEED.

AUSTIN K. . . . . **P. austinae**
BELLFLOWER K. . . **P. campanulatum**
BLACKFRINGE K. . . . . **P. cilinode**
BOLANDER K. . . . . . **P. bolanderi**
BOX K. . . . . **P. buxiforme**
BROADLEAF K. . . . . . **P. minimum**
BUSHY K. . . . . **P. ramosissimum**
DOUGLAS K. . . . . . . **P. douglasi**
ERECT K. . . . . **P. erectum**
FOWLERS K. . . . . **P. fowleri**
HEDGE K. . . . . . . **P. dumetorum**
KELLOGG K. . . . . **P. kelloggi**
LEATHERY K. . . . . . **P. achoreum**
NAILWORT K. . . . . **P. paronychia**
PINKHEAD K. . . . . . **P. capitatum**
POLYGALA K. . . . **P. polygaloides**
PROSTRATE K. . . . . . **P. aviculare**

KNOTWEED, continued
ROSECARPET K. **Polygonum vaccinifolium**
SAKHALIN K. . . . . **P. sachalinense**
SAWATCH K. . . . . **P. sawatchense**
SILVERSHEATH K. . . **P. argyrocoleon**
SLIM K. . . . . **P. tenue**

Knucklegrass . . . . PANICUM, FALL: **Panicum dichotomiflorum**

KOCH'IA . . . . . . SUMMERCYPRESS
america'na . . . . GREENMOLLY S.
califor'nica . . . . . CALIFORNIA S.
childs'i . . . . CHILDS S.
hyssopifo'lia . . . . **Bassia h.**
prostra'ta . . . . . . PROSTRATE S.
scopa'ria . . . . . . BELVEDERE S.
—trichophyl'la
This name is often misspelled trichophila.
vesti'ta . . . . GRAY S.

KOEBERLIN'IA |w . . . . . ALLTHORN
spino'sa |w . . . . SPINY A.

KOELE'RIA . . . . KOELERIA
See **GRASS GENERA.**

KOEL'LIA . . . **PYCNANTHEMUM**

KOELREUTE'RIA . . . GOLDRAINTREE
apicula'ta
bipinna'ta . . . . BOUGAINVILLEA G.
formosa'na . . . . FLAME G.
integrifo'lia
panicula'ta . . . . PANICLED G.
—fastigia'ta . . . . . PYRAMID P.G.

KOHLRABI . **Brassica oleracea gongylodes**

KO'KIA
drynarioi'des

KOLKWIT'ZIA . . . . . KOLKWITZIA
amab'ilis . . . . BEAUTYBUSH

KOMBU . . . . **Arthrothamnus**
FORKED K. . . . . **A. bifidus**
KURILE K. . . . . . . **A. kurilensis**

Kombu . . . . . . WINGKELP: **Alaria**

KO'NIGA . . . . . . **LOBULARIA**

KOORDERSIODEN'DRON
pinna'tum . . . . AMUGIS

KOPIE . . . . **Goupia glabra**

KOP'SIA . . . . KOPSIA
arbo'rea . . . . TREE K.
frutico'sa . . . . SHRUBBY K.

KORTHAL'SIA . . . . . . ANTPALM
See **PALM GENERA.**

Korycar'pus dian'drus **Diarrhena americana**

KOSTELETZ'KYA |w SALTMARSHMALLOW
althaeifo'lia |w . . . . . . ALTHEA S.
his'pida . . . . HAIRY S.
virgin'ica |w . . . . . . VIRGINIA S.

KRAME'RIA . . KRAMERIA (*Ratany*)
argen'tea . . . . BRAZIL K.
canes'cens A. Gray (1852) . . **K. grayi**
canes'cens Willd. (1825) . **K. triandra**
glandulo'sa . . . . RANGE K.
gray'i (*canescens* A. Gray, *not* Willd.) GRAYS K.
parvifo'lia . . . . . . LITTLELEAF K.
secundiflo'ra . . . . . . TRAILING K.
trian'dra (*canescens* Willd., *not* Gray) PERUVIAN K.
The above plant is the source of R(h)atanyroot, used in medicine.

KRAUN'HIA . . . . **WISTARIA**

KRAUS'SIA . . . . . **TRICALYSIA**
floribun'da . . . . . . **T. kraussiana**

KRIG'IA (*CYNTHIA*) |w DWARFDANDELION
monta'na . . . . . . MOUNTAIN D.
occidenta'lis (*Cymbia o.*). WESTERN D.
virgin'ica (*Cynthia v.*) |w VIRGINIA D.

KRUGIODEN'DRON
fer'reum . . . . LEADWOOD

KRYNITZ'KIA . . . **CRYPTANTHA**

KUDZUBEAN . . . . **Pueraria**
THUNBERG K. . . . **P. thunbergiana**

Kudzuvine . . . . KUDZUBEAN: **Pueraria**

KUHN'IA
eupatorioi'des

KUHNIS'TERA . **PETALOSTEMON**
pinna'ta . . . . **P. corymbosus**

KULUI . . **Nototrichium sandwicense**

∞ KUMANDARIN . . **Citrus reticulata × Fortunella spp.**

KUMQUAT . . . . **Fortunella**
GOLDENBEAN HONGKONG K. **F. hindsi chintou**
HONGKONG K. . . . . **F. hindsi**
MALAY K. . . . . **F. polyandra**
MARUMI K. . . . . **F. japonica**
MEIWA K. . . . . **F. crassifolia**
NAGAMI K. . . . . **F. margarita**

KUNZ'EA . . . . MOUNTAINBUSH
ambig'ua (*corifolia*) . BOTTLEGREEN M.
ericifo'lia . . . . HEATH M.
micran'tha
parvifo'lia . . . . . . LITTLELEAF M.
peduncula'ris
pomif'era . . . . APPLE M.
recur'va
seric'ea . . . . SILKY M.

KUNZ'IA . . . . **PURSHIA**

KUPUKATREE . . . **Griselinia littoralis**

KUSSOTREE . . . . **Hagenia abyssinica**

KY'DIA . . . . KYDIA
calyci'na . . . . . . ROXBURGHS K.

KYLLIN'GA |w
odora'ta |w
pu'mila |w

LABOURDONNAI'SIA . . . MATTREE
albes'cens . . . . WHITE M.

+LABURNOCYT'ISUS (graft hybrid: *Cytisus + Laburnum*) LABURNOCYTISUS
Known only by the following:
₵ad'ami (*Laburnum anagyroides + Cytisus purpureus; Cytisus adami; C. laburnum purpurascens; Laburnum adami*) . . . . ADAMS L.
A chimaera graft-hybrid.

LABUR'NUM . . . . . . LABURNUM
ad'ami . . . . **₵Laburnocytisus a.**
alpi'num (*Cytisus alpinus*) SCOTCH L.
₵AUTUMN (*autumnale; biferum*) HV.
₵WEEPING (*pendulum*)
anagyroi'des (*vulgare; Cytisus laburnum*) . . . . GOLDENCHAIN L.
—alschin'geri (*L. vulgare a.*) ALSCHINGER G.L.

LABURNUM anagyroides, continued
₵AUTUMN (*autumnale; semperflorens*) HV. L. anagyroides
₵BUNCHLEAF (*sessilifolium*)
₵CARLIER (*carlieri*)
₵CURLLEAF (*bullatum; L. vulgare involutum*)
₵GOLDLEAF (*aureum*)
₵OAKLEAF (*quercifolium*)
₵WEEPING (*pendulum*)
caraman'icum . . ASIATIC LABURNUM
∞ **waterer'i** (*alpinum × anagyroides; parksi* Hort.; *vossi* Hort.) ∞ WATERER L.

LACEBARKTREE . . . . **Lagetta**
LINT L. . . . . **L. lintearia**

LACEFLOWER . . . . **Trachymene**
AUSTRALIAN L. . . . . . **T. australis**
BLUELEAF L. . . . . . **T. glaucifolia**
HAIRY L. . . . . **T. pilosa**
SKYBLUE L. . . . . **T. coerulea**

LACEGRASS . . . . **Eragrostis capillaris**

LACEWOOD . . . . **Cardwellia sublimis**

LACHENA'LIA . . . . CAPECOWSLIP
orchioi'des . . . . ORCHID C.
pen'dula . . . . NODDING C.
—superb'a . . . . GREAT N.C.
pustula'ta
reflex'a
rood'eae
tri'color . . . . TRICOLOR C.
₵FOURCOLOR (*quadricolor; L. q.*) HV.
₵LEMON (*luteola; L. luteola*)
₵NELSON (*nelsoni*)
₵ONECOLOR (*unicolor*)
unifo'lia . . . . SINGLELEAF C.

LACHNAN'THES (*GYROTHECA*) |w REDROOT
tincto'ria (*Gyrotheca t.*) |w . BLOOD R.

LACINA'RIA . . . . **LIATRIS**

LACQUERTREE, JAPANESE **Toxicodendron vernicifluum**

LACTA'RIUS . . . . . . LACTARIUS
delicio'sus . . . . DELICIOUS L.
in'digo . . . . INDIGO L.

LACTREE . . . . **Schleichera**
MALAY L. . . . . **S. oleosa**
PHILIPPINE L. . . . . **S. subundulata**

LACTU'CA (*MULGEDIUM*) |w LETTUCE
alpi'na (*Mulgedium alpinum*) ALPINE L.
angusta'na . . . **L. sativa asparagina**
bourgae'i (*Mulgedium b.*) BOURGET L.
canaden'sis |w . . . . . . CANADA L.
graminifo'lia |w . . . GRASSLEAF L.
hasta'ta
lessertia'na
peren'nis . . . . PERENNIAL L.
plumier'i . . . . PLUMIERS L.
pulchel'la |w . . . . CHICORY L.
sati'va |w . . . . GARDEN L.
—asparagi'na (*L. angustana*) ASPARAGUS G.L.
—capita'ta . . . . HEAD G.L.
—cris'pa . . . . CRINKLE G.L.
—longifo'lia . . . . LONGLEAF G.L.
₵COS. HV. L. s. longifolia
₵ROMAINE
serri'ola (*scariola; virosa* U. S. Auth., *not* L.) . . . . PRICKLY L.
—integra'ta (*L. integrata; L. scariola i.*) |w
spica'ta . . . . BLUE L.
viro'sa . . . . BITTER L.

Ladiestresses . . . . **Spiranthes**
Becks L. . . . . **S. becki**
Continental L. . . **S. romanzoffiana**
Creamy L. . . . . **S. porrifolia**
Fragrant L. . . . . **S. odorata**
Nodding L. . . . . **S. cernua**
October L. . . . . **S. ovalis**
Painted L. . . . . **S. picta**
Shortleaf L. . . . . . . **S. brevifolia**
Slender L. . . . . **S. gracilis**
Southern L. . . . . . . **S. praecox**
Upland L. . . . . **S. vernalis**
Wildleaf L. . . . . **S. lucida**

Ladybell . . . . **Adenophora**
Broadleaf L. . . . . . . **A. latifolia**
Bulleys L. . . . . . . **A. bulleyana**
Bush L. . . . . **A. potanini**
Fickle L. . . . . . . **A. polymorpha**
Lilyleaf L. . . . . **A. lilifolia**
Lovely L. . . . . **A. ornata**
Nikko L. . . . . **A. nikoensis**

Ladyfern . . . . **Athyrium filixfemina**

Ladyofthenight
Selenicereus macdonaldiae

Ladypalm . . . . **Rhapis**
Broadleaf L. . . . . **R. excelsa**
Slender L. . . . . **R. humilis**

Ladyslipper . . . . **Cypripedium**
Brownie L. . . . . **C. fasciculatum**
California L. . . . **C. californicum**
Canada L. . . . . . **C. passerinum**
European L. . . . . . . **C. calceolus**
Largeyellow L.
C. parviflorum pubescens
Mountain L. . . . . . **C. montanum**
Pink L. . . . . **C. acaule**
Ramshead L. . . . . . **C. arietinum**
Showy L. . . . . **C. reginae**
Smallyellow L. . . . **C. parviflorum**
White L. . . . . **C. candidum**
Yellow European L.
C. calceolus pubescens

Ladysmantle . . . . **Alchemilla**
Common L. . . . . **A. vulgaris**
Field L. . . . . **A. arvensis**
Large L. . . . . **A. major**
Mountain L. . . . . **A. alpina**

Ladysthumb . . . . **Polygonum**
See also Bistort, Cornbind, Fleeceflower, Knotweed, Smartweed.
Bigroot L. . . . . **P. muhlenbergi**
Curltop L. . . . . **P. lapathifolium**
Floating L. . . . . **P. natans**
Princesplume L. . . . . **P. orientale**
Spotted L. . . . . . . **P. persicaria**
Water L. . . . . . . **P. amphibium**

LAE'LIA . . . . Laelia
See **ORCHID GENERA.**

LAELIOCAT'TLEYA
See **ORCHID GENERA.**

LAGENA'RIA . . . . Gourd
sicera'ria (*leucantha; vulgaris*)
Calabash G.

LAGERSTROE'MIA . . . Crapemyrtle
flosregi'nae . . . . **L. speciosa**
hypoleu'ca . . . . Andaman C.
in'dica . . . . Common C.
¢Dwarf (*nana*) hv.
¢Dwarf Blue (*lavandula*)
¢Pink
¢Purple (*purpurea*)
¢Red (*magenta; rubra*)
¢White (*alba*)

LAGERSTROEMIA, continued
parviflo'ra
Littleflower Crapemyrtle
pirifor'mis . . . . Batitinan C.
specio'sa (*flosreginae*) . . . Queen C.

LAGET'TA . . . . Lacebarktree
lintea'ria . . . . Lint L.

LAGOPHYL'LA |w
ramosis'sima |w

LAGO'TIS
glau'ca

LAGUNA'RIA . . . . Sugarplumtree
paterso'ni . . . . Paterson S.

LAGUNCULA'RIA . . Falsemangrove
racemo'sa . . . . . . Falsemangrove

LAGU'RUS . . . . Harestail
See **GRASS GENERA.**

Lakoocha . . . . **Artocarpus lakoocha**

LALLEMAN'TIA
canes'cens
ibe'rica
pelta'ta

LAMARCK'IA (*ACHYRODES*)
Goldentop
See **GRASS GENERA.**

LAMBERT'IA
ericifo'lia
formo'sa
iner'mis
multiflo'ra

Lambsuccory . . . . **Arnoseris**
Small L. . . . . **A. minima**

LAMINA'RIA . . . . Bladekelp
sacchari'na . . . . Sugar B.

LA'MIUM |w . . . . Deadnettle
al'bum . . . . White D.
amplexicau'le |w . . . . . Henbit D.
galeob'dolon . . . . . Archangel D.
longiflo'rum
macula'tum . . . . Spotted D.
—al'bum . . . . White S.D.
¢Variegated (*variegatum*) hv. L. maculatum
orva'la . . . . Orvala D.
purpu'reum . . . . Purple D.

LAMPRAN'THUS
MESEMBRYANTHEMUM
See **SUCCULENTS.**

LAMPSA'NA . . . . . . **LAPSANA**

Lancepod . . . . **Lonchocarpus**
Honduras L. . . . . **L. hondurensis**

Lancewood . . **Oxandra; O. lanceolata**

LANDOL'PHIA . . . . . . Gumvine
droogmansia'na
heudelot'ti . . . . Guinea G.
kirk'i . . . . Mozambique G.
owarien'sis . . . . . WestAfrican G.

Langsat . . . . **Lansium**
Domestic L. . . . . . **L. domesticum**

LAN'GUAS . . . . **ALPINIA**

LAN'SIUM . . . . Langsat
domes'ticum . . . . Domestic L.

LANTA'NA . . . . Lantana
aculea'ta
brasilien'sis . . . Yerbasagrada L.
ca'mara . . . . Common L.
¢Yellow (*flava*) hv.

LANTANA, continued
depres'sa
involucra'ta
lila'cina . . . . Lilac Lantana
sellowia'na (*delicatissima*) . Trailing L.
A. Clavean. hv. Lantana
A. Cook
Amiel
Aurora
Cicerone
Comtesse Debiencourt
Corbeille d'Argent
Craig (*craigi*)
E. Bayard
Goldenplume
Grand Sultan
Harkett Perfection
Helvia
Iolande
Jacob Schultz
Jannia
Javotte
Juan d'Or
Lapleur d'Or
Leo Dex
Lyre
Meldissipolia
Merjaune
Michael Schmidt
Pinkbeauty
Pluie d'Or
Protee
Radiation
Rosequeen
Sensation
Snowqueen
Sunset
Tethys
Violetking

LANU'GIA
latifo'lia

LAOTH'OE . . . **CHLOROGALUM**

LAPAGE'RIA . . . . Chilebells
rose'a . . . . Red C.
—albiflo'ra (*alba*) . . . . . . White C.

LAPEIROU'SIA (*ANOMATHECA; LAPEYROUSIA*) . Falsefreesia
cruen'ta (*Anomatheca c.*) . . Red F.
fissifo'lia
jun'cea . . . . Sedge F.

LAPIDA'RIA
margaret'ae

LAPOR'TEA . . . . . . Woodnettle
canaden'sis (*Urticastrum divaricatum*)
Canada W.

LAP'PA . . . . **ARCTIUM**
ed'ulis; ma'jor . . . . **A. lappa**

LAP'PULA (*ECHINOSPERMUM*) |w
Stickseed

The biennial and perennial species with nutlets attached to a pyramidal base are now referred to the genus Hackelia; the annuals with nutlets attached to awl-shaped base are retained in Lappula.

consanguin'ea
deflex'a . . . . **Hackelia d.**
diffu'sa . . . . **Hackelia d.**
echina'ta . . . . European S.
floribun'da . . . . **Hackelia f.**
redow'ski (*occidentalis; texana*) |w
virginia'na . . . . **Hackelia v.**

LAPSA'NA (*LAMPSANA*) Nipplewort
commu'nis . . . . Common N.

Larch . . . . **Larix**
Alpine L. . . . . **L. lyalli**
Carpathian L. . **L. decidua carpathica**
Chinese L. . . . . **L. potanini**
Dahurian L. . . . . **L. gmelini**
∞ Dunkfeld L. . . . . ∞ **L. eurolepis**
Eastern L. . . . . **L. laricina**
European L. . . . . . . **L. decidua**
Himalaya L. . . . . **L. griffithi**
Japanese L. . . . . . . **L. leptolepis**
Korean Dahurian L.
L. gmelini olgensis
Kurile D. L. . . . . . . **L. g. japonica**
∞ Marschlins L. . . . ∞ **L. marschlinsi**
Masters L. . . . . . **L. mastersiana**
Polish L. . . . . **L. decidua polonica**
PrinceRupprecht Dahurian L.
L. gmelini principis-rupprechti
Siberian L. . . . . **L. sibirica**
Sudetic L. . . . **L. decidua sudetica**
Weeping European L. **L. d. pendula**
Western L. . . . . . **L. occidentalis**

LARDIZABA'IA
biterna'ta

LAR'IX |w . . . . Larch
america'na . . . . **L. laricina**
cajan'deri; dahu'rica . . . **L. gmelini**
decid'ua (*europaea*) . . European L.
—carpath'ica . . . . . Carpathian L.
—pen'dula . . . . . . Weeping E.L.
—polo'nica . . . . Polish L.
—sudet'ica . . . . Sudetic L.
∞ **eurol'epis** (*decidua* × *leptolepis*)
∞ Dunkfeld L.
The tree in cultivation is presumably a clon of this cross.

gmeli'ni (*cajanderi; dahurica*)
Dahurian L.
—japon'ica (*L. kamtchatica; L. kurilensis*) . . . . Kurile D.L.
—olgen'sis (*L. koreensis; L. olgensis*)
Korean D.L.
—principis-rupprecht'i
PrinceRupprecht D.L.
grif'fithi (*griffithiana*) . Himalaya L.
laric'ina (*americana*) |w . Eastern L.; Tamarack (Forestry)
leptol'epis Sieb. & Zucc. (*japonica; kaempferi* Sarg., *not* Carr.)
Japanese L.
ly'alli . . . . Alpine L.
∞ **marschlin'si** (*leptolepis* × *sibirica*)
∞ Marschlins L.
mastersia'na (*masteriana*) Masters L.
The tree in cultivation is presumably a clon of this cross.

occidenta'lis . . . . . . Western L.
olgen'sis . . . . **L. gmelini o.**
∞ **pen'dula** (*decidua* × *laricina*)
The tree in cultivation under this name is presumably a clon of this cross.

potani'ni . . . . Chinese L.
sibir'ica . . . . Siberian L.

Larkspur . . . . **Delphinium**
For hort. var. of Larkspur, see **DELPHINIUM.**

Aitchison L. . . . . . **D. aitchisoni**
Albania L. . . . **D. uechtritzianum**
Alpine Bee L. . . **D. elatum alpinum**
Alpine L. . . . . **D. alpestre**
Aman L. . . . . **D. amani**
Anderson L. . . . . . **D. andersoni**
Apache L. . . . . . . **D. apachense**
Arctic L. . . . . **D. frigidum**
Armenian L. . . . **D. armeniacum**

Larkspur, continued
Ashen L. . . . **Delphinium cinereum**
Autumn L. . . . . . . **D. autumnale**
Axilflower L. . . . **D. axilliflorum**
Azure Siberian L.
D. grandiflorum azureum
Baby L. . . . . **D. nanum**
Balansa L. . . . . . . **D. balansae**
Barbey L. . . . . **D. barbeyi**
Barestem L. . . . . . **D. scaposum**
∞ Barlow L. . . . . . . ∞ **D. barlowi**
Batalin L. . . . . **D. batalini**
Batang L. . . . . . **D. batangense**
Bearded L. . . . . . **D. barbatum**
Bee L. . . . . **D. elatum**
Beesian L. . . . . . **D. beesianum**
Bigpod L. . . . . . **D. megacarpum**
Birdsfoot L. . . . **D. pedatisectum**
Biternate L. . . . . **D. biternatum**
Bitter L. . . . . **D. triste**
Blaisdell L. . . . . . **D. blaisdelli**
Blockman L. . . . **D. blockmanae**
Bluewhite L. . . **D. albocoeruleum**
Bog L. . . . . **D. uliginosum**
Bonat L. . . . . **D. bonati**
Bonvalot L. . . . . . **D. bonvaloti**
Borbas L. . . . . **D. borbasi**
Bove L. . . . . **D. bovei**
Bowed L. . . . . . . **D. arcuatum**
Bracted L. . . . . . **D. bracteosum**
Branched L. . . . . . **D. ramosum**
Browns L. . . . . **D. browni**
Bucharic L. . . . . **D. bucharicum**
Bulleys L. . . . . . **D. bulleyanum**
Busch L. . . . . . . **D. buschianum**
California L. . . . **D. californicum**
Caller L. . . . . **D. calleri**
Candid L. . . . . **D. candidum**
Canmore L. . . . . . **D. canmorense**
Cappadocia L. . . **D. cappadocicum**
Cardinal L. . . . . . . **D. cardinale**
Carolina L. . . . **D. carolinianum**
Carrion L. . . . **D. stapeliosmum**
Carrotleaf L. . . . . **D. tenuisectum**
Caucasian L. . . . . **D. speciosum**
Cavalier L. . . . **D. cavaleriense**
Celestial L. . . . . **D. coelestinum**
Cerulean L. . . . . . **D. coeruleum**
Chamisso L. . . . . **D. chamissonis**
Changing L. . . . **D. commutatum**
Chefoo L. . . . . . . **D. chefoense**
Chelan L. . . . . . . **D. viridescens**
Chervil L. . . . **D. anthriscifolium**
Chilliwacen L. . . **D. chilliwacenae**
Clammy L. . . . . **D. viscosum**
Cleft L. . . . . **D. fissum**
Clubstem L. . . . . **D. dasycaulon**
Coast L. . . . . **D. hesperium**
Cockerell L. . . . . . **D. cockerelli**
Columbia L. . . . **D. columbianum**
ColumbiaRiver L. . . **D. trolliifolium**
Corymb L. . . . . . **D. corymbosum**
Cosson L. . . . . . **D. cossonianum**
Coyote L. . . . . **D. luporum**
Cream Menzies L.
D. menziesi ochroleucum
Crowded L. . . . . . . **D. confertum**
Cuyamaca L. . . . . . **D. cuyamacae**
David L. . . . . **D. davidi**
Death L. . . . . **D. venenosum**
Delavay L. . . . . **D. delavayi**
Dell L. . . . . **D. umbrosum**
Denseflower L. . . **D. confertiflorum**
Desert L. . . . . **D. deserti**
Dinaric L. . . . . . . **D. dinaricum**
Dissected L. . . . . . **D. dissectum**
Dotted L. . . . . . . **D. pellucidum**
Doubtful L. . . . . . . **D. ambiguum**

Larkspur, continued
Duhmberg Bee L.
Delphinium elatum duhmbergi
Duncecap L. . . . . . **D. occidentale**
Dwarf Siberian L.
D. grandiflorum minor
EastAfrican L. . . . **D. macrocentron**
Ehrenberg L. . . . . . **D. ehrenbergi**
Elegant L. . . . . **D. elegans**
Emily L. . . . . **D. emiliae**
Engler L. . . . . . . **D. englerianum**
Esquirol L. . . . . **D. esquiroli**
Farges L. . . . . **D. fargesi**
Fenugreek L. . . **D. trigonelloides**
Fewflower L. . . . . **D. oliganthum**
Fivestyle L. . . . . **D. pentagynum**
Flame L. . . . . **D. flammeum**
Flannel L. . . . . . **D. tomentellum**
Flexuous L. . . . . . . **D. flexuosum**
∞ Florists L. . . . . . ∞ **D. cultorum**
Forking L. . . . . **D. consolida**
Forrests L. . . . . **D. forresti**
Freeflower L. . . . . . **D. floribundum**
Freyn L. . . . . **D. freyni**
Fringed L. . . . . **D. ciliatum**
Fuzzystem L. . . . . . **D. hirticaule**
Garland L. . . . . . **D. cheilanthum**
Gautier L. . . . . **D. gautieri**
Georges L. . . . . **D. georgei**
Geranium L. . . . . **D. geraniifolium**
Geyer L. . . . . **D. geyeri**
Giant L. . . . . **D. robustum**
Gilg L. . . . . **D. gilgianum**
Girald L. . . . . **D. giraldi**
Glacier L. . . . . **D. glaciale**
Goetze L. . . . . . . **D. goetzeanum**
Golden Orange L. **D. nudicaule luteum**
Goldhair L. . . . . **D. chrysotrichum**
Gombault L. . . . . . . **D. gombaulti**
Gommingger L. . . . **D. gomminggeri**
Grape L. . . . . **D. vitifolium**
Greenes L. . . . . **D. greenei**
Green L. . . . . **D. viride**
Grooved L. . . . . **D. sulcatum**
Hairy L. . . . . **D. villosum**
Hansen L. . . . . **D. hanseni**
Hardy Garland L.
D. cheilanthum formosum
Hardy L. . . . . **D. formosum**
Heartpetal Mediterranean L.
D. halteratum cardiopetalum
Hedge L. . . . . **D. dumetorum**
Heller L. . . . . **D. helleri**
Henderson L. . . . . **D. hendersoni**
Henry L. . . . . **D. henryi**
Himalayan L. . . . . . **D. altissimum**
Hirschfeld L. . . **D. hirschfeldianum**
Hoary L. . . . . **D. incanum**
Hohenacker L. . . . . **D. hohenackeri**
Hooked L. . . . . **D. uncinatum**
Hop L. . . . . **D. humulinum**
Karategin L. . . . . . . **D. karategini**
Kashmir L. . . . . **D. cashmerianum**
Keteleer L. . . . . **D. keteleeri**
King L. . . . . **D. kingianum**
Kurd L. . . . . **D. kurdicum**
Lacoste L. . . . . **D. lacostei**
Lankong L. . . . . . **D. lankongense**
Largespike L. . . . **D. macrostachyum**
Leafy L. . . . . **D. foliosum**
Lengthy L. . . . . **D. elongatum**
Leroy L. . . . . **D. leroyi**
Likiang L. . . . . **D. likiangense**
Lilac L. . . . . **D. lilacinum**
Lime L. . . . . **D. calcicola**
Lipsky L. . . . . **D. lipski**
Littleflower L. . . . **D. micranthum**
Little L. . . . . **D. bicolor**

Larkspur, continued
Longhead L.
Delphinium macrocephalum
Longleaf L. . . . . **D. macrophyllum**
Longpetal L. . . . **D. macropetalum**
Longstalk L. . **D. longipedunculatum**
Looseflower Hairy L.
D. villosum laxiflorum
Loscos L. . . . . **D. loscosi**
Lovely L. . . . . **D. amabile**
Maack L. . . . . . **D. maackianum**
Madedonian L. . . **D. macedonicum**
Maire L. . . . . **D. mairei**
Manycolor L. . . . . **D. diversicolor**
Manyflower L. . . . **D. multiflorum**
Margined L. . . . **D. emarginatum**
Maria L. . . . . **D. mariae**
Marvel L. . . . . . . **D. mirabile**
Mauretania L. . . **D. mauritanicum**
Maximowicz L. . . **D. maximowiczi**
Maydell L. . . . . **D. maydellianum**
Meadow L. . . . . . . **D. pratense**
Medicine L. . . . . . . **D. officinale**
Mediterranean L. . . **D. halteratum**
Menzies L. . . . . . . **D. menziesi**
Middendorff L. . . **D. middendorffi**
Midzoren L. . . . . . **D. midzorense**
Mitzugen L. . . . . . **D. mitzugense**
Modest L. . . . . . **D. inconspicuum**
Mogollon L. . **D. amplibracteatum**
Mongrel L. . . . . . . **D. hybridum**
Monkshood L. . . . . . . **D. aconiti**
Montana Little L.
D. bicolor montanense
Mountain L. . . . . **D. montanum**
Musk L. . . . . . **D. brunonianum**
Naked L. . . . . **D. apetalum**
Narbonne L. . . . . **D. narbonense**
Narrowlobe L. . . **D. linearilobum**
Narrowpetal L. . . **D. stenosepalum**
Netpod L. . . . . . **D. dictyocarpum**
Nevada L. . . . . . . **D. nevadense**
NewMexican L. . **D. novomexicanum**
Norton L. . . . . **D. nortoni**
Nuttall L. . . . . **D. nuttallianum**
Oakwoods L. . . . **D. quercetorum**
Oliver L. . . . . . . **D. oliverianum**
Orange L. . . . . . . **D. nudicaule**
Oregon L. . . . . . . **D. oreganum**
Oriental L. . . . . . . **D. orientale**
Ornate L. . . . . **D. ornatum**
Painted L. . . . . **D. pictum**
Paleflower L. . . . **D. pallidiflorum**
Panicle L. . . . . **D. paniculatum**
Paphlagonian L. . **D. paphlagonicum**
Parish L. . . . . **D. parishi**
Parry L. . . . . **D. parryi**
Pencilled L. . . . . **D. penicillatum**
Peregrine L. . . . . **D. peregrinum**
Persian L. . . . . **D. persicum**
Phrygian L. . . . . . . **D. phrygium**
Plains L. . . . . **D. virescens**
Pontic L. . . . . **D. ponticum**
Potanin L. . . . . **D. potanini**
Puny L. . . . . **D. exiguum**
Purdom L. . . . . **D. purdomi**
Purpus L. . . . . **D. purpusi**
Pylzow L. . . . . **D. pylzowi**
Pyramid L. . . . . **D. pyramidatum**
Ravey L. . . . . **D. raveyi**
Recurved L. . . . . **D. recurvatum**
Requien L. . . . . . . **D. requieni**
Revolute L. . . . . . . **D. revolutum**
Robert L. . . . . . **D. robertianum**
Rocket L. . . . . **D. ajacis**
Rock L. . . . . **D. tricorne**
RockyMountain L. . **D. stachydeum**
Rosy L. . . . . **D. roseum**

Larkspur, continued
Royal L. . . **Delphinium variegatum**
Rush L. . . . . **D. junceum**
Russian L. . . . . **D. rossicum**
∞ Ruys L. . . . . ∞ **D. ruysi**
Saccate L. . . . . **D. saccatum**
Saloniki L. . . . **D. thessalonicum**
Sanicle L. . . . **D. saniculaefolium**
Sapello L. . . . . . . **D. sapellonis**
Savatier L. . . . . . . **D. savatieri**
Scaly L. . . . . **D. lepidum**
Schmalhausen L. . **D. schmalhauseni**
Seaside L. . . . . . . **D. maritimum**
Sharpleaf L. . . . . **D. apiculatum**
Sharplobe L. . . . . **D. acutilobum**
Sharppetal L. . . . . **D. oxysepalum**
Shorthorn L. . . . . **D. brevicorne**
Siberian L. . . . . **D. grandiflorum**
Sierra L. . . **D. scopulorum glaucum**
Sintenis L. . . . . . . **D. sintenisi**
Siwan L. . . . . **D. siwanense**
Skunk L. . . . . **D. foetidum**
Skyblue Garland L.
D. cheilanthum coelestinum
Slender Siberian L.
D. grandiflorum chinense
Slim L. . . . . . . **D. depauperatum**
Smallflower L. . . . **D. parviflorum**
Smallpetal L. . . . **D. micropetalum**
Smooth Caucasian L.
D. speciosum glabratum
Smoothfruit L. . . . **D. leiocarpum**
Soft L. . . . . **D. molle**
Sonne L. . . . . . . **D. gracilentum**
Sordid L. . . . . **D. sordidum**
Soulie L. . . . . **D. souliei**
Spanish L. . . . . . **D. hispanicum**
Sparse L. . . . . . **D. sparsiflorum**
Spreading L. . . . . . . **D. patens**
Stavesacre L. . . . **D. staphisagria**
Sticky L. . . . . **D. viscidum**
Stiff L. . . . . **D. rigidum**
Stocks L. . . . . . **D. stocksianum**
Strange L. . . . . . **D. paradoxum**
Strict L. . . . . **D. strictum**
Subglobose L. . . . **D. subglobosum**
Sulfur L. . . . . . . **D. sulphureum**
Sweet L. . . . . **D. suave**
Szechwan L. . . . **D. szechuanicum**
Talien L. . . . . **D. taliense**
Tall L. . . . . **D. exaltatum**
Tallmountain L. . . **D. scopulorum**
Tangut L. . . . . . . **D. tanguticum**
Tatsien L. . . . . . . **D. tatsienense**
Teheran L. . . . . . **D. teheranicum**
Ternate L. . . . . **D. ternatum**
Thibetan L. . . . . . **D. thibeticum**
Thickleaf L. . . . . **D. crassifolium**
Thickpod L. . . . . **D. dasycarpum**
Thickstem L. . . . . **D. crassicaule**
Thinleaf L. . . . . **D. leptophyllum**
Threebract L. . **D. tribracteolatum**
Threeleaf L. . . . **D. trifoliolatum**
Threelobe L. . . . . **D. trilobatum**
Tiny L. . . . . **D. minutum**
Toadflax L. . . . . . **D. linarioides**
Tomentose L. . . . . **D. tomentosum**
Tongol L. . . . . . . **D. tongolense**
Trelease L. . . . . . . **D. treleasei**
Tricolor L. . . . . **D. tricolor**
Tuber L. . . . . **D. tuberosum**
Turcoman L. . . . . . **D. turkmenum**
Turkestan L. . . . **D. turkestanicum**
Twohorn L. . . . . . . **D. bicornutum**
Twospike L. . . . . . **D. distichum**
Tyrolean Hairy L.
D. villosum tiroliense
Vanderweyer L. . . **D. vanderweyeri**

Larkspur, continued
Veiny L. . . **Delphinium venulosum**
Velvet L. . . . . **D. velutinum**
Walkers Kashmir L.
D. cashmerianum walkeri
Ward L. . . . . **D. wardi**
Waxleaf L. . . . . . . **D. cerefolium**
Wedge L. . . . . **D. cuneatum**
Wellby L. . . . . **D. wellbyi**
Whitebloom L. . . . . **D. albiflorum**
Whitemargin L. . **D. albomarginatum**
Whitemountain L. **D. sierrae-blancae**
White Siberian L.
D. grandiflorum album
Widepetal L. . . . . **D. latisepalum**
Willamette L. . . . **D. willametense**
Winkler L. . . . . **D. winklerianum**
Wislizenus L. . . . . . **D. wislizeni**
Wolfbane L. . . . . **D. lycoctonum**
Woollyfruit L. . . . **D. eriocarpum**
Woollystyle L. . . . **D. eriostylum**
Wooton L. . . . . **D. wootoni**
Wrinkled L. . . . . . **D. rugulosum**
Yellow L. . . . . **D. flavum**
Yellowroot L. . . . **D. xylorrhizum**
Yellowtinge L. . . . . **D. decorum**
Yellowwhite L. . . **D. xantholeucum**
Yunnan L. . . . . . . **D. yunnanense**
Zalil L. . . . . **D. zalil**

LAR'REA (*COVILLEA*) |w
Creosotebush
divarica'ta . . . . Spreading C.
tridenta'ta (*Covillea t.*) |w . Coville C.
—glutino'sa |w

LASERPIT'IUM . . . . . Laserwort (*Woundwort*)
latifo'lium

Laserwort . . . . **Laserpitium**

LASIA'CIS . . . . Tibisee
See **GRASS GENERA.**

LASIAN'DRA . . . . **TIBOUCHINA**
macran'tha . . . . **T. semidecandra**

LASTHE'NIA |w
glaber'rima |w
glabra'ta |w
—califor'nica (*L. californica*)

LASTRE'A . . . . . **DRYOPTERIS**
See **FERN GENERA.**

LATA'NIA . . . . Latania
See **PALM GENERA.**

Latanierbalai . **Coccothrinax argentea**

LATEX PRODUCTS, INCLUDING RUBBER (Plant Sources of)
See **ECONOMIC PLANTS, LATEX PRODUCTS, INCLUDING RUBBER.**

LATH'YRUS (*OROBUS* in part) |w
Peavine
apha'ca
arizo'nicus . . . . Arizona P.
azu'reus . . . . **L. sativus caeruleus**
bijuga'tus
—sand'bergi (*L. sandbergi*)
Sandberg P.
bolan'deri (*vestitus*) . . Bolander P.
ci'cera . . . . Flatpod P.
clyme'num (*articulatus*)
coria'ceus . . . . **L. lanszwerti**
cya'neus . . . . Blue P.
decaphyl'lus
eucos'mus . . . . Bush P.
gor'goni . . . . Gorgon P.
graminifo'lius . . . . Grassleaf P.
grandiflo'rus . . . . Everlasting P.

LATHYRUS, continued

hirsu'tus . . . . . Rough Peavine
inca'nus . . . . Hoary P.
japon'icus (*maritimus*) . Maritime P.
jep'soni |w . . . . Jepson P.
laetiflo'rus . . . . . . Canyon P.
lanszwer'ti (*coriaceus*) . Thickleaf P.
latifo'lius . . . . . . Perennial P.
Bridesmaid (*grandiflorus*) hv.
Rosy (*rosea*)
Royal (*splendens*)
Whitepearl (*albus*)
White Perennial
leucan'thus . . . . Aspen P.
littora'lis . . . . Beach P.
lute'us (*Orobus l.*) . . . Yellow P.
magellan'icus . . . . Magellan P. (*Lord Anson P.*)
marit'imus . . . . **L. japonicus**
monta'nus . . . . . . Mountain P.
ni'ger (*Orobus n.*) . . . . Black P.
nutt'alli . . . . Nuttall P.
ochroleu'cus . . . . Cream P.
o'chrus
odora'tus . . . . Sweetpea

For hort. var. of Sweetpea see special list below.

—nanel'lus . . . . Dwarf S.
orna'tus . . . . Showy P.
palus'tris |w . . . . Marsh P.
pauciflo'rus . . . . Fewflower P.
polyphyl'lus . . . . . . Pacific P.
praten'sis . . . . Meadow P.
pubes'cens . . . . Downy P.
pusil'lus . . . . Low P.
rose'us (*Orobus r.*) . . . . Pink P.
rotundifo'lius . . . . Roundleaf P.
sand'bergi . . . . . . **L. bijugatus s.**
sati'vus . . . . Grass P.
—caeru'leus (*L. azureus*) . Blue G.P.
setifo'lius . . . . . Bristleleaf P.
spathula'tus . . . . . . Spoon P.
splen'dens . . . . Royal P.
sulphu'reus . . . . Sulfur P.
sylves'tris . . . . Flat P.
—wag'neri . . . . . . Wagner F.P.
tingita'nus . . . . Tangier P.
—rose'us . . . . Pink T.P.
tomento'sus
tor'reyi . . . . Torrey P.
tubero'sus . . . . . Groundnut P.
undula'tus
utahen'sis . . . . Utah P.
veno'sus . . . . Veiny P.
ver'nus (*Orobus v.*) . . . . Bitter P.
—cya'nus . . . . Blue B.P.
vesti'tus . . . . **L. bolanderi**
viola'ceus . . . . Purple P.

Hort. var. of **Lathyrus odoratus**, Sweetpea:

Statement by Editorial Committee

The Editorial Committee wishes to gratefully acknowledge the fine cooperation of Elizabeth M. Bodger in supplying a really up-to-date listing of Sweetpea.

Especial attention is called to Miss Bodger's correct use of the distinctive term "strain," as applied to breeders' "fixed" varieties obtained by careful selection, particularly of annual flowers and vegetables. (Note that new hybrid varieties are not included in this category.) Bodger Seeds, Ltd., follow this procedure.

The questionable practice of many

LATHYRUS odoratus, continued

seedsmen, who for competitive or advertising motives apply their firm name to such a "strain," may be exposed to justifiable criticism; particularly so as its use would in no way detract from, but rather add to, publicity value, and would certainly be more in keeping with fact. Examples: Smith's Strain Hubbard (Squash), not Smith's Hubbard (Squash); Bodger's Strain Hollyhock, not Bodger's Hollyhock.

Statement by Author

Since publication of the first volume of Standardized Plant Names, great strides have been made in the development of Sweetpea strains and varieties. While in the 1923 edition there is but a relatively short list of horticultural varieties, there is at the present time a very long list of horticultural varieties available in three distinct strains of the Spencer type, i. e. Winter or Early Flowering Spencer, Spring or Intermediate Flowering Spencer, and Summer or Late Flowering Spencer. The old Grandiflora type is now virtually out of commerce.

In the following listings, all varieties now included in the catalogs of leading Sweetpea growers of the United States and England have been included. Where possible, the name of the originator is given.

The author is indebted to Mr. Frank Cuthbertson of San Francisco for valuable information obtained from his Sweetpea files.

Elizabeth M. Bodger,
El Monte, Calif.

Abbreviations of Classifications

Impr.	Improved.
SLS.	Summer or Late Spencer.
WES.	Winter or Early Spencer.

Abbreviations of Names of Originators

Ait.	Aitkins.
Ald.	Aldersey.
And.	Anderson & Co., Ltd., Sydney, Australia.
Ball	Geo. J. Ball, West Chicago, Ill.
Bla.	James Bland, England.
Bol.	Robert Bolton & Son, Birdbrook, nr. Halstead, Essex, England.
Bre.	Breadmore.
Bru.	F. H. Brunning Pty., Ltd., Melbourne, Australia.
Bur.	W. Atlee Burpee Co., Philadelphia, Pa.
Car.	Carters Tested Seeds, Ltd., Raynes Park, London, England.
Cole	Cole.
Cul.	Thomas Cullen & Sons, Ltd., Witham, Essex, England.
Cur.	S. F. Curtis.
Dam.	H. J. Damerum, England.
Dic.	Alex Dickson & Sons, Ltd., "Hawlmark," Belfast, Ireland.
Dob.	Dobbie & Co., Edinburgh, Scotland.
Eck.	Eckford, England.
F.-M.	Ferry-Morse Seed Co., San Francisco, Calif.; Detroit, Mich.
Hem.	Hemus.
Hin.	Dr. H. J. Hinton, England.
Hol.	Holmes, Sydenham, England.
Hou.	House.
Hur.	Hurst & Son, London, England.
I.&H.	Ireland & Hitchcock, Mascotts, Marks Tey, England.
King	E. W. King & Co., Ltd., Coggeshall, Essex, England.
Lum.	Lumley.
Mac.	Wm. Macdonald Seed Co., Santa Maria, Calif.
Mad.	Madeleines Floral Farms, Johannesburg, South Africa.
Mal.	A. Malcolm.
Mam.	Mamitsch, England.
Mor.	C. C. Morse & Co. (merged with Ferry-Morse Seed Co.)
MSF.	Moa Seed Farm.
Pea.	Pearson.
Pet.	A. Pettet.
Ryd.	Ryder & Son (1920), Ltd., St. Albans, Herts., England.
San.	W. E. Sands.
Sha.	Chas. Sharpe & Co., Ltd., Sleaford, Lincs., England.
Sme.	J. Smellie, England.
Smi.	E. J. Smith, England.
S.N.	Southfield Nurseries.
Sta.	Stark & Sons, Ltd., Fakenham, Norfolk, England.
Ste.	J. Stevenson, Wimborne, Dorset, England.
Sut.	Sutton & Sons., Ltd., Reading, England.
Unw.	W. J. Unwin, Ltd., Histon, Cambs., England.
Vau.	Vaughans Seed Store, Chicago, Ill.; New York, N. Y.
Ward	Ward.
W.-F.	Waller-Franklin Seed Co., Guadalupe, Calif.
Wilt.	R. F. M. Wiltshire, Netley Abbey, Southampton, England.
Wood.	F. C. Woodcock, Walmer, Kent, England.
Wri.	Wright.
W.&S.	Watkins & Simpson, Ltd., London, England.
Yat.	Arthur Yates & Co., Sydney, Australia.
Zvo., A.	Ant. C. Zvolanek, Lompoc, Calif.
Zvo., W.	Wm. Zvolanek, Lompoc, Calif.

Abundance. SLS. (Bur.)
Admiral. SLS. (Cul.)
Adonis. SLS. (Cul.)
Adorable. SLS. (Bur.)
Advance. SLS. (King.)
Affection. SLS. (Cur.)
All Bright. SLS. (F.-M.)
All White. WES. (W.-F.)
Ambition. SLS. (Cul.-Bur. 1932.)
America. SLS. (Mor.-Vau.)
American Beauty. WES. (F.-M.)
Amethyst. SLS. (Dob.)
Amethyst 2nd. WES. (W.-F.)
Amy Johnson. SLS. (King.)
Anglo. SLS. (Bur. 1934.)
Annie Ireland. SLS.
Annie Laurie. WES. (W.-F.)
Apollo. WES. (F.-M.)
Aristocrat. SLS. (Bol. 1937.)
Artiste. SLS. (F.-M.)
Ascot. SLS. (Cul.)
Asta Ohn. SLS. (F.-M.)
Atlantic. SLS. (Bur.)
Attraction. WES. (F.-M.)
Audrey. SLS. (Ste.)
Aurora. WES. (Bur.)
Austin Frederick. SLS.
Austin Frederick Impr. SLS. (Wood.)
Autocrat. SLS.
Avalanche. SLS. (Sut.-Lum. 1912.)
Aviator. WES. (W.-F.)
Bacchus. WES. (Mac.)
Ball Orange Impr. WES. (W.-F.)
Ballrose. WES. (Ball.)

Hort. var.; hv. = horticultural variety (or varieties); sp. = species (singular); spp. = species (plural).
¢ = clon; × (as a prefix) = hybrid; × (between scientific plant names) = crossed by; ∞ = polybrid; |w = plant useful to wildlife.
See Glossary for definitions of clon, hybrid, and polybrid.

LATHYRUS odoratus, continued
Ballrose Impr. WES.
Ballrose Queen. WES. (Ball.)
Balls Blue. WES. (Ball.)
Ballwhite. WES. (Ball.)
Balmoral. SLS. (Car.)
Baltimore. WES. (Bur.)
Barbara. SLS. (Hol.)
Beatall. SLS. (Bol. 1929.)
Beauty. SLS. (Ste.)
Beauty of Kent. SLS. (Wood.)
Begonia Rose. SLS. (Mac.)
Betsy Ross. WES. (Bur.)
Better Baltimore. WES.
Betty. SLS. (Dob.)
Bigbear. SLS.
Black Bess. SLS. (Bol.)
Black Diamond. SLS. (Sut.)
Blanche Ferry. SLS.-WES. (F.-M.)
Blaze. WES. (Mac.)
Blodwyn. SLS. (Ste.)
Bluebell. SLS. (Bol.)
Bluebird. SLS. (Cul.)
Bluebird 2nd. WES. (Bur.)
Bluebonnet. WES. (W.-F.)
Bluecharm. SLS. (I.&H.)
Bluedanube. WES. (Mac.)
Blueflame. SLS. (F.-M.)
Bluejacket. WES. (Bur.)
Bluejay. WES. (Zvo.)
Bluelagoon. SLS. (Car.)
Bluemonarch. SLS. (Sta.)
Bluemoon. SLS. (Car.)
Bluepicotee. WES. (W.-F.)
Blueribbon. SLS. (Cul.)
Blueshadow. SLS. (Sut.)
Bluewings. SLS.
Bonfire. SLS. (Bol.)
Bonniebriar. SLS. (Mac.)
Bonnie Lassie. SLS. (Bol.)
Bonnie Ruffles. SLS. (Bur. 1927.)
Boon. WES. (F.-M.)
Bountiful. SLS. (Bur.)
Bouquet. SLS.
Boyblue. SLS. (Cul.)
Boyblue 2nd. WES. (A. Zvo.)
Bridalveil. SLS. (F.-M.)
Bridesmaid. SLS. (Mor.)
Bridesmaid 2nd. WES. (Mac.)
Brightlight. WES. (F.-M.)
Brilliant.
Brilliant Rose. SLS. (Bur.)
Burpee. SLS. (Bur.)
Burpee Best White. SLS. (Bur.)
Burpee Blue. SLS. (Bur. 1937.)
Burpee Giant Pink. WES. (Bur.)
Burpee Impr. SLS. (Bur. 1938.)
Burpee Lavender. WES. (Bur.)
Burpee Orange. WES. (Bur.)
Burpee Orange Impr. WES. (Bur.)
Burpee Salmon. WES. (Bur.)
Burpee White. SLS.-WES. (Bur.)
Buy British. SLS. (King.)
Cambridge Blue. SLS. (Hol.-King 1937.)
Campfire. SLS. (F.-M.)
Canarybird. WES. (Bur.)
Capri. SLS. (F.-M. 1936.)
Captain Blood. SLS. (I.&H.)
Captivation. SLS. (Eck.)
Cardinal. SLS. (W.-F.)
Carlotta. SLS. (Car.)
Carmine Gem. SLS.
Cascade. WES. (W. Zvo.)
Cattleya. WES. (Mac.)
Cattleya Queen. SLS. (Mac.)
Cavalcade. SLS. (Bol. 1932.)
Celebrity. SLS. (F.-M.)

LATHYRUS odoratus, continued
Charity. SLS. (Ste.)
Charm. SLS. (Ste.)
Charm 2nd. WES. (Bur.)
Charming. SLS. (Ste.)
Cheerful. WES. (Bur.)
Cheerfulness. SLS. (Sut.)
Cheerio. SLS. (Mac. 1937.)
Chelsea. SLS. (Bol.)
Cherub.
Chevalier. WES. (Bur.)
Chieftain. SLS. (Cul. 1927.)
Chime. WES. (F.-M.)
Chinese Blue. SLS. (W.-F.)
Chloe. SLS. (Cul.)
Christmas Triumph. WES.
Cissie. SLS. (Bol. 1934.)
Claretcup. WES. (W.-F.)
Clematis. SLS. (Unw.)
Clipper. WES. (F.-M.)
Clown. SLS. (Unw.)
Colleen. WES. (Mac.)
Colne Valley.
Colonel. SLS. (Sta.)
Colorado. SLS. (Bol.)
Colossal Rose. WES. (Mac.)
Columbia. WES. (Yat.)
Columbine. SLS. (Unw.)
Colwood. SLS.
Commander Godsall. SLS. (Bol.)
Companion. SLS. (King.)
Conquest. SLS.
Constance Hinton. SLS. (Hin.)
Coquette. SLS. (Eck.)
Corona. SLS. (Cur.)
Coronation. SLS. (Bol.)
Coster Boy. SLS.
Countess. SLS.
Countess Spencer. SLS. (Cole.)
Cream. WES. (W.-F.)
Cream Gigantic. SLS. (Bol.)
Crimson King. SLS. (F.-M.)
Crinkles. SLS. (Bur.)
Crony. SLS. (Mac.)
Crusader. SLS. (Dic.)
Daddy Longlegs. SLS. (Bur.)
Daffodil. SLS. (Bol.)
Daffodil Impr. SLS.
Daintiness.
Daintymaid. SLS. (Cul.)
Daisybud. SLS.
Damask Rose. SLS. (Cul.-Bur.)
Dandy. SLS. (Sha.)
Daphne. WES. (F.-M.)
Daventry. SLS. (King.)
Daybreak.
Daylight. SLS. (Bur.)
Dazzler. SLS. (Bre.)
Debutante. SLS. (F.-M.)
Defiance. SLS. (W.-F.)
Delice. SLS. (Unw.)
Delicious. WES. (W.-F.)
Delightful. SLS. (F.-M.)
Delmonte. SLS. (F.-M.)
Delphinium. SLS. (Sut.)
Derbyday. SLS. (King.)
Diana. SLS. (Mac.)
Discovery. SLS. (F.-M.)
Dobbies Cream. SLS. (Dob.)
Dora. SLS. (Dob.)
Doreen. SLS. (F.-M.)
Doris.
Dubarry. SLS. (Cul.)
Duplex Fandango. WES. (F.-M.)
Duplex Gem. WES. (F.-M.)
Duplex Orchid. WES. (W. Zvo.)
Duplex Pioneer. WES. (F.-M.)
Ebony. SLS.

LATHYRUS odoratus, continued
Ecstasy. SLS. (Ward.)
Edna May Impr. SLS. (Wood.)
Eileen. WES. (Mac.)
Eldorado. WES. (W.-F.)
Eleanor Blue. WES. (Mac.)
Electra. SLS. (Unw.)
Elegance. SLS. (Sta.)
Elfrida Pearson. SLS. (Pea.-Dob.)
Elk Purple. WES. (A. Zvo.)
Elstree. SLS. (Bol.)
Embers. WES. (W. Zvo.)
Emblem. WES. (F.-M.)
Empirex. SLS.
Enchantress. SLS. (Sta.)
Ensign. SLS. (Mac.)
Ethereal. SLS. (Car.)
Etta Dyke. SLS. (Bre.)
Evening Star. WES. (Mac.)
Eventide. SLS. (Mac.)
Excelsior. SLS. (Cul.)
Exhibitionist. SLS. (Sta.)
Exposition Pink. WES. (W.-F.)
Exquisite. SLS. (Unw.)
Fair Lady. SLS. (Ste.)
Fair Maid. WES. (W.-F.)
Fairy.
Fairyland. SLS. (F.-M.)
Fantasy. SLS. (Unw.)
Fascination. SLS. (Eck.)
Fascination 2nd. WES. (W.-F.)
Favorite. SLS. (Bol.)
Favourite. SLS. (Cul.)
Fawn. SLS. (Bur.)
Fawn Impr. SLS.
Fearless. SLS. (Sut.)
Felice Gunther. WES.
Felix. SLS. (Sha.)
Fiancee. SLS. (Cul.)
Fierycross. SLS. (Bur.)
Fire. SLS. (Bur.)
Fireflame. SLS. (Bol.)
Fireglow. SLS. (Dob.)
Fireking. WES. (Bur.)
Flaglieutenant. SLS. (I.&H. 1930.) *The Flag Lieutenant.*
Flagship. SLS. (F.-M. 1937.)
Flamingjune. SLS. (Car.)
Flamingo. WES. (Bur.)
Flamingo 2nd. SLS. (Dob.; Ald. 1910.)
Flamingtorch. SLS.
Flora. SLS. (Mac.)
Floradale. SLS. (Bur.)
Floradale Fairy.
Floradale Purple. SLS. (Bur.)
Florence Nightingale. SLS. (Bur.)
Floristblue. WES. (W.-F.)
Floristrose. WES. (W.-F.)
Fluffyruffles. SLS. (Bur.)
Fordhook Blue. SLS. (Bur.)
Fordhook Orange. SLS. (Bur.)
Fordhook Pink & White. WES. (Bur.)
Fordhook Rose.
Fortune. SLS. (Bol.)
Fortyniner. WES. (Mac.)
Fragrance. WES. (Mac.)
Freckles. WES. (Mac.)
Frilled Lavender. SLS. (Sut.)
Garvey Queen. SLS. (San.)
Gem. SLS. (Ste.)
George Herbert. SLS. (Pre.)
George Shawyer. SLS. (Dob.)
Geo. (*W.*) Kerr. WES. (Bur.)
Giant Attraction. SLS. (King.)
Giantpink. WES. (King.)
Giantrose. WES. (F.-M.)

LATHYRUS odoratus, continued
Giantwhite. SLS. (Bur.)
Gigantic. SLS. (Bol. 1933.)
Gilda Gray. WES. (Bur.)
Gladys Impr. SLS. (King.)
Glamor. WES.
Glamour Girl. SLS. (Bur. 1940.)
Gleam. WES. (Bur.)
Gleneagles. SLS. (Dob.)
Glitters. WES. (Bur.)
Gloria. SLS. (Bla.)
Gloria 2nd. WES. (Mac.)
Gloriosa. SLS. (Bol.)
Glorious. WES. (And.)
Goldcrest. SLS. (Bol.)
Golden Dragon. SLS. (Mac.)
Golden Pink. WES. (Bur.)
Golden Radiance. SLS.
Golden West. SLS. (Sta.)
Golden Wings. SLS. (Ste.)
Goldfinch. SLS. (Unw.)
Good Cheer. SLS. (F.-M.)
Gracie. SLS. (Bol.)
Grandeur. SLS. (F.-M. 1938.)
Grand National. SLS. (King 1934.)
Grandslam. SLS. (F.-M.)
Greeting. WES. (F.-M.)
Grenadier. SLS. (Mal.-Dob.)
Grenadier 2nd. WES. (W.-F.)
Greta. SLS. (Bol. 1936.)
Guinea Gold. SLS. (Ste.)
Gwendolin. SLS. (Hou.)
Halo. SLS. (Bol.)
Happiness. SLS. (Bur.)
Harlequin. WES. (Mad.)
Harmony. WES. (A. Zvo.)
Hawlmark Cerise. SLS.
Hawlmark Lavender. SLS. (Dic.)
Hawlmark Maroon. SSL. (Dic.)
Hawlmark Pink. SLS. (Dic.)
Hawlmark Pink Impr. SLS.
Hawlmark Salmon Pink. SLS. (Dic.)
Hawlmark Scarlet. SLS. (Dic.)
Headlight. SLS. (Cul.)
Heatherbell. WES. (F.-M.)
Heavenly Blue. SLS. (W.-F.)
Hebe. SLS. (Ste.)
Helen Lewis. WES. (W.-F.)
Hercules. WES. (W.-F.)
Hercules 2nd. SLS. (Sta.)
Heyday. SLS. (Bur. 1937.)
Highlander. SLS. (Bol.)
His Majesty. SLS. (MSF.; Bur. 1939.)
Hollyberry. SLS. (King 1935.)
Honour. SLS. (Ste.)
Hope. WES. (Mac.)
Horn of Plenty. SLS. (Bur. 1940.)
Huntsman. SLS. (King.)
Ideal. SLS. (F.-M.)
Idyl. SLS. (F.-M.)
Illumination. WES. (Bur.)
Illuminator. SLS. (Bur.)
Imperial Pink. WES. (W.-F.)
Innocence. SLS. (Cur.)
Inspiration. WES. (A. Zvo.)
International. SLS. (King.)
Irisblue. WES. (Mac.)
Ivory Picture. SLS. (Bol.)
Jack Cornwell. SLS. (King.)
Jack Hobbs. SLS. (King.)
Jean Burpee. WES. (Bur.)
Jean Ireland. SLS. (Dob.)
Jeanne Mamitsch. WES. (Mam.)
Jessie. SLS. (Bol.)
Joan. SLS. (Ait.)
Joan Curtis. SLS. (Bol.)
John Ingman. SLS. (Cole.)

LATHYRUS odoratus, continued
Joseph. WES.
Josie. WES. (A. Zvo.)
Jubilee. SLS. (Dob.)
Jumbo. SLS. (Bol.)
Kames. SLS. (Dob. 1931.)
Kathleen Wiltshire. SLS. (Wilt.)
King. WES. (Bur.)
King Edward. SLS. (Bur.)
King Lavender. SLS. (F.-M. 1938.)
King Manoel. SLS. (Sta.)
King Mauve. SLS. (Wood.)
King White. SLS. (Bur.)
King White Impr. SLS.
Laddie. SLS. (I.&H.)
Laddie 2nd. WES. (Mac.)
Laddie Impr. WES. (Mac.)
Lady Gay. SLS. (Dob.)
Lady Gay 2nd. WES. (W.-F.)
Lady Lilford. SLS. (Bol. 1934.)
Lady Loch. SLS. (Bol.)
Lady Macbeth. SLS. (Mac.)
Lady Ruggles Impr. SLS. (Bur. 1933.)
Lafrance. SLS. (Mac.)
Lavanda. WES. (W.-F.)
Lavender George Herbert. SLS. (Bre.)
Lavender King. WES. (Bur.)
Lavender Lady. SLS. (Car.)
Leader. SLS. (Bol.)
Lemonqueen. SLS. (Car.)
Leslie Rundle. SLS. (King.)
Leviathan. SLS. (Sta.)
Life. SLS. (F.-M. 1937.)
Lilacdomino. SLS. (Unw.)
Lilacqueen. SLS. (Wood.)
Lively. WES.
Lochlomand. SLS. (Bol.)
Lompoc. SLS. (Bur.)
Loveliness. SLS. (Dob.)
Lucifer. SLS. (Dic.)
Lullaby. SLS. (F.-M.)
Lustre. SLS. (Ste.)
Magnet. SLS. (Cul.)
Magnolia. SLS. (Dob.)
Mahogany. SLS. (Sut.)
Majestic Cream. SLS.
Majestic Rose. WES. (W.-F.)
Mammoth. SLS. (Bol.)
Mandarin. SLS. (Dic.)
Margaret Atlee. SLS. (F.-M.)
Margaret Atlee Impr. SLS.
Margaret Rose. SLS. (San.)
Marina. SLS. (Dob.)
Marine. WES. (F.-M.)
Mariner. WES. (F.-M.)
Marion. SLS. (Unw.)
Maroon Prince. WES. (Bur.)
Mars. WES. (F.-M.)
Mary Louise Bok. WES.
Mary Pickford. SLS. (F.-M.)
Mascotts Helio. SLS.
Mascotts Ingman. SLS. (I.&H.)
Mascotts Scarlet. SLS. (I.&H.)
Mascotts White. SLS. (I.&H.)
Mastercream. SLS. (F.-M.)
Matchless. SLS. (Bol.)
Maud Holmes. SLS. (Hol.)
Mauve Beauty. WES. (Bur.)
Mavis. SLS. (King.)
Mayday. SLS. (Dob.)
Mayfair. SLS. (Cul.)
Maytime. SLS. (Mac.)
Meadowlark. WES. (F.-M.)
Meadowlark Impr. WES. (Mac.)
Melba. SLS. (Dob.)
Melody. SLS. (Unw. 1936.)
Memory. WES. (F.-M.)

LATHYRUS odoratus, continued
Mermaid. SLS. (Cul.)
Merrywidow. WES. (A. Zvo.)
Michael. SLS. (S. N.)
Michigan. WES. (A. Zvo.)
Mirth. SLS. (Mac.)
Miss Alabama. WES. (A. Zvo.)
Miss California. SIS. (F.-M.)
Miss (*Louise*) Gude Impr. WES. (Zvo.)
Miss Philadelphia. SLS. (Bur.)
Miss Spokane. WES. (Bur.)
Model. SLS. (Bol.)
Mollie. SLS. (Sme.)
Monterey. WES. (F.-M.)
Montrose. SLS. (Bol.)
Mother Machree. WES. (Mac.)
Mr. Cinders. SLS. (I.&H.)
Mrs. A. Hitchcock.
Mrs. (*Arnold*) Hitchcock. SLS. (Dob.)
Mrs. A. Searles. SLS. (Dam.-Bol.)
Mrs. (*Calvin*) Coolidge. WES. (Bur.)
Mrs. (*C.*) Kay. SLS. (Bol.)
Mrs. (*Herbert*) Hoover. WES. (Bur.)
Mrs. (*Horace*) Wright. SLS. (Unw.)
Mrs. (*H. R.*) Holscher. WES. (A. Zvo.)
Mrs. (*H. S.*) Reddick. WES. (W. Zvo.)
Mrs. (*J.*) Berry. SLS.
Mrs. Kerr. WES. (Bur.)
Mrs. Tom Jones. SLS. (Dob.)
Mrs. (*Warren G.*) Harding.
Mrs. (*Wm.*) Zvolanek. WES. (W. Zvo.)
Muriel. SLS. (San.)
My Choice. SLS. (King.)
Myosotis. SLS. (Car.)
Mystic. SLS. (Dob.)
Navyblue. WES. (W.-F.)
Newblue. WES. (W.-F.)
New Buttercup. SLS. (W.-F.)
Newdawn. SLS.
Nobility. SLS. (Sut.)
Nora Unwin. SLS. (Unw.—W.&S.)
Nouvelle. SLS. (Hur.)
Nubian. SLS. (Hou.)
Nymph. SLS. (Car.)
Olympia. SLS. (King.)
Ophelia. SLS. (Wood.)
Orangecloud. SLS. (Hur.)
Orangeflame. SLS. (Bur. 1931.)
Orangeflare. SLS. (Car.)
Orangeking. WES. (W.-F.)
Orangeking Impr. WES. (W.-F.)
Orange Picture. SLS. (I.&H.)
Orange Supreme. WES.
Orchid. SLS.
Orchid Impr. SLS. (Dic.)
Oriental. WES. (F.-M.)
Othello. SLS. (Eck.)
Othello 2nd. WES. (W.-F.)
Pacific. SLS. (Bur.)
Patricia Unwin. SLS. (Unw.)
Patriot. SLS. (King.)
Peachblossom. SLS. (Eck.)
Peachblossom 2nd. WES. (Bur.)
Peachblow. WES. (Bur.)
Peaches. WES. (W.-F.)
Pearl Buck. WES. (Bur.)
Peche Melba. SLS. (Car.)
Peer. SLS. (F.-M. 1938.)
Peeress. WES. (F.-M.)
Peerlesspink. WES. (Bur.)
Peggy Ann. SLS. (W.-F.)
Penrose. WES. (Bur.)
Perfection. WES. (A. Zvo.)
Personality. SLS. (F.-M.)

LATHYRUS odoratus, continued
Phyllis Simons. SLS.
Picardy. SLS. (Bol. 1937.)
Picture. SLS. (Bol.)
Pierrot. SLS. (Unw.)
Pimpernel. SLS. (King.)
Pinkcockade. SLS. (I.&H.)
Pinkest. SLS. (Wood.)
Pinkfrills. SLS. (Bol.)
Pinkgem. SLS. (Unw.)
Pinkie. SLS. (F.-M.)
Pinkmagnolia. SLS. (Dob.)
Pinkpearl. SLS.
Pinkprofusion. WES. (Bur.)
Pinksuffusion. SLS. (Sut.)
Pinkwonder. WES.
Pinnacle. SLS. (F.-M. 1935.)
Pirate.
Pirate Gold. SLS. (W.-F.)
Poppyday. SLS.
Porcelain. SLS. (I.&H.–Car.)
Powerscourt. SLS. (Cul.)
Premier. SLS. (Bol.)
Pres. Harding. SLS. (Bur.) *The President Harding.*
Prestige. SLS. (Dob. 1936.)
Pride. WES. (F.-M.)
Primrose. SLS. (Eck.)
Prince George.
Prince of Orange. SLS. (Hem.)
Princess. WES. (A. Zvo.)
Princess 2nd. SLS. (Sut.)
Princess Blue. WES. (Mac.)
Princess Royal. SLS. (Bol.)
Progress. SLS. (King.)
Prolific. SLS. (Bur. 1939.)
Prosperity. WES. (Mac.)
Purple King. SLS. (Eck.)
Purple Monarch. SLS. (Sut.)
Purple Perfection. SLS. (Dic.)
Purplerobe. SLS. (Hur.)
Queencrimson. WES. (F.-M.)
Queen Mary. SLS. (Car.)
Queen of the Belgians. SLS. (King.)
Quintuplets. SLS. (Bur.)
Radiance. WES. (Bru.)
Radiant. WES. (Mac.)
Radiant 2nd. SLS. (Ward.)
Ramona. WES. (Mac.)
Rapture. SLS. (F.-M. 1935.)
Rarity. SLS.
Ravenswing. SLS. (Dic.)
Redbeacon. SLS. (Unw.)
Redbird. WES. (Bur.)
Redboy. SLS. (F.-M. 1933.)
Redchief. WES.
Redcross. WES. (Mac.)
Redman. WES.
Redrobin. SLS. (Ste.)
Redrover. SLS. (King.)
Redsupreme. SLS. (W.-F.)
Redwood. WES.
Refinement. SLS. (Sut.)
Reflection. SLS. (F.-M.)
Regal. SLS. (Hur.)
Regal Lady. SLS. (Sut.)
Regal Purple. SLS. (Cul. 1930.)
Renown. SLS. (Dob.)
R. F. Felton. SLS. (Bol.)
Rhapsody. SLS. (Ryd.)
Robustum. SLS. (Bol. 1935.)
Romance. SLS. and WES. (Mac.)
Rosabelle. SLS. (Mal.)
Rosalie. SLS. (Car.)
Rosecharm. WES. (W.-F.)
Roseday. SLS. (Car.)
Rosemarie. WES. (Mac.)
Rosemary. SLS. (Ald.)

LATHYRUS odoratus, continued
Rose Picotee. WES. (Mac.)
Rosequeen. WES. (Pet.)
Rosequeen Impr. WES.
Rosie. SLS. (W.-F.)
Rosita. WES. (Mac.)
Rotarian. WES.
Royalbutterfly. SLS. (Car.)
Royalmauve. SLS. (Bol.)
Royalpink. SLS. (Bol.)
Royalpurple. SLS. (Wri.)
Royalruffles. SLS. (Bur. 1939.)
Royalsalute. SLS.
Royalscot. SLS. (Dob.)
Royalsovereign. SLS. (Dob.)
Rubicund. SLS. (Cul.)
Ruddigore. SLS. (Cul.)
Ruffled Beauty. SLS. (Bur. 1930.)
Ruffled Blue. SLS. (Bur.)
Ruffled Bonnieruffles. SLS. (Bur.)
Ruffled Burpeeblue. SLS. (Bur.)
Ruffled Carmine. SLS. (Bur. 1933.)
Ruffled Cerise. SLS. (Bur.)
Ruffled Crimson. SLS. (Bur. 1937.)
Ruffled Crinkles. SLS. (Bur.)
Ruffled Exquisite. SLS. (Bur.)
Ruffled Fluffyruffles. SLS. (Bur.)
Ruffled Fluffyruffles Impr. SLS. (Bur.)
Ruffled Glamour Girl. SLS.
Ruffled Heyday. SLS. (Bur.)
Ruffled Lady Ruffles. SLS. (Bur.)
Ruffled Lady Ruffles Impr. SLS.
Ruffled Mauve. SLS. (Bur. 1936.)
Ruffled Midblue. SLS. (Bur.)
Ruffled Orchid. SLS. (Bur.)
Ruffled Pink. SLS. (Bur. 1939.)
Ruffled Primrose. SLS. (Bur. 1933.)
Ruffled Purple. SLS. (Bur. 1936.)
Ruffled Rose. SLS. (Bur.)
Ruffled Royal Ruffles. SLS.
Ruffled Sparkle. SLS. (Bur.)
Ruffled White. SLS. (Bur. 1934.)
Sailorboy. SLS. (Hur.)
Salmon Fantasy. SLS.
Salmon Gigantic. SLS. (W.-F.)
Salmon Queen. SLS. (F.-M.)
Sandringham. SLS. (Sta.)
Satinmauve. SLS.
Scarletflame. SLS. (Unw.)
Scarletqueen. SLS. (Wood.)
Schoolmaster. SLS. (Hur.)
Scintillant. SLS. (Ste.)
Senator. SLS. (Eck.)
Senator Spencer. SLS. (Bur.)
Sentiment. SLS.
Sentinel. SLS. (F.-M.)
Sequoia. WES. (Mac.)
Sextet Appleblossom. SLS. (Sut.)
Sextet Lavender. SLS. (Sut.)
Sextetpink. SLS. (Sut.)
Sextetqueen. SLS. (Smi.-Sut.)
Sheba. SLS. (Bol.)
Shirley Temple. WES. (W.-F.)
Siesta. SLS. (F.-M.)
Silverblue. WES. (F.-M.)
Silver Jubilee. SLS. (Bol. 1935.)
Silverking. WES. (Bur.)
Silvermoon. SLS. (Dob.)
Simplicity. SLS. (F.-M.)
Sir Walter. SLS. (Dob.)
Skippy. WES. (W.-F.)
Smiles. SLS. (F.-M.)
Snowball. SLS. (W.-F.)
Snowdon. SLS. (Unw.)
Snowflake. WES. (F.-M.)
Snowqueen. WES. (Yat.)
Snowstorm. WES.

LATHYRUS odoratus, continued
Snowstorm Impr. WES. (Bur.)
Snowwhite. SLS. (Mac.)
Snowwhite 2nd. WES. (F.-M.)
Sonnet. WES. (F.-M.)
Sonnyboy. SLS. (King.)
Souvenir. SLS. (King.)
Sparkle. SLS. (Bur. 1938.)
Sparkle 2nd. WES. (F.-M.)
Spicy. SLS. (Bol.)
Splendour. SLS. (Ste.)
Springsong. WES. (F.-M.)
Springtime. SLS. (Dob.)
Star. WES. (F.-M.)
Starlight. WES. (W.-F.)
Startler. SLS. (Bol. 1937.)
Station Master. SLS. (King.)
Stylist. SLS. (F.-M. 1936.)
Success. WES. (F.-M.)
Sultan. SLS. (King 1921.) *The Sultan.*
Sunburst Impr. WES.
Sunkist. SLS. (F.-M.)
Sunproof Orange. WES. (Mac.)
Sunray. WES. (F.-M.)
Sunrise. SLS. (Car.)
Sunset. SLS. (Bol. F.-M. Vau. 1904.)
Superfine. SLS. (Bol.)
Superior Pink. WES. (F.-M.)
Supreme. SLS. (Bol.)
Supreme Orange. WES. (A. Zvo.)
Susan. SLS. (Bol.)
Susanna. WES. (Mac.)
Sweetbriar. WES. (Mac.)
Sweet Lavender. WES. (W.-F.)
Sweet Lavender 2nd. SLS. (Bol.)
Sybil Henshaw. SLS. (Unw.)
Tahoe. WES. (Mac.)
Tallyho. SLS. (King.)
Tangerine. SLS.
Tangerine Impr. SLS.
The Beauty. WES.
The Flaglieutenant. Flaglieutenant.
The Premier. WES. (King.)
The Pres. Harding. Pres. Harding.
The Sultan. Sultan.
Thriller. SLS. (Bol. 1931.)
Tiptop. SLS. (Hur.)
Titania. SLS. (Car.)
Titania 2nd. WES. (Mac.)
Tom Webster. SLS. (King.)
Tophat. WES. (Mac.)
Tops. SLS. (F.-M.)
Torch. WES. (F.-M.)
Tranquillity. SLS. (F.-M.)
Treasure. SLS. (Ste.)
Treasure Island. WES. (Mac.)
Triumph. WES (F.-M.)
Valencia. WES. (W.-F.)
Valentine. SLS. (Bol. 1918.)
Vanity. SLS. (F.-M.)
Vectis. SLS. (King.)
Venus. SLS. (Unw.)
Vera. WES.
Veronica. SLS. (I.&H.–Car.)
Violet Banner. SLS. (Bur.)
Violet Queen. SLS. (Car.)
Virginia. WES. (Mac.)
Vista. SLS. (F.-M.)
Vivian. WES. (A. Zvo.)
Vivid. SLS.
Vogue. WES. (F.-M.)
Vulcan. WES. (F.-M.)
Warren G. Harding. WES. (Bur.)
Warrior. SLS. (Ste. 1916.)
Wedgewood. SLS. (Dic.–Bur.)
Welcome. SLS. (F.-M.)
Wembley. SLS. (Bol.)

LATHYRUS odoratus, continued
WHATJOY. SLS. (Bol. 1927.)
WHITE CHAMPION. WES. (F.-M.)
WHITE EMBLEM. SLS. (Sha.)
WHITEGIANT. WES.
WHITEHARMONY. WES. (F.-M.)
WHITEHEATHER. SLS. (Dob.)
WHITE JOSIE. WES. (A. Zvo.)
WHITE POWERSCOURT. SLS. (Cul.)
WHITEROSE. WES. (A. Zvo.)
WHITE SPENCER. SLS. (Bur.)
WHITESTAR.
WILDROSE IMPR. SLS. (Ste.)
WINDSOR BLUE. SLS. (Mac.)
WINNIE MORSE. SLS. (F.-M.)
WINSOME. SLS.
WOODVIOLET. SLS.
WORLDSFAIR. WES.
YARRAWA. WES. (Yat.)
YELLOWTIP. SLS. (Bol.)
YOUTH. SLS. (F.-M.)
YULELOG GLOW. SLS. (King.)
ZVOLANEKS PERFECTION. WES. (A. Zvo.)
ZVOLANEKS PINK. WES. (A. Zvo.)
ZVOLANEKS ROSE. WES. (A. Zvo.)
ZVOLANEKS SALMON. WES. (A. Zvo.)
ZVOLANEKS SUPREMEORANGE. WES. (A. Zvo.)

In addition to the above, Spring or Intermediate Flowering Spencer varieties have been originated by the Ferry-Morse Seed Company as follows. The colors are shown but the varieties themselves have not as yet been assigned names. The years indicated are dates of introduction, actual or contemplated:

BLUE. SIFS. (F.-M. 1939.)
CLEAR ROSEPINK. SIFS. (F.-M. 1940.)
CREAM, Black seeded. SIFS. (F.-M. 1942.)
LAVENDER. SIFS. (F.-M. 1939.)
LIGHT CREAMPINK. SIFS. (F.-M. 1942.)
LIGHTLAVENDER. SIFS. (F.-M. 1942.)
MAUVE. SIFS. (F.-M. 1940.)
PURPLE. SIFS. (F.-M. 1942.)
ROSEPINK. SIFS. (F.-M. 1939.)
WHITE, Black seeded. SIFS. (F.-M. 1940.)
WHITE, White seeded. SIFS. (F.-M. 1940.)

LAUREL . . . . **Laurus**
GRECIAN L. . . . . **L. nobilis**

LAURELCHERRY . . . . **Prunus**

The Laurelcherries, often called by the misnomer Cherrylaurel, are the evergreen species belonging to the subgenus Laurocerasus. See also ALMOND, APRICOT, BIRDCHERRY, BUSHCHERRY, CHERRY, CHOKECHERRY, PEACH, PEACHBRUSH, and PLUM.

BIGLEAF COMMON L. **P. laurocerasus magnoliaefolia**
CAROLINA L. . . . . . . **P. caroliniana**
CAUCASIAN COMMON L. **P. laurocerasus caucasica**
COLCHIS C. L. **P. l. colchica**
COMMON L. . . . . **P. laurocerasus**
LITTLELEAF C. L. **P. l. parvifolia**
MYRTLE L. . . . . . . **P. myrtifolia**
NARROWLEAF COMMON L. **P. laurocerasus angustifolia**
PORTUGUESE L. . . . . **P. lusitanica**
ROUNDLEAF COMMON L. **P. laurocerasus rotundifolia**
SALAS L. . . . . **P. salasi**

LAURELCHERRY, continued
SCHIPKA COMMON L. **Prunus laurocerasus schipkaensis**
SERBIAN C. L. . . . . **P. l. serbica**
WESTINDIES L. . . . . **P. occidentalis**
ZABEL COMMON L. **P. laurocerasus zabeliana**

LAURE'LIA
novae-zealan'diae . . . . PUKATEA

LAUROCERA'SUS . . . **PRUNUS**
officina'lis . . . . . **P. laurocerasus**
—caucas'ica . . . . . **P. l. caucasica**
—col'chica . . . . . . **P. l. colchica**
—rotundifo'lia . . . **P. l. rotundifolia**
—schipkaen'sis . . **P. l. schipkaensis**

LAU'RUS . . . . LAUREL
ben'zoin . . . . **Lindera b.**
camph'ora . . . . . **Cinnamomum c.**
glandulif'era **Cinnamomum glanduliferum**
no'bilis . . . GRECIAN L. (*True Bay*)
¢BROADLEAF (*latifolia*) HV.
¢GOLDBAY (*aurea*)
¢NARROWLEAF (*angustifolia*)
¢ROYAL (*regalis*)
¢WILLOWLEAF (*salicifolia*)

LAVAN'DULA . . . . LAVENDER
abrotanoi'des
denta'ta . . . . TOOTHED L.
latifo'lia . . . . BROADLEAF L.
multif'ida . . . . JAGGED L.
officina'lis (*spica; vera*) . . TRUE L.
¢FOLGATE. HV.
¢MIDDACHEN
¢MUNSTEAD DWARF
¢PURPLE (*atropurpurea*)
¢WHITE (*alba*)
peduncula'ta
pinna'ta . . . . FRINGED L.
spi'ca . . . . **L. officinalis**
stoech'as . . . . FRENCH L.
ve'ra . . . . **L. officinalis**
vir'idis . . . . GREEN L.

LAVAN'GA . . . . . . **LUVUNGA**

LAVATE'RA . . . . . . TREEMALLOW
arbo'rea . . . . VELVET T.
¢VARIEGATED (*variegata*) HV.
assurgentiflo'ra . . . CALIFORNIA T.
cachemiria'na
cre'tica . . . . CRETE T.
da'vaei . . . . PORTUGAL T.
insula'ris . . . . ISLAND T.
malopetrif'ida . . . . . . BUSH T.
mauritan'ica . . . . . MAURITIUS T.
ol'bia
—rose'a
puncta'ta
—marocca'na
trimes'tris (*rosea*) . . . . . HERB T.
¢BIGFLOWER (*grandiflora*) HV.
¢SHOWY (*splendens*)
¢WHITE (*alba*)

LAVAUX'IA . . . . **OENOTHERA**

LAVENDER . . . . **Lavandula**
BROADLEAF L. . . . . . . **L. latifolia**
FRENCH L. . . . . **L. stoechas**
FRINGED L. . . . . **L. pinnata**
GREEN L. . . . . **L. viridis**
JAGGED L. . . . . **L. multifida**
TOOTHED L. . . . . **L. dentata**
TRUE L. . . . . **L. officinalis**

LAVENDERCOTTON . . . . . . **Santolina**
CYPRESS L. . . . **S. chamaecyparissus**

LAVENDERCOTTON, continued
GREEN L. . . . . . **Santolina virens**
NAPLES L. . . . . . . **S. neapolitana**
PINNATE L. . . . . **S. pinnata**

Lavendergrass . . . . . . MOORGRASS: **Molinia caerulea**

LAVER . . . . **Porphyra**
COMMON L. . . . . **P. vulgaris**
FINGERFROND L. . . . . **P. laciniata**

LAWNGRASS
JAPANESE L. . . . . **Zoysia japonica**
Korean L. . . . . JAPANESE L.

LAWSO'NIA . . . . HENNA
iner'mis . . . . HENNA
¢RED (*rubra*) HV.
¢WHITE (*alba*)

LAY'IA . . . . TIDYTIPS
calliglos'sa (*Callichroa douglasi; Calliglossa d.*)
chrysanthemoi'des (*Oxyura c.*) CHRYSANTHEMUM T.
el'egans . . . . SHOWY T.
glandulo'sa . . . . . WHITEDAISY T.
platyglos'sa . . . . YELLOWDAISY T.

LEADTREE . . . . **Leucaena**
GREAT L. . . . . . . **L. pulverulenta**
GREGG L. . . . . **L. greggi**
LITTLELEAF L. . . . . **L. retusa**
WHITEPOPINAC L. . . . . . **L. glauca**

LEADWOOD . . . **Krugiodendron ferreum**

Leafcactus . . EPIPHYLLUM: **Epiphyllum**

LEAFCROTON . . . . **Codiaeum**
VARIEGATED L. . . . . **C. variegatum**

LEAFCUP . . . . **Polymnia**
YELLOW L. . . . . **P. uvedalia**

LEAFFLOWER . . . . **Phyllanthus**
BIGCALYX L. . . . . . . **P. calycinus**
BIGLEAF L. . . . . . . **P. grandifolius**
BIRDSEED L. . . . . . . **P. avicularia**
BLUE L. . . . . **P. glaucescens**
EMBLIC L. . . . . **P. emblica**
FLOATING L. . . . . **P. fluitans**
FLYROOST L. . . . . **P. niruri**
JAMAICAGOOSEBERRY L. . **P. acuminatus**
KNOTWEED L. . . . **P. polygonoides**
MIMOSA L. . . . . . . **P. mimosoides**
OTAHEITE-GOOSEBERRY L. . **P. acidus**
SAGE L. . . . . . . **P. salviaefolius**
WIGHTS L. . . . . . . **P. wightianus**

LEAFSTALKGRASS . . . . **Pharus**
CREEPING L. . . . . . . **P. parvifolius**

Leatherflower . . . . CLEMATIS, LEATHERFLOWER: **Clematis viorna**

LEATHERLEAF **Chamaedaphne calyculata**
DWARF L. . . . . **C. c. nana**

LEATHERWOOD . . . . **Dirca**
ATLANTIC L. . . . . **D. palustris**
SANFRANCISCO L. . . . **D. occidentalis**

LEBECK'IA . . . . LEBECKIA
cytisoi'des . . . . BROOM L.

LECANO'RA . . . . LECANORA
candela'ria . . . . CANDELARIA L.
esculen'ta . . . . MANNA L.
haemato'ma . . . . . . BLOODSPOT L.
palles'cens . . . . PALE L.
parel'la . . . . CRABSEYE L.
tatar'ea . . . . LITMUS L.

LECH'EA |w . . . . PINWEED
interme'dia
villo'sa |w . . . . HAIRY P.

LECHENAUL'TIA . **LESCHENAULTIA**

LECHUGUILLA, JAUMAVE. **Agave funkiana**

LECID'EA . . . . LECIDEA
atrovi'rens . . . . MAP L.
sanguina'ria . . . . . BLOODRED L.

LE'CYTHIS . . . . MONKEYPOTTREE
laevifo'lia . . . . . . TRINIDAD M.
zabuca'jo SAPUCAIANUT M. (*Creamnut; Paradisenut; Sapucaianut*)

LE'DUM |w . . . . LEDUM
columbia'num . . . . . COLUMBIAN L.
glandulo'sum . . . . . WESTERN L.
groenland'icum (*latifolium*) |w LABRADORTEA L.
—compac'tum . . . . DWARF L.L.
palus'tre |w . . . . . CRYSTALTEA L.
—decum'bens . . . SPRAWLING C.L.
—dilata'tum . . . . WHITELEAF C.L.

LEE'A
amab'ilis
¢VARIEGATED (*splendens*) HV.
as'pera
sambuci'na

LEEK . . . . **Allium porrum**
LILY L. . . . . **A. moly**
WILD L. . . . . **A. tricoccum**

LEER'SIA (*HOMALOCENCHRUS*) CUTGRASS
See **GRASS GENERA.**

Legou'zia perfolia'ta . . . **Specularia p.**

LEIOPHYL'LUM (*DENDRIUM*) SANDMYRTLE
buxifo'lium (*Dendrium b.*) . . BOX S.
—hu'geri (*Dendrium h.*) . HUGERS S.
—prostra'tum (*Dendrium p.*) ALLEGANY S.

LEITNER'IA . . . . CORKWOOD
florida'na . . . . FLORIDA C.

LEMAIREOCE'REUS (*ARMATOCEREUS*)
See **CACTUS GENERA.**

∞ LEMANDARIN **Citrus limon × C. reticulata**

LEM'NA |w . . . . DUCKWEED
gib'ba |w . . . . SWOLLEN D.
min'ima |w . . . . LEAST D.
mi'nor |w . . . . COMMON D.
perpusil'la |w . . . . . MINUTE D.
triner'vis |w
trisul'ca |w . . . . STAR D.
valdivia'na |w

LEMON . . . . **Citrus limon**
PHILIPPINE L. . . . . . . **C. excelsa**

LEMONGRASS . . . **Cymbopogon citratus**
COCHIN L. . . . . **C. flexuosus**

Lemongum . . . . EUCALYPTUS, LEMON: **Eucalyptus citriodora**

∞ LEMONIME
Citrus aurantifolia × C. limon

LENS' (*LENTILLA*) . . . . LENTIL
culina'ris (*esculenta; Ervum lens; Lentilla l.*) . . . . COMMON L.

Lenscale . . . . SALTBUSH, BIG: **Atriplex lentiformis**

LENTENROSE . . . **Helleborus orientalis**

LENTIL . . . . **Lens**
COMMON L. . . . . **L. culinaris**

LENTIL'LA . . . . **LENS**
lens' . . . . **L. culinaris**

LENTI'NUS . . . . LENTINUS
lecomt'ei . . . . HAIRY L.
lepid'eus . . . . SCALY L.

LEOCE'REUS
See **CACTUS GENERA.**

LEONO'TIS . . . . LIONSEAR
du'bia
dysophyl'la
laxifo'lia
leonu'rus . . . . DRUG L.
nepetaefo'lia

LEON'TODON (*APARGIA*) |w HAWKBIT
autumna'lis (*Apargia a.*) |w . FALL H.
nudicau'lis (*Apargia n.*) . . ROUGH H.
tarax'acum . . . **Taraxacum officinale**

LEONTOPO'DIUM . . . EDELWEISS
alpi'num (*Gnaphalium leontopodium*) COMMON E.
lindav'icum
sibir'icum . . . . SIBERIAN E.
transylvan'icum

LEONU'RUS . . . . . MOTHERWORT
×**amrhein'i**
cardi'aca . . . . COMMON M.
glauces'cens
sibir'icus . . . . SIBERIAN M.

LEOPARDBANE . . . . . . **Doronicum**
AUSTRIAN L. . . . . **D. austriacum**
BIGLEAF L. . . . . **D. macrophyllum**
CAUCASIAN L. . . . . **D. caucasicum**
DOWNY L. . . . . **D. clusi**
HEARTLEAF L. . . . . . **D. cordatum**
PLANTAIN L. . . . . . **D. plantagineum**
SUNFLOWER CAUCASIAN L. **D. caucasicum magnificum**

LEOPOLDIN'IA . . . . . . PIASSAVA
See **PALM GENERA.**

LEPACH'YS . . . . **RATIBIDA**

LEPARGYRE'A . . . **SHEPHERDIA**

LEPID'IUM |w . . . . PEPPERWEED
alyssoi'des . . . . MESA P.
bipinnatif'idum . . . . . WAYSIDE P.
campes'tre . . . . FIELD P.
cardami'nes . . . . SPANISH P.
densiflo'rum (*apetalum*) |w . PRAIRIE P.
dra'ba . . . . **Cardaria d.**
fre'monti . . . . DESERT P.
nit'idum . . . . TONGUE P.
perfolia'tum . . . . . . CLASPING P.
piscid'ium . . . . . FISHPOISON P.
re'pens . . . . LENS P.
sati'vum . . . . . . GARDENCRESS P. (*Garden Cress*)
¢NORMANDY (*crispum*) HV.
vesica'rium . . . . . . BLISTERING P.
virgin'icum |w . . . . . VIRGINIA P.

LEPIDORRHA'CHIS (*CLINOSTIGMA* in part)
See **PALM GENERA.**

LEPIDOSPAR'TUM . . . SCALYBROOM
latisqua'mum . . . . . . WOOLLY S.
squama'tum . . . . . CALIFORNIA S.

LEPIO'TA . . . . LEPIOTA
america'na . . . . AMERICAN L.
mor'gani . . . . GREENGILL L.
nauci'na . . . . SMOOTH L.
pro'cera . . . . PARASOL L.

LEPIS'MIUM
See **CACTUS GENERA.**

LEPRA'RIA . . . . LEPRARIA
chlori'na . . . . BRIMSTONE L.
ioli'thus . . . . VIOLET L.

Leptan'dra virgin'ica **Veronicastrum virginicum**

LEPTARRHE'NA
pyrolifo'lia

LEPTA'SEA . . . . . **SAXIFRAGA**

LEP'TILON . . . . . . **ERIGERON**

LEPTOCE'REUS . . . . . **CEREUS**
See **CACTUS GENERA.**

LEPTOCH'LOA . . . . SPRANGLETOP
See **GRASS GENERA.**

LEPTODAC'TYLON . . . . . **GILIA**

LEPTODER'MIS . . . LEPTODERMIS
kumaonen'sis
lanceola'ta
oblon'ga . . . . CHINESE L.
pilo'sa
pulchel'la
pur'domi . . . . PURDOM L.
rehderia'na . . . . REHDER L.

LEPTOGLOT'TIS . . . **SCHRANKIA**

LEPTOLO'MA
See **GRASS GENERA.**

LEPTOP'TERIS
See **FERN GENERA.**

LEPTOPY'RUM
fumarioi'des (*Isopyrum f.*)

LEPTOSI'PHON . . . . **GILIA**
parviflo'rus . . . . **G. lutea**

LEPTOSPER'MUM . . . . TEATREE
ellip'ticum . . . . SLENDER T.
ericoi'des . . . . HEATH T.
erubes'cens
flaves'cens (*grandiflorum*) YELLOW T.
flexuo'sum . . . . . **Agonis flexuosa**
laeviga'tum . . . . . . VICTORIA T.
¢COMPACT (*compacta*) HV.
¢REEVES (*reevesi*)
liversid'gei
persiciflo'rum
pubes'cens (*lanigerum; nitidum*)
scopa'rium . . . . BROOM T.
¢BIGBLOOM (*grandiflorum*) HV.
¢BOXCAWEN (*boxcaweni*)
¢CHAPMAN (*chapmani*)
¢JUNIPER (*juniperinum*)
¢MYRTLELEAF (*myrtifolium*)
¢NICHOLLS (*nichollsi; Crimson Manuka*)
¢PROSTRATE (*prostratum*)
¢PURSE (*bullatum*)
¢PYGMY (*pygmaeum*)
¢ROSE (*roseum*)
¢ROSE DOUBLE (*roseum plenum*)
¢RUBY (*rubra*)
¢SANDERS (*sandersi*)
¢WALKER (*walkeri*)
¢WHITE DOUBLE (*florepleno; White Manuka*)
spines'cens . . . . SPINY T.
stella'tum

LEPTOSY'NE . . . . . **COREOPSIS**
califor'nica . . . . **C. douglasi**

LEPTOTAE'NIA . . . . LEPTOTAENIA
multif'ida . . . . . . CARROTLEAF L.

LEPTO'TES
See **ORCHID GENERA.**

LEPTU'RUS
See **GRASS GENERA.**

LESCHENAUL'TIA (*LECHENAULTIA*)
bi'loba
floribun'da
formo'sa
linarioi'des

LESPEDE'ZA |w . . . . . Lespedeza
bi'color (*Desmodium b.*) . . . Shrub L.
—al'ba . . . . White S.L.
buer'geri . . . . Buerger L.
capita'ta |w . . . . . . Roundhead L.
chinen'sis . **Campylotropis macrocarpa**
cunea'ta (*sericea*) . . . Chinese L.
cyrtobo'trya
cystoi'des
daur'ica
delavay'i . . . . Delavay L.
formo'sa . . . . **L. thunbergi**
—albiflo'ra . . . . **L. japonica**
hir'ta |w . . . . Hairy L.
inshan'ica
interme'dia (*frutescens*) |w . Wand L.
japon'ica (*L. formosa albiflora; Desmodium japonicum*) . . . Japan L.
jun'cea . . . . Rush L.
kiusia'na
latis'sima . . . . . . Decumbent L.
macrocar'pa . . . . . **Campylotropis m.**
maximowicz'i . . . Maximowicz L.
procum'bens . . . . . . Trailing L.
re'pens |w . . . . . . Creeping L.
seric'ea . . . . **L. cuneata**
stipula'cea |w . . . . . . Korean L.
stria'ta |w . Common L. (*Japanclover*)
Kobe. hv.
Tennessee 76
stuv'ei |w . . . . Stuves L.
thunberg'i (*formosa; sieboldi; Desmodium penduliflorum*) Thunberg L.
—albiflo'ra . . . . . . White T.L.
tomento'sa . . . . Woolly L.
viola'cea |w . . . . Violet L.
virgin'ica |w . . . . . . Slender L.

Lespedeza . . . . **Lespedeza**
Buerger L. . . . . **L. buergeri**
Chinese L. . . . . **L. cuneata**
Common L. . . . . **L. striata**
Creeping L. . . . . **L. repens**
Decumbent L. . . . . . . **L. latissima**
Delavay L. . . . . **L. delavayi**
Hairy L. . . . . **L. hirta**
Japan L. . . . . **L. japonica**
Korean L. . . . . **L. stipulacea**
Maximowicz L. . . . **L. maximowiczi**
Roundhead L. . . . . . . **L. capitata**
Rush L. . . . . **L. juncea**
Shrub L. . . . . **L. bicolor**
Slender L. . . . . **L. virginica**
Stuves L. . . . . **L. stuvei**
Thunberg L. . . . . . . **L. thunbergi**
Trailing L. . . . . . . **L. procumbens**
Violet L. . . . . **L. violacea**
Wand L. . . . . **L. intermedia**
White Shrub L. . . . . . **L. bicolor alba**
White Thunberg L.
L. thunbergi albiflora
Woolly L. . . . . **L. tomentosa**

LESQUEREL'LA (*VESICARIA* in part)
Bladderpod
argen'tea . . . . Silver B.
condensa'ta
engelmann'i . . . . Engelmann B.
globo'sa . . . . Globe B.
stenophyl'la

LESSIN'GIA . . . . Lessingia
germano'rum
lepto'clada

Letterflower . . . . . . **Vauanthes**
Letterpetal . . . . . . **Graptopetalum**
Amethystine L. . . . **G. amethystinum**
Bartram L. . . . . **G. bartrami**
Orpet L. . . . . **G. orpeti**
Paraguay L. . . . . **G. paraguayense**

LETTSO'MIA
capita'ta (*strigosa*)

Lettuce . . . . **Lactuca**
Alpine L. . . . . **L. alpina**
Asparagus Garden L.
L. sativa asparagina
Bitter L. . . . . **L. virosa**
Blue L. . . . . **L. spicata**
Bourget L. . . . . **L. bourgaei**
Canada L. . . . . **L. canadensis**
Chicory L. . . . . **L. pulchella**
Crinkle Garden L. . **L. sativa crispa**
Garden L. . . . . **L. sativa**
Grassleaf L. . . . . . **L. graminifolia**
Head Garden L. . . **L. sativa capitata**
Longleaf G. L. . . . . **L. s. longifolia**
Perennial L. . . . . **L. perennis**
Plumiers L. . . . . **L. plumieri**
Prickly L. . . . . **L. serriola**

LEUCADEN'DRON . Leucadendron
argen'teum . . . . Silver L.
deco'rum
dis'color
plumo'sum . . . . Plume L.
stoko'ei
veno'sum

LEUCAE'NA . . . . Leadtree
glau'ca . . . . . Whitepopinac L.
gregg'i . . . . Gregg L.
pulverulen'ta . . . . Great L.
retu'sa . . . . Littleleaf L.
tricho'des

LEUCAN'THEMUM
CHRYSANTHEMUM
grandiflo'rum; vulga're
C. leucanthemum

LEUCELE'NE . . . . **ASTER**
ericoi'des . . . . **A. leucelene**

LEUCHER'IA (*LEUCERIA*)
senecioi'des

LEUCHTENBER'GIA
See **CACTUS GENERA.**

LEUCOCA'SIA . . . . **COLOCASIA**

LEUCOCORY'NE . . . . Chilestar
ixioi'des (*odorata*)
Glory-of-the-sun C.
uniflo'ra . . . . **Brodiaea u.**

LEUCOCRI'NUM |w . . . . Starlily
monta'num |w . . . . . Common S.

LEUCO'JUM . . . . . . Snowflake
aes'tivum . . . . Summer S.
Gravety Giant. hv.
autumna'le . . . . Autumn S.
hyema'le . . . . April S.
pulchel'lum . . . . . . Sardinian S.
rose'um . . . . Rosy S.
trichophyl'lum . . Mediterranean S.
ver'num . . . . Spring S.
—carpath'icum . . . Carpathian S.S.
—vag'neri . . . . . . Hungarian S.S.

Leuco'phae can'dicans . . . **Sideritis c.**

LEUCOPHYL'LUM . . . Silverleaf
frutes'cens (*texanum*) . . . Texas S.
—floribun'dum
—glau'cum

LEUCOTH'OE (*EUBOTRYS*)
Leucothoe
axilla'ris . . . . Coast L.
cates'baei (*Andromeda c.*)
Drooping L.
—rollisso'ni . . . . Rollisson D.L.
davis'iae . . . . . Blacklaurel L.
graya'na . . . . Grays L.
—interme'dia
keisk'ei . . . . Keisks L.
populifo'lia (*acuminata*) . Florida L.
racemo'sa (*Andromeda r.; Eubotrys r.*)
Sweetbells L.
recur'va (*Eubotrys r.*) . . Redtwig L.

LEU'ZEA
conif'era (*Centaurea c.*)

LEVIS'TICUM . . . . Lovage
officina'le (*Hipposelinum o.*) Garden L.

LEWIS'IA |w . . . . Lewisia
columbia'na . . . . Columbia L.
—rose'a . . . . Pink C.L.
cotyle'don
eastwoodia'na . . . . . Eastwood L.
finch'i . . . . Finch L.
how'elli . . . . Howell L.
—crenula'ta . . . Scallopleaf H.L.
lea'na
min'ima . . . . Little L.
nevaden'sis . . . . Nevada L.
oppositifo'lia
pyg'maea . . . . Least L.
redivi'va |w . . . . . Bitterroot L.
triphyl'la . . . . Threeleaf L.
tweed'yi . . . . Tweedy L.

Lewisia . . . . **Lewisia**
Bitterroot L. . . . . **L. rediviva**
Columbia L. . . . . . **L. columbiana**
Eastwood L. . . . . . **L. eastwoodiana**
Finch L. . . . . **L. finchi**
Howell L. . . . . **L. howelli**
Least L. . . . . **L. pygmaea**
Little L. . . . . **L. minima**
Nevada L. . . . . **L. nevadensis**
Pink Columbia L. **L. columbiana rosea**
Scallopleaf Howell L.
L. howelli crenulata
Threeleaf L. . . . . **L. triphylla**
Tweedy L. . . . . **L. tweedyi**

LEYCESTE'RIA Himalayahoneysuckle
formo'sa (*elegans*) . . . . Showy H.

LHOTZ'KYA
cilia'ta
genetylloi'des

LIA'BUM . . . . Liabum
brown'ei . . . . . Woundwort L.
(*Woundwort*)

LIA'TRIS (*LACINARIA*) |w
Gayfeather
chap'mani . . . . Chapman G.
cylindra'cea . . . . Ontario G.
el'egans (*Lacinaria e.*) . Pinkscale G.
grac'ilis . . . . Slender G.
graminifo'lia (*Lacinaria g.*)
Grassleaf G.
hel'leri . . . . Heller G.
interme'dia . . . . **L. squarrosa i.**
ligulis'tylis (*Lacinaria l.*)
RockyMountain G.
odoratis'sima . . . . **Trilisa o.**
panicula'ta . . . . **Trilisa p.**
pauciflo'ra
pilo'sa . . . . Shaggy G.
puncta'ta (*Lacinaria p.*) . Dotted G.
pycnosta'chya (*Lacinaria p.*) Kansas G.

LIATRIS, continued
scario'sa (*Lacinaria s.*) Tall Gayfeather
—**al'ba** . . . . White T.G.
Magnifica. hv. L. scariosa
September Glory
Superba
spica'ta (*Lacinaria s.*) . . . Spike G.
—**al'ba** . . . . White S.G.
—**monta'na** (*?pumila* Hort.) Dwarf S.G.
squarro'sa (*Lacinaria s.*)
—**interme'dia** (*L. intermedia*)
tenuifo'lia . . . . . . Shortleaf G.

LIBERT'IA . . . . Libertia
formo'sa . . . . Showy L.
grandiflo'ra . . . . . Bigflower L.
ixioi'des . . . . Ixia L.
—**au'rea** . . . . Yellow I.L.
tri'color . . . . Tricolor L.

LIBIDIB'IA . . . . **CAESALPINIA**

LIBOCE'DRUS . . . . Incensecedar
bid'willi . . . . Pahautea I.
chilen'sis . . . . Chilean I.
decur'rens . . . . . . California I.
—**glau'ca** . . . . Blue C.I.
₵Dwarf (*compacta*) hv. L. decurrens
₵Variegated (*aureovariegata*)
macro'lepis . . . . . . Formosa I.
plumo'sa (*doniana*) . . . . Plume I.
uvif'era (*cupressoides; tetragona*)

LIBO'NIA . . . . **JACOBINIA**
floribun'da . . . . **J. pauciflora**

LICA'NIA (*MOQUILEA*) . . . Licania
plat'ypus (*Moquilea p.*) . Sansapote
pyrifo'lia . . . . . Indianmango L.
rig'ida
tomento'sa (*Moquilea t.*)

Licorice . . . . **Glycyrrhiza**
American L. . . . . . . **G. lepidota**
Common L. . . . . **G. glabra**
Russian L. . . . . **G. g. glandulifera**

Licoricefern . **Polypodium glycyrrhiza**

LICUA'LA . . . . Licualapalm
See **PALM GENERA.**

Licualapalm . . . . **Licuala**
Australian L. . . . . . **L. muelleri**
Coast L. . . . . **L. paludosa**
Fan L. . . . . **L. grandis**
Finger L. . . . . **L. pumila**
India L. . . . . **L. peltata**
Molucca L. . . . . **L. rumphii**
Spiny L. . . . . **L. spinosa**

Lidflower . . . . **Calyptranthes**
Myrtle-of-the-river L. . **C. zuzygium**
Pale L. . . . . **C. pallens**

Lig'num ba'phiae . . . . **Baphia nitida**

Lignumvitae . . . . **Guajacum**
Common L. . . . . **G. officinale**
Guatemala L. . . . **G. guatemalense**
Holywood L. . . . . **G. sanctum**

LIGULA'RIA (*FARFUGIUM*) Goldenray
clivo'rum (*Senecio c.*) . . Bigleaf G.
₵Othello. hv.
japon'ica (*Erythrochaete palmatifida; Senecio japonicus*) . . . Japan G.
kaemp'feri (*Senecio k.*) Kaempfer G.
₵Leopard (*aureo-maculata; Farfugium grande; F. maculatum*) hv.
₵Silveredge (*argentea; Farfugium argenteum*)

LIGULARIA, continued
macrophyl'la (*Senecio ledebouri*) Greatleaf Goldenray
sibir'ica (*Senecio sibiricus*) Siberian G.
stenoceph'ala (*Senecio stenocephalus*)
veitchia'na . . . . Veitch G.
wilsonia'na (*Senecio wilsonianus*) Wilson G.

LIGUSTICEL'LA . . . . Ligusticella
east'woodae . . . . . . Eastwood L.

LIGUS'TICUM |w . . . . Ligusticum
canaden'se . . . . Canada L.
filici'num . . . . Fernleaf L.
—**tenuifo'lium** (*L. tenuifolium*) Slim F.L.
gray'i (*oreganum*) . . . . . . Grays L.
por'teri . . . . Porter L.
pyrenae'um . . . . . . Pyrenees L.
sco'ticum |w . . . . Scotch L.

LIGUS'TRUM (*PARASYRINGA*) |w Privet
acumina'tum (*ciliatum* Rehd., *not* Bl. *nor* Sieb.; *medium* Hort., *not* Franch. & Sav.) . . Sharpleaf P.
—**macrocar'pum** . . . Bigberry S.P.
acutis'simum
amuren'se . . . . Amur P.
₵Silverspot (*argenteum variegatum*) hv.
₵Weeping (*pendulum*)
chenault'i . . . . . . Chenault P.
chinen'se . . . . **L. sinense**
cilia'tum Rehd. . . . . **L. acuminatum**
cilia'tum Sieb. . . . . **L. ibota**
compac'tum (*yunnanense*) Yunnan P.
coria'ceum **L. japonicum rotundifolium**
delavaya'num (*ionandrum; pratti*) Delavay P.
formosa'num . . . . . . Formosa P.
grac'ile . . . . Slender P.
hen'ryi . . . . Henrys P.
×**ibo'lium** (*obtusifolium × ovalifolium*) Ibolium P.
ibo'ta (*ciliatum* Sieb., *not* Bl.; *L. i. ciliatum*) . . . . Ibota P.
The plant in general cultivation under this name now appears to be L. obtusifolium! Horticulturists should make sure of *identification.*

in'dicum (*nepalense*) . . . . India P.
₵Variegated (*variegatum*) hv.
insula're . . . . Island P.
ionan'drum . . . . . **L. delavayanum**
japon'icum . . . . . Japanese P.
L. japonicum is often confused in trade with L. lucidum.

—**rotundifo'lium** (*L. coriaceum*) Roundleaf J.P.
₵Goldtip (*aureifolium marginatum*) hv. L. japonicum
₵Silverleaf (*excelsum superbum*)
₵Variegated (*variegatum*)
₵Yellowleaf (*aureifolium*)
lu'cidum (*L. japonicum macrophyllum; spicatum*) . . . . Glossy P.
Often confused in trade with L. japonicum.

₵Bigleaf (*macrophyllum*) hv.
₵Blackleaf (*nigrifolium*)
₵Compact (*compactum*)
₵Crinklyleaf (*recurvifolium*)
₵Graceful (*gracile*)
₵Griffings Waxleaf (*compactum*)
₵Pyramid (*pyramidale*)
₵Spreading (*repandens*)
₵Tricolor

LIGUSTRUM lucidum, continued
₵Upright (*erectum*)
₵Yellowleaf (*aureo-variegatum; aurifolium*)
massalongia'num . Himalayan Privet
me'dium . . . . **L. acuminatum**
nepalen'se . . . . **L. indicum**
obtusifo'lium . . . . Border P.
Horticulturists should note that this species apparently has been long mistakenly cultivated under the name L. ibota.

—**regelia'num** . . . . . Regels B.P.
₵Golden. hv. L. obtusifolium
₵Pygmy (*nanum*)
₵Wattle (*compactum*)
ovalifo'lium . . . . . California P.
₵Dwarf (*nanum*) hv.
₵Golden (*variegatum*)
₵Pyramidal (*pyramidale*)
₵Silverleaf (*argenteum*)
₵Whiteedge (*albomarginatum*)
₵Yellowedge (*aureomarginatum*)
pratt'i . . . . **L. delavayanum**
purpus'i . . . . Purpus P.
quihou'i . . . . Quihou P.
sempervi'rens (*Parasyringa s.*) Evergreen P.
sinen'se (*chinense*) . . . Chinese P.
Erroneously called Amur River Privet "South."

—**staun'toni** . . . . Staunton C.P.
spica'tum . . . . **L. lucidum**
strongylophyl'lum
vulga're |w . . . . . . European P.
₵Boxleaf (*buxifolium*) hv.
₵Darkgreen (*atrovirens*)
₵Golden (*variegatum*)
₵Greenfruit (*chlorocarpum*)
₵Lodense (*nanum*)
₵Netvein (*reticulatum*)
₵Pyramidal (*pyramidale*)
₵Silveredge (*albovariegatum*)
₵Silverspot (*argenteum-variegatum*)
₵Weeping (*pendulum*)
₵Whiteberry (*leucocarpum*)
₵Winterleaf (*sempervirens*)
₵Yellowberry (*xanthocarpum*)
₵Yellowdapple (*aureovariegatum*)
₵Yellowleaf (*aureum*)
yunnanen'se . . . . . **L. compactum**

Lilac . . . . **Syringa**
For hort. var. of Lilac see **SYRINGA.**

Amur L. . . . . **S. amurensis**
Blue Common L. . **S. vulgaris coerulea**
Bulgarian L. . . . . . **S. rhodopea**
Chengtu L. . . . . . **S. sweginzowi**
∞ Chinese L. . . . . . ∞ **S. chinensis**
Common L. . . . . **S. vulgaris**
Cutleaf Persian L. **S. persica laciniata**
Early L. . . . . **S. oblata**
Faurie L. . . . . **S. fauriei**
Felty L. . . . . **S. tomentella**
Hairy L. . . . . **S. pubescens**
Hairy Wolfs L. . . . **S. wolfi hirsuta**
∞ Henry L. . . . . ∞ **S. henryi**
Himalayan L. . . . . **S. emodi**
Hungarian L. . . . . . . **S. josikaea**
∞ Hyacinth L. . . . ∞ **S. hyacinthiflora**
Japanese Tree L. **S. amurensis japonica**
∞ Josiflexa L. . . . . . ∞ **S. josiflexa**
Juliana L. . . . . **S. julianae**
Komarof L. . . . . **S. komarowi**
Korean Early L. . **S. oblata dilatata**
Late L. . . . . **S. villosa**

LILAC, continued
LITTLELEAF L. . **Syringa microphylla**
MANCHURIAN L. . . . . . **S. velutina**
MEYER L. . . . . **S. meyeri**
∞ NANCEIANA L. . . . . ∞ **S. nanceiana**
NODDING L. . . . . . . **S. reflexa**
PALE N. L. . . . . **S. r. pallens**
PEKIN L. . . . . **S. pekinensis**
PERSIAN L. . . . . . . **S. persica**
PINEWOODS L. . . . . **S. pinetorum**
PINNATE L. . . . . . **S. pinnatifolia**
POTANIN L. . . . . . . **S. potanini**
∞ PRESTON L. . . . . ∞ **S. prestoniae**
PURPLE EARLY L. . . **S. oblata giraldi**
∞ SWEGIFLEXA L. . . . ∞ **S. swegiflexa**
∞ VARILEAF L. . . . . ∞ **S. diversifolia**
WHITE COMMON L. . . **S. vulgaris alba**
WHITE EARLY L. . . . **S. oblata a.**
WHITE NODDING L. . . . **S. reflexa a.**
WOLFS L. . . . . **S. wolfi**
YUNNAN L. . . . . **S. yunnanensis**

LILAE'A |w . . . . LILAEA
subula'ta |w . . . . AWLLEAF L.

LILAEOP'SIS |w . . . . . LILAEOPSIS
carolinen'sis |w . . . . . CAROLINA L.
linea'ta |w . . . . STRIPED L.

LIL'IUM |w . . . . LILY
With the kind permission of the author and of the publishers, the Editorial Committee has based this list in part on "Lilies for American Gardens," by George L. Slate, Charles Scribner's Sons, N. Y., 1939. Today many new hybrids are being produced and it is quite important that hybridizers record as accurately as possible, the parentage of the introduced polybrids, coining a suitable group name for such polybrids, made where feasible by combining syllables selected from each parent. ∞CROCEGANS L. (*croceum* × *elegans*) is a good example of such a polybrid name. Horticultural varieties (clons) selected from polybrids should be given appropriate "fancy" or vernacular instead of Latin names in conformity to International Rules and STANDARDIZED PLANT NAMES practice. ₵BROCADE, clon of ∞MARHANSON L. is a typical and good example.

alexan'drae . . . . **L. nobilissimum**
amab'ile . . . . KOREAN L.
₵KOREAN AUREUM (*luteum*) HV.
auranti'acum . **L. bulbiferum croceum**
aura'tum . . . . GOLDBAND L.
—**pic'tum** . . . . . . PAINTED G.L.
—**platyphyl'lum** (*L. macranthum*) BROADLEAF G.L.
—**rubrovitta'tum** . . . . . . RED G.L.
—**wit'tei** (*L. a. virginale* Hort.; *L. wittei*) WITTES G.L.
aurelianen'se Hort.
See hort. var. list below.
bakeria'num (*lowi*) . . . . BAKER L.
₵DELAVAY. HV.
beerens'i Hort.
See hort. var. list below.
bloomeria'num . . . **L. humboldti b.**
bolan'deri . . . . THIMBLE L.
brown'i . . . . BROWNS L.
—**colches'teri** . . COLCHESTER B.L.
₵LINTAN (*lintanense*) HV.
bulbif'erum . . . . BULBIL L.
—**cro'ceum** (*L. aurantiacum; L. croceum*) . . . . ORANGE B.L.
The emblem of the Orangemen in Ireland.
₵CHAIX (*chaixi*) HV.
callo'sum . . . . SLIMSTEM L.

LILIUM, continued
canaden'se . . . . . CANADA LILY
—**coccin'eum** (*L. c. rubrum*) RED C.L.
—**fla'vum** . . . . YELLOW C.L.
—*par'vum* . . . . **L. parvum**
can'didum . . . . MADONNA L.
—**cer'nuum** (*L. c. peregrinum*) SAMBAC M.L.
—**macula'tum** . PURPLESTRIPE M.L.
This may be synonymous with L. c. purpureum.
—**purpu'reum** . . . . PURPLE M.L.
₵CHARLES X. HV. L. candidum
₵MADONNA PLENUM (*plenum*)
₵SALONIKAE
carniol'icum . . . . . . CARNIOLA L.
—**alban'icum** . . . . ALBANIAN C.L.
—**jank'ae** . . . . JANKA C.L.
carolinia'num Michx., *not* Bosc. **L. michauxi**
cates'baei . . . . CATESBY L.
cathaya'num . . . . . . CATHAY L.
centifo'lium **L. leucanthum chloraster**
cer'nuum . . . . NODDING L.
chalcedon'icum . . CHALCEDONIAN L.
₵CHALCEDONIAN MACULATUM. HV.
col'chicum . . . . . **L. monadelphum**
columbia'num (*parviflorum*) COLUMBIA L.
—**in'grami** . . . . . . INGRAM C.L.
con'color . . . . . MORNINGSTAR L.
₵MORNINGSTAR RACEMOSUM. HV.
—**pulchel'lum** . . . . . STOUT M.L.
₵CORIDION. HV.
₵DROPMORE
₵OKIHIME
—**sin'icum** . . . . . . SPOTTED M.L.
corda'tum (*cordifolium*) HEARTLEAF L.
—**glehn'i** (*L. glehni*) . . GLEHN H.L.
cro'ceum . . . . . . **L. bulbiferum c.**
dalhan'soni Hort.
See hort. var. list below.
dalma'ticum . . **L. martagon cattaniae**
daur'icum (*davuricum*) DAHURIAN L.
—**lute'um** . . . . . . YELLOW D.L.
—**venus'tum** (*L. davuricum v.; L. venustum*) . . . . APRICOT D.L.
₵DAHURIAN BATEMAN (*batemanniae*) HV.
—**walla'cei** (*L. wallacei*) WALLACE D.L.
Possibly a hybrid.
—**wil'soni** . . . . . . WILSON D.L.
Some authorities refer this to L. d. pardinum.
₵DAHURIAN ERECTUM. HV. L. dauricum
₵DAHURIAN GRANDIFLORUM
₵DAHURIAN INCOMPARABILE
dav'idi (*thayerae*) . . . . . DAVID L.
—**macran'thum** . . . . . SHOWY D.L.
—**unic'olor** (*L. willmottiae u.*) UNICOLOR D.L.
—**willmot'tiae** (*L. sutchuenense; L. warleyense; L. willmottiae*) SZECHWAN D.L.
₵LADY BYNG. HV. L. davidi
₵ORIOLE
₵QUEEN CHARLOTTE
davur'icum . . . . **L. dauricum**
—*thunbergia'num* . . . . ∞**L. elegans**
—*venus'tum* . . . . . **L. dauricum v.**
dis'tichum . . . . KOCHANG L.
duchar'trei (*farreri*) . . DUCHARTRE L.
∞ **el'egans** (*concolor* × *dauricum; L. davuricum thunbergianum; thunbergianum*) . . . . . . ∞ THUNBERG L.

LILIUM elegans, continued
₵ALICE WILSON. HV.
₵ALUTACEUM (*Kikak*)
₵CRIMSONKING
₵DECORUM
₵DIADEM
₵DOUBLE APRICOT
₵DOUBLE QUEEN
₵DOUBLE SCARLET
₵EARLY DAZZLER
₵HORSMANN
₵KINBUSEN
₵LEONARD JOERG
₵MAHOGANY (*Mahony*)
₵MARMORATUM AUREUM
₵OGON
₵ORANGE HIRTELLUS (Imp.)
₵ORANGEQUEEN
₵PETER BARR
₵PICTUM GRANDIFLORUM
₵PRINCE OF ORANGE
₵PRINCESS
₵PURPLEQUEEN
₵REDEMPEROR
₵REDIMPROVED
₵THE PRESIDENT
₵THUNBERG ATRORUBRUM
₵THUNBERG ATROSANGUINEUM
₵THUNBERG ATROSANGUINEUM RUBROTINCTUM
₵THUNBERG AURANTIACUM
₵THUNBERG AUREUM
₵THUNBERG AUREUM NIGROMACULATUM
₵THUNBERG BICOLOR
₵THUNBERG BREVIFOLIUM
₵THUNBERG CITRINUM
₵THUNBERG FLOREPLENO
₵THUNBERG FULGENS
₵THUNBERG INCOMPARABLE
₵THUNBERG MACULATUM
₵THUNBERG ORANGEGLOW
₵THUNBERG ORNATUM
₵THUNBERG SANGUINEUM
₵THUNBERG SPLENDENS
₵YELLOWPURITY
excel'sum . . . . . ∞**L. testaceum**
exim'ium . . . . . **L. longiflorum e.**
far'gesi . . . . FARGES LILY
far'reri . . . . **L. duchartrei**
formosa'num (*L. philippinense f.*) FORMOSA L.
—**price'i** . . . . PRICE F.L.
formo'sum . . **L. longiflorum insulare**
gigan'teum . . . . GIANT L.
—**yunnanen'se** . . . . YUNNAN G.L.
glehn'i . . . . **L. cordatum g.**
gray'i . . . . GRAYS L.
han'soni . . . . HANSON L.
har'risi Hort. **L. longiflorum eximium**
held'reichi . . . . . . HELDREICH L.
hen'ryi . . . . HENRY L.
₵HENRY CITRINUM. HV.
humboldt'i . . . . . . HUMBOLDT L.
—**bloomeria'num** (*L. bloomerianum*) SMALLER H.L.
—**magnif'icum** . . . . LARGER H.L.
—**ocella'tum** . . . . . . EYED H.L.
—**puber'ulum** (*L. p.*) . . HAIRY H.L.
japon'icum (*krameri*) . . JAPANESE L.
—**al'bum** . . . . WHITE J.L.
—*alexan'drae* . . . **L. nobilissimum**
kel'loggi . . . . KELLOGG L.
kesselringia'num . . . KESSELRING L.
kra'meri . . . . **L. japonicum**
lankongen'se . . . . . LANKONG L.
ledebour'i . . . . . . LEDEBOUR L.
leicht'lini . . . . . . LEICHTLIN L.

LILIUM, continued

leicht'lini maximowicz'i (*L. maximowiczi; L. pseudotigrinum*) Orange Leichtlin Lily
leucan'thum . . . . Ichang L.
—chloras'ter (*L. centifolium*) Greenstripe I.L.
longiflo'rum . . . . Easter L.
—albomargina'tum . . Ribbon E.L.
—alexan'drae . . . **L. nobilissimum**
—exim'ium (*L. eximium; L. harrisi* Hort.; *L. l. harrisi* Hort.) Bermuda E.L.
—insula're (*L. formosum; L. l. formosum*)
₵Creole. hv. L. longiflorum
₵Easter Erabu (*L. longiflorum erabu*)
₵Easter Multiflorum
₵Takesima (*giganteum; takesima*)
₵Whitequeen
low'i . . . . **L. bakerianum**
macran'thum . **L. auratum platyphyllum**
macula'tum . . . . **L. medeoloides**
man'glesi Hort.
See hort. var. list below.
marit'imum . . . . Coast L.
mar'tagon . . . . Martagon L.
—cattan'iae (*L. dalmaticum; L. m. dalmaticum*) . . . Dalmatian M.L.
This may be a clon.
—pilosius'culum . . . . Hairy M.L.
₵Martagon Albiflorum. hv. L. martagon
₵Martagon Album
₵Martagon Albumsuperbum
maximowicz'i. . . . **L. leichtlini m.**
medeoloi'des (*maculatum*) . Wheel L.
michaux'i (*carolinianum* Michx., *not* Bosc.) . . . . Carolina L.
michiganen'se . . . . Michigan L.
monadel'phum (*colchicum*) Caucasian L.
—szovitzia'num . . . **L. szovitzianum**
myriophyl'lum . . . . . . Leafy L.
—superb'um (*L. sulphureum*) Sulfur L.L.
neilgherren'se . . . . . Nilghiri L.
nepalen'se . . . . Nepal L.
nevaden'se . . . . . . Eastwood L.
nobilis'simum (*alexandrae; L. japonicum a.; L. longiflorum a.*) Noble L.
occidenta'le . . . . . . Eureka L.
ochra'ceum . . . . Ocher L.
—primuli'num (*L. primulinum*) Primrose O.L.
papillif'erum . . . . . . Likiang L.
pardali'num . . . . . . Leopard L.
—roez'li . . . . **L. roezli**
₵Dimsdale Yellow. hv. L. pardalinum
₵Johnson
₵Leopard Angustifolium
₵Leopard Californicum
₵Leopard Fragrans
₵Leopard Giganteum
₵Leopard Orangeglow
₵Leopard Pallidifolium
₵Warei
₵Yuba
par'ryi . . . . Parry L.
—kess'leri . . . . . . Kessler P.L.
parviflo'rum . . . . **L. columbianum**
par'vum (*L. canadense p.*) . Sierra L.
—lute'um . . . . . . Yellow S.L.
philadel'phicum . . . . . Wood L.
—andi'num . . . . . Western W.L.
—monta'num . . . Mountain W.L.

LILIUM, continued

philippinen'se . . . Philippine Lily
—formosa'num . . . . **L. formosanum**
polyphyl'lum . . . . . . Afghan L.
pompon'ium . . . . . . Pompon L.
pon'ticum . . . . . . Blacksea L.
primuli'num . . . . **L. ochraceum p.**
prin'ceps Hort.
See hort. var. list below.
pseudotigri'num **L. leichtlini maximowiczi**
puber'ulum . . . . . **L. humboldti p.**
pu'milum (*tenuifolium*) . . Coral L.
₵Goldengleam. hv.
pyrena'icum . . . . . Pyrenees L.
—au'reum . . . . . Golden P.L.
—ru'brum . . . . Maroonspot P.L.
rega'le . . . . Regal L.
roez'li (*L. pardalinum r.*) Santacruz L.
rubel'lum . . . . Rubellum L.
₵Rubellum Album. hv.
rubes'cens (*L. washingtonianum r.*) Chaparral L.
sargen'tiae . . . . Sargent L.
sempervivoi'deum . . Houseleek L.
specio'sum . . . . . . Speciosum L.
—gloriosoi'des . . . . Marbled S.L.
—kraet'zeri . . . Greenstripe S.L.
—puncta'tum . . . . Pinkspot S.L.
—rose'um . . . . Rosy S.L.
—ru'brum . . . . Pink S.L.
₵Melpomene. hv. L. speciosum
₵Speciosum Album
₵Speciosum Erectum
₵Speciosum Magnificum
stewartia'num . . . . . Stewart L.
sulphu'reum **L. myriophyllum superbum**
superb'um . . . . . . Turkscap L.
sutchuenen'se . . **L. davidi willmottiae**
szovitzia'num (*L. monadelphum s.*) Szovitz L.
talien'se . . . . Talien L.
tenuifo'lium . . . . . . **L. pumilum**
∞ **testa'ceum** (*candidum* × *chalcedonicum; excelsum*) . . . . . ∞ Nankeen L.
thay'erae . . . . **L. davidi**
thomsonia'num . . . . . Thomson L.
thunbergia'num . . . . . ∞ **L. elegans**
tigri'num . . . . Tiger L.
₵Tiger Double (*flore pleno*) hv.
₵Tiger Erectum
₵Tiger Fortune
₵Tiger Giant Fortune
₵Tiger Nanum
₵Tiger Splendens
₵Tiger Splendens Burnham
tsingtauen'se . . . . . Tsingtau L.
umbella'tum Western Orangecup L.
∞ *umbella'tum* Hort., *not* Pursh. ∞ Umbel L.
Under the misnomer L. umbellatum are grouped a series of hort. var., including the following, thought to be derived from crossing certain forms of ∞ L. elegans with L. bulbiferum, L. b. croceum, and possibly L. dauricum:
₵Goldenfleece. hv.
₵Orange Brilliant
₵Orangeking
₵Prince of Wales
₵Refulgence
₵Sappho
₵Umbel Erectum
₵Umbel Grandiflorum
₵Umbel Incomparabile
₵Umbel Invincible
₵Umbel Splendidum
₵Umbel Vermillion Brilliant

LILIUM, continued

venus'tum . . . . . . **L. dauricum v.**
walla'cei . . . . **L. dauricum w.**
wallichia'num . . . . Wallich Lily
ward'i . . . . Ward L.
warleyen'se . . . **L. davidi willmottiae**
washingtonia'num . Washington L.
—mi'nor . . . . Shasta W.L.
—purpu'reum . . . . Purple W.L.
—rubes'cens . . . . . . **L. rubescens**
willmot'tiae . . . . . . **L. davidi w.**
—unic'olor . . . . **L. davidi u.**
wil'soni . . . . Wilson L.
wil'tei . . . . **L. auratum w.**

Polybrids of **Lilium**:

Following is a list of the known polybrids of Lilium, Lily. Every *new* hybrid combination should be given at once a polybrid name as indicated on p. 333. Each clon selected from a polybrid should be given a suitable hort. var. name.

∞ Chalceum Lily (*chalcedonicum* × *testaceum*)
∞ Crocegans L. (*croceum* × *elegans*)
∞ Crocelum L. (*croceum* × *pumilum*)
∞ Cromavid L. (*cromattiae* × ∞ Crovidi L.)
∞ Cromott L. (*croceum* × *davidi willmottiae*)
∞ Crotiger L. (*croceum* × *tigrinum*)
∞ Crovidi L. (*croceum* × *davidi*)
∞ Dahlmax L. (₵Dahurian Bateman × *leichtlini maximowiczi*)
∞ Dalhanson L. (*hansoni* × *martagon cattaniae*)
∞ Damottel L. (*dauricum* × *davidi willmottiae* × *elegans*)
∞ Dauriphil L. (*dauricum* × *philadelphicum*)
∞ Davmott L. (*davidi* × *d. willmottiae*)
∞ Dawilgans L. (*davidi willmottiae* × *elegans*)
∞ Hemysup L. (*henryi* × *myriophyllum superbum*)
∞ Marhanson L. (*hansoni* × *martagon*)
∞ Marsoni L. (*hansoni* × ₵Martagon Album)
∞ Maxwill L. (*davidi willmottiae* × *leichtlini maximowiczi*)
∞ Pardaboldt L. (*humboldti* × *pardalinum*)
∞ Pardavum L. (*pardalinum* × *parvum*)
∞ Parrybold L. (*humboldti* × *parryi*)
∞ Parrypard L. (*pardalinum* × *parryi*)
∞ Sargale L. (*regale* × *sargentiae*)
∞ Sargery L. (*henryi* × *sargentiae*)
∞ Sulfurgale L. (*myriophyllum superbum* × *regale*)
∞ Tigrimax L. (*leichtlini maximowiczi* × *tigrinum*)
∞ Wilbel L. (*umbellatum* × ∞ Wilcrovid L.)
∞ Wilcrovid L. (∞ Crovidi L. × *davidi willmottiae*)

Polybrid Hybrid Combinations:

(*chalcedonicum* × *testaceum*) ∞ Chalceum Lily
(*croceum* × *elegans*) ∞ Crocegans L.
(*croceum* × *davidi*) ∞ Crovidi L.
(*croceum* × *davidi willmottiae*) ∞ Cromott L.
(*croceum* × *pumilum*) ∞ Crocelum L.
(*croceum* × *tigrinum*) ∞ Crotiger L.
(*cromattiae* × ∞ Crovidi L.) ∞ Cromavid L.
(∞ Crovidi L. × *davidi willmottiae*) ∞ Wilcrovid L.

LILIUM, continued
(₵DAHURIAN BATEMAN × *leichtlini maximowiczi*) ∞ DAHLMAX LILY.
(*dauricum* × *davidi willmottiae* × *elegans*) ∞ DAMOTTEL L.
(*dauricum* × *philadelphicum*) ∞ DAURIPHIL L.
(*davidi* × *d. willmottiae*) ∞ DAVMOTT L.
(*davidi willmottiae* × *elegans*) ∞ DAWILGANS L.
(*davidi willmottiae* × *leichtlini maximowiczi*) ∞ MAXWILL L.
(*hansoni* × *martagon*) ∞ MARHANSON L.
(*hansoni* × ₵MARTAGON ALBUM) ∞ MARSONI L.
(*hansoni* × *martagon cattaniae*) ∞ DALHANSON L.
(*henryi* × *myriophyllum superbum*) ∞ HEMYSUP L.
(*henryi* × *sargentiae*) ∞ SARGERY L.
(*humboldti* × *pardalinum*) ∞ PARDABOLDT L.
(*humboldti* × *parryi*) ∞ PARRYBOLD L.
(*leichtlini maximowiczi* × *tigrinum*) ∞ TIGRIMAX L.
(*myriophyllum superbum* × *regale*) ∞ SULFURGALE L.
(*pardalinum* × *parryi*) ∞ PARRYPARD L.
(*pardalinum* × *parvum*) ∞ PARDAVUM L.
(*regale* × *sargentiae*) ∞ SARGALE L.
(*umbellatum* × ∞ WILCROVID L.) ∞ WILBEL L.

Common names and hort. var. of **Lilium**, LILY:

ABBREVIATIONS OF CLASS NAMES OF LILIES

Am.	Amabile
Bak.	Bakerianum
Br. c.	Browni colchesteri
Bu. c.	Bulbiferum croceum
Can.	Candidum
Chal.	Chalcedonicum
Co.	Concolor
Co. p.	Concolor pulchellum
Dau.	Dauricum
Dau. v.	Dauricum venustum
Dav.	Davidi
Ele.	Elegans
Hen.	Henryi
Lon.	Longiflorum
Mar.	Martagon
Pard.	Pardalinum
Pum.	Pumilum
Rub.	Rubellum
Spec.	Speciosum
Tig.	Tigrinum
Umb.	*Umbellatum* Hort.

AFGHAN L. **L. polyphyllum.**
ALBANIAN CARNIOLA L. **L. carniolicum albanicum.**
₵ALICE WILSON. Ele.
₵ALUTACEUM (*Kikak*). Ele.
APRICOT DAHURIAN L. **L. dauricum venustum.**
₵AURELIAN. Clon of ∞ SARGERY L.
₵AZALEA.
BAKER L. **L. bakerianum.**
Batemanniae. ₵DAHURIAN BATEMAN.
₵BEERENS. Clon of ∞ CHALCEUM L.
BERMUDA EASTER L. **L. longiflorum eximium.**
BLACKSEA L. **L. ponticum.**
₵BRENDA WATTS (*dauricum* × *davidi willmottiae* × *elegans*).
BROADLEAF GOLDBAND L. **L. auratum platyphyllum.**
₵BROCADE. Clon of ∞ MARHANSON L.
BROWNS L. **L. browni.**
BULBIL L. **L. bulbiferum.**
₵BURBANK. Clon of ∞ PARRYPARD L.

LILIUM, continued
CANADA L. **L. canadense.**
CARNIOLA L. **L. carniolicum.**
CAROLINA L. **L. michauxi.**
CATESBY L. **L. catesbaei.**
CATHAY L. **L. cathayanum.**
CAUCASIAN L. **L. monadelphum.**
₵CHAIX (*chaixi*). Bu. c.
CHALCEDONIAN L. **L. chalcedonicum.**
₵CHALCEDONIAN MACULATUM. Chal.
∞ CHALCEUM L. (*chalcedonicum* × *testaceum*).
CHAPARRAL L. **L. rubescens.**
₵CHARLES X. Can.
Citrinum. HENRY C.; THUNBERG C.
COAST L. **L. maritimum.**
COLCHESTER BROWNS L. **L. browni colchesteri.**
COLUMBIA L. **L. columbianum.**
₵COOLHURST. Clon of ∞ CROCEGANS L.
CORAL L. **L. pumilum.**
₵CORIDION. Co. p.
₵CORONATION. Clon of ∞ DAWILGANS L.
₵CREOLE. Lon.
₵CRIMSONKING. Ele.
∞ CROCEGANS L. (*croceum* × *elegans*).
∞ CROCELUM L. (*croceum* × *pumilum*).
∞ CROMAVID L. (*cromattiae* × ∞ CROVIDI L.)
∞ CROMOTT L. (*croceum* × *davidi willmottiae*).
∞ CROTIGER L. (*croceum* × *tigrinum*).
∞ CROVIDI L. (*croceum* × *davidi*).
₵CROWQUILP.
₵CROWQUINUM. Clon of ∞ CROCEGANS L.
₵CYRUS GATES. Clon of ∞ PARDABOLDT L.
∞ DAHLMAX L. (₵DAHURIAN BATEMAN × *leichtlini maximowiczi*).
₵DAHURIAN BATEMAN (*batemanniae*).
₵DAHURIAN ERECTUM. Dau.
₵DAHURIAN GRANDIFLORUM. Dau.
₵DAHURIAN INCOMPARABILE. Dau.
DAHURIAN L. **L. dauricum.**
∞ DALHANSON L. (*dalhansoni* Hort.; *hansoni* × *martagon cattaniae*).
DALMATIAN MARTAGON L. **L. martagon cattaniae.**
∞ DAMOTTEL L. (*dauricum* × *davidi willmottiae* × *elegans*).
∞ DAURIPHIL L. (*dauricum* × *philadelphicum*).
DAVID L. **L. davidi.**
∞ DAVMOTT L. (*davidi* × *d. willmottiae*).
∞ DAWILGANS L. (*davidi willmottiae* × *elegans*).
₵DECORUM. Ele.
₵DELAVAY. Bak.
₵DEREHAM. Clon of ∞ DALHANSON L.
₵DIADEM. Ele.
₵DIMSDALE. Clon of ∞ PARDABOLDT L.
₵DIMSDALE YELLOW. Pard.
₵DOUBLE APRICOT. Ele.
₵DOUBLE QUEEN. Ele.
₵DOUBLE SCARLET. Ele.
₵DOUGLAS INGRAM. Clon of ∞ PARDABOLDT L.
₵DROPMORE. Co. p.
DUCHARTRE L. **L. duchartrei.**
₵EARLY DAZZLER. Ele.
₵EASTER ERABU. *Erabu.* Lon.
EASTER L. **L. longiflorum.**
₵EASTER MULTIFLORUM. Lon.
EASTWOOD L. **L. nevadense.**
₵EDNA KEAN (*dauricum* × *davidi willmottiae* × *elegans*).
₵E. J. ELWES (*hansoni* × *martagon*).
₵ELLEN WILLMOTT (*hansoni* × *martagon*).
Erabu. ₵EASTER ERABU.
EUREKA L. **L. occidentale.**

LILIUM, continued
EYED HUMBOLDT L. **L. humboldti ocellatum.**
FARGES L. **L. fargesi.**
₵FIREGLOW. Clon of ∞ CROCELUM L.
₵FIREKING. Clon of ∞ WILBEL L.
₵FLAMBEAU.
FORMOSA L. **L. formosanum.**
₵FRANCES LARRABEE. Clon of ∞ PARRYBOLD L.
₵GEORGE (*C.*) CREELMAN. Clon of ∞ SARGALE L.
₵G. F. WILSON (*hansoni* × *martagon*).
GIANT L. **L. giganteum.**
GLEHN HEARTLEAF L. **L. cordatum glehni.**
₵GLOW.
GOLDBAND L. **L. auratum.**
₵GOLDENFLEECE. Umb.
₵GOLDENGLEAM. Pum.
₵GOLDENKING. Clon of ∞ CROMAVID L.
₵GOLDENORB. Clon of ∞ MARHANSON L.
₵GOLDENPARD. Clon of ∞ PARDAVUM L.
GOLDEN PYRENEES L. **L. pyrenaicum aureum.**
₵GRACE MARSHALL. Clon of ∞ DAWILGANS L.
GRAYS L. **L. grayi.**
GREENSTRIPE ICHANG L. **L. leucanthum chloraster.**
GREENSTRIPE SPECIOSUM L. **L. speciosum kraetzeri.**
₵GUINEA GOLD. Clon of ∞ MARHANSON L.
HAIRY HUMBOLDT L. **L. humboldti puberulum.**
HAIRY MARTAGON L. **L. martagon pilosiusculum.**
HANSON L. **L. hansoni.**
HEARTLEAF L. **L. cordatum.**
HELDREICH L. **L. heldreichi.**
∞ HEMYSUP L. (*henryi* × *myriophyllum superbum*).
₵HENRY CITRINUM. Hen.
HENRY L. **L. henryi.**
₵HORSFORD. Clon of ∞ DAHLMAX L.
₵HORSMANN. Ele.
HOUSELEEK L. **L. sempervivoideum.**
HUMBOLDT L. **L. humboldti.**
ICHANG L. **L. leucanthum.**
INGRAM COLUMBIA L. **L. columbianum ingrami.**
JANKA CARNIOLA L. **L. carniolicum jankae.**
JAPANESE L. **L. japonicum.**
₵JOHN MCLAUGHLIN. Clon of ∞ PARDABOLDT L.
₵JOHNSON. Pard.
KELLOGG L. **L. kelloggi.**
KESSELRING L. **L. kesselringianum.**
KESSLER PARRY L. **L. parryi kessleri.**
₵KINBUSEN. Ele.
KOCHANG L. **L. distichum.**
₵KOREAN AUREUM (*luteum*). Am.
KOREAN L. **L. amabile.**
₵KULSHAN.
₵LADY BYNG. Dav.
LANKONG L. **L. lankongense.**
LARGER HUMBOLDT L. **L. humboldti magnificum.**
LEAFY L. **L. myriophyllum.**
LEDEBOUR L. **L. ledebouri.**
LEICHTLIN L. **L. leichtlini.**
₵LEONARD JOERG. Ele.
₵LEOPARD ANGUSTIFOLIUM. Pard.
₵LEOPARD CALIFORNICUM. Pard.
₵LEOPARD FRAGRANS. Pard.
₵LEOPARD GIGANTEUM. Pard.

LILIUM, continued

Leopard L. **L. pardalinum.**
₵Leopard Orangeglow. Pard.
₵Leopard Pallidifolium. Pard.
Likiang L. **L. papilliferum.**
₵Lillian Cummings. Clon of ∞Damottel L.
₵Lintan (*lintanense*). Br. c.
₵Lyla McCann. Clon of ∞Damottel L.
Madonna L. **L. candidum.**
Madonna Plenum. Can.
Magnificum. Spec.
₵Mahogany (*Mahony*). Ele.
₵Mangles. Clon of ∞Crotiger L.
Marbled Speciosum L. **L. speciosum gloriosoides.**
∞Marhanson L. (*hansoni* × *martagon*).
₵Marmoratum Aureum. Ele.
Maroonspot Pyrenees L. **L. pyrenaicum rubrum.**
∞Marsoni L. (*hansoni* ×₵Martagon Album).
₵Martagon Albiflorum. Mar.
₵Martagon Album. Mar.
₵Martagon Albumsuperbum. Mar.
Martagon L. **L. martagon.**
₵Mary Swaythling (*hansoni* × *martagon*).
∞Maxwill L. (*davidi willmottiae* × *leichtlini maximowiczi*).
₵Melpomene. Spec.
₵Mercer Girl. Clon of ∞Parrybold L.
Michigan L. **L. michiganense.**
Morningstar L. **L. concolor.**
₵Morningstar Racemosum. Co.
Mountain Wood L. **L. philadelphicum montanum.**
₵Mrs. (*R. O.*) Backhouse. Clon of ∞Marsoni L.
₵Muriel Condie (*dauricum* × *davidi willmottiae* × *elegans*).
∞Nankeen L. ∞**L. testaceum.**
₵Napier. Clon of ∞Parrypard L.
Nepal L. **L. nepalense.**
Nilghiri L. **L. neilgherrense.**
Noble L. **L. nobilissimum.**
Nodding L. **L. cernuum.**
Ocher L. **L. ochraceum.**
₵Ogon. Ele.
₵Okihime. Co. p.
₵Orange Brilliant. Umb.
Orange Bulbil L. **L. bulbiferum croceum.**
Orangeglow. Leopard O.; Thunberg O.
₵Orange Hirtellus. Ele.
₵Orangeking. Umb.
Orange Leichtlin L. **L. leichtlini maximowiczi.**
₵Orangequeen. Ele.
₵Oriole. Dav.
Painted Goldband L. **L. auratum pictum.**
₵Paradou. Clon of ∞Sargale L.
∞Pardaboldt L. (*humboldti* × *pardalinum*).
∞Pardavum L. (*pardalinum* × *parvum*).
∞Parrybold L. (*humboldti* × *parryi*).
Parry L. **L. parryi.**
∞Parrypard L. (*pardalinum* × *parryi*).
₵Peter Barr. Ele.
₵Peter Puget. Clon of ∞Parrypard L.
∞Philada. Clon of ∞Dauriphil L.
∞Phildauricum. Clon of ∞Dauriphil L.
Philippine L. **L. philippinense.**
₵Philras. Clon of ∞Dauriphil L.
₵Phyllis Cox (*dauricum* × *davidi willmottiae* × *elegans*).
₵Pictum Grandiflorum. Ele.

LILIUM, continued

Pink Speciosum L. **L. speciosum rubrum.**
Pinkspot Speciosum L. **L. speciosum punctatum.**
Pompon L. **L. pomponium.**
Price Formosa L. **L. formosanum pricei.**
₵Pride of Charlotte. Clon of ∞Sargale L.
Primrose Ocher L. **L. ochraceum primulinum.**
₵Prince of Orange. Ele.
₵Prince of Wales. Umb.
₵Princeps. Clon of ∞Sargale L.
₵Princess. Ele.
₵Priscilla. Clon of ∞Marhanson L.
Purple Madonna L. **L. candidum purpureum.**
₵Purplequeen. Ele.
Purplestripe Madonna L. **L. candidum maculatum.**
Purple Washington L. **L. washingtonianum purpureum.**
Pyrenees L. **L. pyrenaicum.**
₵Queen Charlotte. Dav.
Red Canada L. **L. canadense coccineum.**
₵Redemperor. Ele.
Red Goldband L. **L. auratum rubrovittatum.**
₵Redimproved. Ele.
Redstar.

Dr. Slate reports that Redstar breeds true from seed and may even be a new sp.; while listed as a hv. of L. elegans, its true status has not yet been determined.

₵Refulgence. Umb.
Regal L. **L. regale.**
Ribbon Easter L. **L. longiflorum albomarginatum.**
Rosy Speciosum L. **L. speciosum roseum.**
₵Rubellum Album. Rub.
Rubellum L. **L. rubellum.**
₵Russet.
₵Sacajawea. Clon of ∞Pardaboldt L.
₵Salonikae. Can.
Sambac Madonna L. **L. candidum cernuum.**
SantaCruz L. **L. roezli.**
₵Sappho. Umb.
∞Sargale L. (*regale* × *sargentiae*).
Sargent L. **L. sargentiae.**
∞Sargery L. (*henryi* × *sargentiae*).
₵Sceptre. Clon of ∞Marhanson L.
₵Scott. Clon of ∞Dawilgans L.
Shasta Washington L. **L. washingtonianum minor.**
₵Shelburne. Clon of ∞Sargale L.
Showy David L. **L. davidi macranthum.**
₵Shuksan. Clon of ∞Pardaboldt L.
Sierra L. **L. parvum.**
₵S. J. Harmeling.
₵Skinners Orange. Clon of ∞Dauriphil L.
Slimstem L. **L. callosum.**
Smaller Humboldt L. **L. humboldti bloomerianum.**
₵Speciosum Album. Spec.
₵Speciosum Erectum. Spec.
Speciosum L. **L. speciosum.**
₵Speciosum Magnificum. Spec.
Spotted Morningstar L. **L. concolor sinicum.**
₵Star of Oregon (*humboldti* × *pardalinum*).
Stewart L. **L. stewartianum.**

LILIUM, continued

₵St. Nicholas. Clon of ∞Marhanson L.
₵Stooke. Clon of ∞Crotiger L.
Stout Morningstar L. **L. concolor pulchellum.**
∞Sulfurgale L. (*myriophyllum superbum* × *regale*).
Sulfur Leafy L. **L. myriophyllum superbum.**
₵Sunset.
₵Suttoncourt. Clon of ∞Marhanson L.
Szechwan David L. **L. davidi willmottiae.**
Szovitz L. **L. szovitzianum.**
₵T. A. Havemeyer. Clon of ∞Hemysup L.
₵Takesima (*giganteum; takesima*). Lon.
Talien L. **L. taliense.**
₵The President. Ele.
Thimble L. **L. bolanderi.**
Thomson L. **L. thomsonianum.**
₵Thunberg Atrorubrum. Ele.
₵Thunberg Atrosanguineum. Ele.
₵Thunberg Atrosanguineum Rubrotinctum. Ele.
₵Thunberg Aurantiacum. Ele.
₵Thunberg Aureum. Ele.
₵Thunberg Aureum Nigromaculatum Ele.
₵Thunberg Bicolor. Ele.
₵Thunberg Brevifolium. Ele.
₵Thunberg Citrinum. Ele.
₵Thunberg Florepleno. Ele.
₵Thunberg Fulgens. Ele.
₵Thunberg Incomparable. Ele.
∞Thunberg L. ∞**L. elegans.**
₵Thunberg Maculatum. Ele.
₵Thunberg Orangeglow. Ele.
₵Thunberg Ornatum. Ele.
₵Thunberg Sanguineum. Ele.
₵Thunberg Splendens. Ele.
₵Tiger Double (*florepleno*). Tig.
₵Tiger Erectum. Tig.
₵Tiger Fortune. Tig.
₵Tiger Giant Fortune. Tig.
Tiger L. **L. tigrinum.**
₵Tiger Nanum. Tig.
₵Tiger Splendens. Tig.
₵Tiger Splendens Burnham. Tig.
∞Tigrimax L. (*leichtlini maximowiczi* × *tigrinum*).
Tsingtau L. **L. tsingtauense.**
Turkscap L. **L. superbum.**
∞Umbel L. ∞*L. umbellatum* Hort.
₵Umbel Erectum. Umb.
₵Umbel Grandiflorum. Umb.
₵Umbel Incomparabile. Umb.
₵Umbel Invincible. Umb.
₵Umbel Splendidum. Umb.
₵Umbel Vermillion Brilliant. Umb
Unicolor David L. **L. davidi unicolor.**
₵Vashon. Clon of ∞Parrybold L.
Wallace Dahurian L. **L. dauricum wallacei.**
Wallich L. **L. wallichianum.**
Ward L. **L. wardi.**
₵Warei. Pard.
Washington L. **L. washingtonianum.**
Western Orangecup L. **L. umbellatum.**
Western Wood L. **L. philadelphicum andinum.**
Wheel L. **L. medeoloides.**
White Japanese L. **L. japonicum album.**
₵Whitequeen. Lon.

LILIUM, continued
∞Wilbel L. (*umbellatum* × ∞Wilcrovid L.).
∞Wilcrovid L. (∞Crovidi L. × *davidi willmottiae*).
Wilson Dahurian L. **L. dauricum wilsoni.**
Wilson L. **L. wilsoni.**
Wittes Goldband L. **L. auratum wittei.**
Wood L. **L. philadelphicum.**
Yellow Canada L. **L. canadense flavum.**
Yellow Dahurian L. **L. dauricum luteum.**
¢Yellowpurity. Ele.
Yellow Sierra L. **L. parvum luteum.**
¢Yuba. Pard.
Yunnan Giant L. **L. giganteum yunnanense.**

Lillipillitree . . . . . **Acmena smithi**

Lily
See **LILIUM.**

Lilyofthevalley . . **Convallaria majalis**
Fortunes L. . . . . . **C. m. fortunei**
Pink L. . . . . **C. m. rosea**

Lilythorn . . . . **Catesbaea**
Hedge L. . . . . **C. spinosa**

Lilytree . . . . **Crinodendron**
Red L. . . . . **C. patagua**
White L. . . . . . . **C. dependens**

Lilyturf . . . . **Mondo**
Dwarf L. . . . . . . **M. japonicum**
White L. . . . . **M. jaburan**

Lilyturf . . . . Liriope: **Liriope**

Lime . . . . **Citrus aurantifolia**

Limeberry . . . **Triphasia; T. trifolia**

∞Limequat . . . **Citrus aurantifolia × Fortunella spp.**

LIMNAN'THEMUM . **NYMPHOIDES**
nymphaeoi'des . . . . . **N. peltatum**

LIMNAN'THES |w . . . Meadowfoam
doug'lasi (*Floerkea d.*) |w Douglas M.

LIMNO'BIUM |w . Occident-frogbit
sinclair'i . . . . Mexican O.
spon'gia (*Hydrocharis s.*) |w Common O.
stolonif'erum . . . . WestIndies O.

LIMNOCH'ARIS . . . . . Velvetleaf
fla'va (*emarginata; plumieri*) Yellow V.
humboldt'i . . **Hydrocleis nymphoides**

LIMNOCIT'RUS . . . . Swamporange
littora'lis

LIMNO'DEA
See **GRASS GENERA.**

LIMNOPH'ILA . . . . . Marshweed
gratioloi'des . . . . Browns M.
javan'ica . . . . Java M.

LIMNOR'CHIS . . . **HABENARIA**
See **ORCHID GENERA, HARDY TERRESTRIAL GROUP.**

LIMODO'RUM . . . . **CALOPOGON**
Calopogon, a later name, is conserved under International Rules. See **ORCHID GENERA, HARDY TERRESTRIAL GROUP.**

LIMO'NIA L. (1763)
This old generic name for certain plants of the Citrus subfamily is now discarded as too uncertain of application.

acidis'sima . . . . . **Feronia limonia**

LIMO'NIUM (*GONIOLIMON; STATICE* in part) |w . Sea-lavender
angusta'tum |w . . . Narrowleaf S.
arbores'cens . . . . Tree S.
bellidifo'lium . . . . . **L. reticulatum**
binervo'sum (*Statice auriculaefolia*) Twonerve S.
bonduel'li (*Statice b.*) . . Algerian S.
brasilien'se (*Statice brasiliensis*) Brazil S.
brassicaefo'lium (*Statice brassicaefolia*) Canaries S.
califor'nicum (*L. commune c.; Statice limonium californica*) |w California S.
carolinia'num (*Statice caroliniana*) |w Carolina S.
cas'pia . . . . **L. reticulatum**
exim'ium (*Goniolimon e.; Statice eximia*) Sungari S.
¢Superb (*superbum*) hv.
¢White (*album*)
fru'ticans (*Armeria f.*) . . Woody S.
globulariaefo'lium (*salsuginosum*) Violettuft S.
gmel'ini (*Statice g.*) . . . Siberian S.
gougetia'num . . . . . . Gouget S.
imbrica'tum (*Statice imbricata*) Teneriffe S.
latifo'lium . . . . . . Wideleaf S.
—al'bum . . . . White W.S.
—rose'um . . . . Rosy W.S.
¢Elegance (*elegantissimum*) hv. L. latifolium
leptosta'chyum . . . . . Persian S.
lychnidifo'lium . . . . . Morocco S.
macrophyl'lum (*Armeria macrophylla; Statice m.*) . . . . . . Bigleaf S.
macrop'terum . . . . Broadwing S.
minu'tum . . . . Little S.
nash'i |w . . . . Nash S.
pectina'tum (*Statice pectinata*) Chalkdot S.
perez'i (*Statice p.*) . . . . Perez S.
perfolia'tum . . . . . Thorowort S.
preaux'i . . . . Preaux S.
puber'ulum . . . . . Yellowshrub S.
reticula'tum (*bellidifolium; caspia; Armeria caspia; Statice c.*) . Caspian S.
rupic'ola . . . . Crag S.
salsugino'sum . **L. globulariaefolium**
sinen'se . . . . Chinese S.
sinua'tum (*Statice sinuata*) Notchleaf S.
—candidis'simum . . . White N.S.
Album. hv. L. sinuatum
Atrocaeruleum
Carmineum
Roseum
spica'tum . . . . . Littlespike S.
∞**super'bum** (*leptostachyum × suworowi*) ∞Superbum S.
suworo'wi (*Statice s.*) . . Suworow S.
—al'bum . . . . White S.S.
tatar'icum (*Goniolimon t.; Statice tatarica*) . . . . Tatarian S.
—al'bum . . . . White T.S.
—angustifo'lium (*Statice incana; S. i. alba*) . . . . . . Lanceleaf T.S.
—na'num (*Statice incana nana*) Dwarf T.S.
trichog'onum |w . . . . Hairycup S.
virga'tum . . . . . . Seaviolet S.
vulga're . . . . Mediterranean S.

LIMOSEL'LA |w . . . . Mudwort
aquat'ica |w . . . . Water M.
subula'ta |w . . . . . . Awlleaf M.

LI'MU . . . . Limu
ko'la . . . . Ceremonial L.

Linaloe, Cayenne . . **Aniba panurensis**

LINAN'THUS . . . . **GILIA**
dianthiflo'rus . . . . . **G. dianthoides**
grandiflo'rus . . . . . . **G. densiflora**
parviflo'rus . . . . **G. lutea**

LINA'RIA |w . . . . Toadflax
aequitrilo'ba . . . . . **Cymbalaria a.**
alpi'na . . . . Alpine T.
×**—hy'brida** . . . . Hybrid T.
¢Dwarfrose (*nanarosea*) hv. L. alpina
amethyst'ea . . . . . . Amethyst T.
antica'ria
aparinoi'des . . . . . **L. heterophylla**
biparti'ta . . . . . . Clovenlip T.
—al'ba . . . . White C.T.
—splen'dida . . . . . . Royal C.T.
broussonnet'ia (*multipunctata*)
canaden'sis |w . . . . . . Oldfield T.
cymbala'ria . . . **Cymbalaria muralis**
dalmat'ica . . . . . . Dalmatian T.
delphinioi'des . . . . . **L. sapphirina**
elati'ne . . . . **Kickxia e.**
faucic'ola
filicau'lis
genistifo'lia . . . . . Broomleaf T.
hepaticaefo'lia . . . . . **Cymbalaria h.**
heterophyl'la (*aparinoides*)
ital'ica . . . . Italian T.
jat'tae
macedon'ica . . . . Macedonian T.
—specio'sa . . . . Showy M.T.
macrou'ra
marocca'na . . . . Morocco T.
mi'nor . . . . Small T.
multipuncta'ta . . . **L. broussonnetia**
origanifo'lia (*Anarrhinum crassifolium*)
panci'ci Hort. . . . . Golddollar T.
perez'i . . . . **L. tourneforti**
pilo'sa . . . . **Cymbalaria p.**
purpu'rea . . . . Purple T.
¢Canon Went. hv.
re'pens . . . . Palebluet T.
reticula'ta . . . . . . Purplenet T.
sapphiri'na (*delphinioides*) Sapphire T.
spu'ria . . . . **Kickxia s.**
supi'na
tournefort'i (*perezi*) . Tournefort T.
triornithoph'ora
triphyl'la . . . . . . Threeleaf T.
tris'tis (*melanantha*) . . . . Bitter T.
ventrico'sa . . . . Inflated T.
vulga'ris . . . . Butter-and-eggs T. (*Butter-and-eggs*)

LINDELO'FIA
longifo'lia (*spectabilis*)

Linden . . . . **Tilia**
Alabama L. **T. floridana alabamensis**
American L. . . . . . . **T. americana**
Amur L. . . . . **T. amurensis**
Appalachian L. . . . . . . **T. australis**
Beetree L. . . . . . **T. heterophylla**
Bigleaf L. . . . . . **T. platyphyllos**
Blueridge L. . . . . **T. venulosa**
Carolina L. . . . . . . **T. caroliniana**
Caucasian L. . . . . . . **T. dasystyla**
Chinese L. . . . . **T. chinensis**
ColonelsIsland L. . . . . **T. littoralis**
∞Crimean L. . . . . ∞**T. euchlora**
∞European L. . . . . . ∞**T. europaea**
Floribunda L. . . . . ×*T. floribunda*
Florida L. . . . . **T. floridana**
Georgia L. . . . . **T. georgiana**
Gulf L. . . . . **T. leucocarpa**

LINDEN, continued
HAIRY L. . . . . . . Tilia eburnea
HENRY L. . . . . T. henryana
HIGHLANDS L. . . . . . T. monticola
∞ HUNGARIAN L. . . . ∞ T. juranyana
JAPANESE L. . . . . . . T. japonica
KENDALLCOUNTY L. . . T. phanera
KOREAN L. . . . . . . T. insularis
KYUSHU L. . . . . . . T. kiusiana
LITTLELEAF L. . . . . . . T. cordata
LOUISIANA L. . . . . T. cocksi
MANCHURIAN L. . . T. mandshurica
MAXIMOWICZ L. . T. maximowicziana
MICHAUX L.
T. heterophylla michauxi
∞ MOLTKE L. . . . . . . ∞ T. moltkei
MONGOLIAN L. . . . . T. mongolica
OKALOOSA L. . . . . . T. porracea
OLIVER L. . . . . T. oliveri
QUEBEC L. . . . . T. neglecta
∞ ROUNDLEAF L. . . . ∞ T. orbicularis
SILVER L. . . . . . . T. tomentosa
SILVERPENDENT L. . . . T. petiolaris
SMOOTH HENRY L.
T. henryana subglabra
SPAETH L. . . . . × *T. spaethi*
TEXAS L. . . . . T. texana
TUAN L. . . . . T. tuan
WOOLLYTWIG T. L. . . T. t. chinensis
∞ YELLOW L. . . . . ∞ T. flavescens

LIN'DERA (*BENZOIN*) |w . SPICEBUSH
ben'zoin (*Benzoin aestivale; Laurus b.*) |w . . . . COMMON S.
—**xanthocar'pa** (*Benzoin aestivale xanthocarpum*) |w . YELLOWBERRY C.S.
cercidifo'lia
commu'nis (*Benzoin c.*). . CHINESE S.
megaphyl'la (*Benzoin grandifolium*)
GREAT S.
obtusilo'ba (*Benzoin obtusilobum*)
JAPANESE S.
prae'cox (*Benzoin p.*) . . FEBRUARY S.
seric'ea . . . . SILKY S.
trilo'ba . . . . THREELOBE S.
umbella'ta (*Benzoin umbellatum*)
UMBELED S.
—**hypoglau'ca** . . . . SILKYRIB U.S.

LINDERN'IA (*ILYSANTHES*) |w
FALSEPIMPERNEL
anagallid'ea |w
du'bia (*Ilysanthes d.*) |w

LINNAE'A |w . . . . . TWINFLOWER
borea'lis |w
—**america'na** (*L. americana*)
AMERICAN T.
—**longiflo'ra** (*L. longiflora*)
LONGTUBE T.

LINO'MA . . . . **DICTYOSPERMA**
See **PALM GENERA.**

LINOSPA'DIX (*BACULARIA*)
See **PALM GENERA.**

LINOSPA'DIX Becc., *not* Wendl.
PARALINOSPADIX
See **PALM GENERA.**

LINO'SYRIS
vulga'ris (*Aster linosyris; Chrysocoma l.*) . . . . EUROPEAN GOLDILOCKS

LI'NUM (*CATHARTOLINUM*) |w
FLAX
abyssin'icum Hort. . **L. usitatissimum**
₵ABYSSINIAN
africa'num . . . . AFRICAN F.
alpi'num . . . . ALPINE F.
angustifo'lium . . . NARROWLEAF F.

LINUM, continued
arbo'reum . . . . BUSH FLAX
austri'acum . . . . . AUSTRIAN F.
berlandier'i |w
BERLANDIER YELLOW F.
campanula'tum . . . . HAREBELL F.
capita'tum
cathar'ticum . . . . . . PURGING F.
colli'num . . . . HILL F.
corymbif'erum
crep'itans . . . . **L. usitatissimum c.**
fla'vum . . . . GOLDEN F.
—**compac'tum**
gal'licum . . . . FRENCH F.
grandiflo'rum . . . . FLOWERING F.
SCARLET (*coccineum*) HV.
hirsu'tum . . . . HAIRY F.
holog'ynum
hu'mile . . . . LOW F.
lew'isi . . . . LEWIS F.
monog'ynum . . . . NEWZEALAND F.
narbonnen'se . . . . NARBONNE F.
neomexica'num (*Cathartolinum n.*) |w
NEWMEXICO F.
nervo'sum
peren'ne (*sibiricum*) . PERENNIAL F.
WHITE (*album*) HV.
rig'idum (*Cathartolinum r.*) |w
STIFFSTEM F.
salsoloi'des . . . RUSSIANTHISTLE F.
—**na'num** . . . . . . DWARF R.F.
sibir'icum . . . . **L. perenne**
stria'tum |w . . . . RIGID F.
sulca'tum (*Cathartolinum s.*)
GROOVED F.
tenuifo'lium . . . . . SLIMLEAF F.
trig'ynum . . . . **Reinwardtia indica**
usitatis'simum |w . . . . COMMON F.

See notes and names of types and hort. var. of Linum usitatissimum under Flax in **CEREALS** and **FIBER PLANTS.**

—**crep'itans** (*L. crepitans*)
DEHISCENT C.F.
₵ABYSSINIAN (*abyssinicum*) HV. L. usitatissimum
₵AMERICAN (*americanum; White-flowered*)
virginia'num (*Cathartolinum v.*) |w
WOODLAND F.
visco'sum . . . . STICKY F.

LIONSEAR . . . . **Leonotis**
DRUG L. . . . . **L. leonurus**

LIONSHEART . . . . . . **Physostegia**
VIRGINIA L. . . . . . **P. virginiana**

LIP'ARIS . . . . TWAYBLADE
See **ORCHID GENERA, HARDY TERRESTRIAL GROUP.**

LIPFERN . . . . **Cheilanthes**
ALABAMA L. . . . . **C. alabamensis**
CALIFORNIA L. . . . . **C. californica**
COVILLE L. . . . . **C. covillei**
EATON L. . . . . **C. eatoni**
FEE L. . . . . **C. feei**
FENDLER L. . . . . . . **C. fendleri**
HAIRY L. . . . . **C. lanosa**
LACE L. . . . . **C. gracillima**
LINDHEIMER L. . . . . **C. lindheimeri**
SHAGGY L. . . . . **C. villosa**
SOUTHERN L. . . . . . **C. microphylla**
WOOLLY L. . . . . . . **C. tomentosa**
WRIGHT L. . . . . **C. wrighti**

LIPOCAR'PHA |w
macula'ta |w

LIP'PIA (*ALOYSIA*) |w . . . LIPPIA
canes'cens (*repens*) . . . CREEPING L.
chamaedrifo'lia
citriodo'ra (*Aloysia c.; Verbena c.*)
LEMONVERBENA L.
cuneifo'lia
dul'cis
gemina'ta |w
lanceola'ta |w
ligustri'na . . . . PRIVET L.
nodiflo'ra |w
re'pens . . . . **L. canescens**
urticoi'des
wright'i . . . . WRIGHT L.

LIQUIDAM'BAR |w . . . SWEETGUM
chinen'sis . . . . **Altingia c.**
formosa'na . . . . . . FORMOSA S.
—**montic'ola**
orienta'lis . . . . ORIENTAL S.
styracif'lua |w . . . . AMERICAN S.

LIRIODEN'DRON |w . . . TULIPTREE
chinen'se . . . . CHINESE T.
tulipif'era |w . . . . . TULIPTREE;
YELLOW POPLAR (Forestry)
—**obtusilo'bum** . . . . ROUNDLOBE T.
PYRAMID (*fastigiatum*) HV.
WHOLELEAF (*integrifolium*)
YELLOW (*aureo-marginatum*)

LIRI'OPE . . . . . LIRIOPE (*Lilyturf*)
graminifo'lia
Usually the plant grown under this name is L. spicata.
musca'ri (*L. graminifolia densiflora*)
BIGBLUE L.
EXILIFLORA. HV.
VARIEGATA
spica'ta . . . . CREEPING L.

LIRIOS'MA
ova'ta

Lisian'thus russellia'nus
Eustoma russellianum

LISSOCHI'LUS
heudelott'i

LIS'TERA (*OPHRYS*) . . . LISTERA
See **ORCHID GENERA, HARDY TERRESTRIAL GROUP.**

LI'TCHI . . . . LYCHEE
chinen'sis (*Nephelium litchi*) . LYCHEE

LITHOCAR'PUS (*PASANIA*) . TANOAK
Some authors regard Lithocarpus as feminine, the same as Quercus, presumably because in classic Latin, trees are feminine, but under present International Rules Lithocarpus is masculine.
cleistocar'pus (*Quercus cleistocarpa*)
cor'neus (*Quercus cornea*)
densiflo'rus (*Pasania densiflora; Quercus d.*) . . . . TANOAK
—**monta'nus** (*L. echinoides; L. densiflorus e.*) . . . . SCRUB T.
ed'ulis . . . . JAPANESE T.
gla'ber (*thalassica; Quercus g.*)
hen'ryi . . . . HENRY T.

LITHODO'RA . . . . . . LITHODORA
This genus is united by some botanists with Lithospermum.
diffu'sa (*Lithospermum diffusum; L. prostratum*) . . . . . . ACIDSOIL L.
GRACE WARD. HV.
HEAVENLY BLUE
frutico'sa (*Lithospermum fruticosum*)
LIME L.

LITHOPHRAG'MA (*LITHOFRAGMA*) WOODLANDSTAR
The spelling adopted above agrees with the original publication as a *genus*.
affi'nis (*Tellima a.*)
austra'lis . . . . SOUTHERN W.
parviflo'ra . . . . SMALLFLOWER W.
tenel'la . . . . SLENDER W.

LI'THOPS **MESEMBRYANTHEMUM**
See **SUCCULENTS.**

LITHOSPER'MUM lw . . GROMWELL (*Puccoon*)
angustifo'lium (*breviflorum; linearifolium*) lw . . . . . NARROWLEAF G.
arven'se lw . . . . CORN G.
as'perum . . . . WYOMING G.
canes'cens lw . . . . . . HOARY G.
carolinen'se (*hirtum*) . CAROLINA G.
diffu'sum . . . . . **Lithodora diffusa**
dis'tichum
frutico'sum . . . . **Lithodora fruticosa**
gme'lini lw
graminifo'lium . **Moltkia suffruticosa**
interme'dium
latifo'lium . . . . . . AMERICAN G.
linearifo'lium . . . **L. angustifolium**
multiflo'rum lw . . . MANYFLOWER G.
oblon'gum
officina'le lw . . . . . . COMMON G.
oleifo'lium
petrae'um . . . . . **Moltkia petraea**
prostra'tum . . . . **Lithodora diffusa**
purpureo-caeru'leum
rosmarinifo'lium
rudera'le . . . . WAYSIDE G.
sibir'icum . . . . **Mertensia sibirica**
tenuiflo'rum

LITHRAE'A
caus'tica
molleoi'des
veneno'sa

LIT'SEA . . . . LITSEA
calica'ris . . . . . . NEWZEALAND L.
dealba'ta . . . . . PIGEONBERRY L.
ferrugin'ea . . . . . RUSTYLEAF L.
glau'ca
leyten'sis (*obtusata*) . . BATICULIN L.
philippinen'sis . . . . . . BAKAN L.
reticula'ta . . . . . . BOLLYGUM L.

LITTOREL'LA lw . . . . SHOREWEED
america'na (*uniflora* U. S. Auth., *not* (L.) Asch.) lw . . . . AMERICAN S.
uniflo'ra . . . . EUROPEAN S.

Liveforever . . . SEDUM, LIVEFOREVER: **Sedum telephium**

LIVERBALSAM . . . . **Erinus**
ALPINE L. . . . . **E. alpinus**

Livingrock LIVINGROCKCACTUS: **Ariocarpus**

LIVINGROCKCACTUS . . . . . **Ariocarpus**
CHAUTLE L. . . . . **A. fissuratus**
COBBLERSTHUMB L. . . . . **A. retusus**
KOTSCHOUBEY L. **A. kotschoubeyanus**
LLOYD L. . . . . **A. lloydi**

LIVISTO'NA (*SARIBUS*) . FANPALM
See **PALM GENERA.**

LIZARDARUM . . . . . . **Sauromatum**
SIMLEN L. . . . . **S. simlense**
VEINY L. . . . . **S. venosum**

LIZARDTAIL . . . . **Saururus**
COMMON L. . . . . **S. cernuus**
ORIENTAL L. . . . . . . **S. loureiri**

LLOYD'IA . . . . ALPLILY
serot'ina . . . . COMMON A.

LLUMEPALM . . . . **Gaussia**
CUBAN L. . . . . **G. princeps**
PUERTORICAN L. . . . **G. attenuata**

LOA'SA . . . . CHILENETTLE
tri'color . . . . TRICOLOR C.
triphyl'la
u'rens . . . . **Eucnide u.**
vulcan'ica (*wallisi*)

Loba'ria pulmona'ria . . . . **Sticta p.**

LOBE'LIA lw . . . . LOBELIA
cardina'lis lw . . . CARDINALFLOWER
cavanil'lesi . . **L. laxiflora angustifolia**
da'vidi
dortman'na lw . . . . . . WATER L.
eri'nus . . . . EDGING L.
BASKET (*gracilis*) HV.
BLUE DWARF (*pumila*)
DOUBLE (*flore pleno*)
KERMESINA
LINDLEY (*lindleyana*)
LOW (*compacta*)
PAXTON (*paxtoniana*)
WHITE (*alba*)
WHITE-EYE (*speciosa*)
ful'gens . . . . MEXICAN L.
QUEEN VICTORIA. HV.
×**ger'ardi** (*fulgens* × *siphilitica*)
glandulo'sa
grac'ilis . . . . SLENDER L.
The name L. gracilis is often misapplied to Basket Lobelia, hort. var. of L. erinus.
heterophyl'la . . . . . HANDLEAF L.
hy'brida Hort.
Apparently a group name for a varied assortment of garden hybrids.
infla'ta . . . . . INDIANTOBACCO L.
kalm'i lw . . . . ONTARIO L.
laxiflo'ra
—angustifo'lia (*L. cavanillesi*)
paludo'sa lw
siphilit'ica (*syphilitica*) lw. BIGBLUE L.
LARGE WHITE (*alba*) HV.
spica'ta . . . . PALESPIKE L.
splen'dens WESTERN CARDINALFLOWER
tenu'ior (*ramosa*)
triquet'ra
tu'pa . . . . BLOOD L.
CERISE QUEEN. HV. Lobelia
FIREFLY
HUNTSMAN
JACK MCMASTERS
JACOBY
MRS. HUMBERT
PURPLE EMPEROR
PURPLE KING
RUBY
SILVER KING
SILVER QUEEN
STANDARD

LOBELIA . . . . **Lobelia**
BIGBLUE L. . . . . **L. siphilitica**
BLOOD L. . . . . **L. tupa**
CARDINALFLOWER . . . . **L. cardinalis**
EDGING L. . . . . **L. erinus**
HANDLEAF L. . . . . **L. heterophylla**
INDIANTOBACCO L. . . . . . **L. inflata**
MEXICAN L. . . . . **L. fulgens**
ONTARIO L. . . . . **L. kalmi**
PALESPIKE L. . . . . **L. spicata**
SLENDER L. . . . . **L. gracilis**
WATER L. . . . . **L. dortmanna**
WESTERN CARDINALFLOWER **L. splendens**

LOBIV'IA (*REBUTIA* in part)
See **CACTUS GENERA.**

LOBULA'RIA (*KONIGA*) SWEETALYSSUM
marit'ima (*Alyssum maritimum*)
—lutes'cens (*Alyssum l.*)
¢BENTHAMI. HV. L. maritima
¢COMPACTA
¢GIGANTEA
¢MINIMUM
¢ROCKMAT (*procumbens*)
¢TOMTHUMB
¢WHITEFLEECE

LOCH'NERA
rose'a (*Vinca r.*) MADAGASCAR-PERIWINKLE

LOCKHART'IA
See **ORCHID GENERA.**

LOCO . . . . **Astragalus**
See also MILKVETCH and POISONVETCH.
ARIZONA L. . . . . . . **A. arizonicus**
BARESTEM L. . . . . . . **A. scaposus**
BLUE L. . . . . **A. diphysus**
COLTON L. . . . . **A. coltoni**
CURVEPOD L. . . . . . **A. curvicarpus**
EARL L. . . . . **A. earlei**
EGGPOD L. . . . . **A. oocarpus**
HALFMOON L. . . . . . **A. allochrous**
HORN L. . . . . **A. horni**
MENZIES L. . . . . **A. menziesi**
MORTON L. . . . . **A. mortoni**
PATTERSON L. . . . . . **A. pattersoni**
PURSH L. . . . . **A. purshi**
SHEEP L. . . . . **A. nothoxys**
SPECKLEPOD L. . . . . **A. lentiginosus**
THOMPSON L. . . . . **A. thompsonae**
THURBER L. . . . . **A. thurberi**
TOWLINE L. . . . . **A. remulcus**
TWOGROOVED L. . . . . **A. bisulcatus**
UTAH L. . . . . **A. utahensis**
WARD L. . . . . **A. wardi**
WOOLLY L. . . . . . . **A. mollissimus**
WOOLLYLEAF L. . . . **A. leucophyllus**
WOOTON L. . . . . **A. wootoni**
YAQUI L. . . . . **A. yaquianus**

LOCUST . . . . **Robinia**
ASHES L. . . . . **R. ashei**
BOYNTON L. . . . . **R. boyntoni**
CLAMMY L. . . . . **R. viscosa**
ELLIOTT L. . . . . **R. elliotti**
HARTWIG L. . . . . **R. hartwigi**
∞ HOLDT L. . . . . ∞ **R. holdti**
KELSEY L. . . . . **R. kelseyi**
LITTLE L. . . . . **R. nana**
LONGLOBE L. . . . . **R. longiloba**
∞ MARGARET L. . . . . ∞ **R. margaretta**
NEWMEXICO L. . . . **R. neomexicana**
PALLID L. . . . . **R. pallida**
PANACOCO L. . . . . . . **R. panacoco**
ROSEACACIA L. . . . . . . **R. hispida**
RUSBY L. . . . . **R. rusbyi**
∞ SLAVIN L. . . . . ∞ **R. slavini**
SMOOTH ROSEACACIA L. **R. hispida macrophylla**
SOUTHWESTERN L. . . **R. subvelutina**
WESTERN L. . . . . . . **R. luxurians**

LODOI'CEA . . . . DOUBLE-COCONUT
See **PALM GENERA.**

LOESE'LIA
mexica'na (*coccinea*)
tenuifo'lia

LOGANBERRY . . . **Rubus loganobaccus**

LOGA'NIA
longifo'lia

LOGWOOD. **Haematoxylon campechianum**

LOISELEU'RIA (*CHAMAECISTUS*) |w Alpineazalea
procum'bens (*Azalea p.*) |w Alpineazalea

LO'LIUM . . . . Ryegrass
See **GRASS GENERA.**

LOMA'RIA . . . . . . **BLECHNUM**
See **FERN GENERA.**

LOMA'TIA . . . . Lomatia
ferrugin'ea (*pinnatifolia*)
fraxinifo'lia . . . . . . Ashleaf L.
ilicifo'lia . . . . Hollyleaf L.
longifo'lia
obli'qua . . . . Chilean L.
silaifo'lia . . . . . Crinklebush L.
tincto'ria . . . . . Guitarbush L.

LOMA'TIUM (*COGSWELLIA*) |w Lomatium
The species of Lomatium with thick rounded bulblike edible corms are known as Biscuitroot.

ambig'uum (*Cogswellia ambigua*) Wyeth Biscuitroot
anom'alum . . . . . **L. triternatum a.**
bi'color . . . . . . **L. leptocarpum**
circumda'tum . . . . Wallowa B.
cous' (*Cogswellia c.*) . . . . Cous B.
foenicula'ceum
gey'eri . . . . Geyer B.
leptocar'pum (*bicolor; Cogswellia b.*) Bicolor B.
macdou'gali (*jonesi*) . MacDougal L.
macrocar'pum (*Cogswellia macrocarpa*) Bigseed L.
nudicau'le (*Cogswellia nudicaulis; C. platyphylla*) . . . . Barestem L.
orienta'le |w
sim'plex (*Cogswellia s.*) Narrowleaf L.
triterna'tum (*Cogswellia triternata*) Nineleaf L.
—anom'alum (*L. anomalum; Cogswellia anomala*)
utricula'tum

LO'NAS
inodo'ra (*Athanasia annua*)
This monotypic Mediterranean Everlasting-like composite is often called by the misleading and inappropriate name "African Daisy."

LONCHOCAR'PUS . . . . Lancepod
black'i
honduren'sis . . . . . Honduras L.
latifo'lius
nic'ou
puncta'tus
seric'eus
specio'sus . . . . . . **Bolusanthus s.**
viola'ceus

Longan . . . . **Euphoria longan**

Longtom . . . . . **Paspalum lividum**

Longtube . . . . **Macrosiphonia**
Arizona L. . . . . **M. brachysiphon**

LONIC'ERA (*CHAMAECERASUS; DISTEGIA; NINTOOA; XYLOSTEON*) |w . . Honeysuckle
adenoph'ora
affi'nis
—pubes'cens

LONICERA, continued
al'berti . . . . **L. spinosa a.**
albiflo'ra
alpig'ena . . . . Alps Honeysuckle
₵Dwarf (*nana*) hv.
alt'manni . . . . . . Altmann H.
∞ **america'na** (*caprifolium* × *etrusca; italica*) . . . . ∞ Purplestem H.
₵Purple (*atrosanguinea*) hv.
₵Rubella
∞ **amoe'na** (*korolkowi* × *tatarica*) ∞ Gotha H.
₵Arnold (*arnoldiana*) hv.
₵Rosy (*rosea*)
₵White (*alba*)
angustifo'lia
arbo'rea
—per'sica
arizo'nica . . . . Arizona H.
au'cheri (*aurea*)
au'rea . . . . **L. aucheri**
This name unfortunately is often misapplied to L. periclymenum, hv. Golden.

∞ **bel'la** (*morrowi* × *tatarica*) ∞ Belle H.
₵Candida. hv.
₵Pink (*atrorosea*)
₵White (*albida*)
∞ **brown'i** (*hirsuta* × *sempervirens*) ∞ Browns H.
₵Coral (*plantierensis*) hv.
₵Orange (*punicea*)
₵Scarlet Fuchsia (*fuchsioides* Hort., *not* Hemsl.)
₵Youngs (*youngi*)
califor'nica . . . **L. hispidula vacillans**
canaden'sis (*ciliata*) American Fly H.
caprifo'lium . . . . Sweet H.
₵Purple (*pauciflora*) hv.
₵White (*alba*)
caucas'ica . . . . . . **L. orientalis c.**
chaetocar'pa
chamisso'i
chinen'sis . . . . . . **L. japonica c.**
chrysan'tha . . . . Coralline H.
—latifo'lia (*L. c.* form *turkestanica*) Turkestan C.H.
—lon'gipes
—regelia'na . . . . . Regels C.H.
Villous (*vellosa*) hv. L. chrysantha
cilio'sa |w . . Western Trumpet H.
coeru'lea (*caerulea*) . Sweetberry H.
—alta'ica
—angustifo'lia
—ed'ulis
₵Turkestan (*graciliflora*) hv. L. coerulea
confu'sa
conjugia'lis (*Xylosteon conjugiale*) Purpleflower H.
deflexica'lyx
—xeroca'lyx (*L. xerocalyx*)
demis'sa
denuda'ta . . . . . **L. subspicata d.**
dioi'ca (*glauca; parviflora*). Limber H.
dis'color
etrus'ca . . . . Etruscan H.
₵Cream (*gigantea; superba*) hv.
₵Esau (*gigantea* Zab., *not* Carr.; *pubescens*)
ferdinand'i . . . . . Ferdinand H.
—leycesterioi'des
fla'va . . . . Yellow H.
fragrantis'sima . . . . . Winter H.

LONICERA, continued
fuchsioi'des . Fuchsia Honeysuckle
fuchsioi'des Hort., *not* Hemsl. ∞ **L. browni** ₵Scarlet Fuchsia
gir'aldi . . . . Girald H.
glau'ca . . . . **L. dioica**
glauces'cens . . . . Donald H.
gracil'ipes . . . . Spangle H.
grif'fithi . . . . Griffith H.
gynochlamy'dea
∞ **heckrot'ti** (? ∞ *americana* × *sempervirens*) . . . . ∞ Everblooming H.
₵Goldflame (*Golden Flame*) hv.
hen'ryi . . . . Henry H.
heterolo'ba
heterophyl'la
hildebrandia'na . . . . . Giant H.
hirsu'ta |w . . . . Hairy H.
his'pida
hispid'ula
—vac'illans (*L. californica; L. h. californica*) . . . . . California H.
ibe'rica . . . . Iberian H.
implex'a
interrup'ta . . . . . Chaparral H.
involucra'ta (*Distegia i.*) |w Bearberry H.
—flaves'cens
—ledebour'i . . . . . . **L. ledebouri**
₵Serotina. hv. L. involucrata
ital'ica . . . . . . ∞ **L. americana**
japon'ica (*Nintooa j.*) |w . Japanese H.
—chinen'sis (*L. chinensis*) Purple J.H.
—hallia'na . . . . Halls J.H.
—repens
₵Yellownet (*aureo-reticulata*) hv. L. japonica
john'stoni (*L. subspicata j.*) Johnston H.
kesselring'i . . **L. orientalis longifolia**
koehnea'na . . . . . . Koehne H.
korolkow'i . . . . . . Blueleaf H.
—zabel'i
₵Aurora. hv. L. korolkowi
₵Broad (*floribunda*)
lanceola'ta
ledebour'i (L. *involucrata l.; Distegia l.*) . . . . Ledebour H.
longiflo'ra
Regarded by some botanists as indistinguishable from and a synonym of L. involucrata.

maack'i (*Chamaecerasus m.*) . Amur H.
₵Pink (*erubescens*) hv.
₵Podocarpa
maximowicz'i
—sachalinen'sis . . . Sakhalin H.
microphyl'la
∞ **minutiflo'ra** (*morrowi* × ∞ *xylosteoides*) ∞ Bunchberry H.
mor'rowi . . . . Morrow H.
₵Yellowfruit (*xanthocarpa*) hv.
∞ **muendenien'sis** (∞ *bella* × *ruprechtiana*) ∞ Muenden H.
∞ **muscavien'sis** (*morrowi* × *ruprechtiana*) . . . . ∞ Muscovy H.
myrtilloi'des
myrtil'lus
nervo'sa
ni'gra
nit'ida . . . . Box H.
∞ **no'tha** (*ruprechtiana* × *tatarica*) ∞ Rutarian H.

Hort. var.; hv. = horticultural variety (or varieties); sp. = species (singular); spp. = species (plural).
₵ = clon; × (as a prefix) = hybrid; × (between scientific plant names) = crossed by; ∞ = polybrid; |w = plant useful to wildlife.
See Glossary for definitions of clon, hybrid, and polybrid.

LONICERA, continued
oblongifo'lia SWAMP FLY HONEYSUCKLE
—altis'sima
obova'ta
ol'gae . . . . OLGA H.
orienta'lis . . . . . BUCKTHORN H.
—caucas'ica (*L. caucasica*)
—longifo'lia (*L. kesselringi*)
parviflo'ra . . . . **L. dioica**
pericly'menum
WOODBINE H. (*Woodbine*)
₵AUTUMN (*serotina*) HV.
₵DUTCH (*belgica*)
₵GOLDEN (*aurea*)
pilea'ta . . . . PRIVET H.
praeflo'rens
prolif'era (*sullivanti*) . . . GRAPE H.
∞ **propin'qua** (*alpigena* × *ledebouri*)
prostra'ta . . . . . CREEPING H.
∞ **pseudochrysan'tha** (*chrysantha* × *xylosteum*)
purpuras'cens
∞ **pur'pusi** (*fragrantissima* × *standishi*)
∞ PURPUS H.
pyrena'ica . . . . . . PYRENEES H.
quinquelocula'ris . . . MISTLETOE H.
WHITEFRUIT (*translucens*) HV.
ramosis'sima
The true L. ramosissima is not in cult.
rupic'ola
ruprechtia'na . . . MANCHURIAN H.
₵YELLOWFRUIT (*xanthocarpa*) HV.
sacca'ta
∞ **salicifo'lia** (*ruprechtiana* × ∞ *xylosteoides*) ∞ WILLOWLEAF H.
∞ **sar'genti** (*hirsuta* × *prolifera*)
∞ SARGENT H.
segrezien'sis
Possibly a form of L. xylosteum.
sempervi'rens . . . . . TRUMPET H.
₵MINOR. HV.
₵SCARLET (*superba*)
₵YELLOW (*sulphurea*)
sim'ilis
—delavay'i . . . . . . DELAVAY H.
spino'sa . . . . THORN H.
—al'berti (*L. alberti; Chamaecerasus a.*)
ALBERT T.H.
splen'dida (*splendens*)
stan'dishi (*sinensis*) . . . STANDISH H.
₵NARROWLEAF (*lancifolia*) HV.
strophioph'ora
subses'silis
subspica'ta . . . . . . MORONEL H.
—denuda'ta (*L. denudata*)
—john'stoni . . . . **L. johnstoni**
sullivant'i . . . . **L. prolifera**
syringan'tha . . . . . . LILAC H.
—wolf'i . . . . WOLFS L.H.
tangut'ica . . . . BLUSH H.
tatar'ica . . . . . . TATARIAN H.
₵BRIDE (*grandiflora*) HV.
₵GREAT (*latifolia*)
₵LEROYANA
₵LOW (*nana*)
₵MAIDEN (*virginalis*)
₵NARROWLEAF (*angustifolia*)
₵PALLENS
₵RED (*sibirica*)
₵ROSY (*rosea*)
₵SMALLFLOWER (*parvifolia*)
₵WHITE (*alba*)
₵YELLOW (*lutea*)
tatarino'vi
tatsienen'sis
∞ **tellmannia'na** (*sempervirens* × *tragophylla*) . . . . . ∞ TELLMANN H.

LONICERA, continued
tenu'ipes
thibet'ica . . . TIBET HONEYSUCKLE
tomentel'la
tragophyl'la . . . . . . CHINESE H.
trichop'oda
trichosan'tha . . . . . . SLENDER H.
utahen'sis . . . . UTAH H.
villo'sa
∞ **vilmori'ni** (*deflexicalyx* × *quinquelocularis*) . . . . . . ∞ VILMORIN H.
webbia'na . . . . WEBB H.
xeroca'lyx . . . . . . **L. deflexicalyx x.**
∞ **xylosteoi'des** (*tatarica* × *xylosteum*)
∞ VIENNA H.
xylos'teum . . . EUROPEAN FLY H.
₵YELLOW (*lutea*) HV.
yunnanen'sis . . . . . . YUNNAN H.
₵ROSEGLO. HV. Lonicera

LOOSESTRIFE . . . . **Lysimachia**
CLETHRA L. . . . . . **L. clethroides**
FORTUNE L. . . . . . . **L. fortunei**
FOURLEAF L. . . . . . **L. quadrifolia**
GOLDEN L. . . . . **L. vulgaris**
JAPANESE L. . . . . . . **L. japonica**
MONEYWORT . . . . . **L. nummularia**
SPOTTED L. . . . . . . **L. punctata**
SWAMPCANDLE L. . . . . **L. terrestris**
WATER L. . . . . **L. thyrsiflora**

LOPE'ZIA
albiflo'ra
corona'ta
hirsu'ta
linea'ta
minia'ta

LOPHIO'LA
america'na (*aurea*)

LOPHI'RA . . . . LOPHIRA
ala'ta . . . . WINGED L.
proce'ra (*L. alata p.*) . . . EKKI L.

LOPHOCE'REUS
See **CACTUS GENERA.**

LOPHOPH'ORA . . . . PEYOTE
See **CACTUS GENERA.**

LOPHOSPER'MUM . . **MAURANDIA**
scan'dens . . . . **M. lophospermum**

LOPHOTOCAR'PUS |w
calyc'inus |w

LOPSEED . . . . **Phryma**
AMERICAN L. . . . . **P. leptostachya**
LOQUAT . . . . **Eriobotrya; E. japonica**
LORDSANDLADIES . . . **Arum maculatum**

LORINSE'RIA . . . **WOODWARDIA**
See **FERN GENERA.**

LORO'MA . . **ARCHONTOPHOENIX**
See **PALM GENERA.**

LOROPET'ALUM
chinen'se

LO'TUS (*ACMISPON; ANISOLOTUS; HOSACKIA; TETRAGONOLOBUS*) |w . . DEERVETCH
america'nus (*Acmispon americanum; Hosackia americana; H. purshiana*) |w . . . . . . SPANISHCLOVER D.
angustis'simus . . . SLENDERPOD D.
arab'icus . . . . ARABIAN D.
argophyl'lus . . . . SILVER D.
—deco'rus
—fre'monti
—niv'eus

LOTUS, continued
argophyl'lus ornith'opus
argyrae'us
ben'thami . . BENTHAM DEERVETCH
bertholet'i (*peliorhynchus*)
CORALGEM D.
cornicula'tus |w BIRDSFOOT D. (*Crowfoot*)
DOUBLE (*florepleno*) HV.
crassifo'lius (*Anisolotus c.; Hosackia crassifolia*) . . . . BIG D.
davidso'ni
denticula'tus . . . . . RIVERBAR D.
doug'lasi (*Anisolotus decumbens*)
DOUGLAS D.
erioph'orus . . . . MAT D.
filicau'lis
formosis'simus (*Hosackia gracilis*) |w
COAST D. (*Witchesteeth*)
gla'ber . . . . **L. scoparius**
glau'cus
grandiflo'rus . . . . . CHAPARRAL D.
—mutab'ilis
green'ei
hay'doni
humistra'tus (*Anisolotus h.; Hosackia h.*) |w . . . . FOOTHILL D.
inca'nus
jacobae'us . . . . . . ST. JAMES D.
jun'ceus . . . . RUSH D.
leucophyl'lus . . . . WHITELEAF D.
longebractea'tus (*Anisolotus l.*)
LONGBRACT D.
ma'jor . . . . **L. uliginosus**
mascaen'sis
micran'thus (*parviflorus*)
LITTLEFLOWER D.
mol'lis |w . . . . SOFT D.
ni'gricans . . . . **Kennedia n.**
oblongifo'lius (*Hosackia oblongifolia*)
STREAM D.
—tor'reyi (*L. torreyi; Hosackia t.*)
TORREY S.D.
ornithopodioi'des
ornith'opus
peliorhyn'chus . . . . . **L. bertholeti**
pinna'tus . . . . MEADOW D.
rig'idus (*Hosackia rigida*) . SHRUBBY D.
salsugino'sus
—brevivexil'lus
scopa'rius (*glaber; Hosackia glabra*) |w
BROOM D.
siliquo'sus (*Tetragonolobus s.*)
stipula'ris
—subgla'ber
subpinna'tus . . . . . . CHILEAN D.
tetragonolo'bus (*Tetragonolobus purpureus*) . . . . SQUAREPOD D.
tomentel'lus |w . . . . . DESERT D.
tor'reyi . . . . . . **L. oblongifolius t.**
uligino'sus (*major*) . . . WETLAND D.
wright'i |w . . . . WRIGHT D.
(*Red-and-Yellow Pea*)

LOTUS . . . . **Nelumbium**
AMERICAN L. . . . . **N. pentapetalum**
Apple L. . . . WATERLILY, DISHLEAF:
Nymphaea lekophylla
BLUE EGYPTIANLOTUS
Nymphaea caerulea
BLUE INDIALOTUS . **Nymphaea stellata**
HINDU L. . . . **Nelumbium nelumbo**
KERMES H. L. . . **N. n. kermesianum**
KINSHIREN H. L. . . **N. n. kinshiren**
WHITE EGYPTIANLOTUS
Nymphaea lotus
Lousewort . . PEDICULARIS: **Pedicularis**
LOUVI . . . . **Flacourtia inermis**

LOVAGE . . . . **Levisticum**
GARDEN L. . . . . **L. officinale**

LOVEGRASS . . . . Eragrostis
ALKALI L. . . . . . . **E. obtusiflora**
BAHIA L. . . . . . . **E. bahiensis**
BIGTOP L. . . . . **E. hirsuta**
BOER L. . . . . . **E. chloromelas**
BRISTLY L. . . . . . **E. cyperoides**
CANDY L. . . . . . **E. suaveolens**
CAROLINA L. . . . . **E. pectinacea**
CHIHUAHUA L. . . . . **E. erosa**
CHILEAN L. . . . . . . **E. virescens**
CHINESE L. . . . . . **E. unioloides**
COASTAL L. . . . . . . **E. refracta**
CREEPING L. . . . . . **E. reptans**
DESERT L. . . . . **E. arida**
ELLIOTT L. . . . . . . **E. elliotti**
FEATHER L. . . . . . **E. amabilis**
FLARESCALE L. . . . . . **E. obtusa**
FLORIDA L. . . . . **E. acuta**
FORTYFLOWER L. . . . . **E. simplex**
GLENHAVEN SANDBAR L.
E. franki brevipes
GOPHERTAIL L. . . . . . . **E. ciliaris**
GULF L. . . . . . **E. tephrosanthos**
GUMMY L. . . . **E. curtipedicellata**
HAIRYSHEATH L. . . . **E. trichocolea**
INDIA L. . . . . **E. pilosa**
JAPANESE L. . . . . **E. tenella**
KIMBERLY L. . . . . **E. brizanthes**
KOREAN L. . . . . . **E. ferruginea**
LEHMANN L. . . . . **E. lehmanniana**
LITTLE L. . . . . . **E. poaeoides**
MEDITERRANEAN L. . . . **E. barrelieri**
MEXICAN L. . . . . . . **E. mexicana**
MOURNING L. . . . . . . **E. lugens**
NEWMEXICO L. . . **E. neo-mexicana**
ORCUTT L. . . . . . **E. orcuttiana**
PEREGRINE L. . . . . . **E. peregrina**
PLAINS L. . . . . . . **E. intermedia**

LOVEGRASS, continued
POND L. . . . . **Eragrostis glomerata**
PURPLE L. . . . . . . **E. spectabilis**
RED L. . . . . . . **E. secundiflora**
RIOGRANDE L. . . . . **E. palmeri**
SANDBAR L. . . . . **E. franki**
SANDHILL L. . . . . **E. pilifera**
SAND L. . . . . **E. trichodes**
SANIBELISLAND L. . . . . . **E. tracyi**
SILVEUS L. . . . . . . **E. silveana**
SIXWEEKS L. . . . . . **E. lutescens**
SLIMFLOWER L. . . . **E. stenophylla**
SPIKE L. . . . . **E. spicata**
SPREADING L. . . . . . . **E. diffusa**
SWALLEN L. . . . . . . **E. swalleni**
TEAL L. . . . . **E. hypnoides**
THALIA L. . . . . **E. chariis**
TUMBLE L. . . . . . **E. sessilispica**
WEEPING L. . . . . . . **E. curvula**
WICHITA L. . . . . . . **E. beyrichi**

LOVEINAMIST . . . . **Nigella damascena**

LOVE-LIES-BLEEDING
Amaranthus caudatus

LOVO'A . . . . LOVOA
brown'i . . . . BROWNS L.
klainea'na . . . . . . TIGERWOOD L.

LOXOPTERYG'IUM
sago'ti

LUCU'LIA . . . . LUCULIA
gratis'sima . . . . . FRAGRANT L.
interme'dia
pincea'na

LUCU'MA . . . . LUCUMA
caimi'to . . . . **Pouteria c.**
mammo'sa . . . . **Calocarpum sapota**
nervo'sa (*L. rivicoa angustifolia*)
CANISTEL L. (*Eggfruit*)

LUCUMA, continued
salicifo'lia . . WILLOWLEAF LUCUMA (*Yellowsapote*)
vir'ide . . . . GREEN L. (*Greensapote*)

Ludo'via lauchea'na . . . **Carludovica l.**

LUDWIG'IA |w . . . . . . SEEDBOX

The original spelling of this name, Ludvigia, is used by some botanists.

ala'ta |w
alternifo'lia
arcua'ta . . . . . . **Ludwigiantha a.**
cur'tissi |w
glandulo'sa |w
lanceola'ta |w
microcar'pa |w
na'tans (*mulertti*) |w . . . WATER S.

See note on L. natans in **AQUARIUM PLANTS.**

palus'tris . . . . **Isnardia p.**
polycar'pa |w
sphaerocar'pa |w

LUDWIGIAN'THA |w . LUDWIGIANTHA
arcua'ta (*Ludwigia a.*) |w COMMON L.

LUE'HEA . . . . WHIPTREE
divarica'ta . . . . COMMON W.
grandiflo'ra

LUET'KEA (*LUTKEA*)
pectina'ta (*Lutkea p.; Spiraea p.*)

LUF'FA . TOWELGOURD (*Dishclothgourd*)
acutan'gula (*Cucumis acutangulus*)
SINGKWA T.
cylin'drica (*aegyptiaca*)
SUAKWA VEGETABLESPONGE

LUI'NA
hypoleu'ca

LUMBANG, SOFT . . **Aleurites trisperma**

LUMBER TRADE NAMES

The Editorial Committee has been unsuccessful in obtaining either from wood specialists or interested organizations a single complete list of standardized lumber trade names suitable for this book. The list which follows has been obtained chiefly from the sources indicated below, and correlated with the accepted STANDARDIZED PLANT NAMES botanical and common names. In no field of plant nomenclature is the need for adequate name standardization more apparent than in the case of lumber names. Among the mass of synonymous names which appear in the trade for many a kind of lumber, a confusion which is apparent to the most casual observer, we have selected one name only for standardization purposes, endeavoring to do this on the basis of prevalent common trade usage, appropriateness, and avoidance of homonymity.

We recognize, of course, the justice of the claim that in many cases two or more closely related though botanically distinguishable species produce wood that is practically indistinguishable for the purposes of wood users. Red Oak and White Oak, for example, are each generally accepted names for the lumber of at least eight species of Quercus. In this list the Editorial Committee accepts such trade group-names where consistent with fair trade practices, honest business and the protection of the public from deceit and serious loss, and where they do not disguise important differences in wood qualities and uses. The practice of applying the same lumber trade name to woods from trees of two or more different genera is more seriously objectionable and is not accepted.

As examples of the present confusion in lumber trade names, attention might be called to the fact that "Satinwood" is applied to wood from species belonging to at least 10 genera of six different families. "Ironwood" is used for wood of trees of at least 35 different genera belonging to 20 botanical families and in many cases differing widely in other qualities of the wood than hardness. According to Meyer, the wood of 13 different genera of trees is marked "Corkwood." African, Philippine, and other exotic woods are sold as "Mahogany" which do not belong to the Mahogany genus (Swietenia) and which frequently are very different from that wood in qualities, use and appearance. Such Old World woods definitely are not entitled to be called Mahogany, and the misapplication of that name to them, for whatever reason, misleads the public, is bad nomenclatural practice, and should not be tolerated. Many of these woods have qualities no less admirable in their own way than those of Mahogany, though certainly not the same, and ought to be prized and used for their real qualities under their real names instead of being treated as substitutes.

The Editorial Committee believes that this is the first attempt to correlate closely a list of important lumber names with standardized plant names, both scientific and common. For obvious reasons this list is incomplete and imperfect. A full, adequate list would require years of effort by competent, fair-minded, and specially qualified experts, but its importance is so great that its accomplishment should immediately be undertaken, preferably on the initiative of the lumber organizations themselves. Such an authoritative work, expertly prepared as above indicated, should be published with a view to general adoption by trade and public alike.

The committee gratefully acknowledges its indebtedness to Warren D. Brush, Wood Technologist, U.S. Forest Service, for valuable criticism and suggestions, as well as to C. A. Rishell, J. C. Nellis and Henry Bahr, of the National Lumber Manufacturers Association staff; J. L. Stearns, of the Southern Hardwood Producers Association; Stuart Moir, forester of the Western Pine Association; Emanuel Fritz, of the University of California and California Redwood Manufacturers Association; B. R. Ellis, of the Southern Cypress Manufacturers Association; Warren G. Tilton, of the West Coast Lumbermen's Association, and George N. Lamb, of the Mahogany Association.

ABBREVIATIONS OF SOURCE MATERIAL

Ah. Ahern, G. P., "Important Philippine Woods." Manila, 1901.
Ain. Ainslie, J. R., "The Export Timbers of Nigeria." 1938.
And. Anderson, R. H., "The Trees of New South Wales." N. S. W. Dept. Agr. Ed. 2. 1936.
Aud. Audas, J. W., "Native Trees of Australia." Melbourne (1937?).
Bak. Baker, R. T., "The Hardwoods of Australia." N. S. W. Dept. Educ., Tech. Educ. Ser. 23. Sydney, 1919.
Bat. Baterden, J. R., "Timber." New York, 1908.
Ben. Bentham, G., assisted by Mueller, F., "Flora Australiensis," Vol. 3. London, 1866.
Bo. Boulger, G. S., "Wood." London, 1908.
Br. Brush, W. D., (1) "Khaya," 1940; (2) "Greenheart," 1941; (3) "Mahogany," 1941. U. S. Forest Service. Processed.
Ch. Chalk, L., et al., "Forest Trees and Timbers of the British Empire," Nos. I to III. Oxford, 1932–1935.
Da. Davy, J. B., et al., "Check-lists of the Forest Trees and Shrubs of the British Empire, No. I, Uganda Protectorate." Oxford, 1935.

E&H. Eggeling, W. J., and Harris, C. M., "Fifteen Uganda Timbers. Forest Trees and Timbers of the British Empire IV." Oxford, 1939.
ET. Empire Timber Exhibition Catalogue. London, 1920.
FNCV. Field Naturalists' Club of Victoria, "A Census of the Plants of Victoria." Ed. 2. Melbourne, 1928.
Fox. Foxworthy, F. W., "Indo-Malayan Woods." Phil. Journ. Sci. 4(4): 409–592. 1909.
F&W. Freeman, W. G., and Williams, R. O., "The Useful and Ornamental Plants of Trinidad and Tobago." Port-of-Spain, 1927.
FW. Division of Forest Products, Forest Service, U. S. Dept. Agriculture. "Foreign Woods Imported into the United States." Processed. 1939.
Gam. Gamble, J. S., "A Manual of Indian Timbers." Reprinted. London, 1922.
Guil. Guilfoyle, W. R., "Australian Plants." Melbourne (1911?).
How. Howard, A. L., "A Manual of the Timbers of the World." London, 1920.
Kew. Hill, A. W., et al., "Hand-list of Coniferae and other Gymnosperms." Royal Botanical Gardens, Kew. London, 1938.
Ki. Kirk, T., "The Forest Flora of New Zealand." Wellington, 1889.
Leg. Legat, C. E., "The Empire Forestry Handbook, 1938." London, 1938.
LP. Lane-Poole, C. E., "Statement Prepared for the British Empire Forestry Conference, London, 1920." Perth (W. Australia), 1920.
Mar. Marloth, R., "Dictionary of the Common Names of Plants." Cape Town (South Africa), 1917.
Mc. McClatchie, A. J., "Eucalypts Cultivated in the United States." U. S. Dept. Agr., Bur. For. Bull. 35. 1902.
Mey. Meyer, H., "Buch der Holznamen." Hanover, 1936.
P&B. Pearson, R. S., and Brown, H. P., "Commercial Timbers of India." 2 vols. Calcutta, 1932.
Rec. Record, S. J., "Boxwoods of Commerce." Bull. Torrey Bot. Club 48: 297–306. 1921.
Reh. Rehder, A., "Manual of Cultivated Trees and Shrubs." New York, 1940.
Rey. Reyes, L. J., "Philippine Woods." Phil. Dept. Agr. and Comm. Tech. Bull. 7. 1938.
RL. Roddis Lumber and Veneer Company, "Characteristics of Modern Woods." Ed. 2. 1939.
R&M. Record, Samuel J., and Mell, C. D., "Timbers of Tropical America." New Haven, 1924.
Sud. Sudworth, G. B., "Check List." U. S. Dept. Agr. Misc. Cir. 92. 1927.
Sud,L. ———, "Standard Names of Lumber" (pp. 239–242 of "Check List" cited above).
TNC. (U. S.) Forest Service Tree Name Committee, "Approved Changes in Sudworth's Check List." Mimeographed. 1940.
Tr. Troup, R. S., "Indian Woods and Their Uses." Indian For. Mem., Econ. Prod. Ser. I(1). Calcutta, 1909.
VW. Van Wijk, H. L. G., "A Dictionary of Plant-Names." 2 vols. The Hague, 1911.
Wil. Wilson, C. C., "Some Indian Timbers Suitable for Export." Third British Empire Forestry Conference, 1928.
Winn Winn, W., "Timbers and Their Uses." London, 1919.
Y,TW. Yale University, School of Forestry, "Tropical Woods." 1925— (Continuing series).
Z&S. Zon, R., and Sparhawk, W. N., "Forest Resources of the World." 2 vols. New York, 1923.

Lumber Trade Name	Plant Source: Botanical Name	Plant Source: S.P.N.Common Name
Abachi. Obeche		
Abiache. Opepe		
Aboudikro(u). Sapele		
Abura (Ch;How;Leg;Mey; RL. *Bahia; Subaha*)	**Mitragyna stipulosa** (*macrophylla*)	Abura Mitragyna
Acacia (Mey;RL. *Gidgee*)	**Acacia** spp.	Acacia
Acana. Almique; Bulletwood		
Acapu. Angelin		
Accra. Sapele Dr. Brush reports that this is merely a trade name for wood shipped from Accra, Gold Coast, believed to be Entandrophragma.		
Acle (FW;Mey;RL. *Akle*)	**Albizzia acle**	Acle Albizzia
Acoita-cavallo. Estribeira(o)		
Acurel (F&W)	**Trichilia cruegeriana**	Trinidad Bitterwood
Afara (Ain;Ch;ET;How; Leg;Mey. *Frake; Limbo*)	**Terminalia superba**	Afara Terminalia
Black A. Framerie		
African-mahogany. Sapele		
Agallocha; Agallochum. Eaglewood		
Agba (Ain;ET;Leg;RL. *Moboron; Pink Mahogany*)	**Gossweilerodendron balsamiferum**	Agba Gossweilertree
Agboin. Ekhimi		
Aguano. Mahogany, Honduras		
Aiele. Papo		
Ailon. Magnolia		
Akle. Acle		
Akomu (Ain;RL. *Boxboard; Cardboard; Ilomba; Walile*)	**Pycnanthus kombo**	Akomu Pycnanthus
Akume. Copaiba		
Albarco (RL;R&M. *Colombian Mahogany*)	**Cariniana pyriformis**	Albarco Cariniana
Albarco. Jequitiba		
Albawood. Oak, White		
Alder	**Alnus**	Alder
Black A. (Bat;Bo;ET; How;Leg;Mey. *Common A.; European A.*)	**glutinosa**	European A.
Red A. (Bo;Mey;RL)	**rubra** (*oregana*)	Red A.
Red A. Els, Rood		
White A. (Bo;Mey)	**rhombifolia**	Sierra A.
White A. Els, Wit		
Alerce. Arar		
Aligna (Ch;RL. *Apa; Lingue*)	**Afzelia africana**	African Afzelia
Almendro	**Dipteryx panamensis**	Panama Tonkabean
Almique (Mey;RL;R&M. *Acana*)	**Labourdonnaisia albescens**	White Mattree
Almon (Mey;Rey;RL. *Philippine Mahogany*)	**Shorea eximia**	Almon Shorea
Almon. Seraya		
Alona. Tigerwood		
Amaranth (RL;Y,TW. *Amarante; Bois Violet; Guarabu; Morado; Palo Morado; Pao Roxo; Zapateri*) *See also* Purpleheart. It would seem better to call the lumber of this species "Purpleheart."	**Peltogyne paniculata**	Guiana Purpleheart
Amarello. Arariba; Brazilian-satinwood; Brazilian-yellowwood		
Amargoso. Angelim Amargoso		
Amboyna. Padauk, India		
Amoteak; Amotique. Sucupira		
Ampira. Framerie		
Amugis (Mey;Rey;RL)	**Koordersiodendron pinnatum**	Amugis
Amyris (FW;Mey;Y,TW. *West Indian Sandalwood*)	**Amyris balsamifera**	Balsam Amyris
Anan (Bo;ET;How;Mey; Tr)	**Fagraea fragrans**	Sweet Fagraea
Andiroba. Crabwood		
Angelim Amargoso (Mey; RL; R&M. *Amargoso*)	**Andira vermifuga**	Brazilian Angelintree
Angelim Pedra (Mey;RL)	**A. spectabilis**	Showy A.

The name Angelim Pedra (Mey;RL) is also used in the lumber trade for Rock Hymenolobium (**Hymenolobium petraeum**). This is another instance of the urgent need of lumber name standardization.

Lumber Trade Name	Plant Source: Botanical Name	Plant Source: S.P.N.Common Name
Angelin (Leg;Mey. *Acapu*) See note under **Andira**, p. 15.	**Andira** (*Vouacapoua*)	Angelintree
Angelin (Leg;Mey. *Bitterwood; Cabbage Bark; Macayo; Partridgewood*)	**A. inermis** (*jamaicensis; V. americana*)	Cabbage A.
Angelique (Bo;How)	**Dicorynia paraensis**	Para Angelwood
Angsana; Angsena. Padauk, India		
Anyaran. Movingui		
Apa. Aligna		
Apaya. Avodire		
Apitong (How; Mey; Rey; RL)	**Dipterocarpus grandiflorus**	Apitong Gurjunoiltree
Apopo. Tigerwood		
Apple (Bat;Bo;ET;How; Leg;Mey;RL;Tr)	**Malus pumila** (*Pyrus malus*)	Common Apple
Aprono. Mansonia		

Lumber Trade Name	Plant Source Botanical Name	 S.P.N. Common Name
Apru. DANTA		
ARACA (Mey;RL)	**Terminalia januarensis** The exact identity of this species is disputed.	RIOJANEIRO TERMINALIA
ARAR (Mey. *Alerce*)	**Tetraclinis articulata** (*Callitris quadrivalvis*)	ARARTREE
ARARIBA (Mey;RL) Shipments of Arariba from Rio de Janeiro are called *Amarello; Branca; Rosa;* and *Vermelha.* Called *Balaustre* or *Canarywood* in United States.	**Centrolobium** spp.	PORCUPINEPODTREE
ARAUCARIA (Mey;RL. *Monkey Puzzle*)	**Araucaria araucana** (*imbricata*)	MONKEYPUZZLE ARAUCARIA
Arborvitae		
Eastern A. CEDAR, NORTHERN WHITE		
Giant A. REDCEDAR, WESTERN		
Arere. OBECHE		
Argento. EUCALYPTUS, GIANTGUM		
Aromilla. NARGUSTA		
ARYIAN (Ain;Ch;RL)	**Afzelia bipindensis**	ARYIAN AFZELIA
ASH. *See also* TAMO.	**Fraxinus**	ASH
Australian A. EUCALYPTUS, GIANTGUM		
Bennett A. BENNETT-ASH		
BLACK A. (RL;Sud,L. *Brown A.*)	**nigra**	BLACK A.
Brown A. BLACK A.		
Canary A. EUCALYPTUS, GIANTGUM		
Cane A. WHITE A.		
Common A. EUROPEAN A.		
Crows A. FLINDERSIA		
English A. EUROPEAN A.		
EUROPEAN A. (How;RL. *Common A.; English A.; Hungarian A.; Italian Olive A.; Olive A.*)	**excelsior**	EUROPEAN A.
GREEN A. (RL;Sud,L.) *See also* WHITE A.	**pennsylvanica lanceolata**	GREEN A.
Hungarian A. EUROPEAN A.		
Italian Olive A. EUROPEAN A.		
JAPANESE A. (Mey;RL; *Yachidamo*)	**mandshurica**	MANCHURIAN A.
Mountain A. EUCALYPTUS, GIANTGUM; SILVERPINE The true Mountain-ash genus is Sorbus, whose members are of little importance for lumber.		
Olive A. EUROPEAN A.		
Silver A. CUDGERIE		
WHITE A. (How;RL; Sud,L. *Cane A.*)	**americana**	WHITE A.
WHITE A. (Sud;Sud,L. *Biltmore White Ash*)	**biltmoreana**	BILTMORE A.
WHITE A. (Sud, L. *Oregon White A.*)	**oregona**	OREGON A.
WHITE A. (Mey;Sud,L)	**pennsylvanica**	RED A.
WHITE A. (RL;Sud,L) *See also* GREEN A.	**p. lanceolata**	GREEN A.
WHITE A. (Sud,L)	**quadrangulata**	BLUE A.
ASPEN (Sud) *See also* COTTONWOOD and POPLAR	**Populus tremuloides aurea**	GOLDEN QUAKING ASPEN
EUROPEAN A. (How;Leg)	**P. tremula**	EUROPEAN A.
LARGETOOTH A. (Mey; RL; Sud. *Bigtooth Poplar; Largetooth P.; Popple*)	**P. grandidentata**	BIGTOOTH A.
QUAKING A. (Bat;ET; Leg;Mey;RL;Sud. *Popple; White Poplar*)	**P. tremuloides**	QUAKING A.
Aspen. POPLAR, WHITE		
ASSEGAI (Bat;Bo;Mey)	**Curtisia faginea**	ASSEGAITREE

Lumber Trade Name	Plant Source Botanical Name	 S.P.N. Common Name
Atherton Penda. PENDA		
Australian-hickory. EUCALYPTUS, SPOTTEDGUM		
AUSTRALIAN-SANDALWOOD (And; Bak; Bat; Bo; Gui; How; Mey; Y,TW. *Australian Sandalwood; West Australian Sandalwood*)	**Eucarya spicata**	AUSTRALIA-SANDALWOOD
AVOCADO (Bat;Bo;Mey; RL;R&M)	**Persea americana** (*gratissima*)	AMERICAN AVOCADO
AVODIRE (Leg;Mey;RL. *Apaya*)	**Turraeanthus africana**	AFRICAN AVODIRE
AXLEWOOD (Leg;Mey)	**Anogeissus latifolia**	BAKLIGUM AXLEWOOD
Ayan. MOVINGUI		
AYO (Ch)	**Holoptelea grandis**	AYO INDIANELM
Ayous. OBECHE		
Azobe. EKKI		
BABUL		
AFRICAN B. (RL. *Babul*)	**Acacia senegal**	GUMARABIC ACACIA
INDIAN B. (Bat;Fox; Mey;RL. *Babul*)	**A. arabica**	BABUL A.
Badi. BILINGA; OPEPE		
BAGTIKAN (FW;Mey;Rey; RL. *Philippine-mahogany*)	**Parashorea malaanonan**	COMMON BAGTIKAN
Bagtikan. SERAYA		
Bahia. ABURA		
Bahia Rosewood. ROSEWOOD, BRAZILIAN		
Bahia Wood. BRAZILWOOD		
Baitoa. SERON		
BAKAN (Mey;Rey)	**Litsea philippinensis**	BAKAN LITSEA
Baku. MAKORE		
BALAK (Mey. *Philippine-mahogany; White Lauan*)	**Pentacme contorta**	BALAK PENTACME
BALATA (ET;Mey;RL)	**Manilkara bidentata** (*Mimusops balata; Mim. bidentata globosa*)	COMMON BALATA
PANAMA B. (Mey; R&M. *Balata*) This genus is often confused with Bulletwood (**Mimusops**).	**M. darienensis** (*Mimusops d.*)	PANAMA B.
Balaustre. ARARIBA		
Ballygum. BOLLYGUM		
Balm-of-Gilead. POPLAR, BALM-OF-GILEAD		
BALSA (ET;Leg;RL. *Corkwood*)	**Ochroma pyramidale** (*lagopus*)	WESTINDIES BALSA
Balsam. FIR, BALSAM; PERUBALSAM; POPLAR, BALSAM		
Balsamito. CABREUVA		
Balsamo. OLEO VERMELHO; PEPPERTREE; ROSEWOOD, EAST INDIAN; ROSEWOOD, HONDURAS		
BAMBOO (RL) *See also* **BAMBOO GENERA**, p. 40.		
BANABU (How;Mey;Rey; RL. *Jarul; Pyinna*)	**Lagerstroemia speciosa** (*flosreginae*)	QUEEN CRAPEMYRTLE
BANAK (Leg;Mey;RL. *Sangre*)	**Virola merendonis**	MERENDON VIROLA
BANAK (Mey)	**V. panamensis**	PANAMA V.
Bangalay. EUCALYPTUS, BANGALAY		
BANUYO (Mey;Rey;RL)	**Wallaceodendron celebicum**	CELEBES WALLACETREE
Bari. SANTAMARIA		
Baria. CANALETTA		
Barwood. PADAUK, AFRICAN		
BASSWOOD (ET; How; Mey;RL;Sud,L. *American Linden; Limewood*)	**Tilia americana** (*glabra*)	AMERICAN LINDEN; AMERICAN BASSWOOD (Forestry)
WHITE B. (Mey;Sud,L)	**T. heterophylla**	BEETREE L.; WHITE BASSWOOD (Forestry)
Bastard Tallowwood. EUCALYPTUS, TALLOWWOOD		
Bastard Yellowwood. YELLOWWOOD		
Bataan. TANGILE		

Lumber Trade Name	Plant Source	
	Botanical Name	*S.P.N. Common Name*
BATETE (Mey;Rey;RL)	**Kingiodendron alternifolium**	PHILIPPINE KINGSTREE
BATICULIN (How;Mey. *Batikuling*)	**Litsea leytensis** (*obtusata*)	BATICULIN LITSEA
BATITINAN (Mey;Rey;RL)	**Lagerstroemia piriformis**	BATITINAN CRAPEMYRTLE
Batoa. ZAPATERO		
Batuan. DAO		
Batulinau. EBONY, BATULINAU		
Baumier. POPLAR, BALSAM		
Bayott. PALOSAPIS		
Baytree; Sweet B. LAUREL		
Baywood. MAHOGANY, HONDURAS		
Beanwood. BLACKBEAN		
Bedaru. DARU		
BEECH	**Fagus**	BEECH
AMERICAN B. (Mey;RL; Sud,L)	**grandifolia** (*americana*)	AMERICAN B.
Blue B. HORNBEAM, AMERICAN		
Chilean B. SOUTHLAND B.		
Clinker B. HARD B.		
Common B. EUROPEAN B.		
EUROPEAN B. (Mey;RL. *Common B.*)	**sylvatica**	EUROPEAN B.
Evergreen B. TASMANIAN B.		
HARD B. (Leg;Mey. *Clinker B.*)	**Nothofagus truncata**	CLINKER FALSEBEECH
JAPANESE B. (FW;How) Presumably the true Japanese Beech (**F. japonica**) is a valuable timber species.	**Fagus sieboldi** (*F. sylvatica s.*)	SIEBOLD BEECH
Myrtle B. TASMANIAN B.		
NEGROHEAD B. (And; Aud)	**Nothofagus moorei**	NEGROHEAD FALSEBEECH
RED B. (Leg;Mey)	**N. fusca**	BLACK F.
Redbeech. SILKWOOD, MAPLE		
She B. BOLLYGUM		
SOUTHLAND B. (Leg; Mey;RL. *Chilean Beech; Melica; Rauli*)	**N. menziesi**	SILVER F.
TASMANIAN B. (Aud; How;Mey. *Evergreen B.; Myrtle B.; Tasmanian Myrtle*)	**N. cunninghami**	TASMANIAN F.
White B. WHITEBEECH		
BEEFWOOD (Mey;Tr)	**Casuarina equisetifolia**	HORSETAIL BEEFWOOD
Beefwood. BULLETWOOD; SILKYOAK		
Belle Rosa. PALOSAPIS		
Benin. TIGERWOOD		
BENNETTASH (And; Aud; Bak. *Australian Teak; Bennett Ash; Native Teak; She Teak*)	**Flindersia bennettiana**	BENNETT FLINDERSIA
Bera. LIGNUMVITAE		
Bethabara. OCOBO.		
Bibolo. TIGERWOOD		
BIJASAL (Mey;Wil)	**Terminalia marsupium**	BIJASAL TERMINALIA
BILINGA (FW;RL. *Badi*)	**Nauclea trillesi** (*Sarcocephalus t.*)	BILINGA FATHEADTREE
BILLIAN (Bat;ET;How; Leg;Mey. *Borneo-ironwood; Tambulian*)	**Eusideroxylon zwageri**	BORNEO BILLIAN
BILLYWEBB (ET;Mey;RL. *Chichipate*)	**Sweetia panamensis**	BILLYWEBB SWEETIA
Bilsted. REDGUM		
BINGGAS (Fox;Mey;Rey; RL)	**Terminalia comintana**	BINGGAS TERMINALIA
Bintangor. POON		
BIRCH	**Betula**	BIRCH
Alaska B. ALASKA WHITE B.		
ALASKA WHITE B. (RL; Sud. *Alaska B.*)	**papyrifera neoalaskana** (*B. neoalaskana*)	ALASKA PAPER B.
Alpine Burl B. EUROPEAN B.		

Lumber Trade Name	Plant Source	
	Botanical Name	*S.P.N. Common Name*
BIRCH, continued		
American B.; Black B.; Cherry B. SWEET B.		
Common B. EUROPEAN B.		
EUROPEAN B. (Mey. *Alpine Burl B.; Common B.; Flamy B.; Karelian Burl B.; Norway Burl B.; Shira-Kamba*)	**Betula pendula** (*alba* in large part)	EUROPEAN WHITE BIRCH
Flamy B. EUROPEAN B.		
GRAY B. (Mey;Sud)	**populifolia**	GRAY B.
INDIAN B. (How;Mey)	**utilis**	HIMALAYA B.
Karelian Burl B. EUROPEAN B.		
KENAI B. (Sud)	**papyrifera kenaica** (*B. kenaica*)	KENAI PAPER B.
Mahogany B. SWEET B.		
Norway Burl B. EUROPEAN B.		
PAPER B. (Leg;Mey;RL; Sud,L. *White B.*)	**papyrifera**	PAPER B.
RED B. (Sud)	**fontinalis**	WATER B.
Red B. YELLOW B.		
RIVER B. (Mey;RL;Sud,L)	**nigra**	RIVER B.
Sap B.; Silver B.; Swamp B. YELLOW B.		
SWEET B. (Mey;RL; Sud,L. *American B.; Black B.; Cherry B.; Mahogany B.*)	**lenta**	SWEET B.
White B. PAPER B.; YELLOW B.		
YELLOW B. (Bat;Leg; Mey;RL;Sud,L. *Canadian Silkywood; Red B.; Sap B.; Silver B.; Swamp B.; White B.*) Sapwood of Yellow B. sold as White B.	**lutea**	YELLOW B.
BISHOPWOOD (How;Mey; Wil. *Toog; Tuai*)	**Bischofia javanica**	JAVA BISHOPWOOD
BITTERWOOD (FW;Mey; Rey)	**Quassia amara**	SURINAM QUASSIA
Bitterwood. ANGELIN; MARUPA; QUASSIA; QUASSIAWOOD		
BLACKBEAN (Bak;Bat; How;RL. *Beanwood; Moretonbay-chestnut*)	**Castanospermum australe**	MORETONBAY-CHESTNUT
Blackbox. EUCALYPTUS, BLACKBOX		
BLACKBOY (ET;LP;Mey)	**Xanthorrhoea preissi**	PREISS GRASSTREE (*Blackboy*)
Blackbutt. EUCALYPTUS, BLACKBUTT		
BLACKGUM (Mey; RL; Sud,L)	**Nyssa sylvatica**	BLACK TUPELO
Blackgum. TUPELO		
Blackpeppermint. EUCALYPTUS, BLACK PEPPERMINT		
BLACKPLUM (And;Bak; VW)	**Diospyros cargillia**	ILLAWARA EBONY PERSIMMON
Black Sally. BLACKWOOD, AUSTRALIAN		
BLACKTREE (Mey. *Black Mangrove*)	**Avicennia marina**	BLACKMANGROVE
BLACKWOOD		
AFRICAN B. (Bo;Ch; Mey;RL. *Congowood; Mozambique Ebony*)	**Dalbergia melanoxylon**	AFRICAN BLACKWOOD
AUSTRALIAN B. (Bat;Bo; FW;How;Mey;RL. *Black Sally*)	**Acacia melanoxylon**	BLACKWOOD ACACIA
Blackwood. ROSEWOOD, EAST INDIAN		
Bleeding Heart. MACAWOOD		
Bloodwood. EUCALYPTUS, BLOODWOOD; PADAUK		
Bluebeech. HORNBEAM, AMERICAN		
Bluegum. EUCALYPTUS, BLUEGUM; EUCALYPTUS, MAIDENGUM		

	Plant Source	
Lumber Trade Name	*Botanical Name*	*S.P.N. Common Name*
Bocote. CANALETTA		
BODI (FW;Mey;RL. *Bodia*)	**Pynaertia occidentalis**	BODI PYNAERTIA
Bodia. BODI		
Bogo. CEDAR, SPICY		
Bois de Citron. French for Satinwood		
Bois de Fer. EKKI		
Bois Violet. AMARANTH		
BOLLYGUM (And;Bak; Mey;RL. *Ballygum; Brown Bollywood; She Beech*)	**Litsea reticulata**	BOLLYGUM LITSEA
Bollywood, Brown. BOLLYGUM		
BOMBWAY (*Bombwe*)		
RED B. (ET;How;Mey)	**Planchonia andamanica**	BOMBWAY PLANCHONIA
WHITE B. (How;Leg; Mey;RL)	**Terminalia procera**	BOMBWAY TERMINALIA
Bombwe. BOMBWAY		
Bongosi Bole; Bongossi. EKKI		
Borneo-ironwood. BILLIAN		
Bosse. GUAREA		
Box. BOXWOOD		
Boxboard. AKOMU		
BOXELDER (Mey;RL;Sud)	**Acer negundo**	BOXELDER
BOXWOOD (Bat;Bo;How; Leg;Mey;Rec;RL. *Box; Common Boxwood; English B.; European B.; Indian B.*)	**Buxus sempervirens**	COMMON BOX
African B. CAPE BOXWOOD		
Bairnsdale Grey B. EUCALYPTUS, BAIRNSDALE GRAYBOX		
Bastard B.; Brush B. BRISBANEBOX		
CAPE B. (Bo;ET;Leg; Mey;Rec. *African B.; East London B.*)	**B. macowani**	MACOWAN B.
Ceylon B. BUTULANG		
Common B. BOXWOOD		
East London B. CAPE B.		
English B.; European B. BOXWOOD		
Gray B. EUCALYPTUS, GRAYBOX		
India B. GARDENIA, BOXWOOD		
Knysna B. KAMASSIWOOD		
Maracaibo B. ZAPATERO		
Red B. EUCALYPTUS, REDBOX		
Red B. BRISBANEBOX		
San Domingan B. SERON		
West Indies B. OCOBO; ZAPATERO		
Branca. ARARIBA		
BRAZILIAN-YELLOWWOOD (R&M. *Amarello; Vinhatico Amarello*)	**Plathymenia reticulata**	
Brazilletto. BRAZILWOOD		
BRAZILNUT (Mey;RL. *Castanheira*)	**Bertholletia excelsa**	BRAZILNUT
BRAZILWOOD (FW;RL. *Bahia Wood; Brazilletto; Pau Brazil; Pernambuco*)	**Caesalpinia echinata**	PRICKLY BRAZILWOOD
Breadnut. CAPOMO		
BRIARROOT (RL)	**Erica arborea**	TREE HEATH
Brimstone-wood. FRAMERIE		
BRISBANEBOX (Mey. *Bastard Boxwood; Brush B.; Red B.*)	**Tristania conferta**	BRISBANEBOX TRISTANIA
Browngum. EUCALYPTUS, BROWNGUM		
Brownheart. SUCUPIRA		
Brownmallet. EUCALYPTUS, BROWNMALLET		
BUBINGA (FW;Mey;RL. *African Rosewood*)	**Didelotia africana**	BUBINGA DIDELOTIA
Bubinga. OKWEIN		
Bucketwood. REWAREWA		
BUCKEYE (RL)	**Aesculus glabra**	OHIO BUCKEYE
BUCKEYE (Mey;Sud,L)	**A. octandra** (*flava*)	YELLOW B.
BULLETWOOD (FW;Mey; RL. *Acana; Balata; Beefwood; Horseflesh Wood; Massaranduba; Red Lancewood; South African Mahogany; Wild Dilly*) Other species of **Mimusops** also produce Bulletwood. This genus has often been confused with Balata (**Manilkara**).	**Mimusops elengi**	ELENGI BULLETWOOD
Bulloak. LACEWOOD		
Bumpy Ash. CUDGERIE		
BUNYA BUNYA. (Mey;RL. *Bunya-pine*)	**Araucaria bidwilli**	BUNYABUNYA ARAUCARIA
Buruta. SATINWOOD, CEYLON		
BUTTERNUT (Mey;ET; Sud,L. *White Walnut*)	**Juglans cinerea**	BUTTERNUT
BUTTERTREE (Fox;Mey; RL. *Mahwa*) Buttertree is applicable also to other spp. of Madhuca.	**Madhuca indica**	ILLIPE BUTTERTREE
Buttonwood. FALSE-MANGROVE; SYCAMORE		
BUTULANG (Fox. *Ceylon Boxwood*)	**Canthium dicoccum**	BUTULANG CANTHIUM
Cabbage Bark. ANGELIN		
Cabiuna. ROSEWOOD, BRAZILIAN		
CABREUVA (RL;R&M. *Balsamito; Oleo Pardo*)	**Myrocarpus frondosus**	BRAZILIAN MYROCARPUS
Cabreuva. OLEO VERMELHO		
CAIRNSHICKORY (Aud;Bak)	**Flindersia ifflaiana**	IFFLA FLINDERSIA
Calaba. SANTAMARIA		
Calabar. EBONY, GABOON		
Calamander. EBONY, CALAMANDER		
Calamansanay. KALAMANSANAI		
Calantas. KALANTAS		
Calico Ash A trade name, incorrectly used for veneer from American Elm.		
CALIFORNIALAUREL (*Oregon Myrtle*)	**Umbellularia californica**	CALIFORNIALAUREL
CAMAGON (Ah;How;Mey; Rey;RL)	**Diospyros discolor** (*mabola*)	MABOLA PERSIMMON
Cambage Blackbutt. EUCALYPTUS, BLACKBUTT		
Cambala. IROKO		
Camboata Blanca. MUSKWOOD		
CAMPHORWOOD (FW;How; Mey;RL)	**Cinnamomum camphora**	CAMPHORTREE
BORNEO C. (Bo;Leg; Mey;RL. *Kapur Barus*)	**Dryobalanops aromatica**	COMMON BORNEOCAMPHOR
East African C. MUZAITI		
NEPAL C. (Bo;Mey)	**Cinnamomum glanduliferum**	NEPAL CAMPHORTREE
CAMWOOD (Ain;Bo;Mey; Winn)	**Baphia nitida**	SHINY CAMWOOD
Camwood. PADAUK, BURMA		
Canadian Silkywood. BIRCH, YELLOW		
CANA FISTOLA (RL. *Horse Cassia; Stinking Toes*)	**Cassia grandis**	PINKSHOWER SENNA
CANALETTA (RL. *Baria; Bocote; Canalete; Cyp(re); Princewood; Solera; Ziricote*)	**Cordia** spp.	CORDIA
Canarium. PAPO		
Canarywood. ARARIBA; YELLOW-POPLAR		
CANCHARANA (Mey;RL; R&M. *Cangerana*)	**Cabralea congerana**	CANCHARANA CABRALEA
Candlebark. EUCALYPTUS, CANDLEBARK		
Caoba. MAHOGANY, HONDURAS		
CAPA (Mey;RL. *Fiddlewood*)	**Petitia domingensis**	CAPA PETITIA

Lumber Trade Name	Plant Source: Botanical Name	Plant Source: S.P.N. Common Name
Cape-ebony (FW;Mey; RL. *Cape Ebony*)	**Euclea pseudebenus**	CapeEbony Euclea
Cape Laurel. Stinkwood		
Capomo (FW;Mey;RL; R&M. *Breadnut; Capome; Laredo; Ogechi; Ojoche; Ramon; Ujusti*)	**Brosimum alicastrum**	Ramon Breadnut-tree
Caracoli (Mey;RL;R&M. *Carocoli; Espave; Giant Cashew*)	**Anacardium rhinocarpus**	Guiana Cashew
Carallia (ET;Fox;How; Mey;RL. *Maniawga*)	**Carallia brachiata**	India Carallia
Carapa. Crabwood		
Cardboard. Akomu		
Cardinalberry (*Yellowcedar; Yellowwood*)	**Rhodosphaera rhodanthema**	Big Cardinalberry
Caroba; Carobocu. Copaia		
Carocoli. Caracoli		
Cashew, Giant. Caracoli		
Castanheira. Brazilnut		
Catalpa (Mey;RL;Sud)	**Catalpa bignonioides**	Southern Catalpa
Hardy C. (Bat;Sud)	**C. speciosa**	Northern C.
Cativo (Mey;RL;R&M. *Florisa; Tabasara*)	**Prioria copaifera**	Cativo
Catmon (Ah;Mey;Rey; RL;R&M. *Katmon*)	**Dillenia philippinensis**	Catmon Dillenia
Cedar	**Cedrus**	Cedar
African C. Guarea		
Alaska C. (RL;Sud,L. *Alaska Cypress; Alaska Yellow Cedar; Nootka Cypress; Sitka Cypress; Yellow Cedar; Yellow Cypress*)	**Chamaecyparis nootkatensis**	Nootka Falsecypress; Alaska Yellowcedar (Forestry)
Alaska Yellow C. Alaska C.		
Aromatic Red C. Eastern Redcedar		
Borneo C. Seraya		
Brazilian C. Cedrela		
British Guiana C. Cigarboxcedar		
Central American C. Cedrela		
Cigarboxcedar (Bat; Bo;Leg;Mey. *British Guiana Cedar; Spanish C.*)	**Cedrela odorata**	Cigarbox Cedrela
Eastern Redcedar (Bat;Mey;RL;Sud,L. *Aromatic Red Cedar; Pencil Cedar; Red Cedar; Southern Red Cedar; Tennessee Red Cedar*)	**Juniperus virginiana**	Eastern Redcedar
East Indian C. Seraya		
Gold Coast C. Sapele		
Honduras C. Cedrela		
Incensecedar (Bat; R&M;Sud,L)	**Libocedrus decurrens**	California Incensecedar
Lebanon C. (ET;Mey; RL)	**Cedrus libani** (*libanotica*)	Cedar-of-Lebanon
Mexican C. Cedrela		
Michigan White C. Northern Whitecedar		
Mountain C. (Sud)	**Juniperus mexicana**	Mexican Juniper
New Brunswick C. Northern Whitecedar		
New Zealand C. (Bo; ET;How;Mey. *Pahautea*)	**Libocedrus bidwilli**	Pahautea Incensecedar
Nigerian C. Guarea		
Northern Whitecedar (RL;Sud,L. *Michigan White Cedar; New Brunswick Cedar; White Cedar*)	**Thuja occidentalis**	Eastern Arborvitae; Northern Whitecedar (Forestry)
Pencil C. Eastern Redcedar		
Philippine C. Kalantas		
PortOrford C. (Mey; RL;Sud,L)	**Chamaecyparis lawsoniana**	Lawson Falsecypress; PortOrford Whitecedar (Forestry)

Redcedar (And;Aud;ET)

"Redcedar" has become standardized for certain Juniperus species. This is unfortunate, for Juniper is a preferable name for Juniperus.

The species and wood of the genus Cedrela, also sometimes called "Red Cedar," should uniformly be called Cedrela. This is a particularly striking example of a needless misnomer. See Redcedar.

Lumber Trade Name	Plant Source: Botanical Name	Plant Source: S.P.N. Common Name
Cedar, continued		
Red Cedar. Eastern Redcedar; Els, Rood		
Rockymountain Redcedar (Mey;Sud)	**Juniperus scopulorum**	RockyMountain Juniper
South American C. Cedrela		
Southern Redcedar (Sud)	**J. silicicola**	Southern Redcedar
Southern Red Cedar. Eastern Redcedar		
Southern Whitecedar (RL;Sud,L)	**Chamaecyparis thyoides**	Whitecedar Falsecypress; Atlantic Whitecedar (Forestry)
Spanish C. Cedrela; Cigarboxcedar		
Spicy C. (Ain;RL. *Pogo*)	**Tylostemon crassifolius**	
Spicy C. (Ain;Mey;RL. *Bogo*)	**T. manni**	
Tasmaniancedar (Bo. *King William Pine*)	**Athrotaxis selaginoides**	
Tennessee Red C. Eastern Redcedar		
Western Redcedar (RL;Sud,L. *Giant Arborvitae*)	**Thuja plicata**	Giant Arborvitae; Western Redcedar (Forestry)
White C. Northern Whitecedar		
Yellow C. Alaska C.		
Cedre. French for Cedar		
Cedrela (RL. *Brazilian Cedar; Cedro; Central American Cedar; Honduras Cedar; Mexican Cedar; South American Cedar; Spanish Cedar*) *See also* Cigarboxcedar; Toon	**Cedrela mexicana**	Mexican C.
Cedro. Cedrela		
Cedron. Guarea		
Ceiba (Fox;FW;RL. *Kapok; Odoum; Silk Cotton Tree*)	**Ceiba pentandra** (*casearia; Eriodendron anfractuosum*)	Kapok Ceiba
Celery(top)pine (Bat; ET;How;Mey;Tr)	**Phyllocladus rhomboidalis**	Tasmania Celery-pine
Celtis (Ain;RL. *Ita; Itako; Chia*)	**Celtis soyauxi**	Nigerian Hackberry
Cercocarpus (RL. *Mountain Mahogany*)	**Cercocarpus ledifolius**	Curlleaf Mountainmahogany
Cerirello. Ciruela		
Cerise. French for Cherry		
Champ (Fox;Mey;RL;Tr. *Champa(c); Champaca(m); Champak(an)*)	**Michelia champaca**	Champac Michelia
Chaplash (Fox;RL;Tr. *Chaplach; Chaplis*)	**Artocarpus chaplasha**	Chaplash Breadfruit
Chataignier(ne). French for Chestnut		
Chechem (Mey;RL)	**Metopium brownei**	Brownes Poisontree
Chee (Fox;Mey;RL;Tr. *Indian Oak*)	**Barringtonia acutangula**	Chee Barringtonia
Chene. French for Oak		
Chengal (Fox;Mey;RL. *Chengai*)	**Balanocarpus heimi**	
Cherry. Some of the woods called Cherry belong in the Chokecherry (Padus) section of Prunus.	**Prunus** (section Cerasus)	Cherry
African C. Makore		
Black C. (Leg;Mey; RL). The lumber of this species is ordinarily sold simply as Cherry.	**serotina**	Black C.
Chokecherry (Mey; RL. *Choke-Cherry*)	**virginiana**	Common Chokecherry
French C. (RL)	**cerasus**	Sour Cherry
Wild C. (RL. *Gean*). This is the official Cherry lumber of Great Britain.	**avium**	Mazzard C.

Lumber Trade Name	Plant Source: Botanical Name	Plant Source: S.P.N. Common Name
Cherrystone Juniper. ONESEED J.		
CHESTNUT (Mey;RL; Sud,L)	**Castanea dentata**	AMERICAN CHESTNUT
English C. SWEET C.		
Spanish C. SWEET C.		
SWEET C. (ET;Leg; Mey. *English C.; Spanish C.*)	**C. sativa** (*vulgaris*)	EUROPEAN C.
Chewinggum Tree. SAPODILLA		
Chi. NANCHE		
Chichipate. BILLYWEBB		
CHICKRASSY (How;Leg; Mey;RL;Tr. *Chickrassee; Chicrasei; Chikrassi; Chittagong; Yinma*)	**Chukrasia tabularis**	CHITTAGONG CHICKRASSY
Chico Zapote. SAPODILLA		
CHINKAPIN (Mey;Sud. *Chinquapin*)	**Castanea pumila**	ALLEGANY CHINKAPIN
GOLDEN C. (Mey;Sud) Golden Evergreen-chinkapin is the dwarf var. **minor** of this species.	**Castanopsis chrysophylla**	GIANT EVERGREEN-CHINKAPIN
Chittagong. CHICKRASSY		
Chittamwood. SHITTIMWOOD; SMOKETREE, AMERICAN		
CHITTIMWOOD (Mey;RL)	**Bumelia lanuginosa**	WOOLLYBUCKET BUMELIA
CHOKECHERRY (Mey;RL)	**Prunus virginiana**	COMMON CHOKECHERRY
CHUGLAM	**Terminalia**	TERMINALIA (*Myrobalantree*)
BLACK C. (How;Leg; Mey;RL;Tr;Wil. *Chugalam; Chuglan; Chuglum; Kala-chuglam*)	**mani**	MANI T.
Black C. MUTWINDA		
WHITE C. (FW;Leg; Mey;RL;Tr. *Chugalam; India Silver Greywood; India Walnut; Indiawood; Ixora; Verda*)	**bialata**	TWO-WING T.
CIGARBOXCEDAR (Bat;Bo; Leg;Mey. *British Guiana Cedar; Spanish Cedar*)	**Cedrela odorata**	CIGARBOX CEDRELA
Cimarron. SANTAMARIA Cimarron is a very indefinite name, applicable to many trees, woods and other plants.		
CIRUELA (RL. *Cerirello; Ciruello*)	**Astronium** spp.	STARTREE
Citron, Bois de. French for Satinwood		
Claro Walnut. WALNUT, CALIFORNIA		
COACHWOOD (Aud;Bak; Bat;ET;Leg;Mey)	**Ceratopetalum apetalum**	FRAGRANT COACHWOOD
COCOBOLO(A) (Mey;RL; R&M. *Granadillo; Nambar*)	**Dalbergia granadillo**	GRANADILLO ROSEWOOD
COCOBOLO(A) (Mey;RL; R&M. *Nambar*)	**D. hypoleuca**	COSTARICA R.
COCOBOLO(A) (Mey;RL; R&M. *Nambar*)	**D. retusa**	PANAMA R.
COCONUT (Mey. *Porcupinewood*)	**Cocos nucifera**	COCONUT
COCUS (How;Leg;Mey; RL;R&M. *American Ebony; Granadillo; Green Ebony; Jamaica Ebony; West Indian Ebony*)	**Brya ebenus**	EBONY COCUSWOOD
COFFEETREE (Mey;RL)	**Gymnocladus dioica** (*canadensis*)	KENTUCKY COFFEETREE
COGWOOD	**Zizyphus chloroxylon**	COGWOOD JUJUBE
Colombian-mahogany. ALBARCO		
Common Lime. LINDEN, COMMON		
Conacaste. GUANACASTE		
Congo Cypress. VERAWOOD		
Congowood. BLACKWOOD, AFRICAN; TIGERWOOD		
Coolibah. EUCALYPTUS, COOLIBAH		
Copahiba. COPAIBA		
COPAIA (Mey. *Caroba; Carobocu; Fotui; Fut(u)i*)	**Jacaranda copaia**	COPAIA JACARANDA
COPAIBA (Mey;RL;R&M. *Akume; Copahiba*)	**Copaifera officinalis**	COPAIBA COPALTREE
RHODESIAN C. (*Rhodesian-mahogany; Rhodesian Copalwood*)	**C. coleosperma**	RHODESIAN C.
Copalwood. COPAIBA		

In view of the application of the names Copal, Copaltree, and Copalwood to numerous, unrelated genera (see Meyer and Van Wijk, for example) it would seem desirable to encourage the use of Copaiba for lumber from the genus Copaifera.

Lumber Trade Name	Plant Source: Botanical Name	Plant Source: S.P.N. Common Name
Copi(e). KOPIE		
Corail. PADAUK, AFRICAN		
CORALWOOD (Mey;RL)	**Adenanthera pavonina**	SANDAL BEADTREE
CORDIA (Mey;RL. *Cordiawood; Freijo*)	**Cordia goeldiana**	GOELDI CORDIA
CORDIA (Fox;How)	**C. fragrantissima**	FRAGRANT C.
CORK (The commercial bark)	**Quercus suber**	CORK OAK
Cork Elm. ELM, ROCK		
Corkwood		

According to Meyer, the wood of thirteen different genera of trees is marketed as Corkwood. The name appears to be applied indiscriminately to any light wood, perhaps especially to Balsa and the genus **Leitneria.**

Lumber Trade Name	Plant Source: Botanical Name	Plant Source: S.P.N. Common Name
Corkwood, Uganda. MUSODO		
Coromandel. EBONY, CALAMANDER; EBONY, MACASSAR		
COTTONWOOD *See also* ASPEN and POPLAR	**Populus**	POPLAR (*Cottonwood*); ASPEN
Balm C. BLACK C.		
Balsam C. BLACK C.		
BLACK C. (ET;Leg;Mey; Sud,L. *Balm C.; Balsam C.; Western Balm C.*)	**trichocarpa**	CALIFORNIA P. (*Black C.*)
Canadian C. EASTERN C.		
Common C. EASTERN C.		
EASTERN C. (How;Leg; Mey;RL;Sud,L. *Canadian C.; Carolina Poplar; Common C.; Necklace P.; Swiss P.*)	**deltoides** (*monilifera*)	EASTERN P.
FREMONT C. (Sud)	**fremonti**	FREMONT P. (*Fremont C.*)
MACDOUGAL C. (Sud)	**macdougali**	MACDOUGAL P. (*MacDougal C.*)
NORTHERN BLACK C. (RL;Sud,L)	**trichocarpa hastata**	PACIFIC P. (*Northern Black C.*)
NORTHERN C.	**deltoides virginiana**	NORTHERN C.
PLAINS C. (Sud)	**sargenti**	PLAINS P. (*Plains C.*)
SWAMP C. (Sud)	**heterophylla**	SWAMP P. (*Swamp C.*)
Western Balm C. BLACK C.		
Courbaril. GUAPINOL		
COWTREE (R&M;VW. *Milktree*)	**Brosimum utile** (*galactodendron*)	COW B.
Craboo. NANCHE		
CRABWOOD (Bat;Bo;Leg; Mey;RL;R&M. *Andiroba; British Guiana Mahogany; Carapa; Demara M.; Para M.*)	**Carapa guianensis**	GUIANA CRABWOOD
UGANDA C. (Ch)	**C. grandiflora**	UGANDA C.
Cuanacaztle. GUANACASTE		
Cucumbertree. MAGNOLIA		
CUDGERIE (And;Aud;Mey; RL. *Bumpy Ash; Cudgery; Silver Ash*)	**Flindersia schottiana**	CUDGERIE FLINDERSIA
Cupiuba. KOPIE		
CURUPAY (Mey;RL;R&M)	**Piptadenia** spp., especially **P. cebil, macrocarpa,** and **rigida**	PIPTADENIA

Lumber Trade Name	Plant Source: Botanical Name	Plant Source: S.P.N. Common Name
CUTCH (Bat;Bo;How; Mey;RL;Winn)	**Acacia catechu**	CATECHU ACACIA
Cyp(re). CANALETTA		
CYPRESS	**Cupressus**	CYPRESS
Alaska C. CEDAR, ALASKA		
ARIZONA C. (And;Mey; Sud)	**arizonica**	ARIZONA C.
British Honduras C. YACCA		
Congo C. VERAWOOD		
HIMALAYAN C. (And;Tr. *Nepal C.*)	**duclouxiana**	BHUTAN C.
Nepal C. HIMALAYAN C.		
Nootka C. CEDAR, ALASKA		
Red C. SOUTHERN C.		
Sitka C. CEDAR, ALASKA		
SMOOTH C. (Sud)	**arizonica bonita** (*C. glabra*)	SMOOTH ARIZONA C.
SOUTHERN C. (Sud,L. *Red C.; White C.; Yellow C.*)	**Taxodium distichum**	COMMON BALDCYPRESS
Yellow C. CEDAR, ALASKA; SOUTHERN CYPRESS		
CYPRESSPINE (Bo;ET)	**Callitris robusta**	STURDY CYPRESSPINE
Dabema; Dahoma. EKHIMI		
DAKAMA (Mey;RL;R&M)	**Dimorphandra latifolia**	BROADLEAF DIMORPHANDRA
Daman. DHAMAN		
Damo. TAMO		
DAMSON, NATIVE (VW) *See* PODO; *also* MATAI; TOTARA; YACCA.	**Podocarpus elatus**	TALL PODOCARPUS
DANTA (Ch;Mey;RL. *Apru; Otutu; Redwood*)	**Cistanthera papaverifera**	DANTA
DAO (FW;Mey;Rey;RL; Y,TW. *Batuan; New Zealand Wood; Paldao*)	**Dracontomelum dao**	DAO DRAGONPLUM
DARU (Fox;Mey;RL. *Bedaru*)	**Urandra corniculata**	DARU URANDRA
Deal, Red. PINE, SCOTS		
Deal, White. SPRUCE, NORWAY		
Deal, Yellow. PINE, SCOTS		
DEGAME (Bat;FW;Mey; RL;R&M. *Degamiwood; Lemonwood*)	**Calycophyllum candidissimum**	DEGAME CALYCOPHYLLUM
Denya. OKAN		
Determa. IMBUYA		
DHAMAN (Mey;RL. *D(h)aman(a); Dhamani; Dhamin*)	**Grewia tiliaefolia**	LINDEN GREWIA
DHUP (ET;Mey;RL. *Indian White Mahogany; White Dhup*) Dhup, however, seems to be loosely used for other Indian timbers.	**Canarium euphyllum**	ANDAMAN CANARYTREE
Dibetou. TIGERWOOD		
DILLENIA (RL;R&M)	**Dillenia** spp.	DILLENIA
Dilly, Wild. BULLETWOOD		
DOGWOOD (Bat;Mey;RL; Sud)	**Cornus florida**	FLOWERING DOGWOOD
DOUGLASFIR (Bat;Bot;ET; How;Leg;Mey;RL; R&M. *Douglas Yellow F.; Golden Rod D. F.; Montana F.; National Yellow F.; Oregon F.; Pacific Coast Douglas F.; Red F.; Santiam Quality F.; Yellow Douglas F.; Yellow F.*)	**Pseudotsuga taxifolia** (*douglasi; mucronata*)	DOUGLASFIR
Duali. PALOSAPIS		
DUNGON (Mey;Rey)	**Tarrietia sylvatica**	DUNGON STONEWOOD
EAGLEWOOD (Bo;Fox;Mey; R&M;Tr. *Agallocha(um); Lignaloes; Indian Eaglewood*)	**Aquilaria agallocha**	AGALLOCH EAGLEWOOD (*Lignaloes*)
EASTINDIESLAUREL (Leg; Mey;RL. *East India Walnut*)	**Terminalia tomentosa**	WOOLLY TERMINALIA
Eba. EKKI		
EBONY *See also* BLACKPLUM; PERSIMMON	**Diospyros**	PERSIMMON
American E. COCUS		
BATULINAU E. (Mey; Rey. *Batulinau*)	**ferrea** (*Maba buxifolia*)	PHILIPPINE EBONY P.
BENIN E. (Ain;RL. *Uhu*)	**insculpta**	BENIN E. P.
BLACK E. (RL;Tr)	**tomentosa**	NEPAL E. P.
Black E. GABOON E.		
BURMESE E. (How;Tr)	**burmanica**	BURMESE E. P.
CALAMANDER E. (Bat; ET; Fox; FW; How; RL. *Coromandel*)	**quaesita**	CALAMANDER E. P.
Cape E. CAPE-EBONY		
Coromandel E. CALAMANDER E.; MACASSAR E.		
EAST INDIAN E. (ET; Fox;FW;Leg;RL;Tr. *Speckled E.; Streaked E.*)	**ebenum**	EBONY P.
GABOON E. (Bo;FW; How;RL. *Black E.; Calabar; Gabun; Lagos; Niger E.*)	**dendo**	GABOON E. P.
GREEN E. (How;Mey)	**chloroxylon**	GREEN E. P.
Green E. COCUS		
INDIAN E. (Bat. *Zapote*)	**ebenaster**	INDIAN E. P.
Jamaica E. COCUS		
MACASSAR E. (Fox;RL. *Coromandel; Marblewood*)	**melanoxylon**	COROMANDEL E. P.
MACASSAR E. (FW. *Coromandel*)	**macassar**	MACASSAR E. P.
Mozambique E. BLACKWOOD, AFRICAN		
MYRTLE E. (And;Aud; Bak;How;Mey. *Gray Plum*)	**pentamera**	MYRTLE E. P.
Niger E. GABOON E.		
Speckled E.; Streaked E. EAST INDIAN E.		
WEST AFRICAN E. (Da; ET;How;Leg. *Kawraw*)	**mespiliformis**	MEDLAR P.
WEST AFRICAN E. (Leg)	**crassiflora**	WEST AFRICAN E. P.
WEST AFRICAN E. (Leg)	**piscatoria**	FISHERMANS P.
West Indian E. COCUS		
Eginfifen. OBECHE		
EKHIMI (Ain;Ch;RL. *African Greenheart; Agboin; Dabema; Dahoma; Ikkimi; Redwood*) The wood of Millettia is known as Ekimi; also as Moulmein-rosewood.	**Piptadenia africana**	AFRICAN PIPTADENIA
EKKI (Ain;Bat;ET;Leg; RL. *Azobe; Bois de Fer; Bongosi Bole; Bongossi; Eba; Kaku; Red Ironwood*)	**Lophira procera** (*L. alata p.*)	EKKI LOPHIRA
Ekusawa. KUSIA; OPEPE		
Elemi. PAPO		
ELM	**Ulmus**	ELM
American E. SOFT E.		
British E. ENGLISH E.		
CHINESE E. (Mey)	**parvifolia**	CHINESE E.
Common E. ENGLISH E.		
Cork E.; Corkbark E. ROCK E.		
Crowsfoot E. TARTAN, ROYAL		
DUTCH E. (Leg.)	∞**hollandica** (*? carpinifolia × glabra; dippeliana; major*)	∞DUTCH E.
ENGLISH E. (Bat;Bo; Leg;Mey;RL. *British E.; Common E.; European E.*)	**procera** (*campestris* in large part)	ENGLISH E.
European E. ENGLISH E.; WYCH E.		
Gray E. SLIPPERY E.; SOFT E.		
Hard Gray E. SOFT E.		
HIMALAYAN E. (Tr.)	**wallichi**	HIMALAYAN E.
Indian E. INDIAELM		
MEXICAN E. (Mey;R&M)	**mexicana**	MEXICAN E.

Lumber Trade Name	Plant Source: Botanical Name	Plant Source: S.P.N. Common Name
ELM, continued		
Mountain E. WYCH E.		
RED E. (Sud)	**Ulmus serotina**	SEPTEMBER ELM
Red E. SLIPPERY E.		
ROCK E. (Bat;Bo;How; Leg;Mey;RL;Sud,L. *Cork E.; Corkbark E.*)	**thomasi**	ROCK E.
Scotch E. WYCH E.		
SLIPPERY E. (Bat;Bo; Mey;RL. *Gray E.; Red E.*)	**fulva**	SLIPPERY E.
SOFT E. (Sud,L. *American E.; Gray E.; Hard Gray E.; Prinzwood; Swamp E.; Water E.; White E.*)	**americana**	AMERICAN E.
SOUTHERN ROCK E.	**crassifolia**	CEDAR E.
Swamp E.; Water E.; White E. SOFT E.		
WINGED E. (Bat;Bo; Mey;Sud)	**alata**	WINGED E.
WYCH E. (And;Bat;ET; Leg. *European E.; Mountain E.; Scotch E.*)	**glabra** (*montana; scabra*)	SCOTCH E. (*Wych E.*)
ELS, ROOD (Bo;Mey;VW. *Red Alder; Red Cedar; Red Els*) Rood Els is Dutch for Red Alder.	**Cunonia capensis**	CAPE CUNONIA
WIT E. (Bat;Bo;Ch;ET; Mey;VW. *White Alder; White Els*) Wit(te) Els is Dutch for White Alder. Cunonia and Platylophus are not related to Alder (**Alnus**) and their aspect is quite different from that genus.	**Platylophus trifoliatus**	TOWER-OF-PISA-TREE
Embuia. IMBUYA		
Emri. FRAMERIE		
ENG (Bat;How;Leg; Mey. *In*) *See also* YANG	**Dipterocarpus tuberculatus**	ENG GURJUNOIL-TREE
Espave. CARACOLI		
ESPINA CORONA (Mey; R&M. *Espinillo*)	**Gleditsia amorphoides**	AMORPHA HONEYLOCUST
ESTRIBEIRA(o) (Mey;RL. *Acoita-cavallo; Estriveiro*)	**Luehea divaricata**	COMMON WHIPTREE
EUCALYPTUS (Bat;FW; Mey;RL)	**Eucalyptus**	EUCALYPTUS

In the interests of name standardization and good business practice, it seems highly desirable to have the woods of all species of this genus marketed as various sorts of Eucalyptus. Terms such as Blackbutt and Peppermint that are current in the lumber trade are accepted in the following list as adjectives followed by E. (for Eucalyptus) not standing alone as names complete in themselves, though they are often used in that way in Australia where they were first applied to these woods. Some of them are at least as properly applied to trees of other genera, as Karri to an African tree and Bloodwood to trees of many genera.

Lumber Trade Name	Plant Source: Botanical Name	Plant Source: S.P.N. Common Name
AUSTRALIAN WHITEASH (Bak;Leg) E.	**fraxinoides**	ASH E.
BANGALAY (Bak; Mey) E.	**botryoides**	BANGALAY E.
BLACKBOX (And;Bak; Mey. *Flooded Box*) E.	**bicolor**	COOBURN E.
BLACKBUTT (Bak;ET; How;Mey) E.	**patens**	SWANRIVER E.
BLACKBUTT (Bak;ET; Fox;How;Leg;Mey. *Cambage B.*) E.	**pilularis**	BLACKBUTT E.
BLOODWOOD (Aud;Bak; Mey;RL) E.	**gummifera**	DARK BLOODWOOD E.
BLOODWOOD (Bak) E.	**intermedia**	PINK B. E.
YELLOW B. (Bak; Mey) E.	**eximia**	YELLOW B. E.
BLUEGUM (Fox;How; Leg;Mey;RL;R&M. *Bluegum*) E.	**globulus**	TASMANIAN BLUE E.
SYDNEY B. (Bak;ET; Mey) E.	**saligna**	SYDNEY B. E.
VICTORIA B. (Aud) E.	**bicostata**	EURABBIE E.
EUCALYPTUS, continued		
BROWNGUM (Bak;Mey; RL;R&M. *Swamp-mahogany*) E.	**Eucalyptus multiflora**	BEAKPOD EUCALYPTUS
BROWNMALLET (LP) E.	**astringens**	ALUM E.
CANDLEBARK (And;Aud; FNCV) E.	**rubida**	FLOODEDBOX E.
COOLIBAH (And;Aud; Mc;Mey) E.	**microtheca**	CANDLEBARK E.
FLOODEDGUM (And) E.	**grandis**	TOOLUR E.
GIANTGUM (Bak;Mey. *Argento; Australian Ash; Canary Ash; Messmate; Mountain Ash; Tasmanian Oak*) E.	**regnans**	GIANT E.
GIMLET (How) E.	**salubris**	GIMLET E.
GRAYBOX (Bat;ET;Mey. *Gray Boxwood*) E.	**hemiphloia**	GRAYBOX E.
BAIRNSDALE G. (Bat. *Bairnsdale Grey Boxwood*) E.	**bosistoana**	BOSISTO G. E.
GRAYGUM (Bak;ET; Mey) E.	**punctata**	LEATHERJACKET E.
GRAYGUM (Bak;Mey) E.	**propinqua**	GRAY E.
IRONBARK (Bak;ET; FNCV;Leg;Mey) E.		
BROADLEAF I. (Bak) E.	**caleyi**	CALEY IRONBARK E.
BROADLEAF I. (ET;Leg;Mey) E.	**siderophloia**	BROADLEAF I. E.
BLOODWOOD I. (Bak) E.	**fergusoni**	FERGUSON E.
GRAY I. (Bak;Leg; Mey) E.	**paniculata**	GRAY IRONBARK E.
NARROWLEAF I. (Bak) E.	**beyeri**	BEYER I. E.
NARROWLEAF I. (Bak; ET;Leg) E.	**crebra**	NARROWLEAF I. E.
PINK I. (ET) E.	**paniculata**	GRAY I. E.
RED I. (ET) E.	**sideroxylon**	MULGA I. E.
WHITE I. (FNCV) E.	**leucoxylon**	WHITE I. E.
IRONGUM (Aud;Mey) E.	**raveretiana**	IRON E.
JARRAH (Bak;ET;Fox; How;Leg;Mey;RL) E.	**marginata**	JARRAH E.
KARRI (Bak;ET;How; Leg;RL) E.	**diversicolor**	KARRI E.
KINOGUM (Aud. *Red-mahogany*) E.	**resinifera**	KINO E.
KUTCHA (Aud.) E.	**terminalis**	KUTCHA BLOODWOOD E.
LEMONGUM (Bak;Mc; Mey. *Lemon-scented-gum*) E.	**citriodora**	LEMON E.
MAIDENGUM (Aud;Bak. *Bluegum*) E.	**maideni**	MAIDENS E.
MANNAGUM (Bak) E.	**viminalis**	RIBBON E.
MORRELL (Bak;ET; How;Mey) E.	**longicornis**	RED MORRELL E.
MOUNTAINGUM (Bak; Mey) E.	**goniocalyx**	BIGLEAF E.
PEPPERMINT E.		
BLACK P. (Aud;Bak; Bat;Bo;Mey. *Peppermintgum*) E.	**salicifolia**	WILLOWLEAF E.
BROADLEAF P. (Bak; Mey) E.	**dives**	BROADLEAF PEPPERMINT E.
NARROWLEAF P. (Aud;Bak) E.	**radiata australiana**	
NEW ENGLAND P. (Bak) E.	**andrewsi**	ANDREWS P. E.
SYDNEY P. (Bak;Bo; ET;Mey. *Australian Redwood; Messmate*) E.	**piperita**	SYDNEY PEPPERMINT E.
PEPPERMINTGUM (Bak; Mey. *Peppermint-gum*) E.	**odorata** (*cajuputea*)	PEPPERMINT E.
REDBOX (Bak;Bo;Mey. *Red Boxwood*) E.	**polyanthemos**	REDBOX E.
COAST R. (Bak) E.	**rudderi**	RUDDERBOX E.
REDGUM (Bak;Bo;ET; How) E.	**calophylla**	MARRI E.
FOREST R. (Bak;Mey; RL) E.	**umbellata**	HORNCAP E.
MURRAY R. (Bak; ET) E.	**camaldulensis**	LONGBEAK E.
TASMANIAN R. (Bak) E.	**gunni acervula** (*E. acervula* Hook. f., *not* Sieb.)	TASMANIAN CIDER E.

Lumber Trade Name	Plant Source: Botanical Name	Plant Source: S.P.N. Common Name
EUCALYPTUS, continued		
SALMONGUM (Bak;Bat; ET;How;Mey) E.	**Eucalyptus salmonophloia**	SALMONBARK EUCALYPTUS
SCRIBBLYGUM (Aud; Mey) E.	**haemastoma**	SCRIBBLY E.
SLATYGUM (Bak;ET; Mey) E.	**dawsoni**	DAWSON E.
SPOTTEDGUM (Bak;ET; Fox;Leg;Mey. *Australian-hickory*) E.	**maculata**	SPOTTED E.
STRINGYBARK E.		
BROWN S. (Bak; Mey) E.	**capitellata**	BROWN STRINGYBARK E.
CUTTAIL S. (And;Bak; FNCV) E.	**fastigata**	CUTTAIL E.
MESSMATE S. (Aud; Bak;FNCV. *Yuba*) E.	**obliqua**	MESSMATE STRINGYBARK E.
RED S. (Bak;Mey) E.	**macrorhynca**	RED S. E.
ROUGH S. (Bak; Bo) E.	**baileyana**	BLACK S. E.
SILVERTOP S. (Bak. *Mountain Ash*) E.	**laevopinea**	SILVERTOP S. E.
WHITE S. (Bak;ET; Mey) E.	**eugenioides**	WHITE S. E.
YELLOW S. (Leg. *White Mahogany*) E.	**triantha**	
YELLOW S. (Bak;Bat; Mey) E.	**muelleriana**	MUELLER E.
SUGARGUM (Bak;Gu; Mey) E.	**cladocalyx** (*corynocalyx*)	SUGAR E.
TALLOWWOOD(Bak;Bat; Bo;ET;Fox;How; Leg;Mey) E.	**microcorys**	TALLOWWOOD E.
TALLOWWOOD (Aud; Bak. *Bastard Tallowwood*) E.	**planchoniana**	PLANCHON T. E.
TASMANIANOAK (Aud. *Tasmanianoak*) E.	**gigantea**	DELEGATE E.
TINGLETINGLE E.		
RED T. (Bak;LP; Mey) E.	**jacksoni**	REDTINGLE E.
YELLOW T. (LP; Mey) E.	**guilfoylei**	YELLOW TINGLETINGLE E.
TUART (Bak;Bat;Bo; ET;How;Mey. *Tooart*) E.	**gomphocephala**	TUART E.
WANDOO (Bak;ET;How; Leg;LP;Mey. *Whitegum*) E.	**redunca**	BLACKMARLOCK E.
POWDERBARK W. (Mey) E.	**accedens**	POWDERBARK E.
WHITEBOX (Aud; Mey) E.	**albens**	WHITEBOX E.
WHITEMAHOGANY (Aud; Bak. *White Mahogany*)E.	**umbra**	SHADOW E.
WOOLLYBUTT (Bak; ET) E.	**longifolia**	LONGLEAF WOOLLYBUTT E.
CAMDEN W. (Bak) E.	**macarthuri**	MACARTHUR E.
YATE (Aud;Bak;Mc; Mey;VW. *Flattop*) E.	**occidentalis**	FLATTOP YATE E.
YATEGUM (Bak;ET; How) E.	**cornuta**	YATE E.
YELLOWBOX (Bak;Bat; Mey) E.	**melliodora**	YELLOWBOX E.
YORKGUM (Aud. *Yorkgum*) E.	**foecunda**	FREMANTLE MALLEE E.
Ewowo. OBECHE		
False Acacia. LOCUST		
FALSE-MANGROVE (*Buttonwood; White Mangrove*)	**Laguncularia racemosa**	FALSEMANGROVE
FAVEIRO (Mey;RL. *Red Faveiro; Yellow Faveiro*)	**Pterodon pubescens**	FUZZY FAVEIRO
FIDDLEWOOD (Bat;Bo; Mey)	**Citharexylum**	FIDDLEWOOD
WHITE F.	**spinosum**	SPINY F.
Fiddlewood. CAPA		
FIR	**Abies**	FIR
ALPINE F. (Kew;Leg; Sud,L)	**lasiocarpa** (*subalpina*)	ALPINE F.
ALPINE F. (Sud,L. *Corkbark F.*)	**l. arizonica** (*A. arizonica*)	CORKBARK F.
BALSAM F. (Mey;RL; Sud, L. *American Silver F.; Balsam, Eastern F.*)	**balsamea**	BALSAM F.
BALSAM F.	**fraseri**	FRASER B. F.
Balsam F. WHITE F.		

Lumber Trade Name	Plant Source: Botanical Name	Plant Source: S.P.N. Common Name
FIR, continued		
CALIFORNIA RED F. (Sud,L. *Golden F.*)	**Abies magnifica**	RED FIR; CALIFORNIA RED F. (Forestry)
Colorado F. WHITE F.		
Common Silver F. SILVER F.		
Corkbark F. ALPINE F.		
DOUGLASFIR (Bat;Bo; ET;Leg;Mey;Sud,L.)	**Pseudotsuga taxifolia** (*douglasi;mucronata*)	DOUGLASFIR
Eastern F. BALSAM F.		
Giant F. WHITE F. (**grandis**)		
Golden F. CALIFORNIA RED F.		
Golden Rod Douglas F. DOUGLASFIR		
Grand F. WHITE F. (**grandis**)		
Lovely Silver F. SILVER F. (**amabilis**)		
Lowland White F. WHITE F. (**grandis**)		
Montana F. DOUGLASFIR		
National Yellow F. DOUGLASFIR		
NOBLE F. (Bat;Kew; Sud,L. *Larch; White F.*)	**Abies procera** (*nobilis*)	NOBLE F.
Oregon F. DOUGLASFIR		
Pacific Coast Douglas F. DOUGLASFIR		
Red F. DOUGLASFIR		
Red Silver F. SILVER F. (**amabilis**)		
Santiam Quality F. DOUGLASFIR		
SILVER F. (Bat;Bo;ET; How;Leg;Mey. *Common Silver F.; Swiss Pine*)	**alba** (*pectinata*)	SILVER F.
SILVER F. (Sud,L. *Larch; Lovely Silver F.; Red Silver F.; Western F.; White F.*)	**amabilis**	CASCADES F.; PACIFIC SILVER F. (Forestry)
SOUTHERN BALSAM F.	**fraseri**	FRASER BALSAM F.
Tall Silver F. WHITE F.		
Western F. SILVER F.		
Western Hemlock F. WESTERN HEMLOCK		
White F. NOBLE F.; SILVER F.		
WHITE F. (Bat;Kew; Mey;RL;R&M; Sud,L. *Balsam F.; Colorado F.*)	**concolor**	WHITE F.
WHITE F. (Bat;Mey; RL;Sud,L. *Balsam F.; Giant F.; Grand F.; Great F.; Tall Silver F.*)	**grandis**	GRAND F.
Yellow Douglas F. DOUGLASFIR		
Yellow F. DOUGLASFIR		
FIRETREE (Mey;VW. *Silkyoak*)	**Stenocarpus sinuatus**	TALL FIREWHEELTREE
Flattop. EUCALYPTUS, YATE		
FLINDERSIA (Mey. *Crows Ash; Flinderosa; Flindosy; Rasppod Tree; Teak*)	**Flindersia australis**	BALLROOM FLINDERSIA

Other species in this genus are known in the lumber trade as Bennett-ash; Cairns-hickory; Cudgerie; Leopardtree; Longjack; Redbeech and Silkwood, which see.

Lumber Trade Name	Plant Source: Botanical Name	Plant Source: S.P.N. Common Name
Flooded Box. EUCALYPTUS, BLACKBOX		
Floodedgum. EUCALYPTUS, FLOODEDGUM		
Florisa. CATIVO		
FOOCADIE (ET;RL. *Fucadie; Fukadi; Olivier; Phokadie*)	**Bucida buceras** (*Terminalia b.*)	OXHORN BUCIDA
Fotui. COPAIA		
Frake. AFARA		
FRAMERIE (Ain;Ch;Mey; RL. *Ampira; Black Afara; Brimstone-wood; Emri; Frameri; Framire; Indigbo; Satinwood; Yellow Terminalia*)	**Terminalia ivorensis**	IVORYCOAST TERMINALIA

Lumber Trade Name	Plant Source: Botanical Name	Plant Source: S.P.N. Common Name
Framire(i). FRAMERIE		
Freijo. CORDIA		
Frene (RL). French for Ash		
Fucadie; Fukadi. FOOCADIE		
FUSTIC (Bat;Bo;ET;FW; Mey;RL;R&M. *Mora; Old Fustic; Yellowwood)*	**Chlorophora tinctoria**	DRUG FUSTICTREE
Fut(u)i. COPAIA		
Gaboon. OKOUME		
Gabun. EBONY, GABOON		
Galaba; Galba. SANTA-MARIA		
Gambari. GUMBAR		
Garabu. GUARABU		
Garapa. GRAPIAPUNHA		
GARDENIA, BOXWOOD *(India Boxwood)*	**Gardenia latifolia**	BOXWOOD GARDENIA
Gateado. GONCALO ALVES		
Gean. CHERRY, WILD		
Gedunohor. SAPELE		
GENIP (F&W. *Genipa; Jagua)*	**Genipa americana**	MARMALADEBOX GENIP
Genizero. GUANACASTE		
Giac. LIGNUMVITAE		
GIAM (Mey;RL)	**Hopea lowi**	LOWS MERAWAN
GIAM (Mey)	**H. nutans**	NODDING M.
Giantgum. EUCALYPTUS, GIANTGUM		
Gidgee. ACACIA		
Gimlet. EUCALYPTUS, GIMLET		
GLUTA (Fox;Mey;RL)	**Gluta** spp.	GLUTA
Goldia. YON		
Goldspanglewood. LACEWOOD		
GOLDWOOD (Mey;R&M. *Vinhatico de Espinho)*	**Pithecellobium vinhatico**	GOLDWOOD APES-EARRING
Gommier. GUMBOLIMBO		
GONCALO ALVES (Mey; RL;R&M. *Gateado; Jobillo; Kingwood; Mura; Palo Mulatto; Tigerwood; Zebrawood)*	**Astronium fraxinifolium**	ASHLEAF STARTREE
GONCALO ALVES (RL; R&M. *Gateado)*	**A. graveolens**	FETID S.
Goomar Teak. GUMBAR		
Granadillo. COCOBOLO; COCUS; MACAWOOD		
GRAPEFRUIT (Mey;RL)	**Citrus paradisi**	GRAPEFRUIT
GRAPIAPUNHA (How;Mey; R&M. *Garapa)*	**Apuleia praecox**	
GRASSTREE (LP. *Grasstree Fibre)* The name Grasstree is best applied to the genus Xanthorrhoea.	**Kingia australis**	AUSTRALIAN BROOMTREE
Graybox. EUCALYPTUS, GRAYBOX		
Graygum. EUCALYPTUS, GRAYGUM		
Gray Plum. EBONY, MYRTLE		
Graywood, English. MAPLE, SYCAMORE		
GREENHEART (Ain;ET; Leg; Mey; RL; R&M)	**Ocotea rodioei** (*Nectandra r.*)	GREENHEART OCOTEA
Greenheart, African. EKHIMI		
Greywood, India Silver. CHUGLAM, WHITE		
GRIGNON (Bo. *Wane)*	**Bucida angustifolia**	NARROWLEAF BUCIDA
GRUMIXABA (RL. *Grumichaba)*	**Eugenia brasiliensis**	BRAZIL EUGENIA
GUAMBO (Mey;RL)	**Phoebe ambigens**	HONDURAS PHOEBE
GUANACASTE (Mey;R&M; Y,TW. *Conacaste; Cuanacaztle; Genizero; Jenisero; Kelobra; Parota; South American Walnut)*	**Enterolobium cyclocarpum**	GUANACASTE EARPODTREE
Guapeaqu. PAQUE		

Lumber Trade Name	Plant Source: Botanical Name	Plant Source: S.P.N. Common Name
GUAPINOL (Mey;RL. *Courbaril; South American Locust; Surinam Teak; West Indian Locust)*	**Hymenaea courbaril**	COURBARIL
GUARABU (Bo;RL. *Garabu)*	**Terminalia acuminata**	GUARABU TERMINALIA
GUARANTAN (Mey;RL. *Guaranta; Larangeira)*	**Esenbeckia leiocarpa**	GUARANTAN GASPARILLO
GUAREA (Ain;Leg. *African Cedar; Bosse; Cedron; Nigerian Cedar; Obobo; Obobonufua; Pequa; Scented Guarea; White Guarea)*	**Guarea cedrata**	PINK MUSKWOOD
GUAREA (Ain;Leg. *Black Guarea; Nigerian Cedar; Obobonekwi; Obobonerkhui)*	**G. thompsoni**	BLACK M.
Guaruba. AMARANTH		
GUATACARE (F&W;Mey. *Watercare)*	**Lecythis laevifolia**	TRINIDAD MONKEY-POTTREE
Guatambu. PIQUIA PEROBA		
GUAYAIBI (Mey;RL. *Guayabira)*	**Patagonula americana**	GUAYAIBI PATAGONIATREE
Guayacan. LIGNUMVITAE; VERAWOOD		
GUIJO (Ah;Mey;Rey;RL. *Orion)*	**Shorea guiso**	GUIJO SHOREA
Gumar. GUMBAR		
GUM *See also* EUCALYPTUS; TUPELO		
BLACKGUM (Mey;RL; Sud,L. *Pepperidgegum; Sourgum)*	**Nyssa sylvatica**	BLACK TUPELO; BLACKGUM (Forestry)
Bluegum. EUCALYPTUS, BLUEGUM		
Browngum. EUCALYPTUS, BROWNGUM		
Delta Red G. REDGUM		
Floodedgum. EUCALYPTUS, FLOODEDGUM		
Giantgum. EUCALYPTUS, GIANTGUM		
Graygum. EUCALYPTUS, GRAYGUM		
Irongum. EUCALYPTUS, IRONGUM		
Kinogum. EUCALYPTUS, KINOGUM		
Lemongum. EUCALYPTUS, LEMONGUM		
Maidengum. EUCALYPTUS, MAIDENGUM		
Mannagum. EUCALYPTUS, MANNAGUM		
Mountaingum. EUCALYPTUS, MOUNTAINGUM		
Peppermintgum. EUCALYPTUS, PEPPERMINT		
REDGUM (Mey;RL;Sud, L. *Bilsted; Delta Redgum)*	**Liquidambar styraciflua**	AMERICAN SWEETGUM
Redgum. EUCALYPTUS, REDGUM		
Redgum, Forest. EUCALYPTUS, FOREST REDGUM		
Redgum, Murray. EUCALYPTUS, MURRAY REDGUM		
Redgum, Tasmanian. EUCALYPTUS, TASMANIAN REDGUM		
Salmongum. EUCALYPTUS, SALMONBARK		
Scribblygum. EUCALYPTUS, SCRIBBLYGUM		
Slatygum. EUCALYPTUS, SLATYGUM		
Sourgum. BLACKGUM		
Spottedgum. EUCALYPTUS, SPOTTEDGUM		

Lumber Trade Name	Plant Source: Botanical Name	Plant Source: S.P.N. Common Name
GUM, continued		
Sugargum. EUCALYPTUS, SUGARGUM		
Tasmanian Redgum. EUCALYPTUS, TASMANIAN REDGUM		
Whitegum. EUCALYPTUS, WANDOO		
Yategum. EUCALYPTUS, YATE		
Yorkgum. EUCALYPTUS, YORKGUM		
GUMBAR (Bo;How;Mey; Tr. *Gambari; Goomar Teak; Gumadi; Gumaldi; Gumar; Gumar Teak; Gummadi; Gumudu*)	**Gmelina arborea**	MALAY BUSHBEECH
GUMBOLIMBO (Mey;R&M. *Gommier*)	**Bursera simaruba**	GUMBOLIMBO
GURJUN (Bo;Gam;How; Leg;Mey;Tr. *Gurjum; Kanyin*)	**Dipterocarpus turbinatus**	COMMON GURJUN-OILTREE (*Gurjun*)
GURJUN (RL. *Hora*)	**D. zeylanicus**	CEYLON G.
HACKBERRY (And;Bo; Mey;RL;Sud,L)	**Celtis occidentalis**	COMMON HACKBERRY
HACKBERRY (Mey;RL; Sud,L. *Sugarberry*)	**C. laevigata** (*mississippiensis*)	SUGAR H.
HADANG (Mey;RL)	**Cordia macleodi**	MACLEOD CORDIA
HALDU (Fox;Leg;Mey;RL. *Hnaw; Modelwood*)	**Adina cordifolia**	HEARTLEAF ADINA
Halmililla. TRINCOMALIWOOD		
Harewood. PRICKLYASH.		
Harewood, English. MAPLE, SYCAMORE		
HAWTHORN (RL. *Thornapple*)	**Crataegus crusgalli**	COCKSPUR HAWTHORN
HAWTHORN (Tr.)	**C. oxyacantha**	ENGLISH H.
HEMLOCK	**Tsuga**	HEMLOCK
CAROLINA H. (Sud,L.)	**caroliniana**	CAROLINA H.
EASTERN H. (Leg;RL; Sud,L. *Huron Pine; Pennsylvania H.; Pennsylvania White H.; West Virginia H.; Wisconsin White H.*)	**canadensis**	CANADA H; EASTERN H. (Forestry)
MOUNTAIN H. (Sud,L)	**mertensiana**	MOUNTAIN H.
Pacific H.; Pacific Coast H. WESTERN H.		
Pennsylvania H.; Pennsylvania White H. EASTERN H.		
West Coast H. WESTERN H.		
WESTERN H. (Leg;RL; Sud,L. *Alaska Pine; Hemlock Spruce; Pacific H.; Pacific Coast H.; Westcoast H.; Western Hemlock Fir*)	**heterophylla**	PACIFIC H.; WESTERN H. (Forestry)
West Virginia H.; Wisconsin White H. EASTERN H.		
HICKORY. *See also* PECAN. In general, the different species of Hickory are not now distinguished in the lumber trade.	**Carya** (*Hicoria*)	HICKORY
Australian H. EUCALYPTUS, SPOTTEDGUM		
Bigbud H. MOCKERNUT H.		
Big H.; Bigleaf Shellbark H.; Big Shellbark H. SHELLBARK H.		
Birds-eye H. MOCKERNUT H.		
BITTERNUT H. (Mey; Sud. *Pecan*)	**cordiformis** (*amara; Hicoria c.; H. minima*)	BITTERNUT H.
BITTERNUT H. (Sud)	**c. elongata**	ASHE B. H.
Black H. MOCKERNUT H.; PIGNUT H.		
Brown H. PIGNUT H.		

Lumber Trade Name	Plant Source: Botanical Name	Plant Source: S.P.N. Common Name
HICKORY, continued		
Curly H. MOCKERNUT H.		
MOCKERNUT H. (Bat; Bo;Mey;RL. *Bigbud H.; Birds-eye H.; Black H.; Curly H.; Whiteheart H.*)	**Carya tomentosa** (*alba* K. Koch *not* Nutt.)	MOCKERNUT HICKORY
NUTMEG H. (Mey. *Pecan*)	**myristicaeformis**	NUTMEG H.
Pecan H. PECAN		
PIGNUT H. (Bat;Bo; Mey. *Black H.; Brown H.*)	**glabra** (*porcina*)	PIGNUT H.
RED H. (TNC)	**ovalis** (*H. o.*)	RED H.
SHAGBARK H. (Bat;Bo; RL. *Shellbark H.; White H.*)	**ovata** (*alba* Nutt., *not* K. Koch; *H. ovata*)	SHAGBARK H.
SHELLBARK H. (Mey. *Big H.; Big S. H.; Bigleaf S. H.; Thick S. H.*)	**laciniosa** (*sulcata; H. laciniosa; H. sulcata*)	SHELLBARK H.
Swamp H. WATER H.		
Thick Shellbark H. SHELLBARK H.		
WATER H. (Bat;Bo; Mey. *Bitter Pecan; Swamp H.*)	**aquatica**	WATER H.
White H. SHAGBARK H.		
Whiteheart H. MOCKERNUT H.		
Hillgooseberry. ROSEMYRTLE		
HIMALAYA HOLLY (Tr)	**Ilex dipyrena**	HIMALAYA HOLLY
Hnaw. HALDU		
HOLLOCK (Mey;RL. *Lepcha; Panisaj; Sunlock*)	**Terminalia myriocarpa**	PROLIFIC TERMINALIA
HOLLONG (Gam;Mey;RL)	**Dipterocarpus pilosus**	PROLIFIC GURJUN-OILTREE
HOLLY (Mey;RL;Sud)	**Ilex opaca**	AMERICAN H.
HOLLY (Leg;Mey)	**I. aquifolium**	ENGLISH H.
HONEYLOCUST (And. *Honey L.*)	**Gleditsia triacanthos**	COMMON HONEYLOCUST
Honeysuckle. REWAREWA; WALLUM		
HOOBOOBALLI (RL;R&M. *Hububalli; Snakewood; Surinam; Surinam Snakewood*)	**Loxopterygium sagoti**	
Hooppine. MORETONBAYPINE		
Hora. GURJUN		
HORCO CEBIL (Mey;RL)	**Piptadenia communis**	COMMON PIPTADENIA
Hormigo. MACAWOOD		
HORNBEAM (Leg;Mey; RL. *Blue Beech*)	**Carpinus betulus**	EUROPEAN HORNBEAM
HORNBEAM, AMERICAN (Mey. *Bluebeech; Canadian H.*)	**C. caroliniana**	AMERICAN H.
Horse Cassia. CANA FISTOLA		
HORSECHESTNUT (Leg; Mey) *See also* BUCKEYE	**Aesculus hippocastanum**	COMMON HORSECHESTNUT
Horseflesh Wood. BULLETWOOD		
Hububalli. HOOBOOBALLI		
Hudoke. SUCUPIRA		
HUNGCHAI (Mey;RL)	**Ormosia** spp.	ORMOSIA
HUONPINE (ET;How; Mey)	**Dacrydium franklini**	HUONPINE DACRYDIUM
HURA (RL. *Hurawood; Possum Wood; Rakuda*)	**Hura crepitans**	SANDBOXTREE
IBIRANIRA (RL)	**Bumelia obtusifolia**	IBIRANIRA BUMELIA
IBIRARO (RL)	**Pterogyne nitens**	
Ikkimi. EKHIMI		
Ilomba. AKOMU		
IMBUYA (Mey;RL. *Brazilian Walnut; Determa; Embuia; Imbuia*)	**Phoebe porosa**	IMBUYA PHOEBE
In. ENG		
INCENSECEDAR (Bat; R&M;Sud,L)	**Libocedrus decurrens**	CALIFORNIA INCENSECEDAR
INCENSETREE (Tr)	**Boswellia serrata**	INDIA FRANKINCENSE
INCENSEWOOD (And)	**Amoora nitidula**	
India Copal. PINEYVARNISHTREE		

Lumber Trade Name	Plant Source: Botanical Name	Plant Source: S.P.N. Common Name
India Eaglewood. EAGLEWOOD		
INDIAELM (How;Mey;Tr. *Indian Elm*)	**Holoptelea integrifolia**	INDIAELM
INDIA HORSECHESTNUT (Mey;Tr)	**Aesculus indica**	INDIES HORSECHESTNUT
INDIALABURNUM (Mey;Tr; VW)	**Cassia fistula**	GOLDENSHOWER SENNA
India Silver Graywood; India Walnut; Indiawood. CHUGLAM, WHITE		
Indigbo. FRAMERIE		
IPE (RL. *Pao d'arco*)	**Tabebuia** spp. (*Tecoma* in part)	TRUMPETTREE
PEROBA I. (R&M. *White Peroba*)	**Paratecoma peroba** (*Tecoma p.*)	
IPIL (Mey;Rey;RL) *See also* MERBAU	**Intsia bijuga**	COMMON IPIL
IROKO (Bat;Ch;Mey;RL; Y,TW. *African Oak; African Teak; Cambala; Kambala; Odoum; Oloko; Oroko*)	**Chlorophora excelsa**	IROKO FUSTICTREE
Ironbark. EUCALYPTUS, IRONBARK		
Irongum. EUCALYPTUS, IRONGUM		
IRONWOOD		

It is a physical impossibility to standardize such a plant name as "ironwood" or its foreign equivalents such as palo de hierro, bois de fer, eisenholtz, etc. Van Wijk, in his "Dictionary of Plant-Names," gives trees of 34 genera bearing the name "Ironwood." Meyer, in his "Buch der Holznamen," lists 44 species of trees belonging to 35 genera and 20 families called "Ironwood." It is a most trite and unimaginative name for any strong wood; a pity somebody has not used "Steelwood,' just for variety.

Lumber Trade Name	Plant Source: Botanical Name	Plant Source: S.P.N. Common Name
Ita; Itako. CELTIS		
ITA-UBA	**Endiandra ita-uba**	ITA-UBA
Iti. ROSEWOOD, EAST INDIAN		
IVORYWOOD (Mey;VW)	**Siphonodon australe**	AUSTRALIAN IVORYWOOD
Ixora. CHUGLAM, WHITE		
JACARANDA (Mey. *Palisander; Cayenne P.*)	**Jacaranda**	JACARANDA
BRAZIL J.	**brasiliensis**	BRAZIL J.
Jacaranda. ROSEWOOD, BRAZILIAN		
Jagua. GENIP		
Jak. JAKWOOD		
JAKWOOD (Bo;Mey;Tr. *Jak*)	**Artocarpus heterophyllus**	JAKFRUIT
JAMAN (Bat;Mey;RL. *Black Plum*)	**Syzygium cumini** (*jambolanum; Eugenia c.*)	JAMBOLAN
Jamba. PYINKADO		
Jamwood. RASPBERRY JAMWOOD		
Jarrah. EUCALYPTUS, JARRAH		
Jarul. BANABU		
Jenisero. GUANACASTE		
JEQUITIBA (RL;R&M. *Albarco*)	**Cariniana** spp.	CARINIANA
JIGGERWOOD	**Bravaisia floribunda**	JIGGERWOOD
Jobillo. GONCALO ALVES		
Jobo. MOMBIN, YELLOW		
JUJUBE (Mey;Tr)	**Zizyphus jujuba**	COMMON JUJUBE
JUNIPER	**Juniperus**	JUNIPER
ALLIGATOR J. (Kew; Mey;Sud)	**pachyphloea**	ALLIGATOR J.
Cherrystone J. ONESEED J.		
COMMON J. (Kew;Mey. *Dwarf J.*)	**communis**	COMMON J.
Desert J. UTAH J.		
Drooping J. WEEPING BLUE J.		
Dwarf J. COMMON J.		
ONESEED J. (Sud. *Cherrystone J.*)	**monosperma**	ONESEED J.
UTAH J. (Kew;Sud. *Desert J.*)	**utahensis**	UTAH J.
WEEPING BLUE J. (Tr. *Drooping J.*)	**recurva**	HIMALAYAN J.
WESTERN J.	**occidentalis**	SIERRA J.
Kajat. MLOMBWA		
Kaku. EKKI		
Kala-chuglam. CHUGLAM, BLACK		
KALAMANSANAI (Mey; Rey;RL. *Calamansanay*)	**Neonauclea calycina**	KALAMANSANAI
KALANTAS (Mey;Rey;RL. *Calantas; Kalantus; Philippine Cedar*)	**Toona calantas**	PHILIPPINE TOON
KALUNTI (Rey. *Yellow Lauan*)	**Shorea kalunti**	KALUNTI SHOREA
KALUNTI (Mey;RL)	**S. mindanensis**	MINDANAO S.
KAMASSIWOOD (Leg;Mey. *Knysna Boxwood*)	**Gonioma kamassi**	KAMASSIWOOD
Kambala. IROKO		
Kanyin. GURJUN		
Kapok. CEIBA		
Kapur Barus. CAMPHORWOOD, BORNEO		
Karelian Burl. BIRCH, EUROPEAN		
Karri. EUCALYPTUS, KARRI		
Katmon. CATMON		
KAURI (Bak;Mey. *Kauri Pine*)	**Agathis australis**	KAURI DAMMARPINE
KAURI (Leg)	**A. microstachys**	
KAURI (Leg)	**A. palmerstoni**	PALMERSTON D.
Kawraw. EBONY, WEST AFRICAN		
Kelobra. GUANACASTE		
KERUING (Mey;RL)	**Dipterocarpus cornutus**	KERUING GURJUN-OILTREE
Kevazingo. KEWAZINGO		
KEWAZINGO (Mey;RL; *Kevazingo*)	**Copaifera demeusei**	CONGO COPALTREE
KEWAZINGO (Mey;RL; *Kevazingo*)	**C. tessmanni**	TESSMANN C.
KHAYA (Mey. *Uganda Mahogany*)	**Khaya**	KHAYA
DRYZONE K.	**senegalensis**	SENEGAL K.
RED K.	**ivorensis**	IVORYCOAST K.
RED K.	**nyasica**	NYASSA K.
WHITE K.	**anthotheca**	WHITE K.
WHITE K. This lumber is usually sold as African Mahogany (or variations of it, as Senegal M.) or simply as Mahogany. But it is not true Mahogany. *See* MAHOGANY.	**grandifoliola**	BIGLEAF K.
KINGWOOD (Mey;RL. *Violet-Kingwood; Violetta; Violetwood*)	**Dalbergia cearensis**	CEARA ROSEWOOD
Kingwood. GONCALO ALVES		
Kinogum. EUCALYPTUS, KINOGUM		
KOA (Bat;Mey;RL)	**Acacia koa**	KOA ACACIA
Kokko; Koko. SIRIS		
KOPIE (Mey;VW. *Copi(e); Cupiuba; Cupiuva; Red Copie*)	**Goupia glabra**	KOPIE
KUSIA (Mey;RL. *Ekusawa*) *See also* OPEPE	**Nauclea esculenta**	GUINEAPEACH FATHEADTREE
Kussia. OPEPE		
Kutcha. EUCALYPTUS, KUTCHA		
LABURNUM (Bat;Bo;ET; How;Leg;Mey)	**Laburnum anagyroides** (*vulgare*)	GOLDENCHAIN LABURNUM
ALPINE L. (ET;Mey)	**L. alpinum** (*Cytisus alpinus*)	SCOTCH L.
INDIALABURNUM (Mey; Tr;VW)	**Cassia fistula**	GOLDENSHOWER SENNA
LACEWOOD (RL. *Australian Silkyoak; Bulloak; Gold-spanglewood; Queensland Silkyoak; Selano; Silkyoak; Western Plane*)	**Cardwellia sublimis**	LACEWOOD (*Gold-spanglewood*)
Lagos. EBONY, GABOON		
LANCEWOOD (Mey;RL. *Yaya*)	**Oxandra lanceolata**	LANCEWOOD

The name "lancewood" is considerably overworked. In Van Wijk's encyclopaedic "Dictionary of Plant-Names," 8 *genera* are called by this name. In Meyer's "Buch der Holznamen," 9 *genera* and 12 *species* are called "lancewood." Professor Record and others claim that the true lancewood is **Oxandra lanceolata.** The "lancewood" of Australian commerce is **Backhousia australis** and **B. myrtifolia.** Among other commonly called "lancewoods" are spp. of the genera Duguetia, Guatteria, and Rollinia of Guiana.

Lumber Trade Name	Plant Source: Botanical Name	Plant Source: S.P.N. Common Name
Lancewood, Red. Bulletwood		
Lanete (Mey;RL;R&M)	**Wrightia laniti**	
Larangeira. Guarantan		
Larch	**Larix**	Larch
Alpine L. (Mey;Sud)	**lyalli**	Alpine L.
American L. Tamarack		
Eastern L. Tamarack		
European L. (Bat;Leg; Mey;RL)	**decidua** (*europaea*)	European L.
Japanese L. (Leg;Mey)	**leptolepis**(*kaempferi*)	Japanese L.
Western L. (Leg;Mey; RL;Sud,L. *Larch; Montana L.*)	**occidentalis**	Western L.
Larch. Fir, Noble		
Laredo. Capomo		
Lasrin (Bo;Gam;Tr. *Ceylon Rosewood*)	**Albizzia odoratissima**	Fragrant Albizzia
Lauan	**Shorea** spp.	Shorea
See also Almon; Sal		
Red L. (Mey;Rey;RL. *Philippine Mahogany*)	**S. negrosensis**	Redlauan S.
Lauan. Palosapis		
White L. Balak		
Yellow L. Kalunti; Malaanonang; Manggosinoro		
Laurel (RL. *Baytree; Sweet B.*)	**Laurus nobilis**	Grecian Laurel
Alexandrian L. Poon		
American L. Mountainlaurel		
Australian L. Orientalwood		
Californialaurel (*Oregon Myrtle*)	**Umbellularia californica**	Californialaurel
Eastindieslaurel (Leg;Mey;RL. *East India Walnut; Siris*)	**Terminalia tomentosa**	Woolly Terminalia
Mountainlaurel (*American L.*)	**Kalmia latifolia**	Mountainlaurel Kalmia
Leadwood	**Krugiodendron ferreum**	Leadwood
Leche Maria. Santamaria		
Lega. Siris		
Lemongum. Eucalyptus, Lemongum		
Lemonwood. Degame; Piquia Peroba		
Lepcha. Hollock		
Leopardtree (Aud;Bak. *Leopardwood*)	**Flindersia maculosa**	Leopard Flindersia
Broadleaf L. (And; Aud;Mey)	**F. collina**	Hill F.
Leopardwood. Leopardtree; Snakewood		
Letterwood. Snakewood		
Lignaloes. Eaglewood		
Lignumvitae (How;Mey; RL. *Bera; Giac; Guayacan; Ironwood; Vera*)	**Guajacum officinale**	Common Lignumvitae
Holywood L.	**G. sanctum**	Holywood L.
Limbo. Afara		
Limewood. Basswood		
Linden	**Tilia**	Linden; Basswood (Forestry)

Here again occurs needless confusion in terms. The Old World Tilias are called Lindens by the Lumber Trade while American Tilias are unfortunately called Basswoods by both Forestry and the Lumber Trade.

Lumber Trade Name	Botanical Name	S.P.N. Common Name
American L. Basswood		
Bigleaf L. (Bat)	**platyphyllos** (*grandifolia*)	Bigleaf L.
Common L. (Bat. *Common Lime*)	**europaea** (*vulgaris*)	European L.
Littleleaf L. (Bat; Mey)	**cordata** (*ulmifolia*)	Littleleaf L.
Lingoa. Padauk		
Lingue. Aligna		
Locust (Sud,L. *Black L.; False Acacia; Honey L.; Red L.; Yellow L.*)	**Robinia pseudoacacia**	Black Locust
Honey L. Honeylocust; Locust		
Red L. Locust		
South American L.; West Indian L. Guapinol		
Yellow L. Locust		

Lumber Trade Name	Plant Source: Botanical Name	Plant Source: S.P.N. Common Name
Logwood (Bo;Leg;R&M)	**Haematoxylon campechianum**	Logwood
Longjack (And;Aud;Bak; Bo;Mey)	**Flindersia oxleyana**	Longjack Flindersia
Lovoa (Da. *Uganda Walnut*)	**Lovoa browni**	Browns Lovoa
Lovoa. Tigerwood		
Lumbayao (Ah;Mey;Rey; RL. *Lumbayan*)	**Tarrietia javanica**	Java Stonewood
Macacahuba; Macacauba. Macawood		
Macawood (Mey;RL. *Bleeding Heart; Brazilian Padauk; Granadillo; Hormigo; Macacahuba; Macacauba; Roble Colorado; Vencola*) *See also* Quira	**Platymiscium** spp.	Macawood
Macayo. Angelin		
Madou. Maidou		
Madrone Burl (RL. *Madrona; Madrono*)	**Arbutus menziesi**	Pacific Madrone
Magkono. Mancono		
Magnolia	**Magnolia**	Magnolia
Bay M.	**virginiana australis**	Southern Sweetbay M.
Cucumber M. (RL; Sud,L. *Ailon; Cucumbertree*)	**acuminata**	Cucumbertree M.
Evergreen M. (RL; Sud,L. *Ailon; Cucumbertree*)	**grandiflora**	Southern M.
Mahoe, Red. Saltfishwood		
Mahogany	**Swietenia** spp.	Mahogany

African, Philippine, and other exotic woods are sold as "Mahogany" which do not belong to the Mahogany genus (**Swietenia**) and which frequently are very different from that wood in qualities, use, and appearance. Such Old World woods definitely are not entitled to be called Mahogany, and the misapplication of that name to them, for whatever reason, misleads the public, is bad nomenclatural practice, and should not be tolerated. Many of these woods have qualities no less admirable in their own way than those of Mahogany, though certainly not the same; and ought to be prized and used for their real qualities under their real names instead of being treated as substitutes.

Lumber Trade Name	Botanical Name	S.P.N. Common Name
African M. See note under Khaya		
American Tropical M. Honduras M.		
Australian M. Rosamay		
Bataan M. Tangile		
Benin M.; Bigleaf M. See note under Khaya		
Brazilian M. Honduras M.		
British Guiana M. Crabwood		
Brown M. Sapele		
Burma M. Thitka		
Cedar M. Guarea; Sapele		
Cherry M. Makore		
Colombian M. Albarco		
Costa Rica M.; Cuban M.; Curlet M. West Indies M.		
Demerara M. Crabwood		
East Indian M. Padauk, Andaman		
Gaboon M. Okoume		
Guatemalan M. Honduras M.		
Honduras M. (*Aguano; American Tropical M.; Baywood; Brazilian M.; Caoba; Guatemalan M.; Mexican M.; Nicaraguan M.; Panama M.; Peruvian M.; Tabasco M.*)	**macrophylla**	Honduras M.
Indian White M. Dhup		

Lumber Trade Name	Plant Source: *Botanical Name*	Plant Source: *S.P.N. Common Name*
Mahogany, continued		
Jamaica M. West Indies M.		
Lagos M. Khaya		
Mexican M. (*Oaxaca M.*)	**Swietenia humilis**	Mexican Mahogany
Mexican M. Honduras M.		
Mountain M. Cercocarpus		
Nicaraguan M. Honduras M.		
Nigerian M. Khaya		
Oaxaca M. Mexican M.		
Panama M. Honduras M.		
Para M. Crabwood		
Peruvian M. Honduras M.		
Philippine M. An untenable trade name for various Philippine hardwoods. *See* Almon; Bagtikan; Balak; Mayapis; Red Lauan; Tangile		
Pink M. Agba		
Porto Rico M. West Indies M.		
Rhodesian M. Copaiba, Rhodesian		
Rose M. Rosamay		
San Domingo M. West Indies M.		
Sapele M.; Scented M. Sapele		
Senegal M. See note under Khaya		
South African M. Bulletwood		
Spanish M. West Indies M.		
Swamp M. Eucalyptus, Browngum		
Tabasco M. Honduras M.		
Tangile M. Tangile		
Tenasserium M. Padauk, Burma		
True M. West Indies M.		
Uganda M. Khaya		
Venezuela M.	**candollei**	Venezuela M.
West Indies M. (Bo; Mey;Sud,L. *Costa Rica M.; Cuban M.; Curlet M.; Jamaica M.; Porto Rico M.; San Domingo M.; Spanish M.; True M.; West Indian M.*)	**mahagoni**	WestIndies M.
White M. Primavera; Eucalyptus, Yellow Stringybark		
Mahwa. Buttertree		
Maidengum. Eucalyptus, Maidengum		
Maidou (Mey;RL. *Madou; Mai Padu*)	**Pterocarpus pedatus**	
Majagua (RL)	**Hibiscus** spp.	Hibiscus
Makore (RL. *African Cherry; Baku; Cherry Mahogany; Makora; Makori*)	**Mimusops heckeli**	Heckel Bulletwood
Malaanonang (Rey. *Yellow Lauan*)	**Shorea polita**	Polished Shorea
Malabar. Rosewood, East Indian		
Malugai (RL)	**Pometia pinnata**	
Mamee Apple. Sapote		
Manbarklak	**Eschweilera corrugata**	Manbarklak
Mancono (Ah;Mey;Rey. *Magkono*)	**Xanthostemon verdugonianus**	
Mangeao	**Litsea calicaris**	NewZealand Litsea
Manggachapui (Fox;Rey; RL)	**Hopea acuminata**	

Lumber Trade Name	Plant Source: *Botanical Name*	Plant Source: *S.P.N. Common Name*
Manggasinoro (Rey;RL. *Yellow Lauan*)	**Shorea philippinensis**	Philippine Shorea
Mangrove (Mey;R&M)	**Rhizophora mangle**	American Mangrove
Black M. Blacktree		
White M. False-mangrove		
Maniawga. Carallia		
Mannagum. Eucalyptus, Mannagum		
Mansonia (Leg. *Aprono; Ofun; Opruno*)	**Mansonia altissima**	
Maple	**Acer**	Maple
Australian M. Silkwood, Maple		
Bigleaf M. Oregon M.		
Black M. (Bat;Mey; RL;Sud,L. *Hard M.*)	**nigrum**	Black M.
Hard M. Black M.; Sugar M.		
Oregon M. (Bat;Mey; RL. *Bigleaf M.; Soft M.*)	**macrophyllum**	Bigleaf M.
Queensland M. Silkwood, Maple		
Red M. (Bat;Mey;RL. *River M.; Soft M.; Water M.*)	**rubrum**	Red M.
Rock M. Sugar M.		
Silver M. (Leg;RL. *Scarlet M.; Soft M.; Swamp M.; Water M.*)	**saccharinum**	Silver M.
Soft M. Oregon M.; Red M.; Silver M.		
Sugar M. (Bat;Mey; RL;Sud,L. *Hard M.; Rock M.*)	**saccharum**	Sugar M.
Swamp M. Silver M.		
Sycamore M. (Bat; Mey. *English Graywood; English Harewood; English Sycamore*)	**pseudoplatanus**	Planetree M. (*Sycamore M.*)
Water M. Silver M.		
Maracaibo-wood. Verawood		
Marblewood, Andaman	**Diospyros marmorata**	Andaman Marblewood
Marblewood. Ebony, Macassar		
Marinheiro. Muskwood		
Marmalade Tree. Sapote		
Marupa (RL. *Bitterwood; Maruba; Negrito; Paradisetree; Simaruba*)	**Simaruba glauca**	Paradisetree
Massaranduba. Bulletwood		
Matai (Leg)	**Podocarpus spicatus**	Matai Podocarpus
Matchwood (F&W;Mey. *Trinidad M.*)	**Didymopanax morototoni**	Matchwood
Mayapis (RL. *Philippine Mahogany*)	**Shorea palosapis**	Palosapis Shorea
Mayapis. Palosapis		
Melica. Beech, Southland		
Meranti (Bat;Leg;Mey. *Sepang*)	**Hopea maranti**	
Merbau (Leg) *See also* Ipil	**Intsia bakeri**	Merbau Ipil
Merawan (Fox;Mey)	**Hopea** spp.	Merawan
Mersawa. Palosapis		
Messmate. Eucalyptus, Giantgum; Eucalyptus, Sydney Peppermint		
Milktree. Cowtree		
Miorri. Sapele		
Mlombwa (Mey;TW. *Kajat; Muninga*)	**Pterocarpus angolensis**	Angola Padauk
Moboron. Agba		
Modelwood. Haldu		
Molave (Ah;Bo;Fox; Mey;Rey) Used for certain Philippine species of this genus.	**Vitex** spp.	Chastetree

	Plant Source	
Lumber Trade Name	*Botanical Name*	*S.P.N. Common Name*
MOMBIN (Mey;R&M)	**Spondias**	MOMBIN
PURPLE M.	**purpurea**	PURPLE M.
YELLOW M. (*Jobo*)	**mombin** (*axillaris; lutea*)	YELLOW M.
Monkey Puzzle. ARAUCARIA		
MORA (Leg)	**Mora excelsa** (*Dimorphandra mora*)	GUIANA MORA
Mora. FUSTIC		
Morado. AMARANTH		
Moretonbay-chestnut. BLACKBEAN		
MORETONBAY-PINE (Bat; Bo;ET. *Hooppine*) Species of Araucaria should be called Araucaria rather than by the misnomer "Pine."	**Araucaria cunninghami**	CUNNINGHAM ARAUCARIA
Morrell. EUCALYPTUS, MORRELL		
MORURO (Mey;R&M)	**Peltophorum adnatum**	MORURO PELTOPHORUM
Mountaingum. EUCALYPTUS, MOUNTAINGUM		
MOUNTAINLAUREL (*American Laurel*)	**Kalmia latifolia**	MOUNTAINLAUREL KALMIA
MOVINGUI (*Anyaran; Ayan; Movinga; Movingue; Nigerian Satinwood*)	**Distemonanthus benthamianus**	
MUIRACOATIARA	**Centrolobium paraense**	PARA PORCUPINEPODTREE
Muirapiranga. SATINEE		
MULGA (And;Guil)	**Acacia aneura**	MULGA ACACIA
Muninga. MLOMBWA		
Munyama. KHAYA		
Mura. GONCALO ALVES		
Musengera. PODO		
MUSIZI (Ch;Mey)	**Maesopis emini**	
MUSKWOOD (Mey. *Camboata Blanca; Marinheiro*)	**Guarea trichilioides**	AMERICAN MUSKWOOD
JAMAICA M. (R&M)	**G. glabra**	JAMAICA M.
MUSODO (Da;Mey. *Uganda Corkwood*)	**Ricinodendron africanum**	MUSODO MANKETTINUT
Mutiral. SATINWOOD, CEYLON		
MUTWINDA (How;Mey. *Black Chuglam*)	**Myristica irya**	MUTWINDA NUTMEG
MUZAITI (ET;Leg;Mey; RL. *East African Camphorwood; Muzaita*)	**Ocotea usambarensis**	MUZAITI OCOTEA
Myrtle, Golden. PENDA		
Myrtle, Oregon. CALIFORNIALAUREL		
Myrtle, Tasmanian. BEECH, TASMANIAN		
Nacastillo. NARGUSTA		
Nambar. COCOBOLO		
NANCHE (How;Mey;RL. *Chi; Craboo; Nance*)	**Byrsonima crassifolia**	
NARGUSTA (Leg;Mey;RL. *Aromilla; Nacastillo*)	**Terminalia obovata**	NARGUSTA TERMINALIA
Narra. PADAUK, INDIA		
Narrowleaf Peppermint. EUCALYPTUS, NARROWLEAF PEPPERMINT		
Naseberry. SAPODILLA		
Negrito. MARUPA		
New South Wales Beefwood. SILKYOAK		
New Zealand Honeysuckle. REWAREWA		
New Zealand Teak. PUIRI		
New Zealand Wood. DAO		
NIANGON (FW)	**Tarrietia utilis**	
Nikiba. IDAGBON		
NOPO (RL)	**Cordia glabra**	NOPO CORDIA
Noyer. French for Walnut.		
NSAMBYA (Ch;Mey)	**Markhamia platycalyx**	
OAK	**Quercus**	OAK
African O. IROKO		
ARIZONA WHITE O. (Sud. *White O.*)	**arizonica**	ARIZONA WHITE O.
Australian Silky O. LACEWOOD		

	Plant Source	
Lumber Trade Name	*Botanical Name*	*S.P.N. Common Name*
OAK, continued		
Austrian O. EUROPEAN O.		
Bay O. DURMAST O.		
Black O. RED O. (**velutina**)		
BLACKJACK O. (Sud)	**Quercus marilandica**	BLACKJACK OAK
British O.; Brown O. EUROPEAN O.		
BUR O. (Bat;Bo;Mey. *Burr O.; Mossycup O.*) *See also* WHITE O.	**macrocarpa**	BUR O.
Bur(r) O. EUROPEAN O.		
CALIFORNIA BLACK O. (Sud)	**kelloggi**	CALIFORNIA BLACK O.
CALIFORNIA BLUE O. (Sud. *White O.*)	**douglasi**	BLUE O.
California White O. VALLEY WHITE O.		
Chestnut O. WHITE O. (**montana**)		
Chinquapin O. WHITE O. (**muhlenbergi**)		
CORK O. (Bo;How) The commercial bark is Cork.	**suber**	CORK O.
DURMAST O. (Bat;ET; Mey. *Bay O.; Scrub Sessile O.; Sessile O.*)	**petraea** (*sessiliflora*)	DURMAST O.
EMORY O. (Sud)	**emoryi**	EMORY O.
English Brown O. EUROPEAN O.		
EUROPEAN O. (ET;RL. *Austrian O.; British O.; Brown O.; Bur(r) O.; English Brown O.; French O.; German O.; Gothic O.; Hungarian O.; Pedunculate O.; Pollard O.; Russian O.; Slavonian O.*)	**robur** (*pedunculata*)	ENGLISH O.
Forkedleaf White O. WHITE O. (**alba**)		
French O.; German O.; Gothic O. EUROPEAN O.		
HOLLY O. (And;ET; Mey;Tr. *Holm O.*)	**ilex**	HOLLY O.
Hungarian O. EUROPEAN O.		
Indian O. CHEE		
Iron O. WHITE O. (**stellata**)		
KERMES O. (Bo)	**coccifera**	KERMES O.
LAUREL O. (Sud)	**laurifolia** (*hybrida*)	LAUREL O.
LIVE O. (Mey;Sud. *American Live O.*)	**virginiana** (*sempervirens*)	LIVE O.
CALIFORNIA L. O. (Bo. *Canyon L. O.*)	**chrysolepis**	CANYON L. O. (*Goldencup O.*)
COAST L. O. (And; Sud)	**agrifolia**	CALIFORNIA L. O.
INTERIOR L. O.	**wislizeni**	INTERIOR L. O.
MEXICAN BLUE O. (Sud)	**oblongifolia**	MEXICAN BLUE O.
Mossycup O. BUR O.		
NORTHERN PIN O.	**ellipsoidalis**	NORTHERN PIN O.
OREGON WHITE O. (Sud. *White O.*)	**garryana**	OREGON WHITE O.
Overcup O. WHITE O. (**lyrata**)		
Pedunculate O. EUROPEAN O.		
Pin O. RED O. (**palustris**)		
Pollard O. EUROPEAN O.		
Post O. WHITE O. (**stellata**)		
Queensland Silky O. LACEWOOD		
RED O. (Mey;RL;Sud, L. *West Virginia Soft Red O.*)	**borealis maxima**	EASTERN RED O.
RED O. (Sud,L. *Black O.*)	**velutina** (*tinctoria*)	BLACK O.
RED O. (Bat;Bo;ET; RL;Sud,L. *Southern Red O.*)	**falcata** (*rubra* L., *not* Du Roi)	SOUTHERN RED O. (*Spanish O.*)

Lumber Trade Name	Plant Source: Botanical Name	Plant Source: S.P.N. Common Name
OAK, continued		
RED O. (RL;Sud,L) In addition Black, Pin, Southern Red, Swamp Red, Texas Red, Water, and Willow Oaks (*which see*) are officially recognized as sources of Red Oak lumber.	**Quercus borealis** (incl. *rubra* Du Roi, *not* L.)	NORTHERN RED OAK
RED O. (Sud,L. *Swamp Red O.*)	**falcata pagodaefolia** (*Q. rubra p.*)	SWAMP R. O.
RED O. (Sud,L. *Pin O.*)	**palustris**	PIN O.
RED O. (Sud,L. *Water O.*)	**nigra** (*aquatica*)	WATER O.
RED O. (RL;Sud,L. *Texas Red O.*)	**texana**	TEXAS O.
RED O. (RL;Sud,L. *Willow O.*)	**phellos**	WILLOW O.
Rock O. WHITE O. **(prinus)**		
ROCKY MOUNTAIN WHITE O. (Sud)	**utahensis**	UTAH WHITE O.
Russian O. EUROPEAN O.		
Scrub Sessile O.; Sessile O. DURMAST O.		
SHUMARD RED O. (Sud)	**shumardi** (*Q. texana s.*)	SHUMARD O.
Silky O. LACEWOOD; SILKYOAK		
Slavonian O. EUROPEAN O.		
Southern Red O. RED O. **(falcata)**		
Swamp Chestnut O. WHITE O. **(prinus)**		
Swamp Red O. RED O. **(falcata pagodaefolia)**		
Swamp White O. WHITE O. **(bicolor)**		
TANOAK (Sud)	**Lithocarpus densiflorus** (*Pasania densiflora*)	TANOAK
Tasmanian O. EUCALYPTUS, TASMANIANOAK		
Texas Red O. RED O. **(texana)**		
TURKEY O. (And;Bo; ET;Gam)	**Quercus cerris**	EUROPEAN TURKEY OAK
TURKEY O. (Sud)	**laevis** (*catesbaei*)	TURKEY O.
VALLEY WHITE O. (Sud. *California White O.; White O.*)	**lobata**	CALIFORNIA WHITE O. (*Valley O.*)
Water O. RED O. **(nigra)**		
West Virginia Soft Red O. RED O. **(borealis maxima)**		
West Virginia Soft White O. WHITE O. **(alba)**		
WHITE O. (Sud,L. *Albawood; Forkedleaf White O.; West Virginia Soft White O.*)	**alba**	WHITE O.
WHITE O. (Sud,L. *Swamp White O.*)	**bicolor** (*platanoides*)	SWAMP W. O.
WHITE O. (Sud,L. *Overcup O.*)	**lyrata**	OVERCUP O.
WHITE O. (Sud,L. *Bur O.*)	**macrocarpa**	BUR O.
WHITE O. (Sud,L. *Chestnut O.*)	**montana** (*prinus* Engelm, *not* L.)	CHESTNUT O.
WHITE O. (Sud,L. *Chinquapin O.; Yellow Chestnut O.; Yellow O.*)	**muhlenbergi**	CHINKAPIN O.
WHITE O. (Sud,L. *Rock O.; Swamp Chestnut O.*)	**prinus** (*michauxi*)	SWAMP CHESTNUT O. (*Basket O.*)
WHITE O. (Sud,L. *Iron O.; Post O.*)	**stellata** (*minor; obtusiloba*)	POST O.
White O. ARIZONA WHITE O.; CALIFORNIA BLUE O.; OREGON W. O.; VALLEY W. O.		
Willow O. RED O. **(phellos)**		
Yellow Chestnut O.; Yellow O. WHITE O. **(muhlenbergi)**		

Lumber Trade Name	Plant Source: Botanical Name	Plant Source: S.P.N. Common Name
Oba Suluk. SERAYA		
OBECHE (Leg;Mey;RL. *Abachi; African Whitewood; Arere; Ayous; Eginfifen; Ewowo; Okpo; Owowa; Samba-ayous; Wawa*)	**Triplochiton scleroxylon**	
Obobo; Obobonekwi; Obobonerkhui; Obobonufua. GUAREA		
OCOBO (Mey;R&M. *Bethabara; Roble; Robleyugo; West Indies Boxwood*)	**Tabebuia pentaphylla** (*Tecoma leucoxylon; T. pentaphylla*)	
ODOKO (Leg;RL)	**Scottellia coriacea**	
Odoum. CEIBA; IROKO		
Ofun. MANSONIA		
Ogechi. CAPOMO		
Ohia. CELTIS		
OITY (RL)	**Licania tomentosa**	
Ojoche. CAPOMO		
OKAN (RL. *Denya*)	**Cylicodiscus gabunensis**	
OKOUME (Mey;RL. *Gaboon; Gaboon Mahogany; Okume*)	**Aucoumea klaineana**	KLAINE OKOUME
Okpo. OBECHE		
OKWEIN (ET;RL. *Bubinga; Okwen; Zingana*)	**Brachystegia spicaeformis**	SPIKE BARKCLOTHTREE
Old Fustic. FUSTIC		
Oleo Pardo. CABREUVA		
OLEO VERMELHO (RL. *Balsamo; Cabreuva; Quina; Quina-Quina*)	**Myroxylon balsamum** (*toluiferum*)	TOLUBALSAM BALMTREE
OLIVE	**Olea**	OLIVE
AFRICAN O. (Leg;Mey)	**hochstetteri**	AFRICAN O.
INDIA O. (Mey;Tr)	**ferruginea** (*cuspidata*)	INDIA O.
ITALIAN O. (RL)	**europaea**	COMMON O.
Olivier. FOOCADIE		
Oloko. IROKO		
OMBUYA	**Phoebe porosa**	IMBUYA PHOEBE
Omu. SAPELE		
OPEPE (Ain;Leg;RL. *Abiache; Badi; Ekusawa; Kussia; Ubulu*) See also KUSIA	**Nauclea diderichi** (*Sarcocephalus d.*)	OPEPE FATHEADTREE
Opruno. MANSONIA		
ORANGE	**Citrus sinensis**	SWEET ORANGE
ORIENTALWOOD (Mey;RL. *Australian Laurel; Australian Walnut; Oriental Walnut; Queensland Walnut*)	**Endiandra palmerstoni**	ORIENTALWOOD
Orion. GUIJO		
Orme. French for Elm		
Oro. TINDALO		
Oroko. IROKO		
OSOL (RL)	**Symphonia gabonensis**	GABON SYMPHONIA
Otutu. DANTA		
OVAGA (RL)	**Panda oleosa**	
Owowa. OBECHE		
PACARA (Mey. *Pacara Timbo*)	**Enterolobium contortisiliquum**	PACARA EARPODTREE
Pacara. TIMBOUVA		
PADAUK. *Bloodwood; Lingoa; Sangre Toro Vermillion; Yomawood*)	**Pterocarpus** spp.	PADAUK
AFRICAN P. (Mey;RL. *Barwood; Corail*)	**soyauxi**	
ANDAMAN P. (Bat;Fox; Gam;How;Mey;RL; R&M;Tr. *Andaman Redwood; Coromandel Redwood; East Indian Mahogany*)	**dalbergioides**	ANDAMAN P.
Brazilian P. MACAWOOD		
BURMA P. (ET;Fox; How; Leg; Mey; R&M; Tr. *Brown P.; Camwood; Inland P.; Red P.; Tenasserium Mahogany; Yellow P.*)	**macrocarpus**	BURMA P.

	Plant Source	
Lumber Trade Name	Botanical Name	S.P.N.Common Name
PADAUK, continued		
INDIA P. (Bat. *Amboyna; Angsana; Angsena; Burmese Rosewood; Narra; Philippine P.; Sena*) Narra is used for woods of genus Pterocarpus in Philippines.	**Pterocarpus indicus**	BURMACOAST PADAUK
VENGAI	**marsupium**	VENGAI P.
PAGATPAT (Mey;Rey;RL)	**Sonneratia caseolaris**	
Pahautea. CEDAR, NEW ZEALAND		
PAHUTAN (Mey;Rey;RL)	**Mangifera altissima**	PAHUTAN MANGO
Paldao. DAO A coined, veneer-trade term.		
Palisander. JACARANDA; ROSEWOOD, BRAZILIAN; ROSEWOOD, MADAGASCAR		
PALMETTO (Mey)	**Sabal palmetto**	CABBAGE PALMETTO
Paloblanco		

"Paloblanco" is a general term applied to a varied assemblage of chiefly tropical, white-wooded or white-barked trees from Spanish-speaking countries. Meyer (*op. cit.*) lists woods of 12 different genera under this name.

Lumber Trade Name	Botanical Name	S.P.N.Common Name
Palomaria. POON		
Palo Morado. AMARANTH		
Palo Mulatto. GONCALO ALVES		
PALOSAPIS (Mey;Rey;RL. *Bayott; Belle Rosa; Duali; Lauan; Mayapis; Mersawa*)	**Anisoptera thurifera** (*Dipterocarpus thurifer*)	PALOSAPIS MERSAWA
Panacoco. WAMARA		
Panisaj. HOLLOCK		
Pao Amarello. BRAZILIAN-SATINWOOD		
Pao d'arco. IPE		
PAO MULATTO (Mey; R&M)	**Calycophyllum spruceanum**	MULATTO CALYCOPHYLLUM
Pao Roxo. AMARANTH		
PAPO (Leg;RL. *Aiele; Canarium; Elemi*)	**Canarium schweinfurthi**	PAPO CANARYTREE
PAQUE (RL. *Guapaque*)	**Ostrya guatemalensis**	GUATEMALA HOP-HORNBEAM
Paradisetree. MARUPA		
PARANA-PINE (Mey; R&M; RL) Species of Araucaria should be called Araucaria rather than by the misnomer "Pine."	**Araucaria angustifolia** (*brasiliana*)	PARANA ARAUCARIA
Parota. GUANACASTE		
Partridgewood. ANGELIN		
PATTERNWOOD (Da; Mey)	**Alstonia congensis**	CONGO ALSTONIA
Pau Brazil. BRAZILWOOD		
PEAR (Bat;Mey;RL;Sud)	**Pyrus communis**	COMMON PEAR
PECAN (And;RL;Sud,L. *Pecan Hickory;Sweet P.*)	**Carya illinoensis**	PECAN
Pecan. HICKORY, BITTERNUT; HICKORY, NUTMEG; HICKORY, WATER		
PENDA (Aud;Bak;Guil; Mey;RL. *Golden Myrtle*)	**Xanthostemon oppositifolius**	
PENDA (Bak. *Atherton P.*)	**X. pubescens**	
Penkwa. SAPELE; TIGERWOOD		
Pepperidge. BLACKGUM		
Peppermint. EUCALYPTUS, PEPPERMINT		
Peppermintgum. EUCALYPTUS, BLACK PEPPERMINT; EUCALYPTUS, PEPPERMINTGUM		
PEPPERTREE (Mey. *Balsamo*)	**Schinus molle**	CALIFORNIA PEPPERTREE
Pequa. GUAREA		
Pequia. PIQUIA PEROBA		
Pernambuco. BRAZILWOOD		
PEROBA		
RED P. (Mey;RL; R&M)	**Aspidosperma polyneuron**	
White P. IPE, PEROBA		
PERSIMMON (Bat;Bo; How;Mey;RL)	**Diospyros virginiana**	COMMON PERSIMMON
PERUBALSAM (*Balsam*)	**Myroxylon pereirae** (*Toluifera p.*)	PERUBALSAM BALMTREE

	Plant Source	
Lumber Trade Name	Botanical Name	S.P.N.Common Name
Philippine Mahogany. ALMON; BAGTIKAN; BALAK; LAUAN, RED; MAYAPIS; TANGILE An untenable trade name for various Philippine hardwoods.		
Phokadie. FOOCADIE		
PICHO (RL)	**Vatairea lundelli**	
PIGEONBERRYTREE (And; Aud;Guil)	**Litsea dealbata**	PIGEONBERRY LITSEA
PINE	**Pinus**	PINE
Alaska P. HEMLOCK, WESTERN		
ALEPPO P. (Bat;Bo; Mey;Winn)	**halepensis**	ALEPPO P.
Arizona Soft P. PONDEROSA P.		
Arkansas Shortleaf P.; Arkansas Soft P. SHORTLEAF P.		
AUSTRIAN P. (Bat;Bo; Leg;Mey)	**nigra** (*austriaca; P. nigra a.*)	AUSTRIAN P.
Banksia P. JACK P.		
BLUE P. (Bat;Mey;Tr. *Bhotan P.*)	**griffithi** (*excelsa* Wall., *not* Lam.; *nepalensis* De Chambray, *not* Forbes)	HIMALAYAN P.
British Honduras P.; British Honduras Pitch P. SLASH P.		
Bull P. PONDEROSA P.		
Bunya-pine. BUNYA BUNYA		
California Sugar P. SUGAR P.		
California White P. PONDEROSA P.		
Canada White P. NORTHERN WHITE P.		
Canadian Red P. RED P.		
CELERY(TOP)PINE (Bat; Bo;ET;How;Mey;Tr)	**Phyllocladus rhomboidalis**	TASMANIA CELERY-PINE
Cembra P. SWISS STONE P.		
Chir P. LONGLEAF P.		
CLUSTER P. (Bo;ET; Leg;Mey. *Maritime P.*)	**Pinus pinaster**	CLUSTER PINE
Colonial P. MORETONBAY-P.		
CORSICAN P. (Bat;Bo; ET;Leg;Mey)	**nigra poiretiana** (*P. laricio; P. l. calabrica; P. l. corsicana*)	CORSICAN P.
Cuban P. SLASH P.		
CYPRESSPINE (Bo;ET. *Red Australian P.*)	**Callitris robusta**	CYPRESSPINE
Danzig P. SCOTS P.		
Eastern White P. NORTHERN W. P.		
Florida Longleaf Yellow P.; Georgia Yellow P. LONGLEAF P.		
Gray P. JACK P.		
Hard P. PITCH P.		
Hoop P. MORETONBAY-P.		
Hudson Bay P. JACK P.		
HUONPINE (ET;How; Mey)	**Dacrydium franklini**	HUONPINE DACRYDIUM
Huron P. HEMLOCK, EASTERN		
IDAHO WHITE P. (*Idaho P.; Mountain P.; Silver P.; Soft Idaho White P.; Western W. P.; Weymouth Mountain P.*)	**Pinus monticola**	WESTERN WHITE PINE
JACK P. (Bo;ET;Leg; Mey. *Banksia P.; Gray P.; Hudson Bay P.*)	**banksiana** (*divaricata*)	JACK P.
JAPANESE RED P. (Bat;Bo;How;Mey)	**densiflora**	JAPANESE RED P.

Lumber Trade Name	Plant Source: Botanical Name	Plant Source: S.P.N. Common Name
Pine, continued		
Kauri P. Kauripine		
Khasia P. (Bat;Tr)	**Pinus khasya**	Khasia Pine
King William P. Tasmaniancedar		
Loblolly P. (Bat;Bo; Mey;RL. *North Carolina P.; Virginia P.*) Often sold in the trade, in conjunction with 7 other yellow pines, as Southern Yellow Pine.	**taeda**	Loblolly P.
Lodgepole P. (Bo;Leg; Mey;RL;Sud,L. *Tamarack P.*)	**contorta latifolia** (*P. murrayana*)	Lodgepole P.
Longleaf P. (Bat;Bo; Mey;RL. *Florida Longleaf Yellow P.; Georgia Y. P.; Longleaf Y. P.; Pitch P.; Southern Yellow P.*) Often sold in the trade, in conjunction with 7 other yellow pines, as Southern Yellow Pine.	**palustris**	Longleaf P.
Longleaf P. (of Himalayas) (Bat;How; Mey;Tr. *Chir P.*)	**roxburghi**	Chir P.
Longleaf Yellow P. Longleaf P.		
Lowland Spruce P. Spruce P.		
Maritime P. Cluster P.		
Memel P. Scots P.		
Minnesota White P. Northern White P.		
Moretonbay-p. (Bat; Bo;ET;Mey. *Colonial P.; Hoop P.; Richmond River P.*) Species of Araucaria should be called Araucaria rather than by the misnomer "Pine."	**Araucaria cunninghami**	Cunningham Araucaria
Mountain P. (Sud)	**Pinus pungens**	TableMountain Pine
Mountain P. Idaho White P.		
New England P. Northern White P.		
North Carolina P. Loblolly P.; Shortleaf P.; Virginia P.		
Northern P. A trade name recognized for a mixture of lower grades of lumber from Pinus strobus with P. resinosa in which the former usually predominates.		
Northern P. Northern White P.; Scots P.		
Northern White P. (Leg;Mey;RL;Sud,L. *Canada W. P.; Eastern W. P.; Minnesota W. P.; New England P.; Northern P.; Soft Cork W. P.; Soft Minnesota W. P.; Soft P.; Soft W. P.; Weymouth P.; White P.; Wisconsin W. P.*)	**strobus**	Eastern White P.
Norway P. Red P.		
Oregon P.; Oregon White P. Ponderosa P.		
Parana-pine (Mey; R&M; RL) See note above under Moretonbay-p.	**Araucaria angustifolia** (*brasiliana*)	Parana Araucaria
Pitch P. (Bo;Mey. *Hard P.; Southern Yellow P.*)	**Pinus rigida**	Pitch Pine
Pitch P. Longleaf P.		
Pond P. (Bo;Mey;RL. *Southern Yellow P.*)	**rigida serotina** (*P. serotina*)	Pond P.

Lumber Trade Name	Plant Source: Botanical Name	Plant Source: S.P.N. Common Name
Pine, continued		
Ponderosa P. (Bat;Leg; Mey;RL;Sud. *Arizona Soft P.; Bull P.; California White P.; Oregon P.; Oregon White P.; Western P.; Western Soft P.; Western Yellow P.*) The wood of the closely related Jeffrey Pine (**Pinus jeffreyi**) is usually marketed with its more abundant associate, Ponderosa Pine, under the same name.	**Pinus ponderosa**	Ponderosa Pine
Red Australian P. Cypresspine		
Red Baltic P. Scots P.		
Red Deal. Scots P.		
Red New Zealand P. Rimu		
Red P. (Bat;Bo;ET; Mey;RL;Sud,L. *Canadian Red P.; Norway P.*)	**resinosa**	Red P.
Richmond River P. Moretonbay-p.		
Riga P. Scots P.		
Rosemary P. A trade name for mature, slow-growing southern Pine (usually Loblolly P.) other than Longleaf P.		
Scots (Scotch) P. (Bat; ET;Leg;Mey. *Baltic Redwood; Danzig P.; Memel P.; Northern P.; Red Baltic P.; Red Deal; Riga P.; Yellow Deal*)	**sylvestris**	Scotch P.
Shore P. (CL)	**contorta**	Shore P.
Shortleaf P. (Bat;Bo; Mey;RL. *Arkansas S. P.; Arkansas Soft P.; North Carolina P.; Shortleaved Yellow P.; Southern Yellow P.*)	**echinata** (*mitis*)	Shortleaf P.
Shortleaved Yellow P. Shortleaf P.		
Silver P. IdahoWhite P.		
Silverpine (Ah;Bat; Bo;ET;Ki;Mey. *Westland P.*)	**Dacrydium westlandicum**	Westland Dacrydium
Yellow S. (Bat; Ki)	**D. intermedium**	Fire D.
Slash P. (Mey;RL. *British Honduras P.; British Honduras Pitch P.; Cuban P.; Southern Yellow P.*)	**Pinus caribaea** (*elliotti; heterophylla*)	Slash Pine
Soft Cork White P. Northern White P.		
Soft Idaho White P. Idaho White P.		
Soft Minnesota White P. Northern White P.		
Soft P. Northern White P.		
Soft White P. Northern White P.		
Southern P.; Southern White P. Spruce P.		
Southern Yellow P. Composite lumber name for: Loblolly P.; Longleaf P.; Pitch P.; Pond P.; Shortleaf P.; Slash P.; Spruce P.; Virginia P. See these names.		
Spruce P. (Sud,L. *Lowland Spruce P.; Southern P.; Southern White P.; Southern Yellow P.*)	**glabra**	Spruce P.
Stone P. (Bat;Bo;Mey. *Umbrella P.*)	**pinea**	Italian Stone P.
Sugar P. (Bat;Bo;Mey; RL;Sud,L. *California Sugar P.*)	**lambertiana**	Sugar P.

	Plant Source	
Lumber Trade Name	*Botanical Name*	*S.P.N. Common Name*
PINE, continued		
SWISS STONE P. (Bo; Mey. *Cembra P.*)	**Pinus cembra**	SWISS STONE PINE
Swiss P. FIR, SILVER		
Tamarack P. LODGEPOLE P.		
Umbrella P. STONE P.		
UMBRELLAPINE (Bo)	**Sciadopitys verticillata**	UMBRELLAPINE
VIRGINIA P. (Sud,L. *North Carolina P.; Southern Yellow P.*)	**Pinus virginiana**	VIRGINIA PINE
Virginia P. LOBLOLLY P.		
Western P.; Western Soft P. PONDEROSA P.		
Western White P. IDAHO WHITE P.		
Western Yellow P. PONDEROSA P.		
Westland P. SILVERPINE		
Weymouth P. NORTHERN WHITE P.		
Weymouth Mountain P. IDAHO WHITE P.		
White P. NORTHERN WHITE P.		
Wisconsin White P. NORTHERN WHITE P.		
Yellow Deal. SCOTS P.		
Yellow P. LOBLOLLY P.; LONGLEAF P.; PITCH P.; POND P.; SHORTLEAF P.; SLASH P.; VIRGINIA P.		
Pineytree. POON (**angustifolium**)		
PINEYVARNISHTREE (Mey; Tr;Winn. *India Copal; White Dammar*)	**Vateria indica**	
PIQUIA (Mey; R&M. *Piquia-ete*)	**Caryocar villosum**	PIQUIA-ETE
PIQUIA PEROBA (RL. *Guatambu; Lemonwood; Pequia*)	**Aspidosperma tomentosum**	WOOLLY WHITE-QUEBRACHO
PLANE	**Platanus**	PLANETREE; SYCAMORE (Forestry)
CALIFORNIA P. (Bat;Bo)	**racemosa**	CALIFORNIA P.
EASTERN P. (Ah;Bat; Bo;Mey;Tr. *Oriental P.*)	**orientalis**	ORIENTAL P.
LONDON P. (Ah;ET; Leg;Mey)	**acerifolia**	LONDON P.
Oriental P. EASTERN P.		
Western P. LACEWOOD; SYCAMORE		
PLUM (Bat;Bo;Mey) The use of Plum (except perhaps in combination) for Lumber of genera other than Prunus, should be discouraged.	**Prunus domestica**	GARDEN PLUM
Black P. JAMAN		
Gray P. EBONY, MYRTLE		
SEBASTANPLUM (Bo; Fox;Mey;Winn. *Sebesten*)	**Cordia myxa**	SEBASTANPLUM
SOURPLUM (Bo;Guil; Mey;Winn)	**Owenia venosa**	
PODO (Ch;Mey. *Musengera; Yellowwood*)	**Podocarpus** spp.	PODOCARPUS
Pogo. CEDAR, SPICY		
POLAK (Leg;Mey)	**Ochroma bicolor**	
Pollard Oak. OAK, EUROPEAN		
POON (Ah;Mey;RL. *Alexandrian Laurel; Bintangor; Palomaria*)	**Calophyllum inophyllum** L., *not* Lam., *nor* Sieb. ex. Presl.	INDIAPOON BEAUTYLEAF
POON (Bo;Fox;Mey)	**C. tomentosum**	CEYLONPOON B.
POON (Bo. *Pineytree*)	**C. angustifolium**	PENANGPOON B.
POPLAR *See also* ASPEN and COTTONWOOD	**Populus**	POPLAR
BALM-OF-GILEAD P. (CL; RL. *Balm-of-Gilead*)	**candicans** (*P. balsamifera c.*)	BALM-OF-GILEAD P.

	Plant Source	
Lumber Trade Name	*Botanical Name*	*S.P.N. Common Name*
POPLAR, continued		
BALSAM P. (Bat;Mey; RL. *Balsam; Baumier; Tacamahac*)	**Populus tacamahaca** (*balsamifera* Muenchh., and Auth., *not* L.)	TACAMAHAC POPLAR
Bigtooth P. ASPEN, LARGETOOTH		
BLACK ITALIAN P. (ET; Leg;Mey)	**canadensis serotina** (*P. serotina*)	LATE CAROLINA P.
BLACK P. (Bat;Bo;ET; Leg;RL)	**nigra**	BLACK P.
Carolina P. COTTONWOOD, EASTERN		
GRAY P. (Ah;Bat;Bo; ET;Leg;Mey)	**canescens** (*alba* Willd., *not* L.)	GRAY P.
Largetoothed P. ASPEN, LARGETOOTH		
LOMBARDY P. (Mey;Tr)	**nigra** ₵LOMBARDY (*P. italica; P. n. pyramidalis*)	
Necklace P. COTTONWOOD, EASTERN		
Silver P. WHITE P.		
Soft Yellow P. YELLOWPOPLAR		
Swiss P. COTTONWOOD, EASTERN		
TANA P. (ET)	**denhardtiorum**	TANA P.
WHITE P. (Bat;Bo;ET; Leg;Mey. *Aspen; Silver P.*)	**alba**	WHITE P.
White P. ASPEN, QUAKING		
Yellow P. YELLOWPOPLAR		
Poplar. YELLOWPOPLAR		
Popple. ASPEN, QUAKING; ASPEN, LARGETOOTH		
Porcupinewood. COCONUT		
PORTIATREE (Ah;Mey;Tr; Winn. *Tuliptree*)	**Thespesia populnea**	PORTIATREE
Possum Wood. HURA		
PRICKLYASH (Mey;Sud. *Harewood; Ruda*)	**Zanthoxylum** spp. (*Xanthoxylum*)	PRICKLYASH
PRIMAVERA (Mey;RL; R&M. *White Mahogany*)	**Cybistax donnell-smithi**	PRIMAVERA
Princewood. CANALETTA		
Prinzwood. ELM, SOFT A trade name for veneer of American Elm.		
PUIRI (Bat;Bo;ET;Mey. *New Zealand Teak*)	**Vitex littoralis**	TIMOR CHASTETREE
PURPLEHEART (Leg;Mey; R&M. of Trinidad)	**Peltogyne** spp.	PURPLEHEART
PYINGADO (Ah;Bat;Bo; ET;Leg;Mey. *Jamba; Pyinkado*)	**Xylia xylocarpa** (*dolabriformis*)	BURMA PYINGADO
Pyinma. BANABU		
PYINMA ANDAMAN (Leg; Mey)	**Lagerstroemia hypoleuca**	ANDAMAN CRAPEMYRTLE
QUASSIA (Mey;R&M;VW. *Bitterwood*)	**Quassia amara**	SURINAM QUASSIA
QUASSIAWOOD (F&W. *Bitterwood*)	**Picrasma excelsa** (*Picraena e.*)	JAMAICA QUASSIAWOOD
QUEBRACHO (How;Mey; R&M. *Red Q.*)	**Schinopsis lorentzi**	LORENTZ REDQUEBRACHO
QUEBRACHO	**S. balansae**	WILLOWLEAF R.
QUEBRACHOBLANCO (Bo; How;Mey;R&M. *White Quebracho*)	**Aspidosperma quebracho-blanco**	COMMON WHITE-QUEBRACHO
Queensland Maple. SILKWOOD, MAPLE		
Queensland Silky Oak. LACEWOOD		
Queensland Walnut. ORIENTALWOOD		
Quina. OLEO VERMELHO		
Quina-Quina. OLEA VERMELHO		
QUIRA (Mey;R&M. *Panama-redwood*) *See also* MACAWOOD	**Platymiscium polystachyum**	QUIRA MACAWOOD
Rabo Lagarto. RUDA		
Rakuda. HURA		
Ramon. CAPOMO		
Rangoon Teak. TEAK		
RASAMALA (Gam;Mey; VW)	**Altingia excelsa**	RASAMALA ALTINGIA

Lumber Trade Name	Plant Source: Botanical Name	Plant Source: S.P.N. Common Name
RASPBERRY JAMWOOD (Bo. *Jamwood*)	**Acacia acuminata**	RASPBERRY ACACIA
Rasppod Tree. FLINDERSIA		
Rauli. BEECH, SOUTHLAND		
REDASH (Bo;Guil. *Silky Oak*)	**Orites excelsa**	
REDBEECH (Aud;Bo. *Maple*) *See also* BEECH, RED (**Nothofagus fusca**)	**Flindersia chatawaiana** Perhaps hardly more than a variety of F. brayleyana.	CHATAWAY FLINDERSIA
Redbeech. SILKWOOD, MAPLE		
Redbox; Red Boxwood. EUCALYPTUS, REDBOX		
REDCEDAR		
EASTERN R. (Bat;Mey; RL;Sud,L. *Aromatic R.; Pencil R.; Savin; Southern R.; Tennessee R.*)	**Juniperus virginiana**	EASTERN REDCEDAR
ROCKY MOUNTAIN R. (Mey;Sud)	**J. scopulorum**	ROCKY MOUNTAIN JUNIPER
SOUTHERN R. (Sud)	**J. silicicola**	SOUTHERN REDCEDAR
Southern R.; Tennessee R. EASTERN R.		
WESTERN R. (RL; Sud,L.)	**Thuja plicata**	GIANT ARBORVITAE; WESTERN REDCEDAR (Forestry)
Red Cedar. ELS, ROOD		
Red Copie. KOPIE		
Red Els. ELS, ROOD		
Red Faveiro. FAVEIRO		
REDGUM (Mey; RL; Sud, L. *Bilsted; Delta R.*)	**Liquidambar styraciflua**	AMERICAN SWEETGUM
Redgum. EUCALYPTUS, REDGUM		
Red Ironwood. EKKI		
Redmahogany. EUCALYPTUS, KINOGUM		
Red Sanders. SANDERSWOOD, RED		
REDWOOD (Bat;Bo;How; Mey;RL;Sud,L. *Sequoia*)	**Sequoia sempervirens**	REDWOOD
Andaman R. PADAUK, ANDAMAN		
Australian R. EUCALYPTUS, SYDNEY PEPPERMINT		
Baltic R. PINE, SCOTS		
BIGTREE R. (Bat;ET)	**S. gigantea** (*washingtoniana*)	GIANT SEQUOIA
Coromandel R. PADAUK, ANDAMAN		
Panama-redwood. QUIRA		
Redwood. DANTA; EKHIMI		
REWAREWA (Bat;ET; How;Ki;Mey. *Bucketwood; Honeysuckle; New Zealand H.*)	**Knightia excelsa**	REWAREWA
RHODESIANTEAK (Leg; Mey;RL)	**Baikiaea plurijuga**	RHODESIANTEAK
RIMU (Bat;Bo;ET;How; Leg;Mey. *Red New Zealand Pine*)	**Dacrydium cupressinum**	RIMU DACRYDIUM
Rio Rosewood. ROSEWOOD, BRAZILIAN		
Roble This is the Spanish word for Oak and is loosely used in the lumber trade for wood of at least 12 other genera (*fide* Meyer).		
Robleyugo. OCOBO		
Roble Colorado. MACAWOOD		
Rosa. ARARIBA		
ROSAMAY (Bat;Mey;RL. *Australian Mahogany; Australian Rosewood; Rose Mahogany; Rosewood*) This is neither a Mahogany nor a Rosewood.	**Dysoxylum fraseranum**	FRASER PENCILWOOD
ROSA MORADA (RL)	**Lonchocarpus hondurensis**	HONDURAS LANCEPOD

Lumber Trade Name	Plant Source: Botanical Name	Plant Source: S.P.N. Common Name
ROSEMYRTLE (*Hillgooseberry*)	**Rhodomyrtus tomentosa**	DOWNY ROSEMYRTLE
ROSEWOOD *See also* COCOBOLO	**Dalbergia**	ROSEWOOD
African R. BUBINGA; COPAIBA		
Australian R. ROSAMAY		
Bahia R. BRAZILIAN R.		
Bombay R. EAST INDIAN R.		
BRAZILIAN R. (Bat;Bo; Fox;Mey;RL;R&M. *Bahia R.; Cabiuna; Jacaranda; Palisander; Rio R.*)	**nigra**	BLACK R.
Burmese R. PADAUK, INDIA		
Ceylon R. LASRIN		
EAST INDIAN R. (Bat; Fox;How;Leg;Mey; RL;Tr. *Balsamo; Blackwood; Bombay R.; Indian R.; Iti; Malabar; Rosetta R.; Shisham*)	**latifolia**	EAST INDIAN R.
French R. MADAGASCAR R.		
HONDURAS R. (Bo;ET; Leg. *Balsamo*)	**stevensoni**	HONDURAS R.
Indian R. EAST INDIAN R.		
MADAGASCAR R. (Mey; RL. *French R.; Madagascar Palisander*)	**greveana**	MADAGASCAR R.
Rio R. BRAZILIAN R.		
Rosetta R. EAST INDIAN R.		
RUSTYLEAF LITSEA (Aud; Guil. *White Sassafras*)	**Litsea ferruginea**	RUSTYLEAF LITSEA
SABICU (Bo;How;Mey)	**Lysiloma latisiliqua** (*sabicu*)	SABICU LYSILOMA
SACKYSAC (F&W)	**Inga laurina**	SACKYSAC INGA
SAL (Mey;RL;Tr)	**Shorea robusta**	SAL SHOREA
Salmongum. EUCALYPTUS, SALMONGUM		
SALTFISHWOOD (F&W. *Red Mahoe*)	**Sterculia caribaea**	CARIB STERCULIA
Samba-ayous. OBECHE		
SANDALWOOD (Bat;Bo; How;Leg;Tr)	**Santalum**	SANDALWOOD
Australian S. AUSTRALIAN-SANDALWOOD		
FIJI S. (Fox. *Yellow S.*)	**freycinetianum**	YELLOW FIJI S.
FIJI S. (Bo;Mey)	**yasi**	FIJI S.
LANCELEAF S. (And; Aud;Guil;Mey)	**lanceolatum**	LANCELEAF S.
Mysore S. WHITE S.		
NEW CALEDONIA S. (Bo;Mey)	**austro-caledonicum**	NEW CALEDONIA S.
Red S. SANDERSWOOD, RED		
True S. WHITE S.		
West Australian S. AUSTRALIAN-SANDALWOOD		
West Indian S. AMYRIS		
WHITE S. (Bat;Bo;Fox; FW;Leg. *Mysore S.; True S.; Yellow S.*)	**album**	WHITE S.
Yellow S. FIJI S.; WHITE S.		
SANDERSWOOD, RED (Bat; Bo;How;Mey;R&M; Tr;Winn. *Red Sandalwood*)	**Pterocarpus santalinus**	SANDALWOOD PADAUK
Sanderswood, Yellow. TALLOWWOOD		
Sangre. BANAK		
SANGRE DE TORO (Mey)	**Ruprechtia deami**	BULLSBLOOD VIRARU
Sangre Toro. PADAUK		
SANTAMARIA	**Calophyllum** spp.	BEAUTYLEAF
SANTAMARIA (Bat;Bo;Leg; Mey. *Calaba; Galaba; Galba*) This and **C. rekoi** have been frequently confused in literature with the Ceylonese **C. calaba**.	**brasiliense antillanum** (*C. antillanum; C. calaba* Jacq., *not* L.; *C. inophyllum* Sieb. *ex.* Presl., *not* L., *nor* Lam.; *C. jacquini*)	CALABA B.

Lumber Trade Name	Plant Source	
	Botanical Name	*S.P.N. Common Name*
SANTAMARIA (Mey;RL. *Bari; Calaba; Cimarron; Leche Maria*)	**Calophyllum rekoi**	REKO BEAUTYLEAF
SAPELE (Ain;Ch;Leg;Mey; RL. *Aboudikro(u); Accra; African Mahogany; Brown Mahogany; Cedar Mahogany; Gedunohor; Gold Coast Cedar; Ivory Coast Sapele; Miovu; Omu; Penkwa; Sapele Mahogany; Sassandra; Scented Mahogany; Sipo; Tiama; Uganda Sapele Mahogany*)	**Entandrophragma** spp., especially **E. cylindricum**	SAPELE
HEAVY S. (Br)	**E. candollei**	HEAVY S.
Ivory Coast S. SAPELE		
SAPLUNGAN (Mey;Rey)	**Hopea plagata**	
SAPODILLA (Leg;Mey;RL. *Chewinggum Tree; Chico Zapote; Naseberry; Zapota*)	**Achras zapota** (*Sapota achras; S. zapotilla*)	SAPODILLA
SAPOTE (Mey;R&M. *Mamee Apple; Marmaladetree; Zapote*)	**Calocarpum sapota** (*mammosum; Lucuma mammosa*)	SAPOTE
Sassandra. SAPELE		
Satina. BRAZILIAN-SATINWOOD		
SATINAY, RED (Leg;Mey)	**Syncarpia hilli**	HILLS TURPENTINE-MYRTLE
Satine Rubanne. SATINEE		
SATINEE (Mey;RL. *Muirapiranga; Satine Rubanne*)	**Brosimum paraense**	PARA BREADNUTTREE
SATINWOOD	**Chloroxylon**	SATINWOOD
BRAZILIAN-S. (Mey;RL. *Amarello; Pao Amarello; Satina*)	**Euxylophora paraensis**	BRAZILIAN-SATINWOOD
CEYLON S. (Bat;Bo; Mey;RL. *Buruta; East Indian S.; Flowered S.; Mutiral; Tonquin*)	**Chloroxylon swietenia**	CEYLON SATINWOOD
DOMINICAN-S. (*San Dominigan S.; West Indian S.*)	**Zanthoxylum flavum**	YELLOWHEART PRICKLYASH
East Indian S. CEYLON S.		
Flowered S. CEYLON S.		
Nigerian S. MOVINGUI		
San Dominigan S. DOMINICAN-S.		
West Indian S. DOMINICAN-S.		
Satinwood. FRAMERIE		
Savin. REDCEDAR, EASTERN		
SAVONETTE	**Lonchocarpus latifolius**	
Scented Guarea. GUAREA		
Scribblygum. EUCALYPTUS, SCRIBBLYGUM		
Scrub Beefwood. SILKY-OAK		
SEBASTANPLUM (Bo;Fox; Mey;Winn)	**Cordia myxa**	SEBASTANPLUM CORDIA
Selano. LACEWOOD		
Senegal Mahogany. KHAYA		
Sena. PADAUK, INDIA		
Sepang. MERANTI		
Sequoia. REDWOOD		
SERAYA (Mey;RL. *Almon; Bagtikan; Borneo Cedar; Borneo Mahogany; East Indian Cedar; Oba Suluk*)	**Shorea curtisi**	CURTIS SHOREA
SERON (Mey;R&M. *Baitoa; San Domingan Boxwood*)	**Phyllostylon brasiliensis**	SERON
She-beech. BOLLYGUM		
Shellbark. HICKORY, SHAGBARK *See also* HICKORY, SHELLBARK		
SHE-OAK (ET;Leg;Mey)	**Casuarina fraseriana**	FRASER BEEFWOOD
Shira-Kamba. BIRCH, EUROPEAN		
Shisham. SISSOO; ROSEWOOD, EAST INDIAN		
SHITTIMWOOD (Bo;RL. *Chittamwood*)	**Acacia seyal**	SEYAL ACACIA

Lumber Trade Name	Plant Source	
	Botanical Name	*S.P.N. Common Name*
SIDA (ET;Mey)	**Lagerstroemia parviflora**	LITTLEFLOWER CRAPEMYRTLE
Sida. TIGERWOOD		
Silk Cotton Tree. CEIBA		
Silkoak. SILKYOAK		
SILKWOOD (Leg. *Rose S.*)	**Flindersia pimenteliana**	PIMENTEL FLINDERSIA
MAPLE S. (Mey. *Australian Maple; Queensland M.; Queensland S.; Redbeech; Warri*)	**F. brayleyana**	BRAYLEY F.
SILKYOAK (And;Aud;Bo; Guil;How. *Beefwood; New South Wales Beefwood; Scrub Beefwood; Silkoak; Southern Silkyoak; Tuggan-tuggan*)	**Grevillea robusta**	SILKOAK GREVILLEA
WHITE S. (Aud;Guil; Mey)	**G. hilliana**	YIELYIEL G.
Silky Oak. FIRETREE; LACEWOOD; REDASH		
Silkywood. BIRCH, YELLOW		
SILVERPINE (*Mountain Ash*)	**Dacrydium westlandicum**	WESTLAND DACRYDIUM
Silvertop. EUCALYPTUS, SILVERTOP		
Simaruba. MARUPA		
Sipo. SAPELE		
SIRIS (Bat;Bo;ET;Fox; Leg;Mey;Tr. *Koko; Kokko*)	**Albizzia kalkora** (*lebbek* Hemsl., *not* Benth.)	LEBBEK ALBIZZIA
PINK S. (Bo;Fox;Mey; Tr)	**A. julibrissin**	SILKTREE A.
WHITE S. (Fox;Mey;Tr)	**A. procera**	TALL A.
Siris. EASTINDIESLAUREL		
SISSOO (Ah;Bo;Mey;RL; Tr. *Shisham*)	**Dalbergia sissoo**	SISSOO
Slatygum. EUCALYPTUS, SLATYGUM		
SMOKETREE	**Cotinus**	SMOKETREE
AMERICAN S. (Mey;RL. *Chittamwood*)	**americanus** (*Rhus cotinoides*)	AMERICAN S.
SNAKEWOOD (Mey;RL; R&M. *Leopardwood; Letterwood*)	**Piratinera guianensis** (*Brosimum aubleti*)	SNAKEWOOD
Snakewood. HOOBOOBALLI		
Surinam S. HOOBOOBALLI		
WEST INDIAN S. (Mey; R&M)	**Colubrina ferruginosa**	BAHAMA COLUBRINA
SNEEZEWOOD (Ah;Bat; Bo;Mey)	**Ptaeroxylon utile**	
SNEEZEWOOD (E&H)	**P. obliquum**	
SOCKETWOOD (Aud;Mey. *Australian-sassafras; Satinwood; Yellowwood*)	**Daphnandra micrantha**	SASSAFRAS DAPHNANDRA
Solera. CANALETTA		
SOURPLUM (Bo;Guil;Mey; Winn)	**Owenia venosa**	CROWSAPPLE EMUPLUM
South American Locust. GUAPINOL		
Southern Silkyoak. SILKYOAK		
Spottedgum. EUCALYPTUS, SPOTTEDGUM		
Spanish Cedar This name, an obvious misnomer, is probably the commonest in use for CIGARBOXCEDAR.		
SPRUCE	**Picea**	SPRUCE
Adirondack S. EASTERN S.		
BIGCONE-S. (Mey; Sud,L)	**Pseudotsuga macrocarpa**	BIGCONE DOUGLASFIR
Black S. EASTERN S.		
BLUE S. (Bo;Mey; Sud,L. *Colorado S.*)	**Picea pungens** (*parryana*)	COLORADO SPRUCE
Canadian S. EASTERN S.		
Colorado S. BLUE S.		
Common S. EUROPEAN S.		
EASTERN S. (Sud,L. *Adirondack S.; Canadian S.; White S.*) See note under WESTERN WHITE SPRUCE	**glauca** (*alba; canadensis*)	WHITE S.

Lumber Trade Name	Plant Source: Botanical Name	Plant Source: S.P.N. Common Name
SPRUCE, continued		
EASTERN S. (Sud,L. *Black S.*)	**Picea mariana** (*nigra*)	BLACK SPRUCE
EASTERN S. (Sud,L. *Adirondack S.; Canadian S.; Red S.; West Virginia S.*) Lumber of Picea glauca, mariana, and rubens are generally included in the same commercial shipment of Eastern Spruce, and their separation is commercially impossible.	**rubens** (*rubra* [Dur.] Link, *not* A. Dietr.)	RED S.
ENGELMANN S. (Bat; ET;Leg;Sud,L)	**engelmanni**	ENGELMANN S.
European S. NORWAY S.		
Hemlock S. HEMLOCK, WESTERN		
HIMALAYAN S. (Mey)	**smithiana** (*morinda*)	HIMALAYAN S.
Menzies S. SITKA S.		
NORWAY S. (*European S.*) This timber, if imported from the Baltic, is called White Fir, White Deal, or Norway Spruce, but if imported by way of Canada, it is called *Yellow Spruce.*	**abies** (*excelsa*)	NORWAY S.
Red S. EASTERN S.		
Sequoia Silver S.; Silver S. SITKA S.		
SITKA S. (Bat; Bo; ET; How; Leg; Mey; Sud, L. *Menzies S.; Sequoia Silver S.; Silver S.; Tideland S.; West Coast S.; Western Sitka S.; Western S.; Yellow S.*)	**sitchensis**	SITKA S.
Tideland S.; West Coast S. SITKA S.		
West Virginia S. EASTERN S.		
Western Sitka S.; Western S. SITKA S.		
WESTERN WHITE S. A term generally recognized in the trade for lumber produced from the western extension of Picea glauca.		
White S. EASTERN S.		
Yellow S. NORWAY S.; SITKA S.		
Stinking Toes. CANA FISTOLA		
STINKWOOD (Ch;ET;Mey. *Cape Laurel*)	**Ocotea bullata**	STINKWOOD OCOTEA
Stringybark. EUCALYPTUS, STRINGYBARK		
Subaha. ABURA		
SUCUPIRA (Mey;RL; R&M. *Amoteak; Amotique; Brownheart; Hudoke*)	**Bowdichia nitida**	
Sugarberry. HACKBERRY		
Sugargum. EUCALYPTUS, SUGARGUM		
SUGI (Ah;Bat;Bo;Mey)	**Cryptomeria japonica**	CRYPTOMERIA
Sunloch. HOLLOCK		
SUPA (Mey;Rey;RL)	**Sindora supa**	SUPA SINDORA
Surinam Snakewood. HOOBOOBALLI		
Swampmahogany. EUCALYPTUS, BROWNGUM		
Sweet Bay. LAUREL		
SYCAMORE (Bo;Mey;RL; R&M; Sud,L. *Buttonwood; Western Plane*)	**Platanus occidentalis**	AMERICAN PLANETREE; AMERICAN SYCAMORE (Forestry)
English S. MAPLE, SYCAMORE		
Tabasara. CATIVO		

Lumber Trade Name	Plant Source: Botanical Name	Plant Source: S.P.N. Common Name
Tacamahac. POPLAR, BALSAM		
TALLOWWOOD (Mey;Sud. *Yellow Sanderswood*)	**Ximenia americana**	TALLOWWOOD
Tallowwood. EUCALYPTUS, TALLOWWOOD		
TAMARACK (Ah;Bat;Bo; ET;Leg;Mey;RL; Sud,L. *American Larch; Eastern L.*)	**Larix laricina** (*americana*)	EASTERN LARCH; TAMARACK (Forestry)
TAMARIND (Bat;Bo;Mey; Tr)	**Tamarindus indica**	TAMARIND
Tambulian. BILLIAN		
TAMO (Mey;RL. *Damo*)	**Fraxinus longicuspis sieboldiana** (*F. sieboldiana*)	SIEBOLD JAPANESE ASH
TANGILE; TANGUILE (Mey;Rey;RL. *Bataan Mahogany; Philippine M.; Tangile M.*)	**Shorea polysperma**	TANGILE
TANOAK	**Lithocarpus densiflorus** (*Pasania densiflora*)	TANOAK
TAPANA (Bat;Mey;R&M)	**Hieronyma alchorneoides**	
TARAIRE (Ah;Bo;ET; Mey)	**Beilschmiedia tarairi**	TARAIRE SLUGWOOD
TARTAN, ROYAL (Bak;RL. *Crowsfoot Elm*)	**Tarrietia argyrodendron**	SILVER STONEWOOD
Tasmanian Myrtle. BEECH, TASMANIAN		
TASMANIANCEDAR (Bo. *King William Pine*)	**Athrotaxis selaginoides**	
Tasmanianoak. EUCALYPTUS, TASMANIANOAK		
TAVOYWOOD (Ah;Fox; Mey)	**Parashorea stellata**	TAVOY BAGTIKAN
TAWA (Bo;Ki;Leg;Mey)	**Beilschmiedia tawa**	TAWA SLUGWOOD
TEAK (Ah;Bat;Bo;Leg; Mey;RL;Tr. *Rangoon T.*)	**Tectona grandis**	COMMON TEAK
African T. IROKO		
Australian T. BENNETTASH		
Gray T. WHITEBEECH		
Native T. BENNETTASH		
New Zealand T. PUIRIRI		
RHODESIANTEAK (Mey; RL)	**Baikiaea plurijuga**	RHODESIANTEAK
She T. BENNETTASH		
Surinam T. GUAPINOL		
TEPESUCHIL (RL)	**Cordia alliodora**	ONION CORDIA
Thick Shellbark Hickory. HICKORY, BIG SHELLBARK		
THINGAN (Bat;Bo;ET; Fox;How;Leg;Mey)	**Hopea odorata**	THINGAN
THITKA (Ah;Bo;ET;Leg; Mey. *Burma Mahogany*)	**Pentace burmanica**	BURMA THITKA
Thornapple. HAWTHORN		
Tiama. SAPELE		
TIAONG (Mey;Rey)	**Shorea teysmanniana**	TIAONG SHOREA
TIGERWOOD (Mey;RL. *African Walnut; Alona; Apopo; Benin; Bibola; Congowood; Dibetou; Lovoa; Nigerian Golden Walnut; Penkwa; Sida*)	**Lovoa klaineana**	TIGERWOOD LOVOA
Tigerwood. GONCALO ALVES		
Tilleul. French for Linden		
TIMBROUVA (Mey. *Pacara*)	**Enterolobium timbouva**	TIMBOUVA EARPODTREE
TINDALO (Fox;Mey;Rey; RL. *Oro*)	**Pahudia rhomboidea**	PHILIPPINE PAHUDIA (*Tindalo*)
Tingletingle. EUCALYPTUS, TINGLETINGLE		
TOMAN (E&H;Mey)	**Pseudocedrela kotschyi**	
Tonquin. SATINWOOD, CEYLON Ornamental grades sold as Ceylon Satinwood; plainer cuts sold as Tonquin.		

Lumber Trade Name	Plant Source: Botanical Name	Plant Source: S.P.N. Common Name
Tooart. EUCALYPTUS, TUART		
Toog. BISHOPWOOD		
TOON (Mey)	**Toona australis**	AUSTRALIAN TOON
TOON (Ah;Bat;Bo;ET; Leg;Mey;Tr)	**T. ciliata** (*Cedrela toona*)	BURMA T.
HIMALAYA T. (*Hill T.*)	**T. serrata** (*C. serrata*)	HIMALAYA T.
See also CEDRELA; KALANTAS		
TOTARA (Ah;Bat;Bo;ET; Leg;Mey)	**Podocarpus totara**	TOTARA PODOCARPUS
BIGLEAF T. (Ki;Mey. *Large-leaved T.*)	**P. t. halli** (*P. halli*)	HALLS T. P.
TOWHAI (Ah;Bo;ET;Mey; R&M. *Kamahl*)	**Weinmannia racemosa**	KAMAHI
TRINCOMALIWOOD (Mey; RL. *Halmililla*)	**Berrya cordifolia**	TRINCOMALIWOOD
Trinidad Matchwood. MATCHWOOD		
Tuai. BISHOPWOOD		
Tuart. EUCALYPTUS, TUART		
Tuggan-tuggan. SILKY-OAK		
Tuliptree. PORTIATREE; YELLOWPOPLAR		
TULIPWOOD (Bak;Bat;Bo; Mey)	**Harpullia pendula**	TULIPWOOD
The name Tulipwood is occasionally misapplied to Rosewood.		
TUPELO (Mey;Sud,L. *Blackgum; Tupelo Gum*)	**Nyssa aquatica**	WATER TUPELO
Ubulu. OPEPE		
Uganda Sapele-Mahogany. SAPELE		
Uganda Walnut. LOVOA		
Uhu. EBONY, BENIN		
Ujusti. CAPOMO		
UMBRELLAPINE (Bo)	**Sciadopitys verticillata**	UMBRELLAPINE
Vencola. MACAWOOD		
VENGAI (Bat;Mey. *Kinotree; Venga*)	**Pterocarpus marsupium**	VENGAI PADAUK
Vera. LIGNUMVITAE		
VERAWOOD (Mey;RL. *Congo Cypress; Guayacan; Maracaibo-wood; Vera Amarillo*)	**Bulnesia arborea**	VERAWOOD BULNESIA
Verda. CHUGLAM, WHITE		
Vermelha. ARARIBA		
Vermillion. PADAUK		
Victoria Bluegum. EUCALYPTUS, VICTORIA BLUEGUM		
Vinhatico		

"'Vinhatico' (*Amarello Vinhatico*) is a general name applied to a group of woods that are typically yellow in color and are easy to work" (R&M, p. 222). Meyer (op. cit.) lists 21 plant names, belonging to 5 different genera, under Vinhatico or variations thereof. A name so uncertain and confusing should be remanded to synonymy and discarded.

Lumber Trade Name	Plant Source: Botanical Name	Plant Source: S.P.N. Common Name
Vinhatico Amarello. BRAZILIAN-YELLOWWOOD		
Vinhatico de Espinho. GOLDWOOD		
Violet-Kingwood; Violetta; Violetwood. KINGWOOD		
VIRARU (R&M)	**Ruprechtia** spp.	VIRARU
See also SANGRE DE TORO		
Walile. AKOMU		
WALLABA	**Eperua**	WALLABATREE
BIMITI W. (Mey;R&M)	**schomburgkiana**	BIMITI W.
ITURI W. (Mey;R&M)	**jenmani**	ITURI W.
SOFT W. (Bat;How;Leg; Mey)	**falcata**	SOFT W.
WALLUM (Guil. *Honeysuckle*)	**Banksia marginata**	HONEYSUCKLE BANKSIA
WALNUT	**Juglans**	WALNUT
African W. TIGERWOOD		
American Black W. BLACK W.		
American W. BLACK W.		
Ancona W.		

A term applied to Persian Walnut to indicate dark, streaky-figured wood whether produced from French, Italian, Spanish or Circassian sources.

Lumber Trade Name	Plant Source: Botanical Name	Plant Source: S.P.N. Common Name
Australian W. ORIENTALWOOD		
WALNUT, continued		
Austrian W. PERSIAN W.		
Benin W. TIGERWOOD		
BLACK W. (Bo;Mey; RL;Sud. *American Black W.; Canadian W.; Walnut*)	**Juglans nigra**	EASTERN BLACK WALNUT
Brazilian W. IMBUYA		
Bulgarian W. PERSIAN W.		
CALIFORNIA W. (Mey; RL. *California Black W.; Claro W.*)	**californica**	CALIFORNIA B. W.
CALIFORNIA W. (RL. *Hinds Black W.; Hinds W.*)	**hindsi**	HINDS B. W.
Canadian W. BLACK W.		
Circassian W. PERSIAN W.		
Claro W. CALIFORNIA W. (**californica**)		
East India W. EASTINDIESLAUREL		
English W.; European W. PERSIAN W.		
Hinds W.; Hinds Black W. CALIFORNIA W. (**hindsi**)		
India W. GREYWOOD, INDIAN SILVER		
Italian W. PERSIAN W.		
Nigerian Golden W. TIGERWOOD		
Oriental W. ORIENTALWOOD		
PERSIAN W. (Mey;RL. *Austrian W.; Bulgarian W.; Circassian W.; English W.; European W.; French W.; Italian W.; Royal W.; Russian W.; Spanish W.; Turkish W.*)	**regia**	PERSIAN W.
Queensland W. ORIENTALWOOD		
Royal W.; Russian W. PERSIAN W.		
Satin W. REDGUM		
South American W. GUANACASTE		
Spanish W.; Turkish W. PERSIAN W.		
Uganda W. LOVOA		
Walnut. BLACK W.		
White W. BUTTERNUT		
WAMARA (ET;R&M. *Panacoco*)	**Swartzia tomentosa**	WAMARA SWARTZPEA
Wandoo. EUCALYPTUS, WANDOO		
Wane. GRIGNON		
Warri. SILKWOOD, MAPLE		
Watercare. GUATACARE		
WATTLE, BLACK (Mey; Winn)	**Acacia decurrens**	GREENWATTLE ACACIA
Wawa. OBECHE		
Whiteash, Australian. EUCALYPTUS, AUSTRALIAN WHITE		
WHITEBEECH (And;Aud; Bo;ET;Mey. *White Beech*)	**Gmelina leichhardti**	LEICHHARDT GMELINA (*Whitebeech*)
Whitebox. EUCALYPTUS, WHITEBOX		
WHITE-CEDAR		
NORTHERN W. (RL; Sud,L)	**Thuja occidentalis**	EASTERN ARBORVITAE; NORTHERN WHITE-CEDAR (Forestry)
SOUTHERN W. (RL; Sud,L)	**Chamaecyparis thyoides**	ATLANTIC FALSE-CYPRESS; ATLANTIC WHITE-CEDAR (Forestry)
White Dammar. PINEY-VARNISHTREE		
White Dhup. DHUP		
WHITE FIDDLEWOOD (F&W)	**Citharexylum spinosum**	SPINY FIDDLEWOOD

Lumber Trade Name	Plant Source: Botanical Name	Plant Source: S.P.N. Common Name
White Guarea. GUAREA		
Whitegum. EUCALYPTUS, WANDOO		
White Mahogany. EUCALYPTUS, WHITEMAHOGANY; EUCALYPTUS, YELLOW STRINGYBARK		
White-mangrove. FALSEMANGROVE		
WHITEPEAR (Ch;Mey)	**Apodytes dimidiata**	
White Quebracho. QUEBRACHOBLANCO		
White Sassafras. LITSEA, RUSTYLEAF		
Whitewood, African. OBECHE		
Whitewood, American. YELLOWPOPLAR		
WILLOW	**Salix**	WILLOW
BLACK W. (Sud,L)	**nigra**	BLACK W.
CRICKETBAT W. (ET; Leg)	**alba calva** (*S. coerulea*)	PYRAMIDAL WHITE W. (*Cricketbat W.*)
GULF BLACK W. (Sud)	**nigra altissima**	GULF BLACK W.
WHITE W. (ET;Leg)	**alba**	WHITE W.
Woollybutt. EUCALYPTUS, WOOLLYBUTT		
YACCA (Bo;Leg;Mey. *British Honduras Cypress*)	**Podocarpus coriaceus**	YACCA PODOCARPUS
YACHIDAMO (RL)	**Fraxinus mandshurica**	MANCHURIAN ASH
YAKAL (Mey;Rey;RL. *Mingan*)	**Shorea balangeran**	YAKAL SHOREA
Yamane. GUMBAR		
YANG (Mey;RL) The name is probably appropriate for Siamese species only. *See also* ENG; PADAUK	**Dipterocarpus** spp.	GURJUNOILTREE
Yate. EUCALYPTUS, YATE		
Yategum. EUCALYPTUS, YATEGUM		
Yaya. LANCEWOOD		
Yellowbox. EUCALYPTUS, YELLOWBOX		
Yellowcedar. CARDINALBERRY		
Yellow Deal. PINE, SCOTS		
Yellow Faveiro. FAVEIRO		
YELLOW OLIVIER (F&W; Mey. *Yellow Sanders*)	**Buchenavia capitata**	
YELLOWPOPLAR (Sud,L. *American Whitewood; Canarywood; Poplar; Soft Yellow P.; Tuliptree; Whitewood; Yellow P.*)	**Liriodendron tulipifera**	TULIPTREE; YELLOWPOPLAR (Forestry)

Lumber Trade Name	Plant Source: Botanical Name	Plant Source: S.P.N. Common Name
Yellow Sanders. TALLOWWOOD; YELLOW OLIVIER		
Yellow Terminalia. FRAMERIE		
YELLOWWOOD (Mey;Sud. *Bastard Yellowwood*)	**Cladrastis lutea**	AMERICAN YELLOWWOOD
Yellowwood. CARDINALBERRY; FUSTIC; HAREWOOD; LONGJACK; PODO; PRICKLYASH; SANDOMINGO; SOCKETWOOD		

Distinctive lumber trade names are needed for the woods of Acronychia laevis, Combretum imberbe, and Plathymenia reticulata—all sold as Yellowwood or by other homonymous names.

Lumber Trade Name	Plant Source: Botanical Name	Plant Source: S.P.N. Common Name
YEW	**Taxus**	YEW
AMERICAN Y. (Sud. *Pacific Y.*)	**brevifolia**	PACIFIC Y.
CANADA Y. (Mey. *American Y.*)	**canadensis**	CANADA Y.
ENGLISH Y. (Leg. *Common Y.; European Y.*)	**baccata**	ENGLISH Y.
FLORIDA Y. (Mey;Sud)	**floridana**	FLORIDA Y.
Yinma. CHICKRASSY		
YOKEWOOD (Bat;Mey) *See also* CATALPA	**Catalpa longissima**	HAITI CATALPA
Yoma Wood. PADAUK		
YON (Leg;Mey. *Goldia*)	**Anogeissus acuminata**	YON AXLEWOOD
Yorkgum. EUCALYPTUS, YORKGUM		
Yuba. EUCALYPTUS, MESSMATE STRINGYBARK		
Zapateri. AMARANTH		
ZAPATERO (R&M. *Batoa; Maracaibo Boxwood; West Indies B.*)	**Gossypiospermum praecox**	
Zapatero. OCOBO		
Zapota. SAPODILLA		
Zapote. EBONY, INDIAN; SAPOTE		
ZEBRAWOOD (Bo;Mey) Species of **Brachystegia** and **Macrolobium** are also sold as Zebrawood.	**Connarus guianensis**	GUIANA ZEBRAWOOD
Zebrawood. GONCALO ALVES; MARBLEWOOD; MARBLEWOOD, ANDAMAN		
ZELKOVA (Bo)	**Zelkova** spp.	ZELKOVA
Zingana. OKWEIN		
Ziricote. CANALETTA		

Plant Source: Botanical Name	Plant Source: S.P.N. Common Name	Lumber Trade Name
Abies	FIR	FIR
alba (*pectinata*)	SILVER F.	SILVER F.
amabilis	CASCADES F.; PACIFIC SILVER F. (Forestry)	SILVER F.
balsamea	BALSAM F.	BALSAM F.
concolor	WHITE F.	WHITE F.
fraseri	FRASER BALSAM F.	SOUTHERN BALSAM F.
grandis	GRAND F.	WHITE F.
lasiocarpa (*subalpina*)	ALPINE F.	ALPINE F.
l. arizonica (*A. arizonica*)	CORKBARK F.	ALPINE F.
magnifica	RED F.; CALIFORNIA R. F. (Forestry)	CALIFORNIA RED F.
procera (*nobilis*)	NOBLE F.	NOBLE F.
Acacia	ACACIA	ACACIA (*Gidgee*)
acuminata	RASPBERRY A.	RASPBERRY JAMWOOD
aneura	MULGA A.	MULGA
arabica	BABUL A.	INDIAN BABUL
catechu	CATECHU A.	CUTCH
decurrens	GREENWATTLE A.	BLACK WATTLE
koa	KOA A.	KOA
melanoxylon	BLACKWOOD A.	AUSTRALIAN BLACKWOOD
senegal	GUMARABIC A.	AFRICAN BABUL
seyal	SEYAL A.	SHITTIMWOOD (*Chittamwood*)
Acer	MAPLE	MAPLE
macrophyllum	BIGLEAF M.	OREGON M.
negundo	BOXELDER	BOXELDER
nigrum	BLACK M.	BLACK M.
Acer, continued		
pseudoplatanus	PLANETREE MAPLE (*Sycamore M.*)	SYCAMORE MAPLE
rubrum	RED M.	RED M.
saccharinum	SILVER M.	SILVER M.
saccharum	SUGAR M.	SUGAR M.
Achras zapota (*Sapota achras; S. zapotilla*)	SAPODILLA	SAPODILLA
Adenanthera pavonina	SANDAL BEADTREE	CORALWOOD
Adina cordifolia	HEARTLEAF ADINA	HALDU
Aesculus glabra	OHIO BUCKEYE	BUCKEYE
A. hippocastanum *See also* BUCKEYE	COMMON HORSECHESTNUT	HORSECHESTNUT
A. indica	INDIES H.	INDIA H.
A. octandra (*flava*)	YELLOW BUCKEYE	BUCKEYE
Afzelia africana	AFRICAN AFZELIA	ALIGNA
A. bipindensis	ARYIAN A.	ARYIAN
Agathis australis	KAURI DAMMARPINE	KAURI
A. microstachys		KAURI
A. palmerstoni	PALMERSTON D.	KAURI
Albizzia acle	ACLE ALBIZZIA	ACLE
A. julibrissin	SILKTREE A.	PINK SIRIS
A. kalkora (*lebbek*)	LEBBEK A.	SIRIS
A. odoratissima	FRAGRANT A.	LASRIN
A. procera	TALL A.	WHITE SIRIS
Alnus	ALDER	ALDER
glutinosa	EUROPEAN A.	BLACK A.
rhombifolia	SIERRA A.	WHITE A.
rubra (*oregana*)	RED A.	RED A.

Botanical Name (Plant Source)	S.P.N. Common Name (Plant Source)	Lumber Trade Name
Alstonia congensis	Congo Alstonia	Patternwood
Altingia excelsa	Rasamala Altingia	Rasamala
Amoora nitidula		Incensewood
Amyris balsamifera	Balsam Amyris	Amyris
Anacardium rhinocarpus	Guiana Cashew	Caracoli
Andira (*Vouacapoua*)	Angelintree	Angelim; Angelin For Brazilian timbers the Portuguese form (Angelim) is used.
inermis (*jamaicensis; V. americana*)	Cabbage A.	Angelin
spectabilis	Showy A.	Angelim Pedra
vermifuga	Brazilian A.	Angelim Amargoso
Anisoptera thurifera (*Dipterocarpus thurifer*)	Palosapis Mersawa	Palosapis
Anogeissus acuminata	Yon Axlewood	Yon
A. latifolia	Bakligum A.	Axlewood
Apodytes dimidiata		Whitepear
Apuleia praecox		Grapiapunha
Aquilaria agallocha	Agalloch Eaglewood (*Lignaloes*)	Eaglewood
Araucaria angustifolia (*brasiliana*)	Parana Araucaria	Parana-pine
A. araucana (*imbricata*)	Monkeypuzzle A.	Araucaria
A. bidwilli	Bunyabunya A.	Bunya Bunya
A. cunninghami	Cunningham A.	Moretonbay-pine
Arbutus menziesi	Pacific Madrone	Madrone Burl
Artocarpus chaplasha	Chaplash Breadfruit	Chaplash
A. heterophyllus	Jakfruit	Jakwood
Aspidosperma polyneuron		Red Peroba
A. quebracho-blanco	Common Whitequebracho	Quebrachoblanco
A. tomentosum	Woolly W.	Piquia Peroba
Astronium	Startree	Ciruela
fraxinifolium	Ashleaf S.	Goncalo Alves
graveolens	Fetid S.	Goncalo Alves
Athrotaxis selaginoides		Tasmaniancedar
Aucoumea klaineana	Klaine Okoume	Okoume
Avicennia marina	Blackmangrove	Blacktree
Baikiaea plurijuga	Rhodesianteak	Rhodesianteak
Balanocarpus heimi		Chengal
Banksia marginata	Honeysuckle Banksia	Wallum
Baphia nitida	Shiny Camwood	Camwood
Barringtonia acutangula	Chee Barringtonia	Chee
Beilschmiedia tarairi	Taraire Slugwood	Taraire
B. tawa	Tawa S.	Tawa
Berrya cordifolia	Trincomaliwood	Trincomaliwood
Bertholletia excelsa	Brazilnut	Brazilnut
Betula	Birch	Birch
fontinalis	Water B.	Red B.
lenta	Sweet B.	Sweet B.
lutea	Yellow B.	Yellow B.
nigra	River B.	River B.
papyrifera	Paper B.	Paper B.
p. kenaica (*B. kenaica*)	Kenai P. B.	Kenai B.
p. neoalaskana (*B. neoalaskana*)	Alaska P. B.	Alaska White B.
pendula (*alba* in large part)	European White B.	European B.
populifolia	Gray B.	Gray B.
utilis	Himalaya B.	Indian B.
Bischofia javanica	Java Bishopwood	Bishopwood
Boswellia serrata	India Frankincense	Incensetree
Bowdichia nitida		Sucupira
Brachystegia spicaeformis	Spike Barkclothtree	Okwein
Bravaisia floribunda	Jiggerwood	Jiggerwood
Brosimum alicastrum	Ramon Breadnuttree	Capomo
B. paraense	Para B.	Satinee
B. utile (*galactodendron*)	Cow B.	Cowtree
Brya ebenus	Ebony Cocuswood	Cocus
Buchenavia capitata		Yellow Olivier
Bucida angustifolia	Narrowleaf Bucida	Grignon
B. buceras (*Terminalia b.*)	Oxhorn B.	Foocadie
Bulnesia arborea	Verawood Bulnesia	Verawood

Botanical Name (Plant Source)	S.P.N. Common Name (Plant Source)	Lumber Trade Name
Bumelia lanuginosa	Woollybucket Bumelia	Chittimwood
B. obtusifolia	Ibiranira B.	Ibiranira
Bursera simaruba	Gumbolimbo	Gumbolimbo
Buxus macowani	Macowan Box	Cape Boxwood
B. sempervirens	Common B.	Boxwood
Byrsonima crassifolia		Manche
Cabralea congerana	Cancharana Cabralea	Cancharana
Caesalpinia echinata	Prickly Brazilwood	Brazilwood
Callitris robusta	Sturdy Cypresspine	Cypresspine
Calocarpum sapota (*mammosum; Lucuma mammosa*)	Sapote	Sapote
Calophyllum	Beautyleaf	Santamaria
angustifolium	Penangpoon B.	Poon
brasiliense antillanum (*C. antillanum; C. calaba* Jacq., *not* L.; *C. inophyllum* Sieb. *ex* Presl, *not* L., *nor* Lam.; *C. jacquini*)	Calaba B.	Santamaria
inophyllum L., *not* Lam., *nor* Sieb. *ex* Presl	Indiapoon B.	Poon
rekoi	Reko B.	Santamaria
tomentosum	Ceylonpoon B.	Poon
Calycophyllum candidissimum	Degame Calycophyllum	Degame
spruceanum	Mulatto C.	Pao Mulatto
Canarium euphyllum	Andaman Canarytree	Dhup
C. schweinfurthi	Papo C.	Papo
Canthium dicoccum	Butulang Canthium	Butulang
Carallia brachiata	India Carallia	Carallia
Carapa grandiflora	Uganda Crabwood	Uganda Crabwood
C. guianensis	Guiana C.	Crabwood
Cardwellia sublimis	Lacewood (*Goldspanglewood*)	Lacewood
Cariniana	Cariniana	Jequitiba
pyriformis	Albarco C.	Albarco
Carpinus betulus	European Hornbeam	Hornbeam
C. caroliniana	American H. (*Bluebeech*)	American H.
Carya (*Hicoria*)	Hickory	Hickory *See also* Pecan
aquatica	Water H.	Water H.
cordiformis (*amara; Hicoria c.; H. minima*)	Bitternut H.	Bitternut H.
c. elongata	Ashe B. H.	Bitternut H.
glabra (*porcina*)	Pignut H.	Pignut H.
illinoensis	Pecan	Pecan
laciniosa (*sulcata*)	Shellbark H.	Shellbark H.
myristicaeformis (*H. m.*)	Nutmeg H.	Nutmeg H.
ovalis (*H. o.*)	Red H.	Red H.
ovata (*alba* Nutt., *not* K. Koch; *H. ovata*)	Shagbark H.	Shagbark H.
tomentosa (*alba* K. Koch, *not* Nutt.)	Mockernut H.	Mockernut H.
Caryocar villosum	Piquia-ete	Piquia
Cassia fistula	Goldenshower Senna	Indialaburnum
C. grandis	Pinkshower S.	Cana Fistola
Castanea dentata	American Chestnut	Chestnut
C. pumila	Allegany Chinkapin	Chinkapin
C. sativa (*vulgaris*)	European Chestnut	Sweet Chestnut
Castanopsis chrysophylla	Giant Evergreenchinkapin	Golden Chinkapin
Castanospermum australe	Moretonbaychestnut	Blackbean
Casuarina equisetifolia	Horsetail Beefwood	Beefwood
C. fraseriana	Fraser B.	She-oak
Catalpa bignonioides	Southern Catalpa	Catalpa
C. longissima	Haiti C.	Yokewood
C. speciosa	Northern C.	Hardy Catalpa
Cedrela mexicana	Mexican Cedrela	Cedrela
C. odorata	Cigarbox C.	Cigarboxcedar (*Spanish Cedar*)
Cedrus	Cedar	Cedar
libani (*libanotica*)	Cedar-of-Lebanon	Lebanon C.

Botanical Name	Plant Source S.P.N. Common Name	Lumber Trade Name
Ceiba pentandra (*casearia; Eriodendron anfractuosum*)	Kapok Ceiba	Ceiba
Celtis laevigata (*mississippiensis*)	Sugar Hackberry	Hackberry
C. occidentalis	Common H.	Hackberry
C. soyauxi	Nigerian H.	Celtis
Centrolobium	Porcupinepodtree	Arariba
paraense	Para P.	Muiracoatiara
Ceratopetalum apetalum	Fragrant Coachwood	Coachwood
Cercocarpus ledifolius	Curlleaf Mountainmahogany	Cercocarpus
Chamaecyparis lawsoniana	Lawson Falsecypress; PortOrford Whitecedar (Forestry)	PortOrford Cedar
C. nootkatensis	Nootka F.; Alaska Yellowcedar (Forestry)	Alaska C.
C. thyoides	Whitecedar F.; Atlantic Whitecedar (Forestry)	Southern Whitecedar
Chlorophora excelsa	Iroko Fustictree	Iroko
C. tinctoria	Drug F.	Fustic
Chloroxylon swietenia	Ceylon Satinwood	Ceylon Satinwood
Chukrasia tabularis	Chittagong Chickrassy	Chickrassy
Cinnamomum camphora	Camphortree	Camphorwood
C. glanduliferum	Nepal C.	Nepal C.
Cistanthera papaverifera	Danta	Danta
Citharexylum spinosum	Spiny Fiddlewood	White Fiddlewood
Citrus paradisi	Grapefruit	Grapefruit
C. sinensis	Sweet Orange	Orange
Cladrastis lutea	American Yellowwood	Yellowwood
Cocos nucifera	Coconut	Coconut
Colubrina ferruginosa	Bahama Colubrina	West Indian Snakewood
Connarus guianensis	Guiana Zebrawood	Zebrawood
Species of Brachystegia and Macrolobium are also sold as Zebrawood.		
Copaifera	Copaltree	Copaiba
coleosperma	Rhodesian C.	Rhodesian C.
demeusei	Congo C.	Kewazingo
officinalis	Copaiba C.	Copaiba
tessmanni	Tessmann C.	Kewazingo
Cordia	Cordia	Canaletta
alliodora	Onion C.	Tepesuchil
fragrantissima	Fragrant C.	Cordia
glabra	Nopo C.	Nopo
goeldiana	Goeldi C.	Cordia
macleodi	MacLeod C.	Hadang
myxa	Sebastanplum C.	Sebastanplum
Cornus florida	Flowering Dogwood	Dogwood
Cotinus americanus (*Rhus cotinoides*)	American Smoketree	American Smoketree
Crataegus crusgalli	Cockspur Hawthorn	Hawthorn
C. oxyacantha	English H.	Hawthorn
Cryptomeria japonica	Cryptomeria	Sugi
Cunonia capensis	Cape Cunonia	Rood Els
Cupressus	Cypress	Cypress
arizonica	Arizona C.	Arizona C.
a. bonita (*C. glabra*)	Smooth A. C.	Smooth C.
duclouxiana	Bhutan C.	Himalayan C.
Curtisia faginea	Assegaitree	Assegai
Cybistax donnell-smithi	Primavera	Primavera
Cylicodiscus gabunensis		Okan
Dacrydium	Dacrydium	
cupressinum	Rimu D.	Rimu
franklini	Huonpine D.	Huonpine
intermedium	Fire D.	Yellow Silverpine
westlandicum	Westland D.	Silverpine
Dalbergia	Rosewood	Rosewood
cearensis	Ceara R.	Kingwood
granadillo	Granadillo R.	Cocobolo(-a)
greveana	Madagascar R.	Madagascar R.
hypoleuca	CostaRica R.	Cocobolo
latifolia	EastIndian R.	East Indian R.

Botanical Name	Plant Source S.P.N. Common Name	Lumber Trade Name
Dalbergia, continued		
melanoxylon	African Blackwood	African Blackwood
nigra	Black Rosewood	Brazilian Rosewood
retusa	Panama R.	Cocobolo
sissoo	Sissoo	Sissoo
stevensoni	Honduras R.	Honduras R.
Daphnandra micrantha	Sassafras Daphnandra	Socketwood
Dicorynia paraensis	Para Angelwood	Angelique
Didelotia africana	Bubinga Didelotia	Bubinga
Didymopanax morototoni	Matchwood	Matchwood
Dillenia	Dillenia	Dillenia
philippinensis	Catmon D.	Catmon
Dimorphandra latifolia	Broadleaf Dimorphandra	Dakama
Diospyros	Persimmon	Ebony *See also* Blackplum; Persimmon
burmanica	Burmese Ebony P.	Burmese E.
cargillia	Illawara E. P.	Blackplum
chloroxylon	Green E. P.	Green E.
crassiflora	WestAfrican E. P.	West African E.
dendo	Gaboon E. P.	Gaboon E.
discolor (*mabola*)	Mabola P.	Camagon
ebenaster	Indian Ebony P.	Indian E.
ebenum	Ebony P.	East Indian E.
ferrea (*Maba buxifolia*)	Philippine E. P.	Batulinau E.
insculpta	Benin E. P.	Benin E.
macassar	Macassar E. P.	Macassar E.
marmorata	Andaman Marblewood P.	Andaman Marblewood
melanoxylon	Coromandel Ebony P.	Macassar E.
mespiliformis	Medlar P.	West African E.
pentamera	Myrtle Ebony P.	Myrtle E.
piscatoria	Fishermans P.	West African E.
quaesita	Calamander Ebony P.	Calamander E.
tomentosa	Nepal E. P.	Black E.
virginiana	Common P.	Persimmon
Dipterocarpus	Gurjunoiltree	Yang
cornutus	Keruing G.	Keruing
grandiflorus	Apitong G.	Apitong
pilosus	Hollong G.	Hollong
tuberculatus	Eng G.	Eng
turbinatus	Common G. (*Gurjun*)	Gurjun
zeylanicus	Ceylon G.	Gurjun (*Hora*)
Dipteryx panamensis	Panama Tonkabean	Almendro
Distemonanthus benthamianus		Movingui
Dracontomelum dao	Dao Dragonplum	Dao
Dryobalanops aromatica	Common Borneocamphor	Borneo Camphorwood
Dysoxylum fraseranum	Fraser Pencilwood	Rosamay
Endiandra ita-uba	Ita-uba	Ita-uba
E. palmerstoni	Orientalwood	Orientalwood
Entandrophragma spp. esp. E. cylindricum	Sapele	Sapele
E. candollei	Heavy S.	Heavy S.
Enterolobium contortisiliquum	Pacara Earpodtree	Pacara
E. cyclocarpum	Guanacaste E.	Guanacaste
E. timbouva	Timbouva E.	Timbrouva
Eperua	Wallabatree	Wallaba
falcata	Soft W.	Soft W.
jenmani	Ituri W.	Ituri W.
schomburgkiana	Bimiti W.	Bimiti W.
Erica arborea	Tree Heath	Briarroot
Eschweilera corrugata	Manbarklak	Manbarklak
Esenbeckia leiocarpa	Guarantan Gasparillo	Guarantan
Eucalyptus	Eucalyptus	Eucalyptus
accedens	Powderbark E.	Powderbark Wandoo E.
albens	Whitebox E.	Whitebox E.
andrewsi	Andrews Peppermint E.	New England Peppermint E.
astringens	Alum E.	Brownmallet E.
baileyana	Black Stringybark E.	Rough Stringybark E.
beyeri	Beyer Ironbark E.	Narrowleaf Ironbark E.
bicolor	Cooburn E.	Blackbox E.
bicostata	Eurabbie E.	Victoria Bluegum E.
bosistoana	Bosisto Graybox E.	Bairnsdale Graybox E.

Botanical Name	Plant Source S.P.N. Common Name	Lumber Trade Name
Eucalyptus, continued		
botryoides	Bangalay Eucalyptus	Bangalay Eucalyptus
caleyi	Caley Ironbark E.	Broadleaf Ironbark E.
calophylla	Marri E.	Redgum E.
camaldulensis	Longbeak E.	Murray Redgum E.
capitellata	Brown Stringybark E.	Brown Stringybark E.
citriodora	Lemon E.	Lemongum E.
cladocalyx	Sugar E.	Sugargum E.
cornuta	Yate E.	Yategum E.
crebra	Narrowleaf Ironbark E.	Narrowleaf Ironbark E.
dawsoni	Dawson E.	Slatygum E.
diversicolor	Karri E.	Karri E.
dives	Broadleaf Peppermint E.	Broadleaf Peppermint E.
eugenioides	White Stringybark E.	White Stringybark E.
eximia	Yellow Bloodwood E.	Yellow Bloodwood E.
fastigata	Cuttail E.	Cuttail Stringybark E.
fergusoni	Ferguson E.	Bloodwood Ironbark E.
foecunda	Fremantle Mallee E.	Yorkgum E.
fraxinoides	Ash E.	Australian Whiteash E.
gigantea	Delegate E.	Tasmanianoak E.
globulus	Tasmanian Blue E.	Bluegum E.
gomphocephala	Tuart E.	Tuart E.
goniocalyx	Bigleaf E.	Mountaingum E.
grandis	Toolur E.	Floodedgum E.
guilfoylei	Yellow Tingletingle E.	Yellow Tingletingle E.
gummifera	Dark Bloodwood E.	Bloodwood E.
gunni acervula	Tasmanian Cider E.	Tasmanian Redgum E.
haemastoma	Scribbly E.	Scribblygum E.
hemiphloia	Graybox E.	Graybox E.
intermedia	Pink Bloodwood E.	Bloodwood E.
jacksoni	Redtingle E.	Red Tingletingle E.
laevopinea	Silvertop Stringybark E.	Silvertop Stringybark E.
leucoxylon	White Ironbark E.	White Ironbark E.
longicornis	Red Morrell E.	Morrell E.
longifolia	Longleaf Woollybutt E.	Woollybutt E.
macarthuri	MacArthur E.	Camden W. E.
macrorhyncha	Red Stringybark E.	Red Stringybark E.
maculata	Spotted E.	Spottedgum E.
maideni	Maidens E.	Maidengum E.
marginata	Jarrah E.	Jarrah E.
melliodora	Yellowbox E.	Yellowbox E.
microcorys	Tallowwood E.	Tallowwood E.
microtheca	Floodedbox E.	Coolibah E.
muelleriana	Mueller E.	Yellow Stringybark E.
multiflora	Beakpod E.	Browngum E.
obliqua	Messmate Stringybark E.	Messmate Stringybark E.
occidentalis	Flattop Yate E.	Yate E.
odorata (*cajuputea*)	Peppermint E.	Peppermintgum E.
paniculata	Gray Ironbark E.	Gray Ironbark E.; Pink I. E.
patens	SwanRiver E.	Blackbutt E.
pilularis	Blackbutt E.	Blackbutt E.
piperita	Sydney Peppermint E.	Sydney Peppermint E.
planchoniana	Planchon Tallowwood E.	Tallowwood E.
polyanthemos	Redbox E.	Redbox E.
propinqua	Gray E.	Graygum E.
punctata	Leatherjacket E.	Graygum E.
radiata australiana		Narrowleaf Peppermint E.
raveretiana	Iron E.	Irongum E.
redunca	Blackmarlock E.	Wandoo E.
regnans	Giant E.	Giantgum E.
resinifera	Kino E.	Kinogum E.
rubida	Candlebark E.	Candlebark E.
rudderi	Rudderbox E.	Coast Redbox E.
salicifolia	Willowleaf E.	BlackPeppermint E.
saligna	Sydney Blue E.	Sydney Bluegum E.
salmonophloia	Salmonbark E.	Salmongum E.
salubris	Gimlet E.	Gimlet E.

Botanical Name	Plant Source S.P.N. Common Name	Lumber Trade Name
Eucalyptus, continued		
siderophloia	Broadleaf Ironbark Eucalyptus	Broadleaf Ironbark Eucalyptus
sideroxylon	Mulga I. E.	Red I. E.
sieberiana	Sieber E.	Silvertop Stringybark E.
terminalis	Kutcha Bloodwood E.	Kutcha E.
triantha		Yellow Stringybark E.
umbellata	Horncap E.	Forest Redgum E.
umbra	Shadow E.	Whitemahogany E.
viminalis	Ribbon E.	Mannagum E.
Eucarya spicata	Australia-sandalwood	Australian-sandalwood
Euclea pseudebenus	CapeEbony Euclea	Cape-ebony
Eugenia brasiliensis	Brazil Eugenia	Grumixaba
Eusideroxylon zwageri	Borneo Billian	Billian
Euxylophora paraensis	Brazilian-satinwood	Brazilian-satinwood
Fagraea fragrans	Sweet Fagraea	Anan
Fagus	Beech	Beech
grandifolia	American B.	American B.
sieboldi (*F. sylvatica s.*)	Siebold B.	Japanese B.
sylvatica	European B.	European B.
Flindersia	Flindersia	Flindersia
australis	Ballroom F.	
bennettiana	Bennett F.	Bennettash
brayleyana	Brayley F.	Maple Silkwood
chatawaiana	Chataway F.	Redbeech
collina	Hill F.	Broadleaf Leopardtree
ifflaiana	Iffla F.	Cairnshickory
maculosa	Leopard F.	Leopardtree
oxleyana	Longjack F.	Longjack
pimenteliana	Pimentel F.	Silkwood
schottiana	Cudgerie F.	Cudgerie
Fraxinus	Ash	Ash
americana	White A.	White A.
biltmoreana	Biltmore A.	White A.
excelsior	European A.	European A.
longicuspis sieboldiana (*F. sieboldiana*)	Siebold Japanese A.	Tamo
mandshurica	Manchurian A.	Japanese A.
nigra	Black A.	Black A.
oregona	Oregon A.	White A.
pennsylvanica	Red A.	White A.
p. lanceolata	Green A.	White A.
quadrangulata	Blue A.	White A.
Gardenia latifolia	Boxwood Gardenia	Boxwood Gardenia
Genipa americana	Marmaladebox Genip	Genip
Gleditsia amorphoides	Amorpha Honeylocust	Espina Corona
G. triacanthos	Common H.	Honeylocust
Gluta spp.	Gluta	Gluta
Gmelina arborea	Malay Bushbeech	Gumbar
G. leichhardti	Leichhardt B. (*Whitebeech*)	Whitebeech
Gonioma kamassi	Kamassiwood	Kamassiwood
Gossweilerodendron balsamiferum	Agba Gossweilertree	Agba
Gossypiospermum praecox		Zapatero
Goupia glabra	Kopie	Kopie
Grevillea hilliana	Yielyiel Grevillea	White Silkyoak
G. robusta	Silkoak G.	Silkyoak
Grewia tiliaefolia	Lindenleaf Grewia	Dhaman
Guajacum officinale	Common Lignumvitae	Lignumvitae
G. sanctum	Holywood L.	Holywood L.
Guarea cedrata	Pink Muskwood	Guarea
G. glabra	Jamaica M.	Jamaica Muskwood
G. thompsoni	Black M.	Guarea
G. trichilioides	American M.	Muskwood
Gymnocladus dioicus (*canadensis*)	Kentucky Coffeetree	Coffeetree
Haematoxylon campechianum	Logwood	Logwood
Harpullia pendula	Tulipwood	Tulipwood
Hibiscus spp.	Hibiscus	Majagua
Hieronyma alchorneoides		Tapana
Holoptelea grandis	Ayo Indiaelm	Ayo
H. integrifolia	Indiaelm	Indiaelm
Hopea	Merawan	Merawan
acuminata		Manggachapui

Plant Source Botanical Name	S.P.N. Common Name	Lumber Trade Name
Hopea, continued		
lowi	Lows Merawan	Giam
maranti		Meranti
nutans	Nodding M.	Giam
odorata	Thingan M.	Thingan
plagata		Saplungan
Hura crepitans	Sandboxtree	Hura
Hymenaea courbaril	Courbaril	Guapinol
Ilex aquifolium	English Holly	Holly
I. dipyrena	Himalaya H.	Himalaya H.
I. opaca	American H.	Holly
Inga laurina	Sackysac Inga	Sackysac
Intsia bakeri	Merbau Ipil	Merbau
I. bijuga	Common I.	Ipil
Jacaranda	Jacaranda	Jacaranda
brasiliensis	Brazil J.	Brazil J.
copaia	Copaia J.	Copaia
Juglans	Walnut	Walnut
californica	California Black W.	California W.
cinerea	Butternut	Butternut
hindsi	Hinds Black W.	California W.
nigra	Eastern B. W.	Black W.
regia	Persian W.	Persian W.
Juniperus	Juniper	Juniper
communis	Common J.	Common J.
mexicana	Mexican J.	Mountain Cedar
monosperma	Oneseed J.	Oneseed J.
occidentalis	Sierra J.	Western J.
pachyphloea	Alligator J.	Alligator J.
recurva	Himalayan J.	Weeping Blue J.
scopulorum	RockyMountain J.	Rocky Mountain Redcedar
silicicola	Southern Redcedar	Southern R.
utahensis	Utah J.	Utah J.
virginiana	Eastern Redcedar	Eastern R.
Kalmia latifolia	Mountainlaurel Kalmia	Mountainlaurel
Khaya	Khaya	Khaya
anthotheca	White K.	White K.
grandifoliola	Bigleaf K.	
ivorensis	Ivorycoast K.	Red K.
nyasica	Nyassa K.	
senegalensis	Senegal K.	Dryzone K.
Kingia australis	Australian Broomtree	Grasstree
Kingiodendron alternifolium	Philippine Kingstree	Batete
Knightia excelsa	Rewarewa	Rewarewa
Koordersiodendron pinnatum	Amugis	Amugis
Krugiodendron ferreum	Leadwood	Leadwood
Labourdonnaisia albescens	White Mattree	Almique
Laburnum alpinum (*Cytisus alpinus*)	Scotch Laburnum	Alpine Laburnum
L. anagyroides (*vulgare*)	Goldenchain L.	Laburnum
Lagerstroemia hypoleuca	Andaman Crapemyrtle	Pyinma Andaman
L. parviflora	Littleflower C.	Sida
L. piriformis	Batitinan C.	Batitinan
L. speciosa	Queen C.	Banabu
Laguncularia racemosa	Falsemangrove	Falsemangrove
Larix	Larch	Larch
decidua (*europaea*)	European L.	European L.
laricina (*americana*)	Eastern L.; Tamarack (Forestry)	Tamarack
leptolepis (*kaempferi*)	Japanese L.	Japanese L.
lyalli	Alpine L.	Alpine L.
occidentalis	Western L.	Western L.
Laurus nobilis	Grecian Laurel	Laurel
Lecythis laevifolia	Trinidad Monkeypottree	Guatacare
Libocedrus bidwilli	Pahautea Incensecedar	New Zealand Cedar
L. decurrens	California I.	Incensecedar
Licania tomentosa		Oity
Liquidambar styraciflua	American Sweetgum	Redgum
Liriodendron tulipifera	Tuliptree; Yellowpoplar (Forestry)	Yellowpoplar
Lithocarpus densiflorus (*Pasania densiflora*)	Tanoak	Tanoak
Litsea	Litsea	
calicaris	NewZealand L.	Mangeao

Plant Source Botanical Name	S.P.N. Common Name	Lumber Trade Name
Litsea, continued		
dealbata	Pigeonberry Litsea	Pigeonberrytree
ferruginea	Rustyleaf L.	Rustyleaf Litsea
leytensis (*obtusata*)	Baticulin L.	Baticulin
philippinensis	Bakan L.	Bakan
reticulata	Bollygum L.	Bollygum
Lonchocarpus hondurensis	Honduras Lancepod	Rosa Morada
L. latifolius		Savonette
Lophira procera	Ekki Lophira	Ekki
Lovoa browni	Browns Lovoa	Lovoa
L. klaineana	Tigerwood L.	Tigerwood
Loxopterygium sagoti		Hoobooballi
Luehea divaricata	Common Whiptree	Estribeira
Lysiloma latisiliqua (*sabicu*)	Sabicu Lysiloma	Sabicu
Madhuca indica	Illipe Buttertree	Buttertree
Maesopis emini		Musizi
Magnolia	Magnolia	Magnolia
acuminata	Cucumbertree M.	Cucumber M.
grandiflora	Southern M.	Evergreen M.
macrophylla	Bigleaf M.	Cucumbertree
virginiana australis	Southern Sweetbay M.	Bay M.
Malus pumila (*Pyrus malus*)	Common Apple	Apple
Mangifera altissima	Pahutan Mango	Pahutan
Manilkara bidentata (*Mimusops balata; M. bidentata globosa*)	Common Balata	Balata
M. darienensis (*Mimusops d.*)	Panama B	Panama B.
Mansonia altissima		Mansonia
Markhamia platycalyx		Nsambya
Metopium brownei	Brownes Poisontree	Chechem
Michelia champaca	Champac Michelia	Champ
Mimusops elengi	Elengi Bulletwood	Bulletwood
M. heckeli	Heckel B.	Makore
Mitragyna stipulosa (*macrophylla*)	Abura Mitragyna	Abura
Mora excelsa (*Dimorphandra mora*)	Guiana Mora	Mora
Myristica irya	Mutwinda Nutmeg	Mutwinda
Myrocarpus frondosus	Brazilian Myrocarpus	Cabreuva
Myroxylon balsamum (*toluiferum*)	Tolubalsam Balmtree	Oleo Vermelho
M. pereirae (*Toluifera p.*)	Perubalsam B.	Perubalsam
Nauclea diderichi	Opepe Fatheadtree	Opepe
N. esculenta	Guineapeach F.	Kusia
N. trillesi	Bilinga F.	Bilinga
Neonauclea calycina	Kalamansanai	Kalamansanai
Nothofagus	Falsebeech	Beech
cunninghami	Tasmanian F.	Tasmanian B.
fusca	Black F.	Red B.
menziesi	Silver F.	Southland B.
moorei	Negrohead F.	Negrohead B.
truncata	Clinker F.	Hard B.
Nyssa aquatica	Water Tupelo	Tupelo (**Blackgum**)
N. sylvatica	Black T.	Blackgum
Ochroma bicolor		Polak
O. pyramidale (*lagopus*)	WestIndies Balsa	Balsa
Ocotea bullata	Stinkwood Ocotea	Stinkwood
O. rodioei (*Nectandra r.*)	Greenheart O.	Greenheart
O. usambarensis	Muzaiti O.	Muzaiti
Olea	Olive	Olive
europaea	Common O.	Italian O.
ferruginea (*cuspidata*)	India O.	India O.
hochstetteri	African O.	African O.
Orites excelsa		Redash
Ormosia spp.	Ormosia	Hungchai
Ostrya guatemalensis	Guatemala Hophornbeam	Paque
Owenia venosa	Crowsapple Emuplum	Sourplum
Oxandra lanceolata	Lancewood	Lancewood
Pahudia rhomboidea	Philippine Pahudia	Tindalo
Panda oleosa		Ovaga
Parashorea malaanonan	Common Bagtikan	Bagtikan
P. stellata	Tavoy B.	Tavoywood
Paratecoma peroba (*Tecoma p.*)		Peroba Ipe
Patagonula americana	Guayaibi Patagoniatree	Guayaibi

Plant Source		
Botanical Name	*S.P.N. Common Name*	*Lumber Trade Name*
Peltogyne	Purpleheart	Purpleheart
paniculata	Guiana P.	Amaranth
Peltophorum adnatum	Moruro Peltophorum	Moruro
Pentace burmanica	Burma Thitka	Thitka
Pentacme contorta	Balak Pentacme	Balak (*White Lauan*)
Persea americana (*gratissima; persea*)	American Avocado	Avocado
Petitia domingensis	Capa Petitia	Capa
Phoebe ambigens	Honduras Phoebe	Guambo
P. porosa	Imbuya P.	Imbuya
Phyllocladus rhomboidalis	Tasmania Celery-pine	Celery(top)pine
Phyllostylon brasiliensis	Seron	Seron
Picea	Spruce	Spruce
abies (*excelsa*)	Norway S.	Norway S.
engelmanni	Engelmann S.	Engelmann S.
glauca (*alba; canadensis*)	White S.	Eastern S. Lumber from the western extension of this species is generally recognized in the trade as Western White Spruce.
mariana (*nigra*)	Black S.	Eastern S.
pungens (*parryana*)	Colorado S.	Blue S.
rubens (*rubra* [Dur.] Link, *not* A. Dietr.)	Red S.	Eastern S.
sitchensis	Sitka S.	Sitka S.
smithiana (*morinda*)	Himalayan S.	Himalayan S.
Picrasma excelsa (*Picraena e.*)	Jamaica Quassiawood	Quassiawood
Pinus	Pine	Pine
banksiana (*divaricata*)	Jack P.	Jack P.
caribaea (*elliotti; heterophylla*)	Slash P.	Slash P.
cembra	Swiss Stone P.	Swiss Stone P.
contorta	Shore P.	Shore P.
c. latifolia (*P. murrayana*)	Lodgepole P.	Lodgepole P.
densiflora	Japanese Red P.	Japanese Red P.
echinata (*mitis*)	Shortleaf P.	Shortleaf P.
glabra	Spruce P.	Spruce P.
griffithi (*excelsa* Wall., *not* Lam.; *nepalensis* De-Chambray, *not* Forbes)	Himalayan P.	Blue P.
halepensis	Aleppo P.	Aleppo P.
khasya	Khasia P.	Khasia P.
lambertiana	Sugar P.	Sugar P.
monticola	Western White P.	Idaho White P.
nigra (*austriaca; P. nigra a.*)	Austrian P.	Austrian P.
n. poiretiana (*P. laricio; P. l. calabrica; P. l. corsicana*)	Corsican P.	Corsican P.
palustris	Longleaf P.	Longleaf P.
pinaster	Cluster P.	Cluster P.
pinea	Italian Stone P.	Stone P.
ponderosa	Ponderosa P.	Ponderosa P.
pungens	TableMountain P.	Mountain P.
resinosa	Red P.	Red P.
rigida	Pitch P.	Pitch P.
r. serotina (*P. serotina*)	Pond P.	Pond P.
roxburghi	Chir P.	Longleaf P. (of Himalayas)
strobus	Eastern White P.	Northern White P.
sylvestris	Scotch P.	Scots (Scotch) P.
taeda	Loblolly P.	Loblolly P.
virginiana	Virginia P.	Virginia P.
Piptadenia spp.; especially **P. cebil, macrocarpa,** and **rigida**	Piptadenia	Curupay
africana	African P.	Ekhimi
communis	Common P.	Horco Cebie
Piratinera guianensis (*Brosimum aubleti*)	Snakewood	Snakewood
Pithecellobium vinhatico	Goldwood Apes-earring	Goldwood
Planchonia andamanica	Bombway Planchonia	Red Bombway
Platanus	Planetree; Sycamore (Forestry)	Plane
acerifolia	London P.	London P.
Platanus, continued		
occidentalis	American Planetree; American Sycamore (Forestry)	Sycamore
orientalis	Oriental P.	Eastern Plane
racemosa	California P.	California P.
Plathymenia reticulata		Brazilian-yellowwood
Platylophus trifoliatus	Tower-of-pisatree	Wit Els
Platymiscium	Macawood	Macawood
polystachyum	Quira M.	Quira
Podocarpus	Podocarpus	Podo
coriaceus	Yacca P.	Yacca
elatus	Tall P.	Native Damson
spicatus	Matai P.	Matai
totara	Totara P.	Totara
t. halli (*P. halli*)	Halls T. P.	Bigleaf Totara
Pometia pinnata		Malugai
Populus	Poplar; Aspen (*Cottonwood*)	Poplar *See also* Aspen and Cottonwood
alba	White P.	White P.
canadensis serotina	Late Carolina P.	Black Italian P.
candicans (*P. balsamifera c.*)	Balm-of-Gilead P.	Balm-of-Gilead P.
canescens (*alba* Willd., *not* L.)	Gray P.	Gray P.
deltoides (*monilifera*)	Eastern P.	Eastern Cottonwood
d. virginiana	Northern P.	Northern C.
denhardtiorum	Tana P.	Tana P.
fremonti	Fremont P. (*Fremont C.*)	Fremont C.
grandidentata	Bigtooth A.	Largetooth Aspen
heterophylla	Swamp P. (*Swamp C.*)	Swamp C.
macdougali	MacDougal P. (*MacDougal C.*)	MacDougal C.
nigra	Black P.	Black P.
nigra ¢Lombardy (*P. italica; P. n. pyramidalis*)		Lombardy P.
sargenti	Plains P. (*Plains C.*)	Plains C.
tacamahaca (*balsamifera* Muenchh. and Auth., *not* L.)	Tacamahac P.	Balsam P.
tremula	European A.	European A.
tremuloides	Quaking A.	Quaking A.
t. aurea	Golden Q. A.	Aspen
trichocarpa	California P. (*Black C.*)	Black C.
t. hastata	Pacific P. (*Northern Black C.*)	Northern B. C.
Prioria copaifera	Cativo	Cativo
Prunus	Cherry (section Cerasus)	Cherry
avium	Mazzard C.	Wild C.
cerasus	Sour C.	French C.
domestica	Garden Plum	Plum
serotina	Black C.	Black C.
virginiana	Common Chokecherry	Chokecherry
Pseudocedrela kotschyi		Toman
Pseudotsuga macrocarpa	Bigcone Douglas-fir	Bigcone-spruce
P. taxifolia (*douglasi; mucronata*)	Common D.	Douglasfir
Ptaeroxylon obliquum		Sneezewood
P. utile		Sneezewood
Pterocarpus	Padauk	Padauk
angolensis	Angola P.	Mlombwa
dalbergioides	Andaman P.	Andaman P.
indicus	Burmacoast P.	India P.
macrocarpus	Burma P.	Burma P.
marsupium	Vengai P.	Vengai
pedatus		Maidou
santalinus	Sandalwood P.	Red Sanderswood
soyauxi	African P.	African P.
Pterodon pubescens	Fuzzy Faveiro	Faveiro
Pterogyne nitens		Ibiraro
Pycnanthus kombo	Akomu Pycnanthus	Akomu
Pynaertia occidentalis	Bodi Pynaertia	Bodi
Pyrus communis	Common Pear	Pear
Quassia amara	Surinam Quassia	Bitterwood
Quercus	Oak	Oak
agrifolia	California Live O.	Coast Live O.
alba	White O.	White O.
arizonica	Arizona W. O.	Arizona W. O.

Botanical Name	Plant Source S.P.N. Common Name	Lumber Trade Name
Quercus, continued		
bicolor (*platanoides*)	Swamp White Oak	White Oak
borealis	Northern Red O.	Red O.
b. maxima	Eastern R. O.	Red O.
cerris	European Turkey O.	Turkey O.
chrysolepis	Canyon Live O. (*Goldencup O.*)	California Live O.
coccifera	Kermes O.	Kermes O.
douglasi	Blue O.	California Blue O.
ellipsoidalis	Northern Pin O.	Northern Pin O.
emoryi	Emory O.	Emory O.
falcata (*rubra* L., *not* Du Roi)	Southern Red O. (*Spanish O.*)	Red O.
f. pagodaefolia	Swamp R. O.	Red O.
garryana	Oregon White O.	Oregon White O.
ilex	Holly O.	Holly O.
kelloggi	California Black O.	California Black O.
laevis (*catesbaei*)	Turkey O.	Turkey O.
laurifolia (*hybrida*)	Laurel O.	Laurel O.
lobata	California White O. (*Valley O.*)	Valley White O.
lyrata	Overcup O.	White O.
macrocarpa	Bur O.	Bur O.; White O.
marilandica	Blackjack O.	Blackjack O.
montana (*prinus* Engelm., *not* L.)	Chestnut O.	White O.
muhlenbergi	Chinkapin O.	White O.
nigra (*aquatica*)	Water O.	Red O.
oblongifolia	Mexican Blue O.	Mexican Blue O.
palustris	Pin O.	Red O.
petraea (*sessiliflora*)	Durmast O.	Durmast O.
phellos	Willow O.	Red O.
prinus (*michauxi*)	Swamp Chestnut O. (*Basket O.*)	White O.
robur (*pedunculata*)	English O.	European O.
shumardi (*Q. texana s.*)	Shumard O.	Shumard Red O.
stellata (*minor; obtusiloba*)	Post O.	White O.
suber	Cork O.	Cork O.
texana	Texas O.	Red O.
utahensis	Utah White O.	Rocky Mountain White O.
velutina (*tinctoria*)	Black O.	Red O.
virginiana (*virens*)	Live O.	Live O.
wislizeni	Interior L. O.	Interior L. O.
Rhizophora mangle	American Mangrove	Mangrove
Rhodomyrtus tomentosa	Downy Rosemyrtle	Rosemyrtle
Rhodosphaera rhodanthema	Big Cardinalberry	Cardinalberry
Ricinodendron africanum	Musodo Manketti-nut	Musodo
Robinia pseudoacacia	Black Locust	Locust
Ruprechtia	Viraru	Viraru
R. deami	Bullsblood V.	Sangre de Toro
Sabal palmetto	Cabbage Palmetto	Palmetto
Salix	Willow	Willow
alba	White W.	White W.
a. calva (*S. coerulea*)	Pyramidal W. W. (*Cricketbat W.*)	Cricketbat W.
nigra	Black W.	Black W.
n. altissima	Gulf B. W.	Gulf B. W.
Santalum	Sandalwood	Sandalwood
album	White S.	White S.
austro-caledonicum	NewCaledonia S.	New Caledonia S.
freycinetianum	Yellow Fiji S.	Fiji S.
lanceolatum	Lanceleaf S.	Lanceleaf S.
yasi	Fiji S.	Fiji S.
Schinopsis balansae	Willowleaf Red-quebracho	Quebracho
S. lorentzi	Lorentz R.	Quebracho
Schinus molle	California Peppertree	Peppertree
Sciadopitys verticillata	Umbrellapine	Umbrellapine
Scottellia coriacea		Odoko
Sequoia gigantea (*washingtoniana*)	Giant Sequoia	Bigtree Redwood
S. sempervirens	Redwood	Redwood
Shorea	Shorea	Lauan
balangeran	Yakal S.	Yakal
curtisi	Curtis S.	Seraya
eximia	Almon S.	Almon
guiso	Guijo S.	Guijo
kalunti	Kalunti S.	Kalunti
mindanensis	Mindanao S.	Kalunti

Botanical Name	Plant Source S.P.N. Common Name	Lumber Trade Name
Shorea, continued		
negrosensis	Redlauan Shorea	Red Lauan
palosapis	Palosapis S.	Mayapis
philippinensis	Philippine S.	Manggasinoro
polita	Polished S.	Malaanonang
polysperma	Tangile S.	Tangile
robusta	Sal S.	Sal
teysmanniana	Tiaong S.	Tiaong
Simaruba glauca	Paradisetree	Marupa
Sindora supa	Supa Sindora	Supa
Siphonodon australe	Australian Ivorywood	Ivorywood
Sonneratia caseolaris		Pagatpat
Spondias	Mombin	Mombin
mombin (*axillaris; lutea*)	Yellow M.	Yellow M.
purpurea	Purple M.	Purple M.
Stenocarpus sinuatus	Tall Firewheeltree	Firetree
Sterculia caribaea	Carib Sterculia	Saltfishwood
Swartzia tomentosa	Wamara Swartzpea	Wamara
Sweetia panamensis	Billywebb Sweetia	Billywebb
Swietenia	Mahogany	Mahogany
candollei	Venezuela M.	Venezuela M.
humilis	Mexican M.	Mexican M.
macrophylla	Honduras M.	Honduras M.
mahagoni	WestIndies M.	West Indies M.
Symphonia gabonensis	Gabon Symphonia	Osol
Syncarpia hilli	Hilis Turpentine-myrtle	Red Satinay
Syzygium cumini (*jambolanum; Eugenia c.*)	Jambolan	Jaman
Tabebuia pentaphylla (*Tecoma leucoxylon; T. pentaphylla*)		Ocobo
Tamarindus indica	Tamarind	Tamarind
Tarrietia argyrodendron	Silver Stonewood	Royal Tartan
T. javanica	Java S.	Lumbayao
T. sylvatica	Dungon S.	Dungon
T. utilis		Niangon
Taxodium distichum	Common Baldcypress	Southern Cypress
Taxus	Yew	Yew
baccata	English Y.	English Y.
brevifolia	Pacific Y.	American Y.
canadensis (*minor*)	Canada Y.	Canada Y.
floridana	Florida Y.	Florida Y.
Tectona grandis	Common Teak	Teak
Terminalia	Terminalia	Chuglam
acuminata	Guarabu T.	Guarabu
bialata	Two-wing T.	White C.
comintana	Binggas T.	Binggas
ivorensis	Ivorycoast T.	Frameri
januarensis	RioJaneiro T.	Araca
mani	Mani T.	Black C.
marsupium	Bijasal T.	Bijasal
myriocarpa	Prolific T.	Hollock
obovata	Nargusta T.	Nargusta
procera	Bombway T.	White Bombway
superba	Afara T.	Afara
tomentosa	Woolly T.	Eastindieslaurel
Tetraclinis articulata (*Callitris quadrivalvis*)	Arartree	Arar
Thespesia populnea	Portiatree	Portiatree
Thuja occidentalis	Eastern Arborvitae; Northern White-cedar (Forestry)	Northern White-cedar
T. plicata	Giant A.; Western Redcedar	Western Redcedar
Tilia	Linden; Basswood (Forestry)	Linden
americana (*glabra*)	American L.; American Basswood (Forestry)	Basswood
cordata (*ulmifolia*)	Littleleaf L.	Littleleaf L.
europaea (*vulgaris*)	European L.	Common L.
heterophylla	Beetree L.	White Basswood
platyphyllos	Bigleaf L.	Bigleaf L.
Toona australis	Australian Toon	Toon
T. calantas	Philippine T.	Kalantas
T. ciliata (*Cedrela toona*)	Burma T.	Toon
T. serrata (*C. serrata*)	Himalaya T.	Himalaya T.
Trichilia cruegeriana	Trinidad Bitterwood	Acurel

Plant Source Botanical Name	Plant Source S.P.N. Common Name	Lumber Trade Name
Triplochiton scler-oxylon		OBECHE
Tristania conferta	BRISBANEBOX TRISTANIA	BRISBANEBOX
Tsuga	HEMLOCK	HEMLOCK
canadensis	CANADA H.; EASTERN H. (Forestry)	EASTERN H.
caroliniana	CAROLINA H.	CAROLINA H.
heterophylla	PACIFIC H.; WESTERN H. (Forestry)	WESTERN H.
mertensiana	MOUNTAIN H.	MOUNTAIN H.
Turraeanthus africana	AFRICAN AVODIRE	AVODIRE
Tylostemon crassi-folius		SPICY CEDAR
T. manni		SPICY C.
Ulmus	ELM	ELM
alata	WINGED E.	WINGED E.
americana	AMERICAN E.	SOFT E.
crassifolia	CEDAR E.	SOUTHERN ROCK E.
fulva	SLIPPERY E.	SLIPPERY E.
glabra (*montana; scabra*)	SCOTCH E.	WYCH E.
∞ **hollandica** (*?carpinifolia × glabra; dippeliana; major*)	∞ DUTCH E.	DUTCH E.
mexicana	MEXICAN E.	MEXICAN E.
parvifolia	CHINESE E.	CHINESE E.
procera (*campestris* in large part)	ENGLISH E.	ENGLISH E.
serotina	SEPTEMBER E.	RED E.

Plant Source Botanical Name	Plant Source S.P.N. Common Name	Lumber Trade Name
Ulmus, continued		
thomasi	ROCK ELM	ROCK ELM
wallichi	HIMALAYAN E.	HIMALAYAN E.
Umbellularia californica	CALIFORNIALAUREL	CALIFORNIALAUREL
Urandra corniculata	DARU URANDRA	DARU
Vatairea lundelli		PICHO
Vateria indica		PINEYVARNISHTREE
Virola merendonis	MERENDON VIROLA	BANAK
V. panamensis	PANAMA V.	BANAK
Vitex	CHASTETREE	MOLAVE
littoralis	TIMOR C.	PUIRI
Wallaceodendron celebicum	CELEBES WALLACETREE	BANUYO
Weinmannia racemosa	KAMAHI	TOWHAI
Wrightia laniti		LANETE
Xanthorrhoea preissi	PREISS GRASSTREE (*Blackboy*)	BLACKBOY
Xanthostemon oppositifolius		PENDA
X. pubescens		PENDA
X. verdugonianus		MANCONO
Ximenia americana	TALLOWWOOD	TALLOWWOOD
Xylia xylocarpa (*dolabriformis*)	BURMA PYINGADO	PYINGADO
Zanthoxylum	PRICKLYASH	PRICKLYASH
Z. flavum	YELLOWHEART P.	DOMINICAN-SATINWOOD
Zelkova spp.	ZELKOVA	ZELKOVA
Zizyphus chloroxylon	COGWOOD JUJUBE	COGWOOD
Z. jujuba	COMMON J.	JUJUBE

LUNA'RIA . . . . HONESTY
an'nua (*biennis*) . . . DOLLARPLANT
redivi'va . . . . . . PERENNIAL H.

LUN'DIA
umbro'sa

LUNGWORT . . . . **Pulmonaria**
AZURE COWSLIP L.
P. angustifolia azurea
BETHLEHEM L. . . . . **P. saccharata**
COMMON L. . . . . . **P. officinalis**
COWSLIP L. . . . . **P. angustifolia**
MOUNTAIN L. . . . . . **P. montana**

LUPINE . . . . Lupinus
ARIZONA L. . . . . . **L. arizonicus**
ARROYO L. . . . . . **L. succulentus**
BAJADA L. . . . . . . **L. concinnus**
BICOLOR L. . . . . **L. bicolor**
BIGPOD L. . . . . . **L. pachylobus**
BISHOP L. . . . . **L. ludovicianus**
BREWERS L. . . . . **L. breweri**
BRITTONS BUSH L. . . . . **L. brittoni**
BROADLEAF L. . . . . . **L. latifolius**
BROOM L. . . . . **L. cytisoides**
BURKE L. . . . . **L. burkei**
CHICK L. . . . . . **L. microcarpus**
CLOVER L. . . . . . . **L. tidestromi**
COLUMBIA BROADLEAF L.
L. latifolius columbianus
COULTER L. . . . . . **L. sparsiflorus**
COVILLE L. . . . . **L. covillei**
CROWDED L. . . . . . . **L. confertus**
DEER L. . . . . **L. cervinus**
DESERT L. . . . . **L. shockleyi**
DUNE L. . . . . . . **L. chamissonis**
EUROPEAN BLUE L. . . . **L. hirsutus**
EUROPEAN YELLOW L. . . . **L. luteus**
FIELD L. . . . . . . **L. micranthus**
GRAYS L. . . . . **L. grayi**
GROUND L. . . . . **L. onustus**
GULLY L. . . . . . . **L. densiflorus**
HARTWEG L. . . . . . . **L. hartwegi**
HILLS L. . . . . **L. hilli**
HOARY VELVET L.
L. leucophyllus canescens
HOLLOWSTEM L. . . . . **L. pratensis**
INYO L. . . . . **L. excubitus**
KINGS L. . . . . **L. kingi**

LUPINE, continued
LEAST L. . . . . . **Lupinus minimus**
LOBB L. . . . . **L. lyalli lobbi**
LODGEPOLE L. . . . . **L. parviflorus**
LONE L. . . . . **L. peirsoni**
LONGSPIKE L. . . . **L. macrostachys**
LONGSPUR L. . **L. laxiflorus calcaratus**
LONGSTALK BROADLEAF L.
L. latifolius longipes
LUNARA L. . . . . **L. formosus**
LYALL L. . . . . **L. lyalli**
MEADOW L. . . . . **L. superbus**
MOHAVE L. . . . . **L. odoratus**
MONTANA L. . . . **L. pseudoparviflorus**
MOUNTAIN L. . . . . . . **L. alpestris**
MOUNTDANA L. . . . **L. lyalli danaus**
NEBRASKA L. . . . . . . **L. plattensis**
NOOTKA L. . . . . . **L. nootkatensis**
ORANGE L. . . . . **L. citrinus**
OREAD L. . . . . **L. monticola**
ORNATE L. . . . . **L. ornatus**
PACIFIC L. . . . . **L. lepidus**
PALMER L. . . . . **L. palmeri**
PANAMINT L. . . . . . . **L. magnificus**
PARTICOLOR L. . . . . . **L. variicolor**
PAYNES L. . . . . **L. paynei**
PINE L. . . . . **L. albicaulis**
PIPER L. . . . . **L. piperi**
ROCK L. . . . . **L. saxosus**
RUSTY L. . . . . **L. pusillus**
SAND L. . . . . **L. ammophilus**
SATIN L. . . . . **L. sericatus**
SHORE L. . . . . **L. littoralis**
SHORTSTEM L. . . . . . **L. brevicaulis**
SILKY L. . . . . **L. sericeus**
SILVERY L. . . . . **L. argenteus**
SKY L. . . . . **L. nanus**
SOUTHAMERICAN L. . . . **L. mutabilis**
SPATULATE L. . . . . **L. spathulatus**
SPIDER L. . . . . **L. benthami**
SPREADINGHAIR L. . . . . **L. comatus**
SPUR L. . . . . **L. laxiflorus**
STEMLESS L. . . . . . **L. caespitosus**
STINGING L. . . . . **L. hirsutissimus**
STIVERS L. . . . . **L. stiversi**
STREAM L. . . . . **L. rivularis**
SUBALPINE L. . . . . . **L. subalpinus**
SULFUR L. . . . . . . **L. sulphureus**
SUNDIAL L. . . . . **L. perennis**

LUPINE, continued
TAHOE L. . . . **Lupinus meionanthus**
TAILCUP L. . . . . **L. caudatus**
TEXAS L. . . . . . . **L. subcarnosus**
TORREY L. . . . . . **L. aridus torreyi**
TREE L. . . . . **L. arboreus**
VELVET L. . . . . . . **L. leucophyllus**
VOLCANO L. . . . . **L. volcanicus**
WASHINGTON L. . . . . **L. polyphyllus**
WHITEFACE L. . . . . **L. albifrons**
WHITE L. . . . . **L. albus**
WOOD L. . . . . **L. truncatus**
WYETH L. . . . . **L. wyethi**
YELLOWEYE L. . . . . **L. rubens**

LUPI'NUS |w . . . . LUPINE
Botanically this large genus is difficult and its nomenclature controversial.

adsur'gens
—lilaci'nus
affi'nis Agardh. . . . . **L. nanus**
affi'nis Brew. & Wats., *not* Agardh.
L. succulentus
agardhia'nus . . . . . **L. concinnus**
albicau'lis (*sylvestris; L. albicaulis s.*)
PINE L.
—brid'gesi
—shasten'sis
—sylves'tris . . . . . . **A. albicaulis**
al'bifrons . . . . . . WHITEFACE L.
al'bus (*termis*) . . . . . . WHITE L.
alpes'tris . . . . MOUNTAIN L.
ammoph'ilus . . . . SAND L.
anderso'ni
Regarded by some botanists as synonymous with L. albicaulis or varieties thereof.
—aper'tus
—fulcra'tus
angustifo'lius
arbo'reus . . . . TREE L.
LIGHT OF LONDON. HV.
SNOWQUEEN
SUNSHINE
WHITE (*albus*)
argen'teus (*decumbens*) . SILVERY L.
argenti'nus . . . . **L. caudatus**
ar'idus
—lobb'i . . . . **L. lyalli l.**

LUPINUS, continued
ar'idus tor'reyi (*L. torreyi*) TORREY LUPINE
arizo'nicus . . . . ARIZONA L.
barba'tus
bar'biger . . . . **L. sericeus**
ben'thami . . . . SPIDER L.
bi'color . . . . BICOLOR L.
—microphyl'lus
—pipersmith'i
—tetrasper'mus
—tridenta'tus
—trif'idus
—umbella'tus
brevicau'lis . . . . . SHORTSTEM L.
brew'eri . . . . BREWERS L.
brit'toni . . . . . BRITTONS BUSH L.
burk'ei . . . . BURKE L.
caespito'sus (*watsoni*) . . STEMLESS L.
calcara'tus . . . . . . **L. laxiflorus c.**
can'dicans
canes'cens . . . . **L. leucophyllus c.**
cauda'tus (*argentinus; montigenus; oreophilus* Greene, *not* Phillipi) TAILCUP L.
cervi'nus . . . . DEER L.
chamisso'nis . . . . . . DUNE L.
citri'nus . . . . ORANGE L.
columbia'nus . . . . . **L. latifolius c.**
coma'tus . . . . SPREADINGHAIR L.
concin'nus (*agardhianus; gracilis* Agardh, *not* Nutt.; *micensis*). BAJADA L.
confer'tus . . . . CROWDED L.
corymbo'sus (*L. laxiflorus c.*)
covil'lei . . . . COVILLE L.
cya'neus
cytisoi'des . . . . BROOM L.
dana'us . . . . **L. lyalli d.**
decum'bens . . . . **L. argenteus**
deflex'us
densiflo'rus (*menziesi*) . . . GULLY L.
—lac'teus
diffu'sus
excu'bitus . . . . INYO L.
floribun'dus . . . . . **L. parviflorus**
formo'sus . . . . LUNARA L.
gracilen'tus
grac'ilis Agardh, *not* Nutt. **L. concinnus**
gray'i . . . . GRAYS L.
hart'wegi . . . . . . HARTWEG L.
COELESTINUS. HV.
RED (*ruber*)
ROSY (*roseus*)
WHITE (*albus*)
hill'i . . . . HILLS L.
hirsutis'simus . . . . . STINGING L.
hirsu'tus . . . EUROPEAN BLUE L.
CAERULEUS. HV.
CARNEUS
RED (*ruber*)
WHITE (*albus*)
horizonta'lis
—platypet'alus
hypola'sius
inyoen'sis
—erioca'lyx
king'i |w . . . . KINGS L.
latifo'lius . . . . . . BROADLEAF L.
—columbia'nus (*L. columbianus*) COLUMBIA B.L.
—dud'leyi
—lon'gipes (*L. longipes*) LONGSTALK B.L.

LUPINUS, continued
latifo'lius par'ishi
laxiflo'rus . . . . . . SPUR LUPINE
—calcara'tus (*L. calcaratus*) LONGSPUR L.
—corymbo'sus . . . . **L. corymbosus**
—multitinc'tus (*L. multitinctus*)
—silvic'ola (*L. silvicola*)
lep'idus . . . . PACIFIC L.
leucophyl'lus . . . . VELVET L.
—canes'cens (*L. canescens*) HOARY V.L.
leucop'sis
littora'lis . . . . SHORE L.
lobb'i . . . . **L. lyalli l.**
longifo'lius
lon'gipes . . . . **L. latifolius l.**
ludovicia'nus . . . . BISHOP L.
lute'us . . . EUROPEAN YELLOW L.

The name L. luteus is sometimes misapplied to L. arboreus.

ly'alli . . . . LYALL L.
—dana'us (*L. danaus*) . MOUNTDANA L.
—lobb'i (*L. aridus l.; L. lobbi*) . LOBB L.
macrostach'ys . . . . LONGSPIKE L.
magnif'icus . . . . . PANAMINT L.
—glarec'ola
—hesper'ius
meionan'thus . . . . . . TAHOE L.
menzies'i . . . . **L. densiflorus**
micen'sis . . . . . . **L. concinnus**
micran'thus . . . . FIELD L.
microcar'pus . . . . CHICK L.
—ru'ber
min'imus . . . . LEAST L.
montic'ola . . . . OREAD L.
monti'genus . . . . **L. caudatus**
multitinc'tus . . . . **L. laxiflorus m.**
mutab'ilis . . . . SOUTHAMERICAN L.
CRUCKSHANKS (*cruckshanksi*) HV.
ROSY (*rosea*)
VERSICOLOR
na'nus (*affinis* Agardh, *not* Brew. & Wats.) . . . . SKY L.
nootkaten'sis |w . . . . NOOTKA L.
obtusilo'bus
odora'tus . . . . MOHAVE L.
onus'tus . . . . GROUND L.
oreoph'ilus Greene, *not* Phillipi **L. caudatus**
orna'tus . . . . ORNATE L.
pachylo'bus . . . . BIGPOD L.
pal'meri . . . . PALMER L.
panicula'tus
parviflo'rus (*floribundus*) LODGEPOLE L.
payn'ei . . . . PAYNES L.
peir'soni . . . . LONE L.
peren'nis . . . . SUNDIAL L.
pilo'sus
pi'peri . . . . PIPER L.
platten'sis . . . . . . NEBRASKA L.
polyphyl'lus . . . . WASHINGTON L.
ARTIST. HV.
BLACKPOOL TOWERS
BLUE BOY
BLUSH (*roseus*)
CHOCOLATE SOLDIER
C. M. PRICHARD
CODSALL ORANGE
CORPHALE
DOWNERS DELIGHT
DRESDEN CHINA
EDNA
ELIZABETH ARDEN

LUPINUS polyphyllus, continued
FIREFLY
FORTUNATUS
GOLDCREST
GOLD DUST
GOLDEN THOUGHTS
HAPPINESS
HIGHLANDER
JULIANA
LAVENDER BEE
MAJESTIC
MERMAID
MOERHEIM (*moerheimi*)
MOLLY FOSTER
MRS. STEPHENS
OLYMPIADE
PENELOPE
PINK PEARLS
POWERFUL
PRINCESS ELIZABETH
RIVERSLEA
ROWENA
RUBY KING
RUSSELL HYBRIDS
SAXE BLUE
SUTTONS HYBRIDS
TANGERINE
TAPLOW PRIMROSE
TAPLOW PURPLE
21ST LANCERS
TWYNHAM
WEBER
WHITE (*albiflorus*)
WISTARIA
ZULU
praten'sis . . . HOLLOWSTEM LUPINE
pseudoparviflo'rus . . . MONTANA L.
pubes'cens
DUNNETT (*dunnetti*) HV.
pusil'lus . . . . RUSTY L.
—intermonta'nus
rivula'ris . . . . STREAM L.
ru'bens . . . . YELLOWEYE L.
—flavocula'tus
saxo'sus . . . . ROCK L.
serica'tus . . . . SATIN L.
seric'eus (*barbiger*) . . . . SILKY L.
shock'leyi . . . . DESERT L.
silvic'ola . . . . . . **L. laxiflorus s.**
sparsiflo'rus |w . . . . . COULTER L.
spathula'tus . . . . . SPATULATE L.
sti'versi . . . . STIVERS L.
subalpi'nus . . . . . SUBALPINE L.
subcarno'sus . . . . TEXAS L.
subvex'us
—albilana'tus
—phoenic'eus
—transmonta'nus
succulen'tus (*affinis* Brew. & Wats., *not* Agardh) . . . . . . ARROYO L.
sulphu'reus . . . . SULFUR L.
super'bus . . . . MEADOW L.
—bernardi'nus
—elonga'tus
sylves'tris . . . . **L. albicaulis**

L. sylvestris Drew (1889) should not be confused with L. silvestris Lam. (1779).

ter'mis . . . . **L. albus**
texa'nus
tidestrom'i . . . . CLOVER L.
tor'reyi . . . . **L. aridus t.**
trunca'tus . . . . WOOD L.
variicol'or . . . . . . PARTICOLOR L.

Hort. var.; HV. = horticultural variety (or varieties); sp. = species (singular); spp. = species (plural).
₵ = clon; × (as a prefix) = hybrid; × (between scientific plant names) = crossed by; ∞ = polybrid; |w = plant useful to wildlife.
See Glossary for definitions of clon, hybrid, and polybrid.

LUPINUS, continued
villo'sus
viridifo'lius
volcan'icus . . . . Volcano Lupine
wat'soni . . . . **L. caespitosus**
wy'ethi . . . . Wyeth L.

LUT'KEA . . . . **LUETKEA**

LUVUN'GA (*LAVANGA*) . . Luvunga
philippinen'sis . . . . Philippine L.
scan'dens . . . . India L.

LUZI'OLA . . . . Luziola
See **GRASS GENERA.**

LU'ZULA (*JUNCOIDES*) |w Woodrush
campes'tris (*J. campestre*) |w Field W.
—*multiflo'ra* . . . . . . **L. multiflora**
campes'tris Auth., *not* L. . **L. comosa; L. multiflora; L. sudetica**
como'sa (*campestris* Auth., *not* L., in part; *J. comosum*) . . . Hairy W.
kjellmannia'na |w
multiflo'ra (*campestris* Auth., *not* L.; *L. campestris m.*)
nemoro'sa (*J. nemorosum*) . Grove W.
parviflo'ra (*Juncoides parviflorum*) |w Millet W.
pi'peri . . . . **L. wahlenbergi**
saltuen'sis |w
spica'ta (*J. spicatum*) |w . . Spike W.
subconges'ta (*J. subcongestum*) Donner W.
sudet'ica (*campestris* Auth., *not* L., in part) . . . . Sudetic W.
wahlenberg'i (*piperi; Juncoides p.*) Wahlenberg W.

LYCAS'TE
See **ORCHID GENERA.**

Lychee . . . . . . **Litchi; L. chinensis**

LYCH'NIS (*CORONARIA; VISCARIA*) |w . . . . . Campion
al'ba (*vespertina*) . . . . Evening C.
alpi'na . . . . Arctic C.
Doublered (*rubra plena*) hv.
White (*alba*)
apet'ala |w
×**ark'wrighti** (*chalcedonica* × ×*haageana*) Arkwright C.
chalcedon'ica . . . Maltesecross C.
Flesh (*salmonea*) hv.
White (*alba*)
coeliro'sa (*Agrostemma c.*) Roseofheaven
Fringed (*fimbriata*) hv.
Purple-eye (*oculata*)
Red (*kermesina*)
White (*alba*)
corona'ria (*Agrostemma c.*) . . Rose C.
Atrosanguinea. hv.
Rosea
Rubra
White (*alba*)
corona'ta (*grandiflora*) . . . Crown C.
Siebold (*sieboldi*) hv.
cors'ica . . . . Corsica C.
dioi'ca (*diurna*) . . . . . . Red C.
drum'mondi . . . . . Drummond C.
floscu'culi . . . . . Raggedrobin
Double (*plenissima*) hv.
Red (*rosa plena*)
flosjo'vis (*Agrostemma f.*) Flowerofjove
×**for'resti**
ful'gens . . . . Brilliant C.
githa'go . . . . **Agrostemma g.**
grandiflo'ra . . . . **L. coronata**

LYCHNIS, continued
×**haagea'na** (*coronata* × *fulgens*) Haage Campion
lagas'cae . . . . **Petrocoptis l.**
miquelia'na
monta'na
pres'li
pyrena'ica . . . . . . Pyrenees C.
sarto'ri
tris'tis
vesperti'na . . . . **L. alba**
visca'ria . . . . Clammy C.
Cardinal (*cardinalis*) hv.
Double Rosepink (*splendens flore-pleno*)
Dunnett (*dunnetti*)
Flag (*elegans*)
Rosepink (*splendens*)
Rosy (*rosea*)
White (*alba*)
White Bigflower (*grandiflora alba*)
×**wal'keri** (*coronaria* × *flosjovis*)

LY'CIUM |w . . . . Wolfberry (*Desertthorn; Squawbush*)
af'rum
anderso'ni |w . . . . Anderson W.
bar'barum . . . . Barbary W.
brev'ipes
califor'nicum . . . . California W.
carolinia'num . . . . Carolina W.
chilen'se
chinen'se . . . . Chinese W.
—**ova'tum** (*L. rhombifolium*)
coo'peri . . . . Cooper W.
europae'um . . . . . European W.
fre'monti . . . . Fremont W.
grevillea'num
halimifo'lium (*vulgare*) ! Matrimonyvine
hor'ridum
pal'lidum |w . . . . Pale W.
par'ishi . . . . Parish W.
rhombifo'lium . . **L. chinense ovatum**
ruthen'icum
tor'reyi . . . . Torrey W.
turcoman'icum
vulga're . . . . **L. halimifolium**

LYCOP'ERDON . . . . . Lycoperdon
pyrifor'me . . . . Pear L.

LYCOPER'SICON (*LYCOPERSICUM*) |w . . . . Tomato
esculen'tum |w . . . . Common T.
—**cerasifor'me** |w . . . . Cherry T.
—**grandifo'lium** . . . . Bigleaf T.
—**pyrifor'me** . . . . Pear T.
—**val'idum** . . . . . . Upright T.
pimpinellifo'lium . . . . Currant T.

LYCOPO'DIUM |w . . . . . Clubmoss
adpres'sum . . . . . . Southern C.
alopecuroi'des . . . . . Foxtail C.
billardier'i . . . . . . Billardier C.
carolinia'num . . . . . Carolina C.
cer'nuum . . . . Staghorn C.
clava'tum . . . . . . Runningpine
complana'tum
—**flabellifor'me** . . . Groundcedar (*Crowfoot*)
lucid'ulum |w . . . . . . Shining C.
obscu'rum (*dendroideum*) |w Groundpine (*Crowfoot*)
prostra'tum . . . . Carpet C.
sela'go . . . . Fir C.
trista'chyum . Slender Groundcedar

LYCOP'SIS
arven'sis

LYCO'PUS |w . . . . . . Bugleweed
america'nus |w . . . . American B.
europae'us . . . . . . European B.
lu'cidus |w
rubel'lus |w
sessilifo'lius |w
uniflo'rus |w
virgin'icus |w . . . . . Virginia B.

LYCO'RIS . . . . Lycoris
al'ba . . . . White L.
au'rea (*Amaryllis a.*) . . Golden L.
incarna'ta . . . . Fragrant L.
radia'ta (*Amaryllis r.*) . Shorttube L.
—**al'ba** . . . . White S.L.
—**pu'mila** . . . . Dwarf S.L.
sanguin'ea . . . . Orange L.
spreng'eri . . . . . . Sprenger L.
squamig'era (*Amaryllis halli*) Autumn L.
—**purpu'rea** . . . . . . Purple A.L.
stramin'ea . . . . Straw L.

LYCOS'ERIS
oblongifo'lia

LYCU'RUS . . . . Wolftail
See **GRASS GENERA.**

LYGE'UM
See **GRASS GENERA.**

LYGODES'MIA . . . Skeletonplant
exig'ua
jun'cea . . . . Rush S.
spino'sa . . . . Thorn S.

LYGO'DIUM . . . . Climbingfern
See **FERN GENERA.**

Lymegrass . . . . . Wildrye: **Elymus**

LYO'NIA (*NEOPIERIS; XOLISMA*) Lyonia
ferrugin'ea
ligustri'na (*Arsenococcus ligustrinus; Xolisma ligustrina*) He-huckleberry
—**foliosiflo'ra** . . . . . Bracted H.
—**pubes'cens** . . . . Downy H.
lu'cida (*nitida; Desmothamnus lucidus; Neopieris nitida; Pieris lucida; P. nitida*) . . . . . Fetterbush L.
—**ru'bra** . . . . Red F.L.
maria'na (*Neopieris m.; Pieris m.*) Staggerbush L.
ovalifo'lia . . . . Tibet L.
—**ellip'tica** . . . . . Thinleaf T.L.
—**lanceola'ta** . . . . Narrowleaf T.L.

LYONOTHAM'NUS . . . . Lyontree
floribun'dus . . . . Lyontree
—**asplenifo'lius** . . . . Fernleaf L.

Lyontree **Lyonothamnus; L. floribundus**
Fernleaf L. . . . . **L. f. asplenifolius**

LY'SIAS . . . . . . **HABENARIA**
See **ORCHID GENERA.**

LYSICH'ITUM (*LYSICHITON*)
america'num (*camtschatense* Am. Auth. in part)
American Yellowskunkcabbage
camtschatcen'se
Yellowskunkcabbage

LYSID'ICE
rhodoste'gia

LYSIEL'LA . . . . . . **HABENARIA**
See **ORCHID GENERA.**

LYSILO'MA . . . . Lysiloma
bahamen'sis . . . . Bahama L.
latisili'qua (*sabicu*) . . . Sabicu L.
wat'soni . . . . Watson L.

LYSIMACH'IA ⌊w . . . . Loosestrife
atropurpu'rea
baryst'achys
cilia'ta . . . . **Steironema ciliatum**
clethroi'des . . . . . . Clethra L.
du'bia
ephem'erum
fortun'ei . . . . Fortune L.
fra'seri
japon'ica . . . . . . Japanese L.
—minutis'sima
lobelioi'des
nummula'ria . . . . . . Moneywort
pseudo-hen'ryi
puncta'ta . . . . Spotted L.
quadrifo'lia . . . . . . Fourleaf L.
terres'tris ⌊w . . . Swampcandle L.
thyrsiflo'ra ⌊w . . . . . Water L.
vulga'ris . . . . Golden L.

LY'THRUM ⌊w . . . . . Lythrum
ala'tum ⌊w . . . . . . Winged L.
flexuo'sum (*graefferi*)
hyssopifo'lia ⌊w . . . . . . Hyssop L.
linea're ⌊w
salica'ria ⌊w . . . . . . Purple L.
Atropurpureum. hv.
Brightness
Brilliant
Crimson Dwarf
Lady Sackville
Rose (*roseum*)
virga'tum . . . . Wand L.

MAACK'IA . . . . Maackia
amuren'sis (*Cladrastis a.*) . Amur M.
—buer'geri
chinen'sis (*hupehensis*) . Chinese M.
faur'iei
tashiro'i

MA'BA
buxifo'lia . . . . . **Diospyros ferrea**
natalen'sis (*Ebenus n.*) . Natalebony
sandwicen'sis (*Ebenus s.*)

MACADA'MIA . . . . . Macadamia
integrifo'lia
ternifo'lia . . . Queenslandnut M.

This tree produces the Macadamia (Queenslandnut) nuts of commerce.

Macawood . . . . . . **Platymiscium**
Quira M. . . . . . . **P. polystachyum**

Macawpalm . . . . . . **Aiphanes erosa**

MACDOUGAL'IA . . . . **ACTINEA**

MACFADYE'NA
corymbo'sa
cynanchoi'des . . . . . **Dolichandra c.**

MACHAERAN'THERA . . . **ASTER**

Machae'rium ti'pu . . . . . **Tipuana t.**

MACHAEROCE'REUS
See **CACTUS GENERA.**

MACHI'LUS
gammiea'na

MACKAY'A
bel'la (*Asystasia b.*)

MACLEAY'A . . . . . . Plumepoppy
corda'ta (*Bocconia c.; B. japonica*) Pink P.
microcar'pa (*Bocconia m.*)

×**MACLUDRA'NIA** (*CUDRANIA* × *MACLURA*)
×**hy'brida** (*Cudrania tricuspidata* × *Maclura pomifera*)

MACLUR'A (*TOXYLON*) ⌊w Osageorange
pomif'era (*aurantiaca; Toxylon pomiferum*) ⌊w . . . . . Osageorange
—iner'mis (*Toxylon pomiferum inerme*) Thornless O.
tricuspida'ta . . . . . . **Cudrania t.**

MACRADE'NIA
See **ORCHID GENERA.**

MACROCATAL'PA . . . **CATALPA**

MACROCYS'TIS . . . . . Giantkelp
pyrif'era . . . . Giantkelp

Reported to reach occasional lengths of 700 feet, making it the longest of all living organisms.

MACRONE'MA . . . **APLOPAPPUS**
discoi'deum . . . . . . **A. macronema**

MACROPHLO'GA
See **PALM GENERA.**

MACROPI'PER
excel'sum

MACROSIPHO'NIA . . . . Longtube
brachysi'phon . . . . . Arizona L.

MACROTO'MIA
echioi'des

MACROZA'MIA . . . . . Macrozamia
See **CYCAD GENERA.**

Macrozamia . . . . **Macrozamia**
Broadshaft M. . . . **M. platyrachis**
Coralfoot M. . . . . **M. corallipes**
Denison M. . . . . . . **M. denisoni**
Douglas M. . . . . . . **M. douglasi**
Fraser M. . . . . **M. fraseri**
Giant M. . . . . **M. hopei**
Miquel M. . . . . . . **M. miqueli**
Monsterseed M. . . **M. macdonnelli**
Moore M. . . . . **M. moorei**
Spiral M. . . . . **M. spiralis**
Woollycone M. . . **M. paulo-gulielmi**
Zigzag M. . . . . **M. flexuosa**

Madagascargrass
Neyraudia madagascariensis

Madagascar-jasmine . . . Stephanotis, Madagascar: **Stephanotis floribunda**

Madagascar-periwinkle **Lochnera rosea**

Madagascar-piassava . . Vonitrapalm, Piassava: **Vonitra thouarsiana**

Maddencherry . **Maddenia hypoleuca**

MADDE'NIA
hypoleu'ca . . . . . Maddencherry
hypoxan'tha

Madder . . . . **Rubia**
Common M. . . . . . . **R. tinctorum**
India M. . . . . **R. cordifolia**
Levant M. . . . . . . **R. peregrina**

Madeiravine . . . . . **Boussingaultia**
Mignonette M. . . . . . **B. ramosa**

Madflower . . . . **Antholyza**
Ethiopian M. . . . . . **A. aethiopica**
Panicled M. . . . . . **A. paniculata**

MADHU'CA (*BASSIA* Koen. *ex* L. (1771); *ILLIPE*)
butyra'cea (*Bassia b.*)
in'dica (*latifolia; Bassia l.; Illipe l.*) Illipe Buttertree
longifo'lia (*Bassia l.*) . . Mowra B.

MA'DIA ⌊w . . . . Tarweed
dissitiflo'ra
el'egans (*corymbosa*)
glomera'ta ⌊w . . . . . . Cluster T.
sati'va ⌊w . . . . Chilean T.

Madrone . . . . **Arbutus**
Arizona M. . . . . . . **A. arizonica**
Canary M. . . . . . . **A. canariensis**
Mexican M. . . . . . **A. xalapensis**
Pacific M. . . . . . . **A. menziesi**
Strawberry M. . . . . . **A. unedo**
Texas M. . . . . **A. texana**

MAE'SA
chis'ia
in'dica

MAESO'PIS
e'mini

MA'GA . . . . **MONTEZUMA**

MAGNO'LIA ⌊w . . . . . . Magnolia
acumina'ta . . . Cucumbertree M.
—ludovicia'na . . . Louisiana C.M.
ash'ei . . . . Ashe M.
biond'i
camp'belli . . . . . . Campbell M.
co'co (*pumila*)
compres'sa . . . . **Michelia c.**
corda'ta (*M. acuminata c.*) Yellow Cucumbertree M.
dawsonia'na . . . . . . Dawson M.
delavay'i . . . . Delavay M.
denuda'ta (*conspicua; yulan*) Yulan M.
—purpuras'cens

The plant now in cultivation under this name is M. sprengeri.

dis'color . . . . **M. liliflora**
fra'seri . . . . Fraser M.
fusca'ta . . . . **Michelia f.**
glau'ca . . . . **M. virginiana**
globo'sa
grac'ilis . . . . **M. liliflora g.**
grandiflo'ra (*foetida*) ⌊w Southern M.
¢Exmouth. hv.
¢Gallisson (*gallissoniensis*)
¢Glorious (*gloriosa*)
¢Goliath
¢Narrowleaf (*lanceolata*)
¢Roundleaf (*rotundifolia*)
hallea'na . . . . **M. stellata**
hypoleu'ca . . . . **M. obovata**
ko'bus . . . . Kobus M.
—borea'lis
liliflo'ra (*discolor; purpurea*) . Lily M.
—grac'ilis (*M. gracilis*)
¢Purple (*nigra*) hv. M. liliflora
∞ **loeb'neri** (*kobus* × *stellata*) ∞ Loebner M.

The cultivated plant is presumably a clon of this cross.

macrophyl'la . . . . . . Bigleaf M.
nicholsia'na Hort., *not* Rehd. & Wils. **M. sinensis**
nicholsia'na Rehd. & Wils. **M. wilsoni taliensis**
nit'ida . . . . Shinyleaf M.
obova'ta (*hypoleuca*) Whiteleaf Japanese M.

This name has been misapplied to M. liliflora.

officina'lis
parviflo'ra . . . . . . **M. sieboldi**
∞ **proctoria'na** (*salicifolia* × *stellata*) ∞ Proctor M.

The cultivated plant is presumably a clon of this cross.

MAGNOLIA, continued
pu'mila . . . . **M. coco**
purpu'rea . . . . **M. liliflora**
pyramida'ta . . . PYRAMID MAGNOLIA
rostra'ta
salicifo'lia . . . . ANISE M.
sargentia'na . . . . SARGENT M.
sie'boldi (*parviflora*) . . . OYAMA M.
sinen'sis (*nicholsiana* Hort., *not* Rehd. & Wils.) . . . . CHINESE M.
∞ **soulangea'na** (*denudata* × *liliflora*) ∞ SAUCER M.
₵ALEXANDER (*alexandrina*) HV.
₵BROZZONI
₵CANDOLLEANA
₵LENNE (*lennei*)
₵NORBERT (*norbertiana*)
₵PURPLE (*rustica*)
₵SHOWY (*spectabilis*)
₵STRIPED (*speciosa*)
₵WHITE (*alba superba*)
spreng'eri . . . . . . SPRENGER M.
—**elonga'ta**
stella'ta (*halleana*) . . . . STAR M.
₵PINK (*rosea*) HV.
talien'sis . . . . **M. wilsoni t.**
∞ **thompsonia'na** (*tripetala* × *virginiana*) ∞ THOMPSON M.
The cultivated plant is presumably a clon of this cross.
tripet'ala . . . . UMBRELLA M.
∞ **veitch'i** (*campbelli* × *denudata*) ∞ VEITCH M.
The cultivated plant is presumably a clon of this cross.
virginia'na (*glauca*) |w . SWEETBAY M.
—**austra'lis** . . . . SOUTHERN S.M.
×**wat'soni** (*obovata* × *sieboldi*) WATSON M.
wil'soni . . . . WILSON M.
—**talien'sis** (*M. nicholsiana* Rehd. & Wils., *not* Hort.; *M. taliensis*) TALIEN W.M.
yulan' . . . . **M. denudata**

MAGNOLIA . . . . **Magnolia**
ANISE M. . . . . . . **M. salicifolia**
ASHE M. . . . . **M. ashei**
BIGLEAF M. . . . . **M. macrophylla**
CAMPBELL M. . . . . . **M. campbelli**
CHINESE M. . . . . . . **M. sinensis**
CUCUMBERTREE M. . . **M. acuminata**
DAWSON M. . . . . **M. dawsoniana**
DELAVAY M. . . . . . . **M. delavayi**
FRASER M. . . . . **M. fraseri**
KOBUS M. . . . . **M. kobus**
LILY M. . . . . **M. liliflora**
∞ LOEBNER M. . . . . . ∞ **M. loebneri**
LOUISIANA CUCUMBERTREE M. **M. acuminata ludoviciana**
OYAMA M. . . . . **M. sieboldi**
∞ PROCTOR M. . . . . ∞ **M. proctoriana**
PYRAMID M. . . . . **M. pyramidata**
SARGENT M. . . . . **M. sargentiana**
∞ SAUCER M. . . . ∞ **M. soulangeana**
SHINYLEAF M. . . . . . . **M. nitida**
SOUTHERN M. . . . . . **M. grandiflora**
SOUTHERN SWEETBAY M. **M. virginiana australis**
SPRENGER M. . . . . . **M. sprengeri**
STAR M. . . . . **M. stellata**
SWEETBAY M. . . . . . **M. virginiana**
TALIEN WILSON M. **M. wilsoni taliensis**
∞ THOMPSON M. . ∞ **M. thompsoniana**
UMBRELLA M. . . . . . **M. tripetala**
∞ VEITCH M. . . . . . . ∞ **M. veitchi**
WATSON M. . . . . . ×**M. watsoni**

MAGNOLIA, continued
WHITELEAF JAPANESE M. **Magnolia obovata**
WILSON M. . . . . . . **M. wilsoni**
YELLOW CUCUMBERTREE M. **M. cordata**
YULAN M. . . . . **M. denudata**

MAGNOLIAVINE . . . . . . **Schisandra**
ANGLETWIG M. . . . . . **S. propinqua**
BIGBLOOM M. . . . . **S. grandiflora**
BLACK M. . . . . **S. nigra**
CAROLINA M. . . . . . **S. coccinea**
CHINESE M. . . . . . . **S. chinensis**
FUZZY M. . . . . . . **S. pubescens**
LITTLELEAF BIGBLOOM M. **S. grandiflora cathayensis**
ORANGE M. . . . . **S. sphenanthera**
RED BIGBLOOM M. **S. grandiflora rubriflora**
UNDERBLUE M. . . . . . . **S. henryi**
WHIPLASH ORANGE M. **S. sphenanthera lancifolia**
YELLOW ANGLETWIG M. **S. propinqua sinensis**

MAHAPENGIRI . **Cymbopogon winterianus**

MAHER'NIA
verticilla'ta (*odorata*)

×**MAHOBER'BERIS**
Strictly speaking, this hybrid name might be applied to any hybrid between the genera Berberis and Mahonia, but in practice it is applicable only to the single polybrid species below.
∞ **neuber'ti** (*Berberis vulgaris* × *Mahonia aquifolium; B. ilicifolia* Hort., *not* Forst.; ∞ *B. neuberti; M. n. ilicifolia*)
—**latifo'lia**

MAHOGANY . . . . **Swietenia**
HONDURAS M. . . . . **S. macrophylla**
MEXICAN M. . . . . . . **S. humilis**
VENEZUELA M. . . . . **S. candollei**
WESTINDIES M. . . . . **S. mahagoni**

MAHO'NIA (*BERBERIS* in part; *ODOSTEMON*) |w . . . MAHONIA
This group is included in Berberis by some botanists. Mahonia is conserved under International Rules. The thanks of the Editorial Committee are extended to S. B. Fracker and L. M. Ames for review of this Mahonia list and for their valuable suggestions.
aquifo'lium (*Berberis a.; Odostemon a.*) |w . . . . OREGONGRAPE
—**grac'ilis** . . . . SLIM O.
—**juglandifo'lia** . . . . . . PURPLE O.
DARKPURPLE (*atropurpureum*) HV.
M. aquifolium
MOSER (*moseri*)
ROUNDLEAF (*rotundifolia*)
VICAR (*vicari*)
beal'ei (*japonica* Hort., *not* DC.; *Berberis b.*) . . . . . LEATHERLEAF M.
See note under M. japonica.
chocho'co (*Berberis c.; Odostemon c.*) CHOCHOCO M.
dictyo'ta (*Berberis californica; B. dictyota; Odostemon dictyotus*) NETVEIN M.
fascicula'ris . . . . **M. pinnata**
fortun'ei (*Berberis f.; Odostemon f.*) CHINESE M.
fre'monti (*Berberis f.; Odostemon f.*) |w FREMONT M.
grac'ilis (*Berberis g.; Odostemon g.*)
haematocar'pa (*Berberis h.; Odostemon haematocarpus*) |w . . . . . RED M.

MAHONIA, continued
hartweg'i (*Berberis h.; Odostemon h.*) HARTWEG MAHONIA
∞ **heterophyl'la** (*aquifolium* × *fortunei; toluacensis; Berberis h.* Zabel, *not* Juss.) . . . . . ∞ HOLLYGRAPE M.
japon'ica . . . . . . JAPANESE M.
The plant ordinarily grown under this name is M. bealei. The true M. japonica is rarely cultivated in North America.
napaulen'sis (*Berberis nepalensis; Odostemon n.*) . . . . NEPAL M.
nervo'sa (*Berberis n.; Odostemon nervosus*) . . . . CASCADES M.
nev'ini (*Berberis n.; Odostemon n.*) NEVIN M.
pinna'ta (*fascicularis; Berberis p.; B. fascicularis; Odostemon pinnatus*) CLUSTER M.
—*wag'neri* . . . . . . ∞ **M. wagneri**
piperia'na (*Berberis p.*) . . PIPER M.
Perhaps not more than a var. of M. aquifolium.
pu'mila (*Berberis p.; Odostemon pumilus*) . . . . PYGMY M.
re'pens (*Berberis r.; Odostemon r.*) |w CREEPING M.
M. sonnei (*Berberis s.*), Truckee M., seems doubtfully separable from M. repens.
—**macrocar'pa** . . . BIGBERRY C.M.
—**rotundifo'lia** . . ROUNDLEAF C.M.
—**subcorda'ta** . . . . LAPLEAF C.M.
swa'seyi (*Berberis s.; Odostemon s.*) TEXAS M.
toluacen'sis . . . . **M. heterophylla**
trifoliola'ta (*Berberis t.; Odostemon trifoliolatus*) . . LAREDO M. (*Algerita*)
∞ **wag'neri** (*aquifolium* × *pinnata; M. pinnata w.*) . . . . ∞ WAGNER M.
wilcox'i (*Berberis w.; Odostemon w.*) WILCOX M.
zimapa'na (*Odostemon zimapanus*) ZIMAPAN M.

MAHONIA . . . . **Mahonia**
BIGBERRY CREEPING M. **M. repens macrocarpa**
CASCADES M. . . . . . . **M. nervosa**
CHINESE M. . . . . . . **M. fortunei**
CHOCHOCO M. . . . . **M. chochoco**
CLUSTER M. . . . . . . **M. pinnata**
CREEPING M. . . . . . . **M. repens**
FREMONT M. . . . . . . **M. fremonti**
HARTWEG M. . . . . . **M. hartwegi**
∞ HOLLYGRAPE M. . ∞ **M. heterophylla**
JAPANESE M. . . . . . . **M. japonica**
LAPLEAF CREEPING M. **M. repens subcordata**
LAREDO M. . . . . . **M. trifoliolata**
LEATHERLEAF M. . . . . . **M. bealei**
NEPAL M. . . . . . **M. napaulensis**
NETVEIN M. . . . . . . **M. dictyota**
NEVIN M. . . . . **M. nevini**
OREGONGRAPE . . . . **M. aquifolium**
PIPER M. . . . . . . **M. piperiana**
PURPLE OREGONGRAPE **M. aquifolium juglandifolia**
PYGMY M. . . . . **M. pumila**
RED M. . . . . . . **M. haematocarpa**
ROUNDLEAF CREEPING M. **M. repens rotundifolia**
SLIM OREGONGRAPE **M. aquifolium gracilis**
TEXAS M. . . . . **M. swaseyi**
∞ WAGNER M. . . . . . ∞ **M. wagneri**
WILCOX M. . . . . **M. wilcoxi**
ZIMAPAN M. . . . . . **M. zimapana**

MAIAN'THEMUM (*UNIFOLIUM*) |w BEADRUBY
bifo'lium (*Smilacina bifolia; Unifolium bifolium*) . . . . . . TWOLEAF B.
canaden'se |w . . . . . CANADA B.
dilata'tum

MAIDENBUSH . . . . **Savia**
BAHAMA M. . . . . . **S. bahamensis**
MISSOURI M. . . **S. phyllanthoides**

MAIDENCANE . . . **Panicum hemitomon**

MAIDENGRASS
Miscanthus sinensis gracillimus

MAIDENHAIR . . . . **Adiantum**
AMERICAN M. . . . . . . **A. pedatum**
AUSTRALIAN M. . . . . **A. formosum**
BARBADOS M. . . . . **A. tenerum** HV.
BAUSE M. . . . . . **A. tenerum** HV.
BERMUDA M. . . . . **A. bellum**
BRITTLE M. . . . . . **A. concinnum**
CALIFORNIA M. . . . . . . **A. jordani**
CHILEAN M. . . . . **A. excisum**
CROWE M. . . . . . . **A. cuneatum** HV.
DELTA M. . . . . **A. cuneatum**
DIAMOND M. . . . . **A. trapeziforme**
FAN M. . . . . **A. tenerum**
FILMY M. . . . . . . **A. diaphanum**
FRAGRANT M. . . . **A. cuneatum** HV.
GIANT M. . . . . . **A. polyphyllum**
LATHOM M. . . . . **A. tenerum** HV.
MIST M. . . . . . **A. cuneatum** HV.
MOORE M. . . . . **A. moorei**
NEWZEALAND M. . . . . . **A. affine**
PERUVIAN M. . . . . . . **A. wagneri**
ROSY M. . . . . . . **A. tenerum** HV.
ROUGH M. . . . . . . **A. hispidulum**
SOUTHERN M. . . **A. capillus-veneris**
ST. CATHARINE M.
A. trapeziforme HV.
TASSEL M. . . . . . **A. cuneatum** HV.
TRAILING M. . . . . . . **A. caudatum**
TWINLEAF M. . . . **A. macrophyllum**
WALKING M. . . . . **A. philippense**
WILLIAMS M. . . . . . **A. williamsi**

MAIHUE'NIA . . . . . . MAIHUENIA
See **CACTUS GENERA.**

Maikoa . . . . DATURA, FLORIPONDIO: **Datura arborea**

Maira'nia alpi'na . . . **Arctous alpinus**

MAIZE . . . . **Zea mays**
STRIPED M. . . . . . . **Z. m. japonica**

MAJORA'NA . . . . MARJORAM
horten'sis (*Origanum majorana*) SWEET M.
oni'tes (*Origanum o.*) . . . . POT M.

MALABARGOURD . . **Cucurbita ficifolia**

MALABARNUT . . . . **Adhatoda vasica**

MALA'CHE . . . . . . **PAVONIA**

MALA'CHRA
radia'ta

MALACOCAR'PUS
See **CACTUS GENERA.**

MALACOTHAM'NUS **MALVASTRUM**

MALACO'THRIX
califor'nica
glabra'ta (*M. californica g.*)
saxat'ilis
—tenuifo'lia (*M. tenuifolia*)

MALANGA . . . . **Xanthosoma**
BATAVIAN M. . . . *X. bataviense* Hort.
DARKLEAF M. . . . . . **X. atrovirens**
LINDENS M. . . . . **X. lindeni**
MARSHALL M. . . . *X. marshalli* Hort.
PRIMROSE M. . . . . **X. violaceum**
SPOTTED M. . . . . . **X. maculatum**
YAUTIA M. . . . . **X. sagittaefolium**

MALAX'IS (*MICROSTYLIS*)
ADDERMOUTH ORCHID
See **ORCHID GENERA, HARDY TERRESTRIAL GROUP.**

Malayapple. OHIA: **Syzygium malaccense**

MALCO'MIA
flexuo'sa
litto'rea
—gof'fardi
marit'ima

MALEFERN . . . . **Dryopteris filixmas**

MALEPH'ORA
MESEMBRYANTHEMUM
See **SUCCULENTS.**

Maljoe . . . . HORSEBEAN, JACK: **Canavalia ensiformis**

MALLO'TUS
a'pelta
philippinen'sis . . . . KAMALATREE
ricinoi'des
tenuifo'lius

MALLOW . . . . **Malva**
CLUSTER M. . . . . . **M. verticillata**
CURLY M. . . . . **M. crispa**
HIGH M. . . . . **M. sylvestris**
HOLLYHOCK M. . . . . **M. alcea**
LITTLE M. . . . . . . **M. parviflora**
MUSK M. . . . . . . **M. moschata**
RUNNING M. . . . . **M. rotundifolia**

MALO'PE . . . . MALOPE
tri'fida
BIGFLOWER (*grandiflora*) HV.
PURPLE (*purpurea*)
ROSY (*rosea*)
WHITE (*alba*)

MALOR'TIEA . . . **REINHARDTIA**
See **PALM GENERA.**

Malos'ma lauri'na . . . . . . **Rhus l.**

MALOUET'IA
nit'ida

MALPIGH'IA . . . . . . MALPIGHIA
biflo'ra
coccig'era . . . . HOLLY M.
gla'bra . . . . . BARBADOSCHERRY M. (*Barbadoscherry*)
punicifo'lia

MA'LUS |w . . . . APPLE; CRABAPPLE

Some botanists include Apples in the Pear genus (Pyrus). It is of interest in this connection that no natural or artificial hybrid between Apple and Pear appears to be recorded.

For hort. var. of Apple and Crabapple (*Crab*) cultivated for their fruit, see **FRUIT AND EDIBLE NUT NAMES.**

∞**adstrin'gens** (*baccata* × *pumila*)
angustifo'lia (*Pyrus a.*) |w SOUTHERN C.
₵DOUBLEROSY (*rosea plena*) HV.
₵PENDULOUS (*pendula*)
∞**arnoldia'na** (*baccata* × *floribunda*; ∞*Pyrus floribunda a.*) . ∞ARNOLD C.
∞**astracan'ica** (*prunifolia* × *pumila*)
∞**atrosanguin'ea** (*halliana* × *sieboldi*; *Pyrus a.*)
₵CARMINE. HV.

MALUS, continued
bacca'ta (*Pyrus b.*)
SIBERIAN CRABAPPLE
—grac'ilis
—himala'ica
—jack'i . . . . JACK C.
—mandshur'ica (*M. cerasifera; M. mandshurica* Hort.) MANCHURIAN C.
₵DARTMOUTH. HV. M. baccata
bractea'ta (*Pyrus b.*) . BUNCOMBE C.
brev'ipes
corona'ria (*Pyrus c.*) |w WILD SWEET C.
—elonga'ta . . . . . . REHDER S.C.
₵CHARLOTTE (*plena*) HV. M. coronaria
₵NIEUWLAND (*nieuwlandiana*)
∞**dawsonia'na** (*fusca* × *pumila*; ∞*Pyrus d.*) . . . . ∞DAWSON C.
florenti'na (*crataegifolia; Pyrus f.*)
FLORENTINE C.
floribun'da (*Pyrus f.* Kirchn., *not* Lindl.; *P. pulcherrima*)
JAPANESE FLOWERING C.
₵KELSEY. HV.
formosa'na (*Pyrus f.*) . . FORMOSA C.
fus'ca (*rivularis; Pyrus diversifolia; P. fusca; P. rivularis*) |w . OREGON C.
glabra'ta (*Pyrus g.*) . . BILTMORE C.
glauces'cens (*Pyrus g.*) . DUNBAR C.
hallia'na (*Pyrus h.*) . . . . HALLS C.
₵PARKMAN (*parkmani*) HV.
∞**hart'wigi** (*baccata* × *halliana*)
∞HARTWIG C.
∞**heterophyl'la** (*coronaria* × *pumila*)
₵MATTHEWS. HV.
honanen'sis . . . . HONAN C.
hupehen'sis (*theifera; Pyrus t.*)
₵ROSE (*rosea*) HV.
ioen'sis (*Pyrus i.*) . . . PRAIRIE C.
—bush'i . . . . MISSOURI C.
—creniserra'ta . . . . LOUISIANA C.
—pal'meri . . . . PALMER C.
—texa'na . . . . TEXAS C.
₵BECHTEL (*plena*) HV. M. ioensis
₵FRINGEPETAL (*fimbriata*)
kansuen'sis (*Pyrus k.*) . . KANSU C.
lancifo'lia (*Pyrus l.*) . LANCELEAF C.
∞**magdeburgen'sis** (*pumila* × *spectabilis*)
∞MAGDEBURG C.
mandshur'ica Hort. . . **M. baccata m.**
∞**microma'lus** (*?baccata* × *spectabilis*; ∞*Pyrus m.*) . . . . ∞MIDGET C.
platycar'pa (*Pyrus p.*) . . BIGFRUIT C.
pratt'i (*Pyrus p.*) . . . . PRATTS C.
prunifo'lia (*Pyrus p.*) . . PEARLEAF C.
—rink'i (*M. ringo; Pyrus p. rinki*)
CHINESE P.C.
₵COLUMN (*fastigiata*) HV. M. prunifolia
₵PENDENT (*pendula*)
pu'mila (*sylvestris* Hort., *not* Mill.; *Pyrus malus*) |w . . COMMON APPLE

Professor Rehder reports that Malus pumila "is the parent of most of our cultivated Apples, though some probably are the offspring of hybrids with M. sylvestris, M. prunifolia, and also M. baccata."

₵DOUBLEPINK (*translucens*) HV.
₵ELISE RATHKE
₵NIEDZWETSKYANA
₵WEEPING (*pendula*)
∞**purpu'rea** (∞*atrosanguinea* × *pumila*)
∞PURPLE C.
₵ALDENHAM (*aldenhamensis*) HV.
₵ELEY (*eleyi*)
₵LEMOINE (*lemoinei*)
₵WEEPING (*pendula*)

MALUS, continued
rivula'ris . . . . **M. fusca**
∞**robus'ta** (*baccata* × *prunifolia*) ∞CHERRY CRABAPPLE
₵COLUMN (*erecta*) HV.
₵PEACHLEAF (*persicifolia*)
sar'genti (*Pyrus s.*) . . . SARGENT C.
∞**scheideck'eri** (*floribunda* × *prunifolia*; ∞*Pyrus pulcherrima s.*) ∞SCHEIDECKER C.
sie'boldi (*toringo; Pyrus s.; P. toringo*) TORINGO C.
—**arbores'cens**
sikkimen'sis . . . . SIKKIM C.
∞**sou'lardi** (*ioensis* × *pumila;* ∞*Pyrus s.*) . . . . ∞SOULARD C.
spectab'ilis (*Pyrus s.*) CHINESE FLOWERING C.
The so-called hort. var. rosea plena of the trade appears to be either typical M. spectabilis or ₵Rivers.
₵DOUBLEWHITE (*albiplena*) HV.
₵RIVERS (*riversi*)
∞**subloba'ta** (*prunifolia* × *sieboldi*) ∞YELLOW AUTUMN C.
sylves'tris
See note under M. pumila.
theif'era . . . . **M. hupehensis**
torin'go . . . . **M. sieboldi**
toringoi'des (*M. transitoria t.; Pyrus toringoides*) . . . . . CUTLEAF C.
transito'ria (*Pyrus t.*) . . TIBETAN C.
triloba'ta (*Pyrus t.*)
tschonosk'i (*Pyrus t.*)
yunnanen'sis (*Pyrus y.*) . YUNNAN C.
—**veitch'i**
∞**zu'mi** (*baccata mandshurica* × *sieboldi;* ∞*Pyrus z.*) . . . . . . ∞ZUMI C.
₵BOBWHITE. HV.
₵CALOCARPA

MAL'VA |w . . . . MALLOW
al'cea |w . . . . . . HOLLYHOCK M.
—**fastigia'ta**
borea'lis
capen'sis . . . **Malvastrum capense**
chinen'sis . . . . . . **M. verticillata**
cris'pa . . . . CURLY M.
minia'ta . . . **Sphaeralcea cisplatina**
moscha'ta . . . . MUSK M.
WHITE (*alba*) HV.
neglec'ta |w
parviflo'ra . . . . LITTLE M.
peda'ta . . . . . **Callirhoe leiocarpa**
rotundifo'lia |w . . . . RUNNING M.
sylves'tris . . . . HIGH M.
—**mauritia'na** (*M. mauritiana*)
verticilla'ta (*chinensis; pulchella*) |w CLUSTER M.

MALVAS'TRUM (*EREMALCHE; MALACOTHAMNUS*) . FALSEMALLOW
ab'botti . . . . SALINAS F.
aborig'inum . . . . INDIAN F.
arcua'tum (*Malacothamnus arcuatus; Sphaeralcea arcuata*)
campanula'tum
capen'se (*Malva capensis*)
clementi'num . . . SANCLEMENTE F.
coccin'eum . . . **Sphaeralcea coccinea**
davidso'ni (*Malacothamnus d.; Sphaeralcea d.*) . . . . SAND F.
densiflo'rum (*Malacothamnus densiflorus; Sphaeralcea densiflora*)
ex'ile (*Eremalche exilis*)
fascicula'tum (*thurberi; Malacothamnus fasciculatus; Sphaeralcea fasciculata*) MESA F.

MALVASTRUM, continued
fascicula'tum laxiflo'rum
fre'monti . FREMONT FALSEMALLOW
grac'ile . . . . SLENDER F.
grossulariaefo'lium **Sphaeralcea grossulariaefolia**
hypomada'rum
jones'i . . . . JONES F.
lateri'tum
leptophyl'lum . **Sphaeralcea leptophylla**
marrubioi'des . . . . . SOUTHERN F.
munroa'num. . **Sphaeralcea munroana**
nesiot'icum . . . . . SANTACRUZ F.
nutt'alli . . . . NUTTALL F.
orbicula'tum
pal'meri (*Malacothamnus p.; Sphaeralcea p.*) . . . . PALMER F.
par'ryi (*Eremalche p.*)
rotundifo'lium (*Eremalche rotundifolia*)
thur'beri . . . . . . **M. fasciculatum**
tricuspida'tum

MALVAVIS'CUS (*ACHANIA*) WAXMALLOW
arbo'reus (*Achania arborea*) SOUTHAMERICAN W.
can'didus
conzat'ti
drum'mondi . . . . DRUMMOND W.
grandiflo'rus
mol'lis

MAMEY . . . **Mammea; M. americana**

MAMILLOP'SIS . **MAMMILLARIA**
See **CACTUS GENERA.**

MAM'MEA . . . . MAMEY
america'na . MAMEY (*Mammeeapple*)

MAMMILLA'RIA (*Bartschella; Cactus* in part; *Dolichothele; Mamillopsis; Neomammillaria; Pelecyphora; Phellosperma; Porfiria; Solisia*) MAMMILLARIA
See **CACTUS GENERA.**

MAMMILLARIA . . . . . **Mammillaria**
BAXTER M. . . . . . **M. baxteriana**
BLOOD M. . . . . **M. carnea**
BLOSSFELD M. . . . **M. blossfeldiana**
BOCASA M. . . . . . . **M. bocasana**
BOEDEKER M. . . **M. boedekeriana**
BOGOTA M. . . . . . **M. bogotensis**
BULLARD M. . . . . . **M. bullardiana**
DENSESPINE M. . . . **M. densispina**
DESERT M. . . . . **M. arida**
EVERMANN M. . . **M. evermanniana**
FEATHERBALL M. . . . . **M. plumosa**
FERTILE M. . . . . **M. fertilis**
FISHHOOK M. . . . . **M. microcarpa**
FLATTENED M. . . . . **M. applanata**
GOLDEN M. . . . . . . **M. xanthina**
GOLDENSTAR M. **M. elongata stella-aurata**
GRANNY M. . . . . . . **M. hahniana**
GREATSPREAD M. . . . . **M. gigantea**
GREENFLOWER M. . . **M. viridiflora**
GUM M. . . . . **M. gummifera**
HAAGE M. . . . . **M. haageana**
HATCHET M. . . . . **M. asselliformis**
HERRERA M. . . . . . . **M. herrerae**
HEYDER M. . . . . **M. heyderi**
HUTCHISON M. . . **M. hutchisoniana**
JOHNSTON M. . . . . . **M. johnstoni**
KARWINSKY M. . . **M. karwinskiana**
KEW M. . . . . **M. kewensis**
KLISSING C. . . . . **M. klissingiana**
KUNZE C. . . . . **M. kunzeana**
LACE M. . . . . **M. elongata**
LLOYD M. . . . . **M. lloydi**

MAMMILLARIA, continued
MACDOUGAL M. **Mammillaria macdougali**
MARSHALL M. . . . **M. marshalliana**
MAZATLAN M. . . . **M. mazatlanensis**
MENDEL M. . . . . . **M. mendeliana**
MESA M. . . . . **M. collinsi**
MOELLER M. . . . . **M. moelleriana**
NIPPLE M. . . . . **M. sphaerica**
OLIVIA M. . . . . **M. oliviae**
ORCUTT M. . . . . **M. orcutti**
PACIFIC M. . . . . **M. pacifica**
PAINTERS M. . . . . **M. painteri**
PALE M. . . . . **M. albicans**
PALMER M. . . . . **M. palmeri**
PARKINSON M. . . . . **M. parkinsoni**
PETTERSSON M. . . . **M. petterssoni**
PIEBALD M. . . . . **M. discolor**
POWDERPUFF M. **M. bocasana inermis**
PRINGLE M. . . . . **M. pringlei**
PYGMY M. . . . . **M. pygmaea**
RITTER M. . . . . . . **M. ritteriana**
RUNYON M. . . . . **M. runyoni**
SCHUMANN M. . . . . **M. schumanni**
SHELDON M. . . . . . . **M. sheldoni**
SLEVIN M. . . . . **M. slevini**
SNOWY M. . . . . **M. nivosa**
STANDLEY M. . . . . . **M. standleyi**
SWINGLE M. . . . . **M. swinglei**
THIMBLE M. . . . . **M. fragilis**
VIERECK M. . . . . . . **M. viereckі**
VIPER M. . . . . **M. viperina**
WALTHER M. . . . . . . **M. waltheri**
WHITEHAIR M. . . . . . . **M. candida**
WHITEWASH M. . . . . . **M. dealbata**
WILCOX M. . . . . **M. wilcoxi**
WILDS M. . . . . **M. wildi**
WINTERS M. . . . . . . **M. winteriae**
WRIGHTS M. . . . . **M. wrighti**
ZAHN M. . . . . **M. zahniana**
ZEILMANN M. . . . **M. zeilmanniana**
ZEYER M. . . . . **M. zeyeriana**
ZUCCARINI M. . . . **M. zuccariniana**

MAMONCILLO . . . . . **Melicocca bijuga**

MANATEEGRASS . . . . **Cymodocea**
GULF M. . . . . **C. manatorum**

MANBARKLAK . **Eschweilera corrugata**

MANCHINEEL . **Hippomane mancinella**

MANDEVIL'LA
suave'olens . . . . . CHILEJASMINE

MANDRAG'ORA . . . . MANDRAKE
autumna'lis . . . . . . AUTUMN M.
officina'rum

MANDRAKE . . . . **Mandragora**
AUTUMN M. . . . . . **M. autumnalis**

MANET'TIA . . . . MANETTIA
bi'color
gla'bra (*cordifolia*)
infla'ta

MANFRE'DA
brachysta'chys (*Agave b.*)
maculo'sa (*Agave m.*)
variega'ta (*Agave v.*)
virgin'ica (*Agave v.*)
₵GIANT (*gigantea*) HV.

MANGIF'ERA . . . . MANGO
altis'sima . . . . PAHUTAN M.
cae'sia . . . . BINJAI M.
foet'ida BACHANG M. (*Ambatjang M.*)
in'dica . . . . COMMON M.
lauri'na . MONJET M. (*Manga Monjet; Manga Pari*)
odora'ta . KUWINI M. (*Bumbum M.*)
sylvat'ica . . . . NEPAL M.

MANGIFERA, continued
verticilla'ta . . . . . Bauno Mango
zeylan'ica . . . . Ceylon M.

Mango . . . . **Mangifera**
Ambatjang M. . . . . . . Bachang M.
Bachang M. . . . . **M. foetida**
Bauno M. . . . . . . **M. verticillata**
Binjai M. . . . . **M. caesia**
Bumbum M. . . . . . . Kuwini M.
Ceylon M. . . . . . . **M. zeylanica**
Common M. . . . . **M. indica**
Kuwini M. . . . . **M. odorata**
Manga Monjet; Manga Pari Monjet M.
Monjet M. . . . . . . **M. laurina**
Nepal M. . . . . **M. sylvatica**
Pahutan M. . . . . . . **M. altissima**

Mangosteen . . **Garcinia mangostana**

Mangrove . . . . **Rhizophora**
American M. . . . . . **R. mangle**

MANICA'RIA (*TIMLIS*). Sleevepalm
See **PALM GENERA.**

MAN'IHOT
ai'pi . . . . Aipi Cassava
carthaginen'sis
dichot'oma
dul'cis
esculen'ta (*utilissima; Jatropha manihot*) . . . . Common C.
glazio'vi . . . . Ceararubberplant

Manilagrass . . . . **Zoysia matrella**

MANILKA'RA . . . . Balata

This genus, united by some botanists with Mimusops, is considered distinct by most recent authors. If united, Mimusops L. (1753) has priority over Manilkara Adans. (1763).

bidenta'ta (*Mimusops balata; M. bidentata globosa*) . . . . Common B.
darienen'sis (*Mimusops d.*). Panama B.
kau'ki (*Mimusops k.*) . . . . Pekola
parvifo'lia (*Mimusops p.*)
roxburghia'na (*Mimusops r.*) Roxburgh B.

MANISU'RIS . . . . Jointtail
See **GRASS GENERA.**

Mankettinut . . . . . **Ricinodendron**
Musodo M. . . . . . **R. africanum**

Mannagrass . . . . **Glyceria**
American M. . . . . . **G. grandis**
Arkansas M. . . . . **G. arkansana**
Atlantic M. . . . . . . **G. obtusa**
Canada M. . . . . Rattlesnake M.
Clubhead M. . . . . . . Atlantic M.
Creeping M. . . . . **G. acutiflora**
Eastern M. . . . **G. septentrionalis**
Fernald M. . . . . **G. fernaldi**
Fewflower M. . . . . Weak M.
Fowl M. . . . . **G. striata**
Melic M. . . . . . . **G. melicaria**
Northern M. . . . . . **G. borealis**
Northwestern M. . **G. occidentalis**
Pale M. . . . . **G. pallida**
Rattlesnake M. . . **G. canadensis**
Slimhead M. . . . **G. leptostachya**
SmokyMountains M. . . **G. nubigena**
Spike M. . . . . **G. erecta**
Tall M. . . . . **G. elata**
Tall Rattlesnake M. **G. canadensis laxa**
Washington M. . . . . . . **G. otisi**
Water M. . . . . **G. fluitans**
Weak M. . . . . . . **G. pauciflora**

Mannagum . . . Eucalyptus, Manna: **Eucalyptus mannifera**

MANSO'NIA
altis'sima

MANTIS'IA
saltato'ria . . . . . . Dancinggirls

MANULE'A
viola'cea

Manyseed . . . . **Polycarpon**
Fourleaf M. . . . **P. tetraphyllum**

Manzanita . . . . . **Arctostaphylos**
Bearberry . . . . . . **A. uva-ursi**
Bigberry M. . . . . **A. glauca**
Brittleleaf M. . . . . **A. crustacea**
Common M. . . . . . **A. manzanita**
Delnorte M. . . . . . . **A. cinerea**
Dune M. . . . . **A. pumila**
Eastwood M. . . . . . **A. glandulosa**
Eldorado M. . . . . . **A. nissenana**
Fire M. . . . . **A. nummularia**
Greenleaf M. . . . . **A. patula**
Hairy M. . . . . . . **A. columbiana**
Heartleaf M. . . . . . **A. andersoni**
Hoary M. . . . . **A. canescens**
Hooker M. . . . . **A. hookeri**
Howell M. . . . . . . **A. hispidula**
Indian M. . . . . **A. mewukka**
Ione M. . . . . **A. myrtifolia**
Island M. . . . . **A. insularis**
Konocti M. . . . . **A. elegans**
Littleberry M. . . . . **A. sensitiva**
Lompoc M. . . . . . . **A. viridissima**
Mariposa M. . . . . . . **A. mariposa**
Mission M. . . . . **A. bicolor**
Monterey M. . . . . . **A. bracteosa**
Morro M. . . . . . . **A. morroensis**
Otay M. . . . . **A. otayensis**
Pajaro M. . . . . . . **A. pajaroensis**
Parry M. . . . . **A. parryana**
PechoMountain M. . . **A. pechoensis**
Pine M. . . . **A. parryana pinetorum**
Pinemat M. . . . . . **A. nevadensis**
Pointleaf M. . . . . . . **A. pungens**
Pringle M. . . . . **A. pringlei**
SantaRosaIsland M. **A. confertiflora**
Serpentine M. . . . **A. obispoensis**
Shagbark M. . . . . **A. rudis**
Silverleaf M. . . . . . **A. silvicola**
Sonoma M. . . . . . . **A. densiflora**
Stanford M. . . . . **A. stanfordiana**
Stripeberry M. . . . . . **A. pilosula**
Toothed M. . . . . . **A. diversifolia**
Whiteleaf M. . . . . **A. viscida**
Woolly M. . . . . . . **A. tomentosa**

Maple . . . . **Acer**
Amur M. . . . . **A. ginnala**
Arizona Boxelder **A. negundo arizonicum**
Austrian Hedge M. **A. campestre austriacum**
Balkan M. . . . . **A. heldreichi**
Bigkey Planetree M. **A. pseudoplatanus euchlorum**
Bigleaf M. . . . . **A. macrophyllum**
Bigtooth M. . . **A. grandidentatum**
Black M. . . . . **A. nigrum**
∞ Bornmueller M. ∞ **A. bornmuelleri**
∞ Bosc M. . . . . ∞ **A. bosci**
Boxelder . . . . **A. negundo**
California Boxelder **A. n. californicum**
Campbell M. . . . . . . **A. campbelli**
Catalpa M. . . . . . **A. catalpifolium**
Chalk M. . . . . **A. leucoderme**
Chinese M. . . . . **A. sinense**

Maple, continued
Coliseum M. . . **Acer cappadocicum**
Cutleaf Mono M. **A. mono dissectum**
David M. . . . . **A. davidi**
Devil M. . . . . **A. diabolicum**
Douglas RockyMountain M. **A. glabrum douglasi**
Drummond Red M. **A. rubrum drummondi**
∞ Durett M. . . . . . . ∞ **A. duretti**
Farges M. . . . . **A. fargesi**
Florida M. . . . . . . **A. floridanum**
Forrests M. . . . . **A. forresti**
Franchet M. . . . . . . **A. francheti**
Fullmoon M. . . . . . **A. japonicum**
Golden Coliseum M. **A. cappadocicum aureum**
Grossers M. . . . . . . **A. grosseri**
Hairy Florida M. **A. floridanum villipes**
Hawthorn M. . . . **A. crataegifolium**
Hedge M. . . . . **A. campestre**
Henry M. . . . . **A. henryi**
Hooker M. . . . . **A. hookeri**
Hornbeam M. . . . **A. carpinifolium**
Inland Boxelder **A. negundo interius**
Japanese M. . . . . **A. palmatum**
Kimball Bigleaf M. **A. macrophyllum kimballae**
Littleleaf Siebold M. **A. sieboldianum microphyllum**
Lobel M. . . . . **A. lobeli**
Manchurian M. . . **A. mandshuricum**
Manchustripe M. . **A. tegmentosum**
Maximowicz M. . . **A. maximowiczi**
Mayrs M. . . . . **A. mayri**
Miyabe M. . . . . **A. miyabei**
Mono M. . . . . **A. mono**
Montpelier M. **A. monspessulanum**
Mountain M. . . . . . . **A. spicatum**
Nikko M. . . . . **A. nikoense**
Norway M. . . . . . . **A. platanoides**
Oliver M. . . . . . . **A. oliverianum**
Oriental M. . . . . . . **A. orientale**
Pagoda M. . . . . . . **A. micranthum**
Painted Mono M. **A. mono marmoratum**
Paleflower Red M. **A. rubrum pallidiflorum**
Palmer Black M. **A. nigrum palmeri**
Paperbark M. . . . . **A. griseum**
Persian Velvet M. **A. velutinum glabrescens**
Planetree M. . . . **A. pseudoplatanus**
Purple Balkan M. **A. heldreichi purpuratum**
Purplebloom M. **A. pseudo-sieboldianum**
Purpleblow M. . . . . **A. truncatum**
Redbud M. . . . . . . **A. trautvetteri**
Red Coliseum M. **A. cappadocicum rubrum**
Red Devil M. **A. diabolicum purpurascens**
Red M. . . . . **A. rubrum**
Redvein M. . . . . **A. rufinerve**
RockyMountain M. . . . **A. glabrum**
Rugel Sugar M. **A. saccharum rugeli**
Schneck S. M. . . . . . **A. s. schnecki**
Schwerin M. . . . . **A. schwerini**
Sevenlobe Japanese M. **A. palmatum heptalobum**
Siebold M. . . . . . **A. sieboldianum**
Sikkim M. . . . . **A. sikkimense**
Silver M. . . . . **A. saccharinum**
Smoothkey Hedge M. **A. campestre leiocarpum**

MAPLE, continued
SOUTHWESTERN BIGTOOTH M.
Acer grandidentatum brachypterum
STRIPED M. . . . A. pensylvanicum
SUGAR M. . . . . . . A. saccharum
Sycamore M. . . . . . PLANETREE M.
SYRIAN M. . . . . A. syriacum
TARON M. . . . . A. taronense
TATARIAN M. . . . . . . A. tataricum
TAURUS HEDGE M.
A. campestre tauricum
TEXAS BOXELDER A. negundo texanum
∞ THICKLEAF M. . . . ∞ A. coriaceum
THREEFLOWER M. . . . A. triflorum
THREELEAF ROCKYMOUNTAIN M.
A. glabrum tripartitum
TRICOLOR COLISEUM M.
A. cappadocicum tricolor
TRIDENT M. . . . . A. buergerianum
TRIDENT RED M. . A. rubrum trilobum
TSCHONOSKI M. . . . A. tschonoski
VANVOLXEM VELVET M.
A. velutinum vanvolxemi
VEITCH M. . . . . A. veitchi
VELVET M. . . . . . . A. velutinum
VINE M. . . . . A. circinatum
VIOLET BOXELDER A. negundo violaceum
WILD HEDGE M.
A. campestre hebecarpum
WILSON M. . . . . A. wilsoni
WOOLLY PLANETREE M.
A. pseudoplatanus tomentosum

MAPLEWORT . . . . Aceranthus
DOUBLELEAF M. . . . . A. diphyllus

MA'RAH . . . . . . **MEGARRHIZA**

MARANG . . . **Artocarpus odoratissimus**

MARAN'TA . . . . ARROWROOT
arundina'cea . . . . . . BERMUDA A.
—variega'ta
bi'color (*Calathea b.*)
clo'soni . . . . CLOSON A.
conspic'ua . . . . . **Calathea lietzei**
govenia'na . . . . SPOTTED A.
illus'tris . . . . **Calathea i.**
insig'nis . . . . **Calathea i.**
kegelia'na . . . **Calathea bachemiana**
leuconeu'ra . . . . BANDED A.
LIEGE (*massangeana*) HV.
REDSPOT (*kerchoveana*)
lin'deni . . . . **Calathea lindeniana**
lucia'na . . . . **Calathea l.**
makoya'na . . . . **Calathea m.**
oppenheimia'na . . . . . **Ctenanthe o.**
pulchel'la . . . . **Calathea p.**
roseo-pic'ta . . . . **Calathea r.**
sanderia'na . . . . **Calathea s.**
smaragdi'na **Monotagma smaragdinum**
vandenheck'i . **Calathea vandenheckei**
vitta'ta . . . . **Calathea v.**
zebri'na . . . . **Calathea z.**

MARA'RA . . . . **AIPHANES**
See **PALM GENERA.**

MARAS'MIUS . . . . . . MARASMIUS
orea'des . . . . . . FAIRYRING M.
ro'tula . . . . COLLARED M.

MARAT'TIA . . . . MARATTIA
See **FERN GENERA.**

MARBLESEED . . . . . . **Onosmodium**
WESTERN M. . . . . **O. occidentale**

MARCGRA'VIA
el'egans
hart'i

MARCHAN'TIA . . . . . MARCHANTIA
polymor'pha . . . . COMMON M.
MARESTAIL . . . **Hippuris; H. vulgaris**
MARGOSA . . . . . . **Melia azadirachta**

MARGYRICAR'PUS
seto'sus . . . . PEARLFRUIT

MAR'ICA . . . . . . **NEOMARICA**

MARIGOLD . . . . **Tagetes**
AZTEC M. . . . . **T. erecta**
FRENCH M. . . . . **T. patula**
LITTLE M. . . . . **T. micrantha**
RAYLESS M. . . . . **T. apetala**
STRIPED M. . . . . **T. tenuifolia**
SWEET M. . . . . **T. lucida**

MARIPOSA . . . . **Calochortus**
BROADFRUIT M. . . . . . . **C. nitidus**
CATALINA M. . . . . . . **C. catalinae**
CLUBHAIR M. . . . . . . **C. clavatus**
CHARMING M. . . . . . . **C. venustus**
DESERT M. . . . . **C. kennedyi**
DOUGLAS M. . . . . **C. douglasianus**
DUNNS M. . . . . **C. dunni**
GOLDENBOWL M. . . . . . **C. concolor**
GOLDENLANTERN M. . **C. pulchellus**
GOLDEN SEGOLILY M. **C. nuttalli aureus**
GREENES M. . . . . **C. greenei**
GUNNISON M. . . . . . . **C. gunnisoni**
HOWELLS M. . . . . **C. howelli**
LEAST M. . . . . **C. minimus**
LILAC M. . . . . **C. splendens**
LOBBS M. . . . . **C. lobbi**
LONGHAIR M. . . . **C. longebarbatus**
LOVELY M. . . . . **C. amabilis**
LYALL M. . . . . **C. lyalli**
MONTEREY M. . . . . . . **C. uniflorus**
NORTHWESTERN M. . . . . **C. elegans**
OAKLAND M. . . . . . . **C. umbellatus**
OBISPO M. . . . . **C. obispoensis**
ONELEAF M. . . . . . **C. monophyllus**
PALMERS M. . . . . **C. palmeri**
PERSISTENT M. . . . . . . **C. persistens**
PLAINS M. . . . . . . **C. invenustus**
PLUMMER M. . . . . . . **C. plummerae**
PURPLE M. . . . . **C. amoenus**
SAGEBRUSH M. . . . **C. macrocarpus**
SEGOLILY M. . . . . **C. nuttalli**
SIERRA M. . . . . **C. nudus**
SKYBLUE M. . . . . . . **C. coeruleus**
SMOKY M. . . . . **C. leichtlini**
TOLMIE M. . . . . **C. tolmiei**
WEAKSTEM M. . . . . . **C. flexuosus**
WEEDS M. . . . . **C. weedi**
WHITE M. . . . . **C. albus**
YELLOW M. . . . . **C. luteus**
Mariposalily . . MARIPOSA: **Calochortus**
Mariposatulip . MARIPOSA: **Calochortus**

MARIS'CUS (*CLADIUM*) hw SAWGRASS
califor'nicus hw . . . . CALIFORNIA S.
jamaicen'sis hw . . . . . JAMAICA S.
mariscoi'des hw . . . . . SMOOTH S.

MARJORAM . . . . **Majorana**
POT M. . . . . **M. onites**
SWEET M. . . . . **M. hortensis**
Wild M. . . . . ORIGANUM, COMMON:
Origanum vulgare
Winter M. . . . ORIGANUM, WINTER:
Origanum heracleoticum

MARKHAM'IA
hildebrandt'i
lute'a
platyca'lyx

MARKINGNUT . . . . **Semecarpus**
CASHEW M. . . . . . . **S. anacardium**
LONGLEAF M. . . . . . . **S. longifolius**
VEINY M. . . . . **S. venosus**

MARRU'BIUM hw . . . . HOARHOUND
(*Horehound*)
candidis'simum
catariaefo'lium
leonuroi'des (*astracanicum*)
MOTHERWORT H.
libanot'icum
vulga're hw . . . . . . COMMON H.

MARSDE'NIA
cunduran'go . . . . . . CONDORVINE
erec'ta (*Cynanchum erectum*)
verruco'sa

MARSHAL'LIA . . . . . MARSHALLIA
caespito'sa
grandiflo'ra
triner'via

MARSHCRESS
AMPHIBIOUS M. . **Rorippa amphibia**
BOG M. . . . . **R. palustris**

MARSHFERN . . . **Dryopteris thelypteris**

Marsh-fleabane . . PLUCHEA, CAMPHOR:
Pluchea camphorata

MARSHMALLOW . . . **Althaea officinalis**

MARSHMARIGOLD . . . . **Caltha**
BIG ELKSLIP M.
C. leptosepala grandiflora
CELANDINE M. . . . . . . **C. chelidoni**
COMMON M. . . . . **C. palustris**
ELKSLIP M. . . . . . **C. leptosepala**
FLOATING M. . . . . **C. natans**
GREAT M. . . . . **C. polypetala**
TWINFLOWER M. . . . . . . **C. biflora**

MARSHPURSLANE . . . **Isnardia palustris**

MARSHWEED . . . . **Limnophila**
BROWNS M. . . . . . **L. gratioloides**
JAVA M. . . . . **L. javanica**

MARSIL'EA . . . . PEPPERWORT
See **FERN GENERA.**

MARTINE'ZIA Auth., *not* Ruiz & Pav.
AIPHANES
See **PALM GENERA.**

MARTYN'IA . . . . MARTYNIA
an'nua . . . . ANNUAL M.
craniola'ria . . . **Craniolaria annua**
fra'grans . . . . . . **Proboscidea f.**
integrifo'lia . . . . **Craniolaria i.**
louisia'na . . . **Proboscidea jussieui**
lute'a . . . . **Ibicella l.**
proboscid'ea . . **Proboscidea jussieui**

MARVOLANUT . . . . **Sclerocarya**
ETHIOPIAN M. . . . . **S. birroea**
KAFIR M. . . . . **S. caffra**
MASCARENE M. . . . . **S. shakua**
MAURITIUS M. . . . . . . **S. castanea**

MASCARENEGRASS . . . **Zoysia tenuifolia**

MASCARENHA'SIA
arbores'cens
elas'tica

MASDEVAL'LIA
See **ORCHID GENERA.**

MASKFLOWER . . . . **Alonsoa**
FLAXLEAF M. . . . . **A. linearis**
HEARTLEAF M. . . . . **A. warscewiczi**
LANCELEAF M. . . . . . . **A. acutifolia**
WHITE L. M. . . . . **A. a. candida**

MASTERWORT . . . . **Astrantia**
BIEBERSTEIN M. . . . **A. biebersteini**
BLACK M. . . . . . . **A. helliborifolia**
DWARF M. . . . . **A. minor**
GREAT M. . . . . **A. major**

MATCHWOOD . **Didymopanax morototoni**
MATGRASS . . . . **Nardus**
Matgrass . . . . . . PASPALUM, MAT: **Paspalum minus**

MATHI'OLA (*MATTHIOLA*) . STOCK
bicor'nis . . . . GRECIAN S.
fenestra'lis
inca'na . . . . COMMON S.
—an'nua . . . . ANNUAL S.

MATILIJA-POPPY . . **Romneya coulteri**
BRISTLECUP M. . . **R. c. trichocalyx**

MATRICA'RIA . . . . . . MAYWEED
au'rea (*Cotula a.*)
capen'sis **Chrysanthemum parthenium**
chamomil'la (*Chamomilla matricaria*) GERMAN-CAMOMILE
exim'ia . **Chrysanthemum parthenium**
grandiflo'ra

The plant in the trade under this name is Double Scentless Camomile, hort. var. of M. inodora, not M. grandiflora of botanists.

inodo'ra (*Chrysanthemum inodorum*) SCENTLESS M.
DOUBLE (*plenissima*) HV.
matricarioi'des (*discoidea; suaveolens*) PINEAPPLEWEED
orea'des
parthenoi'des **Chrysanthemum parthenium**
tchihat'chewi (*Chrysanthemum t.*) TURFINGDAISY
GOLDEN BALL. HV. Matricaria
SILVER BALL
SNOWBALL

MATRIMONYVINE . **Lycium halimifolium**

MATTEUC'CIA . . . . **PTERETIS**
See **FERN GENERA.**

MATTHI'OLA . . . . . **MATHIOLA**

MATTREE . . . . . . **Labourdonnaisia**
WHITE M. . . . . **L. albescens**

MATUCA'NA
See **CACTUS GENERA.**

MAURAN'DIA (*LOPHOSPERMUM*) MAURANDIA
antirrhiniflo'ra (*Antirrhinum a.; A. maurandioides*)
barclaia'na . . . . . . BARCLAY M.
erubes'cens
lophosper'mum (*Lophospermum scandens*) . . . . . . PLUMESEED M.
petroph'ila . . . . . . ROCKLADY M.
pur'pusi
scan'dens

MAURI'TIA . . . . MAURITIA
See **PALM GENERA.**

MAXILLA'RIA
See **ORCHID GENERA.**

MAXIMILIA'NA (*ENGLEROPHOENIX*) . . . . MAXIMILIANA
See **PALM GENERA.**

MAXIMILIANE'A **COCHLOSPERMUM**

MAXIMOWIC'ZIA Rupr., *not* Cogn. **SCHISANDRA**
sinen'sis . . . . **S. chinensis**

MAYA'CA |w . . . . MAYACA
aublet'i |w
fluviat'ilis |w . . . . RIVER M.

MAYAPALM . . . . **Opsiandra; O. maya**
MAYAPPLE . . . . **Podophyllum**
COMMON M. . . . . . . **P. peltatum**
HIMALAYAN M. . . . . . . **P. emodi**
Maye'nia erec'ta . . . . **Thunbergia e.**

MAYTE'NUS . . . . MAYTEN
boa'ria (*chilensis*) . . . . . CHILE M.
ilicifo'lia . . . . HOLLYLEAF M.
phyllanthoi'des . . GUTTAPERCHA M.

MAYWEED . . . . **Matricaria**
GERMAN-CAMOMILE . . **M. chamomilla**
PINEAPPLEWEED . **M. matricarioides**
SCENTLESS M. . . . . . **M. inodora**
TURFINGDAISY . . . **M. tchihatchewi**

MAZARIPALM **Nannorrhops; N. ritchieana**

MA'ZUS
japon'icus (*rugosus*)
pumil'io

MEADOWBEAUTY . . . . **Rhexia**
COMMON M. . . . . . . **R. virginica**
MARYLAND M. . . . . . **R. mariana**
NASH M. . . . . **R. nashi**
YELLOW M. . . . . **R. lutea**

MEADOWFOAM . . . . . **Limnanthes**
DOUGLAS M. . . . . . . **L. douglasi**

MEADOWRUE . . . . **Thalictrum**
ALPINE M. . . . . **T. alpinum**
BAIKAL M. . . . . . . **T. baicalense**
BIGFRUIT M. . . . . **T. macrocarpum**
CELANDINE M. . . . . . **T. chelidoni**
COLUMBINE M. . . **T. aquilegifolium**
CRITICAL M. . . . . . . **T. confine**
DELAVAY M. . . . . . . **T. delavayi**
DUSTY M. . . . . **T. glaucum**
EARLY M. . . . . **T. dioicum**
FENDLER M. . . . . . . **T. fendleri**
FETID M. . . . . **T. foetidum**
GREATER M. . . . . . . **T. majus**
LOW M. . . . . **T. minus**
NARROWLEAF M. . . . . **T. lucidum**
NODDING M. . . . . . **T. squarrosum**
PURPLE M. . . . . . **T. dasycarpum**
SIERRA M. . . . . . **T. polycarpum**
SLIMTOP M. . . . . **T. simplex**
SNOUTSEED M. . **T. rhynchocarpum**
TALL M. . . . . . . **T. polygamum**
VEINY M. . . . . . . **T. venulosum**
WESTERN M. . . . . **T. occidentale**
WHITE YUNNAN M. **T. dipterocarpum album**
YELLOW M. . . . . **T. flavum**
YUNNAN M. . . . . **T. dipterocarpum**

MEADOWSAFFRON . . . . **Bulbocodium**
SPRING M . . . . **B. vernum**

MEADOWSWEET . . . . . **Filipendula**
DROPWORT . . . . . **F. hexapetala**
EUROPEAN M. . . . . . . **F. ulmaria**
JAPANESE M. . . . . . **F. purpurea**
KAMCHATKA M. . . . **F. camtschatica**
PRAIRIE M. . . . . **F. rubra**

MECONEL'LA
linea'ris
—pulchel'lum

MECONOP'SIS
aculea'ta
bel'la
betonicifo'lia (*Cathartia b.*)
—bai'leyi (*M. baileyi*)
cam'brica . . . . WELSHPOPPY
DOUBLE (*floreplena*) HV.
YELLOW (*aurantiaca*)
gran'dis

MECONOPSIS, continued
heterophyl'la . . . . . FLAMINGPOPPY
horrid'ula
integrifo'lia . YELLOW CHINESEPOPPY
panicula'ta (*nepalensis*)
₵PURPLE (*fusco-purpurea*) HV.
₵WHITE (*alba*)
pratt'i
pseudo-integrifo'lia
quintupliner'via
re'gia
ru'dis
simplicifo'lia
sinua'ta
—latifo'lia
wal'lichi . . . . SATINPOPPY

MEDE'MIA . . . . MEDEMIA
See **PALM GENERA.**

MEDE'OLA . . . . MEDEOLA
virginia'na . . . . CUCUMBERROOT M.

MEDIC . . . . **Medicago**
ALFALFA . . . . **M. sativa**
BARREL M. . . . . . **M. tribuloides**
BLACK M. . . . . **M. lupulina**
BUTTON M. . . . . . **M. orbicularis**
CALIFORNIA BURCLOVER . **M. hispida**
CALVARY M. . . . . . . **M. echinus**
COGWHEEL M. . . . . **M. tuberculata**
FIVECOIL BURCLOVER **M. hispida reticulata**
LITTLE M. . . . . **M. minima**
SICKLE ALFALFA . . **M. sativa falcata**
SNAIL M. . . . . **M. scutellata**
SPOTTED M. . . . . **M. arabica**
THREECOIL BURCLOVER **M. hispida confinis**
TIFTON M. . . . . **M. rigidula**
TOOTHED BURCLOVER **M. hispida denticulata**
TREE M. . . . . **M. arborea**

MEDICA'GO |w . . . . MEDIC
apicula'ta
arab'ica (*maculata*) . . . SPOTTED M.
arbo'rea . . . . TREE M.
creta'cea
echi'nus . . . . CALVARY M.
hemicyc'la
his'pida |w . . CALIFORNIA BURCLOVER
—confi'nis . . . . . . THREECOIL B.
—denticula'ta (*M. denticulata*) TOOTHED B.
—reticula'ta . . . . . . FIVECOIL B.
intertex'ta
lupuli'na |w . . . . BLACK M.
macula'ta . . . . **M. arabica**
min'ima . . . . LITTLE M.
orbicula'ris . . . . BUTTON M.
rigid'ula . . . . TIFTON M.
sati'va |w . . . . ALFALFA
—falca'ta . . . . SICKLE A.
COSSACK. HV. M. sativa
GRIMM
PERUVIAN
SAND (SAND LUCERN)
TURKESTAN
VARIEGATED
scutella'ta . . . . SNAIL M.
tribuloi'des . . . . BARREL M.
tubercula'ta . . . . . . COGWHEEL M.

MEDICINETREE . . . . . **Codonocarpus**
MUSTARD M. . . . . . . **C. cotinifolia**

MEDINIL'LA . . . . MEDINILLA
magnif'ica
teys'manni (*amabilis*)

MEDIOCAC'TUS
See CACTUS GENERA.

MEDIOLOBIV'IA (*REBUTIA* in part)
See CACTUS GENERA.

MEDITERRANEANGRASS . . . **Schismus barbatus**

MEDITERRANEANPALM . . . **Chamaerops; C. humilis**
CANARY M. . . . . . **C. h. canariensis**
DATEFRUIT M. . . . **C. h. dactylocarpa**

MEDLAR . . . **Mespilus; M. germanica**

MEDUSAHEAD . **Elymus caput-medusae**

MEGACLIN'IUM (*Bulbophyllum*)
See ORCHID GENERA.

Megapte'rium missourien'se . . . **Oenothera missouriensis**

MEGARRHI'ZA (*MARAH*). . BIGROOT
califor'nica (*fabacea; Echinocystis c.; Marah c.; Micrampelis c.*) . . . CALIFORNIA B.
orega'na (*Echinocystis o.; Marah o.*) . . . OREGON B.
Some botanists regard this as a form or var. of M. californica.

MEGA'SEA . . . . **BERGENIA**

MEGOTIGE'A . . **HELICODICEROS**

MEIBO'MIA . . . . **DESMODIUM**
purpu'rea . . . . . . **D. tortuosum**

MELALEU'CA . . . . . MELALEUCA
acumina'ta
armilla'ris (*alba*) . . . DROOPING M.
bu'gelli
citriodo'ra . . . . LEMON M.
crassifo'lia
decussa'ta . . . . LILAC M.
ellip'tica
ericifo'lia . . . . HEATH M.
ful'gens
genistifo'lia
gibbo'sa
hue'geli . . . . CHENILE M.
hypericifo'lia . . . . . . DOTTED M.
imbrica'ta
inca'na . . . . GRAY M.
laterit'ia . . . . ROBINREDBREAST M.
leucaden'dron . . . . CAJEPUTTREE
linariifo'lia
longico'ma
microme'ria
microphyl'la
nesoph'ila . . . . PINK M.
nodo'sa
parviflo'ra (*preissiana*)
rad'ula
rhaphiophyl'la
squa'mea
styphelioi'des
tenel'la
teretifo'lia
thymifo'lia
viola'cea
web'steri
wil'soni . . . . WILSON M.

MELAMPO'DIUM . . . . BLACKFOOT
cine'reum
leucan'thum . . . . PLAINS B.
perfolia'tum

MELAMPY'RUM |w . . . COWWHEAT
linea're |w . . . . . NARROWLEAF C.

MELANORRHOE'A
usita'ta

MELAN'THIUM . . . . BUNCHFLOWER
virgin'icum (*canadense*) BUNCHFLOWER

MELASPHAE'RULA
gramin'ea

MELASTO'MA
ackerman'i
malaba'thricum
molkenboe'ri

MELEGUETAPEPPER
DRUG M. . . **Aframomum melegueta**
PARADISE M. . . . . **A. grana-paradisi**

ME'LIA |w . . . . CHINABERRY
azadirach'ta (*indica; Azadirachta i.*) . . . MARGOSA
azed'arach (*sempervirens*) |w . . . CHINABERRY
—umbraculifor'mis (*M. a. umbraculifera*) . . . . UMBRELLA C.
candol'lei

MELIAN'THUS . . . . . HONEYBUSH
como'sus
ma'jor . . . . BIGLEAF H.
mi'nor

MELIC . . . . **Melica**
BEARDED M. . . . . **M. aristata**
CALIFORNIA M. . . . **M. californica**
COASTRANGE M. . . . **M. imperfecta**
HARFORD M. . . . . **M. harfordi**
PORTER M. . . . . **M. porteri**
ROCK M. . . . . **M. stricta**
SIBERIAN M. . . . . . . **M. altissima**
SILKYSPIKE M. . . . . **M. ciliata**
SMITH M. . . . . **M. smithi**
THREEFLOWER M. . . . . . **M. nitens**
TORREY M. . . . . **M. torreyana**
TRANSYLVANIA M. **M. transsilvanica**
TWOFLOWER M. . . . . . **M. mutica**
WOODY M. . . . . **M. frutescens**

ME'LICA . . . . MELIC; ONIONGRASS
See GRASS GENERA.

MELICOC'CA (*MELICOCCUS*) . . . HONEYBERRY
bi'juga (*Melicoccus bijugatus*) . . . MAMONCILLO (*Spanishlime*)

MELICO'PE
terna'ta

MELICY'TUS
ramiflo'rus . . . . HINAHINA

MELILO'TUS |w . . . . SWEETCLOVER
al'ba |w . . . . WHITE S.
—an'nua . . . . HUBAM S.
caeru'lea . . . . **Trigonella c.**
denta'ta
grac'ilis
in'dica |w . . . . ANNUAL YELLOW S.
officina'lis . . . . YELLOW S.
parviflo'ra
suave'olens . . . . . DAGHESTAN S.

MELI'NIS
See GRASS GENERA.

MELIOS'MA
beania'na
cuneifo'lia
myrian'tha
old'hami
panno'sa
pen'dens
ten'uis
veitchio'rum

MELIS'SA . . . . BALM
officina'lis . . . . COMMON B.
—au'rea . . . . GOLDEN C.B.

MELIT'TIS
melissophyl'lum

MELOCAC'TUS (*CACTUS* in part) . . . MELONCACTUS
See CACTUS GENERA.

MELOCAN'NA . . . . . MELOCANNA
See BAMBOO GENERA.

MELO'CHIA |w
corchorifo'lia |w
pyramida'ta

MELON
DUDAIM M. . . **Cucumis melo dudaim**
SNAKE M. . . . . . . **C. m. flexuosus**

MELONBARRELS . . . **Ferocactus melocactiformis**

MELONCACTUS . . . . **Melocactus**
ANTON M. . . . . **M. antoni**
BAHIA M. . . . . **M. bahiensis**
BROADWAY M. . . . . **M. broadwayi**
GRAY M. . . . . **M. caesius**
LEMAIRE M. . . . . **M. lemairei**
MATANZAS M. . . . **M. matanzanus**
MAXON M. . . . . **M. maxoni**
MIQUEL M. . . . . **M. miqueli**
NERY M. . . . . **M. neryi**
PERUVIAN M. . . . . **M. peruvianus**
TOWNSEND M. . . . . **M. townsendi**
TURKSCAP M. . . . . . . **M. intortus**
VIOLET M. . . . . **M. violaceus**
ZUCCARINI M. . . . . . **M. zuccarini**

MELO'THRIA (*PILOGYNE*) |w
pen'dula |w
puncta'ta (*Pilogyne suavis*)
sca'bra
uligino'sa

MEMECY'LON
spathan'dra

MEMPHISGRASS . . **Cutandia memphitica**

MENISPER'MUM |w . . MOONSEED
acu'tum . . . . **Sinomenium a.**
canaden'se |w . . . . . COMMON M.
daur'icum . . . . ASIATIC M.

MENODO'RA |w . . . . . MENODORA
integrifo'lia
lae'vis . . . . SMOOTH M.
longiflo'ra . . . . SHOWY M.
sca'bra |w . . . . ROUGH M.
scopa'ria . . . . BROOM M.
spines'cens . . . . SPINY M.

MEN'THA |w . . . . MINT
aquat'ica |w . . . . WATER M.
arven'sis . . . . FIELD M.
—piperas'cens . . . . JAPANESE F.M.
canaden'sis (*M. arvensis c.; penardi*) . . . CANADA M.
cardi'aca |w . . . . LITTLELEAF M.
citra'ta . . . . BERGAMOT M.
cris'pa |w . . . . CRISPLEAF M.
gen'tilis . . . . RED M.
Thought by some botanists to be a hybrid between M. arvensis and M. spicata.

gen'tilis Hort., *not* L. . . . **M. spicata**
lind'leyi
longifo'lia (*sylvestris*) . . . HORSE M. (*Horsemint*)

MENTHA, continued
nilia'ca . . . . EGYPTIAN MINT
Thought by some botanists to be a hybrid.
penard'i . . . . **M. canadensis**
piperi'ta |w . . . . . PEPPERMINT
—citra'ta . . . . ORANGE P.
MITCHAM RED. HV. M. piperita
MITCHAM WHITE
PURPLESTEM (*vulgaris*)
pule'gium . . . . . PENNYROYAL M.
requien'i . . . . REQUIEN M.
rotundifo'lia . . . . APPLE M.
—variega'ta Hort. . . . PINEAPPLE M.
sati'va
spica'ta (*gentilis* Hort.; *viridis* of trade lists) |w . . . . SPEARMINT
sylves'tris . . . . **M. longifolia**

MENTOCA'LYX
veluti'na

MENTZE'LIA (*ACROLASIA; BARTONIA* Pursh, *not* Muhl.; *NUTTALLIA* Raf., *not* Barton) MENTZELIA
The species of the subgenus Nuttallia, with large showy flowers, are known as Blazingstar.
albes'cens (*Nuttallia a.*)
albicau'lis (*Acrolasia a.*) WHITESTEM M.
decapet'ala (*Nuttallia d.*) . . . TENPETAL M. (*Tenpetal Blazingstar*)
florida'na . FLORIDA M. (*Florida B.*)
involucra'ta . SAMIJA M. (*Samija B.*)
laevicau'lis (*Nuttallia l.*) BLAZINGSTAR M. (*Common B.*)
lind'leyi (*Acrolasia aurea*) LINDLEY M.
multiflo'ra (*Nuttallia m.*) DESERT M. (*Desert B.*)
nu'da (*Nuttallia n.*) . . BRACTLESS M. (*Bractless B.*)

MENTZELIA . . . . **Mentzelia**
BLAZINGSTAR M. . . . **M. laevicaulis**
BRACTLESS M. . . . . . . **M. nuda**
DESERT M. . . . . . . **M. multifida**
FLORIDA M. . . . . . . **M. floridana**
LINDLEY M. . . . . . . **M. lindleyi**
SAMIJA M. . . . . . . **M. involucrata**
TENPETAL M. . . . . **M. decapetala**
WHITESTEM M. . . . . **M. albicaulis**

MENYAN'THES |w . . . . BOGBEAN
trifolia'ta |w . . . . . . COMMON B.

MENZIES'IA |w . . . . . . MENZIESIA (*Skunkbush*)
ciliica'lyx
—multiflo'ra
ferrugin'ea . . . . RUSTY M.
glabel'la . . . . SMOOTH M.
multiflo'ra
pentan'dra
pilo'sa |w . . . . . . ALLEGANY M.
purpu'rea (*daboecia*)

MERA'TIA . . **CHIMONANTHUS**

MERAWAN . . . . **Hopea**
LOWS M. . . . . **H. lowi**
NODDING M. . . . . **H. nutans**
THINGAN M. . . . . . . **H. odorata**

MERCURIA'LIS |w . . . . MERCURY
an'nua |w . . . . . HERBMERCURY
peren'nis

MERCURY . . . . **Mercurialis**
HERBMERCURY . . . . . . **M. annua**

MERIA'NA . . . . . . **WATSONIA**

MERIDIA'NA . . . . . . **GAZANIA**

MERIO'LIX . . . . . **OENOTHERA**

MERMAIDWEED . . . . . **Proserpinaca**
COMBLEAF M. . . . . . **P. pectinata**
MARSH M. . . . . **P. palustris**

MER'OPE . . . . MEROPE
angula'ta . . . . MEROPE

MERRIL'LIA . . . . MERRILLIA
calox'ylon

Merrit . . . EUCALYPTUS, FLOCKTON: **Eucalyptus flocktoniae**

MERRYBELLS . . . . **Uvularia**
BIG M. . . . . **U. grandiflora**
LITTLE M. . . . . . . **U. sessilifolia**
WOOD M. . . . . **U. perfoliata**
YELLOW W. M. . . . . . **U. p. flava**

MERSAWA . . . . **Anisoptera**
PALOSAPIS M. . . . . . **A. thurifera**

MERTEN'SIA . . . . . . BLUEBELLS
alpi'na
amoe'na . . . . . . YELLOWSTONE B.
ba'keri
brevis'tyla . . . . . . SHORTSTYLE B.
cilia'ta (*M. c. longipedunculata; polyphylla*) . . . . . . MOUNTAIN B.
—stomatechoi'des . . SIERRA M.B.
coria'cea . . . . . **M. viridis dilatata**
echioi'des
folio'sa . . . . LEAFY B.
francisca'na (*pratensis*) . FRANCISCAN B.
fusifor'mis . . . . SPINDLEROOT B.
hor'neri . . . . **M. longiflora**
hu'milis
interme'dia
laeviga'ta . . **M. paniculata borealis**
lanceola'ta . . . . . . LANCELEAF B.
leonard'i (*sampsoni*) . . . . TALL B.
longiflo'ra (*horneri; pulchella; M. p. glauca*) . . . . SMALL B.
marit'ima . . . . SEA B.
moltkioi'des
oblongifo'lia . . . . OBLONGLEAF B.
—nevaden'sis (*M. nutans*)
panicula'ta . . . . PANICLE B.
—borea'lis (*M. laevigata*)
platen'sis
platyphyl'la
—subcorda'ta (*M. paniculata s.*)
polyphyl'la . . . . **M. ciliata**
praten'sis . . . . . . **M. franciscana**
primuloi'des
pulchel'la . . . . **M. longiflora**
—glau'ca . . . . **M. longiflora**
samp'soni . . . . **M. leonardi**
sibir'ica (*Lithospermum sibiricum*)
tweed'yi . . . . TWEEDY B.
virgin'ica . . . . VIRGINIA B.
vir'idis . . . . GREENLEAF B.
—dilata'ta (*M. coriacea*)

MERU'LIUS . . . . MERULIUS
lac'rymans . . . . . . WEEPING M.

MER'YTA
sin'clairi

MESEMBRYAN'THEMUM (*Acrodon; Aptenia; Argeta; Argyroderma; Aridaria; Astridia; Bergeranthus; Carpanthea; Carpobrotus; Cephalophyllum; Cerochlamys; Chasmatophyllum; Cheiridopsis; Conicosia; Conophytum; Corpuscularia; Cryophytum; Dactylopsis; Delosperma; Disphyma; Dorotheanthus; Drosanthemum; Erepsia; Faucaria; Fenestraria; Gibbaeum; Glottiphyllum; Hereroa; Hymenocyclus; Lampranthus; Lithops; Malephora; Mesembrianthemum; Nananthus; Odontophorus; Oscularia; Pleiospilos; Punctillaria; Rabiea; Rhombophyllum; Rimaria; Ruschia; Sceletium; Stomatium; Titanopsis; Trichodiadema; Verrucifera*)
MESEMBRYANTHEMUM (*Figmarigold*)
See **SUCCULENTS.**

MESEMBRYANTHEMUM **Mesembryanthemum**
BOLUS M. . . . . **M. bolusi**
BRUNNTHALER M. . . **M. brunnthaleri**
CHILEAN M. . . . . **M. chilense**
EIGHTLEAF M. . . . **M. octophyllum**
HEARTLEAF M. . . . . **M. cordifolium**
HERRE M . . . . **M. herrei**
HOTTENTOTFIG . . . . **M. edule**
ICEPLANT M. . . . . **M. crystallinum**
KARKALLA M. . . . **M. aequilaterum**
LESLIE M. . . . . **M. lesliei**
PICKLEPLANT . . . . **M. echinatum**
ROSE M. . . . . **M. roseum**
SCHOENLAND M. **M. schoenlandianum**
TIGERSCLAW M. . . . . **M. tigrinum**
TRICOLOR M. . . . . . **M. gramineum**

MES'PILUS . . . . MEDLAR
german'ica . . . . MEDLAR
¢BIGFRUIT (*gigantea; macrocarpa*) HV.
¢SEEDLESS (*abortiva*)

MESQUITE . . . . **Prosopis**
COMMON M. . . . . . . **P. chilensis**
HONEY M. . . . . . . **P. glandulosa**
VELVET M. . . . . **P. velutina**

Mesquitegrass . . . . . MUHLY, BUSH: **Muhlenbergia porteri**

MESU'A
fer'rea

METALLEAF . . . . **Phyllagathis**
SUMATRA M. . . . . . **P. rotundifolia**

METO'PIUM . . . . . . POISONTREE
brown'ei . . . . BROWNES P.
toxif'erum (*Rhus metopium*) FLORIDA P.

METROSIDE'ROS . . . . . IRONTREE
colenso'i
diffu'sa
floribun'da . . **Callistemon lanceolatus**
flor'ida
lu'cida
parkinso'ni
robus'ta . . . . RATA
—retu'sa
scan'dens (*perforata*)
semperflo'rens. **Callistemon lanceolatus**
tomento'sa
—angus'ta
—la'ta
tremuloi'des
villo'sa

METROX'YLON (*COELOCOCCUS; SAGUS*). SAGOPALM; IVORYNUTPALM
See **PALM GENERA.**

ME'UM
athaman'ticum

MEXICANBUCKEYE **Ungnadia; U. speciosa**

MEXICANCLOVER . **Richardia; R. scabra**
MEXICANORANGE . . . . . . **Choisya**
STARLEAF M. . . . . . . **C. dumosa**
TERNATE M. . . . . **C. ternata**
MEXICANSTAR . . . . **Milla; M. biflora**

MEYEROPHY'TUM
mey'eri

MIBO'RA . . . . MIBORA
See **GRASS GENERA.**

MICHAUX'IA
campanuloi'des

MICHEL'IA
champa'ca . . . CHAMPAC MICHELIA
compres'sa (*Magnolia c.*)
fusca'ta (*Magnolia f.*) . BANANASHRUB

MICO'NIA
magnif'ica (*Cyanophyllum magnificum*)

MICRAM'PELIS . **ECHINOCYSTIS**
califor'nica . . . . . . **Megarrhiza c.**

MICRAN'THEMUM [w] MICRANTHEMUM
micranthemoi'des [w]
umbro'sum [w]

MICRAN'THES . . . **SAXIFRAGA**

MICROCIT'RUS
FINGERLIME; WILDLIME
∞ **australas'ica** . . . . ∞ AUSTRALIAN F. (∞ *Faustrimedin*)
—**sanguin'ea** . . . . . REDPULP A.F.
austra'lis . . AUSTRALIAN ROUND W.
inodo'ra . . . . . . QUEENSLAND W.

MICROCY'CAS . . . . . MICROCYCAS
See **CYCAD GENERA.**

MICROGLOS'SA
albes'cens (*Aster cabulicus*)
staticifo'lius

MICROLE'PIA
See **FERN GENERA.**

MICROME'LES . . . . . **SORBUS**

MICROME'LUM . . . MICROMELUM
compres'sum . . . . PHILIPPINE M.

MICROME'RIA . . . . . MICROMERIA
chamisso'nis (*douglasi*). YERBABUENA
croat'ica (*Satureia c.; Thymus croaticus*) CROATIAN M.
dalmat'ica . . . . . . DALMATIAN M.
grae'ca . . . . GREEK M.
julia'na . . . . TURKISH M.
monta'na . . . . **Satureia m.**
piperel'la . . . . . PEPPERMINT M.
rupes'tris
CORSICA. HV.
The identity of this plant is obscure. It may be Satureia corsica.
va'ria (*Thymus ericaefolius*)

MICROMYR'TUS
microphyl'la

MICRO'SERIS . . . . . MICROSERIS
linearifo'lia . **Uropappus linearifolius**
nu'tans (*Ptilocalais n.*) . NODDING M.

MICROS'TERIS [w]
micran'tha (*Collomia m.; Gilia m.* (Kell.) A. Nels., *not* Steud.) [w]

MICROS'TYLIS . . . . **MALAXIS**
See **ORCHID GENERA, HARDY TERRESTRIAL GROUP.**

MI'DA . . . . **FUSANUS**

MIGNONETTE . . . . **Reseda**
CANARYISLAND M. . . **R. crystallina**
COMMON M. . . . . **R. odorata**
WELD M. . . . . **R. luteola**
WHITE M. . . . . **R. alba**
YELLOW M. . . . . **R. lutea**

Mignonettewood PITTOSPORUM, DIAMONDLEAF: **Pittosporum rhombifolium**

MIKA'NIA
scan'dens . . CLIMBING HEMPWEED

MI'LA
See **CACTUS GENERA.**

MIL'IUM . . . . MILLETGRASS
See **GRASS GENERA.**

MILKBERRY . . . . **Chiococca**
DAVIDS M. . . . . **C. alba**

MILKBUSH . . . . **Synadenium**
GRANTS M. . . . . **S. granti**
ZEBRAPOISON M. . . . **S. arborescens**

MILKPEA . . . . **Galactia**
DOWNY M. . . . . **G. volubilis**
ERECT M. . . . . **G. erecta**
HOARY M. . . . . **G. mollis**
SHAPELY M. . . . . . . **G. regularis**
WRIGHT M. . . . . **G. wrighti**

MILKTHISTLE . . . . **Silybum**
BLESSED M. . . . . **S. marianum**

MILKVETCH . . . . **Astragalus**
See also LOCO and POISONVETCH.

ALPINE M. . . . . **A. alpinus**
BALLOONPOD M. . . . **A. sonneanus**
BECKWITH M. . . . . . . **A. beckwithi**
BIGELOW M. . . . . **A. bigelovi**
CANADA M. . . . . . . **A. canadensis**
DECUMBENT M. . . . . **A. decumbens**
DIFFUSE M. . . . . **A. diffusus**
DRUMMOND M. . . . . **A. drummondi**
DRYPLAINS M. . . . . . **A. araneosus**
FLEXILE M. . . . . **A. flexuosus**
FOXTAIL M. . . . . **A. alopecuroides**
GROUNDPLUM M. . . **A. crassicarpus**
INDIAN M. . . . . **A. aboriginum**
LOOSEFLOWER M. . . . . . **A. tenellus**
NICKLEAF M. . . . . **A. goniatus**
PRAIRIE M. . . . . **A. striatus**
PREUSS M. . . . . **A. preussi**
PURPLE M. . . . . **A. agrestis**
THISTLE M. . . . . **A. impensus**
TRAGACANTH M. . . . . . **A. gummifer**
TUFTED M. . . . . **A. spatulatus**
ZION M. . . . . **A. zionis**

MILKVINE . . . . **Vincetoxicum**
ANGLEPOD M. . . . . . **V. gonocarpos**
CORKPOD M. . . . . . . **V. suberosum**
HAIRY M. . . . . **V. hirsutum**

MILKWEED . . . . **Asclepias**
BLOODFLOWER M. . . . **A. curassavica**
BROADLEAF M. . . . . **A. latifolia**
BUTTERFLY M. . . . . . . **A. tuberosa**
COMMON M. . . . . **A. syriaca**
DESERT M. . . . . **A. erosa**
DWARF M. . . . . **A. involucrata**
HAIRY SWAMP M. **A. incarnata pulchra**
HALLS M. . . . . **A. halli**
KOTOLO M. . . . . **A. fremonti**
MEXICAN M. . . . . **A. mexicana**
PACIFIC M. . . . . **A. lanceolata**
PINK SWAMP M. . **A. incarnata rosea**
PLAINS M. . . . . **A. pumila**
POISON M. . . . . **A. galioides**
PURPLE M. . . . . . **A. purpurascens**

MILKWEED, continued
RED M. . . . . **Asclepias rubra**
SHOWY M. . . . . **A. speciosa**
SKELETON M. . . . . **A. subulata**
SULLIVANT M. . . . . . . **A. sullivanti**
SWAMP M. . . . . **A. incarnata**
WESTCOAST M. . . **A. phytolaccoides**
WHITE SWAMP M. . **A. incarnata alba**
WHORLED M. . . . . . . **A. verticillata**
WOOLLYPOD M. . . . . . . **A. eriocarpa**

MIL'LA . . . . MEXICANSTAR
biflo'ra . . . . MEXICANSTAR
el'egans . . . . **Bessera e.**
uniflo'ra . . . . **Brodiaea u.**

MILLET . . . . **Panicum; Setaria**
Africanmillet . . . . RAGIMILLET
Broomcorn M. . . . . PROSO
Browntop M. . . BROWNTOP PANICUM
BROWNTOPMILLET **Panicum ramosum**
Cattailmillet . . . . . . PEARLMILLET
Coracanmillet . . . . . . RAGIMILLET
Fingermillet . . . . RAGIMILLET
FOXTAIL M. . . . . . . **Setaria italica**
Hog M. . . . . PROSO
Italian M. . . . . . . FOXTAIL MILLET
JAPANESEMILLET . **Echinochloa crusgalli frumentacea**
PEARLMILLET . **Pennisetum glaucum**
Proso M. . . . . PROSO
RAGIMILLET . . . **Eleusine coracana**
Sanwamillet . . . . JAPANESEMILLET
Shanwamillet . . . . . . JUNGLERICE
Texas M. . . . . . . TEXAS PANICUM

MILLETGRASS . . . . **Milium**
AMERICAN M. . . . . **M. effusum**

MILLET'TIA . . . . . . MILLETTIA
caf'fra . . . . KAFIR M.
japon'ica . . . . **Wistaria j.**
megasper'ma . . . . . . **Wistaria m.**
pen'dula . . . . THINWIN M.
reticula'ta (*Wistaria r.*) LEATHERLEAF M.

MILLINGTO'NIA
horten'sis

MILO . . . . . **Sorghum vulgare form**

MILTO'NIA . . . . . . PANSYORCHID
See **ORCHID GENERA.**

MILTONIO'DA
See **ORCHID GENERA.**

MILTONIOP'SIS . . . **MILTONIA**
See **ORCHID GENERA.**

MIMO'SA [w] . . . . MIMOSA
aculeaticar'pa (*acanthocarpa*)
al'bida
argen'tea
bimucrona'ta
biuncif'era [w] . . . . . CATCLAW M.
borea'lis (*fragrans*) [w]. FRAGRANT M.
dysocar'pa . . . . . . VELVETPOD M.
lem'moni [w] . . . . LEMMON M.
ni'gra
polydac'tyla
pu'dica . . . . SENSITIVEPLANT
rubicau'lis
sepia'ria
spegazzi'ni

MIM'ULUS (*DIPLACUS*) [w]
MONKEYFLOWER
ala'tus [w] . . . . . SHARPWING M.
alpi'nus . . . . **M. luteus a.**
ar'idus (*Diplacus a.*) . SANDIEGO M.
auranti'acus (*glutinosus; Diplacus a.*) BUSH M.

MIMULUS, continued
brev'ipes . Canary Monkeyflower
brew'eri
cardina'lis ⌊w . . . Crimson M.
cleve'landi (*Diplacus c.*) Cleveland M.
cu'preus . . . . Chilean M.
doug'lasi
flem'ingi . . . . . . Fleming M.
floribun'dus
fre'monti . . . . . Fremont M.
glabra'tus ⌊w
glutino'sus . . . . . **M. aurantiacus**
—brach'ypus . . . . . **M. longiflorus**
—punic'eus . . . . . **M. puniceus**
gutta'tus (*langsdorfi*) ⌊w . Common M.
leptan'thus (*Diplacus l.; D. grandiflorus*) . . . . Slender M.
lew'isi . . . . Lewis M.
longiflo'rus (*M. glutinosus brachypus; Diplacus l.*) . . . . . Bush M.
lute'us . . . . Golden M.
—alpi'nus (*M. alpinus*) . Alpine M.
—rivula'ris
—variega'tus
—youngea'nus
moscha'tus ⌊w . . . Muskplant M.
na'nus . . . . Dwarf M.
nasu'tus
parviflo'rus (*Diplacus p.*). . Island M.
primuloi'des . . . . . Primrose M.
punic'eus (*M. glutinosus p.; Diplacus p.*) . . . . Red M.
rin'gens ⌊w . . . . . . Allegany M.
rubel'lus
∞ **tigri'nus** (*guttatus × luteus*) ∞ Tiger M.
til'ingi
tri'color . . . . Tricolor M.

MI'MUSOPS . . . . . Bulletwood
bala'ta; bidenta'ta globo'sa **Manilkara bidentata**
caf'fra . . . . Kafir B.
darienen'sis . . . . . **Manilkara d.**
elen'gi . . . . Elengi B.
heck'eli . . . . Heckel B.

Mimusops heckeli is placed by some botanists in the genus Dumoria.

kau'ki . . . . **Manilkara k.**
parvifo'lia . . . . . . **Manilkara p.**
roxburghia'na . . . . . **Manilkara r.**

MI'NA . . . . **QUAMOCLIT**
sanguin'ea . . **Q. coccinea hederifolia**

Minerslettuce . . **Claytonia perfoliata**

Mint . . . . **Mentha**
Apple M. . . . . . **M. rotundifolia**
Bergamot M. . . . . . . **M. citrata**
Canada M. . . . . **M. canadensis**
Crispleaf M. . . . . . . **M. crispa**
Egyptian M. . . . . . . **M. niliaca**
Field M. . . . . . . **M. arvensis**
Horse M. . . . . . . **M. longifolia**
Japanese Field M. **M. arvensis piperascens**
Littleleaf M. . . . . . **M. cardiaca**
Orange Peppermint **M. piperita citrata**
Pennyroyal M. . . . . **M. pulegium**
Peppermint . . . . . . **M. piperita**
Pineapple M. **M. rotundifolia variegata**
Red M. . . . . **M. gentilis**
Requien M. . . . . . . **M. requieni**
Spearmint . . . . **M. spicata**
Water M. . . . . **M. aquatica**

Mintbush . . . . **Prostanthera**
Cutleaf M. . . . . **P. incisa**
Greenflower M. . . . **P. chlorantha**
Hoary M. . . . . **P. incana**
Roundleaf M. . . . . **P. rotundifolia**
Siebers M. . . . . **P. sieberi**
Snowy M. . . . . **P. nivea**
Victorian M. . . . . . **P. lasianthos**
Wedgeleaf M. . . . . . . **P. cuneata**

MIRAB'ILIS (*HESPERONIA; QUAMOCLIDION*) ⌊w . Four-o'clock
bigelo'vi (*Hesperonia b.*)
califor'nica . . . . . California F.
dichot'oma
divarica'ta
froe'beli

The original spelling of the specific name, by Dr. H. Behr, is froebelli but, as the eponym is J. Froebel, the spelling is corrected as shown above.

green'ei
jala'pa . . . . Common F.
lae'vis (*Hesperonia l.*)
longiflo'ra . . . . Sweet F.
multiflo'ra (*Quamoclidion multiflorum*) Colorado F.
retror'sa (*Hesperonia laevis r.; H. retrorsa*) . . . . . Wishboneplant
tenuilo'ba . . . . . . Slender F.
visco'sa (*Oxybaphus v.*)

MISAN'TECA . . . . . . Misanteca
trian'dra . . . . Gulf M.

MISCAN'THUS (*XIPHAGROSTIS*) Silvergrass
See **GRASS GENERA.**

Mistletoe, European . **Viscum album**

Mistmaiden . . . . **Romanzoffia**
Sitka M. . . . . **R. sitchensis**
Unalaska M. . . **R. unalaschkensis**

MITCHEL'LA ⌊w . . . Partridgeberry
re'pens ⌊w . . . . . Partridgeberry
—leucocar'pa

Mitchellgrass . . . . . . **Astrebla**
Bull M. . . . . **A. pectinata**
Curly M. . . . . **A. lappacea**
Hoop M. . . . . . . **A. elymoides**

MITEL'LA ⌊w . . . . . . Miterwort (*Bishopscap; Mitrewort*)
brew'eri
caules'cens (*Mitellastra c.*)
diphyl'la ⌊w . . . . . . Common M.
nu'da ⌊w. . . . . Naked M.
oppositifo'lia
pentan'dra (*Pectiantia p.*) Fivestamen M.
stenopet'ala . . . . Smallflower M.
trif'ida

Mitellas'tra caules'cens . . . . **Mitella c.**

Miterwort . . . . **Mitella**
Common M. . . . . **M. diphylla**
Fivestamen M. . . . . **M. pentandra**
Naked M. . . . . **M. nuda**
Smallflower M. . . . **M. stenopetala**

MITRAG'YNA . . . . . . Mitragyna
africa'na . . . . Josswood
stipulo'sa (*macrophylla*) . . . Abura M.

MITRA'RIA
coccin'ea

MITROPHYL'LUM
mitra'tum

Mixedflower . . . . **Phyteuma**
Apennine M. . . . . **P. sieberi**
Ballhead M. . . . . . **P. orbiculare**
Black M. . . . . **P. nigrum**
Charmel M. . . . . . . **P. charmeli**
Dense M. . . . . **P. scorzonerifolium**
Dwarf M. . . . . **P. serratum**
Grasstuft M. . . **P. hemisphaericum**
Gray M. . . . . **P. canescens**
Hallers M. . . . . **P. halleri**
Harebell M. . . . **P. campanuloides**
Limecleft M. . . . . . . **P. comosum**
Lobelia M. . . . . **P. lobelioides**
Sardinian M. . . . . **P. micheli**
Spike M. . . . . **P. spicatum**
Thrift M. . . . . . . **P. limonifolium**
Wagners M. . . . . **P. vagneri**
Weakstem M. . . . . **P. scheuchzeri**

Mlanjicedar . Widdringtonia, Mlanji: **Widdringtonia whytei**

Mockaster . . . . **Eastwoodia**
Yellow M. . . . . **E. elegans**

Mockbishopweed . . . . **Ptilimnium**

Mockcucumber . . . . . **Echinocystis**
Chilicothe M. . . . . **E. macrocarpa**
Wild M. . . . . **E. lobata**

Mockorange . . . . . . **Philadelphus**
Beadle M. . . . . **P. floridus**
Big Scentless M. . . **P. grandiflorus**
∞ Burkwood M. . . . . ∞ **P. burkwoodi**
California M. . . . . **P. californicus**
Caucasus M. . . . . . **P. caucasicus**
Coulter M. . . . . **P. coulteri**
∞ Cymosus M. . . . . . . ∞ **P. cymosus**
Delavay M. . . . . **P. delavayi**
Drooping M. . . . . **P. laxus**
∞ Falconers M. . . . . . ∞ **P. falconeri**
∞ Floribundus M. . . ∞ **P. floribundus**
Gordon M. . . . . . . **P. gordonianus**
Gray M. . . . . **P. incanus**
Hairy Drooping M. **P. laxus strigosus**
Hairy M. . . . . **P. hirsutus**
Heartleaf M. . . . . . . **P. cordifolius**
Hoary M. . . . . **P. pubescens**
Karwinsky M. . . **P. karwinskyanus**
∞ Koch Zeyher M. ∞ **P. zeyheri kochianus**
∞ Latvian M. . . . . ∞ **P. latvicus**
∞ Lemoine M. . . . . . . ∞ **P. lemoinei**
Lewis M. . . . . **P. lewisi**
Littleleaf M. . . . . **P. microphyllus**
Magdalena M. . . . **P. magdalenae**
∞ Maximus M. . . . . . . ∞ **P. maximus**
Mexican M. . . . . . . **P. mexicanus**
Nepal M. . . . . **P. nepalensis**
Peking M. . . . . **P. pekinensis**
Pipers M. . . . . **P. confusus**
∞ Polyanthus M. . . . ∞ **P. polyanthus**
Purplecup M. . . . . **P. purpurascens**
∞ Purplespot M. ∞ **P. purpureo-maculatus**
Rehders Silk M. **P. sericanthus rehderianus**
Satsuma M. . . . . . . **P. satsumanus**
Scentless M. . . . . **P. inodorus**
Schrenk M. . . . . **P. schrenki**
Silk M. . . . . **P. sericanthus**
Small Beadle M. . . **P. floridus faxoni**
∞ Snowbank M. . . . . ∞ **P. nivalis**
∞ Splendens M. . . . . . ∞ **P. splendens**
∞ Summer M. . . . . ∞ **P. insignis**
Sweet M. . . . . **P. coronarius**
Thymeleaf M. . . . . **P. serpyllifolius**
Tibet M. . . . . **P. venustus**
∞ Umbel Zeyher M. ∞ **P. zeyheri umbellatus**
∞ Virginalis M. . . . . ∞ **P. virginalis**

Mockorange, continued
Warty M. . . **Philadelphus verrucosus**
Willowleaf Sweet M.
P. coronarius salicifolius
Wilson M. . . . **P. subcanus wilsoni**
Woollyleaf M. . . . **P. tomentosus**
∞Zeyher M. . . . ∞**P. zeyheri**

Mockstrawberry . . . . **Duchesnea**
India M. . . . . **D. indica**

MODI'OLA . . . . Modiola
carolinia'na (*multifida*). . Carolina M.
Stock sicknesses charged to this plant in the Southeast should be further studied.

Mogargro . . . . . Eucalyptus, Beyer
Ironbark: **Eucalyptus beyeri**

MOHAVE'A . . . . Mohavea
confertiflo'ra

Molassesgrass . . **Melinis minutiflora**

MOLDA'VICA . **DRACOCEPHALUM**
suave'olens . . . . **D. moldavica**

Moleplant; Moleweed. Euphorbia, Caper: **Euphorbia lathyrus**

MOLI'NIA
See **GRASS GENERA.**

MOLLU'GO |w . . . . . Carpetweed
cervia'na |w
verticilla'ta . . . . . Carpetweed

MOLOPOSPER'MUM
cicuta'rium

MOLT'KIA
coeru'lea
petrae'a (*Lithospermum petraeum*)
suffrutico'sa (*graminifolia; Lithospermum graminifolium*)

Moluccabalm . . . . **Molucella**
Asian M. . . . . **M. laevis**

MOLUCEL'LA (*MOLUCCELLA*)
Moluccabalm
lae'vis . . . . Asian M.
spino'sa

Mombin . . . . **Spondias**
Ambarella . . . . **S. cytherea**
Andaman M. . . . . . . **S. pinnata**
Imbu M. . . . . **S. tuberosa**
Purple M. . . . . . . **S. purpurea**
Yellow M. . . . . . . **S. mombin**

MOMOR'DICA
balsam'ina . . . . Balsamapple
charan'tia . . . . Balsampear
cochinchinen'sis
elate'rium . . . . **Ecballium e.**

MONADE'NIUM
See **SUCCULENTS.**

MONAN'THES (*PETROPHYES*)
Monanthes
See **SUCCULENTS.**

MONANTHOCH'LOE . . Shoregrass
See **GRASS GENERA.**

MONANTHOCIT'RUS
Monanthocitrus
cornu'ta

MONAR'DA |w . . . . Beebalm
bradburia'na
citriodo'ra . . . . Lemon B.
did'yma . . . . Oswego B.
Amaranth (*violacea superba*) hv.
Blazing (*splendens*)
Cambridge Scarlet

MONARDA didyma, continued
Cerise Queen
Mrs. Perry
Rose (*rosea*)
Rose Queen
Salmon (*salmonea*)
Sunset
White (*alba*)
fistulo'sa . Wildbergamot Beebalm
—al'ba . . . . White W.B.
—mol'lis (*M. mollis*) . . . Soft W.B.
—ru'bra (*M. f. media; M. media*)
Redpurple W.B.
lasiodon'ta
menthaefo'lia . . . . Mintleaf B.
pectina'ta . . . . Pony B.
puncta'ta |w . . . . . . Spotted B.
rama'leyi . . . . Ramaley B.
russellia'na . . . . Russell B.

MONARDEL'LA . . . . Monardella
austra'lis . . . . . . Southern M.
cine'rea . . . . Ashy M.
cris'pa . . . . Curlleaf M.
lana'ta . . . . Woolly M.
lanceola'ta
linoi'des . . . . . . Narrowleaf M.
macran'tha . . . . Red M.
na'na . . . . Dwarf M.
odoratis'sima . . . . . Pacific M.
parvifo'lia
robinso'ni . . . SanBernardino M.
villo'sa
vir'idis . . . . Green M.

MON'DIA . . . . **CHLOROCODON**

MON'DO (*OPHIOPOGON*). Lilyturf
jabu'ran (*Ophiopogon j.*) . . White L.
japon'icum (*Ophiopogon japonica*)
Dwarf L.

MONE'SES
uniflo'ra (*Pyrola u.*) . . Woodnymph

Moneywort . . **Lysimachia nummularia**

MONIER'A B. Juss. *ex* P.Br. (1756)
BACOPA

MONIER'A Loefl. (1758) **MONNIERIA**

MONILA'RIA
chrysoleu'ca

Monkeycomb . . . . **Pithecoctenium**
Argentine M. . . . **P. cynanchoides**
Aublet M. . . . . **P. aubleti**
Mexican M. . . . . . **P. echinatum**

Monkeyflower . . . . **Mimulus**
Allegany M. . . . . . . **M. ringens**
Alpine M. . . . . **M. luteus alpinus**
Bush M. . . . . **M. longiflorus**
Canary M. . . . . **M. brevipes**
Chilean M. . . . . **M. cupreus**
Cleveland M. . . . . **M. clevelandi**
Common M. . . . . . . **M. guttatus**
Crimson M. . . . . . **M. cardinalis**
Dwarf M. . . . . **M. nanus**
Fleming M. . . . . **M. flemingi**
Fremont M. . . . . **M. fremonti**
Golden M. . . . . **M. luteus**
Island M. . . . . . . **M. parviflorus**
Lewis M. . . . . **M. lewisi**
Muskplant M. . . . . **M. moschatus**
Orange M. . . . . . **M. aurantiacus**
Primrose M. . . . . . **M. primuloides**
Red M. . . . . **M. puniceus**
SanDiego M. . . . . **M. aridus**
Sharpwing M. . . . . . . **M. alatus**
Slender M. . . . . . **M. leptanthus**
∞Tiger M. . . . . ∞**M. tigrinus**
Tricolor M. . . . . **M. tricolor**

Monkeyjack . . . **Artocarpus rigidus**

Monkeypottree . . . . **Lecythis**
Sapucaianut M. . . . . **L. zabucajo**
Trinidad M. . . . . **L. laevifolia**

Monkshood . . . . **Aconitum**
Aconite M. . . . . **A. napellus**
Autumn M. . . . . **A. autumnale**
Azure M. . . . . **A. fischeri**
Baker M. . . . . **A. bakeri**
Caucasian M. . . . . . . **A. orientale**
Chinese M. . . . . **A. chinense**
Clambering M. . . . **A. uncinatum**
Columbia M. . . . . **A. columbianum**
Early Aconite M. . **A. napellus praecox**
Heller M. . . . . **A. helleri**
Howell M. . . . . **A. howelli**
Hungarian M. . . . . . **A. cammarum**
Japanese M. . . . . . . **A. japonicum**
Kusnezoff M. . . . . . **A. kusnezoffi**
Leiberg M. . . . . **A. leibergi**
Manchurian M. . . . . **A. variegatum**
Panicled M. . . . . . **A. paniculatum**
Pyrenees M. . . . . **A. anthora**
Smooth M. . . . . . **A. glaberrimum**
Vilmorin M. . . . **A. vilmorinianum**
White Aconite M. **A. napellus album**
Wilson M. . . . . **A. fischeri wilsoni**
Wolfbane M. . . . . . **A. lycoctonum**
Yellow M. . . . . **A. lutescens**

Monkshoodvine. **Ampelopsis aconitifolia**
Threeleaf M. . . . . **A. a. glabra**

MONNIER'IA (*MONIERA* Loefl., *not* B. Juss. *ex* P.Br.)
trifo'lia

MONODO'RA
grandiflo'ra
tenuifo'lia

MONOLE'PIS |w . . . . Monolepis
nuttallia'na |w . . . . . Nuttall M.

MONOLO'PIA
ma'jor

Monosplum . . **Eugenia umbellulifera**

MONOTAG'MA
smarag'dinum (*Calathea smaragdina; Maranta s.*)

MONOT'ROPA . . . . . . Indianpipe
hypop'itys
uniflo'ra . . . . Indianpipe

MONSO'NIA . . . . Monsonia
heliotropoi'des . . . . Egyptian M.
loba'ta . . . . Cutleaf M.
senegalen'sis . . . . . Senegal M.
specio'sa . . . . Showy M.

MONSTE'RA
delicio'sa (*Philodendron pertusum*)
Ceriman

Monsterflower . . . . **Rafflesia**
Sumatra M. . . . . **R. arnoldi**

MONTANO'A
bipinnatif'ida (*Polymnia grandis*)
hibiscifo'lia

MONTBRET'IA . . . . **TRITONIA**

MONTEZU'MA (*MAGA*)
cuben'sis
speciosis'sima (*Thespesia grandiflora*)

MON'TIA |w . . . . . Indianlettuce
chamisso'i . . . . **Claytonia c.**
fonta'na |w
lamprosper'ma

MONTIA, continued
linea'ris |w
nevaden'sis . . . . **Claytonia n.**
parvifo'lia . . . . **Claytonia p.**
perfolia'ta . . . . **Claytonia p.**

MONVIL'LEA
See **CACTUS GENERA.**

Moonflower . . . . . . **Calonyction**
Large M. . . . . . . **C. aculeatum**
Small M. . . . . . . **C. muricatum**
Trumpet M. . . . . **C. tuba**

Moonlightcactus . . . . **Selenicereus**
Bigbloom M. . . . . **S. pteranthus**
Boeckmann M. . . . **S. boeckmanni**
Coneflower M. . . . **S. coniflorus**
Honduras M. . . . . **S. hondurensis**
Kunth M. . . . . . . **S. kunthianus**
Ladyofthenight . . **S. macdonaldiae**
Murrill M. . . . . **S. murrilli**
Queenofthenight . . **S. grandiflorus**
Slimstem M. . . . . **S. donkelaari**
Spineless M. . . . . . . **S. inermis**
Urbans M. . . . . . **S. urbanianus**

Moonpod . . **Selinocarpus; S. diffusus**

Moonseed . . . . **Menispermum**
Asiatic M. . . . . . **M. dauricum**
Common M. . . . . . **M. canadense**

Moonwort . . . . **Botrychium lunaria**

Moorgrass . . . . . **Molinia caerulea**

MOQUILE'A . . . . **LICANIA**

MO'RA . . . . Mora
conjuga'ta
excel'sa (*Dimorphandra mora*)
Guiana M.

MORAE'A (*DIETES; MOREA*)
Moraea
bi'color . . . . Yellow M.
catenula'ta
glauco'pis
gutta'ta
iridioi'des . . . . Iris M.
—john'soni
papiliona'cea
pavo'nia (*Iris p.*)
polysta'chya
ramo'sa
robinsonia'na
sisyrin'chium . . . . **Iris s.**
spatha'cea (*Dietes huttoni*)
tricus'pis (*Iris t.*)
tripet'ala

MORCHEL'LA
esculen'ta . . . . . Common Morel

Morel, Common . **Morchella esculenta**

MORE'NIA (*CHAMAEDOREA* in part; *NUNNEZHAROA* in part)
Morenopalm
See **PALM GENERA.**

Morenopalm . . . . **Morenia**
Coral M. . . . . **M. corallina**
Lindens M. . . . . . **M. lindeniana**
Sweet M. . . . . **M. fragrans**

Moretonbaychestnut
Castanospermum australe

Mori . . . . Laver: **Porphyra**

MORICAN'DIA
sonchifo'lia

MORI'NA
kokan'ica
longifo'lia

MORIN'DA . . . . . Indianmulberry
citrifo'lia
corei'a (*tinctoria*) . . . . . Dyers I.
ro'yoc . . . . . . Royoc I. (*Redroot*)

MORIN'GA (*HYPERANTHERA*)
ap'tera (*arabica*)
Arabian Horseradishtree
oleif'era (*moringa; pterygosperma*)
Horseradishtree

MORIS'IA
monan'tha (*hypogaea*)

MORMO'DES
See **ORCHID GENERA.**

Morningglory . . . . . . **Ipomoea**
Bigroot M. . . . . . . **I. pandurata**
Brazilian M. . . . . . . **I. setosa**
Bush M. . . . . . . **I. leptophylla**
Cairo M. . . . . **I. cairica**
Common M. . . . . . . **I. purpurea**
Cypressvine M. . . . . **I. quamoclit**
Dawnflower M. . . . . . . **I. leari**
Fingerleaf M. . . . . . . **I. digitata**
Handleaf M. . . . . . . **I. palmata**
Horsfall M. . . . . . **I. horsfalliae**
Ivyleaf M. . . . . . . **I. hederacea**
Magenta Horsfall M.
I. horsfalliae briggsi
Mexican M. . . . . . . **I. hirsutula**
Orizaba M. . . . . . **I. orizabensis**
Soilbind M. . . . . . **I. pes-caprae**
Sweetpotato . . . . **I. batatas**
Tobago M. . . . . . . **I. pterodes**
Tree M. . . . . . . **I. arborescens**
Tricolor M. . . . . **I. tricolor**
Trinidad M. . . . . **I. sinuata**
Tuxtlas M. . . . . . . **I. tuxtlensis**
White Common M. . **I. purpurea alba**
Whiteedge M. . . . . **I. nil**
Whitetube M. . . . . . **I. mutabilis**

MORON'GIA . . . . . **SCHRANKIA**

MORTO'NIA . . . . Mortonia
utahen'sis . . . . Utah M.

MO'RUS |w . . . . Mulberry
acido'sa . . . . **M. australis**
al'ba |w . . . . White M.
—constantinopolita'na. Turkish W.M.
—macrophyl'la . . . . Bigleaf W.M.
—multicau'lis (*M. multicaulis*)
Silkworm M.
—rose'a . . . . . . Pinkfruit W.M.
—skeletonia'na (*M. a. laciniata*)
Skeletonleaf W.M.
—*stylo'sa* . . . . **M. australis**
—tatar'ica (*M. tatarica*) . Russian M.
—veno'sa . . . . . . Whitevein M.
¢Globe (*globosa*) hv. M. alba
¢Pyramidal (*pyramidalis*)
¢Weeping (*pendula*)
austra'lis (*acidosa; M. alba stylosa*)
Japanese M.
cathaya'na . . . . Chinese M.
microphyl'la . . . . Texas M.
mongol'ica . . . . . . Mongolian M.
multicau'lis . . . . **M. alba m.**
ni'gra . . . . Black M.
ru'bra |w . . . . Red M.
—tomento'sa . . . . . . Woolly R.M.
tatar'ica . . . . **M. alba t.**

MOSCHA'RIA . . . . . . Muskdaisy
pinnatif'ida . . . . Muskdaisy

Moschos'ma ripa'rium . . . **Iboza riparia**

Mosquitofern . . . **Azolla caroliniana**

Mosquitoplant . . . **Agastache cana**

Mother-of-thyme . **Thymus serpyllum**

Motherwort . . . . **Leonurus**
Common M. . . . . . . **L. cardiaca**
Siberian M. . . . . . . **L. sibiricus**

Mothorchid . . . . . . **Phalaenopsis**

Mountainash . . . . **Sorbus**
American M. . . . . . **S. americana**
Amur M. . . . . **S. amurensis**
Arizona M. . . . . **S. dumosa**
∞ Arnold M. . . . . . ∞ **S. arnoldiana**
Browndot M. . . . . . **S. caloneura**
Cascade M. . . . . . **S. cascadensis**
Checkertree M. . . . **S. torminalis**
Densehead M. . . . . . . **S. alnifolia**
Edible M. . . . . **S. mougeoti**
European M. . . . . . **S. aucuparia**
Flameberry M. . **S. rufo-ferruginea**
Folgner M. . . . . **S. folgneri**
Greenes M. . . . . . . **S. scopulina**
Harrows M. . . . . . **S. harrowiana**
Helens M. . . . . **S. helenae**
∞ Hosts M. . . . . ∞ **S. hosti**
Hupeh M. . . . . . . **S. hupehensis**
Japanese M. . . . . **S. japonica**
Keissler M. . . . . **S. keissleri**
Koehnes M. . . . . . **S. koehneana**
Korean M. . . . . **S. commixta**
Matsumura M. . . . **S. matsumurana**
∞ Oakleaf M. . . . . . . ∞ **S. hybrida**
Pacific M. . . . . **S. sitchensis**
Pratt M. . . . . **S. pratti**
Rehder M. . . . . . . **S. rehderiana**
Sargent M. . . . . . **S. sargentiana**
Servicetree M. . . . . **S. domestica**
Showy M. . . . . **S. decora**
Siberian M. . . . . **S. sambucifolia**
Snowberry M. . . . . . . **S. discolor**
Swedish M. . . . . . . **S. intermedia**
Tinyleaf M. . . . . . **S. microphylla**
Vilmorin M. . . . . **S. vilmorini**
Western M. . . . . . **S. occidentalis**
Whitebeam M. . . . . **S. aria**
Wilson M. . . . . **S. wilsoniana**
Yellowberry Japanese M.
S. japonica calocarpa
Zahlbruckner M. . **S. zahlbruckneri**

Mountainbluet . . **Centaurea montana**

Mountain Bunchgrass . Fescue, Green: **Festuca viridula;** Muhly, Mountain: **Muhlenbergia montana**

Mountainbush . . . . **Kunzea**
Apple M. . . . . **K. pomifera**
Bottlegreen M. . . . . . **K. ambigua**
Heath M. . . . . **K. ericifolia**
Littleleaf M. . . . . . . **K. parvifolia**
Silky M. . . . . **K. sericea**

Mountainfringe . . **Adlumia fungosa**

Mountainheath . . . . . **Phyllodoce**
Aleutian M. . . . . **P. aleutica**
Blue M. . . . . **P. caerulea**
Brewer M. . . . . **P. breweri**
Cream M. . . . . . . **P. glanduliflora**
Littleleaf Nippon M.
P. nipponica amabilis
Nippon M. . . . . **P. nipponica**
∞ Redcream M. . . . . ∞ **P. intermedia**
Red M. . . . . **P. empetriformis**

Mountainholly
Nemopanthus; N. mucronata

Mountainlaurel . . . . Kalmia, Mountainlaurel: **Kalmia latifolia**

Mountainmahogany . . . **Cercocarpus**
Alderleaf M. . . . . . . **C. alnifolius**
Arizona M. . . . . . . **C. arizonicus**

Mountainmahogany, continued
Birchleaf M. . **Cercocarpus betuloides**
Catalina M. . . . **C. traskiae**
Curlleaf M. . . . **C. ledifolius**
Littleleaf M. . . . **C. intricatus**
SanDiego M. . . . **C. minutiflorus**
Shaggy M. . . . **C. paucidentatus**
Silver M. . . . **C. argenteus**
True M. . . . **C. montanus**
Wright M. . . . **C. breviflorus**

Mountainmint . . . **Pycnanthemum**
Atlantic M. . . . **P. incanum**
Slender M. . . . **P. flexuosum**
Virginia M. . . . **P. virginianum**

Mountainmisery . . . Bearmat: **Chamaebatia foliolosa**

Mountainpride . . . **Spathelia**
Jamaica M. . . . **S. simplex**

Mountainsorrel . . . **Oxyria**
Alpine M. . . . **O. digyna**

Mouseearcress . **Arabidopsis thaliana**

Mousetail . . . **Myosurus**
Tiny M. . . . **M. minimus**

MUCU'NA . . . Mucuna
See note under **STIZOLOBIUM.**

deeringia'na. **Stizolobium deeringianum**
pru'riens . . . **Stizolobium pruritum**
u'rens (*Stizolobium u.*) . Cowage M.
u'tilis . . . **Stizolobium utile**

Mudgrass . . . **Coleanthus; C. subtilis**

Mudmidget . . . **Wolffiella**

Mudplantain . . . **Heteranthera**

Mudwort . . . **Limosella**
Awlleaf M. . . . **L. subulata**
Water M. . . . **L. aquatica**

MUEHLENBECK'IA (*CALACINUM*) Wirevine
axilla'ris (*nana*) . . . Matbush W.
chilen'sis (*Calacinum chilense*) Chile W.
complex'a (*Calacinum complexum*) Common W.
platycla'dos **Homalocladium platycladum**

Mugwort, Sweet . . Wormwood, Sweet: **Artemisia annua**

MUHLENBER'GIA (*EPICAMPES*) Muhly
See **GRASS GENERA.**

Muhly . . . **Muhlenbergia**
Alkali M. . . . **M. asperifolia**
Arizona M. . . . **M. arizonica**
Bamboo M. . . . **M. dumosa**
Bearded Leafy M. **M. foliosa setiglumis**
Bearded Rock M. **M. sobolifera setigera**
Bearded Wirestem M. **M. mexicana commutata**
Bog M. . . . **M. uniflora**
Bush M. . . . **M. porteri**
California M. . . . **M. californica**
Canyon M. . . . **M. involuta**
Cliff M. . . . **M. polycaulis**
Creeping M. . . . Red M.
Curlyleaf M. . . . **M. setifolia**
Cutover M. . . . **M. expansa**
Desert M. . . . **M. glauca**
Ear M. . . . **M. arenacea**
Forest M. . . . **M. sylvatica**
Foxtail M. . . . **M. andina**
Green M. . . . **M. racemosa**

Muhly, continued
Gulf Hairawn M. **Muhlenbergia capillaris filipes**
Hairawn M. . . . **M. capillaris**
Inland M. . . . **M. glabriflora**
Leafy M. . . . **M. foliosa**
Lindheimer M. . . . **M. lindheimeri**
Littleseed M. . . . **M. microsperma**
Longawn M. . . . **M. parviglumis**
Longtongue M. . . . **M. longiligula**
Marsh M. . . . Green M.
Mat M. . . . **M. squarrosa**
Mesa M. . . . **M. monticola**
Metcalfe M. . . . **M. metcalfei**
Modoc M. . . . **M. jonesi**
Mountain M. . . . **M. montana**
Navaho M. . . . **M. arsenei**
NewJersey M. . . . **M. torreyana**
NewMexico M. . . . **M. pauciflora**
Nodding M. . . . **M. brachyphylla**
Pine M. . . . **M. dubia**
Pullup M. . . . **M. filiformis**
Purple M. . . . **M. rigida**
Red M. . . . **M. repens**
Reverchon M. . . . Seep M.
Ring M. . . . **M. torreyi**
Rock M. . . . **M. sobolifera**
Sandhill M. . . . **M. pungens**
Sand M. . . . **M. arenicola**
Screwleaf M. . . . **M. virescens**
Seep M. . . . **M. reverchoni**
Sixweeks M. . . . **M. depauperata**
Slimflower M. . . . **M. tenuiflora**
Slimstem M. . . . **M. filiculmis**
Spike M. . . . **M. wrighti**
Stonyhills M. . . . **M. cuspidata**
Texas M. . . . **M. texana**
Thurber M. . . . **M. thurberi**
Utah M. . . . **M. curtifolia**
Whiskgrass M. . . . **M. macroura**
Wirestem M. . . . **M. mexicana**

MUIL'LA
marit'ima
serot'ina

Mulberry . . . **Morus**
Bigleaf White M. **M. alba macrophylla**
Black M. . . . **M. nigra**
Chinese M. . . . **M. cathayana**
Japanese M. . . . **M. australis**
Mongolian M. . . . **M. mongolica**
Pinkfruit White M. . **M. alba rosea**
Red M. . . . **M. rubra**
Russian M. . . . **M. alba tatarica**
Silkworm M. . . . **M. a. multicaulis**
Skeletonleaf White M. **M. a. skeletoniana**
Texas M. . . . **M. microphylla**
Turkish White M. **M. alba constantinopolitana**
White M. . . . **M. alba**
Whitevein M. . . . **M. a. venosa**
Woolly Red M. . **M. rubra tomentosa**

MULGE'DIUM . . . **LACTUCA**

Mullein . . . **Verbascum**
Black M. . . . **V. nigrum**
Chaix M. . . . **V. chaixi**
Clasping M. . . . **V. phlomoides**
Flannel M. . . . **V. thapsus**
Goldengate Longleaf M. **V. longifolium pannosum**
Longleaf M. . . . **V. longifolium**
Macedonian M. . . . **V. macedonicum**
Mediterranean M. . . . **V. sinuatum**
Moth M. . . . **V. blattaria**

Mullein, continued
Olympic M. . **Verbascum olympicum**
Portugal M. . . . **V. crassifolium**
Purple M. . . . **V. phoeniceum**
Purplestamen M. . . . **V. virgatum**
∞ Pyramid M. . . . ∞ **V. pyramidale**
Violetstamen M. . **V. pulverulentum**
White Chaix M. . . **V. chaixi album**
White Moth M. **V. blattaria albiflorum**
Wiedemann M.. **V. wiedemannianum**
Willmott M. . . . **V. willmottiae**
Wool M. . . . **V. thapsiforme**
Yellowwand M. . . . **V. leianthum**

Mundiroot . . . **Chlorocodon**
Whites M. . . . **C. whitei**

MUNDT'IA
spino'sa

MUNDULE'A
subero'sa

Munj . Sweetcane, Munj: **Saccharum**

MUNRO'A
See **GRASS GENERA.**

MUNTING'IA
calabu'ra . . . Jamaicacherry

Mu-oiltree . . . **Aleurites montana**

Murity . . . Mauritia, Wine: **Mauritia vinifera**

Murlin . . . Wingkelp: **Alaria**

MUR'RAYA (*CHALCAS; MURRAEA*) Jasminorange
exot'ica (*Chalcas e.*) . . . Chinabox J.
koe'nigi (*Murraea k.*). Curryleaftree
panicula'ta (*Chalcas p.*) . Common J.

MU'SA . . . Banana
arnoldia'na . . . Arnold B.
bank'si . . . Queensland B.
bas'joo . . . Japanese B.
ense'te . . . Abyssinian B.
glau'ca
na'na (*cavendishi; chinensis*) Dwarf B.
paradisi'aca . . . Plantain B.
—sapien'tum (*M. sapientum*) Common B.
Ladyfinger (*champa*). hv. M. paradisiaca
Redfruit (*rubra*)
rosa'cea . . . India B.
sumatra'na . . . Sumatra B.
tex'tilis . . . Abaca B. (*Abaca*)
zebri'na
A botanically uncertain form with brown-striped leaves.

MUSCA'RI . . . Grapehyacinth
armeni'acum . . . Armenian G.
¢Early Giant. hv.
azu'reus . . . **Hyacinthus a.**
botryoi'des . . . Common G.
—al'bum . . . White C.G.
—car'neum . . . Fleshpink C.G.
commuta'tum
como'sum . . . Tassel G.
¢Monstrosum (*plumosum*) hv.
con'icum
hel'dreichi . . . Heldreich G.
latifo'lium
masseya'num
micran'thum
moscha'tum . . . Musk G.
—fla'vum . . . Yellow M.G.
¢Majus. hv.
¢Minus
neglec'tum

MUSCARI, continued
paradox'um CAUCASUS GRAPEHYACINTH
polyan'thum
racemo'sum . . . . STARCH G.
szovitsia'num
ARGAEI. HV. Muscari
WHITE ARGAEI (*argaei album*)
The two above hort. var. are presumably clons, but their identity is still uncertain.

MUSCA'RIA . . . . . **SAXIFRAGA**

MUSHROOM
A general term applied to fleshy fungi of the class Basidiomycetes, especially if with a gill-bearing cap, and (popularly) if edible. See **CRYPTOGAMS, ECONOMIC.**

MUSKDAISY . **Moscharia; M. pinnatifida**
MUSKMALLOW . **Hibiscus abelmoschus**
MUSKMELON . . . . . . **Cucumis melo**
MUSKROOT . . . . **Adoxa moschatellina**
MUSKWOOD . . . . **Guarea**
AMERICAN M. . . . . . **G. trichilloides**
BLACK M. . . . . . . **G. thompsoni**
JAMAICA M. . . . . **G. glabra**
PINK M. . . . . **G. cedrata**
RUSBY M. . . . . **G. rusbyi**

MUSSAEN'DA
erythrophyl'la
lute'ola
macrophyl'la

MUSTARD
BLACK M. . . . . . . **Brassica nigra**
CABBAGE M. . . . . . **B. alboglabra**
INDIA M. . . . . **B. juncea**
JAPANESE M. . . . . . . **B. japonica**
POTHERB M. . . **B. juncea crispifolia**
WHITE M. . . . . **B. hirta**

MU'TINUS . . . . MUTINUS
cani'nus . . . . . DOGSTINKHORN M.

MUTIS'IA . . . . MUTISIA
clem'atis
decur'rens
ilicifo'lia . . . . HOLLYLEAF M.
viciaefo'lia . . . . VETCHLEAF M.

Muttongrass . . . BLUEGRASS, MUTTON: **Poa fendleriana**
Longtongue M. . . . BLUEGRASS, LONGTONGUE MUTTON: **Poa longiligula**

MYCE'NA . . . . MYCENA
galericula'ta . . . . PEAKCAP M.

MYGIN'DA . . . . . **RHACOMA**
rhaco'ma . . . . **R. crossopetalum**

MYOP'ORUM . . . . . . MYOPORUM
acumina'tum . . . WINDSTAYBUSH M.
lae'tum
sandwicen'se. SANDALWOOD M. (*Naio*)

MYOSOTID'IUM
horten'sia (*nobile*)

MYOSO'TIS W . . . . FORGETMENOT
alpes'tris (*rupicola*) . . . . ALPINE F.
BLUE GEM. HV.
DWARF (*robusta grandiflora*)
GOLDEN (*aurea*)
HEATH (*stricta*)
ROYAL BLUE
VICTORIA
arven'sis . . . . FIELD F.
azo'rica . . . . AZORES F.
cespito'sa (*rehsteineri*) . . . TUFTED F.

MYOSOTIS, continued
dissitiflo'ra . . SWISS FORGETMENOT
JACKFROST (*elegantissima*) HV.
lax'a W . . . . BAY F.
lithospermifo'lia
rupic'ola . . . . **M. alpestris**
scorpioi'des (*palustris*) W . . TRUE F.
DWARF PERPETUAL (*semperflorens*) HV.
stric'ta
This name is often misapplied to Heath Forgetmenot, HV. of M. alpestris. The true M. stricta of botanists is not in the trade.
sylvat'ica . . . . . . WOODLAND F.
tra'versi
wel'witschi

MYOSU'RUS W . . . . . MOUSETAIL
min'imus W . . . . TINY M.

MYRCIA'RIA . . . . . . JABOTICABA
cauliflo'ra

MYR'ICA W . . BAYBERRY; WAXMYRTLE
asplenifo'lia . . **Comptonia peregrina; C. p. asplenifolia**
califor'nica W . . . . . PACIFIC W.
carolinien'sis Auth., *not* Mill. **M. pensylvanica**
cerif'era (*caroliniensis* Mill., *not* Auth.) W . . . . . . SOUTHERN W.
cordifo'lia
fa'ya . . . . . . CANARYISLANDS W.
ga'le W . . . . SWEETGALE
hart'wegi . . . . SIERRA W.
heterophyl'la
inodo'ra (*Cerothamnus inodorus*) ODORLESS W.
∞ **macfarla'nei** (*cerifera* × *pensylvanica*) ∞ MACFARLANE W.
The cultivated plant is presumably a clon of this.
pensylvan'ica (*caroliniensis* Auth., *not* Mill.) . . . . NORTHERN B.
This more northern, seashore, *deciduous* species is frequently confused with M. cerifera, which gets no farther north than New Jersey, and has narrower, *evergreen*, sharp-tipped, and less pubescent leaves, and smaller berries.
ru'bra

MYRICA'RIA . . . . . FALSETAMARIX
dahur'ica . . . . . . DAHURIAN F.
german'ica (*Tamarix g.*) . GERMAN F.

MYRIOCEPH'ALUS . . . WOOLLYMAT
stu'arti (*Polycalymma s.*) . STUART W.

MYRIOPHYL'LUM W . PARROTFEATHER
alterniflo'rum W
brasilien'se W . . . . BRAZILIAN P.
exalbes'cens
far'welli W . . . . . . FARWELL P.
heterophyl'lum W
hippuroi'des W
hu'mile W
lax'um W
pinna'tum . . . . GREEN P.
proserpinacoi'des . . . . . CHILE P.
scabra'tum W
spica'tum W
tenel'lum W . . . . SLENDER P.
verticilla'tum W . . . . CANADA P.

MYRIS'TICA . . . . NUTMEG
argen'tea . . . . . . MACASSAR N.
fra'grans . . . . COMMON N.
ir'ya . . . . MUTWINDA N.
surinamen'sis

Myrobalan . . . LEAFFLOWER, EMBLIC: **Phyllanthus emblica;** TERMINALIA, TROPICAL-ALMOND; **Terminalia catappa;** PLUM, MYROBALAN: **Prunus cerasifera**
Myrobalan, a controversial plant name, derives from myrobalanos, a scentless oil (thought to be our modern "oil of ben," obtained from the Horseradishtree, Moringa oleifera) anciently used in mixing unguents. In modern Greek, however, myrobalanos is the Emblic, fruit of Phyllanthus emblica. Myrobalan is also the trade name for commercial tanning material derived from two Oriental species of Terminalia.

MYROCAR'PUS . . . . MYROCARPUS
frondo'sus . . . . . . BRAZILIAN M.

MYROSPER'MUM
frutes'cens

MYROX'YLON (*TOLUIFERA*) BALMTREE
bal'samum (*toluiferum*) TOLUBALSAM B.
perei'rae (*Toluifera p.*) PERUBALSAM B.
peruif'erum . . . . . . ECUADOR B.

MYRRHI'NIUM
salic'inum

MYR'RHIS . . . . . . SWEETCICELY
odora'ta . . . . SWEETCICELY

MYRRHTREE . . . . **Commiphora**
ABYSSINIAN M. . . . . **C. abyssinica**
AFRICAN M. . . . . . . **C. africana**
BISABOL M. . . . . . **C. erythraea**
COMMON M. . . . . **C. myrrha**
MECCA M. . . . . . **C. opobalsamum**
MUKUL M. . . . . **C. mukul**
OPOPANAX M. . . . . **C. kataf**

MYRSI'NE
africa'na
chatham'ica
semiserra'ta
variab'ilis

MYRSIPHYL'LUM . . **ASPARAGUS**

MYRTE'OLA
microphyl'la (*Myrtus m.*)
nummula'ria (*Myrtus n.*)

MYRTILLOCAC'TUS
See **CACTUS GENERA.**

MYRTLE . . . . **Myrtus**
BIDWILL M. . . . . **M. bidwilli**
ITALIAN TRUE M. **M. communis italica**
RALPH M. . . . . **M. ralphi**
RAMARANA M. . . . . . . **M. bullata**
ROMAN TRUE M. **M. communis romana**
TARENTINE T. M. . . . **M. c. tarentina**
TRUE M. . . . . **M. communis**

MYR'TUS . . . . MYRTLE
bid'willi . . . . BIDWILL M.
bulla'ta . . . . RAMARANA M.
commu'nis (*buxifolia* Raf., *not* Swartz) TRUE M.
—**ital'ica** . . . . . . ITALIAN T.M.
—**roma'na** . . . . . . ROMAN T.M.
—**tarenti'na** . . . TARENTINE T.M.
¢COMPACT (*compacta*) HV. M. communis
¢DOUBLE (*floreplen o*)
¢DWARF (*minima*)
¢ROSEMARY (*microphylla*)
¢VARIEGATED (*variegata*)

MYRTUS, continued
lu'ma . . . . . . **Eugenia apiculata**
microphyl'la . . . . . . **Myrteola m.**
Unfortunately the name Myrtus microphylla is commonly misapplied to M. communis ₵Rosemary.
moli'nae . . . . **Ugni m.**
nummula'ria . . . . . . **Myrteola n.**
obcorda'ta
peduncula'ta
pseudocaryophyl'lus
ralph'i . . . . RALPH MYRTLE
—purpu'rea
tomento'sa . . . . . **Rhodomyrtus t.**
ug'ni . . . . **Ugni molinae**
MYSORETHORN . . **Caesalpinia sepiaria**

MYSTACID'IUM
See **ORCHID GENERA.**

NAB'ALUS . . . . . **PRENANTHES**

NAEGE'LIA
cinnabari'na (*Gesneria c.*)
multiflo'ra (*Gesneria amabilis*)
zebri'na (*Gesneria z.*)

NAI'AS |w . . . . NAIAD
The original spelling of this name, Najas, is used by some botanists.
confer'ta |w
flex'ilis |w
—robus'ta
gracil'lima |w
guadalupen'sis |w . . . SOUTHERN N.
maria'na |w . . . . SPINY N.

NAILWORT . . . . **Paronychia**
ALLEGANY N. . . . . **P. argyrocoma**
CREEPING N. . . . . **P. serpyllifolia**
FORKING N. . . . . . **P. dichotoma**
GREEK N. . . . . **P. kapela**
HEAD N. . . . . **P. capitata**
JAMES N. . . . . **P. jamesi**
KURD N. . . . . **P. kurdica**
LINDHEIMER N. . . . **P. lindheimeri**
ROCKYMOUNTAIN N. . . . **P. pulvinata**
SANFRANCISCO N. . . . **P. franciscana**
SILVER N. . . . . **P. argentea**
WHITEMOUNTAINS N.
P. argyrocoma albimontana

Naio . . . . MYOPORUM, SANDALWOOD: **Myoporum sandwicense**

Naked-Indian . APES-EARRING, CARIB: **Pithecellobium caribaeum**

NA'MA (*CONANTHUS*) . . . NAMA
lobb'i . . . . WOOLLY N.
par'ryi (*Eriodictyon p.*) . . PARRY N.

NAMAQUALAND-DAISY . . . . **Venidium**
MONARCH N. . . . . . **V. fastuosum**
SUNBURST N. . . . . **V. decurrens**

NANAN'THUS
MESEMBRYANTHEMUM
See **SUCCULENTS.**

NANDI'NA . . . . NANDINA
domes'tica . . . . NANDINA
—al'ba . . . . . . WHITEBERRY N.

NAN'NORRHOPS . . . . MAZARIPALM
See **PALM GENERA.**

NANO'DES
See **ORCHID GENERA.**

NAPAE'A . . . . GLADEMALLOW
dioi'ca

NAPIERGRASS . **Pennisetum purpureum**

NAPOLEO'NA
imperia'lis

NARCIS'SUS . . . . NARCISSUS
The Editorial Committee is chiefly indebted to the Division of Plant Exploration and Introduction, Bureau of Plant Industry, U. S. Department of Agriculture, for the following treatment of the genus Narcissus. Special attention is called to the "fancy" or hort var. names of Narcissus, which are as a rule (with some notable exceptions such as "Mrs. Walter H. Brewster"), models for brevity.
It is extremely desirable that this admirable practice of giving suitable single or binomial names to plants and plant products be adopted universally in the plant world.
abscis'sus (*N. pseudonarcissus muticus; Ajax a.*)
—graciliflo'rus
—serot'inus
—tubulo'sus
albes'cens (*albicans* Hort., *not* Haw.)
al'bus Haw. . . . . . **N. moschatus**
al'bus Hort. . . **N. triandrus a.** Hort.
alpes'tris (*moschatus* Hort., *not* L. *nor* Haw.)
asturien'sis (*minimus* Auth., *not* Haw.; *minor* Brot., *not* L.)
—brevicorona'tus
∞ **barr'i**
A horticultural hybrid group; has no relation to N. juncifolius.
bi'color (*N. pseudonarcissus b.*)
—lorifo'lius (*N. loriflorus; N. rugilobus* Hort., *not* Haw. *nor* Steud.)
biflo'rus . . . . PRIMROSE N.
biflo'rus Gren. & Godr.
N. pseudonarcissus
biflo'rus Schur . . . . **N. radiiflorus**
bulboco'dium . PETTICOAT DAFFODIL
—citri'nus
₵**—conspic'uus** Hort.
₵**—graells'i** Hort. (*N. graellsi*)
—monophyl'lus (*N. clusii*)
₵FOLIOSUS. HV.
—niv'alis (*N. nivalis*)
calathi'nus DC. . **N. triandrus c.** Hort.
calathi'nus L. . . . . . . **N. odorus**
campernel'li Hort. . . . . **N. odorus**
cer'nuus Hort. . . . . . **N. moschatus**
—ple'nus Hort. ₵**N. moschatus p.** Hort.
cer'nuus Roth, *not* Salisb. **N. tortuosus**
clus'ii . **N. bulbocodium monophyllus**
confu'sus
cyclamin'eus (*N. pseudonarcissus c.*)
el'egans
exer'tus (*N. majalis e.*)
—orna'tus (*N. poeticus o.* Barr)
gadita'nus . . . . . . **N. juncifolius**
gay'i (*princeps* Hort.)
—praelon'gus
×*goua'ni* . . . . ∞ **N. incomparabilis**
N. incomparabilis is not in trade and exists now only as a group name.
grac'ilis . . . . . RUSHLEAF JONQUIL
—ten'uior Hort. (*N. tenuior*)
SILVER R.J.
graells'i . ₵**N. bulbocodium g.** Hort.
hellen'icus
hispan'icus (*N. pseudonarcissus major*)
—con'color
—propin'quus (*N. propinquus*)
—spu'rius
CORONATUS (*major spurius coronatus*) HV.
∞ **incomparab'ilis** ∞ NONESUCH DAFFODIL
This is no longer an entity—merely a group name for natural or artificial hybrids of a specific lineage.

NARCISSUS, continued
∞ **interme'dius**
This is also a group name.
john'stoni (*N. pseudonarcissus j.*)
—mirab'ilis
jonquil'la . . . . JONQUIL
—floreple'no . . . . QUEEN ANNES J.
—jonquilloi'des Hort. (*N. jonquilloides*)
—mi'nor Hort.
—webb'i Hort. (*N. webbi*)
juncifo'lius (*gaditanus; requieni*)
—gadita'nus Hort.
—minutiflo'rus Hort. (*N. minutiflorus*)
—rupic'ola Hort. . . . . **N. rupicola**
lago'i
∞ **leeds'i**
A group name for natural or artificial hybrids of a specific lineage.
leonen'sis
lobula'ris Haw. . . . . **N. obvallaris**
lobula'ris Hort. . . . . . . **N. nanus**
lobula'ris Schult. **N. pseudonarcissus l.**
longispa'thus
loriflo'rus . . . . **N. bicolor l.**
macrolo'bus
—palles'cens
maja'lis
—exer'tus . . . . **N. exertus**
—patella'ris (*N. poeticus p.* Hort.)
marvie'ri Hort.
max'imus . . . . . **N. obvallaris m.**
min'imus Auth. . . . **N. asturiensis**
min'imus Haw. . . . . **N. minor m.**
mi'nor
—min'imus (*N. minimus* Haw., *not* Auth.)
—na'nus (Spach) Herb. . . **N. nanus**
—ple'nus Hort.
mi'nor Brot. . . . . . **N. asturiensis**
mi'nor Hort. . . . . . . **N. pumilus**
minutiflo'rus . **N. juncifolius m.** Hort.
moscha'tus (*albus* Haw., *not* Hort.; *cernuus* Hort., *not* Roth *nor* Salisb.; *N. pseudonarcissus m.* Hort.)
₵**—ple'nus** Hort. (*N. cernuus p.* Hort.)
moscha'tus Haw. . . . . **N. tortuosus**
moscha'tus Hort. . . . . **N. alpestris**
na'nus (*lobularis* Hort., *not* Haw. *nor* Schult.; *N. minor n.* (Spach) Herb.)
×**nel'soni**
nevaden'sis
niv'alis . . . . . **N. bulbocodium n.**
no'bilis . . . . **N. pseudonarcissus n.**
obvalla'ris (*lobularis* Haw., *not* Hort. *nor* Schult.; *N. pseudonarcissus bromfieldi; N. p. obvallaris* Hort.; *rugilobus* Haw., *not* Hort., *nor* Steud.)
TENBY DAFFODIL
—con'color (*N. pseudonarcissus c.*)
—max'imus (*N. maximus*)
—tosca'nus
odo'rus (*calathinus* L., *not* DC.; *campernelli* Hort.)
CAMPERNELLE JONQUIL
—gigan'teus
—hemina'lis Hort.
—mi'nor Hort.
—ple'nus Hort.
—rugulo'sus Hort.
₵MAXIMUS. HV.
—tril'obus Hort.
orna'tus . . . . **N. poeticus o.**
pallidiflo'rus (*N. pallidus praecox* Hort.)
—astur'icus
—interme'dius

NARCISSUS, continued
pisa'nus
∞**po'etaz** . . . . ∞POETAZ NARCISSUS
A group name for hybrids of poeticus × tazetta or reverse.

poet'icus . . . . POETS N.
—**grandiflo'rus** Hort.
—**hellen'icus** Hort.
—**maja'lis** Hort.
—**orna'tus** (*N. ornatus*)
—*orna'tus* Barr . . . . **N. exertus o.**
—*patella'ris* Hort. . . **N. majalis p.**
—**prae'cox** Hort.
₵GRANDIFLORUS. HV.
—*radiiflo'rus* . . . . . **N. radiiflorus**
—*recur'vus* Hort. . . . . **N. recurvus**
—**reflex'us** Hort.
—**tripoda'les** Hort.
—*verbanen'sis* . . . **N. verbanensis**
ORNATUS MAXIMUS. HV. N. poeticus
prin'ceps Hort. . . . . **N. gayi**
propin'quus . . . . **N. hispanicus p.**
pseudonarcis'sus (*biflorus* Gren. & Godr., *not* Curt. *nor* Schur; *rugilobus* Steud., *not* Haw. *nor* Hort.)
COMMON DAFFODIL
—*bi'color* . . . . **N. bicolor**
—*brom'fieldi* . . . . . . **N. obvallaris**
—**cam'bricus** Hort. (*Ajax c.*)
—*con'color* . . . . . **N. obvallaris c.**
—*cyclamin'eus* . . . **N. cyclamineus**
—**festi'nus** (*Ajax f.*)
—**hu'milis**
—**insig'nis**
—*john'stoni* . . . . . . **N. johnstoni**
—**lobula'ris** (*N. lobularis* Schult., *not* Hort. *nor* Haw.)
—*ma'jor* . . . . **N. hispanicus**
—**minorifor'mis**
—**monti'nus** (*Ajax m.*)
—*moscha'tus* Hort. . . **N. moschatus**
—*mu'ticus* . . . . **N. abscissus**
—**no'bilis** (*N. nobilis*)
—*obvalla'ris* Hort. . . **N. obvallaris**
—**platylo'bus**
—**ple'nus** Hort.
—**por'rigens**
—**scot'icus** Hort.
₵PLENUS. HV.
—**tortuo'sus** Hort.
—**variifor'mis** Hort.
pu'milus (*minor* Hort., *not* Brot. *nor* L.)
radiiflo'rus (*biflorus* Schur.; *N. poeticus r.*)
recur'vus (*N. poeticus r.* Hort.)
—**gracil'ior**
requien'i . . . . **N. juncifolius**
rugilo'bus Haw. . . . **N. obvallaris**
rugilo'bus Hort. . **N. bicolor lorifolius**
rugilo'bus Steud. . **N. pseudonarcissus**
rupic'ola (*N. juncifolius r.* Hort.)
sa'bini
serot'inus . . . . AUTUMN JONQUIL
stella'ris
tazet'ta . . . . . . POLYANTHUS N.
₵PAPERWHITE. HV.
ten'uior . . . . . **N. gracilis t.** Hort.
tortuo'sus (*cernuus* Roth, *not* Hort. *nor* Salisb.; *moschatus* Haw., *not* Hort. *nor* L.)
trian'drus . . . . . . ANGELS-TEARS
—**al'bus** Hort. (*N. albus* Hort.)
—**auranti'acus** Hort.
—**calathi'nus** Hort. (*N. calathinus* DC., *not* L.)
—**con'color** Hort.
—**nu'tans** Hort.

NARCISSUS, continued
trian'drus pal'lidus Hort.
—**pulchel'lus** Hort.
—**ryen'sis** Hort.
Probably a garden hybrid.
verbanen'sis (*N. poeticus v.*)
viridiflo'rus GREEN AUTUMN JONQUIL
watier'i
webb'i . . . . . **N. jonquilla w.** Hort.

Common names and hort. var. of **Narcissus:**

EXPLANATION OF NARCISSUS TYPE CLASSIFICATION

As adopted by the Royal Horticultural Society

1a Yellow Trumpets.
1b White Trumpets.
1c Bicolor Trumpets.
2a Yellow Perianth Incomparabilis.
2b White Perianth Incomparabilis.
3a Yellow Perianth Barri.
3b White Perianth Barri.
4a Largecrown Leedsi (Giant Leedsi).
4b Smallcrown Leedsi (Leedsi).
5 Triandrus Hybrids.
6 Cyclamineus Hybrids.
7 Jonquil Hybrids.
8 Tazetta and Tazetta Hybrids, including Poetaz and other small bunch-flowered varieties.
9 Poeticus.
10 Doubles.
11 Various.

ABBREVIATIONS OF NAMES OF ORIGINATORS OR INTRODUCERS

Adams C. Lemesle Adams, Pendeford Hall, Wolverhampton, England.
Back. Mrs. O. R. Backhouse, England.
Back. H. Henry Backhouse, Bournemouth, England.
Back. W. William Backhouse.
Baker Baker.
Barr Barr & Sons, London, W. C., England.
Bath R. H. Bath, Ltd., The Floral Farms, Wisbeck, England.
Bier. Miss Mary McD. Bierne, "Rhodeen," Ashland, Va.
Bro. The Brodie of Brodie, Brodie Castle, Forres, England.
Buck. Leonard Buckland, formerly Keyham, Camperdown, Australia.
Cal. Roderick Frank Calvert, Carnsulan, Coverack, Helston, Cornwall, England.
Cart. Cartwright & Goodwin, Ltd., Kidderminster, England.
Cave Sir Charles H. Cave, Sidbury Manor, Sidmouth, England.
Chap. F. Herbert Chapman, West Mead, Peasmarsh, Sussex, England.
Cob. Cobley.
Cope. W. M. F. Copeland, West View, St. James' Road, Southampton, England.
Cros. E. M. Crosfield.
Cul. Culpin.
Daw. Charles Dawson, The Chantreys, Lymington, Hants, England.
deB. de Bruin.
deG. de Graff Brothers, Ltd., Noordwijk, Holland.
dGro. Probably J. de Groot & Son, Noordwijk, Holland.
Don. Donald Nursery, Newcastle, Ireland.
Eld. W. J. Eldering & Son, Ltd., Sassenheim, Holland.
Eng. Rev. George Herbert Engleheart, Salisbury, England.
Gib. A. Gibson, Australia or New Zealand.

NARCISSUS, continued
Hall J. Hall, Remura, Auckland, New Zealand.
Hart. William Baylor Hartland, Cork, Ireland.
Hay Rev. George Philip Hay, Westbere, Canterbury, England.
Heere Heere.
Hem. Hemorik.
Ho. Homan.
Ken. John Kendall.
Konig von Konig.
Kou. Kouwenhoven.
Kre. Ernst Krelage, Haarlem, Holland.
Laur. Mrs. Laurenson.
L. & B. Edward Leeds & William Backhouse.
Lowe Arthur E. Lowe, Otahuna, Tai Tapu, New Zealand.
Lower Dr. Nynian Yeo Lower, Presteigne, Radnorshire, England.
Lower P. P. Lower, The Cottage, Carlton Road, Harpenden, Herts., England.
Lubbe G. Lubbe & Son, Oezstgeest, Holland.
Mar. Mrs. E. Martin.
Mil. William A. Milner, Totley Hall, Sheffield, England.
Mooy L. Pulman Mooy, Haarlem, Holland.
Ouds. Oudshoorn.
Pap. Papendrecht.
Pear. J. R. Pearson & Sons, Lowdham, Nottinghamshire, England.
Pow. Edwin C. Powell, R.F.D. 1, Rockville, Md.
Prins H. Prins & Co., Wisbeck, Cambridgeshire, England.
Rich. J. Lionel Richardson, Prospect House, Waterford, Ireland.
Sec. F. A. Secrett, Bell Farm, Felcott Road, Hershan, Walton-on-Thames, England.
Seg. Johan Segers, Lisse, Holland.
Smi. Probably Charles Smith & Son, Caledonia Nursery, Guernsey, England.
Spu. Miss Katherine Spurrell, Bessingham, Norfolk, England.
Thom. Prof. Sir Algernon. P W. Thomas, Mt. Eden, Auckland, New Zealand.
Thur. Thurston.
Tro. Tromp.
vDeu. P. van Deursen, Sassenheim, Holland.
Veitch Veitch.
Vis. Albert Vis, Limmen, Holland.
vLeeu. L. vanLeeuwen & Son, Ltd., Sassenheim, Holland.
vSch. Anthony C. van der Schoot, Ltd., Hillegom, Holland.
vTub. G. H. van Tubergen & Sons, Haarlem, Holland.
vWav. M. van Waveren & Sons, Ltd., Leeuwenstein Nurseries, Hillegom, Holland.
vZon. van Zonneveld Bro. & Philippo, Ltd., Sassenheim, Holland.
War. Warnaar & Co., Ltd., Sassenheim, Holland.
Ware Walter T. Ware, Inglescombe, Near Bath, England.
Watts W. A. Watts, The Welch Bulb Fields, St. Asaph, Wales.
Welch. William Welchman, Birdbeck House, Upwell, Wisbeck, England.
West D. U. West, West & Fell, Swanley, Casterton, Victoria, Australia.
White J. T. White.
Will. J. John Charles Williams, Caerhays Castle, Gorran, Cornwell, England.
Will. P. Percival D. Williams, Lanarth, St. Keverne, Cornwall, England.

NARCISSUS, continued

Wils. A. Alexander M. Wilson, Middlemoor, Presteigne, Radnorshire, England.

Wils. G. Guy L. Wilson, The Knockan, Broughshane, Co. Antrim, Ireland.

Wor. Philip John Worsley, Clifton, Bristol, England.

Zand. G. Zandbergen, Terwegen, Sassenheim, Holland.

Zees. C. Zeestraten, Chautauqua Flower Fields, Greenhurst, N. Y.

All the following hort. var. are clons.

Abelard. 2a. (Back.; deG. 1927.)
Abiad. 1c. (deG. 1923.)
Abundance. 8. (Back.; deG. 1930.)
Ace of Diamonds. 9. (Eng. 1923.)
Actaea. 9. (Lubbe 1927.)
Ada Finch. 1b. (deG. 1927.)
Adler. 2b. (deG. 1929.)
Admiration. 8. (vWav. 1913.)
Adsum. 4a. (Lowe 1927.)
Advance Guard. 1a. (Bath 1923.)
Aerolite. 1a. (deG. 1923.)
Afghanistan. 2b. (Will. P. 1927.)
Afiena. 2b. (Back.; deG. 1929.)
Afterglow. 3a. (vLeeu. 1931.)
Agnes Harvey. 5b. (Spu. 1902.)
Agra. 2b. (Lower; War. 1936.)
Alaska. 1a. (deG. 1928.)
Alasnam. 1a. (deG. 1923.)
Albaran. 3b. (Back.; deG. 1929.)
Albast. 1b. (Back.; deG. 1929.)
Albatross. 4b. (Eng. 1891.)
Albert Vis. 8. (Vis 1913.)
Albingia. 3b. (Back.; deG. 1929.)
Albusplenus Odoratus. 10.
Alceste. 2b. (vTub. 1927.)
Alcibiades. 3b. (deG. 1927.)
Alcida. 3a. (Back. 1923.)
Aleppo. 3b. (Bro.; Wils. G. 1928.)
Aletta. 2a. (Back.; deG. 1929.)
Alfred Hartley. 1a. (Eng.; Sec. '30.)
Alice Knights. 1b. (Barr 1905.)
Alicia. 4a. (Barr 1923.)
Allure. 2b. (vLeeu. 1933.)
Almee. 1b. (vZon. 1931.)
Alpine Snow. 4b. (Eng. 1913.)
Alroi. 2a. (Rich. 1926.)
Alsace. 8. (vSch. 1907.)
Amasis. 2a. (Back.; deG 1929.)
Amir. 2a. (Back.; Lower P. 1928.)
Anaconda. 2a. (Back.)
Anak. 1a. (Cob. 1932.)
Anna Croft. 3a. (Back.; deG. 1927.)
Apotheosis. 1a. (vTub. 1927.)
Apricot. 1c. (deG. 1898.)
Apricotine. 2a. (Buck. 1926.)
Apricot Phoenix. 10. (deG. 1907.)
Archeron. 2a.
Argent. 10. (Eng. 1907.)
Argonne. 3b. (Back.; deG. 1929.)
Arion. 4b. (deG. 1923.)
Arizona. 2a. (Back.; deG. 1928.)
Arthur Bowman. 3b. (Back. 1927.)
Artistic. 2b. (West 1932.)
Asmode. 2b. (deG. 1930.)
Aspasia. 8. (vSch. 1910.)
Atreus. 3b. (Back.; deG. 1929.)
Atropos. 1c. (deG. 1927.)
Aubrey. 1a. (deG. 1928.)
Aurelia. 7. (Barr 1913.)
Aurigny. 2b. (Back.; deG. 1929.)
Autocrat. 2a. (L. & B. 1890.)
Balisand. 2b. (deG. 1927.)
Barbara Pratt. 2c. (deG. 1932.)
Barbaric. 3a. (Chap.; Pear. 1927.)

NARCISSUS, continued

Barri Conspicuus. 3a. (L. & B. 1886.) *Conspicuus.*
Batavier. 2a. (deG. 1929.)
Baths Flame. 3a. (Bath 1914.)
Baucis. 2b. (Back.; deG. 1929.)
Beauty of Radnor. 2b. (Lower '23.)
Bedouin. 2b. (Will. J. 1908.)
Beersheba. 1b. (Eng. 1923.)
Bellamy. 2b. (Back.; deG. 1929.)
Bellbro. 3b. (Back.; deG. 1929.)
Belle Jaune. 2a.
Ben Hur. 1a. (deG. 1927.)
Beppy. 1c. (Prins 1929.)
Berdas. 2a. (Watts 1923.)
Berdina. 3b. (Back.; deG. 1929.)
Bernardino. 2b. (Wor. 1907.)
Bertha Aten. 2b. (Back.; deG. 1933.)
Beryl. 6. (Will. P. 1907.)
Betty King. 2b. (Back.; deG. 1927.)
Birdofparadise. 2b. (vTub. 1927.)
Blackprince. 9. (Eng. 1913.)
Blazina. 2b. (Back.; deG. 1929.)
Blazing Sword. 2a. (—; vLeeu. '31.)
Blizzard. 4a. (Eng. 1927.)
Bloemlust. 2a. (vLeeu. 1931.)
Bodilly. 2b. (Will P. 1925.)
Boerhaave. 8. (vZon. 1930.)
Bohemienne. 3b. (deG. 1926.)
Bokhara. 2a. (Bro. 1927.)
Bonfire. 3a. (Will. P. 1910.)
Bonny Winkfield. 1c. (Bro. 1927.)
Borderqueen. 2a. (West 1928.)
Bradwardine. 4a. (Bro.; Cal. 1927.)
Bridegroom. 3b. (Bro.; Cal. 1927.)
Brigand. 1a. (Watts 1923.)
Brightling. 3a. (Back. 1922.)
Brilliancy. 3a. (Eng. 1906.)
Brotonne. 2a. (Back. 1927.)
Broussoneti. 11.
Brunswick. 4a. (Will. P. 1934.)
Bulbocodium Citrinus. 11.
Bulbocodium Conspicuus. 11.
Bulbocodium Monophyllus. 11.
Bulwark. 1a. (Bro. 1923.)
Butterbowl. 2a. (Wils. G. 1931.)
Buttercup. 7. (Eng. 1890.)
Caedmon. 9. (Eng. 1913.)
Caesar. 9. (Eng. 1913.)
Calcutta. 3b. (Back.; Rich. 1930.)
Calif. 2a. (Wils. A. 1927.)
Calorama. 3a. (deG. 1930.)
Campernelli. 7. Odorus Campernelli.
Canaliculatus. 11.
Cardinal. 3b. (Eng. 1907.)
Carleen. 3b. (Back.; White 1930.)
Carlton. 2a. (Will. 1927.)
Carmel. 1c. (Bro 1926.)
Carmencita. 2b. (Back.; deG. '29.)
Carminowe. 3b. (Will. 1927.)
Carnlough. 4a. (Wils. 1934.)
Carnsulan. 8. (Will.; Cal. 1927.)
Carveth. 3b. (Will. 1927.)
Cassandra. 9. (Eng. 1899.)
Cassia. 2b. (Back.; deG. 1929.)
Cennedy. 1c. (deG. 1927.)
Challenger. 3b. (Cros. 1890.)
Chancellor. 2b. (vLeeu. 1931.)
Charming. 4a. (Wils. G. 1923.)
Charter. 3b. (Back. 1927.)
Cheerfulness. 10. (vSch. 1923.)
Cheerio. 2a. (Bro.; Wils. G. 1932.)
China Clay. 1b. (Bro.; Cal. 1928.)
Chippendale. 3b. (vLeeu. 1933.)
Chit Chat. 1c. (Wils.; Cal. 1927.)
Christine. 5. (Back. 1927.)

NARCISSUS, continued

Chrysolite. 7. (deG. 1927.)
Cicely. 4a. (Wils. A. 1927.)
Cinderella. 3b. (Back.; deG. 1927.)
Circlet. 3b. (Eng. 1907.)
Citronella. 1a. (vTub. 1927.)
Clava. 2b. (Bro. 1929.)
Cleopatra. 1a. (Barr 1903.)
Clifton. 2a. (deG. 1927.)
Cocarde. 2a. (vLeeu. 1931.)
Codlins and Cream. Sulphur Phoenix.
Cokefield. 1b. (Bro.; Cal. 1928.)
Col. d'Anternes. 1b. (deG. 1927.)
Comely. 1c. (Wils. G. 1923.)
Comrade. 4a. (Welch 1923.)
Comus. 9. (Eng. 1907.)
Confield. 2b. (Back.; deG. 1929.)
Connemara. 1b. (Wils. G. 1930.)
Conspicuus. 3a. Barri Conspicuus.
Copperbowl. 2a. (Bro.; Wils. G. '27.)
Corinth. 1b. (Bro. 1928.)
Cornish Cross. 4a. (Bro.; Cal. '28.)
Cornish Fire. 2a. (Will.; Wils. 1930.)
Corython. 3b. (Back.; deG. 1929.)
Coverack Beauty. 1c. (Bro.; Cal. 1928.)
Coverack Gem. 2b. (Bro.; Cal. 1928.)
Coverack Glory. 2a. (Will. P.; Cal. 1927.)
Coverack Lad. 2b. (Bro.; Cal. 1928.)
Coverack Perfection. 2b. (Bro.; Cal. 1930.)
Crimsonbraid. 3b. (Chap. 1918.)
Crocus. 2a. (Will. P. 1927.)
Croesus. 2a. (Will. J. 1912.)
Crowned Beauty. 3a.
Crusader. 2b. (West 1929.)
Crystal. 4b. (Bro.; Cal. 1928.)
Cushlake. 4b. (Wils. G. 1934.)
Cyclamineus. 11. (Baker)
Cydonia. 2b. (Back.; deG. 1929.)
Cymricqueen. 2b. (deG. 1929.)
Cyrus. 1c. (Barr 1923.)
Dactyl. 9. (Eng. 1923.)
Dahomey. 2b. (Back.; deG. 1930.)
Daisy Schaeffer. 4a. (deG. 1927.)
Dalila. 2a. (deG. 1931.)
Damson. 2a. (Will. P. 1925.)
Dan. 2b. (Back.; deG. 1930.)
Danesfield. 1c. (Barr 1923.)
Danger. 3a. (Back.; Rich. 1927.)
Daphne. 10. (Cul. 1914.)
Darius. 1a. (Wils. G. 1923.)
David Griffiths. 1a. (Pow. 1936.)
Dawson City. 1a. (vTub. 1925.)
Delaware. 4a. (deG. 1927.)
Delhi. 2b. (Back.; Lower P. 1928.)
Derwent. 3a. (deG. 1930.)
Diana Kasner. 3a. (Back.; deG. '27.)
Dick. 1c. (Konig 1923.)
Dick Turpin. 3b. (Cros.; Wils. A. '30.)
Dick Wellband. 2b. (Back.; deG. '29.)
Dingo. 2a. (Wils. G. 1923.)
Dinkie. 3a. (Chap.; Cal. 1927.)
Dinton Red. 9. (Eng. 1923.)
Diotima. 1a. (deG. 1927.)
Discus. 3b. (Back. H. 1913.)
Distingue. 4a. (Back. H. 1923.)
Dolly Warden. 2b. (Back.; deG. '30.)
Donatello. 2a. (deG. 1927.)
Donax. 2a. (Back. 1910.)
Dorine. 2b. (—; vZon. 1931.)
Dosoris. 3b. (Will. P. 1910.)
Dragoon. 3b. (Wil. J. 1913.)
Drina. 2b. (Back.; deG. 1930.)
Drivensnow. 1b. (Wils. G. 1923.)
Dubloon. 10. (Eng. 1907.)

NARCISSUS, continued

DUCHANEL. 1a. (deG. 1923.)
DUCHESS OF WESTMINSTER. 4b. (Back. H. 1886.)
DUKE OF BEDFORD. 1c. (Barr 1899.)
DUKE OF MARLBOROUGH. 4a. (deG. '27.)
DULCIMER. 9. (Eng. 1913.)
DUNCAN. 4a. (Will. P. 1927.)
DUPLEX. 8. (Dutch origin.)
EARLY SURPRISE. 3a. (Mooy; deG. '27.)
ECLAIR. 3b. (Back.; deG. 1928.)
EDDA. 2b. (Back.; deG. 1930.)
EDITH. 3b. (Back.; deG. 1929.)
EDWINA. 9. (deG. 1927.)
EFFIE. 3a. (Back.; deG. 1927.)
Eggs and Bacon. ORANGE PHOENIX.
EIFINA. 9. (Back.; deG. 1929.)
ELIZABETH RYAN. 3a.
ELLY NEY. 3b. (deG. 1927.)
ELSPETH. 2b. (Will. 1913.)
ELVIRA. 8. (vSch. 1904.)
EMERALDEYE. 4b. (Eng. 1913.)
EMPEROR. 1a. (L. & B. 1890.)
EMPRESS. 1c. (L. & B. 1890.)
ENOSIS. 2b. (Back.; deG. 1930.)
EPAMINONDAS. 1c. (deG. 1927.)
ERINI. 10. (Hart. 1907.)
ESKIMO. 1b. (Bro. 1927.)
ESTELLE. 2b. (Back. 1907.)
ETTRICK. 4a. (Bro. 1923.)
EUCHARIS. 2b. (Hay 1907.)
EVADNE. 9. (Back. 1927.)
EVANGELINE. 4b. (Eng. 1908.)
EVE. 4a. (deG. 1928.)
EVEREST. 1b. (Wils. G. 1926.)
EXCELSIOR. 8. (vSch. 1931.)
EXPECTATION. 2b. (1931.)
EYEBRIGHT. 3b. (Eng. 1907.)
FAIRYCIRCLE. 4b. (Bro. 1913.)
FAIRY KING. 2a. (Wils. A.; Wils. G. '33.)
FAIRYSNOW. 4b. (Eng. 1927.)
FAKIR. 1a. (vTub. 1927.)
FANFARE. 1a. (Will. P. 1927.)
FANNY CURREY. 4a. (Rich. 1925.)
FANTIN LATOUR. 1a. (deG. 1923.)
FEBRUARY GOLD. 6. (deG. 1923.)
FESTIVE. 2b. (Back. 1923.)
FIREBRAND. 3b. (Eng. 1907.)
FIRETAIL. 3b. (Cros. 1910.)
FLAMINGTORCH. 2a. (Back.; War. '33.)
FLEUR. 3b. (Back.; deG. 1927.)
FLORIDA. 2a. (Back.; deG. 1927.)
FLORISTS DELIGHT. 1a. (Wils. 1923.)
FOLLY. 2b. (Will. 1926.)
FORTUNE. 2a. (Ware 1923.)
FORTUNES BLAZE. 2a. (Bro.; Cal. '30.)
FORTUNES BOWL. 2a. (Bro.; Cal. '30.)
FORTUNES CHAMPION. 2a. (Bro.; Cal. 1930.)
FORTUNES CREST. 2a. (Bro.; Cal. '30.)
FORTUNES PRIDE. 2a. (Bro.; Cal. '28.)
FORTUNES QUEEN. 2b. (Back.; Barr 1929.)
FRANCISCUS DRAKE. 2b. (Back.; deG. 1927.)
FRANS HALS. 1a. (Kre. 1914.) There is also a variety in group 8.
FRAU MARGARETHE HOFFMANN. (deG. 1928.)
FRED HOWARD. 1a.
FREIFRAU VON FRIESEN. 3b. (Back.; deG. 1929.)
FRICKLESTIN V. C. 2b. (West)
FRILLED ROBIN. 2b. (Back. 1927.)
FRORE. 4a. (Rich.; Cal. 1931.)
FUGA. 3b. (deG. 1929.)
GABY. 3b. (Back.; deG. 1929.)

NARCISSUS, continued

GALATA. 3b. (Bro. 1927.)
GALLIPOLI. 2a. (Bro. 1923.)
GALOPIN. 2b. (Back. 1927.)
GARIBALDI. 2a. (Wils. A. 1933.)
GARLIDNA. 3a. (Will. 1927.)
GAZA. 1b. (Eng. 1923.)
GENERAL PERSHING. 7. (deG. 1923.)
GEORGE (*Rogers*) CLARK. 4a. (vLeeu. 1931.)
GERMAINE. 2b. (Back.; deG. 1930.)
GERTIA. 2a. (Back.; deG. 1930.)
GERTIE MILLAR. 4a. (deG. 1927.)
GHANDI. 2a. (Back.; deG. 1927.)
GIANT KILLER. 1a. (deG. 1927.)
GIANT MUTICUS. 1a. (Wils. 1927.)
GIANT RING. 2b. (deG. 1932.)
GIONESIUS. 3a. (deG. 1927.)
GLADBOY. 3a. (Back.; deG. 1929.)
GLADIATOR. 2b. (Back. 1914.)
GLADYS DOBIE. 9. (deG. 1927.)
GLITTER. 3a. (Eng. 1907.)
GLORIAMUNDI. 2a. (Back. 1887.)
GLORIANA. 2a. (Buck. 1925.)
GLORIOUS. 8. (Will. J.; Rich. 1923.)
GLORY OF LISSE. 9. (Seg. 1907.) *Glory.*
GLORY OF SASSENHEIM. 1c. (Konig 1923.)
GLORY OF THE MORN. 2a. (deG. 1932.)
GODOLPHIN. 1a. (Will. P. 1925.)
GOLDDUST. 1a.
GOLDEAGLE. 1a.
GOLDEN BANTAM. 2a. (vLeeu.; Cal. 1929.)
GOLDEN BEAUTY. 1c. (vZon. 1930.)
GOLDEN CHIEF. 1a. (1914.)
GOLDEN CITY. 1a. (West 1923.)
GOLDEN EMBLEM. 1a. (Bath 1923.)
GOLDEN FLAG. 1a. (Wils. G. 1923.)
GOLDEN FRILLED. 2a. (—; vLeeu. '28.)
GOLDEN GLORY. 1a. (Bath 1923.)
GOLDEN GOBLET. 7. (vTub. 1927.)
GOLDEN HARVEST. 1a. (War. 1927.)
GOLDEN KING. 1a. (Will. J. 1914.)
GOLDEN PEDESTAL. 2a. (Rich. 1922.)
GOLDEN PERFECTION. 8. (deG. 1927.)
GOLDEN RAY. 1a. (Wat. 1927.)
GOLDEN SCEPTRE. 7. (deG. 1914.)
GOLDENSPUR. 1a. (1889.)
GOLDEN SUNRISE. 1a. (Bath 1916.)
GOLDONA. 2b. (Back.)
GOLDRIM. 2b. (vLeeu. 1933.)
GOLDSHELL. 2b. (Back.)
GOVILEY. 3b. (Will. P. 1928.)
GRACIOUS. 4a. (vLeeu. 1931.)
GRACKLE. 2a. (Will. P.; Rich. 1929.)
GRAND CANYON. 4a. (deG. 1927.)
GRAND OPERA. 9. (Chap.; Will.P. '29.)
Grand Soleil d'Or. SOLEIL D'OR.
GRAYLING. 4a. (Will. P. 1927.)
GREAT WARLEY. 2b. (Eng. 1904.)
GREENMANTLE. 4b. (Don. 1932.)
GRENADE. 2a. (Eng. 1916.)
GRUNO. 2b. (Back.; deG. 1929.)
HADES. 3b. (Back.; Rich. 1925.)
HAEMON. 8. (vWav. 1916.)
HALFA. 1c. (Bro. 1927.)
HALLMARK. 1a. (Hall 1927.)
HALVOSE. 8. (Will. P. 1927.)
HARPAGON. 3b. (Wils. A. 1913.)
HAVELOCK. 2a. (Will. P. 1907.)
HEBRON. 1a. (Bro. 1923.)
HECTOR TREUB. 1a. (deG. 1923.)
HELA. 3b. (Back.; deG. 1929.)
HELEN O'HARA. 1b. (Rich. 1927.)
HELIOS. 2a. (Eng. 1912.)
HELSTON. 4b. (Bro.; Cal. 1928.)

NARCISSUS, continued

HENDRIK IBSEN. 1a. (deG. 1927.)
HENNA. 2a. (Back.; Watts 1929.)
HENRIETTA. 2a. (Cope.; Cart. 1927.)
HERA. 4b. (deG. 1914.)
HER GRACE. 4a. (vTub. 1914.)
HEROD. 1c. (Cros. 1907.)
HESLA. 7. (Will. P. 1908.)
HEXAGON. 4a. (Wils. G. 1923.)
HEXAMETER. 9. (Bro. 1927.)
HIGHLAND CHIEF. 1c. (Bro.; Cal. '28.)
HIS EXCELLENCY. 1a. (Wils. G. 1931.)
HOLLANDS GLORY. 10. (vLeeu. 1927.)
HOMER. 9. (Eng. 1898.)
HOMESPUN. 2a. (Eng. 1907.)
HONEY. 4b. (Back. 1929.)
HONEYBOY. 1a. (Wills. G. 1923.)
HOPEFUL. 2a. (Wils. G. 1927.)
HOPE OF HOLLAND. 1a. (Kre. 1913.)
HORACE. 9. (Eng. 1907.)
HOSPODAR. 2a. (Will. J. 1914.)
HOTSPOT. 3b. (Eng. 1923.)
HUON. 9. (Eng.; Sec. 1927.)
HUSKY. 3a. (Will.; Cal. 1927.)
HYMETTUS. 4a. (Bro. 1923.)
IDEAL. 8. (vSch. 1907.)
IDRIS. 2b. (Watts 1914.)
IDUNA. 4b. (deG. 1933.)
IMPERATOR. 1b. (deG. 1923.)
INDIAN CHIEF. 10. (Back.; deG. '27.)
INNOCENCE. 8.
INNOVATION. 1a. (Eld. 1928.)
INSURPASSABLE. 1a.
INVERGORDON. 2a. (Bro. 1930.)
INVINCIBLE. 2b. (vTub. 1927.)
IRENE BORDONI. 2b. (War. 1936.)
IRENE COPELAND. 10. (Cope. 1923.)
IRISH PEARL. 4a. (Wils. 1923.)
IRMELIN. 8. (vSch. 1930.)
ISIDOOR. 2b. (Back.; deG. 1930.)
IVORINE. 4b. (Will. 1910.)
IXION. 2a. (Barr 1915.)
JAMES HOGG. 9. (Bro. 1913.)
JEAN HOOD. 2b. (West 1931.)
JECUNDA. 2b. (deG. 1928.)
JEFFERSON DAVIS. 2b. (Back.; deG. '29.)
JEFTA. 1c. (deG. 1927.)
JERSEY CREAM. 1c. (Bro. 1923.)
JESTER. 2a. (deG. 1923.)
JIM. 1b. (deG. 1927.)
JOHN EVELYN. 2b. (Cope. 1920.)
Johnstoni Queen of Spain. QUEEN OF SPAIN.
JONQUILLA FLOREPLENO. 10.
JONQUILLA SIMPLEX. 7.
JOSEPHINE. 5b.
JUBILANT. 2a. (Will. 1925.)
JULIET. 9. (Eng. 1907.)
JUNCIFOLIUS. 11.
JUNGFRAU. 1b. (deG. 1927.)
JUNGLEFIRE. 2b. (Back.; Rich. 1927.)
JUPITER. 3a. (Wils. A. 1908.)
KANDAHAR. 1a. (Bro. 1927.)
KANTARA. 1b. (Eng. 1927.)
KATONAH. 1a. (Pow. 1937.)
KENBANE. 1b. (Wils. G. 1927.)
KENNACK. 2b. (Will. P. 1927.)
KENTUCKY. 9. (deG. 1928.)
KESTREL. 9. (Will. P. 1907.)
KHIVA. 4a. (Bro. 1927.)
KILLIGREW. 2a. (Will. 1907.)
KILTER. 3a. (Will. 1927.)
KING ALFRED. 1a. (Ken. 1899.)
KING ARTHUR. 1a. (deG. 1923.)
KINGDOM. 4a. (Mil. 1908.)
KING OF MAY. 1a. (Wils. 1923.)
KING OF THE NORTH. 1a. (Bro. 1927.)

NARCISSUS, continued

Klondyke. 8. (vSch. 1907.)
Lady Arnott. 2a. (Hart. 1907.)
Lady Derby. 2b. (War. 1927.)
Lady (*Diana*) Manners. 3b. (Back. 1925.)
Lady Hillingdon. 7. (deG. 1927.)
Lady Kesteven. 3b. (Back.; deG. '33.)
Lady Lilford. 3b. (Back. 1927.)
Lady Moore. 3b. (Mooy 1916.)
Lady Superior. 3b. (Back. 1914.)
L'Aiglon. 2b. (Back.; deG. 1929.)
Lanarth. 7. (Will. 1907.)
Lantwit. 2a. (Will.)
Last Out. 1a. (Wils. G. 1931.)
Latendresse. 4a. (vLeeu. 1931.)
Laurens Koster. 8. (Vis. 1923.)
Lavestale. 1b. (deG. 1927.)
Lavolunteer. (West 1935.)
Lemonstar. 4a. (Cope. 1910.)
Leontes. 2a. (Wils. A. 1913.)
Liberty. 1a. (Hem.; vZon. 1931.)
Lido. 4a. (Bro. 1927.)
Liscarton. 3a. (Will. P.; Cal. 1927.)
Littlejohn. 2b. (Lowe 1925.)
Livia. 10. (Back.; deG. 1929.)
Lobularis. 1c.
Locarno. 1c. (Ouds.; vSch. 1930.)
Lochfyne. 2b. (Bro. 1914.)
Lord Antrim. 1a. (Wils. 1927.)
Lord Kitchener. 4a. (Back. 1905.)
Lord (*Louis*) Mountbatten. 1c. (deG. 1928.)
Lord Wellington. 1a. (Eng. 1931.)
Loreley. 4b. (Eng. 1910.)
Loudspeaker. 2a. (Back.; deG. 1927.)
Louis Capet. 4a. (deG. 1927.)
Lovenest. 1c. (Back.; deG. 1928.)
Loyalist. 1a. (Rich. 1923.)
Lucifer. 2b. (Laur. 1890.)
Lucinius. 2a. (—; vLeeu. 1928.)
Luckystrike. 3a. (vLeeu. 1931.)
Mabel. 2b. (deG. 1930.)
Macebearer. 2b. (Will. P. 1910.)
MacMahon. 1a. (deG. 1927.)
Magnificence. 1a. (Eng. 1914.)
Magog. 1a. (Eng. 1907.)
Mainsail. 9. (Eng. 1923.)
Majestic. 8. (vWav. 1916.)
Manacles. 1b. (Bro.; Cal. 1928.)
Mangosteen. 3a. (Wils. A.; Rich. '33.)
March Sunshine. 6. (deG. 1923.)
Margaret Fell. 2b. (West 1932.)
Marketglory. 2a. (Back. 1923.)
Marketmerry. 3a. (Bro. 1933.)
Marmora. 4a. (Bro. 1923.)
Marquis. 3a. (Back. 1927.)
Marshlight. 2b. (Will. P. 1907.)
Martha Clarke. 4a. (West 1934.)
Marton Beacon. 2a. (Gib. 1928.)
Mary Bierne. 4a. (vTub.; Bier. '37.)
Mary Copeland. 10. (Cope. 1914.)
Mary Longstreet. 2a. (Back.; deG. 1927.)
Mary Pickford. 2a. (deG. 1933.)
Mascotte. 2b. (West 1932.)
Masterpiece. 3b. (Eng. 1906.)
Master Robert. 1a. (Rich. 1927.)
Matamax. 1a. (deG. 1923.)
Maude Adams. 2b. (deG. 1931.)
Maunganui. 1c. (Lowe 1927.)
May. 1b.
Mayblossom. 3b. (Wils. G. 1927.)
Mayflower. 3b. (Back.; Sec. 1927.)
May Maloney. 4a. (Wils. G. 1927.)
Medusa. 8. (Will. P. 1907.)
Megaphone. 1a. (deG. 1929.)

NARCISSUS, continued

Meonia. 2a. (deG. 1934.)
Mephisto. 2a. (Will. P. 1927.)
Merapi. 2a. (Back.; War. 1930.)
Merkara. 2a. (Back.; Lower P. '27.)
Merryhill. 2a. (Back.; War. 1933.)
Messina. 3b. (Will. P. 1908.)
Micareme. 2a. (Back.; deG. 1907.)
Michigan. 2b. (Back.; deG. 1928.)
Midas. 3a. (Will. J. 1913.)
Milan. 9. (Wils. A.)
Milana. 1a.
Milford Haven. 2b. (Back.; deG. '27.)
Milkmaid. 4a. (Will. 1907.)
Milo. 1b. (Eng. 1923.)
Minimus. 1a.
Minister Talma. 1a. (Philippo.)
Minor. 1a.
Minuet. 9. (Chap. 1923.)
Miss Willmott. 3b. (vTub. 1907.)
Mitylene. 4a. (Eng. 1923.)
Mme. Degraaff. 1b. (deG. 1887.)
Mme. Vanwaveren. 1c. (vWav. '30.)
Moira O'Neill. 1c. (Eng.; Wils. G. 1923.)
Mongolia. 1a. (vTub. 1931.)
Montecarlo. 2a. (Will.; Ho. 1931.)
Moongold. 1a. (Wils. 1929.)
Moonlight. 1a. (vDeu.; deG. 1930.)
Moonshine. 5. (deG. 1927.)
Morea. 2a. (Back.; Lower P. 1929.)
Morningglow. 2b. (deG. 1930.)
Mortlake. 1a. (West 1930.)
Moschatus of Haworth. 1b.
Moulinrouge. 10. (Back.; deG. '27.)
Mount Erebus. 4a. (vTub. 1931.)
Mountroyal. 1a. (deG. 1931.)
Mrs. (*Alfred*) Pearson. 8. (deG. '23.)
Mrs. Barclay. 3a. (Mooy 1924.)
Mrs. (*E. C.*) Mudge. 1c. (Back. '27.)
Mrs. (*E.*) Martin. 10. (Mar. 1923.)
Mrs. (*Ernst H.*) Krelage. 1b. (Kre. 1912.)
Mrs. (*Geo.*) Chandler. 2a. (deG. '27.)
Mrs. (*John*) Bodger. 1b. (deG. '27.)
Mrs. Langtry. 4b. (Back. 1890.)
Mrs. (*Nette*) O'Melveny. 4b. (Back.; deG. 1928.)
Mrs. (*Percy*) Neale. 4a. (Cope.; Barr 1923.)
Mrs. (*Richard*) Tobin. 2b.
Mrs. (*R. O.*) Backhouse. 4a. (Back. 1923.)
Mrs. (*Walter H.*) Brewster. 3b. (Back.)
Much the Miller. 1c. (Cart. 1910.)
Muriel Bibby. 3b. (Back. 1927.)
Muriel Evans. 1a.
Musichall. 1c. (Rich. 1923.)
Myrmidon. 2b. (Back.; deG. 1929.)
Mystic. 4b. (Wils. G. 1923.)
Nabob. 3b. (Chap.; Cal. 1931.)
Nannie Netticoat. 2b. (Back. 1927.)
Nanny Nunn. 3a. (Back. 1923.)
Nanus. 1a.
Narrabri. 9. (Eng.; Sec. 1927.)
Naxos. 4a. (Eng. 1923.)
Nelly. 4b. (Will. P. 1927.)
Nero. 1c. (Barr 1927.)
Nevis. 1b. (Bro. 1916.)
New Amsterdam. 2b. (deG.; War. '31.)
Nightingale. 9. (Eng. 1914.)
Nillumbik. 2b. (West 1927.)
Nimrod. 2a. (Will. P. 1927.)
Niobe. 3b. (deG. 1927.)
Niphetos. 4b. (Will. P. 1927.)
Nissa. 2b. (Bro. 1923.)

NARCISSUS, continued

Niveth. 5b. (Back. H.; Wils. 1931.)
Nobility. 3b. (—; vLeeu. 1928.)
Norfolk. 2a. (Back.; deG. 1928.)
Notos. 2a. (Back.; deG. 1929.)
Numapompilius. 7. (deG. 1927.)
Nursemaid. 3b. (Back.; deG. 1928.)
Oconee. 5a. (Pow. 1939.)
Octavianus. 1b. (deG. 1929.)
Odorus Campernelli. 7. *Campernelli.*
Odorus Campernelli Plenus. 10.
Odorus Rugulosus. 7.
Odorus Rugulosus Maximus. 7.
Odysseus. 3b. (deG. 1927.)
Olympia. 1a. (vWav. 1900.)
Opera. 9. (Eng. 1923.)
Optima. 2b. (Back.; deG. 1933.)
Orangecup. 8. (Tro.)
Orangeglory. 6. (deG. 1920.)
Orangeglow. 2a. (Back. 1922.)
Orangeking. 3a. (Back.; deG. 1927.)
Orange Ophelia. 2b. (Back.; deG. '29.)
Orange Phoenix. 10. *Eggs and Bacon.*
Orangeprince. 8. (deG. 1907.)
Orangequeen. 7. (Cart. 1908.)
Orangesplendour. 2a. (Bath 1929.)
Orangesun. 3a. (Back.; deG. 1927.)
Orangetriumph. 1a. (Kou.; Zand. '35.)
Ornatus. 9.
Ornatus Maximus. 9.
Osiris. 2a. (Wils. G. 1907.)
Osprey. 4b. (Will. J. 1927.)
Ottawa. 3a. (deG. 1932.)
Owen. 3a. (Back. 1923.)
Pacificspur. 1a.
Pandion. 2b. (Back.; deG. 1929.)
Papyrus. 9. (Eng.; Sec. 1926.)
Pearl of Dew. 5b. (Back.; Barr '27.)
Pearlyqueen. 5b. (deG. 1927.)
Peerless. 8. (Back. 1927.)
Peggy. 3b. (Will. 1927.)
Peggy Bauer. 3b. (Back.; deG. '29.)
Peking. 3b. (deG. 1933.)
Pelleas. 3b. (deG. 1934.)
Penny-come-quick. 3b. (Will. P. '27.)
Penwith. 2b. (Bro.; Cal. 1930.)
Pera. 3b. (Bro.; Cal. 1927.)
Perfection. 10. (—; vSch. 1931.)
Peril. 3a. (Lowe 1925.)
Peter Barr. 1b. (Barr 1902.)
Phoebe. 2b. (Back.; deG. 1927.)
Phyllida. 4a. (Cope. 1916.)
Pilgrim. 2b. (Eng. 1907.)
Pilgrimage. 2a. (Bro. 1923.)
Pink'un. 2b. (Buck. 1914.)
∞Poetaz N. ∞**N. poetaz.**
Poets N. **N. poeticus.**
Point d'Aigu. 1b. (deG. 1927.)
Poldhu. 4a. (Bro.; Cal. 1930.)
Polyanthus N. **N. tazetta.**
Porthilly. 2a. (Will. P. 1927.)
President Carnot. 1b. (deG. 1923.)
Pride of Cambridge. 2b. (Bath '30.)
Pride of Virginia. 2b. (Will.; vWav. 1930.)
Primrose Girl. 4a. (Bath 1927.)
Primrose N. **N. biflorus.**
Primrose Phoenix. 10. (1902.)
Prince Fushimi. 2b. (Welch 1908.)
Prince of Orange. 2b. (Welch 1923.)
Prince of Wales. 1a. (vWav. 1927.)
Princess Astrid. 3a. (deG. 1927.)
Princess Miriam. 3b. (Back.; Pear. 1927.)
Princess Yolande. 8. (Mooy 1930.) *Yolande.*

NARCISSUS, continued

Profusion. 8. (1930.)
Prospector. 1a. (Eng.)
Prosperity. 2a. (vLeeu. 1931.)
Prudence. 4. (Daw. 1907.)
Ptolemy. 1c. (Barr 1923.)
Pucelle. 4b. (Eng.; Rich. 1930.)
Puritan Maiden. 4a. (Pear. 1915.)
Puzzle. 2a. (Buck. 1925.)
Pygmalion. 2b. (Back., deG. 1929.)
Quartz. 1c. (Bro. 1923.)
Queen of Denmark. 1b. (deG. 1927.)
Queen of Hearts. 3b. (Eng. 1911.)
Queen of Spain. 5a. *Johnstoni Queen of Spain.*
Queen of the North. 4b. (Barr 1908.)
Queen of the West. 1a. (Mooy '07.)
Queen of the Whites. 5a.
Quetta. 3b. (Bro. 1927.)
Quicksilver. 4a. (Wils. 1923.)
Radium. 4a. (deG. 1927.)
Raeburn. 9. (Eng. 1913.)
Raider. 2a. (Back. 1925.)
Recurvus. 9.
Redabbot. 2b. (Back.; Barr 1931.)
Redbeacon. 3b. (Will. P. 1916.)
Redchief. 3b. (Will. P. 1910.)
Redcross. 2a. (Back. 1928.)
Redemperor. 3b. (Will. P. 1910.)
Redgiant. 2a. (Back.; deG. 1930.)
Redguard. 3a. (Back. 1923.)
Redknight. 2b. (Back.; Barr 1931.)
Redmonarch. 2b. (Back.; War. '31.)
Redrim. 9. (Eng.; Sec. 1923.)
Redsea. 3a. (Bro. 1927.)
Redshadow. 3a. (Back.; deG. 1929.)
Redstar. 2b.
Rembrandt. 1a. (Lubbe 1930.)
Rewa. 2b. (Lower 1928.)
Rhapsody. 9. (Eng. 1923.)
Rheingold. 1a. (Eng. 1923.)
Ringdove. 9. (Cros. 1913.)
Riva. 4a. (Bro. 1927.)
Riviera. 4b. (Bro.; Cal. 1928.)
Roanna. 2b. (Back.; deG. 1929.)
Rob Berkeley. 1b. (1922.)
Robert E. Lee. 1c. (deG. 1929.)
Robert Sydenham. 1a. (vWav. '16.)
Robinhood. 1a.
Rockery Beauty. 1c. (Eld. 1928.)
Roman Star. 3a. (Back.; deG. 1929.)
Rosabella. 1b. (deG. 1930.)
Rosary. 1c. (Eng. 1926.)
Rosebud. 3b. (Will. P. 1927.)
Rosemarie. 3a. (deG. 1927.)
Rosemorran Giant. 1c. (Daw. '27.)
Rosymorn. 3b. (Pow. 1938.)
Roxane. 1b. (vTub. 1927.)
Royalflush. 1a. (Wils. G.; Cal. '27.)
Royalist. 1a. (Lower 1914.)
Royal Lancer. 2a. (Back. 1927.)
Royal Sovereign. 10. (Cope. 1908.)
Ruby. 3b. (Cave 1907.)
Rupert Brooke. 9. (Eng. 1927.)
Rustom Pasha. 2a. (Evelyn; Rich. 1930.)
Salembo. 2b. (Back.; deG. 1928.)
Sallandia. 2b. (Back.; deG. 1929.)
Samaria. 4b. (Bro. 1923.)
Samothrace. 1a. (Eng. 1923.)
San Iiario. 4b. (Cart. 1910.)
Sarchedon. 9. (Eng. 1913.)
Sassenheims Giant. 1a. (vLeeu. '28.)
Satara. 1c. (Gib. 1927.)
Scarletgem. 8. (Will. 1910.)
Scarletlancer. 2a. (Back. 1928.)

NARCISSUS, continued

Scarletleader. 2a. (Back.; deG. 1933.)
Scarletqueen. 2a. (West 1925.)
Seagull. 3b. (Eng. 1895.)
Seraglio. 3a. (Bro. 1926.)
Seraphine. 1a. (vTub. 1930.)
Serotinus. 11.
Seville. 2b. (Will. 1908.)
Shackleton. 3b. (deG. 1921.)
Sheba. 3b. (Will. 1908.)
Sheherasade. 2a. (Back.;deG.1927.)
Sherman. 2b. (deG.1929.)
Shot Silk. 5a. (deG. 1933.)
Siegfried. 1a. (deG. 1927.)
Silvanite. 1c. (deG. 1923.)
Silverfox. 4a. (Eng. 1923.)
Silverglory. 1b. (deG. 1923.)
Silverpink. 4a. (deG. 1935.)
Silverplane. 4a. (Lowe 1927.)
Silversalver. 4b. (Bro. 1922.)
Silverstar. 4a. (Back. 1927.)
Sincerity. 1c. (Lower; Wils. G. '30.)
Sir (*Francis*) Drake. 1a. (Ken. 1902.)
Sir Watkin. 2a. (Back. 1884.)
Smyrna. 9. (Bro. 1927.)
Snowbird. 5b. (Back. 1923.)
Snowdrift. 4a. (Eng. 1907.)
Snowking. 9. (Daw. 1910.)
Snowsprite. 10. (Barr 1913.)
Socrates. 9. (Eng. 1890.)
Soleil d'Or. 8. *Grand Soleil d'Or.*
Solferino. 1a. (vTub.; deG. 1930.)
Solid Gold. 1a. (Don. 1931.)
Solleret. 7. (Eng. 1929.)
Solon. 2b. (Back.; deG. 1930.)
Songster. 4b. (Watts 1916.)
Spanish Flag. 2a. (Back. 1927.)
Sparkler. 2a. (Eng. 1914.)
Springglory. 1c. (deG. 1914.)
Stability. 4a. (Wils. 1923.)
St. Agnes. 8. (Will. P. 1926.)
Starlight. 8. (Veitch 1907.)
Star of West. 2a.
Stateliness. 4a. (Wils. G. 1923.)
Statendam. 1a. (deG. 1929.)
St. Egwin. 2a. (Will. P. 1927.)
Stella Pratt. 2a. (Back. 1923.)
St. Erme. 4a. (Will. P. 1927.)
St. George. 3b. (Eng. 1910.)
Stillwaters. 4b. (Eng.; Wils. G. '31.)
St. Ives. 2a. (Will. P. 1927.)
Stoke. 5a. (Will. 1934.)
St. Olaf. 4b. (Eng. 1913.)
St. Patrick. 8. (Smi. 1908.)
Strabo. 3b. (Back.; deG. 1929.)
Striking. 3b. (deG. 1927.)
Styx. 3b. (deG. 1927.)
Sublime. 4a. (Back.; deG. 1933.)
Suda. 4a. (Bro. 1927.)
Sulphur. 1a. (Will. 1927.)
Sulphur Phoenix. 10. *Codlins and Cream.*
Sunburst. 2a. (Buck. 1924.)
Sunfirm. 2a. (Back.; deG. 1929.)
Sunnyboy. 2b. (War. 1938.)
Sunrise. 3b. (Back. 1907.)
Sunstar. 3b. (Back. 1927.)
Surprise. 2b. (deG. 1931.)
Suvla. 2b. (Bro. 1927.)
Sycamore. 8. (Prins 1923.)
Sycorax. 10. (deG. 1932.)
Sylvester. 1b. (vTub. 1927.)
Syra. 4a. (Eng. 1927.)
Tagore. 2b. (Back.; deG. 1928.)
Tampa. 2a. (Back. 1928.)
Tapin. 1c.

NARCISSUS, continued

Tara Ranee. 3b. (Cros. 1914.)
Tashkend. 2a. (Bro. 1927.)
Telema. 3b. (Back.; deG. 1929.)
Telopea. 2b. (West 1929.)
Tenedos. 4a. (Eng. 1923.)
Terracotta. (Gib.)
Texas. 10. (Back.; deG. 1928.)
Thackeray. 1a. (Kre. 1914.)
Thalia. 8. (vWav. 1916.)
The Admiral. 3b. (Back. 1927.)
The First. 1a. (vZon. 1930.)
Thelma. 9. (vWav. 1931.)
The Pearl. 10. (Zees. 1923.)
The Perfect Gentleman. 1a. (Adams 1923.)
Therapia. 3b. (Bro. 1927.)
The Star. 9. (vSch. 1923.)
Thetis. 9. (Eng. 1923.)
Timon. 9. (Eng. 1910.)
Tongariro. 2a. (Thom. 1930.)
Torina. 2b. (Back.; deG. 1923.)
Torrid. 2a. (Back.; Lower P. 1928.)
Trappist. 1b. (Bro. 1923.)
Treasure. 1a. (vTub. 1925)
Tredore. 2a. (Will. P. 1927.)
Tregoose. 2a. (Will. P. 1927.)
Trenoon. 2a. (Will. P. 1930.)
Treskerby. 3a. (Will. P. 1927.)
Tresserve. 1a. (Heere; vTub. 1923.)
Trevisky. 2a. (Will. P. 1930.)
Trevithian. 7. (Will. 1927.)
Triandrus Albus. 11.
Triandrus Calathinus. 11.
Triandrus Concolor. 11.
Triandrus Pulchellus. 11.
Triomphator. 2b. (deG. 1930.)
Tropicsun. 2a. (Back.)
Tullia. 4b. (deG. 1929.)
Tullus Hostilius. 7. (deG. 1927.)
Tunis. 4a. (Will. P. 1927.)
Twink. 10. (deG. 1927.)
Twinkle. 3a. (Back. 1927.)
Tydens. 2a. (deG. 1930.)
Undine. 5a.
Valencia. 10. (deG.; deB. 1931.)
Valiant. 1a. (Wils. G. 1927.)
Vanilla. 1c. (vSch. 1910.)
Vanwaverens Giant. 1a. (vWav. 1900.)
Varna. 3a. (Bro. 1927.)
Vera. 3b. (deG. 1929.)
Veronica. 4a. (deG. 1927.)
Victoria. 1c. (vLeeu. 1897.)
Village Beauty. 3b. (Mooy 1923.)
Viridiflorus. 11.
Vivian. 2a. (Back. 1929.)
Volunteer. 1a. (West 1935.)
Von Sion. 10.
Wagners Rheingold. 1a. (Kou.; Pap. 1932.)
Walter Hampden. 2a. (deG. 1930.)
Warley Scarlet. 3a. (Eng. 1904.)
Warlock. 2b. (Will. P. 1927.)
Warwick. 1a. (deG. 1923.)
Waterlily. 4a. (Eng. 1907.)
Watieri. 11.
Weebud. 3b. (Back. 1927.)
W. F. Gates. 2a. (West)
Wheel of Fortune. 2a. (Cope. 1923.)
Whistler. 1a. (vWav. 1931.)
White Conqueror. 1b. (Back.; Wils. G. 1927.)
White Emperor. 1b. (Eng. 1913.)
White Giant. 8. (vSch. 1931.)
White Jasmine. 8. (Thur. 1932.)
Whiteley Gem. 2a. (Bro.; Cal. '28.)

NARCISSUS, continued
White Nile. 4a. (Bro. 1922.)
Whitepearl. 4a. (Cope. 1907.)
White Sentinel. 4a. (Eng. 1926.)
Whitestar. 3b. (Will. 1910.)
White Wedgewood. 7. (deG. 1927.)
Whitewell. 2b. (Mooy 1910.)
Widewing. 9. (Eng.; Sec. 1923.)
Will Scarlett. 2b. (Eng. 1898.)
Winsome Girl. 4a. (Gib. 1927.)
Wintergold. 1a. (Barr 1928.)
Winterjoy. 2a. (vLeeu. 1931.)
W. P. Milner. 1b. (Back. 1890.)
Wrestler. 1a. (—; vSch. 1930.)
Yeka. 2a. (deG. 1927.)
Yellow Puppy. 2a.
Yolande. Princess Yolande.
Youth. 1a. (vTub. 1931.)
Yukon. 1a. (Eng. 1923.)
Zanzibar. 3b. (Back. 1923.)
Zingara. 3b. (Back. 1903.)
Zionist. 1b. (Rich. 1927.)
Zoe. 2b. (West 1928.)

Nardgrass . . . . . Citronellagrass: **Cymbopogon nardus**

NAR'DUS . . . . Matgrass
See **GRASS GENERA.**

NAREGA'MIA
ala'ta

NARTHE'CIUM . . . . Bogasphodel
america'num . . . . NewJersey B.
califor'nicum . . . . . California B.
ossif'ragum

NASSEL'LA
See **GRASS GENERA.**

Nastur'tium officina'le
Rorippa nasturtium-aquaticum

Nasturtium . . . . **Tropaeolum**
For hort. var. of Nasturtium, see **TROPAEOLUM.**
Azure N. . . . . **T. azureum**
Bush N. . . . . **T. minus**
Canary N. . . . . . . **T. peregrinum**
Common N. . . . . **T. majus**
Cornucopia N. . . . . . **T. tricolor**
Featherflower N. . . **T. pinnatum**
Fivefinger N. . . . **T. pentaphyllum**
Shield N. . . . . . **T. peltophorum**
Slender N. . . . . . **T. brachyceras**
Thinleaf N. . . . . **T. leptophyllum**
Tomthumb N. . . . **T. majus nanum**
Tuber N. . . . . . . **T. tuberosum**
Venezuela N. . . . . . . **T. digitatum**
Vermilion N. . . . . . **T. speciosum**
Whitevein N. . . . . . . **T. lindeni**
Wreath N. . . . . . **T. polyphyllum**
Natalebony . . . . . **Maba natalensis**
Natalgrass . . . . **Tricholaena repens**
Natotree . . . . **Palaquium**
Barnes N. . . . . **P. barnesi**
Borneo N. . . . . . **P. borneense**
Java N. . . . . **P. javense**
Malay Guttapercha N. . . **P. gutta**
Philippine N. . . . **P. philippinense**

NAU'CLEA (*SARCOCEPHALUS*) Fatheadtree
diderich'i (*Sarcocephalus d.*). Opepe F.
esculen'ta (*Sarcocephalus esculentus*) Guineapeach F.
trilles'i (*Sarcocephalus t.*) . Bilinga F.

NAU'CLEA Bl., *not* L. . **NEONAUCLEA**

NAUCO'RIA . . . . Naucoria
semiorbicula'ris . . . . Halfball N.

NAVARRE'TIA . . . . **GILIA**

Navelseed . . . . **Omphalodes**
Cappadocian N. . . . **O. cappadocica**
Creeping N. . . . . **O. verna**
Flaxleaf N. . . . . **O. linifolia**
Greek N. . . . . **O. luciliae**
Portuguese N. . . . . **O. lusitanica**
White Creeping N. . . **O. verna alba**

Navelspurge . . . . **Omphalea**
Dominican N. . . . . . **O. triandra**
Jamaica N. . . . . . . **O. diandra**
Trinidad N. . . . . . **O. megacarpa**

Navelwort . . . . **Umbilicus**
Nodding N. . . . . . **U. pendulinus**

NA'ZIA . . . . **TRAGUS**
See **GRASS GENERA.**

NEAN'THE (*CHAMAEDOREA* in part) . . . . Neanthe
See **PALM GENERA.**

Necklaceorchid . . **Coelogyne dayana**

NECTAN'DRA . . . . . . **OCOTEA**
co'to . . . . **Aniba c.**
willdenowia'na . . . . . **O. coriacea**

Nectarine . **Prunus persica nectarina**

Needleandthread . . . **Stipa comata**
Tweedy N. . . . . **S. c. intermedia**

Needlegrass . . . . **Stipa**
Araucanian N. . . **S. brachychaeta**
Big Subalpine N. **S. columbiana nelsoni**
Blackseed N. . . . . . **S. avenacea**
California N. . . . . . **S. pulchra**
Chee N. . . . . Cheegrass
Colorado N. . . . . . . **S. porteri**
Columbia N. . . . . . Subalpine N.
Crested N. . . . . . **S. coronata**
Desert N. . . . . . . **S. speciosa**
Elmer N. . . . . **S. elmeri**
Esparto N. . . . . **S. tenacissima**
Finestem N. . . . . **S. tenuissima**
Florida N. . . . **S. avenacioides**
Foothill N. . . . . **S. lepida**
Green N. . . . . **S. viridula**
Guadalupe N. . . . . **S. curvifolia**
Lemmon N. . . . . . . **S. lemmoni**
Letterman N. . . . . **S. lettermani**
Littleawn N. . . . . . . **S. lobata**
Mormon N. . . . . **S. arida**
NewMexico N. NewMexico Feathergrass
Nodding N. . . . . California N.
Pacific N. . . . . . **S. californica**
Pinewoods N. . . . . **S. pinetorum**
Pringle N. . . . . **S. pringlei**
Purple N. . . . . . . California N.
Richardson N. . . . **S. richardsoni**
Scribner N. . . . . . **S. scribneri**
Sierra N. . . . . **S. stillmani**
Slim N. . . . . . **S. lepida andersoni**
Small Crested N. **S. coronata depauperata**
Southwestern N. . . . **S. eminens**
Subalpine N. . . . . **S. columbiana**
Texas N. . . . . . . **S. leucotricha**
Thurber N. . . . . . **S. thurberiana**

Needlegrass, continued
Uruguay N. . . . . . **Stipa neesiana**
Western N. . . . . **S. occidentalis**
Williams N. . . . . . . **S. williamsi**
Yosemite N. . . . . . **S. latiglumis**

Needlegrass . . . Threeawn: **Aristida**

Needlepalm . **Rhapidophyllum; R. hystrix**

Needlestar . . . . **Oxyanthus**
Earleaf N. . . . . **O. tubiflorus**
Natal N. . . . . **O. natalensis**

NEGUN'DO . . . . **ACER**
aceroi'des; fraxinifo'lium . **A. negundo**

NEIL'LIA . . . . Neillia
affi'nis
longiracemo'sa
opulifo'lia . . **Physocarpus opulifolius**
ribesioi'des . . . . . . Currant N.
sinen'sis . . . . Chinese N.
thibet'ica . . . . Tibet N.
thyrsiflo'ra . . . Whiteflower N.
tor'reyi . . **Physocarpus monogynus**
uek'i

NELUM'BIUM (*NELUMBO*) . Lotus
See **WATERLILY GENERA.**

NEMAS'TYLIS
acu'ta
florida'na

NEME'SIA . . . . Nemesia
chamaedrifo'lia
floribun'da
foe'tens
lilac'ina
strumo'sa . . . . Pouch N.
Dwarf (*nana compacta*) hv.
Sutton (*suttoni*)
versicol'or . . . . Spurred N.
Dwarf (*versicolor*) hv.

NEMOPAN'THUS |w . Mountainholly
mucrona'ta (*canadensis*) |w Mountainholly

NEMOPH'ILA . . . . . . Nemophila
atoma'ria . . . . **N. menziesi**
auri'ta . . . . Purple N.
breviflo'ra . . . . . Great Basin N.
integrifo'lia
interme'dia . . . . . Bluevein N.
linifo'lia
macula'ta . . . . Spotted N.
—grandiflo'ra . . . . . Showy S.N.
—purpu'rea . . . . . . Purple S.N.
menzies'i (*insignis*) Babyblue-eyes N.
—al'ba . . . . White B.N.
—atoma'ria (*N. atomaria*) Blackdot B.N.
—crambeoi'des
—discoida'lis . . . Browneye B.N.
—grandiflo'ra . . . . . Showy B.N.
—liniflo'ra (*N. liniflora*) . Flax B.N.
—margina'ta
parviflo'ra . . . . . Smallflower N.
phacelioi'des

NEOABBOT'TIA
See **CACTUS GENERA.**

NEO-BENTHA'MIA
See **ORCHID GENERA.**

NEOBES'SEYA . . **CORYPHANTHA**
See **CACTUS GENERA.**

Hort. var.; hv. = horticultural variety (or varieties); sp. = species (singular); spp. = species (plural).
¢ = clon; × (as a prefix) = hybrid; × (between scientific plant names) = crossed by; ∞ = polybrid; |w = plant useful to wildlife.
See Glossary for definitions of clon, hybrid, and polybrid.

NEODYP'SIS . . . . . . NEODYPSIS
See **PALM GENERA.**

NEOGLAZIO'VIA
variega'ta . . . . CAROA

NEOLLOYD'IA
See **CACTUS GENERA.**

NEOMAMMILLA'RIA
MAMMILLARIA
See **CACTUS GENERA.**

NEOMAR'ICA (*MARICA* in part)
FALSEFLAG
grac'ilis (*Marica g.*) . . . SLENDER F.
longifo'lia (*Marica l.*) . . LONGLEAF F.
northia'na (*Marica n.*) . NORTHS F.

NEONAU'CLEA (*NAUCLEA* Bl., *not* L.)
calyc'ina . . . . . KALAMANSANAI

NEOPIE'RIS . . . . **LYONIA**
nit'ida . . . . **L. lucida**

NEOPORTE'RIA
See **CACTUS GENERA.**

Neoraimon'dia macrosti'bas . **Cereus m.**

NEOWASHINGTO'NIA
WASHINGTONIA
See **PALM GENERA.**

NEPEN'THES . . . . . . NEPENTHES
The hybrids listed below are presumably polybrids and represented in cultivation by clons.
×**atrosanguin'ea** (*?distillatoria* × *sedeni*)
REDBOTTLE N.
×**chel'soni** (*domini* × *hookeriana*)
CHELSON N.
×**court'i** (*?* × *domini*) . . . . COURT N.
×**dickinsonia'na** (*rafflesiana* × *veitchi*)
DICKINSON N.
distillato'ria . . . . . . CEYLON N.
×**do'mini** (*?* × *rafflesiana; dominiana*)
DOMIN N.
×**edinen'sis** (*chelsoni* × *rafflesiana*)
grac'ilis
×**henrya'na** (*hookeriana* × *sedeni*)
HENRY N.
hookeria'na . . . . . . HOOKER N.
×**interme'dia** (*?* × *rafflesiana*) MIDWAY N.
khasia'na . . . . INDIA N.
×**lawrencia'na** (*hookeriana* × *polymorpha*) . . . . LAWRENCE N.
×**mastersia'na** (*khasiana* × *sanguinea*)
MASTERS N.
max'ima
×**paradis'ae** (*?* × *phyllamphora*)
PARADISE N.
×**paterso'ni** . . . . . . PATERSON N.
Parentage unknown.
phyllam'phora
rafflesia'na . . . . . . RAFFLES N.
sanguin'ea
×**se'deni** . . . . SEDEN N.
Parentage unknown.
×**splen'dida** (*hookeriana* × *phyllamphora*)
veitch'i . . . . VEITCH N.

NEPENTHES . . . . **Nepenthes**
CEYLON N. . . . . . . **N. distillatoria**
CHELSON N. . . . . . . ×**N. chelsoni**
COURT N. . . . . ×**N. courti**
DICKINSON N. . . . ×**N. dickinsoniana**
DOMIN N. . . . . ×**N. domini**
HENRY N. . . . . . . ×**N. henryana**
HOOKER N. . . . . . **N. hookeriana**
INDIA N. . . . . **N. khasiana**
LAWRENCE N. . . . ×**N. lawrenciana**

NEPENTHES, continued
MASTERS N. ×**Nepenthes mastersiana**
MIDWAY N. . . . . ×**N. intermedia**
PARADISE N. . . . . . ×**N. paradisae**
PATERSON N. . . . . . ×**N. patersoni**
RAFFLES N. . . . . . **N. rafflesiana**
REDBOTTLE N. . . ×**N. atrosanguinea**
SEDEN N. . . . . ×**N. sedeni**
VEITCH N. . . . . **N. veitchi**

NEP'ETA |w . . . . NEPETA
amethyst'ina
barba'ta
cata'ria |w . . . . CATNIP
cya'nea . . . . CAUCASIAN N.
dis'tans
grandiflo'ra
hedera'cea . . . . **Glecoma h.**
macran'tha . . . . ENGLISH N.
mussi'ni . . . . PERSIAN N.
nepetel'la (*lanceolata*)
nervo'sa
—**al'ba**
nu'da
ucran'ica (*ukranica*) . . UKRAINE N.
viola'cea
wil'soni . . . . WILSON N.

NEPHE'LIUM
lappa'ceum . RAMBUTAN (*Ramboetan; Rambotang; Rambustan*)
li'tchi . . . . **Litchi chinensis**
longa'na . . . . . . **Euphoria longan**
mutab'ile . . PULASAN (*Capulasan; Kapoelasan; Pulassan*)

NEPHRO'DIUM . . . **DRYOPTERIS**
See **FERN GENERA.**

NEPHROLE'PIS . . . . . SWORDFERN
See **FERN GENERA.**

NEPHRO'MA . . . . . . NEPHROMA
This name is treated by some authors as feminine; by others, as neuter. It seems best to regard it as feminine, following the author of the genus, Acharius.
par'ilis . . . . CHOCOLATE N.

NEPHTHY'TIS
afze'li (*liberica*)
pictura'ta. . . **Rhektophyllum mirabile**

NEPTU'NIA |w . . . . . . NEPTUNIA (*Sensitivebrier*)
lute'a . . . . YELLOW N.
ple'na . . . . FLOATING N.

NERI'NE . . . . NERINE
bow'deni . . . . . . CAPECOLONY N.
curvifo'lia . . . . . . CURVELEAF N.
—**fothergill'i** (*N. fothergilli*)
FOTHERGILL N.
MAJOR. HV.
flexuo'sa . . . . NODDING N.
—**pulchel'la** . . . . . REDKEEL N.N.
—**sanderso'ni** . . . . STURDY N.N.
ALBA. HV. N. flexuosa
hu'milis . . . . GOODHOPE N.
SPLENDENS. HV.
∞ **man'selli** (*?curvifolia fothergilli* × *?flexuosa*) . . . . . ∞ MANSELL N.
The cultivated plant may be a clon of this.
pu'dica . . . . PINKKEEL N.
—**elwes'i** . . . . ELWES P.N.
ALBA. HV. N. pudica
sarnien'sis (*Amaryllis s.*)
GUERNSEYLILY N.
CORUSCA. HV.
CORUSCA MAJOR. *Scarlet-beauty*

NERINE sarniensis, continued
INSIGNIS
PLANT (*planti*)
ROSE QUEEN (*rosea*)
undula'ta . . . . KALAHIRI NERINE
—**ma'jor** . . . . BIG K.N.
AFTERGLOW. HV. Nerine
AGLAIN
AURORA
BARCAROLLE
BEACON
BEDOUIN
BERENICE
BETTY
CALPURNIA
COMUS
ELEGANTISSIMA
FELICITY
FILIFOLIA
HERA
HER MAJESTY
HILDA
INGENS
JUDITH
KNIGHT ERRANT
KNIGHT TEMPLAR
LADY (*Clementina*) MITFORD
LADY FOLKES
LADY (*Mary*) SHELLEY
LUCIFER
LYDIA
MEADOWBANK
MINERVA
MIRANDA
PETER BARR
PINKBEAUTY
PRINCESS MARY
QUEEN ALEXANDRA
QUEEN MARY
QUEEN NATHALIE
RED HUSSAR
ROBERT BERKELEY
RONALD
ROSE BARTON
ROSEBEAUTY
ROSELLA
SALMON PERFECTION
SCARLETTA
TALISMAN
VIEUX ROSE

NERINE . . . . **Nerine**
BIG KALAHIRI N. . **N. undulata major**
CAPECOLONY N. . . . . . **N. bowdeni**
CURVELEAF N. . . . . . . **N. curvifolia**
ELWES PINKKEEL N. **N. pudica elwesi**
FOTHERGILL N.. **N. curvifolia fothergilli**
GOODHOPE N. . . . . **N. humilis**
GUERNSEYLILY N. . . . **N. sarniensis**
KALAHIRI N. . . . . **N. undulata**
∞ MANSELL N. . . . . . . ∞ **N. manselli**
NODDING N. . . . . **N. flexuosa**
PINKKEEL N. . . . . **N. pudica**
REDKEEL NODDING N.
N. flexuosa pulchella
STURDY N. N. . . . . . **N. f. sandersoni**

NE'RIUM . . . . OLEANDER
in'dicum (*odorum*). SWEETSCENTED O.
olean'der . . . . COMMON O.
CARDINAL. HV.
COM. BARTHELEMY
DR. GOLFIN
LILIAN HENDERSON WHITE
LUTEUM
MME. PEYRE
MME. SARAH BERNHARDT
MRS. ROEDING

NERIUM **oleander**, continued
PROF. BODKIN
ROSEPINK
RUBRA
SHELLPINK
SINGLE RED
SISTER AGNES
SPLENDENS

NERTE'RA
granaden'sis (*depressa*) . BEADPLANT
Nesae'a verticilla'ta. **Decodon verticillatus**

NES'LIA
panicula'ta . . . . . . BALLMUSTARD

NETBUSH . . . . **Calothamnus**
BLOOD N. . . . . **C. sanguineus**
CLIFF N. . . . . **C. rupestris**
CRIMSONCLUSTER N. . **C. quadrifidus**
CRIMSONSPIKE N. . **C. homalophyllus**
DWARF N. . . . . **C. longissimus**
GILES N. . . . . **C. gilesi**
GOLDEN N. . . . . **C. chrysantherus**
ROUGH N. . . . . **C. asper**

NETTLE . . . . **Urtica**
BIGSTING N. . . . . **U. dioica**
CALIFORNIA SLIM N.
U. gracilis holosericea
DOG N. . . . . **U. urens**
LYALL N. . . . . **U. lyalli**
ROMAN N. . . . . . . **U. pilulifera**
SLIM N. . . . . **U. gracilis**
TALL N. . . . . **U. procera**

NETTLESPURGE . . . . **Jatropha**
BARBADOSNUT . . . . . . **J. curcas**
BELLYACHE N. . . . . **J. gossypifolia**
BERLANDIER N. . . . **J. berlandieri**
CORALPLANT N. . . . . **J. multifida**
PEREGRINA N. . . . . . . **J. hastata**
TARTOGO N. . . . . . . **J. podagrica**

NEVIUS'IA . . . . . . SNOWWREATH
alabamen'sis . . . . . SNOWWREATH

NEWYORK FERN
Dryopteris noveboracensis

NEWZEALAND-SPINACH
Tetragonia expansa

NEYRAUD'IA
See **GRASS GENERA.**

NIBONGPALM . **Oncosperma filamentosum**

NICAN'DRA (*PHYSALODES*)
APPLEOFPERU
physalo'des . . . . APPLEOFPERU
violac'ea

NICOTIA'NA . . . . . . TOBACCO
acumina'ta
ala'ta . . . . WINGED T.
JASMINE (*affinis; grandiflora*) HV.
attenua'ta . . . . COYOTE T.
auricula'ta
bigelo'vi . . . . INDIAN T.
chinen'sis . . **N. tabacum angustifolia**
colosse'a . . . . **N. tomentosa**
forgetia'na
fra'grans . **N. suaveolens macrantha**
glau'ca . . . . TREE T.
glutino'sa
langsdorf'fi
longiflo'ra
macrophyl'la . . . . . **N. tabacum m.**
noctiflo'ra
panicula'ta
petiola'ris
plumbaginifo'lia
quadrival'vis

NICOTIANA, continued
rus'tica . . . . . . AZTEC TOBACCO
∞ **san'derae** (*alata × forgetiana*)
∞ SANDER T.
CRIMSON KING. HV.
suave'olens
—**macran'tha** (*N. fragrans*)
sylves'tris
tabac'um . . . . COMMON T.
—**angustifo'lia** (*N. chinensis*)
NARROWLEAF C.T.
—**macrophyl'la** (*N. macrophylla*)
BIGLEAF C.T.
tomento'sa (*colossea*) . . . GIANT T.
trigonophyl'la . . . . . DESERT T.
visco'sa
wigandioi'des

NIDULA'RIUM
ful'gens (*pictum*)
innocen'ti

NIEPABARKTREE . . . **Samadera indica**

NIEREMBER'GIA . . . . CUPFLOWER
frutes'cens . . . . TALL C.
grac'ilis . . . . SLENDER C.
hippoman'ica . . . . DWARF C.
rivula'ris . . . . WHITE C.

NIGEL'LA . . . . . FENNELFLOWER
arven'sis
damasce'na . . . . . LOVEINAMIST
diversifo'lia
hispan'ica . . . . SPANISH F.
WHITE (*alba*) HV.
sati'va . . . . GARDEN F.

NIGERSEED . . . . **Guizotia**
ETHIOPIAN N. . . . . . **G. abyssinica**

NIGGERHEAD . . **Rudbeckia occidentalis**

Niggermouth . SLIPPERFLOWER, REDBIRD:
Pedilanthus tithymaloides

Niggertoe . . . . BRAZILNUT:
Bertholettia excelsa

NIGHTBLOOMING-CEREUS . . **Hylocereus**
ANTIGUA N. . . . . . **H. antiguensis**
COMMON N. . . . . . . **H. undatus**
COSTA RICA N. . . . **H. costaricensis**
GUATEMALA N. . . **H. guatemalensis**
LEMAIRE N. . . . . . . **H. lemairei**
ONESPINE N. . . . **H. monacanthus**
PURPUS N. . . . . **H. purpusi**

NIGHTJASMINE
Nyctanthes; N. arbor-tristis

NIGHTPHLOX . . . . . . **Zaluzianskya**
CAPE N. . . . . **Z. capensis**
HAIRY N. . . . . **Z. villosa**

NIGHTSHADE . . . . **Solanum**
See also EGGPLANT, HORSENETTLE, JERUSALEMCHERRY, PEPINO, and POTATO.
APPLE-OF-SODOM N. . . **S. sodomeum**
AUSTRALIAN N. . . . . . **S. aviculare**
BITTER N. . . . . **S. dulcamara**
BLACK N. . . . . **S. nigrum**
BRAZIL N. . . . . . **S. atropurpureum**
BUFFALOBUR N. . . . . **S. rostratum**
CALIFORNIA N. . . . . **S. californicum**
CATALINA N. . . . . **S. wallacei**
CLEVELAND N. . . . . . . **S. clevelandi**
COSTARICAN N. . . . . . **S. wendlandi**
CROTON N. . . . . . . **S. crotonifolium**
CUTLEAF N. . . . . **S. triflorum**
DOUGLAS N. . . . . **S. douglasi**
ETHIOPIAN N. . . . . . **S. aethiopicum**
GAYS N. . . . . **S. gayanum**
GIANT N. . . . . **S. giganteum**

NIGHTSHADE, continued
GREAT JASMINE N.
Solanum jasminoides grandiflorum
GUINEA N. . . . . **S. guineense**
HAIRY BITTER N.
S. dulcamara villosissimum
HORNED N. . . . . **S. cornutum**
INLAND N. . . . . **S. interius**
JASMINE N. . . . . . . **S. jasminoides**
LANCELEAF N. . . . . . **S. lanceolatum**
LAURELLEAF N. . . . . **S. laurifolium**
MELONLEAF N. . . . . . **S. heterodoxum**
MULLEIN N. . . . . . **S. verbascifolium**
PARAGUAY N. . . . . . **S. rantonetti**
PARISH N. . . . . **S. parishi**
POTATOTREE N. . . . . **S. macranthum**
PURPLE N. . . . . **S. xanti**
RUSTYWOOL N. . . . . **S. warscewiczi**
SANDIEGO N. . . . . . **S. tenuilobatum**
SEAFORTH N. . . . . **S. seaforthianum**
SHRUB N. . . . . **S. robustum**
SILVERLEAF N. . . . **S. elaeagnifolium**
SODA-APPLE N. . . **S. aculeatissimum**
SOLANBERRY BLACK N.
S. nigrum guineense
TEXAS N. . . . . **S. triquetrum**
TORREY N. . . . . **S. torreyi**
TUCUMAN N. . . . . . **S. tucumanense**
UMBELLED N. . . . . **S. umbelliferum**
VIOLET N. . . . . **S. auriculatum**
WATERMELON N. . . . **S. citrullifolium**
WHITE BITTER N. **S. dulcamara album**
WHOLELEAF B. N. . . **S. d. indivisum**
YELLOW N. . . . . **S. luteum**

NIKKONUTTREE **Afrolicania eleosperma**

NIMBLEWILL . . **Muhlenbergia schreberi**
ILLINOIS N. . . . . . . **M. curtisetosa**
WASHINGTON N. **M. schreberi palustris**

NINEBARK . . . . **Physocarpus**
ALABAMA N. . . . . **P. stellatus**
AMUR N. . . . . **P. amurensis**
COLORADO N. . . . . **P. glabratus**
COMMON N. . . . . . . **P. opulifolius**
DWARF ILLINOIS N.
P. intermedius parvifolius
DWARF N. . . . . **P. alternans**
ILLINOIS N. . . . . . . **P. intermedius**
MALLOW N. . . . . . . **P. malvaceus**
MOUNTAIN N. . . . . . **P. monogynus**
PACIFIC N. . . . . **P. capitatus**
TWINPOD N. . . . . . . **P. bracteatus**

NINTOO'A . . . . **LONICERA**

NIO'BE . . . . **HOSTA**

NI'PA . . . . NIPAPALM
See **PALM GENERA.**

NIPHOB'OLUS . . **CYCLOPHORUS**
See **FERN GENERA.**

NIPPLEWORT . . . . **Lapsana**
COMMON N. . . . . . . **L. communis**

NIPPONBELLS . . . . . **Shortia uniflora**

NIPPONLILY . . . . **Rohdea**
OMOTO N. . . . . **R. japonica**

NISSO'LIA
frutico'sa
schott'i

NITEL'LA |w . . . . NITELLA
batrachosper'ma . . . FROGSPERM N.
cer'nua . . . . NODDING N.
clava'ta . . . . CLUB N.
flex'ilis . . . . PLIANT N.
grac'ilis . . . . SLENDER N.

NITGRASS . . . **Gastridium ventricosum**

NITTATREE . . . . **Parkia**
AFRICAN N. . . . . **P. africana**
FERNLEAF N. . . . . . **P. filicoidea**
MALAYA N. . . . . **P. biglandulosa**
ROXBURGH N. . . . . . **P. roxburghi**
TWOBALL N. . . . . . . **P. biglobosa**

Noglumegrass . . . . . MUDGRASS: **Coleanthus subtilis**

NOLA'NA . . . . NOLANA
atriplicifo'lia (*grandiflora; paradoxa*) DARK BLUE N.
lanceola'ta
prostra'ta

NOLI'NA . . . . NOLINA
bel'dingi
bigelo'vi . . . . BIGELOW N.
green'ei . . . . GREENE N.
longifo'lia
microcar'pa . . . . . . SACAHUISTA
pal'meri
par'ryi (*Dasylirion p.*) . . . PARRY N.

NOLTE'A
africa'na
—au'rea

NOMOCH'ARIS
mair'ei
na'na
pardanthi'na
—far'reri

NOPALCACTUS . . . . **Nopalea**
AUBER N. . . . . **N. auberi**
COCHINEAL N. . . . **N. cochenillifer**
PANAMA N. . . . . **N. dejecta**

NOPA'LEA . . . . . . NOPALCACTUS
See **CACTUS GENERA.**

NOPALXO'CHIA . . **EPIPHYLLUM**
See **CACTUS GENERA.**

NORANTE'A
guianen'sis

NORFOLKISLANDPINE. . **Araucaria excelsa**

NORMAN'BYA . . . NORMANBYPALM
See **PALM GENERA.**

NORMANBYPALM
Normanbya; N. normanbyi

NORON'HIA
emargina'ta

NOR'TA . . . . . . **SISYMBRIUM**

NOSEBURN . . . . **Tragia**

NOTHOFA'GUS . . . . FALSEBEECH
antarc'tica (*Fagus a.*) . ANTARCTIC F.
—uligino'sa
cliffortioi'des . . . . . MOUNTAIN F.
cunningham'i . . . . TASMANIAN F.
dom'beyi . . . . . . SOUTHERN F.
fus'ca (*Fagus f.*) . . . . . BLACK F.
—colenso'i
menzies'i . . . . SILVER F.
moor'ei . . . . NEGROHEAD F.
obli'qua (*Fagus o.*)
pro'cera
solan'dri
trunca'ta . . . . CLINKER F.

NOTHOLAE'NA . . . . CLOAKFERN
See **FERN GENERA.**

NOTHOL'CUS . . . . . . **HOLCUS**
See **GRASS GENERA.**

NOTHOPAN'AX . . . . FALSEPANAX
anom'alus (*Panax anomalum*)
arbo'reus . . . . TREE F.

NOTHOPANAX, continued
colenso'i
da'vidi (*Panax d.*) DAVID FALSEPANAX
lae'tus
sim'plex

NOTHOSCOR'DUM [W] . FALSEGARLIC
bival've [W] . . . . YELLOW F.
fra'grans . . . . . . FRAGRANT F.

Notoba'sis syria'ca . **Cirsium syriacum**

NOTOCAC'TUS
See **CACTUS GENERA.**

NOTO'NIA . . . . NOTONIA
See **SUCCULENTS.**

NOTOSPAR'TIUM
carmichel'iae
glabres'cens

NOTOTHLAS'PI
rosula'tum

NOTOTRICH'IUM
sandwicen'se . . . . KULUI

NUNNEZHA'RIA . **CHAMAEDOREA**
See **PALM GENERA.**

NUNNEZHA'ROA
CHAMAEDOREA; MORENIA
See **PALM GENERA.**

NUNNE'ZIA . . . **CHAMAEDOREA**
See **PALM GENERA.**

NU'PHAR (*NYMPHOZANTHUS*) COWLILY
See **WATERLILY GENERA.**

NUT GROUP COMMON NAMES

Prepared by C. A. Reed, Bureau of Plant Industry, U. S. Department of Agriculture

ACORN . . . . . **QUERCUS** species
ALMOND . . . . . **Prunus amygdalus**
ARAUCNUT (*Araucarian Pinenut*) **Araucaria araucana**
BEECHNUT . . . . . **FAGUS** species
BETELNUT . . . . **Areca cathecu**
BRAZILNUT (*Castanha; Niggertoe*) **Bertholletia excelsa**
BREADNUT . . . **Brosimum alicastrum**
∞ BUARTNUT . . . . ∞ **Juglans bixbyi**
BUFFALONUT . . . . **Pyrularia pubera**
BUTTERNUT (*White Walnut*) **Juglans cinerea**
CANDLENUT . . **Aleurites moluccana**
CASHEW . . . **Anacardium occidentale**
Castanha . . . . BRAZILNUT
CHESTNUT . . . **CASTANEA** species
CHILENUT (*Chilehazel*) **Gevuina avellana**
CHINKAPIN . . **CASTANEA** species; **CASTANOPSIS** species
∞ CHINKNUT . . . ∞ **Castanea neglecta**
COCONUT . . . . . . **Cocos nucifera**
COHUNENUT **Orbignya cohune** (*Attalea c.*)
COLANUT, SUDAN . . **Cola acuminata**
FILBERT (*Hazelnut*) **CORYLUS** species
Flat Siebold Walnut; Flat W. HEARTNUT
GINKGONUT . . . . . **Ginkgo biloba**
Hazelnut . . . . FILBERT
HEARTNUT (*Flat Siebold Walnut; Flat W.*) . **Juglans sieboldiana cordiformis**
HICKORYNUT . . . . **CARYA** species
India-almond . . . TROPICAL-ALMOND
Intermediate Walnut . . ∞ REGRANUT
IVORYNUT . . **Phytelephas seemanni**

NUT GROUP COMMON NAMES, continued
Javaalmond . . . . PILINUT
LYCHEE (*Lycheenut*) . **Litchi chinensis**
This fruit is listed here, as it is popularly (though not accurately) referred to as a nut.
MACADAMIA (*Queenslandnut*) **Macadamia ternifolia**
MORETONBAYCHESTNUT **Castanospermum australe**
Niggertoe . . . . BRAZILNUT
OYSTERNUT . . . . **Telfairia pedata**
Paradisenut . . . . . SAPUCAIANUT
PEANUT . . . . . **Arachis hypogaea**
PECAN . . . . . . **Carya illinoensis**
Pekeanut; Peruvianalmond SAWARRINUT
Pignolia
Trade name for shelled seeds of any edible Pine.
PILINUT (*Javaalmond*) **Canarium ovatum**
PINENUT . . . . . . **PINUS** species
PISTACHIONUT . . **PISTACIA** species
POTATOBEAN . . . **Apios americana**
QUANDONGNUT . **Fusanus acuminatus**
Queenslandnut . . . . . MACADAMIA
Rattlenut . . . . . WATERCHINKAPIN
∞ REGRANUT (*Intermediate Walnut*) ∞ **Juglans intermedia**
SAPUCAIANUT (*Paradisenut*) **Lecythis zabucajo**
SAWARRINUT (*Pekeanut; Peruvianalmond; Souarinut*) **Caryocar nuciferum**
SINGHARANUT . . . **Trapa bispinosa**
Souarinut . . . . SAWARRINUT
TROPICAL-ALMOND (*India-almond*) **Terminalia catappa**
TUNGNUT . . . . . . **Aleurites fordi**
WALNUT . . . . . **JUGLANS** species
WATERCHESTNUT . . . **Trapa natans**
WATERCHINKAPIN (*Rattlenut*) . **Nelumbium pentapetalum** (*luteum*)
WATERNUT . . **Eleocharis tuberosa**
White Walnut . . . . . BUTTERNUT

NUTMEG . . . . **Myristica**
COMMON N. . . . . . . **M. fragrans**
MACASSAR N. . . . . . **M. argentea**
MUTWINDA N. . . . . **M. irya**

NUTTAL'LIA Raf., *not* Barton **MENTZELIA**

NUTTAL'LIA Torr. & Gray, *not* Barton . . . . . . **OSMARONIA**

NUYT'SIA . . . . FIRETREE
floribun'da . . . . . AUSTRALIAN F.

NYCTAN'THES . . . NIGHTJASMINE
arbor-tris'tis . . . . NIGHTJASMINE

NYCTE'LEA . . . . . . **ELLISIA**
ambig'ua . . . . **E. nyctelea**

NYCTERIN'IA . **ZALUZIANSKYA**

NYCTOCE'REUS
See **CACTUS GENERA.**

NYMPH'AEA (*CASTALIA*) WATERLILY
See **WATERLILY GENERA.**

NYMPHOI'DES (*LIMNANTHEMUM*) [W] . . . FLOATINGHEART
aquat'icum [W]
in'dicum (*Limnanthemum i.*). . INDIA F.
lacuno'sum (*Limnanthemum l.*) [W]
pelta'tum (*Limnanthemum nymphaeoides*) [W]

NYMPHOZAN'THUS . . . **NUPHAR**
See **WATERLILY GENERA.**

NYS'SA (*TUPELO*) |w . . . . TUPELO
aquat'ica |w . . . . WATER T.
oge'che |w . . . . . . OGEECHEE T.
sessiliflo'ra
sinen'sis . . . . CHINESE T.
sylvat'ica (*multiflora*) |w . . BLACK T.; BLACKGUM (Forestry)
—biflo'ra (*N. biflora*) |w SWAMP B.T.; BLACKGUM (Lumber trade)
—pen'dula . . . . WEEPING B.T.
ursi'na . . . . BEAR T.

OAK . . . . **Quercus**
ALBERMARLE O. . . . . ×**Q. atlantica**
ALEPPO O. . . . . **Q. infectoria**
ALVORD O. . . . **Q. dumosa alvordiana**
ANDREWS O. . . . . . ×**Q. andrewsi**
ARIZONA WHITE O. . . . **Q. arizonica**
∞ ARKANSAS O. . . . . . ∞ **Q. arkansana**
ARKANSAS POST O. **Q. stellata attenuata**
ASHE BLACKJACK O. **Q. marilandica ashei**
ASHE O. . . . . ×**Q. ashei**
∞ AUDLEY O. . . . . . ∞ **Q. audleyensis**
AUSTRIAN TURKEY O. **Q. cerris austriaca**
BARON O. . . . . **Q. baroni**
BARTRAM O. . . . ×**Q. heterophylla**
BAYOU POST O. . . **Q. stellata similis**
BEADLE O. . . . . ×**Q. beadlei**
BEAUMONT O. . . ×**Q. beaumontiana**
BEBB O. . . . . ×**Q. bebbiana**
∞ BENDER O. . . . . . . ∞ **Q. benderi**
BIENNIAL CORK O. **Q. suber occidentalis**
BIGELOW O. . . . . . . **Q. breviloba**
BLACKJACK O. . . . . **Q. marilandica**
BLACK O. . . . . **Q. velutina**
BLUEJACK O. . . . . **Q. cinerea**
BLUE JAPANESE O. . . . . **Q. glauca**
BLUE O. . . . . **Q. douglasi**
BLUFF O. . . . . **Q. austrina**
BLUFFTON O. . . . ×**Q. blufftonensis**
BOTTOM O. . . . . ×**Q. runcinata**
BOYNTON POST O. **Q. stellata boyntoni**
BRAY O. . . . . **Q. muhlenbergi brayi**
BREWER O. . . . . . . **Q. oerstediana**
BRITTON O. . . . . . . ×**Q. brittoni**
BROADTIP DIAMONDLEAF O. **Q. obtusa obovatifolia**
BROWNWOOD POST O. **Q. stellata parviloba**
BUR O. . . . . **Q. macrocarpa**
BUSHES O. . . . . ×**Q. bushi**
CALIFORNIA BLACK O. . . **Q. kelloggi**
CALIFORNIA LIVE O. . . . **Q. agrifolia**
CALIFORNIA SCRUB O. . . **Q. dumosa**
CALIFORNIA WHITE O. . . . **Q. lobata**
CANARY O. . . . . . . **Q. canariensis**
CANYON LIVE O. . . . **Q. chrysolepis**
CAROLINA O. . . . ×**Q. carolinensis**
CHAPMAN O. . . . . **Q. chapmani**
CHERRYBARK O. **Q. falcata leucophylla**
CHESTNUTLEAF O. . **Q. castaneaefolia**
CHESTNUT O. . . . . . . **Q. montana**
CHINKAPIN O. . . . . **Q. muhlenbergi**
COCKS O. . . . . ×**Q. cocksi**
COLORADORIVER O. . ×*Q. coloradensis*
COMPTON O. . . . . ×**Q. comptonae**
CORK O. . . . . **Q. suber**
COVINGTON O. . . . . . . ×**Q. byarsi**
CUTLEAF TURKEY O. **Q. cerris laciniata**
CYPRIAN GOLDEN O. . . . **Q. alnifolia**
DAIMYO O. . . . . **Q. dentata**

OAK, continued
DEAM O. . . . . . ×**Quercus deami**
DEMAREE O. . . . . . . ×**Q. demarei**
DIAMONDLEAF O. . . . . . . **Q. obtusa**
DURAND O. . . . . **Q. durandi**
DURMAST O. . . . . **Q. petraea**
DWARF CALIFORNIA LIVE O. **Q. agrifolia frutescens**
DWARF CANYON L. O. **Q. chrysolepis nana**
DWARF CHINKAPIN O. . . **Q. prinoides**
DWARF POST O. **Q. stellata margaretta**
EASTERN RED O. . **Q. borealis maxima**
EHRENBERG O. . . . . . **Q. ehrenbergi**
EMORY O. . . . . **Q. emoryi**
ENGELMANN O. . . . . **Q. engelmanni**
ENGLER O. . . . . **Q. engleriana**
ENGLISH O. . . . . **Q. robur**
EUROPEAN TURKEY O. . . . **Q. cerris**
FAXON O. . . . . ×**Q. faxoni**
FENDLER O. . . . . **Q. fendleri**
FERNOW O. . . . . ×**Q. fernowi**
GAMBEL O. . . . . **Q. gambeli**
GEORGIA O. . . . . . . **Q. georgiana**
GIFFORD O. . . . . . . ×**Q. giffordi**
GLANDBEARING O. . **Q. glandulifera**
Goldencup O. . . . . CANYON LIVE O.
GRAVES O. . . . . **Q. gravesi**
GRAY O. . . . . **Q. grisea**
GUADALOUPE O. . ×**Q. guadelupensis**
GUNNISON O. . . . . . **Q. gunnisoni**
HARBISON O. . . . . ×**Q. harbisoni**
HASTINGS O. . . . . ×**Q. hastingsi**
HAVARD O. . . . . **Q. havardi**
HENRY O. . . . . **Q. henryi**
HICKEL O. . . . . ×**Q. hickeli**
HILLS O. . . . . ×**Q. hilli**
∞ HISPANIA O. . . . . . ∞ **Q. hispanica**
HOLLY O. . . . . **Q. ilex**
HUCKLEBERRY O. . . **Q. vaccinifolia**
IBERIAN O. . . . . **Q. iberica**
INTERIOR LIVE O. . . . . **Q. wislizeni**
ISLAND L. O. . . . . . **Q. tomentella**
ITALIAN O. . . . . **Q. frainetto**
JACKS O. . . . . ×**Q. jackiana**
JAPANESE EVERGREEN O. . **Q. acuta**
KAWEAH WHITE O. **Q. garryana semota**
KERMES O. . . . . **Q. coccifera**
KEW O. . . . . ×**Q. kewensis**
KNAPHILL SCARLET O. **Q. coccinea splendens**
LACEY O. . . . . **Q. laceyi**
LAUREL O. . . . . **Q. laurifolia**
LEA O. . . . . ×**Q. leana**
LEATHER O. . . . . **Q. durata**
LEBANON O. . . . . **Q. libani**
LIVE O. . . . . **Q. virginiana**
LOBED BLUEJACK O. **Q. cinerea dentato-lobata**
LOUISIANA LIVE O. **Q. virginiana eximia**
LOUISIANA WHITE O. **Q. alba repanda**
LOWELL O. . . . . ×**Q. lowelli**
MACEDONIAN O. . . . . . . **Q. trojana**
MACNAB O. . . . . ×**Q. macnabiana**
MAPLELEAF SHUMARD O. **Q. shumardi acerifolia**
MELLICHAMP O. . . ×**Q. mellichampi**
MEXICAN BLUE O. . . **Q. oblongifolia**
MISSOURI BLACK O. **Q. velutina missouriensis**
MOHR O. . . . . **Q. mohriana**
MONGOLIAN O. . . . . . **Q. mongolica**
MYRTLE O. . . . . **Q. myrtifolia**
NARROWLEAF HOLLY O. **Q. ilex angustifolia**
NETLEAF O. . . . . **Q. reticulata**
NEWMEXICAN O. . **Q. novomexicana**

OAK, continued
NORTHERN PIN O. **Quercus ellipsoidalis**
NORTHERN RED O. . . . **Q. borealis**
NUTTALL O. . . . . **Q. nuttalli**
OKALOOSA O. . . . . . ×**Q. venulosa**
ORACLE O. . . . . ×**Q. morehus**
OREGON WHITE O. . . . . **Q. garryana**
ORGANMOUNTAINS O. ×**Q. organensis**
ORIENTAL O. . . . . . . **Q. variabilis**
ORIENTAL WHITE O. . . . . **Q. aliena**
ORLANDO LAUREL O. **Q. laurifolia tridentata**
OVERCUP O. . . . . **Q. lyrata**
OVIEDO O. . . . . . ×**Q. oviedoensis**
PALESTINE O. . . . . . **Q. calliprinos**
PALMER O. . . . . **Q. palmeri**
PIN O. . . . . **Q. palustris**
PLEASANTON LIVE O. **Q. virginiana macrophylla**
PLUME DAIMYO O. **Q. dentata pinnatifida**
PONTIC O. . . . . **Q. pontica**
PORTER O. . . . . ×**Q. porteri**
PORTUGUESE O. . . . . . **Q. lusitanica**
POST O. . . . . **Q. stellata**
PRICE O. . . . . **Q. pricei**
PUBESCENT O. . . . . . **Q. pubescens**
PYRENEES O. . . . . . . **Q. pyrenaica**
REHDER O. . . . . ×**Q. rehderi**
RICHTER O. . . . . . . ×**Q. richteri**
ROBBINS O. . . . . . . ×**Q. robbinsi**
ROUNDLEAF HOLLY O. **Q. ilex rotundifolia**
RUDDY POST O. . **Q. stellata rufescens**
RUDKIN O. . . . . ×**Q. rudkini**
SADLER O. . . . . **Q. sadleriana**
SAND LIVE O. . **Q. virginiana geminata**
SAND POST O. . **Q. stellata araneosa**
∞ SARGENT O. . . . . . ∞ **Q. sargenti**
SARGENT SCARLET O. **Q. coccinea tuberculata**
SAUL O. . . . . ×**Q. sauli**
SAWTOOTH O. . . . . . **Q. acutissima**
SCARLET O. . . . . **Q. coccinea**
SCHNECK O. . . **Q. shumardi schnecki**
SCRUB O. . . . . **Q. ilicifolia**
SEMINOLE LIVE O. **Q. virginiana virescens**
SHALLOWCUP MONGOLIAN O. **Q. mongolica grosseserrata**
SHINGLE O. . . . . **Q. imbricaria**
SHRUB LIVE O. . . . . . **Q. turbinella**
SHUMARD O. . . . . **Q. shumardi**
SILVERLEAF O. . . . . . . **Q. hypoleuca**
SMALLS O. . . . . ×**Q. smalli**
SMOOTHBARK O. . . . . **Q. leiodermis**
SOCORRO O. . . . . . . **Q. leptophylla**
SOUTHERN RED O. . . . . . **Q. falcata**
Spanish O. . . . . . SOUTHERN RED O.
ST.LANDRY O. . . . . ×**Q. ludoviciana**
ST.LOUIS O. . . . . . ×**Q. tridentata**
SWAMP CHESTNUT O. . . . . **Q. prinus**
SWAMP RED O. **Q. falcata pagodaefolia**
SWAMP WHITE O. . . . . . . **Q. bicolor**
TEXAS O. . . . . **Q. texana**
THREELOBE RED O. . **Q. falcata triloba**
TOUMEY O. . . . . **Q. toumeyi**
TRIDENT O. . . . **Q. nigra tridentifera**
TURKEY O. . . . . **Q. laevis**
∞ TURNERS O. . . . . . . ∞ **Q. turneri**
UTAH WHITE O. . . . . . **Q. utahensis**
Valley O. . . . CALIFORNIA WHITE O.
VALONIA O. . . . . . . **Q. macrolepis**
VASEY O. . . . . **Q. vaseyana**
VREELAND O. . . . . **Q. vreelandi**
WALTER O. . . . . . ×**Q. walteriana**

OAK, continued
WATER O. . . . . . . Quercus nigra
WAVYLEAF O. . . . . . . Q. undulata
WEEPING TURKEY O. Q. cerris pendula
WHITE O. . . . . Q. alba
WILCOX O. . . . . Q. wilcoxi
WILLDENOW O. . × Q. willdenowiana
WILLOW O. . . . . Q. phellos

OAKE'SIA . . . . **UVULARIA**

OAKFERN . . . . **Dryopteris disjuncta**

OAKLEECH . . . . **Aureolaria**
ATLANTIC O. . . . . . . **A. pedicularia**
VIRGINIA O. . . . . . . **A. virginica**

OAT . . . . **Avena**
See also **CEREALS**.
ALPINE O. . . . . . . **A. mortoniana**
ANIMATED O. . . . . . . **A. sterilis**
COMMON O. . . . . **A. sativa**
HAIRY O. . . . . . . **A. pubescens**
LITTLE O. . . . . **A. brevis**
LOPSIDED O. . . . . . . **A. strigosa**
NAKED O. . . . . **A. nuda**
RED O. . . . . **A. byzantina**
SIDE O. . . . . . **A. sativa orientalis**
SLENDER O. . . . . . . **A. barbata**
SPIKE O. . . . . **A. hookeri**
TREEPANICLE O. . . **A. sativa diffusa**
WILD O. . . . . **A. fatua**

OATGRASS . . . . . . **Arrhenatherum**
TALL O. . . . . **A. elatius**
TUBER O. . . . . . . **A. e. bulbosum**

Oatgrass . . . . DANTHONIA: **Danthonia**

Obedientplant . . LIONSHEART, VIRGINIA: **Physostegia virginiana**

OBELISCA'RIA . . . . **RATIBIDA**

Obio'ne suckleya'na . . . . **Suckleya s.**

OBOLA'RIA . . . . PENNYLEAF
virgin'ica . . . . VIRGINIA P.

OBREGO'NIA . . . **ARIOCARPUS**
See **CACTUS GENERA**.

OCCIDENT-FROGBIT . . . . **Limnobium**
COMMON O. . . . . **L. spongia**
MEXICAN O. . . . . . . **L. sinclairi**
WESTINDIES O. . . . **L. stoloniferum**

Oceano'rus leimanthoi'des . . **Zigadenus l.**

OCH'NA . . . . OCHNA
arbo'rea . . . . CAPE O.
atropurpu'rea
mauritia'na . . . . . . MAURITIUS O.
mossambicen'sis . . MOZAMBIQUE O.
multiflo'ra

OCHRO'MA . . . . BALSA
bi'color
pyramida'le (*lagopus*) . WESTINDIES B.

OCHRO'SIA . . . . OCHROSIA
borbon'ica . . . . BOURBON O.
ellip'tica

OC'IMUM . . . . BASIL
basil'icum . . . . SWEET B.
—purpu'reum . . . . . . PURPLE S.B.
ca'num . . . . HOARY B.
cris'pum . . . . JAPANESE B.
gratis'simum . . . . . . EASTINDIES B.
guineen'se . . . . GUINEA B.
micran'thum . . . . . . AMERICAN B.
min'imum . . . . LEAST B.
Hardly more than a var. of O. basilicum.
—purpu'reum . . . . . PURPLE L.B.
sanc'tum . . . . HOLY B.

OCIMUM, continued
sua've . . . . TREE BASIL
tenuiflo'rum . . . . SLIMFLOWER B.
vir'ide . . . . FEVER B.

OCONEEBELLS . . . **Shortia galacifolia**

OCOTE'A (*NECTANDRA*) . OCOTEA
bulla'ta . . . . STINKWOOD O.
canalicula'ta
catesbya'na (*Nectandra c.*) . GULF O.
coria'cea (*Nectandra c.; N. willdenowiana*) . . . . JAMAICA O.
co'to . . . . **Aniba c.**
pseudoco'to . . FALSE COTOBARK O.
rodioe'i (*Nectandra r.*) GREENHEART O.
ru'bra . . . . RED O.
strumo'sa (*Nectandra s.*) WHITELAUREL O.
usambaren'sis . . . . . MUZAITI O.

OCOTILLO . . . . **Fouquieria splendens**

OCTOMER'IA
See **ORCHID GENERA**.

ODONTADE'NIA . . BRAZILTRUMPET
specio'sa . . . . REDTUBE B.

ODONTIO'DA
See **ORCHID GENERA**.

ODONTI'TES (*BARTSIA*) . . BARTSIA
ru'bra . . . . RED B.

ODONTOGLOS'SUM
See **ORCHID GENERA**.

ODONTONE'MA (*THYRSACANTHUS*) . . . . FIRESPIKE
callistach'yum . . . . TALL F.
schomburgkia'num (*Thyrsacanthus rutilans*) . . . . COLOMBIA F.
stric'tum

ODONTO'NIA
See **ORCHID GENERA**.

ODONTOPH'ORUS **MESEMBRYANTHEMUM**
See **SUCCULENTS**.

ODONTOSO'RIA in part **SPHENOMERIS**
See **FERN GENERA**.

ODONTOSPER'MUM . . . COWSEYE
aquat'icum . . . . SWEET C.
seric'eum . . . . CANARIES C.

ODOS'TEMON . . . . . **MAHONIA**
Mahonia is a conserved name under International Rules.

OEDOGO'NIUM |w . . OEDOGONIUM
autumna'le . . . . . . AUTUMN O.
bosc'i . . . . BOSC O.
gran'de . . . . GREAT O.
landsbor'oughi . . LANDSBOROUGH O.
rufes'cens . . . . REDDISH O.
stagna'le . . . . STAGNANT O.

OENAN'THE |w . . . WATERDROPWORT
croca'ta . . . . HEMLOCK W.
fistulo'sa
phellan'drium . . . FENNELLEAF W.
sarmento'sa (*californica; O. s. californica*) |w . . . . . . PACIFIC W.

OENOTHE'RA (*Anogra; Chylismia; Eulobus; Galpinsia; Hartmannia; Kneiffia; Lavauxia; Meriolix; Onagra; Pachylophus; Raimannia; Sphaerostigma; Taraxia*) |w EVENINGPRIMROSE; SUNDROPS
acau'lis (*taraxacifolia*) . DANDELION S.

OENOTHERA, continued
albicau'lis . . . . **O. pallida**
alyssoi'des (*Sphaerostigma a.*) ALYSSUM EVENINGPRIMROSE
andi'na (*Sphaerostigma andinum*) ANDEAN SUNDROPS
argillic'ola
berteria'na (*Raimannia b.*)
bien'nis (*Anogra b.*) |w . COMMON E.
bistor'ta (*Sphaerostigma b.*) TWISTED S.
—veitchia'na . . . . . . VEITCH T.S.
brachycar'pa (*Lavauxia b.*)
breviflo'ra (*Taraxia b.*)
brev'ipes . . . . GOLDEN E.
caespito'sa (*Pachylophus caespitosus*) TUFTED E.
—crini'ta (*Pachylophus crinitus*)
—margina'ta (*Pachylophus marginatus*)
califor'nica (*Eulobus californicus*) DESERT E.
campyloca'lyx
cardiophyl'la . . . . . HEARTLEAF E.
cheiranthifo'lia . . . . . . **O. spiralis**
clavaefor'mis . . . . BROWNEYED E.
clut'ei . . . . CLUTES E.
cockerell'i . . . . . COCKERELLS E.
coronopifo'lia (*Anogra c.*)
crucia'ta . . . . . . CROSSFLOWER E.
densiflo'ra . . . . **Boisduvalia d.**
denta'ta
drum'mondi . . . . . DRUMMOND E.
exim'ia (*Pachylophus eximius*) WHITE E.
fla'va (*Lavauxia f.*) . . . YELLOW E.
frutico'sa (*serotina; Kneiffia f.*) COMMON S.
MAJOR. HV.
W. CUTHERTSON
YOUNGS (*youngi*)
glau'ca (*Kneiffia g.*) . . BLUELEAF S.
—fra'seri (*O. fraseri*) . . FRASER B.S.
heteran'tha . . . . . . **O. subacaulis**
hook'eri . . . . HOOKER E.
john'soni . . . . JOHNSON E.
lacinia'ta (*Raimannia l.*) |w CUTLEAF E.
lamarckia'na . . . . . . LAMARCK E.
lavandulaefo'lia (*Galpinsia l.*) LAVENDERLEAF E.
linea'ris
missourien'sis (*macrocarpa; Megapterium missouriense*) . . . OZARK S.
—latifo'lia . . . . BROADLEAF O.S.
mollis'sima
odora'ta
ova'ta . . . . GOLDENEGGS S.
pal'lida (*albicaulis; Anogra a.; A. pallida*) . . . . PALE E.
parviflo'ra (*muricata*) SMALLFLOWER E.
peren'nis (*pumila; pusilla*) PERENNIAL S.
—pil'grimi (*O. pilgrimi*). PILGRIM P.S.
praten'sis (*Kneiffia p.*) . MEADOW S.
rhizocar'pa . . . . **O. triloba**
ripa'ria . . . . STREAM S.
rose'a (*Hartmannia r.*) . . . ROSE S.
scapoi'dea (*Chylismia s.*)
serot'ina . . . . **O. fruticosa**
serrula'ta (*Meriolix s.*)
specio'sa (*Hartmannia s.*)
—rose'a
spinulo'sa
spira'lis (*cheiranthifolia*) . BEACH E.
strigo'sa
subacau'lis (*heterantha; Taraxia h.; T. subacaulis*)
tanacetifo'lia (*Taraxia t.*) TANSYLEAF E.
taraxacifo'lia . . . . **O. acaulis**

OENOTHERA, continued
tetrap'tera (*Hartmannia t.*)
FOURWING EVENINGPRIMROSE
trichoca'lyx (*Anogra t.*)
tril'oba (*rhizocarpa*)
utahen'sis (*Sphaerostigma utahense*)
UTAH E.
villo'sa
virides'cens
whit'neyi . . . . **Godetia grandiflora**

OHIA . . . . . . **Syzygium malaccense**

OILNUT . . . . **Pyrularia**
ALLEGANY O. . . . . **P. pubera**

OILPALM . . . . **Elaeis**
AFRICAN O. . . . . . . **E. guineensis**

OILVINE . . . . **Telfairia**
ZANZIBAR O. . . . . **T. pedata**

OKOUME . . . . **Aucoumea**
KLAINE O. . . . . **A. klaineana**

OKRA . . . . . . **Hibiscus esculentus**

OLDFIELD'IA
africa'na . . . . . . AFRICAN-TEAK

OLDMANCACTUS . . **Cephalocereus senilis**

O'LEA |w . . . . OLIVE
america'na . . . . . . **Osmanthus a.**
aquifo'lium . . **Osmanthus ilicifolius**
chrysophyl'la . . . . . GOLDLEAF O.
cunningham'i . . . CUNNINGHAM O.
europae'a |w . . . . . . COMMON O.
—commu'nis . . . . CULTIVATED C.O.
—oleas'ter . . . . WILD C.O.
ferrugin'ea (*cuspidata*) . . INDIA O.
fra'grans . . . . . . **Osmanthus f.**
hochstet'teri . . . . . . AFRICAN O.
ilicifo'lia . . . **Osmanthus ilicifolius**
lanceola'ta . . . . MAIRE O.
monta'na . . . . RORORO O.
verruco'sa . . . . WARTY O.

OLEANDER . . . . **Nerium**
COMMON O. . . . . . . **N. oleander**
SWEETSCENTED O. . . . **N. indicum**

OLEA'RIA (*SHAWIA*) . . DAISYBUSH
al'bida
angula'ta
angustifo'lia . . . . TETEAWEKA D.
(*Permanentwave-plant*)
arbores'cens (*nitida*)
—capilla'ris (*O. capillaris*)
₵COMPACTA. HV. O. arborescens
argophyl'la . . . . . MUSKTREE D.
avicenniaefo'lia . . . . AKEAKE D.
chatham'ica . . . . . . CHATHAM D.
colenso'i . . . . COLENSO D.
coria'cea . . . . . . LEATHERLEAF D.
cunningham'i . . . . HEKETARA D.
denta'ta (*tomentosa*)
erubes'cens . . . . **O. myrsinoides e.**
floribun'da
for'steri . . . . **O. paniculata**
fragrantis'sima . . . . FRAGRANT D.
furfura'cea . . . . BRANNY D.
gunnia'na . . . . **O. stellulata**
haas'ti . . . . HAAST D.
ilicifo'lia . . . . . . HOLLYLEAF D.
insig'nis . . . . . . **Pachystegia i.**
lacuno'sa
linea'ta
macrodon'ta
CASTLEWELLAN. HV.
MAJOR
MINOR (*nana*)
moscha'ta . . . . MUSKY D.
myrsinoi'des . . . . . . MYRSINE D.

OLEARIA, continued
myrsinoi'des erubes'cens (*O. erubescens*)
BIGHEAD MYRSINE DAISYBUSH
nit'ida . . . . **O. arborescens**
nummularifo'lia . . . COINLEAF D.
odora'ta
oleifo'lia . . . . OLIVELEAF D.
pachyphyl'la . . . . . THICKLEAF D.
panicula'ta (*forsteri*) . . AKIRAHO D.
—ellip'tica
—purpu'rea
panno'sa
ramulo'sa . . . . TWIGGY D.
semidenta'ta
solan'dri . . . . SOLANDER D.
specio'sa
stellula'ta (*gunniana*) . TASMANIAN D.
—lira'ta . . . . RIDGE T.D.
sua'vis . . . . SWEET D.
subrepan'da
thom'soni . . . . THOMSON D.
tomento'sa . . . . **O. dentata**
traill'i . . . . TRAILLS D.
tra'versi . . . . TRAVERS D.
virga'ta
wil'coxi . . . . WILCOX D.

OLIVE . . . . **Olea**
AFRICAN O. . . . . . **O. hochstetteri**
COMMON O. . . . . **O. europaea**
CULTIVATED C. O. **O. e. communis**
CUNNINGHAM O. . . **O. cunninghami**
GOLDLEAF O. . . . . **O. chrysophylla**
INDIA O. . . . . **O. ferruginea**
MAIRE O. . . . . **O. lanceolata**
RORORO O. . . . . **O. montana**
WARTY O. . . . . **O. verrucosa**
WILD COMMON O. **O. europaea oleaster**

OLIVERAN'THUS . . **ECHEVERIA**
See **SUCCULENTS.**

OLIVIER, YELLOW . . **Chuncoa obovata**

OL'NEYA
teso'ta . . . . TESOTA

OLONA . . . . . . **Touchardia latifolia**

OLY'RA . . . . OLYRA
See **GRASS GENERA.**

OMAN'THE (*CHAMAEDOREA* in part) . . . . OMANTHE
See **PALM GENERA.**

OMPHALE'A . . . . . NAVELSPURGE
dian'dra . . . . JAMAICA N.
megacar'pa . . . . . . TRINIDAD N.
trian'dra . . . . DOMINICAN N.

OMPHA'LIA . . . . OMPHALIA
campanel'la . . . . BELL O.

OMPHALO'DES . . . . . NAVELSEED
cappado'cica (*cornifolia*)
CAPPADOCIAN N.
linifo'lia (*Cynoglossum linifolium*)
FLAXLEAF N.
lucil'iae . . . . GREEK N.
lusitan'ica (*nitida*) . PORTUGUESE N.
ver'na . . . . CREEPING N.
—al'ba . . . . WHITE C.N.

OMPHALOGRAM'MA
vincaeflo'ra

ONA'GRA . . . . **OENOTHERA**

ONCIDIO'DA
See **ORCHID GENERA.**

ONCID'IUM
See **ORCHID GENERA.**

ONCO'BA . . . . ONCOBA
echina'ta . . . . GORLI O.
ficifo'lia . . . . **Caloncoba f.**
kraussia'na . . . . KRAUSS O.
routled'gei . . . . . . ROUTLEDGE O.
spino'sa . . . . SPINY O.

ONCOSPER'MA . . . . ONCOSPERMA
See **PALM GENERA.**

ONGOKE'A
klainea'na

ONION . . . . **Allium**
See also CHIVE, GARLIC, LEEK, RAMPS, RAMSONS, and SHALLOT.
ALLEGANY O. . . . **A. allegheniense**
ALPS O. . . . . **A. montanum**
ANGLE O. . . . . **A. angulosum**
BALLHEAD O. . . **A. sphaerocephalum**
BEES O. . . . . **A. beesianum**
BIGBLOOM O. . . . . **A. macranthum**
BIGFLOWER ROSY O.
A. roseum grandiflorum
BLACK O. . . . . **A. nigrum**
BLOODTUNIC O. . . . **A. haematochiton**
BLUEGLOBE O. . . . . . . **A. caeruleum**
BLUEMOUNTAINS O. . . . **A. fibrillum**
BOLANDER O. . . . . . . **A. bolanderi**
BRANDEGEE O. . . . . . **A. brandegei**
BREWER O. . . . . **A. breweri**
CORY O. . . . . **A. coryi**
CURLED MEXICALI O.
A. peninsulare crispum
DIOSCORIDES O. . . . **A. dioscoridis**
DOUGLAS O. . . . . **A. douglasi**
DWARF ALPS O.
A. montanum petraeum
ELDORADO O. . . . . . . **A. hyalinum**
FARRER O. . . . . **A. farreri**
FRAGRANT O. . . . . **A. odorum**
GARDEN O. . . . . **A. cepa**
GEYER O. . . . . **A. geyeri**
GIANT O. . . . . **A. giganteum**
GLACIER O. . . . . **A. glaciale**
GOLDBALL O. . . . . **A. ammophilum**
HELDREICH O. . . . . . **A. heldreichi**
JAPANESE O. . . . . . . **A. japonicum**
KANSU O. . . . . **A. kansuense**
KEELED O. . . . . **A. carinatum**
LEAFY O. . . . . . . **A. polyphyllum**
LEBANON O. . . . . **A. libani**
LEDEBOUR O. . . . **A. ledebourianum**
LEMMONS O. . . . . **A. lemmoni**
LONGROOT O. . . . . . . **A. victorialis**
MEDITERRANEAN O. . . **A. paniculatum**
MEXICALI O. . . . . . . **A. peninsulare**
MILK O. . . . . **A. galanthum**
MULTIPLIER O. . . **A. cepa solanium**
MUSK O. . . . . **A. moschatum**
NAPLES O. . . . . . **A. neapolitanum**
NARCISSUS O. . . . **A. narcissiflorum**
NEVADA O. . . . . **A. nevadense**
NODDING O. . . . . **A. cernuum**
NUTTALL O. . . . . **A. nuttalli**
ONELEAF O. . . . . **A. unifolium**
OSTROWSKY O. . . **A. ostrowskianum**
PACIFIC O. . . . . **A. validum**
PALE O. . . . . **A. pallens**
PEARL O. . . . . . **A. margaritaceum**
PERSIAN O. . . . . . . **A. albopilosum**
POTHERB O. . . . . . . **A. oleraceum**
PRAIRIE O. . . . . **A. stellatum**
PURDOM O. . . . . **A. purdomi**
PYRENEES O. . . . . . . **A. pyrenaicum**
ROSENBACH O. . . **A. rosenbachianum**
ROSEPURPLE O. . . . **A. atropurpureum**
ROSESTRIPE O. . . . . . . **A. globosum**
ROSY O. . . . . **A. roseum**

ONION, continued
SCHUBERT O. . . . . . **Allium schuberti**
SERRATE O. . . . . . . **A. serratum**
SHORTSTYLE O. . . . **A. brevistylum**
SICKLELEAF O. . . . . **A. falcifolium**
STELLERS O. . . . . **A. stellerianum**
STEPPES O. . . . . **A. nutans**
TANGUT O. . . . . . **A. tanguticum**
TAPERTIP O. . . . . **A. acuminatum**
TARTAR O. . . . . **A. tataricum**
TEXTILE O. . . . . **A. textile**
THREEBRACT O. . . **A. tribracteatum**
TIBET O. . . . . **A. tibeticum**
TOLMIE O. . . . . **A. tolmiei**
TOP O. . . . . . . **A. cepa viviparum**
TRIANGLE O. . . . . . **A. triquetrum**
TURKESTAN O. . . . **A. karataviense**
TWOCLOAK O. . . **A. dichlamydeum**
URN O. . . . . **A. urceolatum**
VIVIPAROUS O. . . . . . **A. viviparum**
WELSH O. . . . . **A. fistulosum**
WHITE STELLERS O.
A. stellerianum album
WINKLER O. . . . . **A. winklerianum**
YELLOW O. . . . . **A. flavum**
YUNNAN O. . . . . . **A. yunnanense**

ONIONGRASS . . . **Melica; M. bulbosa**
ALASKA O. . . . . **M. subulata**
GEYER O. . . . . **M. geyeri**
LITTLE O. . . . . **M. fugax**
Purple O. . . . . SHOWY O.
SHOWY O. . . . . **M. spectabilis**
YOSEMITE O. . . . . **M. inflata**

ONOBRY'CHIS . . . . . . SAINFOIN
arena'ria . . . . . . HUNGARIAN S.
caputgal'li . . . . . . COCKSHEAD S.
cristagal'li . . . . . . COCKSCOMB S.
pulchel'la . . . . SUNGARI S.
viciaefo'lia (*sativa; vulgaris*) COMMON S.

ONOCLE'A
See **FERN GENERA.**

ONO'NIS . . . . ONONIS (*Restharrow*)
angustis'sima . . . . . SLIMLEAF O.
aragonen'sis . . . . . . ARAGON O.
cenis'ia . . . . CENIS O.
colum'nae . . . . . . COLUMNAS O.
frutico'sa . . . . SHRUBBY O.
hirci'na (*arvensis*) . . . . GOATROOT O.
na'trix . . . . SNAKEROOT O.
re'pens . . . . CAMMOCK O.
rotundifo'lia . . . . . . COINLEAF O.
serra'ta . . . . YELLOW O.
spino'sa . . . . THORNY O.

ONOPOR'DUM (*ONOPORDON*) lw
COTTONTHISTLE
acan'thium lw . . . . . . SCOTCH C.
According to some authorities this is the "Scotch Thistle," floral emblem of Scotland.
ROBERT BRUCE. HV.
alexandri'num . **O. sibthorpianum a.**
anato'licum . . . **O. sibthorpianum**
ara'bicum . . . . MOORS C.
bractea'tum . . . . CURLYBRACT C.
illyr'icum . . . . ILLYRIAN C.
polyceph'alum . . . . . . HYDRA C.
sal'teri Hort.
Dr. L. H. Bailey reports this "a hort. plant of unknown origin."
sibthorpia'num (*anatolicum*)
TURKISH C.
—alexandri'num (*O. alexandrinum*)
EGYPTIAN C.
tau'ricum . . . . TAURUS C.

ONOS'MA . . . . ONOSMA
albo-ro'seum . . . . VELVETBLOOM O.
bulgar'icum . . . . . BULGARIAN O.
cas'sium . . PURPLE-OF-CASSIUS O.
echioi'des . . . . HAIRY O.
emo'di . . . . EMOD O.
rupes'tre . . . . . . CAUCASIAN O.
stellula'tum . . . . . GOLDDROP O.
—helvet'icum (*O. helveticum*)
SWISS G.O.
—tau'ricum (*O. tauricum*)
LONGTUBE G.O.
tubiflo'rum . . . . . . TRUMPET O.

ONOSMO'DIUM lw . . MARBLESEED
occidenta'le . . . . . WESTERN M.

ONY'CHIUM . . . . . . CLAWFERN
See **FERN GENERA.**

OONOP'SIS . . . . . **APLOPAPPUS**
condensa'ta . . . . . . **A. fremonti**

OOPHY'TUM
MESEMBRYANTHEMUM
See **SUCCULENTS.**

OPHIOGLOS'SUM . ADDERSTONGUE
See **FERN GENERA.**

OPHIOPO'GON . . . . . . **MONDO**

O'PHRYS . . . . **LISTERA**
See **ORCHID GENERA, HARDY TERRESTRIAL GROUP.**

OPIZ'IA
See **GRASS GENERA.**

OPLISME'NUS
See **GRASS GENERA.**

OPLOPAN'AX (*ECHINOPANAX*)
DEVILSCLUB
hor'ridus (*Echinopanax h.; Fatsia horrida; Panax horridum*) AMERICAN D.

OPOPAN'AX . . . . OPOPANAX
chiro'nium . . . . . . SURGEONS O.
(*Hercules-allheal; Woundwort*)

OPSIAN'DRA . . . . MAYAPALM
See **PALM GENERA.**

OPULAS'TER . . . **PHYSOCARPUS**
Opulaster has 80 years' priority, but Physocarpus is conserved under International Rules.

OPUN'TIA (*BRASILIOPUNTIA; CONSOLEA; CORYNOPUNTIA; TEPHROCACTUS*) lw
PRICKLYPEAR; CHOLLA
See **CACTUS GENERA.**

ORACH
GARDEN O. . . . **Atriplex hortensis**
RED G. O. . . . **A. h. atrosanguinea**
TUMBLING O. . . . . **A. rosea**

ORANGE
BERGAMOT O. . . . **Citrus bergamia**
CALAMONDIN O. . . . . . **×C. mitis**
INDIA WILD O. . . . . **C. indica**
JAPANESE TACHIBANA O. . **C. tachibana**
KING O. . . . . **C. nobilis**
MANDARIN O. . . . . . **C. reticulata**
MYRTLELEAF O.
C. aurantium myrtifolia
SATSUMA O. . . . . **C. nobilis unshiu**
SOUR O. . . . . **C. aurantium**
SWEET O. . . . . **C. sinensis**
TAHITI O. . . . . **C. taitensis**
Trifoliate-orange . . . HARDYORANGE:
Poncirus trifoliata

ORANGEASTER . . . . . **Pleiospermium**
BORNEO O. . . . . . . **P. latialatum**
CEYLON O. . . . . **P. alatum**
JAVA O. . . . . **P. dubium**
LONGSEPAL O. . . . **P. longisepalum**
SUMATRA O. . . . . . **P. sumatranum**

ORANGE-GLOWVINE . . **Senecio confusus**

∞ ORANGEQUAT . **Citrus nobilis unshiu × Fortunella spp.**

ORA'NIA . . . . ORANIAPALM
See **PALM GENERA.**

ORBIG'NYA . . . . ORBIGNYA
See **PALM GENERA.**

ORCHARDGRASS . **Dactylis; D. glomerata**

ORCHID
ADDERMOUTH O. . . . . . . **Malaxis**
BUTTERFLY O. . . . **Oncidium papilio**
GRASSPINK O. . . **Calopogon pulchellus**
JUMPING O. **Catasetum macrocarpum**
LEAFY ADDERMOUTH O.
Malaxis paludosa
ONELEAF A. O. . . . . . . **M. unifolia**
SHEATH A. O. . . . . **M. monophyllos**
WINDMILL O. **Cirrhopetalum refractum**

ORCHID GENERA

We regret that a revised list of Orchid Genera, other than the hardy native terrestrial ones, p. 422, and the genus Cordula, is not available for this edition of S.P.N. In response to the Committee's request, the Ames Botanical Laboratory which furnished the Orchid Genera for the first edition found it impossible, owing to time limitations, to supply a revision, while a similar request to the American Orchid Society did not bring the desired results.

For the benefit of those especially interested in this very important plant family, and for the important announcement contained therein, we are quoting the reply to our invitation received from David Lumsden, Secretary:

AMERICAN ORCHID SOCIETY
October 13, 1939

Mr. William A. Dayton,
Standardized Plant Names,
930 F Street, N. W.,
Washington, D. C.

Dear Mr. Dayton:

As per my promise to write you relative to the action taken by the Trustees of the American Orchid Society at their meeting held in Philadelphia, October 4, regarding any assistance they may desire to give, the secretary was instructed to write you stating that it was the opinion of the Society the Committee on Standardized Plant Names could get the information they are seeking from the publication "Sanders List of Orchid Hybrids." This publication contains about 100,000 names of hybrid orchids. It contains a complete list of the hybrids raised with parentage.

An addenda may be obtained bringing up the list to 1936. The list is published by authority of the Royal Horticultural Society, London, England. American hybrids are included in the list.

Sincerely yours,
DAVID LUMSDEN, *Secretary.*

The Committee thinks it desirable, however, to include the following compilation prepared for the first edition, together with the explanatory statement accompanying the list. Orchid Genera, excepting the hardy species noted above, is the only list in this new edition of S.P.N. which has not been revised.

ORCHID GENERA, continued

1923 Edition Foreword

For convenience of reference the genera, species, and varieties of Greenhouse and Exotic Orchids are here brought together in one consolidated list.

The American Joint Committee wishes to acknowledge its great indebtedness to the Ames Botanical Laboratory, North Easton, Massachusetts, and to Mr. F. Tracy Hubbard, Compiler, for supplying the material for Orchid Genera. A careful reading of Mr. Hubbard's statement below will show the lamentable chaos and confusion now existing in Orchid names, especially other than American terrestrial forms, occasioned by a lack of generally accepted standard principles for plant naming, and the almost inextricable tangle of Latin polynomials occasioned by the efforts of the hybridizer to *carry the plant's pedigree in the name*, and his reluctance to translate such polynomials into good English common names.

It is an unfortunate fact perhaps that very few Orchids, excepting the comparatively few terrestrial forms, are known under common or vernacular English names. Also, it is quite possible that with many rare species, which will probably never be generally distributed, a common English name would serve no useful purpose.

It is only fair to state here that Mr. Hubbard supplied common names for a large percentage of the Orchids in this list; but owing to the fact that usually such common names were literal translations of the Latin names (a device that has proved rarely satisfactory in other plant groups), and for the other reasons given above, it seemed to the American Joint Committee wise to omit them in Standardized Plant Names.

Considering these severe handicaps, and many others not discussed here, Mr. Hubbard has done an exceedingly creditable piece of work, and has conformed so far as could be done at the present time to the principles practiced by the American Joint Committee.

It is a notable beginning and should lead to the formation of an expert committee on Orchid nomenclature to the end of simplifying and standardizing the names of species, natural varieties, and horticultural varieties of this remarkable and beautiful family of plants.

American Joint Committee
Harlan P. Kelsey, *Secretary.*

Statement of F. Tracy Hubbard

The genera, species, and varieties of Orchids in this list are in cultivation or have been offered for sale in America.

The Orchids present certain difficulties in conforming to the precedent, established in this work, of using common names in alphabetic sequence for horticultural varieties.

In this list the exact spelling as applied in horticulture or in the trade has been followed, except in such cases as incorrect termination or obvious transposition of letters, and if such spelling differs from the accepted spelling it has been attempted to point out, wherever possible, what was presumably intended. Many minor misspellings have been omitted as being superfluous.

In the case of hybrids the parentage has been designated, wherever known, and Rolfe and Hurst's Orchid Stud-book has been accepted as authoritative with certain qualifications:

1. In some instances in which the horticultural name of a parent differs from the botanically correct name, the horticultural name has been maintained; for instance, Cattleya gigas, the horticultural name, is adopted instead of Cattleya warscewiczi, the older and botanically correct name.

2. The Stud-book gives only the species name of the two parents. Where clearly designated in literature, the varietal form of the parent has been added.

3. If one of the parents as commonly cited is given a name which has been made a synonym in this list, the name here accepted is given, followed by the synonym in parentheses.

4. Where a varietal name has been carelessly raised to the rank of a species, the omission of the species name has been rectified by its insertion in brackets []. Furthermore, many hybrids accepted horticulturally are in reality minor variations of the same major cross and are not considered worthy of separation. Following the Stud-book, these have been treated as synonyms, and the name applied by the Stud-book, even though in some instances not in horticultural usage, has been adopted.

Throughout the Orchid list certain forms and abbreviations have been used. Parentheses () indicate that the enclosed portion is as in horticulture or the trade; brackets [ ] that the enclosure is our insertion. ABL signifies Ames Botanical Laboratory, and is used to designate the name which is botanically best according to our conception. Cy, as usual, designates the name used in Bailey's Standard Cyclopedia of Horticulture, when different from the name adopted in the list. Hyb. stands for hybrid and Nat. hyb. for natural hybrid.

Finally, certain genera, although more or less commonly known in horticulture under a given name, have been reduced to the more correct scientific name, where it has been judged best. The most noticeable of these changes are the replacement of Platyclinis by Dendrochilum and Pescatorea by Zygopetalum. A few species usually known in horticulture under genera to which they certainly do not belong have been referred to their correct genera, for example Saccolabium retusum, also known quite as commonly as S. blumei, has been changed to Rhynchostylis retusa.

Ames Botanical Laboratory
F. Tracy Hubbard, *Compiler.*

ACAM'PE
grandiflo'ra
Not found in botanical literature, probably a horticultural variety.
multiflo'ra
papillo'sa

ACANTHOPHIP'PIUM
javan'icum

ACINE'TA
bark'eri
super'ba (*A. humboldti* Cy)

ACRO'PERA . . . . **GONGORA**
loddige'si . . . . **G. galeata**

A'DA
auranti'aca

AERI'DES
af'fine . . . . **A. multiflorum**
—rose'um
Hort. var. of A. multiflorum.
crassifo'lium
expan'sum . . . . . . **A. falcatum**
—leo'niae . . . . **A. falcatum leonaei**
—leo'nis . . . . . **A. falcatum leonaei**
falca'tum (*expansum; larpentae*)
—houlletia'num (*Aerides houlletianum* Cy)
—leonae'i (*expansum leoniae; expansum leonis*)

ORCHID GENERA (AERIDES), continued
field'ingi
houlletia'num Cy
A. falcatum houlletianum
larpen'tae . . . . **A. falcatum**
lawren'ciae
—sanderia'num (*sanderianum*)
lobb'i . . . . . **A. multiflorum lobbi**
maculo'sum
multiflo'rum (*affine*)
—lobb'i (*lobbi*)
odora'tum
—ma'jus (*A. virens* Cy)
quinquevul'nera
sanderia'num
A. lawrenciae sanderianum
vanda'rum
viola'ceum
Not found in botanical literature, probably a horticultural variety.
vi'rens Cy . . . . **A. odoratum majus**

ANAETOCHI'LUS
ANOECTOCHILUS

ANGRAE'CUM
articula'tum
citra'tum
dis'tichum . . **Mystacidium distichum**
eburne'um
—super'bum
eichleria'num
fra'grans . . . Bourbontea Orchid
leo'nis
modes'tum (*sanderianum*)
sanderia'num . . . . . **A. modestum**
scottia'num
sesquipeda'le

ANGULO'A . . . Cradle-orchid
can'dida
Not found in botanical literature, probably a horticultural variety.
clowes'i . . . . Clowes C.
—eburne'a . . . . Ivory C.
eburne'a . . . . . **A. clowesi eburnea**
modes'tans
Not found in botanical literature, probably a horticultural variety.
ruck'eri . . . . Rucker C.

ANOECTOCHI'LUS
marmora'ta
Not found in botanical literature, probably Dossinia marmorata.

ANSEL'LIA
africa'na

ARACHNAN'THE
clark'ei (*Arachnis clarkei* ABL)
lowe'i (*Arachnis lowei* ABL; *Renanthera lowei* Cy; *Vanda lowei*)

ARACH'NIS . **ARACHNANTHE**

ARPOPHYL'LUM
gigan'teum

ASCOTAI'NIA . . . . . **TAINIA**

ASPA'SIA
luna'ta
variega'ta

BARKER'IA
Botanically only a section of Epidendrum.
hindleya'na . . . . . **B. lindleyana**
lindleya'na (*Epidendrum lindleyanum* ABL-Cy)
spectab'ilis (*E. spectabile* ABL-Cy)

BATEMAN'NIA
burt'i . . . . . . **Zygopetalum burti**

ORCHID GENERA, continued

BIFRENA'RIA

atropurpu'rea

dallemag'nei . . . . . **B. tyrianthina**

harriso'niae (*Lycaste harrisoniae*)

tyrianthi'na (*dallemagnei*)

BLET'IA

hyacinthi'na . . . **Bletilla hyacinthina**

BLETIL'LA . . . . . . BLETILLA

hyacinthi'na (*Bletilla striata* ABL) HYACINTH B.

BOL'LEA . . **ZYGOPETALUM**

BRASSAVO'LA

For hybrids, see also **Brassocattlaelia.**

cuculla'ta

digbya'na (*Laelia digbyana* Cy)

fra'grans

glau'ca (*L. glauca* Cy)

nodo'sa

The following crosses have appeared in horticulture without names:

B. digbyana × *Lc. martineti* Brassocattlaelia ASTARTE

B. digbyana × *Lc. rubens.* This is a Brassocattlaelia. ABL.

BRAS'SIA . . . . . SPIDERORCHID

brachia'ta

gigan'tea

Not found in botanical literature, probably a horticultural variety.

lawrencea'na . . . . . LAWRENCE S.

—longis'sima

macula'ta . . . . SPOTTED S.

verruco'sa

BRASSOCATTLAE'LIA

Also written Brasso-Cattleya-Laelia. Crosses between Brassavola and Laeliocattleya or Cattleya and Brassolaelia.

ASTARTE (*Brassavola digbyana* × *L. martineti*)

HELEN SKINNER (*Brassolaelia Helen* × *C. skinneri*)

mackay'i (*B. digbyana* × *L. elegans*)

ROWENA (*B. digbyana* × *Lc. Doris*)

WOTAN (*Brassocattlaelia leemanniae* × *Lc. callistoglossa*)

BRASSOCAT'TLEYA

Also written Brasso-Cattleya. Crosses between Brassavola and Cattleya.

ADMIRAL JELLICO (*Brassocattleya veitchi* × *C. rothschildiana*)

CALYPSO (*Dante; Brassavola digbyana* × *C. bicolor*)

CARMEN (*B. digbyana* × *C. Mrs. Myra Peters*)

conspic'ua (*B. digbyana* × *C. leopoldi*)

CORDELIA (*B. digbyana* × *C. intermedia*)

cy'clops

Parents unknown.

Dante . . . . CALYPSO

Empress of Russia . . . . **B. maroni**

enter'pe . . . . **B. euterpe**

euter'pe (*enterpe; Brassocattleya langleyensis* × *C. schilleriana*)

EVA (*Brassavola digbyana* × *C. lawrenceana*)

fournier'ae (*fournieri; B. digbyana* × *C. labiata*)

fournier'i . . . . . . **B. fournierae**

heatonen'sis (*Brassovola digbyana* × *C. hardyana*)

hol'fordi (*B. digbyana* × *C. forbesi*)

hye'ae (*Mme. Hye; B. digbyana* × *C. harrisoniana*)

ORCHID GENERA (BRASSOCATTLEYA), continued

ILENE (*Brassocattleya maronae* × *C. dowiana*)

Imperatrice de Russie . . . **B. maroni**

jes'sopi

Hyb.—probably the same as Brassolaelia jessopi.

KING EDWARD VII

Hyb.—possibly the same as Brassolaelia veitchi.

langleyen'sis (*Brassavola digbyana* × *C. schroederiana*)

—em'inens

lee'mani . . . . **B. leemanniae**

leeman'niae (*leemani; B. digbyana* × *C. dowiana*)

mari'ae (*Brassavola digbyana* × *C. warneri*)

MARIE

Hyb.—not found in botanical literature, probably the same as B. mariae.

maro'nae (*B. digbyana* × *C. gigas*)

maro'ni (*Empress of Russia; Imperatrice de Russie*)

MARS (*Brassocattleya leemanniae* × *C. rafaeliae*)

men'da (*B. veitchi* × *C. labiata*)

Mme. Hye . . . . **B. hyeae**

NESTOR (*B. maronae* × *C. labiata*)

OBERON (*B. digbyana-mossiae* × *C. schroederiana*)

POCAHONTAS (*Brassavola digbyana* × *C. Eldorado*)

prae'ti (*B. digbyana* × *C. leopoldi*)

Queen Alexandra . . . . . **B. veitchi**

regi'na

Hyb.—parents not known.

se'deni (*B. digbyana* × *C. trianae*)

—ROSALIND

SIREN (*B. digbyana* × *C. skinneri*)

ST. ALBANS (*B. digbyana* × *C. schilleriana*)

thorn'toni (*B. digbyana* × *C. gaskelliana*)

TRIUNE

Hyb.—not known.

veitch'i (*Queen Alexandra; B. digbyana* × *C. mossiae*)

—al'ba

—SUNSET

WATTEAU

Hyb.—not known.

WOTAN

Probably the same as Brassocattlaelia Wotan.

The following crosses have appeared in horticulture without names.

Brassavola digbyana × *C. leopoldi* Brassocattleya conspicua

gressi × *digbyana*

grossi × *digbyana.* This and the last are undoubtedly the same cross, but whether gressi or grossi (probably a Cattleya hybrid) is correct it has been impossible to ascertain as no such name has been found; digbyana is of course a Brassavola.

Brassocattleya leemanniae × *C. labiata*

B. leemanniae × *C. schroederiana*

B. leemanniae × *Laeliocattleya Nella.* This is a Brassocattlaelia.

B. maronae × *Laeliocattleya Gertrude.* This is a Brassocattlaelia.

B. maronae × *Laeliocattleya Voltaire.* This is a Brassocattlaelia.

C. peetersiae (*Mrs. Myra Peters*) × *Brassavola digbyana*

BRASSO-CATTLEYA-LAE'LIA **BRASSOCATTLAELIA**

ORCHID GENERA, continued

BRASSOLAE'LIA

Also written Brasso-Laelia. Crosses between Brassavola and Laelia.

gratrix'iae (*Brassavola digbyana* × *Laelia cinnabarina*)

HELEN (*B. digbyana* × *L. tenebrosa*)

jes'sopi (*B. digbyana* × *L. xanthina*)

LOUIS-BEL (*B. digbyana* × *L. boothiana*)

rolf'ei (*B. digbyana* × *L. crispa*)

veitch'i (*B. digbyana* × *L. purpurata*)

BROUGHTO'NIA

sanguin'ea

BULBOPHYL'LUM

barbig'erum

bear'i

Not found in botanical literature, probably an error for B. deari.

careya'num

como'sum

congoen'sis

Not found in botanical literature, probably B. congolanum is intended.

cu'preum

daya'num

dear'i

falca'tum ABL. **Megaclinium falcatum**

grandiflo'rum

lilaci'num

lobb'i

odoratis'simum

reinward'ti

sauroceph'alum

suavis'simum

vires'cens

BURLINGTO'NIA (*RODRIGUEZIA* ABL)

can'dida (*Rodriguezia candida* ABL)

deco'ra (*R. decora* ABL)

fra'grans (*R. fragrans* ABL)

CALAN'THE

bel'ia (*harrisi; turneri* × *veitchi*)

Bry'an . . . . **C. darblayana**

CLIVE (*veitchi* × ?)

Cornelius Vanderbilt . . . **C. sedeni**

darblaya'na (*Bryan; William Murray; regnieri* × *vestita*)

dis'color

furca'ta ABL . . . . . **C. veratrifolia**

har'risi . . . . **C. bella**

JOBSTOWN

Hyb.—not found in botanical literature.

masu'ca

mcwil'liamsi

Probably the same as C. veitchi McWilliams.

MRS. CORNELIUS VANDERBILT

Hyb.—not found in botanical literature.

orpetia'na

regnier'i (*vestita regnieri* ABL-Cy)

—sanderia'na (*vestita* form ABL)

rubro-ocula'ta . **C. vestita rubro-oculata**

sanderia'na

sandhurstia'na **C. veitchi sandhurstiana**

se'deni (*Cornelius Vanderbilt; veitchi* × *vestita rubro-oculata*)

summiten'sis. Hyb.

veitch'i (*rosea* × *vestita*)

—al'ba

—MCWILLIAMS

—rose'a

—sandhurstia'na (*sandhurstiana*)

—super'ba

—WHITIN

ORCHID GENERA (CALANTHE), continued
veratrifo'lia (*furcata* ABL)
vesti'ta
—igneo-ocula'ta gigan'tea
Form not known.
—*regnier'i* ABL-Cy . . . **C. regnieri**
—rubro-ocula'ta (*rubro-oculata*)
—wil'liamsi (*williamsi*)
William Murray . . . **C. darblayana**
wil'liamsi . . . . **C. vestita williamsi**

CAMARO'TIS
mann'i
purpu'rea (*C. rostrata* ABL-Cy; *Sarcochilus purpureus*)

CATASE'TUM
bungeroth'i
callo'sum
macrocar'pum . . JUMPING ORCHID
macula'tum
scur'ra
tabula're
viridifla'vum
viridiflo'rum
Not found in botanical literature, probably an error for viridiflavum.

CAT'TLEYA
ACHINE (*C. labiata alba* × *C. rafaeliae alba*)
acland'iae . . . . ACLAND CATTLEYA
ADONIS (*Enid; mossiae* × *gigas*)
ad'ula (*bicolor* × *hardyana*)
ALCESTIS (*bicolor* × *mendeli*)
ALEX (*Tunis* × *aurea*)
ALFRED DIMMOCK (*lawrenceana* × *aurea*)
amab'ilis (*labiata* × *gigas*)
amethysti'na . . . . . **C. intermedia**
amethystoglos'sa (*prinzi*)
armainvillieren'sis (*mendeli* × *gigas*)
armstrong'iae (*hardyana* × *harrisoniana*)
ARTEMIS (*Iris* × *gaskelliana*)
ATLANTA (*leopoldi* × *gigas*)
auranti'aca. **Epidendrum aurantiacum**
au'rea (*dowiana aurea* Cy)
Certainly for horticultural purposes C. aurea should be separated from C. dowiana; its scientific status is open to question, just as many of the recognized species of the labiata group are quite probably more correctly to be classed as varieties of C. labiata rather than as distinct species.
—al'ba
ballantinea'na (*ballantina* Cy)
Said to be a nat. hyb., trianae × gigas sanderiana.
—CLEMENT MOORE
bert'i (*harrisoniana* × *labiata*)
bi'color
black'i (*gaskelliana* × *mendeli*)
boadice'a (*hardyana* × *gaskelliana*)
bogoten'sis (*trianae* ABL)
—al'ba (*trianae* var. ABL)
bowringia'na
—caeru'lea
—caerules'cens
bren'da (*dusseldorfi* × *gaskelliana alba*)
cap'pei al'ba (*schroederiana* × *trianae alba*)
CARMEN (*lueddemanniana* (*speciosissima*) × *gigas*)
Cecilia . . . . **C. ceciliae**
cecil'iae (*Cecilia; lawrenceana* × *trianae*)
C. G. ROEBLING (*harrisoniana* × *mendeli*)

ORCHID GENERA (CATTLEYA), continued
child s'i
Hyb.—not found in botanical literature.
chocoen'sis (*trianae chocoensis* Cy)
The scientific status of this species is in doubt.
chrysot'oxa . . . . **C. dowiana**
citri'na . . . . TULIP ORCHID
claesia'na (*intermedia* × *loddigesi*)
CLARISSA (*loddigesi* × *mendeli*)
clark'iae (*labiata* × *bicolor*)
COMET (*dowiana* × *warneri*)
cook'soni (*hardyana* × *trianae*)
cris'pa . . . . **Laelia crispa**
CYBELE OAKWOOD. Hyb.
dietrichia'na (*schilleriana* × *trianae*)
DIRCE (*Vulcan* × *gigas*)
DOMOS
Hyb.—not found in botanical literature.
dowia'na (*chrysotoxa*) QUEEN CATTLEYA
—roset'ti
This may be an error for C. dowiana rosita.
duprea'na (*dupreyana; warneri* × *gigas*)
dupreya'na . . . . **C. dupreana**
dusseldorf'i UNDINE (*mackayi* var. ABL; *intermedia alba* × *mossiae alba*)
ed'wardi (*Prince Edward; schilleriana* × *gigas*)
ELDORADO
ELLA (*bicolor* × *gigas*)
elonga'ta
Empress Frederick . **C. frederickiae**
Enid . . . . ADONIS
Enid alba . . . . ADONIS var.
EURYDICE (*aclandiae* × *labiata*)
FABIA (*dowiana* × *labiata*)
—ALBA (*dowiana* × *labiata alba*)
Ferdinand Denis . . . . **C. fernandi**
fernand'i (*Ferdinand Denis; gigas* × *aclandiae*)
forbes'i
fow'leri (*leopoldi* × *hardyana*)
frederick'iae (*Empress Frederick; aurea* × *mossiae*)
FREYA (*dowiana* × *mantini*)
gaskellia'na
—al'ba
—albes'cens
—caeru'lea
GENERAL FRENCH (*dowiana* × *Ella*)
GENERAL PAU (*labiata* × *lueddemanniana* (*speciosissima*))
german'ia (*granulosa* × *hardyana*)
gi'gas (*warscewiczi* ABL; *warscewiczi gigas* Cy)
—al'ba
—albes'cens
—atropurpu'rea
—beyrodt'i (*gigas Frau Melani Beyrodt*)
—caerules'cens
—*Frau Melani Beyrodt* **C. gigas beyrodti**
—hardya'na
—mandaia'na
—METEOR
—rochellen'sis
—sanderia'na
granulo'sa
gutta'ta (*Epidendrum elatius*)
—*leopold'i* . . . . **C. leopoldi**
hardya'na (*gigas* × *dowiana*)
Nat. hyb.
—al'ba (*gigas alba* × *dowiana*)
—grandiflo'ra
—rose'a

ORCHID GENERA (CATTLEYA), continued
hardya'na RUTHERFORD
—SPRING BROOK
har'risi (*mendl* × *leopoldi*)
harriso'niae . . . . **C. harrisoniana**
harrisonia'na (*harrisoniae*)
—gigan'tea
—viola'cea
has'selli (*frederickiae* (*Empress Frederick*) × *labiata*)
Heloise . . . . **C. heloisiae**
heloi'siae (*Heloise; forbesi* × *mossiae*)
H. S. Leon . . . . **C. leoni**
hye'ae (*Suzanne Hye de Crom; gaskelliana* × *mossiae*)
interglos'sa (*amethystoglossa* × *intermedia*)
interme'dia (*amethystina*)
—al'ba
irides'cens (*Eldorado* × *bicolor*)
IRIS (*bicolor* × *dowiana*)
JOCASTA (*schroederiana* × *mossiae*)
kienastia'na (*dowiana* × *lueddemanniana* (*speciosissima*))
labia'ta
—al'ba
—atropurpu'rea
—caerules'cens
—cook'soni
Probably the same as C. labiata cooksoniae.
—cookson'iae
—EMPEROR
Not found.
—MRS. G. B. WILSON
—MRS. JULIUS ROEHRS
—MRS. M. ROEHRS
—polychi'lus
—rose'a
LADY EVELYN (*Atalanta* × *hardyana*)
lawrencea'na . . LAWRENCE CATTLEYA
LEDA (*dowiana* × *percivaliana*)
leo'ni (*H. S. Leon; schroederiana* × *gigas*)
leopold'i (*guttata leopoldi*) LEOPOLD CATTLEYA
loba'ta . . . . **Laelia boothiana**
lod'digesi
In scientific work this species usually includes C. harrisoniana which is maintained in this list as distinct for horticultural purposes.
Lord Rothschild . . . **C. rothschildiana**
Lord Rothschild alba (*dowiana* × *gaskelliana alba*) . **C. rothschildiana** var.
lueddemannia'na (*speciosissima*)
—al'ba (*speciosissima alba*)
—stan'leyi (*speciosissima stanleyi*)
lue'geae (*Adonis* (*Enid*) × *dowiana*)
luteo'la
MABEL (*peetersiae* (*Mrs. Myra Peters*) × *warneri*)
Maggie Raphael alba **C. rafaeliae alba**
MAGNET (*mossiae* × *whitei*)
man'tini (*bowringiana* × *aurea*)
—nobil'ior
maro'ni (*dowiana* × *velutina*)
martinet'i
Hyb.—not found in botanical literature.
max'ima
—al'ba
mcmasters'iae (*schilleriana* × *mendeli*)
men'deli
Frequently spelled mendelli.
—al'ba
—al'ba ROEHRS
—COLUMBIA
—RUTHERFORD

ORCHID GENERA (CATTLEYA), continued

mimic'ia . . . . **C. minucia**
minu'cia (*mimicia; loddigesi* × *gigas*)
miran'da (*amethystoglossa* × *trianae*)
Miss Williams . . . . **C. williamsiae**
MOIRA (*Fabia* × *mantini splendens*)
—**al'ba**
MOONBEAM
Hyb.—not known.

mos'siae
—**al'ba**
—**au'rea**
—**caeru'lea**
—**caerules'cens**
—C. BROWN
—**grandiflo'ra**
—**gravesia'na**
—**hardya'na**
—H. GRAVES
Presumably the same as C. mossiae gravesiana.

—**lilaci'na**
—MRS. H. KOMITSCH
—MRS. J. ROEHRS, SR.
—MRS. J. T. BUTTERWORTH
—MRS. JULIUS ROEHRS
—**reineckia'na**
—**reineckia'na lilaci'na**
Possibly C. mossiae lilacina is the same.

—**rousselia'na**
—**rutherforden'sis**
—**super'ba**
—VICTORIA
—**wag'eneri**
M. RAPHAEL . . . . . . **C. rafaeliae**
MRS. J. W. WHITELEY (*bowringiana* × *hardyana*)
Mrs. Pitt . . . . **C. pittiae**
M. SANDER (*dusseldorfi* × *mossiae alba*)
mur'rayi (*William Murray; mendeli* × *lawrenceana*)
Octave Doin . . . . OCTAVIA
OCTAVIA (*Octave Doin; dowiana* × *mendeli*)
OLIVIA (*intermedia* × *trianae*)
parthe'nia (*Isabella* × *mossiae*)
peet'ersi (*hardyana* × *labiata*)
percivalia'na
—**al'ba**
—**atropurpu'rea**
—**auro'ra**
—**caeru'lea**
—**expan'sa**
—**gigan'tea**
—**grandiflo'ra**
—KAISER
—OREOL
—**resplen'dens**
—**roeblingia'na**
—**spectab'ilis**
—STANLEY RANGER
—**super'ba**
phryg'ia (*Adonis* (*Enid*) × *Portia*)
pit'tiae (*Mrs. Pitt; aurea* × *harrisoniana*)
pittia'na (*dowiana* × *granulosa*)
PORTIA (*bowringiana* × *labiata*)
Prince Edward . . . . . **C. edwardi**
PRINCE JOHN (*dowiana* × *hardyana*)
PRINCE OLAF (*parthenia* × *labiata*)
PRINCE ROYAL (*Fabia* × *hardyana*)
PURPLE EMPEROR (*gigas* × *Earl Grey*)
QUIBO (*dowiana* × *williamsiae*)
radia'ta (*dowiana* × *edwardi* (*Prince Edward*))
rafae'liae (*Maggie Raphael; Maggie Rafael; raphaelae; dowiana* × *trianae*)

ORCHID GENERA (CATTLEYA), continued

rafae'liae al'ba (*raphaelae alba; dowiana* × *trianae alba*)
raphae'lae . . . . **C. rafaeliae**
—*al'ba* . . . . . . **C. rafaeliae alba**
REMBRANDT (*elongata* × *labiata*)
rex'
Robert de Wavrin . . . . . **C. roberti**
robert'i (*Robert de Wavrin; schilleriana* × *schroederiana*)
roehrsia'na (*hardyana* × *mendeli*)
rothschildia'na (*Lord Rothschild; dowiana* × *gaskelliana*)
schilleria'na
schofieldia'na (*granulosa schofieldiana* Cy)
schroe'derae . . . . **C. schroederiana**
schroederia'na (*schroederae; trianae schroederae* Cy)
—**al'ba**
—**albes'cens**
—BARONESS
—**caeru'lea**
—**citri'na**
—**lilaci'na**
—**me'ta**
—**reful'gens**
—**rose'a**
—SUNSET
—WILLIAM DUCKHAM
SIBYL (*iridescens* × *aurea*)
skin'neri
—**al'ba**
—**rose'a**
SNOWDON (*labiata alba* × *hyeae* (*Suzanne Hye de Crom*))
SNOWFLAKE (*labiata alba* × *dusseldorfi Undine*)
SNOW QUEEN (*gaskelliana* × *hyeae* (*Suzanne Hye de Crom*))
SOULANGE
Hyb.—not known in botanical literature.

speciosis'sima . **C. lueddemanniana**
—*al'ba* . . . . **C. l. alba**
—*gigan'tea* . **C. lueddemanniana** var.
—*stan'leyi* . . . . **C. l. stanleyi**
stu'arti (*mendeli* × *mossiae*)
sua'vior (*mendeli* × *intermedia*)
super'ba (*violacea* ABL-Cy)
—**splen'dens** (*violacea splendens* ABL-Cy)
Suzanne Hye de Crom . . . **C. hyeae**
thayeria'na (*intermedia* × *schroederiana alba*)
thurgoodia'na (*hardyana* × *lueddemanniana* (*speciosissima*))
tria'nae
—A. C. BURRAGE
—**al'ba**
—ALICE
—**amesia'na**
—A. N. COOLEY
—**atropurpu'rea**
—**auranti'aca**
—**backhousia'na**
—BRIGHTNESS
—**caeru'lea**
—**caerules'cens**
—**compac'ta**
—**delica'ta**
—**dodgeso'ni**
—E. B. DANE
—**leea'na**
—**lumino'sa**
—MRS. EARL G. BARTELS
—MRS. EDWARD S. HARKNESS
—MRS. H. J. LUTCHER

ORCHID GENERA (CATTLEYA), continued

tria'nae nigres'cens
—**os'mani**
—PEARL
—PRESIDENT
—**purpu'rea**
—**rose'a**
—**schiffmann'i**
—**splen'dens**
—**virgina'lis**
veluti'na
Possibly a nat. hyb., C. bicolor × C. guttata.

VENUS (*dowiana* × *Iris*)
vesta'lis (*dowiana* × *maxima*)
viola'cea ABL-Cy . . . . **C. superba**
—*splen'dens* ABL-Cy
C. superba splendens
walkeria'na
war'neri
—**al'ba**
—**marmora'ta**
—**super'ba**
warscewicz'i ABL . . . . . . **C. gigas**
wavrinia'na (*granulosa* × *gigas*)
weedonien'sis (*schofieldiana* × *mendeli*)
wendlandia'na (*bowringiana* × *gigas*)
wi'gani (*T. W. Wigan; dowiana* × *schilleriana*)
William Murray . . . . **C. murrayi**
williamsi'ae (*Miss Williams; gaskelliana* × *harrisoniana*)
ZENIA
Hyb.—not known.

ZEPHYR (*schroederiana* × *aurea*)

The following crosses have appeared in horticulture without names:

Adonis (*Enid* × *dowiana*) . **C. luegeae**
Atalanta × *hardyana* . . LADY EVELYN
aurea × *gigas alba*. Probably a form of C. hardyana.
aurea × *hardyana alba*
aurea × *hyeana*. Close to C. Prince John.
aurea × *labiata*. Close to C. Fabia.
aurea × *Laelia crispa*
Laeliocattleya PALLAS
aurea × *suavior*
bowringiana × *Laelia crispa*. This is a Laeliocattleya.
dowiana × *aurea*
dowiana × *gigas alba* . **C. hardyana alba**
dowiana × *hardyana* . . . PRINCE JOHN
dusseldorfi × *dowiana*
edwardi (*Prince Edward*) × *dowiana*
C. radiata
gaskelliana × *mossiae* . . . . **C. hyeae**
gigas × *labiata* . . . . . . **C. amabilis**
guttata × *hardyana*
hardyana × *leopoldi* . . . . . **C. fowleri**
labiata × *Laelia cinnabarina*
Laeliocattleya coronis
lueddemanniana (*speciosissima*) × *dowiana* . . . . **C. kienastiana**
lueddemanniana (*speciosissima*) × *hardyana* . . . . **C. thurgoodiana**
lueddemanniana (*speciosissima*) × *labiata*
GENERAL PAU
maxima × *aurea* . . . . . **C. vestalis**
mendeli × *hardyana* . . . **C. roehrsiana**
mossiae rouseliana × *Laelia tenebrosa*
Laeliocattleya martineti
mossiae × **Hippolyta.** Misspelled Hyppolita.
schilleriana × *Laeliocattleya callistoglossa*
Laeliocattleya TARQUINIAS
schofieldiana × *aurea* . . . **C. pittiana**
schofieldiana × *hardyana* . . **C. germania**
schofieldiana × *mendeli*. **C. weedoniensis**
trianae × *aurea* . . . . . . **C. rafaeliae**
williamsiae (*Miss Williams*) × *aurea*
QUIBO

ORCHID GENERA, continued

CHONDRORHYN'CHA

chesterto'ni

CHY'SIS

au'rea

bractes'cens

chel'soni (*laevis* × *limminghei*)

CIRRHOPET'ALUM

Considered by many botanists to be a section of Bulbophyllum.

appendicula'tum

cylindra'ceum

Not found in botanical literature, possibly a garden variety.

lendya'num

medu'sae

pictura'tum

pul'chrum

refrac'tum . . . . WINDMILL ORCHID

rox'burghi

thouars'i

COCHLIO'DA

noezlia'na (*noetzliana* Cy)

rose'a (*Odontoglossum roseum*)

sanguin'ea

COE'LIA

baueria'na

macrostach'ya

COELOGLOS'SUM **HABENARIA**

COELOGY'NE

aspera'ta (*lowi*)

barba'ta

corruga'ta (*nervosa* ABL-Cy)

crista'ta

—*al'ba* . . . . **C. cristata hololeuca**

—**chats'worthi**

—**hololeu'ca** (*cristata alba*)

—*lem'oni* . . . **C. cristata lemoniana**

Also misspelled lemoini.

—**lemonia'na** (*cristata lemoni*)

—**max'ima**

daya'na . . . . . NECKLACE ORCHID

ela'ta

fimbria'ta

flac'cida

fra'grans

fuligino'sa

lac'tea

lawrencea'na

lentigino'sa

low'i . . . . **C. asperta**

massangea'na

mayeria'na (*meyeriana*)

meyeria'na . . . . . . **C. mayeriana**

moorea'na Cy

nervo'sa ABL-Cy

ocella'ta (*nitida* ABL-Cy)

—**max'ima**

pandura'ta

prolif'era

sanderia'na

spar'sa

specio'sa

stolonif'era

Not found in botanical literature.

tomento'sa

CORD'ULA . . . . SLIPPERORCHID

The plants in cultivation carrying the below polybrid names may in fact be merely selected clons of these polybrids.

actae'us . . . . ∞ *C. simoni*

∞ *alexan'drae* (*godefroyae* × ∞ *nitens*)

∞ *aman'dum* (*insignis* × *venusta*)

appletonia'na

ar'gus

ORCHID GENERA (CORDULA), continued

∞ *arthuria'na* (*fairieana* × *insignis*)

∞ *ashbur'tonae* (*barbata* × *insignis*)

∞ *augus'ta* (*haynaldiana* × *villosa*)

∞ *au'rea* (∞ *nitens* × *spiceriana*)

barba'ta

∞ *beeck'mani* (*bellatula* × *villosa boxalli*)

bellatu'la

Form of **C. bellatula:**

LOWI

bragaia'na . . . . . ∞ *C. godseffiana*

∞ *brand'tiae* (*iva* × *insignis* YOUNGIANA)

∞ *brunia'na* (∞ *leeana* × ∞ *oenantha*)

callo-rothschildia'na . . . ∞ *C. fowleri*

callo'sa

—**gigan'tea**

—**san'derae**

∞ *calyp'so* (*spiceriana* × *villosa boxalli*)

∞ *canham'i* (*superbiens* × *villosa*)

chamberlainia'na

∞ *charlesia'na* (∞ *leeana* × ∞ *nitens*)

charles'worthi

ciliolar'is

∞ *clark'i* (*charlesworthi* × ∞ *swaniana*)

concol'or

∞ *crossia'na* (*insignis* × *venusta*)

∞ *curtemann'i* (∞ *beeckmani* × ∞ *schlesingeriana*)

cur'tisi

∞ *cymato'des* (*curtisi* × *superbiens*)

dauthier'i . . . . . ∞ *C. harrisiana*

dayan'a

∞ *deedmania'na* (*chamberlainiana* × *spiceriana*)

∞ *dicksonia'na* (×*hera* × *villosa*)

drur'yi

∞ *ed'wardi* (*fairieana* × *superbiens*)

∞ *enfielden'sis* (*hookerae* × *lawrenceana*)

ex'ul

fairiea'na

∞ *fow'leri* (*callosa* × *rothschildiana*; *callo-rothschildiana*)

fulshawen'sis . . ∞ *C. schlesingeriana*

∞ *germinya'na* (*hirsutissima* × *villosa*)

∞ *gi'gas* (∞ *harrisiana* × *lawrenceana*; *prewetti*)

glaucophyl'la

godefroy'ae

∞ *godseffia'na* (*hirsutissima* × *villosa boxalli*; *bragaiana*)

∞ *gratrixia'na* (*bellatula* × ∞ *enfieldensis*)

∞ *grovesia'na* (∞ *lathamiana* × ∞ *leeana*)

∞ *han'seni* (*haynaldiana* × *villosa*)

∞ *harrisia'na* (*barbata* × *villosa*; *dauthieri*; *hybrida*)

∞ *harveya'na* (∞ *leeana* × *stonei*)

haynaldia'na

×**he'ra**

hirsutis'sima

∞ *hitchen'siae* (*charlesworthi* × *insignis*)

hook'erae

∞ *hornia'na* (*spiceriana* × *superbiens*)

hy'brida . . . . . . ∞ *C. harrisiana*

∞ *in'gens* (*insignis* × *rothschildiana*)

insig'nis

Forms (probably clons) of **C. insignis:**

AMESIANA
BALLIAE
BRUGENSIS
CHANTINI
COBBIANA
CORRUGATA
COULSONIANA
DOMINAIANA
EDENIANA
ERNESTI
FOSTERMANNI

ORCHID GENERA (CORDULA), continued

GIGANTEA
GRAVESIANA
HEATONENSIS
HURRELLIANA
IMMACULATA NIGRA
LAGERAE
LEOPARDINA
LINDENIAE
LUCIANI
LUTEO-ALBA
MACFARLANEI
MAULEI
MAXIMA
PUNCTATISSIMA
RUTHERFORDENSIS
SADLERI
SANDERAE
SANDERIANA
SYLHETENSIS
WATSONI
WESTGATENSIS
XANTHINA
YOUNGIANA
ZEBRINA

javan'ica

∞ *josephia'na* (*druryi* × *sementa*)

∞ *kamil'i* (*chamberlainiana* × *villosa boxalli*)

laeviga'ta . . . . . **C. philippinensis**

∞ *laires'sei* (*curtisi* × *rothschildiana*)

∞ *lathamia'na* (*spiceriana* × *villosa*; *thompsoni*)

lawrencea'na

—**hyea'na**

∞ *leea'na* (*insignis* × *spiceriana*)

Form of ∞ *C. leeana:*

ALBERTIANA

∞ *leo'nae* (*callosa* × *insignis*)

∞ *longwooden'se* (*charlesworthi* × ∞ *leeana*)

∞ *lu'rida* (*lawrenceana* × *villosa* SUPERBA)

∞ *ma'beliae* (*rothschildiana* × *superbiens*)

∞ *macrop'tera* (*bellatula* LOWI × *superbiens*)

∞ *mahl'erae* (*lawrenceana* × *rothschildiana*)

mastersia'na

∞ *mat'thewsi* (*lawrenceana* × *mastersiana*)

∞ *maud'iae* (*callosa sanderae* × *lawrenceana hyeana*)

∞ *morgan'iae* (*stonei* × *superbiens*)

∞ *ni'tens* (*insignis* MAULEI × *villosa*; *sallieri*)

niv'ea

∞ *oenan'tha* (∞ *harrisiana* × *insignis* MAULEI)

os'bornei . . . . . . ∞ *C. savangeana*

par'ishi

∞ *pavoni'na* (*venusta* × *villosa boxalli*)

philippinen'sis (*laevigata*)

∞ *pitcheria'na* (∞ *harrisiana* × *spiceriana*)

∞ *polletia'na* (*calophylla* × ∞ *oenantha*)

prew'etti . . . . ∞ *C. gigas*

purpura'ta

∞ *rega'lis* (*insignis* MAULEI × *purpurata*)

₵ *rol'fei magnif'ica* (*bellatula* × *rothschildiana*)

rothschildia'na

sallier'i . . . . ∞ *C. nitens*

∞ *san'deri* (∞ *calypso* × ∞ *nitens*)

sanderia'na

∞ *savangea'na* (∞ *harrisiana* × *spiceriana*; *osbornei*)

∞ *schlesingeria'na* (*insignis* MAULEI × *villosa boxalli*; *fulshawensis*)

∞ *sellig'era* (*barbata* × *philippinensis*)

ORCHID GENERA (CORDULA), continued
∞*siebertia'na* (*dayana* × *insignis*)
∞*si'moni* (*insignis* SANDERAE × ∞*leeana; actaeus*)
spiceria'na
∞*ste'vensi* (∞*calypso* × ∞*lathamiana*)
ston'ei
super'biens
∞*supercilia'ris* (*barbata* × *superbiens*)
∞*swania'na* (*barbata* × *dayana*)
₵*swinburn'ei magnif'ica* (*argus* × *insignis* MAULEI)
thomp'soni . . . . . ∞ *C. lathamiana*
ton'sa
∞*triumph'ans* (∞*nitens* × ∞*oenantha*)
∞*truffaut'iae* (*ciliolaris* × *stonei*)
venus'ta
∞*vexilla'ria* (*barbata* × *fairieana*)
victoriae-mari'ae
villo'sa
—boxal'li

Form of **C. villosa:**
SUPERBA

CYCNO'CHES . . . . SWANORCHID
chlorochi'lon . . . . . . COMMON S.
egertonia'num . . . . . EGERTON S.

CYMBID'IUM
alexan'deri (*C. eburneo-lowianum* × *insigne*)
aloifo'lium
—swartz'i
BEATRICE (*lowianum* × *schlegeli*)
BUTTERFLY (*insigne* × *lowio-grandiflorum*)
capel'la (*pauwelsi* × *wiganianum*)
CASTAR (*insigne* × *woodhamsianum*)
CHAFFINCH (*Doris* × *gottianum*)
coo'peri (*insigne sanderi* × *schroederianum*)
CORONA (*lowianum* × *schlegeli*)
CYBELE
Hyb.—not known.
DIANA (*eburneo-lowianum* × *pauwelsi*)
DORIS (*insigne* × *tracyanum*)
eburneo-lowia'num . . . . **C. veitchi**
eburne'um
EGRET (*gottianum* × *pauwelsi*)
el'egans (*Cyperorchis elegans* ABL-Cy)
ELFIN (*parishi sanderae* × *pauwelsi*)
ensifo'lium
erythrosty'lum
findlaysonia'num . **C. finlaysonianum**
finlaysonia'num (*findlaysonianum*)
George Woodham. **C. woodhamsianum**
gigan'teum
gottia'num (*eburneum* × *insigne*)
grandiflo'rum
hamburya'num (*erythrostylum* × *tracyanum*)
holfordia'num (*eburneum* × *grandiflorum*)
ian'soni
Hyb.—not known.
insig'ne (*sanderi*)
JASPER (*veitchi* (*eburneo-lowianum*) × *parishi*)
low'i . . . . **C. lowianum**
lowia'num (*lowi*)
—au'reum
—con'color
—grandiflo'rum . . . . . . **C. sedeni**
lowio-eburne'um . . . . . **C. veitchi**
MAGPIE
Hyb.—not known.
mas'tersi (*Cyperorchis mastersi* ABL)
miran'da (*alexanderi* × *sedeni*)

ORCHID GENERA (CYMBIDIUM), continued
MOIRA (*pauwelsi* × *tracyanum*)
paulwels'i . . . . **C. pauwelsi**
pauwels'i (*paulwelsi; pawelsi*)
pawels'i . . . . **C. pauwelsi**
pen'dulum
schle'geli (*insigne* × *wiganianum*)
schroederia'num
Not found in botanical literature, probably an error for C. schroederi.
se'deni (*lowio-grandiflorum; lowianum grandiflorum; grandiflorum* × *lowianum*)
SWALLOW (*alexanderi* × *pauwelsi*)
SYBIL (*eburneum* × *pauwelsi*)
Also misspelled Sibyl.
tigri'num
traceya'num . . . . . **C. tracyanum**
tracya'num (*traceyanum* Cy)
Probably the same as C. grandiflorum; by some considered a nat. hyb.
veitch'i (*eburneo-lowianum; lowio-eburneum; lowianum* × *eburneum*)
wigania'num (*eburneum* × *tracyanum*)
winnia'num (*giganteum* × *mastersi*)
woodhamen'se
Probably the same as C. woodhamsianum.
woodhamsia'num (*George Woodham; lowianum* × *veitchi*)

CYPRIPE'DIUM . . LADYSLIPPER
For horticultural purposes this name is probably best retained for all forms. In science, today, the genus Cypripedium is split into four genera: Selenipedium, containing about three reed-like plants none of which is known in cultivation; Cypripedium, the North American and a few Chinese and Japanese species, maintaining the Linnean use of the name; Cordula, the Old World tropical species which constistute the bulk of the greenhouse species and hybrids (these are all classed as Paphiopedilum by Bailey [Cy] and others); and Paphiopedilum (in its correct usage) for the Central and South American species which have been known in horticulture as Selenipedium (these are all classed as Phragmopedilum by Bailey [Cy] and others).

In the following list the section and our preference will be abbreviated to Cyp. for Cypripedium; Cord. for Cordula, and Paph. for Paphiopedilum; but no new binomial or trinomial Latin names will be made, notwithstanding the fact that such names are not now in existence, especially in the case of hybrids and variations of species. (For discussion of the generic names see Rolfe in Orchid Review, vol. 20 (1912), pp. 1–3.) In synonymy, C. will be used for Cypripedium, Pa. for Paphiopedilum, Ph. for Phragmopedilum, and S. for Selenipedium.

A'cis . . . . **C. eucharis**
ACME. Cord. (*C. nitens* × *C. Leander* (*Bessie K. Pitcher*); *Pa. Acme* Cy)
Actae'us (*acteus*) . . . . . **C. simoni**
—langleyen'se. (*Pa. Actaeus langleyen'se* Cy; *C. insigne sanderae* × *C. leeanum*) . . . . . **C. simoni var.**
—vic'tor . . . . **C. simoni var.**
Acteus Julius Roehrs
C. simoni JULIUS ROEHRS
ad'amsi. Cord. (*C. John Quincy Adams; C. Calypso* × *C. regale*)
A. de Lairesse . . . . . **C. lairessei**
Adrastus mariae . . . . . HERA var.
AESON. Cord. (*C. druryi* × *C. insigne*)

ORCHID GENERA (CYPRIPEDIUM), con.
ains'worthi. Paph. (*C. browni; C. calurum; Ph. ainsworthi* Cy; *Ph. browni* Cy; *Ph. calurum* Cy; *S. browni; C. longifolium* × *C. sedeni*)
AJAX. Cord. (*C. chamberlainianum* × *C. germinyanum*)
albanen'se. Cord. (*C. insigne* × *C. mastersianum*)
albertia'num. **C. leeanum albertianum**
—super'bum . . **C. leeanum superbum**
Albert Truffaut . . . **C. savageanum**
albopurpu'reum. Paph. (*Ph. albo-purpureum* Cy; *C. schlimi* × *C. dominianum*)
Alcibi'ades . . . . **C. lasellei**
—magnif'icum . . . . . . **C. lasellei**
—super'bum (*Pa. Alcibiades superbum* Cy; *C. leeanum* × *C. schlesingerianum* (*Mons. de Curte*)). **C. lasellei var.**
ALCIDES. Cord. (*Pa. Alcides* Cy; *C. insigne maulei* × *C. hirsutissimum*)
—C. G. Roebling . ALCIDES **superbum**
—CLIO
—super'bum (*C. Alcides C. G. Roebling*)
ALECTOR. Cord. (*Pa. Alector* Cy; *C. barbatum crossi* × *C. spicerianum; C. eyermannianum* ABL)
alexan'drae. Cord. (*C. godefroyae* × *C. nitens*)
Alfred Dimmock . . . . **C. castalia**
ALICE. Cord. (*Pa. Alice* Cy; *C. stonei* × *C. spicerianum*)
ALMA GEVAERT. Cord. (*C. lawrenceanum* × *C. maudiae*)
al'mum. Cord. (*Pa. almum* Cy; *C. barbatum* × *C. lawrenceanum*)
—atropurpu'reum
aman'dum . . . . . . **C. crossianum**
ames'i. Cord. (*C. Oakes Ames; Pa. Oakes Ames* Cy; *C. ciliolare* × *rothschildianum*)
amesia'num . . . **C. measuresianum**
APHRODITE. Cord. (*Pa. Aphrodite* Cy; *C. niveum* × *C. lawrenceanum*)
appletonia'num. Cord. (*Pa. appletonianum* Cy)
ARCHIE NIEL. Cord. (*C. leeanum compactum* × *C.* [*insigne*] *Harefield Hall*)
ARGUS. Cord. (*Pa. Argus* Cy)
ARTEMIS. Cord. (*Pa. Artemis* Cy; *C. dayanum* × *C. swanianum*)
arthuria'num. Cord. (*Pa. arthurianum* Cy; *C. insigne* × *C. fairieanum*)
—grandiflo'rum
—pulchel'lum (*Pa. arthurianum pulchellum* Cy)
ashbur'tonae. Cord. (*C. barteti; Pa. ashburtonae* Cy; *Pa. barteti* Cy; *C. barbatum* × *C. insigne*)
—calospi'lum (*Pa. ashburtonae calospilum* Cy)
—expan'sum (*Pa. ashburtonae expansum* Cy)
—laforcade'i (*C. laforcadei; Pa. laforcadei* Cy; *C. barbatum* × *C. insigne chantini*)
—super'bum
ASTRAEA. Cord. (*Pa. Astraea* Cy; *C. philippinense* × *C. spicerianum*)
angus'tum . . . . **C. hanseni**
au'reum. Cord. (*Pa. aureum* Cy; *C. nitens* × *C. spicerianum*)
—al'bum
—can'didum
—CYRUS (*C. Cyrus*)

ORCHID GENERA (CYPRIPEDIUM), con.
au'reum hyea'num (*C. hyeanum; Pa. aureum hyeanum* Cy)
—OEDIPPE (*C. Oedippe*)
—SURPRISE
—virgina'le (*C. virginale; Pa. aureum virginale* Cy)
aurore'um. Cord. (*Pa. auroreum* Cy; *C. lawrenceanum* × *C. venustum*)
baco'nis. Paph. (*C. conchiferum* × *C. schlimi*)
barbato-mas'tersi . . . . ENDYMION
barba'tum. Cord. (*Pa. barbatum* Cy)
—biflo'rum (*Pa. barbatum biflorum* Cy)
—grandiflo'rum (*Pa. barbatum grandiflorum* Cy)
—illus'tre (*Pa. barbatum illustre* Cy)
—super'bum (*Pa. barbatum superbum* Cy)
—war'neri (*Pa. barbatum warneri* Cy)
bar'beyae. Cord. (*C. Mme. Barbey; Pa. Mme. Barbey* Cy; *C. lawrenceanum* × *tonsum*)
Baron Schroeder . . . . **C. schroederi**
bartet'i . . . . . **C. ashburtonae**
BEATRICE. Cord. (*Pa. Beatrice* Cy; *C. boxalli* × *C. lowei*)
beeck'mani. Cord. (*C. berkleyanum* ABL; *Pa. beeckmani* Cy; *C. bellatulum* × *C. boxalli*)
bella'tulum. Cord. (*Pa. bellatulum* Cy)
BERYL WEST POINT. Cord. (*C. beeckmani* × *C. Mrs. Martin*)
Bessie K. Pitcher . . . . . LEANDER
BLACK PRINCE. Cord. (*C. Hera* × *C. rothschildianum*)
BLANCHE MOORE
Hyb.—parents unknown.

boadicea Flamboyant . **C. sanderi** var.
box'alli. Cord. (*Pa. villosum boxalli* Cy)
—albomargina'tum
—atra'tum
—dilec'tum
—super'bum
bragaia'num . . . . **C. godseffianum**
brandt'iae. Cord. (*C. Frau Ida Brandt; Pa. Frau Ida Brandt* Cy; *C. Io* × *C. youngianum*)
brown'i . . . . **C. ainsworthi**
—leucoglos'sum (*Ph. browni leucoglossum* Cy) . . . . **C. ainsworthi** var.
brunia'num. Cord. (*C. leeanum* × *C. oenanthum*)
BRYSA. Paph. (*Ph. Brysa* Cy; *S. Brysa; C. bossierianum* × *C. sedeni candidulum*)
buchania'num. Cord. (*Pa. buchanianum* Cy; *C. druryi* × *C. spicerianum*)
buckingham'i ABL . **C. gratrixianum**
bullier'i. Cord. (*C. tonso-villosum; Pa. tonso-villosum* Cy; *C. tonsum* × *C. villosum*)
calan'thum. Cord. (*C. Sappho; Pa. calanthum* Cy; *Pa. Sappho* Cy; *C. barbatum* × *C. lowei*)
calceo'lus . EUROPEAN LADYSLIPPER
—*pubes'cens* . . . . YELLOW E.L.
callo-rothschildia'num . . . **C. fowleri**
callo'sum. Cord. (*Pa. callosum* Cy)
—gigan'teum (*Pa. callosum giganteum* Cy)
—san'derae (*Pa. callosum sanderae* Cy)

ORCHID GENERA (CYPRIPEDIUM), con.
calu'rum . . . . . . **C. ainsworthi**
—rougier'i . . . . **C. lemoinierianum**
CALYPSO. Cord. (*Pa. Calypso* Cy; *C. boxalli* × *C. spicerianum*)
CALYPSO OAKWOOD
can'hami. Cord. (*C. Charles Canham; C. Mrs. Charles Canham; Pa. canhami* Cy; *Pa. Mrs. Canham* Cy; *C. superbiens* × *C. villosum*)
cardina'le. Paph. (*Ph. cardinale* Cy; *S. cardinale; C. sedeni* × *C. schlimi albiflorum*)
carici'num. Paph. (*Ph. caricinum* Cy; *C. pearcei*)
CASTALIA. Cord. (*C. Alfred Dimmock; C. druryi* × *C. godseffianum*)
cauda'tum. Paph. (*Ph. caudatum* Cy; *S. caudatum*)
cenan'thum . . . . **C. oenanthum**
Typographical error.

chamberlainia'num. Cord. (*Pa. chamberlainianum* Cy)
chamberleea'num. Cord. (*C. morteni; Pa. morteni* Cy; *C. chamberlainianum* × *C. leeanum*)
Charles Canham . . . . **C. canhami**
charlesia'num. Cord. (*C. nitens* × *C. leeanum*)
charles'worthi. Cord. (*Pa. charlesworthi* Cy)
—NORMAN
chloroneu'rum. Cord. (*C. Ianthe; C. williamsianum; Pa. chloroneurum* Cy; *Pa. Ianthe* Cy; *Pa. williamsianum* Cy; *C. harrisianum* × *C. venustum*)
chlo'rops . . . . . . **C. conchiferum**
ciliola're. Cord. (*Pa. ciliolare* Cy)
clark'i. Cord. (*C. charlesworthi* × *C. swanianum*)
CLEOLA. Paph. (*C. boissierianum* × *C. schlimi*)
col'mani. Cord. (*C. harrisianum* × *C. javanicum*)
—ni'grum (*Pa. colmani nigrum* Cy)
COLOSSUS. Cord. (*C. nitens* × *C. villosum*)
conchif'erum. Paph. (*C. chlorops; Ph. conchiferum* Cy; *Ph. chlorops* Cy; *C. caricinum* × *C. longifolium hartwegi*)
concin'num. Cord. (*Pa. concinnum* Cy; *C. purpuratum* × *C. harrisianum*)
—super'bum
con'color. Cord. (*Pa. concolor* Cy)
conspic'uum. Cord. (*C. wallaertianum; Pa. conspicuum* Cy; *Pa. wallaertianum* Cy; *C. harrisianum* × *C. villosum*)
—super'bum
CONSTANCE. Cord.
coppinia'num. Paph. (*Ph. coppinianum* Cy; *C. sedeni* × *C. conchiferum*)
CREON. Cord. (*Pa. Creon* Cy; *C. harrisianum superbum* × *C. oenanthum superbum*)
crossia'num. Cord. (*C. amandum; Pa. crossianum* Cy; *Pa. amandum* Cy; *C. insigne* × *C. venustum*)
—au'reum (*C. insigne* × *C. venustum pardinum*)
—pal'lidum (*Pa. crossianum pallidum* Cy)
—psittaci'num
—tautzia'num (*Pa. crossianum tautzianum* Cy)

ORCHID GENERA (CYPRIPEDIUM), con.
CUNIA. Cord. × Paph. (*Ph. Cunia* Cy)
This is the result of a cross between a Cordula species (C. stonei) and a Paphiopedilum species (C. longifolium).

curt'emanni. Cord. (*C. schlesingerianum* × *C. beeckmani*)
—magnif'icum LOWS
cur'tisi. Cord. (*Pa. curtisi* Cy)
—exquis'itum
—purpura'tum
—ROEHRS
cycni'des. Cord. (*C. William Lloyd; C. bellatulum* × *C. swanianum*)
cymato'des. Cord. (*C. curtisi* × *C. superbiens*)
dauthier'i . . . . . . **C. harrisianum**
—marmora'tum
C. harrisianum marmoratum
daya'num. Cord. (*Pa. dayanum* Cy)
—super'bum (*Pa. dayanum superbum* Cy)
deedmania'num. Cord. (*Pa. doodmanianum* Cy; *C. chamberlainianum* × *C. spicerianum*)
DESDEMONA. Cord. (*C. Sophie* ABL; *C. gowerianum* × *C. niveum*)
Dibdin . . . . MURILLO
dicksonia'num. Cord. (*C. Countess of Carnavon; C. Hera* × *C. villosum*)
dilec'tum. Cord. (*Pa. dilectum* Cy; *C. boxalli* × *C. hirsutisissimum*)
The same cross as C. godseffianum and probably identical with it.

dominia'num. Paph. (*Ph. dominianum* Cy; *C. caricinum* × *C. caudatum*)
—rubes'cens (*Ph. dominianum rubescens* Cy)
donatia'num . . . . . **C. oenanthum**
DORA. Cord. (*C. bellatulum* × *C. charlesworthi*)
dra'co. Cord. (*C. Hera* × *C. insigne*)
dru'ryi. Cord. (*Pa. druryi* Cy)
DUCHESS. Cord. (*C. aureum* × *C. insigne*)
Duchess of Sutherland. **C. sutherlandiae**
DUKE OF MARLBOROUGH. Cord. (*C. Hera* × *C. leeanum*)
eas'toni. Paph. (*C. longifolium* × *C. lindleyanum*)
EDITH. Cord. (*C. rothschildiano-boxalli; Pa. rothschildiano-boxalli* Cy; *C. boxalli* × *C. rothschildianum*)
edi'thae . . . . ROWENA
ed'wardi. Cord. (*C. fairieanum* × *C. superbiens*)
eismann'i . . . . **C. eismannianum**
eismannia'num. Cord. (*C. eismanni; C. lobengula; Pa. eismannianum* Cy; *Pa. lobengula* Cy; *C. boxalli* × *C. harrisianum*)
elliottia'num. Cord. (*Pa. rothschildianum elliottianum* Cy)
EMILE. Cord. (*C. Emile Cappe; C. Hera* × *C. lathamianum*)
Emile Cappe . . . . EMILE
EMILY ROEBLING
Hyb.—not known.

e'modi. Cord. (*C. callosum sanderae* × *C. lawrenceanum hyeanum*)
ENDYMION. Cord. (*C. barbato-mastersi; Pa. barbato-mastersi* Cy; *C. barbatum* × *C. mastersianum*)
enfielden'se. Cord. (*Pa. enfieldense* Cy; *C. lawrenceanum* × *C. hookerae*)

ORCHID GENERA (CYPRIPEDIUM), con.

eu'charis. Cord. (*C. Acis; Pa. Acis* Cy; *C. lawrenceanum* × *C. insigne sanderae*)
eurya'des . . . . HERA
—*Black Empress* HERA BLACK EMPRESS
eury'ale. Cord. (*C. robinsonianum; Pa. euryale* Cy; *Pa. robinsonianum* Cy; *C. lawrenceanum* × *C. superbiens*)
euryan'drum. Cord. (*Pa. euryandrum* Cy; *C. barbatum* × *C. stonei*)
EVA. Cord. (*C. aureum hyeanum* × *C. memoria jerninghami*)
EVELYN AMES. Cord. (*C. Evelyn* ABL; *Pa. Evelyn Ames* Cy; *C. Calypso* × *C. leeanum*)
—super'bum (*C. Calypso Oakwood* × *C. leeanum giganteum*)
ex'ul. Cord. (*Pa. exul* Cy)
eyermannia'num ABL . . . ALECTOR
fairiea'num. Cord. (*Pa. fairieanum* Cy)
—ni'grum
FAIRY QUEEN. Cord. (*Pa. Fairy Queen* Cy; *C. curtisi* × *C. druryi*)
FIGARO. Cord. (*C. Tityus; C. oenanthum* × *C. spicerianum*)
—super'bum (*C. oenanthum superbum* × *C. spicerianum*)
fow'leri. Cord. (*C. callo-rothschildianum; Pa. fowleri* Cy; *Pa. callorothschildianum* Cy; *C. callosum* × *C. rothschildianum*)
fra'seri . . . . . **C. porphyrochlamys**
Frau Ida Brandt . . . . **C. brandtiae**
fulshawen'se . . **C. schlesingerianum**
Galate'a . . . . **C. oenanthum**
gandia'num
Not found in botanical literature, very probably an error for gaudianum.
gar'fieldi. Cord. (*C. James Garfield; Pa. James Garfield* Cy; *C. regale* × *C. tonsum*)
Garret A. Hobart . . . . . **C. hobarti**
Gaston Butel . . . . . **C. schroederi**
gaudia'num. Cord. (*Pa. gaudianum* Cy; *C. curtisi* × *C. harrisianum superbum*)
GAY GORDON. Cord. (*C. thompsoni* × *C. Leander (Lady Wimborne)*)
gayo'tiae. Cord. (*C. Mlle. Madeleine Gayot; C. pellucidum; Pa. Mlle. Madeleine Gayot; Pa. pellucidum* Cy; *C. dayanum insigne*)
GEORGE MCWILLIAMS
Hyb.—not known.
GERALDA. Paph. (*Ph. Geralda* Cy; *C. caudatum* × *C. lindleyanum*)
germinya'num. Cord. (*Pa. germinyanum* Cy; *C. hirsutissimum* × *C. villosum*)
gigan'teum. Paph. (*C. macrochilum giganteum; Ph. macrochilum giganteum* Cy; *C. caudatum* × *C. grande*)
gi'gas. Cord. (*C. prewetti; Pa. gigas* Cy; *Pa. prewetti* Cy; *C. lawrenceanum* × *C. harrisianum*)
—CORNDEAN HALL. **C. gigas corndeani**
—corndean'i (*gigas Corndean Hall*)
—CORRUDEAN HALL
Probably the same as C. gigas corndeani.
glaucophyl'lum. Cord. (*Pa. glaucophyllum* Cy)
godefroy'ae. Cord. (*Pa. godefroyae* Cy)
—leucochi'lum (*Pa. g. leucochilum* Cy)

ORCHID GENERA (CYPRIPEDIUM), con.

godseffia'num. Cord. (*C. bragaianum; Pa. godseffianum* Cy; *Pa. bragaianum* Cy; *C. boxalli* × *C. hirsutissimum*)
—albomargina'tum
GORDON HIGHLANDER. Cord. (*C. Dreadnought* × *C. schlesingerianum (Mons. de Curte)*)
goweria'num. Cord. (*Pa. gowerianum* Cy; *C. curtisi* × *C. lawrenceanum*)
—magnif'icum
—schofieldia'num
gran'de. Paph. (*Ph. grande* Cy; *S. grande; C. caudatum* × *C. longifolium*)
—atra'tum (*Ph. grande atratum* Cy)
gratrixia'num. Cord. (*C. buckinghami* ABL; *Pa. gratrixianum* Cy; *C. bellatulum* × *C. enfieldense*)
graves'iae. Cord. (*Pa. gravesiae* Cy; *C. Argus* × *C. niveum*)
grovesia'num. Cord. (*C. lathamianum* × *C. leeanum*)
han'seni. Cord. (*C. augustum; Pa. augustum* Cy; *C. haynaldianum* × *C. villosum*)
hardya'num Penelaus ABL . PENELAUS
HARLEQUIN. Cord. (*Pa. Harlequin* Cy; *C. thompsoni* × *C. Mrs. Mostyn*)
harrisia'num. Cord. (*C. dauthieri; C. hybridum; Pa. harrisianum hybridum* Cy; *C. villosum* × *C. barbatum*)
—linia'tum (*Pa. harrisianum liniatum* Cy)
—luteo'lum
—marmora'tum (*C. dauthieri marmoratum*)
—ni'grum
—pitcheria'num (*Pa. harrisianum pitcherianum* Cy)
—super'bum (*Pa. harrisianum superbum* Cy)
—viridiflo'rum
—vivi'cans
harveya'num. Cord. (*Pa. harveyanum* Cy; *C. stonei* × *C. leeanum*)
haynaldia'num. Cord. (*Pa. haynaldianum* Cy)
haywoodia'num. Cord. (*C. T. B. Haywood; Pa. T. B. Haywood; C. druryi* × *C. superbiens*)
HELENA. Cord. (*C. Helen II; C. bellatulum* × *C. insigne*)
Helen II . . . . HELENA
Helen II Roehrs . . . . HELENA var.
HERA. Cord. (*C. Adrastus; C. euryades; C. boxalli* × *C. leeanum*)
—BLACK EMPRESS (*C. euryades Black Empress*)
—fautzia'num
Probably a misspelling.
—MRS. TAUTZ (*Pa. Hera Mrs. Tautz* Cy)
—SANDERS
HIAWATHA. Cord. (*C. godseffianum* × *C. leeanum*)
hirsutis'simum. Cord. (*Pa. hirsutissimum* Cy)
hitchen'se
Not found, probably the same as C. hitchensiae.
hitchen'siae. Cord. (*C. charlesworthi* × *C. insigne*)
ho'barti. Cord. (*C. Garret A. Hobart; Pa. Garret A. Hobart; C. insigne* × *C. lathamianum*)
Holbrook Gaskel . . **C. longwoodense**

ORCHID GENERA (CYPRIPEDIUM), con.

hook'erae. Cord. (*C. volonteanum; Pa. hookerae* Cy)
hornia'num. Cord. (*C. picturatum; Pa. hornianum* Cy; *C. spicerianum* × *C. superbiens*)
hyb'ridum . . . . . . **C. harrisianum**
hyea'num . . . **C. aureum hyeanum**
Ian'the . . . . . . **C. chloroneurum**
illus'tre. Cord. (*C. lathamianum* × *C. nitens*)
INDRA. Cord. (*C. callosum* × *C. villosum*)
in'gens. Cord. (*Pa. ingens* Cy; *C. insigne* × *C. rothschildianum*)
insig'ne. Cord. (*Pa. insigne* Cy)
—ames'iae
Perhaps the same as C. insigne amesianum.
—amesia'num (*Pa. insigne amesianum* Cy)
—atra'ta
—aureo'la
—bal'liae
—bal'liae super'bum
—BLANCHE MOORE
—BRIGHTNESS
—brown'i (*Pa. insigne browni* Cy)
—brugen'se (*Pa. i. brugense* Cy)
—chanti'ni (*Pa. i. chantini* Cy)
—chanti'ni lin'deni
—chanti'ni lin'deri
Very likely the same as C. insigne chantini lindeni.
—charles'worthi
—citri'num (*Pa. insigne citrinum* Cy)
—cobbia'num
—corruga'tum (*Pa. insigne corrugatum* Cy)
—coulsonia'num (*Pa. insigne coulsonianum* Cy)
—dominia'num (*Pa. insigne dominianum* Cy)
—DOROTHY (*Pa. i. Dorothy* Cy)
—edenia'num
—EDWARD ROEHRS
—er'nesti (*Pa. insigne ernesti* Cy)
—eyermann'i (*Pa. insigne eyermanni* Cy)
—fostermann'i (*Pa. insigne fostermanni* Cy)
—gigan'teum
—GLADYS
—graves'i
Probably the same as C. insigne gravesianum.
—gravesia'num (*Pa. insigne gravesianum* Cy)
—HAREFIELD HALL (*Pa. insigne Harefield Hall* Cy)
—heatonen'se
—HESSLE
—hurrellia'num (*Pa. insigne hurrellianum* Cy)
—immacula'tum ni'grum
—la'gerae (*Pa. insigne lagerae* Cy)
—la'geri
Perhaps the same as C. insigne lagerae.
—LAURA KIMBALL (*Pa. insigne Laura Kimball* Cy)
—leopardi'num
—linden'iae
—lucia'ni (*Pa. insigne luciani* Cy)
—lucia'niae
Very likely the same as **C.** insigne luciani.

ORCHID GENERA (CYPRIPEDIUM), con.
insig'ne luteoal'bum (*Pa. insigne luteoalbum* Cy)
—**macfarla'nei** (*Pa. insigne macfarlanei* Cy)
—**macula'tum**
—**maul'ei** (*Pa. insigne maulei* Cy)
—**max'imum** (*Pa. insigne maximum* Cy)
—**mcnabia'num**
—**merx'emi**
—MONARCH
—MONKSHOOD
—**monta'num** (*Pa. insigne montanum* Cy)
—MRS. GEORGE B. WILSON
—ODDITY
—OLIVINE
—**puncta'tum grandiflo'rum**
—**rutherforden'se**
—**rutherford'i**
Probably the same as C. insigne rutherfordense.
—**sad'leri**
—**san'derae** (*Pa. insigne sanderae* Cy)
—**sanderia'num** (*Pa. insigne sanderianum* Cy)
—SPECIAL VARIETY
—STANDARD
—**statteria'num**
—**summiten'se**
—**sylheten'se** (*Pa. insigne sylhetense* Cy)
—T. MELSTROM
—**wat'soni**
—**westgaten'se**
—W. M. DOW
—**xanthi'num**
—**youngia'num**
—**youngia'num super'bum**
—**zebri'num**
IO GRANDIS. Cord. (*C. Argus* × *C. lawrenceanum*)
James Garfield . . . . . **C. garfieldi**
JAMES H. VEITCH
A form of Constance.
James K. Polk . . . . **C. polki**
javan'icum. Cord. (*Pa. javanicum* Cy)
J. MUELLER
Hyb.—not known.
John Quincy Adams . . . **C. adamsi**
JOSEPH HOWES. Cord. (*C. nitens (sallieri)* × *C. villosum aureum*)
This is undoubtedly the same as C. Colossus.
josephia'num. Cord. (*Pa. josephianum* Cy; *C. druryi* × *C. sementa*)
JUNO. Cord. (*Pa. Juno* Cy; *C. callosum* × *C. fairieanum*)
kamil'i. Cord. (*C. boxalli* × *C. chamberlainianum*)
kimballia'num. Cord. (*Pa. kimballianum* Cy; *Pa. praestans kimballianum* Cy)
Supposed nat. hyb. between C. dayanum and C. rothschildianum. There appears to be much confusion in regard to this name as perhaps two distinct things bear the same name, one of which (possibly both) is a variation of C. praestans.
KING GEORGE V. Cord. (*C. charlesworthi* × *C. Talisman*)
KRISHNA. Cord. (*Pa. Krishna* Cy; *C. insigne* × *C. tonsum*)
laeviga'tum . . . . **C. philippinense**

ORCHID GENERA (CYPRIPEDIUM), con.
laforcade'i . **C. ashburtonae laforcadei**
laires'sei. Cord. (*C. A. de Lairesse; C. curtisi* × *C. rothschildianum*)
lanieria'num
Hyb.—not known.
lasell'ei. Cord. (*C. Alcibiades; C. Alcibiades magnificum; Pa. Alcibiades* Cy; *Pa. Alcibiades magnificum* Cy; *C. leeanum* × *C. schlesingerianum*)
lathamia'num. Cord. (*C. thompsoni; Pa. lathamianum* Cy; *Pa. thompsoni* Cy; *C. spicerianum* × *C. villosum*)
—NEGLEYS
lau'rae. Cord. (*C. Mrs. G. D. Owen; Pa. Mrs. G. D. Owen* Cy; *C. superciliare* × *C. villosum*)
lawrencea'num. Cord. (*Pa. lawrenceanum* Cy)
—**gratrixia'num**
—**hyea'num** (*Pa. lawrenceanum hyeanum* Cy)
—**super'bum** (*Pa. lawrenceanum superbum* Cy)
LEANDER. Cord. (*C. Bessie K. Pitcher; C. Lady Wimborne; Pa. Leander* Cy; *Pa. Bessie K. Pitcher* Cy; *C. leeanum* × *C. villosum*)
ledou'xiae. Cord. (*Pa. ledouxiae* Cy; *C. callosum* × *C. harrisianum*)
leea'num. Cord. (*Pa. leeanum* Cy; *C. insigne* × *C. spicerianum*)
—**albertia'num** (*C. albertianum; Pa. albertianum* Cy; *C. insigne* × *C. spicerianum wallacei*)
—**au'reum** (*Pa. leeanum aureum* Cy)
—**bufordien'se** (*Pa. leeanum bufordiense* Cy)
—**clinkaberrya'num** (*Pa. leeanum clinkaberryanum* Cy)
—E. B. DANE
—**gigan'teum** (*Pa. leeanum giganteum* Cy)
—**grandiflo'rum** (*Pa. leeanum grandiflorum* Cy)
—**gratrix'iae**
—**lutes'cens** (*Pa. leeanum lutescens* Cy)
—**magnif'icum**
—**masereelia'num** (*Pa. leeanum masereelianum* Cy)
—**nigres'cens** (*Pa. leeanum nigrescens* Cy)
—**ni'grum**
—**pulchel'lum** (*Pa. leeanum pulchellum* Cy)
—PURITY
—**roehrsia'num**
—**superbis'simum**
—**super'bum** (*C. albertianum superbum; Pa. leeanum superbum* Cy)
—**virgina'le**
lemoinieria'num. Paph. (*C. calurum rougieri; C. ainsworthi (calurum)* × *C. sedeni*)
leon'ae. Cord. (*C. insigne* × *C. callosum*)
leucorrho'dum. **C. sedeni leucorrhodum**
lindleya'num. Paph. Hyb. (*Ph. lindleyanum* Cy)
Lloyd magnificum Charlesworths **C. cycnides** var.
loben'gula . . . . **C. eismannianum**
longifo'lium. Paph. (*Ph. longifolium* Cy)
—**hart'wegi** (*C. roezli; Selenipedium roezli*)

ORCHID GENERA (CYPRIPEDIUM), con.
longifo'lium magniflo'rum (*Ph. longifolium magniflorum* Cy)
longwooden'se. Cord. (*C. Holbrook Gaskel; Pa. Holbrook Gaskel* Cy; *C. charlesworthi* × *C. leeanum*)
Lord Derby . . . . . . **C. mabeliae**
lourya'num . . . . . **C. lowryanum**
low'ei. Cord. (*C. lowianum; Pa. lowei* Cy)
lowia'num . . . . **C. lowei**
lowrya'num. Cord. (*C. louryanum; C. ashburtonae* × *C. vernixium*)
lu'ridum. Cord. (*Pa. luridum* Cy; *C. lawrenceanum* × *C. villosum superbum*)
—**purpu'reum** (*Pa. luridum purpureum* Cy)
mabel'iae. Cord. (*C. Lord Derby; C. rothschildiano-superbiens; C. W. R. Lee; Pa. Lord Derby* Cy; *Pa. rothschildiano-superbiens* Cy; *Pa. W. R. Lee* Cy; *C. rothschildianum* × *C. superbiens*)
macfar'lanei. Cord. (*Pa. macfarlanei* Cy; *C. calophyllum* × *C. spicerianum*)
macrochi'lum gigan'teum. **C. giganteum**
macrop'terum. Cord. (*Pa. macropterum* Cy; *C. lowei* × *C. superbiens*)
madiotia'num. Cord. (*C. chamberlainianum* × *C. villosum*)
magniflo'rum. Paph.
Hyb.?—possibly the same as C. longifolium magniflorum.
mah'lerae. Cord. (*C. rothschildiano-lawrenceanum; Pa. mahlerae* Cy; *Pa. rothschildiano-lawrenceanum* Cy; *C. rothschildianum* × *C. lawrenceanum*)
man'dae. Cord. (*C. insigne* × *C. javanicum*)
man'goldi. Cord. (*Pa. mangoldi* Cy)
Hyb.—parents not known.
marmorophyl'lum. Cord. (*Pa. marmorphyllum* Cy; *C. hookerae* × *C. barbatum*)
mars'tonae. Cord. (*C. callosum* × *C. insigne sanderae*)
Possibly the same as C. leonae.
massaia'num. Cord. (*Pa. massaianum* Cy; *C. rothschildianum* × *C. superciliare*)
mas'tersi
Not found in botanical literature, probably the same as C. mastersianum.
mastersia'num. Cord. (*Pa. mastersianum* Cy)
mat'thewsi. Cord. (*C. lawrenceanum* × *C. mastersianum*)
maud'iae. Cord. (*Pa. maudiae* Cy; *C. lawrenceanum hyeanum* × *C. callosum sanderae*)
—**magnif'icum** (*Pa. maudiae magnificum* Cy)
—NON PLUS ULTRA
measuresia'num. Cord. (*C. amesianum; Pa. measuresianum* Cy; *Pa. amesianum* Cy; *C. villosum* × *C. venustum*)
MEDEIA. Cord. (*C. spicerianum* × *C. hirsutissimum*)
MELANTHUS. Cord. (*Pa. Melanthus* Cy; *C. hookerae* × *C. stonei*)
memoria-moen'si . . **C. savageanum**
MILO. Cord. (*C. oenanthum superbum* × *C. insigne chantini*)

ORCHID GENERA (CYPRIPEDIUM), con.

MINOS. Cord. (*Pa. Minos* Cy; *C. arthurianum* × *C. spicerianum*)
—**low'i** (*C. arthurianum pulchellum* × *C. spicerianum*)
Apparently has the same parents as C. Minos youngi.
—**young'i** (*C. arthurianum pulchellum* × *C. spicerianum*)
Mlle. Madeleine Gayot . . **C. gayotiae**
Mme. Barbey . . . . . **C. barbeyae**
Mme. Cappe . . . . **C. savageanum**
Mons. de Curte. . **C. schlesingerianum**
morgan'iae. Cord. (*Pa. morganiae* Cy; *C. stonei* × *C. superbiens*)
morten'i . . . . **C. chamberleeanum**
Mrs. Charles Canham . . **C. canhami**
Mrs. G. D. Owen . . . . . **C. laurae**
Mrs. W. A. Roebling . **C. schroederae**
MURILLO. Cord. (*C. Dibdin; Pa. Dibdin* Cy; *C. Argus* × *C. boxalli*)
NELLIE. Cord. (*C. tonso-charlesworthi; Pa. tonso-charlesworthi* Cy; *C. tonsum* × *C. charlesworthi*)
NIEUPORT. Cord. (*C. Hera* × *C. Van Dyck*)
NIOBE. Cord. (*Pa. Niobe* Cy; *C. fairieanum* × *C. spicerianum*)
—ROEHRS
—**shorthillen'se**
ni'tens. Cord. (*C. sallieri; Pa. nitens* Cy; *Pa. sallieri* Cy; *C. villosum* × *C. insigne maulei*)
—ARDEL COURT
—CHILLINGHAM
—**gravesia'num** (*Pa. nitens gravesianum* Cy)
—**hyea'num** (*C. sallieri hyeanum; Pa. nitens sallieri hyeanum* Cy; *Pa. sallieri hyeanum* Cy)
—**ni'grum**
nitidis'simum. Paph. (*Ph. nitidissimum* Cy; *C. caudatum* × *C. conchiferum*)
niv'eum. Cord. (*Pa. niveum* Cy)
Oakes Ames . . . . **C. amesi**
oakes'i. Cord. (*C. curtisi* × *C. purpuratum*)
Oedippe . . . . **C. aureum** OEDIPPE
oenan'thum. Cord. (*C. cenanthum; C. donatianum; C. Galatea; C. thibautianum* Cy; *Pa. Galatea* Cy; *Pa. thibautianum* Cy; *C. harrisianum* × *C. insigne maulei*)
—**super'bum** (*Pa. oenanthum superbum* Cy)
OLIVIA. Cord. (*Pa. Olivia* Cy; *C. niveum* × *C. tonsum*)
ORION. Cord. (*Pa. Orion* Cy; *C. concolor* × *C. insigne*)
orphan'um. Cord. (*Pa. orphanum* Cy; *C. barbatum* × *C. druryi*)
os'bornei . . . . . . **C. savageanum**
par'ishi. Cord. (*Pa. parishi* Cy)
pavonia'num . . . . . **C. pavoninum**
pavoni'num. Cord. (*C. pavonianum; C. ravonianum; Pa. pavoninum* Cy; *C. boxalli* × *C. venustum*)
—**inver'sum**
Probably the same as the species.
pearce'i . . . . **C. caricinum**
pellu'cidum . . . . **C. gayotiae**
PENELAUS. Paph. (*C. hardyanum Penelaus* ABL; *Ph. Penelaus* Cy; *ainsworthi* (*calurum*) × *C. caudatum*)
PERSEUS. Paph. (*Ph. Perseus* Cy; *C. sedeni porphyreum* × *C. lindleyanum*)

ORCHID GENERA (CYPRIPEDIUM), con.

philippinen'se. Cord. (*C. laevigatum*)
pictura'tum . . . . . **C. hornianum**
pitcheria'num . . . **C. savageanum**
poli'tum. Cord. (*Pa. politum* Cy; *C. barbatum* × *C. venustum*)
polk'i. Cord. (*C. James K. Polk; Pa. James K. Polk* Cy; *C. chamberlainianum* × *C. nitens*)
polletia'num. Cord. (*Pa. polletianum* Cy; *C. calophyllum* × *C. oenanthum superbum*)
—**magnif'icum**
polystigmat'icum. Cord. (*Pa. polystigmaticum* Cy; *C. venustum* × *C. spicerianum*)
porphy'reum . **C. sedeni porphyreum**
porphyrochla'mys. Cord. (*C. fraseri; Pa. fraseri* Cy; *C. barbatum* × *C. hirsutissimum*)
prae'stans. Cord. (*Pa. praestans* Cy)
PREMIER. Cord. (*Pa. Premier* Cy; *C. cymatodes* × *C. rothschildianum*)
prew'etti . . . . **C. gigas**
PRIAPUS. Cord. (*Pa. Priapus* Cy; *C. philippinense* × *C. villosum*)
PRINCESS. Cord. (*Pa. Princess* Cy; *C. coffineti* × *C. fairieanum*)
PROSPERO. Cord. (*C. spicerianum* × *C. insigne sanderae*)
purpura'tum. Cord. (*Pa. purpuratum* Cy)
PYGMALION. Cord. (*C. villosum* × *C. ciliare*)
PYTHO **magnif'icum.** Cord. (*C. mastersianum* × *C. callosum magnificum*)
radio'sum. Cord. (*Pa. radiosum* Cy; *C. lawrenceanum* × *C. spicerianum*)
—**shorthillen'se**
ravonia'num . . . . . **C. pavoninum**
Typographical error.
rega'le. Cord. (*Pa. regale* Cy; *C. purpuratum* × *C. insigne maulei*)
reginaldia'num. Cord. (*Pa. reginaldianum* Cy; *C. insigne* × *C. siamense*)
REGINALD YOUNG. Cord. (*C. hitchensiae* × *C. insigne Harefield Hall*)
reynald'i. Cord. (*C. boxalli* × *C. villosum*)
robinsonia'num . . . . . . **C. euryale**
roez'li . . . . **C. longifolium hartwegi**
rolf'ei magnif'icum. Cord. (*C. bellatulum* × *C. rothschildianum*)
ROMULUS. Cord. (*C. Troilus; C. Ville de Paris; C. Zeno; Pa. Troilus* Cy; *C. insigne* × *C. nitens*)
ROSETTI. Cord. (*Pa. Rosetti* Cy; *C. insigne sanderianum* × *C. maudiae*)
—**magnif'icum**
rossia'num. Cord. (*C. tonso-barbatum; C. tonsum* × *C. barbatum*)
rothschildiano-box'alli . . . . EDITH
rothschildiano-lawrencea'num **C. mahlerae**
rothschildiano-super'biens. **C. mabeliae**
rothschildiano-ton'sum . . . . SOLON
rothschildia'num. Cord. (*Pa. rothschildianum* Cy)
ROWENA. Cord. (*C. edithae; Pa. edithae* Cy; *C. bellatulum* × *C. chamberlainianum*)
sallier'i . . . . **C. nitens**
—*au'reum* (*Pa. sallieri aureum* Cy) **C. nitens** var.
—*hyea'num* . . . **C. nitens hyeanum**

ORCHID GENERA (CYPRIPEDIUM), con.

sallier'i nigromacula'tum (*Pa. sallieri nigromaculatum* Cy) . **C. nitens** var.
—*pic'tum* (*Pa. sallieri pictum* Cy) **C. nitens** var.
—*platypet'alum* (*Pa. sallierei platypetalum*) . . . . . **C. nitens** var.
san'deri. Cord. (*C. boadicea; C. Calypso* × *C. nitens*)
sanderia'num. Cord.
Sappho . . . . **C. calanthum**
sargentia'num. Paph. (*Ph. sargentianum* Cy)
saundersia'num. Paph. (*Ph. saundersianum* Cy; *C. caudatum* × *C. schlimi*)
savagea'num. Cord. (*C. Albert Truffaut; C. memoria-moensi; C. Mme. Cappe; C. osbornei; C. pitcherianum; Pa. savageanum* Cy; *Pa. Albert Truffaut* Cy; *Pa. memoriamoensi* Cy; *Pa. Mme. Cappe* Cy; *Pa. osbornei* Cy; *Pa. pitcherianum* Cy; *C. harrisianum* × *C. spicerianum*)
schlesingeria'num. Cord. (*C. fulshawense; C. Mons. de Curte; C. sibyrolense; C. W. W. Lunt; Pa. schlesingerianum* Cy; *Pa. sibyrolense* Cy; *Pa. W. W. Lunt; C. boxalli* × *C. insigne maulei*)
schli'mi. Paph. (*Ph. schlimi* Cy)
schroe'derae. Paph. (*C. Mrs. W. A. Roebling; Ph. schroederae* Cy; *Ph. Mrs. W. A. Roebling* Cy; *S. helenae; C. caudatum* × *C. sedeni*)
—**graves'iae**
—**splen'dens**
schroed'eri. Cord. (*C. Baron Schroeder; C. Gaston Butel; Pa. Baron Schroeder* Cy; *Pa. schroederae* Cy; *C. fairieanum* × *C. oenanthum*)
SEAFORTH HIGHLANDER. Cord. (*C. Dreadnought* × *C. schlesingerianum* (*fulshawense*))
se'deni. Paph. (*C. tenellum; Ph. sedeni* Cy; *Pa. tenellum* Cy; *S. sedeni; C. schlimi* × *C. longifolium*)
—**candid'ulum** (*Ph. sedeni candidulum* Cy)
—**leucorrho'dum** (*C. leucorrhodum; Ph. leucorrhodum* Cy)
—**porphy'reum** (*C. porphyreum; Ph. porphyreum* Cy; *C. longifolium hartwegi* × *C. schlimi*)
—**weidlichia'num** (*C. weidlichianum; Ph. weidlichianum* Cy)
sellig'erum. Cord. (*Pa. selligerum* Cy; *C. barbatum* × *C. philippinense*)
—**ma'jus** (*Pa. selligerum majus* Cy)
Probably not distinct from the species proper.
—**porphy'reum** (*Pa. selligerum porphyreum* Cy)
siamen'se. Cord. (*Pa. siamense* Cy)
Nat. hyb. between C. appletonianum and C. callosum.
sibyrolen'se . . **C. schlesingerianum**
siebertia'num. Cord. (*Pa. siebertianum* Cy; *C. dayanum* × *C. insigne*)
Probably the same as C. gayotiae.
si'moni. Cord. (*C. Actaeus; C. Acteus; Pa. Actaeus* Cy; *C. leeanum* × *C. insigne sanderae*)
—JULIUS ROEHRS (*C. Acteus Julius Roehrs*)
—**niv'ale**
—**puncta'tum**

ORCHID GENERA (CYPRIPEDIUM), con.

SNOWFLAKE. Cord. (*C. godseffianum* × *C. insigne sanderae*)
SOLON. Cord. (*C. rothschildiano-tonsum; Pa. rothschildiano-tonsum* Cy; *C. rothschildianum* × *C. tonsum*)
spiceria'num. Cord. (*Pa. spicerianum* Cy)
—au'reum
—rose'um
spicero-niv'eum. Cord. (*Pa. spicero-niveum* Cy; *C. spicerianum* × *C. niveum*)
ST. ALBANS. Cord. (*C. Antigone* × *C. harrisianum*)
statheria'num. Cord. (*C. chamberlainianum* × *C. mastersianum*)
ste'vensi. Cord. (*C. Calypso* × *C. lathamianum*)
ston'ei. Cord. (*Pa. stonei* Cy)
—cannaertia'num (*Pa. stonei cannaertianum* Cy)
SUNSHINE. Cord. (*C. rothschildianum* × *C. beeckmani*)
super'biens. Cord. (*C. veitchi; C. veitchianum; Pa. superbiens* Cy)
supercilia're. Cord. (*Pa. superciliare* Cy; *C. barbatum* × *C. superbiens*)
sutherland'iae. Cord. (*C. Duchess of Sutherland; Pa. Duchess of Sutherland* Cy; *C. rothschildianum* × *C. youngianum*)
swania'num. Cord. (*Pa. swanianum* Cy; *C. dayanum* × *C. barbatum*)
—excel'sum
swinburn'ei magnif'icum. Cord. (*Pa. swinburnei magnificum* Cy; *C. insigne maulei* × *C. Argus*)
T. B. Haywood . **C. haywoodianum**
tenel'lum . . . . **C. sedeni**
—rose'um . . . . . . **C. sedeni** var.
ten'ue
Hyb.—not known.

tessella'tum porphy'reum. Cord. (*Pa. tessellatum porphyreum* Cy; *C. concolor* × *C. barbatum*)
thayeria'num super'bum. Cord. (*C. boxalli* × *C. lawrenceanum*)
THETIS. Cord. (*C. calophyllum* ABL; *Pa. Thetis* Cy; *C. venustum* × *C. barbatum*)
thibautia'num . . . . **C. oenanthum**
thomp'soni . . . . . **C. lathamianum**
tita'num . . . . **C. urgandae titanium**
Tityus . . . . FIGARO
tonso-arthuria'num. Cord. (*Pa. tonso-arthurianum* Cy)
tonso-barba'tum . . . . **C. rossianum**
tonso-charles'worthi . . . . . NELLIE
tonso-purpura'tum. Cord. (*Ph. tonso-purpuratum* Cy)
tonso-san'derae. Cord. (*Pa. tonso-sanderae* Cy)
Probably either sanderi or sanderianum was intended, or C. tonsum sanderae.

tonso-villo'sum . . . . . . **C. bullieri**
ton'sum. Cord. (*Pa. tonsum* Cy)
—charles'worthi
C. tonso-charlesworthi is probably intended.

—purpura'tum
C. tonso-purpuratum is probably intended.

—san'derae
See note under C. tonso-sanderae, above.

—villo'sum
C. tonso-villosum is probably intended.

ORCHID GENERA (CYPRIPEDIUM), con.

TRANSVAAL. Cord. (*Pa. Transvaal* Cy; *C. chamberlainianum* × *C. rothschildianum*)
trium'phans. Cord. (*Pa. triumphans* Cy; *C. nitens* × *C. oenanthum*)
Troilus . . . . ROMULUS
truffau'tiae. Cord. (*C. ciliolare* × *C. stonei*)
URANUS. Paph. (*Ph. Uranus* Cy; *C. lindleyanum* × *C. grande*)
urgan'dae. Paph. (*Ph. urgandae* Cy; *C. lindleyanum* × *C. longifolium*)
—GRAVES
—tita'nium (*C. titanum; Phragmopedilum titanum* Cy)
U. S. GRANT
Hyb.—not known.

VAN DYCK. Cord. (*C. Vandyke; C. hirsutissimum* × *C. schlesingerianum* (*Mons. de Curte*))
—super'bum
Vandyke . . . . VAN DYCK
veitch'i . . . . **C. superbiens**
venus'tum. Cord. (*Pa. venustum* Cy)
vernix'ium. Cord. (*Pa. vernixium* Cy; *C. Argus* × *C. villosum*)
VERONA. Cord. (*C. beeckmani* × *C. leeanum*)
vexilla'rium. Cord. (*Pa. vexillarium* Cy; *C. barbatum* × *C. fairieanum*)
victo'ria mari'ae
Not found in botanical literature, probably an artificial hyb.

VICTORIA MARIE
Probably the same as the preceding.

Ville de Paris . . . . . . ROMULUS
villo'sum. Cord. (*Pa. villosum* Cy)
—albomargina'tum (*Pa. villosum albomarginatum* Cy)
—au'reum (*Pa. villosum aureum* Cy)
—super'bum
volontea'num Cy . . . . **C. hookerae**
wallertia'num . . . . **C. conspicuum**
war'neri
Not found in botanical literature, probably the same as C. barbatum warneri.

weidlichia'num
C. sedeni weidlichianum
W. H. HARRISON
Hyb.—not known.

WILLIAM MCKINLEY
Hyb.—not known.

—super'bum
williamsia'num . . . **C. chloroneurum**
winnia'num. Cord. (*Pa. winnianum* Cy; *C. villosum* × *C. druryi*)
W. R. Lee . . . . **C. mabeliae**
W. W. Lunt . . **C. schlesingerianum**
youngia'num. Cord. (*Pa. youngianum* Cy; *C. superbiens* × *C. philippinense*)
YVETTE **super'bum**
Hyb.—not known.

ZAMPA (*Pa. Zampa* Cy; *C. hirsutissimum* × *C. leeanum*)
ZENO. Cord. (*C. boxalli* × *C. tonsum*)
Zeno (*C. insigne* × *C. nitens*)
ROMULUS

The following crosses have appeared in horticulture without names:
aureum hyeanum × *memoria jerninghami*
beeckmani × *schlesingerianum* (*Mons. de Curte*) . . . . **C. curtemanni**
boxalli × *thompsoni*
chamberlainianum × *mastersianum*
C. statherianum

ORCHID GENERA (CYPRIPEDIUM), con.

curtisi × *purpureum* . . . . . **C. oakesi**
Purpuratum is undoubtedly intended; there is no C. purpureum.
hitchense [*hitchensiae*] × [*insigne*] *Harefield Hall* . . . . REGINALD YOUNG
insigne Harefield Hall × *oenanthum superbum.* Allied to C. Milo.
—Harefield Hall × *spicerianum.* Allied to C. leeanum.
—Monarch × *nitens*
leeanum × *beeckmani* . . . . VERONA
lindleyanum × [*sedeni*] *leucorrhodum nitens* (*sallieri aureum*) × *insigne sanderae.* Allied to C. Romulus.
sanderae × *insigne lucianiae*
schlesingerianum (*Mons. de Curte*) × *clinkaberryanum*
spicerianum × *Laura Kimball*

CYRTOPO'DIUM

anderso'ni
puncta'tum

DENDRO'BIUM

In this list Sarcopodium is included in Dendrobium; by a majority of botanists it is considered to be only a subgenus.

acumina'tum (*Sarcopodium acuminatum* Cy)
aggrega'tum
—ma'jus
ains'worthi (*Artemis; aureum* × *nobile; Artemus; edithae*)
—leechia'num (*leechianum*)
—splendidis'simum (*splendidissimum*)
albosanguin'eum
amesia'num grandiflo'rum
Not found in botanical literature, probably a garden hybrid.

am'plum (*Sarcopodium amplum* Cy)
an'ceps
Apollo grandiflorum
D. rubens grandiflorum
Artemis . . . . **D. ainsworthi**
Artemus . . . . **D. ainsworthi**
ASPASIA (*wardianum* × *aureum*)
atroviola'ceum
auranti'acum
au'reum . . . . . . **D. heterocarpum**
barba'tulum
It is quite possible that the material grown under this name is in reality D. fytchianum.

barbig'erum (*barbrigium*)
barbrig'ium . . . . . **D. barbigerum**
Misspelling.

bella'tulum
ben'soni . . . . **D. bensoniae**
benso'niae (*bensoni*)
bigib'bum
bronckar'ti
brymeria'num
bufordien'se . . . . **D. dulce**
calceola'ria **D. moschatum calceolaria**
calceo'lus . . . . . . **D. moschatum**
cambridgea'num (*Dendrobium ochreatum* ABL-Cy)
carinif'erum
CASSIOPE (*moniliforme* × *nobile*)
childs'i
Not found in botanical literature, probably a garden hybrid.

chloroste'le (*Juno; xanthocentron* Cy; *linawianum* × *wardianum*)
chrysan'thum (*paxtoni*)
chrysodis'cus . . . . **D. melanodiscus**
chrysotox'um
—**suavis'simum** (*suavissimum*)
cilia'tum annamen'se

ORCHID GENERA (DENDROBIUM), con.
clava'tum
coelogy'ne (*Sarcopodium coelogyne* Cy)
crassino'de (*pendulum* ABL-Cy)
—barberia'num
crepida'tum
creta'ceum
crystalli'num
cupe'ta
Not found in botanical literature, probably a garden hybrid.
cu'preum . . **D. moschatum cupreum**
cur'tisi (*Cassiope* × *aureum*)
CYBELE (*findlayanum* × *nobile*)
cymbidioi'des
dalhousiea'num (*pulchellum* ABL)
dear'ei
densiflo'rum
Desdemona . . . . **D. rubens**
devonia'num
dixan'thum
dominia'num (*linawianum* × *nobile*)
DORIS (*ainsworthi* × *moniliforme*)
dul'ce (*bufordiense; aureum* × *linawianum*)
edi'thae . . . . **D. ainsworthi**
endocha'ris (*aureum* × *moniliforme*)
enos'mum (*endocharis* × *nobile*)
—leucop'terum
eriaeflo'rum
Euryalus . . . . **D. rubens**
Euterpe . . . . . . **D. murrhiniacum**
falconer'i
far'meri
fimbria'tum
—ocula'tum
findlaya'num
formo'sum
—gigan'teum
gol'diei . . . . **D. superbiens**
HAROLD (*findlayanum* × *linawianum*)
—amoe'num
heterocar'pum (*aureum*)
hildebrand'i
infundib'ulum
—jamesia'num (*jamesianum*)
jamesia'num
D. infundibulum jamesianum
johan'nis
Juno . . . . **D. chlorostele**
kingia'num
leechia'num. **D. ainsworthi leechianum**
lituiflo'rum
—free'mani
lu'na . . . . **D. melanodiscus**
luteo'la
macrophyl'lum
There is also a D. macrophyllum of Lindley, which is the same as D. superbum and which is probably the plant more commonly in cultivation.
—daya'num . **D. superbum anosmum**
—gigan'teum . . . . **D. s. giganteum**
melanodis'cus (*chrysodiscus; luna; findlayanum* × *ainsworthi*)
—pal'lens (*pallens*)
meterocar'pum
Not found, probably a garden hybrid.
mi'cans (*wardianum* × *lituiflorum*)
moscha'tum (*calceolus*)
—calceola'ria (*calceolaria*)
—cupre'um (*cupreum*)
MRS. ALFRED ROGERS (*findlayanum* × *hildebrandi*)
murrhinia'cum (*murrhinianum; Euterpe; nobile* × *wardianum*)
murrhinia'num . . . **D. murrhiniacum**

ORCHID GENERA (DENDROBIUM), con.
NIOBE (*tortile* × *nobile*)
no'bile
—al'bum
—ames'iae
—amesia'num
Probably the same as D. nobile amesiae.
—ash'worthi
Probably the same as D. nobile ashworthianum.
—ashworth'iae
Probably the same as D. nobile ashworthianum.
—ashworthia'num
—ballia'num
—cook'soni
Probably the same as D. nobile cooksonianum.
—cooksonia'num
—LARZ ANDERSON
—ma'jus
—MRS. LARZ ANDERSON
This and D. nobile Larz Anderson may be the same.
—murrhini'acum
Possibly the same as D. murrhiniacum.
—nobil'ius
—owenia'num
—pulcher'rimum
—RAJAH
—rose'um
—rothwellia'num
—ru'brum
—SOUTH ORANGE
—summiten'se
—tollia'num
—victo'ria regi'na
—virgina'le
ochrea'tum ABL-Cy **D. cambridgeanum**
ocula'tum
Not found in botanical literature, probably the same as D. fimbriatum oculatum.
oncid'ium
Not found in botanical literature.
pal'lens . . **D. melanodiscus pallens**
par'ishi
pax'toni . . . . . . **D. chrysanthum**
pen'dulum ABL-Cy . . **D. crassinode**
phalaenop'sis
—al'bum
—caerules'cens
—schroe'derae
Probably the same as D. phalaenopsis schroederianum.
—schroederia'num
—schroederia'num albes'cens
—schroederia'num al'bum ROEHRS
—schroederia'num roehrsia'na
Very likely this is the more correct name of D. phalaenopsis schroederianum album Roehrs.
pierard'i
pitcheria'num (*rolfeae; nobile* × *primulinum*)
platycau'lon
primuli'num
pulchel'lum ABL . **D. dalhousieanum**
re'gium
roeblingia'num (*nobile* × *ruckeri*)
rog'ersi
Not found in botanical literature, probably a garden hybrid.
rolf'eae . . . . . . **D. pitcherianum**
ru'bens (*Desdemona; Euryalus; ainsworthi* × *nobile*)
—grandiflo'rum (*Apollo grandiflorum*)

ORCHID GENERA (DENDROBIUM), con.
san'derae
schneideria'num (*findlayanum* × *aureum*)
—grandiflo'rum
schuetz'ei
secun'dum
SIBYL (*bigibbum* × *linawianum*)
specio'sum
splendidis'simum
D. ainsworthi splendidissimum
—grandiflo'rum . . . . . . **D. ainsworthi splendidissimum var.**
—grandiflo'rum Thompsons **D. ainsworthi splendidissimum var.**
statteria'num
Supposed nat. hyb. between D. bigibbum and D. phalaenopsis.
suavis'simum
D. chrysotoxum suavissimum
super'biens (*goldiei*)
super'bum (*macrophyllum* of Lindley)
—anos'mum (*macrophyllum dayanum*)
—dear'ei
—gigan'teum (*macrophyllum giganteum*)
THELMA (*wiganiae album* × *nobile virginale*)
thrysiflo'rum . . . . **D. thyrsiflorum**
thyrsiflo'rum (*thrysiflorum*)
Botanically considered a variety of D. densiflorum.
transpa'rens
veitch'i (*wardiano-japonicum; moniliforme* × *wardianum*)
D. moniliforme is the older and more correct name of D. japonicum.
veluti'num
VENUS (*falconeri* × *nobile*)
virgina'le
Not found in botanical literature, probably the same as D. nobile virginale.
wardiano-japon'icum . . . **D. veitchi**
wardia'num
—al'bum
—gigan'teum
—low'i
wiga'niae (*nobile* × *signatum*)
xanthocen'trum . . . . **D. chlorostele**

DENDROCHI'LUM
cobbia'num (*Platyclinis cobbiana* Cy; *P. gigantea*)
cucumeri'num (*Platyclinis cucumerina* Cy)
filifor'me (*P. filiformis* Cy)
gluma'ceum (*P. glumacea* Cy)
—super'bum
Of little standing as distinct.
latifo'lium (*Platyclinis latifolia* Cy)

DIA'CRIUM . . **EPIDENDRUM**
More correctly only a section of Epidendrum, though often maintained as a distinct genus.
bicornu'tum Cy
Epidendrum bicornutum

DI'SA
lu'na (*racemosa* × *veitchi*)

ELLEAN'THUS
longibractea'tus

EPICAT'TLEYA
Also written Epi-Cattleya. Crosses between Epidendrum and Cattleya.
gautemalen'sis
Hyb.—not found in botanical literature.
MRS. SMITH (*E. aurantiacum* × *C. gigas*)

ORCHID GENERA (EPICATTLEYA), con.
NEBO (*Nibo; E. obrienianum* × *C. claesiana*)
Nibo . . . . NEBO
orpet'i (*orpetiana; E. obrienianum* × *C. amethystoglossa*)
orpetia'na . . . . **E. orpeti**

EPIDEN'DRUM (*EPIDENDRON*)
an'ceps
aromat'icum
atropurpu'reum (*macrochilum*)
—rand'i . . . . **E. randi**
auranti'acum (*Cattleya aurantiaca*)
auri'tum ABL . . . . **E. palleaceum**
bahamen'se
bicornu'tum (*Diacrium bicornutum* Cy)
boothia'num (*erythronioides*)
bound'i (*burtoni* × *radicans*)
brassavo'lae
bur'toni (*ybaguense* × *obrienianum*)
cilia're
cinnabari'num
cochlea'tum
conspic'uum . . . . **E. roseum**
cooperia'num
coria'ceum . . . . . . **E. variegatum**
decip'iens
dellen'se (*radicans* × *xanthinum*)
dichro'mum
diur'num ABL . . . . . . **E. virens**
ela'tius . . . . . . **Cattleya guttata**
erythronioi'des . . . . **E. boothianum**
falca'tum
Probably the form grown is E. parkinsonianum and not the true E. falcatum, which is smaller.

fra'grans
gattonen'se (*boundi* × *xanthinum*)
godseffia'num . . . . . **E. osmanthum**
grac'ile
inver'sum
kewen'se (*evectum* × *xanthinum*)
la'geri
Not known, probably a garden hybrid.

latila'brum
More commonly known as E. latilabre, but the original spelling is latilabrum.

lindleya'num ABL-CY
Barkeria lindleyana
longifo'lium
macrochi'lum . . . **E. atropurpureum**
nemora'le
obri'eni . . . . **E. obrienianum**
obrienia'num (*obrieni; evectum* × *radicans*)
odoratis'simum
oncidioi'des
osman'thum (*godseffianum*)
pallea'ceum (*auritum* ABL)
planila'bris
Not found in botanical literature.

polybul'bon (*Dinema polybulbon*)
porphy'reum
prismatocar'pum
pris'tes
rad'icans (*rhizophorum*)
rand'i (*atropurpureum randianum* Cy; *atropurpureum randi*)
rhizoph'orum . . . . . . **E. radicans**
rig'idum
rose'um (*conspicuum*)
This may also apply to a variety of E. atropurpureum.

skin'neri
spectab'ile ABL-Cy **Barkeria spectabilis**
stamfordia'num
—walla'cei

ORCHID GENERA (EPIDENDRUM), con.
stenopet'alum
variega'tum (*coriaceum*)
vi'rens (*diurnum* ABL)
virga'tum
vitelli'num
—ma'jus
wal'lisi
wat'soni
An unpublished species (that is, without a description). Known only in horticulture. The printed form of the name is watsonianum.

xanthi'num

The following cross has appeared in horticulture without a name.
aurantiacum × *Cattleya gigas.* This is an Epicattleya.

EPIPHRONI'TIS
Crosses between Epidendrum and Sophronitis.

veitch'i (*E. radicans* × *S. grandiflora*)

E'RIA
anchorif'era
barba'ta
bractes'cens
convallarioi'des
corona'ria (*Trichosma suavis* Cy)
densiflo'ra
excava'ta
ferrugin'ea
gigan'tea
lava'ta
Not found in botanical literature, probably an error for E. lanata.

monostach'ys
obe'sa

ERIOP'SIS
rutidobul'bon

EUAN'THE ABL
sanderia'na ABL . **Vanda sanderiana**

GALEAN'DRA
devonia'na
lacus'tris

GOME'SA
planifo'lia

GOME'ZA . . . . . . **GOMESA**

GONGO'RA
charles'worthi
galea'ta (*Acropera loddigesi; Maxillaria galeata*)
macula'ta (*quinquinervis* ABL-CY)

GRAMMATOPHYL'LUM (*GRAMMANGIS* ABL)
el'lisi (*Grammangis ellisi* ABL)

HAEMA'RIA ABL . **GOODYERA**
dis'color dawsonia'na ABL
G. dawsoniana

HARTWE'GIA
purpu'rea

HOULLET'IA
brocklehurstia'na
odoratis'sima
—antioquien'sis

HUNT'LEYA Cy **ZYGOPETALUM**
burt'i Cy . . . . **Z. burti**

LAE'LIA . . . . LAELIA
The name of this genus under the American rules is Amalia.

acumina'ta . . . . . **L. rubescens**
al'bida
an'ceps
—al'ba

ORCHID GENERA (LAELIA), continued
an'ceps al'ba BULLS
—ames'iae
Probably the same as L. anceps amesiana.

—amesia'na
—blan'da
—BULLS
This is very likely the same as L. anceps alba Bulls.

—daw'soni
—grandiflo'ra
—hill'i
Probably the same as L. anceps hilliana.

—hillia'na
—hillia'na rosefielden'sis
—holidaya'na
Not found in botanical literature, probably a garden variety.

—lageria'na
—leea'na
—percivalia'na
—protheroia'na
—rose'a
—sanderia'na
—schroe'derae
—schroe'deri
Probably the same as either L. anceps schroederae or L. anceps schroederiana.

—schroederia'na
—stel'la
—stel'la vesta'lis
—veitchia'na
—wil'liamsi
—winnia'na
arnoldia'na [of Manda]
It is impossible to say whether this and the next are the same.

arnoldia'na **Laeliocattleya callistoglossa**
autumna'lis
—al'ba
—atroru'bens
bel'la . . . . . . **Laeliocattleya bella**
boothia'na (*Cattleya lobata*)
cinnabaero'sa . . . . . **L. cinnabrosa**
cinnabari'na
cinnabro'sa (*cinnabaerosa; cinnabarina* × *tenebrosa*)
cris'pa (*Cattleya crispa*)
—super'ba
crispila'bia (*Laelia cinnabarina crispilabia* Cy)
daya'na . . . . **L. pumila dayana**
digbya'na Cy . . **Brassavola digbyana**
el'egans . . . **Laeliocattleya elegans**
This species has been a source of much confusion, having been treated as a valid species of Laelia, but apparently it is a cross between Cattleya leopoldi and Laelia purpurata.

—schilleria'na
Laeliocattleya schilleriana
fla'va
glau'ca Cy . . . . **Brassavola glauca**
gouldia'na
gran'dis tenebro'sa Cy . . **L. tenebrosa**
harpophyl'la
jonghea'na
lato'na (*cinnabarina* × *purpurata*)
lindleya'na (*Cattleya lindleyana*)
maja'lis (*speciosa* ABL)
—al'ba
monaphyl'la
NORA (*cinnabarina* × *xanthina*)
OLIVIA (*crispa* × *xanthina*)
pat'tini
Not found in botanical literature, probably a garden hybrid.

ORCHID GENERA (LAELIA), continued

per'rini
prae'stans . . . . . **L. pumila major**
pu'mila
—**daya'na** Cy (*dayana*)
—**ma'jor** (*praestans; pumila praestans* Cy)
purpura'ta
—**russellia'na**
—*schroe'derae.* **L. purpurata schroederi**
—**schroe'deri** (*purpurata schroederae*)
—**wil'liamsi**
ragotia'na (*cinnabarina* × *grandis*)
rubes'cens (*acuminata*)
specio'sa . . . . **L. majalis**
super'biens
tenebro'sa (*grandis tenebrosa* Cy)

Whether this is a true species or a variety of L. grandis is open to question. We have followed R. A. Rolfe who considers it a distinct species.

—**gran'dis**
Not found, possibly L. grandis.

—Walton Grange

The following crosses have appeared in horticulture without names:

cinnabarina × *xanthina* . . . . Nora
perrini × *Cattleya aurea* **Laeliocattleya decia**
pumila × *purpurata*
pumila dayana × *anceps stella*
purpurata × *Laeliocattleya balli* (*G. S. Ball*). This is a Laeliocattleya.
tenebrosa × *Laeliocattleya canhamiana* **Laeliocattleya** Kathleen

LAELIOCAT'TLEYA

Also written Laelia-Cattleya and Laelio-Cattleya. Crosses between Laelia and Cattleya or between one of these genera and a Laeliocattleya or between two Laeliocattleyas. In references below the abbreviation L. is used for Laelia, Lc. for Laeliocattleya.

Agnes (*Lc. callistoglossa* × *Lc. schilleriana*)
Alebar (*L. ingrami* × *C. superba*)
Alex (*C. dowiana* × *Lc. Tunis*)
Alphand (*C. Fabia* × *Lc. callistoglossa*)
Antigone (*L. purpurata* × *C. schilleriana*)
Antimachus (*C. gigas* × *Lc. dominiana*)
Aphrodite (*Lc. eudora; C. mendeli* × *L. purpurata*)
Ariel (*C. aurea* × *Lc. cowani*)
armstrong'iae (*C. Iris* × *Lc. G. Woodhouse*)
arnoldia'na . . . . **Lc. callistoglossa**
asto'riae (*Lc. Hon. Mrs. Astor; C. gaskelliana* × *L. xanthina*)
Atalanta (*Lc. Clonia* ABL; *C. gigas* × *Lc. elegans*)
Australia (*L. tenebrosa* × *Lc. luminosa*)
baden-pow'elli (*Lc. Gen. Baden Powell; C. lawrenceana* × *L. tenebrosa*)
ball'i (*Lc. G. S. Ball; C. schroederiana* × *L. cinnabarina*)
Bedouin (*L. purpurata* × *Lc. hyeana*)
bel'la (*L. bella; C. labiata* × *L. purpurata*)
—**al'ba** (*C. labiata alba* × *L. purpurata*)
Berthe Fournier . . . **Lc. fournierae**
Black Prince (*C. hardyana* × *Lc. bletchleyensis*)
bletchleyen'sis (*L. tenebrosa* × *C. gigas sanderiana*)

ORCHID GENERA (LAELIOCATTLEYA), con.

bo'la (*C. labiata* × *Lc. callistoglossa*)
boyl'ei (*Lc. Frederick Boyle; C. trianae* × *L. anceps*)
—**kercho'viae** (*Lc. Frederick Boyle kerchoviae*)
britan'nia (*C. gigas* × *Lc. canhamiana*)
—**al'ba** (*C. gigas alba* × *Lc. canhamiana alba*)
Bryan (*C. gaskelliana* × *L. crispa*)
callistoglos'sa (*Lc. arnoldiana; C. gigas* × *L. purpurata*)
canhamia'na (*Lc. Lady Wigan; C. mossiae* × *L. purpurata*)
—**al'ba** (*C. mossiae alba* × *L. purpurata*)
—**rex'** (*C. mossiae wagneri* × *L. purpurata*)
Carmencita (*C. dowiana* × *Lc. luminosa*)
Celia (*C. superba* × *L. purpurata*)
C. G. Roebling . . . **Lc. roeblingi**
charles'worthi (*C. dowiana* × *L. cinnabarina*)
choletia'na (*C. mossiae* × *L. superbiens*)
Clive (*C. dowiana* × *L. pumila*)
Clonia ABL . . . . Atalanta
colmania'na (*C. dowiana* × *Lc. callistoglossa*)
Coronis (*C. labiata* × *L. cinnabarina*)
cow'ani (*C. mossiae* × *L. cinnabrosa*)
cranstoun'ae (*C. harrisoniana* × *L. tenebrosa*)
de'cia (*C. aurea* × *L. perrini*)
Domas (*C. mossiae* × *Lc. dominiana*)
dominia'na (*C. dowiana* × *L. purpurata*)
Dr. R. Schiffman . . . **Lc. schiffmani**
dun'cani (*Lc. duncaniana; C. hardyana* × *Lc. gottoiana*)
duncania'na . . . . . . **Lc. duncani**
ed'wardi (*C. hardyana* × *L. cinnabarina*)
el'egans (*L. elegans; C. leopoldi* × *L. purpurata*)
Elsie (*C. trianae* × *L. cinnabarina*)
Endymion . . . . Eva
Epicasta (*C. gigas* × *L. pumila*)
eudo'ra . . . . Aphrodite
Eva (*Lc. Endymion; Lc. orpetiana; C. gaskelliana* × *L. tenebrosa*)
exim'ia (*C. warneri* × *L. purpurata*)
—**gigan'tea magnif'ica**
exonien'sis (*C. mossiae* × *L. crispa*)
Fabia
Hyb.—probably the same as Cattleya Fabia.

Fascinator (*C. schroederiana* × *L. purpurata*)
—**magnif'icum**
Felicity (*C. mendeli* × *L. crispa*)
fournier'ae (*Lc. Berthe Fournier; C. dowiana* × *Lc. elegans*)
Frederick Boyle . . . . . . **Lc. boylei**
Frederick Boyle kerchoviae **Lc. boylei kerchoviae**
G. C. Whitelegge . . **Lc. whiteleggei**
Gen. Baden Powell. **Lc. baden-powelli**
General French . . **Lc. warnhamensis**
Golden Oriole (*C. dowiana* × *Lc. charlesworthi*)
—**al'ba**
gottoia'na
Nat. hyb. between C. warneri and L. tenebrosa.

green'woodi (*C. hardyana* × *Lc. schilleriana*)
G. S. Ball . . . . **Lc. balli**

ORCHID GENERA (LAELIOCATTLEYA), con.

haroldia'na (*C. hardyana* × *L. tenebrosa*)
Hector (*C. dowiana* × *Lc. martineti*)
Herga (*C. gaskelliana* × *Lc. elegans*)
herscent'iae (*C. dowiana* × *Lc. boothiana*)
highburien'sis (*C. lawrenceana* × *L. cinnabarina*)
Hon. Mrs. Astor . . . . **Lc. astoriae**
hyea'na (*C. lawrenceana hyeana* × *L. purpurata*)
Isabel Sander (*C. mossiae* × *Lc. canhamiana*)
Josephine (*Lc. massiliensis* ABL; *C. trianae* × *L. crispa*)
Kathleen (*Lc. Kathleen Grey; Lc. Kathline; L. tenebrosa* × *Lc. canhamiana*)
labio'sa (*C. labiata* × *Lc. luminosa*)
Lady Rothschild . . **Lc. rothschildiae**
Lady Wigan . . . . **Lc. canhamiana**
Linda (*C. aurea* × *Lc. Arachne*)
lucasia'na (*C. labiata* × *L. tenebrosa*)
Lucia (*C. mendeli* × *L. cinnabarina*)
—**super'ba**
lumino'sa . . . . . **Lc. truffautiana**
Luster . . . . Lustre
lustra . . . . Lustre
Lustre (*Lc. Luster; Lc. lustra; C. lueddemanniana* (*speciosissima*) × *Lc. callistoglossa*)
Mabel (*C. trianae* × *L. tenebrosa*)
martinet'i (*C. mossiae reineckiana* × *L. tenebrosa*)
maureta'nia (*Lc. canhamiana* × *Lc. martineti*)
Memnon (*C. mendeli* × *Lc. elegans*)
Mercia (*C. schroederiana* × *L.* [*pumila*] *dayana*)
Mme. Brasseur-Hye (*C. gigas* × *Lc. Aphrodite* (*eudora*))
Moonbeam (*C. schroederiana* × *Lc. balli* (*G. S. Ball*))
Mrs. Temple (*C. mossiae* × *Lc. greenwoodi* (*Henry Greenwood*))
Mygdon (*C. trianae* × *Lc. truffautiae* (*luminosa*))
Myra (*C. trianae* × *L. flava*)
—**al'ba**
ny'sa (*Lc. nyssa; C. gigas* × *Lc. crispa*)
nys'sa . . . . **Lc. nysa**
Ophir (*C. dowiana* × *L. xanthina*)
orpetia'na . . . . Eva
paca'via
Not known, probably a garden hybrid.

Pallas (*C. aurea* × *L. crispa*)
Phoebe (*Lc. Hippolyta* ABL; *C. mossiae* × *L. cinnabarina*)
Priam (*C. harrisoniana* × *Lc. callistoglossa*)
Purple Emperor (*C. gigas* × *Lc. callistoglossa*)
Queen of Sheba
Not known, probably a garden hybrid.

roeb'lingi (*Lc. C. G. Roebling; Lc. violetta; C. gaskelliana* × *L. purpurata*)
rothschild'iae (*Lc. Lady Rothschild; C. gigas* × *L. perrini*)
schiff'mani (*Lc. Dr. R. Schiffman; C. mendeli* × *Lc. callistoglossa*)
schilleria'na (*L. elegans schilleriana; C. intermedia* × *L. purpurata*)
Soulange (*C. dowiana* × *Lc. Lustre*)
Tarquinias (*C. schilleriana* × *Lc. callistoglossa*)

ORCHID GENERA (LAELIOCATTLEYA), con.
thurgoodia'na (*C. hardyana* × *Lc. martineti*)
truffautia'na (*Lc. luminosa; C. dowiana* × *L. tenebrosa*)
violet'ta . . . . **Lc. roeblingi**
warnhamen'sis (*Lc. General French; C. trianae* × *L. cinnabarina*)
wellsia'na (*Lc. willsiana* Cy; *C. trianae* × *L. purpurata*)
whiteleg'gei (*Lc. G. C. Whitelegge; C. hardyana* × *Lc. callistoglossa*)
ZIXA (*C. mendeli* × *Lc. bella*)

The following crosses have appeared in horticulture without names:

Lc. Aphrodite (*eudora*) × *C. gigas* MME. BRASSEUR-HYE
L. cinnabarina × *C. schroederiana* **Lc. balli**
Lc. martineti × *C. labiata*
C. mossiae rousseliana × *L. tenebrosa*. A close ally of, if not the same as Lc. martineti.
Lc. schilleriana × *Lc. callistoglossa* AGNES

LEPTO'TES (*TETRAMICRA*)
bi'color (*T. bicolor*)

LOCKHART'IA
el'egans
gigan'tea
Not found, probably a garden variety.

LYCAS'TE
aromat'ica
can'dida
costa'ta
cruen'ta
dep'pei
Named for Deppe, but originally (under Maxillaria) spelled deppii.
fulves'cens
harriso'niae . **Bifrenaria harrisoniae**
hy'brida (*deppei* × *skinneri*)
la'nipes
lasioglos'sa
pla'na
skin'neri
—al'ba
—grandiflo'ra
tri'color
tyrianthi'na . **Bifrenaria tyrianthina**

MACRADE'NIA
brassavo'lae

MASDEVAL'LIA
bel'la
chimae'ra
coccin'ea
—harrya'na ABL-Cy . **M. harryana**
coria'cea
estra'dae
harrya'na (*Masdevallia coccinea harryana* ABL-Cy)
—lute'a
houttea'na (*benedicti*)
ig'nea (*militaris* ABL-Cy)
macru'ra
milita'ris ABL-Cy . . . . **M. ignea**
reichenbachia'na
schli'mi
tovaren'sis
veitch'i . . . . **M. veitchiana**
veitchia'na (*veitchi*)

MAXILLA'RIA
angustifo'lia . . . . . **M. variabilis**

ORCHID GENERA (MAXILLARIA), con.
den'sa . . . . . **Ornithidium densum**
galea'ta . . . . . . **Gongora galeata**
There is also a valid M galeata which is probably not in horticulture.
grandiflo'ra
henchmann'i . . . . . **M. variabilis**
houttea'na
hyacinthin'a. . **Xylobium hyacinthinum**
incarna'ta
Not found, perhaps a garden variety; according to Bailey's Cyclopedia a trade name only.
luteoal'ba
—tur'neri ABL . . . . . **M. turneri**
nigres'cens
pic'ta
porphyroste'le (*porphyrostella*)
porphyrostel'la . . . **M. porphyrostele**
pulsel'la
Not found, evidently a misspelling, possibly for pusilla.
rubes'cens
Not found, probably intended for rufescens.
sanderia'na
setig'era
tenuifo'lia
tur'neri (*luteoalba turneri* ABL)
variab'ilis (*angustifolia; henchmanni*)
venus'ta

MEGACLIN'IUM (*Bulbophyllum* ABL)
This genus is recognized by some authorities and by others is reduced to Bulbophyllum.
falca'tum (*Bulbophyllum falcatum* ABL)

MILTO'NIA . . . . PANSYORCHID
Ajax . . . . **Miltonioda** AJAX
bleua'na (*Miltoniopsis bleui; Miltonia vexillaria* × *roezli*)
—charles'worthi
Presumably the same as M. charlesworthi.
—grandiflo'ra
—hyea'na
Presumably the same as M. hyeana.
—magnif'ica
—nobil'ior
—QUEEN ALEXANDRA
—rose'a
—ST. ANDRE
Presumably the same as M. St. Andre.
blunt'i
Supposed nat. hyb. between M. clowes and M. spectabilis.
—lubbersia'na
can'dida
charles'worthi
clowes'i
cunea'ta
flaves'cens
hyea'na (*bleuana* × *vexillaria*)
lambeaua'na
Not found, probably a garden hybrid or a form of M. vexillaria.
morelia'na . **M. spectabilis moreliana**
phalaenop'sis
—al'ba
regnel'li
roez'li
—al'ba

ORCHID GENERA (MILTONIA), continued
schroe'derae
Not found, probably the same as M. schroederiana.
schroederia'na
spectab'ilis
—morelia'na (*moreliana*)
ST. ANDRE (*bleuana* × *roezli*)
vexilla'ria (*uexillaria*)
—EMPRESS AUGUSTA VICTORIA
—gigan'tea
—H. H. HUNNEWELL
—lambeauia'na
—leopold'i
—leucoglos'sa
—magnif'ica
—MEMORIA G. D. OWEN
—rose'a
warscewicz'i (*Oncidium fuscatum*)

MILTONIO'DA
Crosses between Cochlioda and Miltonia.
AJAX (*Miltonia Ajax; Miltonia schroederiana* × *C. noezliana*)
MILTONIOP'SIS . . **MILTONIA**
bleu'i . . . . **M. bleuana**

MORMO'DES
buccina'tor
—citri'num

MYSTACID'IUM
dis'tichum (*Angraecum distichum*)

NANO'DES
More properly included in Epidendrum. ABL.
medu'sae (*Epidendrum medusae* ABL)

NEO-BENTHA'MIA
grac'ilis

OCTOMER'IA
diaph'ana

ODONTIO'DA
Crosses between Cochlioda and Odontoglossum.
ADRASTIA (*Odontioda bohnhoffiae* × *Odontoglossum crispum*)
bol'toni (*C. noezliana* × *Odontoglossum vuylstekeae*)
bradshaw'iae (*C. noezliana* × *Odontoglossum crispum*)
—GATTON PARK
brew'i (*Odontioda charlesworthi* × *Odontoglossum harryanum*)
charles'worthi (*C. noezliana* × *Odontoglossum harryanum*)
CLEOPATRA (*C. noezliana* × *O. lairessei*)
cookso'niae (*C. noezliana* × *O. armainvillierense* (*ardentissimum*))
DIANA (*C. noezliana* × *O. amabile*)
DON (*C. noezliana* × *O. Othello*)
goodso'niae
Hyb.—parents not known.
JOAN (*Odontioda charlesworthi* × *Odontoglossum armainvillierense* (*ardentissimum*))
keighleyen'sis (*C. noezliana* × *Odontoglossum cirrhosum*)
LADY COLMAN (*C. noezliana* × *O. Queen of Sheba*)
lambeauia'na (*C. noezliana* × *Odontoglossum lambeauianum*)
ludit'ia
Not found, possibly the same as Odontioda Lutetia.

ORCHID GENERA (ODONTIODA), con.
LUTETIA (*C. noezliana* × *Odontoglossum luteopurpureum*)
MADELINE (*Odontioda charlesworthi* × *Odontoglossum crispum*)
PATRICIA (*Odontioda charlesworthi* × *Odontoglossum Phoebe*)
RED CROSS (*Odontioda cooksoniae* × *Odontoglossum armainvillierense* (*ardentissimum*))
ROYAL GEM (*Odontioda vuylstekeae* × *Odontoglossum armainvillierense* (*ardentissimum*))
san'derae (*C. noezliana* × *Odontoglossum percultum*)
thwaites'i (*thwaitesse; C. vulcanica* × *O. harryanum*)
vuylste'keae (*C. noezliana* × *O. pescatorei*)
ZEPHYR (*C. noezliana* × *O. wilckeanum*)

ODONTOGLOS'SUM
ADMIRAL (*pescatorei* × *Beaute Coeleste* (*eximum*))
aire'worthi (*crispum* × *lambeauianum*)
al'bum
Not found, probably a white form of either O. bictoniense or O. citrosmum.
alic'iae (*edwardi* × *spectabile*)
al'tum (*armainvillierense* × *halli*)
amab'ile (*spectabile* × *crispum*)
aman'dum (*denisonae* × *pescatorei*)
amoe'num (*concinnum; pescatorei* × *sceptrum*)
andersonia'num . . . **O. crispum andersonianum**
ardentis'simum Cy **O. armainvillierense**
armainvillieren'se (*ardentissimum; crispum* × *pescatorei*)
—xantho'tis
ashworthia'num (*edwardi* × *ossultoni*)
BEAUTE-COELESTE (*eximea; eximium; armainvillierense* × *crispum*)
bictonien'se
caul'stoni (*crispum* (*alexandrae*) × *harryanum*)
cervan'tesi
charles'worthi (*harryano-triumphans; harryanum* × *triumphans*)
cirrho'sum
citros'mum (*pendulum* ABL)
—al'bum
—rose'um
clay'ti
Not found, probably a garden hybrid.
CLYTIE (*edwardi* × *pescatorei*)
corda'tum
crawshaya'num (*halli* × *harryanum*)
crispod'nei (*crispum* × *coradieni*)
crispo-harrya'num . . **O. spectabile**
cris'pum (*alexandrae*)
—andersonia'num (*andersonianum*)
—E. B. DANE
—xantho'des
deniso'nae (*wilckeanum; crispum* × *luteopurpureum*)
DORA (*lambeauianum* × *pescatorei Duchess of Westminster*)
DORIS (*crispum* × *ossultoni*)
ed'wardi
edwardia'num . . . **O. edwardinum**
edwardi'num (*edwardianum; edwardi* × *eximium*)
el'egans (*cirrhosum* × *halli*)
ex'cellens (*pescatorei* × *triumphans*)
FASCINATOR (*crispum* × *adrianae*)
fletcheria'num (*edwardi* × *cirrhosum*)

ORCHID GENERA (ODONTOGLOSSUM), continued
GLADYS (*cirrhosum* × *spectabile*)
gran'de
Commonly known in horticulture as Baby Orchid, a name which seems so inappropriate that it has been rejected.
hall'i
harryano-trium'phans. **O. charlesworthi**
harrya'num
harvengten'se (*loochristiense; crispum* × *triumphans*)
hastila'bium
hellemen'se (*harvengtense* × *crispum*)
hiber'nicum (*halli* × *hastilabium*)
holmes'i (*spectabile* × *adrianae*)
hunnewellia'num
hyea'num (*Souvenir de Victor Hye de Crom; harryanum* × *luteopurpureum*)
illustris'simum (*lambeauianum* × *armainvillierense* (*ardentissimum*))
insleay'i
ISIDORUS (*cirrhosum* × *Rio Tinlo*)
Japonais ABL . . **O. lambeauianum**
JASPER (*crispum victoria regina* × *amabile*)
lae've
lambeauia'num (*Japonais* ABL; *rolfeae* × *crispum*)
lobb'i (*lobbiae; amabile* × *pescatorei*)
lobb'iae . . . . **O. lobbi**
loochristien'se . . . **O. harvengtense**
luteopurpu'reum
—scep'trum (*sceptrum* ABL)
macula'tum
marita'na (*rolfeae* × *sceptrum*)
mirif'icum (*crispum* × *sceptrum*)
nebulo'sum
nit'idum (*spectabile* × *denisonae* (*wilckeanum*))
no'bile ABL-Cy . . . **O. pescatorei**
oberthu'ri (*adrianae* × *harbengtense*)
ossulston'ei . . . . . . **O. ossultoni**
ossulto'ni (*ossulstonei; pescatorei* × *spectabile*)
OTHELLO (*adrianae* × *harryanum*)
pen'dulum ABL . . . **O. citrosmum**
pescato'rei (*nobile* ABL-Cy)
PHILOMENE (*rolfeae* × *percultum*)
PHOEBE (*cirrhosum* × *crispum*)
pulchel'lum
reichenheim'i
By some this is considered to be variety of O. laeve.
rolf'eae (*harryanum* × *pescatorei*)
ross'i
—ma'jus
ruckeria'num
By some considered to be a variety of O. crispum.
schlieperia'num (*schlipperianum*)
—al'bum
schlipperia'num . **O. schlieperianum**
SOLON (*adrianae* × *armainvillierense* (*ardentissimum*))
SORAMIS (*Phoebe* × *crispum*)
Souvenir de Victor Hye de Crom **O. hyeanum**
spectab'ile (*crispo-harryanum; crispum* × *harryanum*)
thomp'soni
Not found, probably the same as O. thompsonianum.
thompsonia'num (*crispum* × *edwardi*)
tigri'num (*Fascinator* × *harryanum*)
Not to be confused with O. tigrinum of Lindley (probably not in cultivation), which is Oncidium tigrinum.

ORCHID GENERA (ODONTOGLOSSUM), continued
trium'phans
triumpho'sum (*triumphans* × *cirrhosum*)
uro-skin'neri
VENILIA (*cirrhosum* × *pescatorei*)
vuylste'kei (*denisonae* × *triumphans*)
Not to be confused with Odontoglossum vuylstekeae which is the result of a different cross, O. spectabile × O. vuylstekei.
warnhamen'se (*halli* × *pescatorei*)
wilckea'num . . . . . **O. denisonae**
williamsia'num
Nat. hyb. between O. grande and O. schlieperianum.

The following cross has appeared in horticulture without a name:
cirrhosum × *crispum* . . . . . PHOEBE

ODONTO'NIA
Crosses between Miltonia and Odontoglossum.
laires'seae (*M. warscewiczi* × *O. crispum*)

ONCIDIO'DA
Crosses between Oncidium and Cochlioda.
charles'worthi (*O. incurvum* × *C. noezliana*)

ONCID'IUM
altis'simum
Some of the material in cultivation may be O. baueri of which O. altissimum of Lindley, not of Swartz, is a synonym.
amplia'tum
—ma'jus
anthocre'ne
auro'sum . . . . . . **O. excavatum**
barba'tum
bicallo'sum
caloglos'sum (*Oncidium pectorale caloglossum* ABL)
Supposed by some to be a nat. hyb. between O. forbesi and O. marshallianum.
carthaginen'se
cavendishia'num
cebollet'a
con'color
cornig'erum
cris'pum
cur'tum
divarica'tum
excava'tum (*aurosum*)
flexuo'sum
forbes'i
fusca'tum . . . **Miltonia warscewiczi**
gard'neri
graminifo'lium
—wray'i
gutta'tum ABL . . . . . **O. luridum**
harrisonia'num
hasta'tum
incur'vum
jonesia'num
krameria'num
lancea'num
leucochi'lum
lon'gipes
lu'ridum (*guttatum* ABL)
macran'thum
marshallia'num
microchi'lum
oblonga'tum
ornithorhyn'chum
—albiflo'rum (*ornithorhynchum album*)
—al'bum
O. ornithorhynchum albiflorum

ORCHID GENERA (ONCIDIUM), continued
ornithorhyn'chum rose'um
papil'lio . . . . . BUTTERFLY ORCHID
—ma'jus
pectora'le caloglos'sum ABL
O. caloglossum
phymatochi'lum
pu'bes
pulchel'lum
pulvina'tum
reichenheim'i
Not found, presumably an error and Odontoglossum not Oncidium was intended.
rog'ersi . . . . **O. varicosum rogersi**
sarco'des
sphacela'tum
—ban'rei
splen'didum (*tigrinum splendidum* ABL)
thymatochi'lum
Not found, probably an error for phymatochilum.
tigri'num
—unguicula'tum (*unguiculatum*)
unguicula'tum **O. tigrinum unguiculatum**
uniflo'rum
varico'sum
—rog'ersi (*rogersi*)
wentworthia'num

OR'CHIS . . . . ORCHIS
incarna'ta
latifo'lia . . . . MARSH O.
macula'ta . . SPOTLEAF O. (*Crowfoot*)
mas'cula . . . . MALE O. (*Aaronsbeard; Crowfoot*)
milita'ris . . . . SOLDIER O.
mo'rio . . . . MORIO O.
rivi'ni . . . . RIVINI O.
rotundifo'lia . . . . . ROUNDLEAF O.
spectab'ilis (*Galeorchis s.*). . SHOWY O.

ORNITHID'IUM
den'sum (*Maxillaria densa*)
fra'grans

ORNITHOCHI'LUS . . BIRDLIP
fus'cus . . . . BURMESE B.

PAPHIOPED'ILUM Cy
CYPRIPEDIUM

PERISTE'RIA
ela'ta . . . . HOLYGHOSTFLOWER

PESCATO'REA . **ZYGOPETALUM**
Also written Pescatoria, as in Bailey's Cyclopedia. Pescatorea is recognized by some botanists as a distinct genus.
au'rea
Not found, probably some garden form of Zygopetalum.
ceri'na Cy . . . . **Z. cerinum**
clabocho'rum . . . . **Z. klabochorum**
daya'na Cy . . . . . . **Z. dayanum**
—rhoda'cra Cy **Z. dayanum rhodacrum**
klabocho'rum Cy . . **Z. klabochorum**

PHAI'US . . . . . . **PHAJUS**

PHA'JUS
The original spelling of the name and the form now commonly accepted in scientific works is Phajus; the change is so slight that it has been deemed best to adopt the more correct spelling. ABL.
cook'sonae (*grandifolius × humbolti*)
cook'soni (*Norman; simulans × wallichi*)
grandifo'lius
incarvil'lei ABL . . . . . **P. wallichi**
macula'tus

ORCHID GENERA (PHAJUS), continued
mar'thae (*blumei × simulans*)
Norman . . . . **P. cooksoni**
sanderia'nus
Not certain, but probably the same as P. sanderi.
wal'lichi (*incarvillei* ABL)

PHALAENOP'SIS . . MOTHORCHID
amab'ilis (*grandiflora*)
—rimestadtia'na (*rimestadtiana*)
APHRODITE (*Phalaenopsis amabilis Aphrodite* ABL)
CYNTHIA
Supposed nat. hyb. between P. schilleriana and P. amabilis.
eques'tris ABL . . . . **P. rosea**
ESMERALDA
grandiflo'ra . . . . . . **P. amabilis**
grandifo'lia
Not found, probably an error for grandiflora.
leucorrho'da (*Phalaenopsis Aphrodite leucorrhoda* Cy)
Claimed by some to be a nat. hyb. between P. schilleriana and P. amabilis, by others, including Rolfe, a hyb. between P. Aphrodite and P. schilleriana, and by still others, to be a variety of P. Aphrodite, which in turn we feel is a variety of P. amabilis, a treatment reducing this to a sub-variety of that species. ABL.
lueddemannia'na
—ochra'cea
rimestadtia'na
P. amabilis rimestadtiana
A geographical form of P. amabilis.
rose'a (*equestris* ABL)
sanderia'na (*P. Aphrodite sanderiana* Cy)
Considered by some to be a nat. hyb., by others a variety of P. Aphrodite which we believe to be a variety of P. amabilis and this a sub-variety of that species. ABL.
schilleria'na
stuartia'na
viola'cea

PHOLIDO'TA
auricula'ta
Not found, possibly an error for P. articulata.
conchoid'ea . . . . **P. imbricata**
imbrica'ta (*conchoidea*)
monostach'ys
Not found.
variega'ta
Not found, probably some garden variety.

PHRAGMOPED'ILUM Cy
CYPRIPEDIUM

PHYSOSI'PHON
loddige'si (*tubatus* ABL)

PILUM'NA . . . **TRICHOPILIA**
fra'grans . . . . **T. fragrans**
—no'bilis . . . . . **T. fragrans var.**

PLATYCLI'NIS Cy
DENDROCHILUM

PLEIO'NE
Often considered only a section of Coelogyne.
birman'ica
lagena'ria
macula'ta
prae'cox wallichia'na ABL
P. wallichiana
wallichia'na (*Pleione praecox wallichiana* ABL)

ORCHID GENERA, continued
PLEUROTHAL'LIS
gel'ida
roez'li
tridenta'ta
velaticau'lis

POLYSTACH'YA
bractes'cens
Not found, probably an error for P. bracteosa.
ce'rea
lutes'cens
Not found, probably an error for P. luteola.
rufin'ula

PROMENAE'A
Often considered only a section of Zygopetalum.
citri'na (*P. xanthina* ABL-Cy; *Zygopetalum xanthinum*)

RENAN'THERA
coccin'ea
imschootia'na
—al'ba
low'ei Cy . . . . **Arachnanthe lowei**
sto'riei

RHYNCHOS'TYLIS
retu'sa (*Saccolabium retusum; S. blumei*)
—gutta'ta (*S. guttatum*)
viola'cea (*S. violaceum; Anota violacea* ABL)

RODRIGUE'ZIA ABL
BURLINGTONIA

SACCOLA'BIUM
belli'num
blu'mei . . . . **Rhynchostylis retusa**
gigan'teum . . . . . **Vanda densiflora**
gutta'tum **Rhynchostylis retusa guttata**
illus'tre
Probably Vanda densiflora illustris.
retu'sum . . . . **Rhynchostylis retusa**
viola'ceum . . . . **R. violacea**

SARCAN'THUS
williamso'ni

SARCOCHI'LUS
calceo'lus . . **Thrixspermum calceolus**
pal'lidus (*unguiculatus*)
purpu'reus . . . **Camarotis purpurea**

SARCOGLOT'TIS
pic'ta (*Spiranthes picta*)

SCHOMBURGH'IA
SCHOMBURGKIA

SCHOMBURG'KIA
cris'pa
ly'onsi
tibici'nis (*tibicina*)
undula'ta

SCUTICA'RIA
had'weni
steel'i

SELENIPE'DIUM
The plants cultivated under this name belong to Paphiopedilum and are listed under Cypripedium. The true Selenipedium of botanists is, as far as known, not in cultivation.
brown'i . . . **Cypripedium ainsworthi**
Bry'sa . . . . **C. BRYSA**
cardina'le . . . . **C. cardinale**
cauda'tum . . . . **C. caudatum**
gran'de . . . . **C. grande**
hele'nae . . . . . . **C. schroederae**
roez'li . . . . **C. longifolium hartwegi**
se'deni . . . . **C. sedeni**

ORCHID GENERA, continued

SERRAS'TYLIS

modes'ta (*Macradenia* ABL)

SIGMATOSTA'LIX

rad'icans

SOBRA'LIA

amesia'na (*wilsoni* × *xantholeuca*)
leucoxan'tha
macran'tha
—al'ba (*macrantha kienastiana* Cy)
virgina'lis
wilsonia'na
Not found, probably the same as wilsoni.

xantholeu'ca

SOPHROCATLAE'LIA

Also written Sophro-Catlealia. Crosses between Sophronitis, Cattleya, and Laelia.

dana'e (*Sophrolaelia laeta* × *C. harrisoniana*)
MEDEIA (*Sophrolaelia orpeti* × *C. bicolor*)

SOPHROCAT'TLEYA

Also written Sophro-Cattleya. Crosses between Sophronitis and Cattleya.

DORIS (*Sophronitis grandiflora* × *C. dowiana*)
PSYCHE
Hyb. not found, probably Sophrolaelia Psyche.

SOPHROLAE'LIA

Also written Sophro-Laelia. Crosses between Sophronitis and Laelia.

Phrosa . . . . PHROSO
PHROSO (*Sophrolaelia Phrosa; Sophrolaelia laeta* × *L. jongheana*)

SOPHRONI'TIS

cer'nua
coccin'ea . . . . **S. grandiflora**
grandiflo'ra (*coccinea*)

SPATHOGLOT'TIS

aureo-vieillard'i Cy . . . . **S. veitchi**
plica'ta
rubro-vieillard'i
Not found, probably some garden variety.

veitch'i (*aureo-vieillardi* Cy; *aurea* × *vieillardi*)

STANHO'PEA

amesia'na (*lowi* ABL-Cy)
buceph'alus
devonien'sis
eburne'a
grandiflo'ra
This name cannot be placed with certainty. S. grandiflora, of Lindley, is the same as S. eburnea while S. grandiflora of the younger Reichenbach equals S. bucephalus, both of which are in cultivation.

insig'nis
langleyen'sis
Not found, probably a garden form.

low'i ABL-Cy . . . . . **S. amesiana**
ocula'ta
reichenbachia'na
tigri'na
—au'rea
—venus'ta

STENOGLOT'TIS

fimbria'ta
longifo'lia

TAI'NIA (*ASCOTAINIA*)

viridifus'ca

TETRAMI'CRA . . **LEPTOTES**

ORCHID GENERA, continued

THRIXSPER'MUM

calceo'lus (*Sarcochilus calceolus*)

THU'NIA

Joined by some to Phajus.

al'ba
benson'iae (*alba bensoniae* ABL)
marshallia'na (*alba marshalliana* ABL)
wrigleya'na (*bensoniae* × *marshalliana*)
The more correct name (if this form is recognized) is T. veitchiana, but our feeling is that it is nothing but a cross between two plants which we consider to be only varieties of T. alba and is therefore scarcely worthy of notice.

TRICHOPI'LIA

coccin'ea (*marginata* ABL-Cy)
—margina'ta (*marginata* ABL-Cy)
fra'grans (*Pilumna fragrans*)
gigan'tea
Not found.

hen'nesi . . . . **T. hennisiana**
hennisia'na (*hennesi*)
her'misi
Not found, perhaps an error for T. hennisi which is the same as T. hennisiana.

sua'vis
tor'tilis

TRICHOS'MA Cy . . . **ERIA**
sua'vis Cy . . . . **E. coronaria**

TRIGONID'IUM

amesia'num
Not found, probably a garden variety.

egertonia'num

VAN'DA

amesia'na
bate'mani (*Vandopsis lissochiloides* ABL-Cy)
ben'soni
box'alli Cy . . . **V. lamellata boxalli**
caeru'lea (*coerulea* ABL)
—albes'cens
—roehrsia'na
caerules'cens (*coerulescens* ABL)
crista'ta
denisonia'na (*dennisoniae*)
denniso'niae . . . . **V. denisoniana**
densiflo'ra (*Saccolabium giganteum*)
—illus'tris
gigan'tea (*Vandopsis gigantea* ABL-Cy; *Stauropsis gigantea*)
hookeria'na
joaqui'miae (*Miss Joaquim; hookeriana* × *teres*)
kimballia'na
lamella'ta
—box'alli (*boxalli* Cy)
limba'ta
low'ei . . . . . . **Arachnanthe lowei**
luson'ica . . . . **V. luzonica**
luzon'ica (*lusonica*)
Miss Joaquim . . . . **V. joaquimiae**
par'ishi
—mariottia'na
rox'burghi (*tessellata* ABL)
sanderia'na (*Euanthe sanderiana* ABL)
sua'vis (*tricolor suavis* Cy)
te'res
—al'ba
—anderso'ni
—*auro'ra* . . . . . **V. teres aurorea**
—aurore'a (*teres aurora*)
—can'dida
—tri'color
Probably the same as V. tricolor.

ORCHID GENERA (VANDA), continued

tessella'ta ABL . . . . **V. roxburghi**
tri'color
—dodg'soni
—planila'bris
—*sua'vis* . . . . **V. suavis**

VANDOP'SIS

lissochiloi'des

VANIL'LA . . . . VANILLA

aromat'ica . . . SOUTH AMERICAN V.
inodo'ra . . . . TRINIDAD V.
planifo'lia (*fragrans*) . MEXICAN V.
tahiten'sis . . . . TAHITI V.

WARSCEWICZEL'LA

By many joined to Zygopetalum.

aromat'ica
Little known.

dis'color
wend'landi

XYLO'BIUM

hyacinthi'num (*Maxillaria hyacinthina*)
leontoglos'sum

ZYGOPET'ALUM

Including Bollea and Pescatorea.

burk'ei
burt'i (*Huntleya burti* Cy; *Batemania burti*)
ceri'num (*Pescatorea cerina* Cy)
coeles'te (*Bollea coelestis* Cy)
crini'tum . . . **Z. mackayi crinitum**
daya'num (*Pescatorea dayana* Cy)
—rhoda'crum (*Pescatorea dayana rhodacra* Cy)
gairia'num
gautier'i . . . . **Z. maxillare gautieri**
interme'dium **Z. mackayi intermedium**
There is also a valid Z. intermedium which apparently is not in cultivation.

klabocho'rum (*Pescatorea clabochorum; P. klabochorum* Cy)
lalind'ei (*Bollea lalindei* Cy)
mackay'i
—crini'tum (*crinitum* Cy)
—interme'dium (*intermedium*)
maxilla're gautier'i (*gautieri* Cy)
xanthi'num . . . **Promenaea citrina**

ORCHID GENERA, HARDY TERRESTRIAL GROUP.

For convenience of reference the genera, species and varieties of Hardy Terrestrial Orchids are here brought together in one consolidated list.

APLEC'TRUM . . . PUTTYROOT

hyema'le (*shorti*) . . . . PUTTYROOT

ARETHU'SA . . . . . ARETHUSA

bulbo'sa (*spicata*) . . . . . ARETHUSA

BLEPHARIGLOT'TIS **HABENARIA**

CALOPO'GON (*LIMODORUM*) GRASSPINK ORCHID

pulchel'lus (*Limodorum pulchellum; L. tuberosum* L., in part) GRASSPINK O.

CALYP'SO (*CYTHEREA*) CALYPSO

bulbo'sa (*borealis; Cytherea bulbosa*) CALYPSO

CEPHALAN'THERA (*EBUROPHYTON*) . . . . . PHANTOMORCHID

aus'tinae (*oregana*) . . . AUSTIN P.

CORALLORRHI'ZA . CORALROOT

macula'ta (*multiflora*) . . SPOTTED C.
mertensia'na . . . . . . PACIFIC C.
odontorhi'za . . . . LATE C.
stria'ta (*bigelovi*) . . . . HOODED C.

ORCHID GENERA, Hardy Terrestrial Group (CORALLORRHIZA), continued
trif'ida . . . . . EARLY CORALROOT
wisteria'na . . . . . . WISTER C.

CYPRIPE'DIUM . . . LADYSLIPPER
acau'le (*Fissipes acaulis*) . . . PINK L.
arieti'num . . . . . . RAMSHEAD L.
califor'nicum . . . . . CALIFORNIA L.
can'didum . . . . WHITE L.
fascicula'tum . . . . BROWNIE L.
monta'num . . . . . MOUNTAIN L.
parviflo'rum . . . . . SMALLYELLOW L.
—pubes'cens (*C. pubescens; C. veganum*) . . . . LARGEYELLOW L.
passeri'num . . . . . . CANADA L.
regi'nae (*hirsutum; spectabile*) SHOWY L.

CYTHERE'A . . . . **CALYPSO**
EBUROPHY'TON **CEPHALANTHERA**

EPIPAC'TIS (*SERAPIAS*) EPIPACTIS
gigan'tea (*Amesia g.; Serapias g.*) STREAM E.
latifo'lia (*S. helleborine*) BROADLEAF E.

FIS'SIPES . . . **CYPRIPEDIUM**
Galeor'chis spectab'ilis . . **Orchis s.**

GOOD'YERA (*PERAMIUM*) RATTLESNAKEPLANTAIN
dawsonia'na (*dawsoni; Haemaria discolor d.; H. dawsoniana*) DAWSON R.
decip'iens (*menziesi; Epipactis d.; Peramium d.*) . . . . WESTERN R.
pubes'cens (*Epipactis p.; Peramium p.*) DOWNY R.
re'pens (*Epipactis r.*) . CREEPING R.
—ophioi'des (*Epipactis r. o.; Peramium o.*)
tessela'ta (*Epipactis t.; Peramium tesselatum*) . . . . . CHECKERED R.

GYROSTA'CHIS; GYROSTA'CHYS . . . . . **SPIRANTHES**
stric'ta . . . . . . **S. romanzoffiana**

HABENA'RIA (*BLEPHARIGLOTTIS; LIMNORCHIS; LYSIAS; LYSIELLA*) . . . . HABENARIA
×an'drewsi (*lacera × psycodes*) ANDREWS FRINGEORCHID
blephariglot'tis (*Blephariglottis b.*) WHITE F.
bractea'ta . . . . **H. viridis b.**
×can'byi (*blephariglottis × cristata*) CANBY F.
cilia'ris (*Blephariglottis c.*). YELLOW F.
clavella'ta . SMALLGREEN WOODORCHID
crista'ta (*Blephariglottis c.*)CRESTED H.
dilata'ta . . . . . WHITE BOGORCHID
el'egans . . CALIFORNIA HILLSIDE H.
fimbria'ta LARGEPURPLE FRINGEORCHID
fla'va (*virescens*) . . . . TUBERCLE H.
grandiflo'ra (*Blephariglottis g.*) BIGFLOWER FRINGEORCHID
hook'eri (*Lysias hookeriana*) HOOKER H.
hyperbo'rea (*Limnorchis h.*) NORTHERN GREEN H.
integ'ra
lac'era (*Blephariglottis l.*)
leucophae'a (*Blephariglottis l.*) PRAIRIE F.
leucosta'chys . . . MILKWHITE H.
macrophyl'la . . . . . . BIGLEAF H.
marit'ima . . . . SEACLIFF H.
michae'li . . . . MICHAEL H.
niv'ea . . . . SNOWY H.

ORCHID GENERA, Hardy Terrestrial Group (HABENARIA), continued
obtusa'ta (*Lysiella o.*)
peramoe'na (*Blephariglottis p.*)
psyco'des SMALLPURPLE FRINGEORCHID
sacca'ta . . . . . MODOC HABENARIA
scutella'ta . . . . SHIELD H.
sparsiflo'ra . . . . CANYON H.
unalascen'sis . . . . . ALASKA H.
vires'cens . . . . **H. flava**
vir'idis
—bractea'ta (*H. bracteata; Coeloglossum bracteatum*) . . . . . . SATYR H.

HEXALEC'TRIS
spica'ta (*aphylla*) . CRESTEDCORALROOT

IBID'IUM . . . **SPIRANTHES**
stric'tum . . . . **S. romanzoffianum**

ISO'TRIA . . . . . **POGONIA**
LIMNOR'CHIS . **HABENARIA**
LIMODO'RUM . . **CALOPOGON**
tubero'sum L., in part . . **C. pulchellus**

LIPA'RIS . . . . . . TWAYBLADE
liliifo'lia . . . . LILY T.
loes'eli . . . . LOESEL T.

LIS'TERA (*OPHRYS*) . . LISTERA
auricula'ta . . . . . CEDARSWAMP L.
austra'lis . . . . . . ATLANTIC L.
cauri'na . . . . NORTHWEST L.
convallarioi'des (*Ophrys c.*)
corda'ta . . . . NORTHERN L.
small'i . . . . SMALLS L.

LY'SIAS; LYSIEL'LA **HABENARIA**

MALAX'IS (*MICROSTYLIS*) ADDERMOUTH ORCHID
monophyl'los (*Microstylis monophylla*) SHEATH A.O.
paludo'sa . . . . LEAFY A. O.
unifo'lia (*M. ophioglossoides*) ONELEAF A. O.

MICROS'TYLIS . . **MALAXIS**
O'PHRYS . . . . . . **LISTERA**

OR'CHIS . . . . ORCHIS
rotundifo'lia . . . . . ROUNDLEAF O.
spectab'ilis (*Galeorchis s.*) . SHOWY O.

PERAM'IUM . . **GOODYERA**

POGO'NIA (*ISOTRIA; TRIPHORA*) . . . . . POGONIA
affi'nis (*Isotria a.*) . . FULLCREST P.
divarica'ta . . . . . . SOUTHERN P.
ophioglossoi'des . . . . . ROSE P.
trianthoph'ora (*pendula; Triphora p.; T. trianthophora*) . . DROOPING P.
verticilla'ta (*Isotria v.*) . ATLANTIC P.

SERAP'IAS . . . . **EPIPACTIS**

SPIRAN'THES (*GYROSTACHIS; GYROSTACHYS; IBIDIUM*) |w LADIESTRESSES
beck'i . . . . BECKS L.
brevifo'lia . . . . . SHORTLEAF L.
cer'nua (*Ibidium cernuum*)NODDING L.
grac'ilis (*Ibidium gracile*). SLENDER L.
×interme'dia (*gracilis × vernalis*)
lu'cida . . . . WILDLEAF L.
odora'ta . . . . FRAGRANT L.
oval'is . . . . OCTOBER L.
pic'ta (*Sarcoglottis p.*) . . PAINTED L.
porrifo'lia . . . . CREAMY L.
prae'cox . . . . SOUTHERN L.
romanzoffia'na (*Gyrostachis r.; G. stricta; Ibidium romanzoffianum; I. strictum*) |w . . . . . CONTINENTAL L.
verna'lis . . . . UPLAND L.

ORCHID GENERA, Hardy Terrestrial Group, continued

TIPULA'RIA . . CRANEFLYORCHID
unifo'lia (*discolor*) . . AMERICAN C.

TRI'PHORA . . . . **POGONIA**

OR'CHIS . . . . ORCHIS
See **ORCHID GENERA.**

ORCHYL'LIUM
alpi'num (*Utricularia alpina; U. montana* Jacq., *not* Poir.)

ORCUT'TIA . . . . ORCUTTIA
See **GRASS GENERA.**

OREGONGRAPE . . **Mahonia aquifolium**
PURPLE O. . . . . **M. a. juglandifolia**
SLIM O. . . . . **M. a. gracilis**

Oregon-myrtle . . CALIFORNIALAUREL: **Umbellularia californica**

OREOCA'RYA . . **CRYPTANTHA**
glomera'ta . . . . **C. sheldoni**
suffrutico'sa . . . . **C. jamesi**

OREOCE'REUS
See **CACTUS GENERA.**

OREOCH'ARIS
primuloi'des

OREOCHRY'SUM . . . **SOLIDAGO**

OREODAPH'NE . . . . OREODAPHNE
foe'tens . . . . RAINTREE O.

OREODOX'A . . . . . **ROYSTONEA**
See **PALM GENERA.**

OREOPAN'AX . . . . . . OREOPANAX
nymphaeifo'lius
xalapen'sis (*thibauti*) . . XALAPA O.

OREOSTEM'MA . . . . . . **ASTER**

OREOX'IS (*CYMOPTERUS*) OREOXIS
alpi'na . . . . ALPINE O.

ORGANPIPE-CACTUS **Pachycereus marginatus**

ORIENTAL CHERRY
See CHERRIES, ORIENTAL FLOWERING.

ORIENTAL POPPY
See **PAPAVER.**

ORIENTALWOOD . **Endiandra palmerstoni**

ORIENTVINE . . . . **Sinomenium**

ORIG'ANUM . . . . . ORIGANUM
dictam'nus . . . . CRETE-DITTANY O. (*Dittany of Crete*)
heracleot'icum . . . . WINTER O. (*Winter Marjoram*)
hir'tum (*smyrnaeum* in part) HAIRY O.
majora'na . . . **Majorana hortensis**
oni'tes . . . . **Majorana o.**
pulchel'lum
sipyle'um (*hybridum*) MOUNTSIPYLOS O.
smyrnae'um . . **O. hirtum; O. vulgare**
tournefort'i . . . . TOURNEFORT O.
vulga're (*smyrnaeum* in part) COMMON O. (*Wild Marjoram*)
—canes'cens . . . . . . HOARY C.O.
₵GOLDLEAF (*aureum*) HV. **O. vulgare**

ORI'TES
excel'sa

ORIX'A . . . . ORIXA
japon'ica . . . . . . JAPANESE O.

ORMO'SIA . . . . ORMOSIA
coarcta'ta . . . . GUIANA O.
monosper'ma (*dasycarpa*) BEADTREE O.

ORNITHID'IUM
See **ORCHID GENERA.**

ORNITHOCHI'LUS . . . . . BIRDLIP
See **ORCHID GENERA.**

ORNITHOG'ALUM STAR-OF-BETHLEHEM
ara'bicum . . . . ARABIAN S.
au'reum . . . . . . **O. thyrsoides a.**
cauda'tum . . . . . . WHIPLASH S.
graminifo'lium . . . . . . GRASSY S.
×**kewen'se** (*thyrsoides* × *t. aureum*)
KEW CHINKERICHEE
lac'teum (*O. thyrsoides l.*) . . MILK S.
₵DOUBLE (*plenum*) HV.
narbonen'se . . . . . NARBONNE S.
nu'tans . . . . NODDING S.
pyramida'le (*O. narbonense p.*)
PYRAMID S.
specio'sum . . . . SHOWY S.
splen'dens . . . . GLOWING S.
suave'olens . . . . SWEET S.
thunbergia'num . . . THUNBERG S.
thyrsoi'des . . CAPE CHINKERICHEE
—**au'reum** (*O. aureum*) GOLDEN C.C.
—*lac'teum* . . . . **O. lacteum**
umbella'tum . . . . . . COMMON S.

ORNITH'OPUS . . . . . SERRADELLA
perpusil'lus . . . . LITTLE S.
sati'vus . . . . COMMON S.

Or'nus europae'a . . . **Fraxinus ornus**

OROBAN'CHE |w . . . . BROOMRAPE
ludovicia'na |w . . . . LOUISIANA B.
mi'nor . . . . CLOVER B.
ramo'sa . . . . HEMP B.
uniflo'ra . . . . **Thalesia u.**

O'ROBUS . . . **LATHYRUS; VICIA**
lathyroi'des . . . . . . **V. oroboides**
lute'us . . . . **L. luteus**
ni'ger . . . . **L. niger**
rose'us . . . . **L. roseus**
ver'nus . . . . **L. vernus**

OROGE'NIA
linearifo'lia . . . . . INDIANPOTATO

ORON'TIUM |w . . . . . GOLDENCLUB
aquat'icum |w . . . . . GOLDENCLUB

OROPHA'CA . . . . **ASTRAGALUS**
caespito'sa . . . . **A. triphyllus**

OROSTACH'YS . . . . . . **SEDUM**
See **SUCCULENTS.**

OROX'YLUM (*OROXYLON*)
INDIA TRUMPETFLOWER
The spelling of this name in literature is highly inconsistent. Professor Rehder, under date of September 5, 1940, furnishes the Editorial Committee with this note: "Oroxylum seems to be the correct spelling. . . . Pfeiffer in his Nomenclator credits Oroxylum to Ventenat (the author of the genus) and Oroxylon to Steudel as a change in spelling made by the latter."
fla'vum . . **Radermachia pentandra**
in'dicum . . . . INDIA T.

ORO'YA
See **CACTUS GENERA.**

ORPHANIDE'SIA
gaultherioi'des

ORPINE . . . . **Telephium**
COMMON O. . . . . **T. imperati**

ORTHOCAR'PUS . . . . OWLCLOVER
attenua'tus . . . VALLEYTASSELS O.
densiflo'rus

ORTHOCARPUS, continued
erian'thus . JOHNNYTUCK OWLCLOVER
lithospermoi'des . . . CREAMSACS O.
lute'us . . . . YELLOW O.
purpuras'cens . . . . . ESCOBITA O.
purpureo-al'bus . . PURPLEWHITE O.
tol'miei . . . . TOLMIE O.
versicol'or . . . . . VERSICOLOR O.

ORTHOSI'PHON . . . . . JAVATEA
grandiflo'rus (*stamineus*) BIGFLOWER J.

ORTHROSAN'THUS . DAWNFLOWER
chimboracen'sis . . CHIMBORAZO D.

ORY'ZA . . . . RICE
See **CEREALS** and **GRASS GENERA.**

ORYZOP'SIS . . . . . . RICEGRASS
See **GRASS GENERA.**

OSAGEORANGE . **Maclura; M. pomifera**
THORNLESS O. . . . . **M. p. inermis**

OSCULA'RIA
MESEMBRYANTHEMUM
See **SUCCULENTS.**

Osier, Common . . . WILLOW, BASKET:
Salix viminalis

OSMAN'THUS . . . . . OSMANTHUS
america'nus (*Olea americana*)
DEVILWOOD O.
aquifo'lium . . . . . . **O. ilicifolius**
—*myrtifo'lius* . . . **O. i. myrtifolius**
arma'tus . . . . CHINESE O.
auranti'acus . . . . . . ORANGE O.
delava'yi . . . . DELAVAY O.
florida'nus . . . . . HAMMOCK O.
for'resti . . . . FORRESTS O.
∞**fortun'ei** (*fragrans* × *ilicifolius*)
∞FORTUNES O.
fra'grans (*Olea f.*) . . . . . SWEET O.
₵AUREUS. HV.
ilicifo'lius (*aquifolium; Olea a.; Olea ilicifolia*) . . . . HOLLY O.
—**myrtifo'lius** (*O. aquifolium m.*)
MYRTLE H.O.
—**rotundifo'lius** . . ROUNDLEAF H.O.
₵GOLDRIM (*aureomarginatus; aureus*) HV. O. ilicifolius
₵PURPLEGREEN (*atropurpureus; purpurascens; purpureus*)
₵SILVERRIM (*argenteomarginatus; argenteus; variegatus*)
serrula'tus . . . . . . SAWTOOTH O.
sua'vis

OSMANTHUS . . . . **Osmanthus**
CHINESE O. . . . . **O. armatus**
DELAVAY O. . . . . **O. delavayi**
DEVILWOOD O. . . . . **O. americanus**
FORRESTS O. . . . . **O. forresti**
∞FORTUNES O. . . . . . ∞**O. fortunei**
HAMMOCK O. . . . . . . **O. floridanus**
HOLLY O. . . . . **O. ilicifolius**
MYRTLE H. O. . . . . **O. i. myrtifolius**
ORANGE O. . . . . . . **O. aurantiacus**
ROUNDLEAF HOLLY O.
O. ilicifolius rotundifolius
SAWTOOTH O. . . . . . **O. serrulatus**
SWEET O. . . . . **O. fragrans**

∞**OSMA'REA** (*PHILLYREA* × *SIPHONOSMANTHUS*) ∞OSMAREA
∞**burk'woodi** (*P. decora* × *S. delavayi*)
∞BURKWOOD O.

OSMARO'NIA (*NUTTALLIA* Torr. & Gray, *not* Barton)
cerasifor'mis (*Nuttallia c.*) . OSOBERRY

OSMORHI'ZA |w . . . . SWEETROOT
clay'toni (*brevistylis*) . . CLAYTON S.
divarica'ta . . . . . . SPREADING S.
longis'tylis . . . . . . LONGSTYLE S.
obtu'sa . . . . BLUNTSEED S.
occidenta'lis . . . . . . SWEETANISE

OSMUN'DA
See **FERN GENERA.**

OSOBERRY . . . **Osmaronia cerasiformis**

OSTEOME'LES . . . . . BONYBERRY
anthyllidifo'lia . . . . POLYNESIAN B.
schweri'nae . . . . CHINESE B.
—**microphyl'la** . . . LITTLELEAF C.B.
subrotun'da . . . . . ROUNDLEAF B.

OSTERDA'MIA . . . . . . **ZOYSIA**
See **GRASS GENERA.**

OSTO'DES
panicula'ta

OSTRICHFERN . . . **Pteretis nodulosa**

OSTROWS'KIA . . . . . GIANTBELL
magnif'ica . . . . GIANTBELL

OS'TRYA |w . . . . . . HOPHORNBEAM
carpinifo'lia . . . . EUROPEAN H.
guatemalen'sis . . . . GUATEMALA H.
japon'ica . . . . JAPANESE H.
knowl'toni . . . . . . KNOWLTON H.
virginia'na (*virginica*) |w AMERICAN H.
—**glandulo'sa** . . . NORTHERN A.H.
—**la'sia** . . . . WOOLLY A.H.

OSTRYOP'SIS
davidia'na
no'bilis

Otaheiteapple . . . . AMBARELLA:
Spondias cytherea; OHIA **Syzygium malaccense**

OTHA'KE . . . . OTHAKE
Some botanists prefer to regard this as a synonym of Polypteris.
sphacela'tum (*Palafoxia hookeriana; Polypteris h.*)
texa'num (*Palafoxia texana; Polypteris t.*) . . . . TEXAS O.

OTHON'NA . . . . OTHONNA
See **SUCCULENTS.**

OTHONNOP'SIS
cheirifo'lia

OTTE'LIA . . . . OTTELIA
alismoi'des . . . WATERPLANTAIN O.

OURATE'A
agrophyl'la

OURIS'IA . . . . OURISIA
coccin'ea . . . . SCARLET O.
el'egans
macrocar'pa . . . . EVERGREEN O.
macrophyl'la . . . NEWZEALAND O.

Ouroupa'ria gambir' . . . . . **Uncaria g.**

OUVIRAN'DRA . . **APONOGETON**

OWALAOILTREE **Pentaclethra macrophylla**

OWE'NIA . . . . EMUPLUM
acid'ula . . . . MOOLEY E.
cepiodo'ra . . . . . . ONIONWOOD E.
cerasif'era . . . . CHERRY E.
veno'sa . . . . . . CROWSAPPLE E.

OWLCLOVER . . . . **Orthocarpus**
CREAMSACS O. . . **O. lithospermoides**
ESCOBITA O. . . . . **O. purpurascens**
JOHNNYTUCK O. . . . . **O. erianthus**
PURPLEWHITE O. . . **O. purpureo-albus**

OWLCLOVER, continued
TOLMIE O. . . . . . **Orthocarpus tolmiei**
VALLEYTASSELS O. . . **O. attenuatus**
VERSICOLOR O. . . . . . **O. versicolor**
YELLOW O. . . . . **O. luteus**

OX'ALIS (*IONOXALIS; XANTHOXALIS*) |w . . . . . . OXALIS
The correct accent of the Latin name is on the first syllable, though the English name is frequently accented on the second syllable (Oxal'is).

acetosel'la . . . . . WOODSORREL O.
adenophyl'la
albiflo'ra . . . . **O. variabilis**
america'na . . . . **O. montana**
bowiea'na (*bowiei*) . . . . BOWIE O. (*Cape Shamrock*)
bupleurifo'lia . . . . BRAZILBUSH O.
califor'nica (*Xanthoxalis c.*) CALIFORNIA O.
carno'sa . . . . . . SPINDLEROOT O.
cer'nua . . . . BUTTERCUP O.
cornicula'ta (*Xanthoxalis c.*) |w CREEPING O.
By some botanists this species is united with O. europaea.
₵PURPLEBED (*atropurpurea; tropaeoloides; Nasturtium*). HV.
crena'ta . . . . OKA O.
cymo'sa |w
decaphyl'la . . . . . . TENLEAF O.
dep'pei . . . . ROSETTE O.
drum'mondi . . . . . DRUMMOND O.
enneaphyl'la . . . . . NINELEAF O.
₵ROSEA. HV.
europae'a . . . EUROPEAN YELLOW O.
floribun'da Hort.
flor'ida (*filipes*) . . . . TRANSVAAL O.
heterophyl'la
hir'ta
₵ROSEA. HV.
lasian'dra . . . . PRIMROSE O.
magellan'ica . . . . . MAGELLAN O.
martia'na . . . . MARTIUS O.
monta'na (*americana*) AMERICAN WOODSORREL O.
orega'na . . . . OREGON O.
ortgies'i . . . . ORTGIES O.
rose'a . . . . ROSY O.
This name is often misapplied to O. rubra and to O. enneaphylla HV. Rosea.
ru'bra . . . . WINDOWBOX O.
stric'ta (*Xanthoxalis s.*) |w COMMON YELLOW O.
tetraphyl'la (*Ionoxalis t.*) FOURLEAF O.
valdivien'sis . . . . CHILEAN O.
variab'ilis (*albiflora*) . . . . CAPE O.
viola'cea (*Ionoxalis v.*) |w VIOLET WOODSORREL O.

OXALIS . . . . **Oxalis**
AMERICAN WOODSORREL O. **O. montana**
BOWIE O. . . . . **O. bowieana**
BRAZILBUSH O. . . . . **O. bupleurifolia**
BUTTERCUP O. . . . . **O. cernua**
CALIFORNIA O. . . . . . **O. californica**
CAPE O. . . . . **O. variabilis**
CHILEAN O. . . . . . . **O. valdiviensis**
COMMON YELLOW O. . . . . **O. stricta**
CREEPING O. . . . . . . **O. corniculata**
DRUMMOND O. . . . . . **O. drummondi**
EUROPEAN YELLOW O. . **O. europaea**
FOURLEAF O. . . . . . **O. tetraphylla**
MAGELLAN O. . . . . . **O. magellanica**
MARTIUS O. . . . . **O. martiana**
NINELEAF O. . . . . . **O. enneaphylla**
OKA O. . . . . **O. crenata**

OXALIS, continued
OREGON O. . . . . **Oxalis oregana**
ORTGIES O. . . . . **O. ortgiesi**
PRIMROSE O. . . . . . . **O. lasiandra**
ROSETTE O. . . . . **O. deppei**
ROSY O. . . . . **O. rosea**
SPINDLEROOT O. . . . . **O. carnosa**
TENLEAF O. . . . . . **O. decaphylla**
TRANSVAAL O. . . . . . . **O. florida**
VIOLET WOODSORREL O. . **O. violacea**
WINDOWBOX O. . . . . . . **O. rubra**
WOODSORREL O. . . . **O. acetosella**

OXAN'DRA . . . . LANCEWOOD
lanceola'ta . . . . LANCEWOOD

OXAN'THERA . . . . . OXANTHERA
fra'grans . . . . FRAGRANT O.
neocaledo'nica . . NEWCALEDONIA O. (*Bigleaf O.; Falseorange*)

OXE'RA
pulchel'la

OXEYE . . . . **Buphthalmum**
HEARTLEAF O. . . . . **B. speciosum**
SHOWY O. . . . . . **B. grandiflorum**
TALL O. . . . . . **B. speciosissimum**
WILLOWLEAF O. . . . **B. salicifolium**

OXEYEDAISY **Chrysanthemum leucanthemum**
FIELD O. . . . . **C. l. pinnatifidum**
NIPPON O. . . . . . . **C. nipponicum**

OXTONGUE . . . . **Picris**
BRISTLY O. . . . . . . **P. echioides**
HAWKWEED O. . . . . . **P. hieracioides**

OXYAN'THUS . . . . . NEEDLESTAR
isth'mia . . . . . **Posoqueria latifolia**
natalen'sis . . . . NATAL N.
tubiflo'rus . . . . EARLEAF N.

Oxyba'phus visco'sa . . . . **Mirabilis v.**

OXYCOC'CUS (*OXYCOCCOS* Auth.) **VACCINIUM**
Cranberries (Oxycoccus) are placed in a distinct genus by some botanists.
interme'dius **V. oxycoccos intermedium**
palus'tris . . . . **V. oxycoccos**
—interme'dius . . . **V. o. intermedium**

OXYDEN'DRUM |w . . . . SOURWOOD
arbo'reum (*Andromeda arborea*) |w SOURWOOD

OXYLO'BIUM . . . . . . POINTEDPOD
callista'chys . . . WESTAUSTRALIA P.
cordifo'lium . . . . . HEARTLEAF P.
ellip'ticum . . . . TASMANIA P.
procum'bens . . . . TRAILING P.

OXYLO'BUS
arbutifo'lius

OXYPET'ALUM . . . . OXYPETALUM
coeru'leum . . . . SKYBLUE O.

OXYP'OLIS |w . . . . . . COWBANE
fend'leri . . . . FENDLER C.
filifor'mis |w . . . . . LEAFLESS C.
occidenta'lis . . . . PACIFIC C.
rigid'ior |w . . . . STIFF C.

OXYR'IA . . . . . MOUNTAINSORREL
di'gyna . . . . ALPINE M.

OXYTE'NIA . . . . OXYTENIA
acero'sa . . . . PRICKLY O.

OXYTHE'CA . . . . OXYTHECA
dendroi'dea . . . . NARROWLEAF O.
perfolia'ta . . . . . . THOROWORT O.
wat'soni . . . . WATSON O.

OXYT'ROPIS (*ARAGALLUS*) |w CRAZYWEED
Some botanists prefer to unite this genus with the Loco-Poisonweed-Milkvetch genus, Astragalus. Species of Oxytropis known to be harmless are called Pointvetch.

albiflo'ra . . . . . . **O. saximontana**
argenta'ta
bes'seyi . . . . BESSEY POINTVETCH
blankinship'i (*Aragallus b.*) BLANKINSHIP C.
campes'tris . . . . PLAINS C.
deflex'a (*Aragallus deflexus*) DROPPOD C.
hal'leri . . . . **O. uralensis**
johannen'sis . . . . ST.JOHNS C.
lago'pus (*Aragallus l.*) . HARESFOOT C.
lam'berti (*Aragallus l.; Astragalus l.*) LAMBERT C.
macoun'i (*spicata* (Hook.) Standl., *not* (Pall.) O. & B. Fedtsch.; *Aragallus m.*) . . . . SPIKE C.
ochroleu'ca . . . CREAMFLOWER C.
richardso'ni . . . . . . WHORLED C.
saximonta'na (*albiflora; Aragallus albiflorus* A. Nels., *not* Bunge) ROCKYMOUNTAIN C.
seric'ea (*Aragallus sericeus*) . SILKY C.
spica'ta (Hook.) Standl., *not* (Pall.) O. & B. Fedtsch. . . . . . **O. macouni**
splen'dens . . . . SHOWY C.
tenel'la (*Astragalus rubyi*) . RUBY C.
uralen'sis (*halleri*) . . . . URAL C.
villo'sa (*Aragallus villosus*) . HAIRY C.
viscid'ula (*Aragallus viscidulus*) YELLOWHAIR C.

Oxyu'ra chrysanthemoi'des . . . **Layia c.**

OYSTERNUTTREE, COMMON **Telfairia occidentalis**

OYSTERPLANT . . . . **Scolymus**
SPANISH O. . . . . . **S. hispanicus**

Oysterplant . . . . SALSIFY, especially SALSIFY, VEGETABLE-OYSTER: **Tragopogon porrifolius**; RHOEO, OYSTER: **Rhoeo discolor**

OYSTERWOOD . . . . **Gymnanthes**
SHINY O. . . . . **G. lucida**

OZARKGRASS . . . **Limnodea arkansana**

OZOTHAM'NUS (*HELICHRYSUM* in part) . . . . . . OZOTHAMNUS
Botanists are not agreed as to the validity of this shrubby Australian genus, as distinguished from Helichrysum.
antenna'ria (*Helichrysum antennarium*) CUDWEED O.
ledifo'lius (*Helichrysum ledifolium*) LEDUMLEAF O.
rosmarinifo'lius **Helichrysum diosmaefolium**

PACAYA . . . . **Chamaedorea; Edanthe**
GUATEMALA P. . . **C. geonomaeformis**
MONKEYTAIL P. . . . **C. graminifolia**
OERSTED P. . . . . **C. pacaya**
TEPEJILOTE P. . . . . . **E. tepejilote**
VERAPAZ P. . . . . . . **E. veraepacis**

PACHI'RA . . . . PACHIRA
aquat'ica . . . GUIANA-CHESTNUT P.
fastuo'sa . . . . APOMPO P.
insig'nis . . . . TRINIDAD P.

PACHIS'TIMA (*PACHYSTIMA*) |w PACHISTIMA
can'byi . . . . CANBY P.
myrsini'tes |w . . . . MYRTLE P.

PACHYCE'REUS
See **CACTUS GENERA.**

PACHYLO'PHUS . . . **OENOTHERA**
crini'tus . . . . **O. caespitosa crinita**
margina'tus . . . . **O. c. marginata**

PACHYPHY'TUM
See **SUCCULENTS.**

PACHYRHI'ZUS . . . . . . YAMBEAN
angula'tus . . . . WAYAKA Y.
ero'sus
palmatilo'bus
tubero'sus . . . . . WESTINDIES Y.

PACHYSAN'DRA . . . PACHYSANDRA
axilla'ris . . . . . . CHINASPURGE P.
procum'bens . . . . . ALLEGANY P.
termina'lis . . . . JAPANESE P.
¢VARIEGATED (*variegata*) HV.

PACHYSTACH'YS . . CARDINALSGUARD
coccin'ea (*Jacobinia c.*) BLACKSTICK C.

PACHYSTE'GIA
insig'nis (*Olearia i.*)

PACHYS'TIMA . . **PACHISTIMA**

∞**PACHYVE'RIA** (*Echeveria* × *Pachyphytum*) . . . . . . ∞PACHYVERIA
See **SUCCULENTS.**

PACOUR'IA
capen'sis

PADAUK . . . . **Pterocarpus**
AFRICAN P. . . . . **P. soyauxi**
ANDAMAN P. . . . . . **P. dalbergioides**
ANGOLA P. . . . . **P. angolensis**
BURMACOAST P. . . . . . . **P. indicus**
BURMA P. . . . . . . **P. macrocarpus**
DRAGONSBLOOD P. . . . . . . **P. draco**
SANDALWOOD P. . . . . . **P. santalinus**
VENGAI P. . . . . **P. marsupium**
WESTAFRICAN P. . . . . . **P. erinaceus**

PADRITREE . . . . . . **Stereospermum**
FRINGED P. . . . . . **S. fimbriatum**

PA'DUS . . . . **PRUNUS**
racemo'sa . . . . **P. padus**

PAEDE'RIA . . . . FEVERVINE
scan'dens (*chinensis; foetida* Thunb., *not* L.; *tomentosa*) . . . CHINESE F.

PAEO'NIA . . . . PEONY
albiflo'ra (*edulis*) . . . . CHINESE P.
—sinen'sis (*P. chinensis*)
DOUBLECRIMSON C.P.
anom'ala . . . . URAL P.
arbo'rea . . . . **P. suffruticosa**
brown'i . . . . BROWNS P.
califor'nica
chinen'sis . . . **P. albiflora sinensis**
coralli'na (*P. russi* in part) CORAL P.
coria'cea (*P. russi* in part)
MOROCCAN P.
deco'ra . . . . TURKISH P.
—pal'lasi . . . . PALLAS P.
delach'ei . . . . DELACHE P.
delavay'i . . . . DELAVAY P.
ed'ulis . . . . **P. albiflora**
emo'di . . . . HIMALAYA P.
ful'gida . . . . **P. officinalis**
hum'ei . . . . **P. suffruticosa h.**
∞**lemoin'ei** (*lutea* × *suffruticosa*)
∞LEMOINE P.
lute'a . . . . GOLDEN P.
macrophyl'la . . . . . . BIGLEAF P.
microcar'pa . . . . . . SPANISH P.
mlokosewitsch'i . . . CAUCASIAN P.

PAEONIA, continued
moutan' . . . . **P. suffruticosa**
officina'lis (*fulgida*) . COMMON PEONY
paradox'a . . . . LEVANT P.
Perhaps only a variety of P. officinalis.

peregri'na . . . . MEDITERRANEAN P.
Perhaps not specifically separable from P. officinalis.

russ'i Hort. . **P. corallina; P. coriacea**
suffrutico'sa (*arborea; moutan*) TREE P.
—hum'ei (*P. humei*) . . HUME T.P.
—papavera'cea . . . . . POPPY T.P.
tenuifo'lia . . . . . . FERNLEAF P.
wittmannia'na . . . . . IRANGOLD P.

Hort. var. of **Paeonia,** PEONY:

In the former edition of STANDARDIZED PLANT NAMES a list of horticultural varieties of Peonies was furnished by the American Peony Society. As the Editorial Committee has been unable to obtain a Peony list from that Society for this edition, we present below, as the best practicable alternative, a list collated by us from the three following sources: (1) "Peonies: The Manual of the American Peony Society," edited by James Boyd, 1928; (2) "Supplement to the Manual of the American Peony Society," compiled by A. F. Saunders, 1933; (3) "American Peony Society List of Peonies for Rating," by George W. Peyton, 1939.

ABBREVIATIONS OF PEONY CLASSIFICATION TYPES

Ane. Anemone
C. Chinese
D. Double
HH. Herbaceous Hybrids
J. Japanese
S. Single
T. Tree

ABBREVIATIONS OF NAMES OF ORIGINATORS

Amand Amand.
Amer. American Rose and Plant Co., Springfield, Ohio.
Ander. Miss Clara Anderson, Van Wert, Ohio.
Andr. D. M. Andrews, Boulder, Colo.
Appel Conrad Appel, Darmstadt, Germany.
Auten Edward Auten, Jr., Princeville, Ill.
Bab. Babcock Peony Gardens, Jamestown, N. Y.
Banks Sir Joseph Banks, Kew, England.
Bar. Barbier & Co.'s Nursery, Orleans, France.
Barr Barr & Sons, London, England.
Bau. Baumann Bros. Nursery, Bollwiller, Upper Rhine, Germany.
Bec. Bechet.
Bel. Belgian.
Ber. E. J. Berneche, Portland, Ore.
Bet. Carl Betscher, Canal Dover, Ohio.
Bla. Blaauw.
Boc. W. S. Bockstoce, Pittsburgh, Pa.
Bon. Lee R. Bonnewitz, Van Wert, Ohio.
Boyd James Boyd, Haverford, Pa.
Bra.,A. A. M. Brand, Faribault, Minn.
Brant Mrs. Ruth H. Brant, Iowa City, Iowa.
Bra.,O. Oliver Franklin Brand, Faribault, Minn.
Bre. Dr. F. G. Brethour, Toronto, Ont., Canada.
Bro. Brochet.
Bue. E. M. Buechly, Greenville, Ohio.
Bun. Bunting.
Bur. Stabilimento Burdin, Milan, Italy.
Buy. Buyck.
Cal. Jacques Calot, Douai, France.
Call. Douai Callot, Nord, France.

PAEONIA, continued
Cas. Giovanni Casaretto, Genoa, Italy.
Cha. Chauviere, Paris, France.
Chase H. F. Chase, Andover, Mass.
Che. Leon Chenault, Orleans, France.
Chi. Chinese-China.
Chr. W. F. Christman, Robbinsdale, Minn.
C.& LeC. Cayeux & Le Clerc, Paris, France.
Coo. Henry S. Cooper, Kenosha, Wis.
Cou. Courant.
Cra. Mrs. Wm. Crawford, La Porte, Ind.
Cro. Felix Crousse, Nancy, France.
Croux Gustave Croux, Paris, France.
Dana W. A. Dana, Eau Claire, Wis.
David David.
Del. Francois Delache, S. & O. Mer (Pas de Calais), France.
Des. Auguste Dessert, Chenonceaux, France.
Don. T. F. Donahue, Newton Lower Falls, Mass.
Donk. Jean Joseph Donkelaer, Ghent Botanical Garden, Ghent, Belgium.
D.&S. Doriat & Sons, Lapalisse (Allier), France.
Duc. Ducher.
Ear. J. W. Earnshaw, Lowville, N. Y.
Edl. J. V. Edlund, White Bear Lake, Minn.
Engle W. J. Engle, Dayton, Ohio.
Far. James F. Farquhar, Boston, Mass.
Farr Bertrand H. Farr, Wyomissing, Pa.
Few. Arthur Howard Fewkes, Newton Highlands, Mass.
For. Fortune, China.
Fou. Foulard.
Fra. A. Franchet, Jardin des Plantes, Paris, France.
Fran. A.B. Franklin, Franklin Nursery, Richfield Station, Minn.
Fre. Dr. Mary Freeborn, Proctor, Vt.
Gar. The Garden, London, England.
G.C. Gardeners' Chronicle, London, England.
G.&K. Goos & Koenemann, Niederwalluf am Rhein, Germany.
Gla. Lyman D. Glassock, Elwood, Ill.
Goe. Goethals, Ghent, Belgium.
Gom. Charles Gombault, Villecante, Clery, France.
G.&R. Good & Reese Co., Springfield, Ohio.
Grade Desire Grade, Alost (France or Belgium).
Gue. Modeste Guerin, Paris, France.
Gumm Walter L. Gumm, Remington, Ind.
Guppy Col. Benjamin W. Guppy, Melrose, Mass.
Har.,A. Alice Harding, Plainfield, N. J.
Har.,E. Mrs. Edward Harding, Plainfield, N. J.
Harr. Rev. C. S. Harrison, York, Neb.
Hen. I. S. Hendrickson, Jamesport, L. I., N. Y.
Henry Louis Henry, Paris, France.
H.G. Home Garden Co.
Hi-se Hinode-sekai.
Hiss Charles Hiss, Versailles, France.
H.&L. Henry & Lee, New York, N. Y.
Hol. George Hollis, South Weymouth, Mass.
H.&S. Haage & Schmidt, Erfurt, Prussia.
Hume Sir Abraham Hume, Wormelybury, England.
J.N. Japan Nursery Co., Settsu, Japan.
Joa. Joanon.
Kel. Kelway & Son, Langport, Somerset, England.
Ker. Kernberger?
K-keg. Kameno-kegoromo.
Koc. Koch.
Koe. Koenig.

PAEONIA, continued

Kor. Kortenoever?
Kre. E. H. Krelage, Haarlem, Holland.
Kun. A. E. Kunderd, Goshen, Ind.
Lan. W. E. Lanigan, Lincoln, Ill.
Lee. L. van Leeuwen & Son, Sassenheim, Holland.
Lei. Max Leichtlin, Baden-Baden, Germany.
Lem.,E. Emile Lemoine, Nancy, France.
Lemon Nicolas Lemon, Porte St. Denis, France.
Lem.,P. Pierre Louis Victor Lemoine, Nancy, France.
Leroy Andre Leroy, Angers, France.
Lev. Leveque, Ivry, France.
Lewis Mrs. John M. Lewis, Copenhagen, N. Y.
L.H. Lutea Hybrid.
Lit. Harry F. Little, Baldwinsville, N. Y.
Loo. Loorberg Nurseries, Berlin, Germany.
Lym. Lyman.
Mag-S Magome-Shara.
Mak. Jacob Makoy & Co., Liege, Belgium.
Man. Giussepe Manetti, Monza, Italy.
Mas. Masson, Belleville, France.
Mat. Mathieu, Belleville, France.
Mec. Etienne Mechin, Chenonceaux, France.
M.H.S. Massachusetts Horticultural Society.
Mie. Auguste Miellez, Esquermet, France.
Mill Mill & Son, Bourg-la-Reine (Seine), France.
Minot Dr. Charles Sedgwick Minot, Mass.
Mon. Gve. Montigny, Orleans, France.
Mou. Mouchelet.
Mount. Earl of Mountmorris, England.
Mur. A. L. Murawska, River Grove, Ill.
M.vanS. Mann-van Steen.
Nee. Dr. John H. Neeley, Paulding, Ohio.
Nic. Col. J. C. Nicholls, Ithaca, N. Y.
Nie. Abraham Nieuwenhuyzen, Springfield, Ohio.
Nois L. C. Nois, Faubourg Saint Jacques, Paris, France.
Nor. Harry A. Norton, Ayer's Cliff, Que., Canada.
O.F.N. Old Farm Nursery, Holland.
Ole. Miss May Oleson, Ripon, Wis.
Oud. Oudin Aine & Fils, Lisieux (Calvados), France.
Pai. Louis Paillet, Chatenay (Seine), France.
Par. Enghien Parmentier.
Pele Pele.
Per. Perche.
Pet. William A. Peterson, Chicago, Ill.
Pfe. The Pfeiffer Nursery, Winona, Minn.
Pleas Mrs. Sarah A. Pleas, Whittier, Calif.
Por. C. H. Porter, Branford, Conn.
Pre. Capt. James Prendergast, China.
Pur. William Purdom.
Ren. Renault.
Ric. John Richardson, Dorchester, Mass.
Rinz Rinz.
Risk O. A. Risk, North Olmsted, Ohio.
Riv. Benoit Riviere, France.
Rob. Mrs. Elizabeth D. Roberts, Medford, Mass.
Ros. J. F. Rosenfield, Indianapolis, Ind.
Run. Alletta R. Runyan, Valley Road, Millington, N. J.
Ruys B. Ruys, Dedemsvaart, Holland.
Sar. Sarreau.
Sass Hans Peter Sass, Washington, Neb.
Sass,J. J. Sass.
Sau. A. P. Saunders, Clinton, N. Y.

PAEONIA continued

Sch. Schwarzenburg.
Scott A. H. Scott, Media, Pa.
Secor,E. Eugene Secor, Forest City, Iowa.
Secor,N. Miss Nina Secor, Forest City, Iowa.
Seg. Elie Seguenot, France.
Sen. Adrian Seneclauze, France.
Sha. Egbert Jerome Shaylor, Auburndale, Mass.
Sie. Philip Franz von Siebold.
Sim. J. A. Simpson, Everett, Wash.
Smith Geo. N. Smith, Wellesley Hills, Mass.
Snook John S. Snook, Paulding, Ohio.
Sou. Souchet.
Ste. F. A. Stevens, Harrisburg, Pa.
Tal. Talsugashera.
Terry H. A. Terry, Crescent, Iowa.
Tho. Thomas, St. Denis, France.
Toedt Sarah Toedt, Hamburg, Iowa.
Tok. Tokio Nursery Co., Japan.
v.Aer. Van Aerschott.
Van. J. F. Vandermaelen, Etablissement Geographique de Bruxelles.
v.d. Meer Van der Meer?
Ver.,E. Eugene Verdier Fils Aine, Gare d'Ivry, Paris, France.
Verh. Verhille.
Ver.,V. Victor Verdier.
v.Gee. Charles Van Geert, Antwerp, Belgium.
v.Hou. Louis Van Houtte, Ghent, Belgium.
v.Kiel Van Kiel, Malines, Belgium.
Vor. Judge L. A. Vories, St. Joseph, Mo.
Wal. Wallace.
War. Warnaar.
Ward Charles Willis Ward, Queens, L. I., N. Y.
Ware T. S. Ware, Tottenham, England.
Welsh Ward Welsh, Springfield, Ohio.
Wet. C. N. Wettengel, Macomb, Ill.
Wild Frank H. Wild, Sarcoxie, Mo.
Wis. John C. Wister, Philadelphia, Pa.
Wolfe Mrs. Wm. Wolfe, Osceola, Iowa.
Wri. Wright.
Yam. Yamato-Sangai.
Yok. Yokohama Nurseries.

ABBE. C.J. (Lewis 1921.)
ABBOTT. J. (Lewis.)
A. (*B. C.*) NICHOLLS. D. (Nic. 1937.)
A. (*B.*) FRANKLIN. D. (Fran. 1928.)
ABOKIU. T.
ABRAHAM LINCOLN. T. (Sen. 1889.)
ACHILLE. DC. (Cal. 1855.)
ACME. D. (Fran. 1931.)
ADAMSON. D. (Kel. 1907.)
ADANA. SJ. (Kel. 1884?)
ADDIELANCHEA. DC. (Bra. O. 1907.)
ADELAIDE. T. (Koc. 1889.)
ADELAIDE DELACHE. DC.
ADELAIDE (*E.*) HOLLIS. DC. (Hol. 1907.)
ADELE DECURSY. T. (Guer. 1846.)
Adelina Patti. SHIRO-KAGURA.
ADELINE GENEE. DC. (Kel.)
ADJIANA. T.
ADMIRAL BEATTY. DC. (Kel. 1915.)
ADMIRAL DEWEY. DC. (Hol. 1904.)
ADMIRAL SCHLEY. DC. (Terry 1904.)
ADMIRAL STURDEE. DC. (Kel. 1915.)
ADMIRAL TOGO. DC. (Hol. 1907.)
ADOLPHE ROUSSEAU. DC. (Des.& Mec. 1890.)
ADONIS. D. (Sass 1930.)
ADORATION. D. (Lan. 1933.)
ADRIENNE. T. (Hiss. 1859.)
ADZUMA-ERABI. T.
ADZUMA-KAGAMI. T. *Etoile Rose.*
ADZUMA-NISHIKI. T. *Gil Blas.*

PAEONIA, continued

ADZUMA-SAKI. J.; T.
ADZUMA-SIBORI. S.; T. (Jap. 1909.)
A. (*F. W.*) HAYWARD. DC. (Kel.)
AGENORIA. T. (Kel. 1890.)
AGIDA. DC.
AGNES BARR. DC. (Barr)
AGNES KEOGH. DC. (Far. 1920.)
AGNES (*Mary*) KELWAY. DC. (Kel. 1888.)
A. (*G.*) PERRY. D. (Bra. A. 1933.)
AILEEN BRETHOUR. D. (Bre. 1935.)
AISSINA. T. (G. C. 1888.)
A. (*J.*) *Davis.* ANDREW JACKSON DAVIS.
A. (*J.*) HUNTER. DC. (Kel.)
AKA-DAIKAGURA. S.; T. (Jap. 1919.)
AKALU. CJ. (Des.)
AKASHI-GATA. J.; T.; S. (Jap. 1893.)
AKASHI-JISHI. S.; T. (Jap. 1893.) *Magicienne.*
AKASHI-NISHIKI. S.; T. (Jap. 1910.) *Talma.*
AKASHIURA. T.
AKEBONO. J.; T. (J. N. 1910.)
AKSARBEN. DC. (Ros. 1908.)
ALASKA. DC. (Auten 1925.)
ALBABELGICA. T. (Ruit. 1906.)
ALBALILACINA. D.; T. (Gue. 1873.) *Grand Frederic.*
ALBAPLENA. T. (Nois. 1839.)
ALBASULFUREA. DC. (Cal. 1860.)
ALBATRE. DC. (Cro. 1885.)
ALBATROSS. J.
ALBERT. DC.
ALBERT CROUSSE. DC. (Cro. 1893.)
Albert, King of the Belgians. BELGIAN KING ALBERT.
ALBIDA LONGIPETALA. T. (H.&S. 1864.)
ALBIDA PLENA. T. (Mount. 1825.)
ALBIFLORA, THE BRIDE. SC. (Lem. P. 1898.) *Lafiancee.*
ALCHEMIST. T. (Kel. 1897.)
ALCYON. T. (Krel. 1867.) *Alcione.*
ALESIA. DC. (Lem. E. 1927.)
ALEX. (*D.*) VORIES. DC. (Vor. 1924.)
ALEXANDRA. T.
Alexandre de Humboldt. ZENOBIA.
ALEXANDRE DUMAS. DC. (Gue. 1862.)
ALEXANDRIANA. DC. (Cal. 1856.)
ALFRED. J. (Terry 1855?)
ALFRED DEMUSSET. DC. (Cro. 1885.)
ALICE BALFOUR. DC. (Kel. 1915.)
ALICE CROUSSE. DC. (Cal. 1872.)
ALICE DEJULVECOURT. DC. (Pele 1857.)
ALICE HARDING. DC. (Lem. 1922.)
ALLEN WEST. DC. (Kel. 1926.)
ALLETTA. SJ. (Run. 1928.)
ALLURE. D. (Nee. 1936.)
ALMA. C.J. (Sha. 1916.)
ALOPE CUPREA. T. (Kre. 1869.)
ALPHA AND OMEGA. DC. (Pleas 1903.)
Alpheus Hyatt. GRANDIFLORA.
ALPHONSE DECANDOLLE. D.; T. (Bur. 1867.)
ALSACE. DC. (Kel. 1916.)
ALSACE-LORRAINE. DC. (Lem. 1906.)
ALTAR CANDLES. C.J. (Pleas 1908.)
AMABILIS PLENA. D.;T.
AMAGASHITA. T.
AMALIA. DC. (G.&K.)
AMANDA YALE. DC. (Bra. O. 1907.)
AMANO-HERA. T.
AMA-NO-SODE. C.J. (Jap.)
AMARANTE. T. (Lem. P. 1903.)
AMARANTHINA PLENA. D.; T. (Sen. or Gue. 1846.)
AMAZONE. DC. (Lem. E. 1899.)

PAEONIA, continued

Ambroise Verschaffelt. DC. (Par. 1850.)
Amelia Robbins. DC. (Lewis 1921.)
Americanbeauty. DC. (Banks 1805.)
American Legion. D. (Mur. 1932.)
Amitie. SC. (Kel. 1926.)
A. (*M.*) Kelway. SC.
Amoena. T. (Kel. 1889.)
Amoskeog. SJ.
A. (*M.*) Slocum. DC. (Fran. 1920.)
Andre Lauries. Fragrans.
Andrew Jackson Davis. DC. (Bra. O. 1907.) *A. J. Davis.*
Andy. D. (Auten 1936.)
Anemoneflora Rubra. DC. (Del. 1854.)
Angelina. T. (Math. 1839.)
Angelus. SJ. (Auten 1933.)
Angustiloba (Delavayi). (Wils.—)
Anna Pavlowa. DC. (Kel. 1863?)
Anna Sass. D. (Sass 1930.)
Anne Nielsen. D. (G.&R. 1930.)
Anneslei. T. (Mount. 1825.)
Annette Carson. D. (Risk 1929.)
Annibel. T.
Annie Louise. DC. (Hol.)
Ann Pfeiffer. D. (Pfe. 1932.)
Antietam. DC. (Hol. 1905.)
Antigonus. T.
Antoine Poiteau. DC. (Gue. 1845.)
Antwerpen. J.
Anyaha-hikare. J.; T. (H.&L. 1926.)
Anyo-ji. J.; T. (H.&L. 1926.)
Anzac. SC. (Kel. 1926.)
Aofukurin. T.
Aowataseshiro. T.
Aphrodite. T. (Kel. 1897.)
Apollo. T. (Kel. 1889.)
Appleblossom. Rei-kai-zan.
A. (*P.*) Saunders. DC. (Thu. 1919.)
Archduke Louis. T. (Kel. 1889.)
Archer. DC. (Kel. 1884?)
Archiduc Ludovico. D.; T. (Bur. 1867.)
Archie Brand. DC. (Bra. A. 1913.)
Archinta Plena. T.
Arcturus. SJ. (Auten 1933.)
Areos. SC.
Arethusa. DT. (Oud. 1846.)
Arethusa. DC.
Argentine. DC. (Lem. 1924.)
Argosy. T. (Saun. 1928.)
Argus. SC.
Arlequin. DC. (Des. 1921.)
Arlesienne. S.; T. (Des. 1909.)
Armance Dessert. D. (D.&S. 1929.)
Armandine Mechin. DC. (Mec. 1880.)
Armand Rousseau. DC. (Des.&Mec. 1893.)
Armide. D. (Lem. E. 1933.)
Arsene Meuret. DC. (Ver. V. 1854.)
Artemise. DC. (Cal. 1861.)
Artist. DC. (Kel. 1884?)
Asa Gray. DC. (Cro. 1886.)
Asa Gray. T.
Asahi-Minato. S.; T. (Jap. 1893.) *Grenade.*
Asashickuma. T.
Askidatsuru. T.
Assmannshausen. DC. (G.&K.1912.)
Atalante. T. (For. 1846.)
Athelney. SC. (Kel. 1884?)
Athelstance. D. (Brown 1938.)
Athlete. D.; T. (Mou. 1867.)
Atlanta. SJ. (Fran. 1931.)

PAEONIA, continued

Atropurpurea. Zenobia.
Atrorubens. T.
Atrosanguinea. CT. (For. 1846.)
Atrosanguinea. D. (Cal. 1858.)
Atroviolacea. D.; T. (Bel. 1846.)
Atroviolacea Grandiflora. T. (Bel. 1867.)
Attraction. C.J. (Hol. 1906.)
Aubesan. J. *Clementine.*
Audomarensis. DC. (Del. 1850.)
Augusta. T.
Auguste Dessert. DC.; T. (Des. '20.)
Auguste Lemonier. DC. (Cal. 1865.)
Auguste Vangeert. DC. (Par. 1850.)
Auguste Villaume. DC. (Cro. 1895.)
Augustin d'Hour. DC. (Cal. 1865.) *Marechal MacMahon.*
Aunt Ellen. DC. (Bra. O. 1907.)
Aureole. J. (Hol. 1905.)
Aureolin. C.J. (Sha. 1917.)
Aurora. T. (Des. 1905.)
Aurore. DC. (Des. 1904.)
Austin Chamberlain. SC. (Kel. 1905.)
Australia. SC. (Kel. 1884?)
Autens Pride. D. (Auten 1933.)
Autumnus. SC. (Kel. before 1891.)
Avalanche. DC. (Cro. 1886.)
Avant Garde. HH. (Lem. P. 1907.)
Ave Maria. D. (M. van S. 1936.)
Aviateur Lindbergh. DC. (Des.& Dor. 1927.)
Aviateur Reymond. DC. (Des. 1915.)
Avocat Guillon. T.
Awadji. J. (Mill.)
Aya-Nishiki. S.; T. (Jap. 1893.) *Moliere; Momozomo.*
Aya-no-maki. T.
Azumasaki. T.
Baby Kelway. SC. (Kel. 1884?)
Baird. DC. (Kel. 1884?)
Balfour. DC. (Kel. 1884?)
Balliol. SC.
Ball o'Cotton. DC. (Fran. 1920.)
Ball White. DC. (Lewis 1924.)
Baltonsburgh. SC. (Kel. 1884?)
Balzac. D.; T. (Des. 1902.)
Bande d'Or. DC. (Cra. 1922.)
Banksi. D.; T. (Chi.-Banks 1789.)
Banryo. T. (Jap.) (J.N. 1910 as new.)
Barker. DC. (Kel. 1884?)
Baroness Schroeder. DC. (Kel. 1889.)
Baron (*J.*) Hulot. SJ. (Mill 1919.)
Baronne d'Ales. D.; T. (Gom. before 1886.)
Baron Vonhugel. T. (Jap.) (K.Sieb.)
Bayadere. DC. (Lem. 1910.)
Beaconlight. J. (Wet. 1924.)
Beatrice Kelway. J.; T. (Kel. 1891.)
Beatrix. S.; T. (Jap.) (Des. 1905.)
Beaumarchais. DC. (Lem. 1922.)
Beaute Detokio. S.; J. (Des. 1905, 1899.)
Beaute Detwickel. D.; T. (Ver. E. 1869.)
Beaute Devillecante. DC. (Gom. 1856.)
Beaute Francaise. DC. (Gue. 1850.)
Beauty. S.; T. (Kel. 1899.)
Beauty of Canton. T. (Chi.-For. 1846.) *Reevesiana.*
Beautys Mask. DC. (Hol. 1904.)
Beck. T. (Pai. 1889.)
Belgian King Albert. DC. (Far. 1919). *Albert, King of the Belgians; King of the Belgians.*

PAEONIA, continued

Belgium. DC. (Kel. 1884?)
Belisaire. DC. (Lem. P. 1901.)
Bella. T.
Bella Dimonza. T.
Bella Donna. D. (New. 1935.)
Belle. D. (Gla. 1928.)
Belle Alliance. DC. (Cro. 1892.)
Belle Chatelaine. DC. (Gue. 1861.)
Belle Chinoise. D. (Auten 1931.)
Belle d'Orleans. D.; T. (Mon.) (Lem. P. 1892.)
Belle Douaisienne. DC. (Cal. 1861.)
Belle Hortense. T.
Belle Hough. DC. (Jerry 1855?)
Belle Japanaise. T.
Belle Mauve. DC. (Lem. P. 1903.)
Bellini. T.
Beni-Kagu. S.; T. (Jap. 1905.) *Tsarine.*
Beni-Kamada. T. (Jap. 1910.)
Beni-Kirin. T. (Jap.)
Benino-Tsukasa. T. (Jap. 1926.)
Beni-Tsukasa. T. (Jap. 1919.)
Benjamin Franklin. DC. (Bra. O. 1907.)
Benmei. T.
Benoit. DC.
Beranger. DC. (Des. 1895.)
Berenice. D.; T. (Chi.-For. 1846.) *Hebe; Versicolor.*
Berlioz. DC. (Cro. 1886.)
Bernardine. DC. (Kel. 1884?)
Bernard Palissy. DC. (Cro. 1897.)
Bertha. DC. (Terry 1910.)
Bertrade. DC. (Lem. 1909.)
Bessie Magill. DC. (Terry 1855?)
Bethcar. SC. (Kel. 1926.)
Betsey Ross. D. (Auten 1931.)
Betsy (*Jean*) Miller. D. (H.G.)
Betty Alden. DC. (Hol. 1889?)
Betty Barnes. D. (Fran. 1928.)
Betty Blossom. DC. (Thu. 1922.)
Betty Rose. SJ. (Bra. A. 1936.)
Bewitching. DC. (Kel. 1926.)
Bicolor. D.; T. (Oud. 1846.)
Biebrich. DC. (G.&K. 1912.)
Bijou Dechusan. T.
Bilderijk. T. (Kre. 1867.)
Bingen. DC. (G.&K. 1919.)
Birket Foster. DC. (Kel. 1909.)
Bishop Burke. DC. (Vor. 1924.)
Bishops Huish. SC. (Kel. 1884?)
Black Beauty. SC. (Ber. 1924.)
Black Hawk. SJ. (Auten 1933.)
Black Magic. SJ. (Auten 1929.)
Black Peony. T.
Black Prince. SC. (Thu. 1915.)
Blanche Cire. DC. (Des. 1908.)
Blanche Dechateau Futu. D.; T (Mou. 1867.)
Blanche Dehiss. Hissiana.
Blanche Demathieu. Victoria.
Blanche Denoisette. D.; T. (Nois. 1864.) *Emilia; Noisette.*
Blanche Elie. D. (Bre. 1934.)
Blanche King. DC. (Bra. A. 1922.)
Blazing Star. D. (Auten 1937.)
Blonde. D. (Dana 1926.)
Bloodstone. SC. (Kel. 1926.)
Bluebird. DC. (Kel. 1884?)
Blushes of Cream. D. (Kun. 1927.)
Blushing Beauty. D. (Fran. 1931.)
Blushing Bride. SJ. (Pfe. 1932.)
Boadicea. DC.
Bobbie Bee. J. (Hol. 1907.)

PAEONIA, continued
Bokuryo. T. (Jap. 1926.)
Bono. DC.
Boule Blanche. DC. (Cro. 1892.)
Boule Deneige. DC. (Cal. 1867.) *Emile Hoste.*
Bouquet Deflora. DC. (Pleas 1913.)
Boy Kelway. DC. (Kel. 1884?)
Brands Magnificent. DC. (Bra. A. 1918.) *Magnificent.*
Bridesmaid. Marie Jacquin.
Brightness. SC.; T. (Kel. 1892.)
British Beauty. DC. (Kel. 1926.)
British Empire. SC. (Kel. 1884?)
Bubbudo. T.
Buffon. Shine-Kagura.
Bumeikai. S.; T. (Jap. 1919.)
Bunbudo. S.; T. (Jap. 1893.)
Bunch of Perfume. DC. (Kel. 1901.)
Bunker Hill. DC. (Hol. 1906.)
Burdiniana. T. (Bur. 1846.)
Butleigh. SC. (Kel. 1884?)
Buycki. DC. (Gue. 1840.)
Cabbage Rose. DC. (Kel. 1912.)
Calelene. T. (Kel. 1897.)
Calumet. SJ. (Auten 1931.)
Calypso. S.; T. (Des. 1913.)
Calypso. SJ. (Aud. 1925.)
Camelia. T. (Chi.-For. 1846.)
Cameo. DC.
Cameron. DC. (Cro. 1879.)
Camille. SC. (Des. 1908.)
Canaflora Lucida. T. (Kel. 1889.)
Canari. DC. (Gue. 1861.)
Candeur. DC. (Des. 1920.)
Candidissima. DC. (Cal. 1856.)
Cantatrix. T. (Kel. 1889.)
Capitaine Champion. T. (Chi.-For. 1889.)
Captain Alcock. SC.
Captain Blood. DC. (Lewis 1927.)
Captain Cheape. DC. (Kel. 1884?)
Captain Kidd. D. (Auten 1934.)
Captain Lambton. T. (Kel. 1902.)
Caraway. D. (Secor N. 1924.)
Cardinal. D. (Gumm.)
Cardinal Antonelli. T. (Mak. 1869.)
Cardinal Vaughan. T. (Kel. 1890.)
Carli. T.
Carlotta Grisi. DC. (Cal. 1856.)
Carmen. DC. (Lem. P. 1898.)
Carmen Sylva. SC. (Kel. 1884?)
Carmosina Plenissima. T.
Carnea Elegans. DC. (Gue. 1850.)
Carnea Elegans. (Cal. 1860.)
Carnea Grandiflora. T.
Carnea Plena. D.; T. (Mount 1825.)
Carnea Striata. DC.
Carnea Triumphans. DC. (Gue. 1852.)
Carnescens Plenissima. Carolina d'-Italie.
Carnosa. T. (Kel. 1889.)
Carnot. SC. (Des. 1913.)
Carolina. T. (Hiss 1842.)
Carolina. T. (Mat. 1846.)
Carolina. T. (Cha. 1867.)
Carolina. T. (Man. 1887.)
Carolina d'Italie. D.; T. (Ital. 1846.) *Carnescens Plenissima.*
Caroline. J.
Caroline Allain. SC. (Gue. 1855.)
Carolyne (*Mae*) Nelson. D. (Sass 1937.)
Casaretto. T. (Cas. 1842.) *Rossini.*
Cascade. J.
Cashmere. J.

PAEONIA, continued
Cathedral. Hana-no-sato.
Catherine. Katherine.
Catherine Parry. SC. (Hen. 1925.)
Catherine (*S.*) Fox. SC. (Ber. 1920.)
Cats. T. (Kre. 1867.)
Caub. DC. (G.&K. 1919.) *Kaub.*
Cavalleria Rusticana. DC.
Cecilia Kelway. DC. (Kel. 1912.)
Cecil Rhodes. T. (Kel. 1900.)
Celeste Brochet. SC.
Celestial. SC. (Des.)
Celestia Lewis. DC. (Lewis 1921.)
Cendrillon. SC. (Des. 1913.)
Cenjinnosoka. T.
Centifolia Rosea. D.; T. (Sen. 1889.)
Ceres. DC. (Ver. 1860.)
Ceres. T. (Lei. 1884.)
Cerise. J. (Lewis 1922.)
Cerise Beauty. D. (Risk 1929.)
Chabannes Lapolice. D. (Dor. 1924.)
Chalice. HH. (Sau. 1929.)
Challenger. HH. (Sau. 1929.)
Chantecler. D.; T. (Des. 1913.)
Charity. HH. (Sau. 1935.)
Charlemagne. DC. (Cro. 1880.)
Charles Binder. DC. (Gue. 1860.)
Charles Earl Pleas. DC. (Pleas 1855?)
Charles Gosselin. DC. (Gue. 1850.)
Charles Hyacinthe. T. (1889.)
Charles McKellip. DC. (Bra. A. 1907.)
Charles Neidel. DC. (Wet. 1916.)
Charles Rogier. D.; T. (About 1853.)
Charles Rouillard. D.; T. (Gue. after 1863.)
Charles (*Sedgwick*) Minot. DC. (Ric. 1904.)
Charles Verdier. DC. (Cal. 1865.)
Charleys Aunt. T. (Kel. 1897.)
Charlot. DC. (Dor. 1924.)
Charlotte Core. SJ. (Dor. 1932.)
Charlotte Cushman. DC. (Hol. '04.)
Charlotte Lee. D. (Don. 1929.)
Chastity. D. (Bre. 1935.)
Chauvieri. T. (Cha. 1846.)
Cherokee. D. (Fran. 1931.)
Cherry Hill. DC. (Thu. 1915.)
Chestine Gowdy. DC. (Bra. A. 1913.)
Chestnut Hill. D. (Don. 1927.)
Chichester. DC. (Kel. 1884?)
Chief. D. (Fran. 1931.)
Chinensis Rosea. DC.
Chinensis Rubra. Fragrans.
Chinese Departing Sun. SC. *Departing Sun.*
Chiyokagura. T.
Cho-jiraku. T. (Jap.) (H.&L. 1926.)
Chokanshishi. T.
Christabel. DC. (Kel. 1909.)
Christina. D.; T. (Bur. 1846.) *Cristina.*
Christine Kelway. T. (Kel. 1902.)
Christine Richter. DC. (Hol. 1907.)
Christine Shand. DC. (Kel. 1884?)
Chromatella. T. (Lem. E. 1928.)
Chrysanthemiflora. DC. (Gue. 1842.)
Cinderella. SJ. (Jones 1937.)
Claire. Kochomai.
Claire Dubois. DC. (Crow. 1886.)
Clairette. SC. (Des. 1905.)
Clara. T. (Koc. 1874.)
Clara Anderson. DC. *Harriet Beecher Stowe.*

PAEONIA, continued
Clara Barton. DC. (Terry 1906.)
Clara MacQueen. SC. (Kel. 1884?)
Clara Stockwell. DC. (Wet. 1926.)
Clarissa. DC.
Clarisse. Oimatsu.
Claude Gellee. DC. (Lem. P. 1904.)
Claude Lorrain. DC. (Cro. 1884.)
Clemenceau. DC. (Des. 1920.)
Clementine. Aubesan.
Clementine Gillot. DC. (Cro. 1885.)
Clercke. SC. (Kel. 1884?)
Climax. SC. (Kel. 1884?)
Clio. SC. (Pet. 1906.)
Clorinda. DC. (Auten 1926.)
Clothos. SC. (Kel. 1884?)
Cobianchi. T. (Ital. or Bur. 1864.) *Cobienski.*
Coericea Pallida. T. (Bel. 1867.)
Coericea Purpurea. T. (Bel. 1846.)
Coericea Purpurea Superba. T. (Bel. 1846.)
Colberti. T.
Col. d'Andeleau. D.; T. (Sen. 1889.)
Col. Malcolm. D.; T. (Chi.-For. 1864.) *Reine Desbeautes; Sir George Davis.*
Colonel Boles. SC. (Kel. 1884?)
Colonel Hopton. DC. (Kel. 1884?)
Colonel Lindbergh. D. (Kun. 1927.)
Colonel Lockwood. DC. (Kel. 1884?)
Colonel Poe. SC. (Kel. 1884?)
Colorado. T. (Jap. 1911.)
Columbus. SJ.
Comata. D.; T. (Mak. 1846.) *Huppec.*
Comet. DC. (Fran. 1920.)
Commander. D. (Don. 1927.)
Commander Byrd. D.
Commodore Emge. DC. (Bra. A. 1913.)
Compacta. T.
Compacta Plena. T. (Jap. 1846.)
Comte Dechoiseul. S.; T. (Jap. 1897.)
Comte Dediesbach. DC. (Cal. 1873.)
Comte Deflandre. T. (Don. 1846.) *Kochleni; Mme. Laffay; Triomphe de van Aerschott.*
Comte Degomer. DC. (Cal. 1868.)
Comte Dejussier. DC.
Comte Denanteuil. DC. (Cal. 1858.)
Comte Deniepperg. DC. (Ver. V. 1854.)
Comte Deparis. D. (Gue. 1842.)
Comte Deparis. T. (Sen. 1889.)
Comte Derambuteau. D.; T. (Gue. 1867.)
Comte d'Osmont. DC. (Cal. 1856.)
Comtesse d'Arenberg. T.
Comtesse Dechambard. T.
Comtesse Decrawford. D.; T. (Sen. 1889.)
Comtesse Demorny. DC.
Comtesse Demurad. SJ. (Dor. 1932.)
Comtesse d'Estienne d'Orvis. T. (Jap. 1897.)
Comtesse Detudor. D.; T. (Gom. 1889.)
Comtesse Hugo. T.
Comtesse (*Mariana*) Delmes. T.
Comtesse (*Mariana*) Demaino. T. (Bur. 1867.)
Concessa Plena. D.; T. (1846.)
Conciliation. T. (1889.)
Confucius. D.; T. (Chi.-For. 1864.) *Lord Macartney; Superba Deyoung.*
Congress. DC.
Conqueror. DC. (Hol. 1907.)

PAEONIA, continued

CONQUISTADOR. D. (Jones 1937.)
CONSTANCE. J. (Ber. 1924.)
CONSTANT DEVRED. DC. (Cal. 1868.)
COOTE. DC. (Kel. 1884?)
COPENHAGEN. DC. (Lewis 1921.)
COQUELIN. DC. (Des. 1905.)
COQUETTE. DC. (Lem. E. 1914.)
COQUETTE DES BLANCHES. D.; T. (Sen. 1889.)
CORAL QUEEN. D. (Sass 1937.)
CORINNE. SC. (Auten 1926.)
CORINTH. HH. (Sau. 1929.)
CORNELIA. D.; T. (For. 1867.) *Orgueil de Hong Kong.*
CORNELIA SHAYLOR. DC. (Sha. 1917.)
CORNELIA STONE. D. (Gumm 1929.)
Cornelie. FU-JI-MINE.
CORONATION. DC. (Kel. 1902.)
COTTAGE MAID. SJ. (Pleas)
COUNTESS CADOGAN. T. (Kel. 1900.)
COUNTESS CREWE. T. (Kel. 1900.)
COUNTESS OF ALTAMONT. SC. (Kel. 1884?)
COUNTESS OF MARITZA. D. (New. 1935.)
COUNTESS OF WARWICK. SC. (Kel. 1884?)
COUNTESS S. PULLE. SC. (Kel. 1884?)
COUNTRY DANCE. SJ. (Auten 1931.)
COURONNE D'OR. DC. (Cal. 1873.) *Dorothy E. Kibby.*
CRAMOISINA PLENA. T. (Pai. 1889.)
CRIMSON VICTORY. DC. (Ros. 1908.)
Cristina. CHRISTINA.
CRITES. T. (Kel. 1897.)
CROWN OF THORNS. J. (Hol. 1907.)
CROWN ON CROWN. J.
CRYSTAL QUEEN. J.
CRYSTAL SEA. D. (Nee. 1936.)
CRYSTOLA. D. (Andr. 1932.)
CURIOSA. DC. (Barr.)
CURIOSITY. J. (Des.&Mec. 1886.)
CURRANT. J.
C. (*W.*) SCHOCK. DC. (Fran. 1920.)
CYNTHIA. T. (Kel. 1897.)
CZARINA. DC.
DA COSTA. T. (Kre. 1867.)
DAI-JO-KUHAN. J. (Mill.)
DAI-KAGURA. T. (Jap. 1893.) *Nuage Rose.*
DAIMIO. J. (Mill. 1926.)
DAMASK ROSE. DC. (Pleas 1912.)
DANA GARNOCK. D. (Dana 1930.)
DANCE CAPRICE. D. (Auten 1933.)
DANCING NYMPH. SJ. (Auten 1933.)
DANIEL BOONE. D. (Auten 1931.)
DANIEL DEWAR.
DAPHNE. DC. (Ear. 1922.)
DARIUS. SC.
DARKNESS. SC. (Bra. A. 1913.)
DARLING O'MINE. D. (G.&R. 1930.)
DAVID. DC. (Kel. 1884?)
DAVID HARUM. DC. (Bra. A. 1920.)
DAWN. J. (Cal. 1870?)
DAWN FLUSH. D. (Nee. 1936.)
DAYBREAK. DC. (Hol. 1910.)
DEAN HOLE. DC. (Kel. 1884?)
DEARBORN. D. (Auten 1929.)
DEBORAH SAYLES. SC. (Sha. 1916.)
DEBUGNEY. SD.; T. (Amand 1846.)
DECANDOLLE. DC. (Ver. 1860.)
Decandolle. DC. (Cro. 1880.)
DECUS. T. (Kel. 1889.)
DEEDIE MAY. DC. (Vor. 1927.)
DEEMSTER. DC. (Kel. 1909.)
DEFIANCE. S. (Ter.) *Northbrook.*
DEJANIRE. T. (Sen. 1867.)

PAEONIA, continued

Dejazet. SHOKI-KAGURA.
DELACHEI. T. (Mei. 1846.)
Delachei. DC. (Del. 1856.) *Emperor of Russia.*
DELAUN. DC. (Lewis 1921.)
DELECOURT VERHILLE. DC. (Verh. 1860.)
Delicatissima. FLORAL TREASURE.
DELILAH. DC. (Barr.)
DELMOTTE. T. (1873.)
DEMETRIUS. SJ.
DENIS DEBATENE. DC. (Vor. 1926.)
DENISE. DC. (Lem. 1924.)
DENIS HELYE. DC. (Ver. V. 1860.)
DENMARK. J. (Lewis 1921.)
Dentata. VIVID.
DEPARTING SUN. J.S. (Wil.)
Departing Sun. SC. (Wil.)
Departing Sun. CHINESE DEPARTING SUN; JAPANESE DEPARTING SUN.
DESCARTES. DC. (Des.&Mec. 1885.)
DESIRE. DC. (Bra. A. 1923.)
DETIENNE. T.
DEVONSHIRE. T. (Hiss.)
DEVRIESE. T. (Sie.)
D. (*H.*) HUGHES. SC.
DIADEM. D. (Fran. 1931.)
DIAMANT. T. (Lem. E. 1908.)
DIAMOND JUBILEE. T. (Kel. 1898.)
Diane. SHIRO-SOKU.
DIEUDONNE. D. (Bre. 1936.)
DIOGENES.
DIONYSI. T. (Dav. 1839.)
DIRECTEUR URSAT. DC. (Dor. 1925.)
DIRECTOR AUBRY. DC. (Cro. 1897.)
DISRAELI. DC. (Kel. 1908.)
DISTINCTION. J. (Des. 1895.)
DIXIE. D. (Fran. 1931.)
DOCTEUR ANDRY. DC. (Cal. 1864.)
DOCTEUR BOISDUVAL. DC. (Gue. 1850.)
DOCTEUR BRETONNEAU. DC. (Gue. 1850.)
Docteur Bretonneau. (Ver. V. 1854.) LADY (*Leonora*) BRAMWELL.
DOCTEUR CAILLOT. DC. (Ver.V. 1856.)
DOG ROSE. J. (Wal.)
DOKUSBIN-DEN. T. (Jap. 1913.)
DOLORES. DC.
DONKELAARI. T. (Mil. or Don. 1867.)
DONNA MARIA. T. (Sen. 1889.) Perhaps the same as Mme. Thibault.
DON QUIXOTE. T. (Kel. 1896.)
DORCHESTER. DC. (Ric. 1870.)
DORIS. DC. (Sha. 1920.)
DOROTHY. S. (Kel. 1898.)
Dorothy. J.D. (Jones 1937.)
DOROTHY ALLISON. SC. (Sha. 1918.)
DOROTHY DANIELS. DC. (Kel. 1884?)
Dorothy E. Kibby. COURONNE D'OR.
DOROTHY KELWAY. DC. (Kel. 1884?)
DORYS. T. (For. 1874.)
DOSHI. T. (Jap. 1896.)
DRAGONS HEAD. J.
DR. BONAVIA. DC. (Kel. 1884?)
Dr. Bowring. GLOIRE DESHANGHAI.
DR. CHRISTOPHER GRAHAM. D. (Bra. A. 1936.)
DREADNOUGHT. SC. (Barr.)
DR. EDGAR PLEAS. J. (Pleas 1900.) *Ostrich Plume.*
DR. (*F. R.*) HUXLEY. D. (Bra. A. 1936.)
DR. (*H.*) BARNSBY. DC. (Des. 1913.)
DR. (*H.*) VANDERTAK. DC. (Nie. 1916.)
DR. (*J. H.*) NEELEY. D. (G.&R. 1930.)

PAEONIA, continued

DR. (*Joseph Fort*) NEWTON. DC. (Kor.)
DR. SICARD. T.
DUC D'ARENBERG. T. (Par. 1873.)
DUC D'AUMALE. T.
DUC DECAZES. DC. (Gue. 1850.)
DUC DEMASSINO. T.
DUC D'ENGHIEN. DC. (Par. 1850.)
DUC DEWELLINGTON. DC. (Cal. 1859.)
DUCHESSE DEFORENKEIN. T.
DUCHESSE DEMORNY. T. (1899.)
DUCHESSE DENEMOURS. D. (Gue. 1840.)
Duchesse Denemours. DC. (Cal. 1856.)
DUCHESSE DEPARME. T. (Sen. 1867.)
DUCHESSE DETHEBA. DC. (Barr.)
DUCHESSE D'ORLEANS. DC. (Gue. 1846.)
Duchesse d'Orleans. T. (Jap. 1846; K. Sieb. 1889.)
DUCHESS OF ALBANY. DC. (Kel. 1915.)
DUCHESS OF BEDFORD. SC. (Kel. 1884?)
DUCHESS OF MARLBOROUGH. T. (Kel. 1897.)
DUCHESS OF PORTLAND. SC. (Barr.)
DUCHESS OF RUTLAND. T. (Kel. 1897.)
DUCHESS OF SOMERSET. DC. (Kel. 1899.)
DUCHESS OF SUTHERLAND. SC. (Kel. before 1898.)
DUCHESS OF TECK. DC. (Kel. 1884?)
Duchess of Teck. T. (Kel. 1896.)
DUCHESS OF YORK. DC. (Kel. 1923–25.)
DUHAMEL. T. (Gue. 1873.)
DUKE OF ATHOLL. SC. (Kel. 1884?)
DUKE OF CAMBRIDGE. DC. (Kel. 1884?)
DUKE OF CLARENCE. DC. (Kel. 1884?)
DUKE OF DEVONSHIRE. DC. (Kel. 1895.)
DULCINEE. DC. (Lem. E. 1924.)
DULUTH. D. (Fran. 1931.)
DUMONT DECOURSET. T. (Gue. after 1863.)
DUNMANS WHITE. D. (Sass)
EARL OF JERSEY. DC. (Kel. 1884?)
EARLY JUNE. D. (Kun. 1927.)
EASTERN BROCADE. SC. (Kel. 1884?)
EASTERN PRINCE. T. (Kel. 1896.)
EAU CLAIRE. SJ. (Dana 1926.)
Eclair. KUMONA-NISHIKI.
ECLAIREUR. T. (Des. 1905.)
ECSTASY. D. (Bre. 1926.)
Eden. SHISHINDEN.
EDITH ARBEITER. D. (Gla. 1929.)
EDITH CAVELL. DC. (Kel. 1916.)
EDITH (*E.*) GUMM. D. (Gumm 1930.)
EDITH ESTELLE. D. (Gumm 1926.)
EDITH FORREST. DC. (Hol. 1918.)
EDITH LYTTLETON. DC. (Kel. 1884?)
EDITH (*M.*) SNOOK. D. (Snook 1931.)
EDITH SCOVELL. D. (Fran. 1928.)
EDITH WEST. SC. (Bra. A. 1920.)
EDMOND. DC. (Barr.)
EDMOND ABOUT. DC. (Cro. 1885.)
EDMOND LEBON. DC. (Cal. 1864.)
EDOUARD ANDRE. DC. (Mec. 1874.)
Edouard Andre. T. (Jap. 1897.)
EDOUARD DORIAT. D. (Dor. 1929.)
EDULIS ALBA. DC. (1835.)
Edulis Fragrans. FRAGRANS.
EDULIS SUPERBA. DC. (Lemon 1824.)
EDWARD VII. SC.; T.
EDWARDSI. T. (Dav. 1837?)
EDWARD (*W.*) BECKER. DC. (Fra. 1920.)
EDWIN (*C.*) SHAW. DC. (Thu. 1919.)
EDWIN FORREST. DC. (Hol. 1904.)

PAEONIA, continued

E. G. Hill. DC. (Lem. P. 1906.)
Eglantine. SC. (Des. 1913.)
Eileen Kelway. J. (Kel. 1884?)
E. J. Shaylor. DC. (Sha. 1918.)
Elaine Pfeiffer. D. (Pfe. 1932.)
El Capitan. D. (Auten 1937.)
Eldii. T. (1855.)
Eleanor Ann Smith. DC. (Fran. 1820.)
Eleanor Dana. D. (Dana 1926.)
Electric. DC. (Kel. 1909.)
Elegans Superbissima. DC. (Buy. 1842.)
Eleza. T. (1889.)
Elfin Pink. SJ. (Auten 1937.)
Eliane. DC. (Lem. E. 1927.)
Eliarsi Rosea. T. Rosa Eliarsi.
Elie Chevalier. DC. (Des. 1908.)
Elisa. DC. (Des.-Dor. 1922.)
Elise. D. (Dana 1926.)
Elise Renault. DC. (Dor. 1927.)
Elizabeth. T. (Cas. 1853.) *Elizabetta.*
Elizabeth (*Barrett*) Browning. DC. (Bra. O. 1907.)
Elizabeth Huntington. D.
Elizabeth, Queen of the Belgians. D.
Elizabetta. Elizabeth.
Ella Christiansen. DC. (Bra. A. 1925.)
Ella Christine Kelway. DC. (Kel. 1899.)
Ella (*C.*) Stubbs. T. (Kel. 1897.)
Ella Lewis. DC. (Lewis 1925.)
Ella Wheeler Wilcox. DC. (Bra. A. 1907.)
Elmer (*J.*) Wright. SJ. (Auten 1929.)
Eloise. D. (Auten 1934.)
Elsa Sass. D. (Sass 1930.)
Elwood Pleas. DC. (Pleas 1900.)
Emaline. D. (Wolfe 1931.)
Emanuel. DC.
Emelie. J.
Emendata. T. (Kel. 1889.)
Emile Fresart. T. (Mak. 1867.)
Emile Hoste. Boule Deneige.
Emilia. Blanche Denoisette.
Emilia Odorata. T. (Gue. 1873.)
Emily. SC. (Kel. 1884?)
Emma. DC. (Terry 1903.)
Emma. J.
Emma Belgica. T. (1867.) *Emma Belgie.*
Emma Lewis. DC. (Lewis 1923.)
Emma Mack. D. (Bra. A. 1936.)
Emmchen. DC. (G.&K. 1919.)
Emotion. T. (1889.)
Empereur Alexandre II. T. (Jap.& Sie. K. 1867.)
Empereur d'Autriche. T. (Sie. 1889.)
Empereur Dechine. T. (For. 1885.)
Empereur Defrance. T. (Sie. K. 1885?)
Empereur Derussie. T. (Sie. K. 1885.)
Empereur Nicolas. DC. (Cro. 1897.)
Emperor of Russia. Delachei.
Empress Eugenie. DC. (Kel. 1884?)
Empress of Britain. D. (Nor. 1930.)
Empress of India. DC. (Kel. 1912?)
Emy. SC. (Ber. 1924.)
Enchanteresse. DC. (Lem. 1903.) *Enchantress.*
Enchantment. DC. (Hol. 1907.)
Enchantress. SC. (Kel. 1884?)

PAEONIA, continued

Enfant Denancy. DC. (Cro. 1896.)
English Elegance. SC. (Kel. 1926.)
Entente Cordiale. DC. (Riv. 1917.)
Epictetus. SC.
Ernest Jardine. DC. (Kel. 1909-10.)
Ernest (*V.*) Taylor. DC. (Kel. 1923–25.)
Estafette. DC. (Des. 1910.)
Estelle. SJ. (Lym. 1933.)
E. St. Hill. SC. (Kel. 1884?)
Esu-gata. T. (Jap. 1926.)
E. (*T.*) Cook. DC. (Kel. 1884?)
Etendard (*Dugrand*) Homme. DC. (Mie. 1855.)
Ethereal. D. (Jones 1937.)
Etienne Brule. D. (Bre. 1934.)
Etienne Dessert. SC. (Des. 1913.)
Etienne Mechin. DC. (Mec. 1880.)
Etna. T. (Jap. 1911.)
Etoile Blanche. Isani Gidui.
Etoile Delyon. T. (Joa. 1906.)
Etoile Rose. Adzuma-Kagami.
Etta. DC. (Terry 1904.)
Eucharis. DC. (Lem. P. 1909.)
Eugene. T. (1889.)
Eugene Bigot. DC. (Des. 1894.)
Eugene Reignoux. DC. (Des. 1905.)
Eugene Verdier. DC. (Colst. 1864.)
Eugene Verdier. T. (Sen. 1889.)

This homonym is a synonym of another homonym, *Princess Louise.* T. (Sen. 1889), so appears to be without a tenable name.

Eugenie Verdier. DC. (Colst. 1864.)
Eunice Shaylor. DC. (Sha. 1919.)
Euphemia. DC. (Terry 1920.)
Eureka. DC.
Eva. J.
Evangeline. DC. (Lem. 1910.)
Evangeline Newhall. D. (Bra. A. 1936.)
Evelina. J.; T. (Pai. 1889.)
Eveline. J.
Evelyn Buechly. D. (Bue. 1923.)
Evelyn Vories. D. (Vor. after 1908.)
Evening Glow. DC. (Hol. 1907.)
Evening Star. D. (Sass 1937.)
Everett. D. (Sim. 1929.)
Excelsa. D. (Fran. 1931.)
Excelsior. DC. (Terry 1855?)
Exquisite. DC. (Kel. 1912.)
Exquisite First. J.
Exquisite Single. SC.
Fabiola. J.
Fairleigh. D. (Brown 1938.)
Fairy Dance. SJ. (Auten 1931.)
Fairy Queen. D. (Auten 1931.)
Fanny Crosby. DC. (Bra. O. 1907.)
Fanny Lee. DC. (Vor. 1924.)
Fantasy. DC. (Auten 1925.)
Farezzi. Rinzi.
Faribault. DC. (Bra. O. 1918.)
Fascination. D. (Bre. 1936.)
Fascinatus. T. (Kel. 1889.)
Faust. DC. (Mie. 1855.)
Faustine. DC. (Lem. E. 1924.)
Fauvette. J.
Favorite. S.; T. (Des. 1913.)
Favorite. S. (Ber. 1920.)
Felicity. J.
Felix Crousse. DC. (Cro. 1881.) *Victor Hugo.*
Femina. Saigyo-Zakura.
Ferdinand Stoliczka. DC. (Ric. 1904.)
Festiva. DC. (Donk. 1838.)
Festiva Fragrans. SJ.
Festiva Maxima. DC. (Mie. 1851.)

PAEONIA, continued

Fidelina. DC.
Fimbriata Carnea. T. (Mak. 1867.)
Fine Lady. SC. (Kel. 1909.)
Fireball. D. (Bra. A. 1933.)
Firelight. SJ. (Brant 1931.)
Flag of Truce. SC. (Kel. 1900.)
Flag of War. SC. (Kel. 1900.)
Flambeau. DC. (Cro. 1897.)
Flamboyant. C. (J. type.) *Kameno-kegoromo.*
Flamingo. SC. (Andr. 1925.)
Flaming Youth. SJ. (Pfe. 1932.)
Flashlight. C. (J. type.) (Hol. 1906.)
Flavia. DC. (Lewis 1921.)
Flora. S.; T. (Jap. Sie. 1867.) *Papaveracea Flora Plena.*
Floral Treasure. DC. (Ros. 1900.) *Delicatissima.*
Flora MacDonald. SC. (Kel. 1884?)
Flora Plena. D.; T. (V.Hou. 1873.)
Floraplena Rosea. T. (Nois. 1836.)
Florence Bond. D. (Gumm 1936.)
Florence MacBeth. DC. (Sass 1924.)
Florence Nicholls. D. (Nic. 1938.)
Florence Nightingale. DC. (Bra. O. 1907.)
Florestine. SC. (Ber. 1924.)
Floweret of Eden. DC. (Nec. 1924.)
Flower Girl. D. (Auten 1935.)
Foaming Wave. J.
Fontenelle. DC. (Ros. 1916.)
Fontenelli. T. (Hiss.)
Formosa Alba. DC. (Lem. P. 1830.)
Formosa Rosea. DC.
Fortschritt. Mme. (*Stuart*) Low.
Fortunes Gift. D. (Nee. 1930.)
Fortune Teller. SJ. (Auten 1936.)
Fowler. DC. (Kel. 1884?)
Fragrans. DC. (Banks 1805.) *Andre Lauries; Chinensis Rubra; Edulis Fragrans; Fragrantissima; Georges Cuvier.*
Fragrans Maxima. T. (Koe. 1853.) *Fragrans Maxima Plena.*
Fragrantissima. Fragrans.
Fraicheur. DC. (Lem. 1914.)
France. DC. (Kel. 1917.)
Francesca. DC. (Kel. 1884?)
Frances Herndon. D. (Pfe. 1932.)
Frances Shaylor. DC. (Sha. 1916.)
Frances Willard. DC. (Bra. O. 1907.)
Francis. SC.
Francis B. Hayes. DC. (Ric. 1904.)
Francis Nepean. DC. (Kel. 1916.)
Francois. J.
Francois Ortegat. DC. (Par. 1850.)
Francois Rousseau. DC. (Des. 1909.)
Frank Bramwell. SC. (Kel. 1884?)
Frank E. Good. D. (G.&R. 1929.)
Frankie Curtis. DC. (Vor. 1924.)
Franklins Pride. D. (Fran. 1931.)
Frank Wade. D. (Gumm 1930.)
Freckles. D. (Nee. 1926.)
Freedom. DC. (Kel. 1909–10.)
Friedrich Appelino. T. (Appel 1864.)
Fuji-arashi. S.; T. (Jap. 1893.)
Fu-ji-mine. J. *Cornelie.*
Fuji no mine. D.; J; T. (Jap. 1895.)
Fuji-no-mori. S.; T. (Jap. 1919.)
Fuji-oe-ryo. T. (Jap. 1926.)
Fuji-otome. T. (Jap. 1910.)
Fukaikiu. T.
Fuka-shigi. S.; T. (Jap. 1893.)
Fulgens.
Fulgida. DC. (Par. 1850.)
Fullmoon. SC. (Kel. 1884?)

PAEONIA, continued
Fusyama. SC.
Fuyajo. (J.)
Fuyo-ko. D.; T. (Jap. 1919.)
Fuyoren. T.
Gabisan. S.; T. (Jap. 1898.)
Galathee. DC. (Lem. P. 1900.)
Galtee More. DC. (Kel. 1884?)
Gardeners Joy. D. (Nee. 1936.)
Garden Princess. D. (Nee. 1930.)
Garnet. DC. (Kel. 1884?)
Garnet Beauty. SJ. (Wri. 1935.)
Gaston Leveque. T. (Lev. 1882.)
Geisha. J.
Geisho-ui. T. (Jap. 1926.)
Gekkyuden. T. (Jap. 1910.)
Gen. Baden-Powell. T. (Kel. 1901.)
Gen. Botha. SC. (Kel. 1884?)
General Bedeau. DC. (Cal. 1860.)
General Bertrand. DC. (Gue. 1846.)
General Buller. DC. (Kel. 1884?)
General Cavaignac. DC. (Cal. 1858.)
General Custer. DC. (Terry 1905.)
General Davoust. DC. (Cro. 1898.)
General Deboisdeffre. DC. (Cro. 1896.)
General Dodds. DC. (Cro. 1893.)
General Gorgas. DC. (VanL. 1924.)
General Grant. DC. (Terry 1855?)
General Hooker. DC. (Terry 1905.)
General Joffre. DC. (Kel. 1915.)
General Schofield. DC. (Terry 1855?)
Gene Stratton-Porter. DC. (Ros. 1925.)
Genevieve. DC. (Lem. E. 1925.)
Gen. Faidherbe. (*Souv. de*) Downing.
Gen. Hector McDonald. T. (Kel. 1901.)
Gentillesse. T. (1889.)
Gen. Wolfe. SC. (Kel. 1884?)
George Alexander. SC. (Kel. 1909-10.)
G.(*eorge*) B. Sowerby. DC. (Ric. 1857?)
George Hollis. DC. (Hol. 1907.)
George Rollison. T. (Mak. 1867.)
Georges Cuvier. Fragrans.
Georges Paul. T. (Sen. 1886.) (*Souv. d'*) *Adrien Seneclauze.*
Georges Sand. T. (Des. 1905.)
Georgette. J. (Wet. 1924.)
George Washington. DC. (Hol. 1904.)
George (*W.*) Peyton. D. (Nic. 1938.)
George (*W.*) Tryon. DC.
Georgiana Shaylor. DC. (Sha. 1908.)
Geraldine. J. (Kel. 1884?)
Geraldine Kelway. T. (Kel. 1904.)
Germaine. J.
Germaine Bigot. DC. (Des. 1902.)
Germaine Perthuis. SJ. (Mill.)
Germania. Negricans.
Germanie. T. (Mill.)
Gertrude. J.
Gettysburg. DC. (Hol. 1909.)
Giant. DC. (Kel. 1884?)
Gigantea. Lamartine.
Gilbert Barthelot. D. (Dor. 1932.)
Gilberte. DC. (Lem. E. 1927.)
Gil Blas. Adzuma-Nishiki.
Ginette. DC. (Des. 1915.)
Gin-Fukurin. Ginku-Kurin.
Ginko-nishiki. SC.
Ginko-Saki. T. (Jap. 1913.) *Rosette.*
Ginku-Kurin. T. (Jap. 1893.) *Gin-Fukurin.*

PAEONIA, continued
Gioku-Senshiu. T. (Jap. 1893.) *Gyoku-Senshiu; Mignon.*
Gioku-sho-dsurin. T. (Jap. 1893.)
Gioku-sho-haku. T. (Jap. 1898.)
Giovanna. T. (1889.)
Gisele. DC. (Lem. E. 1908.)
Gismonda. DC. (Cro. 1895.)
Giuseppina. T. (1889.)
Gleam of Gold. D. (Sass 1937.)
Glint of Gold. J. (Lewis 1923.)
Globosa. T. (Chi.-For. 1846.)
Gloire Debelges. Gloria Belgarum.
Gloire Deboskoop. DC.
Gloire Decasprit Callot. DC.
Gloire de Charles Gombault. DC. (Gom. 1866, introduced into commerce by Des. 1896.)
Gloire Dechenonceaux. DC. (Mec. 1880.)
Gloire Dedouai. DC. (Cal. 1860.)
Gloire Defrance. T. (1889.)
Gloire Degand. T. (1896.)
Gloire Deshanghai. T. (For. 1846.) *Dr. Bowring; Walneri.*
Gloire Detouraine. DC. (Des. 1908.)
Glomerosa. T. (Kel. 1889.)
Gloria. SJ.
Gloria Belgarum. T. (Goe. 1859–1865.) *Gloire Debelges.*
Gloriamundi. DC.
Gloriana. DC. (Kel. 1884?)
Gloriana. DC. (Nee. 1919.)
Gloriapatria. DC. (Fou. 1855.)
Glori Dedouai. DC. (Cal. 1860.)
Gloriosa. T. (Kel. 1889.)
Glorious. DC. (Kel. 1909.)
Glory. J. (Hol. 1907.)
Glory of Somerset. DC. (Kel. 1887.)
Glory of the Garden. SJ. (Toedt 1929.)
Go-Daigo. J. (Mill. 1926.)
Golden Bracelet. D. (Bra. A. 1939.)
Golden Dawn. DC. (Gumm 1923.)
Golden Glow. HH. (Gla. 1935.)
Golden Harvest. DC. (Ros. 1900.)
Golden Morn. SJ. (Gumm 1930.)
Golden Nugget. J. (Pleas 1913.)
Goldenrose. J.
Golden Wedding. DC. (Pleas 1900.)
Golden West. D. (Andr. 1932.)
Goldmine. J. (Hol. 1907.)
Goliath. DC. (Hol. 1904.)
Goods Dream. D. (G.&R. 1930.)
Goods Ideal. D. (G.&R. 1930.)
Goodwin. DC. (Kel. before 1922.)
Gopher Beauty. SJ. (Fran. 1933.)
Gosho-Zakura. D.; T. (Jap. 1919.)
Governor Fuller. D. (Thu. 1930.)
Governor Johnson. DC. (Bra. A. 1907.)
Governor Morton. DC. (Pleas 1917.)
Grace Batson. D. (Sass 1927.)
Grace (*D.*) Bryan. DC. (Ros. 1908.)
Grace Lewis. DC. (Lewis 1922.)
Grace Loomis. DC. (Sau. 1920.)
Grace Ott. DC. (Gumm 1923.)
Graciosa. T. (1864.)
Grand Duc Debade. T. (For. 1848.)
Grand Duchesse Helene. T. (Sie.)
Grand Duc Saxe Weimar. T. (Sie.)
Grand Duke. T. (Kel. 1897.)
Grand Frederic. Albalilacina.
Grandiflora. DC. (Ric. 1883.) *Alpheus Hyatt; Henry Woodward.*
Grandiflora Carnea Plena. DC.

PAEONIA, continued
Grandiflora Gigantea. T.
Grandiflora Niveaplena. DC. (Lemon 1824.)
Grandiflora Rosea. DC. (Lemon 1824.)
Grandiflora Rubra. DC.
Grandiflora Spectabilis. T. (Sen. 1846.)
Grandiflora Superba. T. (Gue. 1867.)
Grand Master. D. (Ros. 1934.)
Grand Sultan. T. (1846.)
Gravetye. DC. (Kel. 1884?)
Graziella. DC. (Des.)
Grenade. Asahi-Minato.
Gretchen. DC. (G.&K. 1911.)
Grizzel Muir. DC. (Kel. before 1895.)
Grover Cleveland. DC. (Terry 1904.) *Tecumseh.*
Guascoi. T. (1889.)
Guillaume Tell. T. (1887.)
Gumpoo-no-nishki. J.
Gyokuka. T. (Jap. 1896.)
Gyoku-Senshiu. Gioku-Senshiu.
Gyokushokaku. T.
Gyokutengaku. T.
Gyokutenshu. T.
Gypsy. C. (J. type.) (Hol. 1904.)
Habanera. SJ. (Auten 1930.)
Haddesiana. T. (Ital. 1867.) *Haddiyana.*
Hadesiana Superba. T. (1873.)
Hade-Sugata. S.; T. (Jap. 1898.)
H. (*A.*) Hagen. DC. (Ric. 1904.)
Hakodate. J.
Haku-Banriu. D.; T. (Jap. 1898.)
Haku-gan. S.; T. (Jap. 1893.) *Mousseline.*
Hakuo-jishi. T. (Jap. 1910.)
Haku-raku-ten. D.; T. (Jap. 1896.)
Hakuseko. J.
Hakusen-shu. T.
Haku-Shuden. S.; T. (Jap. 1919.)
Haku-wo. T. (Jap. 1896.)
Hamilton. DC. (Kel. 1884?)
Hana-daigin. T. (Jap. 1910.)
Hana-den. S.; T. (Jap. 1913.)
Hana-guruma. S.; T. (Jap. 1919.)
Hanai-Kada. T. (Jap. 1910.)
Hana-Kurabe. T. (Jap. 1926.)
Hana-no-Mikado. T. (Jap. 1926.)
Hana-no-nishiki. D.; T. (Jap. 1919.)
Hana-no-sato. J. *Cathedral.*
Hanano-sito. T. (Jap. 1916.)
Hana-no-Tsukasa. S.; T. (Jap. 1919.)
Hana-Tachibana. S.; T. (Jap. 1893.)
Hansina Brand. DC. (Bra. A. 1925.)
Hans (*P.*) Sass. D. (Sass 1937.)
Harbinger. HH. (Sau. 1929.)
Har-iai-nin. J. (Bab. 1929.)
Harmony. D. (Jones 1937.)
Harriet Beecher Stowe. Clara Anderson.
Harriet Farnsley. DC. (Bra. A. 1916.)
Harriet Olney. SC. (Bra. A. 1920.)
Harry (*F.*) Little. D. (Nic. 1933.)
Harry King. T. (1889.)
Harry (*L.*) Burden. D. (Nee 1930.)
Harry (*L.*) Richardson. DC. (Ros. 1925.)
Harry Moore. D. (Fran. 1928.)
Haruno-Akebono. DT.
Harvard Crimson. D. (Smith 1928.)
Hatsuegi. DJ.
Hatsu-hinode. T. (Jap. 1926.)
Hatsu-tori. Jeanne.

PAEONIA, continued
Hawa. J. (Mill.)
Hazel Kinney. DC. (Bra. A. 1925.)
Hearts Idol. D. (Nee. 1936.)
Hebe. DC. (Ter.)
Hebe. Berenice.
Hecate. T. (Kel. 1889.)
Heinburg. DC. (G.&K.)
Heldi. T. (1867.) *Hildi; Holdi.*
Helen. SC. (Thu. 1922.)
Helena. DC.
Helena Leslie. DC. (Barr)
Helene Williams. D. (Pfe. 1932.)
Helen Glover. DC. (Kel. 1884?)
Helen Robertson. DC. (Terry)
Helen Wolaver. DC. (Bra.A. 1918.)
Hemera. T. (Kel. 1889.)
H. (*E.*) Milner. T. (Kel. 1892.)
Hennepin. SJ. (Auten 1931.)
Henri. D.; T. (1889.)
Henri Core. DC. (Dor. 1925.)
Henri Demay. DC. (Cal. 1866.)
Henri Laurent. DC. (Cro. 1875.)
Henri Murger. DC. (Cro. 1895.)
Henri Pingard. T. (Gue. after 1863.)
Henri Potin. C. (J.type) (Dor. 1924.)
Henry Avery. DC. (Bra. O. 1907.)
Henry Irving. T. (Kel. 1899.)
Henry (*M.*) Vories. DC. (Vor. 1924.)
Henry Webster. D. (Fran. 1928.)
Henry Woodward. Grandiflora.
Hera. T. (Kel. 1889.)
Her Grace. SC. (Kel. 1884?)
Hericartiana. DC. (Gue. 1842.)
Herkomer. T. (Kel. 1897.)
Hermes. SC. (Kel. 1884?)
Hermione. D. (Sass 1932.)
Hespanola. DC. (Andr. 1923.)
Hesperus. SC. (Kel. 1884?)
Heterophylla. T. (Sen. 1846.)
Hettie Elliot. J. (Pleas 1910.)
H. (*F.*) Reddick. DC. (Bra. A. 1913.)
Hiawatha. D. (Fran. 1931.)
Hich-i-fuko-jin. T. (Jap. 1910.)
High Jinks. J. (Auten 1929.)
Highland Lassie. SJ. (Toedt 1929.)
Hildi. Heldi.
Hinode-Dsuru. S.; T. (Jap. 1898.) *L'Aiglon.*
Hinode-gumo. T. (Jap. 1927.)
Hinode-sekai. Sunrise.
Hino-Maru. T. (Jap. 1896.)
Hinomisaki. T.
Hino-tobera. T. (Jap. 1896.)
Hiodoshi. T.
Hiogo. SJ. (Mill. 1909.)
Hippolyte. T. (For. 1873.)
Hirishima. J.
Hiryo. S.; T. (Jap. 1896.) *Hiriu.*
His Majesty. J. (Kel. 1929.)
Hissiana. T. (Hiss. 1867.) *Blanche Dehiss.*
Hogarth. SC. (G.&K. 1912.)
Ho-Gioku. J.
Hohenbuchau. DC. (G.&K. 1926.)
Holbein. SC. (G.&K. 1910.)
Holdi. Heldi.
Holing Kung. T.
Hollywood. J. (Auten 1937.)
Homer. DC. (Kel. 1915.)
Homere. DC. (Lem. E. 1902.)
Hon. Alfred Deakin. SC. (Kel. 1884?)
Honeysweet. D. (Fran. 1933.)
Hope. HH. (Sau. 1929.)
Horaciana. Horatiana.
Horairishishi. T.
Horaisan. T. (Jap. 1926.)

PAEONIA, continued
Horatiana. T. (Hiss 1842.) *Horaciana; Horotiana.*
Hottentot. D. (Dana 1926.)
Hoveys White. DC. (Ric.)
Howden. DC. (Kel. 1884?)
(*H.R.H.*) Princess Louise. DC. (Kel. 1912.)
Hubert Degris. J. (D.&S. 1929.)
Humei. DC. (Ander. 1810.)
Humei. T. (Lem. 1892.) *Humel.*
Humeicarnea. DC. (Gue. 1856.)
Humoresque. DC. (Auten 1925.)
Hunt Cup. SC. (Kel. 1884?)
Huppec. Comata.
Hutton. DC. (Kel. 1884?)
Hyakka. J.
Ianthe.
Ianthina. T. (Kel. 1889.)
Ida. Picta.
Ida Pleas. SC. (Pleas)
Ideal. D. (Fran. 1931.)
Illinois. T. (Jap. 1911.)
Illustris. T. (Kel. 1889.)
Imperatrice d'Autriche. T. (1867.)
Imperatrice Defrance. T. (1867.)
Imperatrice Derussie. T. (Gue. 1873.)
Imperatrice Eugenie. T. (1889.)
Imperatrice Josephine. D.; T. (Hiss. 1839.)
Imperial Queen. J. (Wal.)
Imperial Red. SJ. (Sass 1932.)
Incarnata Plena. T. (Nois. 1839.)
Inclita. T. (Kel. 1889.)
Indiana Moon. D. (Ros. 1934.)
Indian Maid. D. (Dana 1926.)
Ingenieur Doriat. D. (Dor. 1931.)
In Memoriam. D.
Innocence. C. (J.type.) (Hol. 1904.)
Inspecteur Lavergne. DC. (Dor. 1924.)
Institeteur Doriat. J. (Dor. 1925.)
Irene Coe. D. (Pfe. 1932.)
Irma. DC. (Cal. 1859.)
Iroka. J. (Mill.)
Iromasari. T.
Iro-no-seki. D.; T. (Jap. 1893.)
Iroquois. J. (Auten 1931.)
Isani Gidui. *Etoile Blanche; Isami Jishi.*
Isoline. DC. (Lem. 1916.)
Iten-shikai. J.
Ivanhoe. DC. (Pleas 1913.)
Iwatogoe. T.
Iwato-ichi. T. (Jap. 1910.)
Iwato-kagami. S.; T. (Jap. 1895.) *Phenix.*
Iwato-Kagura. T. (Jap. 1926.)
Iwatosaki. T.
Iwato-sh. T. (Jap. 1896.)
Jack Rose. D. (Fran. 1928.)
Jacoba. J.
Jacqueline. J.
Jacques Dessert. D. (Dor. 1929.)
Jacques Doriat. J. (Dor. 1928.)
Jacquini. T. (1889.)
James Boyd. DC. (Thu. 1919.)
James Kelway. T. (Kel. 1898.)
James Kelway. Lady Derby.
James Pillow. D. (Chr.&Pil. 1936.)
James (*R.*) Mann. DC. (Thu. 1920.)
James William Kelway. DC. (Kel. 1926.)
Jane Addams. D. (Bra. A. 1936.)
Janes Oleson. DC. (Ole. 1926.)
Japanese Beauty. J. (Sass 1937.)

PAEONIA, continued
Japanese Departing Sun. JS. *Departing Sun.*
Japanese Fairy. SC. (Secor 1924.)
Jap Giant. J. (Fran. 1933.)
Jappensha-ikku. J. (Mill. 1924.)
Jawi. T. (1889.)
J. (*D.*) Nicholson. DC. (Kel. 1912.)
Jean Ann. J. (Fran. 1928.)
Jean (*Baptiste*) Rendatler. DC. (Cal. 1866.)
Jean Cooperman. D. (Bra. A. 1938.)
Jean Dereszke. T. (Kel. 1899.)
Jean (*E.*) Bockstoce. HH. (Boc. 1933.)
Jean Mackay. DC. (Secor 1924.)
Jeanne. J. *Hatsu-tori.*
Jeanne d'Arc. DC. (Cal. 1858.)
Jeanne d'Arc. T. (Sen. 1889.)
Jeanne Ernould. SC. (Dor. 1926.)
Jeanne Gaudichau. DC. (Mill. 1902.)
Jeanne Lapandry. J. (Dor. 1925.)
Jeannette. HH. (Sau. 1938.)
Jeannette Oppliger. DC. (Bra. O. 1913.)
Jeannot. DC. (Des. 1918.)
Jennie (*E.*) Richardson. DC. (Hol. 1909.)
Jenny Lind. DC. (Barr 1860.)
Jessie (*K.*) Crosby. DC. (Hol. 1907.)
Jessie Kelly. J. (Terry 1855?)
Jessie Shaylor. DC. (Sha. 1916.)
Jewel. HH. (Gla. 1931.)
Jewel of Chusan. T. (1864.)
Jin-Joden. T. (Jap. 1926.)
Jitsugetsu-nichiki. T. (Jap. 1927.)
Jocelyn. DC. (Lem. F. 1923.)
Joehanna. D. (Wolfe 1931.)
John Alden. D. (Dana 1926.)
John (*C.*) Dugar. D. (H.G.)
John Hancock. DC. (Hol. 1907.)
John (*L.*) Crenshaw. D.
John Lindley. T. (Sie.)
John (*M.*) Good. DC. (Welsh 1921.)
John (*M.*) Lewis. D. (Lewis 1921.)
John Richardson. DC. (Ric. 1904.)
Jonathan Gibson.
Josephelus. D. (Guppy 1932.)
Joseph Griffin. DC. (Pleas 1909.)
Josephine. J.
Josephine (*Hope*) Healy. D. (Bra. A. 1936.)
Josephine Kelway. SC. (Kel. 1884?)
Josephine Seneclauze. T. (Sen. 1889.)
Joseph-Maria Serra. Mons. (*Joseph-Maria*) Serra.
Joseph Plague. J. (Dor. 1928.)
Joy. HH. (Sau. 1928.)
Joyce. D. (Auten 1938.)
Joy of Life. DC. (Kel. 1912.)
Jubilee. DC. (Pleas 1908.) *Pleas Jubilee.*
Judge Berry. DC. (Bra. 1907.)
Judge Orr. D. (Edl. 1929.)
Judge Snook. D. (G.&R. 1930.)
Jules Calot. DC. (Cal. 1861.)
Jules Pirlot. T. (Mak. 1867.)
Julia. DC. (Auten 1926.)
Julia Ward Howe. DC. (Hol. 1906.) *Mrs. (Julia Ward) Howe.*
Juliette Dessert. DC. (Des. 1888.)
Julius Caesar. T. (Kel. 1899.)
June Brilliant. D. (Auten 1938.)
June Day. DC. (Fra. 1920.)
June Moon. SJ. (Auten 1931.)
June Rose. D. (Jones 1937.)

PAEONIA, continued
June Welcome. SJ. (Dana 1926.)
Juno. DC.; T. (Ter.)
Jupiter. DC. (Terry 1860?)
Jupiter. SJ. (Kel. 1884?)
Jupiter. Yomo-no-homare.
Jupiter. ST. (Pai. 1889.)
Jupiter. Reine Elizabeth.
Kaba-gasane. T. (Jap. 1927.)
Kagara-kun. J.
Kaguraasobi. T.
Kagura-jishi. T. (Jap. 1926.)
Kagura-Nishiki. S.; T. (Jap. 1908.)
Kai-hako-hatsu. T. (Jap. 1926.)
Kaisairon. J. (Mill. 1926.)
Kaiser Leopold. T. (Rinz. 1851.)
Kajura-Jima. S.; T. (Jap. 1898.) *Mirabeau.*
Kama-asobi. T. (Jap. 1895.)
Kamada. T. (Jap. 1910.)
Kamada-Fuji. D.; T. (Jap. 1823.)
Kamakurako. J.
Kamargo. J. (Lewis.)
Kamatonishiki. T.
Kameno-kegoromo. Flamboyant.
Kamino-reginis. J.
Kamma. SJ.
Kankakee. SJ. (Auten 1931.)
Kansenden. S.; T. (Jap. 1898.)
Kan tsaou hwang. T.
Karafune. J.; T.
Karagoma. J.
Karakoasobi. T.
Karanishiki. T.
Kara-ori. T. (Jap. 1896.)
Kara-ori-nishiki. J.; T.
Karatsu. J. (Mill.)
Karl Haag. T. (Kel. 1901.)
Karl Rosenfield. DC. (Ros. 1908.)
Kasane-jishi. T. (Jap. 1913.) *Rosalind.*
Kashira. Shishi-gashira.
Kasimino Requois. J.
Kaskaskia. SJ. (Auten 1931.)
Kasumi-no-mori. S.; T. (Jap. 1910.)
Kate Barry. J. (Nic. 1938.)
Katharine Havemeyer. DC. (Thu. 1921.)
Katherine. DC. (Bra. A. 1909.) *Catherine.*
Katherine Engle. SC. (Engle 1926.)
Katori-nahiko. J. (Mill. 1924.)
Kaub. Caub.
Kazari-uma. T. (Jap. 1896.)
Kedney. DC. (Kel. 1884?)
Kehai. T.
Kelways Betty. DC. (Kel. 1917.)
Kelways Bridesmaid. DC. (Kel. 1884?)
Kelways Circe. DC. (Kel. 1916.)
Kelways Darling. DC. (Kel. 1884?)
Kelways David. DC. (Kel. 1916.)
Kelways Diana. SC. (Kel. 1884?)
Kelways Eve. SC. (Kel. 1884?)
Kelways Exquisite. DC. (Kel. 1884?)
Kelways Florizel. T. (Kel. 1897.)
Kelways Glorious. DC. (Kel. 1909.)
Kelways Gorgeous. SC. (Kel. 1884?)
Kelways Humorist. SC. (Kel. 1884?)
Kelways Lovely. DC. (Kel. 1912.)
Kelways Lovely Lady. SC. (Kel. 1926.)
Kelways Luck. DC. (Kel. 1884?)
Kelways Malmaison. DC. (Kel. 1926.)
Kelways Peace. DC. (Kel. 1884?)
Kelways Queen. DC. (Kel. 1909.) *Queen.*

PAEONIA, continued
Kelways Remembrance. DC. (Kel. 1916.)
Kelways Rosalie. SJ. (Kel. 1884?)
Kelways Rosemary. DC. (Kel. 1916.) *Rosemary.*
Kelways Rose of Delight. SC. (Kel. 1926.)
Kelways Silvo. SC. (Kel. 1926.)
Kelways Spion Kop. Spion Kop.
Kelways Success. DC. (Kel. 1884?)
Kelways Unique. DC. (Kel. 1917.)
Kelways Wild Rose. Wildrose.
Kemankeag. SJ. (Guppy 1935.)
Kenan Hasselaar. T. (Kre. 1867.)
Kenduskeag. SJ. (Guppy 1935.)
Kenny. T. (Cas. 1867.)
Kewanee. SJ. (Auten 1930.)
Kickapoo. SJ. (Auten 1931.)
Kigyoku. D.; T. (Jap. 1919.)
Kiku-Botan. T. (Jap. 1919.)
Killington. D. (Fre. 1934.)
Kin-Fukurin. S.; T. (Jap. 1896.)
King Albert. SC. (Kel. 1916.)
King Alfred. T. (Kel. 1897.)
King Bee. D. (Wri. 1935.)
King Gustav. D. (Ros. 1934.)
King of England. C. (J. type.) (Kel. 1902.)
King of Peace. DC. (Hol. 1909.)
King of the Belgians. Belgian King Albert.
Kingsbury. SC. (Kel. 1884?)
Kings Daughter. DC. (Kel. 1884?)
Kinipaiseten. S.; T. (Jap. 1913.)
Kinkajka. T.
Kino-kimo. CJ.
Kinsen-shu. T.
Kinsui. J.
Kintajio. S.; T. (Jap. 1913.)
Kioto. J. (Mill. 1926.)
Kiowa. SJ. (Auten 1931.)
Kirin-nishiki. T. (Jap. 1910.)
Kirinshi. T.
Kiya. T. (Jap. 1893.)
Knight of the Thistle. J. (Kel. 1884?)
Kochleni. Comte Deflandre.
Kochomai. J. *Claire.*
Kochs Weisse. T. (Koc. 1889.) *Weisse.*
Koenigin Elizabeth. Reine Elizabeth.
Koenigswinter. DC. (G.&K. 1912.)
Kogane-Zome. T. (Jap. 1926.)
Koi-Kagura. T. (Jap. 1926.)
Kojiki. J. (Mill. 1926.)
Kokirin. S.; T. (Jap. 1893.) *Papillon.*
Kokirin-Kin. T. (Jap.)
Kokiriu-Nishiki. T. (Jap. 1905.) *Tulipe.*
Kokizan. T.
Kokkoshi. T.
Kokuhow. T.
Kokurun-rui. J.
Kokuryu. T.
Kokury Ukaku. J.
Komachi-haku. T.
Koningin Wilhelmina. DC. (Kre. 1912.)
Koron-jishi. T. (Jap. 1927.)
Koron-Koku. S.; T. (Jap. 1893.) *Volcan.*
Koronshibori. T.
Kossi. J. (Mill.)
Krinkled White. SJ. (Bra. A. 1928.)
Kuckko. T.
Kukeni-jishi. J.

PAEONIA, continued
Kumagaya. T.
Kumagoe. J.
Kumoi-dsuru. S.; T. (Jap. 1893.)
Kumoisaka. T.
Kumona-Nishiki. T. (Jap. 1913.) *Eclair.*
Kumonano-Tsuki. T. (Jap. 1893.)
Kumona-uye. T.
Kumo-no-nishiki. T. (Jap. 1913.)
Kuni-mori. J.
Kunitoko. T.
Kurama-yama. T. (Jap. 1916.)
Kuro-botan. S.; T. (Jap. 1896.) *Negresse.*
Kushota. S.; T.
Kusuhana. J.
Kwanjo-raku. T.
Kwausenshu. T.
Kyokkasen. T.
Labelle Helene. DC. (Kel. 1915.)
Labolas. J. (Kel. 1884?)
Labrune. DC. (Ver. 1860.)
Lacanadienne. D. (Bre. 1936.)
Lacepede. SC. (Kel. 1884?)
Laciniata. T. (H.&S. 1864.)
Laciniata. J.
Lacoquette. DC. (Gue. 1861.)
Lactea. T. (Dav. 1839 or Gue. 1853.) *Lactea Alba; Lacteola.*
Lactea Superba. T.
Lacteola. Lactea.
Lady (*Alexandra*) Duff. DC. (Kel. 1902.)
Lady (*Algernon*) Lennox. D.; T. (Kel. 1902.)
Lady Anna. DC. (Cal. 1856.)
Lady Bellew. SC. (Kel. 1884?)
Lady Beresford. DC. (Kel. 1895.)
Lady Bowill. T. (1889.)
Lady Bramwell. DC. (Kel. 1884?)
Lady Byng. J. (Nor. 1926.)
Lady Caillard. DC. (Kel. 1884?)
Lady Carrington. DC. (Kel. 1884?)
Lady Curzon. DC. (Kel. 1901.)
Lady Darmouth. DC. (?about 1850.)
Lady Derby. DC. (Kel. 1884?) *James Kelway* (in part).
Lady Emily. DC. (Pleas 1907.)
Lady Godiva. SC. (Kel. 1884?)
Lady (*Gwendolen*) Cecil. DC. (Kel. 1889?)
Lady Halle. T. (Kel. 1898.)
Lady (*Helen*) Vincent. SC. (Kel. 1902.)
Lady Iris. DC. (Pleas 1907.)
Lady Isadore. DC.
Lady Kate. DC. (Vor. 1924.)
Lady (*Leonora*) Bramwell. DC. (Kel. before 1895.) *Docteur Bretonneau* V.Ver., *not* Gue.
Lady Ley. SC. (Kel. 1884?)
Lady (*Lillian*) Ogle. SC. (Kel. 1884?)
Lady Long. T. (Kel. 1899.)
Lady (*Margaret*) Ferguson. SJ. (Kel. 1884?)
Lady (*Mary*) Dashwood. SC. (Kel. 1884?)
Lady Mayoress. DC. (Kel. 1909?)
Lady Millais. T. (Kel. 1897.)
Lady of Grace. S. (Kel. 1884?)
Lady of Langport. DC. (Kel. 1884?)
Lady of the Lake. DC. (Lewis 1923.)
Lady of the West. DC. (Kel. 1912.)
Lady Pocock. DC. (Kel. 1884?)
Lady (*Renny*) Watson. SC. (Kel. 1884?)

PAEONIA, continued
LADY ROMILLY. DC. (Kel. 1884?)
LADY (*Sarah*) WILSON. T. (Kel. 1901.)
LADY SKELMERSDALE. T. (Kel. 1897.)
LADYSMITH. T. (Kel. 1901.)
LADY SOMERSET. DC. (Barr.)
LADY STRADBROKE. DC. (Kel. 1884?)
LADY WOLSELEY. SC. (Kel. 1884?)
LAFAYETTE. DC. (Des. 1904.)
LAFEE. DC. (Lem. 1906.)
LAFIANCEE. DC.
Lafiancee. ALBIFLORA, THE BRIDE; THE BRIDE.
LAFONTAINE. D. (Des. 1893.)
Lafontaine. DC. (Lem. 1904.)
LAFRAICHEUR. SC. (Des. 1905.)
LAFRANCE. T. (Jap. 1897.)
Lafrance. DC. (Lem. 1901.)
LAGLOIRE. T. (v.Gee. 1873.)
LAGRANGE. DC.
LAHOLLANDE. DC. (Nie. 1918.)
L'Aiglon. HINODE-DSURU.
LAIUS. DC.
LAKE O'SILVER. DC. (Fra. 1920.)
LAKME. T. (Jap. 1897.)
LALORRAINE. DC. (Lem. 1901.)
Lalorraine. T. (Lem. 1913.)
LAMARTINE. DC. (Calot 1860.) *Gigantea.*
Lamartine. DC. (Lem. 1908.)
LAMBERTINAE. D.; T. (Mak. 1846.) (*Mlle.*) *Maria Closon; Mme.* (*Maria*) *Closon.*
LANGPORT QUEEN. DC. (Kel. 1884?)
LANGPORT TRIUMPH. DC. (Kel. 1884?)
LANUIT. SC. (Sha. 1918.)
LAPERLE. DC. (Cro. 1886.) *Pearl.*
Larezzi. RINZI.
LAROSIERE. DC. (Cro. 1888.)
LASALLE. SJ. (Auten 1931.)
LAST ROSE. D. (Sass 1930.)
LASUBLIME. DC. (Par. 1850.)
LATENDRESSE. DC. (Cro. 1896.)
LATULIPE. DC. (Cal. 1872.)
LAURA. SC. (Des. 1913.)
LAURA (*Coates*) REED. SJ. (Hol. 1889?)
LAURA DESSERT. DC. (Des. 1913.)
LAURA PLEAS. DC. (Pleas 1855?)
LAURA VORIES. DC. (Vor. 1924.)
LAURENCE. DC. (Lem. E. 1911.)
LAURENS KOSTER. T. (Kre. 1867.)
LAUTA. T. (Kel. 1889.)
LAVENDER PINK. D. (Fran. 1931.)
LAVERNE. DC.
LAVERNE CHRISTMAN. DC. (Bra. 1925.)
LAVESTALE. DC. (Cal. 1870.)
LAVILLE DE ST. DENIS. T. (Mou. 1854.)
LAVILLE DE VERSAILLES. (Hiss 1873.)
Laville de Versailles. MARIE RATTIER.
LAVOLUPTUEUSE. DC. (Gue. 1861.)
LEANDER (*Starr*) JAMESON. SC. (Kel. 1884?)
L'ECLATANTE. DC. (Cal. 1860.)
LECYGNE. DC. (Lem. 1907.)
Lee's Grandiflora Rubra. (*Souv. d'*) AUGUSTE MIELLEZ.
LEGIONAIRE. HH. (Gla. 1928.)
LEJOUR. SC. (Sha. 1915.)
L'ELEGANTE. DC. (Gue. 1857.)
LEMOINE LEWIS. DC. (Lewis 1921.)
LEMON QUEEN. J.
LENA ASHWELL. DC. (Kel. 1884?)
LENOIR. SC. (Sha. 1916.)
LEODIENSE. T. (1864.)

PAEONIA, continued
LEONA CAUSTIN. D. (Pfe. 1932.)
LEONARD KELWAY. DC.; T. (Kel. 1897.)
LEONIE. J.
Leonie. MME. CALOT.
LEOPOLDO. D.; T. (Ital. 1864.) *Rose Cherie.*
LEORNEM. T. (Jap. 1897.)
LESOLEIL. T. (Oud. 1843.)
L'ESPERANCE. DC. (Gue.)
L'Esperance. T. (Lem. E. 1910.)
L'ETINCELANTE. SC. (Des. 1905.)
LETITIA. SC. (Kel. 1884?)
LEUCADIA. SC.
LEVAL D'AUBRAY. T. (Jap. 1897.)
LEVIATHAN. DC. (Kel. 1899.)
LEWIS AMERICANBEAUTY. DC. (Lewis 1921.)
LEWIS FAIRYQUEEN. DC. (Lewis 1926.)
LEWIS SALMON. J. (Lewis)
LEZINSKA DEMIRBEL. T. (1889.)
LIBELLULE. DC. (Des. 1922.)
LIBERTY. DC. (Hol. 1905.)
LIBERTY BELLE. D. (Nee. 1926.)
LIEUTENANT HOBSON. J. (Hol.)
LIEUT. WARNESFORD V.C. DC. (Kel. 1884?)
LILACINA. D.; T. (Chi.-For. 1846.)
LILACINA PLENISSIMA. T. (Bau. 1836.) *Lilacina Major Plena; Plenissima Lilacina Major.*
LILACINA SEMIPLENA. T. (Bau. 1836.)
LILACINA SUPERBA. DC. (Buy. 1842.)
LILACINA VARIEGATA. DC.
LILLE. DC. (Mil. 1902.)
LILLIAN GUMM. DC. (Gumm 1921.)
LILLIE MCGILL. DC. (Terry 1855?)
LILLIPUTIANA. T. (Hiss before 1841.)
L'ILLUSTRATION. DC. (Gue. 1835–1866?)
LIMOSEL. DC. (Kel. 1898.)
LINA. T. (1889.)
L'INDISPENSABLE. DC.
LINNE. DC. (Ver. 1860.)
L'INNOCENCE. DC. (Sha. 1915.)
LITTLE ARISTOCRAT. DC. (Pleas 1913.)
LITTLE BEAUTY. DC. (Pleas? 1855?)
LITTLE NELL. DC. (Pleas 1855?)
LITTLE SWEETHEART. DC. (Bra. A. 1907.)
LIVINGSTONE. DC. (Cro. 1879.)
LONDINIA. T. (Bel. 1867.)
LONGFELLOW. DC. (Bra. 1907.)
LOOS. SJ. (Kel. 1884?)
LORA DEXHEIMER. DC. (Bra. 1913.)
LORCH. DC. (G.&K.)
LORD AVEBURY. DC. (Kel. 1884?)
LORD BURNHAM. T. (Kel. 1906.)
LORD BYRON. T. (Kel. 1899.)
LORD CAVAN. SC. (Kel. 1884?)
LORD DUNRAVEN. T. (Kel. 1897.)
LORD IVEAGH. T. (Kel. 1896.)
LORD KITCHENER. T. (Kel. 1900.)
Lord Kitchener. SC. (Kel.)
Lord Kitchener. DC. (Ren. 1916.)
LORD LEIGHTON. T. (Kel. 1897.)
LORD LYTTON. DC.
Lord Macartney. CONFUCIUS.
LORD MACAULAY. T. (Kel. 1889.)
LORD MILNER. T. (Kel. 1904.)
LORD MORLEY. SC. (Kel. 1884?)
LORD ROBERTS. T. (Kel. 1901?)
LORD ROSEBERY. DC. (Kel. 1895–96.)
LORD SELBOURNE. T. (Kel. 1897.)
LORD TENNYSON. T. (Kel. 1889.)
LOREN FRANKLIN. D. (Fran. 1931.)
LOTHARIO. J. (Wet. 1921.)

PAEONIA, continued
LOTTIE COLLINS. DC. (Barr.)
LOTUS. J.
LOTUS CUP. D. (Nee. 1936.)
LOUISA BRAND. DC. (Bra. A. 1913.)
LOUIS BARTHELOT. DC. (Dor. 1927.)
LOUISE. T. (Den. 1846.)
Louise. RUIGEGNO.
LOUISE ANN. SJ. (Bra. A. 1936.)
LOUISE MOUCHELET. T. (Mou. 1860.)
LOUISE ODIER. T. (1889.)
LOUISE RENAULT. DC. (Cro. 1881.)
LOUIS JOLIET. D. (Auten 1929.)
LOUIS PARMENTIER. T. (Par. 1867.)
LOUIS VANHOUTTE. DC. (Cal. 1867.)
LOU SHENK. J. (Ros. 1927.)
LOVANCIA. J. (Lym. 1933.)
LOVELINESS. DC. (Hol. 1907.)
LOVERS DREAM. D. (Ros. 1934.)
LOWELL THOMAS. D. (Ros. 1934.)
LOYALTY. D. (Nee. 1936.)
Lucie. OHIRAMA.
LUCIE MALARD. DC. (Cro. 1879.)
LUCIENNE. SC. (Des. 1908.)
LUCILE HARTMAN. D. (Fran. 1931.)
LUCKYDAY. SJ. (Auten 1934.)
LUCKYSTAR. D. (Auten 1938.)
LUCKYSTRIKE. D. (Wri. 1935.)
LUCRECE. SC.
LUCY DUNN. DC. (Wet. 1924.)
LUCY (*E.*) HOLLIS. DC. (Hol. 1907.)
LUCY SHAYLOR. DC. (Sha. 1920.)
LUDWIG RICHTER. SC. (G.&K. 1919.)
LUELLA SHAYLOR. DC. (Sha. 1917.)
LUETTA PFEIFFER. DC. (Bra. 1916.)
LULU CLIFFE. J. (Wri. 1935.)
LULU LITTLE. D. (Lit. 1938.)
LULU WILSON. SJ. (Pfe. 1932.)
LUMENA. T. (Kel. 1889.)
LUNA. T. (Kel. 1889.)
LUTEA. T. (Chi.-Fra. 1902.)
LUTEA PLENISSIMA. DC. (Buy. 1842.) *Victor Durufle.*
LUTEA SUPERBA. T. (Lem. E. 1910 or earlier.)
LUTEA VARIEGATA. DC. (Lem. P. 1830; also attributed to Que. 1842.)
LUXOR. D. (Sass 1933.)
L. W. POLLOCK. D. (Bra. A. 1936.)
LYNDA. DC. (Bra. A. 1907.)
MABEL CLAIRE. DC. (Pleas 1916.)
MABELLE. T. (1846.)
MABEL (*L.*) FRANKLIN. DC. (Fran. 1920.)
MACULOSA. T. (Kel. 1889.)
MADAME BUTTERFLY. J.
MADAME (*Claude*) TAIN. D.
MADAME (*Emile*) DEBATENE. D.
MADAME ESCARY. D.
MADAME (*Henri*) CORE. D.
MADCAP. SJ. (Auten 1931.)
MADELEINE GAUTHIER. SC. (Des. 1908.)
MADELON. DC. (Des. 1922.)
MADONI. T. (Ital. 1864; 1867.)
MAFEKING. SC. (Kel.)
Magicienne. AKASHI-JISHI.
MAGNIFICA. DC.
MAGNIFICENCE. J.; T. (Kel. 1889.)
Magnificent. BRANDS MAGNIFICENT.
MAGNIFLORA LILACINA. T. (1867.)
MAHAL. DJ. (Sass 1934.)
MAHARAJAH OF GWALIOR. DC. (Kel. 1884?)
MAHOGANY. HH. (Gla. 1937.)
MAIDENS BLUSH. DC. (Pleas 1855?)
MAID OF HONOR. DC. (Hol. 1909.)

PAEONIA, continued

MAIFLEURI.
MAINZ. D.; DC. (G.&K. 1926.)
MAIREI.
MAITLAND. DC. (Kel. 1884?)
MAJESTIC. D.
MAJOR LODER. J. (Kel. 1884?)
MAKITATEYAMA. J.
MAKUNO-UCHI. T. (Jap. 1910.)
MAMAN MILLET. DC. (Mil. 1924.)
MAMMOTH. T. (v.Hou. 1867.)
MANATZURU. T.
MANDARIN. T. (Chi.-For. 1867.)
MANETTI. T. (Bur. 1867; 1873.) *Manette.*
MANITOU. DC. (Andr. 1923.)
MANKATO. SJ. (Bra. A. 1936.)
MANOAH. D. (Auten 1933.)
MAN O'WAR. HH. (Sau. 1929.)
Man o'War. SJ. (Bra. A. 1936.)
MARANACOOK. J. (Guppy 1935.)
MARCEAU. T. (Des. 1913.)
MARCELLE DESSERT. DC. (Des. 1899.)
MARCHIONESS OF GRANBY. T. (Kel. 1897.)
MARCHIONESS OF LANSDOWNE. DC. (Kel. 1899.)
MARCHIONESS OF LONDONDERRY. T. (Kel. 1897.)
MARCHIONESS OF SALISBURY. T. (Kel. 1897.)
MARCIA DEWEY. D. (Lym. 1933.)
MARCONI. J. (Kel. 1909.)
Marechal MacMahon. AUGUSTIN D'HOUR.
Marechal Vaillant. (Cal. 1867.) (*Souvenir d'*) AUGUSTE MIELLEZ.
MARGARET ATWOOD. J.
MARGARET (*Elliott*) WAGGAMAN. D. (Dor. 1932.)
MARGARET LOUGH. D. (Gumm 1929.)
MARGARET VIERHELLER. DC. (Vet. 1920.)
MARGINATA. T. (Kel. 1889.)
MARGUERITE. J.; T. (Sen. 1867.)
MARGUERITE DESSERT. SC. (Des. 1913.)
MARGUERITE GAUDICHAU. DC. (Mill. 1903.)
MARGUERITE GERARD. DC. (Cro. 1892.)
MARIA. T. (Pai. 1889.)
MARIANNA. D.; T. (Ital. 1854.)
MARIAN PFEIFFER. D. (Pfe. 1925.)
MARIA-THERESA. T. (Sen. 1846.)
MARIE. DC. (Kel. 1868.)
MARIE BEZANCON. T. (Pai. 1889.)
MARIE CORELLI. T. (Kel. 1902.)
MARIE CROUSSE. DC. (Cro. 1892.)
MARIE DEROUX. DC. (Cro. 1881.)
MARIE D'HOUR. DC. (Cal 1883.)
MARIE HOUILLON. DC. (Cal. 1869.)
MARIE JACQUIN. DC. (Ver. E.) *Bridesmaid; Waterlily.*
MARIE KELWAY. DC. (Kel. 1889.)
MARIE KUNDERD. D. (Kun. 1927.)
MARIE LEMOINE. DC. (Cal. 1869.)
MARIELLEN. J. (Guppy 1932.)
MARIE RATTIER. T. (Gue. 1867.) *La-ville de Versailles; Mme.* (*Marie*) *Rattier.*
MARIE STUART. DC. (Cal. 1856.)
Marie Stuart. S.; T. (Jap. 1867.) *Reine Deprusse.*
MARIETTA SISSON. D. (Sass 1933.)
MARION TALLEY. D. (Sim. 1929.)
MARJORIE ALLISON. SC. (Sha. 1918.)

PAEONIA, continued

MARJORIE DAW. DC. (Lewis 1922.)
MARMONTEL. DC. (Cro. 1898.)
MARMORA. D.; T. (1889.)
MARQUIS. SJ.
MARQUIS (*C.*) LAGERGREN. DC. (Des. 1911.)
MARQUIS D'ALFARES. T. (H.&S. 1864.)
MARQUIS DECLAPIERS. T. (Sen. 1899.)
MARQUISE D'IVRY. DC. (Cal. 1857.)
MARTA. HH. (Sau. 1938.)
MARTHA (*A.*) TWYMAN. DC. (Wet. 1920.)
MARTHA BULLOCH. DC. (Bra. 1907.)
MARTHA (*V.*) LANE. DC. (Wet. 1924.)
MARTHA WASHINGTON. DC. (Hol. 1909.)
MARVEL. DC. (Secor 1924.)
MARY. DC. (Pleas)
MARY (*A.*) LIVERMORE. DC. (Hol. 1907.)
MARY AUTEN. D. (Auten 1933.)
MARY (*Baker*) EDDY. DC. (Hol. 1910.)
MARY BRAND. DC. (Bra. 1907.)
MARY (*B.*) VORIES. DC. (Vor. 1924.)
MARY (*C.*) LEWIS. DC. (Lewis 1921.)
MARY (*C.*) WEDGE. DC. (Secor 1924.)
MARY (*E.*) HALL. HH. (Boc. 1933.)
MARY ELLEN. D. (Fran. 1931.)
MARYGOLD. J.
MARY (*L.*) HOLLIS. DC. (Hol. 1907.)
MARY (*Lou*) KIMMEY. D. (Edl. 1929.)
MARY MAY. J. (Ber. 1924.)
MARY (*P.*) KING. DC. (Fran. 1920.)
MARY REID. SJ. (Reid 1930.)
MARY WOODBURY SHAYLOR. DC. (Sha. 1916.)
MASTERPIECE. DC. (Kel. 1895.) *Mr. Manning.*
MATADOR.
MATCHLESS BEAUTY. D. (Nee. 1936.)
MATHIEU. T. (Ler. 1853.)
MATHILDE DEROSENECK. DC. (Cro. 1883.)
MATHILDE MECHIN. DC. (Mec. 1880.)
MATILDA LEWIS. DC. (Sau. 1921.)
MATTAWAMKEAG. SJ. (Guppy 1935.)
MATTIE CHARLES. DC. (Pleas)
MAUD (*L.*) RICHARDSON. DC. (Hol. 1904.)
MAURICE MAETERLINCK. SC. (Kel. 1884?)
MAURINE. D. (Haupt 1935.)
MAXIMAPLENA. T. (Nois 1839.)
MAX LEICHTLIN.
MAY BEE. SJ. (Ber. 1906?)
MAY DAVIDSON. SC.
MAY OLESON. SC. (Ole. 1924.)
MEADOWVALE. DC. (Hol. 1903.)
MEDIA. DC. (Kel. 1884?)
MEDICINE HAT. SJ. (Auten 1936.)
MEDON. SC.
MEDUSA. D. (Kel.)
Medusa. J.
MEGUNTICOOK. J.
MEIGETSUKO. J.
MEIJI-NO-HOMARA. T. (Jap. 1910.)
MEISSONIER. DC. (Cro. 1886.)
MELLIN KNIGHT. SC. (Bra.A. 1920.)
MELLOW MOON. D. (Jones 1937.)
MELODY. DC. (Auten 1925.)
MEMORIAL QUEEN. D. (Ros. 1934.)
MEMORY. D. (Jones 1937.)
MENDOTA. D. (Auten 1937.)
MENTOR GRAHAM. D. (Lan. 1938.)
MERRIGOLD. J.
MERRIMAC. D. (Thu. 1937.)

PAEONIA, continued

MESSAGERE.
METEORE. T. (Che. 1910.)
METEOR FLIGHT. SC. (Kel. 1884?)
MICHELET. DC. (Cro. before 1900.)
MICHISHIBA. D.; T. (Jap. 1910.)
MIDNIGHT. DC. (Hol. 1904.)
Midnight. DC. (Bra. 1907.)
MIDSUMMER NIGHTS DREAM. DC. (Pleas 1906.)
MIGNON. DC. (Lem. 1908.)
Mignon. GIOKU-SENSHIU.
MIKADO. J.
MIKASA-MONI. S.; T. (Jap. 1913.) *Orphee.*
MIKASO-NO-MARI. S.; T. (Jap. 1919.) *Tabarin.*
MIKASO-YAMA. S.; T. (Jap. 1898.)
MIKUNI-NO-HOMARE. T. (Jap. 1926.)
MILES STANDISH. DC. (Hol. 1904.)
MILLAIS. DC.S. (Kel. 1884?)
MILTON HILL. DC. (Ric. 1891.)
MINAMOTA. DC. (Mill.)
MINE-NO-MOMIJI. J.
MINE-NO-MONEY. J.
MINE-NO-YUKI. J.
MINERVA. DC. (Sass 1930.)
MINERVE. S. (Des. 1908.)
MINNEAPOLIS. SJ. (Dana 1926.)
MINNEHAHA. DC.S. (Pleas 1855?)
MINNIE GERTRUDE. HH. (Gla. 1931.)
MINNIE LUCAS. D. (Fran. 1928.)
MINNIE SHAYLOR. DC. (Sha. 1919.)
MINUET. D. (Fran. 1931.)
MIRABEAU. D. (Len. 1904.)
Mirabeau. KAJURA-JIMA.
MIREILLE. DC. (Cro. 1894.)
MIRIAM. DC. (Chase 1916.)
MIRIAM MARSH. J. (Fre. 1931.)
MIRUM MUNDI. T. (Kel. 1889.)
MISCHIEF. DC.S. (Auten 1925.)
MISHIKI-SHIMA. S.; T. (Jap. 1904.)
MISS AMERICA. D. (M.vanS. 1936.)
(*Miss*) BEATRIX JONES. T. (Kel. 1901.)
MISS BRICE. DC. (Kel. 1884?)
MISS ECKART. D. (v.d.Meer? 1928.)
MISS EMERY. DC. (Sha. 1919.)
MISS (*H. C.*) HULL. DC.; S. (Kel. 1884?)
MISS HENNINGER. DC. (Terry 1885?)
MISS (*Ida*) CHAMBERLAIN. DC.; S. (Kel. 1884?)
MISS MINNEAPOLIS. D. (Fran. 1931.)
MISS MORRIS. DC.; S.
MISS SALWAY. DC. (Kel. 1905.)
MISTRAL. DC.; S. (Des. 1905.)
MISU-KAGE. T. (Jap. 1910.) *Misu-no-Kage.*
MIYA-KAGARA. T. (Jap. 1926.)
MIYA-KINI-HARU. T. (Jap. 1926.)
MIYO-HIKARI. T. (Jap. 1926.)
MIYO-KI-NISHIKI. T. (Jap. 1926.)
MIYO-KOHO-NISHIKI. T. (Jap. 1896.)
MIYO-NO-HANA. J.
M. (*J.*) ASTLE. DC.; S. (Kel. 1912.)
MLLE. CIMOCHOWSKA. DC. (Mill.)
(*Mlle.*) CORNELIE RAIKEN. T. (Pai. 1889.)
MLLE. DESBUISSON. DC. (Cro. 1893.)
(*Mlle.*) JEANNE RIVIERE. DC. (Riv. 1908.)
(*Mlle.*) JULIETTE DESSERT. DC. (Des. 1888.)
(*Mlle.*) LEONIE CALOT. DC. (Cal. 1861.) *Mons.* (*Charles*) *Leveque.*
(*Mlle.*) LOUISE DELATTRE. DC. (Mill. 1925.)

PAEONIA, continued

(*Mlle.*) *Maria Closon*. LAMBERTINAE.
(*Mlle.*) MARIE CALOT. DC. (Cal. 1872.)
(*Mlle.*) RENEE DESSERT. DC. (Mec. 1880.)
MLLE. ROUSSEAU. DC. (Cal. 1886.)
MLLE. SOPHIE. T. (1889.)
MLLE. VAILLANT. DC.
MME. ARMAND. T.
MME. (*A.*) SENECLAUZE. T. (Sen. 1889.)
MME. (*Auguste*) DESSERT. DC. (Des. 1899.)
MME. (*Auguste*) PELTEREAU. DC. (Mec. 1880.)
MME. (*Barillet*) DESCHAMPS. DC. (Cal. 1868.)
MME. (*Benoit*) RIVIERE. DC. (Riv. 1911.)
MME. BERNARD. DC. (Ver.V. 1855.)
MME. BOLLET. DC. (Cal. 1867.)
MME. BOULANGER. DC. (Cro. 1886.)
MME. BREON. DC. (Gue. 1850.)
MME. BUCQUET. DC. (Des. 1888.)
MME. BUTTERFLY. J. (Fran. 1933.)
MME. CALOT. DC. (Mie. 1856.) *Leonie* (in part).
MME. (*Camille*) BANCEL. DC.
MME. CARPENTIER. DC. (Del. 1850.)
MME. CHAUMY. DC. (Cal. 1864.)
MME. (*Claude*) TAIN. DC. (Dor. 1927.)
MME. COSTE. DC. (Cal. 1873.)
MME. COURANT. DC. (Cou. 1850.)
MME. CROUSSE. DC. (Cal. 1866.)
MME. D'ANDREMONT. T. (Ver. 1869.)
MME. D'AREMBERG. DC.
MME. DEBOLLEMONT. DC. (Cro. 1892.)
MME. DECOCK. T. (Jap. Sie.-Kre.)
MME. DEGALHAU. DC. (Cro. 1883.)
MME. DEGOVIN. DC. (Cro. 1875.)
MME. DELACHE. T. (Del. 1867.)
MME. DEMONTMARIN. T. (Gom. 1859.)
MME. DE ST. ROME. T. (Sen. 1867.)
MME. DEVATRY. DC.; T. (Gue. 1863.)
Mme. Devatry. D.; T. (Gue. 1867.)
MME. DEVERNEVILLE. DC. (Cro. 1885.)
MME. D'HOUR. DC. (Cal. 1864.)
MME. (*D.*) TREYERAN. DC. (Des. 1899.)
MME. DUCEL. DC. (Mec. 1880.)
MME. (*Edouard*) DORIAT. DC. (Des.-Dor. 1924.)
Mme. (*Edouard*) *Seneclauze*. REINE ELIZABETH.
MME. (*Emile*) DEBATENE. D.; DC. (Des.-Dor. 1927.)
MME. (*Emile*) DUPRAZ. DC. (Riv. 1911.)
MME. (*Emile*) GALLE. DC. (Cro. 1881.)
MME. (*Emile*) LEMOINE. DC. (Lem. 1899.)
MME. (*E.*) PALLAIN. T. (Jap. 1897.)
MME. ESCARY. D.; DC. (Lem. 1922.)
MME. EVERARD. DC.
MME. (*Felicie*) SIMONIS. D.; T. (Ver. 1869.)
MME. FOREL. DC. (Cro. 1887.)
MME. FOULD. DC. (Cro. 1893.)
MME. (*Francois*) TOSCANELLI. DC. (Riv. 1911.)
MME. FURTADO. DC. (Gue. 1856.)
MME. GAUDICHAU. DC. (Mill. 1902.)
MME. GEISSLER. DC. (Cro. 1880.)
MME. GOMBAULT. T. (Dauv.? 1859.)
MME. (*Gustave*) CROUX. T. (Jap. 1897.)
MME. GUYOT. DC. (Pai.)

PAEONIA, continued

MME. (*Henri*) CORE. D.
MME. (*Henriette*) CAILLOT. D.; T. (Des. 1899.)
MME. HERVE. DC. (Cro. 1892.)
MME. HUTIN. DC. (Cro. 1892.)
MME. (*Joanne*) SAILLIER. DC. (Pai.)
MME. (*Jules*) CALOT. DC. (Cal. 1868.)
MME. (*Jules*) DESSERT. DC. (Des. 1909.)
MME. (*Jules*) ELIE. DC. (Cal. 1873.)
MME. (*Jules*) ORBAN. T. (Ver. 1869.)
MME. KRELAGE. T. (Kre. 1867.)
MME. LACOMTESSE DECHARPIN. T. (Pai. 1889.)
Mme. Laffay. COMTE DEFLANDRE.
MME. LAMARQUISE DE CLAUSONNETTE. T. (Pai. 1889.)
MME. LAMARQUISE DEVOGUE. T. (Pai. 1889.)
MME. LEBON. DC. (Cal. 1888.)
MME. LEHELLE. DC.
MME. LEMOINE. D. (Cal. 1864.)
Mme. Lemoine. D.; T. (Sen. 1889.)
MME. LEMOINIER. DC. (Cal. 1865.)
MME. LOISE MERE. DC. (Cal. 1863.)
MME. (*Louis*) HENRY. T. (Henry 1919.)
MME. MANCHET. DC. (Des. 1913.)
Mme. (*Maria*) *Closon*. LAMBERTINAE.
MME. (*Maria*) SEGUENOT. T. (Seg. 1905.)
Mme. (*Marie*) *Rattier*. MARIE RATTIER.
Mme. Masse. MONS. MASSE.
MME. MECHIN. DC. (Mec. 1880.)
MME. MELINE. T. (Jap. 1897.)
MME. MOREAU. DC. (Cro. 1881.)
MME. MOUTOT. DC. (Cro. 1892.)
MME. MUYSSART. DC. (Cal. 1869.)
MME. OTTIN. T. (Pai. 1889.)
MME. (*Pierre*) DESSERT. S.; T. (Des. 1909.)
MME. PLEAS. DC. (Pleas 1912.)
MME. (*Quoodbach*) DERAS. T. (Ver. 1869.)
MME. REIGNOUX. DC. (Des. 1909.)
MME. REJANE. DC. (Kel. 1884?)
MME. RENKIN. T. (Pai. 1889.)
MME. SAINT-AUGUSTIN. T. (Pai. 1889.)
MME. SAVREAU. DC. (Sav. 1906.)
MME. SCHAENMACKERS. D.; T. (Pai. 1889.)
MME. SCHMIDT. DC. (Cal. 1873.)
MME. (*Stuart*) LOW. D.; T. (Mak. 1863.) *Fortschritt*.
MME. THIBAULT. D.; T. (Sen. 1889.) Perhaps the same as Donna Maria.
MME. THOUVENIN. DC. (Cro. 1881.)
MME. (*Victor*) GILLIER. D.; T. (Pai. 1889.)
MME. (*Victor*) VERDIER. DC. (Cal. 1866.)
MME. VILMORIN. DC. (Gue. 1866.)
MOBUCHI. J. (Mill.)
MODELE DEPERFECTION. DC. (Cro. 1875.)
MODELLA. DC. (Bet. 1920.)
MODESTE GUERIN. DC. (Gue. 1845.)
Modeste Guerin. T. (Ver. 1869.)
MOKU-SETSUEH. T. (Jap. 1926.)
Moliere. AYA-NISHIKI.
MOLLY STARK. DC. (Auten 1927.)
Momozomo. AYA-NISHIKI.
MONSIEUR AMAND. T. (Pai. 1889.)
MONSIEUR ANDRE. DC. (Gue. 1862.)
MONSIEUR (*Auguste*) GAUTHIER. DC. (Gue. 1862.)

PAEONIA, continued

MONSIEUR (*August*) RAVEL. D.; T. (Pai. 1889.)
MONSIEUR BARRAL. DC. (Cal. 1866.)
MONSIEUR (*Bastien*) LEPAGE. DC. (Cro. 1885.)
MONSIEUR (*Boucharlat*) AINE. DC. (Cal. 1868.)
MONSIEUR (*Charles*) JOLY. T. (Des. 1899.)
Monsieur (*Charles*) *Leveque*. (*Mlle.*) LEONIE CALOT.
MONSIEUR CHEVREUL. DC. (Des. 1893.)
MONSIEUR COURANT. T. (Pai. 1889.)
MONSIEUR DACHUTRE. DC. (Kel. 1884?)
MONSIEUR DEVILLENEUVE. DC. (Ver. 1855.)
MONSIEUR DUPONT. DC. (Cal. 1872.)
MONSIEUR DURUFLE. DC.
MONSIEUR FLAQUE. T. (Pai. 1889.)
MONSIEUR GALLAND. DC. (Cro. 1875.)
MONSIEUR (*Germain*) DEMONTANZAN. T. (Sen. 1889.)
MONSIEUR (*Joseph-Maria*) SERRA. T. (H.&S. 1864.) *Joseph-Maria Serra*.
MONSIEUR (*Jules*) ELIE. DC. (Cro. 1888.)
MONSIEUR KLEYER. T. (Pai. 1889.)
MONSIEUR KRELAGE. DC. (Cro. 1883.)
MONSIEUR (*l'Avocat*) RIPOLI. T. (H.&S. 1864.)
MONSIEUR MARTIN CAHUZAC. DC. (Des. 1899.)
MONSIEUR MASSE. T. (Gue. 1867.) *Mme. Masse*.
MONSIEUR MIRON. D.; T. (Gom. 1859.)
MONSIEUR PAILLET. DC. (Gue. 1857.)
MONSIEUR (*Paul*) RISBOURG. DC. (Cal. 1869.)
MONSIEUR PEPIN. T. (Gue. 1873.)
MONSIEUR TRIGER. (Pai. 1889.)
MONSTRUOSA ALBA PLENISSIMA. T. (Bau. 1836.)
MONT BLANC. DC. (Lem. 1899.)
MONTEBANK. J. (Kel. 1884?)
MONTE CRISTO. T. (Pai. 1889.)
MONTEREY. J. (Auten 1931.)
MONTICELLO. SJ. (Auten 1931.)
MONT ROSE. T. (Gue. 1889.)
MONT VESUVE. D.; T. (Sen. 1889.)
MOONBEAM. DC. (Kel. 1884?)
MOONLIGHT. DC. (Kel. 1884?)
MOONMIST. SJ. (Auten 1929.)
MOON OF NIPPON. J.
MOON-YEN-CLAIRE. J. (Pleas 1855?)
MORA. DC. (Secor 1924.)
MORNE. DC. (Kel. 1884?)
MORNINGGLORY. D. (Nee. 1936.)
MORNINGSTAR. DC. (Terry 1855?)
MOROCCO. D. (Auten 1933.)
MORRIS. D.; T. (Bur. 1873.)
MOSES HULL. DC. (Bra. 1907.)
MOUNTEBANK. DC. (Kel. 1884?)
MOUNT EVEREST. D. (Sass 1937.)
Mousseline. HAKU-GAN.
MOUTAN. T. (Pai. 1889.)
MOZUTSUYA. T.
MR. BANCROFT. T. (Kel. 1897.)
MR. (*Beerbohm*) TREE. T. (Kel. 1897.)
MR. (*B. H.*) FARR. J. (Van L. 1926.)
MR. CHAPLIN. T. (Kel. 1897.)
MR. (*G. F.*) HEMERIK. J.
MR. LAUNAY. DC. (Mill.)
MR. (*Leopold*) DEROTHSCHILD. T. (Kel. 1904.)

PAEONIA, continued

Mr. (*L.*) Vanleeuwen. DC. (Lie. 1916.)
Mr. Manning. Masterpiece.
Mr. Thim. SJ. (Van L. 1926.)
Mrs. (*A. B.*) Franklin. D. (Fran. 1928.)
Mrs. (*A. F. W.*) Hayward. DC. (Kel. 1884?)
Mrs. (*A. G.*) Ruggles. DC. (Bra. 1913.)
Mrs. (*A. L.*) Chapin. J. (H.&G.)
Mrs. (*A. M.*) Brand. DC. (Bra. 1925.)
Mrs. (*A. O.*) Norton. D. (Nor. 1928.)
Mrs. (*A. S.*) Gowen. D. (Bra. A. 1936.)
Mrs. Bancroft. T. (Kel. 1897.)
Mrs. Barret. DC. (Pleas 1855?)
Mrs. Becket. DC. (Pleas 1910.)
Mrs. (*Beerbohm*) Tree. DC.; SC. (Kel. 1884?)
Mrs. (*Bryce*) Fontaine. D. (Bra. A. 1936.)
Mrs. Carew. DC. (Bra. A. 1907.)
Mrs. (*Charles*) Gilbert. DC. (Sha. 1916.)
Mrs. (*Colonel*) Lindbergh. D. (Sim. 1929.)
Mrs. (*C. S.*) Minot. DC. (Minot 1914.)
Mrs. (*Edward*) Harding. DC. (Sha. 1918.)
Mrs. (*E.*) Horwood. DC. (Kel. 1884?)
Mrs. (*E. J.*) Shaylor. DC. (Sha. 1920.)
Mrs. (*Ernest*) Dunkels. DC. (Kel. 1912.)
Mrs. (*Eugene*) Secor. DC. (Secor N. 1924.)
Mrs. (*F. A.*) Goodrich. D. (Bra. A. 1925.)
Mrs. (*Fern*) Lough. D. (Gumm 1930.)
Mrs. (*F. J.*) Clark. SC.
Mrs. (*Frank*) Beach. DC. (Bra. A. 1925.)
Mrs. (*Franklin D.*) Roosevelt. D. (Fran. 1933.)
Mrs. (*Frederick*) Davidson. DC. (Kel. 1884?)
Mrs. (*George*) Bunyard. DC. (Kel. 1898.)
Mrs. (*George*) Rawson. D. (All. 1931.)
Mrs. (*Gwyn*) Lewis. DC. (Kel. 1884?)
Mrs. (*Harriet*) Gentry. DC. (Bra. 1925.)
Mrs. (*Harry F.*) Little. D. (Lit. 1936.)
Mrs. (*Helen*) Rooker. SJ. (Mill. 1925.)
Mrs. (*Henry*) Kalle. DC. (Nie. 1918.)
Mrs. (*Hobart M.*) Cable. J. (Cra. 1922.)
Mrs. (*James*) Kelway. DC. (Kel. 1926.)
Mrs. (*Jennie R.*) Gowdy. DC. (Bra. A. 1920.)
Mrs. (*Jessop*) Hulton. T. (Kel. 1900.)
Mrs. (*J. F.*) Rosenfield. D. (Ros. 1934.)
Mrs. (*J. H.*) Neeley. D. (Nee. 1931.)
Mrs. (*J. H.*) Perkins. D. (G.&R. 1930.)
Mrs. (*John M.*) Good. D. (G.&R. 1929.)
Mrs. (*John M.*) Kleitsch. DC. (Bra. A. 1925.)
Mrs. (*John M.*) Lewis. DC. (Lewis 1920.)

PAEONIA, continued

Mrs. (*John*) Smythe Fogg. DC. (Hol. 1907.)
Mrs. (*Julia E.*) Goodwin. D. (Fre. 1929.)
Mrs. (Julia Ward) Howe. Julia Ward Howe.
Mrs. (*J. V.*) Edlund. D. (Edl. 1929.)
Mrs. (*J. W.*) Simcox. T. (Kel. 1896.)
Mrs. (*Kenneth*) Kelway. DC. (Kel. 1923–25.)
Mrs. Key. DC.; SC. (Terry 1855?)
Mrs. (*Laura Coates*) Reed. DC.; SC. (Hol. 1889?)
Mrs. (*Livingston*) Farrand. D. (Nic. 1935.)
Mrs. (*M. B.*) Beckett. DC. (Pleas 1910.)
Mrs. McKinley. DC.; SC. (Terry 1855?)
Mrs. McMillan. T. (Kel. 1896.)
Mrs. (*Morgan*) Lewis. DC. (Lewis 1921.)
Mrs. (*M. P.*) Clough. DC. (Sha. 1915.)
Mrs. (*Philip*) Belben. DC. (Kel. 1884?)
Mrs. Pleas. DC. (Terry 1855?)
Mrs. (*Reginald*) Balfour. DC. (Kel. 1884?)
Mrs. (*R. M.*) Bacheller. D. (Vor. 1930.)
Mrs. (*Romaine B.*) Ware. DC. (Bra. 1925.)
Mrs. (*R. T.*) Whittaker. D. (Rei. 1936.)
Mrs. (*S.*) Gundry. DC.; SC.
Mrs. (*Shaylor*) Force. DC. (Sha. 1919.)
Mrs. Shuttleworth. DC. (Kel. 1917.)
Mrs. (*Springer*) Brooks. D. (Edl. 1934.)
Mrs. Thim. DC.; SC. (Van L. 1926.)
Mrs. Wait. DC. (Terry 1855?)
Mrs. (*Ward*) Welsh. J. (G.&R. 1933.)
Mrs. (*W. D.*) Bennett. DC. (Wet. 1926.)
Mrs. (*Wilder*) Bancroft. J. (Nic. 1935.)
Mrs. (*William*) Metcalfe. DC. (Far. 1920.)
Mrs. (*W. L.*) Gumm. D. (Gumm 1929.)
Mrs. (*Wm.*) Kelway. T. (Kel. 1892.)
Mrs. Woodward. DC.; SC. (Terry 1906.)
Muhensai. T. (Jap. 1893.)
Muhlenbecki. T. (Kre. 1867.)
Mulchelney. DC.; SC. (Kel. 1884?)
Mulligan. DC. (Kel. 1884?)
Multicolor. T. (Jap. 1905.)
Multiflora. D. (Pleas.) *Nellie Pleas.*
Murillo. DC.; SC. (G.&K. 1910.)
Mutsu. J. (Cra. 1922.)
Mutsu-hito. J.
Myrtle Gentry. DC. (Bra. A. 1925.)
Myrtle Reineke. D. (Rei. 1936.)
Myrtle Rosenfield. D. (Ros. 1934.)
Nagasaki. SC. (Mill.)
Nanahingi-shibori. D.
Nance o'Neal. DC. (Hol. 1906.) *Nance o'Neil.*
Nancy Dolman. DC. (Vor. 1924.)
Nanette. DC. (Dor. 1924.)
Naniwagata. T.
Naniwanishiki. T.
Nanticook. D.

PAEONIA, continued

Naomi. D. (Auten 1933.)
Napoleana. T. (Hiss. 1841.)
Naubunishiski. SC.
Nauvoo. D. (Auten 1937.)
Nebraska. T. (Jap. 1911.)
Negresse. Kuro-botan.
Negricans. T. (Jap. 1864.) *Germania; Princess Amelie.*
Nehoiden. DC.
Nehumkeag. SJ. (Guppy 1935.)
Neko-wat. J.
Nellie. SC. (Kel.)
Nellie Pleas. Multiflora.
Nell Shaylor. DC. (Sha. 1919.)
Nemesis. T.
Ne Plus Ultra. D. (Miel. 1856.)
Ne Plus Ultra. T. (Sen. 1889.)
Neptune. J. (Terry.)
Neptune. DC. (Des. 1905.)
Neron. T. (Lem. E. 1908.)
Neumanni. Newmani.
New Delight. D. (Nee. 1930.)
New Kea. T.
Newmani. T. *Newmanni.*
New York. T. (Jap. 1911.)
Nichigekko. T.
Nick Shaylor. D. (All. 1931.)
Nigatsunoyuki. T.
Nigricans. DC.
Nihonbeni. T.
Nihonji. J. (Mill. 1926.)
Nimbus. DC. (Andr. 1923.)
Nina Secor. DC. (Secor 1922.)
Ninon. DC. (Dor. 1925.)
Niobe. J.
Niobe. D. (Kre. 1908.)
Nippon Beauty. C. (J. type.) (Auten 1927.)
Nippon-beni. T. (Jap. 1926.)
Nippon Brilliant. J. (Auten 1933.)
Nippon Chief. J. (Auten 1931.)
Nippon Gold. J. (Auten 1929.)
Nippon-ko. S.; T. (Jap. 1919.)
Nippon Maid. J. (Auten 1931.)
Nippon Parade. J. (Auten 1931.)
Nippon Princess. J. (Auten 1931.)
Nippon Red. J. (Auten 1931.)
Nippon Splendor. J. (Auten 1931.)
Nippon Triumph. J. (Auten 1937.)
Nippon Warrior. J. (Auten 1933.)
Nishigawa. T.
Nishikigawa. T. (Jap. 1893.)
Nishikijishi. T.
Nishikikimme. T.
Nishiki-no-shitone. T. (Jap. 1910.)
Nishiki-shima. S.; T. (Jap. 1893.) *Nishiki-Gima; Psyche.*
Nishi-Kotera. T. (Jap. 1893.)
Nisho-no-shitone. J.
Nisshoki. T. (Jap. 1926.)
Nitida Plena. T. (Sen. 1846.)
Nitta. DC. (Barr.)
Nivea Plena. T. (Pai. 1889.)
Niveaplenissima. DC. (Mak. 1840.)
Nivialis. DC. (Buy. 1840.)
Nobilissima. T. (1846.)
Nobilissima. DC. (Mie. 1858.)
Nobility. D. (Van L. 1929.)
Noblepourpre. T.
Nochida. T. (Jap. 1910.)
Noemie Demay. DC. (Cal. 1867.)
Noisette. Blanche Denoisette.
Nokomis. DC. (Fran. 1920.)
Noonday. SC. (Kel. 1884?)
Norfolk. DC. (Ric. 1904.)
Northbrook. Defiance.

PAEONIA, continued
NORTHERNGLORY. T.
NORUGINU. J.
NORUMBEGA. D. (Don. 1928.)
NOVELTY. DC. (Barr; also Terry 1855?)
Nuage Rose. DAI-KAGURA.
NULLI SECUNDUS. SC. (Kel. 1909.)
NUREGARARASU. T.
NYMPH. DC. (Har.) *The Nymph.*
NYMPHAEA. T. (Jap.-Sie.-Kre. 1867.)
Nymphaea. DC. (Thu. 1919.)
NYMPHE. J. (Des. 1913.)
OAHIO KUN. J.
OBOKI. J. (Pfe. 1937.)
OCELLATA. T. (Kre. 1867.)
OCTAVIE DEMAY. DC. (Cal. 1867.)
ODALISQUE. DC. (Lem. 1923.)
ODETTE. DC. (Des. 1908.)
ODORATA MARIA. T. (Man. 1846.) *Papaveracea Maria; Rosina.*
ODORATA PLENA. T. (Seb. 1846.) *Papaveracea Odorata Plena; Phoenicia fl.-pl.; Phoenicia Odorata Plena.*
ODORATA ROSEA. T. (Chi.-For. 1846.) *Rosea Odorata.*
ODZIANA. T. (Des. 1902.)
O FUGI. J.
OHANAGASA. J.
OHENOSATO. T.
OHGONSOME. D.; T.
OHIRAMA. C.J. *Lucie.*
OHUCHICHIME. T.
OIMATSU. J. *Clarisse.*
OKI. J. (Mill.)
OKINA-JISHI. T. (Jap. 1926.)
OKINAMA. SJ.
OKI-NO-NAMI. J.
OLD HUNDREDTH. D. (Auten 1933.)
OLD SILVERTIP. DC. (Bra. A. 1918.)
OLIVE BARRETT. SC. (Kel. 1884?)
OLIVER F. BRAND. D. (Bra. A. 1928.)
OLIVIA. DC. (Kel. 1895–96.)
OLYMPIA. T. (Kel. 1897.)
OMER PACHA. T. (Pai. 1889.)
ONLOOKER. DC. (Kel. 1884?)
ONONDAGA. D. (Lit. 1935.)
Onyx. REINE ELIZABETH.
OPAL. DC. (Pleas 1908.) *The Jewel.*
OPAL IRIS. DC. (Pleas.)
OPHELIA. T. (Pai. 1889.)
OPHIR. SJ.
OPHIS.
OPPORTUNE. D. (Bra. A. 1933.)
OPTIMA OMNIUM. T. (Kel. 1889.)
ORANGE PRINCE. J. (Pleas 1855?)
ORBY. SJ.
Orgueil de Hong Kong. CORNELIA.
ORIFLAMME. T. (Che. 1910.)
ORME. T. (Kel. 1892.)
ORNEMENT DES MASSIFS. DC. (Cro. 1893.)
Orphee. MIKASA-MONI.
OSAKAZUKI. T. (Jap. 1893.) *Osakadzuki.*
OSHO-KUN. T. (Jap. 1926.)
OSIRIS. T. (Chi.-For. 1864.)
Ostrich Plume. DR. EDGAR PLEAS.
OSTRINA LILACINA. T. (Kel. 1889.)
OSTRINA SATURATA. T. (Kel. 1889.)
OTHELLO. S. (Des. 1908.)
Othello. D. (Lem. 1916.)
OTHONIS. T. (H.&S. 1864.) *Ottonis; Ottonis Silvuregie.*
OTIRI. T. (Jap. 1926.)
OTOKOISHI. T.
OTTO FROEBEL.

PAEONIA, continued
Ottonis; Ottonis Silvuregie. OTHONIS.
OURIKA.
OWATONNA. SJ. (Bra. A. 1936.)
PADEREWSKI. DC. (Kel. 1884?)
PALLAS. DC. (Terry.)
PALLIDA SEMIPLENA. T. (Sen. or Nois. 1839.) *Papaveracea Pallida Semiplena.*
PANAMA. T. (Obe. 1920.)
PANORAMA. T. (Pai. 1889.)
Papaveracea. POMPONIA.
PAPAVERACEA BANKSI. T.
Papaveracea Flora Plena. FLORA.
Papaveracea Maria. ODORATA MARIA.
Papaveracea Odorata Plena. ODORATA PLENA.
Papaveracea Pallida Semiplena. PALLIDA SEMIPLENA.
Papaveracea Plena. PLENA.
Papaveracea Rosea. ROSEA.
Papaveracea Rosea Grandiflora. ROSEA GRANDIFLORA.
Papaveracea Stellata Atropurpurea. STELLATA ATROPURPUREA.
PAPAVERIFLORA. DC. (Lemon 1825.)
Papillon. KOKIRIN.
PARADISE. DC. (Hol. 1907.)
PARMENTIERI. T. (Kre. 1867.)
PARVIFLORA. T. (Chi.-For. 1848.)
PASSADUMKEOG. SJ. (Guppy 1936.)
PASTEUR. DC. (Cro. 1896.)
PATIENCE. D. (Auten 1933.)
PATRICIA. D. (Auten 1931.)
PAUL FISCHER. DC. (Ric. 1904.)
PAULINE. T. (Per. 1873.) *Pauline Perche.*
PAULINE KUNDERD. D. (Kun. 1927.)
Pauline Perche. PAULINE.
PAUL VERDIER. T. (Pai. 1889.)
PEACE. HH. (Sau. 1940.)
PEACH BLOW. D. (Sha. 1938.)
Pearl. LAPERLE.
PEARLED ROSE. DC. (Pleas 1855?)
PEGGY. D. (Auten 1931.)
PEG O' MY HEART. DC. (Kel. 1884?)
PELHAM. D. (Auten 1935.)
PENELOPE.
PENNACOOK. J. (Guppy 1935.)
PENNSYLVANIA. T. (Jap. 1911.)
PEORIA. SJ. (Auten 1931.)
PERE MARQUETTE. SJ. (Auten 1933.)
Perfection. RICHARDSONS PERFECTION.
PERLE BLANCHE. SC. (Des. 1913.)
PERLE DESBLANCHES. D.; T. (Des. 1899.)
PERLE ROSE. SC. (Des. 1913.)
PERNETTI. T. (Pai. 1889.)
PEROSI. T. (Kel. 1900.)
PERRETTE. DC. (Des. 1921.)
PERSICHINI. T. (Pai. 1889.)
PETAGRA. DC. (Fra. 1920.)
PETER BARR.
PETER OLESON. SC. (Ole. 1924.)
PETER PAN. DC. (Hol. 1907.)
PETER THE GREAT. DC. (Kel. 1884?)
PETITE LOUISE. SC. (Nie. 1918?)
PETITE RENEE. J. (Des. 1899.)
PFEIFFERS PRIDE. D. (Pfe. 1932.)
PFEIFFERS RED TRIUMPH. D. (Pfe. 1937.)
Phaenicia Rubra Odorata. RUBRA-ODORATAPLENA.
Phenix. IWATO-KAGAMI.
PHILIPPE RIVOIRE. DC. (Riv. 1911.)
PHILOMELE. DC. (Cal. 1861.) *Vadius.*
PHOEBE CARY. DC. (Bra. 1907.)

PAEONIA, continued
PHOEBUS. T. (Kel. 1889.)
PHOENICEA. T. (Chin. 1846.)
Phoenicia fl.-pl. ODORATA PLENA.
Phoenicia Odorata Plena. ODORATA PLENA.
PHYLLIS KELWAY. DC. (Kel. 1908.)
PICIMELLI. T. (Kel. 1889.)
PICO. SJ. (Fre. 1934.)
PICTA. T. (Chi.-For. 1846.) *Ida.*
PIE IX. T. (Gue. 1873.)
PIE PLATE. SJ. (Wri. 1935.)
PIERRE DESSERT. DC. (Des.&Mec. 1890.)
PIERRE DUCHARTRE. DC. (Cro. 1895.)
PIERRE REIGNOUX. DC. (Des. 1908.)
PIERRE VENTCOURT. D. (Dor. 1933.)
PIH LEANG KIN. T.
PING WING. J.
PINK BARONESS SCHROEDER. DC.
PINK BEAUTY. D. (Sass 1937.)
PINK DELIGHT. SC.
PINK DOMINO. SC. (Kel. 1884?)
PINK GEM. SJ. (M.vanS. 1936.)
PINK GLORY. SJ. (Jones 1937.)
PINK LADY. J. (Secor.)
PINK MONARCH. D. (Auten 1933.)
PINK OPAL. D. (Sass 1934.)
PINK PERFECTION. D. (Risk 1929.)
PINK SOLANGE. D. (Auten 1933.)
PIOU-PIOU. SC. (Kel. 1915.)
PIRATE FLAG. SJ. (Auten 1933.)
PITNEY. SC. (Kel. 1884?)
PITTI SINN. DC. (Vor. 1924.)
Pleas Jubilee. JUBILEE.
PLEAS QUEEN. SC. (Pleas 1855?)
PLEASURE. SC. (Kel. 1926.)
PLENA. T. (Bau. 1836.) *Papaveracea Plena.*
PLENIFOLIA. T. (Nois. 1836.)
Plenissima Lilacina Major. LILACINA PLENISSIMA.
PLENISSIMA ROSEA SUPERBA. DC. (Buy. 1804.)
PLUTARCH. DC. (Kel. 1884?)
PLYMOUTH. D. (Auten 1931?)
POCAHONTAS. J. (Pleas 1914.)
POETE FREDERIC MISTRAL. DC. (Riv. 1911.)
POLAR STAR. J. (Sass 1932.)
POLYPHEMUS. DC. (Kel. 1884?)
POMONA. T. (Kel. 1889.)
POMPADOUR. DC. (Pleas 1913.)
POMPILIA. DC. (Ear. 1920.)
POMPONETTE. DC. (Des. 1909.)
POMPONIA. T. (Mat. 1846.) *Papaveracea.*
PONEMAH. DC. (Fran. 1920.)
PORPENTINE. D. (Guppy 1932.)
PORTIA. DC. (Kel. 1884?)
POTTSI. DC. (Chi. 1822.)
POTTSI ALBA. DC. (Buy. 1840.)
POTTSI PLENA. DC. (Cal. 1857.)
PRAECLARA. T. (Kel. 1889.)
PRAECOX. T. (Mat. 1836.)
PRAIRIE AFIRE. J. (Bra. A. 1932.)
PRAIRIE KING. DC. (Ros. 1908.)
PRAIRIE ROSE. SC.
PRAIRIE SPLENDOR. DC. (Ros. 1908.)
PRES. BRONGNIART. T. (Gue. 1863.)
PRESIDENT COOLIDGE. D. (Bra. A. 1928.)
PRESIDENT GARFIELD. DC.
PRESIDENT LINCOLN. SJ. (Bra. A. 1928.)
PRESIDENT POINCARE. DC. (Kel. 1915.)
PRESIDENT ROOSEVELT. (War. 1905.)

PAEONIA, continued

President Taft. DC. (Bla. 1909.)
President Wilson. DC. (Thu. 1918.)
Pres. Lambinon. T. (Mak. 1863.)
Pres. MacMahon. D.; T. (Sen. 1889.)
Presto. SC. (Auten 1925.)
Pres. Viger. T. (Jap. 1897.)
Priam. D. (Sass 1930.)
Pride of Essex. DC. (Thu. 1916.)
Pride of Hong Kong. T. (For. 1873.)
Pride of Langport. SC. (Kel. 1909.)
Pride of Paulding. DC. (Nee. 1920.)
Pride of Remington. D.; J. (Gumm 1929.)
Prime Minister. T. (Kel. 1906.)
Primevere. DC. (Lem. 1907.)
Prince Albert. Vivid.
Prince Alexander. SC.
Prince Alexandre. T. (Jap. Sie. 1885.)
Prince Bismarck. SC. (Kel. 1884?)
Prince Demetternich. T. (Sie. Kre. 1889.)
Prince Deprusse. T. (Sie. Kre.)
Prince Detalindyke. DC.
Prince Dewagram. T. (Amand 1859.)
Prince d'Orange. T. (Jap. Sie.)
Prince Frederick. T. (Jap. Sie.)
Prince George. J.
Prince Henry. T. (Jap. Sie.)
Prince Imperial. DC. (Cal. 1859.)
Prince Ito. J. (Lewis 1923.)
Prince of Darkness. DC. (Bra. A. 1907.)
Prince of Japs. CJ. type. (Lewis 1922.)
Prince of the Netherlands. D.; DC. (Kre. 1919.)
Prince of Wales. DC. (Kel. 1854?)
Prince of Wales. T. (Kel. 1899.)
Prince of Wales. DC. (Terry 1902.)
Prince Pierre Galitzin. DC.
Prince Prosper. DC.
Princess Amelie. Negricans.
Princess Beatrice. DC. (Kel. 1866.)
Princess Demetternich. T. (Jap. Sie. Kre. 1867.)
Princess (*Duleep*) Singh. C. (J. type.) (Kel.)
Princesse Demidoff. T. (Sie. P.F.)
Princesse Deprusse. T. (Jap. Sie. Kre. 1867.)
Princesse d'Orange. T. (Jap. Sie. P.F.)
Princess Ellen. DC. (Terry 1855?)
Princesse Marie des Pays Bas. T. (Jap. Sie. 1889.)
Princesse Mathilde. SC. (Des. 1908.)
Princesse Sophie. T. (Sie. P.F.)
Princess Frederick. T. (Jap. Sie.)
Princess Irene. DC. (Kel. 1889.)
Princess Juliana. DC. (Kre. 1910.)
Princess Louise. T. (Sie.)
Princess Louise. T. (Sen. 1889.)
Princess Mary. DC. (Kel. 1918-22.)
Princess Mathilda. D.; T. (1899.)
Princess Maud. DC. (Kel. 1884?)
Princess May. DC. (Kel. 1884?)
Princess of Monaco. SC. (Kel. 1884?)
Princess of Wales. SC. (Barr.)
Princess of Wales. DC. (Kel. 1884?)
Princess of Wales. D. (Terry 1885?)
Princess Olga. DC.
Priscilla Alden. D. (Rob. 1926.)
Prof. Dekoninck. T. (Ver. 1869.)
Prof. Desavoye. T. (Ver. 1869.)

PAEONIA, continued

Prof. (*Ed.*) Morren. T. (Mak. 1867.)
Professeur C. Potrat. D. (Dor. 1929.)
Professor Budd. DC. (Terry 1855?)
Prolifera Tricolor. DC. (Lemon 1825.)
Proserpine.
Prosiates. T. (Kel. 1897.)
Prudence. D. (Auten 1933.)
Psyche. D. (Cal. 1846.)
Psyche. Nishiki-shima.
Pulcherima. T. (Nois 1839.)
Pulcherrima. DC. (Gue. 1842.)
Pumila. T. (Nois 1839.)
Punicea. T. (Kel. 1889.)
Pure Delight. DC. (Kel. 1926.)
Pure Love. SC. (Kel. 1884?)
Puritan Maid. D.; SJ. (Auten 1933.)
Purity. T. (Pai. 1889.)
Purity. J. (Bun.)
Purity. S. (Kel.)
Purplecup. J. (Kel. before 1915.)
Purplecup. SC. (Secor N. 1924.)
Purple Emperor.
Purpurascens. T. (Sen. 1846.)
Purpurea. T. (Chi.-For. 1864.)
Purpurea Lilacina. T. (Mat. 1839.)
Purpurea Monstrosa. T. (O.F.N. 1924.)
Purpurea Plena. T. (v.Gee. 1842–1867.)
Purpurea Plena Undulata. T. (Kre. 1867.)
Purpurea Superba. DC. (Del. 1855.)
Purpurea Violacea Plena. T. (Bau. 1836.)
Pyramidal. T. (Nois 1839.)
Quaker Lady. DC. (Pleas 1913.)
Queen. SJ. (Pleas 1855?)
Queen. Kelways Queen.
Queen Alexandra. J. (Kel. 1902.)
Queen Alexandra. T. (Kel. 1903.) *Yaso-okina.*
Queen Bess. SJ. (Terry 1855?)
Queen Emma. DC. (Kre. ?)
Queen of Denmark. T. (Kel. 1892.)
Queen of Hamburg. D. (Sass 1937.)
Queen of May. SC. (Kel. 1884?)
Queen of Sheba. D. (Sass 1937.)
Queen of the Belgians. SC. (Kel. 1884.)
Queen of the Pleasance. DC. (Pleas 1899.)
Queen Sophia. DC. (Barr.)
Queens Perfection. DC. (? 1830.)
Queen Victoria. DC. (Kel. 1884?)
Queen Wilhelmina. DC. (Kre. 1915.)
Quideback Derass. T. (Pai. 1889.)
Quite Content. DC. (Hol. 1909.)
Rabelais. J. (Des. 1922.)
Rachel. DC. (Lem. 1904.)
Radetzky. T. (Pai. 1889.)
Radjiana. T. (Pai. 1889.)
Raiden. T. (Jap. 1867.)
Ralph. DC. (Pleas 1913.)
Ramona. D. (Fra. 1928.)
Ranieri. D.; T. (Ital. 1846.)
Raoul Dessert. DC. (Des. 1910.)
Raphael. DC. (Mec. 1882.)
Rapture. D. (Thu. 1937.)
Rare Brocade. J. (Pleas 1855?)
Rashoomon. C.J.
Rauenthal. DC. (G.&K. 1913.)
Rawesi. T. (Chi. 1820.)
Redbeauty. DC. (Van L. 1924.)
Redbird. DC. (Fra. 1921.)

PAEONIA, continued

Redcross. DC. (Hol. 1904.)
Redcrown. J. (Auten 1931.)
Reddelight. D. (Gla. 1928.)
Redemperor. J. (Auten 1931.)
Redglory. HH. (Auten 1937.)
Redjacket. SC. (Cra. 1922.)
Redknight. DC. (Ward-Lewis 1924.)
Redmonarch. HH. (Auten-Gla. 1937.)
Redqueen. SC. (Kel. 1884?)
Redsatin. D. (Sass 1937.)
Redsplendor. J.
Redwing. J.
Reevesiana. Beauty of Canton.
Reevesii.
Reform. DC. (Kel. 1884?)
Regal. SJ. (Lym. 1933.)
Regalis. T. (Kel. 1889.)
Regia. T. (Pai. 1889.)
Regina Belgica. D.; T. (Mak. 1854.) *Reine Desbelges.*
Reginae. T. (Hiss.)
Rei-kai-zan. *Appleblossom.*
Reine Amelie. D.; T. (Pai. 1889.)
Reine Baronet. DC. (Mill. 1924.)
Reine Blanche. Yaso-no-Mine.
Reine Demai.
Reine Deportugal. D.; T. (Des. 1899.)
Reine Deprusse. Marie Stuart.
Reine Desbeautes. Col. Malcolm.
Reine Desbelges. Regina Belgica.
Reine Desfleurs. DC. (Gue. 1850.)
Reine Desfleurs. (Don. 1873.)
Reine Desfrancais. DC. (Gue. 1842.)
Reine Desfrancais. T. (Pai. 1889.)
Reine Despays Bas. T. (Pai. 1889.)
Reine Desviolettes. T. (Chi.-For. 1889.)
Reine Elizabeth. DT. (Cas. before 1846?) *Jupiter; Koenigin Elizabeth; Mme. (Edouard) Seneclauze; Onyx.*
Reine Hortense. DC. (Cal. 1857.)
Reine Hortense. T. (Pai. 1889.)
Reine Marie. DC.; T. (Des. 1920.)
Reine Victoria. DC. (Gue. 1845.)
Reine Victoria. T. (Jap., Sie.&Kre. 1867.)
Rembrandt. T. (Chi.&For. 1846.)
Rembrandt. SC. (G.&K. 1926.)
Remembrance. T. (O.F.N. 1924.)
Remembrance of (*A. J.*) Downing. T. (v. Hou. 1853.)
Renee-Marie. DC. (Des. 1920.)
Rene Potard. DC. (Bec. 1882.)
Renkaku. T. (Jap.) (Yok. 1898.)
Renny. T. (v.Gee. 1896.)
Resplendent. D. (Fran. 1931.)
Reverie. DC. (Fran. 1920.)
Rev. (*H. N.*) Tragitt. D. (Bra. A. 1928.)
Rev. (*L. W.*) Atwood. DC. (Hol. 1908.)
Rhoda. DC. (Terry 1902.)
Richard Carvel. DC. (Bra. O. 1913.)
Richardsons Perfection. DC. (Ric. 1869.) *Perfection.*
Rigida Violacea. T. (Kre. 1867.)
Rigolote. J. (Dor. 1931.)
Rimpo. T. (Jap. 1926.)
Rinhosen. J.
Rinokino. J.
Rinzi. T. (Cas. 1867.) *Farezzi; Larezzi.* Perhaps the same as Kino-Kimo.
Rio Grande. D. (New. 1935.)
Rita. DC. (Des. 1922.)

PAEONIA, continued

RIU SHIKO. S.; T. (Jap. 1900.)
ROBERTA.
ROBERT BURNS. T. (Kel. 1889.)
ROBERT (*E.*) LEE. D. (Bra. A. 1928.)
ROBERT FORTUNE. T. (Chi.-For. 1846.) *Rosea Superba.*
ROBERT (*Lee*) DAVIS. DC. (Dor. 1922.)
ROBINSON. S.; T. (Des. 1913.)
ROCOCO. T. (Rinz. 1848.)
ROI DEPRUSSE. T. (Sie.)
ROI DESBELGES. T. (Jap. Sie. Kre. 1867.)
ROI DEWURTEMBERG. T. (Jap. Sie. Kre.)
ROSA. J. (Hol. 1906.)
ROSABEL. D. (Sass 1937.)
ROSA BELLA. T. (Sen. 1889.)
ROSA BONHEUR. DC. (Des. 1905.)
ROSACCA. T. (Kel. 1889.)
ROSAEFORMIS. T. (Par. or Mat. 1867.)
ROSA ELIARSI. T. (Kre. 1867.) *Eliarsi Rosea; Rosea Elyaesi.*
ROSA GALLICA. T. (Pai. 1889.)
ROSALIE. DC. (Auten 1927.)
ROSALIND. DC. (Cra. 1922.)
Rosalind. KASANE-JISHI.
ROSALITA. DC. (Hol. 1907.)
ROSA MANETTI. T. (Pai. 1889.)
ROSA MARIA. T. (Pai. 1889.)
ROSAMOND. DC. (Lewis 1922.)
ROSAMOND GRANT. D.
ROSAMUNDI. T. (Mak. 1846.)
ROSEA. T. (Chi. 1795.) *Papaveracea Rosea.*
Rosea Elyaesi. (Kre. 1867.) ROSA ELIARSI.
ROSEA GRANDIFLORA. T. *Papaveracea Rosea Grandiflora.*
Rosea Odorata. ODORATA ROSEA.
ROSEA PLENISSIMA. DC.
ROSEA SEMIPLENA. T. (Chi. 1794.)
Rosea Superba. ROBERT FORTUNE.
ROSE CAVALIER. SC. (Pleas 1855?)
Rose Cherie. LEOPOLDO.
ROSEDALE. HH. (Auten 1937.)
ROSE D'AMOUR. DC. (Cal. 1857.)
ROSEGLORY. J. (Ros. 1898?)
ROSE HERE. DC. (Bra. A. 1907.)
ROSELLA MAY. D.
ROSELTHEA. DC. (Lewis 1922.)
ROSE MARIE. HH. (Auten-Gla. 1937.)
Rosemary. KELWAYS ROSEMARY.
ROSE OF HEAVEN. D. (M.vanS.)
ROSE OF NIPPON. J.
ROSEOLENS. T. (Mat. of Bellville about 1841.)
ROSEOLENS ODORATA. T. (Mat. 1867.)
ROSE QUINTAL. DC. (Cal. 1857.)
ROSE SHAYLOR. DC. (Sha. 1920.)
ROSE STANDISH. DC. (Hol. 1919.)
ROSETTE. DC. (Des. 1918.)
Rosette. GINKO-SAKI.
Rosina. ODORATA MARIA.
ROSINE. DC. (Lem. 1913.)
Rossini. CASARETTO.
ROSY DAWN. SC. (Barr.)
Rosy Dawn. DC. (Pleas 1909.)
ROSYGEM.
ROSYGLOW. SJ. (Gla. 1928.)
ROSYRAPTURE. DC. (Kel. 1884?)
ROTARIAN. D. (Fran. 1928.)
ROTUNDA. T. (Kel. 1889.)
ROWENA. DC. (Lewis 1922.)
ROYAL BABE. T. (Kel. 1896.)
ROY (*W.*) GODDARD. D. (Bra.A. 1936.)
R. (*P.*) WHITFIELD. DC. (Rie.)

PAEONIA, continued

RUBANNE DEFLANDRE. T. (Grade 1851.)
RUBENS. DC. (Del. 1854.)
Rubens. SC.
RUBERRIMA. T. (Bel. 1846.)
RUBICON. D. (Lem. E. 1929.)
RUBIDA. T. (Kel. 1889.)
RUBIE BATTEY. J. (Auten 1933.)
RUBRAGRANDIFLORA. SC.
RUBRAMACULATA. T. (Pai. 1889.)
RUBRAMAJOR. T. (Ler. 1846.)
RUBRAODORATAPLENA. T. (Nois 1837.) *Phaenicia Rubra Odorata.*
RUBRAPLENA. T. (Kre. 1867.)
RUBRASUPERBA. DC. (Ric. 1871.)
RUBRATRIUMPHANS. DC. (Del. 1854.)
RUBY. DC. (Auten 1927.)
RUBYLIGHT. SC. (Kel. 1884?)
RUBYQUEEN.
RUDESHEIM. DC. (G.&K.)
RUDYARD KIPLING. T. (Kel. 1903.)
Rudyard Kipling. DC. (Kel. 1917.)
RUHM VON BELSLIN. T. (Loo. 1851.)
RUIGEGNO. J. *Louise* (in part).
RUIGEJE. J.
RURIBAN. S.; T. (Jap. 1893.)
RUSSI MAJOR. SC.
RUTH BRAND. DC. (Bra. A. 1907.)
RUTH BYRD. SC. (Lewis 1921.)
RUTH ELIZABETH. D. (Bra. A. 1936.)
RUTH FORCE. C.J. type. (Sha. 1921.)
RUTILA. T. (Kel. 1889.)
RUY BLAS. DC. (Des. 1905.)
R. (*W.*) MARSH. SC. (Kel. 1884?)
RYUKO. T.
RYUKYUBENI. T.
SAGOROMA. J. (Mill. 1924.)
SAIGYO-ZAKURA. T. (Jap. 1893.) *Femina.*
SAINFOIN. DC. (Kel. 1890.)
SAISHOJI. T. (Jap. 1898.)
SAKURA-KAGAMI. T. (Jap. 1916.)
SALEM. D. (Auten 1931.)
SALMONEA. D.; T. (Chi.-For. 1864.)
SAMARANG. D.; T. (Chi.-For. 1864.)
SAMOSET. DC. (Hol. 1907.)
SAMUEL HENSHAW. DC. (Ric. 1904.)
SAMUEL HILL. SJ. (Ber. 1932.)
SAMUEL HUGHES. DC. (Kel. 1917.)
SAMURAI. J. (Mill.)
SANCTUARY. D. (Auten 1933.)
SAN DIEGO. J. (Auten 1931.)
SANGUINEOLENTA. T. (Kel. 1889.)
SANKONISHIKI. T.
SANS SOUCI. J. (Auten 1930.)
SANTA FE. D. (Auten 1937.)
SANTORB. SC. (Kel. 1926.)
SAPHO. DC. (Lem. E. 1900.)
SARAH. DC. (Pleas 1913.)
SARAH BERNHARDT. T. (Kel. 1896.)
Sarah Bernhardt. (Des.) *Umbellata Rosea.*
Sarah Bernhardt. DC. (Lem. E. 1909.)
SARAH CARSTENSEN. DC. (Terry 1901.)
SARAH (*K.*) THURLOW. DC. (Thu. 1921.)
SARAH (*M.*) NAPIER. D. (Vor. 1930.)
SARAH (*M.*) WETTENGEL. DC. (Wet. 1919.)
SARCOXIE. DC. (Wild 1914.)
SATELLITE. S.; T. (Des. 1913.)
SATINROSE. S.; T. (Des. 1913.)
SATINROUGE. L.H. (Lem. E. 1926.)
SATSUMA. SC. (Mill.)
SATURA. T. (Kel. 1889.)
SATURN. J.
SAVII. D.; T. (Ler. 1846.)

PAEONIA, continued

SAWA-NO-TAKI. D.; T. (Jap. 1919.)
SCARF DANCE. SC. (Auten 1927.)
SCHICHI-FUKUJIN. T. (Jap. 1896.)
SCHICHISHOGAN. T.
SCHONE VONKOLN. D.; T. (v.Gee. 1874.)
SCHULTHESI. T. (Oud. 1846.) *Schultesi.*
SCHWARZENBERGIANA. T. (H.&S. 1864.)
SCHWINDT. SC. (G.&K. 1910.)
SEAFOAM. DC. (Pet. 1886?)
SEASHELL. SJ. (Sass 1937.)
SEBASTICOOK. J. (Guppy 1935.)
SECRETARY FEWKES. DC. (Sha. 1916.)
SEFTON. DC. (Kel. 1884?)
SEIDAI. T. (Yok. 1927.)
SEIFU-KURU. T. (Jap. 1910.)
SEIOBA. J.
SEIRIU. S.; T. (Jap. 1893.)
SEIRIU SOMAE. J.
SEIRYUDEN. T.
SEISHUSHIRO. T.
SENDONISHIKI. J.
SENORITA. J. (Auten 1931.)
SENRIGU-BOTAN. T. (Jap. 1916.)
SENSATION. D. (Sass 1937.)
SENTINEL. J. (Auten 1931.)
SERAPH. SC. (Terry 1855.)
SERENE. DC. (Fran. 1921.)
SETSUGEKKO. T.
SETSURAN. T.
SETTING SUN. SJ. (Pfe. 1932.)
SHABONA. DC. (Harr. 1890.)
SHATTUCK. D. (Bra. A. 1932.)
SHAVANO. J. (Andr. 1925.)
SHAYLORS DREAM. DC. (Sha. 1918.)
SHAYLORS SUNBURST. J. (All. 1931.)
SHELLPINK.
SHERBROOKE RECORD. J. (Nor. 1924.)
SHICHI-FUKUJIN. T. (Yok. 1927.)
SHICHIHO-DEN. T. (Jap. 1926.)
SHICKI-HENGI-SHIBORI. J.
SHIKO-DEN. T. (Jap. 1926.)
SHIN-ABOKIU. T. (Jap. 1910.)
SHIN-AKEBONO. D.; T. (Jap. 1919.)
SHINE-KAGURA. S.; T. (Jap. 1905; 1927.) *Buffon.*
SHINGETSUNOKASA. T.
SHIN-KAGAMI. T. (Jap. 1926.)
SHINKUROBATAN. T.
SHIN-MOMO-ZONO. T. (Jap. 1926.)
SHINSO-JIBIKI. SC. (Mill.)
SHINTOYEN. T.
SHINYASOOKINA. T.
SHIPENKUE. SC. (Mill.)
SHIRAGINU. J.
SHIRA-ZIKU. T. (Jap. 1896.)
SHIRINE. D. (Bre. 1936.)
SHIRLEY WALKER. SC. (Sha. 1918.)
SHIRO-KAGURA. T. (Jap. 1896.) *Adelina Patti.*
SHIRO-KAGURA-JISHI. T. (Jap. 1896.)
SHIROKIJISHI. T.
SHIRO-NOA. T.
SHIRO-SOKU. S.; T. (Jap. 1913.) *Diane.*
SHISHI-GASHIRA. T. (Jap. 1893.) *Kashira.*
SHISHINDEN. S.; T. (Jap. 1913.) *Eden.*
SHISHINOTATEGAMA. T.
SHISHIODORI. T.
SHIUNDAI. S.; T. (Jap. 1896.)
SHI-UN-RYO. T.
SHOGO-NO-MAI. T. (Jap. 1926.)
SHOGUN. SC. *Shoyun.*
SHOKI-KAGURA. S.; T. (Jap. 1898.) *Dejazet.*
SHOKO-NISHIKI. T. (Jap. 1910.)

PAEONIA, continued

SHON-MEINON. T. (Jap. 1926.)
Shoyun. SHOGUN.
SHUCHIUKA. T. (Jap. 1919.)
SHUGYO-KADEN. T. (Jap. 1926.)
SHUMIN-KAI. T. (Jap. 1916.)
SHY MAID. J. (Auten 1930.)
SIBERI. T. (Ler. 1846.)
SIDONIE. DC. (Mie. 1856.) *Sydonie.*
SIGNAL STATION. J. (Auten 1938.)
SIGNORINETTA. DC. (Kel. 1910.)
SILOAM. D. (Auten 1933.)
SILVERCERISE. SJ. (Por. 1931.)
SILVERCUP. SC. (Kel. 1884?)
SILVERKING. D. (Auten 1933.)
SILVERPLUME. J. (Andr. 1932.)
SILVERSWAN. D. (Ros. 1934.)
SILVIA SAUNDERS. DC. (Sau. 1921.) *Silvia.*
SIMONNE CHEVALIER. DC. (Des. 1902.)
SIMPLICI. T. (Bau. 1836.)
SIR AGA KHAN. SC. (Kel. 1884?)
SIR CLINTON DAWKINS. T. (Kel. 1906.)
SIR ERNEST SHACKLETON. DC. (Kel. 1884?)
SIR (*E. S.*) HILL. T. (Kel. 1896.)
SIR FREDERICK LEIGHTON. DC. (Barr 1899.)
SIR GALAHAD. SC. (Kel. 1884?)
Sir George Davis. COL. MALCOLM.
SIR GEORGE STAUNTON. T. (For. 1864.)
SIR HENRY STONE. DC. (Kel. 1926.)
SIRIUS. T. (Kel. 1889.)
SIR JOHN DAVIS. T. (Kre. 1867.)
SIR JOHN FRENCH. DC. (Kel. 1915.)
SIR JOHN STAUNTON. T. (Kel. 1889.)
SIR MADHO SINGH. DC. (Kel. 1884?)
SIR SPENCER (*P.*) FANE. DC. (Kel. 1884?)
SIR THOMAS LIPTON. DC. (Kel. 1884?)
SIR VISTO. SC.
SIR WALTER SCOTT. T. (Kel. 1889.)
Sir Walter Scott. DC.
SIR WILFRID LAURIER. DC. (Kel. 1884?)
SIR WM. MAXWELL. T. (Kel. 1898.)
SISTERS ANNIE. DC. (Bra. A. 1907.)
SISTIE. D. (Auten 1933.)
SLEEPY HOLLOW. SJ. (Auten 1935.)
SMILES. D. (New. 1934.)
SNOWBALL. DC. (Hol. 1907.)
SNOWBOUND. SJ. (Auten 1931.)
SNOWCREAM. DC. (Kel. 1926.)
SNOWDRIFT. J. (Wal.)
SNOWFLAKE. SC. (Kel. 1884?)
SNOWRIM. SC. (Andr. 1923.)
SNOWSPRITE. SJ. (Auten 1930.)
SNOWWHEEL. J.
SNOWY COLES. DC. (Kel. 1884?)
SOLANGE. DC. (Lem. 1907.)
SOLFATARE. DC. (Cal. 1961.)
SOLO FLIGHT. D. (Sau. 1933.)
SOME-GANOKO. J.
SOMERTON. SC. (Kel. 1884?)
SOMIA-OSHIRO. T. (Jap. 1926.)
SONKOIN. T.
SOPHIA HOUSTON. J.
SOPHIE. T. (Dau. 1859.)
SOPS OF WINE. DC. (Secor 1922.)
SOSHI. J. (Mill.)
SOUTHERN CROSS. HH. (Sau. 1935.)
SOUTHERN SUN. SJ. (Don. 1931.)
(*Souv. d'*) *Adrien Seneclauze.* GEORGES PAUL.
(*Souv. d'*) AUGUSTE MIELLEZ. DC. (Cal. 1861.) *Lee's Grandiflora Rubra; Marechal Vaillant.*
(*Souv. de*) A. MILLET. DC. (Mill. 1924.)

PAEONIA, continued

(*Souv. de*) CHENONCEAUX. T. (Mec. 1889.)
(*Souv. de*) DOWNING. T. (Sen. 1889.) *Gen. Faidherbe; Souv. de Dowening.*
(*Souv. de*) DUCHER. D.; T. (Duc. 1889.)
(*Souv. de*) 1896. DC.
(*Souv. de*) FRANCOIS RUITTON. DC. (Riv. 1908.)
(*Souv. de*) GAND. D.; T. (Goe. 1865?)
(*Souv. de*) GRANGER. T. (Des. 1899.)
(*Souv. de*) GUYNEMER. J.; SJ. (Mill.)
(*Souv. de*) J. B. RUITTON. T. (Riv. 1908.)
(*Souv. de*) JULES DESSERT. D.; T. (Des. 1908.)
(*Souv. de*) LA COUVELLERIE. T. (Mec. 1889.)
(*Souv. de*) L'EXPOSITION DEBORDEAUX. DC. (Des. 1896.)
(*Souv. de*) L'EXPOSITION DELOURDES. (Riv.)
(*Souv. de*) L'EXPOSITION DUMANS. DC. (Mec. 1880.)
(*Souv. de*) L'EXPOSITION UNIVERSELLE. DC. (Cal. 1867.)
(*Souv. de*) LOUIS BIGOT. DC. (Des. 1913.)
(*Souv. de*) LOUIS PAILLET. DC. (Bro.)
(*Souv. de*) MAXIME CORNU. T. (Henry 1897.)
(*Souv. de*) 7 MAI. T. (Pai. 1889.)
(*Souv. de*) MME. COLETTE VEILLET. D. (Riv. 1925.)
(*Souv. de*) MME. KNORR. T. (v.Hou. about 1853.)
(*Souv. d'*) ETIENNE MECHIN. D.; T. (Des.&Mec. 1899.)
(*Souv. de*) ZEPHIR. DC.
(*Souv. d'*) HARAUCOURT. SJ. (Mill.)
(*Souv. du*) DR. BRETONNEAU. DC. (Des. 1880.)
(*Souv. du*) GENERAL GALLIENI. DC. (Riv. 1917.)
SOUVENIR. T. (v.Gee. 1896.)
SOWADABSCOOK. J. (Guppy 1935.)
SPECIOSISSIMA. T. (Chi.-For. 1867 or Nois 1839.)
SPEEDWELL. DC. (Hol. 1907.)
SPINNING WHEEL. J. (Bab.)
SPION KOP. DC. (Kel. 1918–22.) *Kelways Spion Kop.*
SPLENDENS. T. (Oud. 1846.)
SPLENDIDA. DC. (Que. 1850.)
SPLENDIDISSIMA. T. (Kre. 1867.)
SPLENDOR. D. (Sass. 1932.)
SPOON RIVER. D. (Auten 1931.)
SPRING BEAUTY. D. (Nic. 1933.)
SPRING MAID. SC.
STANDARD BEARER. DC. (Hol. 1906.)
STANLEY. DC. (Cro. 1879.)
Stanley. SC. (Kel. 1890.)
STAR OF BEAUTY. D. (Nee. 1930.)
STELLATA ATROPURPUREA. T. (1842.) *Papaveracea Stellata Atropurpurea.*
STELLATA FLOREPLENO. T. (H.&S. 1864.)
STEPHANIE. DC. (Terry 1891.)
ST. GOAR. DC.
STRASSBURG. DC. (G.&K. 1911.)
SUAVISSIMA. T. (Kel. 1889.)
SUBLIMIS. T. (Kel. 1889.)
SUCCESS. SJ.
SUI-BIJIN. T. (Yok. 1927.)
SUIGAN. T.
SUISHO-HAKU. T. (Jap. 1919.)
SUISHOKU. T.

PAEONIA, continued

SUISHO-SHIRO. T. (Jap. 1910.)
SULLY PRUDHOMME. DC. (Cro. 1898.)
SULPHUREA. DC. (Lemon 1830.)
SUMINA-GASHI. T. (Jap. 1896.)
SUMI-NO-ICHI. T. (Jap. 1927.)
SUMMER DAY. DC. (Kel. 1895–96.)
SUNBEAM. J. (Hol. 1906.)
SUNCOOK. J. (Guppy 1935.)
SUNRISE. J. *Hinode-sekai.*
Sunrise. DC. (Kel. 1915.)
SUNSET. J. (Risk. 1929.)
SUN-UP. SJ. (Auten 1937.)
Superba Deyoung. CONFUCIUS.
SUPREME. DC. (Hol. 1907.)
SURPRISE. SC. (Barr.)
Surprise. LH. (Lem. 1920.)
SURUGU. J. (Mill. 1917.)
SUSAN (*B.*) ANTHONY. DC. (Bra. A. 1907.)
SUSAN (*B.*) WHITE. D. (Bra. A. 1933.)
SUZANNE DESSERT. DC. (Des.&Mec. 1890.)
SUZETTE. DC. (Des. 1911.)
SUZUGAMINE. T.
SWAN WHITE. SJ. (G.&R. 1930.)
SWEETHEART. DC. (Hol. 1909.)
SWORD DANCE. J. (Auten 1933.)
SYDONIE. T. (Pai. 1889.)
Sydonie. SIDONIE.
SYLVANUS. DC. (Kel. 1884?)
SYLVIA. DC. (Kre. 1917.)
SYLVIA LOUISE. DC. (Kel. 1915.)
SYLVIANE. DC. (Lem. 1924.)
SYLVIE. T. (v.Hou. 1873.)
SYMPHONY. D. (Bre. 1924.)
Tabarin. MIKASO-NO-MARI.
TAGLIONI. DC. (Gue. 1830.)
TAGO-NO-TSUKI. J.
T. (*A.*) HAVEMEYER. T. (Kel. 1906.)
TAHEI-GATA. T. (Jap. 1910.)
TAIHAI. T.
TAI-HEI-BENI. T. (Jap. 1926.)
TAIHEIKO. T.
TAI-HEI-RAKU. T. (Jap. 1926.)
TAIHO. J.
TAIHOTO. JT.
TAIKAKUSEI. T.
TAIKOON. J.
TAI-SHONO-HOMARE. T. (Jap. 1926.)
TAKARADAMA. J.
TAKITSUSE. T.
Talma. AKASHI-NISHIKI.
TAMA-FUYO. T. (Jap. 1919.)
TAMA-JISHI. T. (Jap. 1926.)
TAMA-MIDORI. T. (Jap. 1916.)
TAMATEBOKU. J. *Tomatbako.*
TAMA-USAGI. ST. (Jap. 1919.)
TAMA-ZURA. T. (Jap. 1916.)
TANAGER. D. (Sass J. 1934.)
TANINA-NO-YUKI. T. (Jap. 1927.)
TARANTELLE. J. (Auten 1934.)
TAR BABY. D. (Auten 1931.)
TATIO. J.
TATIO SHISHI. T.
TATSUGASHIRA. J.
T. B. TERRY. DC. (Pleas 1911.)
Tecumseh. GROVER CLEVELAND.
TEMPEST. D. (Auten 1931.)
TENGO-KUKA. T. (Jap. 1927.)
TENIERS. DC. (Cro. 1880.)
THE BARON. J. (Auten 1934.)
THE BRIDE. D. (Terry 18—)
The Bride. T. (Kel. 1897.)
The Bride. CS. (Des. 1902.) *Lafiancee.*
THE DISC. D. (Sass 1926.)
THE DRAGON. J. (Wal.)

PAEONIA, continued

The Eagle. DC. (Cra. 1922.)
The Gem. DC. (Pleas 1909.)
The Grace. D. (Gumm 1930.)
The Jewel. Opal.
Thelma Barnes. D. (Fran. 1933.)
The Marchioness. T. (Sau. 1940.)
The Moor. SC. (Barr.)
The Nymph. Nymph.
The Oaks. SC. (Kel. 1884?)
The Oyne. J.
The Queen. SC. (Kel. 1902.)
Therese. DC. (Des. 1904.)
Therese DeVilmorin. T. (Jap. 1897.)
The Sultan.
The Tycoon. T. (Jap.)
Thoma. SC. (G.&K. 1919.)
Thomas C. Thurlow. DC. (Thu. 1919.)
Thomas Holloway. D. (Kel. 1912.)
Thomas Meehan. D. (Terry 1855?)
Thor. D. (Sass 1937.)
Thura Hires. D. (Nic. 1938.)
Thurlow Weed. SJ. (Weed)
Tiger-tiger. HH. (Sau. 1935.)
Tillienoone. SJ. (Guppy 1932.)
Titan. SC.
Titian. J.; SC.
Toen. T.
Tokio. C.J. type.
Toki-Wadsu. T. (Jap. 1893.)
Toki-Wayana. T. (Jap. 1910.)
Tokykonoshiki. T.
Tollens. T. (Kre. 1867.)
Tomatbako. Tamateboku.
Tom Thumb. DC. (Terry 1855?)
Tom Tinker. SJ. (Auten 1930.)
Tonti. SJ. (Auten 1933.)
Topeka. HH. (Auten 1938.)
Toreador. SC. (Wet. 1921.)
Toro-no-maki. C.J. type.
Torpilleur. C.J. type. (Des. 1913.)
Torquemada. DC. (Kel. 1895.)
Tourangelle. DC. (Des. 1910.)
Tragedy. DC. (Hol. 1909.)
Trails End. D. (Nee. 1936.)
Treasure Cup. SJ. (Kel. 1910.)
Tricolor Flavescens. DC.
Triomphe d'Artselaer. T. (v.Gee. 1874.)
Triomphe Debourg-argental. T. (Sen. 1889.)
Triomphe Degand. DT. (v.Gee 1873.)
Triomphe Dehaarlem. T. (Kre. 1867.)
Triomphe de l'Exposition Delille. DC. (Cal. 1865.)
Triomphe Demalines. T. (v.Kiel 1854.)
Triomphe Demilan. DT. (Bur. 1860.)
Triomphe Deparis. T. (Gue. 1875.)
Triomphe de van Aerschott. Comte Deflandre.
Triomphe Devandermalen. T. (Van. 1867.)
Triomphe Deversailles. T. (Pai. 1889.)
Triomphe Dunord. DC. (Mie. 1850.)
Triumpf Vonmainz. T. (H.&S. 1864.)
Triumphans. T. (Bel. 1864.)
Triumphans. DC.
Trojan. DC. (Kel. 1884?)
Tsarine. Beni-Kagu.
Ts een Ke. T.
T. S. (*Hope*) Simpson. SC. (Kel. 1884?)
Tsin Tsiou. J.
Tsukasa-botan. T. (Jap. 1927.)

PAEONIA, continued

Tsukasa-jishi. T. (Jap. 1919.)
Tsure-dsuru. T. (Jap. 1893.)
Tsuru-watari. T. (Jap. 1896.)
Tsuya-tsugata. T.
Tsuzure-Nishiki. T. (Jap. 1910.)
Tulipe. Kokiriu-Nishiki.
Tuyerline. J.
Twentieth Century. DC. (Hol. 1908.)
Tydeus. SC. (Barr.)
Ukaregiohi. T.
Ukare-jishi. ST. (Jap. 1899.)
Ukijishi. T.
Uklori-nishiki. T. (Jap. 1910.)
Umbellata Rosea. Sarah Bernhardt.
Uncle Remus. D. (Auten 1931.)
Uranie. DT. (Sen. 1889.)
Urano. D. (Secor 1924.)
Uranos. T. (Kel. 1889.)
Usona. DC. (Hol. 1907.)
Usugesho. T.
Usu-jishi. T. (Jap. 1926.)
Vadius. Philomele.
Valiant. DC.
Vander Maeli. DT. (Van. 1853.)
Vandongen. SJ. (Ruys.)
Vandyck. DC. (Cro. 1879.)
Vanhalli. T. (H.&S. 1864.)
Vanhouttei. DT. (Cas. 1812–1879?)
Variegata. T. (Mount. 1834.)
Variegata. DC. (Terry 1855?)
Vavia. T. (Pai. 1889.)
Veloutine. SC. (Des. 1908.)
Venise. SC. (Des. 1913.)
Venosa. T. (Kel. 1889.)
Venus. SC. (Barr.)
Venus. DC. (Kel. 1888.)
Venusta. T. (Kel. 1889.)
Venusta. Wittmanniana hybrid? (Lem. E. 1916.)
Vera. SC. (Gumm 1923.)
Vera Terry. DC. (Terry 1855?)
Verdun. SC. (Des.-Dor. 1927.)
Veribest. DC. (Hol. 1907.)
Verity. HH. (Sau. 1935.)
Versicolor. Berenice.
Versicolor Plena. T. (Par. 1867.)
Vesta. SC. (Kel. before 1897.)
Vesta Clausen. D. (Cla. 1936.)
Vesticius. SC.
Vestucius. J.
Vesuve. SC. (Des. 1905.)
Vicomte Deforceville. DC. (Cal. 1864.)
Victoire d'Alma. T. (Des. 1899.)
Victoire Delamarne. DC. (Des. 1915.)
Victoire Lemon. DC. (Mie. 1858?)
Victoire Mathieu. T. (v.Hou. 1873.)
Victoire Modeste. DC. (Gue. 1842.)
Victor Durufle. Lutea Plenissima.
Victor Hugo. DM. (Des. 1902.)
Victor Hugo. SC. (Kel. 1915.)
Victor Hugo. Felix Crousse.
Victoria. T. (Mat. 1839 or 1836.) *Blanche Demathieu*.
Victoria. SC.
Victoria Alba. T. (Mat. 1867.)
Victoria Tricolor. DC. (v.Hou. 1873?)
Victorie. DC. (Probably a misspelling for Victory.)
Victorine Leseble. T. (v.Gee. 1896.)
Victor Lemoine. DC. (Cal. 1866.)
Victors Crown. D. (Nee. 1936.)
Victory. DC. (Kel. 1884?)

PAEONIA, continued

Victory Chateau Thierry. DC. (Bra. 1925.)
Viking. D. (Auten 1936.)
Ville Delyon. T. (Sen. 1889.)
Ville Denancy. DC. (Cal. 1872.)
Ville Depoissey. DC. (Cou.)
Vimy Ridge. D. (Bre. 1937.)
Vinacea Duplex. T. (v.Hou. 1873.)
Vincea Plena. T. (Ital. 1846.)
Vindicator. HH. (Sau. 1935.)
Vinette. DC. (Lewis 1922.)
Violacea. T. (Chi.-For. 1846 or Nois. 1839.)
Violacea Purpurea. T. (Mat. 1846.)
Violaris. T. (Kel. 1889.)
Violetta. ST. (Des. 1909.)
Virgata. T. (Kel. 1889.)
Virginia Mary. D. (Pfe. 1932.)
Virginie. DC. (Cal. 1858.)
Virgins Blush. DC. (Pleas 1913.)
Virgo Maria. DC. (Cal. 1859.)
Virgo Maria. T. (1889.)
Viscountess Folkestone. DC. (Barr 1899.)
Vishnu. T. (Kel. 1889.)
Vivid. T. (Chi.-For. 1864.) ***Dentata; Prince Albert.***
Volcan. Konron-Koku.
Vondel. T. (Kre. 1867.)
Von Siebold. T. (Jap. Sie. Kre. 1867.)
Vulcan. SC.
Wah-wah-tay-see. DC. (Fra. 1920.)
Waldafla. DC. (G.&K. 1926.)
Walneri. Gloire Deshanghai.
Walter Brewster. D. (Brew. 1932.)
Walter (*Campbell*) Lyman. D. (Lym. 1933.)
Walter Faxon. DC. (Ric. 1904.)
Walter Lindgren. D. (Bra. A. 1936.)
Walter Morgan. DC. (Pleas 1900.)
Wangpan. T.
War. DC. (Kel. 1916.)
War. SC.
Warai-jishi. T. (Jap. 1916.)
Ward Welsh. D. (Nee. 1929.)
Warren Roy. D. (Gumm 1883?)
Warwick. DC.
Waseca. SJ. (Bra.A. 1936.)
Washington. DC. (Gue. 1850.)
Wataseshiro. T.
Watchman. SJ. (Auten 1933.)
Waterlily. Marie Jacquin.
Waterloo. DC. (Kell. 1908.)
Watteau. SC. (G.&K. 1911.)
Waukeag. SJ. (Guppy 1935.)
Wedding Day. SJ. (Auten 1933.)
Weigetsuko. J.
Weisse. Kochs Weisse.
Welcome Guest. DC. (Hol. 1904.)
Wenonah. DC. (Fran. 1920.)
Westhill. D. (Lit. 1938.)
W. F. Christman. DC. (Fra. 1921.)
W. F. Miller. D. (Wet. 1928.)
Whitebatson. D. (Sass 1925.)
Whitebeauty. D. (Auten 1931.)
Whitecloud. J. (Auten 1931.)
Whitedelight. D. (Auten 1935.)
Whiteeagle. D. (Sass 1937.)
Whitegold. J. (M.vanS. 1936.)
Whitejapan. J.
Whitelady. C.J.type. (Kel. 1900.)
Whitemoth. SJ. (Auten 1933.)
Whitepearl. D. (Auten 1931.)
Whiteperfection. SJ. (Auten 1931.)
Whiteprince. D. (Risk 1929.)

PAEONIA, continued

Whitequeen. J. (Wal.)
Whiteswan. SC. (Pleas 1913.)
Whitleyi. SC.
Whitleyimajor. SC.
Wiesbaden. DC. (G.&K. 1911.)
Wilbur Wright. SC. (Kel. 1909.)
Wildrose. SC. (Kel. 1884?) *Kelways Wild Rose.*
Wilhelmina. DT. (Koc. 1874.)
William (*F.*) Turner. DC. (Sha.1916.)
William Mesman. DC. (Ker. 1914.)
William Penn. DC. (Bra. A. 1907.)
William Robinson. T. (Kel. 1900.)
Will McClelland. DC. (Sha. 1919.)
Will Rogers. D. (Fra. 1935.)
Wilton Lockwood. DC. (Sha. 1916.)
Winnebago Chief. SC. (Secor 1924.)
Winnie Winkle. D. (Fra. 1931.)
Winnifred Domme. DC. (Bra. 1913.)
Winnikenni. DC. (Thu. 1915.)
Wisconsin. T. (Jap. 1911.)
Witches' Dance. SJ. (Auten 1931.)
W. L. Gumm. D. (Gumm 1929.)
Wyoming. J.
Yachiyo-jishi. T. (Jap. 1911.)
Yachyo-nishiki. T. (Jap. 1910.)
Yaekasumi. T.
Yaenishiki. T.
Yaeshishi. T.
Ya Machina. J. (Mil.)
Yamatochiro. T.
Yamato-Sangai. J.
Yamato Tsuka. J.
Yamato Tsukasa. J.
Yamo-okina. T. (Jap. 1900.)
Yaou. T.
Yashimoura. T.
Yaso-no-Mine. T. (Jap.) *Reine Blanche.*
Yaso-okina. Queen Alexandra.
Yatsufusa. T.
Yayoura. J.
Yellow King. J
Yenchi-no-tsuki. J.
Yeso. J.
Yo-boku. T. (Jap. 1926.)
Yochigetsu. T.
Yoki-hi. T.
Yokohama. J.
Yomo-no-homare. T. (Jap. 1893.) *Jupiter.*
Yomo-zackura. T. (Jap. 1927.)
Yoochi-no-tsuki. J.
Yoro-nishiki. T. (Jap. 1910.)
Yoshinogawa. T.
Yo-so-oil. T. (Jap. 1910.)
Yoyoerobi. T.
Yoyonoyuki. T.
Yuhigaoka. T.
Yuki-arashi. T. (Yok. 1893.)
Yuki-doro. T. (Jap. 1919.)
Yukikazari. T.
Yukinoikkyoku. T.
Yukishige. T.
Yukon. D. (Auten 1937.)
Yukon-dano. ST. (Jap. 1919.)
Yutsumi. J. (G.H.G.)
Zansetzu. J.
Zelia. T. (Pai. 1889.)
Zenobia. T. (Chi.-For. 1864.) *Alexandre de Humboldt; Atropurpurea.*
Zephyrus. DC. (Kel. before 1895.)

PAEONIA, continued

Zest. DC. (Hol. 1907.)
Zip Coon. D. (Auten 1931.)
Zoe Calot. DC. (Mie. 1855.)
Zoe Verniory. DC. (Gue. 1863.)
Zorania. T. (Bur. 1867.)
Zulu Bride. D. (Auten 1933.)

Pagodatree, Japanese. **Sophora japonica**

PAHU'DIA . . . . Pahudia
martaban'ica . . . . Martaban P.
rhomboi'dea . Philippine P. (*Tindalo*)
xylocar'pa . . . . Shan P.

Paintbrush, Indian . **Castilleja coccinea**

Paintedcup . . . . **Castilleja**
Bradbury P. . . . . **C. bradburyi**
Hairy P. . . . . **C. lutea**
Indian Paintbrush . . . **C. coccinea**
Magenta P. . . . . . . **C. oreopola**
Northwestern P. . . **C. angustifolia**
Pale P. . . . . **C. pallescens**
Pine P. . . . . **C. pinetorum**
Scarlet P. . . . . **C. miniata**
Shrubby P. . . . . . . **C. hololeuca**
Splitleaf P. . . . . . . **C. rhexifolia**
Sulfur P. . . . . **C. sulphurea**
Texas P. . . . . **C. indivisa**
Western P. . . . . . **C. occidentalis**
White P. . . . . **C. pilosa**
Wholeleaf P. . . . . . . **C. integra**
Woolly P. . . . . **C. foliolosa**
Wyoming P. . . . . . **C. linariaefolia**
Yellowgreen P. . . . **C. luteovirens**
Yellow P. . . . . **C. flava**
Yellowstone P. . . . . . . **C. lauta**

Pakchoi . . . . . . **Brassica chinensis**
False P. . . . . . **B. parachinensis**

PALAFOX'IA . . . . Palafoxia
feay'i . . . . Feay P.
hookeria'na . . **Othake sphacelatum**
leucophyl'la . . . . Baja P.
linea'ris . . . . Desert P.
texa'na . . . . . . **Othake texanum**

PALAQUI'UM . . . . . . Natotree
barnes'i . . . . Barnes N.
borneen'se . . . . Borneo N.
gut'ta (*Isonandra g.*) Malay Guttapercha N.
javen'se . . . . Java N.
philippinen'se . . . . Philippine N.

Known locally by many common names, including Alakaak, Araka, Guttapercha, and Malak.

PALICOUR'EA . . . . . Palicourea
barbiner'via . . . . Showy P.
cro'cea . . . . Yellow P.
leariflo'ra
rig'ida
terna'ta . . . . Threeleaf P.

PALISO'TA
bar'teri
pynaert'i

PALIU'RUS . . . . Paliurus
hemsleya'nus (*orientalis*) Chinese P.
spina-chris'ti (*aculeatus*) Christthorn P.

Palm
Cohune P. . . . **Orbignya cohune**
Illawarra P. . . Kingpalm, Piccabeen: **Archontophoenix cunninghamiana**
Palmadulce . . Braheapalm, Sweet: **Brahea dulcis**

PALMEREL'LA
deb'ilis
—serra'ta

Palmetto . . . . **Sabal**
Beccari P. . . . . . **S. beccariana**
Bermuda P. . . . . . **S. bermudana**
Blackburn P. . . . . **S. blackburnia**
Cabbage P. . . . . . . **S. palmetto**
Cuban P. . . . . **S. parviflora**
Dwarf P . . . . **S. minor**
Etonia P. . . . . **S. etonia**
Guanajuato P. . . . . . **S. dugesi**
Guatemala P. . . . **S. guatemalensis**
Hispaniola P. . . . **S. umbraculifera**
Jamaica P. . . . . . **S. jamaicensis**
Japa P. . . . . **S. yapa**
Louisiana P. . . . . . . **S. louisiana**
Oaxaca P . . . . **S. mexicana**
PuertoRico P. . . . **S. causiarum**
Sonora P. . . . . **S. uresana**
Tepic P. . . . . **S. rosei**
Texas P. . . . . **S. texana**
Trinidad P. . . . **S. mauritiaeformis**
Victoria P. . . . . **S. exul**

PALM GENERA

Taxonomically, palms are among the most difficult of all groups in the entire plant world to classify and systematize, and perhaps may always remain so. Under these severe limitations the Editors of Standardized Plant Names believe that the following treatment by Dr. Bomhard is probably the most authentic and up-to-date of any at present available. On behalf of the American Joint Committee we wish to acknowledge our great indebtedness to the author.

Harlan P. Kelsey, *Chairman,*
Editorial Committee S.P.N.

This list is intended primarily to include palms reported to be in cultivation in this country or of economic interest. The common names necessarily conform to the plan adopted for this book. In recent years, the nomenclature of palms has undergone considerable revision at the hands of various authorities and many new species are being described. The latest publications should be consulted.

Miriam L. Bomhard,
Forest Service,
U. S. Department of Agriculture

ACANTHOPHOE'NIX Spinepalm
crini'ta (*Areca c.*) . . . . Woolly S.
no'bilis . . . . **Deckenia n.**
ru'bra (*Areca r.* Bory, *not* Hort.) Red S.

Palms cultivated at present in this country under the name of Acanthophoenix probably do not belong to this genus.

ACANTHORRHI'ZA **CRYOSOPHILA**

ACANTHOSA'BAL . **PAUROTIS**

ACOELORRA'PHE . . **BRAHEA; PAUROTIS; SERENOA**

ACRIS'TA . . . . . **EUTERPE**

ACROCO'MIA . . . . Acrocomia
aculea'ta . . . . Grugru A.
armenta'lis (*crispa*) Cuban A. (*Corojo*)
fusifor'mis . . . . Jamaica A.
me'dia . . PuertoRico A. (*Corozo*)
mexica'na . . . . Coyol

Hort. var.; hv. = horticultural variety (or varieties); sp. = species (singular); spp. = species (plural).
₵ = clon; × (as a prefix) = hybrid; × (between scientific plant names) = crossed by; ∞ = polybrid; |w = plant useful to wildlife.
See Glossary for definitions of clon, hybrid, and polybrid.

PALM GENERA (ACROCOMIA), continued
sclerocar'pa . . Mucaja Acrocomia
tota'i . . . . Totaipalm
vinif'era

ACTINOPHLOE'US (*ROMANOVIA*) . . . . . Clusterpalm
kerstenia'nus **Ptychosperma kerstenianum**
macar'thuri (*Kentia m.; Ptychosperma m.*) . . . . . . MacArthur C.
—hos'pitus (*A. hospitus; Ptychosperma hospitum*)
nicola'i (*Ptychosperma n.; Romanovia n.*) Purpleleaf C.
sanderia'nus (*Kentia sanderiana; Ptychosperma sanderianum*) . Sander C.

ACTINORHY'TIS
calappa'ria (*Areca c.; A. cocoides; Ptychosperma calapparium; Seaforthia c.*) Calappapalm

ADONID'IA . . . . . . Adonidia
mer'rilli (*Normanbya m.*) Merrill A.

AE'RIA . . . . **GAUSSIA**

AI'PHANES (*CURIMA; MARARA; MARTINEZIA* Auth., *not* Ruiz & Pav.; *TILMIA*) Rufflepalm
acanthophyl'la (*Bactris a.; Curima calophylla; Martinezia a.*) . Coyure R.
aculea'ta (*Euterpe a.; Marara a.; Martinezia a.; M. aiphanes*)
caryotaefo'lia (*caryotifolia; Marara c.; Martinezia c.; Tilmia c.*) . Caryota R.
ero'sa (*Martinezia e.*). . Macawpalm
lindenia'na (*Martinezia l.*) Alvarico R.
min'ima (*corallina; Bactris m.; Curima corallina; Martinezia c.*) . Spice R.
trunca'ta (*Martinezia t.*)

ALFONS'IA . . . . . **COROZO**

ALLAGOP'TERA (*DIPLOTHEMIUM* in part)
campes'tris (*Diplothemium c.*)
caudes'cens . . . **Polyandrococos c.**

AMYLOCAR'PUS . . . **BACTRIS**

ARCHONTOPHOE'NIX (*LOROMA*) Kingpalm
alexan'drae (*Ptychosperma a.*) Alexandra K.
—bea'tricae (*A. beatricae*) . Step K.
cunninghamia'na (*cunninghami; Loroma amethystina; L. cunninghamiana; Ptychosperma cunninghamianum; Seaforthia elegans* Hort., *not* R. Br.) Piccabeen K. (*Illawarra Palm*)
A. cunninghamiana is "Seaforthia elegans" of Hort. The Seaforthia elegans of botanists is Ptychosperma elegans.
el'egans . . . . . . **Ptychosperma e.**

AR'ECA . . . . Arecapalm
al'ba . . . . . **Dictyosperma album**
al'icae
Plants grown under this name may be Arikuryroba schizophylla.
augus'ta . . . . . . **Ptychoraphis a.**
au'rea Hort. **Dictyosperma album aureum**
bau'eri . . . . . . **Rhopalostylis b.**
calappa'ria . . . . . **Actinorhytis c.**
cath'ecu (*catechu*) . Betelnutpalm
cocoi'des . . . **Actinorhytis calapparia**
concin'na . . . . Ceylon A.
corona'ta . . . . **Pinanga c.**

PALM GENERA (ARECA), continued
crini'ta . . . . . **Acanthophoenix c.**
furfura'cea Hort. **Dictyosperma album furfuraceum**
glandifor'mis . Moluccan Arecapalm
grac'ilis Roxb. . . . . . **Pinanga g.**
ilsemann'i Hort.
This name is perhaps not applicable to an Areca.
lutes'cens . . . . **Chrysalidocarpus l.**
madagascarien'sis Hort. **Chrysalidocarpus m.**
madagascarien'sis Mart. . **C. lutescens**
mi'nor . . . . **Linospadix m.**
monosta'chya **Linospadix monostachyos**
norman'byi . . . . . **Normanbya n.**
ru'bra Bory . . . **Acanthophoenix r.**
ru'bra Hort. **Dictyosperma album rubrum**
sa'pida Endl. . **Rhopalostylis baueri**
sa'pida Soland. . . . **Rhopalostylis s.**
sechella'rum Hort. **Stevensonia borsigiana**
singaporen'sis . . . **Ptychoraphis s.**
specio'sa Hort. **Hyophorbe amaricaulis**
spica'ta . . . **Calyptrocalyx spicatus**
trian'dra . . . . Bungua A.
verschaffel'ti Hort. . . . **Hyophorbe v.**

ARECAS'TRUM (*COCOS* in part) Queenpalm
romanzoffia'num (*Cocos plumosa; C. romanzoffiana*) . . . . Queenpalm
—austra'le (*Cocos arechavaletana; C. australis* Mart., *not* Hort.; *C. datil; C. flexuosa* Hort., *not* Mart.) Robust Q.
—botryoph'orum (*Cocos botryophora; C. geriba; C. martiana; Syagrus botryophora*)

AREN'GA (*SAGUERUS*) Sugarpalm
am'bong (*mindorensis; tremula*) Philippine S.
eng'leri . . . . Formosa S.
obtusifo'lia . . . . . Sumatra S.
obtusifo'lia Hook. f., *not* Mart. **A. westerhouti**
pinna'ta (*saccharifera*) . . Gomuti S.
tre'mula . . . . **A. ambong**
undulatifo'lia . . . . Borneo S.
westerhout'i (*obtusifolia* Hook. f., *not* Mart.) . . . . Curry S.
wight'i . . . . Wight S.

ARIKURYRO'BA (*ARIKURY; COCOS* in part) . Arikurypalm
schizophyl'la (*Arikury s.; A. capanemae; Cocos arikuryroba; C. capanemae; C. schizophylla*). Arikurypalm
This species has appeared in cultivation under the name Areca alicae.

ASTROCA'RYUM . Astrocaryum
ala'tum . . . . Limon A.
au'reum
awar'ra (*segregatum*) . . Awarra A.
borsigia'num . **Stevensonia borsigiana**
cohu'ne . . . **Hexopetion mexicanum**
gigan'teum . . . . Giant A.
mal'ybo . . . . Malybo A.
mexica'num . . . . **Hexopetion m.**
murumu'ru . . . . . Murumuru A.
parama'ca . . . . . Paramaca A.
pic'tum . . . **Stevensonia borsigiana**
rostra'tum . . **Hexopetion mexicanum**
segrega'tum . . . . **A. awarra**
standleya'num . . . . Blackpalm

PALM GENERA (ASTROCARYUM), con.
tucuma' . . . Tucuma Astrocaryum
tucuma' Wallace, *not* Mart.
Perhaps referable to A. vulgare.
vulga're (*Bactris v.*)

ATITA'RA . . . . **DESMONCUS**

ATTALE'A (*BORNOA*). . Attalea
amygdali'na
cohu'ne . . . . **Orbignya c.**
crassispa'tha (*Bornoa c.; Maximiliana c.*) . . . . Carossier A.
excel'sa . . . . . **Scheelea martiana**
funif'era Piassava A. (*Bahia-Piassava*)
gomphococ'ca . . . . . . **Scheelea g.**
prin'ceps . . . . **Scheelea p.**
specio'sa Barb. Rodr. **Orbignya cohune**
specio'sa Mart. . . **Orbignya martiana**
spectab'ilis . . . . **Orbignya s.**

AUGUSTIN'EA . . . **BACTRIS**

BAC'TRIS (*AMYLOCARPUS; AUGUSTINEA; PYRENOGLYPHIS*) . . Spinyclubpalm
acanthophyl'la . . . . . . **Aiphanes a.**
augustin'ea (*ovata* Wendl., *not* Stokes; *Pyrenoglyphis o.*) . . Augustine S.
balanoi'dea (*Augustinea b.; Pyrenoglyphis b.*)
bi'fida (*Pyrenoglyphis b.*)
concin'na (*Pyrenoglyphis c.*)
flavispi'na Hort. . . . **B. pallidispina**
gasipa'es . . . . . . **Guilielma g.**
geonomoi'des (*simplicifrons* Spruce, *not* Mart.)
hor'rida
ma'jor (*ovata* Stokes, *not* Wendl.; *Augustinea m.; Pyrenoglyphis m.*) Beach S.
min'ima . . . . **Aiphanes m.**
mi'nor
ova'ta Stokes . . . . **B. major**
ova'ta Wendl. . . . . **B. augustinea**
pallidispi'na (*flavispina* Hort.; *Pyrenoglyphis p.*)
simplic'ifrons (*Amylocarpus s.*)
simplic'ifrons Spruce, *not* Mart. **B. geonomoides**
sworderia'na
trichophyl'la
u'tilis . . . . . . **Guilielma gasipaes**
vulga're . . . . . . **Astrocaryum v.**

BACULA'RIA . . **LINOSPADIX**

BALA'KA . . . . Balaka
Older palms now in cultivation under this genus name are Ptychosperma elegans. Younger ones may prove to be true Balakas.
kerstenia'na **Ptychosperma kerstenianum**
perbre'vis (*Ptychosperma perbreve*)
see'manni (*Ptychosperma s.*) Seemann B.

BENTINCK'IA . . . . Bentinckia
ceram'ica . **Rhopaloblaste hexandra**
nicobar'ica (*Orania n.*). . . Nicobar B.
ren'dah . . . . . . **Cyrtostachys r.**

BISMARCK'IA . . . Bismarckia
no'bilis (*Medemia n.*) . . Stately B.

BORAS'SUS
flabel'lifer . . . . . . Palmyrapalm

BOR'NOA . . . . . **ATTALEA**

BRAHE'A (*ACOELORRAPHE* in part) . . . . Braheapalm
arma'ta . . . . **Erythea a.**

PALM GENERA (BRAHEA) continued
brandeg'eei Hort. . . . . . **Erythea b.**
calca'rea (*calcarata* Hort.; *nitida* Andre, *not* Hort.)
This and B. pimo are perhaps not true Braheas. Purported to be in cultivation.
dul'cis (*Corypha d.*) SWEET BRAHEAPALM (*Palmadulce*)
ed'ulis . . . . **Erythea e.**
filamento'sa Hort. **Washingtonia filifera**
filif'era . . . . **Washingtonia f.**
glau'ca Hort. . . . . . **Erythea armata**
nit'ida Andre . . . . . **B. calcarea**
nit'ida Hort. . . . . . . **Sabal minor**
pi'mo (*Acoelorraphe p.*) . . PIMO B.
roez'li Hort. . . . . **Erythea r.**
serrula'ta . . . . . **Serenoa repens**

BU'TIA (*COCOS* in part). BUTIAPALM
bonnet'i (perhaps *Cocos b.* Hort. and *C. gaertneri* Hort.) . . . . ACORN B.
capita'ta (*Cocos australis* Hort., *not* Mart.; *C. capitata; C. coronata* Hort., *not* Mart.) . . . . . BRAZILIAN B.
—nehrlingia'na (*B. nehrlingiana; Cocos n.*) . . . . . . NEHRLING B.
—odora'ta (*Cocos o.*) . . PERFUME B.
—pulpo'sa (*Cocos p.*) . . BIGFRUIT B.
—stric'tior (*Cocos humilis* Hort. in part)
—vires'cens . . . . . GREENLEAF B.
eriospa'tha (*Cocos e.* Mart., *not* Lindm.) WOOLLY B.
leiospa'tha (*Cocos l.*)
nehrlingia'na . . . . . **B. capitata n.**
paraguayen'sis (*B. yatay p.; Cocos p.*) PARAGUAY YATAY
Palms in cultivation under this name are usually referable to B. yatay.
puncta'ta . . . . . . DOTFRUIT B.
yatay' (*Cocos eriospatha* Lindm., *not* Mart.; *C. yatay*). ARGENTINE YATAY
—paraguayen'sis . . **B. paraguayensis**

CAL'AMUS . . . . RATTANPALM
Calamus, Daemonorops, and Korthalsia are genera of hooked and climbing tropical Asiatic palms obviously not suitable for general ornamental planting in the United States.
cilia'ris
deera'tus
dra'co . . . . **Daemonorops d.**
fis'sus . . . . **Daemonorops f.**
gran'dis Griff. . . . **Daemonorops g.**
jenkinsia'nus . . . . **Daemonorops j.**
ovoi'deus
palemban'icus . . . **Daemonorops p.**
riva'lis
ro'tang . . . . ROTANG R.
—dra'co . . . . . . **Daemonorops d.**

CALYPTROCA'LYX CALYPTROCALYX
spica'tus (*Areca spicata; Pinanga globosa*)

CARYO'TA . . . . FISHTAILPALM
al'berti . . . . **C. rumphiana**
cum'ingi . . . . . . PHILIPPINE F.
furfura'cea Blume **C. mitis; C. rumphiana**
mi'tis (*furfuracea* in part; *griffithi; sobolifera; urens* Jacq., *not* L., *nor* Blanco) . . . . TUFTED F.
plumo'sa Hort.
A name.
rumphia'na (*alberti; furfuracea* in part; *urens* Blanco, *not* L., *nor* Jacq.) RUMPH F.
sobolif'era . . . . **C. mitis**

PALM GENERA (CARYOTA), continued
u'rens . . . . . TODDY FISHTAILPALM (*Kittoolpalm*)
u'rens Blanco, *not* L. . **C. rumphiana**
u'rens Jacq., *not* L. . . . . . **C. mitis**

CA'TIS . . . . . . **EUTERPE**

CEROX'YLON . . . . . WAXPALM
andic'ola
austra'le . . . . . . **Juania australis**
cerif'erum . . . . . SANTAMARTA W.
ferrugin'eum . . . . . . SALENTO W.
quindiuen'se . . . . . . QUINDIO W.

CHAMAEDORE'A CHAMAEDOREA; PACAYA
The male and female spadices are usually borne on separate plants in this genus, which is not well understood botanically. Some of the species are favorite household or patio palms. Among invalid genera synonymous with or related to Chamaedorea, the following should be mentioned: Collinia; Edanthe; Kinetostigma; Neanthe; Nunnezharia; Nunnezharoa; Nunnezia; Omanthe; Spathoscaphe; Stachyophorbe; and Stephanostachys. Several of these are, nevertheless, herein listed as though valid.
adscen'dens (*Kinetostigma a.*)
arenbergia'na (*Spathoscaphe a.*)
atrovi'rens
bambusoi'des Hort.
This name is obscure.
con'color (*lindeniana* Wendl., *not* Hort.; *Nunnezharoa c.*)
coralli'na (*not Morenia c.*) **C. oblongata**
costarica'na . . . . . . **Omanthe c.**
desmoncoi'des (*Nunnezharoa d.*)
ela'tior (*Nunnezharoa e.*). CLIMBING C.
C. scandens, sometimes referred here, appears to be a separate species.
el'egans Auth. **Eleutheropetalum sartorii**
el'egans Mart. . . . . . . **Neanthe e.**
ernesti-augus'ti (*Morenia e.; Nunnezharoa e.*) . . . **Eleutheropetalum e.**
fibro'sa . . . . **Synecanthus fibrosus**
fra'grans (*Nunnezharia f.; Nunnezia f.*)
geonomaefor'mis (*geonomiformis; Nunnezharia g.*) . . . GUATEMALA P.
glaucifo'lia (*Nunnezharoa g.*)
graminifo'lia (*Nunnezharoa g.*) MONKEYTAIL P.
karwinskya'na (*lindeniana* Hort., *not* Wendl.)
lindenia'na Hort. . . **C. karwinskyana**
lindenia'na Wendl. (*not Morenia l.*) **C. concolor**
martia'na (*Stephanostachys m.*)
neurochlam'ys
oblonga'ta (*corallina; lunata; Nunnezharoa l.; N. oblongata*)
oblonga'ta Wendl., *not* Mart. **Eleutheropetalum sartorii**
paca'ya (*Nunnezharoa p.*) OERSTED P.
prin'glei
pulchel'la . . . . . **Neanthe elegans**
pu'mila (*Nunnezharoa p.*)
sarto'rii . . . . . **Eleutheropetalum s.**
scan'dens
Sometimes referred to C. elatior.
schip'pi
simplic'ifrons Hort. **Eleutheropetalum ernesti-augusti**
tepejilo'te Liebm. . . . . **Edanthe t.**
tepejilo'te Wendl. . . **C. wendlandiana**
tuerckhei'mi (*Kinetostigma t.; Malortiea t.*)
veraepa'cis . . . . **Edanthe v.**

PALM GENERA (CHAMAEDOREA), con.
wendlandia'na (*tepejilote* Wendl., *not* Liebm.; *Nunnezharoa w.; Stephanostachys w.*)
Palms planted as this species may be Edanthe tepejilote.

CHAMAE'ROPS MEDITERRANEANPALM (*Hairpalm*)
bi'roo (*byrrho*) . **Livistona rotundifolia**
excel'sa Mart. . **Trachycarpus fortunei**
excel'sa Thunb. . . . . **Rhapis e.**
fortun'ei . . . . . . **Trachycarpus f.**
grif'fithi . . . **Trachycarpus martianus**
hu'milis . . . . MEDITERRANEANPALM (*Hairpalm*)
There are numerous synonymous names for this variable species of a monotypic genus. Some are valid varietal names. The more important varieties in cultivation in this country are listed below.
—arbores'cens
—argen'tea
—canarien'sis . . . . . CANARY M.
—dactylocar'pa . . . DATEFRUIT M.
—el'egans
—macrocar'pa
hys'trix . . . . **Rhapidophyllum h.**
khasia'na . **Trachycarpus martianus**
martia'na . . . . . . **T. martianus**
moci'ni . . . . . **Cryosophila nana**
nepalen'sis. **Trachycarpus wagnerianus**
ritchiea'na . . . . . **Nannorrhops r.**
serrula'ta . . . . . **Serenoa repens**
stauracan'tha Hort.
This name is probably referable to Cryosophila nana.
ta'kil . . . . **Trachycarpus t.**

CHAMBEYRO'NIA (*KENTIOPSIS* in part) CHAMBEYRONIAPALM
hook'eri (*Kentia lindeni* Hort.; *K. macrocarpa* Brongn., *not* Vieill.)
macrocar'pa (*Kentia lindeni* Hort.; *K. macrocarpa* Vieill., *not* Brongn.; *Kentiopsis m.*)

CHRYSALIDOCAR'PUS BUTTERFLYPALM
bar'oni . . . . **Neodypsis b.**
decip'iens . . . . . **Macrophloga d.**
lucuben'sis . . . . LUCUBA B.
lutes'cens (*Areca l.; A. madagascariensis* Mart., *not* Hort.; *Hyphaene indica* Hort., *not* Gaertn.) YELLOW B.
madagascarien'sis (*Areca m.* Hort., *not* Mart.; *Dypsis m.* Hort.) MADAGASCAR B.

CLINOSTIG'MA
moorea'num. **Lepidorrhachis mooreana**

COCCOTHRI'NAX (*THRINAX* in part; *THRINCOMA; THRINGIS*) . . . . . . SILVERPALM
al'ta (*argentea* Brit. & Wils., *not* Sarg.; *latifrons; laxa; Thrincoma a.; Thringis latifrons; T. laxa*) PUERTORICAN S.
Palms of this species are frequently planted under the name Thrinax altissima.
anom'ala . . . . **Zombia antillarum**
argenta'ta (*argentea* Auth., *not* Sarg.; *garberi; jucunda; Thrinax garberi*) FLORIDA S.
argen'tea (*Thrinax a.*) LATANIERBALAI
argen'tea Auth., *not* Sarg. **C. argentata**
argen'tea Brit. & Wils., *not* Sarg. **C. alta**
barbaden'sis (*Thrinax b.*)
Not identified among cultivated palms.

PALM GENERA (COCCOTHRINAX), con.
crini'ta (*Thrinax c.*)
ek'mani . . . . EKMAN SILVERPALM
fra'grans . . . . FRAGRANT S.
gar'beri . . . . **C. argentata**
jucun'da . . . . **C. argentata**
lat'ifrons . . . . **C. alta**
lax'a . . . . **C. alta**
mar'tii
See note under Thrinax martii.
miragua'ma (*miraguano; Copernicia m.; Thrinax m.; T. yuraguana*) MIRAGUAMA S.
pauciramo'sa
radia'ta (*Thrinax r.*)

CO'COS . . . . COCONUT
This genus includes only one species, C. nucifera. Segregated genera of close relationship to Cocos are Arecastrum, Arikuryroba, Barbosa, Butia, Rhyticocos, and Syagrus.
alphon's(e)i Hort.
This name is botanically obscure.
ama'ra . . . . **Rhyticocos a.**
arechavaleta'na . . . . . **Arecastrum romanzoffianum australe**
argen'tea Engel . . . . . . **Syagrus a.**
argen'tea Hort.
This name is misapplied to some palm other than the true Syagrus argentea, which is not cultivated in this country.
arikuryro'ba. **Arikuryroba schizophylla**
austra'lis Hort. . . . . **Butia capitata**
This name has been misapplied to Butia eriospatha.
austra'lis Mart. . . . . . **Arecastrum romanzoffianum australe**
blumena'via Hort.
This name may refer to Butia eriospatha or to B. capitata.
bonnet'i Hort. . . . . . . **Butia b.**
botryoph'ora . . . . . . **Arecastrum romanzoffianum botryophorum**
brazilien'sis Hort.
A name of unknown application.
campes'tris Hort.
Perhaps referable to Butia capitata.
campes'tris Mart. . . . . . **Syagrus c.**
capane'mae. **Arikuryroba schizophylla**
capita'ta . . . . **Butia c.**
como'sa . . . . **Syagrus c.**
Syagrus comosa is apparently not in cultivation. The name has been misapplied to a species of Butia.
corona'ta Hort. . . . . **Butia capitata**
corona'ta Mart. . . . . . **Syagrus c.**
da'til . . . . **Arecastrum romanzoffianum australe**
eriospa'tha Lindm. . . . **Butia yatay**
eriospa'tha Mart. . . . . . **Butia e.**
flexuo'sa Hort. . . . . . **Arecastrum romanzoffianum australe**
flexuo'sa Mart. . . . . **Syagrus f.**
gaert'neri Hort. . . . . **Butia bonneti**
ger'iba . . . . **Arecastrum romanzoffianum botryophorum**
hu'milis Hort. in part **Butia capitata strictior**
insig'nis . . . . **Syagrus i.**
lapid'ea
A name of uncertain application.
leiospa'tha . . . . **Butia l.**
littora'lis Hort.
This name has been applied to some Butia.

PALM GENERA (COCOS), continued
macrocar'pa . . . . . . **Syagrus m.**
mariae-regi'nae Hort.
This name is botanically obscure.
marit'ima Hort.
This name is botanically obscure.
martia'na . . . . **Arecastrum romanzoffianum botryophorum**
maximilia'na
Perhaps referable to a Syagrus.
nehrlingia'na (*nehrlingi*) **Butia capitata n.**
norman'byi . . . . . **Normanbya n.**
nucif'era . . . . COCONUT
KING. HV.
MAKAPUNO
NAWASI
odora'ta . . . . . . **Butia capitata o.**
paraguayen'sis . . . . **Butia p.**
petrae'a . . . . **Syagrus p.**
plumo'sa **Arecastrum romanzoffianum**
procopia'na . . **Syagrus macrocarpa**
pulpo'sa . . . . . . **Butia capitata p.**
romanzoffia'na **Arecastrum romanzoffianum**
rupes'tris . . . . . **Syagrus petraea**
sap'ida Barb. Rodr. . . . . **Syagrus s.**
sap'ida Hort. . . . **Rhopalostylis s.**
schizophyl'la . . . . . **Arikuryroba s.**
sya'grus . . . . . . **Syagrus cocoides**
vinif'era Hort.
This is an unidentified name.
vinif'era Mart. . . **Pseudophoenix v.**
weddellia'na . . . . **Syagrus w.**
yatay' . . . . **Butia y.**
yuruma'guas Hort.
Perhaps referable to a form of Butia yatay.

COELOCOC'CUS. **METROXYLON**
Although Coelococcus is at present considered to be inseparable botanically from Metroxylon, it may on further research again be recognized. The genus name is well established and will likely continue in usage inasmuch as one of the species has long furnished the Polynesian Ivorynuts or Tahitinuts of commerce.

COLEOSPA'DIX
angustifo'lius (*oninensis; Ptychosperma angustifolium*)
oninen'sis . . . . . **C. angustifolius**
Some of the palms in cultivation under the names Ptychosperma angustifolium and C. oninensis are Actinophloeus macarthuri or an undetermined species of Actinophloeus.

COLLIN'IA . **CHAMAEDOREA**

COLPOTHRI'NAX . . BARRELPALM
wright'i (*Pritchardia w.*) . BARRELPALM

COPERNIC'IA . . . . COPERNICIA
C. australis and C. cerifera have been grown in southern California and southern Florida. The remainder of the species here listed are mainly Cuban and of recent introduction.
austra'lis (*Corypha cerifera* Mart. in part, *not* Arr. Camara). CARANDA C.
baileya'na . . . . BAILEY C.
brittono'rum . . . . BRITTONS C.
burretia'na . . . . BURRET C.
cerif'era (*Corypha c.* Arr. Camara, *not* Mart.) . . . . CARNAUBAPALM
clark'i . . . . CLARK C.
cow'elli . . . . COWELL C.
curbelo'i
gi'gas
glabres'cens

PALM GENERA (COPERNICIA), continued
holguinen'sis
miragua'ma . . . . **Coccothrinax m.**
pauciflo'ra
ramosis'sima
rig'ida
sueroa'na
tecto'rum (*Corypha t.*)
torrea'na . . . TORRES COPERNICIA
wright'i . . . . **Paurotis w.**
yarey' . . . . YAREY C.

CORO'ZO (*ALFONSIA*) AMERICAN-OILPALM
oleif'era (*Alfonsia o.; Elaeis melanococca* Auth., *not* Gaertn.) AMERICAN-OILPALM

CORY'PHA . . . . . . CORYPHA
austra'lis . . . . **Livistona a.**
cerif'era Arr. Camara . **Copernicia c.**
cerif'era Mart. in part **Copernicia australis**
dul'cis . . . . **Brahea d.**
ela'ta . . . . **C. utan**
C. elata, a name of long botanical standing, has recently been replaced by the older C. utan.
geban'ga Blume . . . . . . **C. utan**
geban'ga Hort. . **Livistona chinensis**
na'na . . . . **Cryosophila n.**
re'pens . . . . **Serenoa r.**
talie'ra (*taliafera*) . . . . TALIER C.
tecto'rum . . . . . . **Copernicia t.**
theba'ica . . . . **Hyphaene t.**
umbraculif'era . . . . TALIPOTPALM
umbraculif'era Jacq., *not* L. . **Sabal u.**
u'tan (*elata; gebanga* Blume, *not* Hort.) BURIPALM

CRYOSO'PHILA (*ACANTHORRHIZA*) . . . ROOTSPINEPALM
na'na (*Acanthorrhiza aculeata; A. mocini; Chamaerops m.; Corypha n.; Trithrinax aculeata*)
It is doubtful whether the true Cryosophila nana is in cultivation in this country.

CURI'MA . . . . . **AIPHANES**

CYCLOSPA'THE **PSEUDOPHOENIX**

CYRTOSTACH'YS SEALINGWAXPALM
ceram'ica . . **Rhopaloblaste hexandra**
lak'ka (*C. l. singaporensis*) . RAJAH S.
ren'dah (*Bentinckia r.*) . SUMATRA S.
—duvivieria'num

DAEMON'OROPS . DEVILRATTAN
See note under Calamus.
dra'co (*Calamus d.; C. rotang d.*) SUMATRA-DRAGONSBLOOD
fis'sus (*Calamus f.*)
gran'dis Mart., *not* Kurz *nor* Ridley (*Calamus g.* Griff.) . . . GIANT D.
jenkinsia'nus (*Calamus j.*)
palemban'icus (*Calamus p.*) PALEMBANG D.

DECKE'NIA . . . . DECKENPALM
no'bilis (*Acanthophoenix n.*) DECKENPALM

DE'NEA . . . . **HOWEA**

DESMON'CUS (*ATITARA; DESMONCHUS*) . . BRAMBLEPALM
hor'ridus (*major; Atitara h.; A. major*) PICMOC B.
oxyacan'thos (*Atitara o.*)
panamen'sis Hort.
A name applied to an unidentified palm of Colombia.

PALM GENERA, continued

DICTYOSPER'MA (*LINOMA*) PRINCESSPALM
al'bum (*Areca alba; Linoma a.*) WHITE P.
—**au'reum** (*D. aureum; Areca aurea* Hort.; *Linoma alba aurea*) YELLOW P.
—**furfura'ceum** (*D. furfuraceum; Areca furfuracea* Hort.; *Linoma alba furfuracea*)
—**ru'brum** (*D. rubrum; Areca rubra* Hort., *not* Bory; *Linoma alba rubra*) RED P.
fibro'sum . . . . . . **Vonitra fibrosa**

DIDYMOSPER'MA . DRYADPALM
dis'tichum . . . . **Wallichia disticha**
na'num (*Wallichia nana*) . LITTLE D.

DIPLOTHE'MIUM **ALLAGOPTERA; POLYANDROCOCOS**

DRYMOPHLOE'US
norman'byi . . . . . **Normanbya n.**
singaporen'sis . . . **Ptychoraphis s.**

DYP'SIS . . . . DYPSIS
grac'ilis . . **Roscheria melanochaetes**
madagascarien'sis Hort. **Chrysalidocarpus m.**
thouarsia'na . . . . . **Vonitra fibrosa**

EDAN'THE (*CHAMAEDOREA* in part) . . . . PACAYA
tepejilo'te (*Chamaedorea t.*, Liebm., *not* Wendl.; *Nunnezharoa t.; Stephanostachys t.*) . . . . TEPEJILOTE P.
veraepa'cis (*Chamaedorea v.*) VERAPAZ P.

ELAE'IS . . . . OILPALM
guineen'sis . . . . . . AFRICAN O.
melanococ'ca Auth., *not* Gaertn. **Corozo oleifera**

ELEUTHEROPET'ALUM (*CHAMAEDOREA* in part)
ernesti-augus'ti (*Chamaedorea e.; C. simplicifrons* Hort.; *Geonoma latifrons* Hort.; *Morenia e.; Nunnezharoa e.*)
sarto'rii (*Chamaedorea elegans* Auth., *not* Mart.; *C. oblongata* Wendl., *not* Mart.; *C. sartorii; Morenia oblongata; Nunnezharoa aurantiaca; N. sartorii*)

ENGLEROPHOE'NIX **MAXIMILIANA**

EO'RA . . . **RHOPALOSTYLIS**

ERYTHE'A (*GLAUCOTHEA*) ERYTHEA
aculea'ta . . . . SINALOA E.
arma'ta (*Brahea a.; B. glauca* Hort.; *Glaucothea a.*) . . . . . BLUE E.
—*microcar'pa* . . . . . . **E. roezli**
brandeg'eei (*Brahea b.* Hort.; *Glaucothea b.*) . . . . . . BRANDEGEE E.
—**spiral'is** . . . . TLACO E.
ed'ulis (*Brahea e.*) . . GUADALUPE E.
el'egans (*Glaucothea e.*) FRANCESCHI E.
loreten'sis
The palm on which this species was founded proves to be a Sabal.
roez'li (*E. armata microcarpa; Brahea r.* Hort.) . . . . ROEZL E.

EUPRITCHARD'IA (*PRITCHARDIA; STYLOMA*) PRITCHARDIAPALM
gaudichau'di (*Pritchardia g.; Styloma g.*) . . . . GAUDICHAUD P.
mar'tii (*Pritchardia m.; Styloma m.*) MARTIUS P.

PALM GENERA (EUPRITCHARDIA), con.
pacif'ica (*Pritchardia p.; Styloma p.*) FIJI PRITCHARDIAPALM
thurs'toni (*Pritchardia t.; Styloma t.*) THURSTON P.

EUTER'PE (*ACRISTA; CATIS*) EUTERPEPALM
aculea'ta . . . . **Aiphanes a.**
acumina'ta
acumina'ta Waby, *not* Willd. **Roystonea regia**
broad'wayae (*broadwayana*)
ed'ulis (*oleracea* Barb. Rodr., *not* Mart.)
ed'ulis Barb. Rodr., *not* Mart. **E. oleracea**
globo'sa (*oleracea* Griseb., *not* Mart.; *Acrista monticola*)
jen'mani . . . . **Roystonea j.**
olera'cea (*edulis* Barb. Rodr., *not* Mart.; *Catis martiana*) . . ASSAI E.
olera'cea Barb. Rodr., *not* Mart. **E. edulis**
olera'cea Griseb., *not* Mart. **E. globosa**
ventrico'sa . . . . . **Roystonea regia**
vinif'era . . . . . **Pseudophoenix v.**

GAUS'SIA (*AERIA*) . LLUMEPALM
attenua'ta (*Aeria a.*) PUERTORICAN L.
prin'ceps (*splendens*) . . . CUBAN L.
vinif'era . . . . **Pseudophoenix v.**

GEONO'MA . . . SHADOWPALM
biner'via
el'egans
grac'ilis
grac'ilis Linden & Andre, *not* Wendl. **G. riedeliana**
grac'ilis Poepp., *not* Wendl. **Hyospathe g.**
lat'ifrons Hort. **Eleutheropetalum ernesti-augusti**
longepetiola'ta
prin'ceps Hort.
A name referring to some palm of Peru.
pynaertia'na Hort.
A name referring to a Malayan palm, Iguanura spectabilis.
riedelia'na (*gracilis* Linden & Andre, *not* Wendl.) . . . . . . RIEDEL S.
schottia'na . . . . . . ARICANGA S.

GLAUCOTHE'A . . **ERYTHEA**

GLAZIO'VA . . . . **SYAGRUS**

GORGA'SIA . . . **ROYSTONEA**

GUILIEL'MA (*BACTRIS* in part)
gasipa'es (*speciosa; utilis; Bactris g.; B. utilis*) . PEACHPALM (*Pejibaye*)

GULU'BIA . . . . GULUBIAPALM
costa'ta (*Kentia c.*)
molucca'na (*Kentia m.*) MOLUCCA G.

HEDYSCE'PE . . UMBRELLAPALM
canterburya'na (*Kentia c.*) CANTERBURY U.

HETEROSPA'THE(-A). SAGISIPALM
ela'ta . . . . SAGISIPALM

HEXOPE'TION (*ASTROCARYUM* Auth., *not* Mey.)
mexica'num (*Astrocaryum cohune; A. mexicanum; A. rostratum*)

HOW'EA (*DENEA; HOWEIA; HOWIEA; KENTIA* in part) SENTRYPALM
belmorea'na (*Kentia b.*) . BELMORE S.
forsteria'na (*Kentia f.*) . FORSTER S.

PALM GENERA, continued

HYDRIASTE'LE . . HYDRIASTELE
wendlandia'na (*Kentia w.* F. Muell., *not* Benth. in part) . WENDLAND H.
Plants in cultivation under this name are Ptychosperma elegans or P. capitisyorki.

HYOPHOR'BE
amaricau'lis (*Areca speciosa* Hort.; *Hyospathe a.* Hort.). . BOTTLEPALM
verschaffel'ti (*Areca v.* Hort.) SPINDLEPALM

HYOSPA'THE
amaricau'lis Hort. . . **Hyophorbe a.**
grac'ilis (*Geonoma g.* Poepp., *not* Wendl.)

HYPHAE'NE . . . . DOUMPALM
bar'oni . . CENTRALMADAGASCAR D.
crini'ta . . . . . SOUTHAFRICAN D.
guineen'sis
A Hyphaene has recently been introduced under this name. Although this species was formerly referred to H. thebaica, the name has again been considered valid.
hildebrandt'i . . . . . . **H. schatan**
in'dica . . . . INDIAN D.
in'dica Hort., *not* Gaertn. **Chrysalidocarpus lutescens**
natalen'sis . . . . NATAL D.
scha'tan (*hildebrandti*) NORTHMADAGASCAR D.
theba'ica (*Corypha t.*) . EGYPTIAN D.
turbina'ta . . . . ZAMBESI D.

INO'DES . . . . **SABAL**

JUA'NIA . . . . JUANPALM
austra'lis (*Ceroxylon australe*)

JUBAE'A . . . . JUBAEA
spectab'ilis (*chilensis*) . . . SYRUP J.

KENT'IA . . . . KENTIA
Probably none of the true Kentias are at present cultivated in this country. The two best-known florist palms which have long been called Kentias, K. belmoreana and K. forsteriana, are properly placed under Howea.
austra'lis Hort.
A name referring to some palm of Lord Howe's Island, perhaps Howea forsteriana.
belmorea'na . . . . **Howea b.**
canterburya'na . . . . **Hedyscepe c.**
costa'ta . . . . **Gulubia c.**
forsteria'na . . . . **Howea f.**
joan'nis (*johannis*) . . . . **Veitchia j.**
kerstenia'na Hort. **Ptychosperma kerstenianum**
lin'deni Hort. **Chambeyronia hookeri; C. macrocarpa**
macar'thuri . . . . **Actinophloeus m.**
macrocar'pa Brongn. **Chambeyronia hookeri**
macrocar'pa Vieill. **Chambeyronia m.**
molucca'na . . . . **Gulubia m.**
moorea'na . . . . **Lepidorrhachis m.**
olivaefor'mis . . . . . . **Kentiopsis o.**
sanderia'na Hort. **Actinophloeus sanderianus**
wendlandia'na Benth. in part **Ptychosperma capitisyorki**
wendlandia'na F. Muell. **Hydriastele w.**

KENTIOP'SIS
macrocar'pa . . . **Chambeyronia m.**
olivaefor'mis (*Kentia o.*)

KINETOSTIG'MA **CHAMAEDOREA**

KORTHAL'SIA . . . . ANTPALM
See note under Calamus.
junghuhn'i . . . . JAVA A.
macrocar'pa (*robusta* Becc., *not* Blume)

PALM GENERA (KORTHALSIA), continued
robus'ta
robus'ta Becc. *not* Blume **K. macrocarpa**
robus'ta Blume in part. . **K. teysmanni**
teys'manni (*robusta* Blume in part) TEYSMANN ANTPALM
One species cultivated under the name of K. robusta may not be the true robusta of Blume.

LATA'NIA . . . . LATANIA
au'rea . . . . **L. verschaffelti**
borbon'ica Hort. . **Livistona chinensis**
borbon'ica Lam. . . . **L. commersoni**
Palms sold under the name L. borbonica are usually Livistona chinensis.
commerso'ni (*borbonica* Lam., *not* Hort.; *rubra*) . . . . RED L.
lod'digesi (*glaucophylla*) . . SILVER L.
mauri'tius . . . . . . MAURITIUS L.
ru'bra . . . . **L. commersoni**
verschaffel'ti (*aurea*)

LEOPOLDIN'IA . . . . PIASSAVA
The fiber of L. piassaba enters into commerce but it is doubtful whether the species is in cultivation here.
piassa'ba . . . . PARA P.
pul'chra
pul'chra Hort., *not* Mart. **Syagrus weddelliana**

LEPIDORRHA'CHIS (*CLINOSTIGMA* in part)
moorea'na (*Clinostigma mooreanum; Kentia mooreana*)

LICUA'LA . . . . . LICUALAPALM
el'egans . . . . **L. pumila**
gran'dis (*Pritchardia g.* Hort.). FAN L.
hor'rida . . . . **L. spinosa**
jeannen'cyi Hort. (*jeanenceyi; jeannenci*) . . . . **L. muelleri**
muel'leri (*jeannencyi* Hort.) AUSTRALIAN L.
paludo'sa . . . . COAST L.
paludo'sa Kurz, *not* Griff.. **L. spinosa**
pelta'ta . . . . INDIA L.
pu'mila (*elegans*) . . . . FINGER L.
rumph'ii . . . . MOLUCCA L.
spino'sa (*horrida; paludosa* Kurz, *not* Griff.) . . . . SPINY L.

LINO'MA . . **DICTYOSPERMA**

LINOSPA'DIX (*BACULARIA*)
mi'nor (*Areca m.; Bacularia m.*)
monostach'yos (*Areca monostachya; Bacularia m.*)
petrickia'nus . . . . **Paralinospadix p.**

LINOSPA'DIX Becc., *not* Wendl. **PARALINOSPADIX**

LIVISTO'NA (*SARIBUS*) FANPALM
altis'sima . . . . . . **L. rotundifolia**
austra'lis (*inermis* Wendl. & Dr. in part, *not* R. Br.; *Corypha a.*) AUSTRALIAN F.
chinen'sis (*olivaeformis; Corypha gebanga* Hort., *not* Blume; *Latania borbonica* Hort., *not* Lam.) CHINESE F.
—subglobo'sa (*L. subglobosa*)
cochinchinen'sis (*hoogendorpi*) MALAYAN F.
decip'iens (*humilis* Hort., *not* R. Br.; *inermis* Hort., *not* R. Br.) WEEPING F.
hu'milis . . . . BUSH F.
hu'milis Hort., *not* R. Br. **L. decipiens**
iner'mis
The true L. inermis is not in cultivation.

PALM GENERA (LIVISTONA), continued
iner'mis Hort., *not* R. Br. **L. decipiens**
iner'mis Wendl. & Dr. in part, *not* R. Br. . . . . **L. australis**
jenkinsia'na (*jenkensi*) ASSAM FANPALM (*Tokopat*)
mari'ae . . . . BRONZE F.
muel'leri . . . . . BELEMBUNA F.
olivaefor'mis . . . . . . **L. chinensis**
rotundifo'lia (*altissima; Chamaerops biroo*) . . . . JAVA F.
—luzonen'sis . . . . . . LUZON F.
subglobo'sa . . . . . . **L. chinensis s.**

LODOI'CEA . . . DOUBLE-COCONUT
maldi'vica (*callipyge; seychellarum*) DOUBLE-COCONUT
This palm bears probably the largest known seed, up to 50 pounds.

LORO'MA **ARCHONTOPHOENIX**

MACROPHLO'GA
decip'iens (*Chrysalidocarpus d.*)

MALOR'TIEA . **REINHARDTIA**

MANICA'RIA (*TIMLIS*) SLEEVEPALM
saccif'era . . . . SLEEVEPALM

MARA'RA . . . . . **AIPHANES**

MARTINE'ZIA Auth., *not* Ruiz & Pav. . . . . **AIPHANES**

MAURI'TIA . . . . . . MAURITIA
flexuo'sa (*setigera*) FIBER M. (*Burity*)
A handsome and useful fiber-producing palm not yet established in this country.
vinif'era . . . . WINE M. (*Murity*)

MAXIMILIA'NA (*ENGLEROPHOENIX*) . . MAXIMILIANA
crassispa'tha . . . . **Attalea c.**
el'egans (*caribaea; Englerophoenix c.*)
longirostra'ta (*Englerophoenix l.*)
macrogy'ne
re'gia (*martiana; Englerophoenix r.*) REGAL M.

MEDE'MIA . . . . . . MEDEMIA
no'bilis . . . . **Bismarckia n.**

METROX'YLON (*COELOCOCCUS; SAGUS*) . . . . . SAGOPALM; IVORYNUTPALM
amica'rum (*carolinense; Coelococcus a.; C. carolinensis*) . . . POLYNESIAN I. (*Tahitinut*)
This species has long been the source of the Tahitinut of commerce, though other species of the section Coelococcus furnish similar nuts. Not to be confused with Phytelephas macrocarpa.
lae've . . . . **M. sagu**
rumph'ii (*Sagus r.*) . . . . SPINY S.
sa'gu (*laeve; Sagus laevis*) . SMOOTH S.
salomen'se (*Coelococcus s.*) SOLOMON I.

MORE'NIA (*CHAMAEDOREA* in part; *NUNNEZHAROA* in part) . . . . . MORENOPALM
coralli'na (*Nunnezharoa c.; not Chamaedorea c.*) . . . . CORAL M.
ernesti-augus'ti . **Eleutheropetalum e.**
fra'grans (*Nunnezharoa morenia*) SWEET M.
fra'grans Auth., *not* Ruiz & Pav. **M. lindeniana**
lindenia'na (*fragrans* Auth., *not* Ruiz & Pav.; *Nunnezharoa l.; not Chamaedorea l.*) . . . . LINDENS M.
oblonga'ta . **Eleutheropetalum sartorii**

PALM GENERA, continued
NAN'NORRHOPS. . MAZARIPALM
ritchiea'na (*Chamaerops r.*) MAZARIPALM

NEAN'THE (*CHAMAEDOREA* in part) . . . . NEANTHE
bel'la
el'egans (*Chamaedorea e.* Mart., *not* Auth.; *C. pulchella; Collinia e.; Nunnezharoa e.; N. pulchella*)
neesia'na

NEODYP'SIS . . . . NEODYPSIS
bar'oni (*Chrysalidocarpus b.*)

NEOWASHINGTO'NIA **WASHINGTONIA**

NI'PA . . . . NIPAPALM
fru'ticans . . . . NIPAPALM

NORMAN'BYA . NORMANBYPALM
mer'rilli . . . . **Adonidia m.**
norman'byi (*muelleri; Areca n.; Cocos n.; Drymophloeus n.*) NORMANBYPALM

NUNNEZHA'RIA **CHAMAEDOREA**

NUNNEZHA'ROA **CHAMAEDOREA; MORENIA**

NUNNE'ZIA . **CHAMAEDOREA**

OMAN'THE (*CHAMAEDOREA* in part) . . . . OMANTHE
costarica'na (*Chamaedorea c.; Nunnezharoa c.*)

ONCOSPER'MA . . ONCOSPERMA
fascicula'tum . . . . . CEYLON O.
filamento'sum (*tigillarium*) NIBONGPALM

OPSIAN'DRA . . . . MAYAPALM
ma'ya . . . . MAYAPALM

ORA'NIA . . . . . . ORANIAPALM
nicobar'ica . . . . . . **Bentinckia n.**
philippinen'sis (*palindan*) PALINDAN O.
rega'lis . . . . . . NEWGUINEA O.

ORBIG'NYA . . . . . . ORBIGNYA
cohu'ne (*speciosa* Barb. Rodr., *not* Mart.; *Attalea c.; A. speciosa* Barb. Rodr., *not* Mart.) . . COHUNE PALM
hueb'neri . . . . . . HUEBNER O.
martia'na (*barbosiana; speciosa* (Mart.) Barb. Rodr.; *Attalea s.* Mart., *not* Barb. Rodr.) . . MARTIUS BABASSU
oleif'era . . . . BABASSU
It is most unfortunate that the botanical identity of the economically important Babassu palms of Brazil has involved so much change of nomenclature. It is not possible to cite clearly in a list the various transfers and botanical interpretations involved. The publications on this subject should be consulted.
specio'sa Barb. Rodr. . . . **O. cohune**
specio'sa (Mart.) Barb. Rodr. **O. martiana**
spectab'ilis (*Attalea s.*)

OREODOX'A . . . **ROYSTONEA**

PARAJUBAE'A . . . PARAJUBAEA
cocoi'des

PARALINOSPA'DIX (*LINOSPADIX* Becc.)
petrickia'nus (*Linospadix p.*)

PAURO'TIS (*ACANTHOSABAL; ACOELORRAPHE* in part) PAUROTIS
wright'i (*androsana; arborescens; Acanthosabal caespitosa; Acoelorraphe arborescens; A. wrighti; Copernicia w.; Serenoa arborescens*) . . . . SAW P. (*Saw-Cabbagepalm*)

PALM GENERA, continued

PELAGODOX'A

henrya'na

PHOENICOPHO'RIUM **STEVENSONIA**

PHOE'NIX |w . . . . DATE

abyssin'ica . . . . . ABYSSINIAN D.

The true P. abyssinica is not in this country.

acau'lis . . . . . . STEMLESS D.

acau'lis Auth., *not* Roxb. . **P. humilis**

canarien'sis (*jubae; tenuis* Hort.) CANARY D.

Palms grown in this country under the names P. cycadifolia, P. leonensis, and P. leonensis speciosa are sometimes to be referred to P. canariensis.

cycadifo'lia Hort.

This name has referred to various species of Phoenix, including P. canariensis.

dactylif'era |w . . . . DATE

The following hort. var. (all clons) of Date are successfully grown in this country or enter into the trade:

AMIR HADJ.
BARHEE. *Barhi.*
BRAIM. *Buraym.*
DAYRI. *Dairee; Dairi.*
DEGLET NOOR. *Deglet Nur.*
FARD. *Fardh.*
HALAWY. *Halawi; Hallawi.*
HALILY. *Halili.*
HAYANY. *Hayani.*
ITEEMA. *Itima.*
KHADRAWY. *Kadrawi; Khadrawi; Khudrawee.*
KHALASA. *Khalaseh.*
KHUSTAWY. *Khastawi; Kustawy.*
MAKTOOM. *Maktum.*
MEDJOOL. *Majul; Medjhool.*
MENAKHER. *Manakhir.*
RHARS. *Ghars.*
SAIDY. *Saidi.*
SAYER. *Ista'amran; Usta Imran.*
SPHINX.
TAZIZAOOT. *Tazizoot.*
THOORY. *Thuri.*
ZAHIDI. *Zahdi; Zahidee.*

farinif'era Roxb. . . . . . **P. pusilla**

farinif'era Zoll. . . . . . **P. reclinata**

hancea'na (*P. humilis h.*). HANCE D.

hu'milis (*acaulis* Auth., *not* Roxb.; *ouseleyana*) . . . . . DWARF D.

—*hancea'na* . . . . . . **P. hanceana**

—**lourei'ri** (*P. loureiri; P. pusilla* Lour., *not* Gaertn.; *P. roebeleni*) ROEBELEN D.

—**peduncula'ta** (*P. pedunculata*)

hy'brida Hort.

Perhaps referable to P. macrocarpa.

ju'bae . . . . **P. canariensis**

leonen'sis Hort. . . . . . **P. reclinata**

Plants grown under this name may be P. canariensis.

lourei'ri . . . . **P. humilis l.**

macrocar'pa Hort.

This name was applied to a particular hybrid between P. canariensis and P. dactylifera.

natalen'sis Hort.

This name has been referred both to P. canariensis and to P. reclinata.

ouseleya'na . . . . . . **P. humilis**

paludo'sa (*siamensis*) . MALAYAN D.

PALM GENERA (PHOENIX), continued

peduncula'ta . . . . . . **P. humilis p.**

pu'mila . . . . **P. reclinata**

pusil'la (*farinifera* Roxb., *not* Zoll.) SHRUBBY DATE

pusil'la Becc., *not* Gaertn. . **P. zeylanica**

pusil'la Lour., *not* Gaertn. **P. humilis loureiri**

reclina'ta (*farinifera* Zoll., *not* Roxb.; *leonensis* Hort.; *pumila; senegalensis* Hort.; *spinosa*) . . . SENEGAL D.

roebele'ni . . . . **P. humilis loureiri**

rupic'ola . . . . CLIFF D.

siamen'sis . . . . **P. paludosa**

sinpif'era Hort.

An unidentified name, perhaps referable to P. reclinata.

spino'sa . . . . **P. reclinata**

sylves'tris . . . SUGAR D. (*India D.*)

sylves'tris Thwaite, *not* Roxb. **P. zeylanica**

ten'uis Hort. . . . . . . **P. canariensis**

vinif'era Hort.

An unidentified name.

zeylan'ica (*pusilla* Becc., *not* Gaertn.; *sylvestris* Thwaite, *not* Roxb.) CEYLON D.

PHYTEL'EPHAS . . IVORYPALM

macrocar'pa . COMMON I. (*Taguanut*)

This species is the source of the vegetable-ivory of commerce. See note under Metroxylon amicarum, with which it should not be confused.

macrocar'pa Seem., *not* Ruiz & Pav. **P. seemanni**

see'manni (*macrocarpa* Seem., *not* Ruiz. & Pav.) . . . . SEEMANN I.

PIGAFET'TA (*PIGAFETTIA*) PIGAFETTA

fila'ris (*elata*) . . . . MOLUCCAN P.

PINAN'GA . . . . PINANGAPALM

corona'ta (*Areca c.*)

deco'ra

A valid name for a Borneo pinanga but application uncertain. Plants have been introduced under this name.

frut'icans

globo'sa . . . **Calyptrocalyx spicatus**

grac'ilis (*Areca g.* Roxb.)

kuhl'i (*Ptychosperma k.; Seaforthia k.*) BROADLEAF P.

pat'ula

POLYANDROCO'COS (*DIPLOTHEMIUM* in part)

caudes'cens (*Allagoptera c.; Diplothemium c.*)

PRITCHAR'DIA **EUPRITCHARDIA**

PSEUDOPHOE'NIX (*CYCLOSPATHE*) . . . . CHERRYPALM

ela'ta . . . . **P. vinifera**

insig'nis . . . . **P. vinifera**

linea'ris . . . . **P. vinifera**

sao'nae

This species is perhaps referable to P. sargenti.

sar'genti (*Cyclospathe northropi*) SARGENT C.

vinif'era (*elata; insignis; linearis; Aeria v.; Cocos v.* Mart., *not* Hort.; *Euterpe v.; Gaussia v.*) . BUCCANEER C.

PTYCHORA'PHIS . PTYCHORAPHIS

augus'ta (*Areca a.*) . . . NICOBAR P.

Sometimes mislabeled Bentinckia nicobarica.

PALM GENERA (PTYCHORAPHIS), con.

singaporen'sis (*Areca s.; Drymophloeus s.; Ptychosperma s.; Rhopaloblaste s.*) SINGAPORE PTYCHORAPHIS

PTYCHOSPER'MA (*SEAFORTHIA*) . . . . . PTYCHOSPERMA

alexan'drae . . . **Archontophoenix a.**

angustifo'lium **Coleospadix angustifolius**

Palms planted under this name in the United States are species of Actinophloeus.

calappa'rium . **Actinorhytis calapparia**

capitisyork'i (*wendlandianum; Kentia w.* Benth. in part, *not* F. Muell.) CAPEYORK P.

cunninghamia'num **Archontophoenix cunninghamiana**

el'egans (*Archontophoenix e.; Seaforthia e.* R. Br., *not* Hort.) SOLITAIREPALM

This widely cultivated palm has been distributed under the name Hydriastele wendlandiana, and has also been mistaken for Balaka seemanni.

hos'pitum **Actinophloeus macarthuri hospitus**

kerstenia'num (*Actinophloeus kerstenianus; Balaka kersteniana; Kentia kersteniana* Hort.)

kuhl'i . . . . **Pinanga k.**

macar'thuri . . . . **Actinophloeus m.**

nicola'i . . . . . . **Actinophloeus n.**

perbre've . . . . . . **Balaka perbrevis**

sanderia'num **Actinophloeus sanderianus**

see'manni . . . . **Balaka s.**

singaporen'sis . . . **Ptychoraphis s.**

wendlandia'num . . . **P. capitisyorki**

PYRENOGLY'PHIS . **BACTRIS**

RANE'VEA (*RAVENEA; RAVENIA* Benth. & Hook. f., *not* Vell.) . . . . RANEVEA

hildebrandt'i

RA'PHIA . . . . . . RAFFIAPALM

Many of the Old World species of Raphia furnish raffia or piassava fibers and wine for local use. Commercially, certain species furnish a better raffia; others a better piassava. The botany of this genus is confused, although much has recently been published. There is, consequently, some uncertainty as to the exact source of the commercial fibers.

gaert'neri Mann & Wendl. in part **R. palma-pinus**

gaert'neri Mann & Wendl. in part **R. wendlandi**

gigan'tea (*hookeri* Chev., *not* Mann & Wendl.; *R. hookeri mancipiorum*) GIANT R.

hook'eri . . . . IVORYCOAST R. (*Ivorycoast-Piassava*)

hook'eri Chev., *not* Mann & Wendl. **R. gigantea**

palma-pi'nus (*gaertneri* Mann & Wendl. in part; *Sagus p.*) LIBERIAN R.

peduncula'ta (*ruffia*). MADAGASCAR R.

ses'e (*sese-de-wild* Hort.) . CONGO R.

taedig'era (*vinifera* Auth., *not* Beauv.; *R. vinifera t.*) . . . AMERICAN R.

vinif'era . . . . WINE R. (*West African-Piassava*)

vinif'era Auth., *not* Beauv. **R. taedigera**

wend'landi (*gaertneri* Mann & Wendl. in part) . . . . . FERNANDOPO R.

PALM GENERA, continued

RAVE'NEA (*RAVENIA* Benth. & Hook. f., *not* Vell.) . . **RANEVEA**

REINHARD'TIA (*MALORTIEA*) REINHARDTPALM

grac'ilis (*Malortiea g.*)

sim'plex (*Malortiea s.*)

RHAPIDOPHYL'LUM NEEDLEPALM

hys'trix (*Chamaerops h.*). NEEDLEPALM

RHA'PIS . . . . LADYPALM

excel'sa (*flabelliformis; Chamaerops e.* Thunb., *not* Mart.) . BROADLEAF L.

hu'milis . . . . SLENDER L.

RHOPALOBLAS'TE RHOPALOBLASTE

hexan'dra (*exandra; Bentinckia ceramica; Cyrtostachys c.*)

singaporen'sis . . . **Ptychoraphis s.**

RHOPALOS'TYLIS (*EORA*) RHOPALOSTYLIS

bau'eri (*Areca b.; A. sapida* Endl., *not* Soland.; *Eora b.*) . . . . BAUER R.

sap'ida (*Areca s.* Soland., *not* Endl.; *Cocos s.* Hort., *not* Barb. Rodr.; *Eora s.*) . . . . NIKAU R.

RHYTICO'COS (*COCOS* in part)

ama'ra (*Cocos a.; Syagrus a.*)

ROMANO'VIA (*ROMANOWIA*) **ACTINOPHLOEUS**

ROOSEVELT'IA . ROOSEVELTPALM

franklinia'na . . . . ROOSEVELTPALM

ROSCHE'RIA (*ROCHERIA*) BLACKBRISTLEPALM

melanochae'tes (*Dypsis gracilis; Verschaffeltia m.*). . BLACKBRISTLEPALM

ROYSTO'NEA (*GORGASIA; OREODOXA*) . . . ROYALPALM

borinque'na (*caribaea* P. Wils. in part; *Oreodoxa b.*) . . . PUERTORICO R.

caribae'a P. Wils. in part **R. borinquena; R. oleracea**

florida'na . . . . **R. regia**

hispaniola'na . . . . . HISPANIOLA R.

jamaica'na (*Oreodoxa oleracea* Auth., *not* Mart.) . . . . . . JAMAICA R.

jen'mani (*Euterpe j.*) . . JENMAN R.

olera'cea (*caribaea* P. Wils. in part; *Gorgasia o.; Oreodoxa o.*) . CARIB R.

prin'ceps (*Oreodoxa p.*) . MORASS R.

re'gia (*floridana; Euterpe acuminata* Waby, *not* Willd.; *E. ventricosa; Oreodoxa r.*) . . . . . . CUBAN R.

SA'BAL (*INODES*) |w . PALMETTO

acau'lis . . . . **S. minor**

adanso'ni . . . . **S. minor**

beccaria'na (*princeps* Hort. in part) BECCARI P.

bermuda'na (*blackburniana* Hemsl., *not* Glazebr.) . . . . . BERMUDA P.

blackburn'ia (*Inodes blackburniana*) BLACKBURN P.

blackburn'ia(na) Hort.

This name has been used for several species, particularly bermudana, blackburnia, and umbraculifera.

causia'rum (*Inodes c.*) PUERTORICO P. (*Yaray*)

deeringia'na . . . . **S. louisiana**

domingen'sis . . . . **S. umbraculifera**

duge'si . . . . . . GUANAJUATO P.

etoni'a . . . . ETONIA P.

ex'ul (*Inodes e.*) . . . . VICTORIA P.

PALM GENERA (SABAL), continued

flor'ida . . . . **S. parviflora**

ghiesebrech'ti (*giesbreghti*) Hort.

A name of doubtful application.

gla'bra . . . . **S. minor**

glauces'cens Hort. . **S. mauritiaeformis**

guatemalen'sis GUATEMALA PALMETTO

haiten'sis . . . . . **S. umbraculifera**

havanen'sis

A name of no botanical standing.

jamaicen'sis . . . . . . JAMAICA P.

jamesia'na . . . . **S. palmetto**

longepeduncula'ta Hort.

This name of no botanical standing has been applied to S. palmetto.

louisia'na (*deeringiana*). LOUISIANA P.

ma'sonae . . . . **S. minor**

mauritiaefor'mis (*glaucescens* Hort.; *mauritiiformis; Trithrinax mauritiaeformis*) . . . TRINIDAD P. (*Carat*)

megacar'pa

A doubtful species.

mexica'na (*Inodes m.*) . . OAXACA P.

mexica'na S. Wats., *not* Mart. **S. texana**

mi'nor (*acaulis; adansoni; glabra; masonae; Brahea nitida* Hort., *not* Andre) |w . . . . . . DWARF P.

neglec'ta . . . . . . **S. umbraculifera**

palmet'to (*jamesiana; schwarzi; Inodes p.; I. schwarzi*) |w . CABBAGE P.

parviflo'ra (*florida*) . . . CUBAN P.

Some palms of this species are planted as S. causiarum.

prin'ceps Hort. in part **S. beccariana**

The name S. princeps has been widely used in this country for various Palmettos.

ro'sei (*S. uresana roseana; Inodes rosei*) TEPIC P.

schwarz'i . . . . **S. palmetto**

serrula'ta . . . . . **Serenoa repens**

texa'na (*mexicana* S. Wats., *not* Mart.; *Inodes t.*) . . . . TEXAS P.

umbraculif'era (*domingensis; haitensis; neglecta; Corypha u.* Jacq., *not* L.) HISPANIOLA P.

uresa'na (*Inodes u.*) . . SONORA P.

—*rosea'na* . . . . **S. rosei**

ya'pa (*japa; Inodes y.*) . . . JAPA P.

SAGUE'RUS . . . . . **ARENGA**

SA'GUS . . . . **METROXYLON**

SA'RIBUS . . . . . **LIVISTONA**

SCHEE'LEA (*ATTALEA* in part; *MAXIMILIANA* in part)

gomphococ'ca (*Attalea g.*)

lauromuelleria'na

leandroa'na

martia'na (*Attalea excelsa*)

prin'ceps (*Attalea p.*)

urbania'na

zonen'sis

SCHIP'PIA

con'color . . . . PIMENTOPALM

SEAFORTH'IA **PTYCHOSPERMA**

SERENO'A (*ACOELORRAPHE* in part; *SERENAEA*) |w SAWPALMETTO

arbores'cens . . . . **Paurotis wrighti**

re'pens (*serrulata; Brahea s.; Chamaerops s.; Corypha r.; Sabal s.*) |w SAWPALMETTO

SIMPSO'NIA . . . . **THRINAX**

SPATHOSCA'PHE **CHAMAEDOREA**

PALM GENERA, continued

STACHYOPHOR'BE **CHAMAEDOREA**

STEPHANOSTA'CHYS **CHAMAEDOREA**

STEVENSO'NIA (*PHOENICOPHORIUM; STEPHENSONIA*). . . . STEVENSONPALM

borsigia'na (*grandiflora; grandifolia; sechellarum; Areca s.* Hort.; *Astrocaryum borsigianum; A. pictum; Phoenicophorium borsigianum; P. sechellarum*) . . . . . FEATHER S.

STYLO'MA . **EUPRITCHARDIA**

SYA'GRUS (*COCOS* in part; *GLAZIOVA*) . . . . . SYAGRUS

ama'ra . . . . **Rhyticocos a.**

argen'tea (*Cocos a.* Engel, *not* Hort.) GUIRACHE S.

botryoph'ora . . . . . . **Arecastrum romanzoffianum botryophorum**

campes'tris (*Cocos c.* Mart., *not* Hort.) FIELD S.

cocoi'des (*Cocos syagrus*)

como'sa (*Cocos c.*)

corona'ta (*Cocos c.* Mart., *not* Hort.) URICURY S.

flexuo'sa (*Cocos f.* Mart., *not* Hort.) ACUMA S.

insig'nis (*Cocos i.; Glaziova i.*)

macrocar'pa (*Cocos m.; C. procopiana*)

petrae'a (*Cocos p.; C. rupestris*)

sap'ida (*Cocos s.* Barb. Rodr., *not* Hort.)

weddellia'na (*Cocos w.; Glaziova martiana; Leopoldinia pulchra* Hort., *not* Mart.) . . . . . . WEDDELL S.

Except for S. weddelliana, very few species of Syagrus are actually cultivated here, many of the names being misapplied to species of Butia.

SYNECAN'THUS

fibro'sus (*Chamaedorea fibrosa*)

THRI'NAX (*SIMPSONIA*) THATCHPALM

altis'sima Hort.

Palms planted under this name are mostly Coccothrinax alta.

argen'tea . . . . . . **Coccothrinax a.**

bahamen'sis . . . . . **T. microcarpa**

barbaden'sis . . . **Coccothrinax b.**

Specimens of T. parviflora are going under the name T. barbadensis, as are also some Washingtonias.

crini'ta . . . . **Coccothrinax c.**

el'egans Hort.

A confused name.

elegantis'sima Hort.

This name is applied to some undetermined species of Coccothrinax.

excel'sa Brit., *not* Griseb. **T. parviflora**

florida'na . . . . . . **T. parviflora**

gar'beri . . . **Coccothrinax argentata**

mar'tii

A confused name which has been referred both to Coccothrinax and to Thrinax, usually T. parviflora.

microcar'pa (*bahamensis; keyensis; ponceana; praeceps; Simpsonia m.*) BRITTLE T.

miragua'ma; miraguano **Coccothrinax miraguama**

mor'risi . . . . MORRIS T.

parviflo'ra (*excelsa* Brit., *not* Griseb.; *floridana; wendlandiana*) JAMAICA T.

This species is sometimes planted under the name T. barbadensis.

PALM GENERA (THRINAX), continued
poncea'na . . . . . . **T. microcarpa**
prae'ceps . . . . . . **T. microcarpa**
punctula'ta LITTLEFRUIT THATCHPALM
radia'ta . . . . . **Coccothrinax r.**
wendlandia'na . . . . . **T. parviflora**
yuragua'na . **Coccothrinax miraguama**

THRINCO'MA **COCCOTHRINAX**

THRIN'GIS . **COCCOTHRINAX**

TIL'MIA . . . . . . **AIPHANES**

TIM'LIS . . . . . **MANICARIA**

TRACHYCAR'PUS (*CHAMAEROPS* in part) . WINDMILLPALM
caespito'sus . . . . BUSH W.
fortun'ei (*excelsus; Chamaerops excelsa* Mart., *not* Thunb.; *C. fortunei*) FORTUNES W.
khasia'nus (*khasyana*) . . **T. martianus**
martia'nus (*griffithi; khasianus; Chamaerops griffithi; C. khasiana; C. martiana*) . . . . MARTIUS W.
na'nus . . . . DWARF W.
nepalen'sis . . . . . **T. wagnerianus**
ta'kil (*Chamaerops t.*) . . . TAKIL W.
wagneria'nus (*nepalensis; Chamaerops n.*) . . . . WAGNER W.

TRITHRI'NAX . TRITHRINAXPALM
acanthoco'ma . . . . . GREEN T.
aculea'ta . . . . . . **Cryosophila nana**
brasilien'sis . . . . . . BRAZIL T.
campes'tris . . . . SWORD T.
mauritiaefor'mis . . . . . **Sabal m.**

VEITCH'IA . . . . . . VEITCHIA
joan'nis (*johannis; Kentia j.*)

VERSCHAFFELT'IA VERSCHAFFELTIA
melanochae'tes . . . . **Roscheria m.**
splen'dida (*splendens*) . . . TALL V.

VONI'TRA . . . . VONITRAPALM
fibro'sa (*thouarsiana; Dictyosperma fibrosum; Dypsis t.*) . . PIASSAVA V. (*Madagascar-Piassava*)

WALLICH'IA . . . WALLICHPALM
caryotoi'des . . . . FISHTAIL W.
dis'ticha (*Didymosperma distichum*) STRADDLELEAF W.
na'na . . . . **Didymosperma nanum**

WASHINGTO'NIA (*NEOWASHINGTONIA*) |W WASHINGTONPALM
filif'era(*arizonica;filamentosa;W.filifera robusta; Brahea filamentosa* Hort.; *B. filifera; Pritchardia filamentosa; P. filifera*) . . . . . CALIFORNIA W.
robus'ta (*W. filifera sonorae; gracilis; W. robusta g.; sonorae*) MEXICAN W.

ZOM'BIA . . . . . . ZOMBIPALM
antilla'rum (*Coccothrinax anomala*) ZOMBIPALM

PALMGRASS . . . . **Setaria palmifolia**
POIRET P. . . . . **S. poiretiana**

PALMYRAPALM . . . **Borassus flabellifer**

Palo Borracho . . . CHORISIA: **Chorisia**

PALOVERDE . . . . **Cercidium**
BLUE P . . . . **C. floridum**
BORDER P. . . . . **C. macrum**
LITTLELEAF P. . . . **C. microphyllum**
TEXAS P. . . . . **C. texanum**

PAMBU'RUS . . . . . . PAMBURUS
missio'nis

PAMIAN'THE . . . . . . PAMIANTHE
peruvia'na . . . . PERU P.

PAMPASGRASS . . . . . . **Cortaderia**
QUILA P. . . . . . . **C. rudiuscula**
SELLOA P. . . . . **S. selloana**

PANAEO'LUS . . . . . . PANAEOLUS
retiru'gis . . . . WRINKLED P.

PAN'AX . . . . GINSENG

Panax appears to be masculine in the original Greek but was treated as neuter by Linnaeus in Ed. 1 of Species Plantarum. Hence, under Art. 72 (1) of International Rules it is a neuter word. However, Prof. Rehder, who is a member of the Special (International) Committee on plant nomenclature, informs the Editorial Committee of this book that his committee recommended that a generic name retain its classical gender, the International Botanical Congress at Amsterdam (1935) making that a recommendation rather than a rule. This obviously raises a controversy over the gender of such a name as Panax; it can, therefore, be regarded (as Prof. Rehder does) as masculine or else as neuter. S. P. N. adopts the former policy.

anom'alum . . **Nothopanax anomalus**
da'vidi . . . . **Nothopanax d.**
el'egans . . . . . **Tieghemopanax e.**
hor'ridum . . . . **Oplopanax horridus**
mur'rayi. . . . . **Tieghemopanax m.**
quinquefo'lium (*Aralia quinquefolia*) AMERICAN G.
sambucifo'lium **Tieghemopanax sambucifolius**
schin'seng (*ginseng*) . . ASIATIC G.
sessiliflo'rum **Acanthopanaxsessiliflorus**
trifo'lium . . . . DWARF G.
JAPANESE. HV. Panax

PANCRA'TIUM . . . . PANCRATIUM
canarien'se . . . . . . CANARIES P.
declina'tum . **Hymenocallis caribaea**
illyr'icum . . . . ILLYRIAN P.
marit'imum . . . . SEADAFFODIL P.

PAN'DA
oleo'sa

PANDAN'US . . . . . . SCREWPINE
austra'lis . . . . . AUSTRALIAN S.
bap'tisti
—au'reus
carico'sus
grac'ilis
graminifo'lius . . . . . . GRASSY S.

The name Pandanus graminifolius is often misapplied to P. pygmaeus.

javan'icus . . . . JAVA S.
pacif'icus . . . . PACIFIC S.
pyg'maeus . . . . DWARF S.
san'deri . . . . TIMOR S.
—roehrsia'nus . . . . . ROEHRS T.S.
stenophyl'lus
tecto'rius . . . . THATCH S.
u'tilis . . . . COMMON S.
variega'tus . . . . . . VARIEGATED S.
veitch'i . . . . VEITCH S.

PANDO'REA . . . . . . PANDOREA
bryce'i (*Tecoma reginae-sabae*) QUEEN-OF-SHEBA P.
jasminoi'des (*Tecoma j.*) JASMINE P.
pandora'na (*australis; bignonia; Tecoma a.*) . . . . . . WONGAVINE P.
ricasolia'na (*Tecoma mackeni; T. ricasoliana*) . . . . RICASOL P.

PAN'GIUM . . . . PANGIUM
ed'ule . . . . FOOD P.

PANIALA . . . . . **Flacourtia jangomas**

PANICULA'RIA . . . . **GLYCERIA**
See **GRASS GENERA.**

PAN'ICUM . . PANICUM; WITCHGRASS
See **CEREALS** and **GRASS GENERA.**

PANICUM . . . . **Panicum**
ADDISON P. . . . . . . **P. addisoni**
ARIZONA P. . . . . . **P. arizonicum**
ASHE P. . . . . **P. ashei**
BARTOW P. . . . . . **P. bartowense**
BEAKED P. . . . . **P. anceps**
BERG P. . . . . **P. bergi**
BICKNELL P. . . . . . . **P. bicknelli**
BITTER P. . . . . **P. amarum**
BLUE P. . . . . **P. antidotale**
BOG P. . . . . **P. vernale**
BROWNTOP P. . . . **P. fasciculatum**
BULB P. . . . . **P. bulbosum**
CLUTE P. . . . . **P. clutei**
COMBS P. . . . . **P. combsi**
CORAL P. . . . . **P. chapmani**
Creeping P. . . . . TORPEDO P.
CYPRESS P. . . . . **P. sphagnicola**
DEAM P. . . . . **P. deami**
DESERT P. . . . . . . **P. urvilleanum**
DOMINICAN P. . . . . **P. adspersum**
EGYPTIAN P. . . . . **P. geminatum**
FALL P. . . . . . **P. dichotomiflorum**
GAPING P. . . . . **P. hians**
GOUIN P. . . . . **P. gouini**
HALLS P. . . . . **P. halli**
HAVARD P. . . . . **P. havardi**
HELLER P. . . . . **P. helleri**
HEMLOCK P. . . . . . **P. tsugetorum**
HILLMAN P. . . . . . . **P. hillmani**
HUACHUCA P. . . . . **P. huachucae**
JALAPA P. . . . . **P. xalapense**
LEIBERG P. . . . . **P. leibergi**
LINDHEIMER P. . . . **P. lindheimeri**
LITTLE BULB P. . **P. bulbosum minus**
LITTLE P. . . . . **P. polycaulon**
LONGLEAF P. . . . . **P. longifolium**
NEEDLELEAF P. . . . . . **P. aciculare**
PACIFIC P. . . . . **P. pacificum**
PURPLE P. . . . . **P. stipitatum**
REDTOP P. . . . . . . **P. agrostoides**
ROUNDSEED P. . . . **P. sphaerocarpon**
SAND P. . . . . **P. arenicoloides**
SAVANNAH P. . . . **P. gymnocarpon**
SCRIBNER P. . . . **P. scribnerianum**
SHASTA P. . . . . **P. shastense**
SHEEP P. . . . . **P. ovinum**
SLIMLEAF P. . . . . . **P. linearifolium**
SOFTLEAF P. . . . **P. malacophyllum**
SPRAWLING P. . . . . **P. reptans**
TENNESSEE P. . . . **P. tennesseense**
TEXAS P. . . . . **P. texanum**
TORPEDO P. . . . . **P. repens**
VELVET P. . . . . **P. scoparium**
WARTY P. . . . . . . **P. verrucosum**
WATER P. . . . . . . **P. paludivagum**
WEBBER P. . . . . . **P. webberianum**
WERNER P. . . . . **P. werneri**
WILCOX P. . . . . . . **P. wilcoxianum**
WILMINGTON P. . **P. wilmingtonense**
WOOLLY P. . . . . . . **P. lanuginosum**
WRIGHT P. . . . . . **P. wrightianum**

PANSY . . . . **Viola**
GARDEN P. . . . **V. tricolor hortensis**
WILD P. . . . . **V. tricolor**

PANSYORCHID . . . . **Miltonia**

PA'NUS . . . . PANUS
styp'ticus . . . . BITTER P.

PAPA'VER |w . . . . Poppy
alpi'num (*burseri*) . . . . Alpine P.
Alpine Album. hv.
Roseum
ap'ulum . . . . Apulian P.
argemo'ne . . . . Eye P.
atlan'ticum . . . . Atlas P.
bractea'tum . . . Great Scarlet P.
bur'seri . . . . **P. alpinum**
califor'nicum . . . . . Mission P.
caucas'icum (*fugax*) . . Caucasian P.
du'bium . . . . Longpod P.
—laeviga'tum (*P. laevigatum*) Dragon P.
glau'cum . . . . Tulip P.
heldreich'i . . . . . . Heldreich P.
laterit'ium . . . . Armenia P.
macoun'i |w . . . . . . Macoun P.
macrosto'mum . . . . Bell P.
monan'thum . . . . Loneflower P.
nudicau'le . . . . Iceland P.
—al'bum . . . . White I.P.
—auranti'acum . . . . Orange I.P.
—coccin'eum . . . . Crimson I.P.
—lu'teum . . . . . . Yellow I.P.
—rose'um . . . . Rose I.P.

Hort. var. of Iceland Poppy are shown in hort. var. list below.

olym'picum . . . . . . **P. pilosum**
orienta'le . . . . Oriental P.

Hort. var. of Oriental Poppy are shown in hort. var. list below.

paucifolia'tum
pavoni'num . . . . . . Peacock P.
per'sicum . . . . Persian P.
pilo'sum (*olympicum*) . . Olympic P.
pyrena'icum (*rhaeticum*). Pyrenees P.
radica'tum
rhoe'as . . . . Corn P.
—umbro'sum (*P. umbrosum*) Blackspot C.P.

Hort. var. of Corn Poppy are shown in hort. var. list below.

rupifra'gum . . . . . . Spanish P.
schinzia'num. . . . . . . Schinz P.
setig'erum . . . . Hairy P.

Sometimes treated as a form of P. somniferum.

somnif'erum . . . . Opium P.
—ni'grum . . . . Black O.P.
Giganteum. hv. P. somniferum
Monstrosum
Murselli
Paeoniflorum
spica'tum . . . . Spike P.
thibet'icum . . . . . . Tibetan P.
triniaefo'lium . . . . Cappadocia P.
umbro'sum . . . . **P. rhoeas u.**

Ornamental hort. var. (clons) of **Papaver**, Oriental, Iceland and other Poppies:

For the following list, the Editorial Committee is chiefly indebted and expresses hearty thanks to John D. Siebenthaler, Dayton, Ohio. All the hort. var. named below are clons.

CP. Corn P. Ice. Iceland P.
Or. Oriental P.

Admiral
African
American Flag. Or.
Apricot Queen. Or.
Aurora. Ice.
Austin Double Shirley. CP.
Australia. Or.
Ballet Girl. Or.

PAPAVER, continued
Barrs Pink. Or.
Barrs White. Or.
Beauty of Livermere. Or.
Betty Ann. Or.
Big Jim. Or.
Blush Queen. Or.
Bobs. Or.
Boston. Or. *Boston Peerless.*
Brightness. Or.
Brilliant. Or.
California. Ice.
Cardinal. Or.
Cavalier. Or.
Cerise Beauty. Or.
Charles Darwin
Cheerio. Or.
Chinese
Coccineum Aureum. CP.
Colonel Bowles. Or.
Coonara. Ice.
Dainty Lady. Or.
Dannebrog. *Danebrog; Danish; Danish Cross; Danish Flag.*
Delicata. Or.
Delight. Or.
Duke of Teck. Or.
E. A. Bowles. Or.
Echo. Or.
Edna Perry. Or.
Eldorado
Enchantress. Or.
Enfield Beauty. Or.
Ethel Swete. Or.
Excelsior. Or.
Fairy. Or.
Fairy Blush. Or.
Fireking. Or.
Flag-of-Truce
Flaming Ben. Or.
Flanders. Or.
Flanders Field. Or.
Floreplenum. Or.
Fordhook Fairy. CP.
Gaartref. Ice.
Gaiety. Or.
Gerald Perry. Or.
Gibson Giant
Giganteum. Hort. var. of P. somniferum.
Glowing Embers. Or.
Golden Gate
Golden Surprise. Or.
Gold of Ophir. Or.
Goldschmidt. Or.
Goliath. Or.
Grand Mogul. Or.
Grossfurst. Or.
Harmony. Or.
Helen Elizabeth. Or.
Henri Cayeux. Or.
Hercules. Or.
Hooker Single
Immaculata. Or.
Improved Shirley. CP.
Isle of Shoals. CP.
Japanese Pompon. CP.
Jeannie Mawson. Or.
John III. Or.
Joyce. Or.
Julia Buck. Or.
June Delight. Or.
King Edward. Or.
King George. Or.
Lachs Koenigen. Or.
Lady Roscoe. Or.
Leon Laurent. Or.

PAPAVER, continued
Lightness. Or.
Little Prince. Or.
Little Shrimp. Or.
Lord Lambourne. Or.
Loreley. Or.
Lula A. Neeley. Or.
Luminosum. Or.
Magnificum. Or.
Mahony. Or. *Mahonoy; Mahogany.*
Maid-of-the-Mist
Manchus Fan. Or.
Mandarin. Or.
Marie Studholme. Or.
Mary Ellen. Or.
Mary Jane Miller. Or
May Campbell. Or.
Mayqueen. Or.
May Sadler. Or.
Menelik. Or.
Mephisto. Or.
Mikado. Or.
Miss Sherwood. Or.
Mme. Pavlowa. Or.
Mogul. Or.
Monstrosum. Hort. var. of P. somniferum.
Mrs. Baker. Or.
Mrs. Ballego. Or.
Mrs. Carl Skinner. Or.
Mrs. Heenk. Or.
Mrs. (*H. G.*) Stobart. Or.
Mrs. (*John*) Harkness. Or.
Mrs. Perry. Or.
Murselli. Hort. var. of P. somniferum.
Nancy. Or.
Neeleys Lavender. Or.
Neeleys Pink. Or.
Negrillon. Or.
Old Rose. Or.
Olympia. Or.
Orange Beauty. Or.
Orange Queen. Or.
Oriental King. Or.
Oriflamme. Or.
Paeoniflorum. Hort. var. of P. somniferum.
Parkman. Or. *Parkmani; P. orientale parkmani.*
Pearl Pink. Or.
Pearl Queen. Or.
Perfection. Or.
Perrys White. Or.
Peter Pan. Or.
Phenomenal. Or.
Picotee. Or.
Pink Beauty. Or.
Premier. Or.
Prince of Orange. Or.
Prince of Wales. Or.
Princess Ena. Or.
Princess Mary. Or.
Princess Victoria Louise. Or.
Proserpine. Or.
Psyche. Or.
Purity. Or.
Pygmaeum. Or.
Queen Alexandra. Or.
Ranunculus. *Ranunculus-flowered.*
Red Lacquer. Or.
Rembrandt. Or.
Ridgewood Beauty. Or.
Rose Glory. Or.
Rose Queen. Or.
Royal Rose. Or.
Royal Scarlet. Or.

PAPAVER, continued
Salmon Beauty. Or.
Salmon Glow. Or.
Salmon King. Or.
Salmon Perfection. Or.
Salmon Queen. Or.
Sass Pink. Or.
Shell Pink. Or.
Shirley
Shirley Poppies are a strain of P. rhoeas.
Shrimp Pink. Or.
Silver Blick. Or.
Silver King. Or.
Silver Lining. Or.
Silver Queen. Or.
Snowdrift. Or.
Snowflame. Or.
Splendor. Or.
Spotless. Or.
Spotted Giant. Or.
Sturmpackel. Or.
Sun Mist. Or.
Sunny Jim. Or.
Tangerine. Ice.
(*The*) Bride. Or.
The Marne. Or.
Thibet. Ice.
Thora Perry. Or.
Toreador. Or.
Trilby. Or.
Tulipa. Or.
Vestal Flame. Or.
Victoria Louise. Or.
Virginia. Or.
War Lord. Or.
Watteau. Or.
Welcome. Or.
Whirlwind. Or.
White Shirley
White Swan. Or.
Winnie. Or.
Wunderkind. Or.
Wurtembergia. Or.
Yellow Wonder. Ice.

Papaw . . . . . . Pawpaw: **Asimina**
Papaya . . . . . . **Carica; C. papaya**
Mountain P. . . . **C. candamarcensis**
Oakleaf P. . . . . . **C. quercifolia**

Paperbush . . . . . . **Edgeworthia**
Oriental P. . . . . . **E. tomentosa**

Paperflower . . . . . . **Psilostrophe**
Cudweed P. . . . . **P. gnaphalodes**
Greenstem P. . . . . **P. sparsiflora**
Whitestem P. . . . . **P. cooperi**
Woolly P. . . . . . . **P. tagetinae**

Papermulberry . . . . **Broussonetia**
Common P. . . . . . **B. papyrifera**
Kazinoki P. . . . . . **B. kazinoki**

PAPHIOPED'ILUM **CYPRIPEDIUM**
See **ORCHID GENERA.**

PAPPO'PHORUM . . . Pappusgrass
See **GRASS GENERA.**

Pappusgrass . . . . . . **Pappophorum**
Feather P. . . . . . . **P. wrighti**
Pink P. . . . . **P. bicolor**
Spike P. . . . . Feather P.
Whiplash P. . . . . **P. mucronulatum**

PAPY'RIUS . . . **BROUSSONETIA**
Broussonetia L'Her. (1799) is conserved under International Rules for the Papermulberry genus. It should not be confused with the older Broussonetia Orteg. (1798), which is a synonym of the leguminous genus Sophora.

PAPY'RUS . . . . **CYPERUS**
antiquo'rum . . . . **C. papyrus**

Papyrus . . . . . . **Cyperus papyrus**

PARADI'SEA . . . . . St.Brunolily
lilias'trum (*Anthericum l.*) St.Brunolily
—ma'jor . . . . Great S.
Paradisenut . . . . Monkeypottree, Sapucaianut: **Lecythis zabucajo**
Paradisetree . . . . **Simaruba glauca**
Paragrass . . . **Panicum purpurascens**
Paraguaya . . . . **Britoa acida**
Paraguaytea . . . **Ilex paraguariensis**

PARAJUBAE'A . . . . . Parajubaea
See **PALM GENERA.**

PARALINOSPA'DIX (*LINOSPADIX* Becc.)
See **PALM GENERA.**

PARAME'RIA
vulnera'ria

PARAMIG'NYA . . . . . . Vinelime
longipeduncula'ta . . . Philippine V.
monophyl'la . . . . . . Oneleaf V.

PARASHOR'EA . . . . . . Bagtikan
malaanonan' . . . . . . Common B.
stella'ta . . . . Tavoy B.
war'burgi . . . . . . Mindanao B.
Parasoltree, Chinese **Firmiana simplex**
PARASYRIN'GA . . . **LIGUSTRUM**

PARATECO'MA
pero'ba (*Tecoma p.*)

PARDAN'THUS . . **BELAMCANDA**
sinen'sis . . . . **B. chinensis**
Pareiraroot
Chondodendron tomentosum

PARIETA'RIA [w] . . . . Pellitory
officina'lis . . . . Wall P.
pennsylvan'ica [w]. Pennsylvania P.

PARINA'RIUM . . . . . Parinarium
macrophyl'lum Gingerbreadplum P.
mobo'la . . . . Mobolaplum P.
non'da . . . . Nondatree P.

PARIT'IUM . . . . . . **HIBISCUS**
ela'tum . . . . . **H. tiliaceus elatus**

PAR'KIA . . . . Nittatree
africa'na . . . . African N.
biglandulo'sa . . . . . Malaya N.
biglobo'sa . . . . Twoball N.
filicoi'dea . . . . Fernleaf N.
rox'burghi . . . . . . Roxburgh N.

PARKINSO'NIA
aculea'ta . . . . Jerusalemthorn
microphyl'la **Cercidium microphyllum**
torreya'na . . . . **Cercidium floridum**

PARME'LIA . . . . Parmelia
capera'ta . . . . Wrinkled P.
ceratophyl'la . . . . Horny P.
conspers'a . . . . Sprinkled P.
omphalo'des . . . . Blackcrottle P.
parieti'na . . . . Wall P.
perla'ta
physo'des . . . . . . Darkcrottle P.
saxat'ilis . . . . . . Stonecrottle P.

PARMENTIER'A . . . . Candletree
aculea'ta . . . . . Yellowtaper C.
ala'ta . . . . **Crescentia a.**
cereif'era . . . . Panama C.
ed'ulis . . . . Food C.

PARNAS'SIA [w] . . . . Parnassia
asarifo'lia . . . . Brook P.
califor'nica . . . . . . California P.
carolinia'na [w] . . . . . Carolina P.
—monta'na . . . . Dwarf C.P.
cirra'ta
fimbria'ta . . . . RockyMountain P.
grandifo'lia . . . . Bigleaf P.
interme'dia . . . . Nevada P.
montanen'sis . . . . . . Montana P.
palus'tris [w] . . . . . Wideworld P.
parviflo'ra [w] . . . . Smallflower P.

PAROCHE'TUS . . . . . Shamrockpea
commu'nis . . . . Common S.

PARODI'A (*HICKENIA*)
See **CACTUS GENERA.**

PARONY'CHIA Nailwort (*Whitlowwort*)
argen'tea . . . . Silver N.
argyroco'ma . . . . . . Allegany N.
—albimonta'na . WhiteMountains N.
capita'ta (*nivea* DC., *not* C. A. Mey.) Head N.
dichot'oma . . . . Forking N.
francisca'na . . . . SanFrancisco N.
james'i . . . . James N.
kape'la . . . . Greek N.
kurd'ica (*nivea* C. A. Mey., *not* DC.) Kurd N.
lindheim'eri . . . . . Lindheimer N.
niv'ea DC. . . . . **P. capitata**
niv'ea C. A. Mey. . . . . . **P. kurdica**
pulvina'ta . . . RockyMountain N.
serpyllifo'lia . . . . . . Creeping N.
Perhaps only a variety of P. capitata.

PAROSE'LA . . . . **DALEA**

Parrotbeak . . . . **Clianthus**
Albino Red P. . . **C. puniceus albus**
Glorypea P. . . . . . . **C. dampieri**
Red P. . . . . **C. puniceus**

Parrotfeather . . . . **Myriophyllum**
Brazilian P. . . . . . **M. brasiliense**
Canada P. . . . . . **M. verticillatum**
Chile P. . . . **M. proserpinacoides**
Farwell P. . . . . **M. farwelli**
Green P. . . . . **M. pinnatum**
Slender P. . . . . **M. tenellum**

PARRO'TIA . . . . Parrotia
jacquemontia'na . . . **Parrotiopsis j.**
per'sica . . . . Persian P.

PARROTIOP'SIS
jacquemontia'na (*Parrotia j.*)

PAR'RYA . . . . Parrya
menzies'i **Phoenicaulis cheiranthoides**
platycar'pa (*macrocarpa* S. Wats., *not* R. Br.) . . . . Utah P.

PARRYEL'LA
filifo'lia . . . . Dunebroom

Parsley . . . . **Petroselinum**
Common Garden P. **P. crispum latifolium**
Curly G. P. . . . . **P. crispum**
Fernleaf G. P. . . . . **P. c. filicinum**
Turnip G. P. . . . . **P. c. radicosum**

Parsnip . . . . **Pastinaca**
Garden P. . . . . **P. sativa**
Wild G. P. . . . . . . **P. s. sylvestris**

PARSONS'IA . . . . **CUPHEA**

PARTHE'NIUM . . . . . Parthenium
argenta'tum . Guayule P. (*Guayule*)
inca'num . . . . Mariola P.

PARTHENOCIS'SUS lw . . CREEPER
henrya'na (*Ampelopsis h.; Vitis h.*) SILVERVEIN C.
heptaphyl'la (*Ampelopsis h.*) SEVENLEAF C.
himalaya'na (*Vitis h.*) . . HIMALAYA C.
—rubrifo'lia (*Vitis h. r.*) REDLEAF H.C.
inser'ta (*vitacea; Ampelopsis v.; Vitis v.*) THICKET C.
—lacinia'ta . . . . . RAGLEAF T.C.
—macrophyl'la . . . . BIGLEAF T.C.
laetevi'rens
quinquefo'lia (*Ampelopsis q.; Vitis q.*) lw . . . . VIRGINIA C.
—engelmann'i (*Ampelopsis q. e.*) ENGELMANN V.C.
—hirsu'ta . . . . . . REDTWIG V.C.
—mi'nor . . . . . LITTLELEAF V.C.
—muro'rum (*Ampelopsis muralis* Hort.; *A. q. murorum*). . WALL V.C.
—saintpaul'i (*A. q. s.*) . ST.PAUL V.C.
semicorda'ta
sinen'sis . . . . **Vitis piasezki**
thom'soni (*Ampelopsis t.; Vitis t.*) THOMSON C.
tricuspida'ta (*Ampelopsis t.; Vitis inconstans*) . JAPANESE C. (*Boston Ivy*)
—low'i (*Ampelopsis l.*) . . LOWS J.C.
—purpu'rea . . . . . . PURPLE J.C.
—veitch'i (*Ampelopsis v.*). VEITCH J.C.
vita'cea . . . . **P. inserta**

PARTRIDGEBERRY . **Mitchella; M. repens**

PARTRIDGEPEA . . . . . **Chamaecrista**
GREENMAN P. . . . . **C. leptadenia**
SEASHORE P. . . . . . **C. cinerea**
SENSITIVE P. . . . . . **C. procumbens**
SHOWY P. . . . . . . **C. fasciculata**
WRIGHTS P. . . . . . . **C. wrighti**
YELLOWLOCKS P. . . . . **C. flavicoma**

PASA'NIA . . . . . **LITHOCARPUS**

PASITH'EA . . . . PASITHEA
coeru'lea . . . . CHILE P.

PAS'PALUM . . . . PASPALUM
See **GRASS GENERA.**

PASPALUM . . . . **Paspalum**
BARESTEM P. **P. longepedunculatum**
BLUE P. . . . . . . **P. caespitosum**
BROOK P. . . . . . **P. acuminatum**
BROWNSEED P. . . . . **P. plicatulum**
BULL P. . . . . . . **P. boscianum**
COCONUT P. . . . . **P. laxum**
COMBS P. . . . . **P. almum**
CORAL P. . . . . . . **P. blodgetti**
CYPRESS P. . . . . . **P. lentiferum**
DUNE P. . . . . **P. psammophilum**
EARLY P. . . . . **P. praecox**
FIELD P. . . . . **P. laeve**
FLORIDA P. . . . . . **P. floridanum**
FRINGELEAF P. . . . **P. ciliatifolium**
GIANT P. . . . . . . **P. giganteum**
GOLDHAIR P. . . . . **P. debile**

PASPALUM, continued
GULFDUNE P. **Paspalum monostachyum**
HAIRYLEAF P. . . . . . **P. longipilum**
HAIRYSEED P. . . . . **P. pubiflorum**
HARTWEG P. . . . **P. hartwegianum**
HORSETAIL P. . . . . . . **P. repens**
INDIA P. . . . . . **P. scrobiculatum**
LITTLESEED P. . . . . **P. propinquum**
LONGLEAF P. . . . . . . **P. supinum**
MAT P. . . . . **P. minus**
MUDBANK P. . . . . . **P. dissectum**
ONESPIKE P. . . . **P. unispicatum**
PERUVIAN P. . . . . **P. racemosum**
PITCHFORK P. . . . . . . **P. bifidum**
RIBBED P. . . . . **P. malacophyllum**
ROUNDSEED P. . . . . . **P. circulare**
RUSTYSEED P. . . . . . . **P. langei**
SAND P. . . . . **P. stramineum**
SEASHORE P. . . . . . **P. vaginatum**
SMOOTH FLORIDA P. **P. floridanum glabratum**
SOUR P. . . . . **P. conjugatum**
STIFF P. . . . . . . **P. rigidifolium**
THIN P. . . . . **P. setaceum**

PASQUEFLOWER
AMERICAN P. . . **Anemone ludoviciana**
EUROPEAN P. . . . . . **A. pulsatilla**
MEADOW P. . . . . . . **A. pratensis**
SPREADING P. . . . . . . **A. patens**
WESTERN P. . . . . . **A. occidentalis**

PASSIFLO'RA (*TACSONIA*) lw PASSIONFLOWER
ala'ta . . . . WINGSTEM P.
×**alatocaeru'lea** (*alata × caerulea; pfordti*)
al'ba . . . . WHITE P.
antioquien'sis (*vanvolxemi; Tacsonia v.*) ANTIOQUIEN P.
×**atropurpu'rea** (*racemosa × hermesiana*)
banks'i . . . . BANKS P.
caeru'lea . . . . BLUECROWN P.
BIGFLOWER (*grandiflora*) HV.
CONSTANCE ELLIOTT
capsula'ris
coccin'ea . . . . SCARLET P.
×**colvil'lei** (*caerulea × incarnata*) COLVILLE P.
cumbalen'sis
ed'ulis . . . . PURPLE GRANADILLA (*Passionfruit*)
×**exonien'sis** (*antioquiensis × mollissima*)
foe'tida . . . . TAGUA P.
—hasta'ta (*P. hastata*)
grac'ilis . . . . CRINKLED P.
hermesia'na (*raddiana*)
ig'nea . . . . **P. manicata**
incarna'ta lw . . . . . . MAYPOP P.
jameso'ni (*Tacsonia j.*) . JAMESON P.
Sometimes misapplied to P. tomentosa.
lana'ta (*Tacsonia l.*)
laurifo'lia . . . . WATERLEMON (*Yellow Granadilla*)

PASSIFLORA, continued
ligula'ris . . . . SWEET GRANADILLA
lute'a . . . YELLOW PASSIONFLOWER
macrocar'pa . . . **P. quadrangularis**
malifor'mis CURUBA P. (*Kuruba P.*)
manica'ta (*ignea; Tacsonia m.*) RED P.
milita'ris . . . . SOLDIER P.
mix'ta (*Tacsonia m.*)
mollis'sima (*Tacsonia m.*) SOFTLEAF P.
multifor'mis
This name has been misapplied in the past to P. maliformis.
pfordt'i . . . . . ×**P. alatocaerulea**
quadrangula'ris (*macrocarpa*) GIANT GRANADILLA
racemo'sa (*princeps*)
raddia'na . . . . **P. hermesiana**
ru'bra
tomento'sa (*Tacsonia t.*) . WOOLLY P.
trifascia'ta . . . . . . THREEBAND P.
vanvolx'emi . . . . **P. antioquiensis**
viola'cea . . . . VIOLET P.

PASSIONFLOWER . . . . . . **Passiflora**
ANTIOQUIEN P. . . . **P. antioquiensis**
BANKS P. . . . . **P. banksi**
BLUECROWN P. . . . . . **P. caerulea**
COLVILLE P. . . . . . . ×**P. colvillei**
CRINKLED P. . . . . **P. gracilis**
CURUBA P. . . . . . . **P. maliformis**
GIANT GRANADILLA **P. quadrangularis**
JAMESON P. . . . . **P. jamesoni**
Kuruba P. . . . . CURUBA P.
MAYPOP P. . . . . **P. incarnata**
PURPLE GRANADILLA . . . **P. edulis**
RED P. . . . . **P. manicata**
SCARLET P. . . . . **P. coccinea**
SOFTLEAF P. . . . . . **P. mollissima**
SOLDIER P. . . . . **P. militaris**
SWEET GRANADILLA . . . **P. ligularis**
TAGUA P. . . . . **P. foetida**
THREEBAND P. . . . . . **P. trifasciata**
VIOLET P. . . . . **P. violacea**
WATERLEMON . . . . . . **P. laurifolia**
WHITE P. . . . . **P. alba**
WINGSTEM P. . . . . **P. alata**
WOOLLY P. . . . . **P. tomentosa**
YELLOW P. . . . . **P. lutea**

Passionfruit . . . GRANADILLA, PURPLE: **Passiflora edulis**

PASTINA'CA lw . . . . . . PARSNIP
sati'va lw . . . . GARDEN P.
—sylves'tris . . . . WILD G.P.

PATAGONIATREE . . . . . **Patagonula**
GUAYAIBI P. . . . . . **P. americana**

PATAGON'ULA . . . PATAGONIATREE
america'na . . . . . . GUAYAIBI P.

PATCHOULI
CABLIN P. . . . . **Pogostemon cablin**
HEYNE P. . . . . . . **P. heyneanus**

PATENTS, PLANT

This list is compiled from the official records of the United States Patent Office, with the exception of the Introduction Names. As these do not appear on the original Patent Records, the Editorial Committee requested authentic information direct from the present owners or introducers themselves and have included the results so far as they have been received.

Many of these Introduction Names might well be shortened and in other ways changed to comply more nearly to rules of horticultural nomenclature as adopted by the Horticultural Section of the International Botanical Congress, or S.P.N. standards. Some examples are: *Mrs. Francis King* would become FRANCIS KING or MRS. KING; *McGredy's Triumph*, MCGREDYS TRIUMPH; *Sun Glow*, SUNGLOW, etc. See discussion of International Rules in Preface.

In the following alphabetical list the figures following the kinds of plants refer to Plant Patent numbers.

AGROSTIS. 143.
APPLE. 57, 61, 85, 90, 125, 168, 238, 258, 278, 293, 327, 388, 474.
APRICOT. 74, 476.
AVOCADO. 100, 139, 234, 261, 433.
AZALEA. 145, 147.
BARBERRY. 40, 99, 110, 189, 460.
BEGONIA. 265, 406.
BENT (GRASS). 143.
BLACKBERRY. *See* LOGANBERRY.
BRAMBLEBERRY. 39.
BUDDLEIA. 206.
CAMELLIA. 224, 231, 431.
CARNATION. 3, 24, 34, 35, 37, 56, 69, 127, 133, 148, 193, 198, 219, 239, 260, 273–275, 319, 344, 372, 398, 399, 434, 463.
CHERRY. 29, 30, 41, 94, 164, 188, 316, 421.
CHRYSANTHEMUM. 58, 64, 75, 76, 204, 205, 251, 310, 313, 352, 368, 390–392, 401.
CITRUS HYBRID. 142.
CLEMATIS. 471, 472.

PLANT PATENTS

(Through July 1, 1941)

No.	For	Patent Granted	Inventor	Assigned to	Introduction Name
1	Climbing or Trailing Rose	Aug. 18, 1931	Henry F. Bosenberg, New Brunswick, N. J.	Louis C. Schubert, New Brunswick, N. J.	The New Dawn
2	Rose	Oct. 13, 1931	Frank Spanbauer, North Kansas City, Mo.		Senior
3	Carnation	Oct. 20, 1931	Otto A. Muller, Ambler, Pa.	The Florex Gardens, North Wales, Pa.	Joan Marie
4	Thornless Young Dewberry	Oct. 20, 1931	Elmer L. Pollard and Jubal E. Sherrill, Chino, Calif.		Acme
5	Rose	Nov. 10, 1931	Victor Groshens, Roslyn, Pa.		La Vie
6	Hybrid Tea Rose	Feb. 16, 1932	Robert Lee Catron, Richmond, Ind.	The Joseph H. Hill Co., Richmond, Ind.	Sweet Adeline
7	Peach	Feb. 16, 1932	James E. Markham, Xenia, Ill.	Stark Bros. Nurseries & Orchards Co., Louisiana, Mo.	Hal-berta Giant
8	Rose	Feb. 23, 1932	George B. Hart, Brighton, N. Y.		Mary Hart
9	Hybrid Tea Rose	Feb. 23, 1932	Robert Lee Catron, Richmond, Ind.	Joseph H. Hill Co., Richmond, Ind.	Afterglow
10	Climbing Rose	Mar. 8, 1932	Joseph W. Kallay, Painesville, Ohio.	Jackson & Perkins Co., Newark, N. Y.	Blaze
11	Hybrid Tea Rose	Mar. 22, 1932	Christian W. Hjermind, Maywood, Ill., and Paul E. Weiss, River Forest, Ill.	Premier Rose Gardens, Maywood, Ill.	Ambassador
12	Plum	Apr. 5, 1932	Elizabeth Waters Burbank, Known also as Elizabeth Burbank, Executrix of Luther Burbank, Deceased, Santa Rosa, Calif.	Stark Bros. Nurseries & Orchards Co., Louisiana, Mo.	Burbanks June Red Skin
13	Plum	Apr. 5, 1932	"	"	Burbanks Great Yellow
14	Plum	Apr. 5, 1932	"	"	Burbanks Flaming Delicious
15	Peach	Apr. 5, 1932	"	"	Burbanks July Elberta
16	Plum	May 10, 1932	"	"	Burbanks Mammoth Cardinal
17	Freesia	May 24, 1932	William Russell Elder, Indianapolis, Ind.	Elder & Elder Nurseries, Indianapolis, Ind.	
18	Plum	July 19, 1932	Elizabeth Waters Burbank, Known also as Elizabeth Burbank, Executrix of Luther Burbank, Deceased, Santa Rosa, Calif.	Stark Bros. Nurseries & Orchards Co., Louisiana, Mo.	
19	Dahlia	July 19, 1932	Harold L. Ickes, Hubbard Woods, Ill.		Anna W. Ickes
20	Yellow Rose	Aug. 23, 1932	Earl H. Mann, Richmond, Ind.	E. G. Hill Co., Richmond, Ind.	Golden Talisman
21	Cerise Rose	Aug. 23, 1932	"	"	Sterling
22	Rose	Aug. 23, 1932	Charles N. White, Medina, N. Y.		Yellow Joanna Hill
23	Rose	Aug. 23, 1932	Robert Lee Catron, Richmond, Ind.	Joseph H. Hill Co., Richmond, Ind.	Better Times
24	Variety of Plant (Carnation)	Aug. 30, 1932	William Sim, Saugus, Mass.		My Love
25	Hybrid Tea Rose	Aug. 30, 1932	Wallace R. Pierson, Cromwell, Conn.		Souvenir

No.	For	Patent Granted	Inventor	Assigned to	Introduction Name
26	Strawberry	Aug. 30, 1932	Bert W. Keith and Bud H. Keith, Sawyer, Mich.		KEITHS KANNER KING
27	Mushroom	Sept. 20, 1932	Louis F. Lambert, Coatesville, Pa.		GOLDEN WHITE
28	Rose	Oct. 4, 1932	Walter D. Brownell and Josephine D. Brownell, Little Compton, R. I.		MRS. ARTHUR CURTISS JAMES; GOLDEN CLIMBER
29	Cherry	Oct. 4, 1932	Levi R. Taft, East Jordan, Mich.	Stark Bros. Nurseries & Orchards Co., Louisiana, Mo.	MONTLATE
30	Cherry	Oct. 4, 1932	"	"	MONEARLY
31	Peach	Oct. 11, 1932	Maurice A. Blake, New Brunswick, N. J.	New Jersey State Agricultural Exp. Sta., New Brunswick, N. J.	WHITE HALE
32	Freesia	Oct. 11, 1932	Gerald Hew Dalrymple, Bartley, near Southampton, England.	C. J. Van Bourgondien, Babylon, N. Y.	MARYON
33	Hybrid Tea Rose	Oct. 11, 1932	Paul M. Pierson, Ossining, N. Y.		
34	Carnation	Oct. 11, 1932	Abner B. Shaw, North Dartmouth, Mass.	Stephen E. Shaw, North Dartmouth, Mass.	GREATHEART
35	Carnation	Oct. 18, 1932	Russell Engle, Kokomo, Ind.	Thomas L. Knipe, Kokomo, Ind.	CHIEF KOKOMO
36	Dahlia	Oct. 18, 1932	Jesse J. Bromall, Eagle Rock, Calif.	Charles G. Reed, Lawrence, Mass.	
37	Carnation	Oct. 25, 1932	William Sim, Saugus, Mass.		
38	Rose	Oct. 25, 1932	Matthias Leenders, Teyl, Netherlands.	Jackson & Perkins Co., Newark, N. Y.	COMTESSE VANDAL
39	Brambleberry	Oct. 25, 1932	Percy W. Meredith, Oregon City, Ore.		
40	Thornless Barberry	Nov. 8, 1932	William Gordon Sutherland, Boulder, Colo.	Stark Bros. Nurseries & Orchards Co., Louisiana, Mo.	THORNLESS BARBERRY
41	Cherry	Nov. 8, 1932	Elizabeth Waters Burbank, Executrix of the Estate of Luther Burbank, Deceased, Santa Rosa, Calif.	Stark Bros. Nurseries & Orchards Co., Louisiana, Mo.	BURBANKS LATE HEART-HONEY
42	Grape	Nov. 8, 1932	Herman J. B. Wiederkehr, Altus, Ark.	Stark Bros. Nurseries & Orchards Co., Louisiana, Mo.	EARLY GIANT
43	Freesia	Nov. 8, 1932	Edward A. Manda, East Orange, N. J.		JOAN MANDA
44	Freesia	Nov. 22, 1932	Gerald Hew Dalrymple, Bartley, near Southampton, England.	C. J. Van Bourgondien, Babylon, N. Y.	TANGERINE
45	Variety of Rose	Nov. 29, 1932	Emile J. LeDuc, Danville, Pa.		EMILE J. LEDUC
46	Strawberry	Nov. 29, 1932	Ernest W. Townsend, Hannah E. Cordrey, Charles M. Freeman, For Eastern Shore Trust Co., Administrators of the Estate of Oliver C. Cordrey, Deceased, Salisbury, Md.	Ernest W. Townsend, Salisbury, Md.	
47	Pecan	Nov. 29, 1932	William H. Brake, Rocky Mount, N. C.		
48	Plant or Rosebush	Dec. 6, 1932	George B. Hart, Brighton, N. Y.		
49	Hybrid Tea Rose	Dec. 20, 1932	Nicholas Grillo, Milldale, Conn.		AMERICAN PRIDE
50	Hybrid Tea Rose	Dec. 20, 1932	James Didato, Middlesex, N. J.		WATCHUNG
51	Peach	Dec. 20, 1932	William F. Ramsey, Okanogan, Wash.; Andrew T. Gossman, Wenatchee, Wash.	Columbia & Okanogan Nursery Co., Wenatchee, Wash.	CANDOKA
52	Rose	Jan. 10, 1933	John A. Mason, Burlingame, Calif.		VIVID MASON
53	Colored Seedless Grape Fruit	Jan. 24, 1933	Albert E. Henninger, McAllen, Texas.		RUBYRED
54	Evergreen Plant (Juniper)	Jan. 31, 1933	Willis Russell Gray, Oakton, Va.		
55	Water Lily	Feb. 28, 1933	George Harry Pring, St. Louis, Mo.	The Missouri Botanical Garden, St. Louis, Mo.	ST. LOUIS
56	Carnation	Mar. 14, 1933	Adolphe F. J. Baur, Indianapolis, Ind.	Baur-Steinkamp & Co., Inc., Indianapolis, Ind.	LIGHT PINK ABUNDANCE
57	Apple Tree	Mar. 21, 1933	John H. Dickey, Wenatchee, Wash.	Stark Bros. Nurseries & Orchards Co., Louisiana, Mo.	SCARLET STAYMARED
58	Chrysanthemum	Mar. 21, 1933	Alexander Cumming, Jr., Bristol, Conn.	Bristol Nurseries, Inc., Bristol, Conn.	MERCURY
59	Hybrid Tea Rose	Apr. 4, 1933	Albert J. Amling and Ernest C. Amling, Orange, Calif.	Amling Brothers, Santa Ana, Calif.	RED TALISMAN
60	Strawberry	Apr. 18, 1933	Carl E. Schuster, Corvallis, Ore.		CORVALLIS

No.	For	Patent Granted	Inventor	Assigned to	Introduction Name
61	Apple	Apr. 18, 1933	Edwin P. Wray, White Salmon, Wash.		
62	Rose	May 2, 1933	Marguerite Denoyel, Venissieux near Lyon, France.	Jackson & Perkins Co., Newark, N. Y.	GOVERNOR A. E. SMITH
63	Rose	May 2, 1933	Louis Reymond, Villeurbanne, France.	Jackson & Perkins Co., Newark, N. Y.	AMELIA EARHART
64	Chrysanthemum	May 2, 1933	James Wheeler and Francis L. Wheeler, Natick, Mass.; Francis Lionel Wheeler, Executor of said James Wheeler, Deceased.		ALADDIN
65	Rose	May 16, 1933	Elizabeth Waters Burbank, Executrix of the Estate of Luther Burbank, Deceased, Santa Rosa, Calif.	Stark Bros. Nurseries & Orchards Co., Louisiana, Mo.	BURBANKS APPLE BLOSSOM
66	Rose	May 16, 1933	"	"	BURBANKS GOLDEN SUNSET
67	Hybrid Tea Rose	June 20, 1933	Fred H. Howard, Montebello, Calif.	Minnie Jones Howard, Montebello, Calif.	MRS. J. D. EISELE
68	Snap Dragon	June 20, 1933	Cecil C. Chamberlin, Chagrin Falls, Ohio.		
69	Carnation	June 20, 1933	Russell Engle, Kokomo, Ind.	Thomas L. Knipe, Kokomo, Ind.	OPAL
70	Rose	July 18, 1933	Richard Diener, Oxnard, Calif.		DIENER'S ROSE UNDERSTOCK
71	Strawberry Plant	July 25, 1933	Everett C. Howard, Belchertown, Mass.		HOWARD'S SUPREME
72	Pink Rose	July 25, 1933	Frank Schramm, Crystal Lake, Ill.		MRS. FRANK SCHRAMM
73	Pecan Tree	July 25, 1933	James A. Simpson, Uvalde, Texas.	Humble Oil & Refining Co., Houston, Texas.	HUMBLE
74	Apricot	Sept. 26, 1933	Harry Yount, Douglas Co.; Andrew T. Gossman, Wenatchee, Wash.	Andrew T. Gossman, Wenatchee, Wash.	RILAND
75	Single Chrysanthemum .	Sept. 26, 1933	Ryohitsu Shibuya, Menlo Park, Calif.		
76	Single Chrysanthemum .	Sept. 26, 1933	"		
77	Gladiolus	Oct. 3, 1933	Carl Salbach, Berkeley, Calif.		GOLDEN GODDESS
78	Rose	Oct. 3, 1933	Vinzenz Berger, Chomutov (Komotau), Czechoslovakia.	Paul J. Howard, Los Angeles, Calif.	HEIDEKIND
79	Rose	Nov. 7, 1933	Christoph Weigand, Soden, Germany.	Paul J. Howard, Los Angeles, Calif.	SYMPHONY
80	Yellow Rose	Nov. 7, 1933	Frank H. Traendly, Brooklyn, N. Y.	Traendly & Schenck's Rowayton Greenhouses, Inc., Rowayton, Conn.	MRS. FRANKLIN D. ROOSEVELT
81	Plant (Peach)	Nov. 14, 1933	Vincent G. Lucas, Ontario, Calif.	Lucas Ranching Co., Cucamonga, Calif.	LUCAS BEAUTY
82	Thornless Logan Blackberry	Nov. 14, 1933	Beulah E. Bauer and Gordon R. Bauer, San Gabriel, Calif.		BAUER'S THORNLESS LOGANBERRY
83	Viola	Nov. 28, 1933	Stuart R. Weston, Marcy, N. Y.		CORNUTA YORK GEM
84	Peach	Nov. 28, 1933	William F. Yerkes, near Rio Oso, Calif.		RIO OSO GEM
85	Apple Tree	Jan. 16, 1934	William Uecker, Cashmere, Wash.	Stark Bros. Nurseries & Orchards Co., Louisiana, Mo.	JONARED
86	Peach	Feb. 6, 1934	Oliver P. Blackburn, East Bakersfield, Calif.		
87	Rose	Mar. 13, 1934	Max Krause, Hasloh in Holstein, Germany.	The Conard-Pyle Co., West Grove, Pa.	NIGRETTE
88	Seedless Grape	Mar. 13, 1934	Leon O. Bonnet, Berkeley, Calif.		
89	Pendulous Juniperus scopulorum	Mar. 13, 1934	Carl Burton Fox, Tulsa, Okla.	¼ to Geo. X Frey, Santa Fe, N. Mex.	WEEPING SCOPULORUM JUNIPER; Juniperus scopulorum pendula.
90	Apple	Apr. 3, 1934	Harry I. Shotwell, Wenatchee, Wash.	Columbia & Okanogan Nursery Co., Wenatchee, Wash.	SHOTWELL DELICIOUS APPLE
91	Red Rose	Apr. 3, 1934	Frank Spanbauer, Medina, N. Y.		CARMELITA
92	Nectarine	Apr. 3, 1934	Maurice A. Blake, New Brunswick, N. J.	New Jersey State Agricultural Exp. Sta., New Brunswick, N. J.	GARDEN STATE
93	Gardenia Plant	Apr. 17, 1934	Walter E. Lenk, Belmont, Mass.		BELMONT
94	Cherry	Apr. 17, 1934	Menno Gerber, Orville, Ohio.		
95	Hybrid Tea Rose	Apr. 24, 1934	Robt. J. Montgomery, Executor of the Estate of Alexander Montgomery, Deceased, Amherst, Mass.	The Montgomery Co., Inc., Hadley, Mass.	TOKEN
96	Rose Plant	May 15, 1934	Josephine D. Brownell, Little Compton, R. I.		GOLDEN ORANGE CLIMBER
97	Rose	May 15, 1934	Warwick G. Bate, Newton Falls, Ohio.		RADIANT BEAUTY

No.	For	Patent Granted	Inventor	Assigned to	Introduction Name
98	Freesia	May 22, 1934	William Pitt Morgan, Marion County, Ind.	Elder & Elder Nurseries, Indianapolis, Ind.	Miss Blanche Blue
99	Hybrid Barberry	June 26, 1934	Elmer H. Schultz and Michael Henry Horvath, Mentor, Ohio.	Wayside Gardens Co., Mentor, Ohio.	Mentorensis
100	Avocado	Aug. 7, 1934	Jennie C. Gano, Whittier, Calif.		Gano
101	Strawberry	Aug. 7, 1934	Edwin P. Wray, White Salmon, Wash.		
102	Rose	Sept. 18, 1934	Pedro Dot, San Feliu de Llobregat, near Barcelona, Spain.	The Conard-Pyle Co., West Grove, Pa.	Luis Brinas
103	Rose	Sept. 18, 1934	Charles Mallerin, Varces, France.	The Conard-Pyle Co., West Grove, Pa.	Feu Pernet-Ducher
104	Rose	Oct. 16, 1934	Wilhelm John Hinrich Kordes, Sparrieshoop, Germany.	Henry A. Dreer, Inc., Philadelphia, Pa.	Glowing Sunset
105	Rose Variety	Oct. 16, 1934	"	"	Crimson Glory
106	Variety of Rose	Oct. 16, 1934	Gerrit de Ruyter, Hazerswonde, Netherlands.	Jackson & Perkins Co., Newark, N. Y.	Prinses Van Orange
107	Variety of Rose	Oct. 16, 1934	Matthias Leenders, Teyl, Netherlands.	Jackson & Perkins Co., Newark, N. Y.	Permanent Wave
108	Rose	Oct. 16, 1934	Victor Lens, Wavre, Notre Dame, Belgium.	Jackson & Perkins Co., Newark, N. Y.	White Briarcliff
109	Rose	Oct. 23, 1934	Jean H. Nicolas, Newark, N. Y.	Jackson & Perkins Co., Newark, N. Y.	Yosemite
110	Barberry	Oct. 23, 1934	Michael H. Horvath, Mentor, Ohio.	The Cole Nursery Co., Painesville, Ohio.	Truehedge Columnberry; Berberis Thunbergi Erecta
111	Plum	Nov. 13, 1934	Jennie Benedict Thompson, Pasadena, Calif.	Armstrong Nurseries, Inc., Ontario, Calif,	Mariposa Plum
112	Strawberry	Nov. 20, 1934	Geo. D. Aiken, Putney, Vt.		
113	Raspberry Variety . . .	Nov. 20, 1934	Asaph B. Curtis, Sarona, Wis.		
114	Rose	Dec. 4, 1934	Walter Easlea, Leigh-on-Sea, England.	Chas. H. Totty, Madison, N. J.	Easlea's Golden Rambler
115	Hybrid Tea Rose	Dec. 11, 1934	Jason G. Layton, Olean, N. Y.		Lady Layton
116	Rose	Dec. 11, 1934	Lorenzo Pahissa, San Feliu de Llobregat, Spain.	Jackson & Perkins Co., Newark, N. Y.	Alezane
117	Rose	Jan. 15, 1935	Walter M. Elmer, San Jose, Calif.	Andrew J. Elmer, San Jose, Calif.	Rio Rita
118	Phlox	Jan. 15, 1935	John J. Grullemans, Painesville, Ohio.	The Wayside Gardens Co., Mentor, Ohio.	Columbia
119	Mango	Jan. 15, 1935	Edwards G. Wilkinson, Naples, Fla.		Fragrance
120	Peach Tree	Jan. 15, 1935	Donald S. Byers, Clyde, Ohio.		Hardee
121	Rose	Feb. 19, 1935	Ruth Kaucher, Newtown, Pa.		Good Morning
122	Variety of Rose	Feb. 19, 1935	Josephine Moorhead, Thomas Gardner, Geo. C. Thomas, 3d, Executors of the Estate of Geo. C. Thomas, Jr., Deceased, Beverly Hills, Calif.	Armstrong Nurseries, Ontario, Calif.	Mrs. Dudley Fulton
123	Pansy	Feb. 26, 1935	Stanley B. Fillow and Joseph H. Sniffen, Westport, Conn.		
124	Orange Tree	Mar. 5, 1935	Pearl C. Mohn, Anaheim, Calif.		
125	Apple	May 28, 1935	Edgar W. Hartman, Cashtown, Pa.	¼ to Buntings Nurseries, Selbyville, Del. ¼ to Waynesboro Nurseries, Waynesboro, Va. ¼ to Harrisons Nurseries, Berlin, Md.	Red Yorking
126	Orange Tree	May 28, 1935	Roy Robertson, Redlands, Calif.	Armstrong Nurseries, Ontario, Calif.	Robertson Navel Orange
127	Carnation Variety . . .	June 4, 1935	Richard C. Witterstaetter, Executor of the Last Will and Testament of Richard Witterstaetter, Deceased, Cincinnati, Ohio.	R. Witterstaetter, Carnation Co., Partnership of Edw. C. Deller, Wm. H. Deller, and Edw. A. Witterstaetter, Cincinnati, Ohio.	
128	Freesia (Red)	July 30, 1935	Alois Frey, San Fernando, Calif.		
129	Rose	July 30, 1935	Chas. C. Mallerin, Varces, France.	The Conard-Pyle Co., West Grove, Pa.	Mme. Cochet-Cochet
130	Rose	Aug. 13, 1935	Abner Marshall Lowman, Elmira, N. Y.	United States Cut Flower Co., Elmira, N. Y.	Grand Canary
131	Rose	Aug. 13, 1935	Jean H. Nicolas, Newark, N. Y.	Jackson & Perkins Co., Newark, N. Y.	Rochester
132	Rose	Aug. 13, 1935	"	"	Polar Bear
133	Carnation	Aug. 13, 1935	Adolphe Frederick Jacob Baur, Indianapolis, Ind.	Baur-Steinkamp & Co., Inc., Indianapolis, Ind.	Pink Kokomo (undisseminated)
134	Rose	Aug. 20, 1935	Thomas James Wolfe, Waco, Texas.		Forward March
135	Rose	Aug. 20, 1935	"		Texas Gold
136	Rose	Aug. 20, 1935	Jean H. Nicolas, Newark, N. Y.	Jackson & Perkins Co., Newark, N. Y.	Carillon
137	Rose	Aug. 20, 1935	"	"	Gloaming

No.	For	Patent Granted	Inventor	Assigned to	Introduction Name
138	Rose	Aug. 27, 1935	Matthias Leenders, Steyl-Tegelen, Netherlands.	Jackson & Perkins Co., Newark, N. Y.	Rheingold
139	Avocado	Aug. 27, 1935	Rudolph G. Hass, La Habra Heights, Calif.		Hass
140	Rose	Sept. 17, 1935	Olive R. Fitzhardinge, Warrawee, New South Wales, Australia.	The Conard-Pyle Co., West Grove, Pa.	Warrawee
141	Nasturtium	Sept. 17, 1935	David Burpee, Bucks Co., Pa.	W. Atlee Burpee Co., Philadelphia, Pa.	Burpees Double and Super-double Mixed
142	Sport of Citrus Fruit . . (Citrus hybrid)	Oct. 1, 1935	James M. Ater, Chula Vista, Calif.		
143	Agrostis Stolonifera . . .	Oct. 1, 1935	Earle M. Barrows, Minneapolis, Minn.		
144	Hybrid Tea Rose	Oct. 29, 1935	Martin C. Amling, Pana, Ill.	Amling Rose Co., Pana, Ill.	Happy Days
145	Azalea, single	Nov. 5, 1935	Lambertus Christian Bobbink, East Rutherford, N. J.		Caroline Graham; Cherokee Ruby; Constance; Fairy Flame; Jewel; Mary Corcoran; Mrs. W. R. Coe; Mrs. Karl Stefan; Natalie Mai Coe; Planting Fields; Snow Bank.
146	Azalea, semi-double or hose-in-hose	Nov. 5, 1935	"		Dorothy Gish; Firelight; F. L. Atkins; Glory; Indian Chief; L. C. Bobbink; Mother of Pearl; Mrs. Mildred Pepper; Pink Beauty; Pink Lady; Pink Ruffles; Pocahontas; Ruby Dust; Salmon Glow; Salmon Perfection; Sunset; Yuletide.
147	Azalea, double	Nov. 5, 1935	"		Alaska; Albion; Crimson Glory; Delight; Mrs. A. W. Muller; Orange King; Purity; Rhapsody; Rose Queen; Snow Queen.
148	Carnation, scarlet . . .	Nov. 19, 1935	Adolphe Frederick Jacob Baur, Indianapolis, Ind.	Baur-Steinkamp & Co., Inc., Indianapolis, Ind.	King Cardinal
149	Rose	Nov. 26, 1935	Frederick Huber Howard, Montebello, Calif.	Henry A. Dreer, Inc., Philadelphia, Pa.	Little Beauty
150	Rose	Nov. 26, 1935	Richard Theodore Muller, Amherst, Mass.	The Montgomery Co., Inc., Hadley, Mass.	Chieftain
151	Rose	Nov. 26, 1935	Clair Dana Tanner, Holland, N. Y.		
152	Rose	Dec. 3, 1935	Michael H. Horvath, Mentor, Ohio.	Jackson & Perkins Co., Newark, N. Y.	Doubloons
153	Rose	Dec. 3, 1935	Jean H. Nicolas, Newark, N. Y.	Jackson & Perkins Co., Newark, N. Y.	Kismet
154	Rose	Dec. 3, 1935	Roy L. Byrum, Richmond, Ind.	Joseph H. Hill Co., Richmond, Ind.	Justine
155	Rose	Dec. 3, 1935	"	"	Captain Glisson
156	Rose	Dec. 3, 1935	"	"	Lestra Hibberd
157	Rose	Dec. 3, 1935	Robt. Lee Catron, Richmond, Ind.	Joseph H. Hill Co., Richmond, Ind.	Peerless
158	Rose	Dec. 3, 1935	Frederick Huber Howard, Montebello, Calif.	Henry A. Dreer, Inc., Philadelphia, Pa.	Carrie Jacobs Bond
159	Rose	Dec. 10, 1935	Verne Stone Hillock, near Arlington, Texas.		Black Knight
160	Rose	Dec. 10, 1935	Jean H. Nicolas, Newark, N. Y.	Dixie Rose Nursery, Tyler, Texas.	Stratford
161	Peach Variety	Dec. 17, 1935	Edw. Champneys, Arvin, Calif.	Earl Fruit Co., San Francisco, Calif.	
162	Rose	Jan. 21, 1936	Archibald Flint Watkins, Tyler, Texas.	Dixie Rose Nursery, Tyler, Texas.	Texas Centennial
163	Rose	Jan. 21, 1936	"	½ to Dixie Rose Nursery, Tyler, Texas. ½ to Jackson & Perkins Co., Newark, N. Y.	Dixie Climber
164	Cherry Variety	Jan. 21, 1936	Menno Gerber, Orrville, Ohio.		
165	Regal Lily	Feb. 18, 1936	Chester N. Moore, Schenectady, N. Y.	General Electric Co., New York, N. Y.	Roentgen Regal Lily
166	Peach	Feb. 18, 1936	Wm. C. Elliott, Modesto, Calif.		Elliott Special
167	Rose	Feb. 25, 1936	Wm. Spandikow, Jr., Maywood, Ill.	Wm. Spandikow & Sons, Maywood, Ill.	Doris
168	Apple Tree	Mar. 10, 1936	Lloyd Balderston, 3d, Colora, Md.	Bountiful Ridge Nurseries, Princess Anne, Md.	Colora Red York
169	Rose	Mar. 17, 1936	John de Vink, Boskoop, Netherlands.	The Conard-Pyle Co., West Grove, Pa.	Tom Thumb
170	Rose	Apr. 7, 1936	Gerard Adriaan vanRossem, Naarden, Netherlands.	Jackson & Perkins Co., Newark, N. Y.	Matador
171	Rose	Apr. 7, 1936	Jean H. Nicolas, Newark, N. Y.	Jackson & Perkins Co., Newark, N. Y.	Rocket
172	Rose	Apr. 7, 1936	"	"	Eclipse

No.	For	Patent Granted	Inventor	Assigned to	Introduction Name
173	Nectarine	Apr. 7, 1936	Frederic W. Anderson, Merced, Calif.		
174	Rose	Apr. 14, 1936	Pedro Dot, St. Feliu de Llobregat, Spain.	The Conard-Pyle Co., West Grove, Pa.	ANGELS MATEU
175	Peach Tree	Apr. 28, 1936	Lawrence Bellinie Le Duke, Lawrence, Mich.	Greening Nursery Co., Monroe, Mich.	FERTILE HALE
176	Poinsettia	Apr. 28, 1936	Stephen M. Page, Port Arthur, Texas.		
177	Rose	May 12, 1936	Frank Eugene Cremer, Hanover, Pa.		WILLIAM F. EKAS
178	Rose	June 2, 1936	Rena Eveline Wilber, Seattle, Wash.		RUTH ALEXANDER
179	Rose	June 9, 1936	Edw. Richard Asmus, Sr., Closter, N. J.		MANHATTAN
180	Rose	June 9, 1936	Walter L. Armacost, Los Angeles, Calif.	Armacost & Royston, Inc., Los Angeles, Calif.	LUCKY STAR
181	Rose	June 9, 1936	Wm. B. Murray, Atco, N. J.		MUR-RAY
182	Rose	June 9, 1936	Svend Poulsen, Copenhagen, Denmark.	Jackson & Perkins Co., Newark, N. Y.	ANNE POULSEN
183	Rose	June 16, 1936	Robt. H. Kistler, Houston, Texas.		GRAND PRIZE
184	Pomegranate	June 16, 1936	Erich C. Trauernicht, Ft. Worth, Texas.	Baker Bros. Co., Ft. Worth, Texas.	
185	Rose	June 23, 1936	Verne Stone Hillock, Arlington, Texas.		NELLIE E. HILLOCK
186	Peach	June 23, 1936	Chas. Edw. Sullivan, Yuba City, Calif.		SULLIVAN CLING
187	Rose	June 23, 1936	Wm. Spandikow, Jr., Maywood, Ill.		
188	Ornamental Cherry Tree	June 23, 1936	Neville Mitchell Smith, York, Pa.		WASHINGTON MEMORIAL CHERRY
189	Barberry Plant	Aug. 4, 1936	Carlton E. Huber, Groesbeck, Ohio.		GLOBE BARBERRY; Berberis Thunbergi globosa.
190	Rose	Aug. 25, 1936	Walter Irwin Johnston, Portadown, Ireland.	Jackson & Perkins Co., Newark, N. Y.	McGREDY'S TRIUMPH
191	Rose	Sept. 8, 1936	Chas. Mallerin, Varces, France.	The Conard-Pyle Co., West Grove, Pa.	ROCHEFORT
192	Rose Bush	Sept. 15, 1936	Joseph Wm. Cook, Baltimore, Md.	The John Cook Co., Inc., Baltimore, Md.	YOUTH
193	Carnation	Sept. 15, 1936	Shirley Hemmings, Abington, Mass.	Littlefield-Wyman Nurseries, North Abington, Mass.	ORCHID BEAUTY
194	Rose	Sept. 15, 1936	Verne Stone Hillock, Arlington, Texas.		IRELAND HAMPTON
195	Grapevine	Sept. 15, 1936	Tice C. Kevitt, Pompton Lakes, N. J.	Meyer Aronowitz, or the Barclay Nursery Co., New York, N. Y.	
196	Freesia	Sept. 29, 1936	Alois Frey, San Fernando, Calif.		
197	Rose	Sept. 29, 1936	Pedro Dot, St. Feliu de Llobregat, Spain.	The Conard-Pyle Co., West Grove, Pa.	RADIO
198	Carnation	Sept. 29, 1936	Adolphe Frederick Jacob Baur, Indianapolis, Ind.	Baur-Steinkamp & Co., Inc., Indianapolis, Ind.	ROSE CHARM
199	Rose	Sept. 29, 1936	Richard Theodore Muller, Darien, Conn.	The Montgomery Co., Inc., Hadley, Mass.	SIGNET
200	Rose	Oct. 13, 1936	Josephine D. Brownell, Little Compton, R. I.		APRICOT GLOW
201	Rose	Oct. 13, 1936	Domenico Aicardi, San Remo, Italy.	Jackson & Perkins Co., Newark, N. Y.	SIGNORA
202	Rose	Oct. 13, 1936	Charles Mallerin, Varces, France.	Jackson & Perkins Co., Newark, N. Y.	ALICE HARDING
203	Sugar Cane	Oct. 27, 1936	Benj. Arthur Bourne, Clewiston, Fla.		F.31–962
204	White Chrysanthemum	Nov. 17, 1936	Clarence C. Mayhew, Sherman, Texas.	Texas Nursery Co., Sherman, Texas.	"AZALEAMUM-MAGIC WHITE"
205	Bronze Chrysanthemum	Nov. 17, 1936	"	"	BRONZE BEAUTY
206	Buddleia	Nov. 17, 1936	Paul Schmidt, Youngstown, Ohio.		
207	Hybrid Poplar	Nov. 17, 1936	Ralph H. McKee, New York, N. Y.		
208	Rose	Nov. 24, 1936	Jesse F. Hiscox, East Patchogue, N. Y.		GOOD LUCK
209	Rose	Dec. 8, 1936	Geo. E. Lukens, North Wales, Pa.	The Florex Gardens, North Wales, Pa.	SUN GLOW
210	Sugarcane	Dec. 29, 1936	Benj. Arthur Bourne, Clewiston, Fla.		F.30–35
211	Hybrid Poplar	Jan. 5, 1937	Ralph H. McKee, New York, N. Y.		
212	Hybrid Poplar	Jan. 5, 1937	"		
213	Hybrid Poplar	Jan. 5, 1937	"		
214	Hybrid Poplar	Jan. 5, 1937	"		
215	Hybrid Poplar	Jan. 5, 1937	"		
216	Hybrid Poplar	Jan. 5, 1937	"		
217	Hybrid Poplar	Jan. 5, 1937	"		
218	Hybrid Poplar	Jan. 5, 1937	"		
219	Carnation	Jan. 12, 1937	Adolphe Frederick Jacob Baur, Indianapolis, Ind.	Baur-Steinkamp & Co., Inc., Indianapolis, Ind.	PINK TREASURE

No.	For	Patent Granted	Inventor	Assigned to	Introduction Name
220	Sugar Cane	Jan. 19, 1937	Benj. Arthur Bourne, Clewiston, Fla.		F.31–436
221	Lobelia	Jan. 19, 1937	Esther C. Johnson, La Mesa, Calif.	The Johnson Nursery, La Mesa, Calif.	La Mesa
222	Rose	Jan. 19, 1937	Kellar Carbaugh, Lower Yoder Township, Cambria Co., Pa.	Johnstown Greenhouses, Inc., Johnstown, Pa.	Mahaja
223	Rose	Jan. 19, 1937	Alexander Dickson, Jr., Newtownards, near Belfast, Ireland.	Henry A. Dreer, Inc., Philadelphia, Pa.	Dicksons Centennial
224	Camellia	Jan. 19, 1937	Edward A. McIlhenny, Avery Island, La.		Purple Dawn
225	Hybrid Poplar	Jan. 19, 1937	Ralph H. McKee, New York, N. Y.	McKee Poplar Forestation, Inc., New York, N. Y.	
226	Hybrid Poplar	Jan. 19, 1937	"	"	
227	Gladiolus	Jan. 26, 1937	Anna L. Miller, Nashport, Ohio.		Incense
228	Hybrid Poplar	Jan. 26, 1937	Ralph H. McKee, New York, N. Y.	McKee Poplar Forestation, Inc., New York, N. Y.	
229	Hybrid Poplar	Jan. 26, 1937	"	"	
230	Hybrid Poplar	Jan. 26, 1937	"	"	
231	Camellia	Feb. 2, 1937	Edward A. McIlhenny, Avery Island, La.		Leila
232	Peach Tree	Feb. 2, 1937	Jay Perry, Benton Co., near Kennewick, Wash.	Columbia & Okanogan Nursery Co., Wenatchee, Wash.	Redelberta
233	Peach	Feb. 9, 1937	Carl Howard Fisher, Queenston, Ontario, Can.		Howard Fisher Peach
234	Avocado	Feb. 9, 1937	Chas. C. Henry, Escondido, Calif.	½ to Jesse L. Jones, Escondido, Calif.	Henrys Select
235	Rose	Feb. 16, 1937	Elizabeth Waters Burbank, Executrix of the Estate of Luther Burbank, Deceased, Santa Rosa, Calif.	Stark Bros. Nurseries & Orchards Co., Louisiana, Mo.	Burbanks Golden Comet
236	Rose	Mar. 9, 1937	Patsy A. Izzo, Glen Head, N. Y.		Thornless Glory
237	Freesia	Mar. 9, 1937	Edward J. Schroeder, Perry Hall, Md.	½ to Roman J. Irwin, New York, N. Y.	Schroeder's White Perfection
238	Apple	Mar. 16, 1937	Valentine Moore, Visalia, Calif.		
239	Carnation	Mar. 23, 1937	John C. Rasmussen, New Albany, Ind.	Louis Alfred Kintzele, Denver, Colo.	Dictator
240	Rose	Mar. 30, 1937	Carl F. Bertanzel, Jr., Roslyn, N. Y., Harry W. Moore, Mineola, N. Y., Executors, Estate of Carl F. Bertanzel, Sr., Deceased, Roslyn, N. Y.	Carl F. Bertanzel, Jr., Roslyn, N. Y.	Yellow Gloria
241	Rose	Apr. 6, 1937	Edward Richard Asmus, Sr., Closter, N. J.		Lovely Lady
242	Poinsettia	Apr. 6, 1937	Paul Ecke, Encinitas, Calif.		Ruth Ecke
243	Rose	Apr. 13, 1937	John A. Armstrong, Ontario, Calif.	Armstrong Nurseries, Ontario, Calif.	Cl. Golden Dawn
244	Rose	Apr. 13, 1937	"	"	Cl. Hinrich Gaede
245	Rose	Apr. 20, 1937	Warwick G. Bate, Newton Falls, Ohio.		
246	Rose	Apr. 20, 1937	Frank C. Raffel, Stockton, Calif.		Maid of Gold
247	Berry (Loganberry)	Apr. 20, 1937	Hallack F. Greider, Vashon, Wash.		Olympic
248	Rose	June 1, 1937	Josephine D. Brownell, Little Compton, R. I.		Stargold
249	Rose	June 8, 1937	Hendrikus Antonie Verschuren, near Uden, Netherlands.	Henry A. Dreer, Inc., Philadelphia, Pa.	R.M.S. Queen Mary
250	Lily of the Valley Plant	June 8, 1937	Sidney C. Baston, Eggertsville, N. Y.		
251	Chrysanthemum	June 15, 1937	Robt. C. Murphey, Urbana, Ohio.	R. H. Murpheys Sons Co., Urbana, Ohio.	Golden Glorymum
252	Phlox	June 22, 1937	Elmer H. Schultz, Mentor, Ohio.	The Wayside Gardens Co., Mentor, Ohio.	Augusta
253	Rose	June 29, 1937	Jean H. Nicolas, Newark, N. Y.	Jackson & Perkins Co., Newark, N. Y.	Mrs. Francis King
254	Rose	July 6, 1937	Wilhelm Kordes, Sparrieshoop, Germany.	Jackson & Perkins Co., Newark, N. Y.	Golden Main
255	Gladiolus	July 6, 1937	Elizabeth A. Briggs, Encinitas, Calif.		Briggs Lavender
256	Rose	July 13, 1937	Frederick Huber Howard, Montebello, Calif.		Will Rogers
257	Hybrid Perpetual Rose	July 20, 1937	Martin R. Jacobus, Ridgefield, N. J.		Oratam
258	Apple Tree	July 20, 1937	Paul L. Lingamfelter, Hedgesville, W. Va.	Stark Bros. Nurseries & Orchards Co., Louisiana, Mo.	York-a-red
259	Rose	Aug. 3, 1937	John Square, Lake County, Ohio.		John Square

No.	For	Patent Granted	Inventor	Assigned to	Introduction Name
260	Carnation	Aug. 3, 1937	Chas. Augustus Schaefer, York, Pa.		York Beauty
261	Avocado	Aug. 24, 1937	Jos. R. Byrum, Homestead, Fla.	Redland Avocado Grove, Homestead, Fla.	Monroe
262	Peach	Sept. 14, 1937	Wm. Leon Plantz, near Marysville, Calif.		
263	Rose	Oct. 5, 1937	Josephine D. Brownell, Little Compton, R. I.		Golden Glow
264	Rose	Nov. 23, 1937	Jean H. Nicolas, Newark, N. Y.	Jackson & Perkins Co., Newark, N. Y.	Miss America
265	Begonia	Dec. 28, 1937	Rocco Zeparo, Arlington, Mass.		Zeparo Begonia; Salmon Beauty
266	Rose	Jan. 4, 1938	Elizabeth Waters Burbank, Executrix of the Estate of Luther Burbank, Deceased, Santa Rosa, Calif.	Stark Bros. Nurseries & Orchards Co., Louisiana, Mo.	Burbanks Copper Climber
267	Rose	Jan. 4, 1938	"	"	Burbanks Snowhite Climber
268	Rose	Jan. 18, 1938	Frederick Huber Howard, Montebello, Calif.		Springtime
269	Rose	Feb. 1, 1938	Elizabeth Waters Burbank, Executrix of the Estate of Luther Burbank, Deceased, Santa Rosa, Calif.	Stark Bros. Nurseries & Orchards Co., Louisiana, Mo.	Burbanks Dawnglow
270	Rose	Feb. 1, 1938	Gerrit de Ruyter, Hazerswonde, Netherlands.	Jackson & Perkins Co., Newark, N. Y.	Gloire du Midi
271	Peach Tree	Feb. 15, 1938	Marsh Harpole, Mount Vernon, Ill.	Stark Bros. Nurseries & Orchards Co., Louisiana, Mo.	Hardy-berta
272	Rose	Apr. 12, 1938	Harold B. Brookins, Orchard Park, N. Y.	Jerry Brookins, Inc., Orchard Park, N. Y.	Quaker Beauty
273	Carnation	Apr. 19, 1938	Adolphe Frederick Jacob Baur, Indianapolis, Ind.	Baur-Steinkamp & Co., Inc., Indianapolis, Ind.	Royal Purple
274	Carnation	Apr. 19, 1938	"	"	Yellow Gold
275	Carnation	Apr. 19, 1938	Russell Engle, Kokomo, Ind.	Tom Knipe, Kokomo, Ind.	Remembrance
276	Hydrangea	Apr. 19, 1938	John H. Kluis, Boskoop, Netherlands.	Joseph S. Merritt, Dundalk, Md.	Helen Merritt
277	White Rose	Apr. 26, 1938	Fred C. Stielow, Niles Center, Ill.		White Finch
278	Apple Tree	May 17, 1938	Thomas Elwood Graham, Kent Co., Mich.	Greening Nursery Co., Monroe, Mich.	
279	Rose	May 17, 1938	Jean H. Nicolas, Newark, N. Y.	Jackson & Perkins, Co., Newark, N. Y.	Snowbank
280	Gladiolus	June 21, 1938	Carl Salbach, Contra Costa Co., Calif.	Ella S. Salbach, Contra Costa Co., Calif.	Grand Opera
281	Snapdragon	June 21, 1938	Louis A. Michler, Lexington, Ky.	Michler Florist, Inc., Lexington, Ky.	
282	Rose	Aug. 16, 1938	Edward Towill, Roslyn, Pa.		Gilda
283	Peach Tree	Aug. 23, 1938	Robt. Walter Fair, Tyler, Texas.		
284	Rose Plant	Aug. 23, 1938	Jean Gaujard, Feyzin, France.	Jackson & Perkins Co., Newark, N. Y.	Ronsard
285	Rose	Aug. 23, 1938	Jean H. Nicolas, Newark, N. Y.	Jackson & Perkins Co., Newark, N. Y.	Bernice
286	Rose	Aug. 30, 1938	Harry Hofmann, Jacksonville, Ill.		Emeline Rouge
287	Rose	Aug 30, 1938	Michael H. Horvath, Mentor, Ohio.		Federation
288	Rose	Aug. 30, 1938	"		Scarlano
289	Rose Plant	Aug. 30, 1938	James N. Meadowcroft, Kennett Square, Pa.	J. H. Thompsons Sons, Kennett Square, Pa.	Mohican
290	Peach Tree	Sept. 6, 1938	Elizabeth Waters Burbank, Executrix of the Estate of Luther Burbank, Deceased, Santa Rosa, Calif.	Stark Bros. Nurseries & Orchards Co., Louisiana, Mo.	Burbanks Orchid
291	Peach Tree	Sept. 6, 1938	"	"	Burbanks Santa Rosa
292	Rose	Sept. 20, 1938	Fred C. Stielow, Niles Center, Ill.		Red Finch
293	Apple Tree	Oct. 4, 1938	Thomas Elwood Graham, Kent Co., Mich.	Greening Nursery Co., Monroe, Mich.	Graham
294	Water Lily	Oct. 11, 1938	Martin E. Randig, San Bernardino, Calif.		Mrs. Martin E. Randig
295	Rose	Oct. 18, 1938	Ivar Ringdahl, Rome, N. Y.		Romana
296	Rose	Oct. 25, 1938	Michael H. Horvath, Mentor, Ohio.		Hercules
297	Rose	Oct. 25, 1938	"		Mabelle Stearns
298	Rose	Oct. 25, 1938	"		Pink Profusion
299	Rose	Oct. 25, 1938	"		Sonia
300	Rose Plant	Nov. 1, 1938	Mathias Tantau, Utersen, Germany.	The Conard-Pyle Co., West Grove, Pa.	Topaz
301	Rose	Nov. 1, 1938	Eugene R. Dramm, Elmhurst, Ill.	Dramm Greenhouse, Inc. Elmhurst, Ill.	Dream
302	Snapdragon	Nov. 1, 1938	Chester Harper Lothrop, Lexington, Mass.		Lothrops Double Pink
303	Rose	Nov. 8, 1938	Francis Meilland, Tassin-les-Lyon, France.	The Conard-Pyle Co., West Grove, Pa.	Golden State

No.	For	Patent Granted	Inventor	Assigned to	Introduction Name
304	Rose	Nov. 8, 1938	Domenico Aicardi, San Remo, Italy.	Jackson & Perkins Co., Newark, N. Y.	Rome Glory
305	Rose	Nov. 28, 1938	Ray L. Byrum, Richmond, Ind.	Joseph H. Hill Co., Richmond, Ind.	Lucile Hill
306	Peach Tree	Nov. 29, 1938	Leon Maillochon and Ernest Marlaud, Argenton sur Creuse (Indre), France.	Stark Bros. Nurseries & Orchards Co., Louisiana, Mo.	Tom Thumb Dwarf Peach
307	Poinsettia	Jan. 10, 1939	Knud Christensen, Wood-Ridge, N. J.	Madsen & Christensen, Inc., Wood-Ridge, N. J.	Christmas Star
308	Snapdragon	Jan. 17, 1939	John Oder, Denver, Colo.	The Denver Wholesale Florists Co., Denver, Colo.	Helene Lang
309	Pear Tree	Jan. 17, 1939	Rudolf N. Ruedlinger, St. Louis Park, Minn.	Ruedlinger Nursery, St. Louis Park, Minn.	
310	Chrysanthemum	Jan. 17, 1939	Robt. C. Murphey, Urbana, Ohio.	R. H. Murpheys Sons Co., Urbana, Ohio.	Achievement
311	Grape	Jan. 17, 1939	Vahan Mkhalian, Visalia, Calif.		Empress of Grapes
312	Rose	Jan. 24, 1939	Roy L. Byrum, Richmond, Ind.	Jos. H. Hill Co., Richmond, Ind.	Yellow Dot
313	Chrysanthemum	Feb. 14, 1939	Edw. Christopher Geiger, North Wales, Pa.	Wm. A. Geiger & Sons, Inc., North Wales, Pa.	White Beauty
314	Rose	Feb. 21, 1939	Frederick Huber Howard, Montebello, Calif.		Pres. Boone
315	Daphne	Feb. 28, 1939	Arthur Burkwood, Farnham, England.	The Wayside Gardens Co., Mentor, Ohio.	Somerset
316	Cherry	Feb. 28, 1939	Lewis Benj. Reber, Royalton Township, Berrien Co., Mich.	The Greening Nursery Co., Monroe, Mich.	Richmorency
317	Rose	Mar. 7, 1939	Walter Irwin Johnston, Portadown, Ireland.	Jackson & Perkins Co., Newark, N. Y.	McGredy's Sunset
318	Kniphofia or Tritoma . .	Mar. 14, 1939	John James Grullemans, Mentor, Ohio.	The Wayside Gardens Co., Mentor, Ohio.	Springtime
319	Carnation	Mar. 21, 1939	Adolphe Frederick Jacob Baur, Indianapolis, Ind.	Baur-Steinkamp & Co., Inc., Indianapolis, Ind.	Rosalie
320	Peach Tree	Mar. 28, 1939	Willie Marsden Perry, Chase City, Va.	Bountiful Ridge Nurseries, Princess Anne, Md.	Erly-red-fre
321	Rose	Mar. 28, 1939	Jean Gaujard, Feyzin, France.	Jackson & Perkins Co., Newark, N. Y.	Jean Cote
322	Dahlia	Mar. 28, 1939	Roy Yoshikata Kimura, Los Angeles, Calif.		
323	Rose	Apr. 4, 1939	Edw. Richard Asmus, Sr., Closter, N. J.		Red Better Times
324	Delphinium	Apr. 4, 1939	Bonne Ruys, Dedemsvaart, Netherlands.	Jackson & Perkins Co., Newark, N. Y.	Pink Sensation
325	Peach Tree	Apr. 4, 1939	John Ugene Nametz, Benton Harbor, Mich.	Greening Nursery Co., Monroe, Mich.	Early Halehaven
326	Rose	Apr. 18, 1939	Verne Stone Hillock, Arlington, Texas.		Dolly Madison
327	Apple	Apr. 18, 1939	James W. Savely, near Hendersonville, Tenn.		Almeda
328	Nectarine	Apr. 25, 1939	Geo. Edw. Alexander, Venice, Calif.	Karl K. Snyder, Hughson, and A. D. DiGrazia, San Francisco, Calif.	
329	Phlox	Apr. 25, 1939	John J. Grullemans, Mentor, Ohio.	Wayside Gardens Co., Mentor, Ohio.	Atlanta
330	Rose	June 13, 1939	Karel Riesselmann, North Wales, Pa.	The Florex Gardens, North Wales, Pa.	Stardust
331	Rose Plant	June 20, 1939	Fannie Nicolas, Adm. of Estate of Jean H. Nicolas, Deceased, Newark, N. Y.	Jackson & Perkins Co., Newark, N. Y.	Smiles
332	Rose Plant	June 20, 1939	Domenico Aicardi, San Remo, Italy.	Jackson & Perkins Co., Newark, N. Y.	Eternal Youth
333	Rose	June 27, 1939	Joseph Proietti, San Leandro, Calif.		California Beauty
334	Rose, Hybrid Tea . . .	July 4, 1939	Nicholas Grillo, Milldale, Conn.		Sunnymount
335	Rose Plant	July 18, 1939	Walter Irwin Johnston, Portadown, Ireland.	Jackson & Perkins Co., Newark, N. Y.	Rex Anderson
336	Poinsettia	Aug. 8, 1939	Paul Ecke, Encinitas, Calif.		Variegated Ruth Ecke
337	Rose Plant	Aug. 8, 1939	Chas. Mallerin, Varces, France.	The Conard-Pyle Co., West Grove, Pa.	Mme. Henri Guillot
338	Rose Plant	Sept. 19, 1939	Jean Gaujard, Feyzin, France.	Jackson & Perkins Co., Newark, N. Y.	Mme. Jean Gaujard
339	Rose Plant	Sept. 19, 1939	Walter Irwin Johnston, Portadown, Ireland.	Jáckson & Perkins Co., Newark, N. Y.	McGredy's Pride
340	Rose Plant	Sept. 19, 1939	Basil E. Prior, Colchester, England.	Jackson & Perkins Co., Newark, N. Y.	Betty Prior
341	Rose Plant	Sept. 26, 1939	Walter Irwin Johnston, Portadown, Ireland.	Jackson & Perkins Co., Newark, N. Y.	McGredy's Pink
342	Lemon Tree	Oct. 10, 1939	Sanford Johnson, Riverside, Calif.		Armstrong Seedless Lemon
343	Poinsettia	Oct. 10, 1939	Paul Ecke, Encinitas, Calif.		Cathyrn Reed

No.	For	Patent Granted	Inventor	Assigned to	Introduction Name
344	Carnation	Oct. 24, 1939	John Cadwalader Rasmussen, New Albany, Ind.		CHARM
345	Strawberry	Oct. 24, 1939	Evan L. Russell, Jonesville, Va.		MAJESTIC
346	Pyracantha Koidzumii (variety)	Nov. 14, 1939	Edmy Bourdieu, Ventura, Calif.		PYRACANTHA DUVALI
347	Orange Tree	Nov. 21, 1939	John Albert Workman, Riverside, Calif.	Armstrong Nurseries, Ontario, Calif.	WORKMAN NAVEL ORANGE
348	Rose	Nov. 28, 1939	Roy L. Byrum, Richmond, Ind.	Jos. H. Hill Co., Richmond, Ind.	SNOW WHITE
349	Rose Plant	Dec. 12, 1939	Domenico Aicardi, San Remo, Italy.	Jackson & Perkins Co., Newark, N. Y.	SATURNIA
350	Rose	Dec. 19, 1939	Hendrikus Antonie Verschuren, Haps, near Uden, Netherlands.	Henry A. Dreer, Inc., Philadelphia, Pa.	ORANGE NASSAU
351	Peach Tree	Dec. 26, 1939	Vine Carson Campbell, Yakima Co., Wash.	Walter Dibble Plough, Wenatchee, Wash.	
352	Red Chrysanthemum Plant	Jan. 9, 1940	Clarence C. Mayhew, Sherman, Texas.	Texas Nursery Co., Sherman, Texas.	SUNRAY
353	Rose	Jan. 16, 1940	Ivar Ringdahl, Rome, N. Y.		ESKIL
354	Rose	Jan. 16, 1940	Harold Fetzer Yoker, Barberton, Ohio.	Yoder Bros., Barberton, Ohio.	SUNTAN
355	Geranium	Jan. 23, 1940	Chas. A. Brown II, Hinsdale, Ill.	Hinsdale Cemetery Co., Hinsdale, Ill.	FIAT QUEEN
356	Gladiolus	Jan. 30, 1940	Carl Salbach, Contra Costa Co., Calif.	Ella S. Salbach, Contra Costa Co., Calif.	SIR GALAHAD
357	Gladiolus	Jan. 30, 1940	"	"	HELEN OF TROY
358	Gladiolus	Jan. 30, 1940	"	"	JUNE BRIDE
359	Gladiolus	Jan. 30, 1940	"	"	CALIFORNIA
360	Gladiolus	Jan. 30, 1940	"	"	KING OF HEARTS
361	Rose Plant	Feb. 13, 1940	Walter Irwin Johnston, Portadown, Ireland.	Jackson & Perkins Co., Newark, N. Y.	HECTOR DEANE
362	Rose Plant	Feb. 13, 1940	Wilhelm Kordes, Sparrieshoop in Holstein, Germany.	Jackson & Perkins Co., Newark, N. Y.	WORLD'S FAIR
363	Rose Plant	Feb. 13, 1940	"	"	ZULU QUEEN
364	Gardenia Plant	Feb. 27, 1940	Thomas H. Wright, Los Angeles, Calif.		HOLLYWOOD
365	Papaver or Poppy	Mar. 5, 1940	Lulu M. Rector, Clarksburg, W. Va.	Wayside Gardens Co., Mentor, Ohio.	SNOWFLAME
366	Rose Plant	Mar. 5, 1940	Pedro Dot, Barcelona, Spain.	The Conard-Pyle Co., West Grove, Pa.	RAMON BACH
367	Rose	Mar. 5, 1940	Nicholas Grillo, Milldale, Conn.		THORNLESS BEAUTY
368	Yellow Chrysanthemum Plant	Mar. 5, 1940	Clarence C. Mayhew, Sherman, Texas.	The Texas Nursery Co., Sherman, Texas.	GOLDEN WONDER
369	Rose Plant	Mar. 12, 1940	John S. Elliott, Dover, N. Y.		
370	Rose Plant	Mar. 12, 1940	"		
371	Delphinium	Mar. 26, 1940	Max Reuter, Blue Point, N. Y.		EXQUISITE BLUE POINT
372	Carnation	Apr. 2, 1940	Russell Engle, Kokomo, Ind.	Tom Knipe, Kokomo, Ind.	SETH PARKER
373	Rose Plant	Apr. 9, 1940	Frank H. Witter, Evans City, Pa.	Evans City Cut Flower Co., Evans City, Pa.	REVELATION
374	Rose Plant	Apr. 16, 1940	Fannie Nicolas, Adm. of the Estate of Jean H. Nicolas, Deceased, Newark, N. Y.	Jackson & Perkins Co., Newark, N. Y.	FLAMBEAU
375	Rose Plant	Apr. 16, 1940	"	"	JUNE MORN
376	Rose Plant	Apr. 16, 1940	Alexander Dickson, Jr., Newtownards, Belfast, Ireland.	Jackson & Perkins Co., Newark, N. Y.	DICKSONS RED
377	Rose Plant	Apr. 16, 1940	Basil Edmund Prior, Colchester, England.	Jackson & Perkins Co., Newark, N. Y.	DONALD PRIOR
378	Rose Plant	Apr. 16, 1940	Pedro Dot, Barcelona, Spain.	Jackson & Perkins Co., Newark, N. Y.	RIVIERA
379	Rose Plant	Apr. 16, 1940	Lorenzo Pahissa, San Feliu de Llobregat, Spain.	Jackson & Perkins Co., Newark, N. Y.	SATAN
380	Pear Tree	Apr. 23, 1940	Victor A. Silvera, near Milpitas, Calif.		
381	Rose Plant	Apr. 30, 1940	Gerrit de Ruiter, Hazerswoude, Dorp, Netherlands.	Jackson & Perkins Co., Newark, N. Y.	JOYOUS
382	Rose Plant	Apr. 30, 1940	Nicholas Grillo, Milldale, Conn.		JEWEL
383	Rose	Apr. 30, 1940	Clarence Alda Chase, Lane County, Ore.		ROYAL CHINOOK
384	Double Gypsophila	Apr. 30, 1940	Geo. H. Starr, Turlock, Calif.		STARRI
385	Rose	May 7, 1940	Michael H. Horvath, Mentor, Ohio.		MERCURIUS
386	Rose	May 7, 1940	"		POLARIS
387	Rose	May 7, 1940	"		THOR
388	Apple Tree	May 7, 1940	J. Ralph McIlvaine, Vernon M. Barnett, Adm. of Estate of Wrixhem M. McIlvaine, Deceased, Magnolia, Del.	Bountiful Ridge Nurseries, Princess Anne, Md.	WRIXPARENT

No.	For	Patent Granted	Inventor	Assigned to	Introduction Name
389	Rose	May 7, 1940	Chas. B. Hansen, Ontario, Calif.		FIESTA
390	Chrysanthemum Plant	May 7, 1940	John Franklin Styer, Concordville, Pa.		SIEGFRIED
391	Chrysanthemum Plant	May 7, 1940	"		RHEINGOLD
392	Chrysanthemum Plant	May 7, 1940	"		BRUNNHILDE
393	Rose	May 7, 1940	Geo. C. Thomas, 3rd, Josephine Moorhead Thomas Gardner, Ex. of Estate of Geo. C. Thomas, Jr., Deceased, Beverly Hills, Calif.	Armstrong Nurseries, Ontario, Calif.	CAPTAIN THOMAS
394	Rose Plant	May 7, 1940	Theodore J. Morris, Van Nuys, Calif.	Western Rose Co., San Fernando, Calif.	MRS. SAM MCGREDY
395	Rose Plant	May 14, 1940	Wilhelm Kordes, Sparrieshoop in Holstein, Germany.	Jackson & Perkins Co., Newark, N. Y.	HOLSTEIN
396	Rose Plant	May 14, 1940	Robt. Marion Hatton, Harrisburg, Pa.	The Conard-Pyle Co., West Grove, Pa.	FLASH
397	Violet	May 14, 1940	Julia Isabelle Dearborn, Corvallis, Ore.		
398	Carnation	May 14, 1940	Minoru Okada, San Lorenzo, Calif.		PINK BEAUTY
399	Red Carnation	May 14, 1940	"		RED GLORY
400	Rose Plant	May 14, 1940	Alphonse Couteau, Orleans, France.	Jackson & Perkins Co., Newark, N. Y.	CLIMBING SUMMER SNOW
401	Chrysanthemum	June 4, 1940	Itaro Nakata and Daniel Nakata, Tracy, Calif.		GOLDEN TREASURE
402	Rose	June 18, 1940	Martin Samtmann, Wyndmoor, Pa.		CAVALIER
403	Rose Plant	June 18, 1940	Fremont Bernard Abrams, Ossining, N. Y.		SPLENDOR
404	Gladiolus	June 18, 1940	Elizabeth A. Briggs, Encinitas, Calif.	Chas. E. Ogg, Encinitas, Calif.	RUTH GODFREY
405	Rose Plant	June 25, 1940	Lyman B. Coddington, Murray Hill, N. J.	L. B. Coddington Co., Murray Hill, N. J.	MURRAY HILL
406	Begonia	June 25, 1940	Harold E. Traver, Woodbury, Conn.		LUCILLE
407	Rose Plant	July 2, 1940	Pedro Dot, San Feliu de Llobregat, Spain.	The Conard-Pyle Co., West Grove, Pa.	BABY GOLD STAR
408	Rose Plant	July 2, 1940	John de Vink, Boskoop, Netherlands.	The Conard-Pyle Co., West Grove, Pa.	PIXIE
409	Rose Plant	July 2, 1940	Charles Mallerin, Varces, Par Pont de Claix, France.	The Conard-Pyle Co., West Grove, Pa.	MME. CHARLES MALLERIN
410	Rose Plant	July 9, 1940	Walter Irwin Johnston, Portadown, Ireland.	Jackson & Perkins Co., Newark, N. Y.	MCGREDY'S SALMON
411	Rose Plant	July 9, 1940	"	"	PATRICK ANDERSON
412	Tobacco Plant	July 16, 1940	Joseph Rosenberg, Hartford, Conn.	The Rosenberg-Coulter Co., Hartford, Conn.	
413	Plum Tree	July 23, 1940	Carmine Maglio, Nelson, British Columbia, Canada.		MAGLIO PLUM
414	Rose Plant	July 23, 1940	Jean H. Nicolas, Deceased, Fannie Nicolas Adm. of the Estate, Newark, N. Y.	Jackson & Perkins Co., Newark, N. Y.	STARLITE
415	Hydrangea	Aug. 6, 1940	John H. Kluis, Boskoop, Netherlands.	Joseph S. Merritt, Dundalk, Md.	VIRGINIA MERRITT
416	Rose Plant	Aug. 13, 1940	Chas. H. Perkins, Newark, N. Y.	Jackson & Perkins Co., Newark, N. Y.	SUMMER SNOW
417	Rose	Aug. 13, 1940	Nicholas Grillo, Milldale, Conn.		REGINA ELENA
418	Peach Tree	Aug. 27, 1940	Geo. P. Sunday, Baroda, Mich.	The Greening Nursery Co., Monroe, Mich.	
419	Rose	Sept. 10, 1940	Josephine D. Brownell, Little Compton, R. I.		FREDERICK S. PECK
420	Rose	Sept. 10, 1940	"		LILY PONS
421	Cherry Tree	Sept. 17, 1940	Horace B. Faber, John A. C. Ziegler, Jr., York, Pa.	White Rose Seed & Nursery Co., York, Pa.	YORK IMPERIAL
422	Silver-Blue Juniperus	Sept. 17, 1940	Roger W. Haygood, Keithville, La.	Texas Nursery Co., Sherman, Texas.	
423	Rose Plant	Sept. 17, 1940	Wilhelm Kordes, Sparrieshoop in Holstein, Germany.	Jackson & Perkins Co., Newark, N. Y.	PEARL S. BUCK
424	Geranium Plant	Sept. 17, 1940	Felix L. Sturm, Shinnston, W. Va.		
425	Rose Plant	Sept. 17, 1940	Gerard Adriaan van Rossem, Naarden, Netherlands.	Jackson & Perkins Co., Newark, N. Y.	ROSE BAMPTON
426	Rose	Oct. 1, 1940	Francis Meilland, Tassin-les-Lyon, France.	The Conard-Pyle Co., West Grove, Pa.	GOOD NEWS
427	Rose Plant	Oct. 8, 1940	Lyman B. Coddington, Murray Hill, N. J.	L. B. Coddington Co., Murray Hill, N. J.	M. S. HERSHEY
428	Rose Plant	Oct. 15, 1940	Victor Lens, Wavre Notre Dame, Belgium.	Jackson & Perkins Co., Newark, N. Y.	NEVILLE CHAMBERLAIN
429	Ivy Plant	Oct. 15, 1940	Sylvan Hahn, Pittsburgh, Pa.		MAPLE QUEEN
430	Ivy Plant	Oct. 15, 1940	"		SYLVANIAN
431	Camellia	Nov. 19, 1940	Kosaku Sawada, Crichton, Ala.	Overlook Nurseries, Crichton, Ala.	K. SAWADA

No.	For	Patent Granted	Inventor	Assigned to	Introduction Name
432	Rhododendron Plant	Nov. 19, 1940	Otto Kausen, Eureka, Calif.	Cottage Gardens Co., Inc., Eureka, Calif.	Eureka Maid
433	Avocado Tree	Nov. 26, 1940	James H. Macpherson, Encinitas, Calif.	½ to Mildred Macpherson	
434	Carnation	Dec. 3, 1940	Adolphe Frederick Jacob Baur, Indianapolis, Ind.	Baur-Steinkamp & Co., Inc., Indianapolis, Ind.	
435	Pear Tree	Dec. 17, 1940	Joseph T. Guraly, Jr., Fairport Harbor, Ohio.		Guraly Jr.
436	Lily	Dec. 24, 1940	Clarence E. Downing, Sunfield, Mich.		
437	Rose Plant	Jan. 14, 1941	Eugene S. Boerner, Newark, N. Y.	Jackson & Perkins Co., Newark, N. Y.	
438	Hybrid Tea Rose Plant	Jan. 14, 1941	Elisha Allan Peirce, Waltham, Mass.	Peirce Bros., Waltham, Mass.	Fair Maid
439	Hybrid Tea Rose Plant	Jan. 14, 1941	Herbert C. Swim, Ontario, Calif.	Armstrong Nurseries, Ontario, Calif.	Climbing Night
440	Fuchsia	Jan. 14, 1941	George C. Lodge, Painesville, Ohio.	The Cole Nursery Co., Painesville, Ohio.	Scarlet Beauty
441	Hybrid Tea Rose Plant	Jan. 21, 1941	Edith C. Bosley, Mentor, Ohio.		Mrs. Paul R. Bosley
442	Flowering Dogwood Tree	Jan. 21, 1941	Hiram H. Owens, Barbourville, Ky.	Stark Bros. Nurseries & Orchards Co., Louisiana, Mo.	
443	Rose Plant	Jan. 28, 1941	Niels J. Hansen, Washington, D. C.	Bobbink & Atkins, East Rutherford, N. J.	Chevy Chase
444	Lime Tree	Jan. 28, 1941	George L. Polk, Homestead, Fla.		
445	Rose Plant	Feb. 4, 1941	Jac Verschuren, near Uden, Netherlands.	John Parmentier, Bayport, N. Y.	Aviator Parmentier
446	Rose Plant	Feb. 11, 1941	Svend Poulsen, Copenhagen, Denmark.	The Conard-Pyle Co., West Grove, Pa.	Poulsen's Copper
447	Rose Plant	Feb. 11, 1941	Frederick Huber Howard, Montebello, Calif.		Major Shelley
448	Rose Plant	Feb. 11, 1941	"		Indian Summer
449	Rose Plant	Feb. 11, 1941	"		California
450	Rose Plant	Feb. 11, 1941	"		Mrs. Paul J. Howard
451	Mango	Feb. 18, 1941	Michael Fascell, Miami, Fla.		
452	Rose Plant	Feb. 25, 1941	Lyman B. Coddington, Murray Hill, N. J.	L. B. Coddington Co., Murray Hill, N. J.	Royal Beauty
453	Rose Plant	Feb. 25, 1941	Jean Gaujard, Feyzin, France.	Jackson & Perkins Co., Newark, N. Y.	Adoration
454	Rose Plant	Feb. 25, 1941	Walter E. Lammerts, Ontario, Calif.	Armstrong Nurseries, Ontario, Calif.	Boutonniere
455	Rose Plant	Feb. 25, 1941	"	"	Charlotte Armstrong
456	Rose Plant	Feb. 25, 1941	"	"	The Chief
457	Rose Plant	Feb. 25, 1941	Jean H. Nicolas, Deceased, Fannie Nicolas, Adm. of the Estate, Newark, N.Y.	Jackson & Perkins Co., Newark, N. Y.	Dr. J. H. Nicolas
458	Rose	Mar. 4, 1941	Josephine D. Brownell, Little Compton, R. I.		
459	Rose	Mar. 4, 1941	"		
460	Barberry Plant	Mar. 4, 1941	Bonne Ruys, Dedemsvaart, Netherlands.	E. D. Smith & Sons, Ltd., Winona, Ontario, Canada.	Pink Princess
461	Rose Plant	Mar. 18, 1941	Walter Irwin Johnston, Portadown, Ireland.	Jackson & Perkins Co., Newark, N. Y.	Lady Mandeville
462	Hybrid Tea Rose	Apr. 22, 1941	Adolph E. Gude, Rockville, Md.	A. Gude Sons Co., Inc., Washington, D. C.	
463	Carnation Plant	Apr. 29, 1941	Philip J. Goebel, Des Peres, Mo.		
464	Rose Plant	Apr. 29, 1941	Frederick Huber Howard, Montebello, Calif.		Apricot Queen
465	Shasta Daisy	Apr. 29, 1941	Horace Postle Read, Brundall, near Norwich, England.	The Conard-Pyle Co., West Grove, Pa.	Horace P. Read
466	Rose Plant	May 20, 1941	John de Vink, Boskoop, Netherlands.	The Conard-Pyle Co., West Grove, Pa.	Midget
467	Rose	May 27, 1941	Charles L. Fitzgerald, Hawthorne, Calif.		
468	Rose	May 27, 1941	"		
469	Rose	May 27, 1941	"		
470	Sansevieria	June 3, 1941	William Walter Smith, Jr., New Orleans, La.	Sylvan Hahn, Pittsburgh, Pa.	
471	Clematis	June 3, 1941	Edwin Beckett, Red Bank, N. J.		
472	Clematis	June 3, 1941	"		
473	Peach Tree	June 3, 1941	Benjamin Harrison Haley, Lakeside, Calif.	Armstrong Nurseries, Ontario, Calif.	
474	Apple	June 10, 1941	Ingermar Emil Soderlund, Excelsior, Minn.		
475	Rose Plant	June 24, 1941	Wilhelm Kordes, Holstein, Germany.	Jackson & Perkins Co., Newark, N. Y.	A. Grille
476	Apricot	June 24, 1941	Carl Weschcke, St. Paul, Minn.		
477	Seedless Pineapple Orange	June 24, 1941	Robert Lee Ragin, Shiloh, Fla.	Clapp & Clapp, Orlando, Fla.	

PATERSO'NIA . . . AUSTRALIANFLAG
glau'ca . . . . BLUE A.
umbro'sa . . . . DELL A.

PATRIN'IA . . . . PATRINIA
palma'ta
scabiosaefo'lia . . . . DAHURIAN P.
sibir'ica . . . . SIBERIAN P.

PAULLIN'IA . . . . PAULLINIA
cupa'na . . . . GUARANA P.
erian'tha . . . WOOLLYFLOWER P.
fusces'cens . . . . RUSTY P.
thalictrifo'lia . . . . MEADOWRUE P.
turbacen'sis

PAULOW'NIA . . . . . . PAULOWNIA
corea'na . . . . KOREAN P.
far'gesi . . . . FARGES P.
fortun'ei . . . . FORTUNES P.
tomento'sa (*imperialis*) . . ROYAL P.
—lana'ta . . . . . . WOOLLY R.P.
—pal'lida . . . . PALE R.P.

PAURO'TIS (*ACANTHOSABAL; ACOELORRAPHE* in part) PAUROTIS
See **PALM GENERA.**

PA'VIA . . . . **AESCULUS**
macrosta'chya . . . . . **A. parviflora**
ru'bra . . . . **A. pavia**

PAVO'NIA (*MALACHE*) . . PAVONIA
hasta'ta (*Malache h.*) . SPEARLEAF P.
lasiopet'ala (*Malache l.*) . WRIGHTS P.
multiflo'ra
praemor'sa
se'pium (*flava*)
spi'nifex . . . . BARBFRUIT P.

PAWPAW . . . . **Asimina**
BIGFLOWER P. . . . . . **A. obovata**
COMMON P. . . . . **A. triloba**
RUGEL P. . . . . **A. rugeli**
SEMINOLETEA P. . . . . **A. reticulata**
SLIMLEAF P. . . . . . **A. angustifolia**
SLIMPETAL P. . . . . . . **A. pulchella**
SMALLFLOWER P. . . . . **A. parviflora**
SPRAWLING P. . . . . . . **A. pygmaea**
ST. LUCIE P. . . . . . . **A. tetramera**
WOOLLY P. . . . . **A. incana**

PAYE'NA . . . . PAYENA
leer'i . . . . GUTTAPERCHA P.

PEA . . . . **Pisum**
BABY GARDEN P. . **P. sativum humile**
BOUQUET G. P. . . . **P. s. umbellatum**
FIELD P. . . . . **P. s. arvense**
GARDEN P. . . . . **P. sativum**
JOMARD P. . . . . **P. jomardi**
MEDITERRANEAN P. . . . . **P. elatius**
Red-and-Yellow P.
DEERVETCH, WRIGHT: **Lotus wrighti**
SUGARPOD GARDEN P.
P. sativum macrocarpon

PEABUSH . . . . **Brachysema**
LANCELEAF P. . . . . **B. lanceolatum**

PEACH . . . . **Prunus; P. persica**
See also ALMOND, APRICOT, BIRDCHERRY, BUSHCHERRY, CHERRY, CHOKECHERRY, LAURELCHERRY, PEACHBRUSH, and PLUM. For cultivated varieties see **FRUIT AND EDIBLE NUT NAMES.**

∞ ALMOND P. . ∞ **P. amygdalo-persica**
CLINGSTONE P. **P. persica scleropersica**
DAVID P. . . . . **P. davidiana**

PEACH, continued
FLAT P. . . **Prunus persica compressa**
FREESTONE P. . . **P. p. aganopersica**
GOBI P. . . . . **P. pilosa**
KANSU P. . . . . **P. kansuensis**
MONGOL P. . . . . . . **P. mongolica**
NECTARINE . . . **P. persica nectarina**
RED DAVID P. . . **P. davidiana rubra**
SHINYLEAF D. P. . . . **P. d. potanini**
SILVER P. . . . . **P. argentea**
SMOOTHPIT P. . . . . **P. mira**
WHITE DAVID P. . **P. davidiana alba**

PEACHBRUSH
See also ALMOND, APRICOT, BIRDCHERRY, BUSHCHERRY, CHERRY, CHOKECHERRY, LAURELCHERRY, PEACH, and PLUM.

ANDERSON P. . . . **Prunus andersoni**
DESERT P. . . . . . . **P. fasciculata**
FREMONT P. . . . . **P. fremonti**
SMALLFLOWER P. . . . **P. minutiflora**
TEXAS P. . . . . **P. texana**
THORNY P. . . . . **P. spinosissima**

PEACHMYRTLE . . . . . **Hypocalymma**
SWANRIVER P. . . . . . **H. robustum**

PEACHPALM . . . . **Guilielma gasipaes**

PEANUT . . . . . . **Arachis; A. hypogaea**

PEANUTCACTUS . **Chamaecereus silvestri**

PEAR . . . . **Pyrus**
ALMOND P. . . . **P. amygdaliformis**
BIRCHLEAF P. . . . . **P. betulaefolia**
BRETSCHNEIDER P. . **P. bretschneideri**
CALLERY P. . . . . . . **P. calleryana**
COMMON P. . . . . . . **P. communis**
DUSKY P. . . . . . . **P. phaeocarpa**
EVERGREEN P. . . . . . . **P. kawakami**
GLOBE DUSKY P. **P. phaeocarpa globosa**
HONDO P. . . **P. ussuriensis hondoensis**
KOREAN CALLERY P.
P. calleryana fauriei
∞ LECONTE P. . . . . . . ∞ **P. lecontei**
∞ MICHAUX P. . . . . . ∞ **P. michauxi**
OLEASTER P. . . . . **P. elaeagrifolia**
OVOID USSURIAN P.
P. ussuriensis ovoidea
PASHI P. . . . . **P. pashia**
SAND P. . . . . **P. pyrifolia**
SNOW P. . . . . **P. nivalis**
USSURIAN P. . . . . . . **P. ussuriensis**
WILLOWLEAF P. . . . . . . **P. salicifolia**
WOOLLYTWIG CALLERY P.
P. calleryana tomentella

PEARLBERRY . . . . **Chiogenes**
CREEPING P. . . . . **C. hispidula**

PEARLBLOOMTREE . . . . . **Poliothyrsis**
CHINESE P. . . . . **P. sinensis**

PEARLBUSH . . . . **Exochorda**
COMMON P. . . . . **E. racemosa**
REDBUD P. . . . . **E. giraldi**
TURKESTAN P. . . . . . **E. korolkowi**
WILSON REDBUD P. . **E. giraldi wilsoni**

PEARLEVERLASTING . . . . . **Anaphalis**
COMMON P. . . . . . **A. margaritacea**
SUBALPINE C. P. . . . **A. m. subalpina**
WESTERN C. P. . . **A. m. occidentalis**

PEARLFRUIT . . **Margyricarpus setosus**

PEARLMILLET . . **Pennisetum glaucum**

PEARLWORT . . . . **Sagina**
ARCTIC P. . . . . **S. saginoides**
CORSICAN P. . . . . **S. subulata**

PEARLWORT, continued
KNOTTED P. . . . . . **Sagina nodosa**
PROCUMBENT P. . . . **S. procumbens**
SMOOTH P. . . . . **S. glabra**
TRAILING P. . . . . . **S. decumbens**

PEASHRUB . . . . **Caragana**
AFGHANISTAN P. . . . **C. decorticans**
BIGFLOWER RUSSIAN P.
C. frutex macrantha
BOIS P. . . . . **C. boisi**
BROADLEAF RUSSIAN P.
C. frutex latifolia
CAUCASIAN P. . . . . **C. grandiflora**
CHINESE P. . . . . **C. sinica**
DWARF P. . . . . **C. aurantiaca**
FRANCHET P. . . . . **C. franchetiana**
GERARD P. . . . . . . **C. gerardiana**
HIMALAYA P. . . . . . . **C. sukiensis**
LITTLELEAF P. . . . . **C. microphylla**
MAXIMOWICZ P. . **C. maximowicziana**
PEKING P. . . . . . . **C. pekinensis**
PYGMY P. . . . . **C. pygmaea**
RUSSIAN P. . . . . **C. frutex**
SHAGSPINE P. . . . . **C. jubata**
SHORTLEAF P. . . . . . . **C. brevifolia**
SHORTSPINE P. . . . . . **C. brevispina**
SHOWY LITTLELEAF P.
C. microphylla megalantha
SHRUBBY P. . . . . . . **C. fruticosa**
SIBERIAN P. . . . . . **C. arborescens**
SILKYLEAF P. . . . . . . **C. oreophila**
SOPHORALEAF P. . ×**C. sophoraefolia**
SPINY P. . . . . **C. spinosa**
THIBET P. . . . . **C. tibetica**
THICKSTEM P. . . . . **C. crassicaulis**

PEAVINE . . . . **Lathyrus**
ARIZONA P. . . . . . . **L. arizonicus**
ASPEN P. . . . . **L. leucanthus**
BEACH P. . . . . **L. littoralis**
BITTER P. . . . . **L. vernus**
BLACK P. . . . . **L. niger**
BLUE BITTER P. . . **L. vernus cyanus**
BLUE GRASS P. . **L. sativus caeruleus**
BLUE P. . . . . **L. cyaneus**
BOLANDER P. . . . . . . **L. bolanderi**
BRISTLELEAF P. . . . . . **L. setifolius**
BUSH P. . . . . **L. eucosmus**
CANYON P. . . . . . . **L. laetiflorus**
CREAM P. . . . . . . **L. ochroleucus**
DOWNY P. . . . . **L. pubescens**
DWARF SWEETPEA **L. odoratus nanellus**
EVERLASTING P. . . . **L. grandiflorus**
FEWFLOWER P. . . . . **L. pauciflorus**
FLAT P. . . . . **L. sylvestris**
FLATPOD P. . . . . **L. cicera**
GORGON P. . . . . **L. gorgoni**
GRASSLEAF P. . . . **L. graminifolius**
GRASS P. . . . . **L. sativus**
GROUNDNUT P. . . . . . **L. tuberosus**
HOARY P. . . . . **L. incanus**
JEPSON P. . . . . **L. jepsoni**
Lord Anson P. . . . . . MAGELLAN P.
LOW P. . . . . **L. pusillus**
MAGELLAN P. . . . . **L. magellanicus**
MARITIME P. . . . . . . **L. japonicus**
MARSH P. . . . . **L. palustris**
MEADOW P. . . . . **L. pratensis**
MOUNTAIN P. . . . . . . **L. montanus**
NUTTALL P. . . . . **L. nuttalli**
PACIFIC P. . . . . . . **L. polyphyllus**
PERENNIAL P. . . . . . . **L. latifolius**
PINK P. . . . . **L. roseus**

Hort. var.; HV. = horticultural variety (or varieties); sp. = species (singular); spp. = species (plural).
₵ = clon; × (as a prefix) = hybrid; × (between scientific plant names) = crossed by; ∞ = polybrid; [w] = plant useful to wildlife.
See Glossary for definitions of clon, hybrid, and polybrid.

Peavine, continued
Pink Tangier P. **Lathyrus tingitanus roseus**
Purple P. . . . . **L. violaceus**
Rough P. . . . . **L. hirsutus**
Roundleaf P. . . . . **L. rotundifolius**
Royal P. . . . . **L. splendens**
Sandberg P. . . **L. bijugatus sandbergi**
Showy P. . . . . **L. ornatus**
Spoon P. . . . . **L. spathulatus**
Sulfur P. . . . . **L. sulphureus**
Sweetpea . . . . **L. odoratus**
Tangier P. . . . . **L. tingitanus**
Thickleaf P. . . . . . **L. lanszwerti**
Torrey P. . . . . **L. torreyi**
Utah P. . . . . **L. utahensis**
Veiny P. . . . . **L. venosus**
Wagner Flat P. **L. sylvestris wagneri**
Yellow P. . . . . **L. luteus**

Pecan . . . . **Carya illinoensis**
Bitter P. . . . . **C. texana**

Pectian'tia pentan'dra . . . . **Mitella p.**

PEC'TIS |w . . . . Pectis
fil'ipes |w . . . . . Threadstem P.

PECTOCA'RYA . . . . Combseed
linea'ris . . . . Slim C.
penicilla'ta . . . . . . Shortleaf C.

PEDICULA'RIS |w . . . . Pedicularis (*Lousewort; Woodbetony*)
arc'tica . . . . Arctic P.
attol'lens
bracteo'sa . . . . Bracted P.
canaden'sis . . . . Early P.
centran'thera . . . . Dwarf P.
chamisso'nis . . . . . . Chamisso P.
contor'ta . . . . Coiled P.
crenula'ta . . . . Meadow P.
densiflo'ra . . . . Indianwarrior P.
furbish'iae . . . . Furbish P.
gray'i . . . . Grays P.
groenlan'dica . . Elephanthead P.
japon'ica . . . . Japanese P.
labrador'ica . . . . Labrador P.
lanceola'ta |w . . . . . . Swamp P.
langsdorff'i . . . . . Langsdorff P.
lappon'ica . . . . Lapland P.
palus'tris . . . . European P.
parviflo'ra . . . . . Smallflower P.
racemo'sa . . . . Sickletop P.
sudet'ica . . . . Sudetic P.
versicol'or
verticilla'ta . . . . Whorled P.

Pedicularis . . . . **Pedicularis**
Arctic P. . . . . **P. arctica**
Bracted P. . . . . **P. bracteosa**
Chamisso P. . . . . . **P. chamissonis**
Coiled P. . . . . **P. contorta**
Dwarf P. . . . . . . **P. centranthera**
Early P. . . . . **P. canadensis**
Elephanthead P. . . **P. groenlandica**
European P. . . . . **P. palustris**
Furbish P. . . . . . . **P. furbishiae**
Grays P. . . . . **P. grayi**
Indianwarrior P. . . . . **P. densiflora**
Japanese P. . . . . **P. japonica**
Labrador P. . . . . . **P. labradorica**
Langsdorff P. . . . . . **P. langsdorffi**
Lapland P. . . . . **P. lapponica**
Meadow P. . . . . **P. crenulata**
Sickletop P. . . . . . . **P. racemosa**
Smallflower P. . . . . **P. parviflora**
Sudetic P. . . . . **P. sudetica**
Swamp P. . . . . **P. lanceolata**
Whorled P. . . . . . . **P. verticillata**

PEDILAN'THUS . . . Slipperflower
See **SUCCULENTS.**

PEDIOCAC'TUS
See **CACTUS GENERA.**

Pediome'lum esculen'tum **Psoralea esculenta**

PEG'ANUM . . . . Peganum
harma'la . . . . Harmel P.
mexica'num . . . . Mexican P.

PEIRES'KIA . . . . . **PERESKIA**
See **CACTUS GENERA.**

Pejibaye . . . . Peachpalm: **Guilielma gasipaes**

Pekeanut . . . . Sawarrinut: **Caryocar nuciferum**

Pekola . . . . **Manilkara kauki**

PELAGODOX'A
See **PALM GENERA.**

PELARGO'NIUM . . . Pelargonium

This large, essentially South-African genus is the "Geranium" of the gardens as well as of the familiar city windowbox and flowerpot. It is closely related to the true Geranium (Geranium), differing from that genus in technical characters.

In accordance with Standardized Plant Names principles, the common or vernacular name Geranium is confined to the genus Geranium and the common name Pelargonium is applied to the genus Pelargonium.

acerifo'lium . . . . . Mapleleaf P.
alchemilloi'des (*malvaefolium*) Ladiesmantle P.
angulo'sum . . . . . . Stiffleaf P.
artemisiaefo'lium . . . Wormwood P.
betuli'num . . . . Birchleaf P.
bi'color . . . . Bicolor P.
∞ **blandfordia'num** (*echinatum* × *graveolens*) . . . . . . ∞ Blandford P.
capita'tum . . . . . . Rosescent P.
× **citriodo'rum** . . . . Citrus P.
Parentage unknown.
₵Dennisianum. hv.
₵Prince of Orange
₵Vandesiae
clypea'tum . . . . . . **P. peltatum c.**
× *coccin'eum* . . . . . . ∞ **P. hybridum**
corda'tum . . . . . . Heartleaf P.
cotyle'donis . . . . . St.Helena P.
cris'pum . . . . . . Fingerbowl P.
—**latifo'lium** . . . . . . Bigleaf F.P.
cuculla'tum . . . . Hedge P.
denticula'tum . . . Skeletonleaf P.
₵Dr. Livingston. hv.
₵Majus
∞ **denticula'tum × tomento'sum**
∞ **domes'ticum** . ∞ Lady Washington P.
A variable group of cultigens apparently descended from several species.
echina'tum . . . . Spiny P.
endlicheria'num . . . . . Syrian P.
exstipula'tum . . . Pennyroyal P.
ferula'ceum (*parviflorum*) Fennelleaf P.
fissifo'lium . . . . Finger P.
∞ **fra'grans** (*exstipulatum* × *odoratissimum*) . . . . . . ∞ Fragrant P.
ful'gidum . . . . Scarlet P.
₵Old Scarlet Unique. hv.
glutino'sum . . . . Gummy P.
grandiflo'rum . . . . Bigwhite P.
₵Easter Greeting. hv.
₵Edith North
₵Gardeners Joy
₵German Glory

PELARGONIUM grandiflorum, continued
₵Lucy Becker
₵Pride of Quedlinburg
₵Prince Bismarck
₵Springtime
₵Swabian Maid
grave'olens (*roseum* Hort.) Rose Pelargonium
₵Lady Plymouth. hv.
₵Snowflake
₵Variegated
hederaefo'lium . . . . . **P. lateripes**
hirsu'tum . . . . Hoary P.
his'pidum . . . . Hairy P.
∞ **horto'rum** . . . . ∞ Fish P.
A highly variable group of cultigens, apparently derived from several species, perhaps especially P. inquinans and P. zonale.
∞ **hy'bridum** (*inquinans* × *zonale;* × *coccineum*)
in'quinans . . . . Sticky P.
∞ **jatrophaefo'lium** (*denticulatum* × *glutinosum*) . . . ∞ Nettlespurge P.
later'ipes (*hederaefolium; P. peltatum l.*) Ivyleaf P.
∞ **limo'neum** (× *odoratum* Hort.) ∞ Lemon P.
P. crispum is thought to be one of the parents of this cultigen.
malvaefo'lium . . . **P. alchemilloides**
∞ **melis'sinum** (*crispum* × *graveolens*) ∞ Balm P.
multibractea'tum . . . Longstalk P.
odoratis'simum . . . . Nutmeg P.
× *odora'tum* Hort. . . ∞ **P. limoneum**
₵Lady Mary. hv.
parviflo'rum . . . . . **P. ferulaceum**
pelta'tum . . . . Ivyvine P.
—**clypea'tum** (*P. clypeatum*) Fuzzy I.P.
—**gla'brum** . . . . . . Smooth I.P.
—*later'ipes* . . . . . . **P. lateripes**
—**scuta'tum** (*P. scutatum*) Hairycup I.P.
∞ **pinguifo'lium** (*lateripes* × *peltatum*)
quercifo'lium . . . . . . Oakleaf P.
₵Fair Ellen. hv.
₵Fringed Oak
₵Giant Oak
₵Pinnatifidum
₵Prostrate Oak
₵True Oak
quinquevul'nerum . . . Purple P.
Possibly a hybrid between P. bicolor and P. triste.
rad'ula . . . . Curlleaf P.
renifor'me . . . . Kidney P.
rose'um Hort. . . . . . **P. graveolens**
∞ **saepeflo'rens** (?*echinatum* × *reniforme*) ∞ Everblooming P.
sca'brum . . . . Rough P.
₵M. Ninon. hv.
scan'dens
scuta'tum . . . . . . **P. peltatum s.**
∞ **terebinthina'ceum** (*graveolens* × *quercifolium*) . . . . . ∞ Oakrose P.
tomento'sum . . . . . . Woolly P.
transvaalen'se . . . . Transvaal P.
tris'te . . . . Darkspot P.
—**daucifo'lium** . . Carrotleaf D.P.
—**filipendulifo'lium** Meadowsweet D.P.
—**laxa'tum** . . . Fourfeather D.P.
vitifo'lium . . . . . . Grapeleaf P.
zona'le . . . . Horseshoe P.

Common names and hort. var. (clons) of **Pelargonium:**

Abbie Schaffer
Admiral Byrd
Alice of Vincennes
Alliance
Alpha
Alphonse Ricard
America
Anastasie Lacadre
Andeken an Moskow
Anita
Anna Rudloff
Apple Blossom
Attar of Roses
Aurora
Azalea
∞ Balm P. ∞ **P. melissinum.**
Beaute Depoitevine
Beautiful
Beauty
Beckwith Pride
Bertha Priscilla
Bertha Wagner
Beverly Hills
Bicolor P. **P. bicolor.**
Bigleaf Fingerbowl P. **P. crispum latifolium.**
Bigwhite P. **P. grandiflorum.**
Birchleaf P. **P. betulinum.**
Bismarck
Black Douglass
∞ Blandford P. ∞ **P. blandfordianum.**
Blue Mabel
Bronze Beauty
Buxton
Caesar Frank
California
California Beauty
California Giant Pink
Camphor Rose
Capri
Carrotleaf Darkspot P. **P. triste daucifolium.**
Charles Turner
Chicago Market
Citrus P. ×**P. citriodorum.**
Clorinda
Col. Baden Powell
Columbus
Comtesse Degrey
Conejo
Coral Barney
Countess of Scarborough
Crabbe
Curlleaf P. **P. radula.**
Darkspot P. **P. triste.**
Delight
Dennisianum
Dieners Giant
Distinction
Double White
Dr. Livingston
Dr. Livingston, Skeleton
Earliana
Easter Greeting
Eastern Star
Edith North
Elenore (*E.*) Rober
Elkhorn
Elrey
Emile Zola
Enchantress
Ethelyn
Etincelant
∞ Everblooming P. ∞ **P. saepeflorens.**
Fair Ellen

PELARGONIUM, continued

Faiss Triumph
Fennelleaf P. **P. ferulaceum.**
Fiat
Fiat Enchantress
Fingerbowl P. **P. crispum.**
Finger P. **P. fissifolium.**
∞ Fish P. ∞ **P. hortorum.**
Flame
Fourfeather Darkspot P. **P. triste laxatum.**
Fragrantissimum
∞ Fragrant P. ∞ **P. fragrans.**
Frau Krump
Fringed Oak
Fruehlingszauber
Fuzzy Ivyvine P. **P. peltatum clypeatum.**
Gardeners Joy
Gartendirector Siebert
Gen. Grant
German Glory
Gertrude Pearson
Giant Oak
Giant Venus
Glendale
Godfreys Pride
Goleta
Gordens Glory
Graf Zeppelin
Grapeleaf P. **P. vitifolium.**
Gringorie
Grossmama Fischer
Grossularioides
Gummy P. **P. glutinosum.**
Hairycup Ivyvine P. **P. peltatum scutatum.**
Hairy P. **P. hispidum.**
Hall Caine
Happy Thought
Heartleaf P. **P. cordatum.**
Hedge P. **P. cucullatum.**
Helen Michell
Hills of Snow
Hoary P. **P. hirsutum.**
Horseshoe P. **P. zonale.**
Ida Henley
Imp. Poitevine
Improved Mme. Layal
Incomparable
Irvington Beauty
Ivyleaf P. **P. lateripes.**
Ivyvine P. **P. peltatum.**
Jacquerie
Jeanne
Jeanne d'Arc
Jean Pabon
Jean Packer
Jean Viaud
Joseph Warren
Jubilee
Karminkoenigin
Kidney P. **P. reniforme.**
Kunze
Ladiesmantle P. **P. alchemilloides.**
Lady Mary
Lady Plymouth
Lady Ruth
∞ Lady Washington P. ∞ **P. domesticum.**
Lafiesta
Lavender Quedlinburg
Lavender Queen
Lavender Ricard
Lavender Rose
∞ Lemon P. ∞ **P. limoneum.**
Leopard
Light Greenleaf Oak

PELARGONIUM, continued

Littleleaf Rose
Lois Mackay
Longstalk P. **P. multibracteatum.**
Los Angeles
Louise
Lucretia Smith
Lucy Becker
Mabel
Mackensen
Majus
Mapleleaf P. **P. acerifolium.**
Marguerite Delayre
Marie Rober
Marie Vogel
Marquis Decastellane
Marquis Demontmort
Marshall MacMahon
Martha Washington
Marvel
Mary ann
Maxine Kovaleski
Meadowsweet Darkspot P. **P. triste filipendulifolium.**
Michells Sensation
Miss Edith Cavell
Missouri
Mme. Buchner
Mme. Fournier
Mme. Jaulin
Mme. Landry
Mme. Languth. *Mrs. Languith.*
Mme. Salleroi
Mme. Tibout
M. Ninon
Modesto
Mons. Emile David
Montecito
Mountain of Snow
Mrs. Anna Brown
Mrs. Banks
Mrs. Cullum
Mrs. E. G. Hill
Mrs. F. Bachler
Mrs. Kingsley
Mrs. Lawrence
Mrs. Mary Bard
Mrs. Parker
Mrs. Pollock
Mrs. Richard Gloede
Mrs. Sanders
∞ Nettlespurge P. ∞ **P. jatrophaefolium.**
Neuheit C. Faiss
New Life
New (*Velvety*) Maroon
Nuit Poitevine
Nutmeg P. **P. odoratissimum.**
Oakleaf P. **P. quercifolium.**
∞ Oakrose P. ∞ **P. terebinthinaceum.**
Oberle
Odoratissimum
Old Scarlet Unique
Olympic
Onkel Richter
Orchid
Orchid Edith North
Otokar Samohrd
Pamela
Pasadena
Paso Robles
Paul Crampel
Pauline Schroeter
Peggy Craddock
Pennyroyal P. **P. exstipulatum.**
Pink Barney
Pink Phenomenal
Pinnatifidum

PELARGONIUM, continued
Piru
Poinsettia
Pretty Polly
Pride of Quedlinburg
Prince Bismarck
Prince of Orange
Prince Rupert
Prince Rupert, Variegated
Princess
Prostrate Oak
Purple P. **P. quinquevulnerum.**
Radio Red
Red Barney
Red Fiat
Redflowering Rose
Rollinsons Unique
Rose P. **P. graveolens.**
Rosescent P. **P. capitatum.**
Rough P. **P. scabrum.**
Roundleaf Rose
Ruby
Ruth W. McAfee
Salmon Ideal
Salmon Queen
San Diego
Sanguineum
Santa Barbara
Santa Monica
S. A. Nutt
S. A. Nutt, Variegated
Scarlet Beauty
Scarlet P. **P. fulgidum.**
Schottesham Pet
Sensation
Silverleaf
Silverleaf (*S. A.*) Nutt
Skeletonleaf P. **P. denticulatum.**
Skeletons Unique
Skies of Italy
Smooth Ivyvine P. **P. peltatum glabrum.**
Snowflake
Spiny P. **P. echinatum.**
Spring Magic Frulingzauber
Springtime
Stars and Stripes
St.Helena P. **P. cotyledonis.**
Sticky P. **P. inquinans.**
Stiffleaf P. **P. angulosum.**
Sue Jarrett
Sunset
Suzanne
Suzanne Leepre
Swabian Maid
Syrian P. **P. endlicherianum.**
The Princess
Therese
Transvaal P. **P. transvaalense.**
True Oak
Vandesiae
Variegated
Variegated Ivy
Vera N. Watt
Verna
White Madonna
Willy
Wolfgang Goethe
Woolly P. **P. tomentosum.**
Wormwood P. **P. artemisiaefolium.**
Wurtembergia
Wyona

PELECY'PHORA . **MAMMILLARIA**
See **CACTUS GENERA.**

PELLAE'A . . . . Cliffbrake
See **FERN GENERA.**

PELLIO'NIA . . . . Pellionia
daveaua'na
pul'chra

Pellitory . . . . **Parietaria**
Pennsylvania P. . . **P. pennsylvanica**
Wall P. . . . . **P. officinalis**

PELTAN'DRA |w . . . . Arrowarum
glau'ca |w . . . . Redfruit A.
virgin'ica (*undulata*) |w . Virginia A.

PELTA'RIA . . . . Shieldwort
allia'cea . . . . Onion S.

PELTIPHYL'LUM . . **SAXIFRAGA**

PELTOG'YNE . . . . Purpleheart
panicula'ta . . . . Guiana P.
porphyrocar'dia . . . . Trinidad P.

PELTOPH'ORUM (*BARYXYLUM*) Peltophorum
adna'tum . . . . Moruro P.
africa'num . . . . African P.
du'bium
iner'me (*ferrugineum; Baryxylum i.*) Sogabark P.
linnae'i (*braziletto*) . . Brazilwood P.
vogelia'num . . . . Parana P.

Pencilflower . . . . . . **Stylosanthes**
Pencilgrass . . . Itchgrass: **Rottboellia exaltata;** Jointtail: **Manisuris**

Pencilwood . . . . **Dysoxylum**
Fraser P. . . . . . . **D. fraseranum**
Showy P. . . . . . . **D. spectabile**

PENIOCE'REUS
See **CACTUS GENERA.**

PENNAN'TIA . . . . . . Pennantia
corymbo'sa . . . . . . Kaikomako P.

PENNISE'TUM (*GYMNOTHRIX*) Pennisetum
See **GRASS GENERA.**

Pennycress . . . . **Thlaspi**
Alps P. . . . . **T. montanum**
Blue P. . . . . **T. glaucum**
Bulb P. . . . . **T. bulbosum**
Cilician P. . . . . **T. cilicicum**
Early P. . . . . **T. praecox**
Field P. . . . . **T. arvense**
Italian P. . . . . **T. stylosum**
Roundleaf P. . . . **T. rotundifolium**
Thorowort P. . . . . **T. perfoliatum**
Violet P. . . . . **T. violascens**

Pennyleaf . . . . **Obolaria**
Virginia P. . . . . . . **O. virginica**

Pennywort . . . . **Hydrocotyle**
Common P. . . . . **H. vulgaris**
Floating P. . . . . **H. ranunculoides**
Largeleaf P. . . . . **H. bonariensis**
Marsh P. . . . . . . **H. americana**
Shiny P. . . . . . . **H. rotundifolia**
Tasmanian P. . . . **H. peduncularis**
Whorled P. . . . . . **H. verticillata**

PEN'STEMON (*PENTSTEMON*) |w Penstemon

The original spelling of the scientific name, Penstemon, has only recently been adopted by botanists.

abieti'nus . . . . Firleaf P.
acumina'tus . . . . . Sharpleaf P.
adamsia'nus . . . . Adams P.
alberti'nus . . . . Alberta P.
al'bidus |w . . . . White P.
alluvio'rum . . . . . . Mississippi P.
alpi'nus . . . . Alpine P.
amab'ilis . . . . Lovely P.

PENSTEMON, continued
ambig'uus . . . . Gilia Penstemon
angustifo'lius (*coeruleus*) Narrowleaf P.
antirrhinoi'des . . . . Snapdragon P.
arenic'ola . . . . Sand P.
ar'idus . . . . Stiffleaf P.
arizo'nicus . . . . Arizona P.
attenua'tus . . . . Sulfur P.
azu'reus . . . . Azure P.
barba'tus (*Chelone barbata*) Beardlip P.
—*tor'reyi* . . . . **P. torreyi**
Alice Hindley. hv. P. barbatus
Countess Dalkeith
Emperor
George Home
King George V
Middleton Gem
Mrs. Fulford
Newbury Gem
Pink Beauty
Princess Elizabeth
barret'tae . . . . Barrett P.
brandeg'ei . . . . Brandegee P.
breviflo'rus . . . . . Stubflower P.
brevifo'lius (*brevis*) . . Shortleaf P.
brevisep'alus . . . . Appalachian P.
brid'gesi . . . . Bridges P.
brittono'rum . . . . . . Brittons P.
cacu'minis (*pulchellus* Greene, *not* Lindl.) . . . . Dainty P.
cae'sius . . . . . SanBernardino P.
caespito'sus . . . . Mat P.
califor'nicus . . . . . SanJacinto P.
calyco'sus . . . . . . Longsepal P.
campanula'tus . . . . . Harebell P.
canes'cens . . . . Gray P.
cardina'lis . . . . Cardinal P.
card'welli (*P. fruticosus c.*) Cardwell P.
centranthifo'lius . Scarletbugler P.
chionoph'ilus . . . . . Snowland P.
cine'reus . . . . Ashen P.
cleve'landi . . . . Cleveland P.
cobae'a . . . . Cobaea P.
coeru'leus . . . . . . **P. angustifolius**
colli'nus . . . . **P. humilis**
coloraden'sis . . . . Colorado P.
comarrhe'nus . . . . Dusty P.
confer'tus |w . . . . Yellow P.
—coeruleo-purpu'reus
—globo'sus
confu'sus . . . . **P. utahensis**
cordifo'lius . . . . Vine P.
corymbo'sus . . . . . Thymeleaf P.
cran'dalli . . . . Crandall P.
—al'bus . . . . White C.P.
—rose'us . . . . Pink C.P.
crassifo'lius (*P. fruticosus c.*) . Pink P.
crista'tus . . . . **P. eriantherus**
cu'sicki . . . . Cusick P.
cyanan'thus (*P. glaber c.*). Wasatch P.
—subgla'ber . . . Narrowleaf W.P.
cyathoph'orus . . . . . Northpark P.
davidso'ni . . . . Davidson P.
—rose'us . . . . Pink D.P.
deus'tus . . . . Scabland P.
diffu'sus . . . . Coast P.
digita'lis (*P. laevigatus d.*)
diphyl'lus . . . . Mintleaf P.
dissec'tus . . . . . . Featherleaf P.
do'lius . . . . Jones P.
doug'lasi . . . . Douglas P.
eat'oni . . . . Eaton P.
—undo'sus . . . . Wavyleaf E.P.
ellip'ticus . . . . Rockvine P.
erian'therus(*cristatus*). Fuzzytongue P.

PENSTEMON, continued
fend'leri . . . Fendler Penstemon
flor'idus . . . Panamint P.
fre'monti (*leptanthus*) . . Fremont P.
fruticifor'mis . . DesertMountain P.
frutico'sus . . . Bush P.
—*card'welli* . . . **P. cardwelli**
—*crassifo'lius* . . . **P. crassifolius**
gaird'neri . . . Gairdner P.
gar'retti . . . Garretts P.
genicula'tus . . . Bentstem P.
gla'ber (*gordoni*) . . . Sawsepal P.
—**alpi'nus** . . . Alpine S.P.
—*cyanan'thus* . . . **P. cyananthus**
—*specio'sus* . . . **P. speciosus**
Rosy (*roseus*) hv. P. glaber
Splendid (*gordoni splendens*)
glabres'cens . . . **P. teucrioides**
glandulo'sus . . . Stickystem P.
glau'cus . . . Blueleaf P.
gloxinioi'des . . . Gloxinia P.
gor'doni . . . **P. glaber**
gracilen'tus |w . . . Slimstem P.
grac'ilis . . . Slender P.
grandiflo'rus . . . Shell-leaf P.
grinnell'i . . . Grinnell P.
hall'i . . . Halls P.
harbour'i . . . Harbours P.
hart'wegi . . . Hartweg P.
hay'deni . . . Hayden P.
heterodox'us . . . Heretic P.
heterophyl'lus . . . Chaparral P.
—**erec'tus**
—**pur'dyi** . . . Purdy C.P.
hirsu'tus (*pubescens*) . . . Type P.
hu'milis (*collinus*) . . . Low P.
—**al'bus** . . . White L.P.
imber'bis
inca'nus |w . . . Hoary P.
incer'tus . . . Argus P.
isophyl'lus
jaffraya'nus . . . Jaffray P.
james'i . . . James P.
ken'nedyi . . . Kennedy P.
king'i . . . Kings P.
labro'sus . . . Longlips P.
lae'tus . . . Gay P.
laeviga'tus . . . Smooth P.
—*digita'lis* . . . **P. digitalis**
lae'vis . . . **P. speciosus**
laricifo'lius . . . Larchleaf P.
—**exilifo'lius** . . . Nelson L.P.
lax'us . . . Idaho P.
leiophyl'lus . . . **P. subglaber**
lem'moni . . . Lemmons P.
leon'ardi . . . Leonard P.
leptan'thus . . . **P. fremonti**
leptophyl'lus . . . Boise P.
linarioi'des . . . Toadflax P.
lineola'tus . . . Humboldt P.
ly'alli . . . Lyall P.
macran'thus
mensa'rum . . . Grandmesa P.
menzies'i . . . Menzies P.
—*scou'leri* . . . **P. scouleri**
metcalf'ei . . . Metcalfe P.
mexica'nus . . **Allophyton mexicanum**
micran'thus . . . Tinybloom P.
microphyl'lus . . . Littleleaf P.
minidoka'nus . . . **P. perpulcher**
mi'ser . . . Malheur P.
monta'nus (*woodsi*) . . . Cordroot P.
multiflo'rus . . . Pineywoods P.
murraya'nus . . . Cutleaf P.
nemoro'sus (*Chelone nemorosa*) Grove P.
neomexica'nus . . . NewMexico P.

PENSTEMON, continued
neoter'icus . . . Keck Penstemon
newber'ryi . . . Newberry P.
nit'idus . . . Waxleaf P.
nudiflo'rus
oligan'thus . . . Wooton P.
orega'nus . . . Oregon P.
ova'tus . . . Eggleaf P.
o'weni . . . **P. pseudoprocerus**
pachyphyl'lus . . . Thickleaf P.
pal'lidus . . . Pale P.
pal'meri . . . Palmer P.
panicula'tus . . . **P. variabilis**
par'ishi . . . Parish P.
par'ryi . . . Parry P.
pauciflo'rus . . . Hillbilly P.
perpul'cher (*minidokanus*) Minidoka P.
pineto'rum . . . **P. wilcoxi**
praten'sis . . . **P. washoensis**
proce'rus . . . Littleflower P.
—**mi'nor**
produc'tus . . . Longtube P.
pruino'sus . . . Prickleaf P.
pseudoproce'rus (*oweni; pseudohumilis* Rydb., *not* Jones) . . . Bridger P.
pseudospectab'ilis . . . Desert P.
puberulen'tus . . . Jackear P.
pubes'cens . . . **P. hirsutus**
pulchel'lus Lindl. (1828)

This Mexican species is considered by some botanists as a variety (or form) of or else synonymous with P. campanulatus.

pulchel'lus Greene (1898) **P. cacuminis**
pu'milus . . . Pygmy P.
punic'eus . . . Redbells P.
pur'pusi . . . Purpus P.
radico'sus . . . Matroot P.
rat'tani . . . Rattan P.
rex' . . . **P. speciosus**
richardso'ni . . . Richardson P.
roez'li . . . Placer P.
roth'rocki . . . Rothrock P.
rupic'ola . . . Cliff P.
—**ma'jor** . . . Big C.P.
ryd'bergi . . . Rydberg P.
scapoi'des . . . Inyo P.
scou'leri (*P. menziesi s.*) . Scouler P.
—**al'bus** . . . White S.P.
secundiflo'rus . . . Sidebells P.
secundiflo'rus A. Gray, *not* Benth. **P. unilateralis**
sepal'ulus . . . Littlecup P.
sim'ilis . . . Pinyon P.
small'i . . . Smalls P.
specio'sus (*P. glaber s.; laevis; rex*) Royal P.
spectab'ilis . . . Showy P.
stenophyl'lus . . . Grassleaf P.
stenosep'alus . . . **P. whippleanus**
strictifor'mis . . . Mancos P.
stric'tus . . . RockyMountain P.
subgla'ber (*leiophyllus; utahensis* (S. Wats.) A. Nels., *not* Eastw.)
superb'us . . . SantaRita P.
terna'tus . . . Whorled P.
teucrioi'des (*glabrescens*) Germander P.
thompson'iae . . . Thompson P.
thur'beri . . . Thurber P.
tidestrom'i . . . Tidestrom P.
tol'miei . . . Tolmie P.
tor'reyi (*P. barbatus t.*) . Torrey P.
trichan'der . . . Esau P.
triphyl'lus . . . Threeleaf P.
tubiflo'rus . . . Tube P.
—**digita'lis**

PENSTEMON, continued
uintahen'sis . . . Uinta Penstemon
unilatera'lis (*secundiflorus* A. Gray, *not* Benth.) . . . Oneside P.
utahen'sis (*confusus*) . . . Utah P.
utahen'sis (S. Wats.) A. Nels., *not* Eastw. . . . **P. subglaber**
variab'ilis (*paniculatus*). Klickitat P.
venus'tus . . . BlueMountains P.
vi'rens . . . Green P.
virga'tus . . . Wandbloom P.
ward'i . . . Wards P.
washoen'sis (*pratensis*) . Washoe P.
wat'soni . . . Watson P.
whipplea'nus (*stenosepalus*) Whipple P.
wil'coxi (*pinetorum*) . . . Wilcox P.
woods'i . . . **P. montanus**
wright'i . . . Wrights P.
Mauve Beauty. hv. Penstemon
Middleton Gem
Sensation
Six Hills
Southgate Gem

Penstemon . . . **Penstemon**
Adams P. . . . **P. adamsianus**
Alberta P. . . . **P. albertinus**
Alpine P. . . . **P. alpinus**
Alpine Sawsepal P. . . . **P. glaber a.**
Appalachian P. . . . **P. brevisepalus**
Argus P. . . . **P. incertus**
Arizona P. . . . **P. arizonicus**
Ashen P. . . . **P. cinereus**
Azure P. . . . **P. azureus**
Barrett P. . . . **P. barrettae**
Beardlip P. . . . **P. barbatus**
Bentstem P. . . . **P. geniculatus**
Big Cliff P. . . . **P. rupicola major**
Blueleaf P. . . . **P. glaucus**
BlueMountains P. . . . **P. venustus**
Boise P. . . . **P. leptophyllus**
Brandegee P. . . . **P. brandegei**
Bridger P. . . . **P. pseudoprocerus**
Bridges P. . . . **P. bridgesi**
Brittons P. . . . **P. brittonorum**
Bush P. . . . **P. fruticosus**
Cardinal P. . . . **P. cardinalis**
Cardwell P. . . . **P. cardwelli**
Chaparral P. . . . **P. heterophyllus**
Cleveland P. . . . **P. clevelandi**
Cliff P. . . . **P. rupicola**
Coast P. . . . **P. diffusus**
Cobaea P. . . . **P. cobaea**
Colorado P. . . . **P. coloradensis**
Cordroot P. . . . **P. montanus**
Crandall P. . . . **P. crandalli**
Cusick P. . . . **P. cusicki**
Cutleaf P. . . . **P. murrayanus**
Dainty P. . . . **P. cacuminis**
Davidson P. . . . **P. davidsoni**
DesertMountain P. . . **P. fruticiformis**
Desert P. . . . **P. pseudospectabilis**
Douglas P. . . . **P. douglasi**
Dusty P. . . . **P. comarrhenus**
Eaton P. . . . **P. eatoni**
Eggleaf P. . . . **P. ovatus**
Esau P. . . . **P. trichander**
Featherleaf P. . . . **P. dissectus**
Fendler P. . . . **P. fendleri**
Firleaf P. . . . **P. abietinus**
Fremont P. . . . **P. fremonti**
Fuzzytongue P. . . . **P. eriantherus**
Gairdner P. . . . **P. gairdneri**
Garretts P. . . . **P. garretti**
Gay P. . . . **P. laetus**
Germander P. . . . **P. teucrioides**
Gilia P. . . . **P. ambiguus**
Gloxinia P. . . . **P. gloxinioides**

PENSTEMON, continued

GRANDMESA P. Penstemon mensarum
GRASSLEAF P. . . . P. stenophyllus
GRAY P. . . . . . . P. canescens
GREEN P. . . . . P. virens
GRINNELL P. . . . . . . P. grinnelli
GROVE P. . . . . . . P. nemorosus
HALLS P. . . . . P. halli
HARBOURS P. . . . . . . P. harbouri
HAREBELL P. . . . . P. campanulatus
HARTWEG P. . . . . . . P. hartwegi
HAYDEN P. . . . . P. haydeni
HERETIC P. . . . . P. heterodoxus
HILLBILLY P. . . . . P. pauciflorus
HOARY P. . . . . P. incanus
HUMBOLDT P. . . . . . P. lineolatus
IDAHO P. . . . . P. laxus
INYO P. . . . . P. scapoides
JACKEAR P. . . . . P. puberulentus
JAFFRAY P. . . . . . P. jaffrayanus
JAMES P. . . . . P. jamesi
JONES P. . . . . P. dolius
KECK P. . . . . P. neotericus
KENNEDY P. . . . . . . P. kennedyi
KINGS P. . . . . P. kingi
KLICKITAT P. . . . . . P. variabilis
LARCHLEAF P. . . . . P. laricifolius
LEMMONS P. . . . . . . P. lemmoni
LEONARD P. . . . . . . P. leonardi
LITTLECUP P. . . . . . P. sepalulus
LITTLEFLOWER P. . . . . P. procerus
LITTLELEAF P. . . . P. microphyllus
LONGLIPS P. . . . . . . P. labrosus
LONGSEPAL P. . . . . . P. calycosus
LONGTUBE P. . . . . . P. productus
LOVELY P. . . . . P. amabilis
LOW P. . . . . P. humilis
LYALL P. . . . . P. lyalli
MALHEUR P. . . . . P. miser
MANCOS P. . . . . . P. strictiformis
MAT P. . . . . P. caespitosus
MATROOT P. . . . . . . P. radicosus
MENZIES P. . . . . . . P. menziesi
METCALFE P. . . . . . . P. metcalfei
MINIDOKA P. . . . . . P. perpulcher
MINTLEAF P. . . . . . . P. diphyllus
MISSISSIPPI P. . . . . P. alluviorum
NARROWLEAF P. . . . P. angustifolius
NARROWLEAF WASATCH P.
P. cyananthus subglaber
NELSON LARCHLEAF P.
P. laricifolius exilifolius
NEWBERRY P. . . . . P. newberryi
NEWMEXICO P. . . P. neomexicanus
NORTHPARK P. . . P. cyathophorus
ONESIDE P. . . . . . P. unilateralis
OREGON P. . . . . . . P. oreganus
PALE P. . . . . P. pallidus
PALMER P. . . . . P. palmeri
PANAMINT P. . . . . . . P. floridus
PARISH P. . . . . P. parishi
PARRY P. . . . . P. parryi
PINEYWOODS P. . . . . P. multiflorus
PINK CRANDALL P. . P. crandalli roseus
PINK DAVIDSON P. . . P. davidsoni r.
PINK P. . . . . . . P. crassifolius
PINYON P. . . . . P. similis
PLACER P. . . . . P. roezli
PRICKLEAF P. . . . . . P. pruinosus
PURDY CHAPARRAL P.
P. heterophyllus purdyi
PURPUS P. . . . . P. purpusi
PYGMY P. . . . . P. pumilus
RATTAN P. . . . . P. rattani
REDBELLS P. . . . . . . P. puniceus
RICHARDSON P. . . . . P. richardsoni
ROCKVINE P. . . . . . . P. ellipticus

PENSTEMON, continued

ROCKYMOUNTAIN P.
Penstemon strictus
ROTHROCK P. . . . . . P. rothrocki
ROYAL P. . . . . P. speciosus
RYDBERG P. . . . . P. rydbergi
SANBERNARDINO P. . . . . P. caesius
SAND P. . . . . P. arenicola
SANJACINTO P. . . . . P. californicus
SANTARITA P. . . . . . . P. superbus
SAWSEPAL P. . . . . P. glaber
SCABLAND P. . . . . . . P. deustus
SCARLETBUGLER P. P. centranthifolius
SCOULER P. . . . . P. scouleri
SHARPLEAF P. . . . . P. acuminatus
SHELL-LEAF P. . . . . P. grandiflorus
SHORTLEAF P. . . . . . P. brevifolius
SHOWY P. . . . . . . P. spectabilis
SIDEBELLS P. . . . P. secundiflorus
SLENDER P. . . . . P. gracilis
SLIMSTEM P. . . . . . P. gracilentus
SMALLS P. . . . . P. smalli
SMOOTH P. . . . . . . P. laevigatus
SNAPDRAGON P. . . . P. antirrhinoides
SNOWLAND P. . . . P. chionophilus
STICKYSTEM P. . . . P. glandulosus
STIFFLEAF P. . . . . P. aridus
STUBFLOWER P. . . . P. breviflorus
SULFUR P. . . . . . . P. attenuatus
THICKLEAF P. . . . P. pachyphyllus
THOMPSON P. . . . P. thompsoniae
THREELEAF P. . . . . . P. triphyllus
THURBER P. . . . . . . P. thurberi
THYMELEAF P. . . . . P. corymbosus
TIDESTROM P. . . . . . P. tidestromi
TINYBLOOM P. . . . . P. micranthus
TOADFLAX P. . . . . . P. linarioides
TOLMIE P. . . . . P. tolmiei
TORREY P. . . . . P. torreyi
TUBE P. . . . . P. tubiflorus
TYPE P. . . . . P. hirsutus
UINTA P. . . . . . . P. uintahensis
UTAH P. . . . . P. utahensis
VINE P. . . . . P. cordifolius
WANDBLOOM P. . . . . . . P. virgatus
WARDS P. . . . . P. wardi
WASATCH P. . . . . . P. cyananthus
WASHOE P. . . . . . P. washoensis
WATSON P. . . . . P. watsoni
WAVYLEAF EATON P. P. eatoni undosus
WAXLEAF P. . . . . P. nitidus
WHIPPLE P. . . . . . P. whippleanus
WHITE CRANDALL P. P. crandalli albus
WHITE LOW P. . . . . P. humilis a.
WHITE P. . . . . P. albidus
WHITE SCOULER P. . P. scouleri albus
WHORLED P. . . . . . . P. ternatus
WILCOX P. . . . . P. wilcoxi
WOOTON P. . . . . . P. oliganthus
WRIGHTS P. . . . . P. wrighti
YELLOW P. . . . . . . P. confertus

PENTA'CE . . . . THITKA
burman'ica . . . . BURMA T.
grif'fithi . . . . TAVOY T.

PENTACLE'THRA
filamento'sa . . . . IRIPILBARKTREE
macrophyl'la . . . . OWALAOILTREE

PENTAC'ME . . . . PENTACME
contor'ta . . . . BALAK P.

PENTACTI'NA . . . . . . PENTACTINA
rupic'ola . . . . KOREAN P.

PENTAGLOT'TIS . . . **ANCHUSA**

PENTAPTERYG'IUM
ser'pens

PEN'TAS . . . . STARCLUSTERS
coccin'ea . . . . SCARLET S.
lanceola'ta (*carnea*) . . . EGYPTIAN S.

PEN'THORUM |w . . . . PENTHORUM
hu'mile . . . . AMUR P.
interme'dium . . . . CHINESE P.
sedoi'des (*chinense*) . . . VIRGINIA P.
(*Ditch Stonecrop*)

PENTSTE'MON . . **PENSTEMON**

PENTZ'IA . . . . SHEEPBUSH
inca'na . . . . AUSTRALIAN S.

PEONY . . . . **Paeonia**

For hort. var. of Peony see **PAEONIA**.

BIGLEAF P. . . . . . . P. macrophylla
BROWNS P. . . . . P. browni
CAUCASIAN P. . . . P. mlokosewitschi
CHINESE P. . . . . P. albiflora
COMMON P. . . . . . . P. officinalis
CORAL P. . . . . P. corallina
DELACHE P. . . . . P. delachei
DELAVAY P. . . . . P. delavayi
DOUBLECRIMSON CHINESE P.
P. albiflora sinensis
FERNLEAF P. . . . . . . P. tenuifolia
GOLDEN P. . . . . P. lutea
HIMALAYA P. . . . . P. emodi
HUME TREE P. . P. suffruticosa humei
IRANGOLD P. . . . . P. wittmanniana
∞ LEMOINE P. . . . . . . ∞ P. lemoinei
LEVANT P. . . . . P. paradoxa
MEDITERRANEAN P. . . . P. peregrina
MOROCCAN P. . . . . . . P. coriacea
PALLAS P. . . . . . P. decora pallasi
POPPY TREE P.
P. suffruticosa papaveracea
SPANISH P. . . . . . P. microcarpa
TREE P. . . . . . . P. suffruticosa
TURKISH P. . . . . P. decora
URAL P. . . . . P. anomala

PEPERO'MIA . . . . . . PEPEROMIA
argyroneu'ra . . . . SILVERTHREAD P.
arifo'lia . . . . P. sandersi
blan'da
crassifo'lia
maculo'sa . . . . SPOTTED P.
obtusifo'lia . . . . . . OVALLEAF P.
pellu'cida . . . . SHINY P.
rotundifo'lia (*nummularifolia*)
COINLEAF P.
san'dersi (*arifolia*) . . . SANDERS P.
—argyre'ia

PEPINO . . . . . **Solanum muricatum**

PEPPER . . . . **Piper**
BETEL P. . . . . P. betle
BLACK P. . . . . P. nigrum
CELEBES P. . . . . P. ornatum
CUBEB P. . . . . P. cubeba
JABORANDI P. . . . . . . P. jaborandi
KAVA P. . . . . P. methysticum
LONG P. . . . . P. longum
MATICO P. . . . . . P. angustifolium

PEPPERMINT . . . . . **Mentha piperita**

As Peppermints are true Mints, the name logically should appear as two words (Pepper Mint) but long usage has fixed the spelling as one word.

Black P. EUCALYPTUS, WILLOWLEAF: **Eucalyptus salicifolia**
ORANGE P. . . **Mentha piperita citrata**

Peppermintgum . . . . EUCALYPTUS, PEPPERMINT: **Eucalyptus odorata**

PEPPERMINTTREE . . . **Agonis flexuosa**

Peppertree . . . . **Schinus**
Brazil P. . . . . . **S. terebinthifolia**
California P. . . . . **S. molle**
Chilean P. . . . . **S. latifolia**
Longleaf Peru P.
S. dependens longifolia
Peru P . . . . **S. dependens**
Pinkberry P. . . . . **S. lentiscifolia**

Peppervine . . . . **Ampelopsis arborea**

Pepperweed . . . . **Lepidium**
Blistering P. . . . . **L. vesicarium**
Clasping P. . . . . . **L. perfoliatum**
Desert P. . . . . **L. fremonti**
Field P. . . . . **L. campestre**
Fishpoison P. . . . . . **L. piscidium**
Gardencress P. . . . . . **L. sativum**
Lens P. . . . . **L. repens**
Mesa P. . . . . **L. alyssoides**
Prairie P. . . . . . . **L. densiflorum**
Spanish P. . . . . . **L. cardamines**
Tongue P. . . . . **L. nitidum**
Virginia P. . . . . . **L. virginicum**
Wayside P. . . . . **L. bipinnatifidum**

Pepperwort . . . . **Marsilea**
Hooked P. . . . . **M. uncinata**

Peradocampo . . **Eugenia klotzschiana**

PERA'MIUM . . . . **GOODYERA**
See **ORCHID GENERA, HARDY TERRESTRIAL GROUP.**

PERAPHYL'LUM
ramosis'simum . . . . Squawapple

PERDIC'IUM . . . . . **GERBERA**

PERES'KIA (*PEIRESKIA; RHODOCACTUS*) . . . . . . Pereskia
See **CACTUS GENERA.**

PERESKIOP'SIS
See **CACTUS GENERA.**

PERE'ZIA . . . . Perezia
microceph'ala
multiflo'ra

PERICO'ME . . . . . . Pericome
cauda'ta . . . . Tailleaf P.

PERIDERID'IA (*CARUM* Am. Auth., *not* L.; *EULOPHUS*)
bolan'deri (*Eulophus b.*)
gaird'neri (*Carum g.*) . . . . Yampa
orega'na (*Carum oreganum*) . Eppaw

PERIL'LA . . . . Perilla
frutes'cens (*ocymoides*) . Common P.
—cris'pa (*P. f. nankinensis*)
Purple C.P.
—lacinia'ta Hort. (*P. atropurpurea*)
Cutleaf C.P.

PERIPLO'CA . . . . Silkvine
grae'ca . . . . Grecian S.
se'pium . . . . Chinese S.

PERISSOCO'BUS
bij'li

PERISTE'RIA
See **ORCHID GENERA.**

PERIS'TROPHE . . . . Peristrophe
angustifo'lia . . . . Java P.
¢Variegata. hv.
specio'sa . . . . India P.

Perit'oma serrula'tum . **Cleome serrulata**

Periwinkle . . . . **Vinca**
Bigleaf P. . . . . **V. major**
Common P. . . . . **V. minor**

Periwinkle, continued
Herbaceous P. . . **Vinca herbacea**
Mottled Bigleaf P.
V. major variegata
Whitespot B. P. . **V. m. elegantissima**

Permanentwave-plant . . . Daisybush, Teteaweka: **Olearia angustifolia**

PERNET'TYA . . . . . . Pernettya
This generic name, sometimes spelled Pernettia, commemorates A. J. Pernetty (1716–1801), an explorer of the Falkland Islands.
cilia'ris . . . . **Arbutus furiens**
empetrifo'lia . . . . **P. pumila**
mucrona'ta . . . . Chilean P.
—angustifo'lia . . Narrowleaf C.P.
—rupic'ola (*P. rupicola*) Thinleaf C.P.
Alba. hv. P. mucronata
Coccinea
Leucocarpa
Lilacina
Magellan
Major
Nigra
Purpurea
Rosea
Sanguinea
Speciosa
na'na . . . . NewZealand P.
prostra'ta . . . . Creeping P.
—pent'landi (*P. pentlandi*)
Pentland C.P.
pu'mila (*empetrifolia*) . Falklands P.
Purpurea. hv.
rupic'ola . . . . . . **P. mucronata r.**
tasman'ica . . . . . . Tasmanian P.

PEROV'SKIA (*PEROWSKIA*)
Perovskia
abrotanoi'des . . . . . Caspian P.
atriplicifo'lia . . . . . Russiansage P.
scrophulariaefo'lia . . Turkestan P.

PER'SEA |w . . . . Persea
america'na (*gratissima; persea*)
American Avocado
—drymifo'lia (*P. drymifolia*)
Mexican A.
—leiog'yna (*P. leiogyna*) . Trapp A.
borbo'nia (*carolinensis*) |w . Redbay P.
cineras'cens . . . . . . Zacupan P.
flocco'sa . . . . . . Oaxaca Avocado
gratis'sima . . . . . . **P. americana**
in'dica . . . . MadeiraBay P.
leiog'yna . . . . . . **P. americana l.**
meyenia'na . . . . Meyen P.
palus'tris (*pubescens*) |w Swampbay P.
per'sea . . . . **P. americana**
pittier'i . . . . Yas Avocado
schiedea'na . . . . Coyo A.

PER'SICA . . . . **PRUNUS**
vulga'ris . . . . **P. persica**

PERSICA'RIA . . . **POLYGONUM**
mi'tis . . . . **P. persicaria**

Persimmon . . . . **Diospyros**
For hort. var. of Persimmon, see **FRUIT AND EDIBLE NUT NAMES.**
Andaman Marblewood P.
D. marmorata
Benin Ebony P. . . . **D. insculpta**
Bolongeta P. . . . . **D. pilosanthera**
Burmese Ebony P. . . **D. burmanica**
Calamander E. P. . . . **D. quaesita**
Chinese P. . . . . **D. sinensis**
Common P. . . . . . . **D. virginiana**
Coromandel Ebony P. **D. melanoxylon**

Persimmon, continued
Datepalm P. . . . **Diospyros lotus**
Diamondleaf P. . . . **D. rhombifolia**
Ebony P. . . . . **D. ebenum**
Fishermans P. . . . . . **D. piscatoria**
Fuzzy Common P.
D. virginiana pubescens
Gaboon Ebony P. . . . . . **D. dendo**
Gaub P. . . . . **D. embryopteris**
Green Ebony P. . . . . **D. chloroxylon**
Illawara E. P. . . . . . . **D. cargillia**
Indian E. P. . . . . . . **D. ebenaster**
Kaki P. . . . . **D. kaki**
Mabola P. . . . . **D. discolor**
Macassar Ebony P. . . **D. macassar**
Medlar P. . . . . . . **D. mespiliformis**
Mountain P. . . . . **D. montana**
Myrtle Ebony P. . . . **D. pentamera**
Nepal E. P. . . . . **D. tomentosa**
Oklahoma P. **D. virginiana platycarpa**
Philippine Ebony P. . . . . **D. ferrea**
Spiny P. . . . . **D. armata**
Texas P. . . . . **D. texana**
WestAfrican Ebony P. . **D. crassiflora**
Wild Kaki P. . . . **D. kaki silvestris**

PERSOON'IA . . . . . . Persoonia
chamaepeu'ce . . . . . Larchleaf P.
juniperi'na . . . . Juniper P.
oxycoccoi'des . . . . . Cranberry P.
pinifo'lia . . . . Pineleaf P.
salicifo'lia . . . . . . Willowleaf P.
to'ru . . . . Toru P.

PER'TYA . . . . Pertybush
sinen'sis . . . . China P.

Pertybush . . . . **Pertya**
China P. . . . . **P. sinensis**

Perubalm . . . . **Roubieva**
Flatweed P. . . . . . . **R. multifida**

Perunkila . Carissa, Sweet Karanda: **Carissa carandas dulcis**

Peruvianalmond . . . . Sawarrinut: **Caryocar nuciferum**

Peruviandaffodil . . . . . . **Ismene**

PESCATO'REA . **ZYGOPETALUM**
See **ORCHID GENERA.**

PETALO'NYX . . . . Sandpaperplant
linea'ris . . . . Narrowleaf S.
nit'idus . . . . Smooth S.
thur'beri . . . . Thurber S.

PETALOSTE'MON (*KUHNISTERA; PETALOSTEMUM*) |w
Prairieclover
al'bidus |w . . . . Pallid P.
can'didus . . . . White P.
corymbo'sus (*Kuhnistera pinnata*) |w
September P.
decum'bens . . . . . . Tennessee P.
flaves'cens . . . . Yellow P.
multiflo'rus . . . . Roundheaded P.
obova'tus
oligophyl'lus . . . Slender White P.
purpu'reus (*violaceum*) . . Purple P.
searls'iae . . . . Searls P.
stan'fieldi . . . . Stanfield P.
villo'sus |w . . . . Silky P.

PETASI'TES . . . . Butterbur
fra'grans (*Tussilago f.*) . . Sweet B.
hy'brida (*officinalis; vulgaris*)
Purple B.
japon'ica . . . . Japanese B.
—gigan'tea . . . . Giant J.B.
niv'ea . . . . Snowleaf B.
palma'ta . . . . Palmate B.

PETER'IA . . . . PETERIA
nevaden'sis . . . . NEVADA P.
scopa'ria . . . . RUSH P.
thomp'sonae . . . . . THOMPSON P.

PETIT'IA . . . . PETITIA
domingen'sis . . . . CAPA P.

PETIVER'IA . . . . GUINEAHENWEED
allia'cea . . . . GARLIC G.

Petrado'ria pu'mila . **Solidago petradoria**

PETRE'A . . . . PETREA
arbo'rea . . . . BLUETREE P.
volub'ilis . . . . PURPLEWREATH P.

PETROCAL'LIS . . . . . ROCKBEAUTY
pyrena'ica (*Draba p.*) . . PYRENEES R.

PETROCOP'TIS
lagas'cae (*Lychnis l.*)

PETROPH'ILA . . . . . COMBBUSH
bilo'ba . . . . TWINLOBE C.
linea'ris . . . . SLIMLEAF C.
me'dia . . . . ROUNDLEAF C.
peduncula'ta . . . . . LONGSTALK C.
pulchel'la . . . . PRETTY C.
ses'silis . . . . . . QUEENSLAND C.
shuttleworthia'na . SHUTTLEWORTH C.

PETROPHY'ES . . **MONANTHES**
See **SUCCULENTS.**

PETROPHY'TUM . . . . . ROCKMAT
caespito'sum (*Spiraea caespitosa*) TUFTED R.
cineras'cens . . . . GRAY R.
henderso'ni . . . . HENDERSON R.

PETRORHA'GIA . . . . . **TUNICA**

PETROSELI'NUM . . . . . PARSLEY
cris'pum (*P. hortense c.*) CURLY GARDEN P.
—filici'num . . . . FERNLEAF G.P.
—latifo'lium (*P. hortense; P. sativum*) COMMON G.P.
—radico'sum . . . . TURNIP G.P.
₵NAPLES (*neapolitanum*) HV. P. crispum

PETSAI . . . . . **Brassica pekinensis**

PETTER'IA . . . . PETTERPEA
ramenta'cea . . . . . DALMATIAN P.

PETTERPEA . . . . **Petteria**
DALMATIAN P. . . . . . **P. ramentacea**

PETU'NIA . . . . PETUNIA
axilla'ris (*nyctaginiflora*) WHITEMOON P.
∞ **hy'brida** (*?axillaris × violacea*) ∞ COMMON P.

There are many varieties of Petunia in the trade but their names have not yet been standardized.

infla'ta . . . . INFLATED P.
viola'cea . . . . VIOLET P.

PEUCED'ANUM (*IMPERATORIA*) HOGFENNEL
officina'le . . . . COMMON H.
ostru'thium (*Imperatoria o.*) MASTERWORT H.

PEUCEPHYL'LUM . . . SPRUCEBUSH
schott'i . . . . SCHOTTS S.

PEU'MUS (*BOLDEA; BOLDU*)
Peumus is conserved under International Rules.
bol'dus (*Boldea b.; B. fragrans*) BOLDUTREE
ru'bra . . . . **Cryptocarya r.**

PEYOTE . . . . **Lophophora**
MESCALBUTTON P. . . . . **L. williamsi**

PFEIF'FERA
See **CACTUS GENERA.**

PHA'CA . . . . . . **ASTRAGALUS**
pic'ta . . . . **A. ceramicus**

PHACE'LIA (*EUTOCA; WHITLAVIA*) lw . . . . PHACELIA
alpi'na . . . . ALPINE P.
bipinnatif'ida . . LOOSEFLOWERED P.
campanula'ria (*P. minor c.*) HAREBELL P.
cilia'ta . . . . LAVENDER P.
conges'ta
divarica'ta
—wrangelia'na
doug'lasi . . . . DOUGLAS P.
fimbria'ta . . . . FRINGED P.
frank'lini . . . . FRANKLIN P.
glandulo'sa . . . . . GLANDULAR P.
heterophyl'la lw . . . . VARILEAF P.
idahoen'sis . . . . IDAHO P.
leucophyl'la . . . . . SILVERLEAF P.
linea'ris (*Eutoca multiflora*) lw THREADLEAF P.
mi'nor (*whitlavia; Whitlavia grandiflora*) . . . . . BLUEBELL P.
—al'ba . . . . WHITE B.P.
—campanula'ria . . **P. campanularia**
—gloxinoi'des (*Whitlavia g.*) GLOXINIA B.P.
BLUEPLATE. HV.
par'ryi . . . . PARRY P.
pursh'i . . . . PURSH P.
ramosis'sima . . . . . BRANCHING P.
seri'cea . . . . SILKY P.
tanacetifo'lia . . . . TANSY P.
vis'cida (*Eutoca v.*) . . . STICKY P.
whitla'via . . . . **P. minor**

PHACELIA . . . . **Phacelia**
ALPINE P. . . . . **P. alpina**
BLUEBELL P. . . . . **P. minor**
BRANCHING P. . . . . **P. ramosissima**
DOUGLAS P. . . . . **P. douglasi**
FRANKLIN P. . . . . . . **P. franklini**
FRINGED P. . . . . . . **P. fimbriata**
GLANDULAR P. . . . . **P. glandulosa**
GLOXINIA BLUEBELL P. **P. minor gloxinoides**
HAREBELL P. . . . . **P. campanularia**
IDAHO P. . . . . **P. idahoensis**
LAVENDER P. . . . . **P. ciliata**
LOOSEFLOWERED P. . . **P. bipinnatifida**
PARRY P. . . . . **P. parryi**
PURSH P. . . . . **P. purshi**
SILKY P. . . . . **P. sericea**
SILVERLEAF P. . . . . **P. leucophylla**
STICKY P. . . . . **P. viscida**
TANSY P. . . . . . . **P. tanacetifolia**
THREADLEAF P. . . . . . . **P. linearis**
VARILEAF P. . . . . . **P. heterophylla**
WHITE BLUEBELL P. . . **P. minor alba**

PHAEDRANAS'SA . . . . QUEENLILY
carmio'li . . . . . . COSTARICA Q.
chloraca'ra (*obtusa*) . . . . ANDES Q.
leh'manni . . . . COLOMBIA Q.
viridiflo'ra
Perhaps only a variety of P. chloracara.

PHAEDRAN'THUS . BLOODTRUMPET
buccinato'rius (*Bignonia b.; B. cherere*) MEXICAN B.

PHA'JUS (*PHAIUS*)
See **ORCHID GENERA.**

PHALAENOP'SIS . . . MOTHORCHID
See **ORCHID GENERA.**

PHAL'ARIS . . . . . . CANARYGRASS
See **GRASS GENERA.**

PHALSA . . . . **Grewia asiatica**

PHANTOMORCHID . . . . **Cephalanthera**
AUSTIN P. . . . . **C. austinae**

PHA'RIUM . . . . . . **BESSERA**

PHA'RUS . . . . . . LEAFSTALKGRASS
See **GRASS GENERA.**

PHASE'OLUS lw . . . . BEAN
aconitifo'lius . . . . MOTH B.
acutifo'lius . . . . TEXAS B.
—latifo'lius . . . . TEPARY B.
angula'ris . . . . ADSUKI B.
angustifo'lius . . . . NARROWLEAF B.
angustis'simus . . . . . SLIMLEAF B.
au'reus . . . . MUNG B.
calcara'tus . . . . RICE B.
caracal'la . . . . SNAIL B.
coccin'eus (*multiflorus*) SCARLET RUNNER B.
ALBONANUS. HV.
BUTTERFLY
RUBRONANUS
WHITE DUTCH (*albus*)
dilata'tus
lathyroi'des
limen'sis (*P. lunatus macrocarpus*) LIMA B.
luna'tus . . . . SIEVA B.
—lunona'nus . . . . . DWARF S.B.
—sal'icis . . . . WILLOWLEAF S.B.
macropoi'des
metcalf'ei (*retusus* Benth., *not* Moench) METCALFE B.
mun'go. MUNGO B. (*Black Gram; Urd*)
na'nus
A name erroneously applied to dwarf varieties of P. vulgaris.
pandura'tus
peduncula'ris
polystach'ys . . . . . . THICKET B.
riten'sis lw
smilacifo'lius . . . . . HAMMOCK B.
trilo'bus
triner'vius . . . . MALAY B.
vulga'ris lw . . . . KIDNEY B.
—hu'milis . . . . BUSH K.B.

PHEBA'LIUM
argen'teum

PHEGOP'TERIS . . **DRYOPTERIS**
See **FERN GENERA.**

PHELLODEN'DRON . . . . CORKTREE
amuren'se . . . . AMUR C.
chinen'se . . . . CHINESE C.
—glabrius'culum . . . SMOOTH C.C.
japon'icum . . . . JAPANESE C.
laval'lei (*P. amurense l.*) . LAVALLE C.
pirifor'me . . . . . . PEARFRUIT C.
sachalinen'se . . . . . . SAKHALIN C.

PHELLOP'TERUS . . . . CORKWING
macrorhi'zus . . . . BIGROOT C.
utahen'sis . . . . UTAH C.

PHELLOSPER'MA . **MAMMILLARIA**
See **CACTUS GENERA.**

PHIALODIS'CUS
unijuga'tus

PHILADEL'PHUS . . . MOCKORANGE
brachybo'trys . . . . **P. pekinensis b.**
—purpuras'cens . . **P. purpurascens**
∞ **burk'woodi** (∞ *purpureo-maculatus* × ∞ *virginalis*) . . . . ∞ BURKWOOD M.

PHILADELPHUS, continued

califor'nicus (*P. lewisi c.; P. l. parvifolius*) . . CALIFORNIA MOCKORANGE
caucas'icus . . . . . CAUCASUS M.
confu'sus . . . . . . PIPERS M.
×**conges'tus** (*laxus* × *?verrucosus*)
The origin of this hybrid is obscure.

cordifo'lius . . . . HEARTLEAF M.
Some botanists regard this as a variety or form of P. lewisi.

corona'rius . . . . . . SWEET M.
—*acumina'tus* . . . . **P. satsumanus**
—*gordonia'nus* . . . **P. gordonianus**
—**salicifo'lius** . . WILLOWLEAF S.M.
₵BIG (*grandiflorus*) HV. P. coronarius
The above hort. var. should not be confused with the species, P. grandiflorus.

₵DEUTZIA (*deutziaeflorus*). (Lemoine 1917.)
₵DOUBLE (*dianthiflorus; duplex; flore-pleno; plenus*)
₵DWARF SWEET (*nanus; pumilus*)
₵GOLDEN (*aureus*)
₵PRIMROSE (*primulaeflorus*)
₵ROUNDLEAF (*speciosissimus*)
₵VARIEGATED (*variegatus*)
coul'teri . . . . COULTER M.
∞**cymo'sus** (*?grandiflorus* × ∞*lemoinei*) ∞CYMOSUS M.
₵ATLAS. (Lem. 1924.) HV.
₵BANNIERE. (Lem. 1907.)
₵CONQUETE. (Lem. 1903.)
₵MER DE GLACE. (Lem. 1900.)
₵NORMA. (Lem. 1914.)
₵NUEE BLANCHE. (Lem. 1900.)
₵PERLE BLANCHE. (Lem. 1900.)
₵ROSACE. (Lem. 1900.)
₵VOIE LACTEE. (Lem. 1921.)
delavay'i . . . . DELAVAY M.
—**calves'cens**
—**melanoca'lyx**
∞**falconer'i** (*coronarius* × *?laxus*) ∞FALCONERS M.
∞**floribun'dus** (*coronarius* × *?gordonianus*) . . . . . ∞FLORIBUNDUS M.
flor'idus . . . . BEADLE M.
—**fax'oni** . . . . SMALL B.M.
gordonia'nus (*P. coronarius g.*) GORDON M.
—**columbia'nus**
grandiflo'rus (*P. inodorus g.*) BIG SCENTLESS M.
This species should not be confused with hort. var. BIG (grandiflorus) of P. coronarius. Unfortunately, the name grandiflorus is sometimes misapplied to P. pubescens.

hirsu'tus . . . . HAIRY M.
inca'nus . . . . GRAY M.
inodo'rus . . . . . . SCENTLESS M.
∞**insig'nis** (*?californicus* or *cordifolius* × *pubescens*) . . . . ∞SUMMER M.
₵SOUVENIR DE BILLIARD. HV.
intec'tus . . . . . . **P. pubescens i.**
karwinskya'nus . . KARWINSKY M.
kochia'nus . . . . . ∞**P. zeyheri k.**
latifo'lius . . . . . . **P. pubescens**
∞**lat'vicus** (*microphyllus* × *pubescens*) ∞LATVIAN M.
lax'us (*speciosus; undulatus*) DROOPING M.
—**strigo'sus** . . . . . HAIRY D.M.
∞**lemoin'ei** (*coronarius* × *microphyllus*) ∞LEMOINE M.
₵AVALANCHE. (Lem. 1896.) HV.
₵BELLE ETOILE. (Lem. 1925.)
₵BONJE

PHILADELPHUS lemoinei, continued

₵BOULE D'ARGENT. (Lem. 1894.)
₵CANDELABRE. (Lem. 1894.)
₵COUPE D'ARGENT. (Lem. 1916.)
₵CREAM (*ochroleucus*)
₵DAME BLANCHE. (Lem. 1910.)
₵DRESDEN
₵ENCHANTMENT. (Lem. 1924.)
₵ERECT (*erectus; Juno*)
₵FLEUR DE NEIGE. (Lem. 1916.)
₵GIRANDOLE. (Lem. 1916.)
₵INNOCENCE. (Lem. 1927.)
Juno. ERECT
₵MANTEAU D'HERMINE. (Lem. 1898.)
₵MONT BLANC. (Lem. 1896.)
₵PYRAMIDALE. (Lem. 1916.)
₵SYLVIANE. (Lem. 1917.)
lew'isi . . . . LEWIS MOCKORANGE
—*califor'nicus* . . . . **P. californicus**
—*parvifo'lius* . . . . **P. californicus**
magdale'nae . . . . MAGDALENA M.
×**magnif'icus** (*grandiflorus* × *pubescens*)
The origin of this hybrid is unknown.

∞**max'imus** (*pubescens* × *tomentosus*) ∞MAXIMUS M.
mexica'nus . . . . . MEXICAN M.
₵PLENUS. HV.
microphyl'lus . . . LITTLELEAF M.
×**monstro'sus** (*?gordonianus* × *pubescens*)
The origin of this hybrid is unknown.

na'nus Hort. . . . . . **P. coronarius** ₵DWARF SWEET
nepalen'sis . . . . . . NEPAL M.
nepalen'sis Lodd., *not* Koehne **P. tomentosus**
∞**niva'lis** (*coronarius* × *pubescens*) ∞SNOWBANK M.
₵PLENUS. HV.
₵SPECTABILIS
pekinen'sis . . . . . . PEKING M.
—**brachybo'trys** (*P. brachybotrys*)
—**kansuen'sis**
∞**polyan'thus** (*?* ∞*insignis* × ∞*lemoinei*) ∞POLYANTHUS M.
₵FAVORITE. (Lem. 1916.) HV.
₵GERBE DE NEIGE. (Lem. 1894.)
₵PAVILLON BLANC. (Lem. 1896.)
pubes'cens (*latifolius*) . . . HOARY M.
—**intec'tus** (*P. intectus*)
The name P. pubescens is sometimes misapplied to P. laxus.

purpuras'cens (*P. brachybotrys p.*) PURPLECUP M.
∞**purpureo-macula'tus** (*coulteri* × ∞*lemoinei*) . . . . . ∞PURPLESPOT M.
₵AMALTHEE. (Lem. 1924.) HV.
₵ETOILE ROSE. (Lem. 1910.)
₵FANTAISIE. (Lem. 1900.)
₵NUAGE ROSE. (Lem. 1916.)
₵OEIL DE POURPRE. (Lem. 1914.)
₵OPHELIA. (Lem. 1916.)
₵ROMEO. (Lem. 1914.)
₵SIRENE. (Lem. 1910.)
₵SURPRISE. (Lem. 1914.)
₵SYBILLE. (Lem. 1914.)
satsuma'nus (*satsumi; P. coronarius acuminatus*) . . . . . SATSUMA M.
—**nikoen'sis**
schrenk'i . . . . SCHRENK M.
—**jack'i**
serican'thus . . . . SILK M.
—**rehderia'nus** . . . REHDERS S.M.
serpyllifo'lius . . . THYMELEAF M.
specio'sus . . . . **P. laxus**
∞**splen'dens** (*?gordonianus* × *grandiflorus*) . . . . . . ∞SPLENDENS M.

PHILADELPHUS, continued

subca'nus
—**wil'soni** (*P. wilsoni*) WILSON MOCKORANGE
tenuifo'lius
tomento'sus (*nepalensis* Lodd., *not* Koehne) . . . . . WOOLLYLEAF M.
umbella'tus . . . . ∞**P. zeyheri u.**
undula'tus . . . . **P. laxus**
venus'tus . . . . TIBET M.
verruco'sus . . . . WARTY M.
∞**virgina'lis** (∞*lemoinei* × *?* ∞*nivalis* ₵PLENUS) . . . ∞VIRGINALIS M.
The typical form of this polybrid is ₵VIRGINAL.

₵ALBATRE. (Lem. 1914.) HV.
₵ARGENTINE. (Lem. 1914.)
₵BOUQUET BLANC. (Lem. 1903.)
₵GLACIER. (Lem. 1914.)
₵VIRGINAL. (Lem. 1909.)
wil'soni . . . . **P. subcanus w.**
∞**zey'heri** (*coronarius* × *?grandiflorus* or *inodorus*) . . . . . ∞ZEYHER M.
∞—**kochia'nus** (*P. kochianus*) KOCH Z.M.
∞—**umbella'tus** (*P. umbellatus*) ∞UMBEL Z.M.
₵DWARF GOLDEN. HV. Philadelphus

PHILE'SIA . . . . BOXLILY
magellan'ica (*buxifolia*). MAGELLAN B.

PHILIBER'TIA (*FUNASTRUM*) PHILIBERTIA
clau'sa (*Funastrum clausum*) SWEET P.

PHILLYR'EA . . . . PHILLYREA
angustifo'lia . . . . NARROWLEAF P.
₵ROSEMARY (*rosmarinifolia*) HV.
deco'ra (*vilmoriniana*) . LANCELEAF P.
latifo'lia . . . . TREE P.
—**me'dia** (*P. media*). SHARPBERRY T.P.
—**rotundifo'lia** . . . ROUNDLEAF T.P.
—**spino'sa** (*P. ilicifolia*) HOLLYLEAF T.P.

PHILODEN'DRON . . PHILODENDRON
acuminatis'simum . . . TAPERTIP P.
andrea'num
aspera'tum (*imperiale*)
bipinnatif'idum . . . . TWICECUT P.
car'deri . . . . **P. verrucosum**
corda'tum . . . . . . HEARTLEAF P.
×**corsinia'num** Hort. . . . REDRIM P.
devansayea'num
erubes'cens
gigan'teum . . . . . GIANTLEAF P.
glorio'sum
grandifo'lium . . . . . BIGLEAF P.
imperia'le . . . . . **P. asperatum**
lac'erum
ma'mei
pertu'sum . . . . **Monstera deliciosa**
sello'um
spectab'ile . . . . VELVET P.
triparti'tum . . . . TRILEAF P.
verruco'sum (*carderi; lindeni*) WARTY P.
wal'lisi . . . . WALLIS P.

PHILOTHE'CA . . . . PHILOTHECA
ericoi'des . . . . HEATH P.

PHILO'TRIA . . . . **ANACHARIS**

PHIPPS'IA
See **GRASS GENERA.**

PHLEBO'DIUM . . **POLYPODIUM**
See **FERN GENERA.**

PHLE'UM . . . . TIMOTHY
See **GRASS GENERA.**

PHLOGACAN'THUS. Flameacanthus
thyrsiflo'rus

PHLO'MIS . . . . . Jerusalemsage
alpi'na . . . . Alpine J.
cashmeria'na . . . . . Kashmir J.
frutico'sa . . . . Common J.
Goldleaf (*chrysophylla*) hv.
Rusty (*ferruginea*)
lana'ta . . . . Woolly J.
lychni'tis . . . . Lampwick J.
pun'gens . . . . Prickly J.
sa'mia . . . . Greek J.
spectab'ilis . . . . Showy J.
tubero'sa . . . . Tuber J.
visco'sa (*russeliana*) . . . Sticky J.

PHLOX' |w . . . . Phlox
The Editorial Committee acknowledges with thanks and appreciation the expert assistance of Edgar T. Wherry, University of Pennsylvania, Philadelphia, Pa., in the preparation of the Phlox species list, and of Alfred M. S. Pridham, Cornell University, Ithaca, N. Y., for an up-to-date hort. var. list of "Summer Flowering Phlox."

aculea'ta . . . . Idaho P.
adsur'gens . . . . . Periwinkle P.
albiflo'ra . . . . **P. divaricata candida**
amoe'na . . . . Amoena P.
The plant commonly offered under this name is ∞P. procumbens.

amplifo'lia (*P. paniculata a.*)
Broadleaf P.
andic'ola (*planitiarum*) . . Plains P.
∞ **arends'i** (*divaricata* × *paniculata*)
∞ Arends P.
argilla'cea . . . . **P. pilosa a.**
arista'ta; as'pera . . . . **P. pilosa**
austromonta'na . . . . Desert P.
bif'ida . . . . Tenpoint P.
—stella'ria (*P. stellaria*) Smooth T.P.
brit'toni . . . . **P. subulata b.**
bryoi'des . . . . Squarestem P.
buck'leyi . . . . . . Buckley P.
caespito'sa . . . . Tufted P.
—condensa'ta (*P. condensata*)
Dwarf T.P.
cam'la (*camlaensis*) **P. nivalis** ₵Camla
This is claimed to be a hybrid of P. amoena and P. subulata, but is not related to either.

canaden'sis . . . . . **P. divaricata c.**
canes'cens |w . . . . . . Hoary P.
∞ **caroli'na** (*caroliniana*; ∞*decussata* in part; *suffruticosa* in part)
∞ Carolina P.
—altis'sima . . . . Tall C.P.
—car'nea . . . . Pink C.P.
—heterophyl'la . . Changeleaf C.P.
—triflo'ra . . . . Early C.P.
coeru'lea . . . **P. stolonifera violacea**
condensa'ta . . . . **P. caespitosa c.**
corda'ta . . . . **P. paniculata c.**
costa'ta . . . . **P. multiflora**
covil'lei . . . . Coville P.
∞ **criter'ion** (*?drummondi* × *paniculata*)
∞ Criterion P.
cruen'ta . . . . . . **P. paniculata c.**
cuspida'ta . . . . . . **P. drummondi**
Though originally proposed for typical P. drummondi, this name is often misapplied to its ₵Star.

∞ **decussa'ta** . . . . . ∞ Decussata P.
A group name for horticultural half-breeds or mixed-breeds of P. paniculata, and sometimes of ∞P. carolina, P. glaberrima, or P. maculata.

PHLOX, continued
depres'sa . . . . . **P. multiflora d.**
diffu'sa . . . . . Spreading Phlox
divarica'ta . . . . Sweetwilliam P.
—canaden'sis (*P. canadensis*)
Canada S.P.
—candi'da (*P. albiflora*) . Albino S.P.
—lapham'i . . . . . . Lapham S.P.
₵White Lapham (*alba*) hv.
—lilaci'na . . . . Lilac S.P.
dolichan'tha . . . SanBernardino P.
doug'lasi |w . . . . . . Douglas P.
—missoulen'sis . . Missoula D.P.
This var. is occasionally and incorrectly placed under P. kelseyi and the name misspelled missouliensis.

—rig'ida (*P. rigida*) Thickleaf D.P.
drum'mondi (*cuspidata*) |w
Drummond P.
All the following are clons.

Bigbloom (*grandiflora*). hv.
Big Drummond (*rotundata*)
Carmine (*carnea*)
Dusky (*atropurpurea*)
Dwarf Drummond (*nana*)
Giant (*gigantea*)
Heynhold (*wilcoxiana*)
Isabellina
Leopold (*leopoldi*)
Radowitz (*radowitzi*)
Rosy Drummond (*rosea*)
Scarlet (*coccinea*)
Smoothtube (*glabriflora*)
Star (*stellaris*)
To this form the name P. cuspidata is frequently misapplied.

Violet (*violacea*)
White-eye (*alba oculata*)
florida'na . . . . Florida P.
Not in cultivation. P. floridana Hort. is P. glaberrima.

∞ **frondo'sa** (*nivalis* × *subulata*)
₵Perfection. hv.
₵Vivid
glaber'rima (∞*decussata* in part; *suffruticosa* in part) . . . Smooth P.
glabra'ta . . . . **P. hoodi g.**
∞ **glutino'sa** (*divaricata* × *pilosa*)
hentz'i . . . . **P. nivalis**
hirsu'ta . . . . Siskiyou P.
hood'i |w . . . . Hoods P.
—glabra'ta (*P. glabrata*) Smooth H.P.
—muscoi'des (*P. muscoides*)
Dwarf H.P.
kel'seyi . . . . Kelsey P.
lanceola'ta . . . . . . **P. speciosa l.**
∞ **leopoldia'na** (*drummondi* × *paniculata?*) . . . . ∞ Leopold P.
∞ **lilaci'na** (*bifida* × *subulata*). ∞ Lilac P.
₵Bluehill. hv.
₵G. F. Wilson (*wilsoni*)
₵Stellaria
longifo'lia . . . . . . Longleaf P.
macula'ta (∞*decussata* in part; *longiflora*) . . . . Meadow P.
—odora'ta . . . . . Northern M.P.
Alba (*P. alba*) hv.
—pyramida'lis . . . Southern M.P.
Candida. hv.
—suave'olens . . . . . Sweet M.P.
multiflo'ra (*costata*) . . . Flowery P.
—depres'sa (*P. depressa*) Dwarf F.P.
muscoi'des . . . . **P. hoodi m.**
na'na . . . . SantaFe P.
niva'lis (*hentzi; P. n. hentzi; P. subulata h.*) . . . . Trailing P.

PHLOX nivalis, continued
₵Camla. hv.
₵Dixie (*sylvestris*)
₵Mary Alice
₵Sir Guilford
ova'ta . . . . . . Mountain Phlox
—latifo'lia . . . . Purple M.P.
—pul'chra . . . . Pastel M.P.
panicula'ta (∞*decussata* in part; *sickmanni*) . . . . Summer P.
—amplifo'lia . . . . . **P. amplifolia**
—corda'ta (*P. cordata*) Heartleaf S.P.
—cruen'ta (*P. cruenta*) . Blood S.P.
—sca'bra . . . . . Roughleaf S.P.
—undula'ta (*P. undulata*)
Waveleaf S.P.
pilo'sa (*aristata; aspera*) . . Downy P.
—amplexicau'lis . . Southern D.P.
—argilla'cea (*P. argillacea*) Silver D.P.
—deton'sa . . . . Gulf D.P.
—ful'gida . . . . Prairie D.P.
—ozarka'na . . . . . . Ozark D.P.
—villosis'sima (*P. villosissima*)
Texas D.P.
—vi'rens . . . . . . Eastern D.P.
planitia'rum . . . . . . **P. andicola**
∞ **procum'bens** (*stolonifera* × *subulata; verna* Hort.)
Often sold as P. amoena Hort.
₵Variegated (*foliis variegatis*) hv.
rep'tans . . . . **P. stolonifera**
rig'ida . . . . **P. douglasi r.**
roemeria'na . . . . . . Roemer P.
∞ **rugel'i** (*amoena* × *divaricata*)
∞ Rugel P.
sibir'ica . . . . Siberian P.
sickmann'i . . . . **P. paniculata**
specio'sa . . . . Showy P.
—lanceola'ta (*P. lanceolata*)
Broadleaf S.P.
splen'dens Hort. (*divaricata* × *pilosa*)
stansbur'yi . . . . . Stansbury P.
stella'ria A. Gray, *not* Hort. **P. bifida s.**
stella'ria Hort. . . . ∞ **P. lilacina** hv.
stolonif'era (*reptans*) . Creeping P.
—viola'cea (*P. coerulea*) . Violet C.P.
subula'ta . . . . Moss P.
—al'ba . . . . White M.P.
—austra'lis . . . . Southern M.P.
—britto'ni (*P. brittoni*) Britton M.P.
—cilia'ta . . . . . Northern M.P.
—hentz'i . . . . **P. nivalis**
All the following are clons.

Annulata. hv. P. subulata
Appleblossom
Atropurpurea
Big Moss (*grandiflora*)
Caerulescens
Crimsonking
Frondosa
Maysnow
Moerheim
Nelson Moss (*nelsoni*)
Nivalis
Pallida
Red (*rubra*)
Rhonsdorf Beauty
Rochester
Rosemoss (*rosea*)
Samson
(*The*) Bride
suffrutico'sa . . . . . . **P. carolina; P. glaberrima**
—glaber'rima (*P. suffruticosa* in part)
P. glaberrima
ten'uis . . . . Slender P.
undula'ta . . . . . **P. paniculata u.**

PHLOX, continued

ver'na Hort. . . . . . ∞**P. procumbens**
villosis'sima . . . . . . **P. pilosa v.**
vis'cida . . . . Sticky Phlox

Common names and hort. var. (clons) of **Phlox:**

Except as otherwise indicated the plants included in this list are horticultural varieties of Phlox paniculata or of alleged hybrids between that species and P. maculata. However, Dr. Wherry finds no evidence that the latter species enters these hybrids. Hort. var. of ∞P. arendsi, Ar.; P. d varicata, Div.; P. drummondi, Drum.; ∞P. frondosa, Fron.; P. glaberrima (*suffruticosa* in part), Gla.; ∞P. lilacina, Lil.; P. nivalis, Niv.; ∞P. procumbens, Pro.; P. subulata, Sub.

Abbreviations of Names of Introducers

Ald.	Aldersey.
And.	Andrews.
App.	Appleton.
Are.	Arends.
Bec.	Beckett.
B. G.	Beatrice Gardens.
BSN.	Bay State Nurseries.
Cam.	Campbell.
Dic.	Dickson.
Dov.	Dove.
Dre.	Dreer.
D.-T.	Dwyer-Thurlow.
Fai.	Fairbairn.
F. et C.	Fougeot et Cie.
Few.	Fewekes.
Fig.	Figuerredo.
For.	Forbes.
G.&K.	Goos & Koenemann.
Heu.	Heurlin.
H.-R.	Hollis-Rea.
Jon.	Jones.
Lem.	Lemoine.
Lie.	Lierval.
Pfi.	Pfitzer.
Pri.	Pritchard.
Rea	Rea.
Ruys	Ruys.
Sau., A.	A. P. Saunders.
Sch.	Schmeiske.
Smi., G.	G. N. Smith.
S.-R.	Struthers-Rea.
Thu.	Thurlow.
Toe.	Toedt.
W. G.	Wayside Gardens.

In using this list the clon sign (₵) should precede all hort. var. names, but not common names of species and natural varieties; as, ₵Abel Tasman, but Albino Sweetwilliam P.

Abel Tasman.
Adonis.
A. E. Amos. (Jon.)
Aetna.
Africa. (Pfi. 1910.)
Aida. (Pfi. 1934.)
A. J. Macself. (For. 1911.)
Alba.
Albatre.
Albert (*Leo*) Schlageter. (Pfi.)
Albert Leteau.
Albino Sweetwilliam P. **P. divaricata candida.**
Albion. (Dre. 1900.)
Alcestes.
Aldeham. (Pri.)
Amanda. Ar.
Amaranth.
American Legion. (Dov. 1914.)
Amoena P. **P. amoena.**
Amphitryon.
Annie Cook. (Thu.)
Annie Laurie.
Annulata. Sub.
Antoinette Six.
Antonin Mercier. (Lem. 1901.)
Apollo. (Sch. 1930.)
Appleblossom. Sub.
Aquilon.
∞Arends P. ∞**P. arendsi.**
Arete.
Argon.
Asa Gray. (Sch. 1930.)
Asia. (Pfi. 1910.)
Astier Rehu.
Astrild.
Athis.
Atlas.
Atropurpurea. Sub.
Attraction. (Fai.)
Augusta. (W. G. 1937.)
August Fremiet.
Aurora Borealis.
Australia.
Bacchante.
Balzac.
Baron Vondedem. (Ruys.)
Baron Vonheekeren. (Ruys.)
B. Comte. (Lem. 1900.)
Beacon.
Beranger.
Berenice.
Bernice. (Thu.)
Bigbloom (*grandiflora*). Drum.
Big Drummond (*rotundata*). Drum.
Big Moss (*grandiflora*). Sub.
Black Warrior.
Blanc Nain.
Blood Summer P. **P. paniculata cruenta.**
Bluehill. Lil. (Heu.)
Border Queen. (Fai.)
Boule de Feu.
Bouquet Fleuri.
Brantome.
Brenda.
Bridesmaid. (Pri. 1920.)
Brilliant.
Britton Moss P. **P. subulata brittoni.**
Broadleaf P. **P. amplifolia.**
Broadleaf Showy P. **P. speciosa lanceolata.**
Brogniart.
Buckley P. **P. buckleyi.**
Burns.
Caerulescens. Sub.
Cameron.
Camillo Schneider.
Camla. Niv.
Canada Sweetwilliam P. **P. divaricata canadensis.**
Candeur.
Candida.
Caractacus.
Caran d'Ache.
Carl Bleyle.
Carmine (*carnea*). Drum.
∞Carolina P. ∞**P. carolina.**
Caroline Vandenberg.
Cendrillon.
Cerisius. (Sch. 1920.)
Chamois Rose.
Champion Veribest.
Champs Elysee.
Changeleaf Carolina P. **P. carolina heterophylla.**
Charles B. Merrill. (Rea.)
Charles Darwin.
Charlotte. Ar.
Charlotte Saison.
Chateaubriand.

PHLOX, continued

Chatrain.
Clara Benz.
Colibri.
Colorado. (And. 1929.)
Columbia. (W. G. 1935.)
Comtesse Dejarnac. (Pfi.)
Comte Ungerer Sternberg.
Comte von Hochberg. Vonhochberg.
Comus.
Coquelicot. (Lem.)
Cornelie Dotter.
Count Zeppelin.
Coville P. **P. covillei.**
Creeping P. **P. stolonifera.**
Crepuscule. (Lem. 1860.)
Crimsonking. Sub.
∞Criterion P. ∞**P. criterion.**
Cyrano.
Czarina.
Daily Sketch. (Jon. 1930.)
Daniel Leseuer.
Daubigny.
Dawn.
Daybreak.
Debs. (Heu.)
∞Decussata P. ∞**P. decussata.**
Deeside. (Cam.)
Delarey.
Demirbel.
Desert P. **P. austromontana.**
Deutschland. (Are. 1920.)
Diplomat.
Dixie (*sylvestris*). Niv.
Dolly. (H.-R.)
Douglas P. **P. douglasi.**
Downy P. **P. pilosa.**
Dr. Charcot. (Lem. 1904.)
Dr. Konigshofer.
Drummond P. **P. drummondi.**
Dr. Vogel. (Pfi.)
Duquesclin.
Dusky (*atropurpurea*). Drum.
Dwarf Drummond (*nana*). Drum.
Dwarf Flowery P. **P. multiflora depressa.**
Dwarf Hoods P. **P. hoodi muscoides.**
Dwarf Tufted P. **P. caespitosa condensata.**
Early Carolina P. **P. carolina triflora.**
Eastern Downy P. **P. pilosa virens.**
Eclaireur. (Lem. 1889.)
Edmond Bossier.
Edmond Rostand.
Edward Lockroy.
E. I. Farrington. (Smi. G. 1929.)
Eiffel Tower.
Electra.
Elizabeth Campbell.
Embrasement.
Emile Littre.
Emil Kranz.
Enchantress.
Epopee.
Esclamonde.
Especial French.
Etna. (Lem. 1892.)
Ettas Choice.
Eugene Danzanvilliers.
Europa. (Pfi. 1910.)
Europe.
Evangeline. (Jon.)
Evelyn. (Ald. 1905.)
Eventide. Sub.
Fannie Stuart.
Faust.
Fernand Cortez.

PHLOX, continued
Feu Dumonde.
Fiancee.
Fidelio. (Pfi.)
Fireball. Drum.
Firebrand. (Are.)
Flambeau.
Flora Hornung.
Flora Reidi. (Toe. 1925.)
Florence.
Florida P. **P. floridana.**
Flowery P. **P. multiflora.**
Fort de France.
Frau Ackerknecht.
Frau (*Anton*) Buchner. (Pfi. 1907.)
Frau Dr. Klemm. (Pfi. 193–.)
Frau (*Henri*) Gertz. (Pfi. 1909.)
Fraulein von Lassburg. Lassburg.
Frau (*Millie*) Korte. (Pfi.)
Frau (*P.*) Schollhammer. (Pfi.)
Frau (*Richard*) Gross.
Fred Rafferty. (Pfi. 1912.)
Freya.
Frondosa. Sub.
Gefion. (G.&K.)
General Chanzy.
General Petain. (Fai.)
General Vanheutz. (Ruys 1905.)
George Stipp. (Pfi. 1926.)
George Stroehlein. (Pfi. 1905.)
G. F. Wilson (*wilsoni*). Lil.
Giant (*gigantea*). Drum.
Girondin.
Gismonda.
Gladstone.
Glenwood.
Gloire Demaroc.
Glow.
Goethe. *Wolfgang von Goethe.*
Goliath. (BSN. 1922.)
Graf Zepplin. (Pfi. 1918.)
Greta. Ar.
Grideur.
Gruppenkoenigin. (Pfi. 1905.)
Gulf Downy P. **P. pilosa detonsa.**
Gustave Lind. (Pfi. 1904.)
Gustave Nadaud.
Guy Moore. (Sch. 1920.)
Hajo Eilers.
Hanny Pfleiderer. (Pfi. 1907.)
Hans Vollmoller. (Pfi. 1914.)
Harlekin. (Pfi.)
Harvest Fire.
Hauptmann Kohl. (Pfi. 1928.)
H. B. May. (Jon.)
Heartleaf Summer P. **P. paniculata cordata.**
Hector.
Helene. Ar.
Helene Vacaresco.
Henri Martin.
Henri Murger.
Henri Regnault.
Hercules. Gla.
Hermina.
Heroine.
Hervor.
Heynhold (*wilcoxiana*). Drum.
Hindenburg. (Pfi. 1916.)
H. Menior.
Hoary P. **P. canescens.**
Hodur.
Hoffnung. (Pfi. 1919.)
Hoods P. **P. hoodi.**
Hortense.
H. O. Wijers.
Idaho P. **P. aculeata.**
Iduna.

PHLOX, continued
Imperator.
Independence. Mrs. Jenkins.
Indian Chief. Gla.
Ingeborg.
Inspector Elpel.
Iris.
Isabellina. Drum.
Isabey.
James Bennett.
James Galloway.
Japonaise.
Jean Dupois.
Jeanne d'Arc.
J. H. Slocum.
Jocelyn.
Johnsons Favorite.
Jordan.
Joseph Barr.
Josephine Gerbeaux.
Jules Breton.
Jules Cambon.
Jules Sandeau. (Lem. 1911.)
Juliet.
Julius Heurlin.
Junius.
Kapt. Koenig. (Pfi. 1916.)
Karl Bleyle. (Pfi. 1912.)
Karl Foerster. (Ruys.)
Kathe. Ar.
Katina Beeli.
Kelsey P. **P. kelseyi.**
Klara Benz. (Pfi. 1904.)
Lady Greenall. (Fai.)
Lady (*Lunch*) Blosse.
Lafrance.
L'Aiglon.
Lamartine.
Laniboire.
Lapham. Div.
Lapham Sweetwilliam P. **P. divaricata laphami.**
Lassburg. *Fraulein von Lassburg.*
Lavague.
Lavina Ponsonby.
L'Eclaireur. (F. et C. 1890.)
Lecygne.
Lemahdi. (Jon. 1900.)
Lemauve.
Leonardo Da Vinci.
Leopold (*leopoldi*). Drum.
∞ Leopold P. ∞ **P. leopoldiana.**
Le Pole Dunord.
Leprintemps.
Leprophete.
Lesiecle.
Lesoleil.
L'Esperance.
L'Evenement.
Lierwalli.
Light of Godsall.
Lilacmoss. Lilac P.
∞ Lilac P. ∞ **P. lilacina.**
Lilac Sweetwilliam P. **P. divaricata lilacina.**
Lillian. (Fig. 1928.)
Little Dot. Sub.
Lofna.
Loki. (G.&K.)
Longleaf P. **P. longifolia.**
Lord Lambourne.
Lothair.
Louise. Ar.
Louise Abbema.
Lucas Schwinghammer. (Pfi.)
Lumineux.
Luster.
Madagascar.

PHLOX, continued
Magician.
Magnificence. Gla.
Maid Marian. (Thu. 1917.)
Manzelbrunner.
Marechal French. (Lem. 1915.)
Margarete Closs.
Margaret (*Gavin*) Jones. (Ruys.)
Mariana. (Are.)
Maries Jacob.
Marmorata.
Marquise de St. Paul.
Mary Alice. Niv.
Mary Louise. (Sau. A. 193–.)
Mary Wilkins.
Matador.
Mauvequeen.
Maysnow. Sub.
Meadow P. **P. maculata.**
Merry Andrew.
Meteor.
Mia Ruys. (Ruys.)
Michael Buchner.
Milly Vanhoboken.
Minerva.
Minnie West.
Miramer.
Miss (*Ellen*) Willmott.
Miss Lingard. Gla. (App.)
Miss Miller. Gla.
Missoula Douglas P. **P. douglasi missoulensis.**
Miss Pemberton.
Miss Verboom.
Mme. Benzanson.
Mme. Cornudet.
Mme. Mellinger.
Mme. Mueret.
Mme. (*Pape*) Carpentier.
Mme. (*Paul*) Dutrie. (Pfi. 1907.)
Mme. Prosper Langier.
Model. Sub.
Moerheim. Sub.
Mons. Graham.
Montagnard.
Montblanc. Gla.
Morgenrood. (Ruys 1926.)
Moss P. **P. subulata.**
Mountain P. **P. ovata.**
Mozart.
Mrs. (*A.*) Baker.
Mrs. (*Arnold*) Turner.
Mrs. (*Charles*) Dorr.
Mrs. Cook.
Mrs. (*Edwin*) Beckett. (Bec.)
Mrs. (*Ethel*) Pritchard. (Pri. 1923.)
Mrs. (*H. J.*) Jones. (Jon.)
Mrs. Ingalls.
Mrs. Jenkins. *Independence.*
Mrs. (*Livingston*) Farrand. (Sch. 1920.)
Mrs. (*Milly*) Vanhoboken. (Ruys.)
Mrs. Oliver.
Mrs. Rutgers.
Mrs. Scholten. (Ruys.)
Mrs. (*Warren G.*) Harding. (Sch. '20.)
Mrs. (*W.*) Vanbeuninger. (Ruys.)
Nana Coerulea.
Nelson Moss (*nelsoni*). Sub.
Neubert.
Nivalis. Sub.
Nordlicht. (G.&K.)
Northern Meadow P. **P. maculata odorata.**
Northern Moss P. **P. subulata ciliata.**
Norwood.
Obergartner Wittig.
Oriflame. (Lem. 1925.)

PHLOX, continued
Ornament.
Osceola. (And. 1929.)
Ostaris.
O. Wittich.
Ozark Downy P. **P. pilosa ozarkana.**
Painted Lady.
Pallida. Sub.
Pantheon.
Papillon.
Pastel Mountain P. **P. ovata pulchra.**
Paul Fliche.
Paul (*Hoffman*) Arends.
Paul Martin.
P. D. Williams.
Peachblossom.
Peachblow.
Pearl.
Pecheur d'Islande.
Perfection. Fron.
Periwinkle P. **P. adsurgens.**
Pharaon. (Lem. 1900.)
Pinkbeauty.
Pink Carolina P. **P. carolina carnea.**
Plains P. **P. andicola.**
Pluto.
Prairie Downy P. **P. pilosa fulgida.**
Premier Ministre.
Princess Louise.
Professor Schliemann.
Professor Virchow.
Prof. Went. (Ruys.)
Purity.
Purple Mountain P. **P. ovata latifolia.**
Purplequeen. Gla.
Pyramid.
Queen.
Queen of Beatrice Gardens. (B. G. 1930.)
Radowitz (*radowitzi*). Drum.
R. A. Goldie.
Red (*rubra*). Sub.
Redacteur Flammer.
Redoubt.
Reichgraf Vonhochberg. (Pfi. 1899.)
Rheinlander. (G.&K. 1914.)
Rheinstrom. Rijnstroom.
Rhonsdorf Beauty. Sub.
Richard Strauss.
Richard Wallace. (Lie. 1870.)
Riechenau. *Schlossgaertner Riechenau.*
Rijnstroom. (Pfi. 1910.) *Rynstrom; Rheinstrom.*
Ringleader.
Riverton Jewel. (Dre. 1905.)
Robert Werner.
Robinhood. (And. 1929.)
Rochester. Sub.
Roemer P. **P. roemeriana.**
Roi des Massifs.
Rokoko. (Pfi. 1929.)
Rosemoss (*rosea*). Sub.
Rosenberg. (Pfi. 1908.)
Rosenkavalier. (Pfi. 1928.)
Rosetta.
Rossignol.
Rosy Drummond (*rosea*). Drum.
Rosygem. Gla.
Roughleaf Summer P. **P. paniculata scabra.**
Royalpurple. (Bec.)
R. P. Struthers. (S.-R.)
Ruby. (Few. 1924.)
∞ Rugel P. ∞ **P. rugeli.**
Ruth May. (Thu. 193–.)
Rynstrom. Rijnstroom.
Saison Lierval.

PHLOX, continued
Saladin. (G.&K. 1924.)
Salmon Glow.
Salome. (Pfi. 1930.)
Samson. Sub.
SanBernardino P. **P. dolichantha.**
SantaFe P. **P. nana.**
Sarabande.
Savorgnan Debrazza.
Scarlet (*coccinea*). Drum.
Schlossgaertner Riechenau. Riechenau.
Selma. (Ruys 1905.)
Septemberglut. (Pfi.)
September Snow.
Seraph. Sub.
Sherrif Ivory. (Dic.)
Showy P. **P. speciosa.**
Siberian P. **P. sibirica.**
Siebold. (Lem. 1904.)
Sigrid Arnoldson.
Silver Downy P. **P. pilosa argillacea.**
Silvertone. (And. 1927.)
Simplon.
Sir David Beatty. (Vai.)
Sir Edwin Landseer.
Sir Guilford. Niv.
Siskiyou P. **P. hirsuta.**
Slender P. **P. tenuis.**
Smiles. (Pfi. 193–.)
Smooth Hoods P. **P. hoodi glabrata.**
Smooth P. **P. glaberrima.**
Smoothtube (*glabriflora*). Drum.
Snowball. Drum.
Snowcap. (And. 1929.)
Snowdon. Gla.
Sommerkleid.
Southern Downy P. **P. pilosa amplexicaulis.**
Southern Meadow P. **P. maculata pyramidalis.**
Southern Moss P. **P. subulata australis.**
Spatrot.
Spreading P. **P. diffusa.**
Sprite. Sub.
Squarestem P. **P. bryoides.**
Stanislas.
Stansbury P. **P. stansburyi.**
Star (*stellaris*). Drum.
Starlight.
Stella Choice. (D.-T.)
Stellaria. Lil.
Stephanie.
Sticky P. **P. viscida.**
Suffrage.
Summer P. **P. paniculata.**
Sunshine.
Superb. *Superbians.*
Sweetheart.
Sweet Meadow P. **P. maculata suaveolens.**
Sweetwilliam P. **P. divaricata.**
Sylphide.
Tall Carolina P. **P. carolina altissima.**
Tanager. (And. 1929.)
Tapis Blanc. (Lem. 1901.)
Tenpoint P. **P. bifida.**
Terre Neuve.
Texas Downy P. **P. pilosa villosissima.**
Thebaide.
(*The*) Bride. Sub.
(*The*) King. (Fai.)
Thickleaf Douglas P. **P. douglasi rigida.**
Thor. (G.&K. 1915.)
Tigress.
Titanic. (Lem. 1918.)

PHLOX, continued
Tragedian. *Tragedii.*
Trailing P. **P. nivalis.**
Traviata. (Pfi. 1929.)
Tufted P. **P. caespitosa.**
Turandot. (Pfi. 1936.)
Unique.
Variegated (*foliis variegatis*). Pro.
Vesuvius.
Victor.
Viking. (G.&K.)
Violet (*violacea*). Drum.
Violet Creeping P. **P. stolonifera violacea.**
Violetta.
Vivid. Fron.
Vonhochberg. *Comte von Hochberg.*
Walter Groff.
Wanadis.
Waveleaf Summer P. **P. paniculata undulata.**
W. C. Egan.
Wellesley. (G. Smi. 1927.)
White-eye (*alba oculata*). Drum.
Whitelady.
Whitelapham (*alba*).
White Moss P. **P. subulata alba.**
Widar. (G.&K. 1912.)
William Kesselring. (Ruys.)
William Muhle.
William Ramsey.
William Robinson.
William Tell. (Sch. 1920.)
William Wells. (Jon.)
Wolfgang von Goethe. Goethe.
Wurtembergia. (Pfi. 1919.)
W. Watson.
Zouave.
Zukunft. (Pfi. 1919.)

PHOE'BE . . . . Phoebe
am'bigens . . . . . . Honduras P.
nan'mu . . . . Nanmu P.
poro'sa . . . . Imbuya P.

PHOENICAU'LIS . . . Phoenicaulis
cheiranthoi'des (*Parrya menziesi*) Wallflower P.

PHOENICOPHO'RIUM **STEVENSONIA**
See **PALM GENERA.**

PHOE'NIX . . . . Date
See **PALM GENERA.**

PHOLIDO'TA
See **ORCHID GENERA.**

PHOLIO'TA . . . . Pholiota
adipo'sa . . . . Fatty P.
capera'ta . . . . . . Wrinkled P.
margina'ta
squarro'sa . . . . Scaly P.

PHOLIU'RUS . . . . . . Sicklegrass
See **GRASS GENERA.**

PHORADEN'DRON |w American-mistletoe
califor'nicum |w . . . Mesquite A.
coloraden'se . . ColoradoDesert A.
den'sum . . . . Cypress A.
flaves'cens |w . . . . Christmas A.
juniperi'num . . . . . . Juniper A.
liboce'dri |w . . . . Incensecedar A.
liga'tum . . . . Pinchscale A.
macrophyl'lum (*P. flavescens m.*) Bigleaf A.
pauciflo'rum . . . . Fir A.
villo'sum |w . . . . . . Pacific A.

PHOR'MIUM . . . . . . Fiberlily
colenso'i (*cookianum*) . . . Green F.
Pearlstripe (*variegatum*) hv.
hook'eri . . . . Hookers F.
ten'ax . . . . NewZealand F.
—alpi'num . . . . . Alpine N.F.
Golden (*aureum*) hv. P. tenax
Powerscourt (*powerscourti*)
Purpleleaf (*atropurpureum*)
Variegated (*variegatum*)
Veitch (*veitchianum*)

PHOTIN'IA (*HETEROMELES*) lw Photinia
amphidox'a . . . . . Bigfruit P.
arbutifo'lia (*salicifolia; Heteromeles a.; H. salicifolia*) lw . Christmasberry (*Toyon*)
—chrysocar'pa . . . . . Orange C.
—macrocar'pa . . . . . Catalina C.
beauverdia'na . . . . Beauverd P.
—notab'ilis . . . . . Showy B.P.
benthamia'na . . . . . Bentham P.
davidso'niae . . . . . Davidson P.
franchetia'na . . . . . Franchet P.
gla'bra . . . . Japanese P.
integrifo'lia . . . . . Wholeleaf P.
japon'ica . . . . . . **Eriobotrya j.**
parvifo'lia (*subumbellata*) Littleleaf P.
salicifo'lia . . . . . . **P. arbutifolia**
serrula'ta . . . . . . Chinese P.
—rotundifo'lia . . . Roundleaf C.P.
Nova. hv. P. serrulata
villo'sa . . . . Oriental P.
—lae'vis . . . . . . Smooth O.P.
—maximowiczia'na . Veinyleaf O.P.
—sin'ica . . . . . . Thinleaf O.P.

Photinia . . . . **Photinia**
Beauverd P. . . . . **P. beauverdiana**
Bentham P. . . . . **P. benthamiana**
Bigfruit P. . . . . . **P. amphidoxa**
Catalina Christmasberry **P. arbutifolia macrocarpa**
Chinese P. . . . . . . **P. serrulata**
Christmasberry . . . **P. arbutifolia**
Davidson P. . . . . **P. davidsoniae**
Franchet P. . . . . **P. franchetiana**
Japanese P. . . . . **P. glabra**
Littleleaf P. . . . . . **P. parvifolia**
Orange Christmasberry **P. arbutifolia chrysocarpa**
Oriental P. . . . . **P. villosa**
Roundleaf Chinese P. **P. serrulata rotundifolia**
Showy Beauverd P. **P. beauverdiana notabilis**
Smooth Oriental P. **P. villosa laevis**
Thinleaf O. P. . . . . **P. v. sinica**
Veinyleaf O. P. **P. v. maximowicziana**
Wholeleaf P. . . . . **P. integrifolia**

PHRAGMI'TES . . . . Reed
See **GRASS GENERA.**

PHRAGMOPED'ILUM **CYPRIPEDIUM**
See **ORCHID GENERA.**

PHRY'MA lw . . . . Lopseed
leptostach'ya lw . . . American L.

PHYGE'LIUS . . . . Phygelius
capen'sis . . . . Capefuchsia P.
Coccinea. hv.

PHY'LICA . . . . Phylica
ericoi'des . . . . . . Capeheath P.

PHYLLAG'ATHIS . . . . Metalleaf
rotundifo'lia . . . . Sumatra M.

PHYLLAN'THUS (*CICCA; XYLOPHYLLA*) lw . . . . Leafflower
ac'idus (*distichus; Cicca disticha*) Otaheite-gooseberry L.
acumina'tus . Jamaicagooseberry L.
angustifo'lius (*Xylophylla angustifolia*)
avicula'ria lw . . . . . Birdseed L.
calyci'nus . . . . Bigcalyx L.
em'blica . . . . Emblic L.

This small tropical tree is the source of Emblic, one of the fruits known as Myrobalan.

flu'itans . . . . Floating L.
glauces'cens . . . . Blue L.
grandifo'lius . . . . . . Bigleaf L.
latifo'lius . . . . **P. speciosus**
mimosoi'des . . . . Mimosa L.
niru'ri . . . . Flyroost L.
nivo'sus . . . . **Breynia nivosa**
polygonoi'des lw . . . Knotweed L.
salviaefo'lius . . . . Sage L.
specio'sus (*latifolius; Xylophylla speciosa*)
wightia'nus . . . . . . Wights L.

PHYLLAU'REA . . . **CODIAEUM**

PHYLLI'TIS (*SCOLOPENDRIUM*)
See **FERN GENERA.**

PHYLLOCAC'TUS . **EPIPHYLLUM**
See **CACTUS GENERA.**

PHYLLOCA'LYX . . . . . **EUGENIA**

PHYLLOCLA'DUS . . . Celerypine
alpi'nus . . . . Mountain C.
glau'cus . . . . Toatoa C.
rhomboida'lis . . . . . Tasmania C.
trichomanoi'des . . . Tanekaha C.

PHYLLO'DOCE lw . . Mountainheath
aleu'tica . . . . Aleutian M.
brew'eri . . . . Brewer M.
caeru'lea . . . . Blue M.
empetrifor'mis lw . . . . . . Red M.
erec'ta . . . . **Phyllothamnus erectus**
glanduliflo'ra . . . . . . Cream M.
∞**interme'dia** (*empetriformis × glanduliflora*) . . . . . . ∞Redcream M.
nippon'ica . . . . Nippon M.
—amab'ilis . . . Littleleaf N.M.

PHYLLOG'ONUM . . . **GILMANIA**

Phyllogonum has recently been reduced to synonymy on account of an earlier genus of mosses, Phyllogonium, with which it is likely to be confused.

PHYLLOSPA'DIX lw . . . Surfgrass
scou'leri (*serrulatus*) lw . Scouler S.
tor'reyi lw . . . . Torrey S.

PHYLLOSTA'CHYS
See **BAMBOO GENERA.**

PHYLLOS'TYLON . . . . . . Seron
brasilien'sis . . . . Seron

PHYLLOTAE'NIUM **XANTHOSOMA**

×**PHYLLOTHAM'NUS** (*Phyllodoce × Rhodothamnus*) . . Phyllothamnus
∞**erec'tus** (*Phyllodoce empetriformis × Rhodothamnus chamaecistus; Phyllodoce erecta*)

PHYMATO'DES . . **POLYPODIUM**
See **FERN GENERA.**

PHYMO'SIA . . . . **SPHAERALCEA**

PHY'SALIS lw . . . . Groundcherry
alkeken'gi (*bunyardi; francheti*) lw Strawberry G.
angula'ta . . . . Cutleaf G.
heterophyl'la . . . . . . Clammy G.
ixocar'pa . . . . Tomatillo G.
loba'ta . . . . **Quincula l.**
peruvia'na (*edulis*) . . . Peruvian G. (*Cape-gooseberry*)

This plant appears to have originated in Peru but has reached its chief economic importance in the Cape region of South Africa—whence the name "Cape-gooseberry."

pruino'sa . . . . Hairy G.
pubes'cens lw . . . . Downy G.
pu'mila . . . . Prairie G.
rotunda'ta lw . . . . Roundleaf G.
subglabra'ta . . . . . Taperleaf G.
virginia'na . . . . Virginia G.

PHYSALO'DES . . . . **NICANDRA**

PHYSA'RIA (*VESICARIA* in part) lw Twinpod
didymocar'pa lw . . . . Common T.

PHYSE'DRA
bar'teri
eglandulo'sa
heterophyl'la
lon'gipes

Physian'thus al'bens . . **Araujia sericifera**

PHYSOCAR'PUS (*OPULASTER*) lw Ninebark
alabamen'sis . . . . . . **P. stellatus**
al'ternans . . . . Dwarf N.
amuren'sis (*Opulaster a.; Spiraea a.*) Amur N.
bractea'tus (*Opulaster b.*). Twinpod N.
capita'tus . . . . Pacific N.
glabra'tus (*Opulaster g.*). Colorado N.
interme'dius (*ramaleyi; Opulaster i.*) Illinois N.
—parvifo'lius . . . . . Dwarf I.N.
malva'ceus (*pauciflorus; Opulaster m.*) Mallow N.
monog'ynus (*Neillia torreyi; Opulaster m.*) . . . . Mountain N.
opulifo'lius (*Neillia opulifolia; Opulaster opulifolius; Spiraea opulifolia*) lw . . . . Common N.
Dwarf (*nanus*) hv.
¢Goldleaf (*aureus; luteus*)
stella'tus (*alabamensis*) . Alabama N.

PHYSOSI'PHON
See **ORCHID GENERA.**

PHYSOSTE'GIA lw . . . Lionsheart
virginia'na (*virginica; Dracocephalum virginianum*) lw . . . Virginia L. (*Obedientplant*)
Dense (*speciosa*) hv.
Giant (*gigantea*)
Red (*rubra*)
Vivid
White (*alba*)

PHYSOSTIG'MA . . . Calabarbean
veneno'sum . . . . . . Deadly C.

PHYTEL'EPHAS . . . . Ivorypalm
See **PALM GENERA.**

PHYTEU'MA . . . . . Mixedflower
campanuloi'des . . . . Harebell M.
canes'cens . . . . Gray M.
char'meli . . . . Charmel M.
como'sum . . . . . . Limecleft M.
hal'leri . . . . Hallers M.

PHYTEUMA, continued
hemisphaer'icum GRASSTUFT MIXEDFLOWER
limonifo'lium . . . . . THRIFT M.
lobelioi'des . . . . . LOBELIA M.
mi'cheli . . . . . . SARDINIAN M.
ni'grum . . . . BLACK M.
orbicula're . . . . . . BALLHEAD M.
scheuch'zeri . . . . . WEAKSTEM M.
scorzonerifo'lium . . . . DENSE M.
Perhaps only a var. of P. micheli.
serra'tum . . . . DWARF M.
sie'beri . . . . APENNINE M.
spica'tum . . . . SPIKE M.
vag'neri . . . . WAGNERS M.

PHYTOLAC'CA |w . . . . POKEBERRY
acino'sa . . . . INDIA P.
america'na (*decandra*) |w. COMMON P.
dioi'ca . . . . OMBUTREE P.
esculen'ta . . . . FOOD P.
heterosep'ala . . . . . MEXICAN P.
icosan'dra
octan'dra . . . . . EIGHTSTAMEN P.
rig'ida |w
rivinoi'des . . . . . . VENEZUELA P.

PIARAN'THUS
See **SUCCULENTS.**

PIARO'PUS . . . . . **EICHHORNIA**

PIASSAVA . . . . **Leopoldinia**
PARA P. . . . . **L. piassaba**

PI'CEA |w . . . . SPRUCE
a'bies (*excelsa; Abies picea* Mill., *not* Lindl.; *Pinus e.* Lam.) . NORWAY S.
—chlorocar'pa . . . GREENCONE N.S.
—erythrocar'pa . PURPLECONE N.S.
—ni'gra . . . . BLACK N.S.
Probably all of these are clons:
ARROWHEAD (*conica*) HV. P. abies
BARRY (*barryi; clanbrasiliana*)
BRANCHLESS (*monstrosa*)
BURLY (*robusta*)
COLUMNAR (*columnaris*)
CRANSTON (*cranstoni; virgata*)
CREEPING (*repens*)
CYPRESS (*cupressina*)
DROOPING (*inversa*)
DWARF (*pumila*)
DWARFCONIC (*nana*)
DWARFPYRAMID (*parviformis*)
ELLWANGER (*ellwangeriana*)
FERN (*filicoides*)
FINEDON (*finedonensis*)
GLOBE (*compacta*)
GOLDEN (*aurea*)
GREGORY (*gregoryana*)
HEAD (*capitata; dumosa*)
HEDGEHOG (*echinaeformis*)
KNIGHT (*elegans*)
LONGBRANCH (*viminalis*)
MAXWELL (*maxwelli*)
MERK (*merki*)
NEST (*nidiformis*)
OHLENDORFF (*ohlendorffi*)
PARSONS (*parsonsi*)
PROSTRATE (*procumbens*)
PYGMY (*pygmaea*)
PYRAMIDAL (*pyramidalis; pyramidata*)
REDCONE (*erythrocarpa*)
REMONT (*remonti*)
SHARPLEAF (*mucronata*)
SILVER (*argenteospica[ta]*)
SMALLCONE (*microsperma*)
SMITH (*smithi*)
TRAILING (*tabuliformis*)

PICEA abies, continued
VEITCH (*veitchi*)
WEEPING (*pendula*)
WHITELEAF (*argentea; variegata*)
ajanen'sis . . . . **P. jezoensis**
al'ba . . . . **P. glauca**
albertia'na . . . . **P. glauca a.**
alcockia'na . . . . **P. bicolor**
ascen'dens **P. brachytyla rhombisquamea**
aspera'ta . . . . . DRAGON SPRUCE
—heterole'pis (*P. heterolepis*) REDTWIG D.S.
—notab'ilis . . . NARROWSCALE D.S.
—pondero'sa . . . . . BIGCONE D.S.
auranti'aca . . . . YELLOWTWIG S.
austra'lis . . . . **P. rubens**
balfouria'na . . . . **P. likiangensis b.**
bi'color (*alcockiana*) . . . . ALCOCK S.
—acicula'ris . . . WHOLESCALE A.S.
—reflex'a . . . . CURLLEAF A.S.
brachyt'yla (*pachyclada; sargentiana*) SARGENT S.
—complana'ta . . . . GRAYBARK S.S.
—rhombisqua'mea (*P. ascendens*) DIAMONDSCALE S.S.
brevifo'lia . . . . **P. mariana**
breweria'na . . . . BREWER S.
engelmann'i |w . . . . ENGELMANN S.
BLUELEAF (*glauca*). HV.
DWARF GLOBE (*microphylla*)
FENDLER (*fendleri*)
SILVER (*argentea*)
excel'sa . . . . **P. abies**
falca'ta
This is probably a synonym of P. sitchensis. The name still appears in catalogs.
glau'ca (*alba; canadensis* (L.) B.S.P., *not* Link) |w . . . . . . WHITE S.
—albertia'na (*P. albertiana; P. canadensis a.*) . . . . . ALBERTA W.S.
₵DWARF (*conica*) HV.
—densa'ta . . . . BLACKHILLS W.S.
₵BLUELEAF (*coerulea*) HV. P. glauca
₵GOLDEN (*aurea*)
₵PYGMY (*nana*)
₵SPREADING (*parva*)
glehn'i . . . . SAKHALIN S.
hetero'lepis . . . . . . **P. asperata h.**
jezoen'sis (*ajanensis*) . . . YEDDO S.
—hondoen'sis (*P. hondoensis*) HONDO Y.S.
koyama'i (*koraiensis*) . . KOYAMA S.
likiangen'sis . . . . . . LIKIANG S.
—balfouria'na (*P. balfouriana*) BALFOUR S.
—purpu'rea . . . . . . **P. purpurea**
maria'na (*brevifolia; nigra*) |w BLACK S.
BEISSNER (*beissneri*) HV.
DOUMET (*doumeti*)
GLOBE (*globosa*)
HEATH (*ericoides*)
PYRAMIDAL (*fastigiata*)
maximowicz'i . . . . . . MAXIMOWICZ S.
menzies'i . . . . **P. sitchensis**
mey'eri . . . . MEYER S.
montig'ena . . . . CANDELABRA S.
morin'da . . . . **P. smithiana**
morindoi'des . . . . . . **P. spinulosa**
∞ **mo'seri** (*jezoensis* × *mariana*) ∞ MOSER S.
ni'gra . . . . **P. mariana**
∞ **no'tha** (*glehni* × *jezoensis hondoensis*) ∞ NOTHA S.
obova'ta . . . . SIBERIAN S.
—alpes'tris . . . . . . ALPINE S.S.
—fen'nica . . . . . . FINNISH S.S.
omor'ika . . . . SERBIAN S.
₵WEEPING (*pendula*) HV

PICEA, continued
orienta'lis . . . . ORIENTAL SPRUCE
BRONZEGOLD (*aurea*) HV.
COLUMNAR (*gracilis*)
DWARF (*nana*)
PYGMY (*pygmaea*)
YELLOWTIP (*aureospicata*)
pachycla'da . . . . . . **P. brachytyla**
poli'ta . . . . TIGERTAIL S.
pun'gens (*parryana*) |w . COLORADO S.
₵BAKER (*bakeri*) HV.
₵BLUE (*glauca*)
₵CERULEAN (*coerulea*)
₵DWARF (*compacta*)
₵GOLDEN (*aurea*)
₵HUNNEWELL (*hunnewelliana*)
₵KOSTER (*kosteriana*)
₵MOERHEIM (*moerheimi*)
₵SILVER (*argentea*)
₵WEEPING (*pendula*)
₵YELLOW (*lutea*)
purpu'rea (*P. likiangensis p.*) PURPLECONE S.
₵BLUE (*coerulea*) HV.
₵COMPACT (*compacta*)
₵SILVER (*argentea*)
retroflex'a
ru'bens (*australis; rubra* (Dur.) Link, *not* A. Dietr.) |w . . . . . . RED S.
∞ **saagh'yi** (*glauca* × *jezoensis*) ∞ SAAGHY S.
sargentia'na . . . . . . **P. brachytyla**
schrenkia'na . . . . . . SCHRENK S.
sitchen'sis (*menziesi*) |w . . SITKA S.
SPECIOSA. HV.
smithia'na (*morinda*) . HIMALAYAN S.
spinulo'sa (*morindoides*) . . SIKKIM S.
wil'soni (*watsoniana*) . . . WILSON S.

PICKERELWEED . **Pontederia; P. cordata**
LANCE P. . . . . **P. c. lancifolia**

PICKERIN'GIA . . . . CHAPARRALPEA
monta'na . . . . . . CALIFORNIA C.
—tomento'sa . . . . . FUZZY C.C.

PICKLEPLANT **Mesembryanthemum echinatum**

PICKLEWEED **Allenrolfea; A. occidentalis**

PICRADE'NIA . . . . . **ACTINEA**
floribun'da . . . . . . **A. richardsoni**

Picradeniop'sis oppositifo'lia . **Bahia o.**

PICRAE'NA Lindl. (1838) **PICRASMA**

PICRAE'NA Stev. (1832) **ASTRAGALUS**

PICRALI'MA . . . . . . PICRALIMA
klainea'na . . . . KLAINES P.

PICRAM'NIA . . . . . . BITTERBUSH
antides'ma . . . . JAMAICA B.
pentan'dra . . . . FLORIDA B.

PICRAS'MA (*PICRAENA* Lindl., *not* Stev.) . . . . QUASSIAWOOD
excel'sa (*Picraena e.*) . . JAMAICA Q.
quassioi'des . . . . INDIA Q.

Picrid'ium vulga're **Reichardia picroides**

PIC'RIS . . . . OXTONGUE
echioi'des . . . . BRISTLY O.
hieracioi'des . . . . . HAWKWEED O.

PICRODEN'DRON . . . BITTERTREE
bacca'tum (*arboreum; juglans*) JAMAICA B.
The "edible * with caution" fruits of this West Indian tree are known as "Jamaica Walnuts."

Piemarker . . . . ABUTILON, CHINGMA: **Abutilon theophrasti**

PI'ERIS (*ARCTERICA*) . . . PIERIS
This genus, unfortunately, is sometimes confused with Andromeda.

floribun'da . . . . . MOUNTAIN P.
formo'sa . . . . HIMALAYA P.
for'resti . . . . CHINESE P.
japon'ica . . . . JAPANESE P.
¢PYGMY (*pygmaea*) HV.
¢WHITERIM (*albomarginata; variegata*)
lu'cida . . . . **Lyonia l.**
macroca'lyx . . . . . . YUNNAN P.
maria'na . . . . **Lyonia m.**
na'na (*Arcterica n.*) . . KAMCHATKA P.
nit'ida . . . . **Lyonia lucida**
taiwanen'sis . . . . . FORMOSA P.

PIGAFET'TA (*PIGAFETTIA*) PIGAFETTA
See **PALM GENERA.**

Pigeongrass . . BRISTLEGRASS: **Setaria**

PIGEONPEA . . . . . . **Cajanus cajan**

PIGEONWINGS . . . . **Clitoria**
ASIAN P. . . . . **C. ternatea**
ATLANTIC P. . . . . . . **C. mariana**
BIG P. . . . . **C. dendrina**
TROPIC P. . . . . . . **C. cajanifolia**

PIGWEED, RUSSIAN **Axyris amaranthoides**

Pilauai . . . . CANARYTREE, PILINUT: **Canarium ovatum**

PI'LEA |w . . . . CLEARWEED
microphyl'la (*serpyllifolia* Auth., *not* Wedd.) . . . . . . ARTILLERY C.
True P. serpyllifolia appears to be imperfectly known and not in cultivation.
nummulariaefo'lia CREEPINGCHARLEY C.
pu'mila |w . . . . . . CANADA C. (*Coolweed; Richweed*)

PILEOSTE'GIA
viburnoi'des

Pili . . . . TANGLEHEAD: **Heteropogon contortus**

PILOCAR'PUS . . . . . PILOCARPUS
jaboran'di . . . . . . JABORANDI P.
microphyl'lus . . . . LITTLELEAF P.
pennatifo'lius . . . . . . SPIKE P.
racemo'sus . . . . . WESTINDIES P.

PILOCE'REUS (*ESPOSTOA; FACHEIROA*) . . . . . . PILOCEREUS
See **CACTUS GENERA.**

PILOCEREUS . . . . **Pilocereus**
BAHAMAS P. . . . . . . **P. bahamensis**
BAHIA P. . . . . . **P. phaeacanthus**
BARBADOS P. . . . . . **P. barbadensis**
BRAZILCOAST P. . . . . . **P. arrabidae**
BROOKS P. . . . . . . **P. brooksianus**
BROOM P. . . . . **P. scoparius**
CATINGA P. . . . . . . **P. catingicola**
CURACAO P. . . . . . **P. lanuginosus**
GOLDSPINE P. . . . **P. chrysacanthus**
GOUNELLE P. . . . . . . **P. gounellei**
HAITI P. . . . . . . **P. monoclonos**
KEYWEST P. . . . . **P. keyensis**
MATACUMBE P. . . . . . . **P. deeringi**
MAXON P. . . . . **P. maxoni**
MILLSPAUGH P. . . . . **P. millspaughi**
PALMER P. . . . . **P. palmeri**
POLYGON P. . . . . . . **P. polygonus**
PURPUS P. . . . . **P. purpusi**
ROBINS P. . . . . **P. robini**
ROYEN P. . . . . **P. royeni**

PILOCEREUS, continued
RUSSEL P. . . **Pilocereus russelianus**
SALVADOR P. . . . . **P. salvadorensis**
SARTORIUS P. . . . . **P. sartorianus**
SIERRADELALO P. . . . . . . **P. alensis**
SPURGE P. . . . . . **P. euphorbioides**
SWARTZ P. . . . . **P. swartzi**
TEHUACAN P. . . **P. macrocephalus**
ULE P. . . . . **P. ulei**
URBANS P. . . . . . . **P. urbanianus**
VERACRUZ P. . . **P. pentaedrophorus**
WHITELOCK P. . . . **P. leucocephalus**
WHITESPINE P. . . . . **P. albispinus**

PILOG'YNE . . . . **MELOTHRIA**
sua'vis . . . . **M. punctata**

PILULA'RIA |w
america'na |w

PILUM'NA . . . . **TRICHOPILIA**
See **ORCHID GENERA.**

PIME'LEA (*BANKSIA* Forst., *not* L. f.) RICEFLOWER
ferrugin'ea (*decussata; Banksia f.*) ROSY R.
graciliflo'ra . . . . . . DOTLEAF R.
ligustri'na . . . . PRIVET R.
spectab'ilis . . . . . . BIGHEAD R.

PIMEN'TA (*AMOMIS*) . . PIMENTA
officina'lis . . . . . . ALLSPICE P.
racemo'sa (*acris; Amomis caryophyllata*) BAYRUMTREE
—citrifo'lia (*A. c. citrifolia*)

PIMENTOPALM . . . . **Schippia concolor**

PIMPERNEL . . . . **Anagallis**
FLAXLEAF P. . . . . . . **A. linifolia**
SCARLET P. . . . . **A. arvensis**

PIMPINEL'LA . . . . . . PIMPINELLA
ani'sum . . . . ANISE
mag'na (*major*) . . . . GREATER P.
ROSEA. HV.
saxif'raga . . . . . . SAXIFRAGE P.

PINAN'GA . . . . . . PINANGAPALM
See **PALM GENERA.**

PINCK'NEYA . . . . . . PINCKNEYA
pu'bens . . . . PINCKNEYA

Pincushiontree . . . . . . VIBURNUM, EUROPEAN CRANBERRYBUSH: **Viburnum opulus**; HAKEA, SEAURCHIN: **Hakea laurina**

PINE . . . . **Pinus**
ALEPPO P. . . . . . . **P. halepensis**
ARIZONA PONDEROSA P. **P. ponderosa arizonica**
ARMAND P. . . . . **P. armandi**
AUSTRIAN P. . . . . **P. nigra**
AZTEC P. . . . . **P. teocote**
BALKAN P. . . . . **P. peuce**
Bigcone P. . . . . COULTER P.
BISHOP P. . . . . **P. muricata**
Bosnian P. PALEBARK HELDREICH P.
BRISTLECONE P. . . . . . **P. aristata**
CANARY P. . . . . . . **P. canariensis**
CEVENNES P. . . **P. nigra cebennensis**
CHIHUAHUA P. . . . . . **P. leiophylla**
CHILGHOZA P. . . . . . **P. gerardiana**
CHINESE P. . . . . . **P. tabulaeformis**
CHIR P. . . . . **P. roxburghi**
CLUSTER P. . . . . **P. pinaster**
COLORADO PINYON P. **P. cembroides edulis**
CORSICAN P. . . . **P. nigra poiretiana**
COULTER P. . . . . **P. coulteri**
CRIMEAN P. . . . **P. nigra caramanica**

PINE, continued
CUBAN P. . . . . **Pinus occidentalis**
CYPRESSPINE . . . . . **Callitris spp.**
DAMMARPINE . . . . . . **Agathis spp.**
DIGGER P. . . . . **P. sabiniana**
Dwarf Table P. JAPANESE RED P. ¢ GLOBE
EASTERN WHITE P. . . . . **P. strobus**
ERECTCONE ALEPPO P. **P. halepensis brutia**
FORMOSA P. . . . . . **P. taiwanensis**
FOXTAIL P. . . . . . . **P. balfouriana**
Grayleaf P. . . . . DIGGER P.
GROUNDPINE . **Lycopodium obscurum**
HELDREICH P. . . . . . **P. heldreichi**
HIGHLANDS SCOTCH P. **P. sylvestris scotica**
HIMALAYAN P. . . . . **P. griffithi**
HOOPES SWISSMOUNTAIN P. **P. mugo rotundata**
ITALIAN STONE P. . . . . . . **P. pinea**
JACK P. . . . . **P. banksiana**
JAPANESE BLACK P. . . **P. thunbergi**
JAPANESE RED P. . . . . **P. densiflora**
JAPANESE STONE P. . . . . . **P. pumila**
JAPANESE WHITE P. . . . **P. parviflora**
JEFFREY P. . . . . **P. jeffreyi**
JELECOTE P. . . . . **P. patula**
KHASIA P. . . . . **P. khasya**
KNOBCONE P. . . . . . . **P. attenuata**
KOREAN P. . . . . **P. koraiensis**
LACEBARK P. . . . . **P. bungeana**
LAPLAND SCOTCH P. **P. sylvestris lapponica**
LIMBER P. . . . . **P. flexilis**
LOBLOLLY P. . . . . **P. taeda**
LODGEPOLE P. . . **P. contorta latifolia**
LONGLEAF P. . . . . **P. palustris**
LUCHU P. . . . . **P. luchuensis**
LUZON P. . . . . **P. insularis**
MASSON P. . . . . **P. massoniana**
MERKUS P. . . . . **P. merkusi**
MEXICAN PINYON P. . **P. cembroides**
MEXICAN WHITE P. . . . **P. ayacahuite**
MONTEREY P. . . . . **P. radiata**
MONTEZUMA P. . . . . **P. montezumae**
MUGHO SWISSMOUNTAIN P. **P. mugo mughus**
NELSON PINYON P. . . . . **P. nelsoni**
NICARAGUA P. . . . **P. pseudostrobus**
NORFOLKISLANDPINE **Araucaria excelsa**
Norway P. . . . . RED P.
Nut P. . . . . . MEXICAN PINYON P.
PALEBARK HELDREICH P. **P. heldreichi leucodermis**
PARRY PINYON P. **P. cembroides parryana**
PINCEANA P. P. . . . . . **P. pinceana**
PITCH P. . . . . **P. rigida**
PONDEROSA P. . . . . . **P. ponderosa**
POND P. . . . . . . **P. rigida serotina**
RED P. . . . . **P. resinosa**
RHAETIC P. . . . . ×**P. rhaetica**
RIGA SCOTCH P. . **P. sylvestris rigensis**
ROCKYMOUNTAIN PONDEROSA P. **P. ponderosa scopulorum**
RUNNINGPINE . **Lycopodium clavatum**
SAND P. . . . . **P. clausa**
∞SCHWERIN P. . . . . . ∞**P. schwerini**
SCOTCH P. . . . . **P. sylvestris**
SCREWPINE . . . . . . **Pandanus spp.**
Scrub P. . . . . VIRGINIA P.
SHORE P. . . . . **P. contorta**
SHORTLEAF P. . . . . **P. echinata**
SHORTWINGSEED MEXICAN WHITE P. **P. ayacahuite brachyptera**
SHRUBBY SWISSMOUNTAIN P. **P. mugo pumilio**

Pine, continued
Siberian Swiss Stone P. **Pinus cembra sibirica**
Singleleaf Pinyon P. **P. cembroides monophylla**
Slash P. . . . . **P. caribaea**
Sonderegger P. . ×**P. sondereggeri**
Spruce P. . . . . **P. glabra**
Sugar P. . . . . **P. lambertiana**
SwissMountain P. . . . . **P. mugo**
Swiss Stone P. . . . . **P. cembra**
TableMountain P. . . . **P. pungens**
Tanyosho P. . . . . Japanese Red P. ₵Umbrella
Thunberg P. . . . Japanese Black P.
Timberline Montezuma P. **P. montezumae hartwegi**
Torrey P. . . . . **P. torreyana**
Tree SwissMountain P. **P. mugo rostrata**
Tyrolean Scotch P. **P. sylvestris engadinensis**
Umbrellapine . **Sciadopitys verticillata**
Veitch Mexican White P. **P. ayacahuite veitchi**
Virginia P. . . . . . **P. virginiana**
Western White P. . . **P. monticola**
Western Yellow P. . . Ponderosa P.
Whitebark P. . . . . . **P. albicaulis**
Yunnan P. . . . . **P. yunnanensis**
Pineapple . . . . . . **Ananas comosus**
Pineapple-cactus **Sclerocactus polyancistrus**
Pineappleflower . **Eucomis punctata**
Pineappleweed **Matricaria matricarioides**
Pinebarrenpea **Pitcheria; P. galactioides**
Pinedrops . . . . **Pterospora**
Woodland P. . . . **P. andromedea**
Pinefern . . . . **Anemia adiantifolia**
Pinegrass . . **Calamagrostis rubescens**
Purple P. . . . . . **C. purpurascens**
Pinegrass . . . . . Fescue, Arizona: **Festuca arizonica**; Dropseed, Pine: **Blepharoneuron tricholepis**
Pinesap . . . . **Hypopitys latisquama**
Pineweed . . . . **Sarothra**
Drummond P. . . . . **S. drummondi**
Orange P. . . . . . **S. gentianoides**

PINGUIC'ULA |w . . . Butterwort
alpi'na . . . . Mountain B.
ela'tior (*australis*) . . . . Tall B.
grandiflo'ra . . . . . Bigflower B.
lute'a . . . . Yellow B.
planifo'lia |w
vulga'ris . . . . Common B.
Pink . . . . **Dianthus**
Allwood P. . . . . . . **D. allwoodi**
Alpine P. . . . . **D. alpinus**
Alpine Sweetwilliam. **D. barbatus a.**
Anatolian P. . . . . **D. anatolicus**
Atkinson P. . . . . . **D. atkinsoni**
Auvergne P. . . . ×**D. arvernensis**
Banded P. . . . . . . **D. zonatus**
Beard P. . . . . . . **D. banaticus**
Bering P. . . . . **D. repens**
Bitter P. . . . . **D. tristis**
Blood P. . . . . . . **D. cruentus**
Boissier P. . . . . . **D. boissieri**
Boyd P. . . . . **D. boydi**
Branched P. . . . **D. brachyanthus**
Button P. . . . . . . **D. latifolius**
Carnation . . . . **D. caryophyllus**
Carthusian P. . . **D. carthusianorum**
Childing P. . . . . . . **D. prolifer**
Chinese P. . . . . . . **D. chinensis**
Cloudland P. . . . . . **D. alpestris**

Pink, continued
Clove P. . . **Dianthus caryophyllus**
Deptford P. . . . . . . **D. armeria**
Downy P. . . . . . . **D. pubescens**
Dunnett Sweetwilliam **D. barbatus dunnetti**
Erect P. . . . . **D. strictus**
Everblooming Grass P. **D. plumarius semperflorens**
Eyed Sweetwilliam **D. barbatus oculatus**
Field P. . . . . . . **D. campestris**
Finland P. . . . . . **D. arenarius**
Forked P. . . . . **D. furcatus**
Fragrant P. . . . . . . **D. fragrans**
Fringed Chinese P. **D. chinensis laciniatus**
Frost P. . . . . **D. gelidus**
Glacier P. . . . . . **D. neglectus**
Granite P. . . . . . **D. graniticus**
Grass P. . . . . . . **D. plumarius**
Grisebach Sticky P. **D. viscidus grisebachi**
Hardy Garden P. . . . . **D. knappi**
Hillside P. . . . . . . **D. collinus**
Hoeltzer P. . . . . . **D. hoeltzeri**
Ice P. . . . . **D. glacialis**
∞ Lauchean P. . . . ∞ **D. laucheanus**
Lilac P. . . . . **D. superbus**
Maiden P. . . . . . . **D. deltoides**
Montpelier P. . **D. monspessulanus**
Mt. Taurus P. . . . **D. brevicaulis**
Ragged P. . . . . . . **D. seguieri**
Rainbow Chinese P. **D. chinensis heddewigi**
Rosetuft P. . . . . . **D. attenuatus**
Rosy Sweetwilliam **D. barbatus roseus**
Rumanian P. . . . . . **D. acicularis**
Shrubby P. . . . . . **D. fruticosus**
Solomon Sweetwilliam **D. barbatus salamoni**
Sticky P. . . . . . . **D. glutinosus**
Sundermann P. . . **D. sundermanni**
Sweetwilliam . . . . . **D. barbatus**
White Alpine P. . . **D. alpinus albus**
White Grass P. **D. plumarius albiflorus**
Wood P. . . . . **D. sylvestris**
Zoned P. . . . . . . **D. callizonus**
Pinkbells. . . . **Heuchera lithophila**

PI'NUS |w . . . . Pine
albicau'lis . . . . . Whitebark P.
apach'eca . . . . . **P. ponderosa**
arista'ta . . . . . . Bristlecone P.
arizo'nica . . . . . **P. ponderosa a.**
ar'mandi . . . . Armand P.
₵Compacta. hv.
attenua'ta (*tuberculata* Gord., *not* D. Don) . . . . Knobcone P.
austra'lis . . . . **P. palustris**
austri'aca . . . . **P. nigra**
ayacahui'te (*strobiformis*) Mexican White P.
—**brachyp'tera** ShortwingseedM.W.P.
—**veitch'i** (*P. veitchi*). Veitch M.W.P.
balfouria'na . . . . . . Foxtail P.
banksia'na (*divaricata*) |w . . Jack P.
bru'tius . . . . **P. halepensis brutia**
bungea'na . . . . . . Lacebark P.
canarien'sis . . . . Canary P.
caribae'a (*elliotti; heterophylla*) |w Slash P.
cem'bra . . . . . . Swiss Stone P.
—**sibir'ica** . . . . . Siberian S.P.
₵Column (*columnaris*) hv. P. cembra
₵Yellowcone (*chlorocarpa*)

PINUS, continued
cembroi'des . Mexican Pinyon Pine (*Nut P.*)
—**ed'ulis** (*P. edulis*) |w Colorado P.P.
₵Albovariegata. hv.
—**monophyl'la** (*P. monophylla*) Singleleaf P.P.
—**parrya'na** (*P. parryana; P. quadrifolia*) . . . . Parry P.P.
clau'sa . . . . Sand P.
contor'ta |w . . . . Shore P.
—**latifo'lia** (*P. murrayana*) Lodgepole P.
coul'teri . . Coulter P. (*Bigcone P.*)
cuben'sis . . . . **P. occidentalis**
densiflo'ra . . . . . Japanese Red P.
—*fune'bris* Hort. . . . **P. tabulaeformis**
₵Dragonseye (*oculus-draconis*) hv. P. densiflora
₵Globe (*globosa. Dwarf Table P.*)
₵Golden (*aurea*)
₵Umbrella (*umbraculifera. Tanyosho P.*)
₵Weeping (*pendula*)
₵Whitetip (*alboterminata*)
divarica'ta . . . . . . **P. banksiana**
echina'ta (*mitis*) |w . . Shortleaf P.
ed'ulis . . . . . . **P. cembroides e.**
elliott'i . . . . **P. caribaea**
excel'sa Hook. (1865) . . . **P. peuce**
excel'sa Lam. (1778) . . **Picea abies**
excel'sa Wall. (1824) . **Pinus griffithi**
flex'ilis |w . . . . Limber P.
—**reflex'a** (*P. strobiformis* U. S. Auth., *not* Engelm.)
fune'bris . . . . . . **P. tabulaeformis**
gerardia'na . . . . . Chilghoza P.
gla'bra |w . . . . Spruce P.
grif'fithi (*excelsa* Wall., *not* Lam.; *nepalensis* De Chambray 1845; *wallichi*) . . . . Himalayan P.
halepen'sis (*maritima* Lamb. (and Mill.?), *not* R.Br. in Ait., *nor* Lam.) Aleppo P.
—**bru'tia** (*P. brutius; P. pyrenaica* Dav., *not* Lapey.). Erectcone A.P.
held'reichi . . . . . Heldreich P.
—**leucoder'mis** (*P. leucodermis*) Palebark H.P. (*Bosnian P.*)
hen'ryi . . . . . . **P. tabulaeformis**
heterophyl'la . . . . . . **P. caribaea**
in'ops . . . . **P. virginiana**
insig'nis . . . . **P. radiata**
insula'ris (*khasiana*) . . . Luzon P.
jef'freyi |w. . . . . . . Jeffrey P.
khas'ya . . . . Khasia P.
koraien'sis. . . . . . . Korean P.
lambertia'na . . . . Sugar P.
laric'io . . . . **P. nigra poiretiana**
—*calab'rica* . . . . **P. n. poiretiana**
—*corsica'na* . . . **P. n. poiretiana**
leiophyl'la |w. . . . . Chihuahua P.
leucoder'mis . . . . . **P. heldreichi l.**
longifo'lia Roxb. . . . . **P. roxburghi**
longifo'lia Salisb. . . . **P. palustris**
luchuen'sis . . . . Luchu P.
marit'ima R.Br., in Ait. (1813) **P. nigra**
marit'ima Lam. (1778) . **P. pinaster**
marit'ima Lamb. (1803). **P. halepensis**
marit'ima Mill. (1768). **P. halepensis?** Name uncertain.
massonia'na (*sinensis* Lamb., *not* Mayr) Masson P.
This name has often been misapplied to other Old World Pines, and particularly to P. densiflora, luchuensis, pinaster, and thunbergi.

PINUS, continued
mer'kusi . . . . . . Merkus Pine
mi'tis . . . . **P. echinata**
monophyl'la . . . **P. cembroides m.**
monspelien'sis . **P. nigra cebennensis**
monta'na . . . . **P. mugo**
—*mu'ghus* . . . . . . **P. m. mughus**
—*prostra'ta* . . . . . **P. m. pumilio**
—*pumil'io* . . . . . . **P. m. pumilio**
—*rostra'ta* . . . . . . **P. m. rostrata**
—*uncina'ta* . . . . . . **P. m. rostrata**
montezu'mae . . . Montezuma P.
—hart'wegi . . . Timberline M.P.
montic'ola . . . Western White P.
mu'ghus . . . . . **P. mugo mughus**
mu'go (*montana*) . SwissMountain P.
—mu'ghus (*P. montana mughus; P. mughus*) . . . . Mugho S.P.
—pumil'io (*P. montana p.; P. m. prostrata; P. pumilio*) . Shrubby S.P.
—rostra'ta (*P. montana r.; P. m. uncinata; P. uncinata*) . . . Tree S.P.
—rotunda'ta . . . . . . Hoopes S.P.
¢Globe (*compacta*) hv. P. mugo
¢Slavin (*slavini*)
murica'ta . . . . Bishop P.
murraya'na . . . **P. contorta latifolia**
nel'soni . . . . . Nelson Pinyon P.
nepalen'sis De Chambray (1845)
P. griffithi
nepalen'sis Forbes (1839)
The identity of this species is uncertain. Prof. Rehder thinks it may possibly be P. insularis Endl. (1847). If so, being older, it should replace that name.

ni'gra (*austriaca; maritima* R.Br. in Ait., *not* Lam. *nor* Lamb.; *P. n. austriaca; pyrenaica* Lapey., *not* Dav.) |w . . . . . . Austrian P.
—*austri'aca* . . . . **P. nigra**
P. nigra austriaca (*P. austriaca*) is the typical form of this species and is used by some botanists for that form. Standardized Plant Names prefers binomial names for the typical forms of species, as more acceptable to nontaxonomic workers with plants and to the general public.

—caraman'ica (*P. n. pallasiana; P. pallasiana*) . . . . . Crimean P.
—cebennen'sis (*monspeliensis*)
Cevennes P.
—*pallasia'na* . . . . **P. n. caramanica**
—poiretia'na (*P. laricio; P. l. calabrica; P. l. corsicana*) . Corsican P.
Globe (*globosa*) hv. P. nigra
Hornibrook (*hornibrookiana*)
Prostrate (*prostrata*)
Pygmy (*pygmaea*)
Pyramid (*pyramidalis*)
Weeping (*pendula*)
occidenta'lis (*cubensis*) . . Cuban P.
pallasia'na . . . **P. nigra caramanica**
palus'tris (*australis; longifolia* Salisb., *not* Roxb.) |w . . . Longleaf P.
parrya'na . . . . . **P. cembroides p.**
parviflo'ra (*pentaphylla*)
Japanese White P.
Silver (*glauca*) hv.
pat'ula . . . . Jelecote P.
peu'ce (*excelsa* Hook., *not* Lam.)
Balkan P.
pinas'ter (*maritima* Lam., *not* R.Br. in Ait., *nor* Mill.) . . . . Cluster P.
pincea'na . . . Pinceana Pinyon P.
pine'a . . . . . . Italian Stone P.
pondero'sa (*apacheca*) |w Ponderosa P. (*Western Yellow P.*)
—arizo'nica (*P. arizonica*) Arizona P.P.

PINUS, continued
pondero'sa scopulo'rum (*P. scopulorum*) RockyMountain Ponderosa Pine
Weeping (*pendula; penduliformis*) hv. P. ponderosa
pseudostro'bus . . . . Nicaragua P.
pu'mila . . . . . Japanese Stone P.
pumil'io . . . . **P. mugo p.**
pun'gens |w . . TableMountain P.
pyrena'ica Dav. (1833)
P. halepensis brutia
pyrena'ica Lapey. (1818) . . **P. nigra**
quadrifo'lia . **P. cembroides parryana**
radia'ta (*insignis; tuberculata* D. Don, *not* Gord.) |w . . . Monterey P.
resino'sa |w . . Red P. (*Norway P.*)
Globe (*globosa*) hv.
×**rhae'tica** (*mugo × silvestris*)
Rhaetic P.
A natural hybrid.

rigen'sis . . . . **P. sylvestris r.**
rig'ida |w . . . . Pitch P.
—serot'ina (*P. serotina*) |w . Pond P.
roxburgh'i (*longifolia* Roxb., *not* Salisb.)
Chir P.
sabinia'na . . Digger P. (*Grayleaf P.*)
∞ **schwer'ini** (*griffithi × strobus*)
∞ Schwerin P.
scopulo'rum . . . . **P. ponderosa s.**
serot'ina . . . . **P. rigida s.**
sinen'sis Lamb. . . . **P. massoniana**
sinen'sis Mayr, *not* Lamb.
P. tabulaeformis
—*yunnanen'sis* . . . **P. yunnanensis**
×**sondereg'geri** (*palustris × taeda*)
Sonderegger P.
A natural hybrid.

strobifor'mis . . . . . **P. ayacahuite**
strobifor'mis U. S. Auth., *not* Engelm.
P. flexilis reflexa
stro'bus |w . . . Eastern White P.
Blue (*glauca*) hv.
Contorted (*contorta*)
Dwarf (*nana*)
Globe (*globosa*)
Golden (*aurea*)
Prostrate (*prostrata*)
Pyramidal (*fastigiata; pyramidalis*)
Umbrella (*umbraculifera*)
Weeping (*pendula*)
sylves'tris . . . . Scotch P.
—engadinen'sis . . Tyrolean S.P.
—lappon'ica . . . . . Lapland S.P.
—rigen'sis (*P. rigensis*) . . Riga S.P.
—scot'ica . . . . . Highlands S.P.
Dwarf (*nana*) hv. P. sylvestris
Golden (*aurea*)
Littleleaf (*parvifolia*)
Pyramidal (*fastigiata*)
Silver (*argentea*)
Waterer (*watereri*)
Weeping (*pendula*)
tabulaefor'mis (*funebris; henryi; sinensis* Mayr, *not* Lamb.; *wilsoni*)
Chinese P.
—densa'ta
tae'da |w . . . . Loblolly P.
taiwanen'sis . . . . . . Formosa P.
teoco'te . . . . Aztec P.
Teocote is an Aztec word meaning "Pine of the Gods." Only the Aztec nobles were permitted to use the resin of this Pine for incense in worship.

thunberg'i . . . Japanese Black P. (*Thunberg P.*)
torreya'na . . . . Torrey P.
tubercula'ta D. Don (1837) . **P. radiata**

PINUS, continued
tubercula'ta Gord. (1849) . **P. attenuata**
uncina'ta . . . . . **P. mugo rostrata**
veitch'i . . . . . . **P. ayacahuite v.**
virginia'na (*inops*) |w . Virginia Pine (*Scrub P.*)
wal'lichi . . . . **P. griffithi**
wil'soni . . . . . . **P. tabulaeformis**
yunnanen'sis (*P. sinensis y.*)
Yunnan P.

Pinweed . . . . **Lechea**
Hairy P. . . . . **L. villosa**

PI'PER . . . . Pepper
angustifo'lium . . . . . . Matico P.
bet'le . . . . Betel P.
cube'ba . . . . Cubeb P.
jaboran'di . . . . . . Jaborandi P.
lon'gum . . . . Long P.
magnif'icum
methys'ticum . . . . Kava P.
ni'grum . . . . Black P.
orna'tum . . . . Celebes P.
retrofrac'tum (*officinarum*)
tubercula'tum

Pipewort . . . . **Eriocaulon**
Parker P. . . . . **E. parkeri**
Tenangle P. . . . . . **E. decangulare**

Pipsissewa . . . . **Chimaphila**
Common P. . . . . . . **C. umbellata**
Menzies P. . . . . **C. menziesi**
Striped P. . . . . **C. maculata**
Western P.
C. umbellata occidentalis

PIPTADE'NIA . . . . . . Piptadenia
africa'na. African P. (*Agboin; Ekhimi*)
cebil' . . . . Cebil P.
commu'nis . . . . Common P.
macrocar'pa . . . . Longpod P.
peregri'na . . . . Cohoba P.
rig'ida

PIPTANTHOCE'REUS . . **CEREUS**
See **CACTUS GENERA.**

PIPTAN'THUS . . . . . Piptanthus
con'color . . . . . . Greenleaf P.
—yunnanen'sis (*P. bicolor*)
Yunnan P.
laburnifo'lius (*nepalensis*)
Lanceleaf P.
tomento'sus . . . . . . Woolly P.

PIPTOCHAE'TIUM (*ORYZOPSIS* in part) . . . . Ricegrass
See **GRASS GENERA.**

PIQUE'RIA . . . . Piqueria
Unfortunately the common name Stevia is frequently misapplied to this genus by horticulturists. Stevia is a wholly distinct group of composites.

serra'ta . . . . SanLuis P.
triner'via (*Stevia serrata* Hort., *not* Cav.) . . . . Fragrant P.
It is very unfortunate that horticulturists have commonly misapplied the misleading name Stevia serrata to this familiar plant. The true Stevia serrata is an entirely distinct native plant of Arizona and New Mexico.

Piquia-ete . . . . **Caryocar villosum**

Piratebush. **Buckleya; B. distichophylla**

PIRATINE'RA
guianen'sis (*Brosimum aubleti*)
Snakewood

PIRIQUE'TA |w . . . . . PIRIQUETA
carolinia'na |w . . . . . CAROLINA P.
tomento'sa . . . . . . WOOLLY P.

PISCA'RIA . . . **EREMOCARPUS**

PISCID'IA (*ICHTHYOMETHIA*)
FISHFUDDLETREE
commu'nis (*Ichthyomethia c.*)
FLORIDA F.
piscip'ula (*erythrina; Ichthyomethia p.*)
JAMAICA F.

PISO'NIA . . . . PISONIA
aculea'ta . . . . . DEVILSCLAW P.
al'ba . . . . LETTUCETREE P.
brunonia'na
AUSTRALASIA CATCHBIRDTREE
excel'sa . . . . MALAY C.
obtusa'ta Jacq. . . . . . . **Torrubia o.**
obtusa'ta U. S. Auth. **Torrubia longifolia**
zapal'lo . . . . ZAPALLO P.

PISTACHE . . . . **Pistacia**
AFGHAN P. . . . . **P. cabulica**
CHINESE P. . . . . . . **P. chinensis**
COMMON P. . . . . **P. vera**
EGYPTIAN P. . . . . **P. khinjuk**
HIMALAYAN P. . . . . **P. integerrima**
LENTISK P. . . . . . . **P. lentiscus**
MEXICAN P. . . . . . . **P. mexicana**
MOUNT-ATLAS P. . . . . **P. atlantica**
PALESTINE TEREBINTH P.
P. terebinthus palaestina
TEREBINTH P. . . . . . **P. terebinthus**
TEXAS P. . . . . **P. texana**
TURKTEREBINTH P. . . . . **P. mutica**
YUNNAN P. . . . **P. weinmannifolia**

PISTAC'IA . . . . PISTACHE
atlan'tica . . . . MOUNT-ATLAS P.
cabul'ica . . . . AFGHAN P.
This species produces the Bombay Mastic of commerce. See note on P. lentiscus.
chinen'sis (*sinensis*) . . CHINESE P.
integer'rima . . . . . HIMALAYAN P.
khin'juk . . . . EGYPTIAN P.
len'tiscus . . . . LENTISK P.
This species produces the Chios Mastic of commerce. See note on P. cabulica.
mexica'na . . . . MEXICAN P.
mu'tica . . . . . TURKTEREBINTH P.
terebin'thus . . . . . TEREBINTH P.
—palaesti'na . . . . PALESTINE T.P.
texa'na . . . . TEXAS P.
Regarded by some botanists as synonymous with P. mexicana.
ve'ra . . . . COMMON P.
weinmannifo'lia . . . . YUNNAN P.

PIS'TIA |w . . . . . WATERLETTUCE
stratio'tes |w . . . . WATERLETTUCE

PI'SUM |w . . . . PEA
ela'tius . . . MEDITERRANEAN P.
jomard'i . . . . JOMARD P.
sati'vum |w . . . . GARDEN P.
—arven'se (*P. arvense*) . . FIELD P.
—hu'mile . . . . BABY G.P.
—macrocar'pon (*P. s. saccharatum* Hort.) . . . . . . SUGARPOD G.P.
—umbella'tum . . . . . BOUQUET G.P.

PITAFLOJA . . . **Aechmea magdalenae**

PITANGA . . . . **Eugenia uniflora**

PITCAIRN'IA . . . . . . PITCAIRNIA
coralli'na . . . . CORAL P.
integrifo'lia . . . . . . TRINIDAD P.
moritzia'na . . . . MORITZ P.
punic'ea . . . . SCARLET P.

PITCHER'IA . . . . PINEBARRENPEA
galactioi'des . . . . PINEBARRENPEA

PITCHERLILY . . . . **Urceolina**
BROADLEAF P. . . . . . . **U. latifolia**
SCARLET P. . . . . **U. miniata**
YELLOW P. . . . . **U. pendula**

PITCHERPLANT . . . . . . **Sarracenia**
COMMON P. . . . . . . **S. purpurea**
DRUMMOND P. . . . . **S. drummondi**
HOODED P. . . . . **S. minor**
JONES P. . . . . **S. jonesi**
PARROT P. . . . . **S. psittacina**
SLEDGES P. . . . . **S. sledgei**
SWEET P. . . . . **S. rubra**
TRUMPET P. . . . . **S. flava**

PITHECELLO'BIUM . . APES-EARRING
The generic name is frequently misspelled Pithecolobium and Pithecollobium.
arbo'reum . . . . . . TAMARIND A.
brevifo'lium . . . . . . HUAJILLO A.
caribae'um. CARIB A. (*Naked-Indian*)
confi'ne
dul'ce . . . . GUAMACHIL A.
flexicau'le . . . . EBONY A.
grandiflo'rum . TORTOISESHELL A.
junghuhnia'num . . . JUNGHUHN A.
lanceola'tum
pruino'sum . . . . . SNOWWOOD A.
saman' . . . . **Samanea s.**
scala're . . . . LADDER A.
trapezifo'lium . . . . . SOAPTREE A.
unguisca'ti . . . . CATCLAW A.
vinhat'ico . . . . GOLDWOOD A.

PITHECOCTE'NIUM . MONKEYCOMB
aublet'i . . . . AUBLET M.
cynanchoi'des (*clematideum*)
ARGENTINE M.
echina'tum (*muricatum*). MEXICAN M.

PITOMBA. . . . **Eugenia luschnathiana**

PITSCALEGRASS . . . . . **Hackelochloa**

PITTOS'PORUM . . . PITTOSPORUM
bi'color . . . . BANYALLA P.
buchan'ani . . . . . BUCHANAN P.
Perhaps hardly more than a var. of P. tenuifolium.
cauliflo'rum
colenso'i . . . . COLENSO P.
Perhaps hardly more than a var. of P. tenuifolium.
cornifo'lium . . . . . . DOGWOOD P.
crassifo'lium . . . . KARO P.
dall'i . . . . DALLS P.
daphniphylloi'des . . . . DAPHNE P.
eriolo'ma . . . . LORDHOWE P.
eugenioi'des . . . . TARATA P.
₵VARIEGATED (*variegatum*) HV.
fair'childi . . . . FAIRCHILD P.
ferrugin'eum . . . . . RUSTYWOOL P.
floribun'dum
glabra'tum
heterophyl'lum . . . . ROCK P.
hos'meri . . . . HOSMER P.
—longifo'lium . . . . . LONGLEAF H.P.
kirk'i . . . . KIRKS P.
may'i Hort. . . . . MAYS P.
This cultivated plant seems to be without botanical standing.
ni'gricans Hort. . . . **P. tenuifolium**
pat'ulum
phillyraeoi'des . . . . . WILLOW P.
ralph'i . . . . RALPH P.
Perhaps hardly more than a var. of P. crassifolium.

PITTOSPORUM, continued
revolu'tum
BRISBANELAUREL PITTOSPORUM
rhombifo'lium . . . DIAMONDLEAF P. (*Mignonettewood*)
rig'idum
tenuifo'lium (*nigricans* Hort.)
TAWHIWHI P.
₵WHITESPOT (*variegatum*) HV.
timoren'se . . . . TIMOR P.
tobi'ra . . . . TOBIRA P.
₵WHITESPOT (*variegata*) HV.
trunca'tum
tur'neri . . . . TURNER P.
umbella'tum
undula'tum . . . . ORANGEBERRY P.
viridiflo'rum . . . . CAPE P.

PITTOSPORUM . . . . . . **Pittosporum**
BANYALLA P. . . . . **P. bicolor**
BRISBANELAUREL P. . . **P. revolutum**
BUCHANAN P. . . . . **P. buchanani**
CAPE P. . . . . **P. viridiflorum**
COLENSO P. . . . . **P. colensoi**
DALLS P. . . . . **P. dalli**
DAPHNE P. . . **P. daphniphylloides**
DIAMONDLEAF P. . . . **P. rhombifolium**
DOGWOOD P. . . . . . **P. cornifolium**
FAIRCHILD P. . . . . . . **P. fairchildi**
HOSMER P. . . . . **P. hosmeri**
KARO P. . . . . . . **P. crassifolium**
KIRKS P. . . . . **P. kirki**
LONGLEAF HOSMER P.
P. hosmeri longifolium
LORDHOWE P. . . . . . **P. erioloma**
MAYS P. . . . . *P. mayi* Hort.
ORANGEBERRY P. . . . **P. undulatum**
RALPH P. . . . . **P. ralphi**
ROCK P. . . . . . . **P. heterophyllum**
RUSTYWOOL P. . . . . **P. ferrugineum**
TARATA P. . . . . . . **P. eugenioides**
TAWHIWHI P. . . . . . **P. tenuifolium**
TIMOR P. . . . . **P. timorense**
TOBIRA P. . . . . **P. tobira**
TURNER P. . . . . **P. turneri**
WILLOW P. . . . . **P. phillyraeoides**

PITURI . . . . . . **Duboisia hopwoodi**

PITYROGRAM'MA (*CEROPTERIS*)
GOLDFERN
See **FERN GENERA.**

Pityrosper'ma aceri'num
Cimicifuga japonica

PLAGIAN'THUS . . . . . TWINEBARK
betuli'nus . . . . . RIBBONWOOD T.
divarica'tus
ly'alli . . . . **Hoheria l.**
pulchel'lus . . . . HEMPBUSH T.

PLAGIOBO'THRYS (*ALLOCARYA*)
|w . . . . POPCORNFLOWER
hispid'ulus (*Allocarya hispidula*)
HAIRY P.
jones'i |w . . . . JONES P.
nothoful'vus |w . . . . . REDSTAIN P.
reticula'tus
—rossiano'rum (*Allocarya californica*)
CALIFORNIA P.
scou'leri (*Allocarya s.*) . SCOULER P.

PLAINSMUSTARD . . . **Schoenocrambe**
FLAXLEAF P. . . . . **S. linifolia**

PLANCHO'NIA . . . . . PLANCHONIA
andaman'ica . . . . . BOMBWAY P.

PLA'NERA |w . . . . WATERELM
aquat'ica |w . . . . WATERELM
crena'ta . . . . **Zelkova carpinifolia**
japon'ica . . . . . **Zelkova serrata**
rich'ardi . . . . **Zelkova carpinifolia**

PLANETREE . . . . **Platanus**
AMERICAN P. . . . . . . **P. occidentalis**
ARIZONA P. . . . . **P. wrighti**
CALIFORNIA P. . . . . . **P. racemosa**
CHIAPAS P. . . . . . . **P. chiapensis**
FINGERLOBE ORIENTAL P. **P. orientalis digitata**
JALAPA P. . . . . . . **P. lindeniana**
∞ LONDON P . . . . ∞ **P. acerifolia**
MEXICAN P. . . . . . . **P. mexicana**
OAXACA P. . . . . . . **P. oaxacana**
ORIENTAL P. . . . . . . **P. orientalis**
SMALL O. P. . . . . . . **P. o. cuneata**
SMOOTH AMERICAN P. **P. occidentalis glabrata**

PLANTA'GO [w] . . . . . . PLANTAIN
The small native western annuals are called Indianwheat.

alpi'na . . . . ALPS P.
arena'ria . . . . **P. indica**
argyre'a . . . . **P. purshi**
arista'ta. BOTTLEBRUSH INDIANWHEAT
This has been confused with the South American P. patagonica.
asiat'ica . . . . ASIATIC P.
corono'pus . . CROWFOOT P. (*Crowfoot*)
cyn'ops . . . . SHRUBBY P.
decip'iens (*P. maritima* U. S. Auth., *not* L.) [w] . . AMERICAN SEASIDE P.
elonga'ta . . . . **P. pusilla**
erec'ta [w] . . . . DOTSEED P.
eriop'oda [w] . . . . . . REDWOOL P.
fastigia'ta (*gooddingi; scariosa*) DESERT INDIANWHEAT
galeattia'na . . . . BEAK P.
gnaphalioi'des . . . . . . **P. purshi**
heterophyl'la
igno'ta (*picta; xerodea*) FOOTHILL INDIANWHEAT
in'dica (*arenaria*) . . . . WHORLED P.
lago'pus . . . . ROUNDHEAD P.
lanceola'ta [w] . . . . BUCKHORN P.
macrocar'pa . . . . BIGPOD P.
ma'jor [w] . . . . RIPPLESEED P.
marit'ima . . . EUROPEAN SEASIDE P.
marit'ima U. S. Auth., *not* L. **P. decipiens**
me'dia . . . . SWEET P.
ova'ta . . . . BLOND P.
patago'nica PATAGONIA INDIANWHEAT
pic'ta . . . . **P. ignota**
psyl'lium . . . . FLAXSEED P.
pursh'i (*argyrea; gnaphalioides; P. patagonica g.*) [w] WOOLLY INDIANWHEAT
pusil'la (*elongata*) . . . . SLENDER P.
rhodosper'ma . . . . . . REDSEED P.
ru'geli [w] . . . . BLACKSEED P.
scario'sa . . . . **P. fastigiata**
spinulo'sa
tweed'yi . . . . TWEEDY P.
virgin'ica [w] . . . . . . PALESEED P.
wrightia'na . . . . WRIGHT P.
xerode'a . . . . **P. ignota**

PLANTAIN . . . . **Plantago**
ALPS P. . . . . **P. alpina**
AMERICAN SEASIDE P. . . **P. decipiens**
ASIATIC P. . . . . **P. asiatica**
BEAK P. . . . . **P. galeattiana**
BIGPOD P. . . . . . . **P. macrocarpa**
BLACKSEED P. . . . . **P. rugeli**
BLOND P. . . . . **P. ovata**
BOTTLEBRUSH INDIANWHEAT. **P. aristata**

PLANTAIN, continued
BUCKHORN P. . . **Plantago lanceolata**
CROWFOOT P. . . . . . **P. coronopus**
DESERT INDIANWHEAT . . **P. fastigiata**
DOTSEED P. . . . . **P. erecta**
EUROPEAN SEASIDE P. . . **P. maritima**
FLAXSEED P. . . . . **P. psyllium**
FOOTHILL INDIANWHEAT . . **P. ignota**
PALESEED P. . . . . **P. virginica**
PATAGONIA INDIANWHEAT **P. patagonica**
REDSEED P. . . . . **P. rhodosperma**
REDWOOL P. . . . . . . **P. eriopoda**
RIPPLESEED P. . . . . **P. major**
ROUNDHEAD P. . . . . **P. lagopus**
SHRUBBY P. . . . . **P. cynops**
SLENDER P. . . . . **P. pusilla**
SWEET P. . . . . **P. media**
TWEEDY P. . . . . **P. tweedyi**
WHORLED P. . . . . **P. indica**
WOOLLY INDIANWHEAT . . **P. purshi**
WRIGHT P. . . . . . **P. wrightiana**

PLANTAINLILY . . . . **Hosta**
BLUE P. . . . . **H. caerulea**
BLUNT P. . . . . **H. decorata**
FORTUNES P. . . . . . **H. fortunei**
FRAGRANT P. . . . . **H. plantaginea**
JAPANESE P. . . . . . . **H. japonica**
MIDSUMMER P. . . . . . **H. erromena**
SIEBOLD P. . . . . . . **H. sieboldiana**
WAVYLEAF P. . . . . . **H. undulata**

PLANT PATENTS
See **PATENTS, PLANT.**

PLAT'ANUS [w] . . . . . PLANETREE; SYCAMORE (Forestry)
∞ **acerifo'lia** (*occidentalis* × *orientalis*) ∞ LONDON P.
¢CAMBRIDGE (*cantabrigiensis*) HV.
¢KELSEY (*P. a. aureovariegata; P. a. kelseyana*)
¢LITTLELOBE (*parviloba*)
¢LONDON
¢PYRAMID (*P. a. pyramidalis*)
¢SPANISH (*P. a. hispanica*)
¢SUTTNER (*P. a. suttneri; P. occ. argenteo-variegata*)
califor'nica . . . . **P. racemosa**
chiapen'sis . . . . . . CHIAPAS P.
glabra'ta . . . . . . **P. occidentalis g.**
lindenia'na . . . . JALAPA P.
mexica'na . . . . MEXICAN P.
oaxaca'na . . . . OAXACA P.
occidenta'lis [w] . . . AMERICAN P.; AMERICAN S. (Forestry)
—glabra'ta (*P. glabrata*) SMOOTH A.P.; SMOOTH A.S. (Forestry)
orienta'lis . . . . ORIENTAL P.
The name Platanus orientalis is commonly misapplied to ∞ P. acerifolia.
—cunea'ta . . . . SMALL O.P.
Possibly of hybrid origin.
—digita'ta . . . . . FINGERLOBE O.P.
Possibly of hybrid origin.
¢CUTLEAF (*laciniata*) HV. P. orientalis
¢ISLAND (*insularis*)
racemo'sa (*californica*) CALIFORNIA P.; CALIFORNIA S. (Forestry)
wright'i [w] . . . . . . ARIZONA P.; ARIZONA S. (Forestry)

PLATHYME'NIA
reticula'ta

PLATO'NIA . . . . . GUIANAORANGE
insig'nis . . . . BAKURI G.

PLATYCA'RYA
strobila'cea (*Fortunaea chinensis*)

PLATYCE'RIUM (*ALCICORNIUM*) STAGHORNFERN
See **FERN GENERA.**

PLATYCLI'NIS . **DENDROCHILUM**
See **ORCHID GENERA.**

PLATYCO'DON . . . BALLOONFLOWER
grandiflo'rum (*Campanula grandiflora; Wahlenbergia g.*) . BALLOONFLOWER
AUTUMN (*autumnale*) HV.
AZURE (*azureum*)
DWARF (*nanum; pumilum*)
GIANT (*macranthum*)
JAPANESE (*japonicum*)
MARIES (*mariesi*)
SEMIDOUBLE (*semiduplex; semiplenum*)
SKYBLUE (*caeruleum*)
WHITE (*album*)

PLATYLO'PHUS
trifolia'tus . . . TOWER-OF-PISATREE

PLATYMIS'CIUM . . . . MACAWOOD
diadel'phum
polysta'chyum . . . . . . QUIRA M.

PLATYSTE'MON . . . PLATYSTEMON
califor'nicus . . . . . CREAMCUPS P.
—crini'tus

PLECTRAN'THUS . . . SPURFLOWER
esculen'tus . . . . . KAFIRPOTATO
dis'color
sacca'tus

PLECTRI'TIS . . . . . . PLECTRITIS
Some botanists unite this genus with Valerianella, but prevailing usage is to keep them separate.
conges'ta (*Valerianella c.*)
macro'cera (*Valerianella m.*) LONGHORN P.

PLEIOBLAST'US
See **BAMBOO GENERA.**

PLEIOGYN'IUM
solan'dri (*Spondias s.*). BURDEKINPLUM

PLEIO'NE
See **ORCHID GENERA.**

PLEIOSPER'MIUM . . ORANGEASTER
ala'tum . . . . CEYLON O.
du'bium . . . . JAVA O.
latiala'tum . . . . BORNEO O.
longisep'alum . . . . LONGSEPAL O.
sumatra'num . . . . . SUMATRA O.

PLEIOSPI'LOS **MESEMBRYANTHEMUM**
See **SUCCULENTS.**

PLERO'MA . . . . **TIBOUCHINA**

PLEUROG'YNA (*PLEUROGYNE*) [w] FELWORT
rota'ta [w] . . . . MARSH F.

PLEUROPO'GON . . SEMAPHOREGRASS
See **GRASS GENERA.**

PLEUROTHAL'LIS
See **ORCHID GENERA.**

Hort. var.; HV. = horticultural variety (or varieties); sp. = species (singular); spp. = species (plural).
¢ = clon; × (as a prefix) = hybrid; × (between scientific plant names) = crossed by; ∞ = polybrid; [w] = plant useful to wildlife.
See Glossary for definitions of clon, hybrid, and polybrid.

PLEURO'TUS . . . . . . PLEUROTUS
ostrea'tus . . . . OYSTER P.
sap'idus . . . . SAPID P.

PLU'CHEA |w . . . . PLUCHEA
camphora'ta |w . . . . CAMPHOR P.
(*Marsh-fleabane*)
seric'ea |w . . . . . ARROWWEED P.

PLUM . . . . **Prunus**
See also ALMOND, APRICOT, BIRDCHERRY, BUSHCHERRY, CHERRY, CHOKECHERRY, LAURELCHERRY, PEACH and PEACHBRUSH. For cultivated varieties see **FRUIT AND EDIBLE NUT NAMES.**
ALLEGANY P. . . . . **P. alleghaniensis**
AMERICAN P. . . . . . **P. americana**
APRICOT P. . . . . **P. simoni**
ARMENIAN P. . . . . . . **P. curdica**
BEACH P. . . . . **P. maritima**
BEAR P. . . . . **P. ursina**
BIG CHICKASAW P.
P. angustifolia varians
∞ BLIREIANA P. . . . . ∞ **P. blireiana**
BULLACE P. . . . . . . **P. insititia**
CANADA P. . . . . **P. nigra**
CHICKASAW P. . . . . **P. angustifolia**
COCOMILIA P. . . . . . **P. cocomilia**
CREEK P. . . . . **P. rivularis**
DAVIS ALLEGANY P.
P. alleghaniensis davisi
∞ DUNBAR P. . . . . . ∞ **P. dunbari**
FLATWOODS P. . . . . **P. umbellata**
FLOWERING P. . . . . . . **P. triloba**
FULTON MEXICAN P.
P. mexicana fultonensis
GARDEN P. . . . . . . **P. domestica**
∞ GIANT P. . . . . . . ∞ **P. gigantea**
GRAVES P. . . . . **P. gravesi**
GREEK P. . . . **P. pseudoarmeniaca**
HOG P. . . . . **P. reverchoni**
HORTULAN P. . . . . . **P. hortulana**
INCH P. . . . . **P. lanata**
JAPANESE P. . . . . **P. salicina**
KELLOGG KLAMATH P.
P. subcordata kelloggi
KLAMATH P. . . . . . **P. subcordata**
LARISSA P. . . . . . . **P. tenuifolia**
MEXICAN P. . . . . . . **P. mexicana**
MINER HORTULAN P.
P. hortulana mineri
MISSOURI H. P. . . . . . **P. h. pubens**
MYROBALAN P. . . . . **P. cerasifera**
NETVEIN MEXICAN P.
P. mexicana reticulata
OKLAHOMA P. . . . . . . **P. gracilis**
PETZOLD FLOWERING P.
P. triloba petzoldi
POLYANDRA MEXICAN P.
P. mexicana polyandra
SAND CHICKASAW P.
P. angustifolia watsoni
∞ SULTANA P. . . . . . ∞ **P. sultana**
TAURUS P. . . . . . . **P. monticola**
TEXAS P. . . . . **P. venulosa**
WAKULLA AMERICAN P.
P. americana floridana
WILD BULLACE P.
P. insititia subsilvestris
WILD FLOWERING P. **P. triloba simplex**
WILDGOOSE P. . . . . **P. munsoniana**
WILD MYROBALAN P.
P. cerasifera divaricata
YELLOW BEACH P. . **P. maritima flava**

PLUMBA'GO . . . . . . PLUMBAGO
capen'sis . . . . CAPE P.
—al'ba . . . . WHITE C.P.
coccin'ea . . . . **P. rosea c.**

PLUMBAGO, continued
coccin'ea super'ba . . . . **P. rosea c.**
europae'a . . . COMMON PLUMBAGO
larpen'tiae
Ceratostigma plumbaginoides
rose'a (*indica*) . . . . ROSE P.
—coccin'ea (*P. coccinea; P. c. superba*)
SCARLET P.
scan'dens . . . . CLIMBING P.

∞ PLUMCOT
Prunus armeniaca × salicina

PLUMEGRASS . . . . **Erianthus**
BENT-AWN P. . . . . . **E. contortus**
BROWN P. . . . . . . **E. brevibarbis**
FLORIDA SILVER P.
E. alopecuroides hirsutus
NARROW P. . . . . **E. strictus**
SILVER P. . . . . . **E. alopecuroides**
SUGARCANE P. . . . . . **E. giganteus**

PLUMEPOPPY . . . . **Macleaya**
PINK P. . . . . **M. cordata**

PLUMER'IA (*PLUMIER(I)A*)
FRANGIPANI
acumina'ta (*acutifolia*) . MEXICAN F.
al'ba . . . . WHITE F.
emargina'ta . . . . . . CUBAN F.
obtu'sa . . . . BLUNTLOBE F.
ru'bra . . . . NOSEGAY F.

PLUMIE'RA; PLUMIE'RIA
PLUMERIA

∞ PLUMPEACH **Prunus persica × salicina**

PLUMYEW . . . . **Cephalotaxus**
CHINESE P. . . . . **C. fortuni**

PLU'TEUS . . . . PLUTEUS
cervi'nus . . . . . . FAWNCOLOR P.

PO'A . . . . BLUEGRASS
See **GRASS GENERA.**

PODACHAE'NIUM
em'inens (*Ferdinanda e.*)

PODALYR'IA . . . . PODALYRIA
buxifo'lia . . . . BOXLEAF P.
—grandiflo'ra . . . . . SHOWY B.P.
calyptra'ta . . . . . . FRAGRANT P.
seric'ea . . . . SATINLEAF P.

PODFERN . . . . **Cheilanthes siliquosa**

PODGRASS . . . . **Triglochin**
ARROW P. . . . . **T. palustris**
RIDGED P. . . . . **T. striata**
SHORE P. . . . . **T. maritima**

PODOCAR'PUS . . . . . PODOCARPUS
acutifo'lius . . . . . . THINLEAF P.
affi'nis
alpi'nus . . . . TASMANIA P.
andi'nus . . . . ANDES P.
appres'sus . . . . **P. macrophyllus a.**
chinen'sis . . . . **P. m. maki**
coria'ceus . . . . YACCA P.
dacrydioi'des . . . . . . KAHIKA P.
ela'tus . . . . TALL P.
elonga'tus . . . . FERN P.
ferrugin'eus . . . . MIRO P.
gracil'ior . . . . . . MUSENGERA P.
hall'i . . . . **P. totara h.**
macrophyl'lus . . . . YEW P.
—appres'sus (*P. appressus*)
SHORTLEAF Y.P.
—ma'ki (*P. chinensis; P. japonicus*)
SHRUBBY Y.P.
na'gi . . . . JAPANESE P.
neriifo'lius . . . . OLEANDER P.
niv'alis . . . . SNOW P.
nubig'enus . . . . CHILE P.

PODOCARPUS, continued
salig'nus . WILLOWLEAF PODOCARPUS
spica'tus . . . . MATAI P.
spinulo'sus . . . . . . SPINYLEAF P.
tota'ra . . . . TOTARA P.
—hall'i (*P. halli*) . . . . HALLS T.P.

PODOCARPUS . . . . **Podocarpus**
ANDES P. . . . . **P. andinus**
CHILE P. . . . . **P. nubigenus**
FERN P. . . . . **P. elongatus**
HALLS TOTARA P. . . . **P. totara halli**
JAPANESE P. . . . . **P. nagi**
KAHIKA P. . . . . . . **P. dacrydioides**
MATAI P. . . . . **P. spicatus**
MIRO P. . . . . **P. ferrugineus**
MUSENGERA P. . . . . . . **P. gracilior**
OLEANDER P. . . . . . . **P. neriifolius**
SHORTLEAF YEW P.
P. macrophyllus appressus
SHRUBBY Y. P. . . . . . . **P. m. maki**
SNOW P. . . . . **P. nivalis**
SPINYLEAF P. . . . . . **P. spinulosus**
TALL P. . . . . **P. elatus**
TASMANIA P. . . . . **P. alpinus**
THINLEAF P. . . . . . . **P. acutifolius**
TOTARA P. . . . . **P. totara**
WILLOWLEAF P. . . . . . . **P. salignus**
YACCA P. . . . . **P. coriaceus**
YEW P. . . . . **P. macrophyllus**

PODOLE'PIS . . . . PODOLEPIS
arista'ta (*chrysantha*) . . GOLDEN P.
canes'cens (*affinis*) . . . . HOARY P.
grac'ilis . . . . LILAC P.

PODOPHYL'LUM . . . . MAYAPPLE
em'odi . . . . HIMALAYAN M.
pelta'tum . . . . COMMON M.

PODOSTE'MON |w . . . RIVERWEED
abrotanoi'des |w . . . . OLDMAN R.
ceratophyl'lum |w . . . HORNLEAF R.

PODRA'NEA
bryc'ei . . . . . . QUEEN-OF-SHEBA

POGO'NIA (*ISOTRIA; TRIPHORA*)
POGONIA
See **ORCHID GENERA, HARDY TERRESTRIAL GROUP.**

POGONO'PUS
tubulo'sus

POGOSTE'MON
cab'lin . . . . . CABLIN PATCHOULI
heynea'nus (*patchouly*) . . HEYNE P.

POINCIA'NA . . . . . . POINCIANA
conzat'ti (*Coulteria tinctoria*)
CONZATTI P.
gillies'i (*Caesalpinia g.*) . PARADISE P.
(*Bird-of-paradise-flower*)
pulcher'rima (*Caesalpinia p.*)
FLOWERFENCE P.
—fla'va . . . . YELLOW F.P.
re'gia . . . . **Delonix r.**

Poinciana, Royal . . FLAMBOYANTTREE:
Delonix regia

POINSET'TIA . . . . **EUPHORBIA**
See **SUCCULENTS.**

POINSETTIA
Euphorbia (section Poinsettia)
COMMON P. . . . . . **E. pulcherrima**

POINTEDPOD . . . . **Oxylobium**
HEARTLEAF P. . . . . **O. cordifolium**
TASMANIA P. . . . . . **O. ellipticum**
TRAILING P. . . . . **O. procumbens**
WESTAUSTRALIA P. . . **O. callistachys**

POINTVETCH, BESSEY . **Oxytropis besseyi**
POISONHEMLOCK . . **Conium maculatum**
POISONIVY, COMMON
Toxicodendron radicans
WESTERN P. . . . . . . **T. r. rydbergi**
POISONNUT . . . . **Strychnos**
AMAZON P. . . . . **S. castelnaei**
CLEARING P. . . . . . **S. potatorum**
CURARE P. . . . . **S. toxifera**
ICAYA P. . . . . **S. icaja**
KAFIRORANGE P. . . . . . **S. spinosa**
MALACCA P. . . . . . **S. malaccensis**
NUXVOMICA P. . . . . **S. nuxvomica**
ST.IGNATIUS P. . . . . . . **S. ignati**
POISONOAK . **Toxicodendron quercifolium**
ORIENTAL P. . . . . **T. orientale**
PACIFIC P. . . . . . . **T. diversilobum**

POISONOUS PLANTS

The annual losses in the United States from poisonous plants reach astonishing figures. It is estimated that they average around 4 percent per annum for range livestock and, in Colorado alone, the poisonous-plant toll is reported to average about $1,000,000 a year. Crazyweed, Deathcamas, Larkspur, Loco, Lupine, Podgrass (*Arrowgrass*), Poisonvetch, Sneezeweed, and Waterhemlock are perhaps the chief offenders. In addition, there is a considerable annual loss of human life from poisonous plants, such as toxic fungi (bacteria are here eliminated from consideration); children sometimes eat Waterhemlock tubers, Elderberry roots, raw Horsechestnuts, and the like, with occasional fatal results.

The list below, covering about 175 genera and 525 species and varieties of plants, is intended to cover the more important poisonous plants of the United States. The list is intended to be practical, omitting plants which are occasionally reported to be poisonous (often without adequate evidence) and common vegetables (such as Potato, which at certain stages may contain toxic compounds). It is confined to plants which are actually known to have poisoned livestock or human beings and to species (like Nettles and Poisonivy) which are definitely irritating to the human skin. It disregards the very numerous plants (such as Ceanothus) for which chemical analyses have demonstrated the presence of toxic alkaloids such as saponin, but which practical experience shows to be valuable forage plants. It should be remembered that, if every plant in the United States alone were listed against whose record some suspicious report has been raised or for which some chemical analysis has demonstrated the presence of some toxic (actual or alleged) compound, the number would run high in four figures. The list has been compiled from published and unpublished records of the United States Forest Service, including the "Range Plant Handbook" (1937), "Important Western Browse Plants" (1931), and a 14-page mss. list, by W. A. Dayton, "Preliminary List of National Forest Range Plants Poisonous to Livestock" (1931); from the copious toxicological literature of the various State Agricultural Experiment Stations and of the U. S. Department of Agriculture, particularly "Stock-Poisoning Plants of the Range," by the late C. Dwight Marsh (U. S. Dept. Agr. Bull. 1245, rev. 1929); also from the late L. H. Pammel's encyclopedic "A Manual of Poisonous Plants" (1911), and Walter Conrad Muenscher's "Poisonous Plants of the United States" (1939).

W. A. DAYTON and DORIS W. HAYES
Forest Service, U. S. Dept. of Agriculture

POISONOUS PLANTS, continued

ACALY'PHA . . . . . COPPERLEAF
lindheim'eri . . . . LINDHEIMER C.
virgin'ica . . . . VIRGINIA C.

ACERA'TES viridiflo'ra
GREEN ACERATES

ACONI'TUM . . . . MONKSHOOD
ba'keri . . . . BAKER M.
columbia'num . . . . COLUMBIA M.
glaber'rimum . . . . SMOOTH M.
hel'leri . . . . HELLER M.
how'elli . . . . HOWELL M.
leiberg'i . . . . LEIBERG M.
lutes'cens . . . . YELLOW M.
uncina'tum . . . . CLAMBERING M.

ACTAE'A . . . . BANEBERRY
al'ba . . . . WHITE B.
argu'ta (*A. spicata a.*) . . WESTERN B.
eburne'a . . . . IVORY B.
ru'bra (*A. spicata r.*) . . . . RED B.

ACTINE'A (*HYMENOXYS*)
ACTINEA
odora'ta (*Hymenoxys cockerelli; H. multiflora; H. odorata*)
BITTERWEED A.
richardso'ni (*Hymenoxys floribunda*)
PINGUE A. (*Colorado Rubberweed*)

ADE'LIA va'seyi (*Euphorbia v.; Ricinella v.*) . . . . . VASEY ADELIA

ADENOSTE'GIA
CORDYLANTHUS

AES'CULUS . . . . . . BUCKEYE; HORSECHESTNUT

Afze'lia cassioi'des . . **Seymeria c.**

AGROSTEM'MA githa'go (*Lychnis g.*) . . . COMMON CORNCOCKLE

AILAN'THUS altis'sima (*glandulosa*)
TREEOFHEAVEN AILANTHUS

ALE'TRIS farino'sa
WHITETUBE STARGRASS

AMANI'TA . . . . AMANITA
musca'ria . . . . FLY A.
phalloi'des . . . . . . DEATHCUP A.
ver'na . . . . SPRING A.

AMIAN'THIUM muscaetox'icum (*Chrosperma m.; Zigadenus m.*)
CROWPOISON

Ampelop'sis quinquefo'lia
Parthenocissus q.

AMSINCK'IA spectab'ilis
COAST FIDDLENECK
Seeds are toxic.

AMSO'NIA pal'meri
PALMER AMSONIA

ANDROM'EDA . . . ANDROMEDA
cates'baei . . . . **Leucothoe c.**
glaucophyl'la . . . . DOWNY A.
polifo'lia . . . . . . BOGROSEMARY A.
racemo'sa . . . . **Leucothoe r.**

Andropo'gon halepen'sis
Sorghum halepense
sor'ghum . . . . **S. vulgare**
—sudanen'sis . . . **S. v. sudanense**

ANEM'ONE occidenta'lis (*Pulsatilla o.*) WESTERN PASQUEFLOWER

APLOPAP'PUS (*BIGELOVIA* in part; *ISOCOMA; OONOPSIS*)
GOLDENWEED
fre'monti (*Oonopsis condensata*)
FREMONT G.

POISONOUS PLANTS (APLOPAPPUS), con.
frutico'sus (*Bigelovia coronopifolia; Isocoma c.; I. fruticosa*) . BURROWEED
heterophyl'lus (*Bigelovia heterophylla; Isocoma heterophylla; I. wrighti*)
JIMMYWEED

APOC'YNUM . . . . . DOGBANE
androsaemifo'lium . . SPREADING D.
cannab'inum . . . . HEMP D.
pu'milum . . . . LOW D.
scopulo'rum . . . . CLIFF D.
sibir'icum . . . . PRAIRIE D.

ARAGAL'LUS . . **OXYTROPIS**
albiflo'rus . . . . . **O. saximontana**

ARGEMO'NE mexica'na
MEXICAN PRICKLEPOPPY

ARTEMIS'IA filifo'lia
SAND SAGEBRUSH

ASCLE'PIAS . . . . MILKWEED
cordifo'lia . **Gomphocarpus cordifolius**
eriocar'pa . . . . WOOLLYPOD M.
ero'sa . . . . DESERT M.
fre'monti . . . . KOTOLO M.
galioi'des . . . . POISON M.
incarna'ta . . . . SWAMP M.
involucra'ta . . . . . . DWARF M.
latifo'lia . . . . . . BROADLEAF M.
mexica'na . . . . MEXICAN M.
pu'mila . . . . PLAINS M.
specio'sa . . . . SHOWY M.
syri'aca . . . . COMMON M.
tubero'sa . . . . . . BUTTERFLY M.
verticilla'ta . . . . . WHORLED M.

ASCLEPIODO'RA decum'bens
SPIDER ANTELOPEHORN

AS'TER (*XYLORRHIZA*) . ASTER
glabrius'culus (*Xylorrhiza glabriuscula*) . . . . ALKALI A.
par'ryi (*Xylorrhiza p.*) . . . . PARRY A.
xylorrhi'za (*Xylorrhiza scopulorum; X. villosa*) . . . . COMMON WOODY A.

ASTRAG'ALUS (*Ctenophyllum; Cystium; Diholcos; Hamosa; Homalobus; Phaca; Pterophacos; Rydbergiella; Xylophacos*)
LOCO; POISONVETCH

The species causing locoism are called Loco; poisonous species, causing symptoms very different from locoism, are called Poisonvetch.

alloch'rous (*Phaca allochroa*)
HALFMOON L.
arizo'nicus . . . . ARIZONA L.
bisulca'tus (*Diholcos b.*)
TWOGROOVED L.
col'toni . . . . COLTON L.
convalla'rius (*campestris* A. Gray, *not* L.) . . . . TIMBER P.
—diversifo'lius (*A. diversifolius; A. junciformis*)
—hyloph'ilus (*A. hylophilus*)
curvicar'pus . . . . . CURVEPOD L.
diph'ysus (*Cystium diphysum*) BLUE L.
earl'ei . . . . EARL L.
haydenia'nus (*scobinatulus; Diholcos s.*)
HAYDEN P.
horn'i . . . . HORN L.
hyloph'ilus . . . . **A. convallarius h.**
juncifor'mis
A. convallarius diversifolius
lentigino'sus (*Cystium lentiginosum*)
SPECKLEPOD L.
leucophyl'lus . . . . WOOLLYLEAF L.
menzies'i . . . . MENZIES L.

POISONOUS PLANTS (ASTRAGALUS), con.
mollis'simus . . . . . WOOLLY LOCO
mort'oni . . . . MORTON L.
nothox'ys . . . . SHEEP L.
palliser'i (*Homalobus p.*) PALLISER POISONVETCH
patterso'ni (*Rydbergiella p.*) PATTERSON L.
pectina'tus (*Ctenophyllum pectinatum*) NARROWLEAF P.
pursh'i (*Xylophacos p.*) . . PURSH L.
remul'cus . . . . TOWLINE L.
sabulo'sus (*praelongus; Rydbergiella praelonga*) . . . STRAIGHTSTEM P.
scapo'sus (*Hamosa scaposa*) BARESTEM L.
scobinat'ulus . . . . **A. haydenianus**
tetrap'terus (*Pterophacos t.*) FOURWING P.
thomp'sonae . . . . . THOMPSON L.
thur'beri . . . . THURBER L.
utahen'sis (*Xylophacos shortianus; X. utahensis*) . . . . UTAH L.
vesperti'nus (*Xylophacos v.*)
ward'i (*Phaca w.*) . . . . WARD L.
woot'oni . . . . WOOTON L.
yaquia'nus . . . . YAQUI L.

Astrophyl'lum dumo'sum **Choisya dumosa**

A'triplex suckleya'na . **Suckleya s.**

AZA'LEA . . **RHODODENDRON**
califor'nica . . . . . . **R. occidentale**

AZALEAS'TRUM **RHODODENDRON**

BAC'CHARIS . . . BACCHARIS
pteronioi'des (*ramulosa*) YERBADEPASMO B.
sarothroi'des . . . . BROOM B.

BAHI'A oppositifo'lia (*Picradeniopsis o.*) . . . . . . PLAINS BAHIA

BAI'LEYA multiradia'ta DESERT BAILEYA

BERNARD'IA myricaefo'lia SOUTHWEST BERNARDIA

BER'ULA erec'ta . STALKY BERULA

BIGELO'VIA . . **APLOPAPPUS**
coronopifo'lia . . . . . . **A. fruticosus**

BIKU'KULLA . . . **DICENTRA**

BOE'BERA . . . . . **DYSSODIA**

Broussonet'ia secundiflo'ra **Sophora s.**

CAL'THA . . . MARSHMARIGOLD
biflo'ra (*howelli*) . . TWINFLOWER M.
palus'tris . . . . COMMON M.

CALYCAN'THUS . SWEETSHRUB
fer'tilis . . . . PALE S.
flor'idus . . . . COMMON S.
occidenta'lis (*macrophyllus*) CALIFORNIA S.

CAN'NABIS sati'va (*indica*). HEMP

CASSI'OPE . . . . . . CASSIOPE
mertensia'na . . . . . . MERTENS C.
tetrag'ona . . . . FIREMOSS C.

CASTANOP'SIS sempervi'rens SIERRA EVERGREENCHINKAPIN

CATHARTOLI'NUM . . **LINUM**

CEPHALAN'THUS occidenta'lis COMMON BUTTONBUSH

CERA'SUS . . . . . . **PRUNUS**

CES'TRUM . . . . . . CESTRUM

POISONOUS PLANTS, continued

CHAMAESY'CE . **EUPHORBIA**

CHELIDO'NIUM ma'jus GREATER CELANDINE

CHLOROG'ALUM pomeridia'num (*Laothoe pomeridiana*) AMOLE SOAPPLANT

CHOI'SYA dumo'sa (*Astrophyllum dumosum*) STARLEAF MEXICANORANGE

Chrosper'ma muscaetox'icum **Amianthium m.**

CICU'TA . . . . WATERHEMLOCK
bulbif'era . . . . BULB W.
califor'nica . . . . CALIFORNIA W.
cur'tissi . . . . CURTISS W.
doug'lasi . . . . DOUGLAS W.
macula'ta . . . . SPOTTED W.
occidenta'lis . . . . . WESTERN W.
va'gans . . . . TUBER W.

CIMICIF'UGA racemo'sa COHOSH BUGBANE

CLAV'ICEPS purpu'rea ERGOT CLAVICEPS

CNIDOS'COLUS stimulo'sus (*Jatropha stimulosa*) . RISKY TREADSOFTLY

CO'NIUM macula'tum POISONHEMLOCK

CORDYLAN'THUS wright'i (*Adenostegia w.*) . . WRIGHT BIRDBEAK

CORYD'ALIS (*CAPNOIDES*) CORYDALIS
au'rea (*Capnoides aureum*) . GOLDEN C.
casea'na (*Capnoides caseanum*) FITWEED C.
sempervi'rens . . . . PALE C.

COVIL'LEA . . . . . **LARREA**

CRAC'CA . . . . **TEPHROSIA**

CROTALA'RIA . . . CROTALARIA
sagitta'lis . . . . ARROW C.
spectab'ilis . . . . SHOWY C.

CRO'TON . . . . CROTON
capita'tus . . . . WOOLLY C.
fruticulo'sus . . . . BUSH C.
neomexica'nus . . NEWMEXICAN C.
texen'sis . . . . TEXAS C.

CTENOPHYL'LUM **ASTRAGALUS**

CYCLADE'NIA . . . CYCLADENIA
hu'milis . . . . SMOOTH C.
tomento'sa . . . . WOOLLY C.

CYNOGLOS'SUM. HOUNDSTONGUE
occidenta'le . . . . . WESTERN H.
officina'le . . . . . . COMMON H.

CYS'TIUM . . . **ASTRAGALUS**

CY'TISUS scopa'rius (*Genista scoparia; Spartium scoparium*) SCOTCH BROOM

DA'LEA (*PAROSELA*) . DALEA
argyrae'a (*Parosela a.*) . . SILVER D.
frutes'cens (*Parosela f.*) . . BLACK D.
par'ryi (*Parosela p.*) . . . PARRY D.

DAPH'NE meze'reum FEBRUARY DAPHNE

DASYLIR'ION texa'num TEXAS SOTOL

POISONOUS PLANTS, continued

DATU'RA . . . . DATURA
meteloi'des . . . . SACRED D.
quercifo'lia . . . . OAKLEAF D.
stramo'nium (*tatula*). JIMSONWEED D.

DAUBENTO'NIA . . RATTLEBOX
cavanil'lesi (*longifolia; Sesbania c.*) LONGLEAF R.
drum'mondi (*Sesbania d.*) DRUMMOND R.

DELPHIN'IUM . . . . LARKSPUR
abieto'rum . . . . . . **D. occidentale**
aja'cis (*candelabrum; gayanum*) ROCKET L.
albes'cens . . . . **D. virescens**
amplibractea'tum . . . MOGOLLON L.
anderso'ni (*burkei; leonardi*) ANDERSON L.
apicula'tum . . . . . SHARPLEAF L.
azu'reum . . . . . . **D. carolinianum**
bar'beyi (*D. scopulorum subalpinum; subalpinum*) . . . . . BARBEY L.
bi'color (*glareosum*) . . . . LITTLE L.
block'manae . . . . . . BLOCKMAN L.
brown'i . . . . BROWNS L.
burk'ei . . . . **D. andersoni**
califor'nicum . . . . . CALIFORNIA L.
campo'rum . . . . . **D. virescens c.**
candelab'rum . . . . **D. ajacis**
cardina'le . . . . CARDINAL L.
carolinia'num (*azureum; nortonianum; D. c. nortonianum*) . . CAROLINA L.
—*penard'i* . . . . **D. virescens**
columbia'num (*nuttalli; pauciflorum* Nutt., *not* D. Don) . COLUMBIA L.
consol'ida . . . . FORKING L.
cuculla'tum . . . . . **D. occidentale**
deco'rum . . . . . YELLOWTINGE L.
—*pa'tens* . . . . **D. patens**
depaupera'tum (*diversifolium*) . SLIM L.
dis'tichum . . . . TWOSPIKE L.
elonga'tum . . . . LENGTHY L.
gaya'num . . . . **D. ajacis**
geraniifo'lium . . . . GERANIUM L.
gey'eri . . . . GEYER L.
glareo'sum . . . . **D. bicolor**
glauces'cens
glau'cum . . . . . **D. scopulorum g.**
gracilen'tum (*sonnei*) . . . SONNE L.
han'seni . . . . HANSEN L.
hesper'ium . . . . COAST L.
leonard'i . . . . **D. andersoni**
menzies'i (*nelsoni; pauperculum; pinetorum*) . . . . MENZIES L.
—**ochroleu'cum** (*D. leucophaeum; D. ochroleucum*) . . . . . CREAM M.L.
nortonia'num . . . . **D. carolinianum**
nudicau'le . . . . ORANGE L.
nutt'alli . . . . **D. columbianum**
occidenta'le (*abietorum; cucullatum; quercetorum*) . . . . DUNCECAP L.
par'ryi . . . . PARRY L.
pa'tens (*D. decorum p.*). SPREADING L.
pauciflo'rum Nutt., *not* D. Don **D. columbianum**
pauper'culum . . . . . **D. menziesi**
penard'i . . . . **D. virescens**
pineto'rum . . . . **D. menziesi**
recurva'tum . . . . . RECURVED L.
reticula'tum
robus'tum . . . . GIANT L.
sapello'nis . . . . SAPELLO L.
scapo'sum . . . . BARESTEM L.
scopulo'rum . . . . TALLMOUNTAIN L.
—**glau'cum** (*D. glaucum*) . SIERRA L.
—*subalpi'num* . . . . . **D. barbeyi**
sierrae-blan'cae . WHITEMOUNTAIN L.

POISONOUS PLANTS (DELPHINIUM), con.
sim'plex
son'nei . . . . **D. gracilentum**
stachyd'eum (*D. scopulorum s.*) ROCKYMOUNTAIN LARKSPUR
subalpi'num . . . . . . **D. barbeyi**
tenuisec'tum . . . . . CARROTLEAF L.
tricor'ne . . . . ROCK L.
trolliifo'lium . . . COLUMBIARIVER L.
variega'tum . . . . ROYAL L.
veneno'sum . . . . DEATH L.
vires'cens (*albescens; D. carolinianum penardi; penardi; D. v. penardi*) PLAINS L.
—campo'rum (*D. camporum*)
virides'cens . . . . . . CHELAN L.

DENDROME'CON rig'ida STIFF BUSHPOPPY

DICEN'TRA (*BIKUKULLA*) BLEEDINGHEART
canaden'sis (*Bikukulla c.*) SQUIRRELCORN
chrysan'tha (*Bikukulla c.*) GOLDEARDROPS B.
cuculla'ria (*Bikukulla c.*) DUTCHMANS-BREECHES
exim'ia (*Bikukulla e.*) . . FRINGED B.
formo'sa (*Bikukulla f.*) . . PACIFIC B.
ochroleu'ca (*Bikukulla o.*) . CREAM B.
pauciflo'ra . . . . . . CALIFORNIA B.
pusil'la (*Bikukulla p.*) . . . LITTLE B.
uniflo'ra (*Bikukulla u.*) STEERSHEAD B.

DICHROPHYL'LUM **EUPHORBIA**

DIGITA'LIS purpu'rea COMMON FOXGLOVE

DIHOL'COS . . **ASTRAGALUS**
scobina'tulus . . . . **A. haydenianus**

DIR'CA palus'tris ATLANTIC LEATHERWOOD

DITAX'IS . . . . DITAXIS

DODONAE'A visco'sa angustifo'lia NARROWLEAF CLAMMY HOPSEEDBUSH

DRO'SERA rotundifo'lia ROUNDLEAF SUNDEW

DRYMA'RIA holosteoi'des (*pachyphylla*) . . THICKLEAF DRYMARY

DUGAL'DIA . . . **HELENIUM**

DYSSO'DIA pappo'sa (*Boebera p.*) PRAIRIE DOGWEED

EQUISE'TUM . . . . HORSETAIL
arven'se . . . . FIELD H.
hyema'le . . . . . . SCOURINGRUSH
laeviga'tum . . . . . . SMOOTH H.
palus'tre . . . . MARSH H.
praeal'tum (*robustum*) STOUT SCOURINGRUSH
praten'se . . . . MEADOW H.
sylvat'icum . . . . SYLVAN H.
telmatei'a . . . . GIANT H.

ERAGROS'TIS cilianen'sis STINKGRASS

EREMOCAR'PUS setig'erus (*Piscaria setigera*) . TURKEYMULLEIN

ERIG'ERON canaden'sis (*Leptilon canadense*) HORSEWEED FLEABANE

ERYTHRI'NA flabellifor'mis WESTERN CORALBEAN

EUBO'TRYS . . . **LEUCOTHOE**

EUON'YMUS atropurpu'reus EASTERN WAHOO

POISONOUS PLANTS, continued

EUPATO'RIUM . . . EUPATORIUM
perfolia'tum . . . . BONESET
rugo'sum . . . . WHITE SNAKEROOT

EUPHOR'BIA (*Chamaesyce; Dichrophyllum; Poinsettia; Tithymalopsis; Tithymalus; Trichosterigma; Zygophyllidium*) . . EUPHORBIA
corolla'ta (*Tithymalopsis c.*) FLOWERINGSPURGE E.
crenula'ta (*Tithymalus crenulatus*) BEETLE E.
cyparis'sias (*Tithymalus c.*) CYPRESS E.
denta'ta (*Poinsettia d.*) . TOOTHED E.
e'sula (*virgata*) . . . . . . LEAFY E.
glyptosper'ma (*Chamaesyce g.*) RIDGESEED E.
heliosco'pia (*Tithymalus h.*) . SUN E.
heterophyl'la (*Poinsettia h.*) PAINTED E.
hexag'ona (*Zygophyllidium hexagonum*) SIXANGLE E.
la'thyrus . . . . CAPER E.
macula'ta (*nutans; presli; Chamaesyce m.*) . . . . SPOTTED E.
margina'ta (*variegata; Dicrophyllum marginatum*) SNOW-ON-THE-MOUNTAIN E.
pal'meri (*Tithymalus p.*) . PALMER E.
pep'lus (*Tithymalus p.*) . . PETTY E.
serpyllifo'lia (*neomexicana; Chamaesyce s.*) . . . . . . THYMELEAF E.
va'seyi . . . . **Adelia v.**
vermicula'ta (*hirsuta*)

FAGOPY'RUM sagitta'tum (*esculentum*) . . . COMMON BUCKWHEAT

GELSE'MIUM sempervi'rens CAROLINAJESSAMINE

Genis'ta scopa'ria . **Cytisus scoparius**

GLECO'MA hedera'cea (*Nepeta h.*)

Horses are reported to be poisoned occasionally by this plant. The matter should be more fully investigated.

GOMPHOCAR'PUS
cordifo'lius (*Asclepias cordifolia*)
purpuras'cens . . . . . . **Solanoa p.**

Gonolo'bus macrophyl'lus **Vincetoxicum gonocarpos**

GUTIERRE'ZIA . . . SNAKEWEED
microceph'ala (*filifolia*) THREADLEAF S.
saro'thrae . . . . BROOM S.

GYMNO'CLADUS dioi'cus (*canadensis*) . KENTUCKY COFFEETREE

GYROTHE'CA. **LACHNANTHES**

HAMO'SA . . . **ASTRAGALUS**

HELE'NIUM (*DUGALDIA*) SNEEZEWEED
autumna'le . . . . . . COMMON S.
bigelo'vi . . . . BIGELOW S.
hoopes'i (*Dugaldia h.*) . . ORANGE S.
monta'num (*autumnale* D. C. Eaton, *not* L.) . . . . . . MOUNTAIN S.
nudiflo'rum . . . . PURPLEHEAD S.
tenuifo'lium . BITTER S. (*Bitterweed*)

HELLE'BORUS vir'idis GREEN HELLEBORE

HIPPOMA'NE mancinel'la MANCHINEEL

HOL'CUS . . . . . VELVETGRASS
halepen'sis . . . . **Sorghum halepense**
lana'tus . . . . COMMON V.
sor'ghum . . . . . **Sorghum vulgare**
—sudanen'sis . . . . **S. v. sudanense**
sudanen'sis . . . . **S. v. sudanense**

POISONOUS PLANTS, continued

HOMALO'BUS . **ASTRAGALUS**

HYMENOX'YS . . . . **ACTINEA**
cockerel'li . . . . **A. odorata**
floribun'da . . . . **A. richardsoni**
multiflo'ra . . . . **A. odorata**

HYOSCY'AMUS ni'ger BLACK HENBANE

HYPER'ICUM . . . ST.JOHNSWORT
concin'num . . . . . CALIFORNIA S.
perfora'tum . . . . . . COMMON S.
puncta'tum (*maculatum* Walt., *not* Crantz) . . . . SPOTTED S

ICHTHYOME'THIA . **PISCIDIA**

IONOX'ALIS . . . . . **OXALIS**

I'RIS versicol'or . . BLUEFLAG IRIS

The rootstocks of this plant are poisonous.

ISOCO'MA . . . **APLOPAPPUS**
coronopifo'lia . . . . . . **A. fruticosus**
wright'i . . . . **A. heterophyllus**

Jat'ropha stimulo'sa **Cnidoscolus stimulosus**

KAL'MIA . . . . KALMIA
angustifo'lia . . . . . LAMBKILL K.
latifo'lia . . . . MOUNTAINLAUREL K.
polifo'lia (*glauca; occidentalis*) . BOG K.
—microphyl'la . . . . ALPINE B.K.

KARWIN'SKIA humboldtia'na HUMBOLDT COYOTILLO

LACHNAN'THES tincto'ria (*Gyrotheca t.*) . . . . BLOOD REDROOT

LAOTH'OE . . **CHLOROGALUM**

LAPOR'TEA canaden'sis (*Urticastrum divaricatum*) CANADA WOODNETTLE

LAR'REA tridenta'ta (*Covillea t.*) COVILLE CREOSOTEBUSH

LAUROCERA'SUS . . **PRUNUS**

LE'DUM . . . . LEDUM
glandulo'sum . . . . . WESTERN L.
groenland'icum (*latifolium*) LABRADORTEA L.

Leptan'dra virgin'ica **Veronicastrum virginicum**

LEP'TILON . . . . **ERIGERON**

LEUCOCRI'NUM monta'num COMMON STARLILY

LEUCOTH'OE (*EUBOTRYS*) LEUCOTHOE
cates'baei (*Andromeda c.*) DROOPING L.
davis'iae . . . . . . BLACKLAUREL L.
racemo'sa (*Andromeda r.; Eubotrys r.*) SWEETBELLS L.

LIGUS'TRUM vulga're EUROPEAN PRIVET

LINNAE'A borea'lis america'na AMERICAN TWINFLOWER

LI'NUM (*CATHARTOLINUM*) FLAX
neomexica'num (*Cathartolinum n.*) NEWMEXICO F.
rig'idum (*Cathartolinum r.*) STIFFSTEM F.
usitatis'simum . . . . . COMMON F.

LOBE'LIA . . . . . . LOBELIA
cardina'lis . . . . CARDINALFLOWER
infla'ta . . . . . INDIANTOBACCO L.
siphilit'ica (*syphilitica*) . BIGBLUE L.
spica'ta . . . . PALESPIKE L.

POISONOUS PLANTS, continued

LO'LIUM temulen'tum DARNEL RYEGRASS

LONIC'ERA . . . . HONEYSUCKLE
interrup'ta . . . . . . CHAPARRAL H.
involucra'ta . . . . . BEARBERRY H.

LOPHOPH'ORA wil'liamsi MESCALBUTTON PEYOTE

LUPI'NUS . . . . LUPINE

The pods and seeds of many Lupines are poisonous to livestock. In a few cases the herbage also is known to sicken animals which consume it.

albicau'lis . . . . PINE L.
al'bifrons . . . . . . WHITEFACE L.
alpes'tris . . . . . . MOUNTAIN L.
ammoph'ilus . . . . SAND L.
argen'teus (*decumbens*) . SILVERY L.
argenti'nus . . . . **L. caudatus**
ar'idus lobb'i . . . . **L. lyalli l.**
bar'biger . . . . **L. sericeus**
brevicau'lis . . . . . SHORTSTEM L.
caespito'sus (*watsoni*) . STEMLESS L.
calcara'tus . . . . . . **L. laxiflorus c.**
canes'cens . . . . **L. leucophyllus c.**
cauda'tus (*argentinus*) . . TAILCUP L.
columbia'nus . . . . . **L. latifolius c.**
coma'tus . . . . . SPREADINGHAIR L.
concin'nus (*micensis*) . . . BAJADA L.
confer'tus . . . . CROWDED L.
corymbo'sus (*L. laxiflorus c.*)
covil'lei . . . . COVILLE L.
cya'neus
dana'us . . . . **L. lyalli d.**
decum'bens . . . . **L. argenteus**
gray'i . . . . GRAYS L.
hill'i . . . . HILLS L.
king'i . . . . KINGS L.
latifo'lius . . . . BROADLEAF L.
—columbia'nus (*L. columbianus*) COLUMBIA B.L.
—lon'gipes (*L. longipes*) LONGSTALK B.L.
laxiflo'rus . . . . SPUR L.
—calcara'tus (*L. calcaratus*) LONGSPUR L.
—*corymbo'sus* . . . . **L. corymbosus**
—multitinc'tus (*L. multitinctus*)
—silvic'ola (*L. silvicola*)
lep'idus . . . . PACIFIC L.
leucophyl'lus . . . . VELVET L.
—canes'cens (*L. canescens*) HOARY V.L.
leucop'sis
lobb'i . . . . **L. lyalli l.**
lon'gipes . . . . **L. latifolius l.**
ly'alli . . . . LYALL L.
—dana'us (*L. danaus*) MOUNTDANA L.
—lobb'i (*L. aridus l.; L. lobbi*). LOBB L.
macrostach'ys . . . . LONGSPIKE L.
micen'sis . . . . **L. concinnus**
micran'thus . . . . FIELD L.
min'imus . . . . LEAST L.
multitinc'tus . . . . . **L. laxiflorus m.**
onus'tus . . . . GROUND L.
orna'tus . . . . ORNATE L.
pal'meri . . . . PALMER L.
parviflo'rus . . . . . . LODGEPOLE L.
peren'nis . . . . SUNDIAL L.
polyphyl'lus . . . . WASHINGTON L.
pseudoparviflo'rus . . . MONTANA L.
pusil'lus . . . . RUSTY L.
rivula'ris . . . . STREAM L.
saxo'sus . . . . ROCK L.
seric'eus (*barbiger*) . . . SILKY L.
silvic'ola . . . . **L. laxiflorus s.**
spathula'tus . . . . . SPATULATE L.
sti'versi . . . . STIVERS L.

POISONOUS PLANTS (LUPINUS), con.

subalpi'nus . . . SUBALPINE LUPINE
super'bus . . . . MEADOW L.
wat'soni . . . . **L. caespitosus**
wy'ethi . . . . WYETH L.

Lych'nis githa'go . **Agrostemma g.**

LY'CIUM halimifo'lium (*vulgare*) MATRIMONYVINE

LYGODES'MIA jun'cea RUSH SKELETONPLANT

LYO'NIA (*XOLISMA*) . . LYONIA
ligustri'na (*Xolisma l.*) HE-HUCKLEBERRY
maria'na (*Pieris m.*). STAGGERBUSH L.

MACROSIPHO'NIA brachysi'phon ARIZONA LONGTUBE

MAHO'NIA re'pens (*Odostemon r.*) CREEPING MAHONIA

MAN'IHOT esculen'ta (*utilissima*) COMMON CASSAVA

MELAN'THIUM virgin'icum (*canadense*) . . . . . . BUNCHFLOWER

ME'LIA azed'arach . . CHINABERRY

MENISPER'MUM canaden'se COMMON MOONSEED

MENTZE'LIA decapet'ala (*Nuttallia d.*) . . TENPETAL MENTZELIA

Reported as containing selenium, if growing on shale soils bearing that element, and in such cases poisonous if eaten by livestock.

MENZIES'IA . . . . MENZIESIA
ferrugin'ea . . . . RUSTY M.
glabel'la . . . . SMOOTH M.

MERCURIA'LIS an'nua HERBMERCURY

METO'PIUM toxif'erum (*Rhus metopium*) . . FLORIDA POISONTREE

MODI'OLA carolinia'na (*multifida*) CAROLINA MODIOLA

Stock sicknesses charged to this plant in the Southeast should be further studied.

Nep'eta hedera'cea . . **Glecoma h.**

NICOTIA'NA . . . . . TOBACCO
attenua'ta . . . . COYOTE T.
glau'ca . . . . TREE T.
trigonophyl'la . . . . . DESERT T.

Nuttal'lia decapet'ala . **Mentzelia d.**

Obio'ne suckleya'na . . **Suckleya s.**

ODOS'TEMON . . . **MAHONIA**

OENAN'THE sarmento'sa (*californica; O. s. californica*) PACIFIC WATERDROPWORT

This species demands careful study. It is included here because of the known virulent character of the Old World members of the genus.

OONOP'SIS . . . **APLOPAPPUS**
condensa'ta . . . . . . **A. fremonti**

ORNITHOG'ALUM umbella'tum COMMON STAR-OF-BETHLEHEM

OX'ALIS viola'cea (*Ionoxalis v.*) VIOLET WOODSORREL OXALIS

OXYP'OLIS . . . . . . COWBANE
fend'leri . . . . FENDLER C.
occidenta'lis . . . . PACIFIC C.

OXYTE'NIA acero'sa PRICKLY OXYTENIA

POISONOUS PLANTS, continued

OXYT'ROPIS (*ARAGALLUS*) CRAZYWEED
albiflo'ra. . . . . . **O. saximontana**
blankinship'i (*Aragallus b.*) BLANKINSHIP C.
deflex'a (*Aragallus deflexus*) DROPPOD C.
lago'pus (*Aragallus l.*) . HARESFOOT C.
lam'berti (*Aragallus l.*) . LAMBERT C.
macoun'i (*spicata; Aragallus m.*) SPIKE C.
richardso'ni . . . . . . WHORLED C.
saximonta'na (*albiflora; Aragallus albiflorus*) . . . ROCKYMOUNTAIN C.
seric'ea (*Aragallus sericeus*). SILKY C.
splen'dens . . . . SHOWY C.
viscid'ula (*Aragallus viscidulus*) YELLOWHAIR C.

PA'DUS . . . . **PRUNUS**

PAROSE'LA . . . . . . **DALEA**

PARTHENOCIS'SUS quinquefo'lia (*Ampelopsis q.*) VIRGINIA CREEPER

PEG'ANUM harma'la HARMEL PEGANUM

PHA'CA . . . . **ASTRAGALUS**

PHORADEN'DRON flaves'cens CHRISTMAS AMERICAN-MISTLETOE

PHYLLO'DOCE . MOUNTAINHEATH
brew'eri . . . . BREWER M.
empetrifor'mis . . . . RED M.
glanduliflo'ra . . . . . . CREAM M.

PHY'SALIS . . . GROUNDCHERRY
heterophyl'la . . . . . CLAMMY G.
subglabra'ta . . . . . TAPERLEAF G.

PHYTOLAC'CA america'na (*decandra*) . . . COMMON POKEBERRY

Picradeniop'sis oppositifo'lia **Bahia o.**

Pi'eris maria'na . . . . **Lyonia m.**

PISCA'RIA . **EREMOCARPUS**

PISCID'IA commu'nis (*Ichthyomethia c.*). FLORIDA FISHFUDDLETREE

PODOPHYL'LUM pelta'tum COMMON MAYAPPLE

POINSET'TIA . . **EUPHORBIA**

POLANIS'IA trachysper'ma ROUGHSEED CLAMMYWEED

PRU'NUS (*Cerasus; Laurocerasus; Padus*) . CHERRY; CHOKECHERRY; LAURELCHERRY; PLUM
america'na . . . . . AMERICAN P.
a'vium . . . . . . MAZZARD CHERRY
bes'seyi . . . . . . BESSEY CHERRY
carolinia'na (*Laurocerasus c.*) CAROLINA L.
pensylva'nica (*Cerasus p.*) PIN CHERRY
serot'ina (*Cerasus s.*) . BLACK CHERRY
virginia'na (*Padus v.*) COMMON CHOKECHERRY
—demis'sa (*P. demissa*) WESTERN C.C.
—melanocar'pa (*P. demissa m.; P. melanocarpa*) . . . . . BLACK C.C.

PSILOS'TROPHE . PAPERFLOWER
gnaphalo'des. . . . . . CUDWEED P.
sparsiflo'ra . . . . . GREENSTEM P.
tageti'nae . . . . WOOLLY P.

PSORA'LEA tenuiflo'ra SLIMFLOWER SCURFPEA

POISONOUS PLANTS, continued

PTERID'IUM . . . . . Bracken
aquili'num pubes'cens (*Pteris aquilina p.*) . . . . Western B.
latius'culum . . . . Eastern B.

Pter'is aquili'na pubes'cens **Pteridium aquilinum p.**

PTEROPHA'COS . **ASTRAGALUS**

PULSATIL'LA . . . **ANEMONE**

QUER'CUS . . . . Oak
brevilo'ba . . . . Bigelow O.
gam'beli . . . . Gambel O.
hav'ardi . . . . Havard O.
utahen'sis . . . . . Utah White O.

RANUN'CULUS . . . Buttercup
abort'ivus . . . . . . Littleleaf B.
a'cris (*acer*) . . . . Tall B.
bulbo'sus . . . . Bulb B.
re'pens (*speciosus*) . . Creeping B.
scelera'tus (*eremogenes*) . Blister B.

RHAM'NUS cathar'tica Common Buckthorn

RHODODEN'DRON (*AZALEA; AZALEASTRUM*) Rhododendron
albiflo'rum (*Azalea albiflora; Azaleastrum albiflorum*) Cascades Azalea
catawbien'se . . . . . . Catawba R.
macrophyl'lum (*californicum*) Coast R.
max'imum . . . . Rosebay R.
occidenta'le (*Azalea californica; A. occidentalis*) . . . . . Western A.

RHUS' (in part) **TOXICODENDRON**
meto'pium . . . **Metopium toxiferum**
rydberg'i . . . . **T. radicans r.**
toxicoden'dron L., *not* Auth. **T. quercifolium**
toxicoden'dron Auth., *not* L. **T. radicans**
venena'ta . . . . **T. vernix**

Ricinel'la va'seyi . . . . **Adelia v.**

RICI'NUS commu'nis . Castorbean

RIVI'NA portulaccoi'des Currant Rougeplant

ROBIN'IA . . . . Locust
neomexica'na . . . NewMexico L.
pseudoaca'cia . . . . . . Black L.
visco'sa . . . . Clammy L.

RYDBERGIEL'LA **ASTRAGALUS**
praelon'ga . . . . **A. sabulosus**

SAMBU'CUS canaden'sis American Elder

SANGUINA'RIA canaden'sis Bloodroot

SANIC'ULA bipinna'ta Poison Sanicle

Sampson & Malmsten report (Calif. Agr. Expt. Sta. Bul. 593, 1935) that this umbellifer "is known to be poisonous."

SAPIN'DUS drum'mondi Western Soapberry

SAPONA'RIA vacca'ria (*Vaccaria v.; V. vulgaris*) . . Cow Soapwort

SARCOBA'TUS vermicula'tus Black Greasewood

SA'VIA phyllanthoi'des Missouri Maidenbush

Schizono'tus purpuras'cens **Solanoa p.**

SCHOENOCAU'LON drum'mondi Drummond Sabadilla

POISONOUS PLANTS, continued

SENE'CIO . . . . . Groundsel
au'reus . . . . Golden G.
integer'rimus (*dispar; exaltatus; lugens; perplexus*) . . . . Lambstongue G.
jacobae'a . . . . Ragwort G.
longilo'bus (*filifolius*) . Threadleaf G.
platten'sis . . . . Prairie G.
riddell'i . . . . Riddell G.
spartioi'des . . . . Broom G.

Sesba'nia cavanil'lesi **Daubentonia c.**
drum'mondi . . . . **Daubentonia d.**

SEYME'RIA cassioi'des (*tenuifolia; Afzelia c.*) . . . Senna Seymeria

SI'UM sua've Hemlock Waterparsnip

SOLANO'A purpuras'cens (*Gomphocarpus p.; Schizonotus p.; Solanoana p.*)

SOLA'NUM . . . . . Nightshade
dulcama'ra . . . . Bitter N.
inte'rius . . . . Inland N.
ni'grum . . . . Black N.
triflo'rum . . . . Cutleaf N.
umbellif'erum . . . . Umbelled N.
xan'ti . . . . Purple N.

SOPHO'RA . . . . Sophora
secundiflo'ra (*Broussonetia s.*) Mescalbean S.
seric'ea . . . . Silky S.
stenophyl'la . . . . . Fringeleaf S.

SOR'GHUM . . . . . . Sorghum
halepen'se (*Andropogon halepensis; Holcus h.*) . . . . . . Johnsongrass
vulga're (*Andropogon sorghum; Holcus s.*) . . . . Sorghum
—sudanen'se (*Andropogon sorghum sudanensis; Holcus sorghum sudanensis; H. sudanensis*) . . Sudangrass

Spar'tium scopa'rium **Cytisus scoparius**

SPIGE'LIA marilan'dica Pinkroot Spigelia

STAN'LEYA bipinna'ta Alkali Princesplume

Reported as containing selenium if grown on shale soils bearing that element.

STENAN'THIUM occidenta'le Western Stenanthium

STI'PA robus'ta (*vaseyi*) Sleepygrass

SUCK'LEYA suckleya'na (*petiolaris; Atriplex s.; Obione s.*) Poison Suckleya

TAX'US . . . . Yew
brevifo'lia . . . . Pacific Y.
canaden'sis (*minor*) . . . Canada Y.

TEPHRO'SIA virginia'na (*Cracca v.*) Virginia Tephrosia

TETRACOC'CUS . Fourpodspurge
dioi'cus (*engelmanni*) . California F.
hall'i . . . . Hall F.

TETRADYM'IA . . Horsebrush
canes'cens . . . . Gray H.
—iner'mis . . . . . Spineless G.H.
glabra'ta . . . . . . Littleleaf H.

TITHYMALOP'SIS; TITHYMA'LUS . . . . . . **EUPHORBIA**

TOFIELD'IA occidenta'lis (*intermedia*) . . . . Tall Tofieldia

POISONOUS PLANTS, continued

TOXICODEN'DRON (*RHUS* in part)
diversilo'bum (*Rhus diversiloba*) Pacific Poisonoak
quercifo'lium (*Rhus quercifolia; R. toxicodendron* L., *not* Auth.) Poisonoak
rad'icans (*Rhus r.; R. toxicodendron* Auth., *not* L.) . Common Poisonivy
—rydberg'i (*T. rydbergi; Rhus r. r.; R. rydbergi*) . . Western Poisonivy
ver'nix (*Rhus venenata; R. vernix*) Poisonsumac

TOXICOSCOR'DION **ZIGADENUS**
interme'dium . . . . . . **Z. gramineus**

TRICHEROSTIG'MA **EUPHORBIA**

TRIGLO'CHIN . . . . Podgrass

See notes on the common-name nomenclature of this genus, "Range Plant Handbook," write-up GL17, paragraph 1.

marit'ima . . . . Shore P.
palus'tris . . . . Arrow P.
stria'ta . . . . Ridged P.

UNGNA'DIA specio'sa Mexicanbuckeye

URTI'CA . . . . Nettle
dioi'ca . . . . Bigsting N.
ly'alli . . . . Lyall N.
u'rens . . . . Dog N.

Urticas'trum divarica'tum **Laportea canadensis**

VACCA'RIA . . . **SAPONARIA**
vulga'ris . . . . **S. vaccaria**

VERA'TRUM . . Falsehellebore
califor'nicum (*speciosum*) California F.
eschscholtz'i . . . . Eschscholtz F.
fimbria'tum . . . . . . Fringed F.
insoli'tum
specio'sum . . . . . . **V. californicum**
vir'ide . . . . American F.

VERONICAS'TRUM virgin'icum (*Leptandra virginica; Veronica v.*) Culversphysic

VINCETOX'ICUM gonocar'pos (*Gonolobus macrophyllus*) Anglepod Milkvine

XAN'THIUM . . . . Cocklebur
cal'vum . . . . PaloAlto C.
echina'tum . . . . Beach C.
ital'icum . . . . Italian C.
spino'sum . . . . Spiny C.
struma'rium

XEROPHYL'LUM ten'ax Common Beargrass

XOLIS'MA . . . . . . **LYONIA**

XYLOPHA'COS . **ASTRAGALUS**
shortia'nus . . . . **A. utahensis**

XYLORRHI'ZA . . . . **ASTER**
scopulo'rum; villo'sa . . . **A. xylorrhiza**

ZIGADE'NUS (*AMIANTHIUM; TOXICOSCORDION*) Deathcamas
el'egans . . . . Mountain D.
fre'monti (*douglasi*) . . . Fremont D.
gramin'eus (*intermedius; Toxicoscordion intermedium*) . . . Grassy D.
muscaetox'icum . . . **Amianthium m.**
nutt'alli . . . . Nuttall D.

POISONOUS PLANTS (ZIGADENUS), con.
panicula'tus . FOOTHILL DEATHCAMAS
veneno'sus . . . . . . MEADOW D.
—micran'thus . . . . . SMALL M.D.

ZYGOPHYLLID'IUM **EUPHORBIA**

POISONSUMAC . . **Toxicodendron vernix**
DELAVAY P. . . . . . . **T. delavayi**
ORIENTAL P. . . . . . . **T. sylvestre**
PEELBERRY P. . . . **T. trichocarpum**

POISONTREE . . . . **Metopium**
BROWNES P. . . . . . . **M. brownei**
FLORIDA P. . . . . . **M. toxiferum**

POISONVETCH. . . . . . . **Astragalus**
See also Loco and MILKVETCH.
FOURWING P. . . . . **A. tetrapterus**
HAYDEN P.. . . . . **A. haydenianus**
NARROWLEAF P. . . . **A. pectinatus**
PALLISER P. . . . . . . **A. palliseri**
STRAIGHTSTEM P.. . . . **A. sabulosus**
TIMBER P. . . . . . . **A. convallarius**

POKEBERRY . . . . **Phytolacca**
COMMON P. . . . . . . **P. americana**
EIGHTSTAMEN P. . . . . **P. octandra**
FOOD P. . . . . **P. esculenta**
INDIA P. . . . . **P. acinosa**
MEXICAN P. . . . . **P. heterosepala**
OMBUTREE P. . . . . **P. dioica**
VENEZUELA P. . . . . **P. rivinoides**

Pokerplant. . . . TORCHLILY: **Kniphofia**

POLANIS'IA ⌊w . . . . CLAMMYWEED
grave'olens . . . . . STINKING C.
trachysper'ma ⌊w . . . ROUGHSEED C.

POLEMO'NIUM ⌊w . . POLEMONIUM
albiflo'rum . . . . . . WHITE P.
amoe'num . . . . WASHINGTON P.
archibald'ae . . . . . ARCHIBALD P.
borea'le . . . . ARCTIC P.
caeru'leum . . . GREEKVALERIAN P.
—al'bum . . . . WHITE G.P.
—himalaya'num (*P. grandiflorum; P. himalaicum*) . . . HIMALAYA G.P.
VARIEGATED (*variegatum*) HV. P. caeruleum
car'neum . . . . SALMON P.
charta'ceum
confer'tum . . . . SKYPILOT P.
delica'tum
el'egans
exim'ium
filici'num . . . . . . FERNLEAF P.
fla'vum . . . . YELLOW P.
foliosis'simum . . . . . . LEAFY P.
grandiflo'rum; himala'icum
P. caeruleum himalayanum
hu'mile . . . . . **P. pulcherrimum**
melli'tum . . . . CREAM P.
micran'thum . . . . LITTLEBELLS P.
mol'le. . . . . FUZZY P.
occidenta'le . . . . . WESTERN P.
parvifo'lium . . . . . MONTANA P.
pauciflo'rum . . . . . MEXICAN P.
pulcher'rimum (*humile; pulchellum*) SKUNKLEAF P.
MT. HOOD. HV.
rep'tans . . . . . . CREEPING P.
robus'tum . . . . . COLORADO P.
scopuli'num . . . . CLIFF P.
vanbrunt'iae . . . . VANBRUNT P.
visco'sum . . . . STICKY P.

POLEMONIUM. . . . . . **Polemonium**
ARCHIBALD P. . . . . **P. archibaldae**
ARCTIC P. . . . . **P. boreale**
CLIFF P. . . . . . . **P. scopulinum**

POLEMONIUM, continued
COLORADO P. . **Polemonium robustum**
CREAM P. . . . . **P. mellitum**
CREEPING P. . . . . **P. reptans**
FERNLEAF P. . . . . . . **P. filicinum**
FUZZY P. . . . . **P. molle**
GREEKVALERIAN P. . . **P. caeruleum**
HIMALAYA G. P. . **P. c. himalayanum**
LEAFY P. . . . . . **P. foliosissimum**
LITTLEBELLS P. . . . **P. micranthum**
MEXICAN P. . . . . . **P. pauciflorum**
MONTANA P. . . . . . **P. parvifolium**
SALMON P. . . . . **P. carneum**
SKUNKLEAF P. . . . **P. pulcherrimum**
SKYPILOT P. . . . . . . **P. confertum**
STICKY P. . . . . **P. viscosum**
VANBRUNT P. . . . . **P. vanbruntiae**
WASHINGTON P. . . . . **P. amoenum**
WESTERN P. . . . . . **P. occidentale**
WHITE GREEKVALERIAN P. **P. caeruleum album**
WHITE P. . . . . **P. albiflorum**
YELLOW P. . . . . **P. flavum**

POLIAN'THES . . . . . . TUBEROSE
tubero'sa . . . . TUBEROSE

POLIOMIN'THA . . ROSEMARYMINT
inca'na . . . . HOARY R.

POLIOTHYR'SIS . PEARLBLOOMTREE
sinen'sis . . . . CHINESE P.

POL'LIA
condensa'ta
VARIEGATED (*variegata*) HV.

POLYAL'THIA . . . . . . GREENSTAR
longifo'lia . . . . INDIA G.

POLYANDROCO'COS (*DIPLOTHEMIUM* in part)
See **PALM GENERA**.

Polycal'ymma stu'arti . **Myriocephalus s.**

POLYCAR'PEA
niv'ea

POLYCAR'PON . . . . . MANYSEED
tetraphyl'lum . . . . FOURLEAF M.

POLYCO'DIUM . . . **VACCINIUM**

POLYG'ALA ⌊w . . . . . . POLYGALA
acanthoc'lada . . . . THORN P.
al'ba . . . . WHITE P.
ama'ra . . . . TART P.
apopet'ala . . . . BAJA P.
brachyp'oda
calca'rea . . . . LIME P.
califor'nica (*cucullata*) . CALIFORNIA P.
chamaebux'us . . . . GROUNDBOX P.
—grandiflo'ra (*P. c. purpurea*) PURPLE G.P.
∞ **dalmaisia'na** (*P. myrtifolia grandiflora* × ?) . . . . ∞ DALMAIS P.
lute'a . . . . ORANGE P.
myrtifo'lia . . . . MYRTLE P.
—grandiflo'ra (*P. grandiflora*) SHOWY M.P.
neomexica'na ⌊w . . NEWMEXICAN P.
paucifo'lia . . . . FRINGED P.
polyg'ama . . . . BITTER P.
sanguin'ea. . . . . BLOOD P.
sen'ega . . . SENECA-SNAKEROOT P.
subspino'sa . . . . SPINY P.
vayred'iae . . . . PYRENEES P.
virga'ta . . . . CAPE P.

POLYGALA . . . . **Polygala**
BAJA P. . . . . **P. apopetala**
BITTER P. . . . . **P. polygama**

POLYGALA, continued
BLOOD P. . . . . **Polygala sanguinea**
CALIFORNIA P. . . . . . **P. californica**
CAPE P. . . . . **P. virgata**
∞ DALMAIS P. . . . . ∞ **P. dalmaisiana**
FRINGED P. . . . . . . **P. paucifolia**
GROUNDBOX P. . . . **P. chamaebuxus**
LIME P. . . . . **P. calcarea**
MYRTLE P. . . . . **P. myrtifolia**
NEWMEXICAN P. . . **P. neomexicana**
ORANGE P. . . . . **P. lutea**
PURPLE GROUNDBOX P. **P. chamaebuxus grandiflora**
PYRENEES P.. . . . . . . **P. vayrediae**
SENECA-SNAKEROOT P. . . . **P. senega**
SHOWY MYRTLE P. **P. myrtifolia grandiflora**
SPINY P.. . . . . **P. subspinosa**
TART P. . . . . **P. amara**
THORN P. . . . . . . **P. acanthoclada**
WHITE P.. . . . . **P. alba**

POLYGONA'TUM ⌊w . . SOLOMONSEAL
biflo'rum ⌊w . . . . SMALL S.
—ma'jus (*P. majus*)
commuta'tum (*giganteum*) ⌊w. GREAT S.
latifo'lium . . . . BROADLEAF S.
multiflo'rum . . . . . . EURASIAN S.
GIANT (*P. m. giganteum; major*) HV.
officina'le . . . . DRUG S.
verticilla'tum . . . . . WHORLED S.

POLYGONEL'LA ⌊w . . . JOINTWEED
america'na (*ericoides*) . . SOUTHERN J.
articula'ta ⌊w. . . . . COAST J.

POLYG'ONUM (*ACONOGONUM; BILDERDYKIA; BISTORTA; PERSICARIA*) ⌊w . . KNOTWEED
This immense variable genus is divided by some botanists into distinct genera, including Aconogonum (Fleeceflower), Bilderdykia, syn. Tiniaria (Cornbind), Bistorta (Bistort), Persicaria (Smartweed; Ladysthumb), and Polygonum (Knotweed).
acho'reum . . . . LEATHERY K.
a'cre (*Persicaria acris*) BITTER SMARTWEED
a'cre Ell., *not* Lam. . . **P. punctatum**
affi'ne (*brunonis*) HIMALAYAN FLEECEFLOWER
alpi'num . . ALPINE FLEECEFLOWER
amphib'ium (*Persicaria amphibia*) ⌊w WATER LADYSTHUMB
See note under P. natans.
amplexicau'le MOUNTAIN FLEECEFLOWER
RUBY (*rubra*) HV.
SHARPLEAF (*oxyphyllum*)
argyrocole'on . . . SILVERSHEATH K.
arifo'lium . . . . **Tracaulon a.**
au'berti . SILVERVINE FLEECEFLOWER
aus'tinae ⌊w . . . . AUSTIN K.
avicula're ⌊w . . . . . PROSTRATE K.
baldschuan'icum BOKARAVINE FLEECEFLOWER
bistor'ta (*Bistorta officinalis*) EUROPEAN BISTORT
FLESH (*carnea; superba c.*) HV.
SUPERB (*superba*)
bistortoi'des (*Bistorta b.*) AMERICAN BISTORT
bolan'deri . . . . BOLANDER K.
bruno'nis . . . . **P. affine**
buxifor'me . . . . BOX K.
campanula'tum . . . BELLFLOWER K.
capita'tum . . . . PINKHEAD K.
ca'reyi ⌊w . . . . CAREY SMARTWEED

POLYGONUM, continued
cilino'de |w BLACKFRINGE KNOTWEED
convol'vulus (*Bilderdykia c.*) |w
DULLSEED CORNBIND
cris'pulum . . . **Atraphaxis buxifolia**
cuspida'tum (*sieboldi*)
JAPANESE FLEECEFLOWER
—compac'tum (*P. compactum; P. sieboldi c.*) . . . . LOW J.F.
VARIEGATED (*variegatum*) HV. P. cuspidatum
doug'lasi |w . . . . . . DOUGLAS K.
dumeto'rum |w . . . . . HEDGE K.
emer'sum . . . . . **P. muhlenbergi**
equisetifor'me
erec'tum |w . . . . ERECT K.
fagopy'rum . **Fagopyrum sagittatum**
filifor'me **Tovara virginiana filiformis**
fow'leri . . . . FOWLERS K.
frutes'cens . . . . **Atraphaxis f.**
hirsu'tum (*Persicaria hirsuta*) |w
HAIRY SMARTWEED
hydropi'per (*Persicaria h.*) |w
MARSHPEPPER SMARTWEED
hydropiperoi'des (*Persicaria h.*) |w
SWAMP SMARTWEED
kel'loggi . . . . KELLOGG K.
lapathifo'lium (*Persicaria lapathifolia*) |w . . CURLTOP LADYSTHUMB
longis'tylum (*Persicaria longistyla*) |w
LONGSTYLE SMARTWEED
min'imum . . . . . . BROADLEAF K.
muhlenberg'i (*emersum; Persicaria m.*) |w. . . . BIGROOT LADYSTHUMB
multiflo'rum . TUBER FLEECEFLOWER
The name Polygonum multiflorum is often misapplied to P. amplexicaule.
na'tans (*Persicaria n.*)
FLOATING LADYSTHUMB
According to the late Dr. H. Gluck, this is the typical form of P. amphibium. The nomenclature of these plants is much confused.
newber'ryi (*Aconogonum n.*)
NEWBERRY FLEECEFLOWER
omis'sum (*Persicaria omissa*) |w
orienta'le (*Persicaria orientalis*)
PRINCESPLUME LADYSTHUMB
parony'chia . . . . . NAILWORT K.
pensylvan'icum (*Persicaria pennsylvanica*) |w PENNSYLVANIA SMARTWEED
persica'ria (*Persicaria mitis*) |w
SPOTTED LADYSTHUMB
phytolaccaefo'lium (*Aconogonum p.*)
POKEWEED FLEECEFLOWER
polygaloi'des . . . . . POLYGALA K.
polysta'chyum
portoricen'se |w
PUERTORICO SMARTWEED
puncta'tum (*acre* Ell., *not* Lam.; *Persicaria punctata*) |w
DOTTED SMARTWEED
ramosis'simum |w . . . . BUSHY K.
sachalinen'se SAKHALIN K. (*Sacaline*)
sagitta'tum . . . . . . **Tracaulon s.**
sawatchen'se . . . . . SAWATCH K.
scan'dens (*Bilderdykia s.; Tiniaria s.*) |w . . . . . . HEDGE CORNBIND
seric'eum . . SILKY FLEECEFLOWER
seta'ceum (*Persicaria setacea*) |w
BRISTLY SMARTWEED
sie'boldi . . . . . . **P. cuspidatum**
—compac'tum . . . **P. cuspidatum c.**
sphaerosta'chyum
ten'ue |w . . . . SLIM K.
tomento'sum (*Persicaria tomentosa*) |w
WOOLLY SMARTWEED

POLYGONUM, continued
vacciniifo'lium ROSECARPET KNOTWEED
virginia'num . . . **Tovara virginiana**
vivip'arum (*Bistorta vivipara*) |w
VIVIPAROUS BISTORT
wey'richi

POLYM'NIA |w . . . . . . LEAFCUP
gran'dis . . . **Montanoa bipinnatifida**
uveda'lia . . . . YELLOW L.

POLYOS'MA
cunningham'i . . . . FEATHERWOOD (*Wineberry*)

POLYPO'DIUM (*GONIOPHLEBIUM; PHLEBODIUM; PHYMATODES*)
POLYPODY
See **FERN GENERA.**

POLYPODY . . . . **Polypodium**
ASHLEAF P. . . . . **P. fraxinifolium**
CALIFORNIA P. . . . **P. californicum**
COAST P. . . . . **P. scouleri**
COMB P. . . . . **P. pectinatum**
COMMON P. . . . . **P. vulgare**
EAST INDIAN P. . . . . **P. phymatodes**
ELASTIC P. . . . . **P. plumula**
FRAGRANT P. . . . . . **P. pustulatum**
GOLDEN P. . . . . **P. aureum**
JOINTED P. . . . . **P. subauriculatum**
KNIGHT P. . . **P. subauriculatum** HV.
LOWS P. . . . . **P. aureum** HV.
MANDA P. . . . . . . **P. aureum** HV.
NIPPLE P. . . . . . . **P. percussum**
PALMER P. . . . . **P. palmeri**
POLYNESIAN P. . . . . . **P. polycarpon**
REINWARDT P. . **P. subauriculatum** HV.
STRAP P. . . . . **P. phyllitidis**
VARIFORM P. . . . . **P. diversifolium**
WESTERN P. . . . . . . **P. hesperium**

POLYPO'GON . . . . . POLYPOGON
See **GRASS GENERA.**

POLYP'ORUS . . . . . . POLYPORUS
berk'eleyi . . . . . . BERKELEY P.
betuli'nus . . . . BIRCH P.
cro'ceus . . . . . WHITEPIPEROT P.
frondo'sus . . . . . OAKSTRAWROT P.
sulphu'reus . . . . SULFUR P.

POLYP'TERIS . . . . . . POLYPTERIS
hookeria'na . . **Othake sphacelatum**
integrifo'lia . . . . . ALTAMAHA P.
texa'na . . . . . . **Othake texanum**

POLYS'CIAS . . . . POLYSCIAS
balfouria'na (*Aralia b.*) . BALFOUR P.
filicifo'lia (*Aralia f.*) . FERNLEAF P.
frutico'sa (*Aralia f.*) . . . INDIA P.
¢PLUMED (*plumata*) HV.
guilfoyl'ei (*Aralia g.*) . GUILFOYLE P.
¢CUTLEAF (*laciniata*) HV.
¢JAGGEDLEAF (*monstrosa; Aralia m.*)
¢VICTORIA (*victoriae; A. victoriae*)
obtu'sa . . . . JAVA P.

POLYSTACH'YA
See **ORCHID GENERA.**

POLYS'TICHUM . . . . HOLLYFERN
See **FERN GENERA.**

POLYS'TICTUS . . . . . POLYSTICTUS
cinnabari'nus
pergame'nus
versicol'or

POLYT'RIAS
See **GRASS GENERA.**

POLYT'RICHUM |w . . HAIRCAPMOSS
alpi'num |w . . . . . . ALPINE H.

POLYTRICHUM, continued
commu'ne |w . COMMON HAIRCAPMOSS
hyperbo'reum |w
juniperi'num |w . . . . JUNIPER H.
stric'tum |w
yukonen'se |w . . . . YUKON H.

POMADER'RIS . . . . . ANZACWOOD
apet'ala . . . . VIRESCENT A.
ed'gerleyi . . . . . . EDGERLEY A.
ellip'tica . . . . . GOLDEN-TAINUI A.
lanig'era . . . . PETALED A.
phylicaefo'lia . . . . . . SHRUBBY A.
rugo'sa . . . . RUSTYVEIN A.

POMEGRANATE . . . . **Punica**
COMMON P. . . . . . . **P. granatum**
SOCOTRA P. . . . . . **P. protopunica**

POME'TIA
pinna'ta

Pompelmous . PUMMELO: **Citrus grandis**

PONCI'RUS . . . TRIFOLIATE-ORANGE
trifolia'ta (*Citrus t.*) TRIFOLIATE-ORANGE (*Hardyorange*)
—monstruo'sa . . FLYINGDRAGON T.

PONDAPPLE . . . . . . **Annona glabra**

Pondcypress . . . BALDCYPRESS, POND: **Taxodium ascendens**

PONDSCUM . . . . **Spirogyra**
COMMON P. . . . . **S. protecta**

PONDWEED . . . . **Potamogeton**
BABY P. . . . . **P. pusillus**
BLUNTLEAF P. . . . . . **P. obtusifolius**
BROADLEAF P. . . . . . . **P. latifolius**
BUD P. . . . . **P. gemmiparus**
CURLY P. . . . . **P. crispus**
DENSE P. . . . . **P. densus**
FENNELLEAF P. . . . . **P. pectinatus**
FLATSTEM P. . . . . **P. zosteriformis**
FLOATINGLEAF P. . . . . . **P. natans**
FRAGILE P. . . . . . . **P. fragillimus**
FRIES P. . . . . **P. friesi**
HILLS P. . . . . **P. hilli**
ILLINOIS P. . . . . **P. illinoensis**
LARGELEAF P. . . . . . **P. amplifolius**
LEAFY P. . . . . **P. foliosus**
LONGLEAF P . . . . . **P. americanus**
LONGTONGUE P. . . . **P. longiligulatus**
OAKES P. . . . . **P. oakesianus**
PORTER P. . . . . **P. porteri**
RIBBONLEAF P. . . . . . . **P. epihydrus**
RICHARDSON THOROWORT P.
P. perfoliatus richardsoni
ROBBINS P. . . . . **P. robbinsi**
SHEATHED P. . . . . . . **P. vaginatus**
SLIMLEAF P. . . . . . . **P. tenuifolius**
THOROWORT P. . . . . . **P. perfoliatus**
VARIABLELEAF P. . . . . **P. gramineus**
VASEY P. . . . . **P. vaseyi**
WHITESTEM P. . . . . . **P. praelongus**

PONGA'MIA . . . . PONGAMIA
pinna'ta (*glabra*) . . . POONGAOIL P.

PONTEDE'RIA |w . . PICKERELWEED
corda'ta |w . . . . PICKERELWEED
—lancifo'lia . . . . LANCE P.
lanceola'ta |w

PONYFOOT . . . **Dichondra carolinensis**

POOLMAT . . . . **Zannichellia**
COMMON P. . . . . **Z. palustris**

POORROBINS-PLANTAIN **Erigeron pulchellus**

POPCORNFLOWER . . . . **Plagiobothrys**
CALIFORNIA P.
P. reticulatus rossianorum
HAIRY P. . . . . . . **P. hispidulus**

Popcornflower, continued
Jones P. . . . **Plagiobothrys jonesi**
Redstain P. . . . . . **P. nothofulvus**
Scouler P. . . . . . . **P. scouleri**

Poplar . . . . **Populus**
See also Aspen.
Algerian Black P. **P. nigra thevestina**
Andrews P. . . . . . **×P. andrewsi**
Angletwig P. . . . . . **P. angulata**
Arizona P. . . . . . . **P. arizonica**
Balm-of-Gilead P. . . . **P. candicans**
∞ Berlin P. . . . . . **∞ P. berolinensis**
Birchleaf Black P. **P. nigra betulifolia**
Black P. . . . . **P. nigra**
Bloomy P. . . . . **P. pruinosa**
Browntwig P. . . . . . . **P. tristis**
California P. . . . . **P. trichocarpa**
Carolina P. . **P. canadensis eugenei**
Cathay P. . . . . . . **P. cathayana**
Chinese P. . . . . . . **P. lasiocarpa**
Chinese White P. . . **P. tomentosa**
Ducloux Roundleaf P. **P. rotundifolia duclouxiana**
Early Carolina P. **P. canadensis regenerata**
Eastern P. . . . . . . **P. deltoides**
Euphrates P. . . . . **P. euphratica**
∞ False Lombardy P. . . . **∞ P. robusta**
Fremont P. . . . . . . **P. fremonti**
Gray P. . . . . **P. canescens**
Hardy Angletwig P. **P. angulata cordata**
∞ Jacks P. . . . . **∞ P. jacki**
Japanese P. . . . . **P. maximowiczi**
Jones Arizona P. . **P. arizonica jonesi**
Korean P. . . . . . . **P. koreana**
Lanceleaf P. . . . . **P. acuminata**
Late Carolina P. **P. canadensis serotina**
Laurel P. . . . . **P. laurifolia**
Longtip Carolina P. **P. canadensis marilandica**
MacDougal P. . . . . **P. macdougali**
Mexico P. . . . . **P. mexicana**
Michaux Tacamahac P. **P. tacamahaca michauxi**
Mongolian P. . . . . **P. suaveolens**
Narrowleaf P. . . . . **P. angustifolia**
Northern P. . **P. deltoides virginiana**
Pacific P. . . **P. trichocarpa hastata**
Palmer P. . . . . **P. palmeri**
Parry P. . . . . **×P. parryi**
∞ Petrowsky P. . . . **∞ P. petrowskyana**
Plains P. . . . . . . **P. sargenti**
Purdom P. . . . . . . **P. purdomi**
Pyramidal Carolina P. **P. canadensis erecta**
Pyramidal Mongolian P. **P. suaveolens pyramidalis**
Pyramidal Simon P. **P. simoni fastigiata**
∞ Razoumofsky P. . **∞ P. rasumowskyana**
Rehder Lanceleaf P. **P. acuminata rehderi**
Richards White P. . **P. alba richardi**
RioGrande P. . . . . . **P. wislizeni**
Roundleaf P. . . . . **P. rotundifolia**
SanDiego P. . **P. fremonti pubescens**
SilverCity P. . . . **P. f. macrodisca**
Simon P. . . . . **P. simoni**
Southern P. **P. deltoides missouriensis**
Swamp P. . . . . . **P. heterophylla**
Szechwan P. . . . . **P. szechuanica**
Tacamahac P. . . . . **P. tacamahaca**
Tana P. . . . . . **P. denhardtiorum**

Poplar, continued
Texas P. . . . . . **Populus texana**
Thornber P. . **P. fremonti thornberi**
Toumey P. . . . . . . **P. f. toumeyi**
Tweedy P. . . . . . . **P. tweedyi**
Weeping Simon P. **P. simoni pendula**
Western P. . . . . . **P. occidentalis**
White P. . . . . **P. alba**
Wilson P. . . . . **P. wilsoni**
∞ Woobst P. . . . . . . **∞ P. woobsti**
Yunnan P. . . . . **P. yunnanensis**

Poplargum . . . Eucalyptus, Poplar: **Eucalyptus alba**

Poppy . . . . **Papaver**
For hort. var. of Poppy, see **PAPAVER**.
Alpine P. . . . . **P. alpinum**
Apulian P. . . . . **P. apulum**
Armenia P. . . . . . . **P. lateritium**
Atlas P. . . . . **P. atlanticum**
Bell P. . . . . . . **P. macrostomum**
Black Opium P **P. somniferum nigrum**
Blackspot Corn P. **P. rhoeas umbrosum**
Cappadocia P. . . . **P. triniaefolium**
Caucasian P. . . . . **P. caucasicum**
Corn P. . . . . **P. rhoeas**
Crimson Iceland P. **P. nudicaule coccineum**
Dragon P. . **P. dubium laevigatum**
Eye P. . . . . **P. argemone**
Great Scarlet P. . . **P. bracteatum**
Hairy P. . . . . . . **P. setigerum**
Heldreich P. . . . . **P. heldreichi**
Iceland P. . . . . . . **P. nudicaule**
Loneflower P. . . . **P. monanthum**
Longpod P. . . . . **P. dubium**
Macoun P. . . . . . . **P. macouni**
Mission P. . . . . **P. californicum**
Olympic P. . . . . . . **P. pilosum**
Opium P. . . . . . **P. somniferum**
Orange Iceland P. **P. nudicaule aurantiacum**
Oriental P. . . . . . . **P. orientale**
Peacock P. . . . . . **P. pavoninum**
Persian P. . . . . . . **P. persicum**
Pyrenees P. . . . . **P. pyrenaicum**
Rose Iceland P. **P. nudicaule roseum**
Schinz P. . . . . **P. schinzianum**
Spanish P. . . . . **P. rupifragum**
Spike P. . . . . **P. spicatum**
Tibetan P. . . . . . **P. thibeticum**
Tulip P. . . . . **P. glaucum**
White Iceland P. **P. nudicaule album**
Yellow I. P. . . . . . **P. n. luteum**

Poppymallow . . . . **Callirhoe**
Clustered P. . . . **C. triangulata**
Finger P. . . . . **P. digitata**
Low P. . . . . **C. involucrata**
Tall P. . . . . **C. leiocarpa**

POP'ULUS lw . . . . Poplar (*Cottonwood*); Aspen

Cottonwood is in general use in the Far West for Poplars. Aspen is applied to the species of the section Leuce, whose flattened leafstalks cause the leaves to flutter almost continually.

acumina'ta (*coloradensis*) Lanceleaf P. (*Lanceleaf Cottonwood*)
—reh'deri Rehder L.P. (*Rehder L.C.*)
adenop'oda . . . . . . Chinese A.
al'ba . . . . White P.
—canes'cens . . . . . . **P. canescens**
—denuda'ta . . . . . . **P. tomentosa**
—rich'ardi Hort. . . . Richards W.P.
—tomento'sa . . . . . **P. tomentosa**

POPULUS alba, continued
¢Bolleana (*pyramidalis; P. a. bolleana; P. bolleana*) hv. P. alba
¢Globe (*globosa*)
¢Silver (*nivea; P. a. acerifolia; P. a. arembergica* Hort.; *P. a. argentea*)
¢Weeping (*pendula*)
al'ba Willd., *not* L. . . **P. canescens**
×andrews'i (*acuminata × sargenti*) Andrews Poplar (*Andrews Cottonwood*)
Apparently a natural and stable hybrid.
angula'ta (*P. deltoides a.*) Angletwig P.
—corda'ta . . . . Hardy A.P.
angula'ta Auth., *not* Ait. **P. deltoides missouriensis**
angustifo'lia (*fortissima; P. balsamifera a.*) . . . . . Narrowleaf P. (*Narrowleaf C.*)
arizo'nica . Arizona P. (*Arizona C.*)
—jones'i . Jones A.P. (*Jones A.C.*)
au'rea . . . . **P. tremuloides a.**
—cercidiphyl'la . . **P. tremuloides a.**
balsamif'era **P. deltoides missouriensis; P. tacamahaca**
—angustifo'lia . . . . **P. angustifolia**
—can'dicans . . . . . . **P. candicans**
—vimina'lis . . . . . . **P. laurifolia**
—virginia'na . . . . **P. deltoides v.**
∞ **berolinen'sis** (*laurifolia × nigra* ¢Lombardy; ∞ *certinensis*) . ∞ Berlin P.
∞ **canaden'sis** (*deltoides × nigra*)
—au'rea
—erec'ta . . Pyramidal Carolina P.
—euge'nei (*P. eugenei*) . Carolina P.
—mariland'ica (*P. henryana; P. lloydi; P. marilandica*) . . Longtip C.P.
—regenera'ta . . . . . . Early C.P.
—serot'ina (*P. serotina*) . . Late C.P.
can'dicans (*P. balsamifera c.*) Balm-of-Gilead P.
Perhaps a clon.
canes'cens (*alba* Willd., *not* L.; *P. alba c.; hybrida; steiniana*) . . . Gray P.
¢Pendula. hv.
cathaya'na . . . . Cathay P.
cercidiphyl'la . . **P. tremuloides aurea**
∞ *certinen'sis* . . . . . **∞ P. berolinensis**
coloraden'sis . . . . . . **P. acuminata**
deltoi'des (*P. d. monilifera; monilifera*) lw . . . . Eastern P.
—angula'ta . . . . . . **P. angulata**
—missourien'sis (*P. angulata* Auth., *not* Ait.; *P. balsamifera* L., *not* Muenchh. and Auth.) lw Southern P.
—monilif'era . . . . . . **P. deltoides**
—occidenta'lis . . . . . **P. sargenti**
—pilo'sa
—virginia'na (*P. balsamifera v.*) Northern P.
denhardtio'rum . . . . . Tana P.
euge'nei . . . . . **P. canadensis e.**
euphra'tica . . . . Euphrates P.
fortis'sima . . . . . **P. angustifolia**
fre'monti . Fremont P. (*Fremont C.*)
—macrodis'ca . . . . SilverCity P. (*SilverCity C.*)
—pubes'cens . . . . SanDiego P. (*SanDiego C.*)
—thorn'beri . . . . Thornber P. (*Thornber C.*)
—tou'meyi . . . . . Toumey P. (*Toumey C.*)
∞ **genero'sa** (*angulata × trichocarpa*)

POPULUS, continued
grandidenta'ta . . . Bigtooth Aspen
—meridiona'lis . . . Southern B.A.
—pen'dula Hort.
P. pseudo-grandidentata
—pendulifor'mis . . . Weeping B.A.
henrya'na . **P. canadensis marilandica**
heterophyl'la . . . . Swamp Poplar (*Swamp Cottonwood*)
hy'brida . . . . **P. canescens**
∞ **jack'i** (*deltoides* × *tacamahaca*) ∞ Jacks P.
korea'na . . . . Korean P.
lasiocar'pa . . . . Chinese P.
laurifo'lia (*P. balsamifera viminalis*) Laurel P.
—lindleya'na (*P. lindleyana; P. salicifolia* Hort.)
lloyd'i . . . **P. canadensis marilandica**
macdoug'ali . . . . MacDougal P. (*MacDougal C.*)
Very close to P. fremonti.
mariland'ica . . . . **P. canadensis m.**
maximowicz'i . . . . . Japanese P.
mexica'na . . . . Mexico P.
michaux'i . . . . **P. tacamahaca m.**
monilif'era . . . . **P. deltoides**
ni'gra . . . . Black P.
—betulifo'lia . . . . Birchleaf B.P.
∞ **—plantieren'sis** (*?nigra betulifolia* × *nigra* ₵Lombardy; *P. n. elegans*)
—thevesti'na . . . . Algerian B.P.
₵Lombardy (*italica; P. italica; P. n. pyramidalis*) hv. P. nigra
occidenta'lis . . . . . . Western P.
pal'meri . . . Palmer P. (*Palmer C.*)
×**par'ryi** (*fremonti* × *trichocarpa*) Parry P. (*Parry C.*)
Apparently a natural and stable hybrid.
pekinen'sis . . . . . . **P. tomentosa**
∞ **petrowskya'na** (*?deltoides* × *laurifolia*) ∞ Petrowsky P.
pruino'sa . . . . Bloomy P.
pseudo-grandidenta'ta (*P. tremula p.; P. grandidentata pendula* Hort.)
pur'domi . . . . Purdom P.
∞ **rasumowskya'na** (*?laurifolia* × *nigra*) ∞ Razoumofsky P.
∞ **robus'ta** (*angulata* × ∞*nigra plantierensis*) . . . ∞ False Lombardy P.
rotundifo'lia . . . . . Roundleaf P.
—duclouxia'na . . . . Ducloux R.P.
salicifo'lia Hort. **P. laurifolia lindleyana**
sar'genti (*P. deltoides occidentalis*) Plains P. (*Plains C.*)
serot'ina . . . . . . **P. canadensis s.**
sie'boldi . . . . Siebold Aspen
si'moni . . . . Simon P.
—fastigia'ta . . . . Pyramidal S.P.
—pen'dula . . . . . Weeping S.P.
steinia'na . . . . . . **P. canescens**
suave'olens . . . . . . Mongolian P.
This name is sometimes misapplied in cult. to P. cathayana and P. maximowiczi.
—pyramida'lis . . . Pyramidal M.P.
szechua'nica . . . . . Szechwan P.
tacamaha'ca (*balsamifera* Muenchh. and Auth., *not* L.) . Tacamahac P.
The spelling tacamahacca observed by some authors is disapproved by Prof. Rehder, who states that the author of the name (Miller) cites Bauhin's "Pinax" as the source of name, where, as in other pre-Linnean works, the spelling is uniformly tacamahaca.
—michaux'i (*P. michauxi*) Michaux T.P.
texa'na . . . . Texas P. (*Texas C.*)

POPULUS, continued
tomento'sa (*P. alba denudata; P. alba t.; pekinensis*) Chinese White Poplar
trem'ula . . . . . European Aspen
—davidia'na . . . . . . Davids E.A.
—pen'dula . . . . . . Weeping E.A.
—pseudo-grandidenta'ta **P. pseudo-grandidentata**
—villo'sa . . . . Hairy E.A.
tremuloi'des |w . . . . . Quaking A.
—au'rea (*P. aurea; P. a. cercidiphylla; P. cercidiphylla*) . . Golden Q.A.
—pen'dula
—renifor'mis . . Kidneyleaf Q.A.
—vancouveria'na (*P. vancouveriana*) Vancouver Q.A.
trichocar'pa |w . . . . California P. (*Black Cottonwood*)
—hasta'ta Pacific P. (*Northern B.C.*)
tris'tis . . . . . . Browntwig P.
tweed'yi . . . . Tweedy P.
vancouveria'na . . . **P. tremuloides v.**
violas'cens
wil'soni . . . . Wilson P.
wislize'ni RioGrande P. (*RioGrande C.*)
∞ **woob'sti** (*laurifolia* × *?tristis*) ∞ Woobst P.
yunnanen'sis . . . . . Yunnan P.

PORA'NA . . . . Porana
panicula'ta . . . . Christmasvine P.
racemo'sa . . . . . Snowcreeper P.

Porcupinegrass . . . . **Stipa spartea**
Shortawn P. . . . . **S. s. curtiseta**

Porcupinepodtree . . . **Centrolobium**
Para P. . . . . **C. paraense**

Poreleaf . . . . **Porophyllum**
Slender P. . . . . **P. gracile**

PORFI'RIA . . . . . **MAMMILLARIA**
See **CACTUS GENERA.**

PORLIER'IA (*PORLIERA*). Porlieria
angustifo'lia . . . . Texas P.

POROPHYL'LUM . . . . Poreleaf
grac'ile . Slender P. (*Yerbadelvenado*)

PORPHY'RA . . . . Laver (*Mori; Redlaver; Slack*)
lacinia'ta . . . . . Fingerfrond L.
vulga'ris . . . . Common L.

PORTERAN'THUS . . . **GILLENIA**

Portiatree . . . **Thespesia populnea**

PORTLAND'IA . . . . . Portlandia
coccin'ea . . . . Scarlet P.
domingen'sis . . . . Dominican P.
grandiflo'ra . . . . . . Reddish P.
platan'tha . . . . . . Planeleaf P.
pterosper'ma . . . . Oaxaca P.

PORTULAC'A |w . . . . Portulaca
grandiflo'ra . . . . . . Common P.
Thelluson (*thellusoni*) hv.
Thorburn (*thorburni*)
White (*albiflora*)
margina'ta . . . . . . Venezuela P.
olera'cea (*aurea*) |wCommon Purslane
Double Giant (*giganthes*) hv.
Kitchen-garden (*sativa*)
pilo'sa . . . . . Shaggy Portulaca (*Jump-up-and-kiss-me*)
Garden (*hortualis*) hv.
retu'sa |w
suffrutes'cens |w . . . . Shrubby P.

PORTULACA'RIA
See **SUCCULENTS.**

POSOQUE'RIA . . . . . Posoqueria
latifo'lia (*Oxyanthus isthmia*) Panama P.
trinita'tis . . . . Trinidad P.

Possumhaw . . . . **Ilex decidua**
Buswell P. . . . . **I. buswelli**
Curtiss P. . . . **I. decidua curtissi**

POTAMOGE'TON |w . . Pondweed
america'nus |w . . . . Longleaf P.
amplifo'lius |w . . . . Largeleaf P.
bicupula'tus |w
capilla'ceus |w
clystocar'pus |w
confervoi'des |w
cris'pus |w . . . . Curly P.
den'sus . . . . Dense P.
diversifo'lius |w
epihy'drus |w . . . . Ribbonleaf P.
fibrillo'sus |w
filifor'mis |w
folio'sus |w . . . . Leafy P.
fragil'limus |w . . . . . . Fragile P.
fries'i |w . . . . Fries P.
gemmip'arus |w . . . . Bud P.
gramin'eus |w . . . Variableleaf P.
hill'i |w . . . . Hills P.
illinoen'sis |w . . . . . Illinois P.
latera'lis |w
latifo'lius |w . . . . . Broadleaf P.
longiligula'tus |w . . Longtongue P.
na'tans |w . . . . . Floatingleaf P.
oakesia'nus |w . . . . . . Oakes P.
obtusifo'lius |w . . . . Bluntleaf P.
panormita'nus |w
pectina'tus |w . . . . Fennelleaf P.
perfolia'tus |w . . . Thorowort P.
—richardso'ni (*P. richardsoni*) |w Richardson T.P.
por'teri |w . . . . Porter P.
praelon'gus |w . . . . Whitestem P.
pul'cher |w
pusil'lus |w . . . . Baby P.
rob'binsi |w . . . . Robbins P.
rotunda'tus |w
spiril'lus |w
strictifo'lius |w
tenuifo'lius |w . . . . . Slimleaf P.
vagina'tus |w . . . . . Sheathed P.
va'seyi |w . . . . Vasey P.
zosterifor'mis |w . . . . Flatstem P.

Potato . . . . . . **Solanum tuberosum**
Fendler P. . . . . **S. fendleri**

Potatobean . . . . **Apios**
American P. . . . . . . **A. americana**

POTENTIL'LA (*ARGENTINA; DASIPHORA; DRYMOCALLIS*) |w Cinquefoil
adschar'ica . . . . . Caucasian C.
al'ba . . . . White C.
alchemilloi'des . . . Ladysmantle C.
alpes'tris . . . . . Orangespot C.
ambig'ua
andic'ola . . . . Colombian C.
anseri'na (*Argentina a.*) |w Silverweed C.
apenni'na . . . . Apennine C.
argen'tea |w . . . . Silver C.
—**cala'bra** (*P. calabra*) Calabrian S.C.
argu'ta (*Drymocallis agrimonioides*)
argyrophyl'la . . . . Undersnow C.
—atrosanguin'ea . . . . . Ruby U.C.
atrosanguin'ea . . . . Himalayan C.
au'rea (*chrysocraspeda*) . Golden C.
ba'keri . . . . Baker C.
×**bi'color** (*argyrophylla?* × *atrosanguinea?*) . . . . . . Bicolor C.

POTENTILLA, continued
bicrena'ta
bien'nis . . . BIENNIAL CINQUEFOIL
bifur'ca (*imbricata*) . . . TWOFORK C.
blaschkea'na . . . . . BLASCHKE C.
brew'eri . . . . BREWER C.
—expan'sa . . . . . . LARGE B.C.
buccoa'na . . . . . . BUCCOAN C.
cala'bra . . . . **P. argentea c.**
canaden'sis |w . . . . OLDFIELD C.
chrysan'tha . . . . PRIMROSE C.
chrysocras'peda . . . . . **P. aurea**
cine'rea . . . . RUSTY C.
clusia'na . . . . CLUSIUS C.
concin'na (*humifusa*) . . ELEGANT C.
crini'ta
cryptotae'niae . . . . . NIPPON C.
curvise'ta . . . . . . WALTHERS C.
dahur'ica . . . . . **P. fruticosa d.**
detommas'i . . . . . DETOMMAS C.
dissec'ta . . . . . HUDSONBAY C.
diversifo'lia . . . . . VARILEAF C.
dom'beyi . . . . DOMBEY C.
drum'mondi . . . . DRUMMOND C.
effu'sa . . . . . SASKATCHEWAN C.
erec'ta (*tormentilla*) . TORMENTILLA C.
eriocar'pa . . . . . WOOLLYFRUIT C.
fi'lipes . . . . SLIMSTEM C.
fis'sa (*Drymocallis f.*) . BIGFLOWER C.
flabellifo'lia . . . . . . FANLEAF C.
formo'sa . . . . **P. nepalensis**
fragifor'mis . . . . STRAWBERRY C.
frig'ida . . . . ALPS C.
frutes'cens
frutico'sa (*Dasiphora f.*) |w . BUSH C.
—al'bicans . . . . . CHINESE B.C.
—dahur'ica (*P. dahurica*)
DAHURIAN B.C.
—far'reri . . . . . . FARRER B.C.
×**—friedrich'seni** (*fruticosa* × *f. dahurica*) . . . . . FRIEDRICHSEN B.C.
BEANS (*fruticosa beani*) HV.
—grandiflo'ra . . . BIGFLOWER B.C.
—mandschur'ica . MANCHURIAN B.C.
—ochroleu'ca . . . . CREAMY B.C.
—parvifo'lia (*P. parvifolia*)
LITTLELEAF B.C.
—pu'mila . . . . DWARF B.C.
—pur'domi (*P. purdomi*) PURDOM B.C.
—pyrena'ica (*P. prostrata*)
PYRENEES B.C.
—rig'ida . . . . . HIMALAYA B.C.
—tenuilo'ba (*P. f. tenuifolia; Dasiphora f. tenuiloba*) . . SLIMLEAF B.C.
—veitch'i (*P. veitchi*) . VEITCH B.C.
—vilmorinia'na. . . . VILMORIN B.C.
ful'gens . . . . SHINY C.
gel'ida . . . . SIBERIAN C.
glandulo'sa (*Drymocallis g.*) GLAND C.
glaucophyl'la . . . . . BLUELEAF C.
grac'ilis |w . . . . . NORTHWEST C.
grammopet'ala . . . LETTERPETAL C.
grandiflo'ra . . . . SUNNY C.
grif'fithi . . . . GRIFFITH C.
heptaphyl'la (*thuringiaca*) SEVENLEAF C.
hippia'na . . . . HORSE C.
hir'ta . . . . . . CONTINENTAL C.
hookeria'na . . . . . . HOOKER C.
∞**hopwoodia'na** (*nepalensis* × *recta*)
∞HOPWOOD C.
humifu'sa . . . . **P. concinna**
∞**hy'brida** (*argyrophylla* × *nepalensis*)
∞FLORISTS C.
The following appear to be hort. var. of ∞P. hybrida:
BELLISARE. HV.
CARNIVAL

POTENTILLA hybrida, continued
CONGO
DRAP D'OR
ETNA
GIBSONS SCARLET
LEMOINEI
PANORAMA
PERFECTA PLENA
PHOEBUS
VAN DYCK
VELOUR POURPRE
VULCAN
WM. ROLLISON
imbrica'ta . . . . **P. bifurca**
interme'dia . . DOWNY CINQUEFOIL
jucun'da . . . . GAY C.
kleinia'na . . . . KLEIN C.
kur'dica . . . . KURDISH C.
levier'i . . . . LEVIER C.
libanot'ica. . . . . . . LEBANON C.
∞**macnabia'na** (*argyrophylla* × *atrosanguinea*) . . . . . . ∞MACNAB C.
matsumu'rae. . . . MATSUMURA C.
mey'eri . . . . MEYER C.
monspelien'sis . . . MONTPELIER C.
—norveg'ica . . . . . . **P. norvegica**
montenegri'na . . MONTENEGRIN C.
multif'ida (*tonguei*) . . STAGHORN C.
nepalen'sis (*formosa*) . . . NEPAL C.
—mi'nor . . . . SMALL N.C.
MISS WILLMOTT (*willmottiae*) HV.
nevaden'sis . . . . . . SPANISH C.
nit'ida . . . . SNOWLINE C.
ALLANNAH. HV.
LISSADELL
PURPLE (*purpurea*)
WHITE (*alba*)
niv'alis . . . . SNOWY C.
norveg'ica (*P. monspeliensis n.*)
NORWEGIAN C.
—hirsu'ta . . . . HAIRY N.C.
nutt'alli . . . . NUTTALL C.
pacif'ica . . . . PACIFIC C.
palus'tris (*Comarum palustre*) |w
MARSH C.
parvifo'lia . . . . . . **P. fruticosa p.**
pensylva'nica . . PENNSYLVANIA C.
perfec'ta . . . . MAROON C.
pimpinelloi'des . . . . ANISELEAF C.
platten'sis . . . . PLATTE C.
propin'qua |w . . . . . SUMMIT C.
prostra'ta . . . **P. fruticosa pyrenaica**
pseudorupes'tris (*Drymocallis p.*)
ALBERTA C.
pulcher'rima . . . . BEAUTY C.
pu'mila . . . . PETTY C.
pur'domi . . . . **P. fruticosa p.**
purpu'rea . . . . PURPLE C.
pyrena'ica . . . . . . PYRENEES C.
rec'ta . . . . SULFUR C.
—war'reni . . . . . . WARRENS S.C.
rep'tans . . . . CREEPING C.
riva'lis . . . . BROOK C.
rupes'tris . . . . CLIFF C.
—al'ba . . . . WHITE C.C.
—pyg'maea . . . . . . PYGMY C.C.
∞**russellia'na** (*atropurpurea* × *nepalensis*) . . . . ∞RUSSELL C.
salesovia'na (*salesovi; Comarum salesowi*) . . . . SALESOV C.
sanguisor'ba . . . . . . BURNET C.
sanguisorbifo'lia
saxif'raga . . . . . . SAXIFRAGE C.
specio'sa . . . . SHOWY C.
stenophyl'la . . . . . LANKLEAF C.
ster'ilis
supi'na . . . . CARPET C.

POTENTILLA, continued
thur'beri . . THURBER CINQUEFOIL
thuringia'ca . . . . . **P. heptaphylla**
tongue'i . . . . **P. multifida**
tormentil'la . . . . **P. erecta**
transcas'pia . . . . TRANSCASPIAN C.
tridenta'ta (*Sibbaldiopsis t.*)
WINELEAF C.
uniflo'ra. . . . . SINGLEFLOWER C.
veitch'i . . . . **P. fruticosa v.**
ver'na. . . . . SPRING C.
DWARF (*nana*) HV.
villo'sa . . . . HAIRY C.
virga'ta . . . . TWIGGY C.
O'BRIAN (*obriana*) HV. Potentilla

POTE'RIUM . . . . BURNET
This genus is doubtfully separable from the closely related Sanguisorba.
sanguisor'ba . . . **Sanguisorba minor**
spino'sum (*Sanguisorba spinosa*)
SPINY B.

POTHOMOR'PHE
pelta'ta

PO'THOS . . . . POTHOS
Plants cultivated under this name are seldom of this genus.
argyrae'us . . . **Scindapsus pictus a.**
au'reus . . . . **Scindapsus a.**
—wilcox'i . . . . . **Scindapsus a. w.**
corda'tus . . . . **Anthurium cordatum**
lourei'ri . . . . KUYU P.
ni'tens
Dr. L. H. Bailey reports that this is a "hort. name of doubtful botanical standing."

POUTE'RIA
caimi'to (*Lucuma c.*) . . . . . ABIU

Povertygrass . . . **Andropogon furcatus, A. scoparius; Aristida dichotoma, A. divaricata, A. longespica, A. purpurea; Danthonia spicata**

Powderflaskfruit . AFRAEGLE: **Afraegle**
Dwarf P. . . . AEGLOPSIS: **Aeglopsis**

PRAIRIECLOVER . . . . . **Petalostemon**
PALLID P. . . . . **P. albidus**
PURPLE P. . . . . . . **P. purpureus**
ROUNDHEADED P. . . . **P. multiflorus**
SEARLS P. . . . . **P. searlsiae**
SEPTEMBER P. . . . . **P. corymbosus**
SILKY P.. . . . . **P. villosus**
SLENDER WHITE P. . **P. oligophyllus**
STANFIELD P. . . . . . **P. stanfieldi**
TENNESSEE P. . . . . **P. decumbens**
WHITE P. . . . . **P. candidus**
YELLOW P. . . . . . . **P. flavescens**

PRAIRIECONEFLOWER . . . **Ratibida**
UPRIGHT P. . . . . . **R. columnaris**

PRAIRIEGENTIAN . . . . . . **Eustoma**
ANDREWS P. . . . . . . **E. andrewsi**
RUSSELL P. . . . . **E. russellianum**

Prairiegrass . . WEDGESCALE, PRAIRIE: **Sphenopholis obtusata**

Prairiemallow . . . CHECKERMALLOW: **Sidalcea**

PRAN'GOS
ulop'tera

PRA'TIA . . . . BERRYLOBELIA
angula'ta . . . . MAT B.
arena'ria . . . . CHATHAM B.
begonifo'lia . . . . BEGONIALEAF B.
mac'rodon . . . . BIGTOOTH B.

PREM'NA . . . . PREMNA
arbo'rea . . . . Gmelina a.
integrifo'lia . . . HEADACHETREE P.
odora'ta . . . . . . FRAGRANT P.
taiten'sis . . . . TAHITI P.

PRENAN'THES (*NABALUS*) |w
RATTLESNAKEROOT
al'ba . . . . WHITE R.
as'pera (*Nabalus a.*) . . . ROUGH R.
purpu'rea . . . . PURPLE R.
trifoliola'ta . . . . . THREELEAF R.

PRE'NIA
sladenia'na

PRICKLEGRASS . . **Crypsis; C. aculeata**

PRICKLEPOPPY . . . . **Argemone**
CRESTED P. . . . . . **A. platyceras**
HEDGEHOG P. . . . . . **A. p. hispida**
MEXICAN P. . . . . . . **A. mexicana**
ROSY P. . . . . . **A. platyceras rosea**
SHOWY P. . . . . . . **A. grandiflora**
WHITE P. . . . . **A. alba**

Pricklyapple . . APPLECACTUS: **Harrisia**

PRICKLYASH . . . . . . **Zanthoxylum**
AILANTHUS P. . . . . **Z. ailanthoides**
BISCAYNE P. . . . . . **Z. coriaceum**
CHINESE WINGLEAF P.
Z. alatum planispinum
CLIMBING P. . . . . . **Z. stenophyllum**
COMMON P. . . . . . **Z. americanum**
FLATSPINE P. . . . . . **Z. simulans**
HERCULESCLUB P. . **Z. clavaherculis**
HIMALAYA P. . . . **Z. acanthopodium**
JAPANESE P. . . . . . . **Z. piperitum**
LIME P. . . . . **Z. fagara**
MARTINIQUE P. . . . **Z. martinicense**
PEPPERTREE P. . . . **Z. schinifolium**
SENEGAL P. . . . . . **Z. senegalense**
SHARPLEAF P. . . . . **Z. oxyphyllum**
SMALLFRUIT P. . . . **Z. microcarpum**
TEXAS HERCULESCLUB P.
Z. clavaherculis fruticosum
WINGLEAF P. . . . . . . **Z. alatum**
YELLOWHEART P. . . . . . **Z. flavum**

PRICKLYPEAR . . . . . . **Opuntia**
See also CHOLLA.
AARONSBEARD P. . . . **O. leucotricha**
ARIZONA JUMPING P. . . **O. bigelovi**
BEAVERTAIL P. . . . . . **O. basilaris**
BIGFLOWER P. . . . . **O. grandiflora**
BLIND P. . . . . **O. rufida**
BRITTLE P. . . . . **O. fragilis**
CHIMNEY P. . . . . **O. elatior**
COMMON P. . . . . . . **O. vulgaris**
COWSTONGUE P. . . **O. linguiformis**
DILLEN P. . . . . **O. dilleni**
DOBBIE P. . . . . . . **O. dobbieana**
DOG P. . . . . **O. canina**
DOLLARJOINT P. . . . **O. chlorotica**
EICHLAM P. . . . . . . **O. eichlami**
ENGELMANN P. . . . **O. engelmanni**
GOLDEN P. . . . . **O. aurea**
GOLDPLUSH P. . . . **O. microdasys**
GRIZZLYBEAR P. . . . **O. erinacea**
GROUND P. . . . . . **O. decumbens**
HERRFELDT P. . . . . . **O. herrfeldti**
INDIANFIG . . . . . . **O. ficus-indica**
MACDOUGAL P. . . **O. macdougaliana**
MACKENSEN P. . . . . **O. mackenseni**
MEXICANROSE P. . . . . . **O. pottsi**
MISSION P. . . . . **O. megacantha**
MOHAVE P. . . . . . **O. mojavensis**
NARROWPETAL P. . . . **O. stenopetala**
ORANGERED P. . . . . **O. aurantiaca**
PLAINS P. . . . . . **O. polyacantha**

PRICKLYPEAR, continued
POLLARD P. . . . **Opuntia pollardi**
SANTA RITA P. . . . . . **O. santa-rita**
SCHEERS P. . . . . **O. scheeri**
SCHUMANN P. . . . . . **O. schumanni**
SMOOTH P. . . . . **O. laevis**
SOFTHAIR P. . . . . **O. pilifera**
STRAWTOP P. . . . . **O. echinocarpa**
SULFUR P. . . . . **O. sulphurea**
TESAJO . . . . **O. leptocaulis**
TRELEASE P. . . . . . . **O. treleasei**
TUNA P. . . . . **O. tuna**
TWISTSPINE P. . . . . . **O. tortispina**
VASEY P. . . . . **O. vaseyi**
VELVET P. . . . . **O. velutina**
WESTERN P. . . . . . **O. occidentalis**
WHITNEY P. . . . . . **O. whitneyana**

PRICKLYTHRIFT . . . . . **Acantholimon**
COMB P. . . . . **A. glumaceum**
LARGEFLOWER P. . . . . **A. venustum**

PRIDE-OF-MADEIRA . **Echium fastuosum**

PRIMAVERA . **Cybistax; C. donnell-smithi**

PRIMROSE . . . . **Primula**
ALLIONI P. . . . . **P. allioni**
AMBER P. . . . . **P. helodoxa**
AMERICAN P. . . . . . . **P. americana**
ANISE P. . . . . **P. anisodora**
ARABIAN P. . . . . . . **P. verticillata**
AURICULA P. . . . . **P. auricula**
BALKANROSE P. . . . . . . **P. frondosa**
BEAUTY P. . . . . **P. pulchella**
BEES P. . . . . **P. beesiana**
BIG ROSE P. . . . **P. rosea grandiflora**
BIRDSEYE P. . . . . **P. farinosa**
BLOOD JAPANESE P.
P. japonica atrosanguinea
BLUNTLEAF P. . . . . . **P. obtusifolia**
BRISCOE P. . . . . **P. briscoei**
∞ BULLES P. . . . . . . ∞ **P. bullesiana**
BULLEYS P. . . . . **P. bulleyana**
BURMAN P. . . . . **P. burmanica**
BUTTERCUP P. . . . . . . **P. floribunda**
CARNIOLAN P. . . . . **P. carniolica**
CHINESE P. . . . . **P. sinensis**
CLAMMY P. . . . . **P. viscosa**
CLIFF P. . . . . **P. saxatilis**
CLUSIUS P. . . . . **P. clusiana**
COCKBURN P. . . . . . **P. cockburniana**
COLORADO P. . . . . . **P. angustifolia**
CORTUSA P. . . . . . . **P. cortusoides**
COTTIAN P. . . . . **P. cottia**
COWSLIP P. . . . . **P. veris**
CUP SHINYLEAF P.
P. glaucescens calycina
CURLY P. . . . . **P. crispa**
DROOPING P. . . . . **P. deflexa**
∞ EDINA P. . . . . ∞ **P. edina**
ELWES P. . . . . **P. elwesiana**
ENGLISH P. . . . . **P. vulgaris**
ENTIRELEAF P. . . . . . **P. integrifolia**
FAIRY P. . . . . **P. malacoides**
FAURIE P. . . . . **P. fauriei**
FLAMINGO P. . . . . **P. seclusa**
FORBES P. . . . . **P. forbesi**
FORRESTS P. . . . . **P. forresti**
GASPE P. . . . **P. americana gaspensis**
GIRALD P. . . . . **P. giraldiana**
GUMMY P. . . . . **P. hirsuta**
HIMALAYAN P. . . . . . **P. denticulata**
HOKKAIDO P. . . . . **P. jesoana**
JAGGED P. . . . . **P. erosa**
JAPANESE P. . . . . **P. japonica**
JULIA P. . . . . **P. juliae**
KASHMIR P. **P. denticulata cachemiriana**
∞ KEW P. . . . . ∞ **P. kewensis**
KINGS P. . . . . **P. kingi**

PRIMROSE, continued
LAMA P. . . . . **Primula zambalensis**
LEAST P. . . . . **P. minima**
LEDGE P. . . . . **P. rupicola**
LICHIANG P. . . . . . **P. lichiangensis**
LITTONS P. . . . . **P. littoniana**
LONGFLOWER P. . . . . . **P. longiflora**
LONGLEAF P. . . . . . **P. oblanceolata**
LOOSE P. . . . . **P. effusa**
LUSTY P. . . . . **P. grandis**
MAGELLAN P. . . . . . **P. magellanica**
MALLOW P. . . . . **P. malvacea**
MANYBUD P. . . . . **P. gemmifera**
MISTASSINI P. . . . . **P. mistassinica**
MOERHEIM P. . . . . . . **P. moerheimi**
MOORES P. . . . . **P. mooreana**
MOORES PURPLEHEAD P. **P. capitata m.**
MORAINE P. . . . . **P. crispata**
MOUNTAIN TINYTOOTH P.
P. microdonta alpicola
NINEFLOWER P. . . . . **P. florida**
OLYMPUS P. . . . . **P. deorum**
ORANGE-EYE P. . . . . . . **P. conspersa**
ORANGE P. . . . . **P. aurantiaca**
OXLIP P. . . . . **P. elatior**
PALINURUS P. . . . . **P. palinuri**
PARRY P. . . . . **P. parryi**
PAX P. . . . . **P. paxiana**
PERIWINKLE P. . . . . . . **P. vinciflora**
PIEDMONT P. . . . . . **P. pedemontana**
PINNACLE P. . . . . . . **P. involucrata**
POISSON P. . . . . **P. poissoni**
∞ POLYANTHA P. . . . . . ∞ **P. polyantha**
PRATT P. . . . . **P. pratti**
PUFFED COWSLIP P. . . **P. veris inflata**
PURPLECHINA P. . . **P. sinopurpurea**
PURPLEHEAD P. . . . . **P. capitata**
REINS P. . . . . **P. reini**
ROSE P. . . . . **P. rosea**
ROSY JAPANESE P. . . . **P. japonica r.**
ROUGELEAF P. . . . . **P. rufa**
ROUNDHEAD P. . . **P. sphaerocephala**
RUSBY P. . . . . **P. rusbyi**
SCOTCH P. . . . . **P. scotica**
SEVENLOBE P. . . . . . **P. septemloba**
SHINYLEAF P. . . . . . **P. glaucescens**
SHOWY P. . . . . **P. spectabilis**
SIBERIAN P. . . . . **P. sibirica**
SIDEFLOWER P. . . . . **P. secundiflora**
SIEBOLD P. . . . . **P. sieboldi**
SIERRA P. . . . . . . **P. suffrutescens**
SIKKIM P. . . . . **P. sikkimensis**
SILVERDUST P. . . . . . **P. pulverulenta**
SILVEREDGE P. . . . . **P. marginata**
SKY P. . . . . **P. caerulea**
SLEEPY P. . . . . **P. nutans**
SNOWBLOSSOM P. . . . . **P. chionantha**
SNOW P. . . . . **P. nivalis**
STICKY P. . . . . **P. glutinosa**
ST.LAWRENCE P. . . . . **P. laurentiana**
STRIPED P. . . . . **P. vittata**
SULFUR P. . . . . **P. luteola**
SWEET COWSLIP P. **P. veris suaveolens**
SWEET P. . . . . **P. glycyosma**
SZECHWAN P. . . . . . **P. szechuanica**
TIBETAN P. . . . . **P. florindae**
TINYTOOTH P. . . . . . . **P. microdonta**
TOP P. . . . . **P. obconica**
VEITCH P. . . . . **P. veitchi**
VIOLET P. . . . . **P. algida**
WALTON P. . . . . **P. waltoni**
WARDS P. . . . . **P. wardi**
WATTS P. . . . . **P. watti**
WEDGELEAF P. . . . . **P. cuneifolia**
WHITE COWSLIP P. . . . **P. veris alba**
WHITE HIMALAYAN P. **P. denticulata a.**
WHITE JAPANESE P. . . **P. japonica a.**

PRIMROSE, continued

WHITE SIEBOLD P. **Primula sieboldi alba**
WILSON P. . . . . **P. wilsoni**
WINTERS P. . . . . **P. winteri**
WULFEN P. . . . . . . **P. wulfeniana**
YARGONG P. . . . . . **P. yargongensis**
YELLOWEYE P. . . . . . **P. chrysopa**
YELLOWSWEET P. . . . **P. chungensis**

PRIM'ULA . . . . PRIMROSE
acau'lis . . . . **P. vulgaris**
al'gida . . . . VIOLET P.
allio'ni . . . . ALLIONI P.
alpi'na Hort. **P. auricula** HV. ALPINE
america'na (*P. farinosa a.*) AMERICAN P.
—gaspen'sis (*P. farinosa g.*) GASPE P.
angustifo'lia (*P. a. helenae*) COLORADO P.
anisodo'ra . . . . ANISE P.
auranti'aca . . . . ORANGE P.
auric'ula (*lutea; Auricula l.*) AURICULA P.
ALPINE (*alpina*) HV.
DOUBLE (*plena*)
ROSY (*rosea*)
YELLOW QUEEN
beesia'na . . . . BEES P.
briscoe'i (*bulleyana* × *japonica*) BRISCOE P.
∞ **bullesia'na** Hort. (*beesiana* × *bulleyana*) ∞ BULLES P.

See ∞ P. edina. Research is needed to establish which of these two names has priority.

bulleya'na . . . . BULLEYS P.
burman'ica . . . . BURMAN P.
GLASNEVIN. HV.
caeru'lea . . . . SKY P.
calyci'na . . . . . . **P. glaucescens c.**
capita'ta . . . . . . PURPLEHEAD P.
—moorea'na . . . . . . MOORES P.P.
carnio'lica . . . . . . CARNIOLAN P.
cashmiria'na **P. denticulata cachemiriana**
chinen'sis . . . . **P. sinensis**
chionan'tha . . . . SNOWBLOSSOM P.
chryso'pa . . . . YELLOWEYE P.
chungen'sis . . . YELLOWSWEET P.
clusia'na . . . . CLUSIUS P.
cockburnia'na . . . . COCKBURN P.
consper'sa . . . . . ORANGE-EYE P.
cortusoi'des . . . . CORTUSA P.
cot'tia . . . . COTTIAN P.
cris'pa . . . . CURLY P.
crispa'ta . . . . MORAINE P.
cuneifo'lia . . . . . . WEDGELEAF P.
deflex'a . . . . DROOPING P.
denticula'ta . . . . . HIMALAYAN P.
—al'ba . . . . WHITE H.P.
—cachemiria'na (*P. cashmiriana*) KASHMIR P.
deo'rum . . . . OLYMPUS P.
∞ **edi'na** Hort. (*beesiana* × *bulleyana*) ∞ EDINA P.

See ∞ P. bullesiana. Research is needed to establish which of these two names has priority.

effu'sa . . . . LOOSE P.
ela'tior . . . . OXLIP P.
elonga'ta
elwesia'na . . . . ELWES P.
ero'sa . . . . JAGGED P.
farino'sa . . . . BIRDSEYE P.
—america'na . . . . . **P. americana**
—gaspen'sis . . . . . **P. americana g.**
faurie'i . . . . FAURIE P.
floribun'da . . . . . BUTTERCUP P.
GRANDIFLORA. HV.

PRIMULA, continued

flor'ida . . . NINEFLOWER PRIMROSE
florin'dae . . . . TIBETAN P.
forbes'i . . . . FORBES P.
for'resti . . . . FORRESTS P.
frondo'sa . . . . . . BALKANROSE P.
gemmif'era . . . . MANYBUD P.
giraldia'na (*muscarioides*) . GIRALD P.
glauces'cens . . . . . SHINYLEAF P.
—calyci'na (*P. calycina*) . . CUP S.P.
glutino'sa . . . . STICKY P.
glycyos'ma . . . . SWEET P.
grandiflo'ra Hort.

This untenable name is misapplied to large-flowered forms of various species.

grand'is . . . . LUSTY P.
helodox'a . . . . AMBER P.
hirsu'ta . . . . GUMMY P.
in'gens
integrifo'lia . . . . . ENTIRELEAF P.
involucra'ta . . . . . . PINNACLE P.
japon'ica . . . . JAPANESE P.
—al'ba . . . . WHITE J.P.
—atrosanguin'ea . . . . BLOOD J.P.
—rose'a . . . . ROSY J.P.
jesoa'na . . . . HOKKAIDO P.
ju'liae . . . . JULIA P.
DOROTHY. HV.
HELEN (*helenae*)
MERTON
WANDA
∞ **kewen'sis** (*floribunda* × *verticillata*) ∞ KEW P.
₵FARINOSA. HV.
king'i . . . . KINGS P.
laurentia'na . . . . ST. LAWRENCE P.
leucoch'noa
lichiangen'sis . . . . . . LICHIANG P.
littonia'na . . . . LITTONS P.
longiflo'ra . . . . . LONGFLOWER P.
lute'a . . . . **P. auricula**
luteo'la . . . . SULFUR P.
magellan'ica . . . . . MAGELLAN P.
malacoi'des . . . . FAIRY P.
ALBA. HV.
ATROPURPUREA
BABY ROSE
LELAND (*lelandi*)
PETER PAN
PRINCESS MARY
ROBUST (*robusta*)
ROSE (*rosea*)
ROSELLE
malva'cea . . . . MALLOW P.
margina'ta . . . . . . SILVEREDGE P.
microdon'ta . . . . . . TINYTOOTH P.
—alpic'ola . . . . . . MOUNTAIN T.P.
min'ima . . . . LEAST P.
mistassin'ica . . . . . MISTASSINI P.
moer'heimi . . . . MOERHEIM P.
moorea'na . . . . MOORES P.
muscarioi'des . . . . . **P. giraldiana**
niv'alis . . . . SNOW P.
nu'tans . . . . SLEEPY P.
obcon'ica . . . . TOP P.
BIGFLOWER (*grandiflora*) HV.
FRINGED (*fimbriata*)
GIANT (*gigantea*)
ROSY (*rosea*)
SHOWY (*superba*)
WHITE (*alba*)
oblanceola'ta . . . . . . LONGLEAF P.
obli'qua
obtusifo'lia . . . . . . BLUNTLEAF P.
officina'lis . . . . **P. veris**
palinu'ri . . . . PALINURUS P.
par'ryi . . . . PARRY P.

PRIMULA, continued

paxia'na . . . . PAX PRIMROSE
pedemonta'na . . . . . PIEDMONT P.
pois'soni . . . . POISSON P.
∞ **polyan'tha** (*?elatior* × *?veris* × *?vulgaris*) . . . . . . ∞ POLYANTHA P.
praeni'tens . . . . **P. sinensis**
pratt'i . . . . PRATT P.
∞ **pubes'cens** (*auricula* × *hirsuta*)
pudibun'da
pulchel'la . . . . BEAUTY P.
pulverulen'ta . . . . . SILVERDUST P.
rein'i . . . . REINS P.
rose'a . . . . ROSE P.

This name has been misapplied to P. japonica rosea and P. obconica HV. Rosy.

—grandiflo'ra . . . . . . BIG R.P.
ru'fa . . . . ROUGELEAF P.
rupic'ola . . . . LEDGE P.
rus'byi . . . . RUSBY P.
saxat'ilis . . . . CLIFF P.
sco'tica . . . . SCOTCH P.
seclu'sa . . . . FLAMINGO P.
secundiflo'ra . . . . SIDEFLOWER P.
septemlo'ba . . . . . SEVENLOBE P.
sibir'ica . . . . SIBERIAN P.
sie'boldi . . . . SIEBOLD P.
—al'ba . . . . WHITE S.P.
BIGFLOWER (*grandiflora*) HV. P. sieboldi
QUEEN OF WHITES
sikkimen'sis . . . . SIKKIM P.
sinen'sis (*chinensis; praenitens*) CHINESE P.
FRINGED (*fimbriata*) HV.
STAR (*stellata*)
sinopurpu'rea . . . PURPLECHINA P.
spectab'ilis . . . . SHOWY P.
sphaerocephʼala . . . ROUNDHEAD P.
suave'olens . . . . **P. veris s.**
suffrutes'cens . . . . SIERRA P.
szechuan'ica . . . . . SZECHWAN P.
tosaen'sis
veitch'i . . . . VEITCH P.
ve'ris (*officinalis*) . . . . COWSLIP P.

In the U. S., the name Cowslip is often misapplied to the Marshmarigold, Caltha palustris. Its historical application is to the Cowslip Primrose, Primula veris.

—al'ba . . . . WHITE C.P.
—infla'ta (*P. pannonica*) PUFFED C.P.
—suave'olens (*P. suaveolens*) SWEET C.P.
GIANT MUNSTEAD. HV. P. veris
GOLDLACE
LUTEA
PRIMROSE
SPETCHLEY
verticilla'ta . . . . ARABIAN P.
vinciflo'ra . . . . . . PERIWINKLE P.
visco'sa . . . . CLAMMY P.
vitta'ta . . . . STRIPED P.
vulga'ris (*acaulis*) . . . ENGLISH P.
DOUBLE (*floreplena*) HV.
E. R. JAMES
GLORIA
MORTON
PAM
PURPLE SPLENDOR
wal'toni . . . . WALTON P.
ward'i . . . . WARDS P.
watt'i . . . . WATTS P.
wil'soni . . . . WILSON P.
win'teri . . . . WINTERS P.
wulfenia'na . . . . WULFEN P.
yargongen'sis . . . . . . YARGONG P.

PRIMULA, continued
zambalen'sis . . . . LAMA PRIMROSE
HELENE PURPURKISSENS. HV. Primula
JEWELL
JULIANA
PAM
PRIMROSE LODGE

PRINCE-ALBERT-YEW
Saxegothaea; S. conspicua
Princespine . . PIPSISSEWA, COMMON: **Chimaphila umbellata**
PRINCESPLUME . . . . **Stanleya**
ALKALI P. . . . . **S. bipinnata**
ARIZONA P. . . . . **S. albescens**
DESERT P. . . . . **S. pinnata**
PANAMINT P. . . . . **S. elata**
WHOLELEAF DESERT P.
S. pinnata integrifolia
PRINCESSPALM . . . . . **Dictyosperma**
RED P. . . . . **D. album rubrum**
WHITE P. . . . . **D. album**
YELLOW P. . . . . . . **D. a. aureum**
PRINCEWOOD, CARIBBEAN
Exostemma caribaeum
PRINSE'PIA . . . . PRINSEPIA
sinen'sis . . . . CHERRY P.
uniflo'ra . . . . HEDGE P.
—serra'ta . . . . TOOTHEDLEAF H.P.
u'tilis . . . . HIMALAYAN P.
PRIONOP'SIS . . . **APLOPAPPUS**
PRIOR'IA . . . . CATIVO
copaif'era . . . . CATIVO
PRITCHAR'DIA . **EUPRITCHARDIA**
See **PALM GENERA.**
PRITCHARDIAPALM . . . **Eupritchardia**
FIJI P. . . . . **E. pacifica**
GAUDICHAUD P. . . . . **E. gaudichaudi**
MARTIUS P. . . . . **E. martii**
THURSTON P. . . . . . . **E. thurstoni**
PRIVET . . . . **Ligustrum**
AMUR P. . . . . **L. amurense**
BIGBERRY SHARPLEAF P.
L. acuminatum macrocarpum
BORDER P. . . . . **L. obtusifolium**
CALIFORNIA P. . . . . **L. ovalifolium**
CHENAULT P. . . . . . . **L. chenaulti**
CHINESE P. . . . . **L. sinense**
DELAVAY P. . . . . . **L. delavayanum**
EUROPEAN P. . . . . **L. vulgare**
EVERGREEN P. . . . . **L. sempervirens**
FORMOSA P. . . . . . . **L. formosanum**
GLOSSY P. . . . . **L. lucidum**
HENRYS P.. . . . . **L. henryi**
HIMALAYAN P. . . **L. massalongianum**
IBOLIUM P. . . . . **×L. ibolium**
IBOTA P. . . . . **L. ibota**
ISLAND P. . . . . **L. insulare**
JAPANESE P. . . . . . . **L. japonicum**
NEPAL P. . . . . **L. nepalense**
PURPUS P. . . . . **L. purpusi**
QUIHOU P. . . . . **L. quihoui**
REGELS BORDER P.
L. obtusifolium regelianum
SHARPLEAF P. . . . . . **L. acuminatum**
SLENDER P. . . . . **L. gracile**
STAUNTON CHINESE P.
L. sinense stauntoni
YUNNAN P. . . . . . . **L. compactum**
PROBOSCID'EA |w . . DEVILSCLAWS
fra'grans (*formosa; Martynia fragrans*) SWEET D.
jussieu'i (*louisiana; Martynia l.; M. proboscidea*) |w . . . COMMON D.
parviflo'ra . . . . NEWMEXICO D.

∞ PROCIMEQUAT
Fortunella hindsi × ∞ LIMEQUAT
PROMENAE'A
See **ORCHID GENERA.**
PROSAR'TES . . . . **DISPORUM**
PROSERPINA'CA |w . . MERMAIDWEED
amblygo'na |w
palus'tris |w . . . . . . MARSH M.
pectina'ta |w . . . . . COMBLEAF M.
platycar'pa |w
PROSO . . . . . . **Panicum miliaceum**
See **CEREALS.**
PROSO'PIS |w . . . . . . MESQUITE
chilen'sis (*juliflora*) |w . COMMON M.
cineras'cens . . . . **Strombocarpa c.**
glandulo'sa (*P. juliflora g.*) HONEY M.
odora'ta . . . . . . **Strombocarpa o.**
pubes'cens . . **Strombocarpa odorata**
veluti'na . . . . VELVET M.
PROSTAN'THERA . . . . MINTBUSH
chloran'tha . . . GREENFLOWER M.
cunea'ta . . . . . . WEDGELEAF M.
inca'na . . . . HOARY M.
inci'sa . . . . CUTLEAF M.
lasian'thos . . . . . VICTORIAN M.
niv'ea . . . . SNOWY M.
rotundifo'lia . . . . . ROUNDLEAF M.
sie'beri . . . . SIEBERS M.
PRO'TEA . . . . PROTEA
acero'sa . . . . NEEDLE P.
compac'ta . . . . RUBY P.
corda'ta . . . . HEARTLEAF P.
cynarioi'des . . . . . HONEYPOT P.
gran'diceps . . . . GREAT P.
longiflo'ra (*lacticolor*) LONGFLOWER P.
mellif'era . . . . SUGAR P.
obtusifo'lia . . . . . BLUNTLEAF P.
scolymoceph'ala . . . GREENBRACT P.
susan'nae . . . . SUSANNA P.
PRO'TIUM (*ICICA* Engl.) RESINTREE
guianen'se (*Icica guianensis*) INCENSE R.
heptaphyl'lum . . . . . . BRAZIL R.
PRUNE
See **FRUIT AND EDIBLE NUT NAMES.**
PRUNEL'LA (*BRUNELLA*) |w SELFHEAL
grandiflo'ra . . . . . BIGFLOWER S.
—al'ba . . . . WHITE B.S.
—rose'a . . . . PINK B.S.
hastaefo'lia
vulga'ris |w . . . . COMMON S.
webbia'na . . . . WEBB S.
—al'ba . . . . WHITE W.S.
—grandiflo'ra . . . BIGFLOWER W.S.
—rose'a . . . . PINK W.S.
PRU'NUS (*AMYGDALUS; ARMENIACA; CERASUS; EMPLECTOCLADUS; LAUROCERASUS; PADUS; PERSICA*) |w . APRICOT; CHERRY; CHOKECHERRY; LAURELCHERRY; PEACH; PLUM

This large, variable genus contains the cultivated Almonds, Apricots, Cherries, Peaches, Plums, etc. See CHERRIES, ORIENTAL FLOWERING; **FRUIT AND EDIBLE NUT NAMES.**

The species which follow belong to sections or subgenera of the genus: Almonds and Peaches to the section (or subgenus) Amygdalus; Apricots to Armeniaca; Cherries to Cerasus; Chokecherries to Padus; Laurelcherries to Laurocerasus; Plums to Euprunus, etc. These sections (or subgenera) are regarded by some botanists as distinct genera.

PRUNUS, continued
alabamen'sis (*Padus a.*) ALABAMA CHOKECHERRY
alleghanien'sis . . . ALLEGANY PLUM
—da'visi . . . . DAVIS A.P.
america'na |w . . . AMERICAN PLUM
—florida'na . . . . . WAKULLA A.P.
—lana'ta . . . . **P. lanata**
¢NEWPORT (*Purpleleaf*) HV. P. americana
∞ **amygdalo-per'sica** (*amygdalus × persica*) . . . ∞ ALMOND PEACH
amyg'dalus (*communis* Arcang., *not* Huds.; *Amygdalus c.*) . . . ALMOND
—ama'ra (*P. communis a.; Amygdalus c. a.*) . . . . BITTER A.
¢BIGNUT BITTER (*amara macrocarpa*) HV. P. amygdalus
¢DOUBLEPINK (*roseoplena*)
¢DOUBLEPINK BITTER (*amara roseoplena*)
¢DOUBLEWHITE (*alboplena*)
¢DWARF BITTER (*amara nana*)
¢FRAGILESHELL (*fragilis*)
¢ROSEPURPLE (*purpurea*)
¢WEEPING (*pendula*)
anderso'ni (*Amygdalus a.; Emplectocladus a.*) . ANDERSON PEACHBRUSH
angustifo'lia . . . CHICKASAW PLUM
—va'rians . . . . BIG C.P.
—wat'soni (*P. watsoni*) . . . SAND C.P.
apet'ala (*ceraseidos*) NOPETAL CHERRY
argen'tea (*orientalis* Koehne, *not* Walp.; *Amygdalus a.*) . . . SILVER PEACH
armeni'aca (*Armeniaca vulgaris*) |w APRICOT
—an'su . . . . ANSU A.
—sibir'ica . . . . **P. sibirica**
¢CHARLES ABRAHAM. HV. P. armeniaca
¢DAPPLELEAF (*variegata*)
¢WEEPING (*pendula*)
armeni'aca × salici'na . ∞ PLUMCOT
∞ **arnoldia'na** (*cerasifera × triloba*) ∞ ARNOLD FLOWERING ALMOND
austra'lis SOUTH ALABAMA CHOKECHERRY
a'vium |w . . . . MAZZARD CHERRY
—actia'na (*P. a. sylvestris*) WILD M.C.
—rega'lis . . . . ∞ **P. effusa**
—salicifo'lia . . . WILLOWLEAF M.C.
¢DOUBLE (*plena*) HV. P. avium
¢DOUBLEPINK (*plena rosea*)
¢DWARF (*nana*)
¢FERNLEAF (*aspleniifolia*)
¢HARDFLE H (*duracina*). *Bigarrea.*
¢HEART (*juliana*). *Gean.*
¢TENINCHLEAF (*decumana*)
¢WEEPING (*pendula*)
baldshuan'ica
bes'seyi (*P. pumila b.*) BESSEY CHERRY
bi'color (*Padus b.*)
∞ **blireia'na** (*cerasifera* ¢PISSARD ×*mume; ∞ P. cerasifera b.*) ∞ BLIREIANA PLUM
¢MOSER (*moseri; P. b. moseri*) HV.
¢NEWPORT
¢OTHELLO
bokharien'sis
brachyp'oda pubig'era . . **P. pubigera**
briganti'na (*brigantiaca*) BRIANCON APRICOT
buchar'ica (*Amygdalus b.*)
buergeria'na . . . RACEMOSE CHERRY
bun'gei . . . . **P. humilis**
campanula'ta . . . TAIWAN CHERRY
canes'cens . . . UNDERGRAY CHERRY

PRUNUS, continued

cap'ollin . . . . **P. serotina salicifolia**
∞ *capronia'na* . . . . . . ∞ **P. effusa**
cap'uli . . . . **P. serotina salicifolia**
carolinia'na (*Cerasus c.; Laurocerasus c.*) . . CAROLINA LAURELCHERRY
cerasei'dos . . . . **P. apetala**
cerasif'era (*P. domestica myrobalan; korolkowi; myrobalana*) MYROBALAN PLUM
∞ —*blireia'na* . . . . . ∞ **P. blireiana**
—**divarica'ta** (*P. divaricata*) WILD M.P.
¢BLACK (*nigra*) HV. P. cerasifera
¢PISSARD (*atropurpurea; pissardi*). *Purpleleaf.*
¢PURPUS (*purpusi*)
¢VESUVIUS
¢WEEPING (*pendula*)
¢WHITERIM (*elegans*)
¢WOODS (*woodi*)
cerasoi'des (*puddum*)
cera'sus (*Cerasus caproniana*) |w SOUR CHERRY
—**frutes'cens** . . . . SHRUBBY S.C.
—**maras'ca** (*P. marasca*) MARASCA S.C.
—**salicifo'lia** . . . WILLOWLEAF S.C.
¢ALLSAINTS (*semperflorens*). *Everblooming.* HV. P. cerasus
¢AMARELLE (*acida; caproniana*)
¢DOUBLE (*plena*)
¢MORELLO (*austera*)
¢PEACHDOUBLE (*persiciflora*)
¢RHEX (*Cerasus rhexi; P. cerasus r.*)
¢UMBRELLA (*umbraculifera*)
∞ **ciste'na** (*cerasifera* ¢PISSARD × *pumila*)
¢HENSEN. HV.
cocomi'lia . . . . . COCOMILIA PLUM
commu'nis Huds. . . . **P. domestica**
commu'nis Arcang. . . **P. amygdalus**
—*ama'ra* . . . . . **P. amygdalus a.**
conade'nia
concin'na
conradi'nae . . . CONRADINA CHERRY
¢HALFDOUBLE (*semiplena*) HV.
consociiflo'ra
cornu'ta (*pachyclada; Padus c.*) HIMALAYAN BIRDCHERRY
crataegifo'lia . . HAWTHORN CHERRY
curd'ica . . . . . ARMENIAN PLUM
cuth'berti . . GEORGIA CHOKECHERRY
cyclami'na
dasycar'pa (*Armeniaca d.*) PURPLE APRICOT
davidia'na (*Amygdalus d.; Persica d.*) DAVID PEACH
—**al'ba** . . . . WHITE D.P.
—**potani'ni** . . . . SHINYLEAF D.P.
—**ru'bra** . . . . RED D.P.
dehis'cens . . . . **P. tangutica**
demis'sa . . . . . . **P. virginiana d.**
—*melanocar'pa* . . . **P. virginiana m.**
depres'sa . . . . **P. pumila d.**
dielsia'na . . . . . DIELS CHERRY
divarica'ta . . . . . **P. cerasifera d.**
domes'tica (*communis* Huds., *not* Arcang.) . . . . . . GARDEN PLUM
—*insiti'tia* . . . . **P. insititia**
—*myrobal'an* . . . . . . **P. cerasifera**
¢DOUBLE (*domestica plantieri; plantierensis*) HV. P. domestica

The term "Damson" (a corruption of Damascene—from Damascus) appears originally to have been applied to the so-called var. P. domestica damascena, which Prof. Rehder does not regard as distinct. The term is now used to cover certain varieties or forms having a small compact habit, small leaves, and small, firm, ovoid, usually dark purple clustered fruits.

∞ **dun'bari** (*americana* × *maritima*) ∞ DUNBAR PLUM
∞ **effu'sa** (*avium* × *cerasus; P. avium regalis;* ∞ *caproniana*) ∞ DUKE CHERRY
emargina'ta (*Cerasus e.*) |w BITTER CHERRY
—*villo'sa* . . . . **P. prunifolia**
∞ **em'inens** (*cerasus* × *fruticosa*) ∞ SOURBUSH CHERRY
fascicula'ta (*Amygdalus f.; Emplectocladus fasciculatus*) DESERT PEACHBRUSH
fenzlia'na (*Amygdalus f.*) FENZL ALMOND
∞ **fontanesia'na** (*avium* × *mahaleb*) ∞ DESFONTAINES CHERRY
fre'monti (*Amygdalus f.; Emplectocladus f.*) . FREMONT PEACHBRUSH
×**fru'ticans** (*insititia* × *?spinosa*)
This appears to be a natural hybrid.
frutico'sa . . . . . GROUND CHERRY
¢WEEPING (*pendula*) HV.
∞ **gigan'tea** (∞ *amygdalo-persica* × *cerasifera*) . . . . ∞ GIANT PLUM
¢BURBANK. HV.
¢MARIANNA
¢MOTLEY
¢PURPLELEAF KELSEY
glandulo'sa (*Cerasus g.*) ALMOND CHERRY

The double-flowered hort. var. are known as "Flowering Almond." The species is actually a Cherry.

—**al'ba** . . . . WHITE A.C.
—**rose'a** . . . . PINK A.C.
¢DOUBLEPINK (*alboplena*) HV. P. glandulosa
¢DOUBLEWHITE (*sinensis*)
glandulo'sa (Hook.) Torr. & Gray, *not* Thunb. . . . . **P. texana**
grac'ilis . . . . . . OKLAHOMA PLUM
graves'i . . . . GRAVES PLUM
graya'na (*P. padus japonica; Padus g.*) GRAYS CHOKECHERRY
hel'enae . . . . . . HELENA CHERRY
hook'eri . . . . **P. texana**
hortula'na . . . . HORTULAN PLUM
—**mi'neri** . . . . . . MINER H.P.
—**pu'bens** . . . . . MISSOURI H.P.
hu'milis (*bungei*) . . BUNGE CHERRY
ilicifo'lia (*Cerasus i.*) HOLLYLEAF CHERRY
—*integrifo'lia* . . . . **P. lyoni**
—**occidenta'lis** (*Cerasus o.*) WESTERN H.C.
inca'na (*Cerasus incana*) UNDERWOOL CHERRY
inci'sa . . FUJI CHERRY (*Mame C.*)
One of the species of Japanese Flowering Cherry.
—**serra'ta** . . . . BRISTLELEAF M.C.
injucun'da . . . . . . **P. umbellata i.**
insiti'tia (*P. domestica i.*) BULLACE PLUM
—**subsilves'tris** . . . . . WILD B.P.
¢GREENGAGE (*italica*). *Reine Claude.* HV. P. insititia
¢MIRABELLE (*syriaca*)
integrifo'lia . . . . **P. lyoni**
involucra'ta
jacquemont'i (*Cerasus j.*) JACQUEMONT CHERRY
japon'ica . . CHINESE BUSHCHERRY

Despite the name japonica, this species is Chinese rather than Japanese. It is not one of the true Japanese Flowering Cherries. The name P. japonica is often misapplied to the Flowering Almond varieties of P. glandulosa and to some of the true Japanese Flowering Cherries, especially the weeping variety of P. subhirtella, Shidare-higan.

—**eng'leri** . . . . . . ENGLER C.B.
—**naka'i** . . . . NAKAI C.B.
—**thun'bergi** . . . . THUNBERG C.B.
∞ **judd'i** (*sargenti* × *yedoensis*) ∞ JUDD CHERRY
kansuen'sis (*Amygdalus k.*) KANSU PEACH
korolkow'i . . . . **P. cerasifera**
kurilen'sis . . . . . . **P. nipponica k.**
lana'ta (*P. americana l.; palmeri*) INCH PLUM
lannesia'na . . . . . **P. serrulata l.**
∞ **lauchea'na** (*padus* × *virginiana*)
laurocera'sus (*Laurocerasus officinalis*) COMMON LAURELCHERRY
—**angustifo'lia** . . NARROWLEAF C.L.
—**caucas'ica** (*Laurocerasus officinalis c.*) CAUCASIAN C.L.
—**col'chica** (*Laurocerasus officinalis c.*) COLCHIS C.L.
—**magnoliaefo'lia** . . . BIGLEAF C.L.
—**parvifo'lia** . . . . LITTLELEAF C.L.
—**rotundifo'lia** (*Laurocerasus officinalis r.*) . . . . . ROUNDLEAF C.L.
—**schipkaen'sis** (*Laurocerasus officinalis s.*) . . . . . . SCHIPKA C.L.
—**serb'ica** . . . . . . SERBIAN C.L.
—**zabelia'na** . . . . . . ZABEL C.L.
¢BENARD (*benardi*) HV. P. laurocerasus
BERTINI
¢BROADLEAF (*latifolia*)
¢BRUANT (*bruanti*)
¢CAMELLIA (*camelliaefolia*)
¢COMPACT (*compacta*)
¢DWARF (*nana*)
¢MISCHIANA
¢PYRAMID (*pyramidalis*)
¢REYNVAN (*reynvani*)
¢TRIOMPHE DE BORDEAUX
¢VERSAILLES (*versaillensis*)
lobula'ta
lusitan'ica (*Laurocerasus l.*) PORTUGUESE LAURELCHERRY (*Cherrylaurel*)
¢AZORES (*azorica*) HV.
¢MYRTLE (*myrtifolia*)
¢PYRAMID (*pyramidalis*)
¢WHITERIM (*variegata*)
ly'oni (*integrifolia; P. ilicifolia i.; Cerasus integrifolia*) CATALINA CHERRY
maack'i . . . . AMUR CHOKECHERRY
macrade'nia
maha'leb (*Cerasus m.*) MAHALEB CHERRY
—**xanthocar'pa** . . . . YELLOW M.C.
¢MONSTROSA. HV. P. mahaleb
¢WEEPING (*pendula*)
mandshur'ica (*Armeniaca m.*) MANCHURIAN APRICOT
marit'ima |w . . . . . BEACH PLUM
—**fla'va** . . . . YELLOW B.P.
∞ **maur'eri** (*incana* × *pumila*) ∞ MAURER CHERRY
maximowicz'i . . . MIYAMA CHERRY
melanocar'pa . . . . **P. virginiana m.**

PRUNUS, continued

mexica'na . . . . . Mexican Plum
—fultonen'sis . . . . Fulton M.P.
—polyan'dra . . . . Polyandra M.P.
—reticula'ta . . . . . Netvein M.P.
mey'eri . . . Meyer Chokecherry
Perhaps a hybrid between P. maacki and P. maximowiczi.
microcar'pa (*Cerasus m.*) Little Cherry
—tortuo'sa . . . . Twiststem L.C.
minutiflo'ra (*Emplectocladus minutiflorus*). Smallflower Peachbrush
mi'ra (*Amygdalus m.*) Smoothpit Peach
mol'lis Walp., *not* Torr. . **P. prunifolia**
mongo'lica (*Amygdalus m.*) Mongol Peach
montic'ola . . . . . Taurus Plum
mu'me (*Armeniaca m.*) Japanese Apricot
—al'ba . . . . White J.A.
—ton'sa . . . . Smooth J.A.
₵Bonita. hv. P. mume
₵Doublepink (*alphandi*)
₵Doublewhite (*alboplena*)
₵Weeping (*pendula*)
munsonia'na . . . . Wildgoose Plum
myrobala'na . . . . **P. cerasifera**
myrtifo'lia . . Myrtle Laurelcherry
na'na Stokes, *not* Du Roi . **P. tenella**
napaulen'sis . . Nepal Chokecherry
—seric'ea . . . . **P. sericea**
ni'gra . . . . Canada Plum
nippon'ica . . . . . Takane Cherry
One of the species of Japanese Flowering Cherry.
—kurilen'sis (*P. kurilensis*) Kurile T.C.
occidenta'lis (*Laurocerasus o.*) WestIndies Laurelcherry (*Cherrylaurel*)
orienta'lis Koehne, *not* Walp. **P. argentea**
∞ **orthosep'ala** (*americana* × *angustifolia watsoni*)
pachycla'da . . . . **P. cornuta**
pa'dus (*Cerasus p.; Padus racemosa*) European Birdcherry
—chlorocar'pos . . . . Yellow E.B.
—commuta'ta (*P. regeliana*) Harbinger E.B.
—japon'ica . . . . . . **P. grayana**
—lax'a . . . . Korean B.
—leucocar'pa . . . Palefruit E.B.
—parviflo'ra . . . Smallflower E.B.
₵Aucubaleaf (*aucubaefolia*) hv. P. padus
₵Bigflower (*spaethi*)
₵Double (*plena*)
₵Longcluster (*watereri*)
₵Red (*rubra*)
₵Weeping (*pendula*)
pal'meri . . . . **P. lanata**
pauciflo'ra . . . . . **P. pseudocerasus**
peduncula'ta (*Amygdalus p.*)
pensylva'nica (*Cerasus p.*) |w Pin Cherry
—saximonta'na . . Manitoba P.C.
per'sica (*Amygdalus p.; Persica vulgaris*) . . . . Peach
—aganopers'ica . . . Freestone P.
—compres'sa (*P. p. platycarpa; P. platycarpa; Amygdalus p.*) . Flat P.

PRUNUS, continued

per'sica nectari'na (*P. p. nucipersica; Amygdalus persica nectarina*) Nectarine
—scleroper'sica . Clingstone Peach
₵Bloodleaf (*atropurpurea*) hv. P. persica
₵Camellia (*camelliaeflora*)
₵Carmine (*magnifica*)
₵Carnation (*dianthiflora*)
₵Chrysanthemum
₵Doubled red (*duplex; roseoplena; rubroplena*)
₵Doublewhite (*alboplena*)
₵Purple (*purpurea*)
₵Pyramid (*pyramidalis*)
₵Redflowering (*rubra*)
₵Versicolor
₵Weeping (*pendula*)
₵Whiteflowering (*alba*)
per'sica × salici'na . . ∞ Plumpeach
petunniko'wi (*Amygdalus p.*) Turkestan Almond
pilo'sa (*Amygdalus p.*) . Gobi Peach
pilosius'cula
platycar'pa . . . **P. persica compressa**
pleiocera'sus
pleurop'tera
polyt'richa
prostra'ta Mediterranean Ground Cherry
prunifo'lia (*P. emarginata villosa; P. mollis* Walp., *not* Torr.; *Cerasus m.; C. prunifolia*) . Plumleaf Cherry
pseudoarmeni'aca . . Greek Plum
pseudocera'sus (*pauciflora*)
This name is often misapplied to P. serrulata and other Japanese Flowering Cherries.
pubig'era (*P. brachypoda p.*)
—obova'ta
—pratt'i
pud'dum. . . . . . . **P. cerasoides**
pu'mila . . . . Sand Cherry
The name P. pumila is often misapplied to dwarf forms of other species.
—bes'seyi . . . . **P. besseyi**
—depres'sa (*P. depressa*) Sprawling S.C.
—susqueha'nae (*P. susquehanae*) |w Appalachian S.C.
regelia'na . . . **P. padus commutata**
revercho'ni . . . . . . Hog Plum
rivula'ris (*texana* Scheele, *not* Dietr.) Creek Plum
ru'fa . . . . . Himalayan Cherry
sa'lasi. . . . . Salas Laurelcherry
salicifo'lia . . . . . . **P. serotina s.**
salici'na (*triflora*) . . Japanese Plum
sar'genti (*P. serrulata sachalinensis*) Sargent Cherry
seric'ea (*P. napaulensis s.*)
serot'ina (*Cerasus s.; Padus s.*) |w Black Cherry
—cartilagin'ea . . . . . Shiny B.C.
—monta'na . . . . Underblue B.C.
—phelloi'des . . . . Willowoak B.C.
—salicifo'lia (*P. capollin; P. capuli; P. salicifolia; Cerasus capollin*) Capulin B.C.
₵Fernleaf (*asplenifolia*) hv. P. serotina
₵Pyramid (*pyramidalis*)
₵Weeping (*pendula*)

PRUNUS, continued

ser'rula
serrula'ta . . . . Oriental Cherry
The typical form of P. serrulata is the cultivated double white form albo-pleno Schneid. For hort. var. of P. serrulata, see Cherries, Oriental Flowering.
—lannesia'na (*P. lannesiana*)
—sachalinen'sis . . . . **P. sargenti**
—sponta'nea . . . Underbrown O.C.
sibir'ica (*P. armeniaca s.; Armeniaca s.*) Siberian Apricot
₵Doubled red (*plenarubra*) hv.
sie'boldi (*Cerasus s.*) Siebold Cherry
One of the species of Japanese Flowering Cherry.
si'moni . . . . Apricot Plum
sinen'sis **P. glandulosa** ₵Doublewhite
This name is sometimes misapplied to P. japonica.
∞ **skin'neri** (*japonica* × *tenella*)
∞ **sla'vini** (*angustifolia* × *gracilis*)
specio'sa . . . . . **P. serrulata albida**
spino'sa . . . . . Sloe; Blackthorn
₵Double (*plena*) hv.
₵Purpleleaf (*purpurea*)
spinosis'sima (*Amygdalus s.*) Thorny Peachbrush
spreng'eri . . . . Sprenger Cherry
ssio'ri (*Padus s.*)
stellip'ila
subcorda'ta . . . . Klamath Plum
—kel'loggi . . . . . . Kellogg K.P.
subhirtel'la . . . . . Higan Cherry
One of the species of Japanese Flowering Cherry.
—ascen'dens . . . . . . Tall H.C.
₵Autumn (*autumnalis*) hv. P. subhirtella
₵Weeping (*pendula*)
₵Yaeshidare (*pendula floreplena*)
∞ **sulta'na** (*salicina* × *simoni*) ∞ Sultana Plum
₵Wickson. hv.
susqueha'nae . . . . . . **P. pumila s.**
sweginzo'wi (*Amygdalus s.*) Sweginzow Almond
tangu'tica (*dehiscens; Amygdalus t.*) Tangut Almond
tatsienen'sis . . . . Tatsien Cherry
tenel'la (*nana* Stokes, *not* Du Roi; *Amygdalus n.*) . . Russian Almond
—al'ba . . . . White R.A.
—campes'tris . . Roundfruit R.A.
₵Redbud (*gessleriana*) hv. P. tenella
tenuifo'lia . . . . . . Larissa Plum
texa'na (*glandulosa* (Hook.) Torr. & Gray, *not* Thunb.; *hookeri; Amygdalus glandulosa; Emplectocladus glandulosus*) . Texas Peachbrush
texa'na Scheele, *not* Dietr. **P. rivularis**
tomento'sa . . . Manchu Cherry (*Nanking C.*)
—endot'richa Whiteflowered M.C.
—leucocar'pa . . . Palefruit M.C.
triflo'ra . . . . **P. salicina**
tril'oba (*Amygdalus t.*) Flowering Plum
—petz'oldi . . . . . . Petzold F.P.
—sim'plex . . . . Wild F.P.
₵Multiplex. hv. P. triloba
This clon, unfortunately, represents the botanical type of the species, *i.e.*, it is typical Flowering Plum.

Hort. var.; hv. = horticultural variety (or varieties); sp. = species (singular); spp. = species (plural).
₵ = clon; × (as a prefix) = hybrid; × (between scientific plant names) = crossed by; ∞ = polybrid; |w = plant useful to wildlife.
See Glossary for definitions of clon, hybrid, and polybrid.

PRUNUS, continued
umbella'ta . . . . Flatwoods Plum
—injucun'da (*P. injucunda*)
—tar'da
ursi'na . . . . Bear Plum
∞ **utahen'sis** (*angustifolia watsoni* × *besseyi*) . . . . . . ∞ Utah Cherry
velu'tina
venulo'sa . . . . . . Texas Plum
vi'rens (*Padus v.*)
Southwestern Chokecherry
—ru'fula . . . Gila Chokecherry
virginia'na (*Padus v.*) |w
Common Chokecherry
—demis'sa (*P. demissa*) |w
Western C.C.
—duerinck'i . . . . Broadleaf C.C.
—leucocar'pa . . . . . Amber C.C.
—melanocar'pa (*P. demissa m.; P. melanocarpa*) . . . . . Black C.C.
₵Dwarf (*nana*) hv. P. virginiana
wat'soni . . . . . **P. angustifolia w.**
wil'soni (*Padus w.*)
Wilson Chokecherry
yedoen'sis . . . . . Yoshino Cherry

This is supposed to be a hybrid between P. serrulata and P. subhirtella. This species is one of the Oriental Flowering Cherries, of which a list appears in this book.

₵Perpendens. hv.
₵Weeping (*pendula*)

PSATHYREL'LA . . . . Psathyrella
dissemina'ta

PSATHYRO'TES
ramosis'sima

PSED'ERA . . . . . **AMPELOPSIS**

PSEUDABU'TILON . Falseabutilon
lozan'i (*Wissadula l.*) . . . Lozano F.

PSEUDERAN'THEMUM
Pseuderanthemum
atropurpu'reum (*Eranthemum a.*)
Purplespot P.
₵Eldorado. hv.
bi'color (*Eranthemum b.*) . Bicolor P.
kewen'se . . . SolomonIslands P.
reticula'tum (*Eranthemum r.*)
Yellowvein P.
setica'lyx
tubercula'tum (*Eranthemum t.*)
Knotstem P.

PSEUDOCED'RELA
kotsch'yi

Pseudocydo'nia sinen'sis **Chaenomeles s.**

PSEUDOCYMOP'TERUS |w
Pseudocymopterus
anisa'tus
monta'nus |w

PSEUDOCYT'ISUS
integrifo'lius (*Vella pseudocytisus; V. integrifolia*)
spino'sus (*Vella spinosa*)

PSEUDOESPOS'TOA . **BINGHAMIA**
See **CACTUS GENERA.**

PSEUDOLAR'IX . . . . Goldenlarch
amab'ilis (*fortunei; kaempferi*)
Lovely G.
—na'na . . . . Dwarf G.

PSEUDOPAN'AX
chatham'icus
crassifo'lius
—trifoliola'tus

PSEUDOPANAX, continued
dis'color
fe'rox
les'soni

PSEUDOPHOE'NIX (*CYCLOSPATHE*)
Cherrypalm
See **PALM GENERA.**

PSEUDORHIP'SALIS
See **CACTUS GENERA.**

PSEUDOSA'SA
See **BAMBOO GENERA.**

PSEUDOSAS'SAFRAS . **SASSAFRAS**

PSEUDOTSU'GA . . . . Douglasfir
japon'ica . . . . Japanese D.
macrocar'pa . . . . . . Bigcone D.
sinen'sis . . . . Chinese D.
taxifo'lia (*douglasi; mucronata*) |w
Common D.
—brevibractea'ta . Shortbract C.D.
₵Blue (*glauca*) hv. P. taxifolia
₵Columnar (*fastigiata*)
₵Compact (*compacta*)
₵Dwarf (*pumila*)
₵Frets (*fretsi*)
₵Globe (*globosa*)
₵Gray (*caesia*)
₵Green (*viridis*)
₵Silverleaf (*argentea*)
₵Weeping (*pendula*)

PSIDIOP'SIS
moritzia'num

PSID'IUM . . . . Guava
See **FRUIT AND EDIBLE NUT NAMES.**
ara'ca . . . . **P. guineense**
cattleia'num . . . . **P. littorale**
—lu'cidum . . . . **P. littorale l.**
coria'ceum
cujavil'lum . . . . Dwarf G.
friedrichsthalia'num (*laurifolium*)
CostaRican G.
guaja'va . . . . Common G.
guineen'se (*araca*) . . . Brazilian G. (*Araca*)

The name guineense is a misnomer, the plant being native to Brazil rather than Guinea.

littora'le (*cattleianum; variabile*)
Cattley G. (*Strawberry G.*)
—lu'cidum (*P. cattleianum l.*)
Yellow C.G.
mol'le . . . . Guisaro G.

PSILOCAR'PHUS
tenel'lus

PSILOCA'RYA |w . . . . . Baldrush
ni'tens |w . . . . Shiny B.
scirpoi'des |w

PSILOCAU'LON
grandicau'le

PSILOSTE'MON **TRACHYSTEMON**

PSILOS'TROPHE . . . Paperflower
coop'eri . . . . Whitestem P.
gnaphalo'des . . . . . . Cudweed P.
sparsiflo'ra . . . . . Greenstem P.
tageti'nae . . . . Woolly P.

PSOPHOCAR'PUS . . . . . Goabean
tetragonolo'bus . . . . . Indies G.

PSORA'LEA |w . . . . . . Scurfpea
aphyl'la . . . . Bluebroom S.
argophyl'la |w . . . . Silverleaf S.

PSORALEA, continued
bitumino'sa . . . Arabian Scurfpea
canes'cens |w . . . . . . Hoary S.
casto'rea . . . . . Beaverbread S.
corylifo'lia . . . . . . Malaytea S.
cuspida'ta . . . . . . Tallbread S.
drupa'cea . . . . Drupe S.
esculen'ta (*Pediomelum esculentum*)
Common Breadroot S.
glandulo'sa
grac'ilis |w . . . . Slender S.
hypogae'a . . . Little Breadroot S.
lanceola'ta (*micrantha*) . . Lemon S.
macrosta'chya |w . . Leatherroot S.
mephit'ica . . . . Skunktop S.
onobry'chis
physo'des . . . . Californiatea S.
pinna'ta . . . . Pinnate S.
psoralioi'des (*pedunculata*) Bobsroot S.
stenosta'chya
tenuiflo'ra . . . . . Slimflower S.

PSYCHO'TRIA |w . . . . Wildcoffee
bacterioph'ila . . ComoroIslands W.
bahamen'sis . . . . Bahama W.
capen'sis . . . . Cape W.
ipecacuan'ha . . . . . . **Cephaelis i.**
jasminiflo'ra . . . . Jasmine W.
nervo'sa . . . . St.Johns W.
—lanceola'ta . . . St.Augustine W.
ser'pens
sulz'neri . . . . Sulzner W.
tenuifo'lia |w . . . . . Shortleaf W.
unda'ta . . . . Seminole W.

PTAEROX'YLON . . . Sneezewood

This name is often misspelled Pteroxylon.

obli'quum
u'tile

Ptarmiganberry . . . . **Arctous**
Alpine P. . . . . **A. alpinus**
Redfruit P. . . . . **A. ruber**

PTE'LEA . . . . Hoptree
bald'wini . . . . Baldwin H.
lutes'cens . . . . Yellow H.
ni'tens . . . . Shiny H.
polyade'nia
trifolia'ta . . . . Common H.
—mol'lis (*P. mollis; P. tomentosa*)
Woolly C.H.
—pentaphyl'la . . . . Fiveleaf C.H.
—pubes'cens
₵Golden (*aurea*) hv. P. trifoliata
₵Pyramid (*fastigiata*)

PTERE'TIS (*MATTEUCCIA; STRUTHIOPTERIS* Willd., *not* Weis)
See **FERN GENERA.**

PTERID'IUM . . . . Bracken
See **FERN GENERA.**

PTER'IS . . . . Brake
See **FERN GENERA.**

PTEROCAC'TUS . . . Wingcactus
See **CACTUS GENERA.**

PTEROCAR'PUS . . . . . . Padauk
angolen'sis . . . . Angola P.
dalbergioi'des . . . . . Andaman P.
dra'co . . . . . . Dragonsblood P.
erina'ceus . . . . . WestAfrican P.
in'dicus . . . . . . Burmacoast P.
macrocar'pus . . . . Burma P.
marsu'pium . . . . Vengai P.
peda'tus
santali'nus . . . . . Sandalwood P.
soyaux'i . . . . African P.

PTEROCA'RYA . . . . . . WINGNUT
fraxinifo'lia (*caucasica; sorbifolia; spachiana*) . . . . . . CAUCASIAN W.
—dumo'sa (*P. dumosa*) SHRUBBY C.W.
hupehen'sis . . . . . . HUPEH W.
paliu'rus . . . . . . DISKFRUIT W.
∞ **rehderia'na** (*fraxinifolia* × *stenoptera*) ∞ REHDER W.
rhoifo'lia . . . . . . JAPANESE W.
stenop'tera (*japonica* Hort.; *sinensis* Hort.) . . . . CHINESE W.

PTEROCEL'TIS . . . . . WINGCELTIS
tatarino'wi . . . . TATAR W.

PTEROCEPH'ALUS . . . WINGHEAD
parnas'si (*Scabiosa p.; S. pterocephala*) TEASEL W.

PTER'ODON . . . . FAVEIRO
pubes'cens . . . . FUZZY F.

PTEROG'YNE
ni'tens

PTERO'NIA
camphora'ta

PTEROPHA'COS . . **ASTRAGALUS**

PTEROSPER'MUM
acerifo'lium

PTEROS'PORA . . . . . PINEDROPS
andromede'a . . . . . WOODLAND P.

PTEROSTY'RAX . . EPAULETTETREE
corymbo'sa . . . . LITTLE E.
his'pida . . . . FRAGRANT E.

PTEROXYG'ONUM
gir'aldi

PTEROX'YLON . **PTAEROXYLON**

PTERYGO'TA
ala'ta (*Sterculia a.*)

PTILIM'NIUM |w . MOCKBISHOPWEED
capilla'ceum |w

Ptilocala'is nu'tans . . . **Microseris n.**

PTILO'RIA . . **STEPHANOMERIA**

PTILO'TA |w
asplenioi'des |w
pectina'ta |w

PTILO'TUS (*TRICHINIUM*)
man'glesi

PTYCHORA'PHIS . . . PTYCHORAPHIS
See **PALM GENERA.**

PTYCHOSPER'MA (*SEAFORTHIA*) PTYCHOSPERMA
See **PALM GENERA.**

PUCCINEL'LIA . . . . ALKALIGRASS
See **GRASS GENERA.**

PUCCIN'IA . . . . PUCCINIA
gram'inis . . . . STEMRUST P.

Puccoon . . . BLOODROOT: **Sanguinaria canadensis;** GOLDENSEAL: **Hydrastis canadensis;** GROMWELL: **Lithospermum** spp.

PUERA'RIA . KUDZUBEAN (*Kudzuvine*)
thunbergia'na (*hirsuta; Dolichos japonicus*) . . . . THUNBERG K.

PUFFBALL
A general term applied to certain fungi of the families Lycoperdaceae, Sclerodermaceae, and Tylostomaceae. Bovista, Calvatia, and Lycoperdon are familiar genera of Puffballs.

PUKATEA . . **Laurelia novae-zealandiae**

Pulassan PULASAN: **Nephelium mutabile**

PULICA'RIA
dysenter'ica (*Inula d.*)
odo'ra (*Inula o.*)

PULMONA'RIA . . . . LUNGWORT
angustifo'lia . . . . . . COWSLIP L.
—azu'rea . . . . AZURE C.L.
monta'na (*mollis; rubra*) MOUNTAIN L.
officina'lis (*maculata*) . . COMMON L.
sacchara'ta . . . . . BETHLEHEM L.
¢ARVERNE (*arvernensis*) HV. Pulmonaria
¢ARVERNE WHITE (*arvernensis alba*)

PULSATIL'LA . . . . . **ANEMONE**
hirsutis'sima . . . . . **A. ludoviciana**

PULTENAE'A . . . . . PULTENAEA
daphnoi'des . . . . WALLFLOWER P.
ericaefo'lia . . . . HEATHERLEAF P.

PUMMELO . . . . **Citrus grandis**

PUMPKIN . . . . **Cucurbita pepo**
BUSH P. . . . . **C. p. melopepo**

PUMPWOOD . . . . **Cecropia**
AMBAY P. . . . . **C. adenopus**
SHIELDLEAF P. . . . . . . **C. peltata**
SILVERLEAF P. . . . . . **C. palmata**

PUNCTILLA'RIA **MESEMBRYANTHEMUM**
See **SUCCULENTS.**

PUNCTUREVINE . . . **Tribulus terrestris**

PU'NICA . . . . POMEGRANATE
grana'tum . . COMMON P. (*Granada*)
DOUBLE (*plena*) HV.
DWARF (*nana*)
LEGRELLE (*legrellei*)
MULTIPLEX
PALE (*albescens*)
RED (*rubra*)
VARIEGATED (*variegata*)
WHITE (*alba*)
YELLOW (*flavescens*)
protopu'nica . . . . . . SOCOTRA P.

Puriri . . CHASTETREE, NEWZEALAND: **Vitex lucens**

PURPLEHEART . . . . . . **Peltogyne**
GUIANA P. . . . . . . **P. paniculata**
TRINIDAD P. . . . **P. porphyrocardia**

PURPLETOP . . . . . . **Triodia flava**

PURSH'IA (*KUNZIA*) |w BITTERBRUSH
tridenta'ta (*Kunzia t.*) |w ANTELOPE B.
—glandulo'sa . . . . . DESERT B.

PURSLANE, COMMON . **Portulaca oleracea**

PUSCHKIN'IA (*SCILLOIDES* Hort.) PUSCHKINIA
scilloi'des . . . . SQUILL P.
—libanot'ica . . . . . . LEBANON P.

Pussyears
Lobbs P. . . . . MARIPOSA, LOBBS: **Calochortus lobbi**
Northwestern P. NORTHWESTERN M.: **C. elegans**
Skyblue P. SKYBLUE M.: **C. coeruleus**
Tolmie P. . . TOLMIE M.: **C. tolmiei**
Yellow P. ONELEAF M.: **C. monophyllus**

PUSSYPAWS . . . . **Spraguea**
MT.HOOD P. . **S. umbellata candicifera**
UMBELLATE P. . . . . . **S. umbellata**

PUSSYTOES . . . . **Antennaria**
ALPINE P. . . . . **A. alpina**
CANADA P. . . . . . . **A. canadensis**
CARPATHIAN P. . . . . **A. carpathica**

PUSSYTOES, continued
COMMON P. . . . **Antennaria dioica**
FIELD P. . . . . **A. neglecta**
LITTLELEAF P. . . . . **A. microphylla**
LOW P. . . . . **A. dimorpha**
MAGELLAN P. . . . . **A. magellanica**
PLANTAINLEAF P. . . **A. plantaginifolia**
RACEME P. . . . . . . **A. racemosa**
ROCKYMOUNTAIN P. . . . . **A. aprica**
ROSE P. . . . . **A. rosea**
RUSH P. . . . . **A. luzuloides**
SHOWY P. . . . . . . **A. pulcherrima**
SMALLER P. . . . . . . **A. neodioica**
WOOLLY P. . . . . **A. lanata**

PUTAWETA . . . **Carpodetus; C. serratus**

PUTRAN'JIVA . . . . AMULETPLANT
rox'burghi . . . . INDIA A.

PUTTYROOT . . **Aplectrum; A. hyemale**

PU'YA
aequatoria'lis
alpes'tris
caeru'lea
chilen'sis

PYCNAN'THEMUM (*KOELLIA*) MOUNTAINMINT
flexuo'sum (*K. flexuosa*) SLENDER M.
inca'num . . . . . . ATLANTIC M.
virginia'num . . . . . . VIRGINIA M.

PYCNAN'THUS . . . . . PYCNANTHUS
kom'bo . . . . AKOMU P.

PYCNOSTA'CHYS
daw'ei
urticifo'lia

PYGMYWEED . . . . **Tillaea**
COMMON P. . . . . . . **T. aquatica**
DRUMMOND P. . . . . **T. drummondi**

PYINGADO, BURMA . . **Xylia xylocarpa**

PYNAER'TIA . . . . . . PYNAERTIA
occidenta'lis . . . . BODI P.

PYRACAN'THA . . . . . FIRETHORN
angustifo'lia (*Cotoneaster a.*) NARROWLEAF F.
atalantoi'des (*discolor; gibbsi* A. B. Jacks., *not* Rehd.)
coccin'ea (*Crataegus pyracantha*) SCARLET F.
—laland'i (*Crataegus l.*) . . LALAND F.
—pauciflo'ra . . . . SPARSE F.
crenato-serra'ta (*P. crenulata yunnanensis; gibbsi* Rehd., *not* A. B. Jacks.; *yunnanensis*)
¢CHINESE. HV.
crenula'ta (*Cotoneaster c.; Crataegus c.*) NEPAL F.
—fla'va . . . . YELLOW N.F.
—kansuen'sis . . . . . . KANSU F.
—rogersia'na (*P. c. aurantiaca*) ROGERS F.
—serrula'ta
—yunnanen'sis . . **P. crenato-serrata**
discol'or . . . . **P. atalantoides**
gibbs'i A. B. Jacks. . . **P. atalantoides**
gibbs'i Rehd. . . . **P. crenato-serrata**
koidzu'mi (*formosana*) . . FORMOSA F.
yunnanen'sis . . . **P. crenato-serrata**

∞ **PYRACOM'ELES** (*OSTEOMELES* × *PYRACANTHA*)
∞ **vilmori'ni** (*O. subrotunda* × *P. crenata-serrata*)
The cultivated shrub is presumably a clon of this cross.

PYRENOGLY'PHIS . . . **BACTRIS**
See **PALM GENERA.**

PYRE'THRUM **CHRYSANTHEMUM**

Pyrethrum . . . . . Chrysanthemum
Caucasian P. . . . . C. marschalli
Dalmatian P. . . C. cinerariaefolium
Florists P. . . . . . C. coccineum

PYRO'LA |w . . . . Pyrola
america'na . . . . . American P.
aphyl'la . . . . Leafless P.
asarifo'lia . . . . Alpine P.
—incarna'ta (*P. uliginosa*)

The nomenclatural relationship of P. asarifolia, P. a. incarnata, and P. uliginosa is a moot question among botanists. Some recognize all three names as valid; some recognize only asarifolia (the oldest name); others hold to the opinion shown here that var. incarnata is good but that uliginosa is a synonym of it.

chloran'tha . . . . Green P.
denta'ta . . . . Toothleaf P.
ellip'tica . . . . . . Waxflower P.
mi'nor . . . . Snowline P.
pic'ta . . . . Whitevein P.
renifo'lia . . . . . Kidneyleaf P.
rotundifo'lia (*bracteata; uliginosa*)
European P.
secun'da . . . . . . Sidebells P.
uligino'sa . . . P. asarifolia incarnata
uniflo'ra . . . . Moneses u.

Pyrola . . . . Pyrola
Alpine P. . . . . . . P. asarifolia
American P.. . . . . . P. americana
European P. . . . . P. rotundifolia
Green P. . . . . P. chlorantha
Kidneyleaf P. . . . . . . P. renifolia
Leafless P. . . . . P. aphylla
Sidebells P. . . . . P. secunda
Snowline P.. . . . . P. minor
Toothleaf P. . . . . P. dentata
Waxflower P. . . . . P. elliptica
Whitevein P. . . . . P. picta

PYROLIR'ION . . . . . Flamelily
Regarded by some botanists as a synonym of Zephyranthes.

au'reum (*Zephyranthes aurea*)
Golden F.

×**PYRO'NIA** (*CYDONIA* × and + *PYRUS*) . . . . Quinpear
+daniel'i (*C. oblonga* + *P. communis*)
Daniel Q.
Graft hybrid.
×veitch'i (*C. oblonga* × *P. communis*)
Veitch Q.
₵—luxemburgia'na . ₵Luxemburg Q.

PYROSTE'GIA . . . . . **BIGNONIA**

PYRRHOCAC'TUS (*CHILENIA*)
See **CACTUS GENERA.**

PYRROCO'MA . . . **APLOPAPPUS**

PYRULA'RIA . . . . Oilnut
pu'bera . . . . Allegany O.

PY'RUS |w . . . . Pear
For varieties of Pear cultivated for their fruit see **FRUIT AND EDIBLE NUT NAMES.**

america'na . . . . Sorbus a.
amygdalifor'mis . . . . Almond P.
angustifo'lia . . . . Malus a.
arbutifo'lia . . . . Aronia a.
atrosanguin'ea . . . . . . ∞Malus a.
aucupa'ria . . . . Sorbus a.
bacca'ta . . . . Malus b.
betulaefo'lia . . . . . Birchleaf P.
bractea'ta . . . . Malus b.

PYRUS, continued

bretschnei'deri . Bretschneider Pear
callerya'na . . . . Callery P.
—fauri'ei . . . . . . Korean C.P.
—tomentel'la . . Woollytwig C.P.
caloneu'ra . . . . Sorbus c.
commu'nis |w . . . . . Common P.
—corda'ta (*P. cordata*)
corona'ria . . . . Malus c.
∞*dawsonia'na* . . . . . . ∞Malus d.
delavay'i . . . . Docynia d.
dis'color . . . . Sorbus d.
diversifo'lia . . . . . . Malus fusca
elaeagrifo'lia . . . . . . Oleaster P.
florenti'na . . . . Malus f.
floribun'da Kirchn., *not* Lindl. Malus f.
∞—*arnoldia'na* . . . . . . ∞Malus a.
folg'neri . . . . Sorbus f.
formosa'na . . . . Malus f.
fus'ca . . . . Malus f.
glabra'ta . . . . Malus g.
glauces'cens . . . . Malus g.
hallia'na . . . . Malus h.
heterophyl'la . . . . P. regeli
hondoen'sis . . . . P. ussuriensis h.
ioen'sis . . . . Malus i.
japon'ica Sims Chaenomeles lagenaria
japon'ica Thunb. . . Chaenomeles j.
kansuen'sis . . . . Malus k.
kawaka'mi . . . . Evergreen P.
lagena'ria . . . . . . Chaenomeles l.
lancifo'lia . . . . Malus l.
∞lecon'tei (*communis* × *pyrifolia*)
∞Leconte P.
lon'gipes
ma'lus . . . . Malus pumila
maul'ei . . . Chaenomeles japonica
∞michaux'i (*amygdaliformis* × *nivalis*)
∞Michaux P.
∞*microma'lus* . . . . . . ∞Malus m.
miyabe'i . . . . . . Sorbus alnifolia
ni'gra . . . . . . Aronia melanocarpa
niv'alis . . . . Snow P.
ovoid'ea . . . . . . P. ussuriensis o.
pash'ia . . . . Pashi P.
phaeocar'pa . . . . Dusky P.
—globo'sa . . . . Globe D.P.
platycar'pa . . . . Malus p.
pratt'i . . . . Malus p.
prunifo'lia . . . . Malus p.
—*rink'i* . . . . Malus p. r.
pulcher'rima . . . . . Malus floribunda
∞—*scheideck'eri* . . . . . ∞Malus s.
pyrifo'lia (*serotina*) . . . . . Sand P.
re'geli (*heterophylla*)
rivula'ris . . . . Malus fusca
salicifo'lia . . . . Willowleaf P.
sambucifo'lia . . . . Sorbus s.
sar'genti . . . . Malus s.
serot'ina . . . . P. pyrifolia
serrula'ta
sie'boldi . . . . Malus s.
si'moni . . . . P. ussuriensis ovoidea
sor'bus . . . . Sorbus domestica
∞*soulard'i* . . . . ∞Malus s.
spectab'ilis . . . . Malus s.
theif'era . . . . Malus hupehensis
tianshan'ica . . . . Sorbus t.
torin'go . . . . Malus sieboldi
toringoi'des . . . . Malus t.
tormina'lis . . . . Sorbus t.
transito'ria . . . . Malus t.
triloba'ta . . . . Malus t.
tschonosk'i . . . . Malus t.
ussurien'sis . . . . . . Ussurian P.
—hondoen'sis (*P. hondoensis*)
Hondo P.

PYRUS, continued

ussurien'sis ovoid'ea (*P. ovoidea; P. simoni*) . . Ovoid Ussurian Pear
vilmori'ni . . . . Sorbus v.
yunnanen'sis . . . . Malus y.
∞*zu'mi* . . . . ∞Malus z.

PYXIDAN'THERA . . . . Pyxiemoss
barbula'ta . . . . Sand P.
brevifo'lia

Pyxiemoss . . . . Pyxidanthera
Sand P. . . . . P. barbulata

Quackgrass . . . . Agropyron repens
False Q. . . . . . A. pseudorepens
Stiffleaf Q.. . . . . A. pungens

Quailbush . . . . . . Saltbush, Big:
Atriplex lentiformis

Quakinggrass . . . . Briza
Big Q. . . . . B. maxima
Little Q. . . . . B. minor
Perennial Q. . . . . B. media

QUAMA'SIA . . . . . . **CAMASSIA**

QUAMOCLID'ION . . . **MIRABILIS**

QUAM'OCLIT (*MINA*) |w . Starglory
coccin'ea (*Ipomoea c.*) |w . Scarlet S.
—*penna'ta* . . . . Q. sloteri
—hederifo'lia (*Ipomoea h.; Mina sanguinea*) . . . . Ivy S.
loba'ta (*Mina l.*) . . . . . Crimson S.
penna'ta (*Ipomoea quamoclit*) |w
Cypressvine S.
The specific name is frequently misspelled pinnata.
—al'ba . . . . White C.S.
slo'teri (*Q. coccinea pennata*)
Cardinal S.

Quandongnut . . . . . . Spindletree, Quandongnut: Fusanus acuminatus

Quartervine . . . . Crossvine:
Bignonia capreolata

QUAS'SIA . . . . Quassia
ama'ra . . . . Surinam Q.

Quassiawood . . . . Picrasma
India Q.. . . . . . . P. quassioides
Jamaica Q. . . . . P. excelsa

QUEBRA'CHIA . . . . **SCHINOPSIS**

Queenlily . . . . Phaedranassa
Andes Q. . . . . P. chloracra
Colombia Q. . . . . P. lehmanni
CostaRica Q. . . . . P. carmioli

Queen-of-Sheba . . . Podranea brycei

Queenofthenight
Selenicereus grandiflorus

Queenpalm
Arecastrum; A. romanzoffianum
Robust Q. . . . . A. r. australe

QUER'CUS |w . . . . Oak
Oaks frequently hybridize in nature. With about nine exceptions, all the crosses mentioned below are natural, fairly constant hybrids. Of the (at least largely) artificial polybrids (∞) listed, perhaps only clones are in actual cultivation.

acu'ta . . . Japanese Evergreen O.
acutis'sima (*serrata* Sieb. & Zucc., *not* Thunb.) . . . . Sawtooth O.
ae'gilops . . . . Q. macrolepis
agrifo'lia |w . . . California Live O.
—frutes'cens . . . . . Dwarf C.L.O.
al'ba |w . . . . White O.
—latilo'ba
—repan'da . . . . Louisiana W.O.

QUERCUS, continued
alien'a . . . . ORIENTAL WHITE OAK
—acuteserra'ta
alnifo'lia . . . CYPRIAN GOLDEN O.
ambig'ua . . . . **Q. borealis**
×**an'drewsi** (*?macrocarpa* × *?undulata*) ANDREWS O.
annula'ta Buckl., *not* Hook. f., *nor* Korth. . . . . **Q. breviloba**
aquat'ica . . . . **Q. nigra**
aquifolioi'des . . . **Q. semecarpifolia**
arizo'nica . . . . ARIZONA WHITE O.
∞**arkansa'na** (*marilandica* × *nigra; ∞sterilis*) . . . . ∞ARKANSAS O.
—caput-riv'uli
×**ash'ei** (*catesbaei* × *cinerea*) . ASHE O.
×**atlant'ica** (*?cinerea* × *?laurifolia*) ALBEMARLE O.
∞**audleyen'sis** (*ilex* × *petraea*) ∞AUDLEY O.
austri'na . . . . BLUFF O.
ballo'ta . . . . . **Q. ilex rotundifolia**
bambusaefo'lia . . . **Q. myrsinaefolia**
banister'i . . . . **Q. ilicifolia**
bar'oni . . . . BARON O.
×**bead'lei** (*alba* × *prinus*) . BEADLE O.
×**beaumontia'na** (*falcata* × *obtusa*) BEAUMONT O.
×**bebbia'na** (*alba* × *macrocarpa*) BEBB O.
∞**ben'deri** (*borealis maxima* × *coccinea*) ∞BENDER O.
bi'color (*platanoides*) [W] SWAMP WHITE O.
×**blufftonen'sis** (*falcata* × *laevis*) BLUFFTON O.
borea'lis (*ambigua; Q. rubra a.*) NORTHERN RED O.
—max'ima (*Q. rubra* Du Roi, *not* L.) [W] EASTERN R.O.
brevifo'lia . . . . **Q. cinerea**
brevilo'ba (*annulata* Buckl., *not* Hook. f., *nor* Korth.) . . . . BIGELOW O.
brew'eri . . . . **Q. oerstediana**
×**brit'toni** (*ilicifolia* × *marilandica*) BRITTON O.
×**bush'i** (*marilandica* × *velutina*) BUSHES O.
×**by'arsi** (*?macrocarpa* × *?prinus*) COVINGTON O.
×**cadu'ca** (*cinerea* × *nigra*)
callipri'nos. . . . . . PALESTINE O.
canarien'sis (*Q. lusitanica mirbecki; mirbecki*) . . . . CANARY O.
×**carolinen'sis** (*cinerea* × *marilandica*) CAROLINA O.
castaneaefo'lia . . CHESTNUTLEAF O.
—inca'na
cates'baei . . . . **Q. laevis**
cer'ris. . . . EUROPEAN TURKEY O.
—ambrozya'na
—austri'aca . . . . . AUSTRIAN T.O.
—lacinia'ta . . . . . CUTLEAF T.O.
—pen'dula. . . . . WEEPING T.O.
₵VARIEGATED (*variegata*) HV. Q. cerris
chap'mani . . . . . . CHAPMAN O.
chrysol'epis . . . . CANYON LIVE O. (*Goldencup O.*)
—na'na . . . . DWARF C.L.O.
—pal'meri . . . . **Q. palmeri**
—vaccinifo'lia . . . . **Q. vaccinifolia**
cine'rea (*brevifolia*) . . BLUEJACK O.
—dentato-loba'ta . . . . LOBED B.O.
cleistocar'pa . **Lithocarpus cleistocarpus**
coccif'era . . . . KERMES O.
coccin'ea [W] . . . . . SCARLET O.
—splen'dens . . . . KNAPHILL S.O.
—tubercula'ta . . . . SARGENT S.O.

QUERCUS, continued
×**cocks'i** (*obtusa* × *velutina*) . COCKS OAK
×*coloraden'sis* Ashe, *not* Lesq. (*?macrocarpa* × *?virginiana*) COLORADORIVER O.

This name is rendered untenable by the older O. coloradensis Lesq., a fossil species.

×**comp'tonae** (*lyrata* × *virginiana*) COMPTON O.
concord'ia . . . . **Q. robur** ₵GOLDEN
confer'ta . . . . **Q. frainetto**
cor'nea . . . . **Lithocarpus corneus**
cris'pula . **Q. mongolica grosseserrata**
cuspida'ta . . . . **Castanopsis c.**
×**deam'i** (*alba* × *muhlenbergi*) DEAM O.
×**demare'i** . . . . DEMAREE O.
densiflo'ra . . **Lithocarpus densiflorus**
denta'ta . . . . DAIMYO O.

The name Q. dentata is often misapplied to Q. glandulifera.

—pinnatif'ida Hort.. . . . PLUME D.O.
digita'ta . . . . **Q. falcata**
doug'lasi . . . . BLUE O.
×**du'bia**

The parentage of this hybrid Oak, reported from six southeastern States, is dubious. Q. cinerea, laurifolia, phellos, and possibly velutina are suspected to be among its antecedents.

dumo'sa [W] . . CALIFORNIA SCRUB O.
—alvordia'na . . . . . ALVORD O.
—bulla'ta
durand'i. . . . . DURAND O.
dura'ta . . . . LEATHER O.
ehrenberg'i . . . . . EHRENBERG O.
ellipsoida'lis . . . NORTHERN PIN O.
emo'ryi . . . . EMORY O.
engelmann'i . . . . . ENGELMANN O.
engleria'na . . . . . . ENGLER O.
×**exac'ta** (*imbricaria* × *palustris*)

A natural hybrid.

fa'bri
falca'ta (*digitata; rubra* L., *not* Du-Roi) [W] . . . . SOUTHERN RED O. (*Spanish O.*)
—leucophyl'la . . . CHERRYBARK O.
—pagodaefo'lia (*Q. rubra p.*) SWAMP RED O.
—trilo'ba . . . . . THREELOBE R.O.
farnet'to . . . . **Q. frainetto**
×**fax'oni** (*alba* × *prinoides*) . FAXON O.

A natural hybrid.

fend'leri . . . . FENDLER O.
×**fernow'i** (*alba* × *stellata*) . FERNOW O.

A natural hybrid.

ferrugin'ea . . . . . . **Q. marilandica**
frainet'to (*conferta; farnetto; hungarica; pannonica* Hort.) . . . ITALIAN O.
frutico'sa
gam'beli [W] . . . . . . GAMBEL O.
garrya'na [W] . . . OREGON WHITE O.
—brew'eri . . . . **Q. oerstediana**
—semo'ta . . . . . . KAWEAH W.O.
gemina'ta . . . . . . **Q. virginiana g.**
georgia'na . . . . GEORGIA O.
×**gif'fordi** (*?ilicifolia* × *?phellos*) GIFFORD O.
gillia'na
gla'ber . . . . **Lithocarpus g.**
glandulif'era (*serrata* Thunb., *not* Auth.) GLANDBEARING O.
glau'ca . . . . . BLUE JAPANESE O.
grae'ca . . . . **Q. macrolepis**
graves'i (*Q. texana chesosensis; Q. t. stellipila*) . . . . GRAVES O.

QUERCUS, continued
gri'sea . . . . GRAY OAK
grosseserra'ta . . . . **Q. mongolica g.**
×**guadelupen'sis** (*macrocarpa* × *stellata*) GUADALOUPE O.
gunniso'ni . . . . GUNNISON O.
haas'
×**harbiso'ni** (*?stellata margaretta* × *?virginiana geminata*) . . . HARBISON O.

Only one wild tree of this apparent hybrid seems to be known.

hartwissia'na
×**hastings'i** (*marilandica* × *texana*) HASTINGS O.
hav'ardi . . . . HAVARD O.
×*haw'kinsi* . ×**Q. porteri** ₵HAWKINS
hen'ryi . . . . HENRY O.
×**heterophyl'la** (*borealis maxima* × *phellos*) . . . . BARTRAM O.
×**hick'eli** (*pontica* × *robur*) . HICKEL O.
×**hill'i** (*macrocarpa* × *muhlenbergi*) HILLS O.
∞**hispan'ica** (*cerris* × *suber*) ∞HISPANIA O.

This polybrid is reported to occur in nature also, in southern Europe.

₵BROADLEAF (*latifolia*) HV.
₵CURLYLEAF (*crispa*)
₵DEEPLOBE (*heterophylla*)
₵FULHAM (*dentata; lucombeana fulhamensis*)
₵LUCOMBE (*exoniensis; lucombeana*)
₵SMALL (*diversifolia*)

hunga'rica . . . . **Q. frainetto**
hy'brida Bechst. . . . . ∞**Q. rosacea**
hy'brida (Mx.) Small . . . **Q. obtusa**
hypoleu'ca [W] . . . . SILVERLEAF O.
iber'ica . . . . IBERIAN O.
i'lex . . . . HOLLY O.
—angustifo'lia . . NARROWLEAF H.O.
—rotundifo'lia (*Q. ballota*) ROUNDLEAF H.O.
₵CURLLEAF (*crispa*) HV. Q. ilex
₵FORD (*fordi*)
₵GRAMUNTIA
₵LITTLELEAF (*microphylla*)
ilicifo'lia (*banisteri*) [W]. . . SCRUB O.
imbrica'ria. . . . . . . SHINGLE O.
inaequa'lis
inca'na
iner'mis
infecto'ria . . . . ALEPPO O.
×**jackia'na** (*alba* × *bicolor*). . JACKS O.
∞**jolonen'sis** (*douglasi* × *lobata*)
kel'loggi . . . . CALIFORNIA BLACK O.
×**kewen'sis** (*cerris* × *wislizeni*) KEW O.
la'ceyi . . . . LACEY O.
lae'vis (*catesbaei*) . . . . TURKEY O.
lamello'sa
lanugino'sa . . . . . **Q. pubescens**
laurifo'lia [W] . . . . . . LAUREL O.
—tridenta'ta . . . . ORLANDO L.O.
×**lea'na** (*imbricaria* × *velutina*) . LEA O.
leioder'mis . . . . SMOOTHBARK O.
leptophyl'la . . . . . . SOCORRO O.
liaotungen'sis
liban'i. . . . . LEBANON O.
linea'ta
loba'ta [W] . . . CALIFORNIA WHITE O. (*Valley O.*)
×**low'elli** (*?borealis* × *?ilicifolia*) LOWELL O.

Apparently known from one wild tree only.

lucombea'na ∞**Q. hispanica** ₵LUCOMBE
—fulhamen'sis . . . . ∞**Q. hispanica** ₵FULHAM

QUERCUS, continued

×**ludovicia'na** (*falcata* × *phellos*; ×*subfalcata*) . . . . . . St.Landry Oak
¢Littleleaf (*microcarpa; phellos m.; subfalcata m.*) hv.
lusitan'ica . . . . . Portuguese O.
—mirbeck'i . . . . . **Q. canariensis**
lyra'ta |w . . . . Overcup O.
macedo'nica . . . . **Q. trojana**
×**macnabia'na** (*durandi* × *stellata*) MacNab O.
macran'thera
macrocar'pa . . . . Bur O.
macrole'pis (*aegilops; graeca*) Valonia O.
marilan'dica (*ferruginea; nigra* Wangh., *not* L.) |w . . . . . Blackjack O.
—ash'ei . . . . Ashe B.O.
×**mellichamp'i** (*?laevis* × *?laurifolia*) Mellichamp O.
michaux'i . . . . **Q. prinus**
mi'nor . . . . **Q. stellata**
mirbeck'i . . . . . . **Q. canariensis**
mohria'na . . . . Mohr O.
mongol'ica . . . . . . Mongolian O.
—grosseserra'ta (*Q. crispula; Q. grosseserrata*) . . . Shallowcup M.O.
monta'na (*prinus* Engelm., *not* L.) |w Chestnut O.
×**more'hus** (*kelloggi* × *wislizeni*) Oracle O.
muhlenberg'i . . . . Chinkapin O.
—bray'i . . . . Bray O.
×**mutab'ilis** (*palustris* × *shumardi schnecki*)
myrsinaefo'lia (*bambusaefolia; vibreyana*)
myrtifo'lia . . . . Myrtle O.
×**neopal'meri** (*nigra* × *shumardi*)
Apparently known from one wild tree only.
ni'gra (*aquatica*) |w . . . . Water O.
—tridentif'era . . . . . Trident O.
ni'gra Wangh., *not* L. . **Q. marilandica**
novomexica'na (*nitescens*) NewMexican O.
nutt'alli . . . . Nuttall O.
oblongifo'lia . . . Mexican Blue O.
obtu'sa (*hybrida* (Mx.) Small, *not* Bechst.; *rhombica*) Diamondleaf O.
—obovatifo'lia . . . . Broadtip D.O.
obtusa'ta
obtusilo'ba . . . . **Q. stellata**
occidenta'lis . . . . . . **Q. suber o.**
oerstedia'na (*breweri; Q. garryana b.*) Brewer O.
×**organen'sis** (*?arizonica* × *?grisea*) OrganMountains O.
×**oviedoen'sis** (*?cinerea* × *?myrtifolia*) Oviedo O.
oxyo'don
×**palaeolithic'ola** (*ellipsoidalis* × *velutina*)
pal'meri (*Q. chrysolepis p.*) . Palmer O.
palus'tris |w . . . . Pin O.
pannon'ica Hort. . . . . **Q. frainetto**
pectina'ta . . **Q. robur** ¢Combleaf
peduncula'ta . . . . **Q. robur**
—dauves'sei . . . **Q. robur** ¢Weeping
pedunculiflo'ra
petrae'a (*sessiliflora*) . . Durmast O.
¢Cutleaf (*insecata; laciniata*) hv.
¢Medlar (*mespilifolia*)
¢Purple (*purpurea*)
¢Weeping (*pendula*)
phel'los |w . . . . Willow O.
phillyraeoi'des
platanoi'des . . . . **Q. bicolor**

QUERCUS, continued

×**podophyl'la** (*cinerea* × *velutina*)
polycar'pa
pon'tica . . . . Pontic Oak
×**por'teri** (*borealis maxima* × *velutina*) Porter O.
¢Hawkins (×*Q. hawkinsi*)
Apparently known from a single tree only.
pric'ei . . . . Price O.
prinoi'des . . . Dwarf Chinkapin O.
—rufes'cens
pri'nus (*michauxi*) |w . . . . Swamp Chestnut O. (*Basket O.*)
pri'nus Engelm., *not* L. . **Q. montana**
pubes'cens (*lanuginosa*) Pubescent O.
¢Curlleaf (*crispata*) hv.
¢Cutleaf (*pinnatifida*)
pyrena'ica (*tauzin; toza*) Pyrenees O.
¢Weeping (*pendula*) hv.
×**reh'deri** (*ilicifolia* × *velutina*) Rehder O.
reticula'ta . . . . Netleaf O.
rhom'bica . . . . **Q. obtusa**
×**rich'teri** (*borealis maxima* × *palustris*) Richter O.
A natural hybrid but has also been artificially produced and propagated in Europe.
×**rob'binsi** (*coccinea* × *ilicifolia*) Robbins O.
ro'bur (*pedunculata*) . . English O.
¢Combleaf (*pectinata; Q. pectinata*) hv.
¢Dauvesse (*dauvessei*)
¢Fernleaf (*filicifolia*)
¢Golden (*concordia; Q. concordia*)
¢Lobeless (*holophylla*)
¢Longleaf (*heterophylla*)
¢Purple (*atropurpurea*)
¢Pyramidal (*fastigiata*)
¢Royal (*purpurascens*)
¢Spleenwort (*aspleniifolia*)
¢Variegated (*variegata*)
¢Weeping (*pedunculata dauvessei; pendula*)
∞**rosa'cea** (*petraea* × *robur; hybrida* Bechst., *not* (Mx.) Small)
This very variable cultivated polybrid is said to occur occasionally in Europe in nature.
ru'bra . . . . **Q. falcata**
ru'bra Du Roi, *not* L. **Q. borealis maxima**
—ambig'ua . . . . . . **Q. borealis**
—pagodaefo'lia . . . . . **Q. falcata p.**
×**rud'kini** (*marilandica* × *phellos*) Rudkin O.
×**runcina'ta** (*borealis maxima* × *imbricaria*) . . . . Bottom O.
sadleria'na . . . . Sadler O.
∞**sar'genti** (*montana* × *robur*) ∞Sargent O.
×**saul'i** (*alba* × *montana*) . . . Saul O.
∞**schochia'na** (*palustris* × *phellos*)
×**schuet'tei** (*bicolor* × *macrocarpa*)
semecarpifo'lia (*aquifolioides*)
semiserra'ta
serra'ta Carruthers . . . **Q. variabilis**
serra'ta Sieb. & Zucc. . **Q. acutissima**
serra'ta Thunb. . . . . **Q. glandulifera**
sessiliflo'ra . . . . **Q. petraea**
shumard'i (*Q. texana s.*) . Shumard O.
—acerifo'lia . . . . Mapleleaf S.O.
—schneck'i (*Q. schnecki*) Schneck O.
×**small'i** (*georgiana* × *marilandica*) Smalls O.

QUERCUS, continued

stella'ta (*minor; obtusiloba*) . Post Oak
—anom'ala
—araneo'sa . . . . Sand P.O.
The original spelling, araniosa, is, Prof. Rehder states, to be regarded as a misprint or slip of the pen.
—attenua'ta . . . . . Arkansas P.O.
—boyn'toni . . . . . Boynton P.O.
—margaret'ta . . . . . Dwarf P.O.
—parvilo'ba . . . . Brownwood P.O.
—rufes'cens . . . . . . Ruddy P.O.
—sim'ilis . . . . Bayou P.O.
∞*ster'ilis* . . . . ∞ **Q. arkansana**
su'ber . . . . Cork O.
—occidenta'lis (*Q. occidentalis*) Biennial C.O.
×*subfalca'ta* . . . . ×**Q. ludoviciana**
×**subinte'gra** (*cinerea* × *falcata*)
submol'lis . . . . **Q. utahensis**
×*sud'worthi* . . . ×**Q. willdenowiana**
tau'zin . . . . **Q. pyrenaica**
texa'na . . . . Texas O.
—chesosen'sis . . . . . . **Q. gravesi**
—shumard'i . . . . **Q. shumardi**
—stellip'ila . . . . **Q. gravesi**
tincto'ria . . . . **Q. velutina**
tomentel'la . . . . . . Island Live O.
tou'meyi . . . . Toumey O.
to'za . . . . **Q. pyrenaica**
×**tridenta'ta** (*imbricaria* × *marilandica*) St.Louis O.
troja'na (*macedonica*) Macedonian O.
turbinel'la . . . . . . Shrub Live O.
∞**tur'neri** (*ilex?* × *robur*) ∞Turners O.
¢Evergreen (*aizoon; austriaca sempervirens; pseudoturneri*) hv.
undula'ta |w . . . . . . Wavyleaf O.
utahen'sis (*submollis*) |w Utah White O.
vaccinifo'lia (*Q. chrysolepis v.*) Huckleberry O.
variab'ilis (*serrata* Carruthers, *not* Thunb.) . . . . Oriental O.
vaseya'na . . . . Vasey O.
velut'ina (*tinctoria*) |w . . . Black O.
—missourien'sis . . . Missouri B.O.
¢Champion (*albertsi; rubrifolia*) hv.
Q. velutina
×**venulo'sa** (*?arkansana caput-rivuli* × *?cinerea*) . . . . . . Okaloosa O.
vibreya'na . . . . . **Q. myrsinaefolia**
virgilia'na
virginia'na (*virens*) |w . . . . Live O.
—exim'ia . . . . . Louisiana L.O.
—gemina'ta (*Q. geminata*) . Sand L.O.
—macrophyl'la . . . Pleasanton L.O.
—vires'cens . . . . . Seminole L.O.
vree'landi . . . . . . Vreeland O.
×**walteria'na** (*?laevis* × *?nigra*) Walter O.
wil'coxi . . . . Wilcox O.
Prof. Rehder is inclined to think that Q. wilcoxi may prove to be a var. or form or even synonymous with Q. palmeri. However, it seems desirable, pending further field studies at least, to keep the two distinct.
×**willdenowia'na** (*falcata* × *velutina*; ×*sudworthi*) . . . . Willdenow O.
wislize'ni . . . . Interior Live O.
—frutes'cens

QUIABENT'IA . . . . . Quiabentia
See **CACTUS GENERA.**

Quickweed . . . . **Galinsoga**
Fringed Q. . . . . **G. ciliata**
Littleflower Q. . . . **G. parviflora**

QUILA . . . . **Chusquea quila**

QUILLA'JA . . . . . . SOAPBARKTREE
sapona'ria . . . . . . SOAPBARKTREE

QUILLWORT . . . . **Isoetes**
BOLANDER Q. . . . . **I. bolanderi**
BRAUNS Q. . . . . **I. brauni**
EATONS Q. . . . . **I. eatoni**
ENGELMANN Q. . . . . **I. engelmanni**
FLETT Q. . . . . **I. fletti**
HOWELL Q. . . . . **I. howelli**
NUTTALL Q. . . . . **I. nuttalli**
PIPER Q. . . . . **I. piperi**
TUCKERMAN Q. . . . . **I. tuckermani**

QUINCE . . . . **Cydonia**
COMMON Q. . . . . **C. oblonga**

QUIN'CULA |w . . CHINESELANTERN
loba'ta (*Physalis l.*) |w . . PLAINS C.

QUINOA . . . . . **Chenopodium quinoa**

QUINPEAR . . . . **×Pyronia**
DANIEL Q. . . . . **+P. danieli**
₵LUXEMBURG Q.
₵P. veitchi luxemburgiana
VEITCH Q. . . . . **×P. veitchi**

QUINTIN'IA . . . . QUINTINIA
acutifo'lia . . . . . CRINKLELEAF Q.
serra'ta . . . . . . NEWZEALAND Q.

QUISQUA'LIS . . . . . . QUISQUALIS
in'dica . . . . . RANGOONCREEPER

RABBITBRUSH . . . . **Chrysothamnus**
ALKALI R. . . . . **C. albidus**
DESERT R. . . . . . . **C. paniculatus**
DOUGLAS R. . . . . . **C. viscidiflorus**
DOWNY R. . . . . **C. puberulus**
DWARF R. . . . . **C. depressus**
FLAXLEAF R. . . . . **C. linifolius**
GREENES R. . . . . **C. greenei**
GREENPLUME R. . . . **C. graveolens**
HOWARD R. . . . . **C. howardi**
LANCELEAF R. . . . . **C. lanceolatus**
LOW DOUGLAS R.
C. viscidiflorus pumilus
LOW R. . . . . **C. humilis**
NEVADA R. . . . . . . **C. nevadensis**
PARRY R. . . . . **C. parryi**
PINENEEDLE R. . . . . **C. pinifolius**
ROUNDLEAF R. . . . . **C. teretifolius**
RUBBER R. . . . . . . **C. nauseosus**
SAWTOOTH DOUGLAS R.
C. viscidiflorus serrulatus
SMALL R. . . . . . . **C. stenophyllus**
SOUTHWEST R. . . . . . **C. pulchellus**
TALL R. . . . . **C. speciosus**
TWISTLEAF DOUGLAS R.
C. viscidiflorus tortifolius

Rabbitfootgrass POLYPOGON, RABBITFOOT: **Polypogon monspeliensis**

Rabbittailgrass . . . . . . HARESTAIL: **Lagurus ovatus**

RABIE'A . **MESEMBRYANTHEMUM**
See **SUCCULENTS.**

RADERMACH'ERA
fen'icis

RADERMACH'IA . . . ASIABELLTREE
pentan'dra (*Oroxylum flavum*) GRAND A.
sin'ica (*Stereospermum sinicum*) GLORY A.

RADIC'ULA . . . . . . **RORIPPA**

RADISH . . . . **Raphanus**
CHINESE R. . **R. sativus longipinnatus**
GARDEN R. . . . . **R. sativus**

RADISH, continued
RATTAIL R. . **Raphanus sativus caudatus**
WILD R. . . . . **R. raphanistrum**

RAFFIAPALM . . . . **Raphia**
AMERICAN R. . . . . . . **R. taedigera**
CONGO R. . . . . **R. sese**
FERNANDOPO R. . . . **R. wendlandi**
GIANT R. . . . . **R. gigantea**
IVORYCOAST R. . . . . . . **R. hookeri**
LIBERIAN R. . . . . **R. palma-pinus**
MADAGASCAR R. . . . . **R. ruffia**
WINE R. . . . . **R. vinifera**

RAFFLE'SIA . . . . MONSTERFLOWER
arnold'i . . . . SUMATRA M.
Said to be the largest flower in the world.

RAGGEDROBIN . . . **Lychnis floscuculi**

RAGIMILLET . . . . **Eleusine coracana**

RAGWEED . . . . **Ambrosia**
BLOOD R. . . . . **A. aptera**
COMMON R. . . . **A. artemisiaefolia**
DWARF R. . . . . **A. pumila**
GIANT R. . . . . **A. trifida**
LANCELEAF R. . . . . . **A. bidentata**
WESTERN R. . . . . . **A. psilostachya**

RAIMAN'NIA . . . . **OENOTHERA**

RAINLILY . . . . **Cooperia**
EVENINGSTAR R. . . . **C. drummondi**
GREENTIP E. R. . . **C. d. chlorosolen**
KANSAS R. . . . . **C. kansensis**
REDTINGE R. . . . . . **C. pedunculata**
SMALLS R. . . . . **C. smalli**
TRAUB R. . . . . **C. traubi**
WHITE R. . . . . **C. albicans**

RAINTREE . . . . **Brunfelsia**
BLUERING BRAZIL R.
B. calycina macrantha
BRAZIL R. . . . . **B. calycina**
BROADLEAF R. . . . . **B. latifolia**
BIGLEAF R. . . . . . . **B. macrophylla**
FADING BRAZIL R. **B. calycina eximia**
FRANCISCAN R. . . . . . **B. americana**
MANACA R. . . . . **B. hopeana**
MIRE R. . . . **B. hydrangeaeformis**
WHITEEYE BRAZIL R.
B. calycina floribunda

RAISIN
See **FRUIT AND EDIBLE NUT NAMES.**

RAISINTREE . . . . **Hovenia**
JAPANESE R. . . . . **H. dulcis**

RAJA'NIA . . . . TUBERVINE
corda'ta (*pleioneura*) COCKSCOMBYAM T.
pleioneu'ra Bello, *not* Griseb.
Dioscorea pilosiuscula

RAMALI'NA . . . . RAMALINA
farina'cea . . . . MEALY R.
scopulo'rum . . . . IVORY R.

Ramboetan; Rambotang; Rambustan
RAMBUTAN: **Nephelium lappaceum**

RAMBUTAN . . . **Nephelium lappaceum**

RAMIE . . . . **Boehmeria nivea**
RHEA R. . . . . . . **B. n. tenacissima**

RAMO'NA . . . . **SALVIA**
grandiflo'ra . . . . . . **S. spathacea**

RAMON'DA . . . . RAMONDA
heldreich'i . . . . THESSALY R.
pyrena'ica . . . . ROSETTE R.
—al'ba . . . . WHITE R.R.

RAMONTCHI . . . . . **Flacourtia indica**

Ramps . . RAMSONS: **Allium ursinum;** LEEK, WILD: **A. tricoccum**

RAMSONS . . . . **Allium ursinum**

RAN'DIA . . . . RANDIA
dumeto'rum . . . . . . MALABAR R.
formo'sa
sinen'sis . . . . CHINESE R.

RANE'VEA (***RAVENEA; RAVENIA*** Benth. & Hook. f., *not* Vell) RANEVEA
See **PALM GENERA.**

RANGE PLANTS

AUTHORS' STATEMENT

Range plants, and particularly those of the Far West, cover 728,000,000 acres of range, or approximately one-third of the area of the United States, and comprise about 10,000 species of flowering plants in over 1,200 genera. The importance of these plants in the nation's economy is enormous. Not only is the range livestock industry, with all its social and economic implications, dependent on these plants, but they are most intimately associated with soil conservation, runoff and erosion, irrigation and hydroelectric power, agricultural crops, wildlife, timber reproduction and diseases, fire, recreation, and other vital phases of the national life. While this list is primarily of range interest, yet many hundreds of these plants have sufficient beauty or utility to attract, on an increasing scale, the interest of the ornamental and economic horticulturist and others concerned with introducing useful plants into cultivation. Some range plants are already important in the drug, gum, and latex trades; some of the fruits, nuts, and other edible plant products are prized by the white man as well as the Indian, and many merit, and are receiving, the attention of the professional pomologist; some of the native grasses are being introduced into cultivation and experimental effort is being made to improve them. Attention has very recently been directed to the native ranges of the Southeast, and detailed knowledge concerning these plants and their value is still largely lacking.

The list below includes the names of about 500 genera and 1,900 species and varieties of the more important range plants; to avoid unnecessary duplication grasses and poisonous plants are excluded, as these groups are treated in separate lists in this book. Conifers (except Junipers) are also omitted; they are frequently, in a broad sense, range plants as well, but in general, their outstanding value is for timber and their use as browse is ordinarily not desirable. Conifers, of course, appear in their proper alphabetical order in the body of this book. Most of the plants listed here are western, though a few of the more important Alaskan and Southeastern range plants are represented. The list has been compiled from various published and unpublished records of the U. S. Forest Service, including the "Range Plant Handbook" (Forest Service, 1937) and W. A. Dayton's "Important Western Browse Plants" (U. S. Department of Agriculture Misc. Pub. 101, 1931). See also **GRASS GENERA, POISONOUS PLANTS,** and **WEEDS.**

Our thanks are extended to Beryl O Schreiber of the California Forest and Range Experiment Station, for valuable criticism and suggestions.

W. A. DAYTON and DORIS W. HAYES
Forest Service, U. S. Department of Agriculture.

ABRO'NIA . . . . . SANDVERBENA

ABU'TILON . . . . . ABUTILON

ACA'CIA . . . . ACACIA
constric'ta . . . . MESCAT A.

RANGE PLANTS (ACACIA), continued
farnesia'na . . . . . Sweet Acacia
filicioi'des (*filicina*) . . Fernleaf A.
gregg'i . . . . Catclaw A.
lem'moni . . . . Lemmons A.
reticula'ta . . . . . . Netvein A.
suffrutes'cens

ACALY'PHA . . . . Copperleaf

ACAMPTOPAP'PUS sphaeroceph'alus . . . Rayless Goldenhead

A'CER (*NEGUNDO*) . . Maple
arizo'nicum . . . . . **A. negundo a.**
brachyp'terum . . **A. grandidentatum b.**
califor'nicum . . . . **A. negundo c.**
circina'tum . . . . Vine M.
gla'brum . . . RockyMountain M.
—doug'lasi (*A. douglasi*) Douglas R.M.
grandidenta'tum . . . . Bigtooth M.
—brachyp'terum (*A. brachypterum*) Southwestern B.M.
macrophyl'lum . . . . Bigleaf M.
negun'do . . . . Boxelder
—arizo'nicum (*A. arizonicum*) Arizona B.
—califor'nicum (*A. ca ifornicum*) California B.
—inte'rius (*A. interius*) . Inland B.

ACHILLE'A . . . . . . Yarrow
lanulo'sa (*A. millefolium l.*) Western Y.
—alpic'ola (*A. alpicola; A. subalpina*) Subalpine Y.

ACH'LYS triphyl'la Deerfoot Vanillaleaf

ACHYRACHAE'NA mol'lis Blowwives

AC'MISPON . . . . . **LOTUS**

Acomas'tylis turbina'ta **Geum turbinatum**

ACONI'TUM . . . . Monkshood
See also **POISONOUS PLANTS.**
columbia'num (*californicum*) Columbia M.

ACONOG'ONUM . **POLYGONUM**

Acrola'sia albicau'lis . **Mentzelia a.**

ACTAE'A . . . . . . Baneberry
argu'ta (*A. spicata a.*) . Western B.
viridiflo'ra . . . . Green B.

ACTINE'A (*HYMENOXYS; MACDOUGALIA; RYDBERGIA; TETRANEURIS*) Actinea
See also **POISONOUS PLANTS.**
acau'lis (*Tetraneuris a.*) Stemless A.
—arizo'nica (*Tetraneuris arizonica*) Arizona S.A.
—lanig'era (*Tetraneuris l.*) Woolly S.A.
—septentriona'lis (*Tetraneuris s.*) Northern S.A.
—sim'plex (*Tetraneuris s.*) Sagebrush S.A.
brandeg'ei (*Rydbergia b.*) Brandegee A.
grandiflo'ra (*Rydbergia g.*) Graylocks A.
linearifo'lia (*Tetraneuris l.*) Fineleaf A.
scapo'sa (*Tetraneuris s.*)
—linea'ris (*Tetraneuris l.*)

RANGE PLANTS, continued
AC'UAN . . . **DESMANTHUS**

ADE'LIA Michx., *not* L. **FORESTIERA**

ADENOCAU'LON bi'color American Adenocaulon

ADENOSTE'GIA **CORDYLANTHUS**

ADENOS'TOMA . . . . Chamise
fascicula'tum . . . Greasewood C.
sparsifo'lium . . . . . Redshank C.

ADOL'PHIA . . . . . Adolphia
califor'nica . . . . California A.
infes'ta . . . . Texas A.

AGAS'TACHE urticifo'lia Nettleleaf Gianthyssop

AGA'VE . . . . Agave
par'ryi . . . . Parry A.
utahen'sis . . . . Utah A.

AGO'SERIS . . . . . Agoseris
The name Mountaindandelion, accepted for species of Krigia, is often applied also to this genus.
arizo'nica . . . . Arizona A.
auranti'aca . . . . Orange A.
glau'ca . . . . Pale A.
—parviflo'ra . . Littleflower P.A.
grac'ilens . . . . Slender A.
—green'ei . . . . . Greenes S.A.
heterophyl'la (*major*) . . . Annual A.
pu'mila . . . . Low A.
purpu'rea . . . . Purple A.
scorzoneraefo'lia . . Scorzonera A.
taraxacifo'lia . . . . Dandelion A.

ALLENROL'FEA occidenta'lis Pickleweed

ALLIO'NIA (*WEDELIA; WEDELIELLA*) . . . . Allionia
incarna'ta (*Wedeliella i.*) Trailing A.

AL'LIUM . . . . Onion
acumina'tum . . . . Tapertip O.
brandeg'ei . . . . Brandegee O.
brevisty'lum . . . . Shortstyle O.
canaden'se . . . . . Canada Garlic
cer'nuum (*neomexicanum; recurvatum*) Nodding O.
falcifo'lium . . . . . Sickleleaf O.
fibril'lum . . . BlueMountains O.
gey'eri . . . . Geyer O.
nevaden'se . . . . Nevada O.
schoeno'prasum . . . . . . Chive
—sibir'icum (*A. sibiricum*) Siberian C.
serra'tum . . . . . . Serrate O.
tex'tile (*reticulatum*) . . Textile O.
tol'miei . . . . Tolmie O.
tribractea'tum . . . . Threebract O.
val'idum . . . . Pacific O.

ALLOCA'RYA **PLAGIOBOTHRYS**

AL'NUS . . . . Alder
inca'na . . . . Speckled A.
oblongifo'lia . . . NewMexican A.
ru'bra (*oregana*) . . . . . . Red A.
sinua'ta (*sitchensis*) . . . . Sitka A.
tenuifo'lia . . . . . . Thinleaf A.

ALSI'NE . . . . . **STELLARIA**

AMARAN'THUS . . . Amaranth
blitoi'des . . . . Prostrate A.
grae'cizans . . . . Tumbleweed A.
hy'bridus . . . . Slim A.

RANGE PLANTS (AMARANTHUS), con.
pow'elli . . . . . Powell Amaranth
retroflex'us . . . . Redroot A.
spino'sus . . . . Spiny A.

AMAREL'LA . . . . **GENTIANA**

AMBRO'SIA psilosta'chya Western Ragweed

AMELAN'CHIER . Serviceberry
alnifo'lia . . . . Saskatoon S.
flo'rida . . . . Pacific S.
oreoph'ila . . . . . . Mountain S.
polycar'pa . . . . Cluster S.
prunifo'lia (*rubescens*) . . Redbud S.
utahen'sis . . . . Utah S.

AMOR'PHA . . . . . Amorpha
califor'nica . . . . . California A.
canes'cens . . . . . . Leadplant A.
frutico'sa . . . . . . Indigobush A.
na'na (*microphylla*) Dwarfindigo A.

Amphiachy'ris dracunculoi'des **Gutierrezia d.**

AMSINCK'IA . . . . Fiddleneck
douglasia'na . . . . . . Douglas F.
interme'dia (*douglasiana* Auth., *not* DC.) . . . . Fireweed F.
menzies'i . . . . Menzies F.
retror'sa
spectab'ilis (*intermedia* Auth., *not* Fisch. & Mey.) . . . . Coast F.

AMSO'NIA eastwoodia'na Eastwood Amsonia

ANAGAL'LIS arven'sis Scarlet Pimpernel

ANAPH'ALIS . Pearleverlasting
margarita'cea . . . . . Common P.
—subalpi'na (*A. subalpina*) Western C.P.

ANDRO'SACE . . . Rockjasmine

ANEM'ONE (*PULSATILLA*) Anemone
The Pasqueflower section (Pulsatilla) is regarded by some botanists as a distinct genus.
canaden'sis . . . . . . Meadow A.
cylin'drica . . . . Candle A.
globo'sa . . . . Pacific A.
Anemone globosa, perhaps, is hardly more than a southern form of A. hudsoniana.
ludovicia'na (*Pulsatilla l.*) American Pasqueflower
occidenta'lis (*Pulsatilla o.*) Western P.

ANGEL'ICA . . . . . Angelica
brew'eri . . . . Brewer A.
gray'i . . . . Grays A.
ly'alli . . . . Lyall A.
pinna'ta . . . . Small-leaf A.
wheel eri . . . . Wheeler A.

ANHALO'NIUM . **ARIOCARPUS**

ANISACAN'THUS . Anisacanth
insig'nis . . . . Dwarf A.
thur'beri . . . . Thurber A.
wright'i . . . . Wrights A.

ANISOLO'TUS . . . . **LOTUS**

ANO'GRA . . . . **OENOTHERA**

ANTENNA'RIA . . . . Pussytoes
a'prica . . . . RockyMountain P.
dimor'pha . . . . Low P.
luzuloi'des . . . . Rush P.
microphyl'la (*parvifolia*) Littleleaf P.

RANGE PLANTS (ANTENNARIA), continued
pulcher'rima . . . SHOWY PUSSYTOES
racemo'sa . . . . . . RACEME P.
rose'a (*A. dioica r.*) . . . . ROSE P.

ANTHE'RICUM tor'reyi TORREY ANTHERICUM

ANTHOPO'GON . . **GENTIANA**

APLOPAP'PUS (*Bigelovia* in part; *Chrysoma; Ericameria; Eriocarpum; Isocoma; Macronema; Pyrrocoma; Sideranthus; Stenotopsis; Stenotus; Tonestus*) GOLDENWEED
See also **POISONOUS PLANTS.**
acau'lis (*Stenotus a.*) . . STEMLESS G.
arbores'cens (*Bigelovia a.; Ericameria a.*) . . . . FLEECE G.
bloom'eri (*Chrysothamnus b.*) RABBITBRUSH G.
brachyle'pis Hall, *not* Phil. **A. propinquus**
coop'eri (*Bigelovia c.*) . . COOPER G.
cunea'tus (*Ericameria cuneata*) WEDGELEAF G.
falca'tus (*Stenotus caespitosus*) TUFTED G.
green'ei (*Macronema g.*) GREENES G.
—mol'lis
integrifo'lius (*Pyrrocoma integrifolia*) WHOLELEAF G.
lanceola'tus (*Pyrrocoma lanceolata*) LANCELEAF G.
laricifo'lius (*Ericameria laricifolia*) LARCHLEAF G.
linearifo'lius (*Stenotopsis linearifolia*) NARROWLEAF G.
macrone'ma (*Macronema discoideum*) WHITESTEM G.
na'nus (*Ericameria nana*) . DWARF G.
nutt'alli (*Sideranthus grindelioides*) NUTTALL G.
pal'meri (*Ericameria p.*) . PALMER G.
propin'quus (*brachylepis* Hall, *not* Phil.; *Ericameria b.*) . . . CHAPARRAL G.
suffrutico'sus (*Macronema suffruticosum*) . . . . . . SINGLEHEAD G.
uniflo'rus (*Pyrrocoma uniflora*) PLANTAIN G.
vene'tus (*Isocoma veneta*) DAMIANA G.

APOC'YNUM . . . . DOGBANE
androsaemifo'lium . . SPREADING D.
—gla'brum (*A. ambigens*)
cannab'inum . . . . . . HEMP D.
pu'milum . . . . LOW D.

AQUILE'GIA . . . . COLUMBINE
canaden'sis . . . . . AMERICAN C.
coeru'lea . . . . COLORADO C.
flaves'cens . . . . YELLOW C.
formo'sa . . . . SITKA C.
pineto'rum . . . . PINE C.

AR'ABIS . . . . . . ROCKCRESS
brew'eri . . . . BREWER R.
canes'cens . . . . SILVER R.
divaricar'pa
drum'mondi . . . . DRUMMOND R.
ex'ilis . . . . SLIM R.
gla'bra . . . . TOWERMUSTARD R.
hirsu'ta pycnocar'pa (*A. pycnocarpa*) COMMON HAIRY R.
holboell'i . . . . . . HOLBOELL R.
lem'moni . . . . . . LEMMONS R.
ly'alli . . . . LYALL R.
microphyl'la . . . . LITTLELEAF R.

RANGE PLANTS (ARABIS), continued
nutt'alli (*spathulata* Nutt., *not* DC.) NUTTALL ROCKCRESS
platysper'ma . . . . . . PIONEER R.
suffrutes'cens . . . . WOODY R.

ARA'LIA califor'nica CALIFORNIA ARALIA

ARBU'TUS . . . . . . MADRONE
arizo'nica . . . . ARIZONA M.
menzies'i (*procera*) . . PACIFIC M.
texa'na . . . . TEXAS M.

ARCTOSTAPH'YLOS (*COMAROSTAPHYLIS*) . . . MANZANITA
alpi'na . . . . **Arctous alpinus**
anderso'ni (*regismontana*) HEARTLEAF M.
columbia'na . . . . . . HAIRY M.
diversifo'lia (*Comarostaphylis d.*) TOOTHED M.
glandulo'sa . . . . . . EASTWOOD M.
glau'ca . . . . BIGBERRY M.
manzani'ta . . . . . . COMMON M.
mewuk'ka (*pastillosa*) . . INDIAN M.
morroen'sis . . . . MORRO M.
nevaden'sis . . . . . . PINEMAT M.
otayen'sis . . . . OTAY M.
pajaroen'sis . . . . PAJARO M.
parrya'na . . . . PARRY M.
—pineto'rum (*A. pinetorum*) PINE M.
pat'ula . . . . GREENLEAF M.
pilos'ula . . . . . . STRIPEBERRY M.
pring'lei . . . . PRINGLE M.
pun'gens . . . . POINTLEAF M.
ru'dis . . . . SHAGBARK M.
sensiti'va . . . . . LITTLEBERRY M.
silvic'ola . . . . . . SILVERLEAF M.
tomento'sa . . . . WOOLLY M.
uva-ur'si . . . . BEARBERRY
vis'cida . . . . . . WHITELEAF M.

ARCTO'US alpi'nus (*Arctostaphylos alpina; Mairania a*) ALPINE PTARMIGANBERRY

ARENA'RIA . . . . . SANDWORT
burk'ei . . . . BURKE S.
conges'ta . . . . BALLHEAD S.
fend'leri . . . . FENDLER S.
formo'sa (*A. capillaris f.*) . FESCUE S.
king'i . . . . KINGS S.
sajanen'sis . . . . SIBERIAN S.
serpyllifo'lia . . . . . THYMELEAF S.
uintahen'sis . . . . UINTA S.

ARGEMO'NE platyce'ras his'pida (*A. hispida*) HEDGEHOG PRICKLEPOPPY

ARGENTI'NA . . **POTENTILLA**

ARIOCAR'PUS (*ANHALONIUM*) LIVINGROCKCACTUS

AR'NICA . . . . ARNICA
cordifo'lia . . . . . HEARTLEAF A.
folio'sa . . . . LEAFY A.
—inca'na . . . . . . HOARYLEAF A.
ful'gens . . . . ORANGE A.
latifo'lia . . . . . . BROADLEAF A.
longifo'lia . . . . . . LONGLEAF A.
mol'lis . . . . HAIRY A.
par'ryi . . . . RAYLESS A.
peduncula'ta . . . . CORM A.

ARTEMIS'IA . . . . SAGEBRUSH
arbus'cula . . . . LOW S.
bigelo'vi . . . . BIGELOW S.
califor'nica . . . . . CALIFORNIA S.
ca'na . . . . SILVER S.

RANGE PLANTS (ARTEMISIA), continued
carruth'i . . . CARRUTH SAGEBRUSH
dis'color (*incompta*) . . . SWEET S.
dracunculoi'des . FALSETARRAGON S.
filifo'lia . . . . SAND S.
flocco'sa . . . . WOOLLY S.
franserioi'des . . . . . RAGWEED S.
frig'ida . . . . FRINGED S.
This plant is uniformly called Estafiata in the Southwest. In the Northeast, where it is a common pasture weed, it is called Pasture Sagebrush.
gnaphalo'des . . . . . CUDWEED S.
incomp'ta . . . . **A. discolor**
longifo'lia . . . . LONGLEAF S.
ludovicia'na . . . . . . LOUISIANA S.
mexica'na . . . . MEXICAN S.
michauxia'na . . . . . . MICHAUX S.
natronen'sis . . . . ALKALI S.
neomexica'na . . . NEWMEXICAN S.
no'va . . . . BLACK S.
redo'lens . . . . CHIHUAHUA S.
rig'ida . . . . STIFF S.
rothrock'i . . . . ROTHROCK S.
scopulo'rum . . . . ALPINE S.
spines'cens . . . . BUD S.
tridenta'ta . . . . BIG S.
triparti'ta (*A. tridentata trifida; trifida* Nutt., *not* Turcz.) . . THREETIP S.
vulga'ris . . MUGWORT WORMWOOD
wright'i . . . . WRIGHTS S.

ASCLE'PIAS . . . . . MILKWEED
See **POISONOUS PLANTS.**

AS'TER (*EUCEPHALUS; IONACTIS; LEUCELENE; MACHAERANTHERA; OREOSTEMMA*) . . . . . . ASTER
adscen'dens (*denudatus; nelsoni; oxylepis; vallicola*)
alpi'nus . . . . ALPINE A.
amplexifo'lius . . . . **A. integrifolius**
anderso'ni . . . . . . ANDERSON A.
a'pricus . . . . . . **A. foliaceus a.**
burk'ei . . . . **A. foliaceus b.**
canes'cens (*Machaeranthera c.*) HOARY A.
commuta'tus
—cras'sulus (*A. crassulus*)
conspic'uus . . . . SHOWY A.
decur'rens . . . . **A. laevis**
denuda'tus . . . . . **A. adscendens**
eat'oni (*A. foliaceus e.*) . . EATONS A.
engelmann'i . . . . ENGELMANN A.
ericoi'des (*multiflorus*) . . . HEATH A.
folia'ceus . . . . . . LEAFYBRACT A.
—a'pricus (*A. apricus*) . ALPINE L.A.
—burk'ei (*A. burkei*) . BURKE L.A.
—fron'deus (*A. frondeus*) TALL L.A.
glauco'des (*Eucephalus glaucus*)
integrifo'lius (*amplexifolius*) THICKSTEM A.
lae'vis (*decurrens*) . . . . SMOOTH A.
leucanthemifo'lius (*Machaeranthera leucanthemifolia*) . . . DAISYLEAF A.
leucele'ne (*Leucelene arenosa; L. ericoides*) . . . . BABYWHITE A.
modes'tus . . . . . . FEWFLOWER A.
multiflo'rus . . . . **A. ericoides**
nel'soni . . . . **A. adscendens**
occidenta'lis . . . . . WESTERN A.
oxyle'pis . . . . . . **A. adscendens**
perel'egans (*Eucephalus elegans*) NUTTALL A.
scopulo'rum (*Ionactis alpina*) CRAG A.
stenome'res (*Ionactis s.*) NORTHWEST A.

RANGE PLANTS (ASTER), continued

tanacetifo'lius (*Machaeranthera tanacetifolia*) . . . . TANSYLEAF ASTER
vallic'ola . . . . . . **A. adscendens**

ASTRAG'ALUS (*DIHOLCOS; GEOPRUMNON; HAMOSA; HOMALOBUS; KENTROPHYTA; TIUM; XYLOPHACOS*) . . . . MILKVETCH
See also **POISONOUS PLANTS** and note on this genus on p. 30.

aborig'inum . . . . . . INDIAN M.
adsur'gens Auth., *not* Pall. **A. striatus**
agres'tis . . . . PURPLE M.
alpi'nus (*Tium alpinum*) . ALPINE M.
araneo'sus . . . . . DRYPLAINS M.
beck'withi . . . . . BECKWITH M.
bigelo'vi . . . . BIGELOW M.
calyco'sus
crassicar'pus . . . GROUNDPLUM M.
decum'bens . . . . DECUMBENT M.
diffu'sus . . . . DIFFUSE M.
drum'mondi (*Tium d.*) DRUMMOND M.
flexuo'sus (*Homalobus f.*) FLEXILE M.
gonia'tus . . . . . NICKLEAF M.
impen'sus . . . . . THISTLE M.
sonnea'nus (*hookerianus*) BALLOONPOD M.
spatula'tus . . . . . TUFTED M.
stria'tus (*adsurgens* Auth., *not* Pall.) PRAIRIE M.
tenel'lus . . . . . LOOSEFLOWER M.
zi'onis . . . . ZION M.

Astrophyl'lum dumo'sum **Choisya dumosa**

A'TRIPLEX . . . . SALTBUSH
canes'cens . . . . . FOURWING S.
This is generally called Chamiza in New Mexico.
confertifo'lia . . . . SHADSCALE S.
gard'neri (*nuttalli*) . . . GARDNER S.
lentifor'mis . . . . BIG S. (*Lenscale; Quailbush*)
par'ryi . . . . PARRY S.
pat'ula hasta'ta (*A. hastata*) SPEARLEAF FAT-HEN S.
spinif'era

AUDIBERT'IA . . . . **SALVIA**

AZA'LEA; AZALEAS'TRUM **RHODODENDRON**

BAC'CHARIS . . . . . BACCHARIS
emo'ryi . . . . EMORY B.
glutino'sa . . . . SEEPWILLOW B.
pilula'ris . . . . KIDNEYWORT B.
pteronioi'des (*ramulosa*) YERBADEPASMO B.
sarothroi'des . . . . . . BROOM B.

BAER'IA chrysosto'ma (*gracilis*) BRANCHY GOLDFIELDS

BAHI'A dissec'ta (*Villanova d.*) RAGLEAF BAHIA

BAI'LEYA . . . . BAILEYA
multiradia'ta . . . . . DESERT B.
peren'nis . . . . . . LEAFYSTEM B.

BALSAMORHI'ZA . BALSAMROOT
hook'eri . . . . HOOKER B.
inca'na . . . . HOARY B.
macrophyl'la . . . . . CUTLEAF B.
sagitta'ta . . . . . ARROWLEAF B.

BARBARE'A orthoce'ras (*Campe o.*) ERECTPOD WINTERCRESS

BAS'SIA hyssopifo'lia FIVEHOOK BASSIA

RANGE PLANTS, continued

BATRA'CHIUM . **RANUNCULUS**

BECKWITH'IA . **RANUNCULUS**

BELOPERO'NE califor'nica CALIFORNIA BELOPERONE

BER'BERIS fend'leri COLORADO BARBERRY

BET'ULA . . . . BIRCH
fontina'lis (*occidentalis*) . . WATER B.
glandulo'sa . . . . BOG B.
rotundifo'lia . . . . . GROUND B.

BI'DENS . . . . . BEGGARTICKS

BIGELO'VIA in part **APLOPAPPUS**

BIKU'KULLA . . **DICENTRA**

BILDERDY'KIA **POLYGONUM**

BISTOR'TA . . . **POLYGONUM**

BLI'TUM . . **CHENOPODIUM**

BRAS'SICA campes'tris BIRD RAPE

BRICKEL'LIA (*COLEOSANTHUS*) BRICKELLIA
califor'nica (*wrighti* A. Gray, *not* Rothr.; *Coleosanthus californicus*) CALIFORNIA B.
floribun'da (*wrighti* Rothr., *not* A. Gray; *Coleosanthus floribundus*) BIGLEAF B.
glabra'ta (*Coleosanthus glabratus*)
grandiflo'ra (*Coleosanthus grandiflorus*) TASSELFLOWER B.

BRODIAE'A (*HOOKERA*) BRODIEA
capita'ta (*Dichelostemma capitatum*) BLUEDICKS B.
doug'lasi (*Hookera d.; Triteleia grandiflora*) . . . . DOUGLAS B.

Broussonet'ia secundiflo'ra **Sophora s.**

BUDDLE'IA . . BUTTERFLYBUSH
marrubiifo'lia . . . . . . WOOLLY B.
scordioi'des . . . . . ESCOBILLA B.
utahen'sis . . . . UTAH B.

BUR'SA . . . . . **CAPSELLA**

CALLIAN'DRA . . . CALLIANDRA
eriophyl'la . . . FALSEMESQUITE C.
hu'milis . . . . DWARF C.
reticula'ta . . . . . . NETVEIN C.

CALOCHOR'TUS . . . MARIPOSA
coeru'leus (*maweanus* in part) SKYBLUE M.
el'egans . . . . NORTHWESTERN M.
gunniso'ni . . . . . . GUNNISON M.
macrocar'pus . . . . SAGEBRUSH M.
nit'idus (*eurycarpus*) . BROADFRUIT M.
nutt'alli . . . . SEGOLILY M.
tol'miei (*maweanus* in part) TOLMIE M.

CAL'THA leptosep'ala (*rotundifolia*) ELKSLIP MARSHMARIGOLD

CALYCAN'THUS occidenta'lis (*macrophyllus*) CALIFORNIA SWEETSHRUB

CALYP'SO bulbo'sa (*Cytherea b.*) CALYPSO

CAMAS'SIA (*QUAMASIA*). CAMAS
cu'sicki . . . . CUSICK C.
leicht'lini . . . . . LEICHTLIN C.
qua'mash (*esculenta* Lindl., *not* (Ker.) Rob.; *Quamasia q.*) . . COMMON C.
suksdorf'i . . . . SUKSDORF C.

RANGE PLANTS, continued

CAMPAN'ULA . . . BELLFLOWER
par'ryi . . . . PARRY B.
petiola'ta (*rotundifolia* Auth., *not* L.) AMERICAN HAREBELL

CAM'PE . . . . . **BARBAREA**

CAN'NABIS sati'va (*indica*) . HEMP

CANO'TIA holacan'tha . . CANOTIA

CAPNOI'DES . . . **CORYDALIS**

CAPSEL'LA bursa-pasto'ris (*Bursa b.*) . . . . SHEPHERDSPURSE

CARDAM'INE cordifo'lia HEARTLEAF BITTERCRESS

CA'REX . . . . SEDGE
abrup'ta . . . . . . ABRUPTBEAK S.
aquat'ilis . . . . WATER S.
athrosta'chya . . . SLENDERBEAK S.
atra'ta . . . . BLACK S.
au'rea . . . . GOLDEN S.
bel'la
doug'lasi . . . . DOUGLAS S.
ebe'nea . . . . EBONY S.
eleoch'aris (*stenophylla* Auth., *not* Wahl.) . . . . . . NEEDLELEAF S.
exser'ta . . . . . . SHORTHAIR S.
festivel'la . . . . . . OVALHEAD S.
filifo'lia . . . . . . THREADLEAF S.
geoph'ila
gey'eri . . . . ELK S.
helioph'ila . . . . SUN S.
hood'i . . . . HOOD S.
illo'ta . . . . SHEEP S.
kel'loggi . . . . KELLOGG S.
lanugino'sa . . . . WOOLLY S.
liddon'i . . . . **C. petasata**
mar'cida . . . . . . **C. praegracilis**
merten'si . . . . MERTENS S.
microp'tera . . . . . SMALLWING S.
nebrasken'sis . . . . NEBRASKA S.
ni'gricans . . . . . BLACK ALPINE S.
nubic'ola . . . . CLOUD S.
pachystach'ya . . . . CHAMISSO S.
petasa'ta (*liddoni*) . . . . LIDDON S.
phaeoceph'ala . . . . DUNHEAD S.
praegrac'ilis (*marcida*)
pres'li . . . . PRESL S.
raynolds'i . . . . . . RAYNOLDS S.
ross'i . . . . ROSS S.
rostra'ta . . . . BEAKED S.
sicca'ta . . . . SILVERTOP S.
stenophyl'la Auth., *not* Wahl. **C. eleocharis**
teneraefor'mis . . . SIERRASLIM S.
tol'miei . . . . TOLMIE S.

CARLOWRIGHT'IA CARLOWRIGHTIA
arizo'nica . . . . ARIZONA C.
linearifo'lia . . . . HEATH C.

CARNEGIE'A . . . . **CEREUS**

CARPHOCHAE'TE bigelo'vi

Ca'rum gaird'neri . . **Perideridia g.**

Cas'sia chamaecris'ta **Chamaecrista fasciculata**

CASSI'OPE . . . . . CASSIOPE
mertensia'na . . . . . MERTENS C.
tetrag'ona . . . . . FIREMOSS C.

CASTANOP'SIS EVERGREENCHINKAPIN
chrysophyl'la . . . . . . GIANT E.
—mi'nor . . . . GOLDEN E.
sempervi'rens . . . . . . SIERRA E.

RANGE PLANTS, continued

CASTILLE'JA . . . PAINTEDCUP
angustifo'lia (*hispida*) NORTHWESTERN P.
bradbur'yi . . . . . . BRADBURY P.
coccin'ea . . . . INDIAN PAINTBRUSH
confu'sa
fla'va . . . . YELLOW PAINTEDCUP
inte'gra . . . . . . WHOLELEAF P.
lau'ta . . . . . YELLOWSTONE P.
linariaefo'lia . . . . . WYOMING P.
lute'a (*villosa*) . . . . . HAIRY P.
luteovi'rens . . . . YELLOWGREEN P.
minia'ta . . . . SCARLET P.
occidenta'lis . . . . . . WESTERN P.
oreop'ola . . . . MAGENTA P.
palles'cens . . . . PALE P.
pilo'sa . . . . WHITE P.
pineto'rum . . . . PINE P.
rhexifo'lia . . . . . SPLITLEAF P.
sulphu'rea . . . . SULFUR P.
villo'sa . . . . **C. lutea**

CAULAN'THUS crassicau'lis THICKSTEM WILDCABBAGE

CEANO'THUS . . . CEANOTHUS
america'nus . . . . JERSEYTEA C.
arbo'reus . . . . . . FELTLEAF C.
cordula'tus MOUNTAIN WHITETHORN C.
cunea'tus . . . . . BUCKBRUSH C.
divarica'tus . . . . . . **C. oliganthus**
divarica'tus Auth., *not* Nutt. **C. leucodermis**
diversifo'lius (*decumbens*) TRAILING C.
fend'leri . . . . FENDLER C.
fer'risae . . . . COYOTE C.
fresnen'sis (*C. rigidus f.*) FRESNOMAT C.
gregg'i . . . . DESERT C.
integer'rimus . . . . DEERBRUSH C.
The blue-flowered form of this species is commonly called Bluebrush.
jep'soni . . . . JEPSON C.
lem'moni . . . . LEMMONS C.
leucoder'mis (*divaricatus* Auth., *not* Nutt.) CHAPARRAL WHITETHORN C.
mar'tini . . . . MARTIN C.
mogollo'nicus . . . . MOGOLLON C.
oligan'thus (*divaricatus*) . . HAIRY C.
ova'tus . . . . INLAND C.
prostra'tus . . . . SQUAWCARPET C.
rig'idus . . . . MONTEREY C.
—*fresnen'sis* . . . . . . **C. fresnensis**
sanguin'eus . . . . . . REDSTEM C.
soredia'tus . . . . . . JIMBRUSH C.
spino'sus . . . . . . REDHEART C.
thyrsiflo'rus . . . BLUEBLOSSOM C.
—chand'leri . . . . CHANDLER B.C.
veluti'nus . . . . . SNOWBRUSH C.

CELAS'TRUS scan'dens AMERICAN BITTERSWEET

CEL'TIS . . . . HACKBERRY
doug'lasi (*rugulosa*) . . DOUGLAS H.
laeviga'ta (*mississippiensis*) SUGAR H.
pal'lida . . . . SPINY H.
reticula'ta . . . . . . NETLEAF H.

CEPHALAN'THUS occidenta'lis COMMON BUTTONBUSH

CERAS'TIUM . . . CERASTIUM
stric'tum . . . . COMMON C.
visco'sum . . . . STICKY C.
vulga'tum . . . . BIG C.

CERCID'IUM . . . PALOVERDE
flor'idum (*torreyanum*) . . . BLUE P.
ma'crum . . . . BORDER P.

RANGE PLANTS (CERCIDIUM), continued
microphyl'lum (*Parkinsonia microphylla*) . . . LITTLELEAF PALOVERDE
texa'num . . . . TEXAS P.

CER'CIS occidenta'lis CALIFORNIA REDBUD

CERCOCAR'PUS MOUNTAINMAHOGANY
argen'teus . . . . SILVER M.
arizo'nicus . . . . . . ARIZONA M.
betuloi'des . . . . . BIRCHLEAF M.
breviflo'rus . . . . . . WRIGHT M.
exim'ius
intrica'tus . . . . . LITTLELEAF M.
ledifo'lius . . . . . . CURLLEAF M.
monta'nus . . . . TRUE M.

CE'REUS
engelmann'i . . . . **Echinocereus e.**
gigan'teus (*Carnegiea gigantea*) SAGUARO (*Giantcactus*)

CHAENAC'TIS doug'lasi DOUGLAS CHAENACTIS

CHAMAEBA'TIA foliolo'sa BEARMAT (*Mountainmisery*)

CHAMAEBATIA'RIA millefo'lium TANSYBUSH (*Desertsweet*)

CHAMAECRIS'TA fascicula'ta (*Cassia chamaecrista*) SHOWY PARTRIDGEPEA

CHAMAENE'RION **EPILOBIUM**

CHAMAEPERICLY'MENUM **CORNUS**

CHAMAESY'CE . . **EUPHORBIA**

CHEIRIN'IA . . . **ERYSIMUM**

Chelo'ne barba'ta **Penstemon barbatus**

CHENOPO'DIUM (*BLITUM*) GOOSEFOOT
al'bum . . . . . LAMBSQUARTERS G.
atrovi'rens
capita'tum (*Blitum c.*) . . BLITE G.
fre'monti . . . . FREMONT G.
inci'sum (*cornutum*) . . RAGLEAF G.
leptophyl'lum . . . . . SLIMLEAF G.

CHILOP'SIS linea'ris DESERTWILLOW

CHIMA'PHILA . . . . PIPSISSEWA
menzies'i . . . . MENZIES P.
umbella'ta . . . . COMMON P.
—occidenta'lis . . . . WESTERN P.

CHOI'SYA dumo'sa (*Astrophyllum dumosum*) STARLEAF MEXICANORANGE

CHRYSACTIN'IA mexica'na DAMIANITA

Chrysobot'rya odora'ta **Ribes odoratum**

CHRYSO'MA . . **APLOPAPPUS**

CHRYSOP'SIS . . . . GOLDASTER
brew'eri . . . . BREWER G.
folio'sa . . . . LEAFY G.
his'pida . . . . ROUGH G.
villo'sa . . . . HAIRY G.

CHRYSOTHAM'NUS RABBITBRUSH
grave'olens (*C. nauseosus g.*) GREENPLUME R.
green'ei . . . . GREENES R.
how'ardi . . . . HOWARD R.
hu'milis . . . . LOW R.

RANGE PLANTS (CHRYSOTHAMNUS), continued
lanceola'tus LANCELEAF RABBITBRUSH
linifo'lius . . . . FLAXLEAF R.
nauseo'sus . . . . RUBBER R.
nevaden'sis . . . . NEVADA R.
panicula'tus . . . . DESERT R.
par'ryi . . . . PARRY R.
pinifo'lius . . . . . PINENEEDLE R.
puber'ulus . . . . DOWNY R.
pulchel'lus . . . . . SOUTHWEST R.
specio'sus . . . . TALL R.
stenophyl'lus . . . . SMALL R.
teretifo'lius . . . . . ROUNDLEAF R.
turbina'tus
viscidiflo'rus . . . . . DOUGLAS R.
—pu'milus (*C. pumilus*) . LOW D.R.
—serrula'tus (*C. serrulatus*) SAWTOOTH D.R.
—tortifo'lius (*C. tortifolius*) TWISTLEAF D.R.

CHYLIS'MIA . . **OENOTHERA**

CIR'SIUM . . . . THISTLE
drum'mondi . . . . DRUMMOND T.
lanceola'tum . . . . BULL T.
undula'tum . . . . . WAVYLEAF T.

CIS'SUS inci'sa . . IVY TREEBINE

CLARK'IA . . . . CLARKIA

CLAYTO'NIA . . . SPRINGBEAUTY

CLEM'ATIS . . . . . . CLEMATIS
doug'lasi (*hirsutissima*) . DOUGLAS C.
ligusticifo'lia WESTERN VIRGINSBOWER
pseudoalpi'na . . ROCKYMOUNTAIN C.
verticilla'ris columbia'na (*C. columbiana*) . . . . COLUMBIAN ROCK C.

CLEO'ME . . . . SPIDERFLOWER
lute'a . . . . YELLOW S.
serrula'ta . . . . BEE S.

CLINTO'NIA uniflo'ra QUEENCUP BEADLILY

CLISTOYUC'CA . . . . **YUCCA**

COGSWEL'LIA . . **LOMATIUM**

COLDE'NIA nutt'alli NUTTALL COLDENIA

COLEOG'YNE ramosis'sima BLACKBRUSH

COLEOSAN'THUS . **BRICKELLIA**

COLLIN'SIA parviflo'ra (*tenella* (Pursh) Piper, *not* Benth.) LITTLEFLOWER COLLINSIA

COLLO'MIA . . . . . . **GILIA**

COLUBRI'NA . . . COLUBRINA
gla'bra . . . . SMOOTH C.
texen'sis . . . . TEXAS C.

COMAN'DRA umbella'ta (*nudiflora; pallida*) . . COMMON COMANDRA

COMAROSTAPH'YLIS **ARCTOSTAPHYLOS**

COMMELI'NA dianthifo'lia (*linearis*) . . . BIRDBILL DAYFLOWER

CONDA'LIA . . . . . CONDALIA
lycioi'des (*Zizyphus l.*) SOUTHWESTERN C.
—canes'cens . . . . . DESERT S.C.
obova'ta . . . . . . BLUEWOOD C.
obtusifo'lia . . . . . LOTEWOOD C.
par'ryi . . . . PARRY C.
spathula'ta . . . . . KNIFELEAF C.

RANGE PLANTS, continued

CONVOL'VULUS . . . GLORYBIND
arven'sis . . . . . . EUROPEAN G.
polymor'phus . . . . . VARIABLE G.

CORALLORRHI'ZA macula'ta (*multiflora*) . . SPOTTED CORALROOT

CORDYLAN'THUS (*ADENOSTEGIA*) . . . . BIRDBEAK
ramo'sus (*Adenostegia ramosa*) BUSHY B.

COREOP'SIS . . . . COREOPSIS

CORISPER'MUM . . TICKSEED

COR'NUS (*CHAMAEPERICLYMENUM*) . . . . . DOGWOOD
canaden'sis (*Chamaepericlymenum canadense*) . . . . . BUNCHBERRY D.
nutt'alli . . . . PACIFIC D.
occidenta'lis . . . . . WESTERN D.
sanguin'ea . . . . . BLOODTWIG D.
stolonif'era . . . . . . REDOSIER D.

CORYD'ALIS au'rea (*Capnoides aureum*) . . . . GOLDEN CORYDALIS

COR'YLUS . . . FILBERT (*Hazel*)
califor'nica . . . . . CALIFORNIA F.
cornu'ta (*rostrata*) . . . . BEAKED F. (*Beaked H.*)

COS'MOS . . . . COSMOS

COT'ULA coronopifo'lia BIRD BRASSBUTTONS

COVIL'LEA . . . . . . **LARREA**

COWA'NIA stansburia'na STANSBURY CLIFFROSE

CRATAE'GUS . . . HAWTHORN
doug'lasi . . . . DOUGLAS H.
rivula'ris . . . . RIVER H.

CRE'PIS . . . . . HAWKSBEARD
acumina'ta . . . . . . TAPERTIP H.
glau'ca
interme'dia . . . . GRAY H.
montic'ola . . . . . . SISKIYOU H.
na'na (*Youngia n.*) . . . . TINY H.
occidenta'lis . . . . WESTERN H.
runcina'ta . . . . DANDELION H.
scopulo'rum . . YELLOWSTONE H.

CROSSOSO'MA bigelo'vi BIGELOW CROSSOSOMA

CROTALA'RIA pu'mila (*lupulina*) LOW CROTALARIA

CRYPTAN'THA (*OREOCARYA*) CRYPTANTHA

CUCUR'BITA foetidis'sima BUFFALOGOURD

CYMOP'TERUS fend'leri . CHIMAYA

CYP'ERUS fendleria'nus FENDLER FLATSEDGE

CYSTOP'TERIS (*FILIX*) BLADDERFERN
bulbif'era . . . . BERRY B.
frag'ilis . . . . BRITTLE B.

CYTHERE'A . . . . **CALYPSO**

DA'LEA (*PAROSELA*) . DALEA
amoe'na . . . . NAVAHO D.
argyrae'a . . . . SILVER D.
au'rea . . . . SILKTOP D.
formo'sa . . . . FEATHER D.
frutes'cens . . . . BLACK D.
james'i . . . . JAMES D.
john'soni . . . . DESERTBEAUTY D.
par'ryi . . . . PARRY D.
pogonan'thera . . . . . BEARDED D.
polygonoi'des . . . . SIXWEEKS D.
spino'sa . . . . . SMOKETHORN D.

RANGE PLANTS, continued

DASIPH'ORA . . **POTENTILLA**

DASYLIR'ION . . . . . . SOTOL
texa'num . . . . TEXAS S.
whee'leri . . . . WHEELER S.

DASYSTEPH'ANA . **GENTIANA**

DAU'CUS pusil'lus SOUTHWESTERN CARROT

DESCURAI'NIA (*SISYMBRIUM* in part; *SOPHIA*) TANSYMUSTARD
halicto'rum andrena'rum (*Sophia a.*)
inci'sa (*Sisymbrium incisum; Sophia incisa*) . . . . WESTERN T.
longipedicella'ta (*Sophia filipes; S. longipedicellata; S. pinnata* Howell, *not* Br. & Br.) . . . . SLIMSTEM T.
serra'ta (*Sophia s.*) . . . TOOTHED T.
sophi'a (*Sophia parviflora*) FLIXWEED T.

DESMAN'THUS coo'leyi (*jamesi; Acuan j.*) JAMES BUNDLEFLOWER

DESMO'DIUM (*MEIBOMIA*) TICKCLOVER

DICEN'TRA (*BIKUKULLA*) BLEEDINGHEART
chrysan'tha . . . . GOLDEARDROPS B.
formo'sa . . . . PACIFIC B.
uniflo'ra . . . . . . STEERSHEAD B.

DICHELOSTEM'MA **BRODIAEA**

DIHOL'COS . . . **ASTRAGALUS**

DI'PLACUS . . . . **MIMULUS**

DIS'PORUM trachycar'pum WARTBERRY FAIRYBELLS

DISTE'GIA . . . . **LONICERA**

DITHYRAE'A wislize'ni WISLIZENUS SPECTACLEPOD

DODECA'THEON . SHOOTINGSTAR
con'jugens
jef'freyi . . . . JEFFREY S.
pauciflo'rum . . . . DARKTHROAT S.

DODONAE'A visco'sa angustifo'lia NARROWLEAF CLAMMY HOPSEEDBUSH

DON'DIA . . . . . . **SUAEDA**

DOUGLAS'IA monta'na MOUNTAIN DOUGLASIA

DRA'BA . . . . DRABA
au'rea . . . . GOLDEN D.
ni'tida . . . . SHINY D.
sonor'ae . . . . SONORA D.

DRACOCEPH'ALUM (*MOLDAVICA*) . . . . . DRAGONHEAD

DRYMOCAL'LIS . **POTENTILLA**

DYSSO'DIA . . . . . DOGWEED
acero'sa . . . . PRICKLEAF D.
pappo'sa . . . . PRAIRIE D.

ECHINOCAC'TUS . ECHINOCACTUS
polyceph'alus . . . . . COTTONTOP E.

ECHINOCE'REUS engelmann'i (*Cereus e.*) ENGELMANN ECHINOCEREUS

EDWIN'IA . . . . . **JAMESIA**

ELAEAG'NUS commuta'ta (*argentea*) . . . . SILVERBERRY

ELEO'CHARIS . . . SPIKESEDGE

RANGE PLANTS, continued

EMMENAN'THE WHISPERINGBELLS
parviflo'ra . . . . . SAGEBRUSH W.
penduliflo'ra . . . . . YELLOW W.

EMPLECTOCLA'DUS . **PRUNUS**

ENCE'LIA . . . . . . ENCELIA
farino'sa . . . WHITE BRITTLEBUSH
frutes'cens . . . . BUSH E.
—virginen'sis (*E. virginensis*) VIRGINRIVER E.

ENCELIOP'SIS . . . ENCELIOPSIS
argophyl'la . . . . . SILVERLEAF E.
nudicau'lis . . . . . BARESTEM E.

E'PHEDRA . . . . . EPHEDRA
antisyphilit'ica . . . . . . VINE E.
nevaden'sis . . . . . . NEVADA E.
torreya'na . . . . TORREY E.
trifur'ca . . . . . . LONGLEAF E.
vir'idis . . . . GREEN E.

EPILO'BIUM (*CHAMAENERION*) . . . . . WILLOWWEED
adenocau'lon . . . . . . STICKY W.
alpi'num . . . . ALPINE W.
angustifo'lium (*spicatum; Chamaenerion a.*) . . . . FIREWEED
brevisty'lum . . . . . SIERRA W.
hornemann'i . . . . HORNEMANN W.
panicula'tum . . . . . AUTUMN W.

EREMOCA'RYA . . DESERTNUT

ERICAME'RIA . **APLOPAPPUS**

ERIG'ERON . . . . . FLEABANE
an'nuus . . . . ANNUAL F.
argenta'tus
armerifo'lius . . . . **E. lonchophyllus**
bloom'eri . . . . BLOOMER F.
caespito'sus . . . . TUFTED F.
canaden'sis . . . . . HORSEWEED F.
compos'itus . . . . . . FERNLEAF F.
—incer'tus (*E. discoideus*)
concin'nus . . . . HAIRY F.
—aphanac'tis
corymbo'sus . . . PURPLE-DAISY F.
coul'teri . . . . COULTER F.
diver'gens (*wootoni*) . SPREADING F.
ea'toni . . . . EATON F.
engelmann'i . . . . ENGELMANN F.
filifo'lius . . . . . THREADLEAF F.
flagella'ris . . . . . . TRAILING F.
glabel'lus . . . . SMOOTH F.
lonchophyl'lus (*armerifolius; minor; racemosus*) . . . . SPEARLEAF F.
macran'thus . . . . ASPEN F.
nudiflo'rus . . . . . . SPRAWLING F.
philadel'phicus . . PHILADELPHIA F.
pu'milus . . . . LOW F.
re'pens . . . . CREEPING F.
salsugino'sus . . . . ASTER F.
—angustifo'lius . . NARROWLEAF A.F.
sen'ilis
sim'plex
specio'sus . . . . OREGON F.
subtriner'vis . . . THREENERVE F.
ton'sus . . . . SHORN F.
trif'idus . . . . TRIFID F.
ursi'nus . . . . BEARRIVER F.
vis'cidus . . . . VISCID F.
woot'oni . . . . **E. divergens**

ERIOCAR'PUM **APLOPAPPUS**

ERIODIC'TYON . . YERBASANTA
angustifo'lium . . . NARROWLEAF Y.
califor'nicum . . . . CALIFORNIA Y.

RANGE PLANTS, continued

ERIOG'ONUM . . . Eriogonum
ala'tum . . . . Wing E.
ar'idum . . . . Dryland E.
caespito'sum . . . . Mat E.
cer'nuum . . . . . . Nodding E.
chrysoceph'alum . . . Goldball E.
ela'tum . . . . Rush E.
fascicula'tum . . . . . Flattop E.
fla'vum . . . . Yellow E.
heracleoi'des . . . . . . Wyeth E.
infla'tum . . . Deserttrumpet E.
james'i . . . . James E.
lonchophyl'lum . . . Spearleaf E.
microthe'cum . . . Slenderbush E.
neglec'tum
nu'dum . . . . Barestem E.
ovalifo'lium . . . . . . Cushion E.
parvifo'lium . . . . . Seacliff E.
pharnaceoi'des . . . Wirestem E.
pi'peri . . . . Piper E.
polifo'lium . . . . . Rosemary E.
polycla'don . . . . . . Sorrel E.
pyrolaefo'lium . . . . Oarleaf E.
racemo'sum . . . . . Redroot E.
stella'tum . . . . . . Longray E.
subalpi'num . . . . . Subalpine E.
thymoi'des . . . . Thyme E.
umbella'tum . . . . . . Sulfur E.
vimin'eum . . . . Broom E.
wright'i . . . . Wright E.

ERIOPHYL'LUM . Eriophyllum
integrifo'lium
lana'tum . . . . Woolly E.
staechadifo'lium . . . Lizardtail E.

ERO'DIUM cicuta'rium Alfileria

ERYS'IMUM (*CHEIRINIA*) Erysimum
as'perum . . . . Plains E.
ela'tum . . . . Tall E.
parviflo'rum (*inconspicuum*) Smallflower E.

ERYTHRI'NA flabellifor'mis Western Coralbean

ERYTHRO'NIUM . . . Fawnlily
grandiflo'rum . . . Lambstongue F.
—pal'lidum (*E. parviflorum*)

ESCHENBACH'IA Rayless-aster

ESCHSCHOLTZ'IA . . Goldpoppy
califor'nica . . . . Californiapoppy
—cro'cea
glyptosper'ma . . . . . Desert G.
mexica'na . . . . . . Mexican G.

EUCEPH'ALUS . . . . **ASTER**

EUON'YMUS . . . . Euonymus
atropurpu'reus . . . Eastern Wahoo
occidenta'lis . . . Western Wahoo

EUPATO'RIUM . . Eupatorium

EUPHOR'BIA (*CHAMAESYCE; TITHYMALOPSIS; TITHYMALUS*) . . . . Euphorbia
albomargina'ta (*Chamaesyce a.*) Whitemargin E.
capitella'ta (*Chamaesyce c.*). . Head E.
crenula'ta (*Tithymalus crenulatus*) Beetle E.
fend'leri (*Chamaesyce f.*). Fendler E.
glyptosper'ma (*C. g.*) . Ridgeseed E.
pal'meri (*Tithymalus p.*). Palmer E.
robus'ta (*T. robustus*) . . Robust E.
serpyllifo'lia (*Chamaesyce s.*) Thymeleaf E.

RANGE PLANTS, continued

EURO'TIA lana'ta Common Winterfat

EVOL'VULUS . . . Evolvulus

EYSENHARDT'IA polysta'chya (*Viborquia p.*) . . . . Kidneywood

FALLU'GIA paradox'a Apacheplume

FEND'LERA . . . Fendlerbush
rupic'ola . . . . Cliff F.
—falca'ta . . . . . Sickleleaf C.F.

FEROCAC'TUS wislize'ni (*Echinocactus w.*) Southwest Barrelcactus

FI'LIX . . . . **CYSTOPTERIS**

FLOUREN'SIA cer'nua American Tarbush

FORESTIER'A (*ADELIA* Michx., *not* L.) . . . . . . Forestiera
neomexica'na (*F. acuminata parvifolia; Adelia p.*) . . . NewMexican F.

FORSELLE'SIA spines'cens (*Glossopetalon s.*) . Spiny Greasebush

FOUQUIE'RIA splen'dens Ocotillo

FRAGA'RIA . . . Strawberry
bractea'ta . . . . . . Bracted S.
chiloen'sis . . . . Chiloe S.
glau'ca . . . . Blueleaf S.
platypet'ala . . . . . Broadpetal S.

FRANSE'RIA . . . . . Bursage
acanthicar'pa
chenopodiifo'lia . . . . SanDiego B.
deltoi'dea . . . . . . Triangle B.
dumo'sa . . . . White B.
tenuifo'lia . . . . . . Slimleaf B.

FRA'SERA . . Frasera (*Elkweed*)
albomargina'ta . . Whitemargin F.
monta'na . . . . Small F.
ni'tida . . . . Shiny F.
specio'sa . . . . Showy F.

FRAX'INUS . . . . Ash
anom'ala . . . . . Singleleaf A.
cuspida'ta . . . . . Fragrant A.
dipet'ala . . . . . . Twopetal A.
orego'na (*californica*) . Oregon A.
veluti'na (*standleyi*) . . . Velvet A.
—coria'cea (*F. coriacea*) Leatherleaf A.
—tou'meyi (*F. attenuata*) . Toumey A.

FREMONT'IA califor'nica (*Fremontodendron californicum*) California Fremontia

FRITILLA'RIA . . . Fritillary
atropurpu'rea . . . . Purplespot F.
pu'dica . . . . Yellow F.
recur'va (*coccinea*) . . . . Scarlet F.

GAILLAR'DIA arista'ta Common Perennial Gaillardia

GA'LIUM . . . . . Bedstraw
apari'ne . . . . . Catchweed B.
asper'rimum
bifo'lium . . . . Twinleaf B.
borea'le . . . . Northern B.
mollu'go . . . . White B.
multiflo'rum . . . . . Shrubby B.
tincto'rium . . . . Dye B.
triflo'rum . . . . Sweetscented B.
ve'rum . . . . Yellow B.

RANGE PLANTS, continued

GALPIN'SIA . . **OENOTHERA**

GAR'RYA . . . . . Silktassel
ellip'tica . . . . Tree S.
flaves'cens . . . . Yellowleaf S.
fre'monti . . . . Fremont S.
gold'mani . . . . . . Goldman S.
wright'i . . . . Wrights S.

GAULTHE'RIA . . Wintergreen
humifu'sa . . . . Western W.
ovatifo'lia . . . . Oregon W.
shal'lon . . . . Salal

GAU'RA coccin'ea Scarlet Gaura

GAYOPHY'TUM . Groundsmoke
cae'sium . . . . . Kitchenweed G.
diffu'sum . . . . . . Bigflower G.
ramosis'simum

GENTIA'NA (*AMARELLA; ANTHOPOGON; DASYSTEPHANA*) . . . . Gentian
affi'nis (*Dasystephana a.*) RockyMountain Pleated G.
calyco'sa (*Dasystephana c.*) Rainier P. G.
heterosep'ala (*Amarella h.*)
par'ryi (*Dasystephana p.*) . Parry G.
plebei'a (*Amarella p.*) New World Annual G.
romanzo'vi (*Dasystephana r.*) Romanzoff G.
scopulo'rum (*Amarella s.*) RockyMountain G.
therma'lis (*elegans*) RockyMountain Fringed G.

GEOPRUM'NON . **ASTRAGALUS**

GERA'NIUM . . . . . Geranium
atropurpu'reum
dissec'tum . . . . . . Cutleaf G.
fre'monti . . . . Fremont G.
inci'sum . . . . . . Cleftleaf G.
macula'tum . . . . . . Spotted G.
richardso'ni . . . . Richardson G.
robertia'num . . . . Herbrobert G.
viscosis'simum . . . . . Sticky G.

GE'UM . . . . Avens
oregonen'se . . . . . Oregon A.
stric'tum . . . . Yellow A.
turbina'tum (*Acomastylis turbinata*)

GIL'IA (*COLLOMIA; LEPTODACTYLON; LINANTHUS; NAVARRETIA*) . . . . Gilia
aggrega'ta . . . . . Skyrocket G.
brew'eri (*Navarretia b.*) Brewer G.
calca'rea . . . . Sticky G.
califor'nica (*Leptodactylon californicum*) California G.
capilla'ris . . . . Hairstem G.
capita'ta . . . . Globe G.
conges'ta . . . . Ballhead G.
grandiflo'ra (*Collomia g.*) Bigflower G.
greenea'na . . . . Greenes G.
harkness'i (*Linanthus h.*) Harkness G.
hutchinsifo'lia
iberidifo'lia . . . . . Candytuft G.
inconspic'ua . . . . Shy G.
intertex'ta (*Navarretia i.*) Woolly G.
leucophyl'la (*Navarretia l.*) Whitehead G.
linea'ris (*Collomia l.*) Slenderleaf G.

RANGE PLANTS (GILIA), continued
nutt'alli (*Leptodactylon n.*) Nuttall Gilia
pharnaceoi'des (*Linanthus p.*) Threadplant G.
pulchel'la . . . . Tinpiute G.
pun'gens (*Leptodactylon p.*) Granite G.
spica'ta . . . . Spike G.
twee'dyi . . . . Tweedy G.

GLOSSOPET'ALON **FORSELLESIA**

GLYCYRRHI'ZA lepido'ta American Licorice

GOMPHRE'NA . Globeamaranth

GOOD'YERA decip'iens (*menziesi; Peramium d.*) . . . . Western Rattlesnakeplantain

GOSSYP'IUM (*INGENHOUZIA*) Cotton
thur'beri (*Thurberia thespesioides*) Thurber C.

This species is sometimes confused with the rare G. trilobum of Mexico.

GRAY'IA . . . . Hopsage
brandeg'ei . . . . . Spineless H.
spino'sa . . . . Spiny H.

GRINDE'LIA . . . . . Gumweed
robus'ta . . . . Shore G.
squarro'sa . . . . . Curlycup G.
—serrula'ta

GROSSULA'RIA . . . . **RIBES**

GUTIERRE'ZIA . . Snakeweed
dracunculoi'des (*Amphiachyris d.*) Tarragon S. (*Broomweed*)
microceph'ala . . . . Threadleaf S.
saro'thrae . . . . Broom S.

GYMNOLO'MIA . . . **VIGUIERA**

HABENA'RIA (*LIMNORCHIS*) Habenaria
dilata'ta . . . . . White Bogorchid
leucosta'chys . . . . Milkwhite H.

HACKE'LIA

HALE'NIA . . . . . Spurgentian

HALERPES'TES **RANUNCULUS**

HAMO'SA . . . . **ASTRAGALUS**

HEDEO'MA . Falsepennyroyal

HEDYS'ARUM . . . Sweetvetch
borea'le (*pabulare*) . . Northern S.
occidenta'le . . . . . . Western S.
sulphures'cens . . . . . Sulfur S.
utahen'se . . . . Utah S.

HELE'NIUM hoopes'i Orange Sneezeweed

HELIANTHEL'LA Helianthella
arizo'nica . . . . Arizona H.
califor'nica . . . . . California H.
doug'lasi . . . . Douglas H.
quinquener'vis . . . Fivenerve H.
uniflo'ra . . . . . Oneflower H.

HELIAN'THUS . . . Sunflower
an'nuus . . . . Common S.
petiola'ris . . . . Prairie S.

HELIOTRO'PIUM . Heliotrope

HERACLE'UM lana'tum Common Cowparsnip

HESPERO'NIA . . **MIRABILIS**

RANGE PLANTS, continued

HETEROME'LES . **PHOTINIA**

HETEROTHE'CA subaxilla'ris

HEU'CHERA . . . . . Alumroot
america'na . . . . . . American A.
cylin'drica . . . . . Roundleaf A.
his'pida . . . . Rough A.
ovalifo'lia . . . . . . Ovalleaf A.
parvifo'lia . . . . . Littleleaf A.
rubes'cens . . . . Red A.

HIBIS'CUS. Rosemallow; Hibiscus

HIERA'CIUM . . . Hawkweed
albiflo'rum . . . . White H.
auranti'acum . . . . . Orange H.
cynoglossoi'des . Houndstongue H.
grac'ile . . . . Slender H.
scou'leri . . . . . . Woollyweed
villo'sum . . . . Shaggy H.

HOLACAN'THA emo'ryi Crucifixion Thorn

HOLODIS'CUS (*SERICOTHECA*) Rockspirea
dis'color . . . . . . Creambush R.
—ariaefo'lius . . . Oceanspray R.
dumo'sus . . . . Bush R.

HOMALO'BUS . **ASTRAGALUS**

HOOK'ERA . . . . **BRODIAEA**

HORKE'LIA fus'ca Tawny Horkelia

HORSFORD'IA newber'ryi Newberry Horsfordia

HOSACK'IA . . . . . . **LOTUS**

HYDROPHYL'LUM . Waterleaf
capita'tum . . . . . Ballhead W.
fend'leri al'bifrons (*H. albifrons*) Whiteface Fendler W.
occidenta'le . . . . . . Western W.

HYMENOCLE'A monogy'ra Singlewhorl Burrobrush

HYMENOPAP'PUS Hymenopappus
eriop'odus . . . . Woollyfoot H.
filifo'lius . . . . Fineleaf H.

HYMENOX'YS . . . **ACTINEA**

HYPER'ICUM . . St.Johnswort
anagalloi'des . . . . . Trailing S.
androsae'mum . . . . Tutsan S.
formo'sum . . . Southwestern S.
frondo'sum (*aureum* Bartr., *not* Lour.) Golden S.
perfora'tum . . . . . . Common S.
scou'leri . . . . Scouler S.

HYPOP'ITYS latisqua'ma Pinesap

HYP'TIS emo'ryi Emory Bushmint

IBID'IUM . . . **SPIRANTHES**

INGENHOUZ'IA . **GOSSYPIUM**

IONAC'TIS . . . . **ASTER**

IPOMOE'A . . . Morningglory

I'RIS . . . . Iris
missourien'sis . RockyMountain I.
ten'ax . . . . Oregon I.

ISOCO'MA . . . **APLOPAPPUS**

ISOM'ERIS arbo'rea Tree Burrofat

I'VA . . . . Sumpweed
axilla'ris . . . . Poverty S.
xanthifo'lia . . . . Rag S.

RANGE PLANTS, continued

IVES'IA . . . . Ivesia
gor'doni . . . . Gordon I.
utahen'sis . . . . Utah I.

JAMES'IA america'na (*Edwinia a.*) Cliff Jamesia

JANU'SIA . . . . Janusia

JUNCOI'DES . . . **LUZULA**

JUN'CUS . . . . Rush
bal'ticus . . . . Baltic R.
brunnes'cens . . . . . . Button R.
bufo'nius . . . . Toad R.
confu'sus
effu'sus . . . . Common R.
inte'rior . . . . Inland R.
saximonta'nus . RockyMountain R.
tor'reyi . . . . Torrey R.

JUNIP'ERUS . . . . . . Juniper
commu'nis . . . . Common J.
—saxat'ilis (*J. montana; J. sibirica*) Mountain C.J.
monosper'ma . . . . . Oneseed J.
occidenta'lis . . . . . . Sierra J.
pachyphloe'a . . . . . Alligator J.
pin'choti . . . . Redberry J.
scopulo'rum . . RockyMountain J.
utahen'sis . . . . Utah J.

KENTROPHY'TA **ASTRAGALUS**

KOCH'IA america'na Greenmolly Summercypress

KOEBERLIN'IA spino'sa Spiny Allthorn

KRAME'RIA gray'i (*canescens* A. Gray, *not* Willd.) Grays Krameria

KUHNIS'TERA **PETALOSTEMON**

LACINA'RIA . . . . **LIATRIS**

LACTU'CA . . . . Lettuce
pulchel'la . . . . Chicory L.
serri'ola (*scariola*) . . . Prickly L.

LAP'PULA (See also **Hackelia**) Stickseed

LAR'REA tridenta'ta (*Covillea t.*) Coville Creosotebush

LATH'YRUS . . . . Peavine
arizo'nicus . . . . Arizona P.
bijuga'tus sand'bergi (*L. sandbergi*) Sandberg P.
eucos'mus . . . . Bush P.
lanszwer'ti (*coriaceus*) . Thickleaf P.
leucan'thus . . . . Aspen P.
nutt'alli . . . . Nuttall P.
ochroleu'cus . . . . Cream P.
pauciflo'rus . . . . . Fewflower P.
sulphu'reus . . . . Sulfur P.
utahen'sis . . . . Utah P.

LAVATE'RA assurgentiflo'ra California Treemallow

LAVAUX'IA . . **OENOTHERA**

LE'DUM . . . . Ledum
glandulo'sum . . . . . Western L.
groenland'icum (*latifolium*) Labradortea L.
palus'tre . . . . Crystaltea L.
Leon'todon tarax'acum **Taraxacum officinale**

LEPARGYRE'A . **SHEPHERDIA**

LEPID'IUM . . . . Pepperweed

RANGE PLANTS, continued

LEPIDOSPAR'TUM . SCALYBROOM
latisqua'mum . . . . . . WOOLLY S.
squama'tum . . . . CALIFORNIA S.

LEPTODAC'TYLON . . . **GILIA**

LEPTOTAE'NIA multif'ida CARROTLEAF LEPTOTAENIA

LESPEDE'ZA stria'ta COMMON LESPEDEZA

LESQUEREL'LA . . BLADDERPOD

LEUCELE'NE . . . . . **ASTER**

LEWIS'IA redivi'va BITTERROOT LEWISIA

LIA'TRIS (*LACINARIA*) GAYFEATHER

LIGUS'TICUM . . . LIGUSTICUM
filici'num . . . . FERNLEAF L.
—tenuifo'lium (*L. tenuifolium*) SLIM F.L.
gray'i (*oreganum*) . . . . . GRAYS L.
por'teri . . . . PORTER L.

LIMNOR'CHIS . **HABENARIA**

LINAN'THUS . . . . . . **GILIA**

LINOSY'RIS in part **APLOPAPPUS**

LI'NUM lew'isi . . . LEWIS FLAX

LIP'PIA . . . . LIPPIA
ligustri'na . . . . PRIVET L.
wright'i . . . . WRIGHT L.

LITHOCAR'PUS . . . . TANOAK
densiflo'rus . . . . TANOAK
—monta'nus (*L. d. echinoides*) SCRUB T.

LITHOPHRAG'MA WOODLANDSTAR
austra'lis . . . . SOUTHERN W.
parviflo'ra . . . . SMALLFLOWER W.
tenel'la. . . . . SLENDER W.

LITHOSPER'MUM . . GROMWELL
angustifo'lium (*linearifolium*) NARROWLEAF G.
multiflo'rum . . . MANYFLOWER G.
rudera'le . . . . WAYSIDE G.

LOBE'LIA splen'dens WESTERN CARDINALFLOWER

LOMA'TIUM (*COGSWELLIA*) LOMATIUM

The species of Lomatium with thick rounded bulblike edible corms are known as Biscuitroot.

ambig'uum (*Cogswellia ambigua*) WYETH BISCUITROOT
anom'alum . . . . . **L. triternatum a.**
circumda'tum . . . . . WALLOWA B.
cous' (*Cogswellia c.*) . . . . COUS B.
gey'eri . . . . GEYER B.
leptocar'pum (*bicolor*) . . BICOLOR B.
macdou'gali (*jonesi*) . MACDOUGAL L.
macrocar'pum (*Cogswellia macrocarpa*) BIGSEED L.
nudicau'le (*Cogswellia nudicaulis; C. platyphylla*) . . . . BARESTEM L.
sim'plex (*Cogswellia s.*) NARROWLEAF L.
triterna'tum (*Cogswellia triternata*) NINELEAF L.
—anom'alum (*L. anomalum; Cogswellia anomala*)

LONIC'ERA (*DISTEGIA; XYLOSTEON*) . . HONEYSUCKLE
cilio'sa . . . WESTERN TRUMPET H.

RANGE PLANTS (LONICERA), continued

conjugia'lis (*Xylosteon conjugiale*) PURPLEFLOWER HONEYSUCKLE
hispid'ula vac'illans (*L. californica; L. hispidula c.*) . . . CALIFORNIA H.
interrup'ta . . . . . . CHAPARRAL H.
involucra'ta (*Distegia i.*) BEARBERRY H.
ledebour'i (*L. involucrata l.; Distegia l.*) . . . . LEDEBOUR H.
This may be a synonym of L. involucrata.
subspica'ta . . . . . . MORONEL H.
utahen'sis . . . . UTAH H.

LOPHOPH'ORA wil'liamsi MESCALBUTTON PEYOTE

LO'TUS (*ACMISPON; ANISOLOTUS; HOSACKIA*) DEERVETCH
america'nus (*Acmispon americanum; Hosackia americana; H. purshiana*) SPANISHCLOVER D.
crassifo'lius (*Anisolotus c.; Hosackia crassifolia*) . . . . BIG D.
doug'lasi (*Anisolotus decumbens*) DOUGLAS D.
humistra'tus (*Anisolotus h.; Hosackia h.*) . . . . FOOTHILL D.
longebractea'tus (*Anisolotus l.*) LONGBRACT D.
micran'thus (*parviflorus*) LITTLEFLOWER D.
oblongifo'lius (*Hosackia oblongifolia*) STREAM D.
rig'idus (*Hosackia rigida*) . SHRUBBY D.
scopa'rius (*glaber; Hosackia glabra*) BROOM D.
subpinna'tus . . . . . . CHILEAN D.
wright'i . . . . WRIGHT D.
(*Red-and-Yellow Pea*)

LUPI'NUS . . . . LUPINE
See also **POISONOUS PLANTS.**

alpes'tris . . . . . . MOUNTAIN L.
ar'idus tor'reyi (*L. torreyi*) TORREY L.
bi'color . . . . BICOLOR L.
burk'ei . . . . BURKE L.
can'dicans
coma'tus . . . . SPREADINGHAIR L.
concin'nus (*micensis*) . . BAJADA L.
hill'i . . . . HILLS L.
king'i . . . . KINGS L.
orna'tus . . . . ORNATE L.
pal'meri . . . . PALMER L.
parviflo'rus (*floribundus*) LODGEPOLE L.
pi'peri . . . . PIPER L.
polyphyl'lus . . . . . WASHINGTON L.
pseudoparviflo'rus . . . MONTANA L.
rivula'ris . . . . STREAM L.
saxo'sus . . . . ROCK L.
seric'eus . . . . SILKY L.
spathula'tus . . . . . SPATULATE L.
sulphu'reus . . . . SULFUR L.
superb'us . . . . MEADOW L.
tor'reyi . . . . **L. aridus t.**

LU'ZULA (*JUNCOIDES*) WOODRUSH
como'sa . . . . HAIRY W.
multiflo'ra
parviflo'ra . . . . MILLET W.
spica'ta . . . . SPIKE W.
subconges'ta . . . . . . DONNER W.
sudet'ica . . . . SUDETIC W.

LYCH'NIS drum'mondi DRUMMOND CAMPION

LY'CIUM . . . . . . WOLFBERRY
fre'monti . . . . FREMONT W.
pal'lidum . . . . PALE W.

RANGE PLANTS, continued

LYGODES'MIA . SKELETONPLANT
jun'cea . . . . RUSH S.
spino'sa . . . . THORN S.

LYSICH'ITUM america'num (*camtschatense* Auth. in part) AMERICAN YELLOWSKUNKCABBAGE

MACDOUGAL'IA . . **ACTINEA**

MACHAERAN'THERA **ASTER**

MACRONE'MA . **APLOPAPPUS**

MACROSIPHO'NIA brachysi'phon ARIZONA LONGTUBE

MA'DIA glomera'ta CLUSTER TARWEED

MAHO'NIA (*ODOSTEMON*) MAHONIA
aquifo'lium . . . . . OREGONGRAPE
fre'monti . . . . FREMONT M.
haematocar'pa . . . . RED M.
nervo'sa . . . . CASCADES M.
re'pens . . . . CREEPING M.

Maira'nia alpi'na . **Arctous alpinus**

MALA'CHE . . . . . **PAVONIA**

MA'LUS fus'ca OREGON CRABAPPLE

MAL'VA rotundifo'lia RUNNING MALLOW

MALVAVIS'CUS drum'mondi DRUMMOND WAXMALLOW

MAMMILLA'RIA . MAMMILLARIA

MARRU'BIUM vulga're COMMON HOARHOUND

MARSIL'EA . . . . PEPPERWORT

Martyn'ia louisia'na **Proboscidea jussieui**

MATRICA'RIA matricarioi'des (*suaveolens*) . . . PINEAPPLEWEED

MEDICA'GO . . . . MEDIC
his'pida . . CALIFORNIA BURCLOVER
lupuli'na . . . . BLACK M.

MEIBO'MIA . . **DESMODIUM**

MELAMPO'DIUM leucan'thum PLAINS BLACKFOOT

MELILO'TUS . . SWEETCLOVER
al'ba . . . . WHITE S.
in'dica . . . . ANNUAL YELLOW S.
officina'lis . . . . . . YELLOW S.

MELO'CHIA pyramida'ta

MENODO'RA . . . . MENODORA
lae'vis . . . . SMOOTH M.
longiflo'ra . . . . SHOWY M.
sca'bra . . . . ROUGH M.

MEN'THA canaden'sis CANADA MINT

MENTZE'LIA . . . MENTZELIA
albicau'lis (*Acrolasia a.*) WHITESTEM M.
multiflo'ra . . . . DESERT M.

MENZIE'SIA . . . . . MENZIESIA
ferrugin'ea . . . . RUSTY M.
glabel'la . . . . SMOOTH M.

MERTEN'SIA . . . . BLUEBELLS
amoe'na . . . . . YELLOWSTONE B.
brevis'tyla . . . . . SHORTSTYLE B.
cilia'ta (*M. c. longipedunculata; polyphylla*) . . . . . . MOUNTAIN B.

RANGE PLANTS (MERTENSIA), continued
cilia'ta stomatechoi'des SIERRA MOUNTAIN BLUEBELLS
folio'sa . . . . LEAFY B.
francisca'na (*pratensis*) FRANCISCAN B.
fusifor'mis . . . . SPINDLEROOT B.
interme'dia
lanceola'ta . . . . . LANCELEAF B.
leonard'i (*sampsoni*) . . . . TALL B.
longiflo'ra (*pulchella; M. p. glauca*) SMALL B.
oblongifo'lia . . . OBLONGLEAF B.
panicula'ta . . . . PANICLE B.
—borea'lis (*M. laevigata*)
polyphyl'la . . . . **M. ciliata**
tweed'yi . . . . TWEEDY B.

MESEMBRYAN'THEMUM chilen'se (*aequilaterale* Auth., *not* Haw.) . CHILEAN MESEMBRYANTHEMUM (*Seafig*)

MICRO'SERIS nu'tans (*Ptilocalais n.*) . . . NODDING MICROSERIS

MIMO'SA . . . . MIMOSA
biuncif'era . . . . . CATCLAW M.
borea'lis (*fragrans*) . FRAGRANT M.
dysocar'pa . . . . . VELVETPOD M.

MIM'ULUS (*DIPLACUS*) MONKEYFLOWER
auranti'acus (*Diplacus a.*) . BUSH M.
cardina'lis . . . . . . CRIMSON M.
floribun'dus
gutta'tus . . . . COMMON M.
lew'isi . . . . LEWIS M.
moscha'tus . . . . MUSKPLANT M.
na'nus . . . . DWARF M.
rubel'lus

MIRAB'ILIS (*HESPERONIA*) FOUR-O'CLOCK
lae'vis (*Hesperonia l.*)
multiflo'ra (*Quamoclidion multiflorum*) COLORADO F.
retror'sa (*Hesperonia laevis r.; H. retrorsa*) . . . . WISHBONEPLANT

MITEL'LA . . . . . MITERWORT (*Bishopscap*)
pentan'dra . . . . FIVESTAMEN M.
stenopet'ala . . . SMALLFLOWER M.

MOLDA'VICA **DRACOCEPHALUM**

MOLLU'GO verticilla'ta CARPETWEED

MONAR'DA . . . . . BEEBALM
menthaefo'lia . . . . MINTLEAF B.
pectina'ta . . . . PONY B.

MONARDEL'LA odoratis'sima PACIFIC MONARDELLA

MONE'SES uniflo'ra (*Pyrola u.*) WOODNYMPH

MONOLE'PIS . . . MONOLEPIS
nuttallia'na . . . . . . NUTTALL M.

MONOT'ROPA uniflo'ra INDIANPIPE

MYOSO'TIS alpes'tris ALPINE FORGETMENOT

MYOSU'RUS . . . . MOUSETAIL

NAVARRE'TIA . . . . . **GILIA**

NEGUN'DO . . . . **ACER**

NEMOPH'ILA . . NEMOPHILA
breviflo'ra . . . . GREAT BASIN N.
menzies'i . . . . BABYBLUE-EYES N.

NEP'ETA cata'ria . . . . CATNIP

RANGE PLANTS, continued

NICOTIA'NA . . . . . . TOBACCO
attenua'ta . . . . COYOTE T.
glau'ca . . . . TREE T.
trigonophyl'la . . . . . DESERT T.

NOLI'NA microcar'pa . SACAHUISTA

NOR'TA . . . . **SISYMBRIUM**

ODOS'TEMON . . **MAHONIA**

OENOTHE'RA (*Anogra; Chylismia; Galpinsia; Lavauxia; Pachylophus; Sphaerostigma; Taraxia*) EVENINGPRIMROSE; SUNDROPS
alyssoi'des (*Sphaerostigma a.*) ALYSSUM E.
andi'na (*Sphaerostigma andinum*) ANDEAN S.
breviflo'ra (*Taraxia b.*)
caespito'sa (*Pachylophus caespitosus*) TUFTED E.
—crini'ta (*Pachylophus crinitus*)
—margina'ta (*Pachylophus marginatus*)
coronopifo'lia (*Anogra c.*)
fla'va (*Lavauxia f.*) . . YELLOW E.
heteran'tha . . . . . . **O. subacaulis**
hook'eri . . . . HOOKER E.
lavandulaefo'lia (*Galpinsia l.*) LAVENDERLEAF E.
pal'lida (*Anogra p.*) . . . . PALE E.
scapoi'dea (*Chylismia s.*)
strigo'sa
subacau'lis (*heterantha; Taraxia h.; T. subacaulis*)
tanacetifo'lia (*Taraxia t.*) TANSYLEAF E.
utahen'sis (*Sphaerostigma utahense*) UTAH E.

OL'NEYA teso'ta . . . . TESOTA

OPULAS'TER . **PHYSOCARPUS**

OPUN'TIA . PRICKLYPEAR; CHOLLA
dille'ni (*horrida*) . . . . . DILLEN P.
engelmann'i . . . . ENGELMANN P.
imbrica'ta (*arborescens*) WALKINGSTICK C.
polyacan'tha (*missouriensis*) PLAINS P.
treleas'ei . . . . TRELEASE P.

OREOCA'RYA . **CRYPTANTHA**

OREOSTEM'MA . . . . **ASTER**

OROBAN'CHE ludovicia'na LOUISIANA BROOMRAPE

OROGE'NIA linearifo'lia INDIANPOTATO

ORTHOCAR'PUS . . OWLCLOVER
erian'thus . . . . JOHNNYTUCK O.
lute'us . . . . YELLOW O.
purpuras'cens . . . . ESCOBITA O.
purpureo-al'bus . . PURPLEWHITE O.
tol'miei . . . . TOLMIE O.

OSMARO'NIA cerasifor'mis OSOBERRY

OSMORHI'ZA . . . SWEETROOT
divarica'ta . . . . . SPREADING S.
obtu'sa . . . . . . BLUNTSEED S.
occidenta'lis . . . . . SWEETANISE

OX'ALIS . . . . OXALIS

OXYCOC'CUS . . . **VACCINIUM**

OXYR'IA di'gyna ALPINE MOUNTAINSORREL

OXYTE'NIA acero'sa PRICKLY OXYTENIA

OXYTHE'CA . . . . . OXYTHECA

RANGE PLANTS, continued

OXYT'ROPIS bes'seyi BESSEY POINTVETCH
See also **POISONOUS PLANTS.**

PACHIS'TIMA myrsini'tes MYRTLE PACHISTIMA

PACHYLO'PHUS **OENOTHERA**

PAEO'NIA brown'i BROWNS PEONY

PARKINSO'NIA
aculea'ta . . . . . JERUSALEMTHORN
microphyl'la. **Cercidium microphyllum**

PARNAS'SIA . . . . . PARNASSIA

PARONY'CHIA . . . . NAILWORT

PAROSE'LA . . . . . **DALEA**

Par'rya menzies'i **Phoenicaulis cheiranthoides**

PARTHE'NIUM inca'num MARIOLA PARTHENIUM

PARTHENOCIS'SUS inser'ta (*vitacea*) . . . . THICKET CREEPER

PAVO'NIA lasiopet'ala (*Malache l.*) WRIGHTS PAVONIA

PEDICULA'RIS . . . PEDICULARIS
bracteo'sa . . . . . . BRACTED P.
centran'thera . . . . . . DWARF P.
contor'ta . . . . COILED P.
crenula'ta . . . . . . MEADOW P.
densiflo'ra . . . INDIANWARRIOR P.
gray'i . . . . GRAYS P.
groenland'ica . . ELEPHANTHEAD P.
lanceola'ta . . . . SWAMP P.
racemo'sa . . . . . . SICKLETOP P.

PELTIPHYL'LUM **SAXIFRAGA**

PENSTE'MON . . . PENSTEMON
The original spelling of this generic name is Penstemon, and that spelling has recently been adopted by specialists in Scrophulariaceae despite the time-honored usage of the great botanists of the past, such as Torrey and Gray.

al'bidus . . . . WHITE P.
ar'idus . . . . STIFFLEAF P.
attenua'tus . . . . SULFUR P.
barba'tus (*Chelone barbata*) BEARDLIP P.
—tor'reyi . . . . **P. torreyi**
breviflo'rus . . . . STUBFLOWER P.
brevifo'lius (*brevis*) . SHORTLEAF P.
brid'gesi . . . . BRIDGES P.
cacu'minis (*pulchellus* Greene) DAINTY P.
caespito'sus . . . . MAT P.
centranthifo'lius . SCARLETBUGLER P.
comarrhe'nus . . . . . . DUSTY P.
confer'tus . . . . . . YELLOW P.
—coeruleo-purpu'reus
—globo'sus
confu'sus . . . . **P. utahensis**
cyanan'thus . . . . . . WASATCH P.
—subgla'ber . . NARROWLEAF W.P.
davidso'ni . . . . . . DAVIDSON P.
deus'tus . . . . SCABLAND P.
diffu'sus . . . . COAST P.
eat'oni . . . . EATON P.
ellip'ticus . . . . ROCKVINE P.
erian'therus (*cristatus*) FUZZYTONGUE P.
frutico'sus . . . . BUSH P.
gla'ber . . . . SAWSEPAL P.
glabres'cens . . . . . **P. teucrioides**
glau'cus . . . . BLUELEAF P.
gracilen'tus . . . . . . SLIMSTEM P.
heterodox'us . . . . . HERETIC P.
heterophyl'lus . . . . CHAPARRAL P.
hu'milis . . . . LOW P.

RANGE PLANTS (PENSTEMON), continued

ken'nedyi . . KENNEDY PENSTEMON
king'i . . . . KINGS P.
lae'tus . . . . GAY P.
leiophyl'lus . . . . **P. subglaber**
lem'moni . . . . LEMMONS P.
linarioi'des . . . . . . TOADFLAX P.
menzies'i . . . . MENZIES P.
—*scou'leri* . . . . **P. scouleri**
monta'nus (*woodsi*) . . CORDROOT P.
newber'ryi . . . . . NEWBERRY P.
nit'idus . . . . WAXLEAF P.
ova'tus . . . . EGGLEAF P.
pachyphyl'lus . . . . THICKLEAF P.
pal'meri . . . . PALMER P.
proten'sis . . . . . . **P. washoensis**
proce'rus . . . . LITTLEFLOWER P.
pseudoproce'rus (*oweni; pseudohumilis* Rydb., *not* Jones) . BRIDGER P.
radico'sus . . . . . . MATROOT P.
richardso'ni . . . . . RICHARDSON P.
roez'li . . . . PLACER P.
rydberg'i . . . . RYDBERG P.
scou'leri (*P. menziesi s.*). SCOULER P.
secundiflo'rus . . . . . SIDEBELLS P.
specio'sus . . . . ROYAL P.
spectab'ilis . . . . SHOWY P.
stric'tus . . . ROCKYMOUNTAIN P.
subgla'ber (*leiophyllus; utahensis* (S. Wats.) A. Nels., *not* Eastw.)
teucrioi'des (*glabrescens*) GERMANDER P.
tor'reyi (*P. barbatus t.*) . . TORREY P.
unilatera'lis (*secundiflorus* A. Gray, *not* Benth.) . . . . ONESIDE P.
utahen'sis (*confusus*) . . . UTAH P.
venus'tus . . . . BLUEMOUNTAINS P.
virga'tus . . . . . WANDBLOOM P.
washoen'sis (*pratensis*) . WASHOE P.
watso'ni . . . . WATSON P.
whipplea'nus . . . . . WHIPPLE P.
woods'i . . . . **P. montanus**
wright'i . . . . WRIGHTS P.

PENTZ'IA inca'na AUSTRALIAN SHEEPBUSH

PERA'MIUM . . . **GOODYERA**

PERAPHYL'LUM ramosis'simum SQUAWAPPLE

PERIDERID'IA gaird'neri (*Carum g.*) . . . . YAMPA

PERSICA'RIA . **POLYGONUM**

PETALOSTE'MON . (*KUHNISTERA; PETALOSTEMUM*) PRAIRIECLOVER

Petrado'ria pu'mila **Solidago petradoria**

PHACE'LIA . . . . . PHACELIA
alpi'na . . . . ALPINE P.
frank'lini . . . . FRANKLIN P.
glandulo'sa . . . . . . GLANDULAR P.
heterophyl'la . . . . . . VARILEAF P.
idahoen'sis . . . . IDAHO P.
leucophyl'la . . . . . SILVERLEAF P.
linea'ris . . . . . . THREADLEAF P.
ramosis'sima . . . . . BRANCHING P.
seric'ea . . . . SILKY P.

PHASE'OLUS . . . . . . BEAN
angustis'simus . . . SLIMLEAF B.
metcalf'ei (*retusus* Benth., *not* Moench) METCALFE B.

PHELLOP'TERUS utahen'sis UTAH CORKWING

PHILADEL'PHUS. . MOCKORANGE
califor'nicus (*P. lewisi c.*) CALIFORNIA M.

RANGE PLANTS (PHILADELPHUS), con.

gordonia'nus . GORDON MOCKORANGE
lew'isi . . . . LEWIS M.
microphyl'lus . . . . LITTLELEAF M.

PHLOX' . . . . PHLOX
austromonta'na . . . . DESERT P.
caespito'sa . . . . TUFTED P.
canes'cens . . . . HOARY P.
diffu'sa. . . . . SPREADING P.

This variable species is often misidentified as P. douglasi.

drum'mondi (*cuspidata*) DRUMMOND P.
longifo'lia . . . . . . LONGLEAF P.

This species is often misidentified as P. stansburyi.

multiflo'ra (*costata*) . . FLOWERY P.
—**depres'sa** (*P. depressa*) DWARF F.P.
specio'sa . . . . SHOWY P.

PHOENICAU'LIS cheiranthoi'des (*Parrya menziesi*) WALLFLOWER PHOENICAULIS

PHORADEN'DRON juniperi'num JUNIPER AMERICAN-MISTLETOE

PHOTIN'IA arbutifo'lia (*Heteromeles a.; H. salicifolia*) CHRISTMASBERRY

PHYLLO'DOCE . MOUNTAINHEATH
brew'eri . . . . BREWER M.
empetrifor'mis . . . . . . RED M.
glanduliflo'ra . . . . . . CREAM M.

PHY'SALIS . . . GROUNDCHERRY

PHYSA'RIA didymocar'pa COMMON TWINPOD

PHYSOCAR'PUS (*OPULASTER*) NINEBARK
capita'tus . . . . PACIFIC N.
malva'ceus (*pauciflorus*). MALLOW N.
monog'ynus . . . . . MOUNTAIN N.

PISTAC'IA texa'na TEXAS PISTACHE

PITHECELLO'BIUM unguisca'ti CATCLAW APES-EARRING

PLAGIOBO'THRYS (*ALLOCARYA*) . . . . POPCORNFLOWER

PLANTA'GO . . . . . PLANTAIN

The small native annuals of the Southwest are known as Indianwheat and are palatable sheep weeds.

fastigia'ta . DESERT INDIANWHEAT
lanceola'ta . . . . . BUCKHORN P.
ma'jor . . . . . . RIPPLESEED P.
pursh'i . . . WOOLLY INDIANWHEAT
tweed'yi . . . . TWEEDY P.

PLECTRI'TIS macro'cera LONGHORN PLECTRITIS

PLU'CHEA seric'ea ARROWWEED PLUCHEA

POLEMO'NIUM . . POLEMONIUM
albiflo'rum . . . . WHITE P.
caeru'leum . . . GREEKVALERIAN P.
confer'tum . . . . . . SKYPILOT P.
foliosis'simum . . . . . LEAFY P.
occidenta'le . . . . . . WESTERN P.
pulcher'rimum . . . SKUNKLEAF P.
scopuli'num . . . . CLIFF P.

POLIOMIN'THA inca'na HOARY ROSEMARYMINT

POLYCO'DIUM . . **VACCINIUM**

POLYG'ALA . . . . . POLYGALA
acanthoc'lada . . . . . . THORN P.
sen'ega . . . SENECA-SNAKEROOT P.
subspino'sa . . . . SPINY P.

RANGE PLANTS, continued

POLYG'ONUM (*ACONOGONUM; BILDERDYKIA; BISTORTA; PERSICARIA*) KNOTWEED

Many botanists prefer to regard the subgenera or sections of Polygonum as distinct genera. All have well-defined common names as follows: §Aconogonum and allies, Fleeceflower; §Bilderdykia (*Tiniaria*), Cornbind; §Bistorta, Bistort; §Persicaria, Smartweed, Ladysthumb.

amphib'ium (*Persicaria amphibia*) WATER LADYSTHUMB
avicula're. . . . . . . PROSTRATE K.
bistortoi'des (*Bistorta b.*) AMERICAN BISTORT
buxifor'me . . . . BOX K.
convol'vulus (*Bilderdykia c.*) DULLSEED CORNBIND
doug'lasi . . . . DOUGLAS K.
lapathifo'lium (*Persicaria lapathifolia*) CURLTOP LADYSTHUMB
newber'ryi (*Aconogonum n.*) NEWBERRY FLEECEFLOWER
phytolaccaefo'lium (*Aconogonum p.*) POKEWEED FLEECEFLOWER
ramosis'simum . . . . . BUSHY K.
sawatchen'se . . . . . SAWATCH K.
vivip'arum (*Bistorta vivipara*) VIVIPAROUS BISTORT

POP'ULUS POPLAR (*Cottonwood*); ASPEN
acumina'ta (*coloradensis*) LANCELEAF P. (*Lanceleaf C.*)
angustifo'lia . . . . NARROWLEAF P. (*Narrowleaf C.*)
arizo'nica . . ARIZONA P. (*Arizona C.*)
tremuloi'des . . . . . . QUAKING A.
—**au'rea** (*P. aurea; P. a. cercidiphylla; P. cercidiphylla*) . . GOLDEN Q.A.
—**renifor'mis** . . KIDNEYLEAF Q.A.
—**vancouveria'na** (*P. vancouveriana*) VANCOUVER Q.A.
trichocar'pa . CALIFORNIA P. (*Black C.*)

POROPHYL'LUM grac'ile SLENDER PORELEAF (*Yerbedelvenado*)

PORTULAC'A olera'cea COMMON PURSLANE

POTENTIL'LA (*ARGENTINA; DASIPHORA; DRYMOCALLIS*) CINQUEFOIL
anseri'na (*Argentina a.*) SILVERWEED C.
ba'keri . . . . BAKER C.
bien'nis . . . . BIENNIAL C.
blaschkea'na . . . . BLASCHKE C.
brew'eri . . . . BREWER C.
canaden'sis . . . . . . OLDFIELD C.
concin'na (*humifusa*) . . ELEGANT C.
diversifo'lia . . . . VARILEAF C.
drum'mondi . . . . DRUMMOND C.
fi'lipes . . . . SLIMSTEM C.
fis'sa (*Drymocallis f.*) . BIGFLOWER C.
frutico'sa (*Dasiphora f.*) . . BUSH C.
glandulo'sa (*Drymocallis g.*) . GLAND C.
glaucophyl'la . . . . BLUELEAF C.
jucun'da . . . . GAY C.
nutt'alli . . . . NUTTALL C.
platten'sis . . . . PLATTE C.

PROBOSCID'EA . DEVILSCLAWS
jussieu'i (*Martynia louisiana*) COMMON D.

PROSO'PIS . . . . . MESQUITE
chilen'sis (*juliflora*) . . COMMON M.
glandulo'sa . . . . HONEY M.
odora'ta . . . . . **Strombocarpa o.**
veluti'na . . . . VELVET M.

RANGE PLANTS, continued

PRUNEL'LA vulga'ris COMMON SELFHEAL

PRU'NUS (*EMPLECTOCLADUS*) CHERRY; CHOKECHERRY; PEACHBRUSH; PLUM
america'na . . . . AMERICAN PLUM
anderso'ni (*Emplectocladus a.*) ANDERSON PEACHBRUSH
angustifo'lia wat'soni SAND CHICKASAW PLUM
demis'sa . . . . . . **P. virginiana d.**
—melanocar'pa . . . **P. virginiana m.**
emargina'ta . . . . BITTER CHERRY
fascicula'ta (*Emplectocladus fasciculatus*) . . . . DESERT PEACHBRUSH
fre'monti (*Emplectocladus f.*) FREMONT PEACHBRUSH
glandulo'sa . . . . ALMOND CHERRY
melanocar'pa . . . **P. virginiana m.**
minutiflo'ra (*Emplectocladus minutiflorus*). SMALLFLOWER PEACHBRUSH
pensylva'nica . . . . . PIN CHERRY
prunifo'lia . . . PLUMLEAF CHERRY
subcorda'ta . . . . . KLAMATH PLUM
—kel'loggi . . . . . KELLOGG K.P.
vi'rens. SOUTHWESTERN CHOKECHERRY
virginia'na . COMMON CHOKECHERRY
—demis'sa (*P. demissa*) WESTERN C.C.
—melanocar'pa (*P. demissa m.; P. melanocarpa*) . . . . BLACK C.C.

PSEUDOCYMOP'TERUS monta'nus

PSILOS'TROPHE. . PAPERFLOWER
coop'eri . . . . . . WHITESTEM P.
sparsiflo'ra . . . . . GREENSTEM P.

PSORA'LEA . . . . . SCURFPEA

The section of this genus (*Pediomelum*) with deep-seated, tuberous, starchy roots, and which was an important source of food among the Indians, is known as Breadroot.

argophyl'la . . . . SILVERLEAF S.
casto'rea . . . . . BEAVERBREAD S.
cuspida'ta . . . . TALLBREAD S.
esculen'ta . COMMON BREADROOT S.
hypogae'a . . . . . . LITTLE B.S.
lanceola'ta (*micrantha*) . . LEMON S.
macrosta'chya . . LEATHERROOT S.
mephit'ica . . . . . SKUNKTOP S.
physo'des . . . . CALIFORNIATEA S.
stenosta'chya
tenuiflo'ra . . . . . SLIMFLOWER S.

PTE'LEA . . . . HOPTREE
bald'wini . . . . . . BALDWIN H.
trifolia'ta . . . . . . COMMON H.

PTERID'IUM aquili'num pubes'cens WESTERN BRACKEN

PTEROS'PORA andromede'a WOODLAND PINEDROPS

Ptilocala'is nu'tans . **Microseris n.**

PTILO'RIA . **STEPHANOMERIA**

PULSATIL'LA . . **ANEMONE**

PURSH'IA . . . . . BITTERBRUSH
tridenta'ta . . . . ANTELOPE B.
—glandulo'sa . . . . DESERT B.

PYRO'LA . . . . PYROLA
chloran'tha . . . . . . GREEN P.
secun'da . . . . . . SIDEBELLS P.
uniflo'ra . . . . . . **Moneses u.**

PYRROCO'MA . **APLOPAPPUS**

QUAMA'SIA . . . **CAMASSIA**

RANGE PLANTS, continued

QUAMOCLID'ION . **MIRABILIS**

QUAM'OCLIT coccin'ea SCARLET STARGLORY

QUER'CUS . . . . OAK
arizo'nica . . . . ARIZONA WHITE O.
brew'eri . . . . . . **Q. oerstediana**
chrysol'epis . . . . CANYON LIVE O.
—vaccinifo'lia . . . . **Q. vaccinifolia**
dumo'sa . . . . CALIFORNIA SCRUB O.
emo'ryi . . . . EMORY O.
engelmann'i . . . . ENGELMANN O.
fend'leri . . . . FENDLER O.
gam'beli . . . . GAMBEL O.
garrya'na . . . . OREGON WHITE O.
—brew'eri . . . . . **Q. oerstediana**
gri'sea . . . . GRAY O.
hav'ardi . . . . HAVARD O.
hypoleu'ca . . . . . SILVERLEAF O.
kel'loggi . . . CALIFORNIA BLACK O.
loba'ta . . . CALIFORNIA WHITE O.
muhlenberg'i . . . . CHINKAPIN O.
novomexica'na . . NEWMEXICAN O.
oblongifo'lia . . MEXICAN BLUE O.
oerstedia'na (*breweri; Q. garryana b.*) BREWER O.
reticula'ta . . . . . . NETLEAF O.
sadleria'na . . . . SADLER O.
tou'meyi . . . . TOUMEY O.
turbinel'la . . . . . SHRUB LIVE O.
undula'ta . . . . . . WAVYLEAF O.
utahen'sis (*submollis*) UTAH WHITE O.
vaccinifo'lia (*Q. chrysolepis v.*) HUCKLEBERRY O.
vree'landi . . . . . VREELAND O.
wil'coxi . . . . WILCOX O.

RADIC'ULA . . . . **RORIPPA**

RANUN'CULUS (*BATRACHIUM; BECKWITHIA*) . BUTTERCUP
a'cris . . . . TALL B.
alismaefo'lius . . . PLANTAINLEAF B.
—alismel'lus (*R. alismellus*) DWARF P.B.
anderso'ni (*Beckwithia a.*) ANDERSON B.
aquat'ilis (*Batrachium aquatile*) WATERCROWFOOT B.
bon'gardi . . . . BONGARD B.
cymbala'ria saximonta'nus

According to some botanists the range form of this species is R. orthorhyncus platyphyllus.

glaber'rimus . . . . SAGEBRUSH B.
inamoe'nus
macau'leyi . . . . . . MACAULEY B.
occidenta'lis . . . . . WESTERN B.
orthorhyn'cus platyphyl'lus (*R. maximus*) . . . GREAT STRAIGHTBEAK B.

RATIB'IDA columna'ris (*columnifera*) UPRIGHT PRAIRIECONEFLOWER

RHAM'NUS . . . . . BUCKTHORN
alnifo'lia . . . . ALDER B.
califor'nica . . . . . CALIFORNIA B.
cathar'tica . . . . COMMON B.
cro'cea . . . . REDBERRY B.
—ilicifo'lia . . . . HOLLYLEAF R.B.
—insula'ris . . . . GREAT R.B.
—pilo'sa . . . . . . SANDIEGO R.B.
purshia'na . . . . CASCARA B.

RHODODEN'DRON (*AZALEA; AZALEASTRUM*) RHODODENDRON
albiflo'rum (*Azaleastrum a.*) CASCADES AZALEA

RANGE PLANTS (RHODODENDRON), con.
macrophyl'lum (*californicum*) COAST RHODODENDRON
occidenta'le (*Azalea californica; A. occidentalis*) . . WESTERN AZALEA

RHUS' . . . . SUMAC
diversilo'ba **Toxicodendron diversilobum**
emo'ryi . . . . EMORY S.
gla'bra . . . . SMOOTH S.
—cismonta'na (*R. cismontana*) ROCKYMOUNTAIN S.S.
microphyl'la . . . . LITTLELEAF S.
ova'ta . . . . SUGAR S.
rad'icans rydberg'i **Toxicodendron r. r.**
rydberg'i . . . . **Toxicodendron r. r.**
triloba'ta . . . . SKUNKBUSH S.
—anisophyl'la
utahen'sis . . . . UTAH S.

RI'BES (*GROSSULARIA*) CURRANT; GOOSEBERRY
america'num (*floridum*) AMERICAN BLACK CURRANT
au'reum . . . . . GOLDEN CURRANT
ce'reum . . . . WAX CURRANT
cilio'sum . . . . **R. triste**
divarica'tum (*Grossularia divaricata*) STRAGGLY GOOSEBERRY
hall'i . . . . HALLS CURRANT
hirtel'lum (*Grossularia hirtella*) HAIRYSTEM GOOSEBERRY
hudsonia'num. HUDSONBAY CURRANT
ine'brians (*spaethianum*) SQUAW CURRANT
iner'me (*Grossularia inermis*) WHITESTEM GOOSEBERRY
lacus'tre (*echinatum*) PRICKLY CURRANT
lobb'i (*Grossularia l.*) LOBBS GOOSEBERRY
montig'enum (*nubigenum*) GOOSEBERRY CURRANT
odora'tum (*Chrysobotrya odorata*) CLOVE CURRANT
petiola're. WESTERN BLACK CURRANT
pineto'rum (*Grossularia p.*) ORANGE GOOSEBERRY
querceto'rum (*Grossularia q.*) OAKWOODS GOOSEBERRY
roez'li (*Grossularia r.*) SIERRA GOOSEBERRY
sanguin'eum . . . WINTER CURRANT
seto'sum (*Grossularia setosa*) REDSHOOT GOOSEBERRY
spaethia'num . . . . . **R. inebrians**
specio'sum (*Grossularia speciosa*) FUCHSIA GOOSEBERRY
tris'te (*ciliosum*) AMERICAN RED CURRANT
veluti'num (*Grossularia velutina*) DESERT GOOSEBERRY
viscosis'simum . . STICKY CURRANT
watsonia'num (*Grossularia watsoniana*) WATSON GOOSEBERRY
wolf'i . . . . ROTHROCK CURRANT

ROBIN'IA . . . . LOCUST
luxur'ians (*R. neomexicana l.*) WESTERN L.
neomexica'na . . . NEWMEXICO L.
pseudoaca'cia . . . . . BLACK L.
rus'byi . . . . RUSBY L.

ROM'NEYA coul'teri MATILIJA-POPPY

RORIP'PA nasturtium-aquat'icum (*Radicula n.; Sisymbrium n.*) WATERCRESS

RO'SA . . . . ROSE
acicula'ris . . . . . . PRICKLY R.
—bourgeauia'na (*R. a. sayi*) BOURGEAU P.R.

RANGE PLANTS (ROSA), continued
acicula'ris engelmann'i (*R. engelmanni*) ENGELMANN PRICKLY ROSE
califor'nica . . . . . CALIFORNIA R.
fend'leri . . . . **R. woodsi f.**
gymnocar'pa . . . . BALDHIP R.
macoun'i . . . . . . MACOUN R.
man'ca . . . . MANCOS R.
meli'na . . . . . . BLACKSTEM R.
nutka'na . . . . NOOTKA R.
pisocar'pa . . . . . PEAFRUIT R.
pyrif'era . . . . PEARHIP R.
spal'dingi . . . . SPALDING R.
spithame'a . . . . . . GROUND R.
woods'i . . . . WOODS R.
—fend'leri (*R. fendleri*) FENDLER W.R.

RU'BUS . . . . BLACKBERRY; DEWBERRY; RASPBERRY
idae'us aculeatis'simus (*R. melanolasius*) . . . . . WESTERN RED R.
leucoder'mis . . . . WHITEBARK R.
macropet'alus . . . . . TRAILING B.
neomexica'nus . . . NEWMEXICAN R.
parviflo'rus . WESTERN THIMBLEBERRY
spectab'ilis . . . . . SALMONBERRY
—menzies'i . . . . . . MENZIES S.
ursi'nus . . . . CALIFORNIA D.

RUDBECK'IA . . . CONEFLOWER
hir'ta . . . . BLACKEYEDSUSAN
lacinia'ta . . . . CUTLEAF C.
occidenta'lis . . . . . NIGGERHEAD

RU'MEX . . . . DOCK
acetosel'la . . . . . SHEEP SORREL
cris'pus . . . . CURLY D.
hymenosep'alus . . . . . CANAIGRE
mexica'nus . . . . . . MEXICAN D.
paucifo'lius . . . MOUNTAIN SORREL
veno'sus . . . . VEINY D.

RYDBERG'IA . . . . **ACTINEA**

SAGERE'TIA wright'i WRIGHTS SAGERETIA

SAGI'NA saginoi'des ARCTIC PEARLWORT

SALAZA'RIA mexica'na MEXICAN BLADDERSAGE

SALICOR'NIA . . . GLASSWORT

SA'LIX . . . . WILLOW
al'ba . . . . WHITE W.
amygdaloi'des . . . . PEACHLEAF W.
argophyl'la . . . . . SILVERLEAF W.
bar'clayi . . . . BARCLAY W.
bebbia'na (*rostrata*) . . . BEBB W.
caespito'sa . . . . . **S. petrophila c.**
cauda'ta (*S. lasiandra c.*) WHIPLASH W.
commuta'ta . . . . UNDERGREEN W.
eastwood'iae . . . . EASTWOOD W.
exig'ua . . . . COYOTE W.
geyeria'na . . . . GEYER W.
laeviga'ta . . POLISHED W. (*Red W.*)
lasian'dra . . . . . . PACIFIC W.
lasiol'epis . . . . . . ARROYO W.
lem'moni . . . . LEMMONS W.
melanop'sis . . . . DUSKY W.
monochro'ma . . . GREENSIDES W.
montic'ola
ni'gra . . . . BLACK W.
petroph'ila . . . . . . SKYLAND W.
—caespito'sa (*S. caespitosa*) TUFTED S.W.

RANGE PLANTS (SALIX), continued
planifo'lia . . . PLANELEAF WILLOW
purpu'rea . . . . . PURPLEOSIER W.
rostra'ta . . . . **S. bebbiana**
saximonta'na . . . . . SUMMIT W.
scouleria'na . . . . . SCOULER W.
sitchen'sis . . . . SITKA W.
subcoeru'lea . . . . . . BLUE W.
tweed'yi . . . . TWEEDY W.
wolf'i idahoen'sis . IDAHO WOLFS W.

SAL'SOLA ka'li tenuifo'lia (*S. pestifer*) . TUMBLING RUSSIANTHISTLE

SAL'VIA (*AUDIBERTIA*) SAGE
apia'na (*Audibertia polystachya*) WHITE S.
carno'sa (*Audibertia incana*) DESERT S.
columba'riae . . . CALIFORNIA CHIA
eremosta'chya . . . . . . SAND S.
leucophyl'la (*Audibertia nivea*) WHITELEAF S.
mellif'era (*Audibertia stachyoides*) BLACK S.
mohaven'sis (*Audibertia capitata*) MOHAVE S.
sonomen'sis (*Audibertia humilis*) SONOMA S.

SAMBU'CUS . . . . . . ELDER
callicar'pa . . . . PACIFIC RED E.
canaden'sis . . . . . AMERICAN E.
ceru'lea (*glauca*) . . . BLUEBERRY E.
—arizo'nica . . . . . ARIZONA B.E.
—neomexica'na (*S. neomexicana*) NEWMEXICAN B.E.
—veluti'na (*S. velutina*)
melanocar'pa . . . . BLACKBEAD E.
mexica'na . . . . MEXICAN E.
microbo'trys . . . BUNCHBERRY E.
pu'bens . . . . SCARLET E.
vesti'ta . . . . CANYON E.

SANGUISOR'BA sitchen'sis SITKA BURNET

SANIC'ULA tubero'sa TUBER SANICLE

SAPIN'DUS drum'mondi WESTERN SOAPBERRY

SARCOBA'TUS . . . GREASEWOOD
bai'leyi . . . . BAILEY G.
vermicula'tus . . . . . . BLACK G.

SAXIF'RAGA . . . . . SAXIFRAGE
argu'ta . . . . BROOK S.
pelta'ta (*Peltiphyllum peltatum*) UMBRELLA S.
rhomboi'dea . . . DIAMONDLEAF S.

SCHOENOCRAM'BE PLAINSMUSTARD
linifo'lia (*pinnata*) . . . FLAXLEAF P.

SCIR'PUS . . . . . . BULRUSH
acu'tus (*occidentalis*) . . . TULE B.
microcar'pus . . . . PANICLED B.

SCROPHULA'RIA . . FIGWORT
califor'nica . . . . CALIFORNIA F.
occidenta'lis . . . . . WESTERN F.

SCUTELLA'RIA . . . SKULLCAP

SECURINE'GA . . . SECURINEGA

SE'DUM . . . . STONECROP
doug'lasi
stenopet'alum . . . . WORMLEAF S.

SELAGINEL'LA . . SELAGINELLA

RANGE PLANTS, continued
SELINOCAR'PUS diffu'sus MOONPOD

SENE'CIO . . . . . GROUNDSEL
acce'dens . . . COLORADO NODDING G.
ambrosioi'des . . . . . RAGWEED G.
amplec'tens . . . SHOWY ALPINE G.
aronicoi'des . . . . . RAYLESS G.
atra'tus . . . . BLACK G.
au'reus (*pseudaureus*) . GOLDEN G.
canovi'rens . . . . . GRAYGREEN G.
ca'nus . . . . WOOLLY G.
columbia'nus . . . . COLUMBIA G.
cras'sulus . . . . . THICKLEAF G.
croca'tus (*croceus*) . . . SAFFRON G.
cymbalarioi'des . . . CLEFTLEAF G.
doug'lasi . . . . DOUGLAS G.
eremoph'ilus . . . . . DESERT G.
fre'monti . . . . FREMONT G.
glauces'cens . . . . . FLODMAN G.
hydroph'ilus . . . . . . WATER G.
integer'rimus (*perplexus*) LAMBSTONGUE G.
longilo'bus (*filifolius*) THREADLEAF G.
multiloba'tus . . . . . LOBELEAF G.
neomexica'nus . . NEWMEXICO G.
pseudau'reus . . . . . . **S. aureus**
purshia'nus . . . . PURSH G.
ser'ra . . . . . . BUTTERWEED G.
—integrius'cula . . WHOLELEAF B.G.
spartioi'des . . . . BROOM G.
triangula'ris . . . . ARROWLEAF G.
uintahen'sis . . . . . . UINTA G.
vulga'ris . . . . COMMON G.

SERICOTHE'CA . **HOLODISCUS**

SHEPHERD'IA (*LEPARGYREA*) BUFFALOBERRY
argen'tea . . . . SILVER B.
canaden'sis . . . . . . RUSSET B.
rotundifo'lia . . . . ROUNDLEAF B.

SIDAL'CEA . . CHECKERMALLOW
can'dida . . . . WHITE C.
glauces'cens . . . . BIRD C.
nerva'ta . . . . NELSON C.
orega'na . . . . OREGON C.

SIDERAN'THUS **APLOPAPPUS**

SIEVER'SIA . . . . . SIEVERSIA
cilia'ta . . . . . . PRAIRIESMOKE S.
turbina'ta . . . . GOLDEN S.

SILE'NE . . . . SILENE
antirrhi'na SLEEPY S. (*Sleepy Catchfly*)
menzies'i . . . . MENZIES S.
scou'leri . . . . SCOULER S.

SIMMOND'SIA chinen'sis (*californica*) . . . . CALIFORNIA JOJOBA

SISYM'BRIUM altis'simum (*Norta altissima*) . . . TUMBLEMUSTARD
nasturtium-aquat'icum . . **Rorippa n.**

SISYM'BRIUM in part **DESCURAINIA**

SISYRIN'CHIUM. BLUE-EYEDGRASS
angustifo'lium . . . . COMMON B.
occidenta'le . . . . . MONTANA B.

SMELOW'SKIA calyc'ina (*americana*)

SMILACI'NA (*VAGNERA*) SOLOMONPLUME
amplexicau'lis . . . . FAT S.
stella'ta (*lilacea*) . . . . . STARRY S.

Hort. var.; HV. = horticultural variety (or varieties); sp. = species (singular); spp. = species (plural).
¢ = clon; × (as a prefix) = hybrid; × (between scientific plant names) = crossed by; ∞ = polybrid; |w = plant useful to wildlife.
See Glossary for definitions of clon, hybrid, and polybrid.

RANGE PLANTS, continued

SOLA'NUM . . . . NIGHTSHADE
doug'lasi . . . . DOUGLAS N.
fend'leri . . . . . FENDLER POTATO
ni'grum . . . . BLACK N.
rostra'tum . . . . BUFFALOBUR N.
triflo'rum . . . . . . CUTLEAF N.

SOLIDA'GO . . . . GOLDENROD
arizo'nica . . . . ARIZONA G.
califor'nica . . . . . CALIFORNIA G.
canaden'sis . . . . CANADA G.
cilio'sa
concin'na . . . . NELSON G.
decum'bens . . . . . DECUMBENT G.
elonga'ta . . . . CREEK G.
missourien'sis . . . . MISSOURI G.
par'ryi . . . . PARRY G.
petrado'ria (*pumila; Petradoria pumila*) ROCK G.
trinerva'ta . . . . THREENERVE G.

SON'CHUS . . . . SOWTHISTLE

SOPHI'A . . . . **DESCURAINIA**

SOPHO'RA secundiflo'ra (*Broussonetia s.*) MESCALBEAN SOPHORA

SOR'BUS . . . . MOUNTAINASH
america'na . . . . . AMERICAN M.
dumo'sa . . . . ARIZONA M.
occidenta'lis . . . . . WESTERN M.
sambucifo'lia . . . . . SIBERIAN M.
scopuli'na . . . . . GREENES M.
sitchen'sis . . . . . . PACIFIC M.

SPHACE'LE calyc'ina . WOODBALM

SPHAERAL'CEA . GLOBEMALLOW
caespito'sa . . . . . . TUFTED G.
coccin'ea . . . . SCARLET G.
fre'monti . . . . FREMONT G.
grossulariaefo'lia GOOSEBERRYLEAF G.
munroa'na . . . . MUNRO G.
rivula'ris . . . . STREAM G.

SPHAEROSTIG'MA **OENOTHERA**

SPHENOSCIA'DIUM capitella'tum RANGE WOOLLYHEADPARSNIP

SPIRAE'A . . . . SPIREA
densiflo'ra . . . . . SUBALPINE S.
doug'lasi . . . . DOUGLAS S.
lu'cida . . . . SHINYLEAF S.
menzies'i . . . . MENZIES S.
tomento'sa . . . . . HARDHACK S.

SPIRAN'THES romanzoffia'na (*Ibidium romanzoffianum*) CONTINENTAL LADIESTRESSES

STAN'LEYA . . . PRINCESPLUME
pinna'ta (*arcuata*) . . . . DESERT P.
—integrifo'lia (*S. i.*) WHOLELEAF D.P.

STELLA'RIA (*ALSINE*) STARWORT
jamesia'na . . . . TUBER S.
lon'gipes . . . . . . LONGSTALK S.
me'dia . . . . CHICKWEED

STENOTOP'SIS; STENO'TUS **APLOPAPPUS**

STEPHANOME'RIA (*PTILORIA*) WIRELETTUCE

STREPTAN'THUS corda'tus HEARTLEAF TWISTFLOWER

STROMBOCAR'PA . SCREWBEAN

Regarded by some botanists as a section of the Mesquite genus (Prosopis).

cineras'cens . . . . . . DWARF S.
odora'ta (*Prosopis o.*) . FREMONT S.

RANGE PLANTS, continued

STY'RAX califor'nica CALIFORNIA SNOWBELL

SUAE'DA (*DONDIA*). SEEPWEED

SYMPHORICAR'POS. SNOWBERRY
al'bus . . . . COMMON S.
—pauciflo'rus . . . . . DWARF C.S.
longiflo'rus . . . . LONGFLOWER S.
mol'lis . . . . SPREADING S.
orbicula'tus (*vulgaris*) INDIANCURRANT CORALBERRY
oreoph'ilus . . . . . MOUNTAIN S.
rotundifo'lius . . . . ROUNDLEAF S.
vaccinioi'des . . . WHORTLELEAF S.

SYN'THYRIS . . . . KITTENTAILS

TAGE'TES micran'tha LITTLE MARIGOLD

TARAX'ACUM officina'le (*Leontodon taraxacum*). COMMON DANDELION

TARAX'IA . . . **OENOTHERA**

TETRACOC'CUS . FOURPODSPURGE

TETRADYM'IA . . . HORSEBRUSH
axilla'ris . . . . . . LONGSPINE H.
canes'cens . . . . GRAY H.
—iner'mis . . . . SPINELESS G.H.
nutt'alli . . . . NUTTALL H.
spino'sa . . . . . COTTONTHORN H.

TETRANEU'RIS . . **ACTINEA**

THALIC'TRUM . . . MEADOWRUE
fend'leri . . . . FENDLER M.
occidenta'le . . . . . WESTERN M.

THAMNOS'MA . . DESERTRUE
monta'na . . . . MOHAVE D.
texa'na . . . . TEXAS D.

THELESPER'MA . GREENTHREAD

THERMOP'SIS . . . THERMOPSIS
carolinia'na . . . . . . CAROLINA T.
faba'cea . . . . BEAN T.
mol'lis . . . . SOFT T.
monta'na . . . . MOUNTAIN T.
pineto'rum . . . . PINE T.

THLAS'PI . . . . . PENNYCRESS
arven'se . . . . FIELD P.
glau'cum . . . . BLUE P.

Thurber'ia thespesioi'des **Gossypium thurberi**

TITHYMALOP'SIS; TITHYMA'LUS . . . **EUPHORBIA**

TI'UM . . . . **ASTRAGALUS**

TONES'TUS . . . **APLOPAPPUS**

TOWNSEND'IA . . TOWNSENDIA
exsca'pa (*sericea*) . . . STEMLESS T.
inca'na . . . . HOARY T.
par'ryi . . . . PARRY T.
scapig'era . . . . TUFTED T.

TOXICODEN'DRON
diversilo'bum (*Rhus diversiloba*) PACIFIC POISONOAK
rad'icans rydberg'i (*T. rydbergi; Rhus r.r.; R. rydbergi*) WESTERN POISONIVY

TRADESCAN'TIA . SPIDERWORT

TRA'GIA . . . . NOSEBURN

TRAGOPO'GON . . . . SALSIFY
porrifo'lius . . VEGETABLE-OYSTER S.
praten'sis . . . . MEADOW S.

RANGE PLANTS, continued

TRIB'ULUS terres'tris PUNCTUREVINE

TRICHOSTE'MA . . BLUECURLS

TRIENTA'LIS latifo'lia WESTERN STARFLOWER

TRIFO'LIUM . . . . . CLOVER
acicula're . . . . **T. tridentatum**
albopurpu'reum . . . RANCHERIA C.
beck'withi . . . . . . BECKWITH C.
brew'eri . . . . BREWER C.
cyathif'erum . . . . CUP C.
dasyphyl'lum . . . . WHIPROOT C.
erioceph'alum . . . WOOLLYHEAD C.
fend'leri . . . . FENDLER C.
fimbria'tum . . . . . . COLUMBIA C.
gracilen'tum . . . . . PINPOINT C.
gymnocar'pon . . . . HOLLYLEAF C.
hy'bridum . . . . ALSIKE C.
involucra'tum Ortega, *not* Lam. **T. wormskjoldi**
king'i (*productum*) . . . . KINGS C.
lac'erum . . . . CUTCOLLAR C.
latifo'lium . . . . TWIN C.
lon'gipes . . . . LONGSTALK C.
macroceph'alum . . . . BIGHEAD C.
microceph'alum . . . LITTLEHEAD C.
na'num . . . . DWARF C.
par'ryi . . . . PARRY C.
praten'se . . . . RED C.
produc'tum . . . . **T. kingi**
re'pens . . . . WHITE C.
rus'byi . . . . RUSBY C.
rydberg'i . . . . RYDBERG C.
tridenta'tum (*aciculare*) . TOMCAT C.
variega'tum . . . . . . WHITETIP C.
wormskjold'i (*involucratum* Ortega, *not* Lam.) . . . . SIERRA C.

TRIL'LIUM ova'tum PACIFIC TRILLIUM

Tritelei'a grandiflo'ra **Brodiaea douglasi**

TRIX'IS califor'nica AMERICAN TRIXIS

TROL'LIUS albiflo'rus WHITE GLOBEFLOWER

TY'PHA latifo'lia COMMON CATTAIL

U'LEX europae'us. COMMON GORSE

UMBELLULA'RIA califor'nica CALIFORNIALAUREL

UNGNA'DIA specio'sa MEXICANBUCKEYE

URTI'CA . . . . NETTLE

VACCIN'IUM (*OXYCOCCUS; POLYCODIUM*) . BLUEBERRY
angustifo'lium . . . . LOWBUSH B.
canaden'se . . . . CANADA B.
cespito'sum . . . . DWARF B.
—arbus'cula . . . . . TALLER D.B.
corymbo'sum . . . . HIGHBUSH B.
delicio'sum . . . . . DELICIOUS B.
membrana'ceum . BIG WHORTLEBERRY
occidenta'le . . . . WESTERNBOG B.
oreoph'ilum ROCKYMOUNTAIN WHORTLEBERRY
ovalifo'lium . . . . . OVALLEAF W.
ova'tum . . . . BOX B.
oxycoc'cos (*Oxycoccus palustris*) SMALL CRANBERRY
—interme'dium (*Oxycoccus intermedius; O. palustris intermedius*) WESTERN S.C.
parvifo'lium . . RED WHORTLEBERRY

RANGE PLANTS (VACCINIUM), continued
scopa'rium . Grouse Whortleberry
virga'tum . . Rabbiteye Blueberry
vitis-idae'a . . . . Cowberry
—mi'nus . . . . . . Mountain C.

VAG'NERA . . . . **SMILACINA**

VALERIA'NA . . . . . Valerian
ed'ulis (*ceratophylla* Piper, *not* H. B. K.) Edible V.
micran'tha . . . . Smallflower V.
occidenta'lis . . . . . Western V.
scou'leri . . . . Scouler V.
sitchen'sis . . . . Sitka V.

VAUQUELI'NIA califor'nica (*torreyi*) Torrey Vauquelinia

VERA'TRUM . . Falsehellebore
al'bum . . . . White F.
califor'nicum (*speciosum*) California F.
eschscholtz'i . . . Eschscholtz F.
fimbria'tum . . . . . . Fringed F.
vir'ide . . . . American F.

VERBAS'CUM thap'sus Flannel Mullein

VERBE'NA wright'i Wrights Verbena

VERON'ICA america'na American Speedwell

VIBOR'QUIA . **EYSENHARDTIA**

VIBUR'NUM . . . . . Viburnum
ellip'ticum . . . . . . Oregon V.
lenta'go . . . . . Nannyberry V.
pauciflo'rum . . . Mooseberry V.
trilo'bum (*americanum* Auth., *not* Mill.; *opulus* Auth., *not* L.; *oxycoccus; V. opulus americanum*) American Cranberrybush V.

VIC'IA . . . . Vetch
america'na . . . . . . American V.
—orega'na (*V. oregana*) Oregon A.V.
crac'ca . . . . Bird V.
ful'gens . . . . Scarlet V.
gigan'tea . . . . Giant V.
macrocar'pa . . . . Bigpod V.
monan'tha . . . . Bard V.
sati'va . . . . Common V.
semicinc'ta . . . . Modoc V.
sparsifo'lia . . . . . Stiffleaf V.
villo'sa . . . . Hairy V.

VIGUIE'RA (*GYMNOLOMIA*) Goldeneye
an'nua (*Gymnolomia a.*) . Annual G.
cordifo'lia . . . . . Heartleaf G.
deltoi'dea par'ishi (*V. parishi*) Parish G.
denta'ta (*texana*)
lacinia'ta . . . . Cutleaf G.
longifo'lia . . . . . . Longleaf G.
multiflo'ra (*Gymnolomia m.*) Showy G.
—nevaden'sis (*Gymnolomia linearis; G. nevadensis*) . . . . . Nevada S.G.
ova'lis . . . . Ovalleaf G.
reticula'ta . . . . DeathValley G.
stenolo'ba . . . Skeletonleaf G.
tenuifo'lia . . . . . . Slimleaf G.
texa'na . . . . **V. dentata**

Villano'va dissec'ta . . . . **Bahia d.**

VIO'LA . . . . Violet
adun'ca (*drepanophora; monticola* Rydb., *not* Jord.; *oxysepala; subvestita*) . . . . Hook V.

RANGE PLANTS (VIOLA), continued
beck'withi . . . . Beckwith Violet
canaden'sis (*geminiflora; muriculata; neo-mexicana*) . . . . . Canada V.
glabel'la . . . . Pioneer V.
nutt'alli (*vallicola*) . . . Nuttall V.
—linguaefo'lia (*V. erectifolia; V. linguaefolia; V. praemorsa l.*) Tongueleaf V.
purpu'rea . . . . . . Goosefoot V.
—veno'sa (*V. atriplicifolia; V. aurea v.; V. nuttalli v.; V. praemorsa v.; V. venosa*) . . . . Veiny G.V.

VI'TIS arizo'nica . Canyon Grape

WEDE'LIA; WEDELIEL'LA **ALLIONIA**

WHIP'PLEA modes'ta Modest Whipplea

WYE'THIA . . . . Wyethia
amplexicau'lis . . . Mulesears W.
helianthoi'des . . . Whitehead W.
mol'lis . . . . Woolly W.

XAN'THIUM . . . . Cocklebur

XEROPHYL'LUM . . Beargrass
asphodeloi'des . . Turkeybeard B.
doug'lasi . . . . Douglas B.
ten'ax . . . . Common B.

XYLOPHA'COS . **ASTRAGALUS**

XYLOS'TEON . . . **LONICERA**

Young'ia na'na . . . . **Crepis n.**

YUC'CA (*CLISTOYUCCA*) Yucca
bacca'ta . . . . Datil Y.
brevifo'lia (*arborescens; Clistoyucca b.*) Joshuatree Y.
ela'ta (*radiosa*) . . . . Soaptree Y.
glau'ca (*angustifolia*) Small Soapweed
tor'reyi (*macrocarpa* (Torr.) Cov., *not* Engelm.) . . . . Torrey Y.

ZAUSCHNE'RIA . . Firechalice

Ziz'yphus lycioi'des . . **Condalia l.**

Rangooncreeper . . **Quisqualis indica**

RANUN'CULUS (*BATRACHIUM; BECKWITHIA; HALERPESTES*) |w . Buttercup (*Crowfoot*)
abort'ivus |w . . . . Littleleaf B.
aconitifo'lius . . . . . . Aconite B.
₵Double (*florepleno*) hv.
₵Golden (*luteoplenus*)
acrifor'mis . . . . Sharp B.
a'cris (*acer*) |w . . . . . . Tall B.
₵Double (*florepleno*) hv.
ado'neus . . . . Alpine B.
alismaefo'lius . . . Plantainleaf B.
—alismel'lus (*R. alismellus*) Dwarf P.B.
alleghenien'sis |w . . . Allegany B.
alpes'tris . . . . Moraine B.
am'bigens |w
amplexicau'lis . . . . Yelloweye B.
anderso'ni (*Beckwithia a.*) Anderson B.
anemonoi'des . . . . . Anemone B.
aquat'ilis (*Batrachium aquatile*) |w Watercrowfoot B.
—capilla'ceus (*R. trichophyllus; Batrachium trichophyllum*) Hairleaf W.B.
—heterophyl'lus (*R. heterophyllus; Batrachium heterophyllum*) Varileaf W.B.
Perhaps not distinct from R. aquatilis.
arven'sis . . . . Corn B.
asiat'icus . . . . Persian B.
₵Imperial. hv.
bolan'deri |w . . . . . Bolander B.

RANUNCULUS, continued
bon'gardi . . . Bongard Buttercup
bro'teri . . . . Broters B.
bulbo'sus |w . . . . Bulb B.
₵Double (*florepleno*) hv.
califor'nicus . . . . . California B.
circina'tus |w
crena'tus . . . . Crenate B.
cret'icus
cymbala'ria (*Halerpestes c.*) |w Shore B.
—saximonta'nus
eremog'enes . . . . . **R. sceleratus**
eschscholtz'i
fascicula'ris . . . . Tufted B.
fica'ria (*Ficaria verna*) . . Figroot B.
flabella'ris (*delphinifolius*) |w
flam'mula . . . . . . Spearwort B.
—rep'tans . . . . . . Creeping S.B.
glaber'rimus . . . . . Sagebrush B.
glacia'lis . . . . Glacier B.
gramin'eus . . . . Grassy B.
hebecar'pus |w
hedera'ceus |w . . . . Ivy B.
heterophyl'lus . . . . . **R. aquatilis h.**
his'pidus . . . . Bristly B.
hydrocharoi'des |w
illyr'icus . . . . Illyrian B.
inamoe'nus
intertex'tus |w
lappon'icus |w . . . . Lapp B.
lenor'mandi (*Batrachium l.*) Lenormand B.
limo'sus |w
lin'gua . . . . Tongue B.
—grandiflo'rus . . . . Big T.B.
lobb'i |w . . . . Lobb B.
longiros'tris (*Batrachium longirostre*) Longbeak B.
lyall'i . . . . Lyall B.
macau'leyi . . . . . . Macauley B.
max'imus **R. orthorhyncus platyphyllus**
monta'nus . . . . . . Mountain B.
nemoro'sus . . . . . Wildwood B.
oblongifo'lius |w
occidenta'lis . . . . . . Western B.
ophioglossifo'lius (*R. ophioglossoides*) Mediterranean B.
orthorhyn'cus . . . Straightbeak B.
—platyphyl'lus (*R. maximus*) Great S.B.
ova'lis . . . . Labrador B.
parnassifo'lius . . . . Parnassus B.
parviflo'rus |w . . . . Sticktight B.
pennsylvan'icus |w Pennsylvania B.
pusil'lus |w
pyrenae'us . . . . Pyrenees B.
recurva'tus . . . . Hooked B.
re'pens (*speciosus*) |w . Creeping B.
₵Double (*florepleno*) hv.
scelera'tus (*eremogenes*) |w. Blister B.
seguier'i . . . . Seguier B.
septentriona'lis |w . . . . Swamp B.
suks'dorfi . . . . Suksdorf B.
tenuicau'lis . . . . Cream B.
trichophyl'lus . **R. aquatilis capillaceus**
triterna'tus . . . . . Nineleaf B.

RAOU'LIA . . . . Raoulia
austra'lis . . . . . . Silvermat R.
gla'bra . . . . . . Smoothleaf R.
subseric'ea . . . . . . Plaidmat R.

RAPA'NEA . . . . Rapanea
guianen'sis . . . . . . Guiana R.

Rape
Bird R. . . . . **Brassica campestris**
Oilnavew B. R. . . . . **B. c. oleifera**
Winter R. . . . . **B. napus**

RAPH'ANUS |w . . . . RADISH
raphanis'trum |w . . . . . WILD R.
sati'vus |w . . . . . . GARDEN R.
—cauda'tus (*R. caudatus*) . RATTAIL R.
—longipinna'tus . . . . CHINESE R.

RA'PHIA . . . . RAFFIAPALM
See **PALM GENERA.**

RAPHIOLE'PIS . . . . RAPHIOLEPIS
∞ **delacour'i** (*indica* × *umbellata*) ∞ DELACOUR R.
in'dica . . . . INDIA R.
—rose'a . . . . PINK I.R.
umbella'ta (*japonica*) . . . YEDDO R.
—ova'ta . . . . . ROUNDLEAF Y.R.

RASPBERRY . . . . **Rubus**
See also BLACKBERRY and DEWBERRY. For horticultural varieties cultivated for their fruit, see **FRUIT AND EDIBLE NUT NAMES.**
AMERICAN RED R. **R. idaeus strigosus**
BANK R. . . . . **R. palmatus**
BLACKCAP R. . . . . . **R. occidentalis**
BOULDER R. . . . . . **R. deliciosus**
HAWTHORN R. . . . **R. crataegifolius**
JAPANESE R. . . . . . **R. parvifolius**
KOREAN R. . . . . . . **R. coreanus**
LITTLELEAF R. . . . . **R. parvifolius**
NEWMEXICAN R. . . **R. neomexicanus**
PURPLECANE R. . . . . **R. neglectus**
QUEENSLAND R. . . . . . **R. probus**
RED R. . . . . **R. idaeus**
ROSELEAF R. . . . . . **R. rosaefolius**
SNOWPEAKS R. . . . . . . **R. niveus**
STRAWBERRY R. . . . **R. illecebrosus**
TALL R. . . . . **R. gracilis**
WESTERN RED R. **R. idaeus aculeatissimus**
WHITEBARK R. . . . **R. leucodermis**
WINE R. . . . . . **R. phoenicolasius**
WOOLLY R. . . . . . . **R. lasiostylus**
YELLOW HIMALAYAN R. . **R. ellipticus**

RASPPOD . . . . **Trachylobium**
ZANZIBAR R. . . **T. hornemannianum**

RATA . . . . . . **Metrosideros robusta**

Ratany . . . . . KRAMERIA: **Krameria**

RATHBUN'IA . . . RATHBUNCACTUS
See **CACTUS GENERA.**

RATIB'IDA (*LEPACHYS; OBELISCARIA*) . . PRAIRIECONEFLOWER
columna'ris (*columnifera; Rudbeckia columnaris*) . . . UPRIGHT P.
pinna'ta (*Lepachys p.*)

RATTANPALM . . . . **Calamus**
ROTANG R. . . . . **C. rotang**

RATTLEBOX . . . . **Daubentonia**
DRUMMOND R. . . . . **D. drummondi**
GLORYPEA R. . . . . **D. tripetti**
LONGLEAF R. . . . . . **D. cavanillesi**

RATTLEPOT . . . . . . **Alectorolophus**
LITTLE R. . . . . **A. minus**

RATTLESNAKEFERN
Botrychium virginianum

RATTLESNAKEPLANTAIN . . . **Goodyera**
CHECKERED R. . . . . . **G. tesselata**
CREEPING R. . . . . **G. repens**
DAWSON R. . . . . . **G. dawsoniana**
DOWNY R. . . . . **G. pubescens**
WESTERN R. . . . . . . **G. decipiens**

RATTLESNAKEROOT . . . . **Prenanthes**
PURPLE R. . . . . **P. purpurea**
ROUGH R. . . . . **P. aspera**
THREELEAF R. . . . . **P. trifoliolata**
WHITE R. . . . . **P. alba**

RATTLEWEED . . . . **Rhinanthus**
COCKSCOMB R. . . . . **R. crista-galli**
NORTHERN R. . . . . . . **R. borealis**

RAUWOLF'IA . . . . . DEVILPEPPER
canes'cens . . . . TRINIDAD D.
serpenti'na . . . . JAVA D.
tetraphyl'la . . . . . FOURLEAF D.

RAVENA'LA . . . . . TRAVELERSTREE
madagascarien'sis . MADAGASCAR T.

RAVE'NEA (*RAVENIA* Benth. & Hook. f., *not* Vell.) . . . **RANEVEA**
See **PALM GENERA.**

RAVE'NIA . . . . RAVENIA
spectab'ilis . . . . SHOWY R.

RAVENNAGRASS . . . **Erianthus ravennae**

RAYLESS-ASTER . . . . . . **Eschenbachia**
COULTER R. . . . . **E. coulteri**

RAZORSEDGE . . . . **Scleria**
BALDWIN R. . . . . **S. baldwini**
BROADLEAF R. . . . . . . **S. latifolia**
FEWFLOWER R. . . . . **S. pauciflora**
FRINGED R. . . . . **S. ciliata**
LITTLEHEAD R. . . . . . **S. oligantha**
NETTED R. . . . . **S. reticularis**
SLAVESFLAIL R. **S. flagellum-nigrorum**
SMOOTH R. . . . . **S. glabra**
WHIP R. . . . . **S. triglomerata**
WHORLED R. . . . . . . **S. verticillata**

RAZOUMOW'SKYA **ARCEUTHOBIUM**

REBU'TIA . . . . **LOBIVIA; MEDIOLOBIVIA**
See **CACTUS GENERA.**

REDBUD . . . . **Cercis**
CALIFORNIA R. . . . . **C. occidentalis**
CHINESE R. . . . . **C. chinensis**
EASTERN R. . . . . . . **C. canadensis**
HAIRY E. R. . . . . . **C. c. pubescens**
JUDASTREE . . . . . . **C. siliquastrum**
RACEME R. . . . . **C. racemosa**
SMOOTH EASTERN R. **C. canadensis glabrifolia**
TEXAS R. . . . . **C. reniformis**
UTAH R. . . . . **C. orbiculata**
WHITE EASTERN R. **C. canadensis alba**

REDCEDAR
BERMUDA R. . . **Juniperus bermudiana**
EASTERN R. . . . . **J. virginiana**
NORTH E. R. . . . . **J. v. crebra**

REDFIELD'IA . . . . BLOWOUTGRASS
See **GRASS GENERA.**

Redhotpoker . . TORCHLILY: **Kniphofia**

Redlaver . . . . LAVER: **Porphyra**

Redmahogany . . . EUCALYPTUS, KINO: **Eucalyptus resinifera**

REDPEPPER . . . . **Capsicum**
BIRD R. . . . . **C. frutescens typicum**
BUSH R. . . . . **C. frutescens**
CHERRY R. . . . . . **C. f. cerasiforme**
CLUSTER R. . . . . **C. f. fasciculatum**
LONG R. . . . . **C. f. longum**
ORNAMENTAL BUSH R. **C. f. abbreviatum**
SWEETBELL R. . . . . . . **C. f. grossum**
TABASCO R. . . . . . . **C. f. conoides**

REDQUEBRACHO . . . . **Schinopsis**
LORENTZ R. . . . . **S. lorentzi**
WILLOWLEAF R. . . . . . **S. balansae**

REDROOT . . . . **Lachnanthes**
BLOOD R. . . . . **L. tinctoria**

Redroot . . . . . . ALKANET, DYERS: **Alkanna tinctoria**; AMARANTH, REDROOT: **Amaranthus retroflexus**; CEANOTHUS, JERSEYTEA: **Ceanothus americanus**; INDIANMULBERRY, ROYOC: **Morinda royoc**; SPIGELIA, PINKROOT: **Spigelia marilandica**

REDTOP . . . . **Agrostis alba**

REDWATERTREE, CASCA **Erythrophleum guineense**

REDWOOD . . . **Sequoia sempervirens**
Tavoy R. . . . . GLUTA, TAVOY: **Gluta tavoyana**

REED . . . . **Phragmites**
COMMON R. . . . . **P. communis**
GIANTREED . . . **Arundo; A. donax**

REEDGRASS . . . . **Calamagrostis**
BLUEJOINT R. . . . . **C. canadensis**
CAINS R. . . . . **C. caini**
CASCADES R. . . . . **C. tweedyi**
CHEE R. . . . . **C. epigeios**
CUYAMACA R. . . . . **C. densa**
DUDLEY R. . . . . **C. perplexa**
FIRE R. . . . . **C. koelerioides**
HAIRYSEED R. . . . . . **C. cinnoides**
HUMBOLDT R. . . . . **C. foliosa**
JONES R. . . . . **C. scopulorum**
KNOTROOT R. . . . . **C. lactea**
MACOUN BLUEJOINT R. **C. canadensis macouniana**
NEWENGLAND R. **C. inexpansa novae-angliae**
NORTHERN R. . . . . . **C. inexpansa**
PACIFIC R. . . . . . . **C. nutkaensis**
PICKERING R. . . . . . **C. pickeringi**
PLAINS R. . . . . . **C. montanensis**
PORTER R. . . . . **C. porteri**
REDWOODS R. . . . . . . **C. bolanderi**
RIVERBLUFF R. . . . . . . **C. howelli**
ROUGH BLUEJOINT R. **C. canadensis scabra**
SCRIBNER R. . . . . **C. scribneri**
SHORTHAIR R. . . . . **C. breweri**
SIERRA R. . . . . **C. californica**
SLIMSTEM R. . . . . **C. neglecta**
WASHINGTON R. **C. inexpansa barbulata**

REGE'LIA
cilia'ta
grandiflo'ra

REHDERODEN'DRON . REHDERTREE
macrocar'pum . . . LARGEFRUIT R.

REHDERTREE . . . . . **Rehderodendron**
LARGEFRUIT R. . . . **R. macrocarpum**

REHMAN'NIA . . . . . REHMANNIA
angula'ta (*Sparmannia sinensis*) BEVERLYBELLS R.
ela'ta
glutino'sa
¢ALBA. HV. Rehmannia
¢PINK PERFECTION

REICHARD'IA
picroi'des (*Picridium vulgare*)

REIMAROCH'LOA . . REIMARGRASS
See **GRASS GENERA.**

REINDEERMOSS . . **Cladonia rangiferina**

REINECK'IA . . . . REINECKIA
car'nea . . . . PINK R.
¢VARIEGATED (*variegata*) HV.

REINHARD'TIA (*MALORTIEA*) . . . Reinhardtpalm
See **PALM GENERA.**

Reinhardtpalm . . . . . **Reinhardtia**

REINWARD'TIA . . . . Yellowflax
in'dica (*trigyna; Linum trigynum*) . . . Indian Y.
tetrag'yna . . . . Serrate Y.
trig'yna . . . . **R. indica**

RENAN'THERA
See **ORCHID GENERA.**

RENEAL'MIA (*ALPINIA* L., *not* Roxb.)
Renealmia is conserved under International Rules.
exalta'ta (*Alpinia e.*)

Rescuegrass . . . . . Brome, Rescue: **Bromus catharticus**

RESE'DA . . . . Mignonette
al'ba . . . . White M.
crystalli'na . . . CanaryIsland M.
lute'a . . . . Yellow M.
luteo'la . . . . Weld M.
odora'ta . . . . Common M.

Resintree . . . . **Protium**
Brazil R. . . . . . . **P. heptaphyllum**
Incense R. . . . . . . **P. guianense**

Restharrow . . . . . . Ononis: **Ononis**

Resurrectionfern
Polypodium polypodioides

Resurrectionlily . . . . **Kaempferia**
Ovalleaf R. . . . . **K. ovalifolia**
Roundleaf R. . . . . . . **K. rotunda**

Resurrectionmustard . . . **Anastatica**
Jericho R. . . . . . **A. hierochuntica**

Resurrectionplant
Resurrectionmustard: **Anastatica**; Selaginella, Resurrection: **Selaginella lepidophylla**

RETA'MA . . . . Retama
bo'vei
rhodorrhizoi'des

RETANIL'LA
eph'edra

RETINOS'PORA (*RETINISPORA*)
There is no such genus as Retinospora (or Retinispora as it was originally spelled). The plants referred to it are all juvenile states of the genera Chamaecyparis and Thuja.
The use of the name Retinospora only adds to plant-name confusion. Therefore this edition of Standardized Plant Names does not recognize the name Retinospora as having any justifiable standing in horticulture.

Rewarewa . . . . . **Knightia excelsa**

REYNO'SIA . . . . . . Darlingplum
septentriona'lis . . . . Northern D.

RHABDADE'NIA
biflo'ra

RHABDOTHAM'NUS . . . Waiuatua
solan'dri . . . . . NewZealand W.

RHACO'MA (*MYGINDA*) . Rhacoma
Rhacoma has priority over Myginda and must stand for both when, as here, united.
crossopet'alum (*Myginda rhacoma*) . . . Maravedi R.

RHAGO'DIA . . . . Rhagodia
nu'tans . . . . Nodding R.

RHAM'NUS |w . . . . . . Buckthorn
alater'nus . . . . Italian B.
—angustifo'lia . . . . Slimleaf I.B.
—integrifo'lia . . . Entireleaf I.B.
¢Variegated (*argenteo-variegata; R. a. variegata*) hv. R. alaternus
alnifo'lia . . . . Alder B.
alpi'na . . . . Alpine B.
argu'ta . . . . Sharptooth B.
califor'nica |w . . . . California B.
—crassifo'lia . . . . Thickleaf C.B.
carolinia'na (*carolina*) . . Carolina B.
cathar'tica |w . . . . . Common B.
—pubes'cens . . . . . . Hairy C.B.
chad'wicki . . . . **R. davurica**
costa'ta . . . . Ribleaf B.
crena'ta . . . . Oriental B.
cro'cea . . . . Redberry B.
—ilicifo'lia (*R. ilicifolia*) . . . Hollyleaf R.B.
—insula'ris . . . . Great R.B.
—pilo'sa . . . . SanDiego R.B.
davur'ica (*chadwicki*) . Dahurian B.
—nippon'ica . . . . Nippon B.
dumeto'rum . . . . Hedge B.
—crenoserra'ta . . . . Cutleaf H.B.
erythrox'ylon
fal'lax . . . . Carniolian B.
fran'gula . . . . Glossy B.
—angustifo'lia . . Narrowleaf G.B.
—latifo'lia . . . . . Broadleaf G.B.
¢Feathery (*asplenifolia*) hv. R. frangula
¢Mixleaf (*heterophylla*)
globo'sa . . . . Lokao B.
heterophyl'la
∞ **hy'brida** (*alaternus* × *alpina*) . . . ∞Hybrid B.
¢Billard (*billardi*) hv.
ilicifo'lia . . . . **R. crocea i.**
imereti'na . . . . Caucasian B.
infecto'ria . . . . . . Persianberry B.
japon'ica . . . . Japanese B.
koraien'sis . . . . Korean B.
lanceola'ta |w . . . . . Lanceleaf B.
latifo'lia . . . . Broadleaf B.
leptophyl'la . . . . . Slenderleaf B.
—scabrel'la . . . . . . Scabrous S.B.
libanot'ica . . . . Lebanon B.
oleoi'des
pal'lasi
—spathulaefo'lia . . **R. spathulaefolia**
parvifo'lia . . . . Littleleaf B.
petiola'ris . . . . Petioled B.
prunifo'lia . . . . Plumleaf B.
pu'mila . . . . Dwarf B.
purpu'rea . . . . Purple B.
purshia'na |w . . . . . . Cascara B.
ros'thorni . . . . Rosthorns B.
rugulo'sa . . . . Wrinkleleaf B.
rupes'tris (*Frangula r.*) . . Cliff B.
sargentia'na . . . . Sargent R.
saxat'ilis . . . . Rock B.
schnei'deri . . . . Schneider B.
—manshu'rica . . Manchurian S.B.
smith'i . . . . Smith B.
spathulaefo'lia (*R. pallasi s.*)
tincto'ria . . . . Dyers B.
tomentel'la . . . . Whiteleaf B.
u'tilis . . . . Chinese B.
virga'ta . . . . Twiggy B.

RHA'PHIS . . . . Rhaphis
See **GRASS GENERA.**

RHAPHITHAM'NUS
cyanocar'pus

RHAPIDOPHYL'LUM . Needlepalm
See **PALM GENERA.**

RHA'PIS . . . . Ladypalm
See **PALM GENERA.**

Rhapon'ticum cynaroi'des . **Centaurea c.**

Rhatanyroot . . Krameria, Peruvian: **Krameria triandra**

RHAZ'YA
orienta'lis

RHEED'IA . . . . Rheedia
brasilien'sis Bakupari R. (*Bakupari*)
The Bakupari fruit of commerce is derived from this species. The common name has many variants, including Bakpuri, Bakupary, Bakury, and Pacuri.
ed'ulis . Wildlemon R. (*Wildlemon*)
laterifo'lia . . . . Hatstand R.
macrophyl'la . . . . . Longleaf R.
madru'no . . . . Madrone R.

RHEKTOPHYL'LUM
mirab'ile (*Nephthytis picturata*)

RHE'UM . . . . Rhubarb
acumina'tum . . . . . Sharpleaf R.
alexan'drae . . . . . Alexandra R.
collinia'num . . . . Collin R.
emo'di . . . . Himalayan R.
franzenbach'i . . . Franzenbach R.
macrop'terum
no'bile
officina'le . . . . Medicinal R.
palma'tum . . . . Sorrel R.
—atrosanguin'eum . . Scarlet S.R.
—ru'brum . . . . Red S.R.
—tangut'icum . . . . . . Tangut R.
rhapon'ticum . . . . Garden R.
ri'bes . . . . Currant R.
songar'icum . . . . Sungari R.
specifor'me
undula'tum
webbia'num . . . . Webb R.
wit'trocki . . . . Wittrock R.

RHEX'IA . . . . Meadowbeauty
lute'a . . . . Yellow M.
maria'na . . . . Maryland M.
nash'i . . . . Nash M.
virgin'ica . . . . Common M.

RHINAN'THUS . . . . Rattleweed
borea'lis . . . . Northern R.
crista-gal'li . . . . . Cockscomb R.

RHIPOG'ONUM
scan'dens

RHIPSALIDOP'SIS
See **CACTUS GENERA.**

RHIP'SALIS (*HATIORA*) . Rhipsalis
See **CACTUS GENERA.**

RHIZOPH'ORA . . . . . Mangrove
conjuga'ta
man'gle . . . . American M.
mucrona'ta

RHODAN'THE . . . **HELIPTERUM**
macula'ta . . **H. manglesi maculatum**

Rhodesgrass . . . . . **Chloris gayana**
Rhodesianteak . . **Baikiaea plurijuga**

RHODIO'LA . . . . **SEDUM**
See **SUCCULENTS.**

RHODOCAC'TUS . . . . **PERESKIA**
See **CACTUS GENERA.**

RHODOCHI'TON . . . . Bellvine
volu'bile . . . . Purple B.

RHODODEN'DRON (*AZALEA; AZALEASTRUM; BILTIA; RHODORA*) |w . . Rhododendron

The original and major list of Rhododendron (including Azalea) for this volume was prepared by the Arnold Arboretum, Jamaica Plain, Mass. Later Clement G. Bowers' "Rhododendrons and Azaleas" and the yearbooks of The Rhododendron Assn. (England) were drawn upon for additions. John C. Wister, Sec., Penn. Hort. Soc., Philadelphia, Pa., also aided with suggestions and corrections.

To all of these authorities and sources the Committee extends sincere thanks.

Special attention is called to the fact that botanically all Azaleas are properly listed below under Rhododendron. In horticultural practice, however, it is deemed *permissible* to use the generic Latin term Azalea for the (mostly) deciduous forms of Rhododendron. Some horticulturists, however, prefer to use the technically correct botanical name Rhododendron for the entire group, confining the name Azalea to common and hort. names where appropriate. For convenience of reference, a botanical list is also included under Azalea, as well as a full list of common and hv. names. See **AZALEA.**

achroan'thum
ad'amsi . . . Adams Rhododendron
adenog'ynum
adenoph'orum
adenop'odum
aechmophyl'lum . . . Spearleaf R.
aerugino'sum . . . . Blueleaf R.
aganni'phum
agglutina'tum
alabamen'se (*Azalea alabamensis*) Alabama Azalea
∞ **al'bicans** (*molle* × *occidentale*; ∞ *A. albicans*) . . . . . . ∞ Albicans A.
albiflo'rum (*A. albiflora; Azaleastrum albiflorum*) . . . . . . Cascades A.
—**ple'num** (*A. a. plena*) Double C.A.
albrecht'i (*A. albrechti*). Albrecht A.
∞ **altacleren'se** (*arboreum* × ∞ *morelianum*) . . . . ∞ Altaclerense R.
ambig'uum
∞ **annelies'ae** (*arborescens* × *calendulaceum; A. anneliesae*) ∞ Anneliesa A.
anthopo'gon . . . . . . Sulfur R.
aperan'tum . . . . . . Carpet R.
apodec'tum
arbores'cens (*A. arborescens*) Sweet A.
—**richardso'ni** . . . Richardson S.A.
arbo'reum . . . . Tree R.
—**al'bum** . . . . White T.R.
—**cinnamo'meum** Cinnamonleaf T.R.
—**kingia'num** . . . . . Kings T.R.
—**limba'tum** . . . . . Darkrim T.R.
—**nilagir'icum** . . . . . Nilgiri T.R.
—**punic'eum** . . . . . . Purple T.R.
—**wind'sori** . . . . . . Windsor T.R.
∞ **arbutifo'lium** (*ferrugineum* × *minus*) ∞ Rockmount R.
argen'teum . . . . **R. grande**
argyrophyl'lum . . . . Silverleaf R.
arize'lum
astroca'lyx . . . . Starcup R.
atlan'ticum (*A. atlantica*) . Coast A.
—**luteo-al'bum** (*A. a. luteo-alba*) Blueleaf C.A.
—**neglec'tum** (*A. a. neglecta*) Purple C.A.
auck'landi . . . . . **R. griffithianum**
augustin'i . . . . . . Augustine R.
—**al'bum** . . . . White A.R.
—**violas'cens** . . . . . . Violet A.R.
auricula'tum . . . . . . Earleaf R.

RHODODENDRON, continued

auricula'tum rose'um Rosy Earleaf Rhododendron
austri'num (*A. austrina*) Florida Azalea
∞ **azaleoden'dron** (*japonicum* × *subgenus* Eurhododendron hybrids) ∞ Azaleodendron
∞ **azaleoi'des** (*?nudiflorum* × *ponticum*) ∞ Pinxterpont A.
balfouria'num . . . . . Balfour R.
barba'tum . . . . . Giantblood R.
basil'icum . . . . Regal R.
beesia'num . . . . Bees R.
bodinier'i . . . . Bodinier R.
booth'i . . . . Booth R.
brachyan'thum . . . . Sapgreen R.
brachycar'pum . . . . Fujiyama R.
—**lutes'cens** . . . . . . Cream F.R.
—**rosaeflo'rum** . . . . . Pink F.R.
bractea'tum . . . . . . Redspot R.
brevis'tylum
bulla'tum . . . . . Puckerleaf R.
calendula'ceum (*A. calendulacea; A. lutea* in part) . . . . . Flame A.
—**auran'tium** (*A. c. aurantia*) Orange F.A.
—**cro'ceum**
califor'nicum . . . . **R. macrophyllum**
callimorph'um . . . . . Rosebud R.
calophyl'lum . . Oolah Mountains R.
calophy'tum . . . . . . Bigleaf R.
calos'trotum . . . . . Purple-elf R.
caloxan'thum . . . . Orangetip R.
campanula'tum . . . Bellflower R.
—**bate'mani** . . . . . . Bateman B.R.
—*wal'lichi* . . . . **R. wallichi**
campylocar'pum . . . Honeybell R.
campylog'ynum . . . Duskybloom R.
camtschat'icum (*kamtschaticum*) Kamchatka R.
canaden'se (*A. canadensis; Rhodora canadensis*) . . . . . . Rhodora
—**albiflo'rum** (*A. canadensis alba; Rhodora c. album*) . . . . . White R.
canes'cens (*A. canescens*) Piedmont A.
—**can'didum** (*A. candida; A. canescens candida*) . . . . . . White P.A.
—**subgla'brum** (*A. canescens subglabra*) . . . . . . Smooth P.A.
canes'cens Porter, *not* Sweet . **P. roseum**
cantab'ile . . . . Skyland R.
carolinia'num . . . . . Carolina R.
—**al'bum** . . . . White C.R.
—**folia'tum** . . . . Tall C.R.
catawbien'se . . . . . . Catawba R.
—**al'bum** . . . . White C.R.
—**compac'tum** . . . . . Kelsey C.R.
—**insula're** . . . . . . Piedmont C.R.
—**tomopet'alum** . . . . Fringed C.R.
caucas'icum . . . . . Caucasian R.
—**flav'idum** . . . . . . Yellow C.R.
—**roseo-al'bum** . . . . . . Pink C.R.
—**splen'dens** . . . . . . Glory C.R.
—**stramin'eum** . . . . . . Straw C.R.
cephalan'thum . . . Whitebutton R.
chaetomal'lum . . . . Fleeceleaf R.
chamaecis'tus . . . **Rhodothamnus c.**
chap'mani . . . . Chapman R.
charit'opes
chartophyl'lum . . . . Paperleaf R.
chasman'thum . . . . Olivespot R.
chrysan'thum . . . . . Goldmat R.
chrys'eum . . . . Golden R.
cilia'tum . . . . Fringed R.
ciliica'lyx

RHODODENDRON, continued

cinnabari'num Cinnabar Rhododendron
circinna'tum . . . . Russetleaf R.
citriniflo'rum . . . . Citron R.
clementi'nae . . . . Clementine R.
colletti'num . . . . . . Collett R.
compac'tum . . . . . . Thickset R.
concat'enans . . . . Apricotbell R.
concin'num (*yanthinum*) Purplenymph R.
—**laetevi'rens** (*R. y. laetevirens*) Crimson P.R.
—**lepidan'thum** (*R. c. pseudoyanthinum; R. y. lepidanthum*)
coria'ceum . . . . . Leatherleaf R.
cras'sum . . . . Sweetbay R.
crinig'erum . . . . . Earlyflush R.
cro'ceum . . . . . . Goldsaucer R.
cuculla'tum . . . . . . Hoodleaf R.
∞ **cunningham'i** (*arboreum* × *maximum*) ∞ Cunningham R.
cyanocar'pum . . . . . Bluepod R.
cyc'lium . . . . Canebrake R.
dalhous'iae . . . . . Dalhousie R.
daphniflo'rum . . . . . Daphne R.
daur'icum (*dahuricum; A. daurica*) Dahurian R.
—*cilia'tum* . . . **R. mucronulatum c.**
—*mucronula'tum* . **R. mucronulatum**
—**sempervi'rens** . Evergreen D.R.
da'vidi . . . . Abbe David R.
davidsonia'num . . . Davidson R.
deco'rum . . . . . Sweetshell R.
degronia'num (*R. metternichi pentamerum*) . . . . . . Degrow R.
delavay'i . . . . Abbe Delavay R.
desquama'tum . . . Mauvequeen R.
deton'sum . . . . . Yunnanrose R.
diac'ritum . . . . Whitethroat R.
dichroan'thum . . . . Twincolor R.
dictyo'tum
did'ymum . . . . . Bloodbloom R.
dis'color (*mandarinorum*) Mandarin R.
—**car'neum** . . . . Carmine M.R.
drumo'nium . . . . . . Woodelf R.
eclec'teum . . . . Eclectic R.
edgeworth'i . . . . . Edgeworth R.
eriogy'num
erit'imum
erubes'cens . . . . . Blushing R
euchai'tes . . Woodlandglory R.
exaspera'tum . . . Rustybrick R.
exim'ium . . . . . Saffronleaf R.
fa'beri . . . . Faber R.
falconer'i . . . . Falconer R.
far'gesi . . . . Pere Farges R.
fastigia'tum . . . Autumnpurple R.
faur'iei . . . . Pere Faurie R.
ferrugin'eum . . . . Rock R.
—**al'bum** . . . . White R.R.
—**atrococcin'eum** . . . . Scarlet R.R.
fictolac'teum . . . . . Corrietree R.
fimbria'tum . . . Purplemantle R.
flav'idum . . . . . . Amberbloom R.
flavoru'fum . . . . . . Rubyspot R.
fla'vum . . . . **R. luteum**
floccig'erum . . . . . . Tuftwool R.
floribun'dum . . . . Purplequeen R.
formo'sum . . . . Redstripe R.
fortun'ei . . . . Fortunes R.
—*houl'stoni* . . . . . . **R. houlstoni**
∞ **fra'grans** (*catawbiense* × *viscosum*) ∞ Viscataw R.
∞ **fras'eri** (*canadense* × *japonicum*) ∞ Fraser R.
ful'gens . . . . Pompom R.

RHODODENDRON, continued

fulvoi'des Flushrose Rhododendron
ful'vum . . . . Cinnamon R.
∞ **gandaven'se** (*luteum* × *mortieri*; ∞ *A. gandavensis*) . . ∞ Ghent Azalea
∞ —**ple'num** (∞ *A. g. plena*) ∞ Double G.A.
gigan'teum . . . . Giant R.
glau'cum . . . . . Spiceleaf R.
glisch'rum . . . . . Stickyleaf R.
gran'de (*argenteum*) . . . Argent R.
griersonia'num . . . . Grierson R.
griffithia'num (*aucklandi*) Griffith R.
haema'leum . . . . . Redblood R.
haemato'des . . . . . Royalblood R.
∞ **halen'se** (*ferrugineum* × *hirsutum*) ∞ Halense R.
hancea'num . . . . Hance R.
heliol'epis . . . . Glitterscale R.
hemitrich'otum . . . . Brickbud R.
hemsleya'num . . . . . Hemsley R.
herpes'ticum . . . . . Crawling R.
hippophaeoi'des . Seabuckthorn R.
hirsu'tum . . . . Garland R.
—**albiflo'rum** (*R. h. album*) White G.R.
—**lacinia'tum** . . . . Jagleaf G.R.
hodg'soni . . . . Hodgson R.
∞ **holmleaen'se** (*catawbiense* × *discolor*) ∞ Holmlea R.
hook'eri . . . . Hooker R.
hormoph'orum . . . . Necklace R.
houl'stoni (*R. fortunei h.*) Houlston R.
hunnewellia'num . . Hunnewell R.
∞ **hyb'ridum** (*maximum* × *viscosum*) ∞ Viscomax R.
imped'itum . . . . . Cloudland R.
impera'tor . . . . . . Emperor R.
in'dicum (*A. indica*) . . . Indica A.
—**balsaminaeflo'rum** (*R. i. rosaeflorum*; *A. i. balsaminaeflora*; *A. rollisoni*) Balsam I.A.
—**crispiflo'rum** (*A. i. crispiflora*) Curly I.A.
—**lacinia'tum** (*A. i. laciniata*) Fringed I.A.
∞ **interme'dium** (*maximum* × *ponticum*) ∞ Maxpont R.
intrica'tum . . . . Bluet R.
irrora'tum . . . . Mountaindew R.
japon'icum (*A. japonica*) Japanese A.
—**au'reum** (*A. j. aurea*) Golden J.A.
javan'icum . . . . Java R.
kaemp'feri . . . . . . **R. obtusum k.**
kamtschat'icum . . **R. camtschaticum**
keisk'ei . . . . Keisk R.
kelet'icum . . . . Lhasa R.
keys'i . . . . Keys R.
∞ **kosteria'num** (*japonicum* × *molle*; ∞ *A. kosteriana*) . . . . . ∞ Koster A.
kotsch'yi (*myrtifolium* Schott & Kotschy, *not* Lodd.) . . . Kotschy R.
lac'teum . . . . Cream R.
∞ **laetevi'rens** (*carolinianum* × *ferrugineum*; ×*wilsoni* Hort.) ∞ Wilson R.
lana'tum . . . . . . Woolleaf R.
—**luci'ferum** . . . . . . Wick W.R.
lappon'icum ⊯ . . . . . Lapland R.
laxiflo'rum
ledifo'lium (*A. ledifolia*) **R. mucronatum**
—*al'bum* . . . . . **R. mucronatum**
ledoi'des . . . . . Ledumleaf R.
lepido'tum . . . . . Willowleaf R.
leucas'pis . . . . . Whiteshield R.
liliiflo'rum . . . . Lily R.
linearifo'lium (*A. linearifolia*) Spider A.
—**dianthiflo'rum** (*A. l. dianthiflora*) Dianthus S.A.

RHODODENDRON, continued

linearifo'lium macrosep'alum (*A. l. macrosepala*) . Bigsepal Spider Azalea
litien'se . . Litiping Rhododendron
longesquama'tum . . Szechwoods R.
longis'tylum . . . . . Longstyle R.
lutes'cens . . . . Canary R.
lu'teum (*flavum*; *A. flava*; *A. pontica*, not *A. lutea*) . . . . . Pontic A.
—**macran'thum** (*A. pontica macrantha*) Bigflower P.A.
lysol'epis . . . . . . Violetmat R.
macrophyl'lum (*californicum*) Coast R.
maculif'erum . . . Duskyblotch R.
mad'deni . . . . Madden R.
magnif'icum
makino'i (*R. metternichi angustifolium*; *stenophyllum*) . . . . Makino R.
mallo'tum . . . . Easter R.
mandarino'rum . . . . . **R. discolor**
manipuren'se . . . . . Manipur R.
max'imum ⊯ . . . . . Rosebay R.
—**al'bum** . . . . White R.R.
—**purpu'reum** (*R. m. roseum*) Pink R.R.
maxwell'i . . . . . . Maxwell R.
maxwell'i Millais, *not* Bor. **R. pulchrum**
meddia'num
megaca'lyx . . . . . Tuberose R.
megera'tum . . . . . Dwarfgold R.
metternich'i . . . . Metternich R.
—*angustifo'lium* . . . . . **R. makinoi**
—*pentam'erum* . . . **R. degronianum**
micran'thum . . . . Manchurian R.
microphy'tum (*A. microphyta*) Pinkflush A.
mi'nus . . . . Piedmont R.
—**harbiso'ni** . . . . Harbison P.R.
minutiflo'rum (*A. minutiflora*) Tinyflower A.
∞ **mix'tum** (*gandavense* × *molle*; ∞ *A. mixta*) . . . . ∞ Chinaghent A.
mol'le (*sinense*; *A. mollis*; *A. sinensis*) Chinese A.
mollic'omum . . . . . Hairyleaf R.
∞ **morelia'num** (*catawbiense* × *ponticum*) ∞ Ponticataw R.
mo'ri . . . . Mori R.
∞ **mortier'i** (*calendulaceum* × *nudiflorum*; ∞ *A. mortieri*) . . . . ∞ Mortier A.
moupinen'se . . . . . . Moupin R.
mucrona'tum (*ledifolium*; *R. l. album*; *rosmarinifolium* Dipp., *not* Vidal; *A. ledifolia*; *A. mucronata*; *A. rosmarinifolia*) . . . . Snow A.
—**amethys'tinum** (*A. m. amethystina*) Amethyst S.A.
—**narcissiflo'rum** (*A. m. narcissiflora*; *A. rosmarinifolia narcissiflora*) Narcissus S.A.
—**noordtia'num** (*A. m. noordtiana*; *A. ledifolia noordtiana*) . Noordt S.A.
—**ple'num** (*A. m. plena* . Peony S.A.
—**ripen'se** (*A. m. ripensis*) Riverbank S.A.
—**sekide'ra** (*A. m. sekidera*)
mucronula'tum (*R. dauricum m.*; *A. mucronulata*) . . . . . Korean R.
—**acumina'tum** . . . . . . Late K.R.
—**cilia'tum** (*R. d. ciliatum*) Fringeleaf K.R.
mulien'se . . . . Mu-li R.
∞ **myrtifo'lium** (*hirsutum* × *minus*) ∞ Myrtle R.
myrtifo'lium Schott & Kotschy, *not* Lodd. . . . . **R. kotschyi**
myrtilloi'des . . . . Pincushion R.

RHODODENDRON, continued

neriiflo'rum Oleander Rhododendron
niphar'gum . . . . . . Snowleaf R.
nippon'icum . . . . Nippon R.
nitid'ulum . . . . . Violetbloom R.
—**nubig'enum** . . . . . Small V.R.
niv'ale . . . . Glacier R.
niv'eum . . . . Snowy R.
∞ **norbitonen'se** (∞ *intermedium* × *molle*) ∞ Norbiton R.
₵—**au'reum**
₵—**broughtonia'num**
nudiflo'rum (*A. nudiflora*; *A. periclymenoides*) . Pinxterbloom Azalea
—**al'bum** (*A. n. alba*) . . White P.A.
—**glandif'erum** (*A. n. glandifera*)
oblongifo'lium (*A. oblongifolia*) Texas A.
obtu'sum (*A. obtusa*) . . . Hiryu A.
—**al'bum** (*A. o. alba*; *A. ramentacea*) White A.
—**amoe'num** (*A. amoena*; *A. o. amoena*) Amoena A.
∞ —*arnoldia'num* (*R. o. amoenum* × *R. o. kaempferi*) . . . . **R. obtusum hv.**
—**japon'icum** (*A. kurume*; *A. o. japonica*) . . . . Kurume A.

Here belong the many Kurume Azaleas, one of the best known being Hinodegiri.

—**kaemp'feri** (*R. kaempferi*; *A. kaempferi*; *A. o. kaempferi*) . . Torch A.
occidenta'le (*A. californica*; *A. occidentalis*) . . . . Western A.
old'hami . . . . Oldham R.
orbicula're . . . . Globe R.
oreodox'a . . . . Mountainglory R.
oreot'rephes . . . . Oread R.
orthoc'ladum . . . . Penciltwig R.
ova'tum . . . . Eggleaf R.
pachyt'richum . . . . Hairystalk R.
parvifo'lium . . . . . . Tundra R.
pat'ulum . . . . Assam R.
pemakoen'se . . . . . . Pemako R.
∞ **pennsylvan'icum** (*atlanticum* × *nudiflorum*; ∞ *A. pennsylvanica*) ∞ Pennsylvania A.
pentaphyl'lum (*A. pentaphylla*) Fiveleaf A.
phoenic'eum . . . . . **R. pulchrum p.**
plane'tum . . . . Waif R.
pleistan'thum . . . Rockviolet R.
pocoph'orum . . . . . Tengrinor R.
polyl'epis . . . . Batang R.
pon'ticum . . . . . . Ponticum R.
—**al'bum** . . . . White P.R.
—**rose'um** . . . . Pink P.R.
poukhanen'se . . . . . **R. yedoense p.**
∞ **prae'cox** (*ciliatum* × *dauricum*) ∞ Winter R.
₵—**ru'brum** . . . . ₵Red W.R.
praever'num . . . . . February R.
prinophyl'lum . . . . **R. roseum**
prunifo'lium (*A. prunifolia*) Plumleaf A.
przewal'ski . . . . Przewalski R.
pseudoyanthi'num
pul'chrum (*R. maxwelli* Millais, *not* Bor.; *A. pulchra*) . . . Lovely A.
—**calyci'num**
—**phoenic'eum** (*R. phoeniceum*; *A. phoenicea A.*; *A. p. phoenicea*) Purple L.A.
pural'bum . . . . . Smallsaucer R.
quinquefo'lium (*A. quinquefolia*) Cork A.
racemo'sum . . . . Mayflower R.

RHODODENDRON, continued

ra'dians . . CELEBES RHODODENDRON
ra'dicans . . . . . . ROCKMANTLE R.
ra'dinum . . . . . . ALPENROSE R.
ra'vum . . . . CLIFFROSE R.
re'pens . . . . TRUMPETMANTLE R.
reticula'tum (*rhombicum; A. reticulata*) ROSE AZALEA
—pentan'drum (*R. rhombicum pentandrum; A. reticulata pentandra*) FIVESTAMEN R.A.
rhaibocar'pum . . . . . BANDYPOD R.
rir'iei . . . . RIRIE R.
rose'um (*canescens* Porter, *not* Sweet; *prinophyllum; A. prinophylla; A. rosea*) . . . . ROSESHELL A.
rosmarinifo'lium Dipp., *not* Vidal **R. mucronatum**
rubigino'sum . . . . RUSTY R.
ru'fum . . . . TALISPOT R.
rupic'ola . . . . CLIFFPLUM R.
russa'tum . . . . ROYALALP R.
∞ **russellia'num** (*arboreum* × *catawbiense*) ∞ RUSSELL R.
₵**—al'bum** . . . . . . ₵WHITE R.R.
saluenen'se . . . . SALWEEN R.
∞ **san'deri** (*obtusum* × *simsi;* ∞ *A. sanderi*) . . . . . . ∞ SANDER A.
sanguin'eum . . . . . . TIBETBLOOD R.
sargentia'num . . . . . SARGENT R.
sca'brum (*sublanceolatum; A. scabra*) LUCHU A.
schizopep'lum . . . . . TALIROSE R.
schlippenbach'i (*A. schlippenbachi*) ROYAL A.
scin'tillans . . . . MORAINE R.
scyphoca'lyx . . . . BAMBOOBRAKE R.
sears'iae . . . . SEARS R.
selen'se . . . . SIELA R.
semibarba'tum (*A. semibarbata; Azaleastrum semibarbatum*) AUTUMNLEAF A.
sero'tinum
serpyllifo'lium (*A. serpyllifolia*) WILDTHYME A.
serrula'tum (*A. serrulata*) HAMMOCKSWEET A.
seto'sum . . . . . DARJEELING R.
shel'tonae . . . . SHELTON R.
shwelien'se . . . . SHWELI R.
siderophyl'lum . . . . . IRONRUST R.
sigilla'tum . . . . . DAPPLEBLOOM R.
sims'i (*A. simsi*) . . . . . INDIAN A.
sinen'se . . . . **R. molle**
sinogran'de . . . . . GREATLEAF R.
sinonutt'alli . . . CHINA-NUTTALL R.
smirnow'i . . . . SMIRNOW R.
∞ **smith'i** (*arboreum* × *ponticum*) ∞ SMITH R.
soul'iei . . . . SOULIE R.
specio'sum (*A. calendulacea flammea; A. speciosa*) . . . . . OCONEE A.
sperab'ile . . . . . BURMAFLAME R.
sphaeran'thum . . . . . SNOWBALL R.
sphaeroblas'tum . . . . PINKBUD R.
spinulif'erum . . . . . . TORCH R.
∞ **stanwellia'num** (*catawbiense* × *caucasicum*) . . . . ∞ STANWELL R.
stenophyl'lum . . . . . **R. makinoi**
stewartia'num . . . . . STEWART R.
strigillo'sum . . . . SCARLETBALL R.
subero'sum . . . . BLUSHROSE R.
sublanceola'tum . . . . . **R. scabrum**
sutchuenen'se . . . . SZECHWAN R.
—ger'aldi . . . . . . GERALD S.R.
talien'se . . . . TALI-RANGE R.
tephropep'lum . . . . . ASHROBE R.

RHODODENDRON, continued

thom'soni . THOMSON RHODODENDRON
traillia'num . . . . TRAILL R.
triflo'rum . . . . . . TRIFLORUM R.
tsangpoen'se . . . . . . TSANGPO R.
tschonos'ki (*A. tschonoski*) TSCHONOSKI AZALEA
ungern'i . . . . UNGERN R.
valentinia'num . . PERE VALENTIN R.
va'seyi (*A. vaseyi; Biltia v.*) PINKSHELL A.
—al'bum (*A. v. alba*) . . WHITE P.A.
veitchia'num . . . . VEITCH R.
vena'tor . . . . . . HUNTINGCOAT R.
∞ **venus'tum** (*arboreum* × *caucasicum*) ∞ VENUSTUM R.
vernico'sum . . . . . . LACQUER R.
verruculo'sum . . . . . . WARTY R.
villo'sum . . . . . PURPLESHAG R.
virga'tum . . . . . WILLOWTWIG R.
∞ **viscosep'alum** (*molle* × *viscosum;* ∞ *A. viscocephala;* ∞ *A. viscosepala*) ∞ CHINESE SWAMP A.
₵**—da'viesi** (₵*A. viscosepala d.*) ₵DAVIES C.A.
visco'sum (*A. viscosa*) . . . SWAMP A.
—coerules'cens
—glau'cum (*A. v. glauca*) BLUELEAF S.A.
—monta'num . . . . CAROLINA S.A.
—nit'idum (*A. v. nitida*) . SHINY S.A.
—rhodan'thum (*A. v. rhodantha*) PINK S.A.
—rubes'cens (*A. v. rubescens*) RUBY S.A.
—tomento'sum (*A. tomentosa; A. v. tomentosa*) . . . . . WOOLLY S.A.
wal'lichi (*R. campanulatum w.*) WALLICH R.
ward'i . . . . WARD R.
wa'soni . . . . WASON R.
∞ **waterer'i** (*catawbiense* × *matternichi*) ∞ WATERER R.
websteria'num . . . . . WEBSTER R.
∞ **wellesleya'num** (*catawbiense* × *maximum*) . . . . . . ∞ WELLESLEY R.
wey'richi (*A. weyrichi*) . WEYRICH A.
wight'i . . . . WIGHT R.
williamsia'num . . . . . WILLIAMS R.
×*wil'soni* Hort. . . . ∞ **R. laetevirens**
yanthi'num . . . . . **R. concinnum**
—laetevi'rens . . . . **R. concinnum l.**
—lepidan'thum . . . **R. concinnum l.**
yedoen'se (*A. yedoensis; A. yodogawa*) YODOGAWA A.
—poukhanen'se (*R. poukhanense; A. poukhanensis; A. yedoensis poukhanensis*) . . . . . . KOREAN Y.A.
yunnanen'se . . . . . . YUNNAN R.
zaleu'cum . . . . . . MILKLEAF R.

Common names and hort. var. (clons) of **Rhododendron:**

Abbreviations indicating the name of the group to which a horticultural variety is reported to belong, or the species from which it is reported to have been derived, in whole or in part, are as follows:

Arb. Arboreum Series Hybrid.
Azd. Azaleodendron.
Barb. Barbatum.
Boo. Boothi.
Bra. Brachycarpum.
Campa. Campanulatum.
Campy. Campylocarpum.
Car. Carolinianum.
Cat. Catawbiense.
Cau. Caucasicum.
Cin. Cinnabarinum.
Dau. Dauricum.

RHODODENDRON, continued

Dec. Decorum.
Dis. Discolor.
Edg. Edgeworthi.
Fal. Falconeri.
For. Fortunei.
Glau. Glaucum.
Gran. Grande.
Gri. Griersonianum.
Grif. Griffithianum.
Irr. Irroratum.
Jav. Javanicum.
Lac. Lacteum.
Lap. Lapponicum.
Lod. Loderi.
Mad. Maddeni.
Max. Maximum.
Ner. Neriiflorum.
Pont. Ponticum.
Prae. Praecox group of hybrids.
Salu. Saluenense.
Scab. Scabrifolium.
Smir. Smirnowi.
Tali. Taliense.
Thom. Thomsoni.
Tri. Triflorum.
Vir. Virgatum.

Many other varieties not included in this list will be found in C. G. Bowers' "Rhododendrons and Azaleas," J. G. Millais' "Rhododendrons and the Various Hybrids" and especially the yearbooks of The Rhododendron Association (England).

ABBREVIATIONS OF NAMES OF ORIGINATORS

d. Oud. P. den Ouden and Sons, Boskoop, Netherlands.
F.&D. Felix and Dykuis, Boskoop, Netherlands.
Kos. M. Koster and Sons, Boskoop, Netherlands.
Met. T. Methven and Sons, Edinburgh, Scotland.
Moser Moser, Versailles, France.
Noble Charles Noble, England.
Par. Samuel Parsons, Flushing, N. Y.
Sei. T. J. Seidel, Schweiputz, Saxony, Germany.
Sta. Standish, England.
V. Gee. Van Geert.
V. Hou. Louis Van Houtte, Ghent, Belgium.
V. Nes C. B. Van Nes, Boskoop, Netherlands.
Wat., A. Anthony Waterer, Woking, Surrey, England.
Wat., J. J. Waterer, Sons and Crisp, Twyford, Berks, England.

In using names from this list, the clon sign should precede hort. var. names but not species or variety common names. Example, ₵ABALONE, but ABBE DAVID R. For Azalea hort. var. and common names, see **AZALEA.**

ABALONE. Campy.
ABBE DAVID R. **R. davidi.**
ABBE DELAVAY R. **R. delavayi.**
ABBOT. Thom.
A. BEDFORD.
A. (*B.*) MITFORD. (A. Wat.)
ABRAHAM DIXON. (A. Wat.)
ABRAHAM LINCOLN. Cat.
A. (*C.*) KENDRICK.
ADALBERT. (Sei. 1897–1909.)
ADAM.
ADAMS R. **R. adamsi.**
ADDER. Thom.
ADELAIDE. Grif.
ADENOSYNUM.
ADJUTANT. Ner.
ADMIRAL (*Piet*) HEIN.
ADVIE. Arb.
AFTERGLOW.
A. GILBERT. Campy.
AGNES BEAUFORT. Grif.

RHODODENDRON, continued
Aileen Henderson.
Ajax.
Alarm.
Albatross. Lod.
Albert. Cat. (Sei. 1887–1908.)
Albescens.
Albrecht Durer.
Album Elegans. Cat. (A. Wat. before 1851.)
Album Grandiflorum. Cat. (A. Wat. before 1851.)
Album Novum. Cat. (V. Hou. 1882.)
Album Splendens.
Alcesta. Mad.
Alexander Adie. Cat. (J. Wat.)
Alexander Dancer. Cat. (A. Wat. 1865.)
Alice. Grif.
Alice Martineau.
Allah. Cat.
Alpaca. Ner.
Alpenrose R. **R. radinum.**
∞Altaclerense R. ∞**R. altaclerense.**
Alvinda. Thom.
Amalfi. Arb.
Amarantinora. Cat. (Par.)
Amaura. Campy.
Amba. Vir.
Amberbloom R. **R. flavidum.**
America.
Amethyst.
Amkeys. Tri.
Amor. Gri.
Amphion.
Amy.
Androcles. Arb.
Angelo. Grif.
Anica Bricogne.
Annabella. Campa.
Anna Parsons. Cat. (Par. before 1875.)
Anne. Thom.
Annedore. Cat.
Annie (*Lawrence*) Lamb. Max.
Ann (*Willis*) Fleming.
Anton. Cat.
Apache. Arb.
Aphrodite. Jav. *Maximum Superbum.*
Apple Blossom. For.
Apricotbell R. **R. concatenans.**
Arab. Thom.
Arbad. Arb.
Arbcamp. Arb.
Arboreum Gloxinaeflorum.
Arethusa. Grif.
Argent R. **R. grande.**
Argiolus. Tri.
Argosy. Dis.
Ariadne. (V. Nes before 1922.)
Aries. Thom.
Arma. Ner.
Armistice Day. (V. Nes before 1930.)
Arno. Cat.
Arthur Osborn. Ner.
Aruna. Campy.
Ascot Brilliant. Thom.
Ashrobe R. **R. tephropeplum.**
Assamicum.
Assam R. **R. patulum.**
Astarte. Ner.
Asteroid. Cau.
Atalanta. Arb.
Athens. (Met.)
Atrosanguineum. Cat. (A. Wat.)
Attraction.
August. Cat.
Auguste Lemaire.

RHODODENDRON, continued
Auguste Vangeert. Cat. (V. Gee. before 1867.)
Augustine R. **R. augustini.**
Aurora. Grif.
Autumnpurple R. **R. fastigiatum.**
Avalanche. Lod.
Avocet. Dis.
Ayah. Dis.
Ayesha. Dis.
Azaleoides.
Azma. Gri.
Azor. Gri.
Azric. Gri.
Aztec. Arb.
Bacchus. Cat. (J. Wat.)
Bagshot Ruby. Thom.
Balfour R. **R. balfourianum.**
Ballerina. Dis.
Balsam. Jav. *Balsaminaeflorum.*
Balsaminaeflorum album. White Balsam.
Balsaminaeflorum aureum. Yellow Balsam.
Bamboobrake R. **R. scyphocalyx.**
Bandypod R. **R. rhaibocarpum.**
Barbara Wallace.
Barclayanum.
Barclayi. Thom.
Barclayi Helen Fox. Helen Fox.
Barclayi Robert Fox. Robert Fox.
Baron (*Edm.*) Derothschild.
Baroness (*Henry*) Schroeder. Cat. (J. Wat.)
Baroness (*Lionel*) Rothschild.
Baroness Vonpanwitz.
Baron Schroeder. Cat. (J. Wat.)
Batang R. **R. polylepis.**
Bateman Bellflower R. **R. campanulatum batemani.**
Batemani. Campa.
B. Debruin. (A. Wat.)
Beaulieu. Grif.
Beauty of Bagshot. (J. Wat.)
Beauty of Littleworth. Grif.
Beauty of Tremough. Grif.
Bees R. **R. beesianum.**
Beethoven.
Bellflower R. **R. campanulatum.**
Bellona.
Bernard Crisp. (J. Wat.)
Bernard Gill.
Bertha. Cat.
Bertha Parsons. Cat.
Bertram (*Woodhouse*) Currie.
Betty Wormald.
Bibber. Cat.
Bibiani.
Bigleaf R. **R. calophytum.**
Bismark. Cat.
Blackbeauty.
Blanche Superbe.
Blandy. Cat. *Blandianum.*
Blandyanum. (Sta. & Noble before 1851.)
Bloodbloom R. **R. didymum.**
Bloodred. Arb.
Bluebell. Cat.
Blue Ensign. Grif.
Blueleaf R. **R. aeruginosum.**
Bluepeter.
Bluepod R. **R. cyanocarpum.**
Bluetit. Lap.
Bluet R. **R. intricatum.**
Blushing Beauty.
Blushing R. **R. erubescens.**
Blushrose R. **R. suberosum.**
Bodartianum. Campa.

RHODODENDRON, continued
Bodinier R. **R. bodinieri.**
Bodnant Sunrise. Grif.
Bonfire. Dis.
Booth R. **R. boothi.**
Borde Hill.
Botha. Cat.
Boule Deneige. Cau.
Brabantia.
Brachbooth. Glau.
Brachdis. Bra.
Brachydum. Glau.
Brickbud R. **R. hemitrichotum.**
Brilliant. Jav.
Britannia.
Briton Ferry.
Broughtoni.
Broughtoni Aureum. Azd.
Bulstrode Park.
Burmaflame R. **R. sperabile.**
Butler. Cat. *Butlerianum.*
Buttercup.
Butterfly.
B. W. Elliott. (J. Wat.)
Bylsianum.
Caerulescens.
Calfort. For.
Calliope. (d. Oud. 1910.)
Callirhoe. Cau.
Camilla. Campy.
Campirr. Campy.
Campkew. Campy.
Canary R. **R. lutescens.**
Candidissimum. Cat. (Par.) *Catawbiense × maximum.*
Canebrake R. **R. cyclium.**
Cannizaro.
Canon Furze. (J. Wat.)
Caractacus. Cat. (A. Wat. 1865.)
Carew Hunt.
Carex. Irr.
Carex Blush. Irr.
Carex White. Irr.
Carminata Crispiflora.
Carmine Jasmine. Jasminiflorum Carminatum.
Carmine Mandarin R. **R. discolor carneum.**
Carola. Cat.
Carolina R. **R. carolinianum.**
Carpet R. **R. aperantum.**
Cartoni. Azd.
Catawba R. **R. catawbiense.**
Catawbiense Album. Cat.
Catawbiense Boursault.
Catawbiense Grandiflorum.
Catherine Van Thol. Cat.
Caubut. Cau.
Caucasian R. **R. caucasicum.**
Caucasicum Album. Cau.
Caucasicum Fishers (*Variety*). Cau.
Caucasicum Pictum. Cau.
Caucasicum Roseum. Cau.
Caucasicum Splendidum. Cau.
Cauking. Cau.
C. B. Van Nes.
Celebes R. **R. radians.**
Celia.
Ceres. Jav.
Cetewayo.
Chancellor. Cat.
Chapman R. **R. chapmani.**
Charles Bagley. Cat. (A. Wat. 1865.)
Charles Dickens. Cat. (A. Wat. 1865.)
Charles Noble. (Noble)
Charles Sumner.

RHODODENDRON, continued
Charles Thorold. (A. Wat. before 1851.)
Charles Triffault.
Charlie Waterer. Cat.
Cheronia. For.
Cherry Ripe.
Chevalier Felix Desauvage.
China. For.
China-Nuttall R. **R. sinonuttalli.**
Chintz.
Chionoides. (J. Wat.)
Choremia. Ner.
Christmas Cheer. Cau.
Cilbooth. Mad.
Cilpinense. Mad.
Cinnabar R. **R. cinnabarinum.**
Cinnamonleaf Tree R. **R. arboreum cinnamomeum.**
Cinnamon R. **R. fulvum.**
Cinnkeys. Cin.
Cirrus. Smir.
Citronella. Campy.
Citron R. **R. citriniflorum.**
Clementine R. **R. clementinae.**
Cleo. Cau.
Cleopatra. Arb.
Cliffplum R. **R. rupicola.**
Cliffrose R. **R. ravum.**
Clio. Tali.
Clorinda. Jav.
Cloudland R. **R. impeditum.**
Coalition.
Coast R. **R. macrophyllum.**
Cockoftherock. Cin.
Collett R. **R. collettianum.**
Colonel Rogers. Fal.
Compactum Multiflorum.
Comptons Brow. (V. Nes before '22.)
Comte Degomer.
Comtesse Demorello. (Sta.)
Concessum. Cat.
Congestum Roseum. (J. Wat.)
Conical Kate.
Conspicuum.
Constance Carson.
Constance Terry.
Coombe Royal. Grif.
Coral Star.
Coresia. Campy.
Coreta. Lod.
Cornish Cross. Thom.
Cornish Early Red. Southamptonia.
Cornish Loderi. Dec.
Cornsutch. Arb.
Cornubia. Arb.
Corona. Thom. (J. Wat.)
Coronis. Thom.
Corrietree R. **R. fictolacteum.**
Corry Koster. (Kos. before 1922.)
Cosima. Cat.
Cotterill.
Countess.
Countess Fitzwilliam.
Countess of Athlone.
Countess of Derby. Grif.
Countess of Donoughmore.
Countess of Haddington. Mad.
Countess of Normanton.
Countess of Sefton.
Countess of Tankerville. (J. Wat.)
Crawling R. **R. herpesticum.**
Cream Fujiyama R. **R. brachycarpum lutescens.**
Cream R. **R. lacteum.**
Crimson Purplenymph R. **R. concinnum laetevirens.**
Crossbill. Scab.

RHODODENDRON, continued
Crown Prince. Cat.
C. S. Sargent. Cat. (A. Wat. 1888.)
Cunningham. Cat. *Cunninghami.*
∞Cunningham R. ∞**R. cunninghami.**
Cunninghams Blush.
Cunningham Sulphur. Cau.
Cunningham White. Max. (Before 1867.)
Cupid. Grif.
Cynthia. Cat.
Dahurian R. **R. dauricum.**
Dairy Maid.
Daisy. Cat.
Daisy Rand. Cat. (Par.)
Dalhousiae Victorianum. Mad.
Dalhousie R. **R. dalhousiae.**
Damaris. Cau.
Damask. Lod.
Dame (*Nellie*) Melba. Grif.
Dandy.
Daphne Daffarn. Grif.
Daphne Millais.
Daphne R. **R. daphniflorum.**
Dapplebloom R. **R. sigillatum.**
Darjeeling R. **R. setosum.**
Darkrim Tree R. **R. arboreum limbatum.**
Daubuzzi.
Davidson R. **R. davidsonianum.**
Dawn. Grif.
Dawns Delight.
Degrow R. **R. degronianum.**
Delicatissimum. Cat. (A. Wat. before 1851.) *Maximum × catawbiense.*
Delicatum. Fairy.
Delight. Mad.
Delila. Cat.
Desiderius. Cat.
Devonshire Cream. Campy.
Diadem. Jav.
Diamond. Grif.
Diana. Cat.
Dietrich. Cat.
Diphole Pink. (J. Wat.)
Distinction. Campa.
Donald Waterer. (J. Wat.)
Donar. Cat.
Doncaster. Cat.
Dorothea. Grif.
Dorothy Fortescue. (J. Wat.)
Douglas McEwan.
Dr. (*A.*) Blok.
Dr. (*A. W.*) Endtz.
Dr. (*H. C.*) Dresselhuys. (d. Oud. '24.)
Dr. (*H. J.*) Lovink. (d. Oud. 1929.)
Dr. Hogg.
Dr. Stocker. Cau.
Dr. Torrey. Cat.
Dr. (*V. H.*) Rutgers. (d. Oud. 1924.)
Dr. (*W. F.*) Wery.
Duc Debrabant.
Duchess of Bedford. (J. Wat.)
Duchess of Connaught. Jav.
Duchess of Cornwall.
Duchess of Edinburgh. Jav. (J. Wat. before 1885.)
Duchess of Portland. Barb.
Duchess of Teck.
Duchess of York.
Duke of Connaught.
Duke of Cornwall. Arb.
Duke of Portland.
Duke of York. For.
Dulcie Daffarn. Grif.
Duskybloom R. **R. campylogynum.**
Duskyblotch R. **R. maculiferum.**
Dwarfgold R. **R. megeratum.**

RHODODENDRON, continued
Earleaf R. **R. auriculatum.**
Earl of Athlone. (V. Nes 1922.)
Earl of Morley. Campy.
Earl of Shannon. (J. Wat.)
Early Brilliant.
Earlyflush R. **R. crinigerum.**
Early Gem. Prae.
Easter R. **R. mallotum.**
Echse. (Sei. 1897–1908.)
Eclectic R. **R. eclecteum.**
Edgeworth R. **R. edgeworthi.**
Edinense.
Edith.
Edith (*Mackworth*) Praed.
Edmundi.
Edusa. Campy.
Edward (*S.*) Rand. Cat. (A. Wat. 1820.)
Effner. Cat.
Eggleaf R. **R. ovatum.**
Eidam.
Eileen.
Elfrida.
Elisabetae. Cau.
Elizabethae. Fal.
Elsa Crisp.
Elsae. Gran.
Elsie Waterer.
Elspeth.
Emasculum.
Emeline Buckley.
Emil. Cat.
Emily Mangles.
Emma. Cat.
Emperor R. **R. imperator.**
Enchantress.
Endsleigh Pink.
Eos. Jav.
Erna. Smir.
Ernest Gill. Arb.
Esmeralda.
Essex Scarlet. For.
Ethel Edger. (Kos. 1923.)
Ethel Hall. (Kos. 1923.)
Ethel Stocker.
Euterpe.
Eva. (Sei. 1897–1908.)
Everestianum. Cat. (A. Wat. before 1851.)
Evergreen Dahurian R. **R. dauricum sempervirens.**
Exbury.
Exminster. Thom.
Exoniense. Mad.
Exquisite. Jav.
Faber R. **R. faberi.**
Fabia. Ner.
Faggetters Favorite.
Fair Helen.
Fairy. Cat. *Delicatum.*
Falconer R. **R. falconeri.**
Falvia. Thom.
Farnese. Cat.
Fasthip. Lap.
Fastuosum. Cat.
Fastuosum Plenum.
Favorite. Jav.
F. Bettex. (d. Oud. 1928.)
F. (*B.*) Hayes. Cat.
F. (*C.*) Puddle. Ner.
F. (*D.*) Godman. Cat. (A. Wat.)
February R. **R. praevernum.**
Fee.
Fire Ball. Barb.
Flame. Jav.
F. (*L.*) Ames. Cat. (A. Wat.)
Flamme. Cat.

RHODODENDRON, continued
Flare. Grif.
Fleeceleaf R. **R. chaetomallum.**
F. (*L.*) Olmsted.
Florence. Cat.
Florence Gill.
Florence Smith.
Flushing. Cat. (Par. before 1875.)
Flushrose R. **R. fulvoides.**
Fortunes R. **R. fortunei.**
Fortunes Triumph. For.
Fosterianum.
Fragrantissimum.
Francesia.
Francis (*B.*) Hayes. (J. Wat.)
Francis Dickson.
Frank Galsworthy.
Franz. Cat.
∞Fraser R. ∞**R. fraseri.**
Freckles. Ochroleucum.
Freda. For.
Frederick Waterer. (J. Wat.)
Fringed Catawba R. **R. catawbiense tomopetalum.**
Fringed R. **R. ciliatum.**
Fringeleaf Korean R. **R. mucronulatum ciliatum.**
Fujiyama R. **R. brachycarpum.**
Gaiety.
Galathea. Thom.
Gamechick. Grif.
Garibaldi.
Garland R. **R. hirsutum.**
Garnet.
G. (*A.*) Sims. (A. Wat.)
Gauntlet. Grif.
G. (*B.*) Simpson. (A. Wat.)
Gem. Grif.
Gemmiferum. Azd.
General Cavendish. (V. Nes before 1922.)
General Grant. Cat. (Par. before 1875.)
General (*Sir John*) Ducane. Thom.
Genoveva. Cat.
Geoffrey Henslow.
Geoffrey Millais.
George Bennington. For.
George Cunningham.
George Hardy. Grif.
Gerald Szechwan R. **R. sutchuenense geraldi.**
Gerard Moser.
Gertrud. Cat.
G. (*H.*) Maitland King.
Giantblood R. **R. barbatum.**
Giant R. **R. giganteum.**
Gibsoni.
Gilian. Grif.
Gilli. Grif.
Gills Crimson. Grif.
Gills Gloriosa. Grif.
Gills Goliath. Grif.
Gills Triumph. Arb.
Gina.
Gisela. Cat.
Glacier R. **R. nivale.**
Gladys. Campy.
Glenny. Cau. *Glennyanum.*
Glitterscale R. **R. heliolepis.**
Globe R. **R. orbiculare.**
Gloire Deboskoop.
Gloriosum. (J. Wat.)
Glory Caucasian R. **R. caucasicum splendens.**
Glory of Bagshot.
Glory of Keston. Barb.
Glory of Leonardslee. Grif.

RHODODENDRON, continued
Glory of Littleworth. Azd.
Glory of Penjerrick. Arb.
Godesberg. (V. Nes before 1922.)
Goethe. Cat.
Golden R. **R. chryseum.**
Goldfinch.
Goldfort. For.
Goldmat R. **R. chrysanthum.**
Goldsaucer R. **R. croceum.**
Goldsworth Crimson.
Goldsworth Pink.
Goldsworth Purple. Grif.
Goldsworth White.
Goldsworth Yellow. Cau.
Gomer Waterer. Grif. (J. Wat.)
Govenianum. Azd.
Graf Zeppelin.
Granat. Cat.
Grand Arab.
Grandiflorum.
Greatleaf R. **R. sinogrande.**
Grierson R. **R. griersonianum.**
Griffith R. **R. griffithianum.**
Guido.
Gulnare.
Guttatum.
Gylla MacGregor.
Hairyleaf R. **R. mollicomum.**
Hairystalk R. **R. pachytrichum.**
∞Halense R. ∞**R. halense.**
Halopeanum. Grif.
Hammondi.
Hance R. **R. hanceanum.**
Handsworth Brilliant.
Handsworth Early Red.
Handsworth Scarlet.
Handsworth White.
Hanna Felix. Cat. (F.&D. 1913.)
Hannibal. Cat.
Harbinger.
Harbison Piedmont R. **R. minus harbisoni.**
Harrisi. Thom.
Harrisi Superbum. Thom.
Harrows Seedling.
Harvest Moon.
Hebe. Ner.
Helena.
Helen Fox. Thom. *Barclayi Helen Fox.*
Helen Paul. For.
Helen Rogers.
Helen Schiffner. (Sei.)
Helen Waterer.
Hemsley R. **R. hemsleyanum.**
Hendersoni.
Henrietta Sargent. Cat. (A. Wat. 1891.)
Henryanum. Mad.
Henry Probasco. Cat. (Par.)
Henry Shilson.
Herbert Parsons. (Par.)
Herbert (*T.*) Gill.
Herme. Cat.
Hermia.
Hero. Cat.
H. (*H.*) Hunnewell. Cat. (A. Wat. 1865.)
Hipsal. Lap.
Hiraethlyn. Ner.
His Majesty.
H. (*M.*) Arderne. For.
Hodconeri. Fal.
Hodgson R. **R. hodgsoni.**
Holbein. Cat.
Holger. Cat.
Hollandia.

RHODODENDRON, continued
∞Holmlea R. ∞**R. holmleaense.**
Homer. Cat.
Honeybell R. **R. campylocarpum.**
(*Hon.*) John Boscawen.
Hoodleaf R. **R. cucullatum.**
Hooker R. **R. hookeri.**
Horsham.
Houlston R. **R. houlstoni.**
H. (*T.*) Gill. For.
Hugh Koster. (Kos. about 1923.)
Hugh Wormald. (Kos. before 1922.)
Humbold. Cat.
Hummingbird. Ner.
Hunnewell R. **R. hunnewellianum.**
Huntingcoat R. **R. venator.**
H. (*W.*) Sargent. Cat. (A. Wat. 1865.)
Hymen. Cat.
Ida Waterer.
Ignatius Sargent. Cat. *The Boss.*
Ignescens.
Impeanum.
Independence Day.
Indian Yellow.
Ingeborg. Cat.
Ingrami.
Ione. Mad.
Ironrust R. **R. siderophyllum.**
Isabella Mangles. Grif.
Isago.
Ivers Scarlet. *Iverianum.*
Jackie. Azd.
Jack Izod.
Jacksoni. Cau.
Jacksoni Coccineum.
Jagleaf Garland R. **R. hirsutum laciniatum.**
James Bateman. Cat.
James Burchett.
James MacIntosh. Cat.
James Mason.
James Nasmyth. (A. Wat. 1870.)
James Waterman. (A. Wat. 1865.)
Jasminiflorum. Jav.
Jasminiflorum Carminatum. Jav. *Carmine Jasmine.*
Java R. **R. javanicum.**
J. (*G.*) Millais. Thom.
J. (*H.*) Van Nes.
J. (*J.*) Devink.
J. (*Marshall*) Brooks. Cat. (A. Wat. before 1871.)
John (*Bennett*) Poe. For.
John Boscawen.
John Galsworthy.
John Henry Agnew.
John Rashleigh. Campy.
John Spencer.
John Tremayne. Arb.
John Walter. Cat. (J. Wat.)
John Waterer. Cat.
Joseph Martyr. (A. Wat.)
Joseph Whitworth. (J. Wat.)
Joyce Montagu.
J. R. Trumpy. Cat.
J. Spencer.
Jupiter.
Kamchatka R. **R. camtschaticum.**
Kate Greenaway.
Kate Waterer. Cat. (J. Wat.)
Katherine Vanthol.
Kathleen Fielding. (Kos. before 1922.)
Kathleen Mary Dallimore.
Kathleen Wallace.
Katie.
Kaulbach. Cat.

RHODODENDRON, continued
Keay Slocock.
Keisk R. **R. keiskei.**
Kelsey Catawba R. **R. catawbiense compactum.**
Kernick Gem. Barb.
Kesselringi. Smir.
Kettledrum. Cat. (A. Wat. before 1877.)
Kewense. Grif.
Kewense Hybrid. Grif.
Kewense Superba. For.
Kew Pearl.
Kewxen. Grif.
Keys R. **R. keysi.**
King Albert. Pont.
King Carola. Fal.
King Edward VII. Jav.
King George. Grif.
King-of-the-purples. Cat. (A. Wat.)
Kings Tree R. **R. arboreum kingianum.**
Kissena. Cat. (Par.)
Kittiwake. Tri.
Koenigdis. Dis.
Korean R. **R. mucronulatum.**
Kotschy R. **R. kotschyi.**
Lacquer R. **R. vernicosum.**
Lady (*Alice*) Fitzwilliam.
Lady (*Annette*) Detrafford.
Lady Armstrong. Cat. (A. Wat. before 1865.)
Lady Baillie.
Lady Bessborough. Dis.
Ladybird. Dis.
Lady Bligh.
Lady Chamberlain. Cin.
Lady (*Clementina*) Mitford. (A. Wat.)
Lady (*Clementine*) Walsh. Grif.
Lady Clermont. Cat. (A. Wat.)
Lady Decies. (J. Wat.)
Lady Derothschild. Grif. (V. Nes before 1922.)
Lady (*Eleanor*) Cathcart. Cat.
Lady Falmouth.
Lady (*Francis*) Crossley.
Lady (*Grey*) Egerton. Cat. (A. Wat. before 1885.)
Lady (*Gwendoline*) Broderick. (V. Nes)
Lady Hillingdon. Grif. (J. Wat.)
Lady Longman.
Lady (*Mary*) Parker.
Lady Montagu. Grif.
Lady Primrose.
Lady Rosebery. Cin.
Lady (*Stuart of*) Wortley. (Kos. before 1922.)
Lady (*Winifred*) Herbert.
La Fontaine.
Langley Park. (V. Nes before 1922.)
Langworth.
Lapland R. **R. lapponicum.**
La Signora Defaure.
Late Korean R. **R. mucronulatum acuminatum.**
Latona. Jav.
Lavender Girl. For.
Leatherleaf R. **R. coriaceum.**
Leda. Ner.
Ledumleaf R. **R. ledoides.**
Lees Dark Purple. Cat. *Lees Dark.*
Lees Scarlet.
Leopold. Cat.
Lepidoboothi. Lap.
Lessing.
Letty Edwards.
Lewis Carrol.

RHODODENDRON, continued
Lhasa R. **R. keleticum.**
Lilian. Grif.
Lily R. **R. liliiflorum.**
Limbatum.
Lindbull. Mad.
Linley. Lod.
Lionel. (Par. before 1875.)
Litiping R. **R. litiense.**
Little Beauty. Jav.
Liza Stillman. Grif.
Llandaff. (V. Nes before 1922.)
L. L. Liebig.
Loderi. Grif.
Loders White. Grif.
Loki. Arb.
London. (V. Nes before 1922.)
Lone Eagle. Car.
Longstyle R. **R. longistylum.**
Lord Eversley.
Lord Fairhaven.
Lord Roberts.
Lord Swaythling.
Lord Wolseley. Jav.
Louis Pasteur.
Luciferum. (J. Wat. before 1851.)
Luscombei. For.
Luscombes Scarlet.
Luteoroseum. Jav. *Opal.*
Mabel Parsons. Cat.
Maculatum Purpureum.
Madden R. **R. maddeni.**
Maggie Heywood. (J. Wat.)
Maiden Blush. Jav.
Makino R. **R. makinoi.**
Manchurian R. **R. micranthum.**
Mandarin R. **R. discolor.**
Manglesi. Grif.
Manglesi Delicata.
Manipur R. **R. manipurense.**
Manselli. Fal.
Marchioness of Downshire.
Marchioness of Lansdowne. Cat.
Marchioness of Londonderry.
Marchioness of Tweeddale.
Margaret.
Margaret Bean.
Margery Slocock.
Marie Forte.
Marie Stuart. (A. Wat.)
Marie Vanhoutte. (V. Hou.)
Marion.
Marquis of Waterford. Cat. (J. Wat.)
Mars.
Martin (*Hope*) Sutton. (A. Wat.)
Mary Waterer.
Mauvequeen R. **R. desquamatum.**
Maximum Album. Max. (A. Wat.)
Maximum Roseum. Max.
Maximum Superbum. Aphrodite.
Maximum Triumphans. Max.
Maximum Wellsianum. Max. (A. Wat.)
∞Maxpont R. ∞**R. intermedium.**
Maxwell R. **R. maxwelli.**
Maxwell (*T.*) Masters. (A. Wat.)
Maya. For.
Mayday. Ner.
Mayflower R. **R. racemosum.**
Mayqueen.
May Templar.
Meadowbrook. Cat.
Meg Merrilies.
Melpomene.
Melton. Cat.
Memoir. Cat. (A. Wat.)
Mermaid.

RHODODENDRON, continued
Message of Peace.
Meteor. Cat. (Sta., Noble)
Methvens Scarlet.
Metternich R. **R. metternichi.**
Michael Waterer. Cat.
Midsummer.
Milkleaf R. **R. zaleucum.**
Mims. Cat.
Minnie. Cat. (Sta. before 1867.)
Miss (*H.*) Detrafford. (J. Wat.)
Miss (*Mary*) Ames. (A. Wat.)
Miss (*Noreen*) Beamish.
Miss Watson.
Mistress Mary.
Mme. (*A.*) Moser.
Mme. Carvalho. Cau. (Sta. before 1882.)
Mme. Debruin. (Kos. before 1922.)
Mme. (*F. T.*) Chauvin.
Mme. (*Gaston*) Chandon.
Mme. (*Jeanne*) Bois.
Mme. (*Jules*) Porges.
Mme. Masson. Cat.
Mme. Pellerin. (Moser)
Mme. (*Pierrette*) Forestier.
Mme. Thiers. Cat.
Mme. Wagner. Cat.
Modesty. Cat.
Moliere.
Monsieur (*Alfred*) Chauchard. (Moser)
Monsieur Thiers.
Monstrous. Smir.
Mont Blanc. Cau.
Moonstone. Campy.
Moraine R. **R. scintillans.**
Mori R. **R. mori.**
Mosers Maroon.
Motherofpearl.
Mountaindew R. **R. irroratum.**
Mountainglory R. **R. oreodoxa.**
Mount Everest.
Moupin R. **R. moupinense.**
Mozart.
Mrs. (*A. B.*) Bide. (Kos. 1927.)
Mrs. (*A. C.*) Kendrick.
Mrs. (*Alistair*) MacIntosh.
Mrs. (*A. M.*) Williams.
Mrs. (*Anthony*) Waterer. (A. Wat.)
Mrs. (*Arthur*) Hunnewell. (A. Wat.)
Mrs. (*Ashley*) Slocock.
Mrs. (*A. T.*) Delamare.
Mrs. (*A.*) Walter.
Mrs. (*A.*) Waterer.
Mrs. (*Betty*) Robertson.
Mrs. Byrne. (Kos. 1923.)
Mrs. Cameron.
Mrs. (*C. B.*) Van Nes.
Mrs. (*Charles*) Butler.
Mrs. (*Charles*) Pearson. (Kos. before 1923.)
Mrs. (*Charles*) Sargent. Cat. (A. Wat. 1890.)
Mrs. (*Charles*) Thorold. (A. Wat.)
Mrs. (*Davies*) Evans. (A. Wat.)
Mrs. (*Dr.*) Blamey.
Mrs. (*E. C.*) Stirling. Grif. (J. Wat.)
Mrs. (*E.*) Hillier.
Mrs. Ellice. Grif.
Mrs. (*F.*) Hankey.
Mrs. (*F. J.*) Kirchner. (A. Wat.)
Mrs. Florence Smith. Cat.
Mrs. (*Frank*) Mangles.
Mrs. Furnival.
Mrs. (*George*) Hardy.
Mrs. (*George*) Paul. Grif.
Mrs. (*G. W.*) Leak.

RHODODENDRON, continued
Mrs. Hamilton.
Mrs. (*Harry*) Ingersoll. Cat. (A. Wat. 1877.)
Mrs. Heal. Jav.
Mrs. (*Helen*) Koster.
Mrs. (*Henry*) Agnew.
Mrs. (*Henry*) Shilson.
Mrs. H. Smith.
Mrs. (*H.*) Stocker.
Mrs. (*J.*) Comber. For.
Mrs. (*J. C.*) Williams. (A. Wat.)
Mrs. (*J. H.*) Van Nes. (V. Nes before 1922.)
Mrs. (*J. J.*) Crosfield.
Mrs. (*John*) Clutton. Pont. (A. Wat. 1865.)
Mrs. (*John*) Kelk. (J. Wat.)
Mrs. (*John*) Millais.
Mrs. (*John*) Penn. Cat. (J. Wat. before 1882.)
Mrs. John Waterer. Cat. (J. Wat. before 1867.)
Mrs. (*J. P.*) Lade. (A. Wat.)
Mrs. (*Kenneth*) Wilson.
Mrs. Kingsmill. Arb.
Mrs. (*L. A.*) Dunnett.
Mrs. Lindsay Smith. (Kos. before 1922.)
Mrs. Lionel Derothschild.
Mrs. (*L. M. Hayes*) Palmer.
Mrs. (*Mary*) Ashley.
Mrs. (*Matthew*) Rose. For.
Mrs. Mendel. Cat. (A. Wat.)
Mrs. Milner. Cat. (A. Wat.)
Mrs. P. Denouden. (d. Oud.)
Mrs. (*P. D.*) Williams.
Mrs. Peter Koster.
Mrs. (*Philip*) Martineau.
Mrs. (*Randall*) Davison. Grif.
Mrs. Reuthe.
Mrs. (*R. G.*) Shaw. (A. Wat.)
Mrs. (*Richard*) Gill. Arb.
Mrs. (*Robert W.*) Wallace. (Kos. before 1922.)
Mrs. (*R. S.*) Holford. Cat. (A. Wat.)
Mrs. (*Russell*) Sturgess. (J. Wat.)
Mrs. (*Samuel*) Wallrock.
Mrs. (*S.*) Simpson. (A. Wat.)
Mrs. (*Thistleton*) Dyer. For.
Mrs. (*T. H.*) Lowinsky. (A. Wat.
Mrs. (*Tom*) Agnew. (J. Wat.)
Mrs. Tritton. (J. Wat.)
Mrs. (*T.*) Wezelenburg.
Mrs. (*Walter*) Burns. Grif.
Mrs. W. C. Slocock. Campy.
Mrs. (*W. H.*) Gaze.
Mrs. (*W. H.*) Yas. (V. Nes before 1922.)
Mrs. William Agnew.
Mrs. (*William*) Bovill.
Mrs. (*William*) Watson. Grif.
Mrs. (*W. R.*) Dykes.
Mu-li R. **R. muliense.**
Multiforum. Car.
Mum. Cat. (J. Wat. 1897.)
Muriel. Fal.
Muriel Messel. Lod.
∞ Myrtle R. ∞ **R. myrtifolium.**
Nanette.
Naomi. For.
Necklace R. **R. hormophorum.**
Neda. Ner.
Nellie. Azd.
Nelly Debruin. (Before 1851.)
Neptune. Jav.
Neriiapo. Ner.
Neriiarb. Ner.

RHODODENDRON, continued
Neriihaem. Ner.
Nero.
Nilgiri Tree R. **R. arboreum nilagiricum.**
Niobe.
Nippon R. **R. nipponicum.**
(*N. N.*) Sherwood.
Nobleanum. Arb.
Nobleanum Album. Arb.
Nobleanum Bicolor. Arb.
Nobleanum Coccineum. Arb.
Nobleanum Venustum. Arb.
Norah.
∞ Norbiton R. ∞ **R. norbitonense.**
Noreen Beamish.
Norma. Cat.
Norman Gill.
Norman Shaw. Dis.
Notabile.
Novelty. (A. Wat.)
Novum Elegans.
Nuneham Park. (V. Nes before 1922.)
Ochroleucum. Cau. (J. Wat.) *Freckles.*
Oculatum. (J. Wat.)
Oculissimum. (J. Wat.)
Odoratum. Azd.
Oheimb-Woislowitz. Cat.
Oldewig. Cat.
Oldham R. **R. oldhami.**
Old Port. Cat. (A. Wat. 1865.)
Oleander R. **R. neriiflorum.**
Oliver. Lod.
Olivespot R. **R. chasmanthum.**
Omega. Cat.
Oolah Mountains R. **R. calophyllum.**
Opal. Luteoroseum.
Orangetip R. **R. caloxanthum.**
Oread R. **R. oreotrephes.**
Oreocinn. Tri.
Orion.
Ortrud. Cat.
Osceola. (Par. before 1875.)
Otto Foster. Grif.
Painted Lady.
Pallida. Thom.
Pallidum. Vir.
Pamela Fielding. (V. Nes before 1922.)
Pamela Neve.
Paperleaf R. **R. chartophyllum.**
Parsons Gloriosum. Cat. (Par. before 1869.)
Parsons Grandiflorum. Cat. (Par.)
Patience. Grif.
Peggy.
Pelopidas.
Pemako R. **R. pemakoense.**
Penciltwig R. **R. orthocladum.**
Penelope.
Pengaer. Grif.
Penjerrick. Campy.
Penllyn. For.
Penrose Atkinson.
Pentilly Scarlet.
Percyanum.
Pere Farges R. **R. fargesi.**
Pere Faurie R. **R. fauriei.**
Pere Valentin R. **R. valentinianum.**
Perfection.
Perspicuum. (J. Wat.)
Peter Koster. (Kos. before 1922.)
Philippe Devilmorin.
Philip Waterer. Grif.
Phryne. Campy.
Picotee.
Pictum.

RHODODENDRON, continued
Picturatum. (A. Wat.)
Piedmont Catawba R. **R. catawbiense insulare.**
Piedmont R. **R. minus.**
Pierre Moser.
Pilgrim. For.
Pincushion R. **R. myrtilloides.**
Pink Beauty. (V. Nes before 1922.)
Pink Bride. Grif.
Pinkbud R. **R. sphaeroblastum.**
Pink Caucasian R. **R. caucasicum roseo-album.**
Pink Coral. Grif.
Pink Delight. Arb.
Pink Diamond. Grif.
Pink Domino. Dis.
Pink Fujiyama R. **R. brachycarpum rosaeflorum.**
Pink Pearl. Grif.
Pink Perfection.
Pink Ponticum R. **R. ponticum roseum.**
Pink Rosebay R. **R. maximum purpureum.**
Pink Shell. Grif.
Pocahontas. (Par. before 1875.)
Polarbear. For.
Polarstar.
Polly Peachum.
Pompom R. **R. fulgens.**
∞ Ponticataw R. ∞ **R. morelianum.**
Ponticum R. **R. ponticum.**
Praecox. Dau.
President. Jav.
President Lincoln. Cat. (Par.)
President Roosevelt. Cat.
Pretty Polly. Grif.
Pride of Kernick.
Primrose. Jav.
Prince Arthur.
Prince (*Camille*) Derohan.
Prince of Wales.
Princess Alexandra. Jav.
Princess Alice. Edg. (V. Nes before 1922.)
Princess Beatrice. Jav.
Princess Christian. Jav. (J. Wat.)
Princess Elizabeth.
Princess Ena.
Princess Frederica. Jav.
Princess Hortense. (Sta., Noble)
Princess Juliana. Grif. (V. Nes. before 1922.)
Princess Mary (*of Cambridge*). Cat. (J. Wat.)
Princess of Orange. Thom.
Princess Royal. Jav.
Professor (*Dr. J. H.*) Zaayer.
Professor Hugo Devries.
Prometheus. Cat.
Prostigiatum. Salu.
Prostsal. Salu.
Przewalski R. **R. przewalski.**
Puckerleaf R. **R. bullatum.**
Pulcherrimum. Arb.
Punctatum.
Purity. Edg. (A. Wat.)
Purple-elf R. **R. calostrotum.**
Purplemantle R. **R. fimbriatum.**
Purplenymph R. **R. concinnum.**
Purplequeen R. **R. floribundum.**
Purpleshag R. **R. villosum.**
Purple Splendour.
Purple Tree R. **R. arboreum puniceum.**
Purpureum Crispum. Cat. (Par.)

RHODODENDRON, continued
Purpureum Elegans. Cat. (A. Wat. before 1865.)
Purpureum Grandiflorum. Cat. (A. Wat. before 1865.)
Pygmalion.
Pyramus. Lod.
Queen. Jav.
Queen Alexandra. Arb.
Queen Mary. Grif.
Queen o' the May. Grif.
Queen Souriya.
Queen Wilhelmina. Grif.
Querele. Cat.
Racil.
Ragged Robin.
Rainbow. Grif.
Ralph Saunders. Cat.
Randalls Scarlet.
Raoul Millais. (Kos. before 1922.)
Red Admiral. Arb.
Red Argenteum. Gran.
Redblood R. **R. haemaleum.**
Red Ridinghood.
Redspot R. **R. bracteatum.**
Redstripe R. **R. formosum.**
₵Red Winter R. **₵R. praecox rubrum.**
Regale.
Regal R. **R. basilicum.**
Retreat.
Rev. R. Horsham. (V. Nes before 1922.)
(*Rev. R. W.*) Carew Hunt. (V. Nes before 1922.)
Rhodora. **R. canadense.**
Richard Gill.
Rienzi. (Noble before 1867.)
Ririe R. **R. ririei.**
Riviera Beauty.
Robert Croux.
Robert Fox. Thom. *Barclayi Robert Fox.*
Robert (*W.*) Wallace. (Kos. before 1922.)
Robin Hood. For.
Robin Redbreast. For.
Rockmantle R. **R. radicans.**
∞Rockmount R. **∞R. arbutifolium.**
Rock R. **R. ferrugineum.**
Rockviolet R. **R. pleistanthum.**
Romany Chai.
Romany Chal.
Rosabel. Cat. (A. Wat. 1865.)
Rosamene.
Rosamundi. Cat.
Rosamund Millais. (Kos. before 1922.)
Rosebay R. **R. maximum.**
Rose Beauty.
Rosebud R. **R. callimorphum.**
Rose Mangles. Cin.
Rosemary Chipp. For.
Rose Perfection.
Roseum Elegans. Cat. (A. Wat. before 1851.)
Roseum Grandiflorum. (A. Wat. before 1865.)
Roseum Luteum. (Par.)
Roseum Superbum.
Rosybell.
Rosy Earleaf R. **R. auriculatum roseum.**
Rosymorn. Jav.
Rovellianum. Dau.
Royalalp R. **R. russatum.**
Royalblood R. **R. haematodes.**
Royalflush. Cin.
Royalpurple.

RHODODENDRON, continued
R. S. Field. Cat.
R. S. Holford. Cat.
Rubens.
Ruby. Jav.
Rubyspot R. **R. flavorufum.**
Rundles Scarlet. Arb.
Russellianum. Cat.
Russellianum Album. Cat.
Russellianum Superbum. Cat.
Russellianum Tigrinum. Cat.
∞Russell R. **∞R. russellianum.**
Russetleaf R. **R. circinnatum.**
Rustybrick R. **R. exasperatum.**
Rusty R. **R. rubiginosum.**
Saffronleaf R. **R. eximium.**
Salmono. Cat. *Salmono-roseum.*
Salween R. **R. saluenense.**
Samuel Morley. (J. Wat.)
Samuel P. Parsons. Cat.
Sapgreen R. **R. brachyanthum.**
Sappho.
Sargent R. **R. sargentianum.**
Saturne.
Scarletball R. **R. strigillosum.**
Scarlet Rock R. **R. ferrugineum atrococcineum.**
Schiller.
Scipio. Cat.
Seabuckthorn R. **R. hippophaeoides.**
Sears R. **R. searsiae.**
Seashell.
Sefton. Cat. (A. Wat.)
(*Senator*) Charles Sumner. Cat.
Sensation.
Sesterianum. Edg.
Seta. Scab.
Sheila Osborn. Dis.
Shelton R. **R. sheltonae.**
Shepherdi. Arb.
Sherwood. Cat. *Sherwoodianum.*
Shilson. Thom.
Shotsilk. Campy.
Shweli R. **R. shweliense.**
Siberrads Early Pink.
Sidney Herbert. (J. Wat.)
Sidonia. For.
Siela R. **R. selense.**
Sigismund Bucker. (A. Wat.)
Silverleaf R. **R. argyrophyllum.**
Sir (*A.*) Grinness. (J. Wat.)
Sir Harry Veitch.
Sir Henry Havelock. Cat.
Sir Isaac Balfour. (V. Nes before 1922.)
Sir (*John*) Ramsden. Thom.
Sir Joseph Hooker. Grif.
Sir (*Joseph*) Whitworth.
Sir (*Richard*) Garton.
Sir Robert Peel. (J. Wat. before 1867.)
Sir Thomas Sebright.
Sir Walter Scott. (Sta. before 1867.)
Sir William Maxwell.
Skyland R. **R. cantabile.**
Smallsaucer R. **R. puralbum.**
Small Violetbloom R. **R. nitidulum nubigenum.**
Smirnow R. **R. smirnowi.**
Smithi Aureum. Azd.
∞Smith R. **∞R. smithi.**
Smiths Scarlet.
Snowball R. **R. sphaeranthum.**
Snowbunting. Arb.
Snowdrop. Grif.
Snowflake. (A. Wat.)
Snowleaf R. **R. niphargum.**
Snowqueen. Grif.

RHODODENDRON, continued
Snowy R. **R. niveum.**
Sophia Gray. (Before 1922.)
Soularb. Thom.
Soulbut. Thom.
Soulie R. **R. souliei.**
Soulkew. Thom.
Soulking. Thom.
Southamptonia. *Cornish Early Red; Stoneham Scarlet.*
Souvenir de (*A.*) Waterer.
Souvenir de (*Dr. S.*) Endtz. Grif.
Souvenir de (*H. J.*) Mangles. Jav.
Souvenir de (*Mme. J. H.*) Van Nes
Souvenir de (*W. C.*) Slocock.
Spearleaf R. **R. aechmophyllum.**
Spiceleaf R. **R. glaucum.**
Spinulosum. Scab.
Standard of Flanders.
Standishi. Grif.
Stanley Davies. (J. Wat.)
Stanwellianum. Cau. (Met.)
Stanwellianum Album. Cau. (Met.)
∞Stanwell R. **∞R. stanwellianum.**
Starcup R. **R. astrocalyx.**
Starfish. Grif.
Stella. Cat. (A. Wat. 1865.)
Stephen Davies.
Stewart R. **R. stewartianum.**
St. George.
Stickyleaf R. **R. glischrum.**
St. Keverne. Arb.
Stoneham Scarlet. Southamptonia.
Strategist. Grif.
Straw Caucasian R. **R. caucasicum stramineum.**
Stromboli.
St. Simon.
Sulfur R. **R. anthopogon.**
Sulfur Yellow. Thom.
Sulphureum. Cau.
Sun of Austerlitz. Arb.
Sunset. For.
Sunshine. (J. Wat.)
Susan. Campa.
Sweetbay R. **R. crassum.**
Sweetshell R. **R. decorum.**
Sweet Simplicity. (J. Wat.)
Sybil. Jav.
Sylph. (A. Wat.)
Symphony.
Szechwan R. **R. sutchuenense.**
Szechwoods R. **R. longesquamatum.**
Tali-range R. **R. taliense.**
Talirose R. **R. schizopeplum.**
Talispot R. **R. rufum.**
Tall Carolina R. **R. carolinianum foliatum.**
Tallyho.
Taylor. Jav. *Taylori.*
Tecumseh. (Par. before 1875.)
Ted Waterer.
Tengrinor R. **R. pocophorum.**
The Boss. Ignatius Sargent.
The Bride.
The Don.
(*The Hon.*) Joyce Montagu.
The King.
The Queen. Jav. (Noble)
Thetis. Jav.
The Warrior. (J. Wat. before 1867.)
Thickset R. **R. compactum.**
T. H. Mekowich. (J. Wat.)
Thomasine. Thom.
Thomson R. **R. thomsoni.**
Thomwilliams. Thom.
Thunderstorm. Grif.
Tibetblood R. **R. sanguineum.**

RHODODENDRON, continued
Tittenhurst. Lac.
Tittenhurst Belle. Grif.
Tom (*Willis*) Fleming.
Torch R. **R. spinuliferum.**
Torlonianum. Azd.
Traill R. **R. traillianum.**
Trebah Gem. Arb.
Tree R. **R. arboreum.**
Tregedna. Thom.
Triflorum R. **R. triflorum.**
Trilby.
Triumphans. Jav.
Trumpetmantle R. **R. repens.**
Tsangpo R. **R. tsangpoense.**
Tubantia.
Tuberose R. **R. megacalyx.**
Tuftwool R. **R. floccigerum.**
Tundra R. **R. parvifolium.**
Twincolor R. **R. dichroanthum.**
Tyermani. Mad.
Ungern R. **R. ungerni.**
Unique.
Unknown Warrior.
Urania.
Valewood Pink.
Vanderbrocke. (d. Oud. 1928.)
Vanderhoop. (d. Oud. 1928.)
Vanessa. Thom.
Vanity.
Vannesglory.
Vannessensation.
Vanweerden Poeiman. (d. Oud.)
Vauban. (A. Wat.)
Veitchianum.
Veitch R. **R. veitchianum.**
Venus. Grif.
∞Venustum R. ∞**R. venustum.**
Vervaeneana.
Victorianum.
Viola. Cau. (Sei. before 1883.)
Violet Adair. Grif.
Violet Augustine R. **R. augustini violascens.**
Violetbloom R. **R. nitidulum.**
Violetmat R. **R. lysolepis.**
Violet Paget. Grif.
Violet Parsons.
∞Viscataw R. ∞**R. fragrans.**
∞Viscomax R. ∞**R. hybridum.**
Viscountess Elveden.
Viscount Powerscourt. (J. Wat.)
Waif R. **R. planetum.**
Wallich R. **R. wallichi.**
Ward R. **R. wardi.**
Warrior. Cat. (J. Wat.)
Warty R. **R. verruculosum.**
Wason R. **R. wasoni.**
∞Waterer R. ∞**R. watereri.**
Waterers Caucasicum.
Waterers Hybridum. For.
Webster R. **R. websterianum.**
∞Wellesley R. ∞**R. wellesleyanum.**
Wellsianum.
Werei. Arb.
Westward Ho. Dis.
White Augustine R. **R. augustini album.**
White Balsam. Jav. *Balsaminaeflorum album.*
Whitebutton R. **R. cephalanthum.**
White Carolina R. **R. carolinianum album.**
White Catawba R. **R. catawbiense album.**
Whitecloud. Grif.
Whitediamond. Grif.

RHODODENDRON, continued
White Garland R. **R. hirsutum albiflorum.**
Whitepearl. Grif.
White Ponticum R. **R. ponticum album.**
White Rhodora. **R. canadense albiflorum.**
White Rock R. **R. ferrugineum album.**
White Rosebay R. **R. maximum album.**
₵White Russell R. ₵**R. russellianum album.**
Whitesamite.
Whiteshield R. **R. leucaspis.**
Whiteswan. Dec.
Whitethroat R. **R. diacritum.**
White Tree R. **R. arboreum album.**
Wick Woolleaf R. **R. lanatum luciferum.**
Wight R. **R. wighti.**
William Austin. Cat. (J. Wat.)
William Cowper. (J. Wat.)
William (*Ewart*) Gladstone. (J. Wat. before 1882.)
William Godfrey.
Williams R. **R. williamsianum.**
William Watson.
Willowleaf R. **R. lepidotum.**
Willowtwig R. **R. virgatum.**
∞Wilson R. ∞**R laetevirens.**
Windsor Tree R. **R. arboreum windsori.**
Winifred White.
∞Winter R. ∞**R. praecox.**
W. K. Punchard. (J. Wat.)
Woodelf R. **R. drumonium.**
Woodlandglory R. **R. euchaites.**
Woolleaf R. **R. lanatum.**
W. R. Dykes.
Xenarb. Tali.
Yellow Balsam. Jav. *Balsaminaeflorum aureum.*
Yellow Caucasian R. **R. caucasicum flavidum.**
Yellow Hammer. Boo.
Yunnan R. **R. yunnanense.**
Yunnanrose R. **R. detonsum.**
Yvonne. Grif.
Zeelandia.
Zelauka.

RHODOHYPOX'IS
baur'ei

RHODOLEI'A
champio'ni

RHODOMYR'TUS . . . Rosemyrtle
tomento'sa (*Myrtus t.*) . Downy R.

RHODO'RA . . **RHODODENDRON**

Rhodora . . **Rhododendron canadense**
White R. . . . . . **R. c. albiflorum**

RHODORHI'ZA . . . **CONVOLVULUS**

RHODOSPHAE'RA . Cardinalberry
rhodan'thema . . . . Big C.

RHODOSTA'CHYS . . Rhodostachys
andi'na . . . . Chilean R.
pitcairnifo'lia . . . . . . Pitcairn R.

RHODOTHAM'NUS . . Alpineshrub
chamaecis'tus (*Adodendron c.; Rhododendron c.*) . . . . Rosy A.

RHODOT'YPOS . . . . . . Jetbead
scan'dens (*kerrioides*) . . . Black J.

RHODYME'NIA . . . . . Seakale
palma'ta . . . . . . Irishdulse S.

RHOE'O . . . . Rhoeo
dis'color (*Tradescantia d.*). Oyster R. (*Oysterplant*)
—vitta'ta

RHOMBOPHYL'LUM
MESEMBRYANTHEMUM
See **SUCCULENTS.**

RHOPALOBLAS'TE . Rhopaloblaste
See **PALM GENERA.**

RHOPALOS'TYLIS (*EORA*)
Rhopalostylis
See **PALM GENERA.**

Rhubarb . . . . **Rheum**
Alexandra R. . . . . . **R. alexandrae**
Collin R. . . . . . . **R. collinianum**
Currant R. . . . . **R. ribes**
Franzenbach R. . . **R. franzenbachi**
Garden R. . . . . . **R. rhaponticum**
Himalayan R. . . . . **R. emodi**
Medicinal R. . . . . . . **R. officinale**
Red Sorrel R.. **R. palmatum rubrum**
Scarlet S. R. . **R. p. atrosanguineum**
Sharpleaf R. . . . **R. acuminatum**
Sorrel R. . . . . **R. palmatum**
Sungari R. . . . . . **R. songaricum**
Tangut R. . **R. palmatum tanguticum**
Webb R. . . . . . . **R. webbianum**
Wittrock R. . . . . . . **R. wittrocki**

RHUS' (*SCHMALTZIA*) |w . Sumac
See **TOXICODENDRON.**
al'bida . . . . Sandbind S.
america'na . . . **Cotinus americanus**
aromat'ica (*canadensis*) |w
Fragrant S.
—illinoen'sis . . . . . Illinois F.S.
—serot'ina . . . . Late F.S.
chinen'sis (*javanica; osbecki*)
Chinese S.
—rox'burghi . . . . . Roxburgh S.
cismonta'na . . . . . . **R. glabra c.**
cogna'ta . . . . **R. trilobata**
copalli'na (*Schmaltzia c.*) |w
Flameleaf S.
—lanceola'ta . . . . . Prairie F.S.
—leucan'tha . . . . . . White F.S.
coria'ria . . . . Sicilian S.
coriarioi'des . . **R. punjabensis sinica**
cotinoi'des . . . **Cotinus americanus**
cot'inus . . . . . **Cotinus coggygria**
delavay'i . . . . . **Toxicodendron d.**
diversilo'ba
Toxicodendron diversilobum
emo'ryi . . . . Emory S.
gla'bra |w . . . . Smooth S.
—cismonta'na (*R. cismontana*)
RockyMountain S.S.
—flaves'cens . . Yellowfruit S.S.
—lacinia'ta . . . . . . Cutleaf S.S.
hen'ryi . . . . **R. potanini**
hir'ta . . . . **R. typhina**
∞**hy'brida** (*glabra × typhina*)
integrifo'lia . . . . . . Lemonade S.
—serra'ta . . . . . . Toothed L.S.
javan'ica . . . . **R. chinensis**
lan'cea . . . . SouthAfrican S.
lauri'na (*Malosma l.*) |w . . Laurel S.
meto'pium . . . **Metopium toxiferum**
michaux'i . . . . Michaux S.
microphyl'la |w . . . . . Littleleaf S.
orienta'lis . **Toxicodendron orientale**
os'becki . . . . **R. chinensis**
ova'ta . . . . Sugar S.
pentaphyl'la . . . . . . Fiveleaf S.
potani'ni (*henryi*) . . . . Potanin S.

RHUS, continued
punjaben'sis . . . . . PUNJAB SUMAC
—si'nica (*R. coriarioides; R. sinica*)
quercifo'lia
Toxicodendron quercifolium
rad'icans . . . . . **Toxicodendron r.**
—rydberg'i . . . . **Toxicodendron r. r.**
rydberg'i . . . . . **Toxicodendron r. r.**
sempervi'rens (*virens*) . EVERGREEN S.
succeda'nea
Toxicodendron succedaneum
sylves'tris . **Toxicodendron sylvestre**
terebinthifo'lia . . . . TEREBINTH S.
toxicoden'dron Auth., *not* L.
Toxicodendron radicans
toxicoden'dron L., *not* Auth.
Toxicodendron quercifolium
trichocar'pa
Toxicodendron trichocarpum
triloba'ta (*cognata*) |w . SKUNKBUSH S. (*Skunkbush*)

This is one of several American shrubs called Squawbush.

—anisophyl'la
typhi'na (*hirta*) |w . . . STAGHORN S.
—dissec'ta . . . . . SHREDLEAF S.
—lacinia'ta . . . . . CUTLEAF S.S.
—viridiflo'ra . . . . . . GREEN S.S.
utahen'sis . . . . UTAH S.
venena'ta . . **Toxicodendron vernix**
vernicif'lua
Toxicodendron vernicifluum
ver'nix . . . . . **Toxicodendron v.**
vimina'lis
vi'rens . . . . **R. sempervirens**

RHYNCHO'SIA (*DOLICHOLUS*) |w
RHYNCHOSIA
erec'ta |w . . . . ERECT R.
latifo'lia |w . . . . . BROADLEAF R.
min'ima |w . . . . LEAST R.
phaseoloi'des (*precatoria; Dolicholus phaseoloides; D. precatorius*)
CRABSEYE R.
puber'ula (*Desmodium ciliatum*)
simplicifo'lia |w . . DOLLARLEAF R.
texa'na . . . . TEXAS R.
tomento'sa |w . . . . . . HAIRY R.

RHYNCHOSPER'MUM
TRACHELOSPERMUM

RHYNCHOS'PORA (*CLEISTOCALYX* Steud.) |w . . . . . . BEAKRUSH
cornicula'ta |w . . . . . HORNED B.
cymo'sa |w
dodecan'dra |w
microcar'pa |w . . . . LITTLESEED B.
plumo'sa |w . . . . . . PLUMED B.
prolif'era |w
stipita'ta |w

RHYNCHOS'TYLIS
See **ORCHID GENERA.**

RHYTICO'COS (*COCOS* in part)
See **PALM GENERA.**

RHYTIDOPHYL'LUM
tomento'sum

RIBBONBUSH . . . . . **Homalocladium; H. platycladum**

RIBBONGRASS . **Phalaris arundinacea picta**

Ribbongum . . . EUCALYPTUS, RIBBON: **Eucalyptus viminalis**

RIBBONWOOD . . . . **Hoheria**
HARDY R. . . . . **H. glabrata**
LACEBARK R. . . . . **H. lyalli**
OTAGO R. . . . . **H. populnea**

RI'BES (including *GROSSULARIA*) |w
CURRANT; GOOSEBERRY

The Gooseberries are placed by some botanists in a distinct genus (Grossularia). The other (and more typical) species of Ribes are called Currants. For varieties of Currant and Gooseberry cultivated for their fruit, see list of **FRUIT AND EDIBLE NUT NAMES.**

Currants and Gooseberries form a large genus of at least 150 species widespread in the North Temperate Zone and in the high mountains of Mexico and South America. At least 80 species occur naturally in our Western States, more than in any other part of the world. Many of these plants are cultivated because of the beauty or fragrance of their flowers; a few (especially of the Old World species) are grown for their acid fruit, which is prized—and especially abroad—for jellies, jams, etc. The wild species are of great value for wildlife; birds, and small mammals, in particular, relish the berries, frequently produced in enormous quantities. As a rule, deer, elk, and domestic livestock browse the herbage rather lightly, unless other and better feed is scarce. However, these bushes often occur in great abundance and over wide areas so that, in the aggregate, their browse utility is considerable, especially in late summer and fall. These plants are of particular importance to the forester because they serve as alternate hosts for the White Pine blister-rust fungus, Cronartium ribicola, and, for that reason, large sums of money have been spent to eradicate Currants and Gooseberries in the neighborhood of commercial forests of 5-needle Pines.

The relatively full list below covers over 180 species, varieties, and hybrids of this genus. The hybrids marked below by the polybrid sign (∞) are probably, so far as the plants in cultivation are concerned, actually clons of the crosses indicated. The Editorial Committee is grateful to S. B. Fracker and to the field workers of the blister-rust control project, Bureau of Entomology and Plant Quarantine, U. S. Department of Agriculture, for their constructive criticism of this list.

acerifo'lium (*howelli*)
MAPLELEAF CURRANT
acicula're
albes'cens . . . . **R. sanguineum a.**
al'bidum . . . . . . **R. glutinosum a.**
albiner'vium . . . . **R. triste**
alpes'tre (*Grossularia alpestris*)
HEDGE GOOSEBERRY
—gigan'teum . . . . . . BIG H.G.
alpi'num . . . . ALPINE C.
—au'reum . . . . YELLOWLEAF A.C.
—lacinia'tum . . . . CUTLEAF A.C.
—pu'milum . . . . . . EARLY A.C.
ama'rum (*Grossularia amara*) BITTER G.
ambig'uum . . . . EPIPHYTE C.
america'num (*floridum*)
AMERICAN BLACK C.
amic'tum . . . . **R. roezli**
∞ **arcua'tum** (*hirtellum × missouriense*)
au'reum |w . . . . . . GOLDEN C.
—chrysococ'cum . YELLOWBERRY G.C.
—gracil'limum . . . . . **R. gracillimum**
∞ **bethmont'i** (*malvaceum × sanguineum*)
∞ BETHMONT C.
billiard'i . . **R. fasciculatum chinense**
binomina'tum (*Grossularia binominata*)
SISKIYOU G.
bracteo'sum . . . . STINK C. (*California Black C.*)
burejen'se (*Grossularia burejensis*)
BUREJA G.

RIBES, continued
califor'nicum (*Grossularia californica*)
CALIFORNIA GOOSEBERRY
canthariform'e . . MORENO CURRANT
carpa'thicum . . . . . **R. petraeum c.**
∞ **carrier'ei** (*glutinosum albidum × nigrum*) . . . . ∞ CARRIERE C.
ce'reum |w . . . . WAX C.
—farino'sum . . . . PALELEAF W.C.
cilio'sum . . . . **R. triste**
cogna'tum (*Grossularia cognata*)
UMATILLA G.
coloraden'se . . . . . . COLORADO C.
cruen'tum . . . . **R. roezli c.**
∞ **culverwell'i** (*nigrum × uva-crispa*)
∞ CULVERWELL G.
curva'tum (*Grossularia curvata*)
GEORGIA G.
cynos'bati (*Grossularia c.*) PASTURE G.
—inerm'e . . . . SMOOTH P.G.
diacan'thum (*saxatilis*) . SIBERIAN C.
—inerm'e . . . . SMOOTH S.C.
dikusch'a . . . . . . DIKUSCHA C.
dis'tans
divarica'tum (*Grossularia divaricata*)
STRAGGLY G.
—par'ishi . . . . **R. parishi**
—pubiflo'rum
domes'ticum . . . . . . **R. sativum**
echina'tum . . . . **R. lacustre**
echinel'lum (*Grossularia echinella*)
FLORIDA G.
emoden'se (*himalayense*) HIMALAYA C.
—mey'eri
—urceola'tum . . . . . . SIKKIM C.
—verruculo'sum WARTY HIMALAYA C.
erythrocar'pum . . . CRATERLAKE C.
fascicula'tum (*japonicum* Carr, *not* Maxim.) . . . . WINTERBERRY C.
—chinen'se (*R. billiardi*) CHINESE W.C.
flor'idum . . . . . **R. americanum**
∞ **fontenayen'se** (*sanguineum × uva-crispa*) . . . . . ∞ FONTENAY C.
fra'grans
∞ **fusces'cens** (*bracteosum × nigrum*)
∞ TAWNY C.
∞ **futu'rum** (*sativum × warscewiczi*)
∞ FUTURUM C.
gaya'num (*villosum*) . . CHILEAN C.
gir'aldi
glacia'le . . . . NEPAL C.
—angustisep'alum
glandulo'sum (*prostratum*) . SKUNK C.
glutino'sum (*R. sanguineum g.*)
NUTMEG C.
—al'bidum (*R. albidum; R. sanguineum a.*) . . . . WHITE N.C.
∞ **gondui'ni** (*petraeum × sativum*)
∞ GONDUIN C.
∞ **gordonia'num** (*odoratum × sanguineum*)
∞ GORDON C.
∞ **gothoburgen'se** (*divaricatum × stenocarpum*) . . . . . ∞ GOTHOBURG G.
gracil'limum (*R. aureum g.*) BUGLE C.
grossula'ria . . . . . **R. uva-crispa**
—uva-cris'pa . . . . **R. uva-crispa**
grossularioi'des
hall'i . . . . HALLS C.
hen'ryi . . . . HENRY C.
hespe'rium (*Grossularia hesperia*)
SANGABRIEL G.
himalayen'se . . . . . **R. emodense**
hirtel'lum (*Grossularia hirtella*)
HAIRYSTEM G.
∞ **holoseric'eum** (*petraeum biebersteini × rubrum*)
∞ **—pal'lidum** (∞ *holosericeum × petraeum bullatum*)

RIBES, continued
hor'ridum
horten'se . . . . **R. sativum**
∞ **houghtonia'num** (*rubrum × sativum*) ∞ HOUGHTON CURRANT
how'elli . . . . **R. acerifolium**
hudsonia'num . . . . HUDSONBAY C.
indeco'rum . . . WHITEFLOWER C.
ine'brians (*spaethianum*) . SQUAW C.
iner'me (*saxosum; Grossularia inermis*) WHITESTEM GOOSEBERRY
∞ **innomina'tum** (*divaricatum × uva-crispa*) . . . ∞ INNOMINATE G.
irrig'uum (*Grossularia irrigua*) IDAHO G.
japon'icum . . . . . . JAPANESE C.
japon'icum Carr. . . **R. fasciculatum**
klamathen'sis . . . . KLAMATH G.
×**knight'i** (*divaricatum × lobbi*) KNIGHTS G.
A natural hybrid.
∞ **koehnea'num** (*multiflorum × sativum*) ∞ KOEHNE C.
lacus'tre (*echinatum*) . . PRICKLY C. (*Swamp C.*)
—**par'vulum**
lasian'thum (*Grossularia lasiantha*) WOOLLYFLOWER G.
latifo'lium
laurifo'lium . . . . . LAUREL C.
laxiflo'rum . . . TRAILING BLACK C. (*Alaska B.C.*)
leptan'thum (*Grossularia leptantha*) |w TRUMPET G.
leptos'mum (*G. leptosma*) . . BAY G.
lobb'i (*Grossularia l.*) |w . . LOBBS G. (*Gummy G.*)
longeracemo'sum . . . WISTARIA C.
—**wilso'ni** . . . . . . WILSON W.C.
longiflo'rum . . . . . . **R. odoratum**
lur'idum
malva'ceum . . . . . CHAPARRAL C.
manshur'icum . . . MANCHURIAN C.
mar'shalli . . . . HUPA G.
maximowicz'i
—**floribun'dum**
menzies'i (*subvestitum; Grossularia m.*) MENZIES G.
—**ixoder'me** . . . . . STICKY M.G.
mescale'rium . . . . MESCALERO C.
mey'eri . . . . MEYER C.
missourien'se (*Grossularia missouriensis*) . . . . MISSOURI G.
montig'enum (*nubigenum*) GOOSEBERRY C.
moupinen'se (*tripartitum*) . TREE C.
multiflo'rum . . . . . . RUSSIAN C.
nevaden'se . . . . SIERRA C.
ni'grum . . . EUROPEAN BLACK C.
—**apiifo'lium** . . CELERYLEAF E.B.C.
—**chlorocar'pum** . . . GREEN E.B.C.
—**heterophyl'lum** . . CUTLEAF E.B.C.
—**reticula'tum**
—**xanthocar'pum** . . . YELLOW E.B.C.
niv'eum (*Grossularia nivea*) . SNOW G.
non-scrip'tum (*Grossularia non-scripta*)
nubig'enum . . . . **R. montigenum**
odora'tum (*longiflorum; Chrysobotrya odorata*) . . . . CLOVE C.
—**interme'dium**
—**leiobot'rys**
—**xanthocar'pum**
orienta'le (*resinosum*) . . ORIENTAL C.
—**heterot'richum** . . SHINYLEAF O.C.
oxyacanthoi'des (*Grossularia o.*) |w CANADA G.
par'ishi (*R. divaricatum p.; Grossularia p.*) . . . . PARISH G.

RIBES, continued
petiola're . WESTERN BLACK CURRANT
petrae'um . . . . ROCK C.
—**altis'simum**
—**atropurpu'reum**
—**bieberstein'i**
—**bulla'tum**
—**carpa'thicum** (*R. carpathicum*) CARPATHIAN C.
—**tomento'sum**
pineto'rum (*Grossularia p.*) ORANGE GOOSEBERRY
procum'bens
prostra'tum . . . . **R. glandulosum**
pulchel'lum
pur'pusi (*Grossularia p.*) . PURPUS G.
querceto'rum (*Grossularia q.*) OAKWOODS G.
∞ **re'cens** (∞ *holosericeum × sativum*)
reclina'tum . . . . . **R. uva-crispa**
resino'sum . . . . **R. orientale**
∞ **robus'tum** (*inerme × niveum*) ∞ HAWTHORN G.
roez'li (*amictum; Grossularia r.*) SIERRA G.
—**cruen'tum** (*R. cruentum; Grossularia r. cruenta*) . . . . . . BLOOD S.G.
rotundifo'lium (*Grossularia rotundifolia*) ROUNDLEAF G.
ru'brum (*scandicum; spicatum; sylvestre; vulgare* Lam., *not* Jancz.) NORTHERN RED C.
Much, at least, of the R. rubrum of the trade is R. sativum.
—**pubes'cens**
∞ **rus'ticum** (*hirtellum × ?uva-crispa*) ∞ GARDEN G.
sanguin'eum . . . . . . WINTER C. (*Blood C.; Redflowering C.*)
—**albes'cens** (*R. albescens; R. s. albidum* Hort.) . . . . . . WHITE W.C.
—**atroru'bens** (*R. s. atrosanguineum*) RUBY W.C.
—**brocklebank'i** YELLOWLEAF W.C.
—**car'neum** . . . . . . PINK W.C.
—*glutino'sum* . . . . **R. glutinosum**
—**splen'dens** . . . . . SCARLET W.C.
¢KING EDWARD VII. HV. R. sanguineum
sati'vum (*domesticum; hortense; vulgare* Jancz., *not* Lam.) |w COMMON RED C.
—**macrocar'pum** . . . CHERRY R.C.
—**variega'tum**
∞ **saun'dersi** (*hudsonianum × nigrum*) ∞ SAUNDERS C.
saxat'ilis . . . . . . **R. diacanthum**
saximonta'num . . . . . **R. setosum**
saxo'sum . . . . **R. inerme**
scan'dicum . . . . **R. rubrum**
seric'eum . . . . SILKY G.
seto'sum (*saximontanum; Grossularia setosa*) . . . . REDSHOOT G.
spaethia'num . . . . . . **R. inebrians**
specio'sum (*Grossularia speciosa; Robsonia s.*) . . . . FUCHSIA G.
spica'tum . . . . **R. rubrum**
stenocar'pum . . . . . . KANSU G.
subvesti'tum . . . . . . **R. menziesi**
∞ **succiru'brum** (*divaricatum × niveum*)
sylves'tre . . . . **R. rubrum**
ten'ue . . . . ASIATIC C.
tricus'pis
triparti'tum . . . . . **R. moupinense**
tris'te (*albinervium; ciliosum*) AMERICAN RED C.
—**alaska'num**
tularen'se . . . . TULARE G.

RIBES, continued
∞ **urceola'tum** (*multiflorum × petraeum*)
ussurien'se
∞ **u'tile** (*cynosbati × uva-crispa; ×Grossularia utilis*) ∞ HALFBLOOD GOOSEBERRY
uva-crisp'a (*grossularia; R. g. uva-crispa; reclinatum; Grossularia reclinata*) . . . . EUROPEAN G.
∞ **vanfleetia'num** (*missouriense × uva-crispa*) . . . . . ∞ VAN FLEET G.
veluti'num (*Grossularia velutina*) DESERT G.
viburnifo'lium . CATALINA CURRANT
victor'is (*Grossularia v.*) . VICTORS G.
villo'sum . . . . **R. gayanum**
vilmori'ni . . . . VILMORIN C.
viscosis'simum |w . . . . STICKY C.
∞ **vi'treum** (*stenocarpum × uva-crispa*)
vulga're . . . **R. rubrum; R. sativum**
∞ **walli'chi** (*glaciale × luridum*) ∞ WALLICH C.
warscewicz'i . . . . WARSCEWICZ C.
watsonia'num (*Grossularia watsoniana*) WATSON G. (*Mt. Adams G.*)
wolf'i . . . . ROTHROCK C.
RIBSEED . . . . **Aulospermum**

RIC'CIA |w . . . . RICCIA
flu'itans |w . . . . COMMON R.

RICCIOCAR'PUS |w . . RICCIOCARPUS
na'tans |w . . . . COMMON R.

RICE . . . . **Oryza; O. sativa**
See also **CEREALS.**
BROADLEAF R. . . . . . . **O. latifolia**
RICEFLOWER . . . . **Pimelea**
BIGHEAD R. . . . . . . **P. spectabilis**
DOTLEAF R. . . . . . . **P. graciliflora**
PRIVET R. . . . . **P. ligustrina**
ROSY R. . . . . **P. ferruginea**
RICEGRASS . . **Oryzopsis; Piptochaetium**
BLACKSEED R. . . . . . **O. racemosa**
BLOOMERS R. . . . . . **O. bloomeri**
CANADA R. . . . . . . **O. canadensis**
HENDERSON R. . . . . **O. hendersoni**
INDIAN R. . . . . . . **O. hymenoides**
LITTLE R. . . . . **O. exigua**
LITTLESEED R. . . . . **O. micrantha**
PINYON R. . **Piptochaetium fimbriatum**
ROUGHLEAF R. . . . . **O. asperifolia**
SHORTHORN R. . . . . . **O. pungens**
SIERRA R. . . . . **O. kingi**
WEBBER R. . . . . **O. webberi**
RICEPAPERPLANT **Tetrapanax; T. papyriferus**

RICHARD'IA (*RICHARDSONIA*) |w MEXICANCLOVER
Richardia (Houst.) L. (1753), a genus of the Madderwort family, should not be confused with the homonym Richardia Kunth, which is a synonym for the Callalily genus.
sca'bra (*Richardsonia s.*) |w MEXICANCLOVER

RICHARD'IA Kunth, *not* (Houst.) L. **ZANTEDESCHIA**
africa'na . . . . . . **Z. aethiopica**

RICHARDSO'NIA . . **RICHARDIA**
RICHBUSH . . . . **Abrophyllum ornans**
Richweed . . . . . BUGBANE, COHOSH: **Cimicifuga racemosa;** CLEARWEED, CANADA: **Pilea pumila;** HORSEBALM, CITRONELLA: **Collinsonia canadensis;** RAGWEED, GIANT: **Ambrosia trifida;** SNAKEROOT, WHITE: **Eupatorium rugosum**

Ricinel'la va'seyi . . . . . . **Adelia v.**

RICINODEN'DRON . . MANKETTINUT
africa'num . . . . MUSODO M.

RICI'NUS |w . . . . . . CASTORBEAN
commu'nis |w . . . . . CASTORBEAN
—africa'nus . . . . . AFRICAN C.
—borbonien'sis . . . BOURBON C.
₵ARBOREUS. HV.
—cambodgen'sis . . . . CAMBODIA C.
—gib'soni . . . . GIBSON C.
×**—hy'bridus** . . . . . . HYBRID C.
₵PALERMO (*panormitans*) HV.
—macrocar'pus . . . . BIGFRUIT C.
—macrophyl'lus . . . BIGLEAF C.
₵PHILIPPINE (*philippinensis*) HV. R. communis
₵PURPLE (*purpureus*)
₵RED (*sanguineus*)
₵ZANZIBAR (*zanzibarensis*)

RICO'TIA
luna'ria

RIGIOPAP'PUS |w . . . . WIREWEED
leptoc'ladus |w

RIMA'RIA **MESEMBRYANTHEMUM**
See **SUCCULENTS.**

Ringgrass . . . . . . MUHLY, RING: **Muhlenbergia torreyi**
"RING GRASS" is an ecological term applicable to any grass with the "ring" habit of growth, but used in particular for Muhlenbergia torreyi.

RINGWING . . . . **Cycloloma**
TUMBLE R. . . . . **C. atriplicifolium**

Ripgut . BROME, RIPGUT: **Bromus rigidus**
Longarm R. . . . . LONGARM R.B.: **B. r. gussonei**

Ripgutgrass . . . . . BROME, RIPGUT: **Bromus rigidus**

RITCH'IEA
reflex'a

RI'VEA
corymbo'sa (*Ipomoea sidaefolia*)

RIVERGRASS . . . . **Fluminea**

RIVERWEED . . . . **Podostemon**
HORNLEAF R. . . . **P. ceratophyllum**
OLDMAN R. . . . . **P. abrotanoides**

RIVI'NA |w . . . . . ROUGEPLANT
hu'milis |w . . . . BLOODBERRY R.
portulaccoi'des . . . . . CURRANT R.

ROBIN'IA |w . . . . LOCUST
It is probable that many of the Locusts in cultivation named below are clons only of the respective polybrids.

∞ **ambig'ua** (*pseudoacacia* × *viscosa; dubia*)
—bella-rose'a
ash'ei . . . . ASHES L.
boyn'toni (*R. hispida rosea* Hort.) BOYNTON L.
elliot'ti (*R. hispida rosea* Ell.) ELLIOTT L.
fer'tilis
hart'wigi . . . . . . HARTWIG L.
his'pida . ROSEACACIA L. (*Rose-acacia*)
—macrophyl'la . . . . SMOOTH R.L.
∞ **hold'ti** (*luxurians* × *pseudoacacia*) ∞ HOLDT L.
₵BRITZEN (*britzensis*) HV.
kel'seyi . . . . KELSEY L.
longilo'ba . . . . . . LONGLOBE L.
luxur'ians (*R. neomexicana l.*) WESTERN L.

ROBINIA, continued
∞ **margaret'ta** (*?hispida* × *pseudoacacia*) ∞ MARGARET LOCUST
na'na . . . . LITTLE L.
neomexica'na |w . . NEWMEXICO L.
pal'lida . . . . PALLID L.
panaco'co . . . . PANACOCO L.
pauciflo'ra
pseudoaca'cia |w . . . . . BLACK L.
Probably most of these are clons, although some may be natural varieties or forms. Only known clons are so designated.

AMORPHIFOLIA. HV.
₵BESSON (*bessoniana*)
COLUTEOIDES
₵CRINKLELEAF (*crispa*)
₵CUTLEAF (*dissecta*)
₵DECAISNE (*decaisneana*)
DEPENDENS
₵ERECTA
₵GOLDEN (*aurea*)
LINEARIS
₵LITTLELEAF (*microphylla; R. p. angustifolia*)
₵MYRTIFOLIA
₵ONELEAF (*unifoliola; R. p. monophylla*)
₵PERPETUAL (*semperflorens; R. semperflorens*)
₵PURPLELEAF (*purpurea*)
₵PYRAMID (*pyramidalis*)
REHDER (*rehderi*)
₵ROZYNSKY (*rozynskyana*)
₵SHIPMAST (*rectissima*)
₵STRICTA
₵THORNLESS (*inermis; spectabilis*)
₵TWISTED (*tortuosa*)
ULRICH (*ulriciana*)
₵UMBRELLA (*umbraculifera*)
₵WEEPING (*pendula*)
rus'byi . . . . RUSBY L.
∞ **sla'vini** (*kelseyi* × *pseudoacacia*) ∞ SLAVIN L.
specio'sa
subvelut'ina . . . SOUTHWESTERN L.
visco'sa . . . . CLAMMY L.

ROBINSONEL'LA
diver'gens . . . . GUACIMA

Robso'nia specio'sa . . **Ribes speciosum**

ROCCEL'LA . . . . ROCCELLA
tincto'ria . . . . LITMUS R.

RO'CHEA . . . . ROCHEA
See **SUCCULENTS.**

ROCHFORDFERN . **Cyrtomium falcatum** HV.
DWARF R. . . . . . **C. falcatum** HV.

ROCKBEAUTY . . . . **Petrocallis**
PYRENEES R. . . . . . **P. pyrenaica**

ROCKBELL . . . . **Wahlenbergia**
CAPE R. . . . . **W. capensis**
CREEPING R. . . . . . . **W. congesta**
DALMATIAN R. . . . . . **W. dalmatica**
GENTIAN R. . . . . **W. gracilis**
IVY R. . . . . **W. hederacea**
MADEIRA R. . . . . **W. pendula**
MATTHEWS R. . . . . . **W. matthewsi**
TASMANIA R. . . . . **W. saxicola**

ROCKBRAKE . . . . **Cryptogramma**
AMERICAN R. . . . **C. acrostichoides**
SLENDER R. . . . . **C. stelleri**

ROCKCRESS . . . . **Arabis**
BREWER R. . . . . **A. breweri**
COMMON HAIRY R. **A. hirsuta pycnocarpa**

ROCKCRESS, continued
DOUBLE WALL R. **Arabis albida florepleno**
DOWNY R. . . . . **A. mollis**
DRUMMOND R. . . . . . **A. drummondi**
ERECT R. . . . . **A. stricta**
GERARD R. . . . . **A. gerardi**
HAIRY R. . . . . **A. hirsuta**
HALLER R. . . . . **A. halleri**
HOLBOELL R. . . . . **A. holboelli**
ITALIAN R. . . . . **A. muralis**
∞ KELLERER R. . . . . . ∞ **A. kellereri**
LEMMONS R. . . . . **A. lemmoni**
LITTLELEAF R. . . . . . **A. microphylla**
LYALL R. . . . . **A. lyalli**
MOSS R. . . . . **A. bryoides**
NUTTALL R. . . . . **A. nuttalli**
OREGON R. . . . . **A. oregana**
PIONEER R. . . . . **A. platysperma**
PURPLE R. . . . . . . **A. purpurascens**
RED R. . . . . **A. koehleri**
SHORTFRUIT R. . . . . **A. brachycarpa**
SILVER R. . . . . **A. canescens**
SLIM R. . . . . **A. exilis**
SMOOTH R. . . . . **A. laevigata**
STELLER R. . . . . **A. stelleri**
∞ SUENDERMANN R. . ∞ **A. suendermanni**
SUKSDORF R. . . . . **A. suksdorfi**
TOWERMUSTARD R. . . . . . **A. glabra**
WALL R. . . . . **A. albida**
WOODY R. . . . . . . **A. suffrutescens**

ROCKET . . . . **Hesperis**
DAMES R. . . . . **H. matronalis**
PERSIANSNOW R. . . . . . . **H. nivalis**
WHITE DAMES R. . **R. matronalis nivea**

ROCKETSALAD . . . . . . **Eruca sativa**

ROCKETWEED . . **Erucastrum gallicum**

ROCKJASMINE . . . . **Androsace**
AIZOON R. . . . . **A. aizoon**
ALPINE R. . . . . **A. alpina**
DWARF R. . . . . . **A. chamaejasme**
PINE R. . . . . **A. carnea**
PRIMULA R. . . . . **A. primuloides**
SCARLET AIZOON R. **A. aizoon coccinea**
SWISS R. . . . . **A. helvetica**
WESTERN R. . . . . . . **A. occidentalis**

ROCKMAT . . . . **Petrophytum**
GRAY R. . . . . **P. cinerascens**
HENDERSON R. . . . . . **P. hendersoni**
TUFTED R. . . . . **P. caespitosum**

ROCKPURSLANE . . . . . . **Calandrinia**
ARIZONA R. . . . . **C. arizonica**
BURRIDGE R. . . . . **C. burridgei**
COMMON R. . . . . . . **C. grandiflora**
DESERT R. . . . . **C. caulescens**
PERUVIAN R. . . . . **C. umbellata**
REDMAIDS R. . **C. caulescens menziesi**

ROCKROSE . . . . **Cistus**
AFRICAN GUM R. **C. ladaniferus petiolatus**
CRIMSONSPOT G. R. . . **C. l. maculatus**
FLORENTINE R. . . . . ×**C. florentinus**
GUM R. . . . . **C. ladaniferus**
HAIRY R. . . . . **C. hirsutus**
∞ HETIER R. . . . . ∞ **C. hetieri**
LAUREL R. . . . . **C. laurifolius**
LORETS R. . . . . ×**C. loreti**
MONTPELIER R. . . . **C. monspeliensis**
∞ ORCHIDSPOT R. . . . . ∞ **C. purpureus**
POPLARLEAF R. . . . . . **C. populifolius**
∞ PORTUGUESE R. . . . ∞ **C. lusitanicus**
∞ PURPLE R. . . . . ∞ **C. canescens**
SALVIA R. . . . . **C. salvifolius**
∞ SKANBERG R. . . . . . ∞ **C. skanbergi**
∞ SPOTTED R. . . . . ∞ **C. cyprius**
∞ VERGUIN R. . . . . ∞ **C. verguini**

ROCKROSE, continued
WHITE GUM R. **Cistus ladaniferus albiflorus**
WHITELEAF R. . . . . . **C. albidus**
WHITE LORETS R. . **C. loreti albiflorus**
WRINKLELEAF R. . . . . . **C. crispus**

ROCKSPIREA . . . . **Holodiscus**
BUSH R. . . . . **H. dumosus**
CREAMBUSH R. . . . . . **H. discolor**
OCEANSPRAY R. . . **H. d. ariaefolius**

ROCKWEED . . . . **Fucus**
BLADDERWRACK R. . . **F. vesiculosus**
CARTWRACK R. . . . . . **F. serratus**

ROCKWEEP . . . . . . **Ascophyllum**
DRUG R. . . . . **A. nodosum**

RODGERSFLOWER . . . . . . **Rodgersia**
BRONZELEAF R. . . . **R. podophylla**
ELDERLEAF R. . . . **R. sambucifolia**
FEATHERLEAF R. . . . . . **R. pinnata**
FINGERLEAF R. . . . . **R. aesculifolia**
SHIELDLEAF R. . . . . . **R. tabularis**

RODGERS'IA . . . . RODGERSFLOWER
aesculifo'lia . . . . FINGERLEAF R.
pinna'ta . . . . . . FEATHERLEAF R.
podophyl'la . . . . BRONZELEAF R.
sambucifo'lia . . . . ELDERLEAF R.
tabula'ris . . . . . . SHIELDLEAF R.

RODRIGUE'ZIA . **BURLINGTONIA**
See **ORCHID GENERA.**

ROEMER'IA . . . . ASIAPOPPY
refrac'ta . . . . SPOTTED A.

∞ROFAUSTRIME . . . . . **Microcitrus australasica × M. australis**

ROHD'EA . . . . NIPPONLILY
japon'ica . . . . OMOTO N.
¢VARIEGATED (*variegata*) HV.

ROLLIN'IA
delicio'sa . . . . BIRIBA
muco'sa (*sieberi*)

ROMANO'VIA (*ROMANOWIA*) **ACTINOPHLOEUS**
See **PALM GENERA.**

ROMANZOF'FIA . . . . MISTMAIDEN
sitchen'sis . . . . SITKA M.
unalaschken'sis . . . UNALASKA M.

ROM'NEYA
coul'teri . . . . . MATILIJA-POPPY
—**trichoca'lyx** (*R. trichocalyx*) BRISTLECUP M.

RONDELET'IA . . . . . RONDELETIA
amoe'na . . . . . YELLOWTHROAT R.
corda'ta . . . . HEARTLEAF R.
odora'ta . . . . FRAGRANT R.
thyrsoi'dea

ROOSEVELT'IA . . . ROOSEVELTPALM
See **PALM GENERA.**

ROOSEVELTPALM **Rooseveltia; R. frankliniana**

ROOTSPINEPALM . . . . **Cryosophila**

ROPEVINE . . . . **Tanaecium**
TRINIDAD R. . . . . **T. jaroba**

RORIP'PA (*RADICULA; RORIPA*) |w
amphib'ia . AMPHIBIOUS MARSHCRESS
armora'cia . . . **Armoracia lapathifolia**
austri'aca (*Radicula a.*) AUSTRIAN FIELDCRESS

RORIPPA, continued
nasturtium-aquat'icum (*Nasturtium officinale; Radicula nasturtium-aquaticum; Sisymbrium aquaticum; S. nasturtium-aquaticum*) |w . WATERCRESS
obtu'sa . . . . OBTUSE FIELDCRESS
palus'tris (*Radicula p.*) |w BOG MARSHCRESS
sylves'tris |w . . YELLOW FIELDCRESS

RO'SA |w . . . . ROSE

For the rose species list the Editorial Committee is deeply indebted to Alfred Rehder, Arnold Arboretum, Jamaica Plain, Mass. The first edition of STANDARDIZED PLANT NAMES carried 94 species and natural varieties of Rosa, while Prof. Rehder's new list includes 236 species and natural varieties, and 43 polybrids and clons. The polybrid and clon signs, as well as the vernacular or common names, have been added by the Editorial Committee.

For horticultural varieties see American Rose Society's special list on page 542.

abyssin'ica . . . . **R. moschata a.**
acicula'ris (*fauriei* in part; *sayi*) |w PRICKLY R.
—**bourgeauia'na** (*R. a. sayi; R. bourgeauiana*) . . . . BOURGEAU P.R.
—**carel'ica** (*R. carelica*) CARELIAN P.R.
—**engelmann'i** (*R. engelmanni*) ENGELMANN P.R.
—**nipponen'sis** (*R. nipponensis*) NIPPON P.R.
—*say'i* . . **R. acicularis bourgeauiana**
adenosep'ala . . . . PECOS R.
agres'tis (*sepium*) . . GRASSLAND R.
—*inodo'ra* . . . . **R. inodora**
∞**al'ba** (*?dumetorum × gallica*) ∞COTTAGE R.
¢—**suave'olens** . . . . ¢ATTAR C.R.
¢MAIDENSBLUSH (*R. a. incarnata; R. a. rubicunda*) HV. ∞R. alba
albert'i . . . . ALBERT R.
alpi'na . . . . **R. pendulina**
alta'ica . . . . . **R. spinosissima a.**
amblyo'tis . . . . ERECTPRICKLE R.
amoyen'sis . . . . **R. cymosa**
anemoneflo'ra . . . . . . **R. triphylla**
∞**anemonoi'des** (*laevigata × ?odorata*) ∞ANEMONE R.
arkansa'na . . . . . ARKANSAS R.
Name often misapplied to R. suffulta.
∞**arnoldia'na** (∞*borboniana × rugosa*) ∞ARNOLD R.
arven'sis (*repens; silvestris*) . FIELD R.
—**ayreshi'rea** (*R. arvensis capreolata; R. capreolata*) . . . AYRSHIRE F.R. (*Roebuck Rambler*)
∞**aschersonia'na** (*blanda × chinensis*) ∞ASCHERSON R.
austri'aca . . . . . **R. gallica pumila**
banks'iae (*banksiana*) . . . . BANKS R.
—**albo-ple'na** (*B. banksiae plena*) DOUBLEWHITE B.R.
—**lu'tea** (*R. b. lutea-plena*) YELLOW B.R.
—**lutes'cens** . . . . . . BUFF B.R.
—**norma'lis** . . . . . . WILD B.R.
banksiop'sis . . . . . . FALSE B.R.
∞**barbiera'na** (*multiflora × wichuraiana; R. wichuraiana rubra*) ∞BARBIER R.
beggeria'na . . . . . . BEGGER R.
bel'gica . . . . **R. damascena**
bel'la . . . . SOLITARY R.
—**pal'lens** . . . . PALE S.R.

ROSA, continued
bengalen'sis **R. chinensis semperflorens**
berberifo'lia . . . . **R. persica**
bi'color . . . . **R. foetida b.**
bi'fera . . . . **R. damascena**
blan'da (*fraxinifolia; solandri; subblanda; R. virginiana b.*) MEADOW ROSE
—**willmot'tiae** . . . WILLMOTT M.R.
∞**borbonia'na** (*chinensis × damascena;* ∞*borbonica*) . . . . ∞BOURBON R.
bourgeauia'na . . . . **R. acicularis b.**
boursault'i . . . . . ∞**R. lheritierana**
bractea'ta (*macartnea*) MACARTNEY R.
bractea'ta Hort., *not* Wendl. **R. wichuraiana**
britzen'sis . . . . . KURDISTAN R.
∞**bruant'i** (*odorata* (or *dilecta*) × *rugosa*) ∞BRUANT R.
bruno'ni (*browni; R. moschata nepalensis*) . . . . BROWNS R.
burgunden'sis . . . . . **R. centifolia**
burgundi'aca . **R. centifolia parvifolia**
calenda'rum . . . . . **R. damascena**
califor'nica . . . . . CALIFORNIA R.
—**na'na** . . . . DWARF C.R.
—**ple'na** . . . . DOUBLE C.R.
∞**calocar'pa** (*chinensis × rugosa; R. rugosa calocarpa*) . . . ∞CHINOSA R.
camel'lia . . . . **R. laevigata**
cani'na . . . . DOG R.
—*dumeto'rum* . . . . **R. corymbifera**
—**ex'ilis** (*R. exilis*) . . . LITTLE D.R.
—*froe'beli* . . . . **R. coriifolia f.**
capreola'ta . . . **R. arvensis ayreshirea**
carel'ica . . . . **R. acicularis c.**
caroli'na (*humilis; parviflora; R. virginiana h.*) |w . . . . CAROLINA R.
—**al'ba** (*R. lyoni a.; R. virginiana a.*) WHITE C.R.
—**glandulo'sa** (*R. parviflora g.; R. serrulata*) . . . . . . REHDER C.R.
—**grandiflo'ra** (*R. humilis g.; R. obovata*) . . . . LARGEFLOWER C.R.
—*nuttallia'na* . . . . **R. palustris n.**
—**trilo'ba** (*R. humilis t.*) THREELOBE C.R.
—**villo'sa** (*R. humilis v.; R. lyoni*) HAIRY C.R.
caroli'na Auth., *not* L. . . **R. palustris**
caryophylla'cea . . . . . **R. inodora**
cathayen'sis . . . . **R. multiflora c.**
—*platyphyl'la* . . . **R. multiflora p.**
cauda'ta . . . . WHIPLASH R.
centifo'lia (*burgundensis; R. gallica c.*) CABBAGE R.
—**albo-musco'sa** (*R. muscosa cristata*) WHITEMOSS C.R.
—**crista'ta** . . . . . . CRESTED C.R.
—**musco'sa** (*R. muscosa*) . MOSS C.R.
—**parvifo'lia** (*R. burgundiaca; R. parvifolia*) . . . . . . BURGUNDY C.R.
—**pompo'nia** (*R. pulchella; R. dijonensis*) . . . . POMPON C.R.
—*provincia'lis* . **R. gallica officinalis**
cerasocar'pa . . . . . CHERRYHIP R.
cherokeen'sis . . . . . **R. laevigata**
chinen'sis (*R. c. indica; indica* Lindl.; *R. i. vulgaris; sinica* L., *not* Lindl. *nor* Murr.) . . . . CHINESE R.
—*fra'grans* . . . . . . **R. odorata**
—*in'dica* . . . . **R. chinensis**
—**longifo'lia** (*R. longifolia*) LONGLEAF C.R.

Hort. var.; HV. = horticultural variety (or varieties); sp. = species (singular); spp. = species (plural).
¢ = clon; × (as a prefix) = hybrid; × (between scientific plant names) = crossed by; ∞ = polybrid; |w = plant useful to wildlife.
See Glossary for definitions of clon, hybrid, and polybrid.

ROSA, continued
¢**chinen'sis** *manet'ti* Hort. ∞ **R. noisettiana** ¢Manetti
—**min'ima** (*R. indica pumila; R. lawranciana; R. rouletti*) . . Roulett Chinese Rose (*Rouletti R.*)
—**mutab'ilis** (*R. mutabilis*) Variable C.R.
—*pseudin'dica* . . . . **R. odorata p.**
—**semperflo'rens** (*R. bengalensis; R. indica s.; R. semperflorens*) Everblooming C.R.
—**sponta'nea** . . . . . . Single C.R.
—**viridiflo'ra** (*R. viridiflora*) Green C.R.
cinnamo'mea . . . . Cinnamon R.
—**ple'na** (*R. foecundissima; R. majalis*) Double C.R.
cinnamo'mea L. in part. . **R. pendulina**
clinophyl'la (*involucrata; lyelli*) Angleleaf R.
∞**colli'na** (*?dumetorum × gallica*) ∞Hilltop R.
coriifo'lia (*watsoni*) . Leatherleaf R.
—**froeb'eli** (*R. canina f.; R. froebeli* Hort.; *R. laxa* Froeb., *not* Retz.) Froebel L.R.
corus'cans . . . . **R. rugosa**
corymbif'era (*R. canina dumetorum; dumetorum*) . . . . . Corymb R.
corymbo'sa . . . . **R. palustris**
corymbulo'sa . . . . White-eye R.
crocacan'tha . . . Yellowthorn R.
cymo'sa (*amoyensis; indica* L., in part; *microcarpa* Lindl., *not* Bess. *nor* Retz.; *sorbiflora*) . . . . Cyme R.
dalmat'ica . . . . . . **R. glutinosa d.**
damasce'na (*belgica; bifera; calendarum; polyanthos*) . . . Damask R.
—**trigintipet'ala** . Thirtypetal D.R.
—**versic'olor** . . . Variegated D.R.
da'vidi . . . . David R.
—**elonga'ta** (*R. elongata*) Longhip D.R.
davur'ica . . . . . . Dahurian R.
∞**dawsonia'na** (*multiflora* × General Jacqueminot) . . . ∞Dawson R.
dawsonia'na Ellw. & Barry, *not* Hort. **R. multiflora**
dijonen'sis . . **R. centifolia pomponia**
∞**dilec'ta** (*borboniana × odorata*) ∞Bourbontea R.
duma'lis (*glauca* Vill., *not* Pour.; *reuteri*) Scraggle R.
dumeto'rum . . . . **R. corymbifera**
∞**dupont'i** (*gallica × moschata; freundiana; R. moschata alba; R. m. nivea*) ∞Dupont R.
e'cae Aitch. (*xanthina* Auth., *not* Lindl.) Eca R.
e'cae Rehd. . . . . **R. primula**
The plant usually cultivated under this name in America is R. primula; the true R. ecae has only recently been introduced in this country.
eglante'ria L., *not* Mill. (*floribunda* Steven; *rubiginosa*) Sweetbrier R.
The distinct, single, pink-flowered form of this species, naturalized in North America, is Eglantine R.
—**du'plex** . . . . . . Aromatic S.R.
eglante'ria Mill., *not* L. . . **R. foetida**
elegant'ula . . . . Fairy R.
ellip'tica . . . . **R. inodora**
elonga'ta . . . . **R. davidi e.**
elymait'ica . . . . Zigzag R.
engelmann'i . . . . . **R. acicularis e.**
er'nesti . . . . **R. rubus**
ex'ilis . . . . **R. canina e.**

ROSA, continued
far'gesi . . . . Farges Rose
far'gesi Hort., *not* Boul. . **R. moyesi f.**
far'reri . . . . Farrer R.
—**perseto'sa** . . . . . Bristly F.R.
faur'iei . . . . **R. acicularis; R. maximowicziana**
fedtschenkoa'na . . Fedtschenko R.
fend'leri . . . . **R. woodsi f.**
fe'rox Bieb . . . . **R. horrida**
fe'rox Lawr. . . . . **R. rugosa**
ferrugin'ea Deseg., *not* Vill. **R. rubrifolia**
fi'lipes . . . . . . Threadstalk R.
floribun'da Bak. . . . . . **R. henryi**
floribun'da Steven. . . . . **R. eglanteria**
flor'ida . . . . . **R. multiflora carnea**
foecundis'sima. . **R. cinnamomea plena**
foet'ida (*eglanteria* Mill., *not* L.; *lutea*) Austrian Brier R.
—**bi'color** (*R. bicolor; R. lutea b.; R. l. punicea; R. punicea*) Austrian Copper R.
—*hariso'ni*. . . . . . ∞**R. harisoni**
—**persia'na** (*R. lutea p.; R. l. plena*) Persian Yellow R.
foliolo'sa . . . . Leafy R.
—**al'ba** . . . . White L.R.
forrestia'na . . . . . Forrests R.
∞**fortunea'na** (*?banksiae × laevigata*) ∞Fortunes R.
fortunia'na Paxt., *not* **R. fortuneana** Lindl. . . . **R. odorata pseudindica**
∞**francofurta'na** (*cinnamomea × gallica; ∞turbinata*) . . . ∞Frankfort R.
fraxinifo'lia . . . . **R. blanda**
freundia'na . . . . . ∞**R. duponti**
froe'beli Hort. . . . . **R. coriifolia f.**
fujisanen'sis . . . . . . **R. luciae f.**
gal'lica . . . . French R.
—**ag'atha** . . . . . . Agatha F.R.
—*centifo'lia* . . . . . **R. centifolia**
—**condito'rum** . . . . . Titbit F.R.
—**incarna'ta** . . . Narrowleaf F.R.
—*macran'tha* . . . ¢**R. waitziana m.**
—**officina'lis** (*R. g. plena; R. provincialis*) . . . . Apothecaries F.R.
—**pu'mila** (*R. austriaca; R. pumila*) Dwarf F.R.
—**versic'olor** (*R. g. rosamundi*) Rosamundi F.R.
gentilia'na Levl. & Vant. **R. multiflora cathayensis**
gentilia'na Rehd. & Wils. . **R. henryi**
gen'tilis . . . . . . **R. pendulina g.**
gigan'tea. . . . . . . **R. odorata g.**
girald'i . . . . Giraldi R.
—**venulo'sa** . . . . . . Veiny G.R.
glau'ca Pour. . . . . . . **R. rubrifolia**
glau'ca Vill. . . . . . . **R. dumalis**
glaucophyl'la . . . **R. hemisphaerica**
glomera'ta . . . . . . Cluster R.
glutino'sa (*tuschetica*) . . Gummy R.
—**dalmat'ica** (*R. dalmatica*) Dalmatian G.R.
graciliflo'ra . . . . Daintypetal R.
grandiflo'ra . **R. spinosissima altaica**
gratis'sima . . . . . Sweetleaf R.
gymnocar'pa . . . . . . Baldhip R.
hackelia'na. . . . . . **R. heckeliana**
∞**hard'i** (*clinophylla × persica*) ∞Hardys R.
∞**hariso'ni** (*foetida × spinosissima; R. foetida h.*). ∞Harison Yellow R.
—**vorberg'i** (*R. vorbergi*) . Vorberg R.
hawra'na . . . . Hawran R.
heckelia'na (*hackeliana*). . Heckel R.
hel'enae . . . . Helen R.
helioph'ila . . . . **R. suffulta**

ROSA, continued
hemisphaer'ica (*glaucophylla; rapini; sulphurea*) . . . . . Sulfur Rose
hemsleya'na . . . . . . Hemsley R.
hen'ryi (*floribunda* Bak., *not* Stev.; *gentiliana* Rehd. & Wils., *not* Levl. & Vant.) . . . . Henry R.
∞**hiber'nica** (*canina × spinosissima*) ∞Irish R.
∞**highdownen'sis** (*moyesi × ?*) ∞Highdown R.
hill'ieri . . . . . ∞**R. pruhoniciana**
his'pida . . . . . **R. spinosissima h.**
holodon'ta . . . . . **R. moyesi rosea**
hor'rida (*ferox* Bieb., *not* Ait.) Barbstem R. (*Crimean Sweetbrier*)
hugo'nis . . . . . . Father Hugo R. (*Golden R. of China*)
hu'milis . . . . **R. carolina**
—*grandiflo'ra* . . . . **R. carolina g.**
—*lu'cida* . . . . . . **R. virginiana**
—*trilo'ba* . . . . . . **R. carolina t.**
—*villo'sa* . . . . . . **R. carolina v.**
hys'trix . . . . **R. laevigata**
illinoen'sis . . . . . **R. spinosissima**
incarna'ta . . . . ¢**R. alba i.**
in'dica . . **R. chinensis; R. cymosa**
—*ochroleu'ca* . . . . . **R. odorata o.**
—*odoratis'sima* . . . . . . **R. odorata**
—*pu'mila* . . . **R. chinensis minima**
—*semperflo'rens* . . . **R. chinensis s.**
—*vulga'ris* . . . . **R. chinensis**
inodo'ra (*R. agrestis i.; caryophyllacea; elliptica*) . . . . Scentless R.
interme'dia. . . . . . . **R. multiflora**
involucra'ta . . . . . . **R. clinophylla**
∞**involu'ta** (*?spinosissima × tomentosa*) ∞Burnet R.
∞**iwa'ra** (*multiflora × rugosa; ∞yedoensis*) ∞Iwara R.
jack'i . . . . . **R. maximowicziana j.**
∞**jack'soni** (*rugosa × wichuraiana*) ∞Jackson R.
jundzil'li . . . . . . **R. marginata**
kamtchat'ica . . . . . . **R. rugosa k.**
kel'leri Baker, *not* Torre & Sarnth. **R. maximowicziana jacki**
∞**kochia'na** (*carolina × spinosissima; oxyacantha* K. Koch, *not* Bieb.) ∞Koch R.
korea'na . . . . Korean R.
laeviga'ta (*camellia; cherokeensis; hystrix; nivea; sinica* Lindl., *not* Murr.; *ternata*) . . . . . . Cherokee R.
lawrancia'na . . **R. chinensis minima**
lax'a . . . . Turkestan R.
lax'a Froeb., *not* Retz. **R. coriifolia froebeli**
leschenault'i (*R. moschata l.*)
∞**lheritiera'na** (*chinensis × pendulina; boursaulti; reclinata*) ∞Boursault R.
longicus'pis (*lucens; willmottiana*) Longtooth R.
longifo'lia . . . . . . **R. chinensis l.**
lu'ciae . . . . Lucia R.
—**fujisanen'sis** (*R. fujisanensis*)
—*wichuraia'na* . . . . **R. wichuraiana**
lu'cida . . . . **R. virginiana**
lute'a . . . . **R. foetida**
—*bi'color* . . . . . . **R. foetida b.**
—*persia'na* . . . . . . **R. foetida p.**
—*ple'na* . . . . . **R. foetida persiana**
—*punic'ea* . . . . **R. foetida bicolor**
lutes'cens . . **R. spinosissima hispida**
ly'elli . . . . **R. clinophylla**
ly'oni . . . . . . **R. carolina villosa**
—*al'ba* . . . . **R. carolina a.**
macart'nea . . . . **R. bracteata**

ROSA, continued
macdou'gali . . . **R. nutkana hispida**
macoun'i (*woodsi* Lindl. 1826, *not* 1820) . . . . MACOUN ROSE
macran'tha . . . . ₵**R. waitziana m.**
macrocar'pa . . **R. odorata gigantea**
macrophyl'la . . . . . . BIGLEAF R.
—*acicula'ris* . . . . . . **R. persetosa**
—*crasse-aculea'ta* . . . . **R. setipoda**
—*grac'ilis* . . . . **R. persetosa**
—*rubro-stamin'ea* . . . . . **R. moyesi**
maja'lis . . . . **R. cinnamomea plena**
∞**ma'lyi** (*?pendulina* × *spinosissima*) ∞MALY R.
man'ca . . . . MANCOS R.
₵*manet'ti* . ∞**R. noisettiana** ₵MANETTI
∞**marcya'na** (*gallica* × *tomentosa*; ∞*terebinthinacea*) . . . . . ∞MARCY R.
margina'ta (*jundzilli; trachyphylla*) MARGINED R.
∞**mariae-graeb'nerae** (*palustris* × *virginiana*) . . . . . ∞GRAEBNER R.
marret'i . . . . MARRET R.
maximilia'ni . . . . **R. woodsi**
maximowiczia'na (*fauriei* in part) MAXIMOWICZ R.
—**jack'i** (*R. jacki; R. kelleri* Baker, *not* Torre & Sarnth.) . . . . . JACKS M.R.
meli'na . . . . . . BLACKSTEM R.
micran'tha . . . . . . SMALLFLOWER R.
microcar'pa . **R. cymosa; R. multiflora**
microphyl'la Roxb., *not* Desf. **R. roxburghi**
—*hir'tula* . . . . . . **R. roxburghi h.**
∞**micrugo'sa** (*roxburghi* × *rugosa*; ∞*vilmorini*) . . . . . . ∞ROXOSA R.
minutifo'lia . . . . . TINYLEAF R.
mirif'ica . . . . **R. stellata m.**
mitis'sima . . **R. spinosissima inermis**
mohaven'sis (*R. woodsi m.*) MOHAVE R.
mol'lis (*R. villosa mollissima*) BLOOMYSTEM R.
monta'na . . . . . . MOUNTAIN R.
montezu'mae . . . MONTEZUMA R.
moscha'ta (*ruscinonensis*) . MUSK R.
—**abyssin'ica** (*R. abyssinica*) ABYSSINIAN M.R.
—*al'ba* . . . . ∞**R. duponti**
—*leschenault'i* . . . . **R. leschenaulti**
—**nastara'na** (*R. pissardi*) PERSIAN MUSK R.
—*nepalen'sis* . . . . . . **R. brunoni**
—*niv'ea* . . . . ∞**R. duponti**
moyes'i (*R. macrophylla rubro-staminea*) . . . . MOYES R.
—**far'gesi** (*R. fargesi* Hort., *not* Boul.) FARGES M.R.
—**rose'a** (*R. holodonta*) . PINK M.R.
mulliga'ni . . . . . . MULLIGAN R.
multibractea'ta (*reducta*). BRACTED R.
multiflo'ra (*dawsoniana* Ellw. & Barry, *not* Hort.; *intermedia; microcarpa* in part; *R. multiflora thunbergiana; polyantha* Sieb. & Zucc.; *thyrsiflora; wichurae*) . . . . . . JAPANESE R.
—**cal'va** . . . . SMOOTH J.R.
—**car'nea** (*R. florida; R. m. plena*) PINK J.R.
—**cathayen'sis** (*R. cathayensis; R. gentiliana* Levl. & Vant.) . CATHAY J.R.
—**platyphyl'la** (*R. cathayensis p.; R. platyphylla*) . . SEVEN-SISTERS J.R.
—*thunbergia'na* . . . . **R. multiflora**
—*watsonia'na* . . . . **R. watsoniana**
muriel'ae . . . . MURIEL R.
musco'sa . . . . . . **R. centifolia m.**
—*crista'ta* . **R. centifolia albo-muscosa**

ROSA, continued
mutab'ilis . . . . . **R. chinensis m.**
myriacan'tha . . . **R. spinosissima m.**
nipponen'sis . . . . . **R. acicularis n.**
nit'ida . . . . SHINING ROSE
niv'ea . . . . **R. laevigata**
∞**noisettia'na** (*chinensis* × *moschata*) ∞NOISETTE R.
₵MANETTI (*R. chinensis manetti; R. manetti*) HV.
nutka'na . . . . NOOTKA R.
—**his'pida** (*R. macdougali*) BRISTLY N.R.
nuttallia'na . . . . . **R. palustris n.**
obova'ta . . . **R. carolina grandiflora**
ochroleu'ca . . **R. spinosissima luteola**
odora'ta (*R. chinensis fragrans; R. indica odoratissima; thea*) . . TEA R.
—**erubes'cens** . . . . . BLUSH T.R.
—**gigan'tea** (*R. gigantea; R. macrocarpa; R. xanthocarpa*) . GIANT T.R.
—**ochroleu'ca** (*R. indica o.*) AMBER T.R.
—**pseudin'dica** (*R. chinensis p.; R. fortuniana* Paxt., *not* **R. fortuneana** Lindl.) . . . . FALSE-INDIAN T.R. (*Fortunes Double Yellow*)
omeien'sis . . . . OMEI R.
—**chrysocar'pa** . . . GOLDFRUIT O.R.
—**pteracan'tha** (*R. sericea p.*) WINGTHORN O.R.
omis'sa . . . . **R. sherardi**
orbicula'ris . . . . . ROUNDLEAF R.
orienta'lis . . . . . . ORIENTAL R.
oxyacan'tha K. Koch, *not* Bieb. ∞**R. kochiana**
oxyo'don . . . . **R. pendulina o.**
palus'tris (*carolina* Auth., *not* L.; *corymbosa; pennsylvanica*) |w . SWAMP R.
—**nuttallia'na** (*R. carolina n.; R. nuttalliana*) . . . . . . NUTTALL S.R.
parviflo'ra . . . . **R. carolina**
—*glandulo'sa* . . . . . **R. carolina g.**
parvifo'lia . . . . . . **R. centifolia p.**
∞**paul'i** (*arvensis* × *rugosa*). ∞PAULS R.
penduli'na (*alpina; cinnamomea* L. in part) . . . . DROPHIP R.
—**gen'tilis** (*R. gentilis*)
—**oxyo'don** (*R. oxyodon*) HIGHLAND D.R.
—**pyrena'ica** (*R. pyrenaica*) PYRENEES D.R.
pennsylva'nica . . . . . **R. palustris**
∞**penzancea'na** (*eglanteria* × *foetida*) ∞PENZANCE R.
perseto'sa (*R. macrophylla acicularis; R. m. gracilis*) . . . ALLBRISTLE R.
per'sica (*berberifolia; simplicifolia*) ONELEAF R.
phoenic'ea . . . . . PHOENICIAN R.
pimpinellifo'lia L., *not* Auth. **R. spinosissima p.**
pimpinellifo'lia Auth. **R. spinosissima**
—*iner'mis* . . . . . **R. spinosissima i.**
pineto'rum . . . . . PINEYWOODS R.
pisocar'pa . . . . . . PEAFRUIT R.
pissard'i . . . **R. moschata nastarana**
platyphyl'la . . . . **R. multiflora p.**
∞**pokornya'na** (*canina* × *rubrifolia*) ∞POKORNY R.
∞**pollinia'na** (*arvensis* × *gallica*) ∞POLLINI R.
∞*polyan'tha* Hort. . . ∞POLYANTHA R.
polyan'tha Sieb. & Zucc. **R. multiflora**
polyan'thos . . . . . . **R. damascena**
pomif'era (*villosa*) . . . . APPLE R.
—**du'plex** . . . . DOUBLE A.R.
pratin'cola . . . . **R. suffulta**

ROSA, continued
pratt'i . . . . PRATT ROSE
prim'ula (*ecae* Rehd., *not* Aitch.; *xanthina* Auth., *not* Lindl.; *R. x. normalis*) . . . . PRIMROSE R.
This was cultivated in America for a long time as R. ecae.
prostra'ta . . . . **R. sempervirens p.**
provincia'lis . . . **R. gallica officinalis**
∞**pruhonicia'na** (*moyesi* × *willmottiae; hillieri*) . . . . ∞PRUHONITZ R.
pubes'cens . **R. rugosa chamissoniana**
pulchel'la . . **R. centifolia pomponia**
pu'mila . . . . **R. gallica p.**
punic'ea . . . . . . **R. foetida bicolor**
pyrena'ica . . . . . **R. pendulina p.**
pyrif'era . . . . PEARHIP R.
ra'pa . . . . . . **R. virginiana plena**
rapi'ni . . . . . . **R. hemisphaerica**
reclina'ta . . . . . ∞**R. lheritierana**
reduc'ta . . . . . **R. multibracteata**
regelia'na . . . . **R. rugosa**
re'pens . . . . **R. arvensis**
reu'teri . . . . **R. dumalis**
∞**rever'sa** (*pendulina* × *spinosissima; rubella*) . . . . . ∞SCOTCHNOD R.
rich'ardi (*sancta* Rich., *not* Andr.) RICHARD R.
roulet'ti . . . . **R. chinensis minima**
roxburgh'i (*microphylla* Roxb., *not* Desf.) ROXBURGH R.
—**hir'tula** (*R. microphylla h.*) HAIRY R.R.
—**norma'lis** . . . . . . SINGLE R.R.
—**ple'na** . . . . DOUBLE R.R.
rubel'la . . . . ∞**R. reversa**
rubifo'lia . . . **R. setigera tomentosa**
rubigino'sa . . . . . . **R. eglanteria**
rubrifo'lia (*ferruginea* Deseg., *not* Vill.; *glauca* Pour.) . . . . REDLEAF R.
∞**rubro'sa** (*rubrifolia* × *rugosa*) ∞RUBROSA R.
ru'bus (*ernesti*) . . . BLACKBERRY R.
rudius'cula . . . . . BUSHES R.
∞**ru'ga** (*arvensis* × *chinensis*) ∞RUGA R.
rugo'sa (*coruscans; ferox* Lawr.; *regeliana*) . . RUGOSA R. (*Hedgerow R.*)
—**al'ba** (*R. r. albiflora*) . WHITE R.R.
—**albo-ple'na** . DOUBLEWHITE R.R.
—*calocar'pa* . . . . . ∞**R. calocarpa**
—**chamissonia'na** (*R. pubescens*) CHAMISSO R.R.
—**kamtchat'ica** (*R. kamtchatica*) KAMCHATKA R.R.
—**ple'na** (*R. r. rubro-plena*) DOUBLE R.R.
—**rose'a** . . . . PINK R.R.
—**typ'ica** (*R. r. rubra* Hort.; *R. r. thunbergiana*) . . . . . PURPLE R.R.
ruscinonen'sis . . . . . **R. moschata**
sanc'ta . . . . **R. richardi**
sandberg'i . . . . **R. woodsi**
satura'ta . . . . CORAL R.
say'i . . . . **R. acicularis**
scan'dens . . . . **R. sempervirens s.**
∞**scharnkea'na** (*californica* × *nitida*) ∞SCHARNKE R.
semperflo'rens . . . . **R. chinensis s.**
sempervi'rens . . . . EVERGREEN R.
—**prostra'ta** (*R. prostrata*) PROSTRATE E.R.
—**scan'dens** (*R. scandens*) CLIMBING E.R.
se'pium . . . . **R. agrestis**
serafi'ni (*seraphini* Viv., *not* Guss.) SERAFINI R.
seraphi'ni Guss. . . . . . . **R. sicula**
seraphi'ni Viv. . . . . . . **R. serafini**

ROSA, continued

seric'ea (*tetrapetala*) FOURPETAL ROSE
—pteracan'tha . . . **R. omeiensis p.**
serrula'ta . . **R. carolina glandulosa**
serta'ta . . . . GARLAND R.
setig'era. . . . . PRAIRIE R.
—iner'mis . . . . . SPINELESS P.R.
—sere'na . . . . SMOOTHSTEM P.R.
—tomento'sa (*R. rubifolia*) FUZZY P.R.
setip'oda (*R. macrophylla crasseaculeata*) . . . . NODFRUIT R.
sherard'i (*omissa*) . . . SHERARD R.
sic'ula (*seraphini* Guss., *not* Viv.) SICILIAN R.
silves'tris . . . . **R. arvensis**
simplicifo'lia . . . . **R. persica**
sin'ica L., *not* Lindl. *nor* Murr. **R. chinensis**
sin'ica Lindl., *not* Murr. . **R. laevigata**
sinowil'soni . . . . WILSON R.
solan'dri. . . . . **R. blanda**
sonomen'sis . . . . . . SONOMA R.
sorbiflo'ra . . . . **R. cymosa**
souliea'na . . . . SOULIE R.
∞**spaethia'na** (*palustris* × *rugosa*) ∞SPAETH R.
spal'dingi . . . . SPALDING R.
spinosis'sima (*illinoensis; pimpinellifolia* Auth.) . . . . . . SCOTCH R.
—alta'ica (*R. altaica; R. grandiflora*) ALTAI S.R.
—an'drewsi . . . . . ANDREWS S.R.
—his'pida (*R. hispida; R. lutescens*) BRISTLY S.R.
—iner'mis (*R. mitissima; R. pimpinellifolia i.*) . . . . . SMOOTH S.R.
—lute'a . . . . YELLOW S.R.
—luteo'la (*R. ochroleuca*) . PALE S.R.
—myriacan'tha (*R. myriacantha*) MYRIADSPINE S.R.
—na'na . . . . DWARF S.R.
—pimpinellifo'lia (*R. pimpinellifolia* L., *not* Auth.) . . . PIMPINELLA S.R.
∞**spinulifo'lia** (*pendulina* × *tomentosa*) ∞PRICKLYLEAF R.
spithame'a. . . . . . . GROUND R.
stella'ta . . . . DESERT R.
—mirif'ica (*R. mirifica*) GOOSEBERRY D.R.
stylo'sa (*systyla*) . . . LEAFSEPAL R.
subblan'da . . . . **R. blanda**
subserrula'ta. . . SUBSERRULATA R.
sufful'ta (*heliophila; pratincola* Greene, *not* H. Braun) . . . SUNSHINE R.
—al'ba . . . . WHITE S.R.
sulphu'rea . . . . . **R. hemisphaerica**
sweginzow'i . . . . . SWEGINZOW R.
∞*terebinthina'cea* . . . ∞**R. marcyana**
terna'ta . . . . **R. laevigata**
tetrapet'ala . . . . **R. sericea**
the'a . . . . **R. odorata**
thyrsiflo'ra . . . . **R. multiflora**
tomento'sa . . . . TOMENTOSE R.
trachyphyl'la . . . . . **R. marginata**
triphyl'la (*anemoneflora*) THREELEAF R.
∞*turbina'ta* . . . . ∞**R. francofurtana**
tuschet'ica . . . . **R. glutinosa**
villo'sa . . . . **R. pomifera**
—mollis'sima . . . . . . **R. mollis**
∞*vilmori'ni* . . . . . . ∞**R. micrugosa**
virginia'na (*R. humilis lucida; lucida*) VIRGINIA R.
—al'ba . . . . **R. carolina a.**
—blan'da . . . . **R. blanda**
—hu'milis . . . . **R. carolina**
—lamprophyl'la . . . . GLOSSY V.R.
—ple'na (*R. rapa; R. v. flore pleno*) DOUBLE V.R.

ROSA, continued

viridiflo'ra . . . . **R. chinensis v.**
vorberg'i . . . . **R. harisoni v.**
∞**waitzia'na** (*canina* × *gallica*) ∞WAITZ ROSE
¢**—macran'tha** (*R. gallica m.; R. macrantha*) . . . . . . ¢PALE W.R.
∞**warleyen'sis** (*blanda* × *rugosa*) ∞WARLEY R.
wat'soni . . . . **R. coriifolia**
watsonia'na (*R. multiflora w.*) WATSON R.
webbia'na . . . . WEBBS R.
wichu'rae . . . . **R. multiflora**
wichuraia'na (*bracteata* Hort., *not* Wendl.; *R. luciae w.*). . WICHURA R.
—ru'bra . . . . ∞**R. barbierana**
willmot'tiae . . . . . WILLMOTT R.
willmottia'na . . . . . **R. longicuspis**
∞**wintonien'sis** (*moyesi* × *setipoda*) ∞WINTON R.
woods'i (*maximiliani; sandbergi*) WOODS R.
—fend'leri (*R. fendleri*) FENDLER W.R.
woods'i Lindl. 1826 . . . **R. macouni**
xanthi'na (*xanthinoides*) . MANCHU R.
—norma'lis . . . . **R. primula**
—spontane'a. . . . . . WILD M.R.
xanthi'na Auth., *not* Lindl. **R. primula**
xanthinoi'des . . . . . . **R. xanthina**
xanthocar'pa . . **R. odorata gigantea**
∞*yedoen'sis* . . . . ∞**R. iwara**

Hort. var. of Rosa, ROSE:

The following list has been provided by the American Rose Society. It is selected from "Modern Roses II," prepared for the American Rose Society by Dr. J. Horace McFarland and collaborators, to which the reader should refer for a complete list. It should be noted that these names in many instances do not conform to S.P.N. policy, but appear here in the form in which they have been registered with the American Rose Society.

Special attention is called to the unwarranted use of homonyms by introducers in naming new varieties; no less than 27 homonyms appear in this list, and are indicated by italicizing.

CLASS ABBREVIATIONS

Alp.	Alpina
Arv.	Arvensis
B.	Bourbon
C.	China
CB.	Climbing Bourbon
CC.	Climbing China
Cent.	Centifolia
CHP.	Climbing Hybrid Perpetual
CHT.	Climbing Hybrid Tea
CT.	Climbing Tea
D.	Damask
Evbl. Semi-Cl.	Everblooming Semi-Climber
Floribunda	See Hybrid Polyantha
G.	Gallica
HAlba	Hybrid Alba
H.Arv.Cl.	Hybrid Arvensis Climber
HBc.	Hybrid Bracteata
HBlanda	Hybrid Blanda
HCanina	Hybrid Canina
H. chinensis minima	Hybrid Chinensis minima
HFt.	Hybrid Foetida
HG.	Hybrid Gigantea
HHug.	Hybrid Hugonis
HMacrantha	Hybrid Macrantha
HMs.	Hybrid Moschata
HNut.	Hybrid Nutkana
HP.	Hybrid Perpetual
HPol.	Hybrid Polyantha (incl. Floribunda)
HRug.	Hybrid Rugosa
HSb.	Hybrid Sweetbrier
HSet.	Hybrid Setigera
HSp.	Hybrid Species
HT.	Hybrid Tea
LC.	Large-flowered Climber
M.	Moss
Mlt.	Multiflora
N.	Noisette
Pol.	Polyantha
R.	Rambler
Rug.	Rugosa
Rug.-Pol.	Rugosa-Polyantha
Semi-Cl.	Semi-Climber
Semi-Cl.Pol.	Semi-Climbing Polyantha
Semp.	Sempervirens
Sp.	Species
Spn.	Spinosissima
T.	Tea
Wich.-Pol.	Wichuraiana-Polyantha

ABBREVIATIONS OF NAMES OF ORIGINATORS

Adams	Charles E. Adams, San Jose, Calif.
Admsn.	Adamson, Victoria, Australia.
ADR.	Amis des Roses, Societe Alsacienne et Lorraine des Amis des Roses.
Aic.	D. Cav. Domenico Aicardi, San Remo, Italy.
Aleg.	Alegatiere, Lyon, France.
Allen	A. J. and C. Allen, Norwich, England.
A&McA.	Austin & McAslan, Glasgow, Scotland.
Aml., A.F. Co.	Albert F. Amling Co., Maywood, Ill.
Aml. Br.	Amling Bros., Santa Ana, Calif.
Aml., M.C.	M. C. Amling, Pana, Ill.
Appl.	W. R. Appleton, Belgrave, Leicester, England.
A&R.	Armacost & Royston, West Los Angeles, Calif.
Arch.	W. E. B. Archer & Daughter, Sellindge, Ashford, Kent, England.
Arm., J. A.	J. A. Armstrong, Ontario, Calif.
Arm. Nurs.	Armstrong Nurseries, Ontario, Calif.
ARS.	American Rose Society, Harrisburg, Pa.
Asmus	E. R. Asmus, Sr., Closter, N. J.
A&W.	Alderton & Williams, Queensland, Australia.
B&A.	Bobbink & Atkins, East Rutherford, N. J.
Bagg	Richard Bagg, Bridgeton, N. J.
Ball. H. S.	Ballarat Hort. Soc., Ballarat, Victoria, Australia.
Balz.	J. W. Balzer, Steinfurth, Germany.
Bancr.	Hon. George Bancroft.
Barb.	Barbier & Co., Orleans, France.
Baum.	A. N. Baumann, Bollwillers, France.
Beckw.	G. Beckwith & Son, Hoddesdon, Herts, England.
Bees	Bees, Ltd., Sealand Nurseries, Chester, England.
Bell, C. J.	Mrs. C. J. Bell, Washington, D. C.
Bell, J.	John Bell, Bearsden, Dumbartonshire, Scotland.
Belu.	Jean Beluze, Lyon, France.
Benn.	Henry Bennett, Shepperton, England.
Bent.	J. A. Bentall, Havering, Romford, Essex, England. (Successor to J. H. Pemberton.)
Bentl.	Walter Bentley & Sons, Ltd., The Rose Nurseries, Thurmaston, Leicester, England.
Berg., A.	Adolf Berger, Bokau bei Aussig, Czechoslovakia.

ROSA, continued

Berg., V.	Vincent Berger, Bokau bei Aussig, Czechoslovakia.
Berg., W.	Walter Berger, Bokau bei Aussig, Czechoslovakia.
Bern., A.	A. Bernaix, Villeurbanne-Lyon, Rhone, France.
Berne.	H. B. Bernede, Bordeaux, France.
Bern., P.	P. Bernaix, Villeurbanne-Lyon, Rhone, France. (Succeeded by J. Ducroz.)
Bert.	C. F. Bertanzel, Roslyn, L. I., N. Y.
Bertsch	R. C. Bertsch Co., Auburn, Wash.
Bide	S. Bide & Sons, Ltd., Farmham, Surrey, England.
Bloom	C. R. Bloom, Oakington, Cambridge, England.
Bohm	Jan Bohm, Blatna-Cechy, Czechoslovakia.
Bor.	Giovanni Borgatti, Bologna, Italy.
Bos.	Bosley Nurs., Mentor, Ohio.
Bost.	J. A. Bostick, Tyler, Tex.
Bott.	Bottner, German amateur.
Boud.	Jos. Boudler, Mamer, Grand Duchy of Luxembourg.
Bout.	Boutigny, Rouen, France.
Bowd.	James H. Bowditch, Pomfret Center, Conn.
Boyt.	Camille Boytard, Orleans, France.
Brada	Dr. Gustav Brada, Czechoslovakia.
Brclf.	Briarcliff Greenhouses, Scarborough-on-Hudson, N. Y.
Brooks, L.L.	L. L. Brooks, Modesto, Calif.
Brooks & Son.	Brooks & Son, Modesto, Calif.
Brownl.	Mr. & Mrs. Walter D. Brownell, Little Compton, R. I.
Brown, W.&J.	W. & J. Brown, Eastfield, Peterborough, England.
Bruant	Bruant, Poitiers, France.
Brundr.	S. Brundrett, Narre Warren North, Victoria, Australia.
Buat.	Buatois, Dijon, Cote d'Or, France.
Budl.	Budlong & Son Co., Auburn, R. I.
Buis.	G. A. H. Buisman & Son, Heerde, Netherlands.
Bur.	Luther Burbank, Santa Rosa, Calif.
Burb.	Burbage Nurs., Hinckley, Leicestershire, England.
Burr.	J. Burrell & Co., Cambridge, England.
Buyl	Buyl Freres, Cherscamp, Schellebelle, Belgium.
Cal. Roses	California Roses, Inc., Puente, Calif.
Cant, B. R.	Benjamin R. Cant & Sons, Ltd., Colchester, Essex, England.
Cant, F.	Frank Cant & Co., Ltd., Colchester, Essex, Eng.
Cap.	Capiago, Como, Italy.
Carb.	Kellar Carbaugh, Lower Yoder Township, Pa.
Carm.	Elbert S. Carman, River Edge, N. J.
Caron	Berthe Caron (Mme. Mallerin), Varces, Isere, France.
Catt	H. J. Catt, New South Wales, Australia.
Cay.	H. Cayeux, Le Havre, France.
Caz.	G. Cazzaniga, Cologno Monzese (Milano), Italy.

ROSA, continued

C-C.	Cochet-Cochet, Coubert, Seine-et-Marne, France.
Cent. Ex. Farm	Central Experimental Farm, Ottawa, Ont., Canada.
Cham., C.	C. Chambard, Parilly-Venissieux-les-Lyon, Rhone, France.
Cham., M.	M. Chambard, Lyon-Monplaisir, Rhone, France.
Chap.	Chaplin Bros., Ltd., Waltham Cross, England.
Chase	Clarence A. Chase, Eugene, Ore.
Chau.	Chauvry, Bordeaux, France.
Chot.	Chotkove Rosarium, Czechoslovakia.
C&J.	Conard & Jones, West Grove, Pa. (Succeeded by The Conard-Pyle Co.)
Clark	Alister Clark, Bulla, Victoria, Australia.
Clarke Br.	Clarke Bros., Portland, Ore.
Clarke, W. B.	W. B. Clarke & Son, San Jose, Calif.
Clark's Rose Nurs.	Clark's Rose Nurs., Jacksonville, Texas.
Clev. Cut-Fl. Co.	Cleveland Cut-Flower Co., Newton Falls, Ohio.
Coch.	Scipion Cochet, Coubert, Seine-et-Marne, France.
Cock.	James Cocker & Sons, Aberdeen, Scotland.
Cod.	L. B. Coddington, Murray Hill, N. J.
Cole	Cole Nursery Co., Painesville, Ohio.
Colo.	L. Colombier, Macon, Saone-et-Loire, France.
Cook, J.	John Cook, Baltimore, Md.
Cook, J. W.	Joseph William Cook, John Cook, Inc., Baltimore, Md.
Cool.	G. Cooling & Sons, Bath, England.
Corb.	Corboeuf, Orleans, France.
Cottage	Cottage Gardens Co., Queens, L. I., N. Y.
C-P.	The Conard-Pyle Co., West Grove, Pa. (Successor to Conard & Jones.)
Crem.	F. E. Cremer, Hanover, Pa.
Croib.	J. Croibier & Fils, Saint-Tous, Rhone, France.
Cross	Dr. Whitman Cross, Chevy Chase, Md.
Cutb.	W. H. Cutbush & Son, Ltd., Herts, England.
Dahl.	Edward Dahlgren, Boone, Iowa.
Dale	Dale Estate, Ltd., Brampton, Ont., Canada.
Dan.	Daniels Bros., Ltd., Norwich, England.
da Silva	Alfredo Moreira da Silva & Filhos, Lda., Porto, Portugal.
Daw.	Jackson Dawson, Arnold Arboretum, Jamaica Plain, Mass.
D&C.	Dingee & Conard, West Grove, Pa.
de B.	Victor de Bree, Richmond, Maine.
Del.	F. Delaunay, Angers, France.
Dele.	Paul Delepine, Carrieres, Angers, France.
Denn.	Franklin Dennison, Cranford, Leamington, Eng.
Deno.	Mme. or Vve. Denoyel, Venissieux, France.
De P.	Dr. Hiram DePuy, Tacoma, Wash.
de R.	G. de Ruiter, Hazerswonde, Netherlands.
Desc.	Descemet, St. Denis, France.
Desp.	Desprez, Yebles, France.

ROSA, continued

de V.	Jan de Vink, Boskoop, Netherlands.
Dev.	Harry Deverman, Clifton, N. J.
Dick., A.	Alex. Dickson & Sons, Ltd., Newtownards, Ireland.
Dick., H.	Hugh Dickson, Ltd., Belfast, Ireland.
Dick., S.	Sandy Dickson, Belfast, Ireland.
Dicksons	Dicksons & Co., Edinburgh, Scotland.
Did.	James Didato, Middlesex, N. J.
Dien.	Richard Diener Nursery, Oxnard, Calif.
Dixie	Dixie Rose Nurs., Tyler, Texas.
Dobbie	Dobbie & Co., Ltd., Edinburgh, Scotland.
Dorn.	F. Dorner & Sons Co., Lafayette, Ind.
Dot	Pedro Dot, San Feliu de Llobregat, Barcelona, Spain.
Dreer	Henry A. Dreer, Inc., Philadelphia, Pa.
Dub.	Dubreuil, Lyon, France.
Ducr.	J. Ducroz, Villeurbanne-Lyon, Rhone, France. (Successor to P. Bernaix.)
Dunl.	John H. Dunlop & Son, Ltd., Toronto, Ont., Canada.
Dup.	Dupont, Luxembourg Palace, Paris.
Eas.	Walter Easlea & Sons, Ltd., Eastwood, Leigh-on-Sea, Essex, England.
East. Nurs.	Eastern Nurseries, Inc., Holliston, Mass.
E&B.	Ellwanger & Barry, Rochester, N. Y.
Ebel.	P. Ebeling, Bernburg, Germany.
Eddie	H. M. Eddie & Sons, Ltd., Sardis, B. C., Canada.
Eich.	Henry Eichholz, Waynesboro, Pa.
Elmer's Nurs.	Elmer's Nurs., San Jose, Calif.
Elmer, W. M.	W. M. Elmer, San Jose, Calif.
Evans	Frederick Evans, Kings Road, Brighton, England.
Evans City Cut Fl. Co.	Evans City Cut Flower Co., Evans City, Pa.
Fairh.	W. H. Fairhead, Roding Road, Loughton, Eng.
Fauq.	Fauque & Fils, Orleans, France.
Feast	S. & J. Feast, Baltimore, Md.
Ferg., W.	William Ferguson, Dunfermline, Scotland.
F-H.	J. H. Faassen-Hekkens, Tegelen, Netherlands.
Field	Field Bros., Washington, D. C.
Finch	R. M. Finch, Concord, N. S. W., Australia.
Fitz.	Mrs. H. C. Fitzhardinge, Warrawee, N. S. W., Australia.
F-L.	F. Felberg-Leclerc, Trier, Germany.
Florex	Florex Gardens, North Wales, Pa.
Font.	Fontaine, Clamart, France.
Foote	Mrs. Harriett R. Foote, Marblehead, Mass.
Fort.	Robert Fortune, English botanist.
Fou.	Foulard, au Mans, France.
Gauj.	Jean Gaujard, Feyzin, Isere, France.
Ged.	Philipp Geduldig, Kohlscheid bei Aachen, Germany.
Geelong H.S.	Geelong Horticultural Society, Australia.

ROSA, continued

Geig.	William A. Geiger, North Wales, Pa.
Germ.	Germain Seed & Plant Co., Los Angeles, Calif.
Gers.	Chas. E. F. Gersdorff, Washington, D. C.
Gesch.	Geschwind, Karpona, Hungary.
Gill.	Francis Gillot, Trepillot-Besancon, Doubs, France.
Girin	G. Girin, Saint-Romain-de-Popey, par Pontcharra, Rhone, France.
G&M.	Groshens & Morrison, Roslyn, Pa.
Gould	L. C. Gould Co., Chicago, Ill.
G&R.	Good & Reese, Springfield, Ohio.
Gran.	Granger, Grisy-Suisnes, France.
Grant	Patrick Grant, Macksville, N. S. W., Australia.
Grav.	M. Gravereaux, Roserie de l'Hay, Seine, France.
Gray, A. H.	Alexander Hill Gray, Bath, England.
Gray, W. R.	W. R. Gray, Oakton, Va.
Greg.	Charles Gregory, Chilwell, Notts, England.
Grif.	J. Bruce Griffin, Philadelphia, Pa.
Griffg. Br.	Griffing Bros., Beaumont, Texas.
Griffg., W. D.	W. D. Griffing, Mac-Clenny, Fla.
Grillo	Nicholas Grillo, Milldale, Conn.
Grim.	Grimwood, English plantsman of eighteenth century.
Groen	C. J. Groen, Montebello, Calif.
Groot., F. J.	F. J. Grootendorst, F. J. Grootendorst & Sons, Boskoop, Netherlands.
Groot., R.	Rien Grootendorst, Boskoop, Netherlands.
Grosh.	Victor Groshens, Roslyn, Pa.
GRVL	Grandes Roseraies du Val de la Loire, Orleans, France.
Gude	Gude Bros., Washington, D. C.
Guerin	Modeste Guerin, Paris, France.
Guil.	Vve. A. Guillaud & Fils, Grand Lemps, Isere, France.
Guill. f.	Guillot Fils, Lyon-Monplaisir, France.
Guill., H.	Henri Guillot, Saint-Marcellin, Isere, France.
Guill., M.	Marc Guillot, Lyon-Monplaisir, France.
Guill., P.	Pierre Guillot, Lyon-Monplaisir, Rhone, France.
Guill. p.	Guillot Pere, Lyon, France.
Guin.	Guinoisseau Fils, Angers, France.
Gunn	Gunn & Sons, Ltd., Olton, Warwickshire, England.
H-A.	Hemeray-Aubert, Orleans, France.
Hack.	Hackett & Co., Adelaide, Australia.
Hage	W. C. Hage, W. C. Hage & Co., Boskoop, Netherlands.
Hall	Dr. J. Campbell Hall, Rowantree House, Monaghan, Ireland.
Hamo.	Marc Hamoniere, Ivry, Seine, France.
Han., N. E.	Dr. N. E. Hansen, State College, Brookings, S. D.
Han., N. J.	Niels J. Hansen, Chevy Chase, Md.

ROSA, continued

Har.	Rev. Harison, New York City.
Hardy	Hardy, one-time keeper of Luxembourg Gardens in Paris.
Hark.	R. Harkness & Co., Hitchin, Herts, England.
Hart, G. B.	George B. Hart, Rochester, N. Y.
Hart, L. P.	L. P. Hart, Everson, Wash.
Hat.	R. Marion Hatton, Harrisburg, Pa.
Hau.	C. Hausermann Co., Melrose Park, Ill.
Haz.	Hazlewood Bros., Epping, N. S. W., Australia.
H.Br.&T. Co.	Hoopes, Bro. & Thomas Co., West Chester, Pa.
Heers	C. W. Heers, Manly, Queensland, Australia.
Heiz.	E. Heizmann, Vevey, Switzerland.
Hel.	Heller Bros., New Castle, Ind.
Hend. Ex. Gar.	Henderson's Exp. Gardens, Fresno, Calif.
Hend., P.	Peter Henderson & Co., New York, N. Y.
Hend., W. H.	Wm. H. Henderson, Fresno, Calif.
Hesse	H. A. Hesse, Baumschulen, Weener, Ems, Germany.
Hicks	Elisha J. Hicks, Hurst, Twyford, Berks, England.
Hieatt	Forrest L. Hieatt, San Diego, Calif.
Hil.	Hillier & Sons, Winchester, England.
Hillc. Gar.	Hillcrest Gardens, Weston, Mass.
Hill Crest	Hill Crest Greenhouses, Newtown, Pa.
Hill, E. G.	E. G. Hill Co., Richmond, Ind.
Hill. Fl. Prod.	Hill Floral Products Co., Richmond, Ind.
Hill, J. H.	J. H. Hill Co., Richmond, Ind.
Hillk.	V. S. Hillock, Arlington, Texas.
Hin., P.	Peter Hinner, Woodstock, Ill.
Hin., W.	Wilhelm Hinner, Trier, Germany.
His.	Jesse F. Hiscox, East Patchogue, N. Y.
Hob.	Hobbies, Ltd., Dereham, England.
Hof.	Harry Hofmann, Jacksonville, Ill.
Hor.	M. H. Horvath, Mentor, Ohio.
Hosp	F. P. Hosp, Riverside, Calif.
How., F. H.	Fred H. Howard, Howard & Smith, Montebello, Calif.
How., P. J.	Paul J. Howard, Los Angeles, Calif.
How. Rose Co.	Howard Rose Co., Paul W. Howard, Hemet, Calif.
H&S.	Howard & Smith, Montebello, Calif.
Huck	Arno Huck, Dresden-Gostritz, Germany.
Hurst	Dr. C. C. Hurst, Botanic Garden, Cambridge, England.
IHS.	Ivanhoe Horticultural Society, Victoria, Australia.
Ing.	Fratelli Ingegnoli, Milano (119), Italy.
I.-S. Nurs.	Inter-State Nurs., Hamburg, Iowa.
Izzo	Patsy A. Izzo, Glen Head, N. Y.
Jac.	Martin R. Jacobus, Ridgefield, N. J.

ROSA, continued

Jaco.	Jacotot, Dijon, France.
Jacq.	Jacques, gardener at Chateau de Neuilly, France.
Jam.	Hippolyte Jamain, Paris, France.
Johns	A. Johns & Sons, Houghton, South Australia.
Jor.	B. L. Jordan, Sussex, England.
J&P.	Jackson & Perkins Co., Newark, N. Y.
Kal.	Joseph W. Kallay, Painesville, Ohio.
Kau.	Ruth Kaucher, Newtown, Pa.
Ker.	G. W. Kershaw, Wahroonga, N. S. W., Australia.
Kess.	Henry Kessler, Red Bank, N. J.
Ket.	Ketten Bros., Luxembourg, Grand Duchy of Luxembourg.
Kew	Kew Gardens, London, England.
Keynes&Co.	Keynes & Co., Salisbury, England.
Kiese	Herm. Kiese & Co., Vieselbach-Erfurt, Germany.
K&K.	Kluis & Koning, Boskoop, Netherlands.
Kluis	Anth. Kluis, Boskoop, Netherlands.
Klyn	Gerard K. Klyn, Mentor, Ohio.
Knight, G.	George Knight & Sons, Homebush, N. S. W., Australia.
Knight, J. E.	John E. Knight & Son, Tettenhall Nurs., Wolverhampton, England.
Koch	Anthony Koch, Baltimore, Md.
Kordes	W. Kordes Sons, Sparrieshoop, Holstein, Germany.
Kos.	M. Koster & Sons, Boskoop, Netherlands.
Krause	Max Krause, Alveslohe, Holstein, Germany.
Krebs	Alfred Krebs, Montebello, Calif.
Kreis	Franz A. Kreis Wwe., Hofl., Niederwalluf am Rhein, Germany.
Kru.	Dr. D. Kruger, Freiburg, Baden, Germany.
K.-S. Co.	Kemble-Smith Co., Boone, Iowa.
Lach.	Francois Lacharme, Lyon, France.
La F.	La Florida, Asua, Spain.
Laf.	Laffay, Bellevue, France.
Lain.	Fred L. Lainson, Council Bluffs, Iowa.
Lamb., E.	Elie Lambert, Lyon, France.
Lamb., P.	Peter Lambert, Trier, Germany.
Lamm.	W. E. Lammerts, Armstrong Nurseries, Ontario, Calif.
Lap.	L. Laperriere, Champagne-au-Mont-d'Or, Rhone, France.
Law.	T. A. Lawrenson, Newcastle-on-Tyne, England.
Lax.	Laxton Bros., Bedford, England.
Lay.	J. G. Layton, Olean, N. Y.
Lede.	Ledechaux, Willecresne, France.
Lee	Lee, Hammersmith, England.
Leen. Bros.	Leenders Bros., Steyl-Tegelen, Netherlands.
Leen., M.	M. Leenders & Co., Steyl-Tegelen, Netherlands.
Le G.	E. B. LeGrice, North Walsham, Norfolk, England.

ROSA, continued

Lem.	Fred H. Lemon & Co., Richmond, Ind.
Lens	Louis Lens, Wavre-Notre-Dame, Belgium.
Lest.	Francis E. Lester, Monterey, Calif.
Letts	G. F. Letts & Sons, Hadleigh, Suffolk, England.
Lev.	Levavasseur & Sons, Orleans, Loiret, France.
Leveq.	Leveque, Ivry, France.
Levet, A.	Antoine Levet, Lyon, France.
Levet, F.	Francois Levet, Lyon, France.
Ley	F. Ley, Windlesham, Surrey, England.
L'Hay	Roseraie de l'Hay, pres Bourg-la-Reine, France.
Liab.	Jean Liabaud, Lyon, France.
Lig.	C. U. Liggit Co., Philadelphia, Pa.
Lil.	Leonard Lille, Lyon-Villeurbanne, France.
Lill.	George Lilley, Cippenham, Slough, Bucks, England.
Lind.	Herm. Lindecke, Remagen, Germany.
Lip.	W. C. Lippiatt, Otahuhu, Auckland, New Zealand.
Lohr.	Henry Lohrberg, Lomira, Wis.
Long.	G. Longley & Sons, Rainham, Kent, England.
Looy.	P. J. Looymans & Co., Oudenbosch, Netherlands.
Lot.	Victor Lottin, Avranches, Manche, France.
Lov.	J. T. Lovett, Lovett's Nursery, Little Silver, N. J.
Low	Stuart Low & Co., Bush Hill Park, Enfield, Middlesex, England.
Lowe	W. Lowe & Son, Beeston, Notts, England.
Lowm.	Abner M. Lowman, Elmira, N. Y.
L&S.	Lowe & Shawyer, Uxbridge, England.
Lum	Carleton Lum, Chatham, N. J.
Maass	Conrad Maass, Rellingen, Germany.
Mal.	Charles Mallerin, Varces, Isere, France.
Manda	W. A. Manda, South Orange, N. J.
Mare.	Marechal, Angers, France.
Marg.	Margottin, Bourg-la-Reine, France.
Marr.	George Marriott, Carlton, Nottingham, England.
Mart.	Martin, Dundee, Scotland.
Mason	John A. Mason, Burlingame, Calif.
Maton	Paul L. Maton, Pana, Ill.
May	H. B. May, Summit, N. J.
McC.	J. Chas. McCullough Seed Co., Cincinnati, Ohio.
McGr.	Samuel McGredy & Son, Portadown, Ireland.
McI.	J. T. McIntosh, Prahran, Australia.
McL.	E. W. McLellan Co., Colma, Calif.
Mee	Oliver Mee, Alderley Edge, Cheshire, England.
Meill., A.	A. Meilland, Tassin-les-Lyon, France.
Meill., F.	F. Meilland, Tassin-les-Lyon, France.
Melv.	Melville Bros., Purley, Reading, England.
Merk.	Dr. Merkeley, Winnipeg, Man., Canada.
Merm.	Louis Mermet, Lyon-Monplaisir, Rhone, France.

ROSA, continued

Merry.	H. Merryweather & Sons, Ltd., Southwell, Notts, England.
Mes.	Nicholas Mesman, South Ridge, Madison, Ohio.
M&H.	Munch & Haufe, Dresden-Leuben, Germany.
Mich.	Henry F. Michell Co., Philadelphia, Pa.
Miel.	Miellez, Esquermes, France.
Mikes	Mikes, Troja, Czechoslovakia.
Mohr	Mohr, Copenhagen, Denmark.
Mont., A.	Alex. Montgomery, Hadley, Mass.
Mont. Co.	Montgomery Co., Hadley, Mass.
Moore	Ralph S. Moore, Sequoia Gardens Nursery, Visalia, Calif.
Mord.	Mordigan Evergreen Nurs., San Fernando, Calif.
Morse	Henry Morse & Sons, Westfield Nurseries, Eaton, Norwich, England.
Mould.	Dr. A. Moulden, Unley, South Australia.
M-R.	Moreau-Robert, Angers, France.
Muhle	Arpad Muhle, Temesvar, Rumania.
Mul., F.	Dr. Fr. Muller, Weingarten, Bavaria.
Mul., J. F.	J. F. Muller, Rellingen, Germany.
Munne, B.	Blas Munne, Gava, Barcelona, Spain.
Munne, M.	Manuel Munne, Gava, Barcelona, Spain.
Mur.	William B. Murray, Atco, N. J.
Murr., E.	Edwin Murrell, Ltd., Shrewsbury, England.
Murr., R.	R. Murrell, Rose Acre, Bedmond Hill, Herts, England.
Nab.	P. Nabonnand, Golfe Juan, Alpes-Maritimes, France.
Nad.	Camprubi Nadal, San Juan, Desi, Spain.
Neu.	Harry A. Neuner, Erie, Pa.
Nic.	J. H. Nicolas, Jackson & Perkins Co., Newark, N. Y.
Nonin	Auguste Nonin & Fils, Chatillon-sous-Bagneux, Seine, France.
Norf.	Norfolk Nurs., Dereham, England.
N.R.S. of N.S.W.	National Rose Society, New South Wales, Australia.
N.R.S. of S. Aus.	National Rose Society of South Australia, Australia.
N.R.S. Vic.	National Rose Society, Victoria, Australia.
Oger	A. Oger, Caen, France.
Opde.	A. Opdebeeck Sons, Putte-les-Malines, Belgium.
Pac. Rose Co.	Pacific Rose Co., Los Angeles, Calif.
Padr.	Jose Padrosa, San Justo Desvern, Barcelona, Spain.
Page	Courtney Page, Hon. Sec., National Rose Society, London, England.
Pah.	L. Pahissa, San Feliu de Llobregat, Spain.
Parm.	Parmentier, Enghien, Belgium.
Parm., J.	J. Parmentier, Parmentier's Roses, Bayport, L. I., N. Y.
Pasq.	Thomas Pasquill, North Vancouver, B. C., Canada.

ROSA, continued

Paul	Paul & Sons, Cheshunt, Herts, England.
Paul, W.	W. Paul & Son, Ltd., Waltham Cross, Herts, England.
P-C.	Pajotin-Chedane, Maitre-Ecole, Angers, France.
P-D.	J. Pernet-Ducher, Venissieux-les-Lyon, Rhone, France.
Pemb.	Rev. J. H. Pemberton, Havering atte-Bower, Essex, England.
Pen.	Antoine Penny, Clermont-Ferrand, Puy-de-Dome, France.
Penz.	Lord Penzance, Eashing Park, England.
Pfitz.	Wilhelm Pfitzer, Stuttgart, Wurtemburg, Germany.
Pier., A. N.	A. N. Pierson, Inc., Cromwell, Conn.
Pier., F. R.	F. R. Pierson, Tarrytown, N. Y.
Plant.	Plantier, Lyon, France.
Port.	Portemer, Gentilly, France.
Pouls., D.	Dines Poulsen, Copenhagen, Denmark.
Pouls., D. T.	D. T. Poulsen, Copenhagen, Denmark.
Pouls., S.	Svend Poulsen, Copenhagen, Denmark.
Pra.	Henry Pradel, Lyon, France.
Pras.	F. Praskac, Freundorf, Czechoslovakia.
Pre. R. G.	Premier Rose Gardens, Maywood, Ill.
Prince	George Prince, Longworth, Berks, England.
Prior	D. Prior & Son, Ltd., Colchester, England.
Proi.	Joseph Proietti, San Leandro, Calif.
Pross.	D. Prosser & Son, Gloucester, England.
Pt. Stktn. Nurs.	Port Stockton Nurs., Stockton, Calif.
Raf.	Frank C. Raffel, Port Stockton Nursery, Stockton, Calif.
Ramb.	Rambaud, Lyon, France.
Reeves	A. Reeves & Co., Norwich, England.
Reinb.	Peter Reinberg, Chicago, Ill.
R. et M.	Robert et Moreau, Angers, France.
Rey.	L. Reymond, Lyon-Villeurbanne, Rhone, France.
Reyn.	Stephen Reynolds, Reynolds' Farms, Norwalk, Conn.
Rice	Rice Bros. Co., Geneva, N. Y.
Rich.	C. Richardier, Venissieux-les-Lyon, Rhone, France.
Ring.	Ivar Ringdahl, Rome, N. Y.
Rob.	M. Robert, Biarritz, Basses-Pyrenees, France.
Robi.	Marcel Robichon, Pithiviers, Loiret, France.
Robin., H.	Herbert Robinson, Hinckley, Leicester, England.
Robin., T.	T. Robinson, Portchester Nurs., Carlton, Nottingham, England.
Rosen	L. P. Rosen & Son, Carlingford, N. S. W., Australia.
Rous.	Roussel, Montpelier, France.
Royer	Georges Royer, Versailles, Seine-et-Oise, France.
Russ	George Russ, Victoria, Australia.
Samt.	Samtmann Bros., Chestnut Hill, Pa.
Sand.	Sanders & Sons, St. Albans, England.

ROSA, continued

Saund.	Dr. W. Saunders, Central Experimental Farm, Ottawa, Ont., Canada.
Sauv.	Joseph Sauvageot, near Roche, Doubs, France.
Sav.	Messrs. Savage, Barking, Essex, England.
Schmid	R. Schmid, Bad Kostritz 50 (Thur.), Fernruf 372, Germany.
Schmidt, J. C.	J. C. Schmidt, Erfurt, Germany.
Schmidt, R.	Rudolf Schmidt, Rellingen, Holstein, Germany.
Schoe.	Rev. George M. A. Schoener, University of Santa Clara, Santa Clara, Calif.
Schr.	Frank Schramm, Crystal Lake, Ill.
Schul.	H. Schultheis, Steinfurth, Germany.
Schw., A.	Andre Schwartz, Venissieux, Rhone, France.
Schw., J.	Jos. Schwartz and Vve. (Widow), Lyon, France.
Scit.	Peter Scittine, Council Bluffs, Iowa.
Scott	Robert Scott & Son, Inc., Sharon Hill, Pa.
S&H.	Storrs & Harrison Co., Painesville, Ohio.
Sham.	C. S. Shamburger, Winona, Texas.
Simp.	J. Simpson, South Queensferry, N. B., Canada.
Skin.	F. L. Skinner, Dropmore, Manitoba, Canada.
Sliedr.	Sliedrecht & Co., Boskoop, Netherlands.
Smith, E. P.	E. Percy Smith, The Rosery, Boston, Lincolnshire, England.
Smith, J.	John Smith, Hayward, Calif.
Smith, T.	Thomas Smith & Sons, Stranraer, Scotland.
S&N.	Soupert & Notting. (Succeeded by C. Soupert.)
Som.	Somerset Rose Nurs., New Brunswick, N. J.
Soup.	Constant Soupert, Luxembourg, Grand Duchy of Luxembourg.
Span.	F. Spanbauer, Medina, N. Y.
Spand.	Spandikow & Sons, Melrose Park, Ill.
Spath	L. Spath, Berlin, Germany.
Spek	Jan Spek, Boskoop, Netherlands.
Sprunt	Rev. James M. Sprunt, Kenansville, N. C.
Square	John Square & Son, Painesville, Ohio.
Stanw. R. G.	Stanway Rose Gardens, Colchester, Essex, England.
Stark	Stark Bros. Nurseries & Orchards Co., Louisiana, Mo.
Stell	L. H. Stell, Tyler, Texas.
Stell Nurs.	Stell Rose Nurs., Tyler, Texas.
Stev., G. A.	G. A. Stevens, Harrisburg, Pa.
Stev., W.	Walter Stevens, Ltd., Hoddesdon, England.
Stew.	T. G. Stewart, Victoria, Australia.
Stiel.	Fred C. Stielow, Niles Center, Ill.
Stock.	C. H. Stocking, San Jose, Calif.
Stuppy	Stuppy Floral Co., St. Joseph, Mo.
Tanne	R. Tanne, Alveslohe, Holstein, Germany.
Tant.	Mathias Tantau, Uetersen, Holstein, Germany.

ROSA, continued

Tesch.	Victor Teschendorff, Cossebaude, Dresden, Germany.
Thom.	Capt. George C. Thomas, Jr., Beverly Hills, Calif.
Thomp.	J. H. Thompson's Sons, Kennett Square, Pa.
Thomsv.	Thomasville Nurs., Thomasville, Ga.
Timm	J. Timm & Co., Elmshorn, Holstein, Germany.
Timmer.	Jos. Timmermans, Herten, Roermond, Netherlands.
Tot.	Charles H. Totty Co., Madison, N. J.
Tow.	Edward Towill, Roslyn, Pa.
Trouil.	Trouillard, Angers, France.
T&S.	Traendly & Schenck, Inc., Rowayton Greenhouses, New York, N. Y.
Tur.	E. Turbat & Co., Orleans, France.
Turke	Robert Turke, Meissen III, Saxony, Germany.
Turn.	Charles Turner, Slough, England.
Und.	F. R. M. Undritz, West New Brighton, L. I., N. Y.
U.S. Cut Fl. Co.	U. S. Cut Flower Co., Elmira, N. Y.
U.S. Dept. Agric.	U. S. Dept. of Agric., Washington, D. C.
Van B.	John H. van Barneveld, Puente, Calif.
Van F.	Dr. Walter Van Fleet, Glenn Dale, Md.
Van H.	Louis Van Houtte, Ghent, Belgium.
Van H.-C.	Ach. van Herreweghe-Coppitters, Cherscamp, Belgium.
Van N.	P. van Nes, Boskoop, Netherlands.
Van R.	G. A. Van Rossem, Naarden, Netherlands.
Veitch	J. Veitch & Sons, King's Road, Chelsea, England.
Verd., E.	Eugene Verdier, Paris, France.
Verd., V.	Victor Verdier, Paris, France.
Versch.	H. A. Verschuren & Sons, Haps, Netherlands.
Vestal	Jos. W. Vestal & Son, Little Rock, Ark.
Vet.	Vetillard, Mans, France.
Via.	P. Vially, Lyon-Villeurbanne, Rhone, France.
Vib.	Vibert, Angers, France.
Vick	James Vick, Rochester, N.Y.
Vogel, M.	Max Vogel, Sangerhausen, Germany.
Vogel, R.	R. Vogel, Jr., Sangerhausen, Germany.
V.-P.	J. Verschuren-Pechtold, Netherlands.
Waban	Waban Conservatories, Natick, Mass.
Walsh, J.	James Walsh & Sons, Ltd., Portadown, Ireland.
Walsh, M. H.	M. H. Walsh, Woods Hole, Mass.
Walt.	Louis Walter, Saverne, Bas-Rhin, France.
Ward	Ward, Ipswich, England.
Ward, F. B.	F. B. Ward, Bay City, Mich.
Wat.	John Waterer, Sons & Crisp, Ltd., Twyford, Berks, England.
Watk.	A. F. Watkins, Dixie Rose Nursery, Tyler, Texas.
Waym.	Robert Wayman, Bayside, L. I., N. Y.
Ways.	Wayside Gardens Co., Mentor, Ohio.
W&E.	Wirtz & Eicke, Cossmanns Nachf, Rodehleim-Frankfurt, Germany.

ROSA, continued

Weig., C.	Christopher Weigand, Bad Soden a Taunus, Germany.
Weig., L.	L. Weigand, Ban Soden a Taunus, Germany.
Welt.	Nicola Welter, Trier, Germany.
Westb.	Westbury Rose Co., Westbury, L. I., N. Y.
West. Rose Co.	Western Rose Co., San Fernando, Calif.
Wez.	K. Wezelenburg & Son, Hazerswoude, Netherlands.
Wheat.	Wheatcroft Bros., Ruddington, Nottingham, England.
White Br.	White Bros. Rose Corp., Medina, N. Y.
White, C. N.	Charles N. White, Medina, N. Y.
Whitw.	Whitwell, Darlington, England.
W&I.	Wood & Ingram, Huntingdon, England.
Wig.	John H. Wiggin, Attleboro, Mass.
Wight	J. B. Wight, Cairo, Ga.
Wilb.	Rena E. Wilber, Seattle, Wash.
Will., A. H.	Dr. A. H. Williams, Horsham, Sussex, England.
Witter.	R. Witterstaetter, Cincinnati, Ohio.
Wolfe	Tom J. Wolfe, Waco, Texas.
Woos.	Richard Woosnam, St. Olaves, Grimsby, England.
Wyant	Melvin E. Wyant, Mentor, Ohio.
Young	Blamire Young, Victoria, Australia.
Zieg.	H. M. & W. E. Zieger, Willow Grove, Pa.

ABAILLARD. G. (From Angers 1845.)
ABEL CARRIERE. HP. (E. Verd. 1875.)
ABOL. HT. (Evans; Beckw. '27.)
ADAM MESSERICH. B. (P. Lamb. '20.)
ADELE. HT. (Lens '35.)
ADELE COURTOISE. G.
ADELINE. Cent. (Vib.)
A. DENIS. HT. (Bohm '35.)
ADIEU DE BORDIER. G.
ADMIRATION. HT. (McGr. '22.)
ADOLF DEEGEN. HT. (Bohm '35.)
ADOLF GRILLE. HPol. (Kordes; J&P. '40.)
ADORA. Pol. (Beckw. '36.)
ADORABLE. HT. (Eich. '30.)
ADORATION. HT. (Gauj.; J&P. '40.) *Ile de France.*
ADRIENNE MARTIN. HT. (Buat. '30.)
ADVANCE. HT. (Le G. '41.)
A. DVORAK. HT. (Bohm '33.)
AENNCHEN MUFLLER. Pol. (J. C. Schmidt '07.) *Annie Mueller.*
AENNE KREIS. HT. (Kreis '30.)
A FEUILLES LUISANTES. M. (1843.)
AFTERGLOW. HT. (Le G. '38.) *Sam Buff.*
AGAR. G. (From Angers 1843.)
A.-G.-A. RAPPARD. HT. (Buis. '36.)
AGENOR. G. (Vib. or Rob. 1832.)
AGNES. HRug. (Saund. '00; Cent. Ex. Farm '22.)
AGNES DE PUY. HT. (De P. '30.)
AGNES EMILY CARMAN. HRug. (Carm. 1898.)
AGNES KRUSE. Pol. (Tant. '36.)
Agrippina. CRAMOISI SUPERIEUR.
AIMABLE AMIE. G.

ROSA, continued
Aimee Vibert. N. (Vib. 1828.)
Albast. HT. (Van R. '28.)
Alberic Barbier. LC. (Barb. '00.)
Albertine. LC. (Barb. '21.)
Albert Maumene. HHug. (Sauv. '34.)
Alcine. G.
Alexander Hill Gray. T. (A. Dick. '11.) *Yellow Maman Cochet; Yellow Cochet.*
Alexandre Girault. LC. (Barb. '09.)
Alexandrine Chapuis. HT. (Via. '35.)
Alezane. HT. (Pah.; J&P. '35.)
Alfred Colomb. HP. (Lach. 1865.) *Mme. Brosse.*
Alfred K. Williams. HP. (J. Schw. 1877.)
Alfred Petot. HT. (Buat. '35.)
Alice Amos. Pol. (Spek; Prior '22.)
Alice Harding. HT. (Mal.; J&P. '37.)
Alice Leroi. M. (Vib. 1842.)
Alice Marion Whyte. HT. (Evans '32.)
Alice Stern. HT. (Gill. '26.)
Alida. HT. (Lens '38.)
Alida Lovett. LC. (Van F. '05; Lov. '17.)
Alika. Sp. (Brought from Russia '06 by N. E. Han.; in commerce '30.) *Rosa gallica grandiflora.*
Alister Stella Gray. N. (A. H. Gray 1894.) *Golden Rambler.*
Allen Chandler. CHT. (Chandler; Prince '23.)
Allen's Fragrant Pillar. CHT. (Allen '31.)
Allen's Golden Climber. LC. (Allen '33.)
Allen's Jubilee. Jubilee.
Alois Jirasek. HT. (Bohm '31.)
Aloysia Kaiser. LC. (P. Lamb. '37.)
Amalia Jung. HT. (M. Leen. '34.)
Amami. HT. (Eas. '27.)
Ambassador. HT. (Pre. R. G. '30.)
Amber. HT. (Jor.; Beckw. '30.)
Amelia Earhart. President Charles Hain.
Amelie de Mansfield. G.
Amelie Gravereaux. HRug. (Grav. '03.)
American Beauty. HP. (Lede. 1875; Bancr., Field 1886.) *Mme. Ferdinand Jamin.*
American Girl. HT. (Maton '29.)
American Pillar. R. (Van F. '02; C&J. '08.)
American Pride. HT. (Grillo '29.)
Ami F. Mayery. HT. (Deno.; C. Cham. '33.)
Ami L. Crette. HT. (C. Cham.; C-P. '31.)
Ami Quinard. HT. (Mal. '27; C-P. '30.)
Ampere. HT. (F. Meill. '37.)
Amulett. HT. (Tant. '30.)
Amy Johnson. HT. (Clark; NRS. Vic. '31.)
Amy Robsart. HSb. (Penz.; Keynes & Co. 1894.)
Anais Segalas. Cent. (Vib. 1837.)
Andree Perrier. HT. (C. Cham. '32.)
Andree Vanderschrick. R. (Buat. '35.)
Andulka. HT. (Brada; Bohm '35.)
Anemone. *R. anemonoides.* (J. C. Schmidt 1896.) *Pink Cherokee; Anemone Rose.*

ROSA, continued
Angele. HT. (Vestal '33.)
Angele Pernet. HT. (P-D. '24.)
Angelita Ruaix. HT. (Dot '40.)
Angels Mateu. HT. (Dot; C-P. '34.)
Angelus. HT. (Lem. '21.)
A Night in June. HT. (W. M. Elmer; Elmer's Nurs. '35.)
Anna de Diesbach. HP. (Lach. 1858.) *Gloire de Paris; Glory of Paris.*
Anna Hartmannova. HT. (Brada; Bohm '33.)
Anna Neagle. HT. (McGr. '37.)
Anna Ruebsamen. LC. (L. Weig. '04.)
Anna Soupert. HT. (G. Soup.; C. Soup. '34.)
Anne. HT. (Pemb. '25.)
Anne-Marie Milliat. HT. (Gauj. '39.)
Anne Mette Poulsen. HPol. (S. Pouls. '35.) *Anne Poulsen.*
Anne of Geierstein. HSb. (Penz.; Keynes & Co. 1894.)
Anne Poulsen. Anne Mette Poulsen.
Anne Vanderbilt. HT. (Brownl. '41.)
Annie Brandt. HT. (Mal.; C-P. '30.)
Annie Crawford. HP. (Hall '15.) *Miss Annie Crawford.*
Annie de Metz. HT. (Mal.; C-P. '32.)
Annie Drevet. HT. (Caron '38.)
Annie Dupeyrat. HT. (Mal.; C-P. '34.)
Annie Laurie. HT. (Stuppy '18.) *Double Mme. Butterfly.*
Annie Mueller. Aennchen Mueller.
Anni Jebens. HT. (Kordes '32.)
Anni Weber. M. (Welt. '06.)
Antinea. HT. (Gauj.; H&S. and Dreer '34.)
Antoine Rivoire. HT. (P-D. 1895.)
Antonia Pahissa. HT. (Pah. '35.)
A. N. W. B. Rose. HT. (Buis. '33.)
Apeles Mestres. CHP. (Dot '26.)
Aphrodite. HT. (Eas. '28.)
Apollo. HT. (J. A. Arm.; Arm. Nurs. '41.)
Apothecaries' Rose. **R. gallica.**
Apple Blossom. R. (Bur.; Stark '32.)
Appleton's Limelight. HT. (Appl. '34.)
Apricot Dawn. HT. (Wyant '38.)
Apricot Glow. LC. (Brownl.; Dreer, C-P., B&A. '36.)
Apricot Queen. HT. (H&S. '40.)
Arcadia. R. (M. H. Walsh '13.)
Arcadia. HT. (Gauj. '38.)
Arch. Reventos. HT. (M. Leen. '35.)
Ards Rover. CHP. (A. Dick. 1898.)
Arethusa. C. (W. Paul '03.)
Argosy. HT. (Clark; NRS. of N. S. W. '38.)
Aribau. HT. (Dot; H. Guil., C-P. '36.)
Ariel. HT. (Bees '21.)
Aristobule. M. (1849.)
Armenie. HT. (Buat. '36.)
Armosa. Hermosa.
Arndt. Evbl. Semi-Cl. (P. Lamb. '13.)
Arnold. HRug. (Daw.; East. Nurs. 1893.)
Aroma. HT. (B. R. Cant; J&P. '31.)
Arrillaga. HP. (Schoe.; B&A. '29.)
Arthur Cook. HT. (McGr. '24.)
Arthur Young. M. (Port. 1863.)
Aschenbroedel. Pol. (P. Lamb. '03.)
Asepala. M. (In U. S. before 1848.)

ROSA, continued
Asmodee. G. (Vib. 1849.)
Aspirant Marcel Rouyer. HT. (P-D. '19.)
Assemblage des Beautes. G. (1823.)
Atlantida. HT. (Pah. '39.)
Atropurpurea. HRug. (Lev. '10.)
Attar of Roses. HT. (B. R. Cant '36.)
Attraction. HT. (A. Dick. '31.)
Audrey Stell. HT. (Stell; Stell Nurs. '37.)
Auguste Gervaise. LC. (Barb. '18.)
Auguste Kordes. Mlt. (Kordes '28.) *Cl. Lafayette.*
Auguste Roussel. LC. (Barb. '13.)
Augustine Guinoisseau. HT. (Guin. 1889.) *White La France.*
August Noack. HT. (Kordes '28.)
Augustus Hartmann. HT. (B. R. Cant '14.)
Aureate. HT. (A. Dick. '32.)
Aurelia Capdevila. HT. (Dot '33.)
Aureola. HT. (Bohm '34.)
Aurora Boreal. HT. (B. Munne '35.)
Aurore. HT. (Cap. '36.)
Ausonius. Evbl. Semi-Cl. (P. Lamb. '32.)
Australia Felix. HT. (Clark '19.)
Autumn. HT. (Cod. '28.)
Autumn Delight. HMs. (Bent. '33.)
Autumn Queen. HT. (Vestal '33.) *Vice-President Curtis.*
Avalon. HT. (West. Rose Co.; Germ. '35.)
Avenant. G.
Aviateur Bleriot. R. (Fauq. '10.)
Avoca. HT. (A. Dick. '07.)
Babette. R. (M. H. Walsh '06.)
Baby Alan. Pol. (Kess.; Lov. '30.)
Baby Alberic. Pol. (Chap. '32.)
Baby Betty. Pol. (Burb. '29.)
Baby Chateau. HPol. (Kordes '36.)
Baby Doll. Tip-Top.
Baby Faurax. Pol. (Lil. '24.)
Baby Gloria. Pol. (Bohm '36.)
Baby Gold Star. H. Chinensis minima. (Dot; C-P. '40.)
Baby Herriot. Etoile Luisante.
Baby Rosamunde. Pol. (Kess.; Lov. '30.)
Baby Sunbeam. R. (Bur.; Stark '34.)
Baby Tausendschon. Echo.
Balduin. HT. (P. Lamb. 1896.) Int. U. S. as *Helen Gould* by D&C. '01; *Crimson Maman Cochet; Red Maman Cochet.*
Ballerina. HMs. (Bent. '37.)
Baltimore Belle. HSet. (Feast 1843.)
Banshee.
Barbara Richards. HT. (A. Dick. '30.)
Barbara Robinson. HT. (A. Dick. '25.)
Barbara Ward. HT. (F. B. Ward '31.)
Barbarossa. HT. (Welt. '06.)
Barcelona. HT. (Kordes '32.)
Bardou Job. CB. (Nab. 1887.)
Barillet. M. (V. Verd. 1850.)
Baron de Bonstetten. HP. (Liab. 1871.)
Baron de Wassenaer. M. (V. Verd. 1854.)
Baroness A. van Hovell tot Westerflier. HT. (M. Leen. '33.)
Baronesse S. H. W. van Dedem. HT. (M. Leen. '23.)

ROSA, continued

Baronesse van Ittersum. R. (M. Leen. '10.)
Baroness Krayenhoff. HT. (Buis. '31.)
Baroness Rothschild. HP. (Per. p. 1868.) *Baronne Adolphe de Rothschild.*
Baron Jacques Riston. HT. (Ket. '36.)
Baronne Adolphe de Rothschild. Baroness Rothschild.
Baronne de Stael. G.
Baronne Prevost. HP. (Desp. 1842.)
Beatrice McGregor. HT. (Clark; NRS. Vic. '38)
Beaucaire. Pol. (GRVL. '37.)
Beaujolais. HT. (Croib. '32.)
Beauty. HT. (F. B. Ward '31.)
Beauty of Glazenwood. Fortune's Double Yellow.
Beauty of New South Wales. Pol. (G. Knight '31.)
Beauty of the Prairies. Queen of the Prairies.
Bebe Blanc. Pol. (Tur. '22.)
Becky. HT. (Beckw. '25.)
Bedford Crimson. HT. (Lax. '26.)
Bedfordia. HT. (Lax. '31.)
Bedrich Smetana. HT. (Bohm '33.)
Belgica. HT. (Buyl '29.)
Belinda. HMs. (Bent. '36.)
Belle Adelaide. G. (Miel.)
Belle de Marly. G.
Belle des Jardins. G. (Guill. f. 1872.)
Belle de Yebles. G. (Desp.)
Belle Isis. G. (Parm.)
Belle Lyonnaise. CT. (F. Levet 1869.)
Belle of Portugal. Belle Portugaise.
Belle Poitevine. HRug. (Bruant 1894.)
Belle Portugaise. HG. (Cay.) *Belle of Portugal.*
Belle Rosine. G.
Belle Siebrecht. Mrs. W. J. Grant.
Belle Vichysoise. N. (Found at Vichy; Leveq. 1897.)
Belvedere. Pol. (Kiese '28.)
Ben Arthur Davis. HT. (J. A. Bost. '35.)
Benedikt Roezl. HRug. (V. Berg.; A. Faist '25.)
Bennett's Seedling. Arv. (Benn. 1840.) *Thoresbyana.*
Bentall's Scarlet. HT. (Bent. '35.)
Bentveld. HT. (C. J. Posthuma; Low '32.)
Berangere. M. (Vib. 1849.)
Bergers Erfolg. HRug. (V. Berg.; Pfitz. '25.)
Bernice. Pol. (Nic.; J&P. '37.)
Bertha Gorst. HT. (Beckw. '33.)
Bertram Park. HT. (Burb. '29.) *Coquette.*
Bessie Brown. HT. (A. Dick. 1899.)
Bessie Chaplin. HT. (Chap. '21.)
Bess Lovett. LC. (Van F.; Lov. '15.)
Betsy Ross. HT. (Samt. '31.)
Better Times. HT. (J. H. Hill '34.)
Betty. HT. (A. Dick. '05.)
Betty Bland. H. Blanda. (Skin. '26.)
Betty Grace Clark. HT. (Clark's Rose Nurs. '33.)
Betty Prior. HPol. (Prior '35; J&P. '38.)
Betty Sutor. HT. (McGr. '29.)

ROSA, continued

Betty Uprichard. HT. (A. Dick. '22.)
Beverley Nichols. HT. (Burb. '38.)
Bijou. Pol. (de R.; Sliedr. '32.)
Billard et Barre. CT. (P-D. 1898.)
Billy Boiler. CHT. (Clark; NRS. Vic. '27.)
Billy Boy. HT. (Beckw. '26.)
Birdie Blye. C. (Van F.; C&J. '04.)
Bischof Dr. Korum. HP. (P. Lamb. '21.)
Bishop Darlington. Evbl. Semi-Cl. (Thom. '26; Dreer, H&S. '28.)
Black Bess. Mlt. (Kordes; Morse '39.)
Black Boy. CHT. (Clark; NRS. of S. Aus. '19.)
Black Knight. HT. (Hillk. '34.)
Black Prince. HP. (W. Paul 1866.)
Blanc Double de Coubert. HRug. (C-C. 1892.)
Blanche. M.
Blanche Messigny. HT. (Gill. '23.)
Blanche Moreau. M. (M.-R. 1880.) *White Moss.*
Blarney. CHT. (How. Rose Co. '34.)
Blaze. LC. (Kal.; J&P. '32.)
Blaze Superior. Demokracie.
Bloomfield Abundance. HT. (Thom.; B&A. '20.)
Bloomfield Brilliant. HG. (Thom.; H&S. '31.)
Bloomfield Comet. Evbl. Semi-Cl. (Thom. '24; B&A. '29.)
Bloomfield Courage. R. (Thom. '25; B&A., H&S.)
Bloomfield Culmination. Evbl. Semi-Cl. (Thom. '24; B&A.)
Bloomfield Dainty. Evbl. Semi-Cl. (Thom. '24; B&A.)
Bloomfield Dawn. Evbl. Semi-Cl. (Thom.; Arm. Nurs. '31.)
Bloomfield Decoration. Evbl. Semi-Cl. (Thom. '25; B&A., H&S. '27.)
Bloomfield Discovery. Evbl. Semi-Cl. (Thom.; B&A. '25.)
Bloomfield Endurance. W. Freeland Kendrick.
Bloomfield Fascination. Evbl. Semi-Cl. (Thom. '24; B&A.)
Bloomfield Flame. HT. (Thom.; H&S. '30.)
Bloomfield Improvement. Ednah Thomas.
Bloomfield Loveliness. Sophie Thomas.
Bloomfield Lustre. LC. (Thom.; H&S. '31.)
Bloomfield Mystery. Evbl. Semi-Cl. (Thom. '24; B&A.)
Bloomfield Novelty. Changed to Margaret Anderson.
Bloomfield Progress. HT. (Thom.; B&A. '20.)
Bloomfield Quakeress. CT. (Thom.; Arm. Nurs. '31.)
Bloomfield Rocket. Evbl. Semi-Cl. (Thom. '25; B&A.)
Blue Rambler. Veilchenblau.
Blumenschmidt. T. (J. C. Schmidt '06.)
Blumenschmidt's Fairy Queen. HT. (C. Weig.; J. C. Schmidt '39.)
Blush Damask. D.
Blushing Beauty. LC. (Bur.; Stark '34.)
Blushing Lucy. LC. (A. H. Will. '38.)
Blush Rambler. R. (B. R. Cant '03.)

ROSA, continued

Bocca Negra. R. (Dub. '10.)
Boehmorose. HT. (Bohm '35.)
Bohm Junior. HT. (Bohm '35.)
Bohmova Popelka. Pol. (Bohm '34.)
Bohm's Triumph. HT. (Bohm '34.)
Bolero. HT. (Gauj. '37.)
Bonfire. R. (Tur. '28.)
Bonnie Jean. HT. (Arch. '33.)
Bon Silene. T. (Hardy 1835.)
Bossuet. G.
Boule de Nanteuil. G.
Bouquet Charmant. G.
Bouquet d'Or. N. (Duch. 1872.)
Bouquet d'Or. HT. (Lip. '22.)
Boutonniere. HT. (Lamm.; Arm. Nurs. '40.)
Bozena Nemcova. HT. (Bohm '31.)
Braiswick Charm. R. (F. Cant '14.)
Brazier. HT. (Mal. '36; C-P. '38.)
Break o'Day. Pol. (Arch. '37.)
Break o'Day. HT. (Brownl. '39.) Formerly *Delta.*
Breeze Hill. LC. (Van F.; ARS. '26.)
Brenda. HSb. (Penz.; Keynes & Co. 1894.)
Briand-Paneurope. HT. (Bohm '31.)
Briarcliff. HT. (Brclf. '26.)
Bridesmaid. T. (Moore 1893.)
Brilliancy. HT. (Le G. '36.)
Brilliant Echo. Pol. (West. Rose Co. '27.)
Brilliant Red. HT. (Lens '38.)
Britannia. Pol. (Burb. '29.)
British Queen. HT. (McGr. '12.)
Brno. HT. (Bohm '33.)
Brownell Yellow Rambler. R (Brownl. '42.)
B. S. Bhatcharji. HT. (A. Dick. '33.)
Buff King. HSet. (Hor.; Ways. '39.)
Buisson d'Or. HFt. (Barb. '28.)
Burgemeester Berger. HT. (Leen. Bros. '34.)
Burgundy. HT. (H&S. '39.)
Bushfire. R. (Clark '17.)
Buttercup. HT. (Dobbie '30.)
Butterflies of Gold. HT.-Pol. (Brownl. '39.)
Buttermere. R. (Chap. '32.)
Caledonia. HT. (Dobbie '28.)
California. HT. (H&S. '37.)
California Beauty. HT. (Proi. '35.)
California Gold. Pol. (J. Smith '34.)
Cameo. Pol. (de R.; J&P. '32.)
Campina. HT. (Lens '37.)
Canarienvogel. Pol. (N. Welt. '03.) *Sunset Glow.*
Canary. HT. (A. Dick. '29.)
Canberra. HT. (Harrison '28.)
Canberra. Pol. (G. Knight '35.)
Candeur Lyonnaise. HP. (Croib. '14.)
Candlelight. HT. (Hor.; Bos. '32.)
Cantab. HNut. (Hurst '27.)
Capitaine Basroger. M. (M.-R. 1890.)
Capitaine John Ingram. M. (Laf. 1854.)
Caprice. HT. (M. Leen. '34.)
Captain Bligh. HT. (Fitz.; Haz. '39.)
Captain Blood. HT. (Melv.; R. Murr. '38.)
Captain Christy. HT. (Lach. 1873.)
Captain Glisson. HT. (J. H. Hill '35.)
Captain Hayward. HP. (Benn. 1893.)
Captain Kidd. HSet. (Hor. '34.)

ROSA, continued
Captain Kilbee Stuart. HT. (A. Dick. '22.)
Captain Sassoon. HT. (Gauj. '38.)
Captain Thomas. CHT. (Thom.; Arm. Nurs. '38.)
Captain Williams. G.
Capt. F. S. Harvey-Cant. HT. (F. Cant '23.)
Cardinal de Richelieu. G. (Laf. 1840.)
Cardinal Mercier. HT. (Lens '30.)
Caress. HT. (A. Dick. '35.)
Carillon. HT. (Nic.; J&P. '35.)
Carito MacMahon. HT. (Dot '34.)
Carl Kempkes. HPol. (Kordes; Spath '37.)
Carmelita. HT. (Span. '33.)
Carmen. HRug. (P. Lamb. '07.)
Carmen Sistachs. Pol. (Dot '36.)
Carmine Pillar. Paul's Carmine Pillar.
Carne. M. (Rob.)
Carnival. HT. (Arch. '39.)
Carol Howard. HT. (Pfitz.; P. J. How. '35.)
Carpet of Gold. LC. (Brownl. '39.)
Carrie Jacobs Bond. HT. (H&S.; Dreer '35.)
Cascadia. Evbl. Semi-Cl. (Thom. 25; B&A. '27.)
Catalina. HT. (Grillo '40.)
Catalonia. HT. (Dot; C-P. '33.)
Catharina Klein. HT. (V. Berg.; M&H. '30.)
Cathcart Bedder. HT. (A&McA. '38.)
Catherine de Wurtemberg. M. (Rob. 1843.)
Catherine Mermet. T. (Guill. f. 1869.)
Catherine Seyton. HSb. (Penz.; Keynes & Co. 1894.)
Cathrine Kordes. HT. (Kordes; Dreer, H&S. '30.)
Cavalier. HT. (Samt. '39.)
Cayetana Stuart. HT. (Dot; C-P. '31.)
C. Chambard. HT. (Pierre Bel '34.)
Cecil. HT. (B. R. Cant '26.)
Cecile Brunner. HPol. (Duch.; P-D. 1881.) *Mignon; Mlle. Cecile Brunner; Sweetheart Rose.*
Cecile Mann. HT. (Clark; Brundr. '39.)
Cecile Walter. HT. (Mal.; C-P. '26.)
Celestial. H. Alba.
Celina. M. (Hardy 1855.)
Celine Forestier. N. (Trouil. 1842.)
Cerise d'Orlin. G.
Cerise Talisman. HT. (Clark's Rose Nurs. '33.)
Ceska Pohadka. Pol. (Bohm '33.)
Cesonie. D.
Challenger. HT. (B. R. Cant '38.)
Chamisso. Evbl. Semi-Cl. (P. Lamb. '22.)
Champion of the World. HP. (Woodhouse 1894.) *Mrs. De Graw.*
Chanoine Tuaillon. HT. (Gill. '31.)
Chapeau de Napoleon. Crested Moss.
Chapelain d'Arenberg. G.
Chaplin's Crimson Glow. LC. (Chap. '30.)
Chaplin's Pink Climber. LC. (Chap. '28.)
Chaplin's Triumph. HT. (Chap. '36.)
Charles Dingee. William R. Smith.

ROSA, continued
Charles Gater. HP. (Paul 1893.)
Charles Gregory. HT. (Greg. '29.)
Charles H. Rigg. HT. (Chap. '31.)
Charles K. Douglas. HT. (H. Dick. '19.)
Charles Lawson. CB. (Lawson 1853.)
Charles Lefebvre. HP. (Lach. 1861.)
Charles P. Kilham. HT. (Beckw. '26.)
Charlotte Armstrong. HT. (Lamm.; Arm. Nurs. '40.)
Charlotte E. Dedem. HT. (Buis. '37.)
Charlotte von Rathlef. LC. (M. Vogel; Heinemann '36.)
Charmaine. Pol. (Burb. '29.)
Charme. HT. (Unknown; Rice '30.) *Charm; Germania.*
Charmer. HT. (A.Dick. '34.)
Charming Princess. HT. (T. Hancock '26.)
Chastity. CHT. (F. Cant '24.)
Chateau de Clos Vougeot. HT. P-D. '08.)
Chateau de Vaire. Shrub. (Sauv. '34.)
Chatillon Rose. Pol. (Nonin '23.)
Cheerful. HT. (McGr. '15.)
Cheerie. Cherie.
Cheeric. Pol. (Morse '31.) Cherie.
Cheerio. HPol. (Arch. '37.)
Cheerio. HPol. (Kordes; Dreer '40.)
Cherie. Pol. (Morse '31.) Originally *Cheerio*, then *Cheerie.*
Cherry. HT. (McGr. '28.)
Cherub. R. (Clark; Brundr. '23.)
Chevreul. M. (M-R. 1887.)
Chevy Chase. R. (N. J. Han.; B&A. '39.)
Chieftain. HT. (Mont. Co. '36.)
Chiffon. HT. (Grillo '40.)
Chin Chin. Promise.
Chiquita. Mlt. (Moore '37.) *Little Girl.*
C. H. Middleton. HT. (B. R. Cant'39.)
Chot Pestitele. HP. (Bohm '32.)
Christian Curle. R. (Cock. '10.)
Christine. HT. (McGr. '18.)
Christine Wright. LC. (H. Br. & T. Co. '09.)
Christine Wunderlich. HT. (Wunderlich '34.)
Christobel. HT. (Croib. '37.)
Christopher Stone. HT. (H.Robin.; Wheat. '35; C-P. '36.)
Christoph Weigand. HT. (C. Weig. '28.)
Chromatella. N. (Coquereau 1843.) *Cloth of Gold.*
Cicely Lascelles. CHT. (Clark; NRS. Vic. '37.)
Cicely O'Rorke. CHT. (Clark; NRS. Vic. '37.)
Cidade de Lisboa. HG. (Da Silva '39.)
Cimarron. HT. (Hillk. '38.)
Cinderella. R. (M. H. Walsh '09.)
Cineraria. Pol. (M. Leen. '34.)
Citron. HT. (Gauj. '39.)
City of Little Rock. HT. (E. G. Hill; Vestal '24.)
City of Pilsen. Plzen.
Claire Desmet. HT. (Buat. '32.)
Clara d'Arcis. HT. (Gauj.; C-P. '32.)
Clarice Goodacre. HT. (A. Dick. '16.)

ROSA, continued
Clarissa Dana. HT. (Nic.; J&P. '33.)
Claude Petit. HT. (Buat. '36.)
Claudy Chapel. HT. (Dr. Beaumez; Delhaye '30.)
Clemence Robert. M. (R. et M. 1863.)
Climbing American Beauty. LC. (H. Br. & T. Co. '09.)
Cl. Angelus. CHT. (Dixie '33.)
Cl. Aphrodite. CHT. (Hillk. '33.)
Cl. Arthur R. Goodwin. CHT.
Cl. Aspirant Marcel Rouyer. CHT. (E. Claudius Brenier '34.)
Cl. August Noack. CHT. (Lens '35.)
Cl. Belle Siebrecht. Cl. Mrs. W. J. Grant.
Cl. Bernaix. CHT. (Sham. '35.)
Cl. Better Times. CHT. (J. Parm. '37.)
Cl. Betty Uprichard. CHT. (Krause '36.)
Cl. Briarcliff. CHT. (J. Parm. '29.)
Cl. Bride. Ruth Vestal.
Cl. Caledonia. CHT. (Pierre Bel '36.)
Cl. Captain Hayward. CHP. (Paul '06.)
Cl. Captain Ronald Clerk. CHT. (A&McA. '35.)
Cl. Cathrine Kordes. CHT. (Krohn; Kordes '38.)
Cl. Cecile Brunner. Mlt. (Hosp 1894; Ardagh '04.)
Cl. Charles K. Douglas. CHT. (Leen. Bros. '34.)
Cl. Charles P. Kilham. CHT. (How. Rose Co. '31; Morse '34.)
Cl. Chateau de Clos Vougeot. CHT. (Morse '20.)
Cl. Cherry. CHT. (Sav. '34.)
Cl. Clothilde Soupert. Mlt. (P. J. Berckmans Co. 1896.)
Cl. Columbia. CHT. (Vestal '23; Lens '29.)
Cl. Comte F. de Chavanac. CHT. (Ch. Siret-Pernet '29.)
Cl. Comtesse Vandal. CHT. (J&P. '36.)
Cl. Condesa de Sastago. CHT. (Vestal '36.)
Cl. Cramoisi Superieur. CC. (Coquereau 1832.)
Cl. C. V. Haworth. CHT. (F. Cant '32.)
Cl. "Daily Mail" Scented Rose. CHT. (Arch. '30.)
Cl. Dainty Bess. CHT. (Van B.; Cal. Roses '35.)
Cl. Dame Edith Helen. CHT. (H&S. '30.)
Cl. David O. Dodd. CHT. (How. Rose Co.)
Cl. Devoniensis. CT. (S. J. Pavitt; Henry Curtis 1858.) *Magnolia Rose.*
Cl. Distinction. R. (Lens '35.)
Cl. Dorothy. CHT. (Bost. '35.)
Cl. Duchess of Atholl. CHT. (How. Rose Co. '33.)
Cl. Eclipse. CHT. (West. Rose Co. '39.)
Cl. Else Poulsen. Mlt. (Ley '32.)
Cl. Elvira Aramayo. CHT. (Ing. '33.)
Cl. Emma Wright. CHT. (Stanw. R. G. '32.)
Cl. Etoile de Feu. CHT. (H&S. '30.)
Cl. Etoile de France. CHT. (How. Rose Co. '15.)

ROSA, continued

Cl. Etoile de Hollande. CHT. (M. Leen. '31.)
Cl. Federico Casas. CHT. (Stell; Stell Nurs. '37.)
Cl. Feuerschein. Mlt. (Krause '36.)
Cl. Feu Joseph Looymans. CHT. (West. Rose Co. '35.)
Cl. Fontanelle. CHT. (Johns '35.)
Cl. Frances Gaunt. CHT. (Caz. '34.)
Cl. Francis Scott Key. CHT.
Cl. Frank W. Dunlop. CHT. (Dixie '33.)
Cl. Frau Karl Druschki. CHP. (Law. '06.)
Cl. General MacArthur. CHT. (H. Dick. '23.)
Cl. General-Superior Arnold Janssen. CHT. (Bohm '31.)
Cl. Gloria Mundi. R. (Lens '34.)
Cl. Golden Dawn. CHT. (J. A. Arm. '35; G. Knight '37.)
Cl. Golden Emblem. CHT. (Arm. Nurs. '27.)
Cl. Golden Ophelia. CHT. (Hage; Prior '24.)
Cl. Golden Talisman. CHT. (W. M. Elmer; Elmer's Nurs. '35.)
Cl. Grenoble. CHT. (West. Rose Co. '39.)
Cl. Gruss an Aachen. Mlt. (Kordes '37.)
Cl. Gruss an Teplitz. CHT. (S&H. '11.) *Cl. Virginia R. Coxe.*
Cl. Gwynne Carr. CHT. (Eas. '34.)
Cl. Hadley. CHT. (Tesch. '27.)
Cl. Heinrich Wendland. CHT. (Stell; Stell Nurs. '37.)
Cl. Helen Gould. CT. (G&R. '12.)
Cl. Hinrich Gaede. CHT. (J. A. Arm. '35.)
Cl. Hoosier Beauty. CHT. (W. R. Gray '25.)
Cl. Independence Day. CHT. (W.&J. Brown; E. Murr. '30.)
Cl. Innocence. CHT. (J. A. Arm.; Arm. Nurs. '38.)
Cl. Ireland Hampton. CHT. (Hillk. '36.)
Cl. Irish Fireflame. CHT. (A. Dick. '16.)
Cl. Joanna Hill. CHT. (How. Rose Co. '35.)
Cl. John Russell. CHT. (Ket. '30.)
Cl. Jonkheer J. L. Mock. CHT. (Timmer. '23.)
Cl. Joseph Guy. Mlt. (Nonin '29.)
Cl. Julien Potin. CHT. (Bost. '35.)
Cl. Kaiserin Auguste Viktoria. CHT. (A. Dick. 1897.)
Cl. Killarney. CHT. (Reinb. '08.)
Cl. Killarney Double White. CHT. (How. Rose Co. '35.)
Cl. Lady Ashtown. CHT. (Bradley '09.)
Cl. Lady Forteviot. CHT. (How. Rose Co. '35.)
Cl. Lady Hillingdon. CT. (Hicks '17.)
Cl. Lady Sylvia. CHT. (W. Stev.; Low '33.)
Cl. Lafayette. Auguste Kordes.
Cl. La France. CHT. (P. Hend. 1893.)
Cl. Liberty. CHT. (May '08.)
Cl. Little Dorrit. Mlt. (Letts '35.)
Cl. Lord Charlemont. CHT. (Hurcombe '32.)

ROSA, continued

Cl. Lorraine Lee. (McKay '32.)
Cl. Los Angeles. CHT. (H&S. '35.)
Cl. Louise Catherine Breslau. CHT. (Kordes '17.)
Cl. Luxembourg. CHT. (Wight '32.)
Cl. Lyon Rose. CHT. (Ket. '24.)
Cl. Mabel Morse. CHT. (Mould. '31; Ley '32.)
Cl. Maman Cochet. CT. (Upton '09; H&S. '15.)
Cl. Margaret McGredy. CHT. (Dixie '36.)
Cl. Marie Guillot. CT. (D&C. 1898.)
Cl. Marie van Houtte. CT. (Thomsv. '36.)
Cl. Marquise de Sinety. CHT. (J. C. Griffon '12.)
Cl. Mary Hart. CHT. (West. Rose Co. '37.)
Cl. Matador. CHT. (West. Rose Co. '38.)
Cl. McGredy's Yellow. CHT. (West. Rose Co. '37.)
Cl. Meteor. CHT. (D&C. '01.)
Cl. Mevr. G. A. van Rossem. CHT. (Gauj. '37.)
Cl. Miss Rowena Thom. CHT. (Van B.; Cal. Roses '37.)
Cl. Mme. Abel Chatenay. CHT. (Page; Eas. '17.)
Cl. Mme. Butterfly. CHT. (E. P. Smith '26.)
Cl. Mme. Caroline Testout. CHT. (Chau. '01.)
Cl. Mme. Edouard Herriot. CHT. (Ket. '21.)
Cl. Mme. Jules Bouche. CHT. (Cal. Roses '38.)
Cl. Mme. Louis Lens. CHT. (Lens '35.)
Cl. Mrs. Aaron Ward. CHT. (A. Dick. '22.)
Cl. Mrs. A. R. Barraclough. CHT. (Fryer '35.)
Cl. Mrs. Charles Bell. CHT. (Thomsv. '29.)
Cl. Mrs. Dunlop Best. CHT. (Rosen '33.)
Cl. Mrs. Erskine Pembroke Thom. CHT. (Dixie '33.)
Cl. Mrs. Henry Bowles. CHT. (Dobbie '29.)
Cl. Mrs. Henry Morse. CHT. (Chap. '29.)
Cl. Mrs. Henry Winnett. CHT. (P. Bern. '30.)
Cl. Mrs. Herbert Stevens. CT. (P-D. '22.)
Cl. Mrs. Lovell Swisher. CHT. (H&S. '30.)
Cl. Mrs. Philip Russell. CHT. (Clark '27.)
Cl. Mrs. Pierre S. du Pont. CHT. (Hillk. '33.)
Cl. Mrs. Sam McGredy. CHT. (Guil. '38; West. Rose Co. '40.) *Genevieve Genest.*
Cl. Mrs. Samuel McGredy. CHT. (Buis. '37.)
Cl. Mrs. W. C. Egan. CHT. (How. Rose Co. '33.)
Cl. Mrs. W. J. Grant. CHT. (E. G. Hill 1899; W. Paul 1899.) *Cl. Belle Siebrecht.*
Cl. Mrs. W. T. Sumner. CHT. (Haz. '32.)

ROSA, continued

Cl. Nicole. CHT. (Kordes '33.)
Cl. Night. CHT. (J. A. Arm.; Arm. Nurs. '36.)
Cl. Niphetos. CT. (Keynes & Co. 1889.)
Cl. Olympiad. CHT. (Raf.; Pt. Stktn. Nurs. '38.)
Cl. Ophelia. CHT. (A. Dick. '20.)
Cl. Ophelia Queen. CHT. (Westb. '23.)
Cl. Orleans Rose. Mlt. (Lev. '13.)
Cl. Papa Gontier. CT. (Chevrier '03.)
Cl. Patience. CHT. (Sham. '35.)
Cl. Paul Crampel. Mlt. (Appl. '34; Via. '34; Tant. '37.)
Cl. Paul Lede. CHT. (Low '13.)
Cl. Penelope. CT. (Rosen '32.)
Cl. Perle des Jardins. CT. (J. Henderson 1889.)
Cl. Pink Dawn. CHT.
Cl. Pink Pearl. CHT. (Dixie '33.)
Cl. Premier. CHT. (Vestal '27.)
Cl. President Herbert Hoover. CHT. (B. R. Cant '37.)
Cl. President Hoover. CHT. (Dixie '31.)
Cl. Radiance. CHT. (W. D. Griffg. '26; Catt '28.)
Cl. Rapture. CHT. (Dixie '33.)
Cl. Red Moss. CM. (Sport in garden of Mrs. Foote; B&A.)
Cl. Red Radiance. CHT. (Pac. Rose Co. '27; Catt '29.)
Cl. Rev. F. Page-Roberts. CHT. (A. Beverley; W. B. Clarke '31.)
Cl. Richmond. CHT. (A. Dick. '12.)
Cl. Robinow. CHT. (P. Lamb.; C-P. '34.)
Cl. Rodhatte. Mlt. (F. J. Groot. '25.)
Cl. Roselandia. CHT. (Lens '33.)
Cl. Rose Marie. CHT. (Pac. Rose Co. '27.)
Cl. Roslyn. CHT. (Vestal '37.)
Cl. Shot Silk. CHT. (G. Knight '31.)
Cl. Signora. CHT. (West. Rose Co. '37.)
Cl. Souv. de Claudius Pernet. CHT. (West. Rose Co. '25; J. C. Schmidt '32; Gauj. '33.)
Cl. Souv. de Georges Pernet. CHT. (P-D. '27.)
Cl. Souv. de H. A. Verschuren. CHT. (H&S. '27.)
Cl. Souv. de la Malmaison. CB. (Benn. 1893.)
Cl. Souv. de Mme. Boullet. CHT. (H&S. '30.)
Cl. Souv. de Mme. C. Chambard. CHT. (J. A. Arm. '35.)
Cl. Souv. of Wootton. CHT. (Butler 1899.)
Cl. S. S. Pennock. CHT. (Lens; J&P. '32.)
Cl. Sunburst. CHT. (How. Rose Co. '14; Low '15.)
Cl. Sunstar. CHT. (A. Dick. '25.)
Cl. Superba. Mlt. (P. Guill. '33.)
Cl. Talisman. CHT. (West. Rose Co. '30; Dixie '32.)
Cl. Texas Centennial. CHT. (Dixie '36.)
Cl. The Queen Alexandra Rose. CHT. (Lind.; Kordes '29; Hark. '31.)
Cl. Victoria Harrington. CHT. (Mord. '38.)

ROSA, continued
Cl. Ville de Paris. CHT. (J. A. Arm. '35.)
Cl. Virginia R. Coxe. Cl. Gruss an Teplitz.
Cl. W. E. Chaplin. CHT. (Heiz. '36.)
Cl. White Columbia. CHT. (Clark's Rose Nurs. '34.)
Cl. White Maman Cochet. CT. (G. Knight '07; Needle & Co. '11.)
Cl. Wilhelm Kordes. CHT. (W&I. '27.)
Cl. Yellow Cecile Brunner.
Clio. HP. (W. Paul 1894.)
Cloth of Gold. Chromatella.
Clotilde Soupert. Pol. (S&N. 1890.)
Clovelly. HT. (Hicks '24.)
Clytemnestra. HMs. (Pemb. '15.)
Cocarde Jaune. HT. (Ket. '33.)
Cochineal Glory. HT. (M. Leen. '37.)
Colcestria. CHT. (B. R. Cant '16.)
Cole's Pink Lafayette. Pol. (Cole '30.)
Colette. N. (A. Schw. '32.)
Colette Berges. HT. (Dot '40.)
Colette Clement. HT. (Mal. '29; C-P. '31.)
Colonel Campbell Watson. HT. (Bees '36.)
Colonel Nicolas Meyer. HT. (Sauv. '34.)
Colonel Oswald Fitzgerald. HT. (A. Dick. '17.)
Colonel Robert Lefort. M. (E. Verd. 1864.)
Colonel Sharman Crawford. HT. (A. Dick. '33.)
Colonel Svec. Plukovnik Svec.
Col. R. S. Williamson. HT. (A. Dick. '07.)
Columbia. HT. (E. G. Hill '16.)
Comet. LC. (Mes.; Bos. '34.)
Commandant Felix Faure. HP. (Bout. '01.)
Commandeur Jules Gravereaux. HP. (Croib. '08.)
Common Monthly. Old Blush.
Commonwealth. HP. (Mont. Co.; A. N. Pier. '23.)
Communis. M. (Holland about 1596.) *Old Pink Moss; Common Moss.*
Comte de Nanteuil. G.
Comtesse Anne de Bruce. HT. (Mal.; H. Guill. '37.)
Comtesse de Castilleja. HT. (M. Cham. '26.)
Comtesse de Martel. HT. (F. Meill. '39.)
Comtesse de Murinais. M. (Rob. 1843.) *White Moss.*
Comtesse Doria. M. (Port. 1854.)
Comtesse d'Oxford. HP. (Guill. p. 1869.)
Comtesse du Cayla. C. (P. Guill. '02.)
Comtesse Vandal. HT. (M. Leen.; J&P. '32.) *Countess Vandal.*
Conchita. Pol. (J. Jordan; Low '35.)
Condesa de Munter. HT. (B. Munne '32.)
Condesa de Sastago. HT. (Dot; C-P. '33.)
Conqueror. HT. (Chap. '29.)
Conrad Ferdinand Meyer. HRug. (F. Mul. 1899.)
Consolata. HT. (Cap. '36.)
Conspicuous. HT. (A. Dick. '30; B&A. '32.)

ROSA, continued
Constance. HT. (P-D. '15.)
Contrast. HT. (H&S. '37.)
Copper Climber. LC. (Bur.; Stark '38.)
Copper Glow. LC. (Brownl. '40.)
Coquette. HT. (Dobbie '29.)
Coquette. Bertram Park.
Coquette des Blanches. N. (Lach. 1871.)
Coquina. R. (M. H. Walsh '09.)
Corail. LC. (A. Schw. '31.)
Coral. HT. (A. Dick. '31.)
Coral Cluster. Pol. (R. Murr. '20.)
Coral Creeper. LC. (Brownl. '38.)
Coral Cup. Pol. (B&A. '36.)
Corali. CHT. (Dot '31.)
Coralie. LC. (W. Paul '19.)
Coralline. Pol. (J. Smith; Eddie '38.)
Coral Queen. HT. (Reeves '28.)
Cornelia. HMs. (Pemb. '25.)
Cornelie Koch. T. (Koch 1855.) *Cornelia Cook.*
Cornelis Timmermans. HT. (Timmer. '19.)
Coronation. HP. (H. Dick. '13.)
Corrie Koster. Pol. (Kos.; Royer '23.)
Cotorrita Real. Pol. (Padr. '31.)
Couleur de Brennus. G.
Countess Clanwilliam. HT. (H. Dick. '15.)
Countess Mary. CHT. (Dixie '33.)
Countess of Gosford. HT. (McGr. '06.)
Countess of Stradbroke. CHT. (Clark; Haz. '28.)
Countess Vandal. Comtesse Vandal.
Coupe d'Hebe. HBour. (Laf. 1840.)
Coupe d'Or. LC. (Barb. '30.)
Courage. HT. (McGr. '23.)
Covent Garden. HT. (B. R. Cant '19.)
Craigweil. HT. (Hicks '29.)
Cramoisi des Alpes. G. (Introducer unknown, 1838 or earlier.)
Cramoisie Fonce Veloute. M.
Cramoisi Superieur. C. (Coquereau 1832.) *Agrippina.*
Cream Cracker. HT. (A. Dick. '33.)
Creeping Everbloom. LC. (Brownl. '39.)
Creina Murland. HT. (A. Dick. '34.)
Crepuscule. N. (Dub. '04.)
Crested Moss. M. (Discovered on the wall of a convent near Fribourg and sent out by Vib. in 1827.) *Chapeau de Napoleon.*
Crimson Beauty. HT. (D&C. '30.)
Crimson Beauty. HT. (Le G. '35.)
Crimson Chatenay. HT. (Merry. '15.)
Crimson Conquest. LC. (Chap. '31.)
Crimson Emblem. HT. (McGr. '16.)
Crimson Globe. M. (W. Paul 1890.)
Crimson Glory. HT. (Kordes; Dreer '35.)
Crimson Maman Cochet. Balduin.
Crimson Moss. M. (Clergyman of Tinwell, Rutlandshire, England; int. Lee 18—.)
Crimson Orleans. Pol. (Kos. '22.)
Crimson Queen. HT. (A. Mont. '12.)
Crimson Rambler. Mlt. (Imported from Japan as *The Engineers Rose*, the Chinese name being *Shi Tz-mei* or *Ten Sisters*, and the Japanese

ROSA, continued
name *Soukara-Ibara;* int. Turn., 1893, as *Turner's Crimson Rambler;* E. & B. 1895.)
Cristal. HT. (Gauj. '37.)
Crown of Gold. HT. (H&S. '37.)
Crown of Jewels. Little Beauty.
Crusader. HT. (Mont. Co.; A. N. Pier. '20.)
Cuba. HT. (P-D. '26.)
Cumberland Belle. CM. (Dreer '00.)
Cupid. CHT. (B. R. Cant '15.)
C. V. Haworth. HT. (A. Dick. '17.)
Cynthia. HT. (V.-P.; Dreer, H&S. '34.)
Cynthia E. Hollis. R. (Daw.; East. Nurs.)
Dagmar Spath. HPol. (W&E.; Spath '36.)
D'Aguesseau. G. (Vib.)
"Daily Mail" Rose. Mme. Edouard Herriot.
"Daily Mail" Scented Rose. HT. (Arch. '27.)
Dainty. Pol. (de R. '31.)
Dainty Bess. HT. (Arch. '25.)
Dainty Dawn. Pol. (G. Knight '31.)
Dainty Maid. HPol. (Le G. '37.)
Daisy Bud. HT. (A. Dick. '33.)
Daisy Hill. H.Macrantha. (Kordes)
Dakar. HT. (Gauj. '32.)
Damas Franklin. D. (Rob. 1853 or 1856.)
Dame Catherine. HT. (B. R. Cant '37.)
Dame Edith Helen. HT. (A. Dick. '26.)
D. Ana Guedes. HT. (da Silva '38.)
Dance of Joy. (Sauv. '31.)
D. Angelica Pereira da Rosa. HT. (da Silva '36.)
Daphne. HMs. (Pemb. '12.)
Daphne. HT. (Dobbie '25.)
Dardanelle. HT. (Vestal '26.)
Darius. G.
Dark Secret. HT. (A. F. Aml. Co. '37.)
Das Goldene Prag. Zlata Praha.
D'Assas. D. or HP. (Vib. 1850.)
David McKee. HT. (A. Dick. '33.)
David O. Dodd. HT. (Vestal '26.)
Daybreak. Evbl. Semi-Cl. (Pemb. '18.)
Daybreak. HT. (Lax. '35.)
Daydream. CHT. (Clark; Haz. '25.)
Daylight. HT. (N. J. Han.; B&A. '39.)
Dazla. HT. (B. R. Cant '30.)
Debutante. R. (M. H. Walsh '02.)
Decandolle. M. (Port. 1847 or 1857.)
Decorator. HT. (A. Dick. '36.)
Delicata. HRug. (Cool. 1898.)
Delie Communaudat. HT. (Buat. '33.)
Delight. R. (M. H. Walsh '04.)
Delightful. HT. (McGr. '31.)
Delille. M. (Rob. 1852.)
Delta. Break o'Day.
De Luxe. HT. (White Br.; Lig. '31.)
De Meaux. Cent. (Swelt 1814.)
De Meaux White. Cent.
Demokracie. R. (Bohm '35.) *Blaze Superior.*
Denise Lefeuvre. HT. (C. Cham. '30.)
Denis Helye. HP.
Dereham Pride. Pol. (Norf. '32.)
Deschamps. N. (Deschamps 1877.)

ROSA, continued
Desiree Parmentier. G.
Desmond Johnston. HT. (McGr. '27.)
Destiny. HT. (Beckw. '35.)
Devoniensis. CT. (Foster; Lucombe, Prince & Co. 1841.) *Magnolia Rose.*
Diadem. HT. (McGr. '22.)
Diana. HT. (Bees '21.)
Diana Allen. HT. (Clark; NRS. of N. S. W. '39.)
Diane de Broglie. HT. (C. Cham. '29.)
Dick Koster. Pol. (D. A. Koster '35.)
Dicksons Bouquet. HT. (A. Dick. '38.)
Dicksons Centennial. HT. (A. Dick. '36; Dreer '37.)
Dicksons Delight. HT. (A. Dick. '38.)
Dicksons Perfection. HT. (A. Dick. '37.)
Dicksons Red. HT. (A. Dick. '38; J&P. '39.) American name for *Dr. F. G. Chandler.*
Diener's Rose Understock. (Dien. '32.)
Dignity. HT. (Le G. '40.)
Directeur Guerin. HT. (Gauj. '35.)
Director Plumecock. President Plumecocq.
Director Rubio. HT. (Dot '28.)
Distinction. Pol. (Tur. '27.)
Dividend. HT. (Clark; NRS. Vic. '31.)
Dixie. HT. (W. R. Gray '25.)
Dixie Climber. LC. (Watk.; Dixie, J&P. '35.)
D. Laura Pinto de Azevedo. HT. (da Silva '36.)
D. Maria Antonia Pacheco. HT. (da Silva '35.)
D. Maria do Carmo de Fragoso Carmona. HT. (da Silva '39.)
Docteur Marjolin. M. (R. et M. 1860.)
Dolly Madison. HT. (Hillk. '35.) *Super-Dupont.*
Dolly Varden. HRug. (W. Paul '14.)
Dolly Varden. Pol. (de R. '30.)
Dolomiti. HT. (Ing. '33.)
Dominie Sampson. Spn.
Donald Prior. HPol. (Prior; J&P. '38.)
Don Bradman. HT. (Wheat. '38.)
Doreen Thorn. HT. (F. Cant '34.)
Dorina Neave. HT. (Pemb. '26.)
Doris Dickson. HT. (S. Dick. '24.)
Doris Downes. HG. (A. Clark; NRS. Vic. '32.)
Doris Findlater. HT. (A. Dick. '36.)
Doris Osborne. HT. (Clark; NRS. Vic. '37.)
Doris Trayler. HT. (McGr. '24.)
Dorothy Dennison. R. (Denn. '09.)
Dorothy Fowler. HRug. (Skin. '38.)
Dorothy Hodgson. HT. (F. Cant '30.)
Dorothy Howarth. Pol. (Bees '21.)
Dorothy James. HT. (C-P. '39.)
Dorothy Marie. HT. (Scit.; Lain. '35.)
Dorothy McGredy. HT. (McGr. '36.)
Dorothy Page-Roberts. HT. (A. Dick. '07.)
Dorothy Perkins. R. (J&P. '01.)
Dotty. HT. (Tow. '31.)

ROSA, continued
Double Brique. G.
Double Mme. Butterfly. Annie Laurie.
Double Pink Killarney. Killarney, Double Pink.
Double White Killarney. Killarney, Double White.
Doubloons. LC. (HSet.) (Hor.; J&P. '34.)
Dr. A. I. Petyt. HT. (Burr. '24.)
Dr. Andry. HP. (E. Verd. 1864.)
Dr. A. Svehla. HT. (Bohm '35.)
Dr. A. von Erlach. HT. (S. & N. '32.)
Dr. Belville. CHT. (Thom.; H&S. '31.)
Dr. Carneiro Pacheco. HT. (da Silva '38.)
Dream Parade. HT. (Hill '38.)
Dr. Eckener. HRug. (V. Berg.; Tesch. '30.)
Dr. Edvard Benes. HT. (Bohm '35.)
Dr. Edward Deacon. HT. (Morse '26.)
Dr. E. M. Mills. HRug. (Van F.; ARS. '26.)
Dr. F. G. Chandler. Dickson's Red in U.S.
Dr. Gallwey. LC. (V. Reiter '37.)
Dr. Heinrich Lumpe. HT. (V. Berg.; W. Berg. '28.)
Dr. Hess von Kichdorff. HT. (M. Vogel; Heinemann '36.)
Dr. Huey. LC. (Thom. '14; B&A., A. N. Pier. '20.)
Dr. J. G. Fraser. HT. (Eas. '26.)
Dr. J. H. Nicolas. LC. (Nic.; J&P. '40.)
Dr. Kirk. HT. (Mal.; A. Meill. '39.)
Dr. Mendes Correia. HT. (da Silva '38.)
Dr. Merkeley. *R. cinnamomea* (?) (Brought to Manitoba, Canada, from Siberia by Dr. Merkeley.)
Dr. M. Euwe. HT. (Buis. '36.)
Dr. Miroslav Tyrs. HP. (Bohm '32.)
Dr. O'Donel Browne. HT. (A. Dick. '08.)
Dr. Rafael Duque. HT. (da Silva '38.)
Druschki Rubra. HP. (P. Lamb.; C-P. '29.) *Red Frau Karl Druschki.*
Dr. Vasquez. Pol. (Nad. '36.)
Dr. W. E. Hadden. HT. (McGr. '34.)
Dr. W. Van Fleet. LC. (Van F.; P. Hend. '10.)
Dr. Zamenhof. R. (Brada; Bohm '35.)
D. T. Poulsen. HPol. (D. T. Poul. '30.)
Duc d'Angouleme. Cent. (Holland.)
Duc de Bordeaux. G. (Vib. 1820.)
Duc de Fitzjames. G.
Duc de Guiche. G.
Duc de Valny. G.
Duc de Wellington. Duke of Wellington.
Ducher. C. (Duch. 1869.)
Duchesse d'Auerstaedt. CT. (A. Bern. 1888.)
Duchesse de Brabant. T. (Berne. 1857.)
Duchesse de Buccleugh. G. (Rob.)
Duchesse de Montebello. Cent. or G. (Laf.)
Duchesse de Verneuil. M. (Port. 1856.)

ROSA, continued
Duchesse d'Istrie. M. (Laf. 1855.)
Duchess of Albany. HT. (W. Paul 1888.) *Red La France.*
Duchess of Atholl. HT. (Dobbie '28.)
Duchess of Montrose. HT. (Dobbie '29.)
Duchess of Sutherland. HT. (A. Dick. '12.)
Duchess of Wellington. HT. (A. Dick. '09.)
Duchess of York. HT. (S. Dick. '25.)
Duke of Edinburgh. HP. (W. Paul; Paul 1868.)
Duke of Teck. HP. (Paul 1880.)
Duke of Wellington. HP. (Gran. 1864.) *Duc de Wellington.*
Du Maitre d'Ecole. G.
Dumortier. G.
Dundee Rambler. Arv. (Mart.)
Dupuy Jamain. HP. (Jam. 1868.)
Duquesa de Penaranda. HT. (Dot; C-P. '31.)
Dusterlohe. H. Arv. Cl. (Kordes '31.)
Earl Beatty. HT. (Chap. '23.)
Earl Godard Bentinck. HT. (Buis. '31.)
Earl Haig. HT. (A. Dick. '21.)
Earl of Dufferin. HP. (A. Dick. 1887.)
Easlea's Golden Rambler. LC. (Eas.; Tot. '32.)
East Anglia. HT. (Morse '39.)
Ebby van Best. HT. (Buis. '34.)
Eblouissant. Pol. (Tur. '18.)
Ecarlate. HT. (Boyt. '07.)
Echo. Pol. (P. Lamb. '14.) *Baby Tausendschon.*
Eclair. HP. (Lach. 1883.)
Eclipse. HT. (Nic.; J&P. '35.)
Ecstasy. HT. (A. Dick. '35.)
Eddies' Advent. HT. (Eddie '38.)
Edel. HT. (McGr. '19.)
Edina. HT. (Dobbie '34.)
Edith Bellenden. HSb. (Penz. 1895.)
Edith Cavell. Miss Edith Cavell.
Edith Clark. HT. (Clark; Hack. '28.)
Edith Felberg. HT. (F-L. '31.)
Edith Krause. HT. (Krause; J&P. '30.)
Edith Mary Mee. HT. (Mee; Beckw. '36.)
Edith Nellie Perkins. HT. (A. Dick. '28.)
Editor McFarland. HT. (Mal.; C-P. '31.)
Editor Stewart. HT. (Clark; NRS. Vic. '39.)
Edmond Proust. LC. (Barb. '03.)
Ednah Thomas. CHT. (Thom.; H&S. '31.) *Bloomfield Improvement.*
Edo Bergsma. HT. (Buis. '32.)
Edouard Renard. HT. (Dot '33.)
Eduard Schill. HT. (Kordes '31.)
Edward Mawley. HT. (McGr. '11.)
Effective. CHT. (Hob. '13.)
Effekt. HT. (Krause '35.)
E. G. Hill. HT. (E. G. Hill '29.)
Eglantine. Pol. (S&N. '30.)
Eileen Dorothea. HT. (A. Dick. '31.)
Eisenach. R. (Kiese '10.)
E. J. Ludding. HT. (Van R.; Prior, C-P. '31.)
Elaine Stuart. HT. (W. Edwards '32.)

ROSA, continued

ELDORADO. HT. (H&S. '23.)
ELECTRA. R. (Veitch '00.)
ELEGANCE. LC. (Brownl. '38.)
ELEGANTE. HT. (P-D. '18.)
ELENA CASTELLO. HT. (B. Munne '32.)
ELETA. HT. (Dahl.; K-S. Co. '34.)
ELFENREIGEN. HMacrantha. (Krause '39.) *Fairy Dance.*
ELFIN. HPol. (Arch. '39.)
ELIE BEAUVILLAIN. T. (Beauvillain 1887.)
ELISABETH FAURAX. HT. (F. Meill. '37.)
ELISA ROBICHON. R. (Barb. '01.)
ELISA ROVELLA. G.
ELISKA KRASNOHORSKA. HP. (Bohm '32.)
ELITE. HT. (Tant. '36; J&P. '41.)
ELIZABETH. Pol. (Letts '37.)
ELIZABETH LEE. HT. (Chap. '35.)
ELIZABETH OF YORK. HT. (Dobbie '28.)
ELIZABETH ROWE. M.
ELLA GUTHRIE. HT. (Clark; NRS. Vic. '37.)
ELLEN. HT. (P. Hin.; Gould '28.)
ELLEN POULSEN. HPol. (D. T. Pouls. '12.)
ELLEN TERRY. HT. (Chap. '25.)
ELLEN WILLMOTT. HT. (A. Bern. 1898.)
Ellen Willmott. HT. (Arch. '36.)
ELLI KNAB. HT. (Kordes '34.)
ELSE CHAPLIN. Pol. (Chap. '37.)
ELSE POULSEN. HPol. (D. T. Pouls. '24.)
ELSE'S RIVAL. HPol. (Boer '38.)
ELSIE. LC. (Chap. '34.)
ELSIE BECKWITH. HT. (Beckw. '22.)
ELVIRA ARAMAYO. HT. (Looy. '22.)
EMALINE ROUGE. HT. (Hof. '38.)
EMBERGLOW. HT. (Grillo '35.)
EMILE CRAMON. HT. (C. Cham. '37.)
EMILE FORTEPAULE. R. (Barb. '02.)
EMILY GRAY. LC. (A. H. Will.; B. R. Cant '18.)
EMILY RHODES. CHT. (Clark; NRS. Vic. '37.)
EMMA WRIGHT. HT. (McGr. '18.)
EMPEREUR DU MAROC. HP. (Guin.; E. Verd. 1858.)
EMPIRE QUEEN. HT. (Eas. '25.)
EMPIRE STATE. HT. (Nic.; J&P. '34.)
EMPRESS. HT. (Chap. '33.)
ENA GLADSTONE. HT. (Chap. '36.)
ENCHANTRESS. HRug.
ENG. DUARTE PACHECO. HT. (da Silva '38.)
ENID. Pol. (Prior '36.)
ERATO. LC. (Tant. '37.)
ERFURT. Shrub. (Kordes '39.)
ERIC B. MEE. HT. (Mee; Beckw. '37.)
ERICH FRAHM. HPol. (Kordes; Timm '39.)
ERNA GROOTENDORST. Pol. (R. Groot. '38.)
ERNA TESCHENDORFF. Pol. (Tesch. '11.)
ERNESTINE COSME. R. (Tur. '26.)
ERNST GRANDPIERRE. R. (L. Weig. '02.)
ERUPTION. HT. (Van R. '34.)
ESKIL. HT. (Ring. '39.)
ESPERANTO. HT. (Bohm '32.)
ESSENCE. HT. (B. R. Cant '30.)

ROSA, continued

ETERNAL YOUTH. HT. (D. Aic.; J&P. '37.) *Eterna Giovanezza.*
ETHEL JAMES. HT. (McGr. '21.)
ETHEL SOMERSET. HT. (A. Dick. '21.)
ETIENNE LEVET. HP. (F. Levet 1871.)
ETOILE DE FEU. HT. (P-D. '21.)
ETOILE DE FRANCE. HT. (P-D. '04.)
ETOILE DE HOLLANDE. HT. (Versch. '19.)
ETOILE DE LYON. T. (P. Guill. 1881.)
ETOILE D'OR. HT. (P-D.; Gauj. '31.)
ETOILE LUISANTE. Pol. (Tur.; Mich. '18.) *Baby Herriot.*
EUCHARIS. G. (Desc.)
EUGENE DE BEAUHARNAIS. C. (Hardy 1838.) *Prince Eugene.*
EUGENE DE SAVOIE. M. (M-R. 1860.)
EUGENE E. MAR ITT. B. (Gesch. '00.) *Mme. Eugene Marlitt.*
EUGENE FURST. HP. (S&N. 1875.)
EUGENE JACQUET. R. (Tur. '16.)
EUGENE JANVIER. G.
EUGENE VERDIER. M. (E. Verd. 1872.)
EUGENIE GUINOISSEAU. M. (Guin. 1864.)
EUGENIE LAMESCH. Pol. (P. Lamb. 1899.)
EULALIA. HT. (V-P.; Dreer, H&S. '34.)
EUTERPE. LC. (Tant. '37.)
EUTIN. HPol. (Kordes '40.)
EVA. Shrub. (Kordes '33.)
EVA EAKINS. HT. (McGr. '26.)
EVALINE. Pol. (Pross. '20.)
EVANGELINE. R. (M. H. Walsh '06.)
EVA TESCHENDORFF. Pol. (Tesch. '23.)
EVELYN MAY. HT. (W. Edwards '32.)
EVELYN THORNTON. Pol. (Bees '19.)
EVENING NEWS. HT. (Letts '27.)
EVENING SKY. HT. (Moore '39.)
EVENING STAR. HT. (Morse '19.)
EVERBLOOM. Semi-Cl. Pol. (Arch. '39.)
Everblooming Dr. W. Van Fleet. NEW DAWN.
Everblooming Jack Rose. RICHMOND.
EVEREST. HP. (Eas. '27.)
EVERGREEN GEM. R. (Hor.; Manda 1899.)
EVERT VAN DYK. HT. (Van R.; H&S. '31.)
EVIAN CACHAT. HT. (C. Cham. '39.)
E. V. LUCAS. HT. (McGr. '34.)
EXCELLENZ VON SCHUBERT. Evbl. Semi-Cl. (P. Lamb. '09.)
EXCELSA. R. (M. H. Walsh '09.) *Red Dorothy Perkins.*
FABVIER. C. (Laf. 1832.)
FACKEL. HT. (Krause '37.)
FAIENCE. HT. (Van R.'35; C-P. '37.)
FAIRLIE REDE. HT. (Clark; NRS. Vic. '37.)
FAIRY CLUSTER. HPol. (Arch. '35.)
FANCY. HT. (Van R. '28.)
FANNY. HT. (Lens '35.)
FANNY BIAS. G. (Vib. 1819.)
FASCINATION. HT. (Chap. '27.)
FATIME. G. (Desc. 1820.)
F. CAMBO. HT. (Dot '33.)
FEDERATION. LC. (Hor.; Ways. '38.)
FEDERICO CASAS. HT. (Dot; C-P. '32.)
FEERIE. HT. (Gauj. '38.)
FELBERGS ROSA DRUSCHKI. HP. (F-L. '29.)
FELICIA. Evbl. Semi-Cl. (Pemb. '28.)

ROSA, continued

FELICITE BOHAIN. M. (Grown in America before 1866.)
FE ICITE ET PERPETUE. Semp. (Jacq. 1827.)
FELICITY. HT. (Clarke Br. '19.)
FELIX LAPORTE. HT. (Buat. '28.)
FELLEMBERG. C. (Fellemberg 1857.) *La Belle Marseillaise.*
FERDINAND DE BUCK. G. *Feu de Buck.*
FERDINAND PICHARD. HP. (Tanne '21.)
FEU D'ARTIFICE. LC. (Mal. '35; C-P., B&A. '39.)
Feu de Buck. FERDINAND DE BUCK.
FEUERSCHEIN. Pol. (Krause '30.)
FEU JOSEPH LOOYMANS. HT. (Looy. '21.)
FEU PERNET-DUCHER. HT. (Mal.; C-P. '34.)
F. FERRER. LC. (Pah.; J&P. '40.)
FIESTA. HT. (C. E. Hansen; Arm. Nurs. '40.)
FIREBALL. Pol. (de R. '31.)
FIREBRAND. HT. (B. R. Cant '38.)
FIREGLOW. Pol. (Wez. '29.)
FISHER HOLMES. HP. (E. Verd. 1865.) *Fisher & Holmes.*
F. J. GROOTENDORST. HRug. (de Goey; F. J. Groot. '18.) *Nelkenrose.*
FLAMBEAU. HT. (Nic.; J&P. '40.)
FLAMBOYANT. Pol. (Tur. '31.)
FLAME. R. (Turn. '12.)
FLAME OF FIRE. HT. (McGr. '17.)
FLAMING JUNE. Pol. (Cutb. '31.) *Mrs. A. Hudig.*
FLAMINGO. HT. (A. Dick. '29.)
FLASH. LC. (Hat.; C-P. '38.)
FLAVESCENS. Spn.
FLORA McIVOR. HSb. (Penz.; Keynes & Co. 1894.)
FLORENCE HASWELL VEITCH. CHT. (W. Paul '11.)
FLORENCE L. IZZARD. HT. (McGr. '23.)
FLORENCE PEMBERTON. HT. (A. Dick. '03.)
FLORENTINA. Pol. (M. Leen. '38.)
FLOREX. HT. (Geig.; Florex, A. N. Pier. '27.)
FLOWER OF FAIRFIELD. R. (Ludorf; Schul. '09.)
FLUFFY RUFFLES. Pol. (H&S.; Dreer '35.)
FLYING COLOURS. HG. (Clark; Haz. '22.)
FOLIACEE. Cent. (Desc.; grown in America before 1848.)
FOLKESTONE. HPol. (Arch. '36.)
FONTANELLE. HT. (E. G. Hill '27.)
FORNARINA. G. (Vet. 1826.)
Fornarina. M. (M-R. 1862.)
FORST. HT. (Krause '37.)
FORTSCHRITT. HPol. (Kordes '33.)
FORTUNE'S DOUBLE YELLOW. N. (Fort. 1845.) *Beauty of Glazenwood.*
FORWARD MARCH. HT. (Wolfe '34.)
FRAGRANCE. HT. (Chap. '24.)
FRAGRANT PINK TALISMAN. HT. (Moore '38.)
FRAICHEUR. R. (Tur. '21.)
FRANCES ASHTON. HT. (De P.; Stock. '37.)
FRANCESCA. CHT. (Pemb. '22.)
FRANCESCO LA SCOLA. HT. (Ket. '34.)
FRANCES GAUNT. HT. (A. Dick. '18.)
FRANCIS. R. (V. Hauser '33.)
FRANCIS SCOTT KEY. HT. (J. Cook '13.)

ROSA, continued
Francois Bollez. HT. (Gill. '35.)
Francois de Salignac. M. (Rob. 1854.)
Francoise Blondeau. HT. (Mal. '38.)
Francois Guillot. R. (Barb. '07.)
Francois Juranville. R. (Barb. '06.)
Francois Laplanche. HT. (Buat. '34.)
Francois Poisson. LC. (Barb. '02.)
Frank Reader. HT. (Versch.; H&S., Dreer '27.)
Frank W. Dunlop. HT. (Dunl.; Tot. '20.)
Frau Astrid Spath. Pol. (L. Spath '30.)
Frau Dr. Erreth. Pol. (Ged. '15.)
Frau Dr. Schricker. C. (F-L. '27.)
Frau Eduard Bethge. HT. (F-L. '30.)
Frau Elizabeth Balzer. HT. (Balz. '33.)
Frau E. Weigand. HT. (C. Weig.; C. Weig., Schul. '28.)
Frau Hugo Lauster. HT. (H. Lauster; Pfitz.; Dreer '32.)
Frau Karl Druschki. HP. (P. Lamb. '01.) *Reine des Neiges; Snow Queen; White American Beauty.*
Fraulein Octavia Hesse. R. (Hesse '10.)
Frau Robert Turke. HT. (Turke; Tesch. '28.)
Frau Rudolph Schmidt. Pol. (J. C. Schmidt '19.)
Frazer Annesley. HT. (McGr. '35.)
Frederick S. Peck. LC. (Brownl. '38.)
Fred Walker. HT. (McGr. '35.)
Freedom. LC. (Und. '18.)
Freia. HT. (Tant. '36.)
Freidlanderiana. G.
Freifrau von Marschall. R. (P. Lamb. '13.)
Freiherr von Marschall. T. (P. Lamb. '03.)
Freude. HPol. (Kordes '38.)
Frieda Krause. HT. (Krause '35.)
Friedrichsruh. HT. (Turke '08.)
Friendship. HT. (A. F. Aml. Co. '37.)
Friendship. HT. (A. Dick. '38.)
Fritz Hoger. HT. (Kordes '34.)
Fritz Schrodter. HT. (Muhle '28.)
Friuli. HT. (Ing. '33.)
F. R. Patzer. HT. (A. Dick. '09.)
Fruhlingsgold. Spn. (Kordes '37.)
Fuchsine Guy. HPol. (M. Leen. '30.)
F. W. Lowe. HT. (Lowe '36.)
Gabrielle Privat. Pol. (Barthelemy-Privat; Tur. '31.)
Gabriel Lombart. HT. (Buat. '32.)
Gabriel Noyelle. M. (Buat. '33.)
Gaiety. HT. (E. G. Hill; Hill Fl. Prod. Co. '26.)
Gainsborough. CHT. (G&R. '03.)
Garden Gem. HT. (D&C. '30.)
Garden Glow. HT. (B. R. Cant '37.)
Gardenia. R. (Manda 1899.)
Gartendirektor Nose. HT. (Kordes; Dreer, H&S. '30.)
Gartendirektor O. Linne. Pol. (P. Lamb. '34.)
Gava. HT. (M. Munne; Nad. '34.)
Gazelle. G.
Geant des Batailles. HP. (Nerard; Guill. p. 1846.) *Giant of Battles.*
Geheimrat Dr. Mittweg. Evbl. Semi-Cl. (P. Lamb. '09.)

ROSA, continued
Geheimrat Duisberg. HT. (Kordes '33; H&S., Dreer '34.) *Golden Rapture.*
Geheimrat Richard Willstatter. HT. (F-L. '31.)
General Baron Berge. HP. (Pernet pere 1892.)
General Domingos de Oliveira. HT. HT. (da Silva '39.)
General Donnadieu. G.
General Jacqueminot. HP. (Rous. 1853.)
General Kleber. M. (Rob. 1856.)
General MacArthur. HT. (E. G. Hill '05.)
General Stefanik. HP. (Bohm; J&P. '33.) *Krasna Azurea.*
General-Superior Arnold Janssen. HT. (M. Leen. '12.)
General Washington. HP. (Gran. 1860.)
Genevieve Genest. Cl. Mrs. Sam McGredy.
Genius Mendel. HT. (Bohm '35.)
Gen. Robert E. Lee. T. (G&R. 1896.)
Georg Arends. HP. (W. Hin. '10.)
George C. Waud. HT. (A. Dick. '08.)
George Dakin. HT. (Burb. '27.)
George Dickson. HT. (A. Dick. '12.)
George Elger. Pol. (Tur. '12.) *Yellow Baby Rambler.*
George Geuder. HT. (J. C. Schmidt '31.)
Georges Cain. HRug. (F. Mul. '09.)
Georges Chesnel. HT. (P-D.; Gauj. '35; J&P. '39.)
Georges Paquel. HT. (M. Leen. '34.)
Georges Vibert. G. (Rob. 1853.)
George Will. HRug. (Skin. '39.)
Gerald Hardy. HT. (A. Dick. '36.)
Gerbe Rose. LC. (Fauq.; Langue '04.)
Germanea. HT. (Ravenberg '29.)
Germania. Charme.
Gertrud Huck. HT. (Huck '31.)
Ghislaine de Feligonde. R. (Tur. '16.)
Giant of Battles. Geant des Batailles.
Gilda. HT. (Tow. '36.)
Giovanezza. HT. (Ing. '33.)
Gipsy Lass. HT. (A. Dick. '32.) *Gypsy Lass.*
Girlie. Pol. (Wez. '23.)
Girona. HT. (Dot '36; H. Guill., C-P. '39.)
Gisele Alday. HT. (Mal. '34; H. Guill.)
Giuliana Borgatti. HT. (Bor. '36.)
Gladys Benskin. HT. (A. Dick.; Dreer '29.)
Glamour. HT. (M. Leen. '39; T. Robin.)
Glenn Dale. LC. (Van F.; ARS. '27.)
Glitters. CHT. (J. Smith '34.)
Gloaming. HT. (Nic.; J&P. '35.)
Gloire de Chedane-Guinoisseau. HP. (Chedane-Pajotin '07.)
Gloire de Dijon. CT. (Jaco. 1853.)
Gloire de Ducher. HP. (Duch. 1865.)
Gloire de Margottin. HP. (Marg. 1887.)
Gloire de Paris. Anna de Diesbach.

ROSA, continued
Gloire des Lawranceanas. H. chinensis minima. (1837.)
Gloire des Mousseux. M. (Laf. 1852.)
Gloire des Rosomanes. CC. (Vib. 1825.) *Ragged Robin.*
Gloire d'Orient. M. (Belu. 1856.)
Gloire du Midi. Pol. (de R.; Sliedr. & Co., J&P. '32.)
Gloire Lyonnaise. HP. (Guill. 1884.)
Gloria Mundi. Pol. (de R.; Sliedr., Tesch. '29.)
Gloriana. HT. (Hillk. '36.)
Glorious Sunset. Pol. (Allen '31.)
Glory of Hurst. Pol. (Hicks '21.)
Glory of Paris. Anna de Diesbach.
Glory of Steinfurth. HT. (Schul. '21.)
Glory of Surrey. HT. (Ley '35.)
Glowing Carmine. HT. (H&S.; Dreer '36.)
Glowing Sunset. American name for Wilhelm Breder.
Gluckskind. HT. (Berg. '35.)
G. Michel. HT. (F-L. '31.)
Gnome. Pol. (M. Leen. '36.)
Goethe. M. (P. Lamb. '11.)
Gold Dame. HT. (Dobbie '29.)
Golden Beauty. HT. (Van R. '37.)
Golden Butterfly. Goudvlinder.
Golden Charm. HT. (G&M. '33.)
Golden Climber. Mrs. Arthur Curtiss James.
Golden Comet. HT. (Bur.; Stark '37.)
Golden Dawn. HT. (Grant; Haz., Prior '29.)
Golden Day. HT. (Bentl.; Hark. '31.)
Golden Dream. Goldener Traum.
Golden Drop. HT. (Clark '39.)
Golden Druschki. Goldene Druschki.
Goldene Druschki. HP. (P. Lamb. '36.) *Golden Druschki.*
Goldene Gruss an Aachen. HPol. (Kordes '35.)
Golden Emblem. HT. (McGr. '17.)
Goldener Traum. HRug. (Turke; J. C. Schmidt '32.) *Golden Dream.*
Goldenes Mainz. HT. (Kordes; J&P. '33.) *Golden Main.*
Golden Frills. HT. (B&A. '36.)
Golden Gate. T. (D&C. 1891.)
Golden Gleam. HT. (Beckw. '26.)
Golden Glory. HT. (Dobbie '31.)
Golden Glow. LC. (Brownl. '37.)
Golden Ideal. HT. (Lens '39.)
Golden King. HRug. (Beckw. '35.)
Golden Light. LC. (Nic.; J&P. '39.)
Golden Main. Goldenes Mainz.
Golden Moss. HMs. (Dot; C-P. '32.)
Golden Ophelia. HT. (B. R. Cant '18.)
Golden Orange Climber. LC. (Brownl. '37.)
Golden Perfection. Pol. (M. Leen. '37.)
Golden Pernet. Julien Potin.
Golden Poly. Pol. (Pah. '31.)
Golden Poly. Pol. (M. Leen. '35.)
Golden Pyramid. LC. (Brownl. '39.)
Golden Queen. HT. (C. Cham. '37.)
Golden Rambler. *Alister Stella Gray; Easlea's Golden Rambler.*
Golden Rapture. American name for Geheimrat Duisberg.
Golden Salmon. Pol. (Cutb. '26.) *Goldlachs.*

ROSA, continued
Golden Salmon Superieur. Pol. (de R.; Sliedr. '29.)
Golden Sam McGredy. HT. (Lens '35.)
Golden Sastago. HT. (Dot; C-P. '38.)
Golden Spray. HT. (H. Dick. '17.)
Golden State. HT. (F. Meill. '37; C-P. '38.)
Golden Sunset. LC. (Bur.; Stark '34.)
Golden Talisman. HT. (E. G. Hill '31.)
Golden Vandal. HT. (Lens '35.)
Golden Van Rossem. HT. (Lens '37.)
Golden Wedding. HT. (Krebs '38.)
Golden West. HT. (Stock. '36.)
Golden Wonder. HT. (Gunn '36.)
Goldfinch. R. (G. Paul '07.)
Goldlachs. Golden Salmon.
Gold of Ophir. N. Form of Fortune's Double Yellow.
Gold Star. HT. (Vestal '33.)
Golmain. Goldenes Mainz, registered as *Golmain* in Canada.
Good Cheer. HT. (A. F. Aml. Co. '37.)
Good Luck. HT. (His. '37.)
Good Morning. HT. (Kau.; Hill Crest '35.)
Good News. HT. (F. Meill. '40.)
Gooiland Beauty. HT. (Van R.; Van R., Prior '24.)
Gorgeous. HT. (H. Dick. '15.)
Gotha. HT. (Krause '32.)
Goudvlinder. HT. (Van R. '26.) *Golden Butterfly.*
Governor Alfred E. Smith. HT. (Deno.; J&P. '33.)
Governor Phillip. CHT. (Fitz.; Haz. '39.)
Grace. HRug. (Saund. '32.)
Grace Noll Crowell. HT. (Vestal '29.)
Grace Wayman. CHT. (Waym. '36.)
Gracie Fields. HT. (Letts '37.)
Graf Sylva Tarouca. HT. (P. Lamb. '16.)
Granat. HT. (Krause '37.)
Grand Canary. HT. (Lowm.; U. S. Cut Fl. Co. '34.)
Grand Cramoisi. G. (Vib. 1818.)
Grande Duchesse Charlotte. HT. (Ket. '39.)
Grande Duchesse de Luxembourg. Marie Adelaide.
Grande Henriette. L'Enchanteresse.
Grande Renoncule. Cent.
Grange Colombe. HT. (P. Guill. '12.)
Gratia. HT. (M. Leen. '34.)
Green Mantle. HSb. (Penz. 1895.)
Grenadier. HT. (A. Dick. '30.)
Grenoble. HT. (Mal. '27; C-P. '31.) *Ville de Grenoble.*
Greta Kluis. Pol. (K&K. '16.)
Gretel Greul. HT. (Greul '39.)
Grillodale. HT. (Grillo '26.)
Grimm. Semi-Cl. (P. Lamb. '32.)
Grootendorst Supreme. HRug. (F. J. Groot. '36.)
Gros Provins Panache. G.
Gruppenkonigin. HPol. (Kordes '35.)
Gruss an Aachen. Pol. (Ged. '09.)
Gruss an Coburg. HT. (F-L. '27.)
Gruss an Freundorf. R. (Pras. '13.)
Gruss an Teplitz. HT. (Gesch.; P. Lamb. 1897.) *Virginia R. Coxe.*

ROSA, continued
Guardsman. HT. (Arch. '37.)
Guill. Kaempff. HT. (F-L. '31.)
Guinee. CHT. (Mal. '37; C-P. '38.)
Guiseppe Motta. HT. (Heiz. '36.)
Gurney Benham. HT. (B. R. Cant '35.)
Gustave Pegis. HT. (P-D. 1890.)
Gwendoline Collins. HT. (Clark; NRS. Vic. '37.)
Gwen Nash. CHT. (Clark; NRS. of N. S. W. '20.)
Gwyneth. Pol. (Woos.; Eas. '23.)
Gwyneth Jones. HT. (McGr. '25.)
Gypsy Lass. Gipsy Lass.
Hadley. HT. (Mont. Co.; A. N. Pier. '14.)
Hamburg. LC. (Kordes '35.)
Hansa. HRug. (Schaum '05.)
Hans Schmid. R. (M. Vogel; P. Lamb., F. C. Heinemann '34.)
Happy Days. HT. (M. C. Aml.; A. F. Aml. Co. '32.)
Harbinger. HG. (Clark; Hack. '23.)
Harison's Yellow. Spn. (Har. 1830.)
Harlequin. R. (Stanw. R. G. '35.)
Harmony. HP. (Nic.; C-P. '33.)
Harriett. CHT. (Moore '31.)
Harry Kirk. T. (A. Dick. '07.)
Harry Maasz. HMacrantha. (Kordes '30.)
Harvard. HT. (Vestal '26.)
Harvest Moon. (B. R. Cant '38.)
Harvest Time. CHT. (Thom.; Arm. Nurs. '39.)
Hauff. R. (P. Lamb. '11.)
Havering. HMs. (Bent. '37.)
Havering Rambler. R. (Pemb. '20.)
Hawlmark Crimson. HT. (A. Dick. '20.)
Hawlmark Scarlet. HT. (A. Dick. '23.)
Hazel Alexander. HT. (Dicksons '33.)
H. Chaubert. HT. (Barb. '28.)
H. C. Valeton. HT. (Versch. '26.)
H. C. Young. HT. (A&McA. '34.)
H. D. M. Barton. HT. (H. Dick. '17.)
Heart of Gold. R. (Van F.; ARS. '26.)
Heart's Delight. HT. (L. P. Hart '33.)
Heather Paton. HT. (A&McA. '34.)
Hector. G. (Parm.)
Hector Deane. HT. (McGr. '38.)
Hede. HT. (Tant. '34.)
Hedwig Fulda. R. (Leen. Br. '34.)
Heidegruss. Pol. (Tant.; M&H. '37.)
Heidekind. Rug.-Pol. (V. Berg.; M&H. '31; P. J. How. '34.)
Heideroslein. Evbl. Semi-Cl. (P. Lamb. '32.)
Heidezauber. Pol. (Tant.; M&H. '36.)
Heimatlos. HSp. (Lohr. '31.)
Heinrich Conr. Soth. Evbl. Semi-Cl. (P. Lamb. '19.)
Heinrich Munch. HP. (W. Hin.; M&H. '11.)
Heinrich Schultheis. HP. (Benn. 1882.)
Heinrich Wendland. HT. (Kordes; Dreer, H&S. '30.)
Helen. HT. (W. Ferg. '30.)
Helena Van Vliet. Mlt. (Kersbergen '31.)
Helene Dapples. HT. (Heiz. '32.)
Helene de Montbriand. HT. (A. Schw. '33.)

ROSA, continued
Helene Vacaresco. HT. (C. Cham. '39.)
Helen Fox. HT. (Buat. '28.)
Helen Gambier. Mlle. Helene Cambier.
Helen Good. T. (G&R. '07.)
Helen Gould. Balduin.
Helen Leenders. Pol. (M. Leen. '24.)
Helgoland. HPol. (Kordes '36.)
Heliodore Dober. G.
Helios. HT. (M. Leen. '35.)
Henri Barruet. LC. (Barb. '18.)
Henri Declinand. R. (Merm. '34.)
Henrietta. HT. (Merry. '17.)
Henri Fouquier. G.
Henri Linger. LC. (Barb. '28.)
Henri Mallerin. Rouge Mallerin.
Henri Martin. M. (Laf. 1863.) *Red Moss.*
Henri Pauthier. HT. (Sauv.; C-P. '33.)
Henry Nevard. HP. (F. Cant '24.)
Herbert Brunning. HT. (Clark '40.)
Hercules. LC. (Hor.; Ways. '38.)
H. E. Richardson. HT. (A. Dick. '13.)
Her Majesty. HP. (Benn. 1885.)
Hermann Eggers. HT. (Kordes; Dreer, H&S. '30.)
Hermann Lindecke. HT. (H. Lind. '29.)
Hermann Lons. HT. (Tant. '31.)
Hermen Anglada. HT. (Dot '33.)
Hermosa. C. (Marcheseau 1840.) *Armosa; Melanie Lemaire; Mme. Neumann.*
Heroine. HT. (Krause '35.)
Heros. HT. (Tant. '33.)
Herrenhausen. Shrub. (Kordes '38.)
Hiawatha. R. (M. H. Walsh '04.)
Hiawatha Recurrent. R. (Sauv.; C-P. '31.)
Hilda. HT. (B. R. Cant '28.)
Hildenbrandseck. HRug. (P. Lamb. '09.)
Hillcrest Pillar. Spn. (Hillc. Gar. '30.)
Hinrich Gaede. HT. (Kordes '31.)
Hippolyte. G.
His Majesty. HT. (McGr. '09.)
Hispania. HT. (Pah. '38.)
Hoffmann von Fallersleben. Evbl. Semi-Cl. (P. Lamb. '17.)
Hofgartner Kalb. C. (F-L. '14.)
Hollandia. HT. (J. K. Zijverden '30.)
Hollywood. HT. (Scit. '30.)
Holstein. HPol. (Kordes; J&P. '38.)
Holstenrose. HT. (Tant. '37.)
Holt Hewitt. HT. (Beckw. '25.)
Homere. T. (R. et M. 1858.)
Home Sweet Home. HT. (W&I.; C-P. '40.)
Hon. Ina Bingham. HP. (A. Dick. '05.)
Hon. Lady Lindsay. Shrub. (N. J. Han. '38; B&A. '39.)
Hoosier Beauty. HT. (Dorn. '15.)
Horace Vernet. HP. (Guill. f. 1866.)
Hortense de Beauharnais. G.
Hortense Vernet. M. (M-R. 1861.)
Hortulanus Budde. HT. (Versch. '19.)
Hortulanus Fiet. HT. (Versch. '19.)
Hubicka. HT. (Bohm '35.)
Hugh Dickson. HP. (H. Dick. '05.)
Hugh Watson. HP. (A. Dick. '05.)
Hugo Roller. T. (W. Paul '07.)
Huguette Despiney. R. (Girin '11.)

ROSA, continued
Huguette Duflos. HT. (Lil. '37.)
Humboldt. HT. (E. G. Hill; Cottage '22.)
Hummingbird. HT. (Scit.; Lain. '34.)
Hurst Charm. LC. (Hicks '36.)
Hurst Delight. LC. (Hicks '36.)
Hurst Favourite. LC. (Hicks '36.)
Hurst Gem. Pol. (Hicks '31.)
Hurst Glory. HT. (Hicks '36.)
Hurst Scarlet. HT. (Hicks '33.)
H. V. Machin. HT. (A. Dick. '14.)
Hwiezdoslav. HT. (Bohm '36.)
Hypathia. G.
Hythe Cluster. Pol. (Arch. '35.)
Ibiza. HT. (Dot '38.)
Ida Klemm. R. (Walt. '07.)
Ida Scholten. HT. (Buis. '33.)
Ideal. Pol. (Spek '21.)
Ignasi Iglesias. HT. (Dot '34.) *Ignacio Inglesias.*
Ignis. Shrub. (Chot.; Bohm '34.)
Ile de France. R. (Nonin '22.)
Ile de France. Adoration in U.S.A.
Imatra. HPol. (S. Pouls.; Olsson '30.)
Imperial Potentate. HT. (Clarke Br. '21.)
Impress. HT. (A. Dick.; Lig., Dreer '29.)
Improved Lafayette. HPol. (H&S.; Dreer '35.)
Independence Day. HT. (Bees '19.)
Indian Summer. CHT. (H&S. '37.)
Indra. LC. (Tant. '37.)
Inermis. Boursault.
Infante Beatrice. HT. (M. Guill. '30.)
Infante Maria Cristina. HT. (Gauj. '30.)
Ingar Olsson. HPol. (D. T. Pouls.'31.)
Innocence. HT. (Chap. '21.)
Inspecteur Jagourt. Pol. (S&N. '32.)
Iolanthe. HT. (Gauj. '40.)
Ion Phillips. HT. (A. Dick. '34.)
Ireland Hampton. HT. (Hillk. '34.)
Irene Churruca. HT. (La F. '34.)
Iris. Spn.
Irish Beauty. HT. (A. Dick. '00.)
Irish Charm. HT. (McGr.; H&S., Dreer '27.)
Irish Courage. HT. (McGr. '27.)
Irish Elegance. HT. (A. Dick. '05.)
Irish Fireflame. HT. (A. Dick. '14.)
Irish Glory. HT. (A. Dick. '00.)
Irish Hope. HT. (McGr.; H&S., Dreer '27.)
Irish Sweetness. HT. (McGr.; H&S., Dreer '27.)
Iris Patricia Green. HT. (Pemb. '28.)
Isa. HT. (F&L. Evans '31.)
Isabella Sprunt. T. (Sprunt; I. Buchanan 1865.)
Isobel. HT. (McGr. '16.)
Italie Imperiale. HT. (Cap. '36.)
Ivanhoe. HT. (Eas. '28.)
Ivy Alice. R. (Letts '27.)
Ivy May. HT. (Beckw. '25.)
I Zingari. HT. (Pemb. '25.)
Jack McCandless. HT. (McGr. '35.)
Jacotte. LC. (Barb. '20.)
Jacques Latouche. HT. (Mal.; H. Guill. '35.)
J. A. Gomis. HT. (Nad. '33.)
James Gibson. HT. (McGr. '28.)
James Rea. HT. (McGr. '30.)
James Walley. HT. (Eas. '23.)

ROSA, continued
Jan Abbing. HT. (Tant. '33.)
Janet Morrison. CHT. (Clark; NRS. Vic. '36.)
Janet's Pride. HSet. (Whitw. 1862.)
Jarvis Brook. HT. (Low '28.)
J. B. Clark. HP. (H. Dick. '05.)
J. Bienfait. Mr. J. Bienfait.
J. C. Thornton. HT. (Bees '26.)
Jean Bodin. M. (Vib. 1847.)
Jean Bostick. HT. (Bost. '36.) *Yellow Condesa de Sastago.*
Jean C. N. Forestier. HT. (P-D. '19.)
Jean Cote. HT. (Gauj.; J&P. '36.)
Jeanine Defaucamberge. Pol. (Tur. '31.)
Jean Lafitte. LC. (Hor.; J&P. '34.)
Jean Liabaud. HP. (Liab. 1875.)
Jean Mermez. Pol. (R. Chenault; H-A. '37.)
Jean Muraour. Pol. (M. Vogel '35.)
Jeanne d'Arc. Pol. (Lev. '09.)
Jeanne de Montfort. M. (Rob. 1851, 1854.)
Jeanne Hachette. M. (Rob. 1851.)
Jeanne Lassalle. Evbl. Semi-Cl. (M. Lassalle; Via. '36.)
Jeanne Richert. R. (Walt. '29.)
Jeannette. G. (Desc.)
Jeannette Heller. William R. Smith.
Jeannie Deans. HSb. (Penz. 1895.)
Jeannie Dickson. HP. (A. Dick. 1890.)
Jean Renton. HT. (Clark '40.)
Jenny Duval. C.
Jersey Beauty. R. (Manda 1899.)
Jessie. Pol. (Merry. '09.)
Jessie Segrave. HT. (Mee; Beckw. '37.)
Jewel. HT. (Grillo '38.)
J. F. Muller. Pol. (J. F. Mul. '29.)
J. G. Glassford. HT. (H. Dick. '21.)
J. H. Bruce. HT. (Bees '37.)
J. H. Pemberton. HT. (Bent. '31.)
J. H. Van Heyst. HT. (M. Leen. '36.)
Jill. Pol. (Le G. '39.)
Jill Darling. HT. (A&McA. '37.)
J. K. B. Roos. HT. (M. Leen. '33.)
J. K. Tyl. LC. (Brada; Bohm '36.)
J. Michel. HT. (F-L. '30.)
Joan. HT. (Pemb. '19.)
Joan Cant. HT. (B. R. Cant '29.)
Joanna Hill. HT. (J. H. Hill '28.)
Joanna Troutman. HT. (Vestal '29.)
Joan Ross. HP. (Nic.; C-P. '33.)
Joao Pereira da Rosa. HT. (da Silva '36.)
Johanna Ropcke. R. (Tant. '31.)
Johanna Tantau. Pol. (Tant. '28.)
Johanniszauber. HT. (Tant. '26.)
John C. M. Mensing. HT. (Eveleens '24.) *Pink Ophelia.*
John Cranston. M.
John Cronin. HT. (Clark; NRS. Vic. '35.)
John E. Sleath. HT. (Mee; Beckw. '37.)
John Fraser. M. (Gran. 1861.)
John Grow. M. (Laf. 1859.)
John Hopper. HP. (Ward 1862.)
John McNab. HRug. (Skin. '38.)
John Moore. HT. (Gauj. '39.)
John Russell. HT. (Dobbie '24.)
John Square. CHT. (Square '37.)
Jolly. Pol. (M. Leen. '34.)
Jonkheer J. L. Mock. HT. (M. Leen. '10.)

ROSA, continued
Jonkheer Mr. G. Sandberg. HT. (Buis. '36.)
Josef Strnad. HT. (Bohm '32; J&P. '34.)
Joseph Guy. Changed to Lafayette in U. S. A.
Joseph Hill. HT. (P-D. '03.)
Josephine Spiecker. HT. (V-P.; Hark., Bentl. '39.)
Josephine Thomas. HT. (H&S.; Dreer '24.)
Josephine Vestal. HT. (E. G. Hill; Vestal '23.)
Joseph Pernet d'Annemasse. HT. (P-D.; Gauj. '34.)
J. Otto Thilow. HT. (Versch.; H&S., Dreer '27.)
Jovita Perez. HT. (M. Munne '29.)
Joy. HT. (Beckw. '29.)
Joyce Lomax. Name given Satan in England.
Joyful. HT. (Vestal '31.)
Joyous. HPol. (de R.; J&P. '39.)
Joyous Cavalier. HT. (Arch. '26.)
J. S. Baar. HT. (Mikes; Bohm '34.)
Jubilaire de Masaryk. Masarykova Jubilejni.
Jubilee. HT. (Allen '30.) *Allen's Jubilee.*
Judith. HT. (Le G. '38.)
Judith Black. HT. (Clark; Haz. '30.)
Judy. HT. (Grillo '40.)
Jules Finger. T. (Duch. 1879.)
Jules Gaujard. HT. (P-D.; Gauj. '28.)
Jules Margottin. HP. (Marg. 1853.)
Julia Ann Bostick. Pol. (Bost. '35.)
Julia, Countess of Dartrey. HT. (Hall; McGr. '27.)
Julia Mannering. HSb. (Penz. 1895.)
Julie de Mersent. M.
Julie d'Etanges. G.
Julienne. HT. (Grillo '40.)
Julien Potin. HT. (P-D.; Dreer '27.) *Golden Pernet.*
Juliet. HP. (W. Paul '10.)
Juliet Staunton Clark. HT. (Robi. '33.)
Juliette E. Beuningen. HT. (Buis. '37.) *Mme. Juliette* in England.
Julius Gofferje. HT. (J. C. Schmidt '30.)
July Glory. R. (Chap. '32.)
June. HT. (Arch. '37.)
June Morn. LC. (Nic.; J&P. '39.)
Jupiter. Spn.
Justine. Cent. (Vib. 1822.)
Justine. HT. (J. H. Hill '35.)
Kaiserin Auguste Viktoria. HT. (P. Lamb. 1891.)
Kalmia. R. (M. H. Walsh '11.)
Kardinal. HT. (Krause '34.)
Kardinal Piffl. HT. (Leen. Br. '25.)
Karel Hynek Macha. HT. (Brada; Bohm '36.)
Karen Poulsen. HPol. (D. T. Pouls.; J&P. '33.)
Karl Forster. Spn. (Kordes '31.)
Kate Felberg. HT. (F-L. '30.)
Kate Mull. HT. (Eas. '34.)
Kate Rainbow. HT. (Beckw. '35.)
Kate Schmid. R. (R. Vogel; Kordes '31.)
Katharina Zeimet. Pol. (P. Lamb. '01.) *White Baby Rambler.*

ROSA, continued

Katharine Pechtold. HT. (V-P.; Dreer, H&S. '34.)
Kathleen. HMs. (Pemb. '22.)
Kathleen. HT. (A. Dick. '34.)
Kathleen Harrop. B. (A. Dick. '19.)
Kathleen Kennedy. HT. (A. Dick. '39.)
Kathleen King. HT. (Marr. '30.)
Kathleen Mills. HT. (Le G. '34.)
Kathleen Wiggin. CHP. (Wig. '32.)
Kazanlik (*R. damascena trigintipetala*).
Kees Knoppers. Pol. (M. Leen. '30.)
Kersbergen. Pol. (Kersbergen '27.)
Ketje. HT. (Lens '38.)
Kidwai. HT. (P-D.; Gauj., Dreer, H&S. '33.) *Kidway.*
Killarney. HT. (A. Dick. 1898.)
Killarney Brilliant. HT. (A. Dick. '14.)
Killarney, Double Pink. HT. (Vestal '35.)
Killarney, Double White. HT. (Budl.; A. N. Pier. '12.)
Killarney Queen. HT. (Budl. '12.)
King Alexander I. Roi Alexandre.
King Boreas. HT. (Brownl. '41.)
King George's Memorial. Pamatnik Krale Jiriho.
King George V. HP. (H. Dick. '12.)
King of Scots. Spn.
Kirsten Poulsen. HPol. (D. T. Pouls. '24.)
Kismet. HT. (J&P. '30.)
Kitty Kingsbury. HT. (Evans '30.)
Kitty Kininmonth. HG. (Clark; Hack. '22.)
Klondyke. R. (Paul '11.)
Klondyke. HT. (Le G. '34.)
Kluis Scarlet. Pol. (R. Kluis '31.)
K. of K. HT. (A. Dick. '17.) *Kitchener of Khartoum.*
Konigin Carola. HT. (Turke '04.)
Konigin Luise. HT. (C. Weig. '27.)
Konigin von Danemark. Cent. (Booth Br. 1898.)
Koningin Astrid. HT. (M. Leen. '35.) *Queen Astrid.*
Koralle. Pol. (Koopmann; Krause, Tant. '37.)
Korovo. HT. (M. Leen. '31.)
Kralj Alexander I. HT. (Bohm '35.)
Kraljica Marija. HT. (Brada; Bohm '35.)
Kralj Petar II. HT. (Brada '36.)
Kralj Tomislav. HT. (M. Leen. '31.)
Krasna Azurea. General Stefanik.
Krasna Uslavanka. HT. (Bohm '30.)
Kronprinsesse Ingrid. HPol. (S. Pouls.; D. T. Pouls. '38.)
Kurt Scholz. HT. (Kordes '34.)
Kyson. CHT. (Eacott; R. Murr. '40.)
La Belle Marseillaise. Fellemberg.
La Caille. M. (R. et M. 1857.)
La Champagne. HT. (Barb. '19.)
La Couronne Tendre. G.
Laddie. HT. (Beckw. '26.)
Lady Alice Stanley. HT. (McGr. '09.)
Lady Ashtown. HT. (A. Dick. '04.)
Lady Baillie. Spn.
Lady Banks. **R. banksiae.**
Lady Barnby. HT. (A. Dick. '30.)
Lady Betty. HT. (Bees '30.)
Lady Blanche. R. (M. H. Walsh '13.)

ROSA, continued

Lady Bountiful. LC. (Tait; B&A. '38.)
Lady Cahn. HT. (Gauj. '37.)
Lady Charles Townshend. HT. (Dan. '31.)
Lady Craig. HT. (H. Dick. '22.)
Lady Cunliffe Owen. HT. (Ley '32.)
Lady Curzon. G. (Turn. '01.)
Lady Dawson Bates. HT. (McGr. '39.)
Lady Dixon-Hartland. HT. (B. R. Cant '23.)
Lady Duncan. Semi-Cl. or Trailer. (Daw.; East. Nurs. '00.)
Lady Edgeworth David. HT. (Fitz.; Haz. '39.)
Lady English. HT. (B. R. Cant '34.)
Lady Evelyn Guinness. HT. (Evans '32.)
Lady Faire. HT. (W. Paul '08.)
Lady Fairfax. HT. (F. Cant '30.)
Lady Florence Stronge. HT. (McGr. '25.)
Lady Forteviot. HT. (B. R. Cant '28.)
Lady Frost. HT. (Bees '35.)
Lady Gay. R. (M. H. Walsh '05.)
Lady Godiva. R. (Paul '08.)
Lady Gowrie. CHT. (Fitz.; Haz. '38.)
Lady Hamilton. Spn.
Lady Helen Maglona. HT. (A. Dick. '26.)
Lady Helen Stewart. HP. (A. Dick. 1887.)
Lady Hillingdon. T. (L&S. '10.)
Lady Hudson. HT. (Chap. '30.)
Lady Huntingfield. HT. (Clark; NRS. Vic. '37.)
Lady Inchiquin. HT. (A. Dick. '22.)
Lady Lauder. HT. (Morse '31.)
Lady Layton. HT. (Lay. '32.)
Lady Leconfield. HT. (Burb.; C-P. '39.)
Lady Leslie. HT. (McGr. '29.)
Lady Lilford. HT. (Greg. '30.)
Ladylove. HT. (Beckw. '26.)
Lady Mandeville. HT. (McGr. '39.)
Lady Mann. HT. (Clark '40.)
Lady Margaret Stewart. HT. (A. Dick. '26.)
Lady Mary Elizabeth. HT. (A. Dick. '27.)
Lady Miller. HT. (Clark '40.)
Lady Moyra Cavendish. HT. (McGr. '39.)
Lady Nutting. HT. (Wheat. '38.)
Lady Penzance. HSb. (Penz. 1894.)
Lady Pirrie. HT. (H. Dick. '10.)
Lady Plymouth. T. (A. Dick. '14.)
Lady Rachel Verney. HT. (Bees '35.)
Lady Reading. Pol. (Van Kleef & Co. '21.)
Lady Roberts. T. (F. Cant '02.)
Lady Roundway. HT. (B. R. Cant '23.)
Lady Sackville. HT. (McGr. '21.)
Lady Sackville. HT. (B. R. Cant '33.)
Lady Somers. HT. (Clark; NRS. Vic. '30.)
Lady Susan Birch. HT. (B. R. Cant '34.)
Lady Sylvia. HT. (W. Stev. '26.)
Lady Trent. HT. (Dot; Wheat. '40.)
Lady Ursula. HT. (A. Dick. '08.)
Lady Violet Astor. HT. (B. R. Cant '33.)

ROSA, continued

Lady Waterlow. CHT. (Nab. '03.)
Lady Willingdon. HT. (Dale '28.)
Lady Worthington Evans. HT. (A. Dick. '26.)
Lafayette. HPol. (Nonin; H&S., Dreer '24.) *Joseph Guy.*
La Fiamma. R. (M. H. Walsh '09.)
La France. HT. (Guill. f. 1867.)
Lal. HT. (Eas. '33.)
Lallita. HP. (Mal. '29.)
La Marne. Pol. (Barb. '15.)
Lamarque. N. (Mare. 1830.)
La Mascotte. CHT. (A. Schw. '33.)
La Melusine. HRug. (Spath '06.)
Lamia. HT. (Eas. '18.)
Lancashire Lass. HT. (Arch. '39.)
Lane. M. (Rob. 1860.)
La Neige. M. (Moranville '05.)
Laneii. M. (Laf.; Lane & Sons 1846, 1847, or 1854.) *Lane's Moss.*
Langley Gem. HPol. (Eacott; R. Murr. '39.)
La Noblesse. Cent. (S&N. 1856.)
La Parisienne. HT. (Mal. '36; C-P. '38.)
La Plus Belle des Ponctuees. G.
La Pologne. HT. (C. Cham. '38.)
La Reine Elizabeth. Pol.
La Rosiere. Prince Camille de Rohan.
Larry Burnett. Spn. (Skin. '25.)
La Rubanee. G. (Vib. 1845.) *Village Maid; Panachee Double; Perle des Panachees.*
La Tosca. HT. (Vve. Schw. '01.)
Laura. Cent.
Laurent Carle. HT. (P-D. '07.)
Laure Soupert. Mlt. (S&N. '27.)
Laurette Messimy. Mme. Laurette Messimy.
La Vie. HT. (Grosh. '31.)
Lawrence of Arabia. HT. (A. Dick. '38.)
Laxton's Pink Delight. Pol. (Lax. '33.)
Leading Lady. HT. (A. Dick. '35.)
Lee. G. (Vib. 1823.)
Leipsig. Shrub. (Kordes '39.)
Lemania. HT. (Heiz.; A. Meill. '36.)
Lemon Beauty. HT. (B. R. Cant '32.)
L'Enchanteresse. G. (Int. to France 1826.) *Grande Henriette.*
Leni Neuss. HT. (M. Leen. '28.)
Leonard Barron. HT. (Nic.; C-P. '31.)
Leon Chenault. HT. (P-D.; Gauj. '31.)
Leonie Lambert. HT. (P. Lamb. '13.)
Leonie Lamesch. Pol. (P. Lamb. 1899.)
Leontine Contenot. HT. (Ket. '35.)
Leontine Gervais. LC. (Barb. '03.)
Le Reve. LC. (P-D. '23.)
Les Amis de Troyes. HT. (Via. '35.)
Lesley Dudley. HT. (McGr. '32.) *Leslie Dudley.*
Lessing. Evbl. Semi-Cl. (P. Lamb. '14.)
Lestra Hibbard. HT. (J. H. Hill '35.)
Liberty. HT. (A. Dick. '00.)
Libia. HT. (Bor. '34.)
Li Bures. HT. (Dot '28.)
Lida Baarova. HT. (Bohm '34.) *Lida Paar.*
Lidka Bohmova. HT. (Bohm '29.) *Lidka Bohm.*

ROSA, continued
LIEBESBOTE. HT. (C. Weig.; Pfitz. '35.)
LIEUT.-COL. A. FAIRRIE. HT. (Bees '30.)
LIEUTENANT CHAURE. HT. (P-D. '10.)
LILETTE MALLERIN. HT. (Mal. '37.)
LILIAN. HT. (B. R. Cant '31.)
LILLIAN GIBSON. HBlanda. (Han. '38.)
LILY PONS. HT. (Brownl. '39.)
LIMELIGHT. HT. (Appleton & Son '34.)
LIPSTICK. Shrub. (Versch.; Dreer '40.)
LISBETH PRIM. HT. (F-L. '34.)
LISE CHIAVASSA. HT. (Buat. '31.)
LISE PALAIS. HT. (Gauj. '37.) *Opal* in U. S.
LITTLE BEAUTY. HT. (H&S.; Dreer '35.) *Crown of Jewels.*
LITTLE COMPTON CREEPER. LC. (Brownl. '38.)
LITTLE GEM. M. (W. Paul 1880.)
LITTLE MISS MUFFETT. HPol. (Le G.; C-P. '30.)
LITTLE NELL. HT. (Arch. '33.)
LITTLE PRINCESS. Pol. (G. Knight; Beckw. '37.)
L. J. DE HOOG. HT. (Leen. Br. '34.)
LLEIDA. HT. (Dot; H. Guill. '36.)
L'OBSCURITE. M. (Lach. 1848.)
LOCARNO. Pol. (deR. '26.)
LOIS CROUSE. HT. (Moore; Brooks & Son '37.)
LOLITA. HT. (Croib. '37.)
LONG JOHN SILVER. LC. (Hor.; J&P. '34.)
LONGWORTH RAMBLER. CHT. (Liab. 1880.)
LORD ALLENBY. HT. (A. Dick. '23.)
LORD BADEN-POWELL. HT. (M. Leen. '37.)
LORD CASTLEREAGH. HT. (A. Dick. '27.)
LORD CHARLEMONT. HT. (McGr. '22.)
LORD FAIRFAX. HT. (W. R. Gray '25.)
LORD LAMBOURNE. HT. (McGr. '25.)
LORD LONSDALE. HT. (A. Dick.; H&S., Dreer '33.)
LORD PENZANCE. HSb. (Penz. 1894.)
LORD ROSSMORE. HT. (Hall; McGr. '30.)
LORD STAIR. HT. (T. Smith '30.)
LORNA. HT. (B. R. Cant '36.)
LORNA ANDERSON. HT. (Clark '40.)
LORRAINE LEE. HG. (Clark; Hack. '24.)
LOS ANGELES. HT. (F. H. How.; H&S. '16.)
LOUISE. HT. (Prince '24.)
LOUISE BALDWIN. HT. (McGr. '19.)
LOUISE CATHERINE BRESLAU. HT. (P-D. '12.)
LOUISE CRETTE. HP. (C. Cham. '15.)
LOUISE KRAUSE. HT. (Krause '30.)
LOUISE MEHUL. G. (Parm.)
LOUISE ODIER. B. (Marg. 1851.)
LOUISE VERGER. M. (R. et M. 1860.)
LOUISE WALTER. Pol. (Walt.; P. Lamb. '01.)
LOUIS GIMARD. M.
LOUIS LE CARDONNEL. HT. (Mal.; A. Meill. '39.)
LOUIS PAJOTIN. HT. (Mal. '38.)
LOUIS PHILIPPE. C. (Guerin 1834.)
LOUIS RODIGER. HMacrantha. (Kordes '35.)
LOUIS VAN HOUTTE. HP. (Lach. 1869.)

ROSA, continued
LOUIS VAN TYLE.
LOUIS WALTER. HT. (Mal. '38.)
LOVE. CHT. (Caron; H. Guill. '35.)
LOVELINESS. R. (Chap. '35.)
LOVELY. HT. (H&S.; Dreer '36.)
LOVELY LADY. HT. (Asmus '34.)
L. R. MAY. HT. (Chap. '35.)
LUBRA. HT. (Fitz.; Haz. '38.)
LUCIA ZULOAGA. HT. (Dot '32; C-P. '34.)
Lucie Bertram. LUCY BERTRAM.
LUCIE MARIE. HT. (A. Dick. '30.)
LUCILE. R. (M. H. Walsh '11.)
LUCILE BARKER. HT. (Hicks '22.)
LUCILE HILL. HT. (J. H. Hill '39.)
LUCILE RAND. HT. (P-D.; Gauj. '30.)
LUCKY STAR. HT. (W. L. Armacost; A&R. '36.)
LUCY. CHT. (A. H. Will. '36.)
LUCY ASHTON. HSb. (Penz. 1894.)
LUCY BERTRAM. HSb. (Penz. 1895.) *Lucie Bertram.*
LUCYLE. HT. (Vestal '33.)
LUCY NICOLAS. HT. (Mal.; H. Guill., C-P. '35.)
LUDWIG OPPENHEIMER. HT. (Leen. Br. '32.)
LUIS BRINAS. HT. (Dot '32; C-P. '34.)
LULU. HT. (Eas. '19.)
LUMINATOR. Pol. (J. Smith; Eddie '38.)
LUMINOUS. Pol. (de R.; J&P. '32.)
LUM'S DOUBLE WHITE. HT. (Lum; Tot. '30.)
LUNA. HT. (D. T. Pouls.; Prior '25.)
Luxembourg. MARIE ADELAIDE.
LYCORIS. M.
LYDIA. HT. (Versch.; Dreer, H&S. '33.)
LYNDA HURST. HT. (Clark; NRS. Vic. '38.)
LYON ROSE. HT. (P-D. '07.)
MABELLE STEARNS. HSet. (Hor.; Ways. '38.)
MABEL LYNAS. HT. (McGr. '26.)
MABEL MORRISON. HP. (Broughton 1878.)
MABEL MORSE. HT. (McGr. '22.)
MABEL TURNER. HT. (H. Dick. '23.)
MAB GRIMWADE. HT. (Clark; NRS. Vic. '37.)
MACBETH. HT. (Bees '21.)
MADELEINE MONOD. HT. (C. Cham. '39.)
MADGE PRIOR. Pol. (Prior '34.)
MADGE TAYLOR. HT. (Clark; Haz. '30.)
MADGE WHIPP. HT. (Bees '36.)
MADGE WILDFIRE. HT. (Dobbie '32.)
MADISON. T. (Brant-Hentz '12.)
MAGENTA. HT. (M. Leen. '34.)
MAGNA CHARTA. HP. (W. Paul 1876.)
MAGNIFIQUE. Pol. (de R.; Sliedr. '28.)
Magnolia Rose. DEVONIENSIS and CL. DEVONIENSIS.
MAHAJA. HT. (Carb. '36.)
MAHARAJAH. HP. (B. R. Cant '31.)
MAIDEN'S BLUSH. HAlba. (Kew 1797.)
MAID MARION. R. (M. H. Walsh '09.)
MAID OF GOLD. CHT. (Raf.; Pt. Stktn. Nurs. '36.)
MAINZ. HT. (Leen. Br. '30.)
MAISON PERNET-DUCHER. HT. (P-D.; Gauj. '34.)
MAJORCA. HT. (Dot '38; C-P. '40 or '41.)

ROSA, continued
MAJOR FRANK HAYES. HT. (Bees '34.)
MAJOR SHELLEY. HT. (H&S. '37.)
MALAR-ROS. HT. (Kordes '32.)
MALEK-ADEL. G.
MALESHERBES. G. (Vib. 1834.)
MALVA. Pol. (M. Leen. '35.)
MALVINA. M. (V. Verd. 1841.)
MAMA DE MEYER. HT. (Lens '31.)
MAMAN COCHET. T. (Coch. 1893.)
MAMAN TURBAT. Pol. (Tur. '11.)
MAMA PECHTOLD. HT. ('39.)
MANA BOHMOVA. R. (Bohm '25.) *Manja Bohm.*
MANHATTAN. HT. (Asmus '36.) *Passion Rose.*
Manja Bohm. MANA BOHMOVA.
Marcella Baldge. SOUV. DE MARCELLE BALAGE.
MARCHIONESS OF LINLITHGOW. HT. (Dobbie '29.)
MARCHIONESS OF LONDONDERRY. HP. (A. Dick. 1893.)
MARCHIONESS OF LORNE. HP. (W. Paul 1899.)
MARCIA STANHOPE. HT. (Lill. '22.)
MARECHAL DAVOUST. M. (Rob. 1853.)
MARECHAL FOCH. Pol. (Lev. '18.) *Red Orleans Rose.*
MARECHAL LYAUTEY. HT. (Croib. '31.)
MARECHAL NIEL. N. (Pra. 1864.)
MARGARET ANDERSON. LC. (Thom.; H&S. '31.) *Bloomfield Novelty.*
MARGARET ANNE BAXTER. HT. (T. Smith '27.)
MARGARET BELLE HOUSTON. HT. (Vestal '29.)
MARGARET DICKSON. HP. (A. Dick. 1891.)
MARGARET DICKSON HAMILL. HT. (A. Dick. '15.)
MARGARET EGERTON. HT. (Chap. '31.)
MARGARETE GNAU. HT. (Krause '30.)
MARGARETE HERBST. Pol. (Herbst & Co. '34.)
MARGARET ELBOGEN. Pol. (Brada; Bohm '36.)
MARGARET HORTON. HT. (Hicks '21.)
MARGARET MCGREDY. HT. (McGr. '27.)
MARGARET TURNBULL. CHT. (Clark; NRS. of N. S. W. '31.)
MARGO KOSTER. Pol. (D. A. Koster '35.)
MARGOT ASQUITH. HT. (Prince '34.)
MARGUERITE CHAMBARD. HT. (C. Cham. '28.)
MARGUERITE GUILLARD. HT. (C. Cham. '15.)
MARGUERITE HEITZMANN. HT. (Baut. '30.)
MARGUERITE MOULIN. HT. (H. Moulin; Hamo. '38.)
MARGY. Pol. (Sauv.; C-P. '36.)
MARIA DE MELLO. HT. (Ket. '35.)
MARIA GUARRO. HT. (Dot '35.)
MARIA LISA. R. (Liebau & Co. '36.)
MARIANNE. HT. (Krause '33.)
MARI DOT. HT. (Dot '27.)
MARIE ADELAIDE. HT. (S&N. '12.) *Luxembourg; Grande Duchesse de Luxembourg.*
MARIE BAUMANN. HP. (Baum. 1863.)
MARIE-CLAIRE. HT. (A. Meill. '38.)
MARIE DE BLOIS. M. (M-R. 1852.)

ROSA, continued
Marie de Bourgogne. M. (M-R. 1853.)
Marie Gouchault. R. (Tur. '27.)
Marie Guillot. T. (Guill. f. 1874.)
Marie Lambert. T. (E. Lamb. 1886.) *White Hermosa.*
Marie Lavier. HT. (Buat. '35.)
Marie Louise. D.
Marie Maass. HT. (Maass '28.)
Marie Pavic. Pol. (Aleg. 1888.)
Marie-Rose. Mlt. (F. A. Truffault; Tur. '30.)
Marie-Rose Besson. HT. (Mal.; A. Meill. '39.)
Marietta Silva Tarouca. R. (Originated in Dendrological Gardens of Graf Silva Tarouca at Pruhonice '25.)
Marie Tudor. G.
Marie van Houtte. T. (Duch. 1871.)
Marion Cran. HT. (McGr. '27.)
Mariposa. Pol. (Allen '27.)
Marjorie Foster. CHT. (Burb. '34.)
Marjorie Palmer. LC. (Clark; NRS. Vic. '36.)
Marmion. HT. (Dobbie '34.)
Marquise de Castellane. HP. (Pernet p. 1869.)
Marshall P. Wilder. HP. (E&B. 1885.)
Martha Lambert. Pol. (P. Lamb. '36.)
Martha Washington.
Marthe Ancey. HT. (A. Schw. '32.) *Mme. Martha Ancey.*
Marvlous. HT. (B. R. Cant '37.)
Mary. HT. (Bent. '31.)
Mary Casant. Marytje Cazant.
Mary, Countess of Ilchester. HT. (A. Dick. '09.)
Mary Guthrie. HT. (Clark; NRS. Vic. '29.)
Mary Hart. HT. (G. B. Hart '31.)
Mary Hicks. R. (Hicks '27.)
Mary Lovett. LC. (Van F.; Lov. '15.)
Mary McHutchin. Pol. (B. R. Cant '35.)
Mary Merryweather. HT. (Merry. '25.)
Mary Murray. HT. (Prior '30.)
Mary Nish. HT. (Pac. Rose Co. '28.) *White Radiance.*
Mary Pickford. HT. (H&S. '23.)
Mary Russell. HT. (Clark '40.)
Marysa. Pol. (Brada; Bohm '36.)
Marytje Cazant. Pol. (Van N. '27.) *Mary Casant.*
Mary Wallace. LC. (Van F.; ARS. '24.)
Mary Warren. CHT. (Clark; NRS. of N. S. W. '31.)
Masarykova Jubilejni. HT. (Bohm '31.) *Jubilaire de Masaryk; Masaryk's Jubilee; Masaryk Jubileums-Rose.*
Matador. HT. (Van R.; J&P. '35.)
Mathilde Batz. HT. (F-L. '29.)
Mati Bradova. HT. (Brada; Bohm '34.)
Maud Cuming. HT. (A. Dick. '23.)
Maud E. Gladstone. Pol. (Bees '26.)
Mauna Loa. HT. (H&S. '37.)
Maupertuis. M. (R. et M. 1868.)
Maurice. HT. (McGr.; H&S. '33.)
Maurice Bernardin. HP. (Gran. 1861.)

ROSA, continued
Max Graf. HRug. (Bowd. '19.)
Max Haufe. HSb. (Kordes '39.)
Maxime Corbon. R. (Barb. '18.)
Max Krause. HT. (Krause; J&P. '30.)
Max Vogel. HT. (M. Leen. '29.)
May Banks. T. (Mrs. Banks '38.)
Mayfair. HT. (Bent. '35.)
Maylina. CHT. (Gers. '16.) *Mrs. Charles E. F. Gersdorff.*
Mayor Baker. HT. (Thom. '28.)
Mayor Cermak. HT. (Bohm '32; J&P. '34.)
May Robinson. Pol.
May Wettern. HT. (A. Dick. '28.)
McGredy's Coral. HT. (McGr. '36.)
McGredy's Gem. HT. (McGr. '33.)
McGredy's Ivory. HT. (McGr. '29.) *Portadown Ivory.*
McGredy's Orange. HT. (McGr. '36.)
McGredy's Peach. HT. (McGr. '33.)
McGredy's Pink. HT. (McGr. '36.)
McGredy's Pride. HT. (McGr. '36.)
McGredy's Salmon. HT. (McGr.; J&P. '40.)
McGredy's Scarlet. HT. (McGr.'30.)
McGredy's Sunset. HT. (McGr. '36.)
McGredy's Triumph. HT. (McGr. '34.)
McGredy's Wonder. HT. (McGr. '34.)
McGredy's Yellow. HT. (McGr. '33.)
Meg Merrilies. HSb. (Penz.; Keynes & Co. 1894.)
Melanie Lemaire. Hermosa.
Melita. R. (Eas. '34.)
Meme Buy. HT. (C. Cham. '35.)
Memory. HT. (B. R. Cant; J&P. '32.)
Mercedes. G. (Vib. 1847.)
Mercedes Gallart. CHT. (M. Munne; J&P. '32.)
Mercurius. LC. (Hor.; Ways. '40.)
Mermaid. HBc. (W. Paul '18.)
Merveille de Lyon. HP. (Pernet p. 1882.)
Merveille des Rouges. Pol. (Dub. '11.)
Mevrouw A. H. de Beaufort. HT. (Van R. '34.)
Mevrouw G. A. van Rossem. HT. (Van R. '26.)
Mevrouw Lala Philips. HT. (Leen. Br. '31.)
Mevrouw L. C. van Gendt. HT. (Van R. '25.)
Mevrouw Nathalie Nypels. Pol. (M. Leen. '19.) *Nathalie Nypels.*
Mevrouw van Straaten van Nes. HPol. (M. Leen. '32; J&P. '35.) *Permanent Wave* in U. S.; *Van Nes* in England.
Mevrouw Welmoet van Heek. HT. (Buis. '33.)
Micalea. G.
Micurin. R. (Bohm '36.)
Mignon. Cecile Brunner.
Mignonette. Pol. (Guill. 1881.)
Mikado. C. (Dobbie '29.)
Mikulas Ales. HT. (Bojan '36.)
Milady. HT. (Tow.; A. N. Pier. '14.)
Milano. R. (Ing. '23.)
Mildred Cant. HT. (B. R. Cant '35.)
Milkmaid. N. (Clark; Brundr. '25.)
Milky Way. R. (M. H. Walsh '00.)
Millie. Pol. (Russ '37.)
Ministre des Finances Rasin. HT. (Bohm '30.) *Minister Rasin.*

ROSA, continued
Minna. HPol. (Kordes '30.)
Minna Kordes. HPol. (Kordes; J&P. '38.) *World's Fair* in U. S.
Minnehaha. R. (M. H. Walsh '05.)
Minnie Dawson. R. (Daw.; E&B.)
Minnie Francis. T. (Griffg. Br. '05.)
Minuet. HT. (Thomp. '30.)
Miss Amelia Gude. HT. (Lem. '21.)
Miss America. HT. (Nic.; J&P. '38.)
Miss Annie Crawford. Annie Crawford.
Miss Australia. HT. (G. Knight '33.)
Miss C. E. Van Rossem. HT. (Versch. '19.)
Miss Cynthia Forde. HT. (H. Dick. '09.)
Miss Edith Cavell. Pol. (Meiderwyk; Spek '17.) *Edith Cavell.*
Miss England. HT. (B. R. Cant '36.)
Miss Flora Mitten. LC. (Law. '13.)
Miss Helyett. LC. (Fauq. '09.)
Miss Lolita Armour. HT. (H&S. '19.)
Miss Marion Manifold. CHT. (Admsn.; Brundr. '13.)
Miss May Marriott. HT. (T. Robin. '17.)
Miss Modesto. HT. (L. L. Brooks; Brooks & Son '34.)
Miss Rowena Thom. HT. (H&S. '27.)
Miss Willmott. HT. (McGr. '17.)
Mlle. Cecile Brunner. Cecile Brunner.
Mlle. de Morlaincourt. HT. (Walt.; ADR. '34.)
Mlle. Eugenie Verdier. HP. (Guill. f. 1869.)
Mlle. Franziska Kruger. T. (G. Nab. 1880.)
Mlle. Helene Cambier. HT. (P-D. 1895.) *Helen Gambier.*
Mlle. Henriette Martin. HT. (Rey.; Via. '36.)
Mlle. Marie Louise Bourgeois. M. (Corb. 1891.)
Mlle. Marthe Carron. R. (Merm. '31.)
Mlle. Marthe Moisset. HT. (Ducr. '35.)
Mlle. Rosa Bonheur. M. (Laf. 1852.)
Mlle. Sontag. G.
Mlle. Stella Mallerin. HT. (C. Cham. '26.)
Mme. Abel Chatenay. HT. (P-D. 1894.)
Mme. Achille Villey. HT. (Colo. '39.)
Mme. A. Labbey. HP. or G.
Mme. Albert Barbier. HP. (Barb.; Dreer '25.)
Mme. Albert Gilles. HT. (H. Guill.; Mal. '34.)
Mme. Alexandre Dreux. HT. (S&N. '21.)
Mme. Alfred Carriere. N. (J. Schw. 1879.)
Mme. Alfred Schissele. HT. (M. Leen. '30.)
Mme. Andre Gillier. HT. (Rey.; Via. '34.)
Mme. Anth. Kluis. Pol. (Kluis; K&K. '24.)
Mme. Antoine Montagne. HT. (Rich. '30.)
Mme. A. Roure. HT. (Lens '32.)
Mme. Arthaud. HT. (Mal. '38.)

ROSA, continued
MME. ARTHUR OGER. CB. (Oger 1899.)
MME. AUGUSTE NONIN. R. (Nonin '14.)
MME. BERARD. CT. (F. Levet 1870.)
MME. BERTHE DE FORGE. HT. (C. Cham. '35.)
MME. BOLLAERT. HT. (C. Cham. '38.)
Mme. Brosse. ALFRED COLOMB.
MME. BUTTERFLY. HT. (E. G. Hill '18.)
MME. CAMILLE. T. (Guill. f. 1871.)
MME. CARNOT. CN. (M-R. 1889.)
MME. CAROLINE TESTOUT. HT. (P-D. 1890.)
MME. CECCALDI. HT. (C. Cham. '38.)
MME. CHAMOUTON-MURGUE. HT. (C. Cham. '25.)
MME. CHARLES FREDERIC WORTH. HRug. (A. Schw. 1890.)
MME. CHARLES HAAS. HT. (Ket. '30.)
MME. CHARLES MALLERIN. HT. (Mal.; C-P. '39.)
MME. CLAUDE OLIVIER. HT. (Mal.; A. Meill. '39.)
MME. COCHET-COCHET. HT. (Mal.; C-P. '34.)
MME. COUIBES. HT. (F. Meill. '38.)
MME. CROIBIER. HT. (Gauj. '35.)
MME. D'ARBLAY. HMs.
MME. DE LA ROCHELAMBERT. M. (Rob. 1851.)
MME. DESMARS. HT. (Mal. '29; H. Guill. '32.)
MME. EDMOND LABBE. HT. (Mal. '39.)
MME. EDOUARD ESTAUNIE. HT. (Buat. '36.)
MME. EDOUARD HERRIOT. HT. (P-D. '13.) *"Daily Mail" Rose.*
MME. ELISE VILMORIN. HP. (Leveq. 1864.)
MME. EMILE DALOZ. HT. (H. Sauv.; J. Sauv., C-P. '34.)
MME. EMILIE VAN DER GOES. HT. (Versch. '25.)
MME. ERNEST CHARLES. HT. (Buat. '33.)
Mme. Eugene Marlitt. EUGENE E. MARLITT.
MME. EUGENE RESAL. C. (P. Guill. 1894.)
MME. FAURAX-LILLE. HT. (Rey.; Via. '33.)
Mme. Ferdinand Jamin. AMERICAN BEAUTY.
MME. FERNAND GENTIN. HT. (Mall.; A. Meill. '39.)
MME. FOJO. HT. (Dot; H. Guill. '37.)
MME. FRACULY. HT. (Ch. Siret-Pernet '29.)
MME. FRANCOIS BOLLEY. HT. (Gill. '34.)
MME. GABRIEL LUIZET. HP. (Liab. 1877.)
MME. GEORGES BRUANT. HRug. (Bruant 1887.)
MME. GEORGES PETIT. HT. (Ket. '28.)
MME. G. HEKKENS. HT. (F-H. '29.)
MME. GILLET LAFOND. HT. (M. Leen. '30.)
MME. GREGOIRE STAECHELIN. CHP. (Dot '27.) *Spanish Beauty.*
MME. HARDY. D. (Hardy 1832.)
MME. HELENE PARMENTIER. HT. (Sauv. '35.)
MME. HENRI GRIMM. HT. (Buat. '34.)

ROSA, continued
MME. HENRI GUILLOT. HT. (Mal.; C-P. '38.)
MME. HENRI LUSTRE. HT. (Buat. '24.)
MME. HENRI PATE. HT. (P-D.; Gauj. '29.)
MME. HENRI QUEUILLE. HT. (P-D.; Gauj. '28.)
MME. HENRI THIEBAUT. HT. (C. Cham. '31.)
MME. ISAAC PEREIRE. B. (Marg. 1880.)
MME. JEAN GAUJARD. HT. (Gauj. '37; J&P. '38.)
MME. JEAN PAQUEL. HP. (Walt.; ADR. '34.)
MME. JEAN RATY. HT. (Ket. '32.)
MME. JENNY. R. (Nonin '26.)
MME. JENNY GILLEMOT. HT. (P-D. '05.)
MME. J.-M. FRUCTUS. HT. (C. Cham. '35.)
MME. JOSEPH JULLIEN. HT. (C. Cham. '38.)
MME. JOSEPH PERRAUD. HT. (Gauj. 34.)
MME. JULES BOUCHE. HT. (Croib. '11.)
MME. JULES FONTAINE-LAMARCHE. HT. (S&N. '36.)
MME. JULES GOUCHAULT. Pol. (Tur. '13.)
MME. JULES GRAVEREAUX. CT. (S&N. '01.)
MME. JULES GROLEZ. HT. (P. Guill. 1897.)
MME. JULES GUERIN. HT. (Gauj. '31.)
MME. JULIEN POTIN. HRug. (Grav.; C-C. '13.)
Mme. Juliette. Name in England for JULIETTE E. VAN BEUNINGEN.
MME. KAHN. HT (Colo. '39.)
MME. KASTLER. HP. (Walt.; ADR. '34.)
MME. KLATZ. M.
MME. LAURETTE MESSIMY. C. (Guill. f. 1887.) *Laurette Messimy.*
MME. LEON PAIN. HT. (P. Guill. '04.)
MME. LOMBARD. T. (Lach. 1877.)
MME. LOUISE TREMEAU. HT. (Mal.; C-P. '31.)
MME. LOUIS LENS. HT. (Lens; J&P. '32.) *White Briarcliff* in U. S.
MME. LOUIS LEVEQUE. M. (Leveq. 1898, 1903 or '04.)
MME. LUCIEN PERRIER. HT. (Gauj. '38.)
MME. LUCIEN VILLEMINOT. HRug. (L'Hay '03.)
MME. MARIUS DEVIGNE. HT. (Rey. '30.)
Mme. Martha Ancey. MARTHE ANCEY.
MME. MASSON. HP. (Masson 1856.)
MME. MAURICE CAZIN. HT. (A. Schw. '31.)
MME. MELANIE SOUPERT. HT. (P-D. '06.)
MME. MICHEL DUFAY. HT. (Sauv. '32.)
MME. MONSEUR-FONTAINE. HT. (S&N. '31.)
MME. MOREAU. M. (M-R. 1872.)
Mme. Neumann. HERMOSA.
MME. NICOLAS AUSSEL. HT. (P-D.; Gauj. '30.)
MME. NICOLAS BOUDLER. HT. (Boud. '34.)

ROSA, continued
MME. NOEL. HT. (C. Cham. '39.)
MME. NOEL LE MIRE. HT. (Sauv. '34.)
MME. NORBERT LEVAVASSEUR. Pol. (Lev. '03.) *Red Baby Rambler.*
MME. PAUL BOUJU. HT. (C. Cham. '30.)
MME. PAUL DURINGE. HT. (C. Cham. '34.)
MME. PAUL OLLIVARY. HT. (A. Schw. '24.)
MME. PIERRE FORESTIER. HT. (C. Cham. '33.)
MME. PIERRE KOECHLIN. HT. (Sauv.; C-P. '35.)
MME. PIERRE OGER. CB. (Oger; C. Verd. 1878.)
MME. PLANTIER. HAlba. (Plant. 1835.)
MME. PLUMECOCQ. HT. (Lens '31.)
MME. RAOUL FAURAN. HT. (Sauv. '34.)
MME. RAVARY. HT. (P-D. 1899.)
Mme. Raymond Gaujard. Original name of OLYMPIAD.
MME. RENE LEFEVRE. HT. (Robi. '38.)
MME. ROBERT FORTIN. HT. (Buat. '35.)
MME. SAPORTAS. G.
MME. S. CROZA. HT. (Lap. '35.)
MME. SEGOND WEBER. HT. (S&N. '08.)
MME. SOUPERT. M. (M-R. 1851.)
MME. STEINBACH. HT. (Caron '34.)
MME. SUZANNE HERVE. HP. (R. Herve; Via. '36.)
MME. TAHA HUSSEIN. HT. (Colo. '39.)
MME. TROTTIER. HT. (M. Leen. '37.)
MME. VAN DE VOORDE. HT. (Mal.; C-P. '28.)
MME. VICTOR BOZZOLA. HT. (Soup. '35.)
MME. VICTOR LOTTIN. R. (Lot. '21.)
MME. VICTOR VERDIER. HP. (E. Verd. 1863.)
MME. VILLATE. HT. (Walt. '36.)
MME. VIRGILIO PIROLA. HT. (Lens '39.)
MME. VISSEAUX. HT. (Mal.; C-P. '36.)
MME. WALTER BAUMANN. HT. (Rey.; Via. '34.)
MODESTY. HT. (McGr. '16.)
MOHICAN. HT. (Thomp. '37.)
MOLLY DARRAGH. HT. (McGr. '30.)
MOLLY SHARMAN-CRAWFORD. T. (A. Dick. '08.)
MONARCH. HT. (Dobbie '26.)
MONS. LOUIS RICARD. HP. (Bout. 1894.)
MONTE CHRISTO. HP. (Font. 1861.)
MONTEREY. HT. (Lest. '33.)
MONT HAMEL. LC. (M. Constantin '37.)
MONTHYON. G.
MOON GLOW. LC. (Brownl. '37.)
MOONLIGHT. Evbl. Semi-Cl. (Pemb. '13.)
MOORE'S WONDER. (Moore '31.)
MORNING-GLORY. CHT. (Beckw. '37.)
MOSELLIED. Semi-Cl. (P. Lamb. '32.)
MOTHER. HT. (B. R. Cant '39.)
MOTHER'S DAY. HT. (G. Knight '37.)
MOUSSELINE. M. (M-R. 1880.)

ROSA, continued
Mousseux Ancien. M.
Mozart. Evbl. Semi-Cl. (P. Lamb. '37.)
Mrs. Aaron Ward. HT. (P-D. '07.)
Mrs. A. Hudig. Changed to Flaming June.
Mrs. A. J. Allen. HT. (Allen '30.)
Mrs. Ambrose Ricardo. HT. (McGr. '14.)
Mrs. Anthony Spalding. HT. (McGr. '34.)
Mrs. Anthony Waterer. HRug. (Wat. 1898.)
Mrs. A. R. Barraclough. HT. (McGr. '26.)
Mrs. Arthur Curtiss James. LC. (Brownl.; J&P. '33.) *Golden Climber.*
Mrs. Arthur Robert Waddell. HT. (P-D. '08.)
Mrs. Beatty. HT. (B. R. Cant '26.)
Mrs. Beckwith. HT. (P-D. '22.)
Mrs. Bertram J. Walker. HT. (H. Dick. '15.)
Mrs. Blamire Young. HT. (Young '32.)
Mrs. B. R. Cant. T. (B. R. Cant '01.)
Mrs. Brownell. HT. (Brownl. '42.)
Mrs. Calvin Coolidge. HT. (U. S. Cut Fl. Co.; F. R. Pier. '24.)
Mrs. C. E. Prell. HT. (Fitz.; Haz. '38.)
Mrs. Charles Bell. HT. (C. J. Bell; A. N. Pier. '17.)
Mrs. Charles E. F. Gersdorff. Changed to Maylina.
Mrs. Charles E. Pearson. HT. (McGr. '13.)
Mrs. Charles E. Russell. HT. (A. Mont.; Waban '14.) *Pink American Beauty.*
Mrs. Charles Lamplough. HT. (McGr. '20.)
Mrs. Charles Tennant. HT. (F. Cant '36.)
Mrs. Claude Aveling. HT. (Bees '29.)
Mrs. Courtney Page. HT. (McGr. '22.)
Mrs. C. W. Edwards. HT. (McGr. '24.)
Mrs. C. W. Thompson. R. (U. S. Dept. Agric.; S&H. '20.)
Mrs. David McKee. HT. (A. Dick. '04.)
Mrs. De Graw. Champion of the World.
Mrs. Dudley Cross. T. (W. Paul '07.)
Mrs. Dudley Fulton. HPol. (Thom.; Arm. Nurs. '31.)
Mrs. Dunlop Best. HT. (Hicks '16.) *Cleveland II.*
Mrs. Edward Laxton. HT. (Lax. '35.)
Mrs. E. J. Manners. HT. (Burb. '38.)
Mrs. E. M. Gibson. HT. (Clark '40.)
Mrs. Erskine Pembroke Thom. HT. (H&S. '26.)
Mrs. E. Wood. HT. (McGr. '34.)
Mrs. F. J. Jackson. HT. (Le G. '33.)
Mrs. Foley-Hobbs. T. (A. Dick. '10.)
Mrs. Francis King. HT. (Nic.; J&P. '36.)
Mrs. Franklin Dennison. HT. (McGr. '15.)

ROSA, continued
Mrs. Franklin D. Roosevelt. HT. (T&S. '33.)
Mrs. Frank Schramm. HT. (Schr.'34.)
Mrs. Frank Verdon. HT. (Bees '35.)
Mrs. Fred L. Lainson. HT. (Scit.; Lain. '34.)
Mrs. F. R. Pierson. HT. (F. R. Pier. '26.)
Mrs. F. W. Flight. LC. (Flight; Cutb. '05.)
Mrs. George B. Easlea. HT. (Eas. '39.)
Mrs. George C. Thomas. Evbl. Semi-Cl. (Thom.; B&A. '25.)
Mrs. George Geary. HT. (Burb. '29.)
Mrs. George Marriott. HT. (McGr. '18.)
Mrs. George Shawyer. HT. (L&S. '11.)
Mrs. Georgia Chobe. HT. (H&S. '37.)
Mrs. G. M. Smith. HT. (Bees '35.)
Mrs. Harold Alston. CHT. (Clark '40.)
Mrs. Harold Bibby. HT. (Bees '36.)
Mrs. Harold Brookes. HT. (Clark; NRS. Vic. '31.)
Mrs. Henri Daendels. HT. (Buis. '31.)
Mrs. Henry Bowles. HT. (Chap. '21.)
Mrs. Henry Morse. HT. (McGr. '19.)
Mrs. Henry Winnett. HT. (Dunl. '17.)
Mrs. Herbert Carter. HT. (F. Cant '34.)
Mrs. Herbert Hoover. HT. (Cod. '28.)
Mrs. Herbert Nash. HT. (Chap. '25.)
Mrs. Herbert Stevens. HT. (McGr. '10.)
Mrs. H. G. Johnstone. HT. (Bees '30.)
Mrs. H. R. Darlington. HT. (McGr. '19.)
Mrs. Hugh Dettmann. CHT. (Clark; NRS. Vic. '30.)
Mrs. James Garner. HT. (F. Cant '31.)
Mrs. James Shearer. HT. (W. Ferg. '23.)
Mrs. J. D. Eisele. HT. (H&S. '33.)
Mrs. J. D. Russell. HT. (Bees '30.)
Mrs. Jennie Deverman. HT. (Dev. '33.)
Mrs. J. F. Redly. HP.
Mrs. J. J. Hedley-Willis. HT. (Bees '29.)
Mrs. John Bell. HT. (J. Bell; Dobbie '28.)
Mrs. John Laing. HP. (Benn. 1887.)
Mrs. Joseph H. Welch. HT. (McGr. '11.)
Mrs. J. T. McIntosh. HT. (McI.; Brundr. '35.)
Mrs. L. B. Coddington. HT. (Cod. '31.)
Mrs. Lovell Swisher. HT. (H&S. '26.)
Mrs. Mabel V. Socha. HT. (H&S. '35.)
Mrs. MacKellar. HT. (A. Dick. '15.)
Mrs. M. H. Walsh. R. (M. H. Walsh '13.)

ROSA, continued
Mrs. Mina Lindell. (N. E. Han. '27.)
Mrs. Myles Kennedy. T. (A. Dick. '06.)
Mrs. Norman Watson. CHT. (Clark; Geelong H. S. '30.)
Mrs. Norris M. Agnew. HT. (Bees '34.)
Mrs. Oakley Fisher. HT. (B. R. Cant '21.)
Mrs. Oliver Ames. HT. (Versch.; Dreer '41.)
Mrs. Olive Sackett. HPol. (W&E.; Spath '31.)
Mrs. Oswald Lewis. HT. (F. Cant '36.)
Mrs. Oswald Smeaton. HT. (Eas. '32.)
Mrs. Paul Goudie. HT. (McGr. '32.) Formerly *Shining Sun.*
Mrs. Paul J. Howard. CHT. (H&S. '36.)
Mrs. Paul M. Pierson. HT. (Brclf. '30.)
Mrs. Percy V. Pennybacker. HT. (Vestal '29.)
Mrs. Philip Russell. HT. (Clark; Hack. '27.)
Mrs. Pierre S. du Pont. HT. (Mal.; C-P. '29.)
Mrs. Ramon de Escofet. HT. (Eas. '19.)
Mrs. Redford. HT. (McGr. '19.)
Mrs. R. G. Sharman-Crawford. HP. (A. Dick. 1894.)
Mrs. R. M. Finch. Pol. (Finch '23.)
Mrs. Robert Bacon. HT. (Bert. '34.)
Mrs. Roy Green. HT. (Clark '40.)
Mrs. Russell Grimwade. HG. (Grimwade '38.)
Mrs. Sam McGredy. HT. (McGr. '29.)
Mrs. S. K. Rindge. HT. (H&S. '19.)
Mrs. S. Paton. HT. (McGr. '28.)
Mrs. T. B. Doxford. HT. (A. Dick. '32.)
Mrs. Theonville van Berkel. HT. (Buis. '35.)
Mrs. Tom Whitehead. HT. (T. M. Whitehead; Beckw. '38.)
Mrs. Tresham Gilbey. HT. (Chap. '23.)
Mrs. U. M. Rose. HT. (Vestal '31.)
Mrs. van Beresteyn-Frowein. HT. (Buis. '35.)
Mrs. Vandenbergh. HT. (Buis. '38.)
Mrs. Verschuren. HT. (Versch.; Dreer '37.) *R. M. S. Queen Mary* in U. S.
Mrs. Wakefield Christie-Miller. HT. (McGr. '09.)
Mrs. Walter Brace. HT. (Beckw. '39.)
Mrs. Warren E. Lenon. HT. (E. G. Hill; Vestal '24.)
Mrs. Wemyss Quin. HT. (A. Dick. '14.)
Mrs. W. E. Nickerson. HT. (McGr.; H&S., Dreer '27.)
Mrs. W. H. Cutbush. Pol. (Lev. '07.)
Mrs. William C. Egan. HT. (H&S. '22.)
Mrs. William Sprott. HT. (McGr. '38.)
Mrs. W. J. Grant. HT. (A. Dick. 1895.) *Belle Siebrecht.*
Mrs. Wm. G. Koning. Pol. (K&K. '17.)

ROSA, continued
M. S. Hershey. HT. (Cod. '40.)
Muriel. HT. (Arch. '29.)
Mur-Ray. HT. (Mur. '36.)
Murray Hill. HT. (Cod. '39.)
Musette. HPol. (Tant. '36.)
Mutter Brada. HT. (Brada '34.)
Naarden Red. HT. (Van R. '32.)
Nair. Evbl. Semi-Cl. (C. Cham. '36.)
Nancy. HT. (W. Ferg. '30.)
Nancy. HT. (Mal.; H. Guill. '34.)
Nancy Hayward. HG. (Clark; NRS. Vic. '37.)
Nancy Wilson. HT. (Clark '40.)
Nanjemoy. CHT. (Cross '37.)
Napoleon. G. (Hardy 1846.)
Narcisse de Salvandy. G. (Van H. 1843.)
Natalie Bottner. HT. (Bott. '09.)
Nathalie Nypels. Mevrouw Nathalie Nypels.
National Emblem. HT. (McGr. '15.)
National Flower Guild. HT. (Mal. '27; C-P. '30.)
Neala. G. (Vib. 1822.)
Neige d'Avril. R. (Robi. '08.)
Neige Parfum. HT. (Mal.; A. Meill. '39.)
Nelkenrose. F. J. Grootendorst.
Nellie E. Hillock. HT. (Hillk. '34.)
Nemesis. C. (Bizard 1836.)
Nemo. HRug. Probably Amelie Gravereaux.
Neon. HT. (Nic.; Beckw. '36.)
Neron. G. (Laf. 1841.)
Nestor. G.
Nestor Bolderdijk. HT. (M. Leen. '38.)
Nevada. Shrub. (Dot '27.)
Neville Chamberlain. HT. (Lens '39; J&P. '40.)
New Century. HRug. (Van F.; C&J. '00.)
New Dawn. LC. (Som.; Dreer '30.) *Everblooming Dr. W. Van Fleet.*
New Haven Queen. HT. (Grillo '39.)
New Moonlight. HT. (W. M. Elmer; Elmer's Nurs. '35.)
Nicole. HT. (Gauj.; C-P. '31.)
Nigger Boy. HT. (G. Knight '33.)
Night. HT. (McGr. '21.) Formerly *Lady Sackville.*
Nigrette. HT. (Krause; C-P. '34.)
Nilsson Guy. HPol. (M. Leen. '30.)
Ninon Vallin. HT. (Gauj. '36.)
Niphetos. T. (Bougere 1843.)
Nippy. HT. (B. R. Cant '32.)
Noella Nabonnand. CT. (Nab. '01.)
Nokomis. R. (M. H. Walsh '18.)
Nona. HT. (Eas. '24.)
Nonin. HT. (Mal. '38.)
Nora Cuningham. CHT. (Clark; Hack. '20.)
Norfolk Harmony. HT. (Le G. '40.)
Norman. HT. (A. Dick. '34.)
Normandie. R. (Nonin '29.)
Norman Lambert. HT. (McGr. '26.)
Norman Rogers. HT. (Chap. '33.)
Nottingham. HT. (R. Robin.; Wheat. '38.)
Nouveau Vulcain. G.
Nouvelle Pivoine. G.
Nouvelle Transparente. G. (Miel. 1835.)
Nova Zembla. HRug. (Mees '07.)
Nubian. CHP. (B&A. '37.)

ROSA, continued
Nuits d'Young. M. (Laf. 1852.)
Numa Fay. HT. (A. Richard; A. Meill. '38.)
Nuntius Pacelli. HT. (Leen. Br. '27.)
Nuntius Schioppa. HT. (Leen. Br. '31.)
Nuria de Recolona. HP. (Dot '33.)
Nur Mahal. HMs. (Pemb. '23.)
Nutzwedel. HPol. (K. Schmidt; Kordes '37.)
Nypels Perfection. Pol. (M. Leen. '30.)
Oakington Ruby. H. chinensis minima. (Bloom '33.)
Oakley. HT. (Fairh. '37.)
Oakmont. HP. (May 1893.)
Oberburgermeister Dr. Kulb. HT. (K. Nauheimer '31.)
Oberhofgartner A. Singer. HP. (P. Lamb. '04.)
Oberleutnant Immelmann. HT. (W. Henniger '36.)
Octavie. G.
Odine. HT. (Ketten '37.)
Œillet. Cent. (Dup. 1800.)
Œillet Flamand. G. (Vib. 1845.)
Œillet Parfait. G. (Fou. 1841.)
Old Black. M.
Old Blush. C. (Parsons 1796.) *Common Monthly.*
Old Crimson China. C. (1789.)
Old Glory. HT. (Hau. '30.)
Old Gold. HT. (McGr. '13.)
Old Pink Moss. Communis.
Olive Cook. HT. (F. Cant '34.)
Oliver Mee. HT. (S. Dick. '27.)
Olympia. HT. (Tant. '36.)
Olympiad. HT. (P-D.; Gauj. '31.) American name for *Mme. Raymond Gaujard.*
Ombree Parfaite. G. (Vib. 1823.)
Ondine. HT. (Ket. '36.)
Opal. American name for *Lise Palais.*
Opal of Arz. HT. (Brownl. '38.)
Ophelia. HT. (W. Paul '12.)
Ophirie. CN. (Goubault 1841.)
Oporto. HT. (Allen '30.)
Orange Cheer. Pol. (Letts '37.)
Orange Glory. HT. (M. Leen. '36.)
Orange Glow. Pol. (Versch.; Dreer '36.)
Orange King. Pol. (Cutb. '22.)
Orange Nassau. HT. (Versch.; Dreer '41.)
Orange Perfection. Pol. (Spek 27.)
Orange Rapture. HT. (K. Schmidt; Kordes '35.)
Orange Schoon. HT. (Lens '38.)
Orange Triumph. Pol. (Kordes; Dreer '37.)
Oratam. HD. (Jac.; B&A. '39.)
Oriole. R. (P. Lamb. '12.)
Orleans Improved. Pol. (Norf. '31.)
Orleans Rose. Pol. (Lev. '09.)
Oskar Cordel. HP. (P. Lamb. 1898.)
Oswald Sieper. HT. (Krause '32; C-P. '33.)
Otto Krauss. HT. (C. Weig. '31.)
Our Annie. HT. (Letts '37.)
Oxford. HT. (Prince '30.)
Padre. HT. (B. R. Cant '21.)
Painted Lady. HT. (F. B. Ward '31.)
Palacky. HT. (Bohm '36.)
Pamatnik Komenskeho. LC. (Bojan; Bohm '36.)

ROSA, continued
Pamatnik Krale Jiriho. HT. (Bohm '36.) *King George's Memorial.*
Panachee d'Angers. D. (M-R. 1879.)
Panachee Double. La Rubanee.
Papa Gontier. T. (Nab. 1882.)
Papa Gouchault. R. (Tur. '22.)
Papa Klein. HT. (Kat. '34.)
Papa Rouillard. R. (Tur. '23.)
Paradise. R. (M. H. Walsh '08.)
Paris. Pol. (deR. '29.)
Parkfeuer. HFt. (P. Lamb. '08.)
Parkzierde. B. (P. Lamb. '09.)
Passion Rose. Manhattan.
Passport. CHT. (Clark '40.)
Patience. HT. (McGr. '27.)
Patricia. HT. (Chap. '32.)
Patrick Anderson. HT. (McGr. '38; J&P. '40.)
Patsy. HT. (H. Dick.; Morse '30.)
Paul Bouclainville. HT. (Buat. '30.)
Paul Buatois. CHT. (Buat. '31.)
Paul Dauvesse. R. (Barb. '33.)
Paul Delepine. Pol. (Dele.; P-C. '33.)
Paul Duvivier. HT. (Lap. '32.)
Paulette. Pol. (Buat. '34.)
Paul Grampel. Pol. (Kersbergen '30.)
Paul Lucchini. HT. (Buat. '31.)
Paul Neyron. HP. (A. Levet 1869.)
Paul Noel. LC. (Tanne '13.)
Paul's Carmine Pillar. CHT. (Paul 1895.) *Carmine Pillar.*
Paul's Lemon Pillar. CHT. (Paul '15.)
Paul's Scarlet Climber. LC. (W. Paul '16.)
Paul Transon. LC. (Barb. '00.)
Pax. Evbl. Semi-Cl. (Pemb. '18.)
Pax Amanda. HBlanda. (N. E. Han. '38.)
Pax Apollo. HBlanda. (N. E. Han. '38.)
Pax Iola. HBlanda. (N. E. Han. '38.)
Pax Labor. HT. (C. Cham. '18.)
Paz Vila. HT. (M. Munne '31.)
Peach Blossom. Wich.-Pol. (Chap. '32.)
Peachblow. HT. (Cod. '37.)
Peaches and Cream. HT. (H&S.; Dreer '36.)
Pearl. HT. (Bent. '33.)
Pearl S. Buck. HT. (Kordes; J&P. '40.)
Pedralbes. HT. (Nad. '34; J&P. '35.)
Pedro Veyrat. HT. (Dot '32.)
Peerless. HT. (J. H. Hill '35.)
Peggy. HT. (Bees '34.)
Peggy Ann Landon. LC. (Brownl. '38.)
Pelisson. M. (Vib. 1848.)
Pembridge. HT. (E. Stevens '34.)
Penelope. HMs. (Pemb. '24.)
Pennsylvania. HT. (Neu. '34.)
Peon. H. chinensis minima. (de V.; C-P. '35.) *Tom Thumb* in U. S.
Peony of Fragrance. HP. (Pah. '33.)
Pepita. G. (Moreau f.)
Percy Izzard. HT. (H. Robin.; Wheat. '36.)
Perfection. Pol. (Prior '32.)
Perfume. HT. (Marr.; Beckw. '29.)
Pergolese. (R. et M. 1860.)
Perle d'Or. Pol. (Ramb.; Dub. 1884.) *Yellow Cecile Brunner.*

ROSA, continued
PERLE DES JARDINS. T. (F. Levet 1874.)
Perle des Panachees. LA RUBANEE.
Permanent Wave. American name for MEVR. VAN STRAATEN VAN NES.
PERPETUAL WHITE. M. (Laf.) *Quatre Saisons Blanc.*
PERSIAN YELLOW. HFt. (Brought to England from Persia by Sir Henry Willock 1837.)
PERSUE DE GOSSART. Cent.
PETER PAN. HT. (Wheat. '29.)
Peter Pan. HT. (G. Knight '35.)
PETER ROSEGGER. Evbl. Semi-Cl. (P. Lamb. '14.)
PETITE DE HOLLANDE. Cent.
PETITE LOUISE. R.
PETITE ORLEANAISE. Cent.
PETIT JEAN. HT. (Vestal '26.)
PHAENOMEN. HT. (Chot.; Bohm '34.) *Phenomenon.*
PHARISAER. HT. (W. Hin. '03.)
PHENICE. G. (Rob. 1843.)
PHILIBERT BOUTIGNY. HP. (Bout.)
PHOEBUS. HP. (1837.)
PHYLLIS. Pol. (Merry. '08.)
PHYLLIS BIDE. R. (Bide '23.)
PHYLLIS BURDEN. HT. (B. R. Cant '35.)
PHYLLIS GOLD. (G. H. Robinson; Wheat. '35.)
P CCANINNY. HT. (Lamm.; Arm. Nurs. '41.)
PICCIOLA INA. Pol. (Aic. '37)
PICTURE. HT. (McGr. '32.)
PIERRE AGU TANT. HT. (Gauj. '38.)
PIERRE CORMIER. Pol. (Tur. '26.)
PIERRE NOTTING. HP. (Port. 1863.)
PIERRETTE. HT. (Tant. '31.)
PIKE'S PEAK. Shrub. (N. C. Gunter; B&A. '40.)
PILARIN VILELLA. HT. (Dot '36.)
PILGRIM. HT. (Mont. Co.; A. N. Pier. '20.)
Pink American Beauty. MRS. CHARLES E. RUSSELL.
PINK CHARM. HPol. (Kordes; Dreer '38.)
Pink Cherokee. ANEMONE.
PINK CLUSTER. HT. (Morse '38.)
PINK DAWN. HT. (H&S.; Dreer '35.)
PINK DELIGHT. Pol. (Lax. '22.)
PINK GOLDEN DAWN. HT. (Bost. '38.)
PINK GROOTENDORST. HRug. (F. J. Groot. '23.)
PINK GRUSS AN AACHEN. HPol. (K&K. '29.)
PINK JEWEL. HPol. (Kordes; Dreer '40.)
PINK LAFAYETTE. HPol. (Grif. '25.)
Pink Ophelia. JOHN C. M. MENSING.
PINK PEARL. HT. (M. Leen. '24.)
PINK PET. C. (Lill. '28.)
PINK PRINCESS. HT. (Brownl. '39.)
PINK PROFUSION. HSet. (Hor.; Ways. '38.)
PINK PROSPERITY. HMs. (Bent. '31.)
PINSON. LC. (Barb. '09.)
PITTSBURGH. HP. (Schoe.; B&A. '29.)
PIUS XI. HT. (M. Leen. '25.)
PIXIE. H. chinensis minima. (de V.; C-P. '40.)
PLATO. Spn.
PLUKOVNIK SVEC. HT. (Bohm '35.) *Colonel Svec.*
PLZEN. HT. (Bohm '30.) *Stadt Pilsen; City of Pilsen.*

ROSA, continued
POEMA. R. (Brada; Bohm '33.)
POINSETTIA. HT. (H&S.; Dreer '38.)
POLAR BEAR. HP. (Nic.; J&P. '34.)
POLAR'S. LC. (Hor.; Ways. '39.)
POLLY. HT. (Beckw. '27.)
POMPON. Cent.
Pompon. G. (Joly 1835.)
Pompon. G. (R. et M. 1858.)
Pompon Ancien. POMPON DE PARIS.
POMPON DE BOURGOGNE. Cent.
POMPON DE PARIS. H. chinensis minima. (1839.) *Pompon Ancien.*
PONCTUEE. M. (Laf. 1846.)
POPPY. HT. (Arch. '39.)
PORTADOWN. HT. (McGr. '28.)
PORTADOWN BEDDER. HT. (McGr. '29.)
PORTADOWN FRAGRANCE. HT. (McGr. '31.)
PORTADOWN GLORY. HT. (McGr. '32.)
Portadown Ivory. MCGREDY'S IVORY.
PORTADOWN SALLY. HT. (McGr. '31.)
PORTO. HT. (Mal. '34.)
POULSEN'S COPPER. HPol. (S. Pouls.; D. T. Pouls. '40.)
POULSEN'S PINK. HPol. (S. Pouls.; D. T. Pouls. '39.)
POULSEN'S SCARLET. HPol. (D. T. Pouls. '41; C-P.)
POULSEN'S YELLOW. HPol. (S. Pouls. '38; C-P. '39.)
POURPRE DU LUXEMBOURG. M. (Hardy 1848.)
Prairie Belle. QUEEN OF THE PRAIRIES.
PRASIDENT HINDENBURG. Pol. (C. Bom; P. Lamb. '27.)
PRECOCE. M. (Vib. 1843.)
PREMIER. HT. (E. G. Hill '18.)
PREMIER SUPREME. HT. (Zieg. '27.)
PRESIDENT BOONE. HT. (H&S. '35.)
PRESIDENT BOUCHE. HT. (P-D. '17.)
PRESIDENT BRIAND. HP. (Mal.; C-P. '29.)
PRESIDENT CHARLES HAIN. HT. (Rey. '29; J&P. '32.) *Amelia Earhart* in U. S.
PRESIDENT COCHET-COCHET. HT. (Mal. '37.)
PRESIDENT DE SEZE. G. (Mme. Hebert.)
PRESIDENT DUHEIM. Pol. (Rey. '30.)
PRESIDENT DUTAILLY. G. (Dub. 1888.)
PRESIDENTE CARMONA. HT. (da Silva '37.)
PRESIDENT FERIER. HT. (Gauj. '38.)
PRESIDENT FRANKLIN D. ROOSEVELT. HT. (T&S.; Reyn. '33.)
PRESIDENT HERBERT HOOVER. HT. (Cod.; Tot. '30.)
PRESIDENT JAC. SMITS. HT. (Versch.; Dreer '28.)
PRESIDENT MACIA. HT. (M. Leen. '33.)
PRESIDENT MOREL JOURNEL. HT. (C. Cham. '34.)
PRESIDENT PAULMIER. Pol. (Tur. 32)
PRESIDENT PLUMECOCQ. HT. (Gauj ; C-P. '31.) *Director Plumecock.*
PRESIDENT VAN OOST. HT. (Lens '34.)
PRESIDENT W. H. TAFT. HT. (McC. '08.)
PRIDE OF NEW CASTLE. HT. (E. G. Hill; Hel. '30.)
PRIDE OF REIGATE. HP. (J. Brown 1884.)
PRIDE OF WALTHAM. HP. (W. Paul 1881.)

ROSA, continued
PRIMAVERA. HT. (Aic.; Robi. '36.)
PRIMEVERE. LC. (Barb. '29; Dreer.) *Primrose* in U. S.
PRINCE BERNHARD. HT. (Van R. '37; J&P. '40.)
PRINCE CAMILLE DE ROHAN. HP. (E. Verd. 1861.) *La Rosiere.*
PRINCE CHARLIE. HT. (Dobbie '32.)
PRINCE DE BULGARIE. HT. (P-D. '01.)
Prince Eugene. EUGENE DE BEAUHARNAIS.
PRINCE FELIX DE LUXEMBOURG. HT. (Ket. '30.)
PRINCESSE ADELAIDE. M. (Laf. 1845.)
PRINCESSE AMEDEE DE BROGLIE. HT. (Mal. '36.)
PRINCESSE DE BEARN. HP. (Leveq. 1885.)
PRINCESS ELIZABETH OF GREECE. HT. (Chap. '26.)
PRINCESS MARGARET ROSE. HT. (B. R. Cant '33.)
PRINCESS MARINA. HT. (H. Robin.; Wheat. '37.)
PRINCESS ROYAL. HT. (A. Dick. '35.)
Princess van Orange. American name for PRINSES VAN ORANJE.
PRINCIPE DI NAPOLI. HT. (Aic. '37.)
PRINSES BEATRIX. HT. (Buis.; Morse '40.)
PRINSES JULIANA. HT. (M. Leen. '18.)
PRINSES VAN ORANJE. Mlt. (de R.; J&P. '35.) *Princes van Orange* in U. S.
PRINS HAMLET. HT. (Mohr '27.)
PRINZ MAX ZU SCHAUMBURG. HT. (Schaumburg-Lippe '34.)
PRISCILLA. HT. (Mont. Co.; A. N. Pier. '22.)
PRODANA NEVESTA. Shrub. (Brada; Bohm '34.)
PROF. BENTO CARQUEJA. HT. (da Silva '36.)
PROF. C. S. SARGENT. LC. (H. Br. & T. Co. '03.)
PROFESSEUR BERARD. HT. (Lap. '30.)
PROFESSEUR DEAUX. HT. (P-D.; Gauj. '35.)
PROFESSEUR EMILE PERROT. D. (Brought from Persia by Prof. Perrot; Tur. '31.)
PROFESSOR IBRAHIM. HMacrantha. (Krause '37.)
PROFUSION. HT. (A. Dick. '39.)
PROLIFERA OF REDOUTE. Cent.
PROMISE. CHT. (F. Cant '29.) *Chin Chin.*
PROSPERITY. HMs. (Pemb. '19.)
PROSPER LAUGIER. HP. (E. Verd. 1883.)
PROVENCE ROSE. **R. centifolia.**
PRUDENCE. CHT. (Fitz.; Haz. '38.)
PURITY. LC. (H. Br. & T. Co. '17.)
PURPLE BENGAL. C.
PYTHAGORAS. Spn.
Quatre Saisons Blanc. PERPETUAL WHITE.
Queen Astrid. KONINGIN ASTRID.
QUEEN DOROTHY BELL. HT. (Stell; Stell Nurs. '40.)
QUEEN FRANCES CONNALLY. HT. (Stell; Stell Nurs. '39.)
QUEEN GERTRUDE ANNE WINDSOR. HT. (Dixie '36.)
QUEEN LOUISE BOREN. HT. (Nic.; Dixie '35.)

ROSA, continued
Queen Mab. C. (W. Paul 1896.)
Queen Margaret Hunt. HT. (Nic.; Dixie '36.)
Queen Marie of Jugoslavia. HT. (Hicks '35.)
Queen of Bath. HT. (Bees '31.)
Queen of Beauty and Fragrance. Souv. de la Malmaison.
Queen of Fragrance. HT. (W. Paul '15.)
Queen of Hearts. CHT. (Clark; NRS. Vic. '20.)
Queen of the Musks. HMs. (W. Paul '13.)
Queen of the Prairies. HSet. (Feast 1843.) *Beauty of the Prairies; Prairie Belle.*
Queensland Beauty. HT. (A&W. '34.)
Queens Scarlet. C. (Hallock & Thorpe 1880.) *Red Hermosa.*
Rachel. HT. (Pemb. '29.)
Radiance. HT. (J. Cook; P. Hend. '08.)
Radiant Beauty. HT. (Clev. Cut-Fl. Co. '34.)
Radio. HT. (Dot; C-P. '37.)
Rafaela de Pena. Pol. (Dot '38.)
Raffel's Pride. HT. (Raf.; Pt. Stktn. Nurs. '37.)
Ragged Robin. Gloire des Rosomanes.
Ramona. R. anemonoides. (Dietrich & Turner '13.) *Red Cherokee.*
Ramon Bach. HT. (Dot; C-P. '38.)
Raphael. M.
Rapture. HT. (T&S.; Rowayton Greenhouse Inc. '26.)
Raubritter. HMacrantha. (Kordes '36.)
Raymond Privat. Pol. (B. Privat '35.)
Rebecca. HT. (Pemb.; Ben. '30.)
Recuerdo de Doctor Ferrari. HT. (M. Munne '35.)
Recuerdo de Felio Camprubi. HT. (Nad. '31.)
Red Admiral. HPol. (Arch. '40.)
Red Baby Rambler. Mme. Norbert Levavasseur.
Red Better Times. HT. (Asmus '37.)
Red Boy. HT. (N. J. Han.; B&A. '39.)
Red Cherokee. Ramona.
Red Columbia. HT. (J. H. Hill '20.)
Red Damask. G. (Turn. 1551.) *Apothecaries' Rose.*
Red Dorothy Perkins. Excelsa.
Red Druschki. Ruhm von Steinfurth.
Red Echo. Pol. (K&K.; J&P. '32.)
Red Explorer. Mlt. (Pen. '28.)
Red Finch. Pol. (Stiel. '37.)
Red Frau Karl Druschki. Druschki Rubra.
Red Guard. HT. (Versch. '35.)
Red Hermosa. Queens Scarlet.
Red Hoover. (Lens '37.)
Redipuglia. HT. (Ing. '33.)
Red La France. Duchess of Albany.
Red-Letter Day. HT. (A. Dick. '14.)
Red Maman Cochet. Balduin; Niles Cochet.
Red Moss. M.
Red Moss. M. (Laf. 1863.) Henri Martin.

ROSA, continued
Red Orleans Rose. Marechal Foch.
Red Pharisaer. HT. (W. Hin. '27.)
Red Premier. HT. (Scott '24.)
Red Provence. Cent.
Red Radiance. HT. (Gude '16.)
Red Riding-Hood. Rodhatte.
Red Rose Marie. HT. (Mor. '38.)
Red Star. HT. (Versch. '18.)
Red Talisman. HT. (Aml. Br. '31.)
Red Tausendschon. R. (Walt. '31.)
Red Velvet. HPol. (Kordes; Dreer '40.)
Refulgence. HSb. (W. Paul '09.)
Regina. R. (M. H. Walsh '16.)
Regina Elena. HT. (Grillo '38.)
Reichspräsident von Hindenburg. HT. (P. Lamb. '33.)
Reine Astrid. HT. (Gauj. '38.)
Reine Blanche. M. (R. et M. 1858.)
Reine des Amateurs. G. (Mme. Hebert.)
Reine des Neiges. Frau Karl Druschki.
Reine d'Espagne. HP. (Font. 1861.)
Reine des Violettes. HP. (Mille-Mallet 1860.)
Reine Marie Henriette. CT. (F. Levet 1878.)
Reine Olga de Wurtemberg. N. (Nab. 1881.)
Rektor Foerster. HT. (C. Weig.; Pfitz. '36.)
Rembrandt. HP. (Van R. '14.)
Rene Andre. R. (Barb. '01.)
Rene Buatois. LC. (Buat. '36.)
Renee Brightman. HT. (A. Hurran '36.)
Rene Javey. HT. (Gill. '34.)
Reve d'Or. M. (Duch. 1869.)
Reveil Dijonnais. CHT. (Buat. '31.)
Revelation. HT. (Evans City Cut Fl. Co. '38.)
Revenante. G. (Miel.)
Rev. F. Page-Roberts. HT. (B. R. Cant '21.)
Reward. HT. (A. Dick. '34.)
Rex Anderson. HT. (McGr.; J&P. '38.)
Rhea Reid. HT. (E. G. Hill '08.)
Rheingold. HT. (M. Leen.; J&P. '34.)
Ria Wenning. HT. (M. Leen. '32.)
Richard E. West. HT. (A. Dick. '24.)
Richardson Wright. HT. (C-P. '31.)
Richmond. HT. (E. G. Hill '05.) *Everblooming Jack Rose.*
Rio Rita. HT. (J. H. Hill '31.)
Rio Rita. CHT. (W. M. Elmer; Elmer's Nurs. '35.)
Riviera. HT. (Dot '39; J&P. '40.)
R. M. S. Queen Mary. American name for Mrs. Verschuren.
Robert Duncan. HP. (A. Dick. 1897.)
Robin Hood. HMs. (Pemb. '27.)
Rochefort. HT. (Mal.; C-P. '35.)
Rochelle Hudson. HT. (Moore; Brooks & Son '37.)
Rochester. HT. (Nic.; J&P. '34.)
Rocket. HT. (Nic.; J&P. '35.)
Rodhatte. Pol. (D. T. Pouls. '12.) *Red Riding-Hood.*
Roger Lambelin. HP. (Vve. Schw. 1890.)

ROSA, continued
Roi Alexandre I. HT. (Gauj. '37.) *King Alexander I; S. M. Alexandre I.*
Roi de Pays Bas. Cent.
Romana. HT. (Ring. '38.)
Romance. HT. (Tow. '31.)
Romance. CHT. (Beckw. '33.)
Rome Glory. HT. (Aic.; J&P. '37.)
Romeo. LC. (Eas. '19.)
Ronald Healy. HT. (Dobbie '32.)
Ronsard. HT. (Gauj.; J&P. '37.)
Rosa Gallart. HT. (Dot '35.)
Rosa Gruss an Aachen. HPol. (Spek '30.)
Rosa × Hillieri. HSp. (Hil. '35.)
Rosalba. HT. (Bor. '34.)
Rosaleen. HMs. (Bent. '33.)
Rosaleen Dunn. HT. (McGr. '39.)
Rosalie. Rosella Sweet.
Rosalie Richardson. HT. (Evans '32.)
Rosa Mundi. G. (Vib. 1875.) **R. gallica versicolor.**
Rosa × Pteragonis. HSp. (Krause '37.)
Rosary. Roserie.
Rose Anne. CHT. (Thom.; Arm. Nurs. '38.)
Rose a Parfum de l'Hay. HRug. (Grav. '03.)
Rose Apples. HRug. (Paul '06.)
Roseate. CHT. (Clark; IHS. '31.)
Rose Bampton. HT. (Van R.; J&P. '40.)
Rose Berkley. HT. (McGr. '28.) *Souv. de Rose Berkley.*
Rose Bradwardine. HSb. (Penz. 1894.)
Rose Charm. HT. Scit.; Lain. '34.)
Rose d'Amour. HT. (Gauj. '36.)
Rose Dawn. HT. (Tow. '24.)
Rose de Provins. **R. gallica.**
Rose des Peintres. Cent.
Rose d'Or. HT. (Gauj.; J&P. '40.)
Rose du Barri. HT. (Arch. '40.)
Rose Hill. HT. (J. H. Hill '28.)
Roselandia. HT. (W. Stev.; Low '24.)
Rosella. Pol. (Prior '30.)
Rosella. CHP. (Dot; C-P. '31.)
Rosella Sweet. HT. (P-D.; Dreer '30.) Formerly *Rosalie.*
Rose Marie. HT. (Dorn. '18.)
Rosemary. CHT. (F. Cant '25.)
Rose Merk. HT. (F. Cant '31.)
Rosenelfe. HPol. (Kordes; Dreer '39.)
Rosen-Lambert. LC. (M. Vogel; P. Lamb. '38.)
Rosenpfarrer Meyer. HT. (S&N. '30.)
Rosenwunder. HSb. (Kordes '34.)
Rose of Castile. **R. damascena.**
Rose Poncheaux.
Roseraie de l'Hay. HRug. (C-C. '01.)
Roserie. R. (Witter. '17.) *Rosary.*
Rosette. HT. (A. Dick. '34.)
Rosette Delizy. T. (Nab. '22.)
Rosieriste Gaston Leveque. HT. (Dot '32.)
Rosieriste Pajotin-Chedane. Pol. (Dele.; P-C. '34.)
Rosine. HT. (Lens '35.)
Roslyn. HT. (Tow. '29.)
Rostock. Semi-Cl. (Kordes '37.)
Rosy Morn. Pol. (Burb. '30.)
Rotary-Lyon. HT. (C. Cham. '36.)

ROSA, continued
Rote Else Poulsen. Pol. (Koopmann; Tant. '34.)
Rote Mevrouw G. A. van Rossem. HT. (Kordes '34.)
Rote Rapture. HT. (J. Weber '34.)
Rotraut. Pol. (Grunewald '31.)
Rouge. Pol. (Versch.; J&P. '34.)
Rouge Mallerin. HT. (Mal.; C-P. '34.) Formerly *Henri Mallerin.*
Roxana. HT. (A. Dick. '33.)
Royal Beauty. HT. (Cod. '40.)
Royal Chinook. HT. (Chase '39.)
Royal Narbre. G.
Royal Red. HT. (E. G. Hill '24.)
Royal Scarlet Hybrid. LC. (Chap. '26.)
Royal Scot. HT. (Dobbie '28.)
Royal Visit. HT. (Eddie '38.)
Roze Koningin. HT. (Lens '38.)
Ruby. Pol. (de R.; Sliedr. '32.)
Ruby Manwaring. HT. (Long. '32.)
Ruby Talisman. HT. (Eddie '35.)
Rudolf Alexander Schroeder. HT. (Kordes '30.)
Rudolf von Bennigsen. Evbl. Semi-Cl. (P. Lamb. '32.)
Rudolph Kluis. HPol. (K&K. '22.)
Rudolph Kluis Superior. HPol. (Kluis '28.)
Rudolph Valentino. HT. (P-D.; Dreer '29.)
Ruhm von Steinfurth. HP. (C. Weig.; Schul. '20.) *Red Druschki.*
Rusalka. Semi-Cl. (Brada; Bohm '34.)
Ruskin (V. F. 1). HRug. (Van F.; ARS. '28.)
Ruth. HT. (Pemb. '21.)
Ruth Alexander. LC. (Wilb.; Bertsch '37.)
Ruth Shamburger. HPol. (Sham. '34.)
Ruth Vestal. CT. (Vestal '08.) *Cl. Bride.*
Ruzyne. HT. (Mikes '36.)
Sabaudia. HT. (Caz. '34.)
Safrano. T. (Beauregard 1839.)
Salet. M. (Lach. 1854.)
Sally. HT. (Spand.; Eddie '38.)
Sally Tite. HT. (S. Dick.; B&A., Arm. Nurs. '30.)
Salmon Beauty. Pol. (Wez. '29.)
Salmon Spray. HPol. (Grant; Ker. '23.)
Sam Buff. Afterglow.
Sam McGredy. HT. (McGr. '37.)
Sammy. HMs. (Pemb. '21.)
Samuel Pepys. HT. (B. R. Cant '34.)
Sanders' White Rambler. R. (Sand. '12.)
San Diego. HT. (Hieatt; Cal. Roses '37.)
Sangerhausen. Shrub. (Kordes '38.)
Sanguinaire. HRug. (Gill. '33.)
San Joaquin. HT. (Moore '39.)
San Jose. HT. (Vve. Deno.; J&P. '33.)
Santa Anita. HT. (F. H. How. '40.)
Sapho. HT. (Gauj. '33.)
Sarah Bernhardt. CHT. (Dub. '06.)
Sarah Darley. HT. (Wheat. '38.)
Sarah Maud. HT. (Mal. '34.)
Sarah Van Fleet. HRug. (Van F.; ARS. '26.)
Satan. HT. (Pah.; J&P. '39.) *Satanas; Joyce Lomax* in England.

ROSA, continued
Saturnia. HT. (Aic.; Robi.; J&P. '36.)
Saudade de Anibal de Morais. HT. (da Silva '35.)
Saverne. Ville de Saverne.
Scarlano. HSet. (Hor.; Ways. '38.)
Scarlet Beauty. HT. (Vestal '34.)
Scarlet Bedder. HT. (W. H. Hend. '27.)
Scarlet Betty Uprichard. HT. (Allen '30.)
Scarlet Button. Pol. (Dreer '32.)
Scarlet Flame. HT. (Bur.; Stark '34.)
Scarlet Glory. HT. (A. Dick. '25.)
Scarlet Queen. HPol. (Kordes; Morse '39.)
Schmids Rekord. Canina. (Schmid '30.)
Schneekopf. HP. (P. Lamb. '03.)
Schneelicht. HRug. (Gesch. 1894.)
Schneezwerg. HRug. (P. Lamb. '12.)
Schwabenland. HRug. (V. Berg.; Pfitz. '28.)
Schwabische Heimat. HT. (Pfitz. '34.)
Schwerin. LC. (Kordes '37.)
Scorcher. CHT. (Clark; Hack. '22.)
Seagull. R. (Pritchard '07.)
Seashell. R. (Daw. '16.)
Secretaire Belpaire. HT. (Lens '34.)
Semi. (R. Laxa, Rotz., grown from seed collected by Hansen on the dry steppes of Semipalatinsk, Siberia, '13.)
Senateur Potie. HT. (Dot '37.)
Senateur Vaisse. HP. (Guillot p. 1859.)
Senator Joe T. Robinson. HT. (Vestal '38.)
Senior. HT. (Span.; Hill Fl. Prod. '32.)
Senora Gari. HT. (Dot; C-P. '34.)
Senora Leon de Aujuria. HT. (La F. '35.)
Senorita de Alvarez. HT. (B. R. Cant '31.)
Senor Philippe. LC.
Sensation. HT. (J. H. Hill '22.)
Senta Schmidt. Pol. (R. Schmidt '30.)
Sentinel. HT. (Clark; Wyant '34.)
Sequoia. HT. (V-P.; Dreer '39.)
Serafina Longa. HT. (La F. '33.)
Sergent Ulmann. HT. (Mal. '30.)
Setina. CB. (P. Hend. 1879.)
Severine. HT. (P-D. '18.)
Shalimar. R. (Burr. '14.)
Sheelagh Baird. Pol. (F. Cant '34.)
Sheila. Pol. (J. Walsh; Beckw. '30.)
Sheila Bellair. HT. (Clark; NRS. Vic. '37.)
Shenandoah. LC. (Nic.; C-P. '34.)
Shining Sun. HT. (Van R. '32.)
Shining Sun. HT. (McGr. '32.) Changed to Mrs. Paul Goudie.
Shirley. HT. (A. Dick. '33.)
Shirley Temple. HT. (Engle; Wyant '36.)
Shot Silk. HT. (A. Dick. '24.)
Shower of Gold. R. (Paul '10.)
Siberian Rugosa. HRug.
Sierra Snowstorm. Shrub. (Moore; Hend. Ex. Gar.. Brooks & Son '36.)
Signe Relander. Rug.-Pol. (D. Pouls.; D. T. Pouls. '28–'30.)

ROSA, continued
Signet. HT. (Mont. Co. '38.)
Signora Piero Puricelli. HT. (Aic.; J&P. '36.) *Signora* in U. S.
Silver Jubilee. HT. (A. Dick. '37.)
Silver Moon. LC. (Van F.; P. Hend. '10.)
Silver Princess. HT. (Bur.; Stark '34.)
Silvia Leyva. HT. (Dot; C-P. '33.)
Simerose. HT. (F. Meill. '39.)
Simone Guerin. HT. (Mal. '29.)
Simone Mayery. HT. (C. Cham. '37.)
Simplicity. HT. (H. Dick. '09.)
Sincerity. HT. (Le G. '40.)
Sir Arthur Streeton. HT. (Clark '40.)
Sir Basil McFarland. HT. (McGr. '31.)
Sir David Davis. HT. (McGr. '26.)
Sir Henry Segrave. HT. (A. Dick. '32.)
Sirius. CHT. (Fitz.; Haz. '39.)
Sir Thomas Lipton. HRug. (Van F.; C&J. '00.)
Sister Therese. Soeur Therese.
Skyrocket. American name for Wilhelm.
Slava Bohmova. HT. (Bohm '30.)
Slavia. Evbl. Semi-Cl. (Brada; Bohm '34.)
Slavuse. HT. (Brada '36.)
S. M. Alexandre I. Roi Alexandre.
S. M. Gustave V. HP. (Nab. '22.)
Smiles. HPol. (Nic.; J&P. '37.)
S. & M. Perrier. HT. (Mal.; C-P. '36.)
Snowbank. HPol. (Nic.; J&P. '37.)
Snowbird. HT. (Hat.; C-P. '36.)
Snowdrift. R. (M. H. Walsh '13.)
Snowflake. R. (F. Cant '22.)
Snowhite Climber. LC. (Bur.; Stark '38.)
Snow Queen. Frau Karl Druschki.
Snowstorm. Evbl. Semi-Cl. (Paul '07.)
Snow White. HT. (Dot '38.)
Snow White. HT. (J. H. Hill '40 or '41.)
Sodenia. R. (L. Weig. '11.)
Soeur Amic. HG. (Lev.)
Soeur Therese. HT. (Gill. '30.) *Sister Therese.*
Solarium. R. (Tur. '25.)
Soleil de France. HT. (Merm.; J&P. '31.)
Soleil d'Or. Pernetiana. (P-D. '00.)
Soleil d'Orient. CHT. (Croib. '35.)
Solfaterre. N. (Boyeau 1843.) *Solfatare.*
Solliden. HT. (M. Leen. '24.)
Sombreuil. T. (M-R. 1851.)
Sonia. HT. (Hor.; Ways. '38.)
Sonnegold. HT. (Kordes '36.)
Sonnenlicht. HFt. (Kru.; Kiese '13.)
Sophie MacKinnon. HT. (Clark; NRS. Vic. '37.)
Sophie Ortlieb. HP. (Walt. '33.)
Sophie Thomas. CHT. (Thom.; H&S. '31.) *Bloomfield Loveliness.*
Source d'Or. LC. (Tur. '13.)
Southern Cross. HT. (Clark; Ball. H. S. '31.)
Southport. HT. (McGr. '33.)
Souvenir. HT. (A. N. Pier. '30.)
Souvenir d'Alexandre Bernaix. HT. (P. Bern. '26.)

ROSA, continued

Souv. de Amand Opdebeeck. HT. (Belge; Opde. '36.)
Souv. de Catherine Fontaine. HT. (Soup. '34.)
Souv. de Charles Gouverneur. HT. (C. Cham. '27.)
Souv. de Claude Vially. HT. (Rey. '31.)
Souv. de Claudius Denoyel. CHT. (C. Cham. '20.)
Souv. de Claudius Pernet. HT. (P-D. '20.)
Souv. de Denier van der Gon. HT. (V-P. '35.)
Souv. de Francis Borges. HT. (C. Cham. '32.)
Souv. de George Beckwith. HT. (P-D. '19.)
Souv. de Georges Pernet. HT. (P-D. '21.)
Souv. de H. A. Verschuren. HT. (Versch. '22.)
Souv. de Henri Faassen. HT. (F-H. '29.)
Souv. de Henri Venot. HT. (Lens '31.)
Souv. de J. B. Weibel. HT. (Sauv.; Gill. '30; C-P. '33.)
Souv. de Jean Ginet. HT. (E. Claudius Brenier; Buat. '35.)
Souv. de Jean Soupert. HT. (S&N. '29.)
Souv. de J. Mermet. R. (Merm. '34.)
Souv. de John E. Knight. HT. (J. Knight '28.)
Souv. de Josefina Pla. HT. (B. Munne '29.)
Souv. de Joseph Besson. HT. (C. Brenier '31.)
Souv. de Jules Nicolas Mathieu Lamarche. Pol. (Soup. '34.)
Souv. de l'Aviateur Olivier de Montalent. R. (Tanne '13.)
Souv. de la Malmaison. B. (Belu. 1843.) *Queen of Beauty and Fragrance.*
Souv. de Lilette. HT. (C. Cham. '37.)
Souv. de Lucienne Valayer. HT. (C. Cham. '38.)
Souv. de Marcelle Balage. HT. (P. Bern. '30.) *Marcella Baldge.*
Souv. de Maria Clotilde. HT. (Carneiro; Ket. '34.)
Souv. de Marie Therese Privat. Pol. (B. Privat '35.)
Souv. d'Emile Mayrisch. HT. (Ket. '32.)
Souv. de Mlle. Juliet de Bricard. Pol. (Dele.; P-C. '34.)
Souv. d'Emmanuel Buatois. HT. (Buat. '32.)
Souv. de Mme. Achille van Herreweghe. HT. (Van H.-C. '36.)
Souv. de Mme. A. Hess. HT. (C. Cham. '36.)
Souv. de Mme. Boullet. HT. (P-D. '21.)
Souv. de Mme. Canel. HT. (Gill. '32.)
Souv. de Mme. C. Chambard. HT. (C. Cham.; C-P. '31.)
Souv. de Mme. H. Thuret. HP. (Texier; Nab. '22.)
Souv. de Mme. Jules Pages. Mlt. (V. Reiter; Stock. '37.)
Souv. de Mme. Lefebvre. HT. (Rich. '29.)

ROSA, continued

Souv. de Mme. Salati-Mongellaz. HP. (Croib. '37.)
Souv. de Philemon Cochet. HRug. (C-C. 1899.)
Souv. de Pierre Notting. T. (S&N. '02.)
Souv. de Pierre Vibert. M. (M-R. 1867.)
Souv. de Rose Berkley. Rose Berkley.
Souv. de S. A. Prince. T. (Prince 1889.) *The Queen.*
Souv. de William Wood. HP. (E. Verd. 1864.)
Souv. du Capitaine Ferrand. HT. (Gauj. '39.)
Souv. du Docteur Albert Reverdin. HT. (P. Bern. '30.)
Souv. du Reverend Pere Planque. HT. (Pierre Bel '32.)
Souv. du Sergent Crette. HT. (C. Cham. '21.)
Souv. of the Old Rose Garden. HT. (B. R. Cant '29.)
Souv. of Wootton. HT. (J. Cook 1888.)
Sovereign. HT. (B. R. Cant '22.)
Spanish Beauty. Mme. Gregoire Staechelin.
Sparkler. Pol. (de R.; Sliedr. '29.)
Splendor. HT. (Sauv. '34.)
Springtime. HPol. (H&S.; Dreer '35.)
Staatspräsident Pats. HT. (C. Weig.; L. Spath '37.)
Stadt Pilsen. Plzen.
Staffa. Spn.
Stammler. HP. (Tant. '30.)
Stanwell Perpetual. Spn. (Lee.)
Stardust. HT. (Florex '39.)
Stargold. HT. (Brownl.; I.-S. Nurs. '36.)
Starlight. HT. (W&I. '34.)
Star of Persia. HFt. (Pemb. '19.)
Stately. HT. (Clark; Hack. '30.)
State of Maine. HT. (de B. '30.)
Steadfast. HT. (Clark; Stew. '39.)
Stella Polaris. HRug. (Jensen '00.)
Sterling. HT. (E. G. Hill '33.)
Stern von Prag. HRug. (V. Berg.; A. Faist '24.)
St. Ingebert. HP. (P. Lamb. '26.)
Stratford. HT. (Nic.; Dixie '36.)
Striped Moss. M.
Sublime. HT. (Aml. Co. '31.)
Sulcova Kladenska. Pol. (Sulc. '36.)
Summer Joy. R. (M. H. Walsh '11.)
Summer Snow, Cl. R. (A. Couteau; J&P. '36.)
Summer Snow, Dwarf. Pol. (C. H. Perkins; J&P. '39.)
Sunburst. HT. (P-D. '12.)
Sunday Best. CHP. (Clark; NRS. Vic. '24.)
Sundown. HT. (Scit.; Lain. '34.)
Sun Glow. HT. (Florex '34.)
Sunglow. HT. (Wheat. '36.)
Sun God. HT. (Klyn; Ways. '30.)
Sun Gold. HT. (W. M. Elmer; Elmer's Nurs. '35.)
Sungold. CHT. (Thom.; Arm. Nurs. '39.)
Sunkist. HT. (E. G. Hill '32.)
Sunlit. HT. (Clark; NRS. Vic. '37.)
Sunmist. HPol. (Kordes; Dreer '40.)
Sunningdale. HT. (Hicks '29.)
Sunny California. HT. (E. Hanshaw '36.)

ROSA, continued

Sunny Days. HT. (Versch.; Dreer '39.)
Sunnymount. HT. (Grillo '36.)
Sunny South. HT. (Clark; NRS. Vic. '18.)
Sun-Ray. HT. (Bent. '32.)
Sunrise. HT. (Dot '39.)
Sunset Glow. Canarienvogel.
Sunshine. Pol. (Robi.; Cutb. '27.)
Sunstar. HT. (A. Dick. '21.)
Suntan. HT. (N. J. Han.; B&A. '39.)
Super-Dupont. Changed to Dolly Madison.
Susan Louise. HG. (Adams; Stock. '29.)
Suzanne Albrand. Pol. (Tur. '30.)
Suzanne-Marie Rodocanachi. HP. (Leveq. 1883.)
Suzanne Michela. HT. (C. Cham. '32.)
Suzanne Villain. HT. (Ket. '35.)
Svatopluk Cech. LC. (Brada; Bohm '36.)
Svaty Vaclav. HT. (Berg. '36.)
Svornost. Pol. (Bohm '35.)
Swansdown. HT. (A. Dick. '28.)
Swantje. Pol. (Tant. '36.)
Sweet Adeline. HT. (J. H. Hill '29.)
Sweetheart. R. (M. H. Walsh '01.)
Sweetheart Rose. Cecile Brunner.
Sweet Lavender. Mlt. (W. Paul '12.)
Sweet Memorie. HT. (Hieatt '37.)
Sweetness. HT. (McGr. '19.)
Sweetness. HT. (A. Dick. '37.)
Sweet Seventeen. HP. (Clark; NRS. Vic. '23.)
Sweet Sue. HT. (Lamm.; Arm. Nurs. '40.)
Sylvia Groen. HT. (Groen '35.)
Symphony. HP. (C. Weig.; P. J. How. '35.)
Syracuse. HT. (Mal.; C-P. '30.)
Talisman. HT. (Mont. Co. '29.)
Tantallon. HT. (Dobbie '34.)
Tarantella. HT. (Tant. '36.)
Tausendschon. R. (J. C. Schmidt '06.)
Tea Rambler. Mlt. (Paul '04.)
Temno. HT. (Bohm '34; J&P.)
Templar. HT. (Mont. Co.; A. N. Pier. '24.)
Tess. Mlt. (Beckw. '39.)
Tetonkaha. HRug. (N. E. Hans. '12.)
Texas Centennial. HT. (Watk.; Dixie '35.)
Texas Gold. HT. (Wolfe '35.)
The Allies. Pol. (Heers '30.)
The Beacon. R. (W. Paul '22.)
The Bishop. HT. (A. Dick. '37.)
The Chief. HT. (Lamm.; Arm. Nurs. '40.)
The Doctor. HT. (H&S.; Dreer '36.)
The Fairy. Pol. (Bent. '32.)
The General. HT. (Pemb. '20.)
The Indian. HT. (Clark; Brundr. '39.)
Thelma. R. (Eas. '27.)
The Old-Fashioned Rose. HT. (Arch. '30.)
The Princess Elizabeth. HT. (Wheat. '27.)
The Queen. Souv. de S. A. Prince.
The Queen Alexandra Rose. HT. (McGr. '18.)
The Rajah. HT. (Clark; NRS. Vic. '37.)

ROSA, continued

THERESE BONNAVIAT. HT. (C. Cham. '34.)
THERESE SCHOPPER. HT. (Kordes '33.)
THERESE ZEIMET-LAMBERT. HT. (P. Lamb. '22.)
THIRZA. HT. (Bent. '32.)
THISBE. HMs. (Pemb. '18.)
THOMAS A. EDISON. HT. (P. Bern.; C-P. '31.)
THOMAS MILLS. HP. (E. Verd. 1873.)
THOR. LC. (Hor.; Ways. '40.)
Thoresbyana. BENNETT'S SEEDLING.
THORNLESS BEAUTY. HT. (Grillo '38.)
THORNLESS GLORY. LC. (Izzo '35.)
THUSNELDA. HRug. (F. Mul. 1889.)
TIP-TOP. Pol. (P. Lamb. '09.) *Baby Doll.*
TITANIA. Pol. (M. Leen. '38.)
TOKEN. HT. (Mont. Co. '33.)
TOKEN SUPREME. HT. (Grillo '40.)
TOMAS BATA. HP. (Bohm '32.)
TOM BARR. HT. (McGr. '32.)
Tom Thumb. American name for PEON.
TOM WOOD. HP. (A. Dick. 1896.)
TONY SPALDING. HT. (McGr. '33.)
TOPAZ. Pol. (Tant.; C-P. '35.)
TORESKY. Pol. (Padr. '31.)
TOWNSEND. Spn.
TREASURE ISLAND. HT. (Raf.; Pt. Stktn. Nurs. '38.)
TRICOLORE. G. (R. et M. 1863.)
TRICOLORE DE FLANDRE. G. (Van H. 1846.)
TRIGO. HT. (A. Dick. '31.)
TRIOMPHE ANGEVIN. Pol. (G. Dele.; P-C. '34.)
TRIOMPHE DE L'EXPOSITION. HP. (Marg. 1855.)
TRIOMPHE ORLEANAIS. Pol. (Peauger '12.)
TROJA. T. (Mikes; Bohm '27.)
TROUBADOUR. R. (M. H. Walsh '11.)
TURENNE. M. (R. et M. 1858.)
TURKES RUGOSA SAMLING. HRug. (Turke; Tesch. '23.) *Turkes Rugosa Seedling.*
TUSCANY. D.
Tuscany. G.
TWYFORD. HT. (Wat. '39.)
UHLAND. Semi-Cl. (P. Lamb. '16.)
ULRICH BRUNNER. HP. (A. Levet 1882.)
ULSTER GEM. HT. (H. Dick. '17.)
UNA. HCanina. (Paul '00.)
UNA WALLACE. HT. (McGr. '21.)
UNIQUE. M.
UNIQUE BLANCHE. Cent. (Grim. 1778.) *Unique; White Provence.*
URDH. HT. (Tant. '30.)
VAINQUEUR. HT. (Heiz.; A. Meill.'37.)
VALERIE. HPol. (Chap. '32.)
VALERIE PURVES. HT. (Clark '40.)
VAN ARTEVELDE. G.
VANDAEL. M. (Laf. 1850.)
VANGUARD. HRug. (G. A. Stev.; J&P. '32.)
VANITY. HMs. (Pemb. '20.)
Van Nes. Name given to MEVR. VAN STRAATEN VAN NES in England.
VAN ROSSEM'S JUBILEE. HT. (Van R. '37.)
VARIEGATA DI BOLOGNA. Cent. (Lodi '09.)

ROSA, continued

VATERLAND. HT. (V. Ber.; Pfitz. '28.)
VEILCHENBLAU. R. (J. C. Schmidt '09.)
VELSHEDA. HT. (F. Cant '36.)
VENETIAN PINK. HT. (Bur. '37.)
VERA ALLEN. HT. (A. Dick. '39.)
VERA CRUZ. HT. (da Silva '38.)
VERDUN. Pol. (Barb. '18.)
VESTAL'S CORAL GEM. HT. (Vestal '39.)
VESTAL'S RED. HT. (Vestal '37.)
VESTAL'S TORCHLIGHT. HT. (Vestal '39.)
VESUVIUS. HT. (McGr. '23.)
VIANDEN. HT. (Ket. '32.)
Vice-President Curtis. Changed to AUTUMN QUEEN.
VICK'S CAPRICE. HP. (Vick 1891.)
VICOMTESSE PIERRE DU FOU. CHT. (Sauv. '23.)
VICTOR FERRANT. HT. (Ket. '33.)
VICTOR HUGO. HP. (J. Schw. 1885.)
VICTORIA HARRINGTON. HT. (Thom.; H&S. '31.)
VICTORIA REGINA. HT. (Hillk. '38.)
VICTOR MAGNIN. Pol. (J. van Gelderen '30.)
VICTOR TESCHENDORFF. HT. (Ebel.; Tesch. '20.)
VICTOR VERDIER. HP. (Lach. 1852.)
VIERGE DE CLERY. Cent. (Baron Veillard 1888.)
VIERLANDEN. HT. (Kordes '32.)
VIKTORIA ADELHEID. HT. (Kordes '32.)
VILLA DE BILBAO. HT. (La F. '33.)
Village Maid. LA RUBANEE.
VILLE D'ANGERS. HT. (Del. '34.)
Ville de Grenoble. GRENOBLE.
VILLE DE MALINES. HT. (Lens '29.)
VILLE DE PARIS. HT. (P-D. '26.)
VILLE DE SAVERNE. HT. (Heiz. '37.) *Saverne.*
VILLE DU HAVRE. HT. (Cay.; Tur. '31.)
VIOLACEE. M. (S&N. 1876.)
VIOLET SIMPSON. HT. (Simp.; Lax.; H&S. '30.)
VIOLETTE. R. (Tur. '21.)
VIOLET WILTON. HT. (Ket. '30.)
VIOLINISTA COSTA. Pol. (Nad. '36.)
VIRA. HRug. (Bohm '36.)
VIRGINIA. LC. (Nic.; C-P. '34.)
VIRGINIA DARE. HT. (Thomp. '24.)
Virginia R. Coxe. GRUSS AN TEPLITZ.
VISCOUNTESS CHARLEMONT. HT. (McGr. '37.)
VIUDA VERDAGUER. HT. (Dot '34.)
VIVID MASON. HT. (Mason; McL. '34.)
VLTAVA. LC. (Bohm '36.)
VON HOTZENDORF. HP. (J. C. Schmidt '16.)
VON LILIENCRON. Semi-Cl. (P. Lamb. '16.)
W. A. BILNEY. HT. (Eas. '27.)
WALDTRAUT NIELSEN. M.
WALTER BENTLEY. HT. (H. Robin.; Wheat. '38.)
WALTER C. CLARK. HT. (W. Paul '17.)
WAR PAINT. HT. (Clark; Hack. '30.)
WARRAWEE. HT. (Fitz.; C-P. '34.)
WARTBURG. R. (Kiese '10.)
WASAGAMING. HRug. (Skin. '38.)
WATCHUNG. HT. (Did. '32.)
W. C. GAUNT. HT. (A. Dick. '16.)

ROSA, continued

W. E. CHAPLIN. HT. (Chap. '29.)
WEDDIGEN. HT. (P. Lamb. '16.)
WEDDING BELLS. R. (M. H. Walsh '06.)
WELLESLEY. HT. (A. Mont. '05.)
WENDY BARRIE. Pol. (Beckw. '36.)
WERNER DIRKS. HMacrantha. (Kordes '37.)
WESTERN GOLD. HT. (West. Rose Co. '32.)
WESTFIELD SCARLET. HT. (H. Morse '31.)
WESTFIELD STAR. HT. (H. Morse '22.)
W. E. WALLACE. HT. (H. Dick. '22.)
WE ZAIR. Cent.
W. FREELAND KENDRICK. HT. (Thom.; B&A. '20.) *Bloomfield Endurance.*
W. G. A. RIDDER V. RAPPARD. HT. (Buis. '36.)
W. H. DUNALLAN. HT. (Clark; NRS. Vic. '39.)
WHITE AACHEN. Pol. (West. Rose Co. '37.)
White American Beauty. FRAU KARL DRUSCHKI.
White Baby Rambler. KATHARINA ZEIMET.
White Banksia. **R. banksiae alboplena.**
WHITE BATH. M. (Salter 1810 or 1817.) *White Moss.*
White Briarcliff. American name for MME. LOUIS LENS.
White Cherokee Rose. **R. laevigata,** or *Cherokee.*
WHITE DOROTHY. R. (B. R. Cant '08.) *White Dorothy Perkins.*
WHITE ENSIGN. HT. (McGr. '25.)
WHITE FINCH. Pol. (Stiel. '37.)
White Finch. Pol. (Eas. '39.)
White La France. AUGUSTINE GUINOISSEAU.
WHITE MAMAN COCHET. T. (J. Cook 1896.)
White Moss. BLANCHE MOREAU, WHITE BATH and COMTESSE DE MURINAIS.
WHITE OPHELIA. HT. (Clev. Cut-Fl. Co.; E. G. Hill, Clev. Cut-Fl. Co. '20.)
WHITE ORLEANS. Pol. (Van Eyk '20.)
WHITE PET. C. (Henderson 1879.)
White Provence. UNIQUE BLANCHE.
White Radiance. MARY NISH.
WHITE SEDUCTION. Pol.
WHITE TAUSENDSCHON. R. (W. Paul '13.)
WICHMOSS. R. (Barb. '11.)
WILDWOOD. HT. (H&S. '37.)
WILHELM. Shrub. (Kordes '34.) *Skyrocket* in U. S.
WILHELM BREDER. HT. (Kordes; Dreer '33.) *Glowing Sunset* in U. S.
WILHELM KAUTH. HT. (W. Kauth '32.)
WILHELM KORDES. HT. (Kordes '22.)
WILLIAM ALLEN RICHARDSON. N. (Vve. Duch. 1878.)
WILLIAM C. EGAN. LC. (Daw.; H. Br. & T. Co. '00.)
WILLIAM E. NICKERSON. HT. (Eas. '28.)
WILLIAM F. DREER. HT. (H&S. '20.)
WILLIAM F. EKAS. HT. (Crem. '35.)
WILLIAM LOBB. M. (Laf. 1855.)
WILLIAM MOORE. HT. (McGr. '35.)

ROSA, continued
William Orr. HT. (McGr. '30.)
William R. Smith. T. (Bagg; E. G. Hill '08.) *Charles Dingee; Jeannette Heller.*
William Shean. HT. (A. Dick. '06.)
Willmottiae × Moyesi. HSp. (Hil. '35.)
Willowmere. HT. (P-D. '13.)
Will Rogers. HT. (H. S. '36.)
Willy Chapel. HT. (Delhaye '30.)
Windermere. LC. (Chap. '32.)
Windsor. HT. (Chap. '29.)
Winifred. HT. (Chap. '30.)
Winsome. CHT. (Dobbie '31.)
Wolfgang von Goethe. HP. (L. Weig. '33.)
World's Fair. American name for Minna Kordes.
Xavier Olibo. HP. (Lach. 1865.)
Yawa. HBlanda. (N. E. Han. '40.)
Yellow Baby Rambler. George Elger.
Yellow Cecile Brunner. Perle d'Or.
Yellow Cochet. Alexander Hill Gray.
Yellow Condesa de Sastago. Golden Sastago; Jean Bostick; Yellow Sastago.
Yellowcrest. HT. (Le G. '35.)
Yellow Dot. HT. (J. H. Hill '38.)
Yellow Gloria. HT. (Bert. '36.)
Yellow Hoover. HT. (West. Rose Co. '33.)
Yellow Joanna Hill. HT. (C. N. White; White Br. '32.)
Yellow Maman Cochet. Alexander Hill Gray.
Yellow Mme. Albert Barbier. HP. (Lens '37.)
Yellow Moss. M. (Walt.; J&P. '32.)
Yellow Rambler. Aglaia.
Yellow Sastago. HT. (How. Rose Co. '39.)
Yellow Shot Silk. HT. (Beckw. '34.)
Yellow Talisman. HT. (Eddie '35.)
York and Lancaster (*R. damascena versicolor*). D. (Described by Monardes 1551.)
Yosemite. HT. (Nic.; J&P. '34.)
Youth. HT. (J W. Cook '35.)
Yvonne. R. (F. Cant '21.)
Yvonne d'Huart. HT. (Ket. '32.)
Yvonne Millot. HT. (Mal.; C-P. '35.)
Yvonne Printemps. HT. (Gauj. '39.)
Yvonne Rabier. Pol. (Tur. '10.)
Yvonne Vacherot. HT. (S&N. '06.)
Yvonne Virlet. HT. (Walt. '36.)
Zaid. Shrub. (C. Cham. '37.)
Zara Hore Ruthven. HT. (Clark; NRS. of S. Aus. '32.)
Zborov. Pol. (Bohm '35.)
Zenobia. M. (W. Paul 1892.)
Zephirine Drouhin. B. (Bizot 1868.)
Zika. Shrub. (N. E. Han. '27.)
Zlata Praha. HT. (Bohm '31.) *Das Goldene Prag.*
Zlaty Dech. HT. (Bohm '36.) *Golden Breath.*
Zulu Queen. HT. (Kordes; J&P. '39.)

Rosa-de-Montana . . . . . Coralvine, Mountainrose: **Antigonon leptopus**

Rosarypea . . . . **Abrus**
Jequirity R. . . . . . **A. precatorius**
Licorice R. . . . . . **A. laevigatus**
Mauve R. . . . . . . **A. pulchellus**

ROSCHE'RIA (*ROCHERIA*) Blackbristlepalm
See **PALM GENERA.**

ROSCO'EA . . . . Roscoea
alpi'na . . . . Alpine R.
cautleoi'des . . . . . Primrose R.
₵August Beauty. hv.
humea'na . . . . Hume R.
lutes'cens . . . . Yellow R.
purpu'rea . . . . Purple R.
—**capita'ta**
sikkimen'sis . . . . . . Sikkim R.

Rose . . . . **Rosa**
For hort. var. of Rose see **ROSA.**
Abyssinian Musk R.
R. moschata abyssinica
Agatha French R. . **R. gallica agatha**
Albert R. . . . . **R. alberti**
Allbristle R. . . . . . **R. persetosa**
Altai Scotch R.
R. spinosissima altaica
Amber Tea R. . **R. odorata ochroleuca**
Andrews Scotch R.
R. spinosissima andrewsi
∞Anemone R. . . . ∞**R. anemonoides**
Angleleaf R. . . . . **R. clinophylla**
Apothecaries French R.
R. gallica officinalis
Apple R. . . . . . . **R. pomifera**
Arkansas R. . . . . . **R. arkansana**
∞Arnold R. . . . . . ∞**R. arnoldiana**
Aromatic Sweetbrier R.
R. eglanteria duplex
∞Ascherson R. . . ∞**R. aschersoniana**
₵Attar Cottage R.
₵**R. alba suaveolens**
Austrian Brier R. . . . . **R. foetida**
Austrian Copper R. . . **R. f. bicolor**
Ayrshire Field R.
R. arvensis ayreshirea
Baldhip R. . . . . . **R. gymnocarpa**
Banks R. . . . . **R. banksiae**
∞Barbier R. . . . . . ∞**R. barbierana**
Barbstem R. . . . . . . **R. horrida**
Begger R. . . . . . **R. beggeriana**
Bigleaf R. . . . . . **R. macrophylla**
Blackberry R. . . . . . . **R. rubus**
Blackstem R. . . . . . . **R. melina**
Bloomystem R. . . . . . **R. mollis**
Blush Tea R. . **R. odorata erubescens**
∞Bourbon R. . . . . ∞**R. borboniana**
∞Bourbontea R. . . . . ∞**R. dilecta**
Bourgeau Prickly R.
R. acicularis bourgeauiana
∞Boursault R. . . . ∞**R. lheritierana**
Bracted R. . . . **R. multibracteata**
Bristly Farrer R. **R. farreri persetosa**
Bristly Nootka R. **R. nutkana hispida**
Bristly Scotch R. **R. spinosissima h.**
Browns R. . . . . **R. brunoni**
∞Bruant R. . . . . . . ∞**R. bruanti**
Buff Banks R. **R. banksiae lutescens**
Burgundy Cabbage R.
R. centifolia parvifolia
∞Burnet R. . . . . ∞**R. involuta**
Bushes R. . . . . . **R. rudiuscula**
Cabbage R. . . . . . . **R. centifolia**
California R. . . . . . **R. californica**
Carelian Prickly R.
R. acicularis carelica
Carolina R. . . . . . . **R. carolina**
Cathay Japanese R.
R. multiflora cathayensis
Chamisso Rugosa R.
R. rugosa chamissoniana
Cherokee R. . . . . . **R. laevigata**
Cherryhip R. . . . . **R. cerasocarpa**

Rose, continued
Chinese R. . . . . . **Rosa chinensis**
∞Chinosa R. . . . . . ∞**R. calocarpa**
Cinnamon R. . . . . **R. cinnamomea**
Climbing Evergreen R.
R. sempervirens scandens
Cluster R. . . . . . . **R. glomerata**
Coral R. . . . . **R. saturata**
Corymb R. . . . . . **R. corymbifera**
∞Cottage R. . . . . ∞**R. alba**
Crested Cabbage R.
R. centifolia cristata
Crimean Sweetbrier . . Barbstem R.
Cyme R. . . . . **R. cymosa**
Dahurian R. . . . . . **R. davurica**
Daintypetal R. . . . **R. graciliflora**
Dalmatian Gummy R.
R. glutinosa dalmatica
Damask R. . . . . . **R. damascena**
David R. . . . . **R. davidi**
∞Dawson R. . . . . ∞**R. dawsoniana**
Desert R. . . . . **R. stellata**
Dog R. . . . . **R. canina**
Double Apple R. **R. pomifera duplex**
Double California R.
R. californica plena
Double Cinnamon R.
R. cinnamomea p.
Double Roxburgh R. **R. roxburghi p.**
Double Rugosa R. . . . **R. rugosa p.**
Double Virginia R. **R. virginiana p.**
Doublewhite Banks R.
R. banksiae albo-p.
Doublewhite Rugosa R. **R. rugosa a.**
Drophip R. . . . . . . **R. pendulina**
∞Dupont R. . . . . . . ∞**R. duponti**
Dwarf California R.
R. californica nana
Dwarf French R. . **R. gallica pumila**
Dwarf Scotch R.
R. spinosissima nana
Eca R. . . . . **R. ecae**
Engelmann Prickly R.
R. acicularis engelmanni
Erectprickle R. . . . . **R. amblyotis**
Everblooming Chinese R.
R. chinensis semperflorens
Evergreen R. . . . **R. sempervirens**
Fairy R. . . . . . . **R. elegantula**
False Banks R. . . . **R. banksiopsis**
False-Indian Tea R.
R. odorata pseudindica
Farges Moyes R. . **R. moyesi fargesi**
Farges R. . . . . **R. fargesi**
Farrer R. . . . . **R. farreri**
Father Hugo R. . . . . . **R. hugonis**
Fedtschenko R. . **R. fedtschenkoana**
Fendler Woods R. **R. woodsi fendleri**
Field R. . . . . **R. arvensis**
Forrests R. . . . . . **R. forrestiana**
Fortunes Double Yellow
False-Indian Tea R.
∞Fortunes R. . . . ∞**R. fortuneana**
Fourpetal R. . . . . . . **R. sericea**
∞Frankfort R. . . ∞**R. francofurtana**
French R. . . . . **R. gallica**
Froebel Leatherleaf R.
R. coriifolia froebeli
Fuzzy Prairie R.
R. setigera tomentosa
Garland R. . . . . **R. sertata**
Giant Tea R. . . **R. odorata gigantea**
Giraldi R. . . . . **R. giraldi**
Glossy Virginia R.
R. virginiana lamprophylla
Golden Rose of China Father Hugo R.
Goldfruit Omei R.
R. omeiensis chrysocarpa

ROSE, continued
GOOSEBERRY DESERT R. Rosa stellata mirifica
∞GRAEBNER R. ∞R. mariae-graebnerae
GRASSLAND R. . . . . . R. agrestis
GREEN CHINESE R. R. chinensis viridiflora
GROUND R. . . . . . R. spithamea
GUMMY R. . . . . R. glutinosa
HAIRY CAROLINA R. R. carolina villosa
HAIRY ROXBURGH R. R. roxburghi hirtula
∞HARDYS R. . . . . . . ∞R. hardi
∞HARISON YELLOW R. ∞R. harisoni
HAWRAN R. . . . . . . R. hawrana
HECKEL R. . . . . . R. heckeliana
Hedgerow R. . . . . . . RUGOSA R.
HELEN R. . . . . R. helenae
HEMSLEY R. . . . . . R. hemsleyana
HENRY R. . . . . R. henryi
∞HIGHDOWN R. . ∞R. highdownensis
HIGHLAND DROPHIP R. R. pendulina oxyodon
∞HILLTOP R. . . . . . . ∞R. collina
∞IRISH R. . . . . ∞R. hibernica
∞IWARA R. . . . . ∞R. iwara
JACKS MAXIMOWICZ R. R. maximowicziana jacki
∞JACKSON R. . . . . . ∞R. jacksoni
JAPANESE R . . . . . . R. multiflora
KAMCHATKA RUGOSA R. R. rugosa kamtchatica
∞KOCH R. . . . . . . ∞R. kochiana
KOREAN R. . . . . . . R. koreana
KURDISTAN R. . . . . . R. britzensis
LARGEFLOWER CAROLINA R. R. carolina grandiflora
LEAFSEPAL R. . . . . . . R. stylosa
LEAFY R. . . . . R. foliolosa
LEATHERLEAF R. . . . . R. coriifolia
LITTLE DOG R. . . . R. canina exilis
LONGHIP DAVID R. R. davidi elongata
LONGLEAF CHINESE R. R. chinensis longifolia
LONGTOOTH R. . . . . R. longicuspis
LUCIA R. . . . . R. luciae
MACARTNEY R. . . . . . R. bracteata
MACOUN R. . . . . . . R. macouni
∞MALY R. . . . . ∞R. malyi
MANCHU R. . . . . . . R. xanthina
MANCOS R. . . . . R. manca
∞MARCY R. . . . . . ∞R. marcyana
MARGINED R. . . . . . R. marginata
MARRET R. . . . . . . R. marreti
MAXIMOWICZ R. R. maximowicziana
MEADOW R. . . . . R. blanda
MOHAVE R. . . . . . R. mohavensis
MONTEZUMA R. . . R. montezumae
MOSS CABBAGE R. R. centifolia muscosa
MOUNTAIN R. . . . . . R. montana
MOYES R. . . . . R. moyesi
MULLIGAN R. . . . . . R. mulligani
MURIEL R. . . . . . . R. murielae
MUSK R. . . . . R. moschata
MYRIADSPINE SCOTCH R. R. spinosissima myriacantha
NARROWLEAF FRENCH R. R. gallica incarnata
NIPPON PRICKLY R. R. acicularis nipponensis
NODFRUIT R. . . . . . . R. setipoda
∞NOISETTE R. . . . . ∞R. noisettiana
NOOTKA R. . . . . . . R. nutkana
NUTTALL SWAMP R. R. palustris nuttalliana
OMEI R. . . . . R. omeiensis
ONELEAF R. . . . . . . R. persica
ORIENTAL R. . . . . . R. orientalis

ROSE, continued
PALE SCOTCH R. Rosa spinosissima luteola
PALE SOLITARY R. . R. bella pallens
₵PALE WAITZ R. ₵R. waitziana macrantha
∞PAULS R. . . . . ∞R. pauli
PEAFRUIT R. . . . . . . R. pisocarpa
PEARHIP R. . . . . . . R. pyrifera
PECOS R. . . . . . . R. adenosepala
∞PENZANCE R. . . ∞R. penzanceana
PERSIAN MUSK R. R. moschata nastarana
PERSIAN YELLOW R. R. foetida persiana
PHOENICIAN R. . . . . . R. phoenicea
PIMPINELLA SCOTCH R. R. spinosissima pimpinellifolia
PINEYWOODS R. . . . R. pinetorum
PINK JAPANESE R. R. multiflora carnea
PINK MOYES R. . . R. moyesi rosea
PINK RUGOSA R. . . . R. rugosa r.
∞POKORNY R. . . . . ∞R. pokornyana
∞POLLINI R. . . . . . ∞R. polliniana
∞POLYANTHA R. . ∞*R. polyantha* Hort.
POMPON CABBAGE R. R. centifolia pomponia
PRAIRIE R. . . . . . . R. setigera
PRATT R. . . . . R. pratti
∞PRICKLYLEAF R. . . ∞R. spinulifolia
PRICKLY R. . . . . . . R. acicularis
PRIMROSE R. . . . . . . R. primula
PROSTRATE EVERGREEN R. R. sempervirens prostrata
∞PRUHONITZ R. . . ∞R. pruhoniciana
PURPLE RUGOSA R. . R. rugosa typica
PYRENEES DROPHIP R. R. pendulina pyrenaica
REDLEAF R. . . . . . . R. rubrifolia
REHDER CAROLINA R. R. carolina glandulosa
RICHARD R. . . . . . R. richardi
Roebuck Rambler . AYRSHIRE FIELD R.
ROSAMUNDI FRENCH R. R. gallica versicolor
ROULETT CHINESE R. R. chinensis minima
Rouletti R. . . . ROULETT CHINESE R.
ROUNDLEAF R. . . . . R. orbicularis
ROXBURGH R. . . . . . R. roxburghi
∞ROXOSA R. . . . . ∞R. micrugosa
∞RUBROSA R. . . . . . ∞R. rubrosa
∞RUGA R. . . . . ∞R. ruga
RUGOSA R. . . . . R. rugosa
SCENTLESS R. . . . . . R. inodora
∞SCHARNKE R. . . ∞R. scharnkeana
∞SCOTCHNOD R. . . . . . ∞R. reversa
SCOTCH R. . . . . . R. spinosissima
SCRAGGLE R. . . . . . . R. dumalis
SERAFINI R. . . . . . . R. serafini
SEVEN-SISTERS JAPANESE R. R. multiflora platyphylla
SHERARD R. . . . . . . R. sherardi
SHINING R. . . . . R. nitida
SICILIAN R. . . . . . . R. sicula
SINGLE CHINESE R. R. chinensis spontanea
SINGLE ROXBURGH R. R. roxburghi normalis
SMALLFLOWER R. . . . R. micrantha
SMOOTH JAPANESE R. R. multiflora calva
SMOOTH SCOTCH R. R. spinosissima inermis
SMOOTHSTEM PRAIRIE R. R. setigera serena
SOLITARY R. . . . . . . R. bella
SONOMA R. . . . . . R. sonomensis
SOULIE R. . . . . . . R. soulieana

ROSE, continued
∞SPAETH R. . . . . ∞Rosa spaethiana
SPALDING R. . . . . . . R. spaldingi
SPINELESS PRAIRIE R. R. setigera inermis
SUBSERRULATA R. . . R. subserrulata
SULFUR R. . . . . R. hemisphaerica
SUNSHINE R. . . . . . . R. suffulta
SWAMP R. . . . . R. palustris
SWEETBRIER R. . . . R. eglanteria
SWEETLEAF R. . . . . R. gratissima
SWEGINZOW R. . . . . R. sweginzowi
TEA R. . . . . R. odorata
THIRTYPETAL DAMASK R. R. damascena trigintipetala
THREADSTALK R. . . . . . R. filipes
THREELEAF R. . . . . . R. triphylla
THREELOBE CAROLINA R. R. carolina triloba
TINYLEAF R. . . . . . R. minutifolia
TITBIT FRENCH R. R. gallica conditorum
TOMENTOSE R. . . . . R. tomentosa
TURKESTAN R. . . . . R. laxa
VARIABLE CHINESE R. R. chinensis mutabilis
VARIEGATED DAMASK R. R. damascena versicolor
VEINY GIRALDI R. R. giraldi venulosa
VIRGINIA R. . . . . . R. virginiana
VORBERG R. . . R. harisoni vorbergi
∞WAITZ R. . . . . . . ∞R. waitziana
∞WARLEY R. . . . . ∞R. warleyensis
WATSON R. . . . . . R. watsoniana
WEBBS R. . . . . . . R. webbiana
WHIPLASH R. . . . . . R. caudata
WHITE CAROLINA R. R. carolina alba
WHITE-EYE R. . . . R. corymbulosa
WHITE LEAFY R. . . R. foliolosa alba
WHITEMOSS CABBAGE R. R. centifolia albo-muscosa
WHITE RUGOSA R. . . R. rugosa alba
WHITE SUNSHINE R. . . R. suffulta a.
WICHURA R. . . . . . R. wichuraiana
WILD BANKS R. R. banksiae normalis
WILD MANCHU R. R. xanthina spontanea
WILLMOTT MEADOW R. R. blanda willmottiae
WILLMOTT R. . . . . . R. willmottiae
WILSON R. . . . . . . R. sinowilsoni
WINGTHORN OMEI R. R. omeiensis pteracantha
∞WINTON R. . . . ∞R. wintoniensis
WOODS R. . . . . R. woodsi
YELLOW BANKS R. . R. banksiae lutea
YELLOW SCOTCH R. . R. spinosissima l.
YELLOWTHORN R. . . R. crocacantha
ZIGZAG R. . . . . . . R. elymaitica

Rose-acacia . . . LOCUST, ROSEACACIA: Robinia hispida

ROSEAPPLE . . . . Syzygium jambos

ROSEGENTIAN . . . . Sabatia
MARSH R. . . . . . . S. dodecandra
NEWENGLAND R. . . . S. kennedyana
PRAIRIE R. . . . . . S. campestris
SALTMARSH R. . . . . . S. stellaris
SLIM R. . . . . S. gracilis
SQUARESTEM R. . . . S. angularis

ROSELLE . . . . . Hibiscus sabdariffa
TALL R. . . . . . H. s. altissima

ROSEMALLOW . . . . Hibiscus
See also HIBISCUS.
CALIFORNIA R. . . . . H. californicus
COMMON R. . . . . . . H. palustris
CRIMSONEYE C. R. . H. p. oculiroseus
DESERT R. . . . . . H. coulteri

ROSEMALLOW, continued
FLOWEROFANHOUR . **Hibiscus trionum**
GREAT R. . . . . . **H. grandiflorus**
MUSKMALLOW . . . **H. abelmoschus**
OKRA . . . . **H. esculentus**
PALEFACE R. . . . . . **H. denudatus**
ROSELLE . . . . . . **H. sabdariffa**
ROUGH R. . . . . **H. aculeatus**
SCARLET R. . . . . . . **H. coccineus**
SHRUBALTHEA . . . . **H. syriacus**
TALL ROSELLE. **H. sabdariffa altissima**
WOOLLY R. . . . . . **H. lasiocarpos**

ROSEMARY . . **Rosmarinus; R. officinalis**
WHITE R. . . . . **R. o. albus**

ROSEMARYMINT . . . . . . **Poliomintha**
HOARY R. . . . . **P. incana**

ROSEMYRTLE . . . . . . **Rhodomyrtus**
DOWNY R. . . . . . . **R. tomentosa**

ROSEOCAC'TUS . . . **ARIOCARPUS**
See **CACTUS GENERA.**

ROSEOFHEAVEN . . . . **Lychnis coelirosa**

ROSEWOOD . . . . **Dalbergia**
AFRICAN BLACKWOOD. **D. melanoxylon**
BLACK R. . . . . **D. nigra**
CEARA R. . . . . **D. cearensis**
COSTARICA R. . . . . **D. hypoleuca**
EASTINDIAN R. . . . . . **D. latifolia**
GRANADILLO R. . . . . **D. granadillo**
HONDURAS R. . . . . **D. stevensoni**
MADAGASCAR R. . . . . **D. greveana**
PANAMA R. . . . . **D. retusa**
SISSOO . . . . **D. sissoo**

ROSHAGRASS . . . **Cymbopogon martini**

ROSINWEED . . . . **Silphium**
COMPASSPLANT . . . . **S. laciniatum**
CUP R. . . . . . . **S. perfoliatum**
DOCK R. . . . **S. terebinthinaceum**
WHOLELEAF R. . . . **S. integrifolium**

ROSMARI'NUS . . . . . . ROSEMARY
officina'lis . . . . ROSEMARY
—al'bus . . . . WHITE R.
₵PROSTRATE (*prostratus*) HV. R. officinalis
₵PYRAMIDAL (*pyramidalis*). *Robinson*

ROSULA'RIA . . . . . . **SEDUM; UMBILICUS**
See **SUCCULENTS.**

ROTA'LA |w . . . . ROTALA
ramo'sior |w . . . . ROTALA

ROTTBOEL'LIA . . . . . . ITCHGRASS
See **GRASS GENERA.**

ROUBIE'VA . . . . PERUBALM
multif'ida . . . . . . FLATWEED P.

ROUGEPLANT . . . . **Rivina**
BLOODBERRY R. . . . . . . **R. humilis**
CURRANT R. . . . . **R. portulaccoides**

ROUPA'LA . . . . ROUPALA
borea'lis . . . . . . VERACRUZ R.
brasilien'sis . . . . BRAZIL R.
complica'ta . . . . . COSTARICA R.
corcovaden'sis . . . . **R. pohli**
darienen'sis (*panamensis*). PANAMA R.
Perhaps a synonym of R. complicata.
me'dia . . . . GUIANA R.
monta'na . . . . TRINIDAD R.
pohl'i (*corcovadensis*) . . . POHLS R.

ROUR'EA
oblongifo'lia

ROYALFERN . . . . . **Osmunda regalis**
SLENDER R. . . . . . **O. regalis** HV.

ROYALPALM . . . . **Roystonea**
CARIB R. . . . . **R. oleracea**
CUBAN R. . . . . **R. regia**
HISPANIOLA R. . . . **R. hispaniolana**
JAMAICA R. . . . . . . **R. jamaicana**
JENMAN R. . . . . **R. jenmani**
MORASS R. . . . . **R. princeps**
PUERTORICO R. . . . **R. borinquena**

ROYE'NA . . . . ROYENA
lu'cida . . . . SHINYLEAF R.

ROYSTO'NEA (*GORGASIA; OREODOXA*) . . . . ROYALPALM
See **PALM GENERA.**

RUBBERTREE . . . . **Hevea**
PARA R. . . . . **H. brasiliensis**

RUBBERVINE . . . . **Cryptostegia**
MADAGASCAR R. **C. madagascariensis**
PALAY R. . . . . . . **C. grandiflora**

Rubberweed, Colorado. ACTINEA, PINGUE: **Actinea richardsoni**

RU'BIA . . . . MADDER
cordifo'lia . . . . INDIA M.
peregri'na . . . . LEVANT M.
tincto'rum . . . . COMMON M.

RU'BUS (*BOSSEKIA*) |w BLACKBERRY; DEWBERRY; RASPBERRY
For horticultural varieties of Rubus see **FRUIT AND EDIBLE NUT NAMES.**

aceroi'des . . . . **R. trifidus**
acumina'tus
adenoph'orus (*sagatus*)
alexete'rius
alleghenien'sis . . . . ALLEGANY B.
alpes'tris
amab'ilis
anderso'ni
arc'ticus |w . . . . ARCTIC BRAMBLE
argu'tus . . . . **R. ostryifolius**
arundelia'nus . . . . **R. frondosus**
austra'lis (*cissoides*) . . TATARAMOA B.
—gla'ber
—schmidelioi'des . . **R. schmidelioides**
bel'lardi
biflo'rus
—quinqueflo'rus
bifor'mis . . . . DIVERSE-SPINE D.
cae'sius . . . . EUROPEAN D.
—turkestan'icus . . . TURKESTAN D.
canaden'sis |w . . . . THORNLESS B.
The name R. canadensis is often misapplied to R. procumbens.
—rand'i (*R. randi*) . . . . RANDS B.
can'dicans (*thyrsoideus*)
carpinifo'lius
carpinifo'lius Rydb., *not* Weihe & Nees. **R. trivialis**
caucas'icus
chamaemo'rus |w . . . . CLOUDBERRY
chroosep'alus
chrysophyl'lus
cissoi'des . . . . **R. australis**
cockburnia'nus (*giraldianus*)
commerso'ni . . . . . **R. rosaefolius**
continenta'lis . . . . **R. trivialis**
corchorifo'lius
corea'nus . . . . KOREAN R.
corona'rius . . . . . . **R. rosaefolius**
crataegifo'lius . . . . HAWTHORN R.
cuneifo'lius . . . . SAND B.
dalibar'da . . . . **Dalibarda repens**
delicio'sus . . . . . . BOULDER R.
dumeto'rum . . . . . **R. nemorosus**
ellip'ticus . . YELLOW HIMALAYAN R.
euleu'cus . . . . **R. gracilis**

RUBUS, continued
flagella'ris (*procumbens; villosus* Bailey, *not* Ait., *nor* Thunb.) |w NORTHERN DEWBERRY
—geoph'ilus (*R. geophilus*)
—invi'sus (*R. invisus*)
—roribac'cus . . . . LUCRETIA D.
flagelliflo'rus
flor'idus
flosculo'sus
—parvifo'lius
∞**fra'seri** (*odoratus* × *parviflorus; robustus*) . ∞FRASER THIMBLEBERRY
frondo'sus (*arundelianus; philadelphicus; recurvans*) YANKEE BLACKBERRY
frutico'sus . . . . . . EUROPEAN B.
geoph'ilus . . . . . **R. flagellaris g.**
giraldia'nus . . . . **R. cockburnianus**
glandicau'lis . . . . . GLANDSTEM B.
glau'cus
grac'ilis (*euleucus; niveus* Wall., *not* Thunb.) . . . . . TALL RASPBERRY
hen'ryi
his'pidus |w . . . . SWAMP B.
hupehen'sis (*swinhoei*)
ichangen'sis
idae'us . . . . RED R.
—aculeatis'simus (*R. melanolasius*) WESTERN R.R.
—strigo'sus (*R. strigosus*) |w AMERICAN R.R.
illecebro'sus . . . . STRAWBERRY R.
innomina'tus
—kuntzea'nus
invi'sus . . . . **R. flagellaris i.**
irenae'us
koehnea'nus
lacinia'tus . . . . CUTLEAF B.
₵BLACK DIAMOND. HV.
₵ELEGANS (*elegans; minor*)
₵EVERGREEN
₵WADE
₵WONDER
lambertia'nus
lasios'tylus . . . . . . WOOLLY R.
lauda'tus
leucoder'mis . . . . WHITEBARK R.
leucosta'chys BROADLEAF EVERGREEN B.
linkia'nus . . . . LINK B.
Some botanists have questioned the tenability of this species.
∞**loganobac'cus** (*idaeus* × *?ursinus*) ∞LOGANBERRY
The origin of this plant is disputed; some authorities regard it as a variation or mutant of R. ursinus.
louisia'nus
macilen'tus
macrocar'pus
macropet'alus . . . . . TRAILING B.
macrophyl'los
malifo'lius
melanola'sius **R. idaeus aculeatissimus**
mesogae'us
mi'rus
molucca'nus
neglec'tus . . . . . PURPLECANE R.
nemoro'sus (*dumetorum*) CAUCASIAN D.
neomexica'nus . . NEWMEXICAN R.
nessen'sis
niv'alis . . . . SNOW D.
niv'eus . . . . SNOWPEAKS R.
niv'eus Wall., *not* Thunb.. . **R. gracilis**
nu'tans
nutka'nus . . . . **R. parviflorus**
occidenta'lis |w . . . . BLACKCAP R.
—pal'lidus

RUBUS, continued
odora'tus |w FRAGRANT THIMBLEBERRY
—al'bidus . . . . WHITE T.
o'riens . . . . EASTERN DEWBERRY
ostryifo'lius (*argutus*) HIGHBRUSH BLACKBERRY
palma'tus . . . . BANK RASPBERRY
panicula'tus
par'keri
parviflo'rus (*nutkanus*) WESTERN THIMBLEBERRY
parvifo'lius (*triphyllos*) . JAPANESE R.
pergra'tus . . . . . . DELICIOUS B.
philadel'phicus . . . . . **R. frondosus**
phoenicola'sius . WINE R. (*Wineberry*)
platyphyl'los
playfairia'nus (*playfairi*)
plicatifo'lius (*?villosus* Ait., *not* Bailey *nor* Thunb.)
polyt'richus . . . . **R. tricolor**
probabil'is . . . . TREE B.
pro'bus . . . . . . QUEENSLAND R.
pro'cerus (*thyrsanthus*). . HIMALAYA B.
procum'bens . . . . . . **R. flagellaris**
pubes'cens . . . . . DWARF RED B.
pun'gens
rand'i . . . . **R. canadensis r.**
recur'vans . . . . **R. frondosus**
reflex'us
—pic'tus
robus'tus. . . . . **R. fraseri**
rosaefo'lius (*commersoni; coronarius; R. r. coronarius*) . . . ROSELEAF R.

The so-called "Brier-rose," R. rosaefolius coronarius (R. coronarius) is recognized by some botanists as a distinct variety or even species.

saga'tus . . . . . . **R. adenophorus**
schmidelioi'des (*R. australis s.*)
seto'sus . . . . SETOSE B.
spectab'ilis |w . . . . SALMONBERRY
—menzies'i . MENZIES SALMONBERRY
stans'
strigo'sus . . . . **R. idaeus s.**
swinhoe'i . . . . **R. hupehensis**
thibeta'nus (*veitchi*)
thyrsan'thus . . . . . . **R. procerus**
thyrsoi'deus . . . . . **R. candicans**
tita'nus
—espina'tus
trian'thus
tri'color (*polytrichus*)
trif'idus (*aceroides*)
tri'frons . . . . . . TRIFOLIOLATE D.
triphyl'los . . . . **R. parvifolius**
trivia'lis (*carpinifolius* Rydb., *not* Weihe & Nees; *continentalis*) SOUTHERN D.
trullisa'tus
ulmifo'lius . . . . ELMLEAF B.
—bellidiflo'rus
—iner'mis. EVERGREEN THORNLESS B.
—variega'tus
ursi'nus . . . . CALIFORNIA D.
—vitifo'lius (*R. vitifolius*) GRAPELEAF C.D.
veitch'i . . . . **R. thibetanus**
ve'lox
vermonta'nus . . . . . VERMONT B.
villo'sus Ait., *not* Bailey *nor* Thunb. **?R. plicatifolius**
villo'sus Bailey, *not* Ait. *nor* Thunb. **R. flagellaris**
vitifo'lius . . . . . . **R. ursinus v.**

RUBUS, continued
vulga'ris
wil'soni
xanthocar'pus

RUDBECK'IA (*DRACOPIS*) CONEFLOWER
amplexicau'lis (*Dracopis a.*) CLASPING C.
bi'color . . . . PINEWOODS C.
—super'ba . . . . ERFURT C.
califor'nica . . . . . CALIFORNIA C.
columna'ris . . . . . . **Ratibida c.**
ful'gida . . . . ORANGE C.
hir'ta . . . . BLACKEYEDSUSAN
lacinia'ta . . . . CUTLEAF C.
GOLDENGLOW (*flore-pleno; hortensis*) HV.
max'ima. . . . . **GREAT C.**
mol'lis
monta'na
ni'tida
AUTUMN GLORY. HV.
AUTUMN SUN
occidenta'lis . . . . . . NIGGERHEAD
pal'lida . . . . **Echinacea p.**
purpu'rea . . . . **Echinacea p.**
specio'sa (*newmanni*) . . . SHOWY C.
subtomento'sa . . . . . . SWEET C.
thibeta'na
trilo'ba . . . . BROWNEYEDSUSAN
GOLDSTRAHL. HV. Rudbeckia
HERBSTSONNE

RUE . . . . **Ruta**
COMMON R. . . . . . . **R. graveolens**
DWARF R. . . . . **R. patavina**
FRINGED R. . . . . . . **R. chalepensis**

RUEL'LIA (*STEPHANOPHYSUM*) |w . . . . RUELLIA
amoe'na (*longifolia; Stephanophysum longifolium*) . . . . REDSPRAY R.
cilio'sa |w . . . . . . FRINGELEAF R.
devosia'na
formo'sa . . . . SCARLET R.
macran'tha . . . . . LAVENDER R.
macrophyl'la . . . . . . LONGLEAF R.
makoya'na
malacosper'ma . . . . . SOFTSEED R.
nudiflo'ra |w . . . . VIOLET R.
peduncula'ta . . . . . . STALKED R.
spectab'ilis
stre'pens . . . . . . LIMESTONE R.
tubero'sa . . . . . . MINNIEROOT R.

RUFFLEPALM . . . . **Aiphanes**
ALVARICO R. . . . . **A. lindeniana**
CARYOTA R. . . . . . **A. caryotaefolia**
COYURE R. . . . . . **A. acanthophylla**
MACAWPALM . . . . **A. erosa**
SPICE R. . . . . **A. minima**

RUKAM . . . . **Flacourtia rukam**

RU'LAC . . . . **ACER**

RULIN'GIA
parviflo'ra

RU'MEX |w . . . . DOCK

The usually small, acid-tasting, early-flowering (mostly reddish) plants, with rootstocks, belonging to the section Acetosa of this genus, are known as Sorrel.

abyssin'icus . . SPINACH-RHUBARB D.
aceto'sa . . . . . . GARDEN SORREL
acetosel'la |w . . . . SHEEP S.
alpi'nus . . . . ALPINE D.

RUMEX, continued
aquat'icus . . . . POND DOCK
britan'nica . . . . GREAT D.
conglomera'tus . . . . CLUSTERED D.
cris'pus |w . . . . CURLY D.
flexuo'sus
hasta'tulus |w . HEARTWING SORREL
hydrolapa'thum . . . . . WATER D.
hymenosep'alus . . . . . CANAIGRE
marit'imus Auth., *not* L. **R. persicarioides**
mexica'nus . . . . . . MEXICAN D.
obtusifo'lius |w . . . . . . BITTER D.
occidenta'lis |w . . . . WESTERN D.
patien'tia . . . . PATIENCE D.
paucifo'lius . . . MOUNTAIN SORREL
persicarioi'des (*maritimus* Auth., *not* L.) |w . . . . GOLDEN D.
pul'cher . . . . FIDDLELEAF D.
rose'us (*R. vesicarius r.*) . . . ROSY D.
salicifo'lius . . . . WILLOW D.
scuta'tus . . . . . . FRENCH SORREL
veno'sus . . . . VEINY D.
verticilla'tus |w . . . . . . SWAMP D.
vesica'rius rose'us . . . . . . **R. roseus**

RUNNINGPINE . . **Lycopodium clavatum**

RUP'PIA |w . . . . . . WIDGEONWEED
marit'ima |w . . . . . WIDGEONGRASS
occidenta'lis |w

RUPRECHT'IA . . . . VIRARU
deam'i . . . . BULLSBLOOD V.

RUSCH'IA **MESEMBRYANTHEMUM**
See **SUCCULENTS.**

RUS'CUS . . . . . . BUTCHERSBROOM
aculea'tus . . . . . BUTCHERSBROOM
hypoglos'sum
hypophyl'lum
hyrca'nus
racemo'sus . . . . . **Danae racemosa**

RUSH . . . . **Juncus**
ALPINE R. . . . . **J. alpinus**
BALTIC R. . . . . **J. balticus**
BRISTLY R. . . . . **J. setaceus**
BULBOUS R. . . . . **J. bulbosus**
BUTTON R. . . . . . **J. brunnescens**
CANADA R.. . . . . . . **J. canadensis**
COMMON R. . . . . **J. effusus**
COOPER R.. . . . . **J. cooperi**
COVILLE R. . . . . **J. covillei**
CREEPING R.. . . . . **J. repens**
INLAND R. . . . . **J. interior**
JOINTED R. . . . . **J. nodosus**
NEEDLEGRASS R. . . . **J. roemerianus**
PACIFIC R.. . . . . **J. lescuri**
POVERTY R. . . . . **J. tenuis**
ROCKYMOUNTAIN R. **J. saximontanus**
SALTMEADOW R. . . . . . . **J. gerardi**
SOFT R. . . . . **J. macer**
SOLDIER R. . . . . **J. militaris**
SPREADING R. . . . . **J. patens**
TOAD R.. . . . . **J. bufonius**
TORREY R.. . . . . **J. torreyi**

RUSHPEA . . . . **Hoffmannseggia**
INDIAN R. . . . . **H. densiflora**
LITTLELEAF R. . . . . **H. microphylla**
SICKLEPOD R. . . . **H. drepanocarpa**

RUSSE'LIA . . . . CORALBLOW
elegantis'sima Hort. . . . HYBRID C.

Thought to be a cross between R. equisetiformis and R. sarmentosa. See note under R. lemoinei below. The cultivated plant may be a clon.

Hort. var.; HV.=horticultural variety (or varieties); sp.=species (singular); spp.=species (plural).
₵=clon; × (as a prefix)=hybrid; × (between scientific plant names)=crossed by; ∞=polybrid; |w=plant useful to wildlife.
See Glossary for definitions of clon, hybrid, and polybrid.

RUSSELIA, continued
equisetifor'mis (*juncea*) . Coralplant
lemoin'ei Hort. . . . Fountainplant
Reputed to be a cross between R. equisetiformis and R. sarmentosa. See note under R. elegantissima. Research is needed to ascertain whether elegantissima or lemoinei has priority. The cultivated plant may be a clon.
sarmento'sa (*multiflora; paniculata*) Leafy Coralblow
Russianolive . **Elaeagnus angustifolia**
Russianthistle . . . . **Salsola**
Common R. . . . . **S. kali**
Larchleaf R. . . . . **S. laricina**
Tumbling R. . . . **S. kali tenuifolia**

RUS'SULA . . . . Russula
emet'ica . . . . Emetic R.
vires'cens . . . . Green R.

RU'TA . . . . Rue
chalepen'sis . . . . . . Fringed R.
grave'olens Common R. (*Herb of Grace*)
patavi'na . . . . Dwarf R.
Rutabaga . . . **Brassica napobrassica**

RYDBERG'IA . . . . . . **ACTINEA**

RYDBERGIEL'LA . **ASTRAGALUS**
praelon'ga . . . . **A. sabulosus**
Rye . . . . **Secale; S. cereale**
See also **CEREALS.**
Mountain R. . . . . **S. montanum**
Ryegrass . . . . **Lolium**
Beardless Darnel R.
L. temulentum leptochaeton
Crested R. . . **L. perenne cristatum**
Dalmatian R. . . . **L. subulatum**
Darnel R. . . . . **L. temulentum**
Hardy R. . . . . . . **L. remotum**
Italian R. . . . . **L. multiflorum**
Perennial R. . . . . . **L. perenne**
Sicilian R. . . . . . . **L. strictum**
Swiss R. . . . . **L. rigidum**

RY'TILIX . . . **HACKELOCHLOA**
See **GRASS GENERA.**

SABADIL'LA . **SCHOENOCAULON**
Sabadilla and Schoenocaulon were both published the same year (1837) and some botanists maintain that the former has priority and should be used. However, Brandt published Sabadilla as a subgenus of Veratrum and it, therefore, has no standing as a genus under International Rules.
Sabadilla . . . . **Schoenocaulon**
Drug S. . . . . **S. officinale**
Drummond S. . . . . **S. drummondi**

SA'BAL (*INODES*) . . . . Palmetto
See **PALM GENERA.**

SABA'TIA (*SABBATIA*) |w Rosegentian
angula'ris . . . . . Squarestem R.
campes'tris . . . . . . Prairie R.
dodecan'dra (*chloroides*) |w Marsh R.
grac'ilis |w . . . . Slim R.
kennedya'na . . . NewEngland R.
stella'ris |w . . . . . Saltmarsh R.

SA'BIA
latifo'lia
schumannia'na
Sacahuista . . . . **Nolina microcarpa**
Sacaline . . . . Knotweed, Sakhalin: **Polygonum sachalinense**
Sacaton . . . . . . **Sporobolus wrighti**
Alkali S. . . . . **S. airoides**

SACCHARODEN'DRON . . . **ACER**

SACCHAROMY'CES
cerevis'iae . . . . . Brewers Yeast

SAC'CHARUM . . . . . Sweetcane
See **GRASS GENERA.**

SACCIO'LEPIS . . . . . . Cupscale
See **GRASS GENERA.**

SACCOLA'BIUM
See **ORCHID GENERA.**

Safflower . . . **Carthamus tinctorius**
Sage . . . . **Salvia**
Autumn S. . . . . **S. greggi**
Azure S. . . . . **S. azurea**
Bertoloni S. . . . . . . **S. bertoloni**
Bigflower S. . . . . . **S. grandiflora**
Black S. . . . . **S. mellifera**
Bog S. . . . . **S. uliginosa**
Brandegee S. . . . . . **S. brandegei**
Cadmus S. . . . . **S. cadmica**
Candelabra S. . . . **S. candelabrum**
Cardinal S. . . . . **S. fulgens**
Clary S. . . . . **S. sclarea**
Cleveland S. . . . . . **S. clevelandi**
Creeping S. . . . . **S. repens**
Crimson S. . . . . . . **S. spathacea**
DeathValley S. . . . . . **S. funerea**
Desert S. . . . . **S. carnosa**
Doric S. . . . . **S. ringens**
Dospalmos S. . . . . . . **S. greatae**
Garden S. . . . . **S. officinalis**
Gentian S. . . . . **S. patens**
Golden S . . . . **S. aurea**
Graham S. . . . . **S. grahami**
Greek S. . . . . **S. triloba**
Japanese S. . . . . **S. japonica**
Joseph S. . . . . **S. horminum**
Kashmir S. . . . . **S. hians**
Lanceleaf S. . . . . . **S. lanceolata**
Lilac S. . . . . **S. verticillata**
Lindenleaf S. . . . . . . **S. tiliaefolia**
Little Mexican S. **S. mexicana minor**
Meadow S. . . . . **S. pratensis**
Mealycup S. . . . . . . **S. farinacea**
Mexican Bush S. . . . **S. leucantha**
Mexican Chia . . . . . **S. hispanica**
Mexican S. . . . . **S. mexicana**
Mohave S. . . . . . . **S. mohavensis**
Montbret S. . . . . **S. montbreti**
Moorish S. . . . . **S. dichroa**
Moroccan S. . . . . **S. marocana**
Mullein S. . . . . . . **S. verbascifolia**
Munz S. . . . . **S. munzi**
Nile S. . . . . **S. nilotica**
Oriental S. . . . . **S. virgata**
Palmer S. . . . . **S. palmeri**
Peruvian S. . . . . **S. heeri**
Pineapple S. . . . . **S. rutilans**
Pink Autumn S. . . . **S. greggi rosea**
Pitchers S. . . . . **S. pitcheri**
Purple Garden S.
S. officinalis purpurascens
Purplish Selfheal S.
S. prunelloides purpurea
Red Garden S. **S. officinalis rubriflora**
Roseleaf S. . . . . **S. involucrata**
Roundtop S. . . . . **S. globosa**
Sand S. . . . . **S. eremostachya**
Scarlet S. . . . . **S. splendens**
Selfheal S. . . . . . . **S. prunelloides**
Sesse S. . . . . **S. sessei**
Sibthorp S. . . . . **S. sibthorpi**
Silver S. . . . . **S. argentea**
Skyblue S. . . . . **S. caerulea**
Sonoma S. . . . . . . **S. sonomensis**
Spanish S. . . . . **S. bicolor**
Sticky S. . . . . **S. glutinosa**
Syrian S. . . . . **S. indica**

Sage, continued
Tasselleaf S. . . **Salvia cacaliaefolia**
Texas S. . . . . **S. coccinea**
Thickleaf S. . . . . . **S. pachyphylla**
Thistle S. . . . . **S. carduacea**
Vasey S. . . . . **S. vaseyi**
Verbena S. . . . . **S. verbenaca**
Violet Joseph S. **S. horminum violacea**
Violet S. . . . . **S. nemorosa**
White Autumn S. . . **S. greggi alba**
White Garden S.
S. officinalis albiflora
Whiteleaf S. . . . . **S. leucophylla**
White Oriental S. . . **S. virgata alba**
White S. . . . . **S. apiana**
White Woodland S. **S. sylvestris alba**
Woodland S. . . . . . . **S. sylvestris**
Sagebrush . . . . **Artemisia**
See also Wormwood.
Alkali S. . . . . . . **A. natronensis**
Alpine S. . . . . . . **A. scopulorum**
Bigelow S. . . . . **A. bigelovi**
Big S. . . . . **A. tridentata**
Birdfoot S. . . . . **A. pedatifida**
Black S. . . . . **A. nova**
Bolander S. . . . . . . **A. bolanderi**
Bud S. . . . . **A. spinescens**
California S. . . . . . **A. californica**
Canada S. . . . . **A. canadensis**
Carruth S. . . . . **A. carruthi**
Chihuahua S. . . . . . . **A. redolens**
Cudweed S. . . . . . . **A. gnaphalodes**
Falsetarragon S. **A. dracunculoides**
Fringed S. . . . . **A. frigida**
Longleaf S. . . . . **A. longifolia**
Louisiana S. . . . . . . **A. ludoviciana**
Low S. . . . . **A. arbuscula**
Mexican S. . . . . **A. mexicana**
Michaux S. . . . . . . **A. michauxiana**
Mixleaf S. . . . . **A. diversifolia**
Narrowleaf Big S.
A. tridentata angustifolia
NewMexican S. . . . **A. neomexicana**
Palmer S. . . . . **A. palmeri**
Parish S. . . . . **A. parishi**
Pursh S. . . . . **A. purshiana**
Ragweed S. . . . . . **A. franserioides**
Rothrock S. . . . . **A. rothrocki**
Sand S. . . . . **A. filifolia**
Sawtooth S. . . . . **A. serrata**
Silverking S. . . . . **A. albula**
Silvermat S. . . . . **A. minuta**
Silver S. . . . . **A. cana**
Stiff S. . . . . **A. rigida**
Sweet S. . . . . **A. discolor**
Threetip S. . . . . **A. tripartita**
Woolly S. . . . . **A. floccosa**
Wrights S. . . . . **A. wrighti**

SAGERE'TIA . . . . Sageretia
minutiflo'ra . . . . . Gulfcoast S.
pycnophyl'la . . . . Woollytwig S.
thee'zans . . . . Hedge S.
wright'i . . . . Wrights S.

SAGI'NA |w . . . . Pearlwort
decum'bens |w . . . . . Trailing P.
gla'bra . . . . Smooth P.
nodo'sa . . . . Knotted P.
procum'bens . . . . Procumbent P.
saginoi'des (*linnaei*) . . . Arctic P.
subula'ta . . . . Corsican P.
Sagisipalm . . . **Heterospathe; H. elata**

SAGITTA'RIA |w . . . . . Arrowhead
ambig'ua |w
angustifo'lia |w . . . Narrowleaf A.
breviros'tra |w . . . . Shortbeak A.

SAGITTARIA, continued
chap'mani |w . Chapman Arrowhead
crista'ta |w
cunea'ta |w . . . . Duckpotato A.
cyclop'tera |w
engelmannia'na |w . Engelmann A.
falca'ta |w
filifor'mis |w
gramin'ea |w . . . . Grassy A.
gregg'i |w . . . . Gregg A.
heterophyl'la |w . . . . Varileaf A.
isoetifor'mis |w
japon'ica . . . . . . **S. sagittifolia**
lancifo'lia |w . . . . Bulltongue A.
latifo'lia |w . . . . . . Common A.
longilo'ba |w . . . . . Longbarb A.
longiros'tra |w . . . . Longbeak A.
lora'ta |w . . . . . . Strapleaf A.
macrocar'pa |w . . . . . . Bigpod A.
mohr'i |w . . . . Mohrs A.
monteviden'sis |w . . . . Giant A.
na'tans . . . . Beach A.
papillo'sa |w
platyphyl'la |w . . . . . . Delta A.
pubes'cens |w . . . . . . Downy A.
rig'ida . . . . Stiff A.
sagittifo'lia (*japonica; sinensis*)
Oldworld A.
₵Double (*floreplena*) hv.
sand'fordi |w . . . . . . Sandford A.
stagno'rum |w
subula'ta |w . . . . . . Awlleaf A.
te'res |w. . . . . Slender A.
visco'sa |w. . . . . Sticky A.
weatherbia'na |w . . Weatherby A.
Sagofern . . . . . **Cyathea medullaris**
Sagolily . . . . Mariposa: **Calochortus**
Sagopalm . . . . **Metroxylon**
Smooth S. . . . . **M. sagu**
Spiny S. . . . . **M. rumphii**
Saguaro . . . . . . **Cereus giganteus**

SAGUE'RUS . . . . . . **ARENGA**
See **PALM GENERA.**

SA'GUS . . . . . **METROXYLON**
See **PALM GENERA.**

Sainfoin . . . . **Onobrychis**
Cockscomb S. . . . . **O. cristagalli**
Cockshead S. . . . . **O. caputgalli**
Common S. . . . . . **O. viciaefolia**
Hungarian S. . . . . . **O. arenaria**
Sungari S. . . . . . . **O. pulchella**

SAINTPAUL'IA . . . Africanviolet
ionan'tha . . . . Common A.
₵Bigflower (*grandiflora*) hv.
₵Variegated (*variegata*)
kewen'sis . . . . Kew A.
₵Admiral. hv. Saintpaulia
₵Blue Boy
Sal . . . Shorea, Sal: **Shorea robusta**
Saladchervil . **Anthriscus cerefolium**
Salal . . . . **Gaultheria shallon**

SALAZA'RIA . . . . . Bladdersage
mexica'na . . . . Mexican B.

SALICOR'NIA |w . . . . Glasswort
bigelo'vi (*mucronata* Bigel., *not* Lag.) |w
Bigelow G.
europae'a |w . . . . . Marshfire G.
frutico'sa . . . . . . Leadbush G.
peren'nis (*ambigua*) |w . . Woody G.
ru'bra |w . . . RockyMountain G.
Regarded by some botanists as a synonym of the widespread S. europaea.
subtermina'lis |w
utahen'sis . . . . Utah G.

SALISBUR'IA . . . . . . **GINKGO**
adiantifo'lia . . . . **G. biloba**

SA'LIX |w . . . . Willow
acumina'ta
There are at least three different species of Willow bearing this name; two, of course, are homonyms and all are synonyms. In addition, the name has been misapplied to other Willow species.
acutifo'lia (*S. daphnoides a.*)
Sharpleaf W.
adenophyl'la (*syrticola*) . . Furry W.
alaxen'sis . . . . . . Feltleaf W.
al'ba . . . . White W.
—cal'va (*S. coerulea*)
Pyramidal W.W. (*Cricketbat W.*)
—chermesi'na (*S. vitellina britzensis*)
Redstem W.W.
—ova'lis . . . . Broadleaf W.W.
—seric'ea (*S. a. argentea; S. a. regalis*)
Silky W.W.
—vitelli'na (*S. vitellina*)
Yellowstem W.W.
₵Weepinggold (*a. tristis; vitellina pendula*)
∞**ambig'ua** (*aurita* × *repens*).
∞Puzzle W.
amplifo'lia . . . . Yakutat W.
amygdali'na (*triandra*) Almondleaf W.
amygdaloi'des . . . . Peachleaf W.
—wright'i (*S. nigra w.; S. wrighti*)
Wright P.W.
anglo'rum (*arctica* R. Br., *not* Pall.; *browni*) . . . . . Northland W.
arbusculoi'des . . . Littletree W.
arc'tica |w . . . . Arctic W.
arctoph'ila
argophyl'la . . . . . Silverleaf W.
argyrocar'pa . . . . . Labrador W.
athabascen'sis . . . . Athabasca W.
auri'ta . . . . Roundear W.
∞**austri'aca** (*grandifolia* × *purpurea;* ∞ *neriifolia*) . . . . . ∞Austrian W.
babylon'ica . Babylon Weeping W.
—doloro'sa Hort. . . . . ∞**S. blanda**
Golden (*ramulis aureis*) hv. S. babylonica
Ringleaf (*annularis; crispa*)
ba'keri . . . . **S. lasiolepis b.**
balsamif'era . . . . . . **S. pyrifolia**
bar'clayi |w . . . . . . Barclay W.
barrattia'na . . . . . . Barratt W.
—tweed'yi . . . . **S. tweedyi**
bebbia'na (*rostrata* Richards., *not* Thuill.) . . . . Bebb W.
—perrostra'ta . . . Smooth B.W.
bel'la . . . . Beautiful W.
bi'color . . . . **S. phylicifolia**
bigelo'vi . . . . **S. lasiolepis b.**
∞**blan'da** (*babylonica* × *fragilis; S. babylonica dolorosa* Hort.; *S. petzoldi pendula* Hort.)
∞Wisconsin Weeping W.
The cultivated plant is presumably a clon of this cross.
bock'i . . . . Bock W.
bonplandia'na . . . . . Bonpland W.
—tou'meyi (*S. toumeyi*) . Toumey W.
Hardly more than a synonym of the species itself, from typical forms of which there is no sharp demarcation.
brachycar'pa (*desertorum* Anderss., *not* Richards.) . . . Barrenground W.
brew'eri . . . . Brewer W.
brown'i . . . . **S. anglorum**
cae'sia
caespito'sa . . . . . . **S. petrophila c.**

SALIX, continued
calcic'ola
∞**callian'tha** (*daphnoides* × *purpurea*)
∞Purpledaphne Willow
can'dida . . . . Sage W.
ca'prea . . . . Goat W.
This is one of the two common "pussy willows" of florists.
₵Kilmarnock (*pendula*) hv.
₵Variegated (*variegata*)
cascaden'sis . . . . . Cascades W.
cathaya'na . . . . Cathay W.
cauda'ta (*S. lasiandra c.*) Whiplash W.
chamisso'nis . . . . . Chamisso W.
chlorol'epis . . . . Greenscale W.
chlorophyl'la . . . . . . **S. planifolia**
cine'rea . . . . Gray W.
This is one of the two common "pussy willows" of florists.
—oleifo'lia (*S. c. angustifolia*)
Oliveleaf G.W.
₵Tricolor. hv. S. cinerea
coac'tilis
coeru'lea . . . . **S. alba calva**
commuta'ta . . . . Undergreen W.
corda'ta . . . . Heartleaf W.
₵Purpurascens. hv.
cordifo'lia
∞**cottet'i** (*myrsinifolia* × *retusa*)
∞Cottet W.
A natural hybrid.
coul'teri . . . . Coulter W.
cryptodon'ta
daphnoi'des . . . . . . Daphne W.
—acutifo'lia . . . . **S. acutifolia**
—pomera'nica . . Pomeranian D.W.
₵Aglaia. hv. S. daphnoides
dasyc'lados (*acuminata* Auth., *not* Mill.) . . . . . . Woollytwig W.
Perhaps a hybrid.
delnorten'sis . . . . . Delnorte W.
deserto'rum . . . . Desert W.
deserto'rum Anderss., *not* Richards.
S. brachycarpa
∞**dichro'a** (*aurita* × *purpurea*)
∞Twocolor W.
dis'color . . . . Pussy W.
—latifo'lia (*S. d. eriocephala*)
—prinoi'des (*S. prinoides*)
dodgea'na . . . . Dodges W.
∞**donia'na** (*purpurea* × *repens*) ∞Dons W.
drummondia'na . . . Drummond W.
eastwood'iae . . . . . . Eastwood W.
∞**ehrhartia'na** (*alba* × *pentandra; hexandra* Auth., *not* Ehrh.) ∞Ehrhart W.
elaeag'nos (*incana*) . . Elaeagnus W.
elegantis'sima. Thurlow Weeping W.
Possibly a hybrid of S. babylonica × S. fragilis.
∞**erding'eri** (*caprea* × *daphnoides*)
∞Erdinger W.
eucalyptoi'des . . **Chosenia bracteosa**
exig'ua . . . . Coyote W.
—luteoseric'ea (*S. luteosericea*)
fal'lax
far'gesi . . . . Farges W.
far'rae . . . . Farr W.
—walpol'ei . . . . **S. walpolei**
fendleria'na . . . . . . **S. lasiandra**
fer'naldi . . . . . **S. vestita erecta**
∞*ferrugin'ea* . . . . . ∞**S. holosericea**
fluviat'ilis . . . . River W
formo'sa
frag'ilis . . . . Brittle W.
₵Globe (*bullata*) hv.
₵Montpelier (*monspeliensis*)

SALIX, continued
francisca'na . . **S. lasiolepis bigelovi**
∞**friesia'na** (*repens* × *viminalis*) ∞Fries Willow
∞**frutico'sa** (*aurita* × *viminalis*)
fusces'cens |w . . . . Alaskabog W.
geyeria'na . . . . Geyer W.
—argen'tea . . . . . Silvery G.W.
gilgia'na . . . . Gilg W.
gla'bra . . . . Alps W.
glacia'lis . . . . Icy W.
glau'ca . . . . Grayleaf W.
—acutifo'lia (*S. glaucops*)
—glabres'cens . . . Smoothish G.W.
glaucophylloi'des . . . Blueleaf W.
—glaucophyl'la (*S. glaucophylla* Bebb, *not* Schleich.) . . . . Firm B.W.
good'dingi . . . . . . Goodding W.
—vallic'ola (*S. nigra v.; S. vallicola*) Dudley W.
gracilis'tyla (*thunbergiana*) Bigcatkin W.
∞**gra'hami** (*herbacea* × *phylicifolia*) ∞Graham W.
grandifo'lia . . . . . . Bigleaf W.
∞**hankenso'ni** (*alba* × *nigra*) ∞Chiaroscuro W.
harbiso'ni . . . . . . Harbison W.
hasta'ta . . . . Halberd W.
hebecar'pa
helvet'ica . . . . Swiss W.
herba'cea . . . . Pygmy W.
×**heteran'dra** (*?pentandra* × *purpurea*)
Apparently a natural, fairly constant hybrid.
heterochro'ma (*henryi*)
hexan'dra . . . . . . Sixstamen W.
hexan'dra Auth., *not* Ehrh. ∞**S. ehrhartiana**
hindsia'na . . . . Hinds W.
—parishia'na (*S. parishiana*) Parish W.
∞**holoseric'ea** (*cinerea* × *viminalis;* ∞*ferruginea*) . . . ∞Streakwood W.
hookeria'na . . . . . Hooker W.
—tomento'sa . . . . Woolly H.W.
humboldtia'na . . . . Humboldt W.
hu'milis . . . . Prairie W.
hypoleu'ca . . . . . Underblue W.
inca'na . . . . **S. elaeagnos**
inte'rior (*longifolia* Muhl., *not* Lam.) Sandbar W.
—angustis'sima (*S. longifolia a.*) Texas S.W.
—pedicella'ta
irrora'ta . . . . Bluestem W.
jalisca'na . . . . Jalisco W.
japon'ica . . . . Japanese W.
This species is sometimes erroneously listed among "Weeping" Willows.
japon'ica Dipp., *not* Thunb. . **S. pieroti**
jep'soni (*S. sitchensis angustifolia*) Jepson W.
jessoen'sis . . . . Yeddo W.
koreen'sis . . . . Korea W.
∞**laestadia'na** (*caprea* × *lapponum*) ∞Laestad W.
laeviga'ta . . Polished W. (*Red W.*)
lambertia'na . . . . . **S. purpurea l.**
lana'ta . . . . Woolly W.
lanceola'ta . . . . **S. undulata**
lappo'num . . . . . . Lapland W.
lasian'dra (*fendleriana*) . Pacific W.
—cauda'ta . . . . **S. caudata**
—lancifo'lia . . . . Lanceleaf P.W.
—macrophyl'la (*S. lyalli*) Bigleaf P.W.
lasiol'epis . . . . . . Arroyo W.

SALIX, continued
lasiol'epis ba'keri (*S. bakeri*) Baker Arroyo Willow
—bigelo'vi (*S. bigelovi; S. franciscana*) Bigelow A.W.
∞**latifo'lia** (*caprea* × *myrsinifolia*) ∞Broadleaf W.
laurentia'na . . . St.Lawrence W.
laurifo'lia . . . . **S. pentandra**
∞**lauri'na** (*caprea* × *phylicifolia*) ∞Goattea W.
leiocar'pa . . . . . . **S. rotundifolia**
leiol'epis
lem'moni . . . . . . Lemmons W.
ligulifo'lia
liv'ida
longifo'lia Muhl., *not* Lam. . **S. interior**
—angustis'sima . . . . . **S. interior a.**
lon'gipes . . . . Coastalplain W.
—venulo'sa . . . . . . Veiny C.W.
—ward'i (*S. wardi*) . . . Ward C.W.
lu'cida . . . . Shining W.
—inton'sa . . . . Hairy S.W.
∞**ludif'icans** (*aurita* × *phylicifolia*) ∞Sport W.
lute'a . . . . Yellow W.
luteoseric'ea . . . . . . **S. exigua l.**
lyall'i . . . **S. lasiandra macrophylla**
mackenzia'na . . . . Mackenzie W.
This species is sometimes (but apparently incorrectly) called Diamond W., according to Dr. C. R. Ball, Willow authority.
macroblas'ta
magnif'ica . . . . . Footcatkin W.
∞**marit'ima** (*daphnoides* × *repens*)
matsuda'na . . . . . . Hankow W.
₵Contorted (*tortuosa*) hv.
₵Umbrella (*umbraculifera*)
₵Weeping (*pendula*)
mccallia'na
mede'mi . . . . Armenia W.
medwedew'i . . . . Medwedeff W.
melanop'sis . . . . Dusky W.
mexica'na . . . . Mexican W.
∞**meyeria'na** (*fragilis* × *pentandra*) ∞Meyer W.
missourien'sis . . . . . Diamond W.
Dr. C. R. Ball, well-known authority on Willows, informs the Editorial Committee that this species, often listed as Missouri River Willow, is the true Diamond Willow.
miyabea'na . . . . . . Miyabe W.
∞**mollis'sima** (*amygdalina* × *viminalis*) ∞Soft W.
mon'ica . . . . **S. planifolia m.**
monochro'ma . . . Greensides W.
montic'ola
moupinen'sis . . . . . . Moupin W.
∞**multiner'vis** (*aurita* × *cinerea*) ∞Japanese Pussy W.
×**myricoi'des** (*cordata* × *sericea*) Bayberry W.
A natural, fairly stable hybrid.
myrsinifo'lia (*nigricans*)
myrsini'tes . . . . . . Myrtle W.
myrtillifo'lia (*pseudomyrsinites* in part) Blueberry W.
myrtilloi'des . . . Whortleberry W.
myrtilloi'des Tuckerm., *not* L. **S. pedicellaris**
—pedicella'ris . . . . **S. pedicellaris**
nel'soni . . . . **S. planifolia n.**
∞*neriifo'lia* . . . . . . ∞**S. austriaca**
ni'gra (*S. n. falcata*) |w . . Black W.
—altis'sima . . . . Gulf B.W.
—lindheim'eri . . . . Texas B.W.

SALIX, continued
ni'gra vallic'ola . . . . **S. gooddingi v.**
—wright'i . . . . **S. amygdaloides w.**
ni'gricans . . . . . . **S. myrsinifolia**
niphoc'lada . . Mouseleaf Willow
niva'lis . . . . Snow W.
obtusa'ta . . . . . . Bluntleaf W.
orbicula'ris . . **S. reticulata subrotunda**
ores'tera . . . . Sierra W.
ovalifo'lia . . . . . . Ovalleaf W.
ox'ica . . . . Oxus W.
oxyl'epis
padophyl'la . . **S. pseudomonticola p.**
paradox'a
paraple'sia
parishia'na . . . . . **S. hindsiana p.**
parksia'na . . . . . SmithRiver W.
∞**pat'ula** (*aurita* × *elaeagnos*)
pedicella'ris (*myrtilloides* Tuckerm., *not* L.; *S. m. pedicellaris*) . . . Bog W.
—hypoglau'ca . . Interocean B.W.
peduncula'ta
pel'la
pelli'ta
penna'ta. . . . . Feathervein W.
pentan'dra (*laurifolia*) . . Laurel W.
petiola'ris
petroph'ila |w . . . . . Skyland W.
—caespito'sa (*S. caespitosa*) Tufted S.W.
petzold'i pen'dula Hort. . ∞**S. blanda**
phan'era
phlebophyl'la
phylicifo'lia (*bicolor*) . . Tealeaf W.
piero'ti (*japonica* Dipp., *not* Thunb.) Pierrot W.
pi'peri . . . . Piper W.
planifo'lia (*chlorophylla*) Planeleaf W.
—mon'ica (*S. monica*) . . Mono P.W.
—nel'soni (*S. nelsoni*) . Nelson P.W.
pola'ris . . . . Polar W.
∞**pontedera'na** (*cinerea* × *purpurea;* ∞*sordida*)
prinoi'des . . . . . . **S. discolor p.**
pseudocorda'ta (*pseudomyrsinites* in part)
pseudolappo'num
pseudomontic'ola . . . . . Park W.
—padophyl'la (*S. padophylla*) Southern P.W.
pseudomyrsini'tes . . . **S. myrtillifolia; S. pseudocordata**
purpu'rea . . . . . Purpleosier W.
—amplexicau'lis . . Clasping P.W.
—grac'ilis . . . . . . Slender P.W.
—lambertia'na (*S. lambertiana*) Lambert P.W.
—multiner'vis . . . Japanese P.W.
—seric'ea . . . . Silky P.W.
₵Dwarf (*nana*) hv. S. purpurea
₵Weeping (*pendula*)
pyrifo'lia (*balsamifera*) . Balsam W.
pyrolaefo'lia . . . . . Shinleaf W.
rehderia'na . . . . Rehder W.
×**rene'cia** (*cinerea* × *?*)
Apparently a natural, fairly stable hybrid.
re'pens . . . . Creeping W.
—nit'ida (*S. r. argentea*) Silver C.W.
—rosmarinifo'lia (*S. rosmarinifolia*) Rosemary C.W.
reticula'ta |w . . . . . Netleaf W.
—subrotun'da (*S. orbicularis*) Round N.W.
retu'sa . . . . . . Notchleaf W.
∞**reu'teri** (*daphnoides* × *elaeagnos*) ∞Reuter W.
richardso'ni . . . . Richardson W.

SALIX, continued
rosmarinifo'lia . . . . . **S. repens r.**
rostra'ta . . . . . . BEAKED WILLOW
rostra'ta Richards., *not* Thuill.
S. bebbiana
rotundifo'lia (*leiocarpa*) . . LEAST W.
rowlee'i . . . . ROWLEE W.
∞ **ru'bens** (*alba × fragilis*)
∞ WHITECRACK W.
×—**palus'tris** . . . . MARSH W.W.
×—**vir'idis** (×*S. viridis*) GREEN W.W.
∞ **ru'bra** (*purpurea × viminalis*)
∞ RED W.
sachalinen'sis . . . . SAKHALIN W.
salamo'ni . . . . . . **S. sepulcralis**
∞ *salviaefo'lia* . . . . ∞ **S. seringeana**
saximonta'na . . . . . SUMMIT W.
schaff'neri . . . . . . SCHAFFNER W.
scouleria'na . . . . . . SCOULER W.
—**flaves'cens** . . . . YELLOW S.W.
∞ **sepulcra'lis** (*alba × babylonica; S. salamoni*) . ∞ SOLOMON WEEPING W.
seric'ea . . . . SILKY W.
∞ **seringea'na** (*caprea × elaeagnos;* ∞ *salviaefolia*) . . . . . ∞ SERINGE W.
seris'sima . . . . AUTUMN W.
serpyllifo'lia . . . . THYMELEAF W.
∞ **sesquiter'tia** (*aurita × phylicifolia × purpurea*) . . ∞ FOURFOOTSIX W.
sessilifo'lia . . . . . . VELVET W.
setchellia'na . . . . . SETCHELL W.
sieboldia'na . . . . . . SIEBOLD W.
sie'gerti (*purpurea × silesica*)
SIEGERT W.
silesia'ca . . . . SILESIAN W.
silicic'ola
sitchen'sis . . . . SITKA W.
—*angustifo'lia* . . . . **S. jepsoni**
∞ **smithia'na** (*caprea × viminalis*)
∞ SMITH W.
∞ *sor'dida* . . . . . . ∞ **S. pontederana**
∞ **specio'sa** (*amygdalina × fragilis*)
stipula'ris . . . . . . STIPULE W.
Possibly a hybrid, and if so, perhaps a cinerea × viminalis cross.
stolonif'era . . . . . SPROUTING W.
∞ **subalpi'na** (*elaeagnos × repens*)
∞ SUBALPINE W.
subcoeru'lea . . . . BLUE W.
subseric'ea
syrtic'ola . . . . . . **S. adenophylla**
taxifo'lia . . . . YEWLEAF W.
∞ **tetrap'la** (*myrsinifolia × phylicifolia*)
∞ TEA W.
thunbergia'na . . . . . **S. gracilistyla**
tou'meyi . . . . . **S. bonplandiana t.**
tra'cyi . . . . TRACY W.
trevira'ni . . . . . TREVIRANUS W.
trian'dra . . . . **S. amygdalina**
tris'tis |w . . . . DWARF PUSSY W.
tur'nori
tweed'yi (*S. barrattiana t.*) TWEEDY W.
tyrrell'i . . . . TYRRELL W.
undula'ta (*lanceolata*) . WAVYLEAF W.
uva-ur'si . . . . . . BEARBERRY W.
vallic'ola . . . . **S. goodingi v.**
vesti'ta
—**erec'ta** (*S. fernaldi*)
vimina'lis BASKET W. (*Common Osier*)
—**gmeli'ni** . . . . GMELIN B.W.
×*vir'idis* . . . . ×**S. rubens v.**
vitelli'na . . . . **S. alba v.**
—*britzen'sis* . . . **S. alba chermesina**
wallichia'na . . . . . . WALLICH W.
walpol'ei (*S. farrae w.*) . WALPOLE W.
ward'i . . . . **S. longipes w.**
∞ **wardia'na** (*cinerea × phylicifolia*)
∞ WARDIANA W.

SALIX, continued
wilhelmsia'na . . WILHELMS WILLOW
∞ **wimmeria'na** (*caprea × purpurea*)
∞ WIMMER W.
wolf'i . . . . WOLFS W.
—**idahoen'sis** . . . . . IDAHO W.W.
wright'i . . . . . **S. amygdaloides w.**
NIOBE WEEPING. HV. Salix

SALMA'LIA . . . . SIMALTREE
malabar'ica (*Bombax malabaricum*)
MALABAR S.

SALMONBERRY . . . **Rubus spectabilis**
MENZIES S. . . . . . . **R. s. menziesi**

SALO'A . . . . . **BLUMENBACHIA**

SALPICHRO'A
rhomboi'dea . . . . . . COCKSEGGS

SALPIGLOS'SIS . . . . SALPIGLOSSIS
gloxiniaeflo'ra . . . . . GLOXINIA S.
sinua'ta (*hybrida; variabilis*)
SCALLOPED S.
AZURE (*azurea*) HV.
EMPEROR (*superbissima*)
GRANDIFLORA

SALPINGOS'TYLIS
coelesti'na

SALSIFY . . . . **Tragopogon**
MEADOW S. . . . . **T. pratensis**
VEGETABLE-OYSTER S. . **T. porrifolius**

SAL'SOLA |w . . . . RUSSIANTHISTLE
ka'li |w . . . COMMON R. (*Saltwort*)
—**tenuifo'lia** (*S. pestifer*). TUMBLING R.
larici'na . . . . . . LARCHLEAF R.

SALTBUSH . . . . **Atriplex**
AUSTRALIAN S. . . . . **A. semibaccata**
BIG S. . . . . **A. lentiformis**
BREWER B. S. . . . . . . **A. l. breweri**
CATTLE S. . . . . **A. polycarpa**
DESERTHOLLY S. . . **A. hymenelytra**
FAT-HEN S. . . . . **A. patula**
FOURWING S. . . . . . . **A. canescens**
GARDEN ORACH . . . . . **A. hortensis**
GARDNER S. . . . . **A. gardneri**
MATSCALE S. . . . . . . **A. decumbens**
MEDITERRANEAN S. . . . . **A. halimus**
PARRY S. . . . . **A. parryi**
PORTULACA S. . . . **A. portulacoides**
RED GARDEN ORACH
A. hortensis atrosanguinea
SHADSCALE S. . . . . **A. confertifolia**
SPEARLEAF FAT-HEN S.
A. patula hastata
TATARIAN S. . . . . **A. tatarica**
TUMBLING ORACH . . . . . . **A. rosea**
WEDGESCALE S. . . . . . **A. truncata**
WHEELSCALE S. . . . . . . **A. elegans**

Saltcedar . . . . SHOREGRASS:
Monanthochloe littoralis

SALTGRASS . . . . **Distichlis**
INLAND S. . . . . **D. stricta**
LITTLE S. . . . . **D. dentata**
SEASHORE S. . . . . **D. spicata**
TEXAS S. . . . . **D. texana**

SALTMARSHMALLOW . . . **Kosteletzkya**
ALTHEA S. . . . . **K. althaeifolia**
HAIRY S. . . . . **K. hispida**
VIRGINIA S. . . . . **K. virginica**

SALTTREE . . . . **Halimodendron**
PURPLE SIBERIAN S.
H. halodendron purpureum
SIBERIAN S. . . . . **H. halodendron**

SALTWORT . . . . **Batis**
MARITIME S. . . . . **B. maritima**

Saltwort . . RUSSIANTHISTLE, COMMON:
Salsola kali

SAL'VIA (*AUDIBERTIA; RAMONA*) |w . . . . SAGE
apia'na (*Audibertia polystachya*)
WHITE S.
argen'tea . . . . SILVER S.
au'rea . . . . GOLDEN S.
azu'rea . . . . AZURE S.
—**al'ba**
—*grandiflo'ra* . . . . **S. pitcheri**
ballotaeflo'ra
bertolo'ni . . . . BERTOLONI S.
bi'color . . . . SPANISH S.
In the horticultural trade the name S. bicolor is sometimes misapplied to HV. Bicolor of S. coccinea.
brachyca'lyx . . . . **S. indica**
bractea'ta
—**rose'a**
brandeg'ei (*Audibertia stachyoides revoluta*) . . . . BRANDEGEE S.
brasilien'sis . . . . . . **S. splendens**
brunello'des . . . . . **S. prunelloides**
cacaliaefo'lia . . . . . TASSELLEAF S.
cad'mica . . . . CADMUS S.
caeru'lea . . . . SKYBLUE S.
candela'brum . . . . CANDELABRA S.
cardua'cea . . . . THISTLE S.
carno'sa (*Audibertia incana*) DESERT S.
clandesti'na
—**angustifo'lia** (*S. cleistogama*)
cleve'landi (*Audibertia c.*) CLEVELAND S.
coccin'ea . . . . TEXAS S.
The name S. coccinea is sometimes misapplied in the horticultural trade to S. splendens.
BICOLOR. HV.
col'orans . . . . **S. splendens**
columba'riae . . . . CALIFORNIA CHIA
dichro'a . . . . MOORISH S.
eremosta'chya . . . . SAND S.
farina'cea . . . . MEALYCUP S.
ful'gens . . . . CARDINAL S.
fune'rea . . . . . . DEATHVALLEY S.
globo'sa . . . . ROUNDTOP S.
glutino'sa . . . . STICKY S.
gra'hami . . . . GRAHAM S.
grandiflo'ra . . . . . . BIGFLOWER S.
great'ae (*greatai*) . . . DOSPALMOS S.
gregg'i . . . . AUTUMN S.
—**al'ba** . . . . WHITE A.S.
—**rose'a** . . . . PINK A.S.
heer'i . . . . PERUVIAN S.
hi'ans . . . . KASHMIR S.
hispan'ica . . . . . . MEXICAN CHIA
The scientific name hispanica (Spanish) is misleading as this is a New World species; the specific name refers to America Hispanica, rather than to Spain itself.
hor'minum . . . . JOSEPH S.
—**viola'cea** . . . . . . VIOLET J.S.
ianthi'na (*hoveyi*)
in'dica (*brachycalyx*) . . . SYRIAN S.
interrup'ta
involucra'ta . . . . . . ROSELEAF S.
₵BETHEL. HV.
japon'ica . . . . JAPANESE S.
lanceola'ta (*lanceafolia*). LANCELEAF S.
leucan'tha . . . . MEXICAN BUSH S.
leucophyl'la (*Audibertia nivea*)
WHITELEAF S.
maroca'na . . . . . . MOROCCAN S.
mellif'era (*Audibertia stachyoides*)
BLACK S.
mexica'na . . . . MEXICAN S.
—**mi'nor** . . . . LITTLE M.S.

SALVIA, continued
mohaven'sis (*Audibertia capitata*) MOHAVE SAGE
montbret'i . . . . . . MONTBRET S.
munz'i . . . . MUNZ S.
nemoro'sa . . . . VIOLET S.
nilot'ica . . . . NILE S.
nu'tans
officina'lis . . . . GARDEN S.
—albiflo'ra . . . . . WHITE G.S.
—purpuras'cens . . . PURPLE G.S.
—rubriflo'ra . . . . RED G.S.
HOLTS MAMMOTH. HV. S. officinalis
pachyphyl'la . . . . . THICKLEAF S.
pal'meri . . . . PALMER S.
pa'tens . . . . GENTIAN S.
CAMBRIDGE BLUE. HV.
pitch'eri (*S. azurea grandiflora*) PITCHERS S.
praten'sis . . . . MEADOW S.
ALBA. HV.
BAUMGARTEN (*baumgarteni*)
ROSE (*rubicunda*)
TENOR (*tenori*)
prunelloi'des (*brunellodes*) SELFHEAL S.
—purpu'rea . . . . . PURPLISH S.S.
przewal'ski
pulchel'la
re'pens . . . . CREEPING S.
rin'gens . . . . DORIC S.
rugo'sa
ru'tilans . . . . . . PINEAPPLE S.
schiedea'na
scla'rea . . . . . . CLARY S. (*Clary*)
¢VATICAN (*turkestanica*) HV.
sesse'i . . . . SESSE S.
sib'thorpi . . . . SIBTHORP S.
sonomen'sis (*Audibertia humilis*) SONOMA S.
spatha'cea (*Audibertia grandiflora; Ramona g.*) . . . . CRIMSON S.
spelmi'na . . . . . . **S. verbenaca**
splen'dens (*brasiliensis; colorans; salvinia*) . . . . SCARLET S.
COMPACT (*compacta*) HV.
MAROON PRINCE
WHITE PRINCE
sylves'tris . . . . . . WOODLAND S.
—al'ba . . . . WHITE W.S.
tiliaefo'lia . . . . . LINDENLEAF S.
triangula'ris
trilo'ba . . . . GREEK S.
tubif'era
uligino'sa . . . . BOG S.
va'seyi . . . . VASEY S.
verbascifo'lia . . . . . MULLEIN S.
verbena'ca (*spelmina; verbenacea*) VERBENA S.
verticilla'ta . . . . . . LILAC S.
virga'ta . . . . ORIENTAL S.
The name S. virgata is sometimes misapplied to S. nemorosa.
—al'ba . . . . WHITE O.S.

SALVIN'IA . . . . SALVINIA
See **FERN GENERA**.

SAMADE'RA
in'dica . . . . . . NIEPABARKTREE

SAMANE'A . . . . SAMAN
saman' (*Pithecellobium s.*) RAINTREE S.

SAMBU'CUS |w . . . . ELDER
arbores'cens . . . . . . **S. pubens a.**
au'rea Hort. **S. canadensis** ¢GOLDEN; **S. nigra** ¢GOLDEN
califor'nica . . . . **S. cerulea velutina**
callicar'pa (*S. racemosa c.*) |w PACIFIC RED E.

SAMBUCUS, continued
canaden'sis |w . . AMERICAN ELDER
—chlorocar'pa . . GREENBERRY A.E.
—ru'bra . . . . . . REDBERRY A.E.
¢CUTLEAF (*acutiloba; laciniata*) HV. S. canadensis
¢GOLDEN (*aurea*)
¢GREAT (*maxima*)
ceru'lea (*coerulea; glauca*) |w BLUEBERRY E.
—arizo'nica . . . . . ARIZONA B.E.
—neomexica'na (*S. intermedia; S. neomexicana*) . . NEWMEXICAN B.E.
—veluti'na (*S. californica; S. velutina*)
eb'ulus . . MEDITERRANEAN HERB E.
∞**fontenay'si** (*cerulea × nigra*) ∞FONTENAYS E.
kamtschat'ica . . . . KAMCHATKA E.
leiosper'ma . . . . WESTERN RED E.
leucocar'pa Hort. **S. nigra** ¢WHITEBERRY
melanocar'pa . . . . BLACKBEAD E.
A reddish brown form of this sp. is known as S. melanocarpa f. fuerstenbergi.
mexica'na . . . . MEXICAN E.
microbo'trys . . . . BUNCHBERRY E.
neomexica'na . . . . . . **S. cerulea n.**
ni'gra . . . . EUROPEAN E.
—rotundifo'lia . . . ROUNDLEAF E.E.
—vir'idis . . . . GREENBERRY E.E.
CUTLEAF (*laciniata*) HV. S. nigra
¢DOUBLE (*florepleno; plena*)
¢DUSTY (*pulverulenta*)
¢GOLDEN (*aurea*)
¢PYRAMID (*pyramidalis*)
¢RAGLEAF (*heterophylla*)
¢WEEPING (*pendula*)
¢WHITEBERRY (*alba; leucocarpa*)
¢WHITEBLOTCH (*albo-variegata*)
YELLOWBERRY (*fructuluteo*)
YELLOWBLOTCH (*aureo-variegata*)
pu'bens |w . . . . SCARLET E.
—arbores'cens (*S. arborescens*) TREE S.E.
¢AMBER (*chrysocarpa; xanthocarpa*) HV. S. pubens
¢DISSECTED (*dissecta; laciniata*)
¢PEARL (*albicocca; leucocarpa*)
racemo'sa . . . . EUROPEAN RED E.
—callicar'pa . . . . . . **S. callicarpa**
¢CUTLEAF (*laciniata; serratifolia*) HV. S. racemosa
¢GOLDENPLUME (*plumosa; plumoso-aurea*)
¢ORNATE (*ornata*)
¢TASSEL (*tenuifolia*)
¢YELLOW (*flavescens*)
sieboldia'na (*S. racemosa s.*) SIEBOLD E.
simp'soni . . . . FLORIDA E.
veluti'na . . . . **S. cerulea v.**
vesti'ta . . . . CANYON E.
wil'liamsi . . . . WILLIAMS E.

SAMO'LUS |w
ebractea'tus |w
floribun'dus |w
valeran'di

SAMPHIRE . . **Crithmum; C. maritimum**

SAMUEL'A . . . . SAMUELA
These Southwestern-Mexican Yucca relatives are frequently called by the indistinctive name Date Yucca.
carnerosa'na . . . . . . BARRETA S.
faxonia'na . . . . TEXAS S.

SANCHEZ'IA
no'bilis
¢VARIEGATED (*glaucophylla*) HV.

SANDALWOOD . . . . **Santalum**
FIJI S. . . . . **S. yasi**
LANCELEAF S. . . . . **S. lanceolatum**
NEWCALEDONIA S. **S. austro-caledonicum**
WHITE S. . . . . **S. album**
YELLOW FIJI S. . . **S. freycinetianum**

SANDBOXTREE . . . . . **Hura crepitans**

SANDBUR . . . . **Cenchrus**
BIG S. . . . . **C. myosuroides**
COAST S. . . . . **C. incertus**
DUNE S. . . . . **C. tribuloides**
GUINEA S. . . . . **C. barbatus**
INDIA S. . . . . **C. biflorus**
MAT S. . . . . **C. pauciflorus**
SLENDER S. . . . . . **C. gracillimus**
SLIMBRISTLE S. . . . . . . **C. browni**
SOUTHERN S. . . . . . . **C. echinatus**

SANDERSO'NIA
auranti'aca

SANDGRASS . . . . **Triplasis**
PERENNIAL S. . . . . **T. americana**
PURPLE S. . . . . **T. purpurea**

Sandgrass . . . SANDREED: **Calamovilfa**

SANDHEATH . . **Ceratiola; C. ericoides**

SANDMYRTLE . . . . **Leiophyllum**
ALLEGANY S. **L. buxifolium prostratum**
BOX S. . . . . **L. buxifolium**
HUGERS S. . . . . **L. b. hugeri**

SANDNYMPH . . . . **Ammocharis**
KORAN S. . . . . **A. coranica**
SCARLET S. . . . . **A. coccinea**

SANDO'RICUM
koetja'pe (*indicum*) . . . . . SANTOL

SANDPAPERPLANT . . . . . . **Petalonyx**
NARROWLEAF S. . . . . . **P. linearis**
SMOOTH S. . . . . **P. nitidus**
THURBER S. . . . . **P. thurberi**

SANDREED . . . . **Calamovilfa**
BIG S. . . . . **C. gigantea**
FLORIDA S. . . . . **C. curtissi**
GREATLAKES S. . **C. longifolia magna**
PRAIRIE S. . . . . **C. longifolia**
RIVERBANK S. . . . . . . **C. brevipilis**

SANDSPURRY . . . . **Spergularia**
RED S. . . . . **S. rubra**
SALTMARSH S. . . . . **S. marina**

SANDVERBENA . . . . **Abronia**
BEARDED S. . . . . . **A. pogonantha**
DESERT S. . . . . **A. villosa**
PINK S. . . . . **A. umbellata**
SEASIDE S. . . . . **A. maritima**
SHOWY PINK S. **A. umbellata grandiflora**
SNOWBALL S. . . . . **A. fragrans**
WHITE S. . . . . **A. alba**
YELLOW S. . . . . **A. latifolia**

SANDWORT . . . . **Arenaria**
ALPINE S. . . . . **A. alpina**
AUSTRIAN S. . . . . . . **A. austriaca**
BALLHEAD S. . . . . . . **A. congesta**
BANATIAN S. . . . . **A. banatica**
BAUHINS S. . . . . . **A. bauhinorum**
BIGFLOWER MOUNTAIN S. **A. montana grandiflora**
BLUNTLEAF S. . . . . . . **A. lateriflora**
BURKE S. . . . . **A. burkei**
CAROLINA S. . . . . . **A. caroliniana**
COMPACT S. . . . . **A. compacta**
CORSICAN S. . . . . . . **A. balearica**
CREEPING S. . . . . **A. repens**
CRETE S. . . . . **A. cretica**
FENDLER S. . . . . **A. fendleri**

SANDWORT, continued
Fescue S. . . . . . **Arenaria formosa**
Grassleaf S. . . . . **A. graminifolia**
Greenland S. . . . . **A. groenlandica**
Hooker S. . . . . **A. hookeri**
Juniper S. . . . . . . **A. juniperina**
Kings S. . . . . **A. kingi**
Larchleaf S. . . . . . **A. laricifolia**
Ledebour S. . . . . **A. ledebouriana**
Longleaf S. . . . . . . **A. longifolia**
Moss S. . . . . . **A. verna caespitosa**
Mountain S. . . . . . . **A. montana**
Purple S. . . . . . **A. purpurascens**
Rock S. . . . . **A. stricta**
Roundleaf S. . . . . **A. rotundifolia**
Saxifrage S. . . . . . . **A. saxifraga**
Seabeach S. . . . . . . **A. peploides**
Siberian S. . . . . . . **A. sajanensis**
Steven S. . . . . . . **A. steveniana**
Stiff S.. . . . . **A. rigida**
Thymeleaf S. . . . . . **A. serpyllifolia**
Tufted S. . . . . **A. verna**
Twinflower S. . . . . . . **A. biflora**
Uinta S. . . . . **A. uintahensis**

SANGUINA'RIA ꟾw. . . . Bloodroot
canaden'sis ꟾw . Bloodroot (*Puccoon*)
₵Double (*plena*)

SANGUISOR'BA (*POTERIUM* in part) ꟾw. . . . . Burnet
The common name Burnet is applied also to the closely allied and at least partly synonymous genus Poterium.
an'nua (*Poterium annuum*) ꟾw Prairie B.
canaden'sis ꟾw . . . . American B.
dodecan'dra (*vallistellinae*)
menzies'i . . . . Menzies B.
mi'nor (*sanguisorba; Poterium s.*) Small B.
obtu'sa (*obtusata; Poterium obtusum*) Japanese B.
officina'lis . . . . Garden B.
sitchen'sis . . . . Sitka B.
spino'sa . . . . **Poterium spinosum**
tenuifo'lia . . . . Siberian B.
Sanicle . . . . **Sanicula**
Black S. . . . . **S. marilandica**
Canada S. . . . . . . **S. canadensis**
European S. . . . . . . **S. europaea**
Menzies S. . . . . **S. menziesi**
Poison S. . . . . **S. bipinnata**
Trefoil S. . . . . **S. trifoliata**
Tuber S. . . . . **S. tuberosa**

SANIC'ULA ꟾw. . . . . Sanicle
bipinna'ta . . . . Poison S.
canaden'sis ꟾw . . . . . Canada S.
europae'a . . . . European S.
grega'ria
marilan'dica . . . . Black S.
menzies'i . . . . Menzies S.
trifolia'ta . . . . Trefoil S.
tubero'sa . . . . Tuber S.
Sansapote . . . . . . **Licania platypus**

SANSEVIER'IA . . . . . Sansevieria
craig'i . . . . Craig S.
cylin'drica . . . . Ife S.
ehrenberg'i . . . . Seleb S.
grandicus'pis
kirk'i . . . . Kirk S.
longifo'lia . . . . Florida S.
par'va
roxburghia'na . . . . India S.
subspica'ta
suffrutico'sa
thyrsiflo'ra (*guineensis*) . . Sweet S.

SANSEVIERIA, continued
trifascia'ta . . . Snake Sansevieria
—laurent'i (*S. laurenti*) . Congo S.S.
zeylan'ica . . . . Ceylon S.

SAN'TALUM . . . . . Sandalwood
al'bum . . . . White S.
austro-caledo'nicum NewCaledonia S.
freycinetia'num . . . Yellow Fiji S.
lanceola'tum . . . . . Lanceleaf S.
ya'si . . . . Fiji S.
Santol . . . . . **Sandoricum koetjape**

SANTOLI'NA . . . . Lavendercotton
chamaecyparis'sus (*incana; S. c. incana*) . . . . Cypress L.
₵Dwarf (*nana*) hv.
neapolita'na (*rosmarinifolia*) Naples L.
pinna'ta . . . . Pinnate L.
vi'rens (*viridis*) . . . . . . Green L.

SANVITA'LIA . . . . Sanvitalia
abert'i . . . . Abert S.
procum'bens . . . . Trailing S.
Sanwamillet . . . . Japanesemillet: **Echinochloa crusgalli frumentacea**
Sapegrass . . . . . Satintail, Brazil: **Imperata brasiliensis**
Sapele . . . . **Entandrophragma**
Heavy S. . . . . **E. candollei**

SAPIN'DUS ꟾw . . . . . Soapberry
drum'mondi ꟾw. . . . . Western S.
margina'tus . . . . Florida S.
mukoros'si . . . . Chinese S.
—carina'tus
sapona'ria . . . . Southern S.
senegalen'sis . . . . . . Senegal S.
trifolia'tus . . . . . . Threeleaf S.

SA'PIUM . . . . Sapium
biglandulo'sum (*glandulosum*) Brazil S.
japon'icum . . . . Japanese S.
laurocera'sus (*aucuparium*) Birdlime S.
sebif'erum (*Stillingia sebifera*) Chinese Tallowtree
Sapodilla . . . . **Achras zapota**

SAPONA'RIA (*VACCARIA*) ꟾw Soapwort
Some botanists, however, regard Vaccaria as a distinct genus.
bellidifo'lia . . . . . Daisyleaf S.
caespito'sa. . . . . . . Pyrenees S.
cala'brica . . . . Calabrian S.
lute'a . . . . Yellowhead S.
ocymoi'des . . . . Rock S.
—al'ba . . . . White R.S.
₵Splendens. hv. S. ocymoides
₵Versicolor
officina'lis . . . . . . Bouncingbet
₵Caucasus (*caucasica*) hv.
₵Double (*flore-pleno*)
₵Double-rose (*rosea-plena*)
₵Double-white (*alba-plena*)
vacca'ria (*Vaccaria pyramidata; V. vaccaria; V. vulgaris*) ꟾw . . Cow S.
₵Alba. hv.
₵Rosea

SAPO'TA . . . . . **CALOCARPUM**
See also Achras, to which some species originally published as Sapota are now referred.
ach'ras; zapotil'la . . . **Achras zapota**

Sapote . . . . . . **Calocarpum sapota**
Green S. . . . . **C. viride**
Sapucaianut . . . . Monkeypottree, Sapucaianut: **Lecythis zabucajo**

SARA'CA . . . . Saraca
cauliflo'ra . . . . Scarlet S.
in'dica (*Jonesia asoca*) . . Common S. (*India Sorrowlesstree*)

SARCAN'THUS
See **ORCHID GENERA.**

SARCOBA'TUS ꟾw . . . Greasewood
bai'leyi . . . . Bailey G.
vermicula'tus ꟾw . . . . . Black G.

SARCOCEPH'ALUS . . **NAUCLEA**

SARCOCHI'LUS
See **ORCHID GENERA.**

SARCOCOC'CA . . . . . Sarcococca
hookeria'na . . . . . . Himalaya S.
—di'gyna . . . . . . Twostyle H.S.
—hu'milis (*S. humilis*) . Small H.S.
ruscifo'lia . . . . Fragrant S.
—chinen'sis . . . . Narrowleaf F.S.
salig'na (*pruniformis*). Willowleaf S.

SARCO'DES . . . . . . Snowplant
sanguin'ea . . . . Snowplant

SARCOGLOT'TIS
See **ORCHID GENERA.**

Sargasso . . . . **Sargassum**
Gulfweed S. . . . . . **S. bacciferum**

SARGAS'SUM . . . . Sargasso
baccif'erum . . . . . Gulfweed S.
Sargentgloryvine **Sargentodoxa; S. cuneata**

SARGENTODOX'A Sargentgloryvine
cunea'ta (*Holboellia c.*) Sargentgloryvine

SA'RIBUS . . . . **LIVISTONA**
See **PALM GENERA.**

SARO'THRA . . . . Pineweed
drum'mondi . . . . . Drummond P.
gentianoi'des . . . . . . Orange P.

SARRACE'NIA ꟾw . . . Pitcherplant
cates'baei Ell., *not* Hort. . . **S. sledgei**
cates'baei Hort., *not* Ell. . **Sarracenia** ₵Catesby
drum'mondi . . . . . Drummond P.
₵Rubra. hv.
fla'va . . . . Trumpet P.
jones'i . . . . Jones P.
mi'nor (*variolaris*) . . . . Hooded P.
psittaci'na . . . . Parrot P.
purpu'rea . . . . Common P.
ru'bra . . . . Sweet P.
sledg'ei (*catesbaei* Ell., *not* Hort.) Sledges P.
₵Catesby (*catesbaei* Hort.; *flava* × *purpurea*) hv. Sarracenia
Sarsaparilla
Honduras S. . . . . Jamaica S.
Jamaica S. . . . . . . **Smilax regeli**
Mexican S. . . . **S. aristolochiifolia**

SA'SA . . . . Sasa
See **BAMBOO GENERA.**

SAS'SAFRAS (*PSEUDOSASSAFRAS*) ꟾw . . . . Sassafras
al'bidum (*officinale*) ꟾw . . Common S.
—mol'le (*S. officinale; S. variifolium*) Silky S.
tzu'mu (*Pseudosassafras t.*) Chinese S.

SATINPOPPY . . . **Meconopsis wallichi**

SATINTAIL . . . . **Imperata**
BRAZIL S. . . . . . . **I. brasiliensis**
CALIFORNIA S. . . . . . **I. hookeri**
COGON S. . . . . **I. cylindrica**

SATINWOOD . . . . **Chloroxylon**
CEYLON S. . . . . **C. swietenia**

SATUREI'A (*CALAMINTHA; SATUREJA*) . . . . . . SAVORY
ac'inos (*Calamintha a.*) . . SPRING S.
alpi'na (*Calamintha a.*) . . ALPINE S.
calamin'tha (*Calamintha officinalis; Clinopodium c.*) . . . CALAMINT S. (*Calamint*)
carolinia'na **Clinopodium georgianum**
catalon'ica . . . . CATALONIA S.
chand'leri . . . . POTMINT S.
chinen'sis . . . . CHINESE S.
coccin'ea . . . **Clinopodium coccineum**
cor'sica . . . . CORSICAN S.
See note under Micromeria HV. Corsica.
croat'ica . . . . **Micromeria c.**
glabra'ta . . . . OZARK S.
horten'sis . . . . SUMMER S.
mol'lis
monta'na (*pygmaea; Calamintha m.; Micromeria m.*) . . . . WINTER S.
multicau'lis
nep'eta (*Calamintha n.; Clinopodium n.*) CATNIP S.
sylvat'ica . . . . WOOD S.
vulga'ris (*Calamintha leucopodium; Clinopodium vulgare*) . WILDBASIL S.
—al'ba . . . . WHITE W.S.
₵GRANDIFLORA. HV. Satureia
₵STENOPHYLLA

SAUROMA'TUM . . . . LIZARDARUM
gutta'tum (*Arum g.*)
—peda'tum (*S. pedatum; Arum p.*)
—puncta'tum (*S. punctatum*)
simlen'se . . . . SIMLEN L.
veno'sum (*Arum v.*) . . . VEINY L.

SAURU'RUS ⊾w . . . . . LIZARDTAIL
cer'nuus ⊾w . . . . . COMMON L.
loureir'i . . . . ORIENTAL L.

SAUSAGETREE . . . . **Kigelia**
AFRICAN S. . . . . . . **K. africana**
COMMON S. . . . . . . **K. pinnata**
MADAGASCAR S. . **K. madagascariensis**

SAUSSUR'EA . . . . . . SAUSSUREA
affi'nis
deltoi'dea . . . . HIMALAYA S.
gossipiph'ora . . . . COTTON S.
uniflo'ra

SAVANNAFLOWER . . . . **Echites**
DEVILSPOTATO . . . . . **E. umbellata**
WOOLLY S. . . . . . . **E. tomentosa**

SAVASTA'NA . . . **HIEROCHLOE**
See **GRASS GENERA.**

SA'VIA . . . . MAIDENBUSH
bahamen'sis . . . . . BAHAMA M.
phyllanthoi'des (*Andrachne reverchoni*) MISSOURI M.
sessiliflo'ra

SAVORY . . . . **Satureia**
ALPINE S. . . . . **S. alpina**
CALAMINT S. . . . . . **S. calamintha**
CATALONIA S. . . . . . **S. catalonica**
CATNIP S. . . . . **S. nepeta**
CHINESE S. . . . . . . **S. chinensis**
CORSICAN S. . . . . . . **S. corsica**
OZARK S. . . . . **S. glabrata**
POTMINT S. . . . . . . **S. chandleri**

SAVORY, continued
SPRING S. . . . . . **Satureia acinos**
SUMMER S. . . . . . . **S. hortensis**
WHITE WILDBASIL S. **S. vulgaris alba**
WILDBASIL S. . . . . . . **S. vulgaris**
WINTER S. . . . . **S. montana**
WOOD S. . . . . **S. sylvatica**

SAWARRINUT . . . . **Caryocar nuciferum**

Saw-Cabbagepalm . . . PAUROTIS, SAW: **Paurotis wrighti**

SAWFERN . . . . **Blechnum serrulatum**

SAWGRASS . . . . **Mariscus**
CALIFORNIA S. . . . . **M. californicus**
JAMAICA S. . . . . . **M. jamaicensis**
SMOOTH S. . . . . . **M. mariscoides**

SAWPALMETTO . . . **Serenoa; S. repens**

SAWWORT . . . . **Serratula**
DYERS S. . . . . **S. tinctoria**

SAXEGOTHAE'A PRINCE-ALBERT-YEW
conspic'ua . . . PRINCE-ALBERT-YEW

SAXIF'RAGA (*ANTIPHYLLA; LEPTASEA; MICRANTHES; MUSCARIA; PELTIPHYLLUM*) ⊾w SAXIFRAGE
adscen'dens
aestiva'lis . . . . SUMMER S.
affi'nis . . . . **S. hypnoides**
aizoi'des (*Leptasea a.*)
ai'zoon . . . . AIZOON S.
—al'ba . . . . WHITE A.S.
—balca'na (*S. balcana*) . BALKAN A.S.
—balden'sis (*S. baldensis*) PIEDMONT A.S.
—brevifo'lia (*S. brevifolia*) SHORTLEAF A.S.
—church'illi (*S. churchilli*)
—flaves'cens (*S. flavescens*) LEMON A.S.
—lagavea'na (*S. lagaveana*)
—lute'a . . . . YELLOW A.S.
—rose'a . . . . PINK A.S.
—stabia'na (*S. stabiana*)
₵DENSE (*densa*) HV. S. aizoon
₵HAINOLD (*hainoldi*)
₵PARADOX (*paradoxa*)
₵PECTINATE (*pectinata*)
₵PYGMY (*minima*)
₵REX
₵SILVERRIM (*notata*)
al'berti . . . . ALBERT S.
allio'ni . . . . **S. moschata a.**
altis'sima . . . . TALL S.
∞ **ambig'ua** (*aretioides × media*)
∞ **an'drewsi** (*aizoon × geum*) ∞ ANDREWS S.
apenni'na . . **S. cuneifolia subintegra**
aphyl'la . . . . TINYLEAF S.
∞ **apicula'ta** (*rocheliana × sancta*)
₵ALBA. HV.
₵MALYI (*S. malyi* Hort.)
aquat'ica . . . . WATER S.
arachnoi'dea . . . . COBWEB S.
aretioi'des
argu'ta (*Micranthes a.*) . . BROOK S.
as'pera
atropurpu'rea . . . . **S. moschata a.**
austromonta'na (*Leptasea a.*) YELLOWDOT S.
balca'na . . . . **S. aizoon b.**
balden'sis . . . . . . **S. aizoon b.**
bathonien'sis . . . . . **S. decipiens** ₵BATHONIENSIS
beesia'na Hort.
The botanical identity of this plant is uncertain.

SAXIFRAGA, continued
∞ **bertolo'ni** (*friderici-augusti × porophylla*) . ∞ BERTOLONI SAXIFRAGE
bon'gardi . . . . BONGARD S.
∞ **bo'risi** (*ferdinandi-coburgi × marginata*) ∞ BORIS S.
bo'ryi . . . . BORY S.
∞ **boyd'i** (*aretioides × burseriana*) ∞ BOYD S.
₵FALDONSIDE. HV.
₵WHITE (*alba*)
brach'ypus (*Micranthes b.*)
brevifo'lia . . . . **S. aizoon b.**
bronchia'lis
burseria'na . . . . BURSER S.
₵GLORIA. HV.
₵GRANDIFLORA
₵MAGNA
₵MINOR
₵REDSTEM (*speciosa*)
₵SULFUR (*sulphurea*)
cae'sia
caespito'sa (*Muscaria c.*)
califor'nica . . . . CALIFORNIAN S.
cam'posi (*wallacei*) . . . . CAMPOS S.
canalicula'ta . . . . GROOVESTEM S.
capilla'ris . . . . **S. cuneifolia**
capil'lipes . . **S. cuneifolia subintegra**
cartilagin'ea (*kolenatiana*) GRISTLELEAF S.
catalau'nica . . . . . CATALONIA S.
caterhamen'sis Hort. . . **S. cotyledon** ₵REDSPOT
ceratophyl'la . . . . . **S. trifurcata c.**
chrysan'tha . . . . . GOLDBLOOM S.
church'illi . . . . **S. aizoon c.**
cochlea'ris . . . . SNAIL S.
₵FINEPLUME (*longifolia*) HV.
₵MAJOR
₵MINOR
columbia'na . . . . . COLUMBIAN S.
conif'era . . . . CONIFER S.
cordifo'lia . . . . **Bergenia c.**
coriophyl'la
cortusifo'lia
corymbo'sa (*luteoviridis*)
cotyle'don . . . . . . JUNGFRAU S.
₵MONTAVON (*montavoniensis*) HV.
₵PYRAMID (*pyramidalis; S. nepalensis; S. pyramidalis*)
₵REDSPOT (*caterhamensis*)
₵ROSETTE (*prolifera*)
₵SILVERLEAF (*longifolia*)
crassifo'lia . . . . **Bergenia c.**
crusta'ta . . . . SALZBURG S.
cunea'ta
cuneifo'lia (*capillaris*) . WEDGELEAF S.
—subinteg'ra (*S. apennina; S. capillipes*) . . . . . . APENNINE W.S.
cuscutaefor'mis . . . . . DODDER S.
cymbala'ria . . . . IVYLEAF S.
decip'iens
₵ALANNAH. HV.
₵ARKWRIGHT (*arkwrighti*)
₵ASTHORE
₵BATHONIENSIS
₵CLARE ISLAND
₵CRIMSON MOSS
₵HOUSE (*houseana*)
₵HYBRIDA
₵LISSADELL
₵MARSHALL JOFFRE
₵POMPADOUR
₵QUEEN MAY
₵ROSEA
₵SANGUINEA
₵TAPIS ROUGE
₵WHITE (*alba*)

SAXIFRAGA, continued
delavay'i . . . Delavay Saxifrage
den'sa . . . . . **S. moschata** ₵Ball
eastwood'iae . . . . . Eastwood S.
ela'tior . . . . **S. hosti**
∞ **elizabe'thae** (*burseriana* × *sancta*)
∞ **eng'leri** (*aizoon* × *cuneifolia*)
∞ Engler S.
exara'ta
ferdinandi-co'burgi
Ferdinand-Coburg S.
ferrugin'ea . . . . . Rustyhair S.
flagella'ris
flaves'cens . . . . **S. aizoon f.**
friderici-au'gusti Frederick-August S.
∞ **gau'dini** (*aizoon* × *cotyledon*)
∞ Gaudin S.
geranioi'des . . . . . Geranium S.
ge'um (*Micranthes g.*) . Kidneyleaf S.
—**denta'ta** . . . . . . Toothed K.S.
—**hirsu'ta** . . . . . . Hairy K.S.
₵Minor. hv. S. geum
globulif'era
∞ **godseffia'na** (∞ *elizabethae* × *sancta*)
granula'ta . . . . Meadow S.
₵Double (*floreplena*) hv.
grisebach'i. . . . . . Grisebach S.
∞ **gus'musi** (*corymbosa* × *porophylla thessalica*) . . . . ∞ Gusmus S.
∞ **haag'i** (*ferdinandi-coburgi* × *sancta*)
∞ Haag S.
∞ **hauss'manni** (*aizoides* × *mutata*)
∞ Haussmann S.
hiber'nica . . . . . . **S. sternbergi**
hirsu'ta . . . . Hairy S.
host'i (*elatior*) . . . . . . Hosts S.
huetia'na . . . . Huet S.
hypnoi'des (*affinis; sponhemica*) Moss S.
—**gemmif'era** (*S. kingi*) . Kings M.S.
integrifo'lia
irrig'ua
∞ **ir'vingi** (*burseriana* var. × *friderici-augusti*) . . . . ∞ Irving S.
juniperifo'lia (*juniperina*) . Juniper S.
∞ **kestonien'sis** (?*burseriana* × ?)
king'i . . . . **S. hypnoides gemmifera**
kolenatia'na . . . . . **S. cartilaginea**
∞ **ky'rilli** (*ferdinandi-coburgi* × *marginata*) . . . . ∞ Kyrill S.
lagavea'na . . . . **S. aizoon l.**
lantosca'na . . . . . . **S. lingulata l.**
lasiophyl'la . **S. rotundifolia repanda**
latepetiola'ta
leicht'lini . . . . **Bergenia ligulata l.**
leucanthemifo'lia (*michauxi; Hydatica petiolaris*) . . . . . . Allegany S.
ligula'ta . . . . **Bergenia l.**
lilaci'na . . . . Lilac S.
lingula'ta . . . . Tongue S.
—**lantosca'na** (*S. lantoscana*)
Shortleaf T.S.
₵Albida. hv. S. lingulata
₵Australis
₵Bellard (*bellardi*)
₵Leichtlin (*leichtlini*)
₵Superba
longifo'lia . . . . Longleaf S.
₵Lowns (*lowni*) hv.
₵Magnifica
₵Major
luteovir'idis . . . . . **S. corymbosa**
ly'alli (*Micranthes l.*) . . . Lyall S.
∞ **macnabia'na** (*cotyledon* × *lingulata*)
∞ MacNab S.
ma'lyi Hort. . ∞ **S. apiculata** ₵Malyi
margina'ta. . . . . . . Hornrim S.
—**rochelia'na** (*S. rocheliana*)
Rochel H.S.

SAXIFRAGA, continued
me'dia
megase'a Hort.
A name apparently loosely used for various species and forms of the genus Bergenia.
mertensia'na . . Mertens Saxifrage
michaux'i . . . . **S. leucanthemifolia**
micranthidifo'lia (*Micranthes m.*)
Lettuce S.
montavonien'sis . . . . . **S. cotyledon**
₵Montavon
moscha'ta . . . . Musk S.
—**allio'ni** (*S. allioni*) . Allioni M.S.
—**atropurpu'rea** (*S. atropurpurea*)
Purple M.S.
—**rhe'i** (*S. rhei*) . . . . Rose M.S.
₵Ball (*densa*) hv. S. moschata
muscoi'des
—**atropurpu'rea**
muta'ta . . . . Thickroot S.
nelsonia'na (*Micranthes n.*). Nelson S.
nepalen'sis Hort. . . . . **S. cotyledon**
₵Pyramid
newcomb'ei (*Spatularia n.*)
Newcombe S.
niva'lis . . . . Snowball S.
∞ **obrist'i** (*burseriana* × *marginata*)
∞ Obrist S.
∞ **obscu'ra**
Reported by some to be a hybrid between S. geranioides and S. pubescens.
occidenta'lis (*Micranthes o.*) Alberta S.
odontolo'ma . . . . Washington S.
oppositifo'lia (*Antiphylla o.*)
Twinleaf S.
—**al'ba** . . . . White T.S.
—**pyrena'ica** (*S. pyrenaica*)
Pyrenees T.S.
₵Blush (*speciosa*) hv. S. oppositifolia
₵Flaming (*splendens*)
₵W. A. Clark
orbicula'ris Hort. . **Bergenia crassifolia**
₵Orbicular
∞ **pauli'nae** (*burseriana* ₵Minor × *ferdinandi-coburgi*) . . . ∞ Paulina S.
∞ **pectina'ta** (*aizoon* × *crustata*)
pedemonta'na . . . . . Piedmont S.
pelta'ta (*Peltiphyllum peltatum*)
Umbrella S.
pennsylva'nica (*Micranthes p.*)
Pennsylvania S.
petiola'ta
∞ **petrasch'i** (*marginata rocheliana* × *tombeanensis*) . . . . . ∞ Petrasch S.
porophyl'la . . . . . . Poreleaf S.
—**montenegri'na** . Montenegrin P.S.
—**thessa'lica** (*S. thessalica*)
Thessalian P.S.
port'ae . . **S. lingulata** ₵Australis
primuloi'des . . . . . **S. umbrosa p.**
prolif'era . . **S. cotyledon** ₵Rosette
puncta'ta . . . . Dotted S.
∞ **pun'gens** (*juniperifolia* × *marginata rocheliana*)
purpuras'cens . . . . . . **Bergenia p.**
pyramida'lis Hort. . . . **S. cotyledon**
₵Pyramid
pyrena'ica . . . . . **S. oppositifolia p.**
ranunculifo'lia . . . . . **Hemieva r.**
retu'sa . . . . Tricorner S.
rhe'i . . . . **S. moschata r.**
rhomboi'dea . . . . Diamondleaf S.
rochelia'na . . . . . . **S. marginata r.**
rotundifo'lia . . . . . Broadleaf S.
—**repan'da** (*S. lasiophylla*). Wavy B.S.
rufid'ula (*Micranthes r.*) . Redwool S.

SAXIFRAGA, continued
∞ **salomo'ni** (*burseriana* × *marginata rocheliana*) . ∞ Solomon Saxifrage
sanc'ta . . . . Sacred S.
sarmento'sa . . . . Strawberry S.
(*Aaronsbeard*)
scar'dica . . . . Scardic S.
∞ **schott'i** (*corymbosa* × *stribrnyi*)
∞ Schotts S.
sib'thorpi . . . . Sibthorp S.
specio'sa Hort.
This untenable name is sometimes misapplied to various hv., especially Blush, Redstem, and Crimson Rajah.
sponhe'mica . . . . . . **S. hypnoides**
squarro'sa . . . . Crevice S.
stabia'na . . . . **S. aizoon s.**
stella'ris. . . . . Star S.
stenoglos'sa
stern'bergi (*hibernica*) . . . . Irish S.
stra'cheyi . . . . **Bergenia s.**
strib'rnyi
∞ **stu'arti** (*stribrnyi* × ?) . ∞ Stuart S.
taygete'a . . . . Taygetus S.
tellimoi'des . . . . **Boykinia t.**
tenel'la
thessa'lica . . . . . **S. porophylla t.**
∞ **tirolen'sis** (*caesia* × *squarrosa*)
∞ Tyrolese S.
tol'miei . . . . Tolmie S.
tombeanen'sis
tricuspida'ta (*Leptasea t.*)
Threebristle S.
trifurca'ta . . . . . . Threefork S.
—**ceratophyl'la** (*S. ceratophylla*)
Hornleaf T.S.
umbro'sa . . . . . Londonpride S.
—**col'villei** . . . . . . Colville L.S.
—**primuloi'des** (*S. primuloides*)
Primrose L.S.
₵Harrows Crimson. hv. S. umbrosa
₵Variegated (*variegata*)
valden'sis
vanhout'tei Hort. . **Bergenia crassifolia**
₵Vanhoutte
vesperti'na (*Leptasea v.*) . . Vesper S.
virginien'sis (*Micranthes v.*) |w
Virginia S.
walla'cei . . . . **S. camposi**
∞ **wildia'na** (*aizoon* × *geum*)
∞ **zim'meteri** (*aizoon* × *cuneifolia*)
∞ Zimmeter S.
₵Cholentiana. hv. Saxifraga
₵James Brenner
₵Palmata
₵Pulchella
₵Rubella
₵Sanguinea Superba
₵Splendens (*cotyledon* × *longifolia*)
₵Stanborg (*stanborgi*)

Saxifrage . . . . **Saxifraga**
Aizoon S. . . . . **S. aizoon**
Alberta S. . . . . **S. occidentalis**
Albert S. . . . . **S. alberti**
Allegany S. . . . **S. leucanthemifolia**
Allioni Musk S. . **S. moschata allioni**
∞ Andrews S. . . . . . . ∞ **S. andrewsi**
Apennine Wedgeleaf S.
S. cuneifolia subintegra
Balkan Aizoon S. . **S. aizoon balcana**
∞ Bertoloni S. . . . . . ∞ **S. bertoloni**
Bongard S. . . . . **S. bongardi**
∞ Boris S. . . . . ∞ **S. borisi**
Bory S. . . . . **S. boryi**
∞ Boyd S. . . . . ∞ **S. boydi**
Broadleaf S. . . . . . **S. rotundifolia**
Brook S. . . . . **S. arguta**

SAXIFRAGE, continued
Burser S. . . . Saxifraga burseriana
Californian S. . . . S. californica
Campos S. . . . . . . S. camposi
Catalonia S. . . . . . S. catalaunica
Cobweb S. . . . . . S. arachnoidea
Columbian S. . . . . S. columbiana
Colville Londonpride S.
S. umbrosa colvillei
Conifer S. . . . . . . S. conifera
Crevice S. . . . . . . S. squarrosa
Delavay S. . . . . . . S. delavayi
Diamondleaf S. . . . S. rhomboidea
Dodder S. . . . . S. cuscutaeformis
Dotted S. . . . . . . S. punctata
Eastwood S. . . . . . S. eastwoodiae
∞ Engler S. . . . . . . ∞ S. engleri
Ferdinand-Coburg S.
S. ferdinandi-coburgi
Frederick-August S.
S. friderici-augusti
∞ Gaudin S. . . . . . . ∞ S. gaudini
Geranium S. . . . . S. geranioides
Goldbloom S. . . . . . S. chrysantha
Grisebach S. . . . . . S. grisebachi
Gristleleaf S. . . . . S. cartilaginea
Groovestem S. . . . S. canaliculata
∞ Gusmus S. . . . . ∞ S. gusmusi
∞ Haag S. . . . . ∞ S. haagi
Hairy Kidneyleaf S. S. geum hirsuta
Hairy S. . . . . S. hirsuta
∞ Haussmann S. . . . . ∞ S. haussmanni
Hornleaf Threefork S.
S. trifurcata ceratophylla
Hornrim S. . . . . . . S. marginata
Hosts S. . . . . S. hosti
Huet S. . . . . S. huetiana
Irish S. . . . . S. sternbergi
∞ Irving S. . . . . ∞ S. irvingi
Ivyleaf S. . . . . . . S. cymbalaria
Jungfrau S. . . . . . . S. cotyledon
Juniper S. . . . . . . S. juniperifolia
Kidneyleaf S. . . . . S. geum
Kings Moss S. S. hypnoides gemmifera
∞ Kyrill S. . . . . ∞ S. kyrilli
Lemon Aizoon S. S. aizoon flavescens
Lettuce S. . . . S. micranthidifolia
Lilac S. . . . . S. lilacina
Londonpride S. . . . . S. umbrosa
Longleaf S. . . . . S. longifolia
Lyall S. . . . . S. lyalli
∞ MacNab S. . . . . . ∞ S. macnabiana
Meadow S. . . . . S. granulata
Mertens S. . . . . . S. mertensiana
Montenegrin Poreleaf S.
S. porophylla montenegrina
Moss S. . . . . S. hypnoides
Musk S. . . . . S. moschata
Nelson S. . . . . . . S. nelsoniana
Newcombe S. . . . . . S. newcombei
∞ Obrist S. . . . . ∞ S. obristi
∞ Paulina S. . . . . . ∞ S. paulinae
Pennsylvania S. . . S. pennsylvanica
∞ Petrasch S. . . . . . . ∞ S. petraschi
Piedmont Aizoon S. S. aizoon baldensis
Piedmont S. . . . . S. pedemontana
Pink Aizoon S. . . . S. aizoon rosea
Poreleaf S. . . . . . . S. porophylla
Primrose Londonpride S.
S. umbrosa primuloides
Purple Musk S.
S. moschata atropurpurea
Pyrenees Twinleaf S.
S. oppositifolia pyrenaica
Redwool S. . . . . S. rufidula
Rochel Hornrim S.
S. marginata rocheliana
Rose Musk S. . . . S. moschata rhei

SAXIFRAGE, continued
Rustyhair S. . Saxifraga ferruginea
Sacred S. . . . . S. sancta
Salzburg S. . . . . S. crustata
Scardic S. . . . . S. scardica
∞ Schotts S. . . . . ∞ S. schotti
Shortleaf Aizoon S. S. aizoon brevifolia
Shortleaf Tongue S.
S. lingulata lantoscana
Sibthorp S. . . . . . . S. sibthorpi
Snail S. . . . . S. cochlearis
Snowball S. . . . . S. nivalis
∞ Solomon S. . . . . . ∞ S. salomoni
Star S. . . . . S. stellaris
Strawberry S. . . . . S. sarmentosa
∞ Stuart S. . . . . ∞ S. stuarti
Summer S. . . . . . . S. aestivalis
Tall S. . . . . S. altissima
Taygetus S. . . . . . . S. taygetea
Thessalian Poreleaf S.
S. porophylla thessalica
Thickroot S. . . . . . . S. mutata
Threebristle S. . . . S. tricuspidata
Threefork S. . . . . . S. trifurcata
Tinyleaf S. . . . . S. aphylla
Tolmie S. . . . . S. tolmiei
Tongue S. . . . . S. lingulata
Toothed Kidneyleaf S.
S. geum dentata
Tricorner S. . . . . . . S. retusa
Twinleaf S. . . . . . S. oppositifolia
∞ Tyrolese S. . . . . . ∞ S. tirolensis
Umbrella S. . . . . S. peltata
Vesper S. . . . . S. vespertina
Virginia S. . . . . . . S. virginiensis
Washington S. . . . S. odontoloma
Water S. . . . . S. aquatica
Wavy Broadleaf S.
S. rotundifolia repanda
Wedgeleaf S. . . . . . S. cuneifolia
White Aizoon S. . . . S. aizoon alba
White Twinleaf S. S. oppositifolia a.
Yellow Aizoon S. . . S. aizoon lutea
Yellowdot S. . . S. austromontana
∞ Zimmeter S. . . . . . ∞ S. zimmeteri

SCABIO'SA (*KNAUTIA*) . Scabious
africa'na . . . . African S.
amoe'na . . . . Turkish S.
arven'sis (*Knautia a.*) . . Field S.
atropurpu'rea . . . . . . Sweet S.
₵Compact (*compacta*) hv.
₵Double (*flore-pleno*)
₵Dwarf (*minor; nana*)
₵Great (*grandiflora; maxima*)
₵Pygmy (*pumila*)
₵White (*candidissima*)
austra'lis . . . . Succisa a.
brachia'ta
caucas'ica . . . . . . Caucasian S.
—al'ba . . . . White C.S.
₵Clive Greves. hv. S. caucasica
₵Constancy
₵Goldingen (*goldingensis*)
₵Isaac House
₵Magnificent (*magnifica*)
₵Miss Willmott
₵Mrs. J. Smith
₵Violet Walters
columba'ria . . . . Dove S.
—anthemifo'lia . . . Camomile D.S.
fisch'eri . . . . Fischers S.
graminifo'lia . . . . . Grassleaf S.
hook'eri . . . . Hookers S.
japon'ica . . . . Japanese S.
lute'a . . . . Yellow S.
₵Giant (*gigantea*) hv.

SCABIOSA, continued
ochroleu'ca . . . . Cream Scabious
parnas'si; pteroceph'ala
Pterocephalus parnassi
pyrena'ica . . . . Pyrenees S.
silenifo'lia
stella'ta . . . . . . Starflower S.
succi'sa . . . . . . Succisa pratensis
sylvat'ica . . . . Knautia s.
₵Ageratum Blue. hv. Scabiosa
₵Azure Fairy
₵Blue Cockade
₵Loveliness
₵Lyreleaf (*lyrata*)
₵Rose
₵Shasta
₵Strawberry (*prolifera*)

Scabious . . . . Scabiosa
African S. . . . . . . S. africana
Camomile Dove S.
S. columbaria anthemifolia
Caucasian S. . . . . . S. caucasica
Cream S. . . . . . . S. ochroleuca
Dove S. . . . . S. columbaria
Field S. . . . . S. arvensis
Fischers S. . . . . S. fischeri
Grassleaf S. . . . . S. graminifolia
Hookers S. . . . . S. hookeri
Japanese S. . . . . . . S. japonica
Pyrenees S. . . . . . . S. pyrenaica
Starflower S. . . . . . . S. stellata
Sweet S. . . . . . S. atropurpurea
Turkish S. . . . . S. amoena
White Caucasian S. . S. caucasica alba
Yellow S. . . . . S. lutea

Scalybroom . . . . . . Lepidospartum
California S. . . . . L. squamatum
Woolly S. . . . . . L. latisquamum

SCAN'DIX . . . . Shepherds-needle
pecten-ven'eris . . . . Venuscomb S.

Scarboro(ugh)lily . . . Vallota: Vallota

SCELE'TIUM
MESEMBRYANTHEMUM
See SUCCULENTS.

SCHAEFFE'RIA
frutes'cens . . . Florida-boxwood

SCHAUE'RIA
flavico'ma

SCHEDONNARD'US . . Tumblegrass
See GRASS GENERA.

SCHEE'LEA (*ATTALEA* in part; *MAXIMILIANA* in part)
See PALM GENERA.

SCHEFF'LERA
actinophyl'la . . . . . . Brassaia a.
digita'ta

SCHEUCHZE'RIA . . . Scheuchzeria
palus'tris . . . . . . Scheuchzeria

SCHI'MA . . . . Gugertree
noron'hae . . . . Burma G.
wal'lichi . . Darjeeling G. (*Chilauni*)

SCHINOP'SIS (*QUEBRACHIA*)
Redquebracho
balan'sae . . . . . Willowleaf R.
lorentz'i (*Quebrachia l.*) . Lorentz R.

SCHI'NUS (*DUVAUA*) W Peppertree
The gender of Schinus is feminine; it is incorrectly treated as masculine in much of the literature.
depen'dens (*Duvaua d.*) . . . Peru P.
—longifo'lia . . . . . Longleaf P.P.

SCHINUS, continued
latifo'lia (*Duvaua l.*) Chilean Peppertree
lentiscifo'lia . . . . . Pinkberry P.
mol'le |w . . . . . California P.
The specific name molle appears to be a neuter adjective, so that some authors have attempted to correct the spelling to mollis. Actually, however, the word molle is a noun.
terebinthifo'lia . . . . . . Brazil P.

SCHIP'PIA
See **PALM GENERA.**

SCHISAN'DRA (*MAXIMOWICZIA* Rupr., *not* Cogn.; *SCHIZANDRA; SPHAEROSTEMA*) Magnoliavine
chinen'sis (*Maximowiczia sinensis*) Chinese M.
—rubriflo'ra . . . . **S. grandiflora r.**
coccin'ea . . . . . . Carolina M.
glauces'cens
grandiflo'ra . . . . . Bigbloom M.
—cathayen'sis . . Littleleaf B.M.
—rubriflo'ra (*S. chinensis r.; S. rubriflora*) . . . . Red B.M.
hen'ryi (*hypoglauca*) . Underblue M.
ni'gra . . . . Black M.
propin'qua (*Sphaerostema propinquum*) Angletwig M.
—sinen'sis . . . . . Yellow A.M.
pubes'cens . . . . Fuzzy M.
rubriflo'ra . . . . . . **S. grandiflora r.**
sphenan'thera . . . . Orange M.
—lancifo'lia . . . . Whiplash O.M.

SCHISMATOGLOT'TIS. . Droptongue
aspera'ta . . . . . Wartystem D.
—albo-macula'ta (*S. crispata*) Whitespot W.D.
deco'ra . . . . **S. pulchra**
marantifo'lium . . . . **Aglaonema m.**
—macula'tum **Aglaonema commutatum**
neo-guineen'sis (*novo-guineensis; Colocasia neo-guineensis*) NewGuinea D.
pic'ta . . . . Painted D.
pul'chra (*decora*) . . Silverblotch D.

SCHIS'MUS
See **GRASS GENERA.**

SCHIVERECK'IA
bornmuel'leri
podol'ica

SCHIZACH'NE
See **GRASS GENERA.**

SCHIZAE'A
See **FERN GENERA.**

SCHIZAN'DRA . . . **SCHISANDRA**

SCHIZAN'THUS . . Butterflyflower
grac'ilis . . . . Slim B.
gra'hami . . . . Graham B.
pinna'tus (*grandiflorus*). Wingleaf B.
—candidis'simus . . . White W.B.
—carmin'eus . . . . Carmine W.B.
—lilac'inus . . . . . Lilac W.B.
₵Marbled (*papilionaceus*) hv. S. pinnatus
retu'sus . . . . . . Orange-rose B.
₵Threespot (*trimaculatus*) hv.
₵Yellowlip (*albus*)
∞ **wisetonen'sis** (*grahami* × *pinnatus*) ∞ Wiseton B.
₵Excelsior. hv.

SCHIZOBASOP'SIS . . . **BOWIEA**

SCHIZOCEN'TRON Spanish-shawlplant
el'egans . . . . Spanish-shawlplant

SCHIZOCO'DON . . . . Fringebell
soldanelloi'des . . . . . Fringebell
—alpi'nus . . . . Alpine F.
—grandiflo'rus . . . . Bigflower F.
—ilicifo'lius (*S. ilicifolius*) Hollyleaf F.

SCHIZOLO'BIUM
parahy'bum (*excelsum*)

SCHIZONO'TUS Lindl. . **SORBARIA**

SCHIZONO'TUS Raf. . **HOLODISCUS**
dis'color . . . . **Holodiscus d.**
purpuras'cens . . . . . . **Solanoa p.**
tomento'sus . . . **Sorbaria tomentosa**

SCHIZOPET'ALON
wal'keri

SCHIZOPHRAG'MA . Hydrangeavine
hydrangeoi'des . . . . . Japanese H.
The name Schizophragma hydrangeoides is often misapplied to Hydrangea petiolaris.
integrifo'lium (*S. hydrangeoides i.*) Chinese H.
—mol'le . . . . Woolly C.H.

SCHIZOSTA'CHYUM
See **BAMBOO GENERA.**

SCHIZOS'TYLIS. . . . Crimsonflag
coccin'ea . . . . Basuto C.

SCHLEICH'ERA . . . . . . Lactree
oleo'sa (*trijuga*) . . . . . Malay L.
subundula'ta . . . . . Philippine L.

SCHLUMBER'GERA (*EPIPHYLLOPSIS; ZYGOCACTUS*) Crabcactus
See **CACTUS GENERA.**

SCHMALTZ'IA . . . . **RHUS**

SCHOENOCAU'LON . . . . Sabadilla
See note under Sabadilla.
drum'mondi . . . . . Drummond S.
officina'le . . . . Drug S.

SCHOENOCRAM'BE Plainsmustard
linifo'lia (*pinnata*) . . . Flaxleaf P.

SCHOEP'FIA . . . . Graytwig
chrysophylloi'des . . . . . Gulf G.

SCHOMBURG'KIA (*SCHOMBURGHIA*)
See **ORCHID GENERA.**

SCHO'TIA . . . . . Kafirbeantree
brachypet'ala
latifo'lia . . . . Elephant-hedge K.
specio'sa . . . . . . Hottentot K.

SCHRANK'IA (*LEPTOGLOTTIS; MORONGIA*) |w . . Sensitivebrier
angustisili'qua . . . . Narrowpod S.
microphyl'la (*angustata*) |w Littleleaf S.
Perhaps only a variety of S. uncinata.
roemeria'na . . . . . . Roemer S.
uncina'ta . . . . Catclaw S.

SCHRE'BERA . . . . . . Schrebera
saunders'iae . . . . . . Saunders S.
swietenioi'des . . . . . Muccaady S.

SCHWAL'BEA . . . . . . Chaffseed
america'na . . . . . . American C.

SCIADOP'ITYS . . . Umbrellapine
verticilla'ta . . . . Umbrellapine

SCIL'LA . . . . Squill
amoe'na . . . . . . Starhyacinth S.
autumna'lis . . . . Autumn S.
bifo'lia (*laxa*) . . . . Twinleaf S.
—al'ba . . . . White T.S.
—rose'a . . . . Pink T.S.
—ruber'rima . . . . Red T.S.
—splen'dens . . . . . . Cobalt T.S.
chinen'sis . . . . Chinese S.
hispan'ica (*campanulata*) Spanish S.
—al'ba . . . . White S.S.
—rose'a (*S. campanulata r.*) Rose S.S.
₵Blue Queen. hv. S. hispanica
₵Coerulea
₵Excelsior
₵Rosalind
₵Rose Queen
hyacinthoi'des . . . . . Hyacinth S.
ital'ica . . . . Italian S.
lax'a . . . . **S. bifolia**
marit'ima . . . . **Urginea m.**
natalen'sis . . . . Natal S.
nonscrip'ta (*nutans*) . Common Blue S.
Alba. hv.
Caerulea
Cernua
Delicata
Lilacina
Rosea
Rubra
peruvia'na . . . . Peruvian S.
The scientific and common names of this plant are misnomers. It originated in the Mediterranean region.
—al'ba . . . . White P.S.
—caeru'lea . . . . Azure P.S.
praten'sis . . . . Meadow S.
sibir'ica . . . . Siberian S.
Alba. hv.
Amoenula
Atrocaerulea
Azurea
Pallida
Taurica. *Multiflora.*
ver'na . . . . Spring S.

SCILLOI'DES Hort.. . **PUSCHKINIA**
The generic name Scilloides, sometimes in catalogs, has no botanical standing.

SCINDAP'SUS . . . . Ivyarum
au'reus (*Pothos a.*) SolomonIslands I.
—wil'coxi (*Pothos a. w.*) . Wilcox S.I.
cuscua'ria . . . . Poisondart I.
officina'lis . . . . Drug I.
pic'tus . . . . Painted I.
—argyrae'us (*S. argyraeus; Pothos a.*) Silver P.I.

SCIR'PUS (*ISOLEPIS*) |w . . Bulrush
acu'tus (*occidentalis*) |w . . Tule B.
america'nus |w . . . . American B.
atrocinc'tus |w
atrovi'rens |w . . . . Green B.
caespito'sus |w . . . . . Deerhair B.
califor'nicus |w . . . . California B.
carina'tus |w . . . . Keeled B.
cer'nuus (*Isolepis gracilis*) |w Weeping B.
cuben'sis |w . . . . Cuban B.
cyperi'nus |w. . . . . . Woolgrass B.
deb'ilis |w . . . . Weak B.
etubercula'tus |w
fluviat'ilis |w . . . . River B.
hall'i |w . . . . Halls B.
heterochae'tus |w . . . . . Slender B.
holoschoe'nus
lacus'tris . . . . Great B.
—zebri'nus Hort. **S. tabernaemontani** ₵Zebra

SCIRPUS, continued
linea'tus |w
microcar'pus |w . PANICLED BULRUSH
nevaden'sis |w . . . . . NEVADA B.
occidenta'lis . . . . **S. acutus**
ol'neyi |w . . . . OLNEY B.
paludo'sus |w . . . . . . ALKALI B.
polyphyl'lus |w . . . . . LEAFY B.
robus'tus |w . . . . . SALTMARSH B.
ru'fus |w . . . . RED B.
saximonta'nus |w ROCKYMOUNTAIN B.
smith'i |w . . . . SMITHS B.
subtermina'lis |w
supi'nus
sylvat'icus |w . . . . WOODLAND B.
tabernaemonta'ni
TABERNAEMONTANUS B.
¢ZEBRA (*zebrinus; lacustris z.*) HV.
tor'reyi |w . . . . TORREY B.
val'idus |w . . . . . . SOFTSTEM B.

SCLERAN'THUS . . . . . KNAWEL
an'nuus . . . . ANNUAL K.
peren'nis . . . . . PERENNIAL K.

SCLE'RIA |w . . . . . . RAZORSEDGE
bald'wini |w . . . . . . BALDWIN R.
cilia'ta |w . . . . . . FRINGED R.
flagellum-nigro'rum . SLAVESFLAIL R.
gla'bra |w . . . . SMOOTH R.
latifo'lia . . . . BROADLEAF R.
oligan'tha |w . . . . LITTLEHEAD R.
pauciflo'ra |w . . . FEWFLOWER R.
ptero'ta
reticula'ris |w . . . . . NETTED R.
triglomera'ta |w . . . . . WHIP R.
verticilla'ta |w . . . . . WHORLED R.

SCLEROCAC'TUS
See **CACTUS GENERA.**

SCLEROCA'RYA . . . . MARVOLANUT
birroe'a . . . . ETHIOPIAN M.
caf'fra . . . . KAFIR M.
casta'nea . . . . . . MAURITIUS M.
shaku'a . . . . . . MASCARENE M.

SCLEROCH'LOA . . . . HARDGRASS
See **GRASS GENERA.**

SCLEROL'EPIS |w . . . . SCLEROLEPIS
uniflo'ra |w . . . . . . SCLEROLEPIS

SCLERO'POA . . . . . . STIFFGRASS
See **GRASS GENERA.**

SCLEROPO'GON . . . . BURROGRASS
See **GRASS GENERA.**

SCOLOCH'LOA . . . . . **FLUMINEA**
See **GRASS GENERA.**

SCOLOPEN'DRIUM . . **PHYLLITIS**
See **FERN GENERA.**

SCOL'YMUS . . . . . OYSTERPLANT
(*Goldenthistle*)
hispan'icus . . . . . . SPANISH O.

SCOPA'RIA . . . . BROOMWORT
dul'cis . . . . SWEET B.

SCOPO'LIA . . . . SCOPOLIA
carniol'ica . . . . . . EUROPEAN S.
japon'ica . . . . . . JAPANESE S.

SCORPIONTAIL . . . . **Scorpiurus**
CATERPILLARPOD S. . . . **S. subvillosa**
PRICKLY S. . . . . **S. muricata**
WORMPOD S. . . . . . **S. vermiculata**

SCORPIU'RUS . . . . SCORPIONTAIL
murica'ta . . . . PRICKLY S.
subvillo'sa . . . . CATERPILLARPOD S.
sulca'ta
vermicula'ta . . . . . . WORMPOD S

SCORZONE'RA . . . . SERPENTROOT
hispan'ica . . . . . BLACKSALSIFY S.
hu'milis . . . . BOHEMIAN S.
lacinia'ta . . . . MEDITERRANEAN S.

SCOTTEL'LIA
coria'cea

SCOURINGRUSH . . **Equisetum hyemale**
STOUT S. . . . . **E. praealtum**
WESTERN S. . **E. hyemale californicum**

SCRATCHBUSH . . . . **Urera**
BROADLEAF S. . . . . . **U. baccifera**
FLAMEBERRY S. . . . . **U. caracasana**

Scratchgrass . . . . . MUHLY, ALKALI:
Muhlenbergia asperifolia

SCREWBEAN . . . . . . **Strombocarpa**
DWARF S. . . . . . . **S. cinerascens**
FREMONT S. . . . . **S. odorata**

SCREWPINE . . . . **Pandanus**
AUSTRALIAN S. . . . . . **P. australis**
COMMON S. . . . . **P. utilis**
DWARF S. . . . . . . **P. pygmaeus**
GRASSY S. . . . . . **P. graminifolius**
JAVA S. . . . . **P. javanicus**
PACIFIC S. . . . . **P. pacificus**
ROEHRS TIMOR S.
P. sanderi roehrsianus
THATCH S. . . . . **P. tectorius**
TIMOR S. . . . . **P. sanderi**
VARIEGATED S. . . . . **P. variegatus**
VEITCH S. . . . . **P. veitchi**

SCREWTREE . . . . **Helicteres**
JAMAICA S. . . . . . . **H. jamaicensis**

Scribblygum . . EUCALYPTUS, SCRIBBLY:
Eucalyptus haemastoma

SCRIBNE'RIA . . . . . . SCRIBNERIA
See **GRASS GENERA.**

SCROPHULA'RIA . . . . . FIGWORT
aquat'ica . . . . WATER F.
califor'nica . . . . . CALIFORNIA F.
lanceola'ta . . . . . . LANCELEAF F.
langea'na . . . . LANGE F.
lateriflo'ra . . . . . . CAUCASIAN F.
marilan'dica . . . . . MARYLAND F.
nodo'sa . . . . WOOD F.
occidenta'lis . . . . . . WESTERN F.

Perhaps hardly more than a western var. of S. lanceolata.

peregri'na . . . . MEDITERRANEAN F.
smith'i . . . . SMITH F.
verna'lis . . . . SPRING F.

SCURFPEA . . . . **Psoralea**
ARABIAN S. . . . . . **P. bituminosa**
BEAVERBREAD S. . . . . . **P. castorea**
BLUEBROOM S. . . . . . . **P. aphylla**
BOBSROOT S. . . . . . **P. psoralioides**
CALIFORNIATEA S. . . . . **P. physodes**
COMMON BREADROOT S. . **P. esculenta**
DRUPE S. . . . . **P. drupacea**
HOARY S. . . . . **P. canescens**
LEATHERROOT S. . . **P. macrostachya**
LEMON S. . . . . **P. lanceolata**
LITTLE BREADROOT S. . . **P. hypogaea**
MALAYTEA S. . . . . . . **P. corylifolia**
PINNATE S. . . . . **P. pinnata**
SILVERLEAF S. . . . . . **P. argophylla**
SKUNKTOP S. . . . . . . **P. mephitica**
SLENDER S. . . . . **P. gracilis**
SLIMFLOWER S. . . . . . **P. tenuiflora**
TALLBREAD S. . . . . . . **P. cuspidata**

SCURVYWEED . . . . **Cochlearia**
COMMON S. . . . . **C. officinalis**

SCUTELLA'RIA |w . . . . . SKULLCAP
al'bida . . . . WHITE S.
alpi'na . . . . ALPINE S.
—**lupuli'na** (*S. lupulina; S. l. bicolor* Hort.) . . . . YELLOW A.S.
¢ALBA. HV. S. alpina
¢CAERULEA
¢ROSEA
altis'sima . . . . TALL S.
angustifo'lia . . . . NARROWLEAF S.
baicalen'sis . . . . BAIKAL S.
¢AZURE (*coelestina*) HV.
brit'toni . . . . BRITTONS S.
califor'nica . . . . . CALIFORNIA S.
coccin'ea . . . . SCARLET S.
colum'nae . . . . COLUMNAR S.
galericula'ta
in'dica . . . . INDIA S.
—**japon'ica** . . . . SMALL I.S.
integrifo'lia . . . . HYSSOP S.
lateriflo'ra . . . . SIDEFLOWERING S.
lupuli'na . . . . **S. alpina l.**
—*bi'color* Hort. . . . . **S. a. lupulina**
mocinia'na . . . . MOCINO S.
nervo'sa . . . . VEINED S.
orienta'lis . . . . ORIENTAL S.
par'vula . . . . SMALL S.
resino'sa . . . . RESINOUS S.
serra'ta . . . . SHOWY S.
tubero'sa . . . . TUBEROUS S.
ventena'ti . . . . COLOMBIA S.
versicol'or

SCUTICA'RIA
See **ORCHID GENERA.**

SCYTHIANLAMB . . . **Cibotium barometz**

SEABERRY . . . . **Haloragis**
ERECT S. . . . . **H. erecta**

SEABUCKTHORN . . . . **Hippophae**
COMMON S. . . . . . **H. rhamnoides**
WILLOWLEAF S. . . . . **H. salicifolia**

SEAFORTH'IA. . **PTYCHOSPERMA**
See **PALM GENERA.**

SEAGRAPE . . . . **Coccolobis**
COMMON S. . . . . **C. uvifera**
GRANDLEAF S. . . . . **C. grandifolia**
KRUGS S. . . . . **C. krugi**
MIXLEAF S. . . . . . . **C. diversifolia**
PIGEON S. . . . . **C. floridana**

SEAHEATH, YERBAREUMA
Frankenia grandifolia

SEA-LAVENDER . . . . **Limonium**
ALGERIAN S . . . . **L. bonduelli**
BIGLEAF S. . . . . **L. macrophyllum**
BRAZIL S. . . . . **L. brasiliense**
BROADLEAF S. . . . . . . **L. latifolium**
BROADWING S. . . . **L. macropterum**
CALIFORNIA S. . . . . **L. californicum**
CANARIES S. . . . **L. brassicaefolium**
CAROLINA S. . . . . . **L. carolinianum**
CASPIAN S. . . . . . . **L. reticulatum**
CHALKDOT S. . . . . . . **L. pectinatum**
CHINESE S. . . . . **L. sinense**
CRAG S. . . . . **L. rupicola**
DWARF TATARIAN S. **L. tataricum nanum**
GOUGET S. . . . . . . **L. gougetianum**
HAIRYCUP S. . . . . . **L. trichogonum**
LANCELEAF TATARIAN S.
L. tataricum angustifolium
LITTLE S. . . . . **L. minutum**
LITTLESPIKE S. . . . . . . **L. spicatum**
MEDITERRANEAN S. . . . . **L. vulgare**
MOROCCO S. . . . . **L. lychnidifolium**
NARROWLEAF S. . . . . **L. angustatum**
NASH S. . . . . **L. nashi**
NOTCHLEAF S. . . . . **L. sinuatum**
PEREZ S. . . . . **L. perezi**

SEA-LAVENDER, continued
PERSIAN S. **Limonium leptostachyum**
PREAUX S. . . . . **L. preauxi**
ROSY WIDELEAF S. **L. latifolium roseum**
SEAVIOLET S. . . . . . . **L. virgatum**
SIBERIAN S. . . . . **L. gmelini**
SUNGARI S. . . . . . . **L. eximium**
∞SUPERBUM S.. . . . . . **∞L. superbum**
SUWOROW S. . . . . . . **L. suworowi**
TATARIAN S. . . . . . . **L. tataricum**
TENERIFFE S. . . . . . **L. imbricatum**
THOROWORT S. . . . . **L. perfoliatum**
TREE S. . . . . **L. arborescens**
TWONERVE S. . . . . **L. binervosum**
VIOLETTUFT S. . **L. globulariaefolium**
WHITE BROADLEAF S.
L. latifolium album
WHITE NOTCHLEAF S.
L. sinuatum candidissimum
WHITE SUWOROW S.
L. suworowi album
WHITE TATARIAN S. . . **L. tataricum a.**
WOODY S. . . . . **L. fruticans**
YELLOWSHRUB S. . . . **L. puberulum**

SEALETTUCE . . . . **Ulva**
COMMON S. . . . . **U. lactuca**

SEALINGWAXPALM . . . **Cyrtostachys**
RAJAH S. . . . . **C. lakka**
SUMATRA S. . . . . **C. rendah**

SEAMILKWORT . . . **Glaux; G. maritima**

SEAOAK, DRUG . . . **Halidrys siliquosa**

SEAOATS . . . . **Uniola paniculata**

SEAONION . . . . **Urginea**

SEA-OXEYE . . . . **Borrichia**
BUSHY S. . . . . **B. frutescens**
TREE S. . . . . **B. arborescens**

SEAROCKET . . . . **Cakile**
AMERICAN S. . . . . . . **C. edentula**

Sebes'ten sebes'tena . . . . . **Cordia s.**

SECA'LE . . . . RYE
See **CEREALS** and **GRASS GENERA.**

SECAMO'NE . . . . SECAMONE
amygdali'na . . . . . . PEACHLEAF S.
ova'ta
socotra'na . . . . SOCOTRA S.
timoren'sis . . . . TIMOR S.

Seccomaria. . . . DRYMARY: **Drymaria**

SECH'IUM (*CHAYOTA*) . . CHAYOTE
ed'ule (*Chayota edulis*) . . CHAYOTE

SECURIDA'CA . . . . . SECURIDACA
diversifo'lia . . . EASTERFLOWER S.
ellip'tica
tenuifo'lia . . . . TRINIDAD S.

SECURIG'ERA . . . HATCHETVETCH
coronil'la (*Coronilla securidaca*)
HATCHETVETCH

SECURINE'GA . . . . . SECURINEGA
duris'sima . . . . SPOILAXE S.
fascicula'ta . . . . . **Tetracoccus halli**
nit'ida . . . . TAHITI S.
suffrutico'sa (*flueggeoides; ramiflora; Flueggea s.; Geblera s.*)

SEDAS'TRUM . . . . . . **SEDUM**
See **SUCCULENTS.**

SEDGE . . . . **Carex**
ABRUPTBEAK S. . . . . . **C. abrupta**
AWNED HAIRYSEED S.
C. trichocarpa aristata
BEAKED S. . . . . **C. rostrata**

SEDGE, continued
BIGLEAF S. . . . . **Carex amplifolia**
BLACK ALPINE S. . . . . **C. nigricans**
BLACK S. . . . . **C. atrata**
BLISTER S. . . . . **C. vesicaria**
BOLANDER S. . . . . . . **C. bolanderi**
BOTTLEBRUSH S. . . . . **C. hystricina**
BRISTLEBRACT S. . . . **C. tribuloides**
BROOM S. . . . . **C. scoparia**
BUCHANAN S. . . . . . **C. buchanani**
CHAMISSO S. . . . . **C. pachystachya**
CLOUD S. . . . . **C. nubicola**
CORDROOT S. . . . . **C. chordorrhiza**
CRAWFORD S. . . . . . . **C. crawfordi**
CROWFOOT S. . . . . . . **C. cruscorvi**
CUSICK S. . . . . **C. cusicki**
DOUGLAS S. . . . . **C. douglasi**
DUNHEAD S. . . . . **C. phaeocephala**
EBONY S. . . . . **C. ebenea**
ELK S. . . . . **C. geyeri**
EMORY S. . . . . **C. emoryi**
FEWSEED S. . . . . . **C. oligosperma**
FOX S. . . . . **C. vulpinoidea**
FRANKS S. . . . . **C. franki**
FRASER S. . . . . **C. fraseri**
FRINGED S. . . . . **C. crinita**
GIANT S. . . . . **C. gigantea**
GOLDEN S. . . . . **C. aurea**
GREEN S. . . . . **C. viridula**
HAIRYSEED S. . . . . **C. trichocarpa**
HINDS S. . . . . **C. hindsi**
HOOD S. . . . . **C. hoodi**
HOPLIKE S. . . . . . **C. lupuliformis**
HOP S. . . . . **C. lupulina**
INLAND S. . . . . **C. interior**
KELLOGG S. . . . . **C. kelloggi**
LACHENAL S. . . . . . . **C. lachenali**
LIDDON S. . . . . **C. petasata**
LURID S. . . . . **C. lurida**
MERTENS S. . . . . **C. mertensi**
MORROWS S. . . . . **C. morrowi**
MUD S. . . . . **C. limosa**
NEBRASKA S. . . . . **C. nebraskensis**
NEEDLELEAF S. . . . . **C. eleocharis**
NEWZEALAND HAIR S. . . . **C. comans**
OKLAHOMA S. . . . **C. oklahomensis**
OVALHEAD S. . . . . . . **C. festivella**
PLANTAINLEAF S. . . . **C. plantaginea**
PRAIRIE S. . . . . **C. prairea**
PRESL S. . . . . **C. presli**
RAYNOLDS S. . . . . . . **C. raynoldsi**
ROSS S. . . . . **C. rossi**
RYEGRASS S. . . . . **C. loliacea**
SALT S. . . . . **C. salina**
SANTABARBARA S. . . . . **C. barbarae**
SARTWELL S. . . . . **C. sartwelli**
SEA S. . . . . **C. marina**
SHEEP S. . . . . **C. illota**
SHELDON S. . . . . **C. sheldoni**
SHORTHAIR S. . . . . . . **C. exserta**
SIERRASLIM S. . . . **C. teneraeformis**
SILVERTOP S. . . . . **C. siccata**
SITKA S. . . . . **C. sitchensis**
SLENDERBEAK S. . . . **C. athrostachya**
SMALLWING S. . . . . . **C. microptera**
STREAMBANK S. . . . . . . **C. riparia**
SUN S. . . . . **C. heliophila**
THREADLEAF S. . . . . . . **C. filifolia**
TOLMIE S. . . . . **C. tolmiei**
TRACY S. . . . . **C. tracyi**
WARTY S. . . . . **C. verrucosa**
WATER S. . . . . **C. aquatilis**
WHITEBEAR S. . . . . . . **C. albursina**
WIDEFRUIT S. . . . . . . **C. eurycarpa**
WINGSEED S. . . . . **C. alata**
WOODBANK S. . . . . **C. cephalophora**
WOOLFRUIT S. . . . . . **C. lasiocarpa**
WOOLLY S. . . . . . . **C. lanuginosa**

SE'DUM (*ANACAMPSEROS* Haw., *not* L.; *CLEMENTSIA; GORMANIA; OROSTACHYS; RHODIOLA; ROSULARIA* in part; *SEDASTRUM*) . . . STONECROP
See **SUCCULENTS.**

SEEDBOX . . . . **Ludwigia**
WATER S. . . . . **L. natans**

SEEPWEED . . . . **Suaeda**
ALKALI S. . . . . **S. fruticosa**
AMERICAN S. . . . . . . **S. americana**
BUSH S. . . . . **S. ramosissima**
CALIFORNIA S. . . . . . **S. californica**
DESERT S. . . . . . **S. suffrutescens**
PURSH S. . . . . **S. depressa**
SEA S.. . . . . **S. maritima**
TORREY S. . . . . **S. torreyana**
WESTERN S. . . . . . **S. occidentalis**

Segolily . . . . . MARIPOSA, SEGOLILY: **Calochortus nuttalli**

SELAGINEL'LA . . . . SELAGINELLA
africa'na . . . . **S. vogeli**
amoe'na . . . . **S. caulescens**
apo'da (*apus*) . . . . . . BASKET S.
braun'i . . . . BRAUNS S.
brown'i . . . . **S. kraussiana b.**
cae'sia . . **S. uncinata; S. willdenovi**
caules'cens (*amoena*) . . . ERECT S.
—japon'ica (*S. japonica*)
JAPANESE E.S.
cuspida'ta . . . . TUFTED S.
denticula'ta . . . MEDITERRANEAN S.
This name is commonly misapplied to S. kraussiana.
doug'lasi . . . . DOUGLAS S.
emmelia'na . . . . EMMEL S.
₵VARIEGATED (*variegata*) HV.
₵YELLOW (*aurea*)
eryth'ropus
flabella'ta . . . . FAN S.
gran'dis
haemato'des . . . . . . REDSTEM S.
japon'ica . . . . . **S. caulescens j.**
kraussia'na . . . . KRAUSS S.
—brown'i (*S. browni*) . . BROWNS S.
₵VARIEGATED (*variegata*) HV. S. kraussiana
₵YELLOWSPOT (*aurea*)
lepidophyl'la . . . RESURRECTION S.
(*Resurrectionplant*)
mart'ensi . . . . MARTENS S.
₵WHITEMARK (*variegata*) HV.
pilif'era
rupes'tris . . . . ROCK S.
ser'pens
uncina'ta (*caesia* in part) . . BLUE S.
viticulo'sa
vo'geli (*africana*) . . . . . VOGEL S.
walla'cei . . . . WALLACE S.
wal'lichi . . . . WALLICH S.
willdeno'vi (*caesia* in part)
RAINBOW S.
₵ELEGANTISSIMA. HV. Selaginella

SELAGINELLA . . . . **Selaginella**
BASKET S. . . . . **S. apoda**
BLUE S. . . . . **S. uncinata**
BRAUNS S. . . . . **S. brauni**
BROWNS S. . . **S. kraussiana browni**
DOUGLAS S. . . . . **S. douglasi**
EMMEL S. . . . . **S. emmeliana**
ERECT S. . . . . **S. caulescens**
FAN S. . . . . **S. flabellata**
JAPANESE ERECT S.
S. caulescens japonica
KRAUSS S. . . . . **S. kraussiana**

SELAGINELLA, continued
MARTENS S. . . . **Selaginella martensi**
MEDITERRANEAN S. . . . **S. denticulata**
RAINBOW S. . . . . . . **S. willdenovi**
REDSTEM S. . . . . . . **S. haematodes**
RESURRECTION S. . . . **S. lepidophylla**
ROCK S. . . . . **S. rupestris**
TUFTED S. . . . . **S. cuspidata**
VOGEL S. . . . . **S. vogeli**
WALLACE S. . . . . **S. wallacei**
WALLICH S. . . . . **S. wallichi**

SELE'NIA . . . . SELENIA
dissec'ta . . . . TEXAS S.

SELENICE'REUS . MOONLIGHTCACTUS (*Snakecactus*)
See **CACTUS GENERA.**

SELENIPE'DIUM
See **ORCHID GENERA.**
The plants usually cultivated under this name belong to the Paphiopedilum of some botanists and are listed here under Cypripedium.

SELFHEAL . . . . **Prunella**
BIGFLOWER S. . . . . **P. grandiflora**
BIGFLOWER WEBB S. . **P. webbiana g.**
COMMON S. . . . . . . **P. vulgaris**
PINK BIGFLOWER S. **P. grandiflora rosea**
PINK WEBB S. . . . . **P. webbiana r.**
WEBB S. . . . . **P. webbiana**
WHITE BIGFLOWER S. **P. grandiflora alba**
WHITE WEBB S. . . . **P. webbiana a.**

SELINOCAR'PUS . . . . . MOONPOD
diffu'sus . . . . MOONPOD

SELI'NUM . . . . SELINUM
officina'le (*Cnidium o.*) . . DRUG S.
papyra'ceum . . . . PAPER S.
tenuifo'lium . . . . . THINLEAF S.

SEMAPHOREGRASS . . . . . **Pleuropogon**
ANNUAL S. . . . . . **P. californicus**
NODDING S. . . . . . . **P. refractus**

SEMECAR'PUS . . . . MARKINGNUT
anacar'dium . . . . . . CASHEW M.
longifo'lius . . . . LONGLEAF M.
veno'sus . . . . VEINY M.

SEM'ELE . . . . SEMELE
androg'yna (*Danae a.*) . CLIMBING S.

SEMIARUNDINA'RIA
See **BAMBOO GENERA.**

SEMMAN'THE
MESEMBRYANTHEMUM
See **SUCCULENTS.**

SEMPERVI'VUM . . . . HOUSELEEK
See **SUCCULENTS.**

SENE'CIO (*JACOBAEA*) |w GROUNDSEL
See note under **KLEINIA.**
acce'dens . . COLORADO NODDING G.
aconitifo'lius . . . . ACONITELEAF G.
adonidifo'lius (*abrotanifolius*) ADONISLEAF G.
ala'tus . . . . . . WINGSTALK G.
ambrosioi'des . . . . . RAGWEED G.
amplec'tens . . . SHOWY ALPINE G.
anteuphor'bium . . . . . **Kleinia a.**
aronicoi'des . . . . . . RAYLESS G.
articula'tus . . . **Kleinia articulata**
atra'tus . . . . BLACK G.
auranti'acus (*Cineraria aurantiaca*)
au'reus (*pseudaureus*) |w . .GOLDEN G.

SENECIO, continued
balsam'itae . . . . . . **S. pauperculus**
—gaspen'sis . . . . . . **S. gaspensis**
bidwill'i . . . . BIDWILL GROUNDSEL
bloch'manae . . . . . BLOCHMAN G.
canovi'rens . . . . . GRAYGREEN G.
ca'nus . . . . WOOLLY G.
cinera'ria (*Cineraria maritima*) SILVER G.
₵ORANGERIM (*aureo-marginatus*) HV.
cineras'cens (*haworthi; Kleinia c.; K. haworthi; K. tomentosa* Hort.)
clivo'rum . . . . **Ligularia c.**
columbia'nus . . . . COLUMBIA G.
compac'tus
confu'sus . . . . ORANGE-GLOWVINE
crassis'simus
cras'sulus . . . . . . THICKLEAF G.
croca'tus (*croceus*) . . . SAFFRON G.
cruen'tus (*Cineraria cruenta; C. grandiflora; C. stellata*) COMMON CINERARIA
The botanical status of the plants known as Cineraria is in dispute. All are cultivated derivatives of Senecio cruentus or have arisen by the hybridization of that species with related species of Senecio, as is supposed to have been the case with the so-called Cineraria hybrida of gardeners.
Many varieties of Cineraria are in cultivation but their names have not been standardized.
cymbalarioi'des . . . CLEFTLEAF G.
dis'par . . . . . . **S. integerrimus**
doron'icum . . . LEOPARDSBANE G.
do'ria
doug'lasi . . . . DOUGLAS G.
elaeagnifo'lius . . . . ELAEAGNUS G.
—buchan'ani . . . . . SMALL E.G.
el'egans . . . . PURPLE G.
₵GIANT LAVENDER. HV.
el'meri . . . . ELMER G.
eremoph'ilus . . . . . . DESERT G.
exalta'tus . . . . . **S. integerrimus**
fend'leri . . . . FENDLER G.
fibrillo'sus
ficoi'des . . . . **Kleinia f.**
filifo'lius . . . . **S. longilobus**
flett'i . . . . FLETT G.
fre'monti . . . . FREMONT G.
fuchs'i . . . . FUCHS G.
ful'gens . . . . **Kleinia f.**
gaspen'sis (*S. balsamitae g.*) GASPE G.
glauces'cens . . . . . . FLODMAN G.
grandiflo'rus . . . . . BIGBLOOM G.
grandifo'lius . . . . . . BIGLEAF G.
grey'i . . . . GREYS G.
haast'i
har'fordi . . . . HARFORD G.
ha'worthi . . . . . . **S. cinerascens**
heritier'i . . . . . . TENERIFFE G.
hunt'i . . . . HUNTS G.
hydroph'ilus |w . . . . . . WATER G.
inca'nus
integer'rimus (*dispar; exaltatus; lugens; perplexus*) . . . . LAMBSTONGUE G.
jacobae'a . . . . RAGWORT G.
japon'icus . . . . **Ligularia japonica**
kaemp'feri . . . . **Ligularia k.**
kermesi'nus
kirk'i . . . . KIRK G.
lanatifo'lius
laxifo'lius
ledebour'i . . . **Ligularia macrophylla**
leptoceph'alus
leucosta'chys . . . . . ARGENTINE G.
ligula'ria
loba'tus . . . . CRESSLEAF G.
longilo'bus (*filifolius*) THREADLEAF G.

SENECIO, continued
lon'gipes . . . . **Notonia granti**
lu'gens . . . . **S. integerrimus**
ly'alli . . . . LYALL GROUNDSEL
ly'oni . . . . CATALINA G.
macrophyl'lus (*Jacobaea macrophylla*)
mikanioi'des . . . . IVY G.
monro'i . . . . MONRO G.
multibractea'tus
multiloba'tus . . . . . LOBELEAF G.
nebroden'sis
neomexica'nus . . . NEWMEXICO G.
obova'tus
odo'rus . . . . **Kleinia odora**
pauper'culus (*balsamitae*) . BALSAM G.
pen'dulus . . . . . . **Notonia pendula**
perdicioi'des
perplex'us . . . . . **S. integerrimus**
petasi'tis . . . . VELVET G.
petrocal'lis
platten'sis . . . . PRAIRIE G.
pseudau'reus . . . . **S. aureus**
pseudo-ar'nica . . . . . SEABEACH G.
pul'cher . . . . URUGUAY G.
purshia'nus . . . . PURSH G.
quadrangula'ris
remotifo'lius
rep'tans
riddell'i . . . . RIDDELL G.
rob'binsi . . . . ROBBINS G.
rotundifo'lius . . . . ROUNDLEAF G.
salig'nus . . . . WILLOW G.
scan'dens . . . . CLIMBING G.
It is probable that some of the stock in the trade under the name S. scandens is S. mikanioides.
scapo'sus . . . . . . **Kleinia scaposa**
scorzoneroi'des
ser'ra . . . . BUTTERWEED G.
—integrius'cula . . WHOLELEAF B.G.
sibir'icus . . . . . **Ligularia sibirica**
smith'i . . . . SMITH G.
spartioi'des . . . . BROOM G.
specio'sus
stapeliifor'mis . . . . **Kleinia s.**
stenoceph'alus . **Ligularia stenocephala**
subscan'dens
succulen'tus . . . . . **Kleinia repens**
sylvat'icus . . . . . . WOODLAND G.
tangu'ticus . . . . CHINESE G.
thapsoi'des
triangula'ris . . . . . ARROWLEAF G.
tropaeolifo'lius (*Kleinia tropaeolifolia*) NASTURTIUM G.
uintahen'sis . . . . UINTA G.
visco'sus . . . . STICKY G.
visia'nus . . . . . MONTENEGRIN G.
vulga'ris |w . . . . COMMON G.
web'steri . . . . WEBSTER G.
wilsonia'nus . . **Ligularia wilsoniana**

SENNA . . . . **Cassia**
ALEXANDRIAN S. . . . . **C. acutifolia**
AMERICAN S. . . . . . . **C. hebecarpa**
APPLEBLOSSOM S. . . . . **C. javanica**
AVARAM S. . . . . **C. auriculata**
BRAZILIAN S. . . . . . **C. brasiliensis**
COFFEE S. . . . . **C. occidentalis**
CONGO S. . . . . **C. angustifolia**
DESERT S. . . . . **C. armata**
FLOWERY S. . . . . **C. corymbosa**
GLOSSYSHOWER S. . . . . . **C. glauca**
GOLDENSHOWER S. . . . . . **C. fistula**
GOLDENWONDER S. . . . . **C. splendida**
HAIRY S. . . . . **C. covesi**
JOINTWOOD S. . . . . **C. nodosa**
PINKSHOWER S. . . . . . . **C. grandis**
RINGWORM S. . . . . **C. alata**

SENNA, continued
SIAMESE S. . . . . . . Cassia siamea
SIBERIAN S. . . . . . . C. siberiana
SICKLE S. . . . . C. tora
SLIMPOD S.. . . . . . . C. leptocarpa
SMOOTH S. . . . . C. laevigata
SOUTHERN S. . . . . . . C. australis
WILD S. . . . . C. marilandica
WISLIZENUS S. . . . . . C. wislizeni
WOOLLY S. . . . . . . C. tomentosa
WORMWOOD S. . . . C. artemisioides
SENSITIVEBRIER . . . . . . Schrankia
CATCLAW S. . . . . . . S. uncinata
LITTLELEAF S. . . . . S. microphylla
NARROWPOD S. . . . S. angustisiliqua
ROEMER S. . . . . . S. roemeriana
Sensitivebrier . . . NEPTUNIA: **Neptunia**
SENSITIVEFERN . . . Onoclea sensibilis
SENSITIVEPLANT . . . Mimosa pudica
SENTRYPALM . . . . Howea
BELMORE S. . . . . . H. belmoreana
FORSTER S. . . . . . H. forsteriana

SEQUOI'A (*SEQUOIADENDRON*) SEQUOIA
See note on *SEQUOIADENDRON*.
gigan'tea (of (Lindl.) Dec., 1854, based on *Wellingtonia g.* Lindl. (1853), *not* Endl.; *washingtoniana; wellingtonia; Sequoiadendron giganteum; Wellingtonia g.*) . . . . GIANT S.
Although the International Rules of Botanical Nomenclature do not now provide for conserved specific names, the Editorial Committee of STANDARDIZED PLANT NAMES has decided to endorse the name Sequoia gigantea, even though a homonym, because of its appropriateness, because its use is practically unanimous among California botanists and in the Californian manuals, and because it is formally approved by the National Park Service, official guardians of these extraordinary trees. There will probably always be controversy as to whether or not Sequoia washingtoniana was adequately published, and the next oldest name, S. wellingtonia, besides being unpalatable to the American people, is neither accepted nor used except by a very small minority. There is every reason for believing that, Rules or no Rules, Sequoia gigantea will continue to be the name in general use.
¢BLUE (*glauca*) HV.
¢COLUMNAR (*pendula*)
gigan'tea Endl. (1847). **S. sempervirens**
sempervi'rens (*S. gigantea* Endl., *not* (Lindl.) Dec.) . . . . . REDWOOD
¢BLUE (*glauca*) HV.
¢SHORTLEAF (*adpressa*)
¢WEEPING (*pendula*)

SEQUOIADEN'DRON . . **SEQUOIA**
Prof. John T. Buchholz has recently separated the Giant Sequoia (*Bigtree*) into a distinct genus, Sequoiadendron. It seems desirable to retain this tree in Sequoia in the new edition of STANDARDIZED PLANT NAMES.
gigan'teum . . . . . . **S. gigantea**

SERA'PIAS . . . . . . **EPIPACTIS**
See **ORCHID GENERA, HARDY TERRESTRIAL GROUP.**

SERENO'A (*ACOELORRAPHE* in part; *SERENAEA*) SAWPALMETTO
See **PALM GENERA.**

SERICOCAR'PUS
asteroi'des
rig'idus

SERICOTHE'CA . . **HOLODISCUS**

SERINE'A (*APOGON*) |w . . SERINEA
The name is often misspelled Serenea and Serinia.
oppositifo'lia (*Apogon humilis*) COMMON S.

SERIS'SA
foe'tida (*japonica*)
¢YELLOWRIM (*variegata*) HV.

SERJA'NIA . . SERJANIA (*Supplejack*)
The generic name is sometimes spelled Seriania.
curassa'vica . . . . . . CURACAO S.
fuscifo'lia . . . . . . RUSTYWOOL S.
glabra'ta . . . . . . HEARTKEY S.
letha'lis . . . . . . TIMBEEHONEY S.
mexica'na . . . . . . MEXICAN S.
nodo'sa . . . . CURARE S.
paucidenta'ta . . . . . . BALBAC S.
rhom'bea

SERON . . **Phyllostylon; P. brasiliensis**
SERPENTCACTUS **Nyctocereus serpentinus**
SERPENTROOT . . . . . . Scorzonera
BLACKSALSIFY S. . . . . S. hispanica
BOHEMIAN S. . . . . . . S. humilis
MEDITERRANEAN S. . . . S. laciniata
SERRADELLA . . . . . . Ornithopus
COMMON S. . . . . O. sativus
LITTLE S. . . . . . . O. perpusillus

SERRAS'TYLIS
See **ORCHID GENERA.**

SERRA'TULA . . . . SAWWORT
cyranoi'des . . . . **Cnicus c.**
nudicau'lis
tincto'ria . . . . DYERS S.

SERVICEBERRY . . . . . . Amelanchier
ALLEGANY S. . . . . A. laevis
∞APPLE S. . . . . . ∞A. grandiflora
ASIAN S.. . . . . A. asiatica
BARTRAM S. . . . . A. bartramiana
CLUSTER S. . . . . . A. polycarpa
CUSICK S. . . . . A. cusicki
∞DWARF S. . . . . . . ∞A. spicata
DWARF SASKATOON S. A. alnifolia pumila
GARDEN S. . . . . A. ovalis
LOW S. . . . . A. humilis
MOUNTAIN S. . . . . . A. oreophila
PACIFIC S. . . . . A. florida
REDBUD S. . . . . . . A. prunifolia
ROUNDLEAF S. . . . . A. sanguinea
RUDDY APPLE S. A. grandiflora rubescens
RUNNING S. . . . . . A. stolonifera
SASKATOON S. . . . . . A. alnifolia
SHADBLOW S. . . . . . A. canadensis
SNOWY S. . . . . A. amabilis
THICKET S. . . . . . A. oblongifolia
UTAH S. . . . . A. utahensis
Servicetree . MOUNTAINASH, SERVICETREE: **Sorbus domestica**
Wild S. . . . . . CHECKERTREE M.: **S. terminalis**

SES'AMUM |w . . . . SESAME
in'dicum (*orientale*) |w. . ORIENTAL S.
Sesamum indicum is the correct name under International Rules, whereas S. orientale (having line priority) was accepted under American Rules.

SESBA'NIA (*AGATI*) |w . . SESBANIA
bispino'sa (*aculeata*)
cavanil'lesi . . . . . **Daubentonia c.**
drum'mondi . . . . **Daubentonia d.**

SESBANIA, continued
em'erus . . . . DANGLEPOD SESBANIA
exalta'ta (*macrocarpa*) |w . HEMP S.
grandiflo'ra (*Agati g.*) . . . AGATI S.
punic'ea . . . . . . **Daubentonia p.**
tripe'ti . . . . **Daubentonia t.**
vesica'ria . . **Glottidium vesicarium**

SESLE'RIA
See **GRASS GENERA.**

SESU'VIUM . . . . SESUVIUM
See **SUCCULENTS.**

SETA'RIA (*CHAETOCHLOA*) BRISTLEGRASS; MILLET
See **GRASS GENERA.**

SEUTE'RIA |w
palus'tris |w

SEVERIN'IA . . . . BOXORANGE
buxifo'lia (*Atalantia b.; Triphasia b.; T. monophylla*) . . . . CHINESE B.
—**subiner'mis** . . . . . DWARF C.B.
dis'ticha . . . . PHILIPPINE B.
linea'ris . . . . . . NARROWLEAF B.
panicula'ta . . . . BOUQUET B.

SEYME'RIA . . . . SEYMERIA
cassioi'des (*tenuifolia; Afzelia c.*) SENNA S.

Shadblow . SERVICEBERRY: **Amelanchier**
Shadbush . SERVICEBERRY: **Amelanchier**
Shaddock . . PUMMELO: **Citrus grandis**
SHADOWPALM . . . . Geonoma
ARICANGA S. . . . . . G. schottiana
RIEDEL S. . . . . G. riedeliana
SHALLOT . . . . . . Allium ascalonicum
SHALLU . . Sorghum vulgare roxburghi
Shamrock, Cape . . . OXALIS, BOWIE: **Oxalis bowieana**
SHAMROCKPEA . . . . . . Parochetus
COMMON S. . . . . . P. communis
Shanwamillet . . . . . JUNGLERICE: **Echinochloa colonum**

SHAW'IA . . . . **OLEARIA**
SHEEPBUR . . . . Acaena
AUSTRALIAN S. . . . . A. ovina
BUCHANAN S. . . . . . A. buchanani
BURNET S.. . . . . . A. sanguisorbae
CHILEAN S. . . . . . . A. ovalifolia
CYLINDER S. . . . A. cylindrostachya
FEATHERLEAF S. . . . A. pinnatifida
GRAY S. . . . . A. glauca
NAKED REDSPINE S. A. microphylla inermis
NEWZEALAND S. A. novae-zealandiae
PATAGONIAN S. . . . . A. sericea
REDSPINE S. . . . . . A. microphylla
SILKLEAF S. . . . . . A. myriophylla
SILVER S. . . . . A. argentea
SMOOTH S. . . . . A. glabra
SHEEPBUSH . . . . Pentzia
AUSTRALIAN S. . . . . . . P. incana
SHELLSEED . . . . . Cochlospermum
COTTON S. . . . . . . C. religiosum
YELLOWSILK S.. . . . . C. vitifolium

SHEPHERD'IA (*LEPARGYREA*) |w BUFFALOBERRY
Some botanists reduce Shepherdia to synonymy under the older genus Elaeagnus.
argen'tea (*Lepargyrea a.*) |w. SILVER B.
¢YELLOW (*xanthocarpa*) HV.
canaden'sis (*Lepargyrea c.*) |w RUSSET B.
¢YELLOW (*xanthocarpa*) HV.

SHEPHERDIA, continued
∞ **gottingen'sis** (*argentea* × *canadensis*)
rotundifo'lia (*Lepargyrea r.*) ROUNDLEAF BUFFALOBERRY
SHEPHERDS-NEEDLE . . . . . . **Scandix**
VENUSCOMB S. . . . **S. pecten-veneris**
SHEPHERDSPURSE
Capsella; C. bursa-pastoris

SHERARD'IA . . . . . FIELDMADDER
arven'sis . . . . . FIELDMADDER

SHIBATAE'A . . . . . SHIBATAEA
See **BAMBOO GENERA.**

SHIELDWORT . . . . **Peltaria**
ONION S. . . . . **P. alliacea**
SHOALWEED . . . . **Halodule**
CUBAN S. . . . . **H. wrighti**
SHOESTRINGFERN . . . . **Vittaria lineata**
SHOOTINGSTAR . . . . . **Dodecatheon**
ALPINE S. . . . . **D. alpinum**
CLEVELAND S. . . . . **D. clevelandi**
COMMON S. . . . . . . **D. meadia**
CUSICK S. . . . . **D. cusicki**
DARKTHROAT S. . . . **D. pauciflorum**
DENTATE S. . . . . . **D. dentatum**
DWARF S. . . . . **D. patulum**
HENDERSON S. . . . . **D. hendersoni**
HUGER S. . . . . **D. hugeri**
JEFFREY S. . . . . . . **D. jeffreyi**
MANYFLOWER S. . . . **D. multiflorum**
PLAINS S. . . . . . . **D. campestre**
POETS S. . . . . . . **D. poeticum**
SHOWY COMMON S.
D. meadia splendidum
SOUTHERN S. . . . . . **D. radicatum**
STANFIELD S. . . . . . **D. stanfieldi**
VIOLET COMMON S.
D. meadia violaceum
WHITE C. S. . . . . . **D. m. album**
YELLOWRING S. . . . **D. tetrandrum**
YELLOWTHROAT S. . . . **D. salinum**

SHOR'EA . . . . SHOREA
ap'tera . . . . BORNEO S.
balangeran' . . . . YAKAL S.
crassifo'lia . . . . . . **S. hypochra**
cur'tisi . . . . CURTIS S.
exim'ia . . . . ALMON S. (*Almon*)
gui'so . . . . GUIJO S. (*Guijo*)
hypo'chra (*crassifolia*) . . . TEMAK S.
kalun'ti . . . KALUNTI S. (*Kalunti*)
mindanen'sis . . . . MINDANAO S.
negrosen'sis . . . . . REDLAUAN S.
palosa'pis . . . . . . PALOSAPIS S.
philippinen'sis . . . . PHILIPPINE S.
poli'ta . . . . POLISHED S.
polysper'ma . . TANGILE S. (*Tangile*)
robus'ta . . . . . . SAL S. (*Sal*)
teysmannia'na . . . . . TIAONG S.
wies'neri . . . . . . BATAVIAN S.
SHOREA . . . . **Shorea**
ALMON S. . . . . **S. eximia**
BATAVIAN S. . . . . . . **S. wiesneri**
BORNEO S. . . . . **S. aptera**
CURTIS S. . . . . **S. curtisi**
GUIJO S. . . . . **S. guiso**
KALUNTI S. . . . . **S. kalunti**
MINDANAO S. . . . . **S. mindanensis**
PALOSAPIS S. . . . . . . **S. palosapis**
PHILIPPINE S. . . . **S. philippinensis**
POLISHED S. . . . . **S. polita**
REDLAUAN S. . . . . **S. negrosensis**
SAL S. . . . . **S. robusta**
TANGILE S. . . . . . **S. polysperma**
TEMAK S. . . . . **S. hypochra**
TIAONG S. . . . . . **S. teysmanniana**
YAKAL S. . . . . . . **S. balangeran**

SHOREGRASS **Monanthochloe; M. littoralis**
SHOREWEED . . . . **Littorella**
AMERICAN S. . . . . . . **L. americana**
EUROPEAN S. . . . . . . **L. uniflora**
Shorthair . . . REEDGRASS, SHORTHAIR: **Calamagrostis breweri**

SHORTHUSK . . . . . . **Brachyelytrum**
BEARDED S. . . . . . . **B. erectum**

SHORT'IA
galacifo'lia . . . . . . OCONEEBELLS
uniflo'ra . . . . NIPPONBELLS
₵GRANDIFLORA. HV.

SHOWVINE . . . . **Camoensia**
BIG S. . . . . **C. maxima**
SHRUBALTHEA . . . **Hibiscus syriacus**
SHRUBHAREBELL . . . . **Isotoma**
CLIFF S. . . . . **I. petraea**
LONGFLOWER S. . . . . **I. longiflora**
WHITE CLIFF S. . . . **I. petraea alba**

SIBBALD'IA
procum'bens
Sibbaldiop'sis tridenta'ta . . **Potentilla t.**

SIBIRAE'A . . . . SIBIREA
laeviga'ta (*Spiraea l.*) . . . SMOOTH S.
—angustifo'lia . . NARROWLEAF S.S.
—croa'tica . . . . . CROATIAN S.S.
tomento'sa . . . . . . WOOLLY S.

SIBTHORP'IA . . . . . SIBTHORPIA
europae'a . . . . . . PENNYWORT S.
—africa'na (*S. africana*) AFRICAN P.S.
₵GOLDGREEN (*variegata*) HV. S. europaea

SICA'NA
odorif'era . . . . CASABANANA
SICKLEGRASS . . **Pholiurus; P. incurvus**

SIC'YOS |W . . . . . . BURCUCUMBER
angula'tus |W . . . . . . WALL B.

SI'DA |W . . . . SIDA
diffu'sa |W
hasta'ta |W . . . . . . SPEARLEAF S.
hedera'cea . . . . ALKALI S.
hermaphrodi'ta (*napaea*) VIRGINIA S.
rhombifo'lia . . . . . BROOMJUTE S.
spino'sa |W . . . . . . PRICKLY S.

SIDAL'CEA |W . . . CHECKERMALLOW (*Prairiemallow*)
campes'tris . . . . PLAINS C.
can'dida . . . . WHITE C.
glauces'cens . . . . BIRD C.
henderso'ni . . . . . HENDERSON C.
malvaeflo'ra . . . . . FOOTHILL C. (*Checkerbloom*)
₵PURPLE (*atropurpurea*) HV.
₵SATIN (*listeri. Pink Beauty*)
murraya'na . . . . **S. spicata**
neomexica'na . . . NEWMEXICAN C.
—parviflo'ra (*S. parviflora*) |W SMALL N.C.
nerva'ta . . . . NELSON C.
₵ROSY GEM. HV.
orega'na . . . . OREGON C.
spica'ta (*murrayana*) . . . . SPIKE C.
₵HIAWATHA. HV. Sidalcea
₵INTERLAKEN
₵J. DICKSON
₵LOWFIELD PINK
₵MONARCH
₵MRS. DUNBAR
₵NIMMERDOR
₵ROSY QUEEN
₵RUBY KING
₵WENSLEYDALE

SIDERAN'THUS . . **APLOPAPPUS**
grindelioi'des . . . . **A. nuttalli**

SIDERI'TIS . . . . . IRONWOUNDWORT
can'dicans (*Leucophae c.*) MADEIRA I.
euboe'a . . . . EUBOEAN I.
hyssopifo'lia . . . . HYSSOP I.
libanot'ica . . . . LEBANON I.
macrosta'chya . . . . LONGSPIKE I.
roma'na . . . . ROMAN I.
syria'ca . . . . SYRIAN I.

SIDEROX'YLON . . . JUNGLEPLUM
This is one of an almost innumerable group of trees known as Ironwood, because of the very hard and strong wood. Although the scientific name also means Ironwood, that name is considered too homonymous to attempt to preserve. See **LUMBER TRADE NAMES.**

capi'ri . . . . CAPIRI J.
foetidis'simum
mastichoden'dron . . . . MASTIC J.
novo-zelan'dicum (*costatum*) NEWZEALAND J.
pohlmania'num . . . . . POHLMAN J.
quadrilocula're . . . . . TRINIDAD J.
tempis'que . . . . . . TEMPISQUE J.

SIEGESBECK'IA . . . ST.PAULSWORT
orienta'lis . . . . . . COMMON S.
SIERRA LEONE-FRANKINCENSE
Daniella thurifera

SIEVER'SIA . . . . SIEVERSIA
campanula'ta (*Geum campanulatum*)
cilia'ta (*Geum ciliatum*) PRAIRIESMOKE S.
monta'na (*Geum montanum*)
GIANT (*maxima*) HV.
ORANGE (*aurantiaca; heldreichi*)
peck'i (*Geum p.*)
rep'tans (*Geum r.*)
ross'i (*Geum r.*)
turbina'ta . . . . GOLDEN S.

SIGMATOSTA'LIX
See **ORCHID GENERA.**

SIGNALGRASS . . . . **Brachiaria**
PALISADE S. . . . . . . **B. brizantha**

SILA'US . . . . SILAUS
flaves'cens . . . . SULFUR S.
praten'sis . . . . MEADOW S.

SILE'NE |W . . . . SILENE
acau'lis |W . . . . MOSS S.
—al'ba . . . . WHITE M.S.
—carmin'ea . . . . CARMINE M.S.
₵KODIAK. HV. S. acaulis
₵NORICA
₵ROCK (*saxatilis*)
al'ba (*nivea*) . . . . SNOWY S.
alpes'tris (*Heliosperma a.*) . ALPINE S.
—rose'a . . . . PINK A.S.
₵BIGFLOWER (*grandiflora*) HV. S. alpestris
₵DOUBLE (*flore-pleno*)
₵RICHENTREICH (*richentreichi*)
an'glica . . . . **S. gallica**
antirrhi'na |W . . . . . . SLEEPY S. (*Sleepy Catchfly*)
arme'ria . . . . . SWEETWILLIAM S.
aster'ias . . . . BANAT S.
₵CRIMSON GLOBE (*grandiflora*) HV.
be'hen . . . . BEHEN S.
benois'ti . . . . BENOIST S.
ber'geri . . . . **S. regia**
brachypet'ala . . . . SHORTPETAL S.
califor'nica . . . . . CALIFORNIA S.

SILENE, continued
campan'ula . . . HAREBELL SILENE
carama'nica . . . . . CARMANIAN S.
carolinia'na (*pennsylvanica*) PEATPINK S.
chloraefo'lia
chloran'tha . . . YELLOWGREEN S.
compac'ta (*orientalis*) . . ORIENTAL S.
co'nica . . . . CONICAL S.
conoi'dea
cucuba'lus (*inflata; venosa*) BLADDER S.
dianthifo'lia
dichot'oma . . . . FORKED S.
dina'rica . . . . DINARIC S.
el'egans
elizabe'thae . . . . . ELIZABETH S.
faba'ria
flaves'cens . . . . . . YELLOW S.
fortun'ei . . . . FORTUNES S.
frutico'sa . . . . SHRUBBY S.
fruticulo'sa
gal'lica (*anglica*) |w . . . . FRENCH S.
gigan'tea . . . . TALL S.
glau'ca . . . . BLUE S.
gran'dis
hook'eri . . . . HOOKER S.
infla'ta . . . . **S. cucubalus**
in'grami . . . . INGRAM S.
ital'ica (*ocymoides*) . . . . ITALIAN S.
japon'ica . . . . JAPANESE S.
lacinia'ta . . . . MEXICAN S.
lae'ta . . . . GAY S.
latifo'lia (*vulgaris*) |w . . COWBELL S.
lerchenfeldia'na
marit'ima . . . . SEA S.
—rose'a . . . . PINK S.S.
₵DOUBLE (*plena*) HV. S. maritima
menzies'i . . . . MENZIES S.
monacho'rum . . . . . **S. quadrifida**
moorcroftia'na . . . . MOORCROFT S.
multicau'lis
muscip'ula . . . . CATCHFLY S.
niv'ea . . . . **S. alba**
noctiflo'ra . . . NIGHTFLOWERING S.
nu'tans . . . . NODDING S.
ocymoi'des . . . . **S. italica**
orienta'lis . . . . . . **S. compacta**
oti'tes
ova'ta
paradox'a
pen'dula (*rosea* Hort.) . . DROOPING S.
₵BONNETT (*bonnetti*) HV.
₵COMPACT (*compacta*)
₵FLESH (*carnea*)
₵LILAC (*lilacina*)
₵REDSTEM (*ruberrima*)
pennsylva'nica . . . . **S. caroliniana**
petrae'a . . . . **S. saxifraga**
pseudo-ato'cion
pumil'io . . . . PYGMY S.
pusil'la
quadrif'ida (*monachorum*)
re'gia (*bergeri*) . . . . . ROYAL S.
reichenbach'i . . . . DALMATIAN S.
reticula'ta . . . . NETVEIN S.
roem'eri . . . . ROEMERS S.
rose'a Hort. . . . . . . **S. pendula**
rubel'la . . . . LITTLEROSE S.
rupes'tris
ruprecht'i . . . . . . RUPRECHT S.
saxat'ilis . . . . ROCK S.
saxif'raga (*petraea*) . . SAXIFRAGE S.
schaf'ta . . . . SCHAFTA S.
schmuck'eri
scou'leri . . . . SCOULER S.
squamig'era
stella'ta . . . . STARRY S.
suksdorf'i . . . . SUKSDORF S.

SILENE, continued
tatar'ica . . . . . . TATARIAN SILENE
valles'ia
veno'sa . . . . **S. cucubalus**
verecun'da
virgin'ica . . . . FIREPINK S.
viridiflo'ra . . . . . GREENFLOWER S.
viscosis'sima . . . . STICKY S.
vulga'ris . . . . **S. latifolia**
wald'steini . . . . . . WALDSTEIN S.
wher'ryi . . . . WHERRY S.
zawad'ski . . . . ZAWADSKI S.

SILENE . . . . **Silene**
ALPINE S. . . . . **S. alpestris**
BANAT S. . . . . **S. asterias**
BEHEN S. . . . . **S. behen**
BENOIST S. . . . . **S. benoisti**
BLADDER S. . . . . **S. cucubalus**
BLUE S. . . . . **S. glauca**
CALIFORNIA S. . . . . . . **S. californica**
CARMANIAN S. . . . . . . **S. caramanica**
CARMINE MOSS S. **S. acaulis carminea**
CATCHFLY S. . . . . **S. muscipula**
CONICAL S. . . . . **S. conica**
COWBELL S. . . . . **S. latifolia**
DALMATIAN S. . . . . . **S. reichenbachi**
DINARIC S. . . . . **S. dinarica**
DROOPING S. . . . . **S. pendula**
ELIZABETH S. . . . . . **S. elizabethae**
FIREPINK S. . . . . **S. virginica**
FORKED S. . . . . **S. dichotoma**
FORTUNES S. . . . . **S. fortunei**
FRENCH S. . . . . **S. gallica**
GAY S. . . . . **S. laeta**
GREENFLOWER S. . . . . **S. viridiflora**
HAREBELL S. . . . . . . **S. campanula**
HOOKER S. . . . . **S. hookeri**
INGRAM S. . . . . **S. ingrami**
ITALIAN S. . . . . **S. italica**
JAPANESE S. . . . . **S. japonica**
LITTLEROSE S. . . . . **S. rubella**
MENZIES S. . . . . **S. menziesi**
MEXICAN S. . . . . **S. laciniata**
MOORCROFT S. . . . **S. moorcroftiana**
MOSS S. . . . . **S. acaulis**
NETVEIN S. . . . . **S. reticulata**
NIGHTFLOWERING S. . . . **S. noctiflora**
NODDING S. . . . . **S. nutans**
ORIENTAL S. . . . . **S. compacta**
PEATPINK S. . . . . **S. caroliniana**
PINK ALPINE S. . . **S. alpestris rosea**
PINK SEA S. . . . . **S. maritima r.**
PYGMY S. . . . . **S. pumilio**
ROCK S. . . . . **S. saxatilis**
ROEMERS S. . . . . **S. roemeri**
ROYAL S. . . . . **S. regia**
RUPRECHT S. . . . . **S. ruprechti**
SAXIFRAGE S. . . . . **S. saxifraga**
SCHAFTA S. . . . . **S. schafta**
SCOULER S. . . . . **S. scouleri**
SEA S. . . . . **S. maritima**
SHORTPETAL S. . . . . **S. brachypetala**
SHRUBBY S. . . . . **S. fruticosa**
SLEEPY S. . . . . **S. antirrhina**
SNOWY S. . . . . **S. alba**
STARRY S. . . . . **S. stellata**
STICKY S. . . . . **S. viscosissima**
SUKSDORF S. . . . . **S. suksdorfi**
SWEETWILLIAM S. . . . . . . **S. armeria**
TALL S. . . . . **S. gigantea**
TATARIAN S. . . . . **S. tatarica**
WALDSTEIN S. . . . . **S. waldsteini**
WHERRY S. . . . . **S. wherryi**
WHITE MOSS S. . . . . . . **S. acaulis alba**
YELLOWGREEN S. . . . . . **S. chlorantha**
YELLOW S. . . . . **S. flavescens**
ZAWADSKI S. . . . . **S. zawadski**

SILKRUBBER . . . . **Funtumia**
LAGOS S. . . . . **F. elastica**

SILKTASSEL . . . . **Garrya**
BOXLEAF S. . **G. flavescens buxifolia**
FADYEN S. . . . . **G. fadyeni**
FREMONT S. . . . . **G. fremonti**
GOLDMAN S. . . . . **G. goldmani**
INTERIOR S. . . . . **G. congdoni**
LAURELLEAF S. . . . . . . **G. laurifolia**
∞ THURET S. . . . . ∞ **G. thureti**
TREE S. . . . . **G. elliptica**
VEITCH S. . . . . **G. veitchi**
WRIGHTS S. . . . . **G. wrighti**
YELLOWLEAF S. . . . . . **G. flavescens**

SILKVINE . . . . **Periploca**
CHINESE S. . . . . **P. sepium**
GRECIAN S. . . . . **P. graeca**

SILKYSCALE . . . . **Anthaenantia**
GREEN S. . . . . **A. villosa**
PURPLE S. . . . . **A. rufa**

SIL'PHIUM . . . . ROSINWEED
integrifo'lium . . . . WHOLELEAF R.
lacinia'tum . . . . . COMPASSPLANT
perfolia'tum . . . . CUP R.
scaber'rimum
terebinthina'ceum . . . . DOCK R.
trifolia'tum

SILVERBELL . . . . **Halesia**
CAROLINA S. . . . . **H. carolina**
FLORIDA S. . . . . **H. parviflora**
FUZZYLEAF MOUNTAIN S. **H. monticola vestita**
MOUNTAIN S. . . . . . **H. monticola**
PINK M. S. . . . . **H. m. rosea**
SUWANEE CAROLINA S. **H. carolina mollis**
TWOWING S. . . . . **H. diptera**

SILVERBERRY . . **Elaeagnus commutata**

SILVERBUSH . . . . **Argythamnia**
CALIFORNIA S. . . . . **A. californica**
LANCELEAF S. . . . . . **A. lanceolata**

SILVERFERN. **Pityrogramma calomelanos**
MOUNTAIN S. . . . . **P. tartarea**

SILVERGRASS. . . . . **Miscanthus**
AMUR S. . . . . **M. saccharifer**
CAPE S. . . . . **M. capensis**
CHINESE S. . . . . **M. sinensis**
JAPANESE S. . . . . **M. japonicus**
LUZON S. . . . . **M. luzonensis**
NEPAL S. . . . . **M. nepalensis**
STRIPED S. . . **M. sinensis** ₵STRIPED

SILVERLEAF . . . . . . **Leucophyllum**
TEXAS S. . . . . **L. frutescens**

SILVERPALM . . . . **Coccothrinax**
EKMAN S. . . . . **C. ekmani**
FLORIDA S. . . . . **C. argentata**
FRAGRANT S. . . . . **C. fragrans**
LATANIERBALAI . . . . . . **C. argentea**
MIRAGUAMA S. . . . . . **C. miraguama**
PUERTORICAN S. . . . . **C. alta**

SILVEUSGRASS . . **Trichoneura elegans**

SIL'VIA Allem. (1845) . **ENDIANDRA**

SIL'VIA Benth. (1846) . . **SYLVIA**

SIL'VIA Vell. (1825) . **ESCOBEDIA**

SIL'YBUM |w . . . . . MILKTHISTLE
ebur'neum
maria'num (*Carduus marianus*) |w BLESSED M.

SIMA'BA . . . . SIMABA
ce'dron . . . . CEDRON S.

SIMALTREE . . . . **Salmalia**
MALABAR S. . . . . . **S. malabaricum**

SIMARU'BA . . . . SIMARUBA
amar'a . . . . ORINOCO S.
glau'ca . . . . PARADISETREE

SIMMOND'SIA |w . . JOJOBA (*Jajoba*)
chinen'sis (*californica*) |w
CALIFORNIA J.

Until comparatively recently this common and important Southwestern shrub was universally known as Simmondsia californica. The scientific name now approved under International Rules, S. chinensis, is patently preposterous, the plant having nothing to do with China. The Editorial Committee feels that common sense, as well as technical rules of precedence, should enter into botanical (as well as other) legislation and that, if necessary, a list of conserved species names should be made. See Dayton, W. A., "A Few Notes on Plant Names" (Proceedings Biological Society of Washington 40: 119–121. 1927).

SIMPSO'NIA . . . . . **THRINAX**
See **PALM GENERA.**

SIM'SIA . . . . . . BUSHSUNFLOWER
foe'tida (*Encelia adenophora*)
STINKING B.

SINA'PIS . . . . **BRASSICA**
al'ba . . . . **B. hirta**
arven'sis . . . . **B. kaber**

SINARUNDINA'RIA . . . CHINACANE
See **BAMBOO GENERA.**

SINDO'RA . . . . SINDORA
su'pa . . . . SUPA S.

SINGHARANUT . . . . **Trapa bispinosa**

Single-awn . . . . THREE-AWN, SINGLE: **Aristida orcuttiana**

SINNIN'GIA . . . . GLOXINIA

The Gloxinia of florists is Sinningia speciosa. Gloxinia crassifolia and G. gigantea are names loosely and incorrectly applied in the trade to some of the varieties of that species. The genus Gloxinia, of botanists, is not in cultivation.

specio'sa (*Gloxinia s.*) . . COMMON G.

Many varieties of Gloxinia are in cultivation but they are not sufficiently well distinguished to permit the preparation of an authentic list at the present time.

—macrophyl'la . . . . BIGLEAF C.G.

SINOCAL'AMUS . . . SINOCALAMUS
See **BAMBOO GENERA.**

SINOFRANCHET'IA . . FRANCHETVINE
chinen'sis (*Holboellia c.*) . CHINA F.

SINOJACK'IA . . . . JACKTREE
rehderia'na . . . . REHDER J.
xylocar'pa

SINOME'NIUM . . . . . ORIENTVINE
acu'tum (*Cocculus diversifolius; Menispermum a.*) |w
cineras'cens

SINOWILSO'NIA . . . . WILSONTREE
hen'ryi . . . . HENRY W.

SIPHONAN'THUS . . . TUBEFLOWER
in'dicus (*Clerodendron siphonanthus*)
INDIA T.

Sipho'nia ridleya'na
See note under **Hevea brasiliensis.**

SIPHON'ODON . . . . . IVORYWOOD
austra'le . . . . . . AUSTRALIAN I.

SISSOO . . . . **Dalbergia sissoo**

SISYM'BRIUM (*NORTA; STENOPHRAGMA*) |w
allia'ria . . . . . . GARLICMUSTARD
altis'simum (*Norta altissima*) |w
TUMBLEMUSTARD
aquat'icum
Rorippa nasturtium-aquaticum
canes'cens . . . **Descurainia menziesi**
inci'sum . . . . **Descurainia incisa**
—fi'lipes **Descurainia longipedicellata**
—hartwegia'num
Descurainia richardsoni
ir'io (*Norta i.*)
nasturtium-aquat'icum . . . **Rorippa n.**
officina'le (*Erysimum o.*)
pinna'tum . . . **Descurainia menziesi**
sophi'a . . . . **Descurainia pinnata**
thalia'num . . . **Arabidopsis thaliana**

SISYRIN'CHIUM |w . BLUE-EYEDGRASS
alpes'tre . . . . COLORADO B.
angustifo'lium (*anceps*) . COMMON B.
—convolu'tum
atlan'ticum |w . . . . . ATLANTIC B.
bel'lum . . . . WESTERN B.
bermudia'num . . . . . BERMUDA B.
bira'meum
borea'le . . . . SPOKANE B.
califor'nicum . . . . . . GOLDEN B.
convolu'tum
doug'lasi (*grandiflorum*) . DOUGLAS B.
graminoi'des (*gramineum*) |w
idahoen'se . . . . IDAHO B.
inala'tum
iridifo'lium
macroceph'alum
occidenta'le . . . . . . MONTANA B.
pachyrhi'zum . . . . BRAZIL B.
stria'tum . . . . . . ARGENTINE B.
va'rians . . . . TEXAS B.

SITA'NION . . . . . SQUIRRELTAIL
See **GRASS GENERA.**

SI'UM |w . . . . WATERPARSNIP
sisa'rum . . . . SKIRRET W.
sua've (*cicutaefolium*) |w. HEMLOCK W.

SKELETONGRASS . . . . **Gymnopogon**
BEARDED S. . . . . . . **G. ambiguus**
CHAPMAN S. . . . **G. chapmanianus**
FLORIDA S. . . . . . **G. floridanus**
SLIM S. . . . . **G. brevifolius**

SKELETONPLANT . . . . . **Lygodesmia**
RUSH S. . . . . **L. juncea**
THORN S. . . . . **L. spinosa**

SKELETONWEED . . . . . . **Chondrilla**
RUSH S. . . . . **C. juncea**

SKIM'MIA . . . . SKIMMIA
japon'ica . . . . JAPANESE S.
laureo'la
reevesia'na . . . . REEVES S.
—variega'ta . . . . VARIEGATED R.S.

SKINLEAF . . . . **Dermophylla**
TAYUYA S. . . . . . . **D. pendulina**

SKULLCAP . . . . **Scutellaria**
ALPINE S. . . . . **S. alpina**
BAIKAL S. . . . . **S. baicalensis**
BRITTONS S. . . . . **S. brittoni**
CALIFORNIA S. . . . . . . **S. californica**
COLOMBIA S. . . . . **S. ventenati**
COLUMNAS S. . . . . **S. columnae**
HYSSOP S. . . . . **S. integrifolia**
INDIA S. . . . . **S. indica**
MOCINO S. . . . . **S. mociniana**
NARROWLEAF S. . . . **S. angustifolia**
ORIENTAL S. . . . . **S. orientalis**

SKULLCAP, continued
RESINOUS S. . . **Scutellaria resinosa**
SCARLET S. . . . . **S. coccinea**
SHOWY S. . . . . **S. serrata**
SIDEFLOWERING S. . . . **S. lateriflora**
SMALL INDIA S. . . **S. indica japonica**
SMALL S. . . . . **S. parvula**
TALL S. . . . . **S. altissima**
TUBEROUS S. . . . . **S. tuberosa**
VEINED S. . . . . **S. nervosa**
WHITE S. . . . . **S. albida**
YELLOW ALPINE S. **S. alpina lupulina**

Skunkbush . . . MENZIESIA: **Menziesia;** SUMAC, SKUNKBUSH: **Rhus trilobata**

SKUNKCABBAGE **Symplocarpus; S. foetidus**

SKYFLOWER . . . . **Duranta**
BRAZIL S. . . . . . **D. stenostachya**
CREEPING S. . . . . **D. repens**
LORENTZ S. . . . . **D. lorentzi**
VARIEGATED CREEPING S.
D. repens variegata
WHITE C. S. . . . . **D. r. alba**

Slack . . . . LAVER: **Porphyra**

SLEEPYGRASS . . . . . . **Stipa robusta**

SLEEVEPALM . . **Manicaria; M. saccifera**

SLIPPERFLOWER . . . . . **Pedilanthus**
REDBIRD S. . . . . **P. tithymaloides**
WAX S. . . . . **P. pavonis**

SLIPPERTREE . . . . **Bowkeria**
GERRARD S. . . . . . **B. gerrardiana**
NARROWLIP S. . . . . . **B. triphylla**

SLOE . . . . **Prunus spinosa**
See also BLACKTHORN.

SLOUGHGRASS . . . . . . **Beckmannia**
AMERICAN S. . . . . . **B. syzigachne**

SLUGWOOD . . . . **Beilschmiedia**
TARAIRE S. . . . . **B. tarairi**
TAWA S. . . . . **B. tawa**

SMARTWEED
Polygonum (Persicaria section)
See also BISTORT, CORNBIND, FLEECEFLOWER, KNOTWEED, LADYSTHUMB.

BITTER S. . . . . **P. acre**
BRISTLY S. . . . . **P. setaceum**
CAREY S. . . . . **P. careyi**
DOTTED S. . . . . **P. punctatum**
HAIRY S. . . . . **P. hirsutum**
LONGSTYLE S. . . . . . **P. longistylum**
MARSHPEPPER S. . . . . **P. hydropiper**
PENNSYLVANIA S. . **P. pensylvanicum**
PUERTORICO S. . . . . **P. portoricense**
SWAMP S. . . . . **P. hydropiperoides**
WOOLLY S. . . . . . . **P. tomentosum**

SMELOW'SKIA
calyc'ina (*americana*)

SMILACI'NA (*VAGNERA*) |w
SOLOMONPLUME (*False Solomonseal*)
amplexicau'lis . . . . FAT S.
bifo'lia . . . **Maianthemum bifolium**
racemo'sa (*Vagnera r.*) |w FEATHER S.
sessilifo'lia . . . . SLIM S.
stella'ta (*liliacea; Vagnera l.; V. stellata*) . . . . STARRY S.
trifo'lia . . . . LABRADOR S.

SMI'LAX |w . . . . GREENBRIER

The Sarsaparillas of commerce also belong to this genus.

aristolochiifo'lia (*medica*)
MEXICAN SARSAPARILLA
as'pera . . . . EURASIAN G.
—macula'ta . . . . . SPOTTED E.G.
—maurita'nica

SMILAX, continued
biflo'ra . . . . NIPPON GREENBRIER
bo'nanox ⌊w . . . . SAW G.
califor'nica . . . . . CALIFORNIA G.
×**can'tab** . . . . CANTAB G.
chi'na . . . . CHINAROOT G.
disco'tis
—**con'color**
excel'sa . . . . STURDY G.
fe'rox
glau'ca ⌊w . . . . CAT G.
herba'cea ⌊w . . . CARRIONFLOWER G.
his'pida . . . . BRISTLY G.
lanceola'ta . . . . . . LANCELEAF G.
laurifo'lia ⌊w . . . . . . LAUREL G.
lon'gipes
med'ica . . . . . **S. aristolochiifolia**
megalan'tha . . . . . CORALBEAD G.
menispermoi'dea . . . BLUEBEAD G.
microphyl'la . . . . . LITTLELEAF G.
officina'lis
regel'i (*ornata*) . . . . JAMAICA SARSAPARILLA (*Honduras S.*)
rig'ida
ripa'ria
rotundifo'lia ⌊w . . . . . COMMON G.
—**quadrangula'ta** . SQUARETWIG C.G.
scobinicau'lis
sie'boldi . . . . SIEBOLD G.
tamnoi'des . . . . . . BAMBOO G.
trachyp'oda
vagina'ta
wal'teri ⌊w . . . . REDBEAD G.

SMILOGRASS . . . . **Oryzopsis miliacea**

SMOKETREE . . . . **Cotinus**
AMERICAN S. . . . . . **C. americanus**
COMMON S. . . . . . . **C. coggygria**

SMUTGRASS
AUSTRALIAN S. . **Sporobolus elongatus**
RATTAIL S. . . . . **S. poireti**
WESTINDIES S. . . . . . . **S. indicus**

SNAILSEED . . . . **Cocculus**
CAROLINA S. . . . . . . **C. carolinus**
JAPANESE S. . . . . **C. trilobus**
LAURELLEAF S. . . . . **C. laurifolius**

Snakecactus . . . . MOONLIGHTCACTUS: **Selenicereus**

SNAKEGOURD . . . . . . **Trichosanthes**
EDIBLE S. . . . . **T. anguina**
HEARTLEAF S. . . . . **T. cordata**
JAPANESE S. . . . . **T. cucumeroides**
MONGOLIAN S. . . . . **T. kirilowi**
REDBALL S. . . . . **T. bracteata**

SNAKEROOT, WHITE **Eupatorium rugosum**

SNAKEWEED . . . . **Gutierrezia**
BROOM S. . . . . **G. sarothrae**
CALIFORNIA S. . . . . . **G. californica**
STICKY S. . . . . **G. iucida**
TARRAGON S. . . . **G. dracunculoides**
TEXAS S. . . . . **G. texana**
THREADLEAF S. . . . **G. microcephala**

SNAKEWOOD . . . **Piratinera guianensis**

Snakewoodtree . . PUMPWOOD: **Cecropia**

SNAPDRAGON . . . . **Antirrhinum**
CHAPARRAL S. . . . **A. coulterianum**
COASTRANGE S. . . . . . . **A. vagans**
COMMON S. . . . . **A. majus**
CORN S. . . . . **A. orontium**
EVERGREEN S. . . . **A. sempervirens**
GUMMY S. . . . . . . **A. glutinosum**
NUTTALL S. . . . . **A. nuttallianum**

SNAPDRAGON, continued
ORCUTT S. . **Antirrhinum orcuttianum**
PYRENEES S. . . . . **A. molle**
SICILIAN S. . . . . **A. siculum**
SIERRA S. . . . . . **A. glandulosum**
SPANISH S. . . . . . **A. hispanicum**
WIDELEAF S. . . . . . . **A. latifolium**
WILDGINGER S. . . . . **A. asarina**

SNAPWEED . . . . **Impatiens**
BALFOUR S. . . . . **I. balfouri**
GARDEN BALSAM . . . . **I. balsamina**
HOLSTS S. . . . . **I. holsti**
JAVA S. . . . . **I. platypetala**
OLIVER S. . . . . **I. oliveri**
PALE S. . . . . **I. pallida**
PETERS S. . . . . **I. petersiana**
ROYLE S. . . . . **I. roylei**
SPOTTED S. . . . . **I. biflora**
SULTAN S. . . . . **I. sultani**

SNEEZEWEED . . . . **Helenium**
AROMATIC S. . . . . . **H. aromaticum**
BIGELOW S. . . . . **H. bigelovi**
BITTER S. . . . . . . **H. tenuifolium**
COMMON S. . . . . . . **H. autumnale**
MOUNTAIN S. . . . . . **H. montanum**
ORANGE S. . . . . **H. hoopesi**
PURPLEHEAD S. . . . . **H. nudiflorum**

SNEEZEWOOD . . . . **Ptaeroxylon**

SNOWBALLCACTUS . **Pediocactus simpsoni**

SNOWBELL . . . . **Styrax**
AMERICAN S. . . . . . . **S. americana**
BIGLEAF S. . . . . . . **S. grandifolia**
CALIFORNIA S. . . . . . **S. californica**
CHINESE S. . . . . **S. wilsoni**
CORKLEAF S. . . . . . . **S. suberifolia**
DOWNY S. . . . . . . **S. pulverulenta**
DRUG S. . . . . **S. officinalis**
FARGES JAPANESE S. **S. japonica fargesi**
FRAGRANT S. . . . . **S. obassia**
HEMSLEY S. . . . . . . **S. hemsleyana**
JAPANESE S. . . . . **S. japonica**
LANGKONG S. . . . . **S. langkongensis**
PHILADELPHIA S. . **S. philadelphoides**
SIAM S. . . . . **S. benzoides**
SOUTHERN CALIFORNIA S. **S. californica fulvescens**
STRIGILA S. . . . . **S. shiraiana**
SUMATRA S. . . . . **S. benzoin**
SYCAMORELEAF S. . . . **S. platanifolia**
TONKIN S. . . . . **S. tonkinensis**
VEITCH S. . . . . **S. veitchiorum**

SNOWBERRY . . . . . **Symphoricarpos**
BROADLEAF COMMON S. **S. albus ovatus**
∞ CHENAULT CORALBERRY. ∞ **S. chenaulti**
CHINESE CORALBERRY . . **S. sinensis**
COMMON S. . . . . **S. albus**
DWARF C. S. . . . . **S. a. pauciflorus**
GARDEN C. S. . . . **S. a. laevigatus**
INDIANCURRANT CORALBERRY **S. orbiculatus**
LONGFLOWER S. . . . **S. longiflorus**
MOUNTAIN S. . . . . . . **S. oreophilus**
PINK S. . . . . **S. microphyllus**
ROUNDLEAF S. . . . . **S. rotundifolius**
SHARPLEAF S. . . . . **S. acutus**
SPREADING S. . . . . **S. mollis**
THINLEAF WESTERN S. **S. occidentalis heyeri**
UTAH S. . . . . **S. utahensis**
WASHINGTON S. . . . . . **S. hesperius**
WESTERN S. . . . . . . **S. occidentalis**
WHORTLELEAF S. . . . **S. vaccinioides**

SNOWDROP . . . . **Galanthus**
ALLEN S. . . . . **G. alleni**
BIG COMMON S. . **G. nivalis maximus**
BYZANTINE S. . . . . . **G. byzantinus**
CILICIAN S. . . . . **G. cilicicus**
COMMON S. . . . . **G. nivalis**
CRIMEAN S. . . . . **G. plicatus**
GIANT S. . . . . **G. elwesi**
GREEK S. . . . . **G. olgae**
GREENTIP COMMON S. **G. nivalis viridi-apice**
NIKARIAN S. . . . . **G. ikariae**
NOVEMBER COMMON S. **G. nivalis corcyrensis**
OCTOBER C. S. . . . **G. n. octobrensis**
REFLEXED C. S. . . . **G. n. reflexus**
YELLOW C. S. . . . **G. n. flavescens**

SNOWFLAKE . . . . **Leucojum**
APRIL S. . . . . **L. hyemale**
AUTUMN S. . . . . **L. autumnale**
CARPATHIAN SPRING S. **L. vernum carpathicum**
HUNGARIAN S. S. . . . **L. v. vagneri**
MEDITERRANEAN S. . **L. trichophyllum**
ROSY S. . . . . **L. roseum**
SARDINIAN S. . . . . . **L. pulchellum**
SPRING S. . . . . **L. vernum**
SUMMER S. . . . . **L. aestivum**

Snowgum . . . . EUCALYPTUS, SNOW: **Eucalyptus pauciflora**

SNOW-IN-SUMMER **Cerastium tomentosum**

SNOWLOVER . . . . **Chionophila**
JAMES S. . . . . **C. jamesi**

SNOWPLANT . . **Sarcodes; S. sanguinea**

SNOWPOPPY . **Eomecon; E. chionantha**

SNOWWREATH **Neviusia; N. alabamensis**

SOAPBARKTREE . **Quillaja; Q. saponaria**

SOAPBERRY . . . . **Sapindus**
CHINESE S. . . . . . . **S. mukorossi**
FLORIDA S. . . . . . . **S. marginatus**
SENEGAL S. . . . . . **S. senegalensis**
SOUTHERN S. . . . . **S. saponaria**
THREELEAF S. . . . . . . **S. trifoliatus**
WESTERN S. . . . . . . **S. drummondi**

SOAPPLANT . . . . **Chlorogalum**
AMOLE S. . . . . . . **C. pomeridianum**

SOAP SUBSTITUTES (Plant Sources of)
See **ECONOMIC PLANTS, SOAP SUBSTITUTES.**

SOAPWEED
PINK SMALL S. . . **Yucca glauca rosea**
SMALL S. . . . . **Y. glauca**
STEMMED S. S. . . . . . **Y. g. stricta**

SOAPWORT . . . . **Saponaria**
BOUNCINGBET . . . . . **S. officinalis**
CALABRIAN S. . . . . . . **S. calabrica**
COW S. . . . . **S. vaccaria**
DAISYLEAF S. . . . . . **S. bellidifolia**
PYRENEES S. . . . . . . **S. caespitosa**
ROCK S. . . . . **S. ocymoides**
WHITE R. S. . . . . **S. o. alba**
YELLOWHEAD S. . . . . **S. lutea**

SOBRA'LIA
See **ORCHID GENERA.**

Softgrass . . . . VELVETGRASS: **Holcus**

SO'JA . . . . **GLYCINE**
max' . . . . **G. soja**

Hort. var.; HV. = horticultural variety (or varieties); sp. = species (singular); spp. = species (plural).
₵ = clon; × (as a prefix) = hybrid; × (between scientific plant names) = crossed by; ∞ = polybrid; ⌊w = plant useful to wildlife.
See Glossary for definitions of clon, hybrid, and polybrid.

SOLAN'DRA (*SWARTZIA* J. F. Gmel., *not* Schreb.) . . . . CHALICEVINE
grandiflo'ra (*Swartzia g.*) . SHOWY C.
gutta'ta . . . . GOLDCUP C.
hartweg'i . . . . **S. nitida**
longiflo'ra . . . . BUGLE C.
ni'tida (*hartwegi; Swartzia n.*) MILKCUP C.
spectab'ilis . . . . LOVELY C.

SOLANO'A
purpuras'cens (*Gomphocarpus p.; Schizonotus p.; Solanoana p.*)

SOLA'NUM |w . . . . . . NIGHTSHADE

Solanum, of which the cultivated Potato and Eggplant are members, is one of the largest and most diversified genera of plants, and contains considerably more than 1200 species.

aculeatis'simum . . . SODA-APPLE N.
aethio'picum . . . . . ETHIOPIAN N.
ala'tum . . . . **S. robustum**
atropurpu'reum . . . . . BRAZIL N.
auricula'tum . . . . . . VIOLET N.
avicula're . . . . . AUSTRALIAN N.
calda'si
califor'nicum . . . . . CALIFORNIA N.
capsicas'trum FALSE JERUSALEMCHERRY
₵ACORN. HV.
₵BIRDSEYE
₵CELESTIAL
₵CHRISTMAS CHAMELEON
₵MELVIN (*melvini*)
₵TUCUMAN (*tucumanense*)
₵VARIEGATED (*variegatum*)
carolinen'se |w CAROLINA HORSENETTLE
cilia'tum
citrullifo'lium . . . WATERMELON N.
cleve'landi . . . . . . CLEVELAND N.
cornu'tum . . . . HORNED N.
cris'pum
—autumna'le
crotonifo'lium . . . . . CROTON N.
doug'lasi . . . . . . DOUGLAS N.
dulcama'ra |w . . . . . . BITTER N.
—al'bum . . . . WHITE B.N.
—indivi'sum . . . . WHOLELEAF B.N.
—villosis'simum . . . . HAIRY B.N.
₵VARIEGATED (*variegatum*) HV. S. dulcamara
elaeagnifo'lium |w . . SILVERLEAF N.
fend'leri . . . . . . FENDLER POTATO
gaya'num . . . . GAYS N.
gigan'teum . . . . GIANT N.
grac'ile |w
guineen'se . . . . GUINEA N.
henderso'ni HENDERSON JERUSALEMCHERRY
heterodox'um . . . . MELONLEAF N.
hu'mile
integrifo'lium . ETHIOPIAN EGGPLANT
inte'rius . . . . INLAND N.
jasminoi'des . . . . . . JASMINE N.
—grandiflo'rum . . . . GREAT J.N.
lanceola'tum . . . . LANCELEAF N.
laurifo'lium . . . . LAURELLEAF N.
lute'um . . . . YELLOW N.
macran'thum . . . . POTATOTREE N.
mac'rodon
margina'tum
melong'ena . . . GARDEN EGGPLANT
minia'tum
murica'tum . . . . PEPINO
ni'grum |w . . . . BLACK N.

SOLANUM, continued
ni'grum guineen'se SOLANBERRY BLACK NIGHTSHADE
₵GARDENHUCKLEBERRY. HV. S. nigrum
₵SUNBERRY
₵WONDERBERRY
par'ishi . . . . PARISH N.
pseudocap'sicum . JERUSALEMCHERRY
—cleve'landi . . . . . CHRISTMAS J.
pseudo-melong'ena . FALSE EGGPLANT
rantonet'ti . . . . . . PARAGUAY N.
robus'tum (*alatum*) . . . . SHRUB N.
rostra'tum |w . . . BUFFALOBUR N.
seaforthia'num . . . . BRAZILIAN N.
sisymbrifo'lium
sodo'meum . . APPLE-OF-SODOM N.
tenuiloba'tum . . . . SANDIEGO N.
tor'reyi . . . . TORREY N.
triflo'rum |w . . . . . . CUTLEAF N.
—calophyl'lum
trique'trum . . . . TEXAS N.
tubero'sum |w . . . . POTATO
tucumanen'se . . . . TUCUMAN N.
umbellif'erum . . . . UMBELLED N.
verbascifo'lium . . . . MULLEIN N.
walla'cei . . . . . . CATALINA N.
warscewicz'i . . . . RUSTYWOOL N.
wend'landi . . . . . COSTARICAN N.
xan'ti . . . . PURPLE N.

SOLDANEL'LA . . . . ALPENCLOCK
alpi'na . . . . GLACIER A.
₵WHITE (*alba*) HV.
∞ **gan'deri** (*alpina* × *minima*) ∞ GANDERS A.
min'ima . . . . LEAST A.
₵WHITE (*alba*) HV.
monta'na . . . . GREATER A.
pusil'la . . . . LITTLE A.

SOLIDA'GO (*OREOCHRYSUM*) |w GOLDENROD
al'gida . . . . ALPINE G.
altis'sima . . . . TALL G.
argu'ta . . . . ATLANTIC G.
arizo'nica . . . . ARIZONA G.
bellidifo'lia
bi'color . . . . SILVER G.
boott'i . . . . BOOTT G.
brachysta'chys Hort.
buck'leyi . . . . BUCKLEY G.
cae'sia . . . . WREATH G.
califor'nica . . . . . CALIFORNIA G.
canaden'sis . . . . CANADA G.
capulin'sis . . . . CAPULIN G.
cilio'sa
concin'na . . . . NELSON G.
cut'leri . . . . CUTLER G.
decum'bens . . . . DECUMBENT G.
elonga'ta . . . . CREEK G.
erec'ta . . . . SCEPTER G.
fistulo'sa . . . . . . PINEBARREN G.
flexicau'lis (*latifolia*) . . . . ZIGZAG G.
gigan'tea (*S. serotina g.*) . . . GIANT G.
—leiophyl'la (*S. serotina*) NOVEMBER G.
glomera'ta . . . . CLUSTER G.
glaber'rima
graminifo'lia . . . . . GRASSLEAF G.
—nutt'alli . . . . . . NUTTALL G.G.
his'pida . . . . HAIRY G.
jun'cea . . . . PLUME G.
latifo'lia . . . . **S. flexicaulis**
leavenworth'i . . . LEAVENWORTH G.
lep'ida . . . . ELEGANT G.
lindheimeria'na . . . LINDHEIMER G.
missourien'sis . . . . . MISSOURI G.
na'na |w . . . . BABY G.
neglec'ta . . . . SWAMP G.

SOLIDAGO, continued
nemora'lis . DYERSWEED GOLDENROD
occidenta'lis |w . . . . . WESTERN G.
odo'ra (*suaveolens*) . . FRAGRANT G.
ohioen'sis . . . . OHIO G.
pal'lida . . . . PALELEAF G.
par'ryi . . . . PARRY G.
pat'ula . . . . ROUGHLEAF G.
petrado'ria (*pumila; Petradoria pumila*) ROCK G.
pu'bens . . . . FURRY G.
puber'ula . . . . DOWNY G.
rad'ula
rand'i . . . . RAND G.
riddell'i . . . . RIDDELL G.
rig'ida . . . . STIFF G.
rigidius'cula . . . . SHOWYWAND G.
rugo'sa . . . . WRINKLED G.
scopulo'rum
sempervi'rens |w . . . . SEASIDE G.
serot'ina . . . . **S. gigantea leiophylla**
—gigan'tea . . . . **S. gigantea**
short'i . . . . SHORTS G.
spathula'ta . . . . COAST G.
specio'sa . . . . NOBLE G.
spectab'ilis . . . . NEVADA G.
squarro'sa . . . . RUGGED G.
stric'ta . . . . . . WILLOWLEAF G.
suave'olens . . . . **S. odora**
tenuifo'lia (*Euthamia t.*)
trinerva'ta . . . . THREENERVE G.
uligino'sa . . . . BOG G.
ver'na
virgau'rea EUROPEAN G. (*Woundwort*)
₵DWARF (*compacta*) HV.
ward'i . . . . WARD G.

SOLIS'IA . . . . **MAMMILLARIA**
See **CACTUS GENERA.**

SOLITAIREPALM . **Ptychosperma elegans**

SOL'LYA . . . . . BLUEBELLCREEPER
heterophyl'la . . . . AUSTRALIAN B.

SOLOMONPLUME . . . . . . **Smilacina**
FAT S. . . . . . . **S. amplexicaulis**
FEATHER S. . . . . . . **S. racemosa**
LABRADOR S. . . . . **S. trifolia**
SLIM S. . . . . **S. sessilifolia**
STARRY S. . . . . **S. stellata**

SOLOMONSEAL . . . . . **Polygonatum**
BROADLEAF S. . . . . . **P. latifolium**
DRUG S. . . . . **P. officinale**
EURASIAN S. . . . . . **P. multiflorum**
False S. . SOLOMONPLUME: **Smilacina**
GREAT S. . . . . . **P. commutatum**
SMALL S. . . . . **P. biflorum**
WHORLED S. . . . . **P. verticillatum**

SOLORI'NA . . . . SOLORINA
cro'cea . . . . SAFFRON S.

SON'CHUS |w . . . . . . SOWTHISTLE
arven'sis |w . . . . FIELD S.
as'per |w . . . . PRICKLY S.
conges'tus (*jacquini*)
olera'ceus |w . . . . COMMON S.

SONCOYA . . . . **Annona purpurea**

SONERI'LA
margarita'cea

SONNERA'TIA
caseola'ris

SOPHI'A . . . . . . **DESCURAINIA**
andrena'rum . . . **D. halictorum a.**
fi'lipes . . . . . **D. longipedicellata**
ochroleu'ca . . . . . . **D. menziesi o.**
parviflo'ra . . . . **D. sophia**
pinna'ta Howell. . **D. longipedicellata**

SOPHO'RA (*BROUSSONETIA* Orteg., *not* L'Her.) |w . . . . . Sophora
affi'nis . . . . Texas S.
alopecuroi'des
arizo'nica . . . . Arizona S.
chatham'ica . . . . . . Chatham S.
chrysophyl'la
flaves'cens
japon'ica . . Japanese Pagodatree
¢Columnar (*columnaris*) hv.
¢Violacea
¢Weeping (*pendula*)
¢Woolly (*pubescens*)
mol'lis . . . . Hairy S.
platycar'pa . . . . **Cladrastis p.**
secundiflo'ra (*Broussonetia s.*) Mescalbean S.
seric'ea . . . . Silky S.
sitchen'sis . . . . Pacific S.
specio'sa . . . . . . Coralbean S.
stenophyl'la . . . . . Fringeleaf S.
tetrap'tera (*Edwardsia grandiflora*) Fourwing S.
—microphyl'la . . . Littleleaf F.S.
viciifo'lia . . . . . . Vetchleaf S.

Sophora . . . . **Sophora**
Arizona S. . . . . **S. arizonica**
Chatham S. . . . . . . **S. chathamica**
Coralbean S. . . . . . . **S. speciosa**
Fourwing S. . . . . . . **S. tetraptera**
Fringeleaf S. . . . . . **S. stenophylla**
Hairy S. . . . . **S. mollis**
Japanese Pagodatree . **S. japonica**
Littleleaf Fourwing S. **S. tetraptera microphylla**
Mescalbean S. . . . . **S. secundiflora**
Pacific S. . . . . **S. sitchensis**
Silky S. . . . . **S. sericea**
Texas S. . . . . **S. affinis**
Vetchleaf S. . . . . . . **S. viciifolia**

SOPHROCATLAE'LIA
See **ORCHID GENERA.**

SOPHROCAT'TLEYA
See **ORCHID GENERA.**

SOPHROLAE'LIA
See **ORCHID GENERA.**

SOPHRONI'TIS
See **ORCHID GENERA.**

SORBA'RIA (*SCHIZONOTUS* Lindl., *not* Raf.) . . . . . . Falsespirea
aitchiso'ni (*angustifolia; Schizonotus aitchisoni; Spiraea aitchisoni*) Kashmir F.
arbo'rea . . . . Tree F.
—glabra'ta . . . . . Smooth T.F.
assur'gens
grandiflo'ra . . . . Showy F.
millefo'lium . . . **Chamaebatiaria m.**
sorbifo'lia (*Schizonotus sorbifolius; Spiraea sorbifolia*) . . . . Ural F.
—stelli'pila (*S. stellipila*) . Starry U.F.
tomento'sa (*lindleyana; Schizonotus tomentosus; Spiraea l.*). . . Lindley F.

∞**SORBARO'NIA** (*ARONIA* × *SORBUS*) . . . . . ∞Sorbaronia
∞**alpi'na** (*A. arbutifolia* × *S. aria*)
∞**arse'ni** (*A. prunifolia* × *S. decora*)
∞**dip'peli** (*A. melanocarpa* × *S. aria*)
∞**fal'lax** (*A. melanocarpa* × *S. aucuparia*)
∞**hy'brida** (*A. arbutifolia* × *S. aucuparia*)
∞**jack'i** (*A. melanocarpa* × *S. aucuparia*)
∞**sorbifo'lia** (*A. melanocarpa* × *S. americana*)

∞Sorberry . . . ∞**Amelasorbus jacki**

∞**SORBOPY'RUS** (*PYRUS* × *SORBUS*)
∞**auricula'ris** (*P. communis* × *S. aria*)
¢Bulbiformis. hv.

SOR'BUS (*MICROMELES*) |w Mountainash
alnifo'lia (*Micromeles a.; Pyrus miyabei*) . . . . . Densehead M.
america'na (*Pyrus a.*) |w American M.
—deco'ra . . . . **S. decora**
—na'na . . . . **S. scopulina**
—sitchen'sis . . . . . . **S. sitchensis**
amuren'sis . . . . Amur M.
ar'ia . . . . Whitebeam M.
¢Decaisne (*decaisneana*) hv.
¢Edible (*edulis*)
¢Goldleaf (*aurea*)
¢Palegold (*chrysophylla*)
¢Willowleaf (*salicifolia*)
¢Yellowleaf (*lutescens*)
∞**arnoldia'na** (*aucuparia* × *discolor*) ∞Arnold M.
aucupa'ria (*Pyrus a.*) . European M.
¢Beissner (*beissneriana*) hv.
¢Cutleaf (*asplenifolia*)
¢Dirken (*dirkeni*)
¢Integerrima
¢Moravian (*edulis*)
¢Russian (*rossica*)
¢Upright (*fastigiata*)
¢Weeping (*pendula*)
¢Yellowberry (*xanthocarpa*)
¢Yellowspot (*luteo-variegata*)
caloneu'ra (*Micromeles c.; Pyrus c.*) Browndot M.
cascaden'sis . . . . . . Cascade M.
chamaemes'pilus
commix'ta . . . . Korean M.
cuspida'ta (*nepalensis*)
deco'ra (*S. americana d.*) . Showy M.
dis'color (*pekinensis; Pyrus d.*) Snowberry M.
domes'tica (*Pyrus sorbus*) Servicetree M. (*Servicetree*)
¢Appleform (*pomifera*) hv.
¢Pearshape (*pyrifera*)
dumo'sa . . . . Arizona M.
esserteauia'na
epiden'dron
fi'lipes
flabellifo'lia . . . . . . **S. umbellata**
folg'neri (*Micromeles f.; Pyrus f.*) Folgner M.
¢Weeping (*pendula*) hv.
glomerula'ta
grac'ilis
harrowia'na . . . . . Harrows M.
hele'nae . . . . Helens M.
∞**host'i** (*chamaemespilus* × *mougeoti*) ∞Hosts M.
hupehen'sis . . . . . . Hupeh M.
∞**hy'brida** (*aucuparia* × *intermedia*) ∞Oakleaf M.
¢Gibbs (*gibbsi*) hv.
¢Meinich (*meinichi*)
¢Pyramidal (*fastigiata*)
interme'dia (*scandica*) . . Swedish M.
—arranen'sis
—min'ima
japon'ica (*koehnei; Micromeles j.*) Japanese M.
—calocar'pa . . Yellowberry J.M.
keiss'leri . . . . . . Keissler M.
koehnea'na . . . . . Koehnes M.
lana'ta
∞**latifo'lia** (*aria* × *torminalis*)
matsumura'na . . . Matsumura M.

SORBUS, continued
megalocar'pa
meliosmifo'lia
microphyl'la Tinyleaf Mountainash
mougeot'i . . . . Edible M.
mun'da subarachnoi'dea . . . **S. pratti**
nepalen'sis . . . . **S. cuspidata**
occidenta'lis (*pumila*) . Western M.
palles'cens
pekinen'sis . . . . **S. discolor**
plantieren'sis
pluripinna'ta
pohuashanen'sis
poteriifo'lia
pratt'i (*S. munda subarachnoidea*) Pratt M.
—tatsienen'sis
pu'mila . . . . **S. occidentalis**
quercifo'lia . . . . . ∞**S. thuringiaca**
reflexipet'ala
rehderia'na . . . . Rehder M.
—cupreo-ni'tens
rufo-ferrugin'ea . . Flameberry M.
sambucifo'lia (*Pyrus s.*) . Siberian M.
sargentia'na . . . . . . Sargent M.
—warleyen'sis
scala'ris
scan'dica . . . . **S. intermedia**
scopuli'na (*S. americana nana*) Greenes M.
serot'ina
sitchen'sis (*S. americana s.*) |w Pacific M.
∞**splen'dida** (*americana* × *aucuparia*)
∞**thuringi'aca** (*aria* × *aucuparia; quercifolia*)
tianshan'ica (*Pyrus t.*)
tormina'lis (*Pyrus t.; Torminaria t.*) Checkertree M. (*Checkertree; Wild Servicetree*)
umbella'ta (*flabellifolia*)
vilmori'ni (*Pyrus v.*) . Vilmorin M.
wilsonia'na . . . . . . Wilson M.
zahlbruck'neri . . Zahlbruckner M.

SORGHAS'TRUM . . . . Indiangrass
See **GRASS GENERA.**

Sorgho . **Sorghum vulgare saccharatum**
Gooseneck S. . . . . . **S. v. bicolor**
Sumac S. . . . . . . **S. v. nigricans**

SOR'GHUM . . . . Sorghum
See **GRASS GENERA.**

Sorghum . . . . **Sorghum; S. vulgare**
See **CEREALS.**

Sorrel
French S. . . . . . **Rumex scutatus**
Garden S. . . . . **R. acetosa**
Heartwing S. . . . . . **R. hastatulus**
Mountain S. . . . . . **R. paucifolius**
Sheep S. . . . . **R. acetosella**

Sorrowlesstree, India. . Saraca, Common: **Saraca indica**

Sotol . . . . **Dasylirion**
Blueleaf S. . . . . **D. glaucophyllum**
Brushtip S. . . . . . . **D. acrotriche**
Grassleaf S. . . . **D. graminifolium**
Sawtooth S. . . . . **D. serratifolium**
Squareleaf S. . . . . **D. longissimum**
Texas S. . . . . **D. texanum**
Wheeler S. . . . . **D. wheeleri**

Souarinut . . . . Sawarrinut: **Caryocar nuciferum**

Sourgrass. . . . **Trichachne insularis**

Soursop . . . . **Annona muricata**
Mountain S. . . . . . . **A. montana**

SOURWOOD . **Oxydendrum; O. arboreum**
SOUTHERNPLUME . **Elliottia; E. racemosa**
Southernwood . . WORMWOOD, OLDMAN: **Artemisia abrotanum**
SOWTHISTLE . . . . **Sonchus**
COMMON S. . . . . **S. oleraceus**
FIELD S. . . . . **S. arvensis**
PRICKLY S. . . . . **S. asper**
SOYBEAN . . . . **Glycine soja**

SOY'MIDA . . . . SOYMIDA
febrif'uga (*Swietenia f.*) . . ROHAN S.

SPACH'EA
el'egans

Spanishbayonet . . . . YUCCA, TRECUL: **Yucca treculeana**
Spanishdagger . . . . . YUCCA, ALOE: **Yucca aloifolia**
Spanishlime . . . . . . MAMONCILLO: **Melicocca bijuga**
Spanishmoss. . TILLANDSIA, TREEBEARD: **Tillandsia usneoides**
SPANISHNEEDLES . . . **Bidens bipinnata**
SPANISH-SHAWLPLANT **Schizocentron; S. elegans**

SPARAX'IS . . . . WANDFLOWER
grandiflo'ra . . . . BIG W.
—al'ba . . . . WHITE B.W.
pulcher'rima . . . . . . **Dierama p.**

SPARGA'NIUM |w . . . . . BURREED
america'num |w . . . AMERICAN B.
androc'ladum |w
angustifo'lium |w . . NARROWLEAF B.
chlorocar'pum |w
eurycar'pum |w . . . . . . GIANT B.
fluc'tuans |w . . . . . . WATER B.
hyperbo'reum |w
min'imum |w . . . . LEAST B.
multipeduncula'tum |w

SPARMAN'NIA . . . . . SPARMANNIA
africa'na . . . . AFRICAN S.
₵DOUBLE (*flore-pleno*) HV.
palma'ta (*Entelea p.*)
sinen'sis . . . . **Rehmannia angulata**

SPARTI'NA . . . . CORDGRASS
See **GRASS GENERA.**

SPAR'TIUM |w . . . WEAVERSBROOM
jun'ceum (*Cytisus junceus*) |w WEAVERSBROOM
—na'num . . . . DWARF W.
—ochroleu'cum
₵DOUBLE (*plenum*) HV. S. junceum
multiflo'rum . . . **Cytisus multiflorus**
scopa'rium . . . . . **Cytisus scoparius**
Spartocyt'isus nubig'enus **Cytisus fragrans**

SPATHE'LIA . . . . MOUNTAINPRIDE
sim'plex . . . . JAMAICA M.

SPATHO'DEA . . . . FLAMBEAUTREE
campanula'ta . . . . BELL F.

SPATHOGLOT'TIS
See **ORCHID GENERA.**

SPATHOSCA'PHE **CHAMAEDOREA**
See **PALM GENERA.**

SPATHYE'MA . . **SYMPLOCARPUS**

SPATHYPHYL'LUM
cochlearispa'thum (*heliconiifolium*)
floribun'dum
pati'ni (*candidum*)

Spatula'ria newcomb'ei . . **Saxifraga n.**
SPEARLILY . . . . **Doryanthes**
COMMON S. . . . . **D. excelsa**
SPEARMINT . . . . . **Mentha spicata**
As Spearmint is a true Mint, the name would logically be written Spear Mint; long usage, however, has sanctioned its spelling as one word.

SPECTACLEPOD . . . . **Dithyraea**
CALIFORNIA S. . . . . **D. californica**
SEASHORE C. S. . . . . **D. c. maritima**
WISLIZENUS S. . . . . . **D. wislizeni**

SPECULA'RIA |w VENUSLOOKINGGLASS
biflo'ra . . . . SMALL V.
pentago'nia (*Campanula p.*)
perfolia'ta (*Legouzia p.*) |w CLASPING V.
speculum-ven'eris (*speculum; Campanula s.*)

SPEEDWELL . . . . **Veronica**
ALLIONI S. . . . . **V. allioni**
ALPINE S. . . . . **V. alpina**
AMERICAN S. . . . . . . **V. americana**
BACHOFENS S. . . . . . **V. bachofeni**
BASTARD S. . . . . **V. spuria**
BECCABUNGA S. . . . . . **V. beccabunga**
CLUMP S. . . **V. maritima subsessilis**
COMB S. . . . . **V. pectinata**
COMMON S. . . . . **V. arvensis**
CREEPING S. . . . . **V. repens**
CUSICK S. . . . . **V. cusicki**
DRUG S. . . . . **V. officinalis**
FIELD S. . . . . **V. agrestis**
GENTIAN S. . . . . **V. gentianoides**
GERMANDER S. . . . **V. chamaedrys**
HAREBELL HUNGARIAN S. **V. latifolia prostrata**
HEATH SPIKE S. . . **V. spicata erica**
HUNGARIAN S. . . . . **V. latifolia**
IVYLEAF S. . . . . . **V. hederaefolia**
MARSH S. . . . . **V. scutellata**
PINK SPIKE S. . . . **V. spicata rosea**
PURSLANE S. . . . . . . **V. peregrina**
ROSY COMB S. . . **V. pectinata rosea**
SPIKE S. . . . . **V. spicata**
THYMELEAF S. . . . . **V. serpyllifolia**
TOURNEFORT S. . . . . . **V. tourneforti**
WATER S. . . . **V. anagallis-aquatica**
WAYSIDE S. . . . . **V. polita**
WHITESPIKE S. . . . . **V. spicata alba**
WOOLLY S. . . . . **V. incana**

SPEGAZZIN'IA . . **WEINGARTIA**
See **CACTUS GENERA.**

SPELT . . . . **Triticum spelta**

SPER'GULA |w . . . . SPURRY
arven'sis |w . . . . CORN S.
pentan'dra . . . . . . WINGSEED S.
sati'va . . . . FIELD S.

SPERGULA'RIA (*TISSA*) |w SANDSPURRY
Spergularia is conserved, under International Rules, in place of the older Tissa.

mari'na |w . . . . . . SALTMARSH S.
ru'bra (*Tissa r.*) . . . . . . RED S.
sali'na

SPERMACO'CE |w . . . . BUTTONPLANT
gla'bra |w . . . . SMOOTH B.

SPERMO'LEPIS |w
divarica'tus |w
echina'tus |w

SPHACE'LE
calyc'ina . . . . WOODBALM

SPHAERAL'CEA (*PHYMOSIA*) |w GLOBEMALLOW
ambig'ua . . . . DESERT G.
angustifo'lia . . . . NARROWLEAF G.
—cuspida'ta (*S. cuspidata*)
arcua'ta . . . **Malvastrum arcuatum**
bonarien'sis
caespito'sa . . . . TUFTED G.
cisplati'na (*Malva miniata*) BRICK G.
coccin'ea (*Malvastrum coccineum*) |w SCARLET G.
davidso'ni . . . . . . **Malvastrum d.**
densiflo'ra . **Malvastrum densiflorum**
fascicula'ta. **Malvastrum fasciculatum**
fre'monti . . . . FREMONT G.
grossulariaefo'lia (*Malvastrum grossulariaefolium*) . GOOSEBERRYLEAF G.
leptophyl'la (*Malvastrum leptophyllum*)
loba'ta |w . . . . LOBED G.
minia'ta
—rhombifo'lia
munroa'na (*Malvastrum munroanum*) |w MUNRO G.
—subrhomboi'dea (*S. subrhomboidea*)
pal'meri . . . . **Malvastrum p.**
remo'ta
rivula'ris . . . . STREAM G.
rose'a (*vitifolia*) . . . . . . ROSY G.
umbella'ta . . . . MEXICAN G.
Sphaerog'yne latifo'lia **Tococa platyphylla**

SPHAEROPHY'SA . . . . . GLOBEPEA
sal'sula . . . . SALT G.

SPHAEROSTE'MA . **SCHISANDRA**

SPHAEROSTIG'MA . **OENOTHERA**

SPHAG'NUM . . . . . . SPHAGNUM
macrophyl'lum . . . . . LONGLEAF S.
papillo'sum . . . . WARTY S.

SPHENOG'YNE . . . . . . **URSINIA**
specio'sa . . . . **U. pulchra**

SPHENOM'ERIS (*ODONTOSORIA* in part)
See **FERN GENERA.**

SPHENOPH'OLIS . . . WEDGESCALE
See **GRASS GENERA.**

SPHENOSCIA'DIUM WOOLLYHEADPARSNIP
capitella'tum . . . . RANGE W.

SPICEBUSH . . . . **Lindera**
CHINESE S. . . . . **L. communis**
COMMON S. . . . . **L. benzoin**
FEBRUARY S. . . . . **L. praecox**
GREAT S. . . . . . . **L. megaphylla**
JAPANESE S. . . . . . . **L. obtusiloba**
SILKYRIB UMBELED S. **L. umbellata hypoglauca**
SILKY S. . . . . **L. sericea**
THREELOBE S. . . . . **L. triloba**
UMBELED S. . . . . **L. umbellata**
YELLOWBERRY COMMON S. **L. benzoin xanthocarpa**

SPICES (Plant Sources of)
See **ECONOMIC PLANTS, SPICES AND OTHER FLAVORING MATERIALS**

SPIDERFLOWER . . . . **Cleome**
BEE S. . . . . **C. serrulata**
GIANT S. . . . . **C. gigantea**
HAIRY S. . . . . **C. hispida**
PRICKLY S. . . . . **C. aculeata**
SAMBO S. . . . . **C. glabrata**
SPINY S. . . . . **C. spinosa**
YELLOW S. . . . . **C. lutea**
SPIDERGRASS . . . . . **Aristida ternipes**

Spiderherb . . . . . . **Gynandropsis**
African S. . . . . . **G. pentaphylla**
Showy S. . . . . **G. speciosa**
Slender S. . . . . **G. gracilis**
Spiderling . . . . **Boerhaavia**
Erect S. . . . . **B. erecta**
Scarlet S. . . . . **B. coccinea**
Watson S. . . . . **B. watsoni**
Wetleaf S. . . . . . . **B. annulata**
Spiderorchid . . . . **Brassia**
Lawrence S. . . . **B. lawrenceana**
Spotted S. . . . . **B. maculata**
Spiderwort . . . . . . **Tradescantia**
Bracted S. . . . . . . **T. bracteata**
Dracena S. . . . . **T. dracaenoides**
Jamaica S. . . . . **T. multiflora**
Littleflower S. . . . **T. micrantha**
Prairie S. . . . . . . **T. occidentalis**
Queens S. . . . . **T. reginae**
Shortstem S. . . . **T. brevicaulis**
Texas S. . . . . **T. humilis**
Virginia S. . . . . . . **T. virginiana**
Wanderingjew . . . **T. fluminensis**
Zigzag S. . . . . **T. pilosa**
SPIGE'LIA . . . . Spigelia
anthel'mia . . . . . WestIndian S.
marilan'dica . . Pinkroot S. (*Redroot*)
peduncula'ta
Spikefescue . . **Hesperochloa; H. kingi**
Shortawn S. . . . . **H. k. rabiosa**
Spikegrass . . Demazeria: **Desmazeria**
Spikeheath **Bruckenthalia; B. spiculifolia**
Spikenard, American. . **Aralia racemosa**
Spikeprimrose . . . . . **Boisduvalia**
Brook S. . . . . **B. stricta**
Dense S. . . . . . . **B. densiflora**
Spikesedge . . . . **Eleocharis**
Beaked S. . . . . . . **E. rostellata**
Blackfruit S. . . . **E. melanocarpa**
Blunt S. . . . . **E. obtusa**
Brightgreen S. . . . . **E. olivacea**
Canada S. . . . . . . **E. canadensis**
Common S. . . . . . . **E. palustris**
Dwarf S. . . . . **E. parvula**
Engelmann S. . . . . **E. engelmanni**
Fewflowered S. . . . **E. pauciflora**
Flatstem S. . . . . . **E. compressa**
Gulfcoast S. . . . . . **E. cellulosa**
Jointed S. . . . . . **E. equisetoides**
Matted S. . . . . . . **E. intermedia**
Needle S. . . . . . . **E. acicularis**
Ovoid S. . . . . **E. ovata**
Robbins S. . . . . . . **E. robbinsi**
Slender S. . . . . **E. tenuis**
Squarestem S. . . **E. quadrangulata**
Torrey S. . . . . **E. torreyana**
Waternut . . . . **E. tuberosa**
Wolfs S. . . . . **E. wolfi**
SPILAN'THES . . . . Spotflower
olera'cea . . . . . . Paracress S.
Spinach . . . . **Spinacia**
Pricklyseed S. . . . . **S. oleracea**
Roundseed S. . . . . **S. o. inermis**
SPINA'CIA . . . . Spinach
olera'cea . . . . Pricklyseed S.
—iner'mis (*S. o. glabra*). Roundseed S.
Spindlepalm . **Hyophorbe verschaffelti**
Spindletree . . . . **Fusanus**
Quandongnut S. . . . **F. acuminatus**
Tangber S. . . . . . **F. persicarius**
Spinepalm . . . . . **Acanthophoenix**
Red S. . . . . **A. rubra**
Woolly S. . . . . **A. crinita**
Spinepink . . . . . . **Acanthophyllum**
Rockgarden S. . . . . **A. pungens**

Spinyclubpalm . . . . **Bactris**
Augustine S. . . . . **B. augustinea**

SPIRAE'A |w . . . . Spirea
aitchiso'ni . . . . **Sorbaria a.**
al'ba (*lanceolata; S. salicifolia paniculata*) Narrowleaf Meadowsweet S.
albiflo'ra (*S. japonica alba; S. j. albiflora*) . . . . . Japanese White S.
alpi'na . . . . Alpine S.
amoe'na
amuren'sis . . . . **Physocarpus a.**
arcua'ta
∞**argu'ta** (∞*multiflora* × *thunbergi*) ∞Garland S.
ariaefo'lia **Holodiscus discolor ariaefolius**
∞**assim'ilis** (*japonica* × ∞*superba*)
astilboi'des . . . . **Astilbe a.**
bel'la (*coccinea*) . . . Himalayan S.
bethlehemen'sis Hort. . . . **S. latifolia**
betulifo'lia . . . . Birchleaf S.
∞**billiar'di** (*douglasi* × *salicifolia; californica; eximia; lenneana*) ∞Billiard S.
₵White (*alba*) hv.
∞**blan'da** (*cantoniensis* × *chinensis*)
blum'ei
∞**brachybo'trys** (*canescens* × *douglasi; pruinosa*)
bractea'ta . . . . **S. nipponica**
∞**bruma'lis** (*alba?*×*amoena*) ∞Winter S.
bulla'ta (*crispifolia*) . . Crispleaf S.
∞**bumal'da** (*albiflora* × *japonica*) ∞Bumalda S.
₵Anthony Waterer. hv.
₵Froebel (*callosa; froebeli*)
caespito'sa . **Petrophytum caespitosum**
calcic'ola
califor'nica . . . . ∞**S. billiardi**
callo'sa . . . . **S. japonica**
camtschat'ica . . . . . **Filipendula c.**
—rose'a . . . . . . **Filipendula c. r.**
ca'na
canes'cens (*flagelliformis; rotundifolia* Hort.; *vacciniifolia* Hort.) Hoary S.
cantonien'sis (*reevesiana*) . Reeves S.
₵Double (*lanceata*) hv.
carpinifo'lia . . . . **S. latifolia**
chamaedryfo'lia . . . Germander S.
—stenophyl'la
—tran'siens
—ulmifo'lia . . . . . . Elmleaf S.
chinen'sis . . . . Chinese S.
∞**cine'rea** (*cana* × *hypericifolia*)
coccin'ea . . . . **S. bella**
∞**concin'na** (*albiflora* × *amoena*)
∞**conspic'ua** (*albiflora* × *?latifolia*) ∞Showy S.
corymbo'sa
crena'ta . . . . Snow S.
crispifo'lia . . . . **S. bullata**
dasyan'tha
da'vidi . . . . **Astilbe d.**
decum'bens
—tomento'sa . . . . . **S. lancifolia**
densiflo'ra . . . . . . Subalpine S.
∞**diffor'mis** (*alba* × *corymbosa*)
dis'color . . . . **Holodiscus d.**
doug'lasi . . . . Douglas S.
exim'ia . . . . ∞**S. billiardi**
filipen'dula . **Filipendula hexapetala**
flagellifor'mis . . . . . . **S. canescens**
∞**fontenay'si** (*canescens* × *salicifolia*) ∞Fontenays S.
₵Rosy (*rosea*) hv.
₵White (*alba*)
fortu'nei semperflo'rens ∞**S. semperflorens**

SPIRAEA, continued
∞**fox'i** (*corymbosa* × *japonica*) ∞Fox Spirea
fritschia'na
∞**fulves'cens** (*alba* or *tomentosa*×*douglasi*)
gemma'ta . . . . . . Mongolian S.
gigan'tea . . **Filipendula camtschatica**
∞**gieseleria'na** (*cana* × *chamaedryfolia*)
glabra'ta . . . . . **S. japonica glabra**
grac'ilis
hen'ryi . . . . Henry S.
—notab'ilis
humboldt'i . . . . **Aruncus sylvester**
hypericifo'lia
—acu'ta
—obova'ta (*S. obovata*)
inci'sa . . . . . . **Stephanandra i.**
∞**inflex'a** (*cana* × *crenata*)
∞**interme'dia** (*albiflora* × *douglasi*)
japon'ica (*callosa*) . . . Japanese S.
—acumina'ta . . . Taperleaf J.S.
—al'ba . . . . **S. albiflora**
—albiflo'ra . . . . **S. albiflora**
—fortu'nei . . . . . Fortunes J.S.
—gla'bra (*S. glabrata; S. j. glabrata*) Smooth J.S.
—ovalifo'lia . . . . . Ovalleaf J.S.
₵Bigleaf (*macrophylla*) hv. S. japonica
₵Mikado (*atrosanguinea*)
₵Red (*ruberrima*)
kamtschat'ica **Filipendula camtschatica**
laeviga'ta . . . . **Sibiraea l.**
lanceola'ta . . . . **S. alba**
lancifo'lia (*S. decumbens tomentosa*)
latifo'lia (*bethlehemensis* Hort.; *S. carpinifolia salicifolia* U. S. Auth., *not* L.) |w . . Broadleaf Meadowsweet S.
This is an American species, usually catalogued as S. salicifolia, which is an Old World species.
∞**lemoin'ei** (*bullata* × ∞*bumalda*) ∞Lemoine S.
lennea'na . . . . . . ∞**S. billiardi**
lindleya'na . . . **Sorbaria tomentosa**
loba'ta . . . . **Filipendula rubra**
longigem'mis
lu'cida . . . . Shinyleaf S.
∞**macrothyrs'a** (*douglasi* × *latifolia*)
∞**margari'tae** (*japonica* × ∞*superba*) ∞Margarita S.
me'dia . . . . Oriental S.
—glabres'cens
—mol'lis
—seric'ea
menzies'i . . . . Menzies S.
micran'tha
∞**micropet'ala** (*hypericifolia* × *media*)
∞**microthyrs'a** (*alba* × *media*)
millefo'lium . . . **Chamaebatiaria m.**
miya'bei . . . . Miyabe S.
—glabra'ta
—pilo'sula
mollifo'lia
∞**multiflo'ra** (*crenata* × *hypericifolia*) ∞Snowgarland S.
myrtilloi'des . . . . **S. virgata**
nippon'ica (*bracteata*) . . . Nippon S.
—rotundifo'lia (*S. rotundifolia*) Big N.S.
—tosaen'sis
∞**niv'ea** (*amoena* × *canescens*)
noblea'na . . . . . . ∞**S. sansouciana**
∞**no'tha** (*corymbosa* × *latifolia*) ∞Notha S.
∞**nudiflo'ra** (*amoena* × *chamaedryfolia ulmifolia*) . . . . . ∞April S.
obova'ta . . . . . **S. hypericifolia o.**
opulifo'lia . . **Physocarpus opulifolius**

SPIRAEA, continued
∞**oxy'odon** (*chamaedryfolia × media*)
∞**pachysta'chys** (*corymbosa × douglasi*)
∞**pallidiflo'ra** (*menziesi × tomentosa*)
palma'ta . . . . **Filipendula purpurea**
panicula'ta . . . . **S. alba**
pectina'ta . . . . **Luetkea p.**
∞**pikovien'sis** (*crenata × media*)
∞PIKOW SPIREA
pruino'sa . . . . ∞**S. brachybotrys**
prunifo'lia . . . . BRIDALWREATH S.
₵DOUBLE (*plena*) HV.
pubes'cens
∞**pulchel'la** (*amoena × ?bella*)
∞**pumilio'num** (*decumbens × lancifolia*)
∞**pyramida'ta** (*lucida × menziesi*)
∞PYRAMID S.
reevesia'na . . . . . . **S. cantoniensis**
∞**revires'cens** (*amoena × japonica*)
∞EVERBLOOMING S.
∞**rosal'ba** (*alba × salicifolia*)
rose'a . . . . **S. splendens**
rost'horni . . . . . . ROSTHORN S.
rotundifo'lia **S. canescens; S. nipponica r.**
∞**rubel'la** (*latifolia × salicifolia*)
∞**ru'bra** (*amoena × douglasi*)
salicifo'lia . . . . WILLOWLEAF S.
(*Aaronsbeard*)
An Old World species. Its Latin name is often misapplied to S. alba and S. latifolia.
—**grandiflo'ra**
—*panicula'ta* . . . . **S. alba**
salicifo'lia U. S. Auth., *not* L. **S. latifolia**
∞**sansoucia'na** (*douglasi × japonica; nobleana*) . . . . . . ∞SANSOUCI S.
sargentia'na . . . . . SARGENT S.
∞**schinabeck'i** (*chamaedryfolia × salicifolia*) . . . . ∞ARCH S.
∞**semperflo'rens** (*japonica × salicifolia; S. fortunei semperflorens*)
∞PERPETUAL S.
sinobrahu'ica . . . . **S. yunnanensis**
sorbifo'lia . . . . **Sorbaria s.**
splen'dens (*rosea*)
∞**super'ba** (*albiflora × corymbosa*)
∞STRIPED S.
∞**syringiflo'ra** (*albiflora × salicifolia*)
∞LILAC S.
thun'bergi . . . . . THUNBERG S.
tomento'sa . . . . . HARDHACK S.
—**al'ba** . . . . WHITE H.S.
trichocar'pa . . . . . KOREAN S.
triloba'ta . . . . . THREELOBE S.
∞**tris'tis** (*amoena × ?*)
ulma'ria . . . . **Filipendula u.**
uraten'sis
vacciniifo'lia
vacciniifo'lia Hort., *not* D. Don.
S. canescens
∞**vanhout'tei** (*cantoniensis × trilobata*)
∞VANHOUTTE S.
veitch'i . . . . VEITCH S.
venus'ta . . . . **Filipendula rubra v.**
virga'ta (*myrtilloides*)
virginia'na . . . . VIRGINIA S.
∞**watsonia'na** (*douglasi × splendens*)
wil'soni . . . . WILSON S.
yunnanen'sis (*sinobrahuica*) YUNNAN S.
zabelia'na . . . . ZABEL S.
SPIRALFLAG . . . . **Costus**
CANEREED S. . . . . . . **C. speciosus**
SPIRAN'THES (*IBIDIUM*)
LADIESTRESSES
See **ORCHID GENERA, HARDY TERRESTRIAL GROUP.**
SPIREA . . . . **Spiraea**
ALPINE S. . . . . **S. alpina**
∞APRIL S. . . . . ∞**S. nudiflora**

SPIREA, continued
∞ARCH S. . . . ∞**Spiraea schinabecki**
BIG NIPPON S. **S. nipponica rotundifolia**
∞BILLIARD S. . . . . . . ∞**S. billiardi**
BIRCHLEAF S. . . . . . **S. betulifolia**
BRIDALWREATH S. . . . **S. prunifolia**
BROADLEAF MEADOWSWEET S. **S. latifolia**
∞BUMALDA S. . . . . . ∞**S. bumalda**
CHINESE S. . . . . **S. chinensis**
CRISPLEAF S. . . . . **S. bullata**
DOUGLAS S. . . . . . . **S. douglasi**
ELMLEAF S.
S. chamaedryfolia ulmifolia
∞EVERBLOOMING S. . . ∞**S. revirescens**
∞FONTENAYS S. . . . ∞**S. fontenaysi**
FORTUNES JAPANESE S.
S. japonica fortunei
∞FOX S. . . . . ∞**S. foxi**
∞GARLAND S. . . . . . . ∞**S. arguta**
GERMANDER S. . . **S. chamaedryfolia**
HARDHACK S. . . . . . **S. tomentosa**
HENRY S. . . . . **S. henryi**
HIMALAYAN S. . . . . **S. bella**
HOARY S. . . . . **S. canescens**
JAPANESE S. . . . . **S. japonica**
JAPANESE WHITE S. . . . **S. albiflora**
KOREAN S. . . . . . . **S. trichocarpa**
∞LEMOINE S. . . . . . . ∞**S. lemoinei**
∞LILAC S. . . . . . . ∞**S. syringiflora**
∞MARGARITA S. . . . ∞**S. margaritae**
MENZIES S. . . . . . . **S. menziesi**
MIYABE S. . . . . **S. miyabei**
MONGOLIAN S. . . . . . . **S. gemmata**
NARROWLEAF MEADOWSWEET S. **S. alba**
NIPPON S. . . . . **S. nipponica**
∞NOTHA S. . . . . ∞**S. notha**
ORIENTAL S. . . . . **S. media**
OVALLEAF JAPANESE S.
S. japonica ovalifolia
∞PERPETUAL S. . . ∞**S. semperflorens**
∞PIKOW S. . . . . . . ∞**S. pikoviensis**
∞PYRAMID S. . . . . . ∞**S. pyramidata**
REEVES S. . . . . . . **S. cantoniensis**
ROSTHORN S. . . . . **S. rosthorni**
∞SANSOUCI S. . . . . ∞**S. sansouciana**
SARGENT S. . . . . . . **S. sargentiana**
SHINYLEAF S. . . . . **S. lucida**
∞SHOWY S. . . . . . . ∞**S. conspicua**
SMOOTH JAPANESE S. **S. japonica glabra**
∞SNOWGARLAND S. . . . ∞**S. multiflora**
SNOW S. . . . . **S. crenata**
∞STRIPED S. . . . . ∞**S. superba**
SUBALPINE S. . . . . . **S. densiflora**
TAPERLEAF JAPANESE S.
S. japonica acuminata
THREELOBE S. . . . . . . **S. trilobata**
THUNBERG S. . . . . . . **S. thunbergi**
∞VANHOUTTE S. . . . . ∞**S. vanhouttei**
VEITCH S. . . . . **S. veitchi**
VIRGINIA S. . . . . **S. virginiana**
WHITE HARDHACK S. **S. tomentosa alba**
WILLOWLEAF S. . . . . . . **S. salicifolia**
WILSON S. . . . . **S. wilsoni**
∞WINTER S. . . . . ∞**S. brumalis**
YUNNAN S. . . . . . . **S. yunnanensis**
ZABEL S. . . . . **S. zabeliana**
SPIRODE'LA |w . . . . . . DUCKSMEAT
polyrhi'za |w . . . . . . COMMON D.
SPIROGY'RA |w . . . . PONDSCUM
protec'ta . . . . COMMON P.
SPIRONE'MA
fra'grans
SPLEENWORT . . . **Asplenium; Athyrium**
BELANGER S. . . **Asplenium belangeri**
BLACKSTEM S. . . . . **A. resiliens**
BUD S. . . . . **A. gemmiferum**
EBONY S. . . . . **A. platyneuron**

SPLEENWORT, continued
GLOSSY S. . . . . **Asplenium lucidum**
GOERING S. . . **Athyrium goeringianum**
GREEN S. . . . . . **Asplenium viride**
LONGLEAF S. . . . . . **A. longissimum**
MAIDENHAIR S. . . . . **A. trichomanes**
MAURITIUS S. . . . . . . **A. viviparum**
MOTHER S. . . . . **A. bulbiferum**
MOUNTAIN S. . . . . **A. montanum**
NARROWLEAF S. **Athyrium pycnocarpon**
SILVERY S. . . . . . **A. thelypteroides**
STAR S. . . . . **Asplenium palmatum**
SPON'DIAS . . . . MOMBIN
cythere'a (*dulcis*) . . . . AMBARELLA
(*Otaheiteapple; Viapple*)
mom'bin (*axillaris; lutea*) YELLOW M.
pinna'ta . . . . ANDAMAN M.
purpu'rea . . . . PURPLE M.
solan'dri . . . . **Pleiogynium s.**
tubero'sa . . . . IMBU M.
SPORO'BOLUS . . . . DROPSEED
See **GRASS GENERA.**
SPOTFLOWER . . . . **Spilanthes**
PARACRESS S. . . . . **S. oleracea**
Spottedgum . . EUCALYPTUS, SPOTTED:
Eucalyptus maculata
SPRAG'UEA . . . . PUSSYPAWS
umbella'ta . . . . UMBELLATE P.
—**candicif'era** (*multiceps*). MT. HOOD P.
SPRANGLETOP . . . . **Leptochloa**
AMAZON S. . . . . . . **L. panicoides**
ARGENTINE S. . . **L. chloridiformis**
BEARDED S. . . . . . **L. fascicularis**
DOMINICAN S. . . . **L. domingensis**
GREEN S. . . . . **L. dubia**
MEXICAN S. . . . . **L. uninervia**
NEALLEY S. . . . . **L. nealleyi**
RED S. . . . . **L. filiformis**
ROUGH S. . . . . **L. scabra**
STICKY S. . . . . **L. viscida**
TROPICS S. . . . . **L. virgata**
SPREKE'LIA . AZTECLILY (*Jacobeanlily; St. Jameslily*)
formosis'sima (*Amaryllis f.*) AZTECLILY
—**glau'ca** . . . . PALE A.
SPRINGBEAUTY . . . . **Claytonia**
ALPINE S. . . . . . . **C. megarrhiza**
CAROLINA S. . . . . . **C. caroliniana**
LANCELEAF S. . . . . . . **C. lanceolata**
LITTLELEAF S. . . . . . . **C. parvifolia**
MINERSLETTUCE . . . . . **C. perfoliata**
NEVADA S. . . . . **C. nevadensis**
TUBER S. . . . . **C. tuberosa**
VIRGINIA S. . . . . **C. virginica**
WATER S. . . . . **C. chamissoi**
SPRUCE . . . . **Picea**
ALBERTA WHITE S. **P. glauca albertiana**
ALCOCK S. . . . . **P. bicolor**
ALPINE SIBERIAN S. **P. obovata alpestris**
BALFOUR S. **P. likiangensis balfouriana**
BIGCONE DRAGON S.
P. asperata ponderosa
BLACK HILLS WHITE S. **P. glauca densata**
BLACK NORWAY S. . . . **P. abies nigra**
BLACK S. . . . . **P. mariana**
BREWER S. . . . . **P. breweriana**
CANDELABRA S. . . . . . **P. montigena**
COLORADO S. . . . . **P. pungens**
CURLLEAF ALCOCK S. **P. bicolor reflexa**
DIAMONDSCALE SARGENT S.
P. brachytyla rhombisquamae
DRAGON S. . . . . **P. asperata**
ENGELMANN S. . . . . . **P. engelmanni**
FINNISH SIBERIAN S. **P. obovata fennica**

SPRUCE, continued
GRAYBARK SARGENT S. **Picea brachytyla complanata**
GREENCONE NORWAY S. **P. abies chlorocarpa**
HIMALAYAN S. . . . . . . **P. smithiana**
HONDO YEDDO S. **P. jezoensis hondoensis**
KOYAMA S. . . . . **P. koyamai**
LIKIANG S. . . . . . **P. likiangensis**
MAXIMOWICZ S. . . **P. maximowiczi**
MEYER S. . . . . **P. meyeri**
∞ MOSER S. . . . . **∞ P. moseri**
NARROWSCALE DRAGON S. **P. asperata notabilis**
NORWAY S. . . . . **P. abies**
∞ NOTHA S. . . . . **∞ P. notha**
ORIENTAL S. . . . . . . **P. orientalis**
PURPLECONE NORWAY S. **P. abies erythrocarpa**
PURPLECONE S. . . . . . **P. purpurea**
RED S. . . . . **P. rubens**
REDTWIG DRAGON S. **P. asperata heterolepis**
∞ SAAGHY S. . . . . **∞ P. saaghyi**
SAKHALIN S. . . . . **P. glehni**
SARGENT S. . . . . . . **P. brachytyla**
SCHRENK S. . . . . . **P. schrenkiana**
SERBIAN S. . . . . **P. omorika**
SIBERIAN S. . . . . **P. obovata**
SIKKIM S. . . . . **P. spinulosa**
SITKA S. . . . . **P. sitchensis**
TIGERTAIL S. . . . . **P. polita**
WHITE S. . . . . **P. glauca**
WHOLESCALE ALCOCK S. **P. bicolor acicularis**
WILSON S. . . . . **P. wilsoni**
YEDDO S. . . . . **P. jezoensis**
YELLOWTWIG S. . . . **P. aurantiaca**

SPRUCEBUSH . . . . . . **Peucephyllum**
SCHOTTS S. . . . . **P. schotti**

SPURFLOWER . . . . **Plectranthus**

SPURGE
A plant belonging to the Spurge family (Euphorbiaceae). As the name cannot be confined to any one genus, it is employed in S. P. N. as a suffix or prefix only.

SPURGENTIAN . . . . **Halenia**
AMERICAN S. . . . . **H. deflexa**

SPURGEOLIVE . . . . **Cneorum tricoccon**

SPURRY . . . . **Spergula**
CORN S. . . . . **S. arvensis**
FIELD S. . . . . **S. sativa**
WINGSEED S. . . . . . . **S. pentandra**

SPYRID'IUM
globulo'sum

SQUASH, WINTER . . **Cucurbita maxima**

SQUAWAPPLE **Peraphyllum ramosissimum**

Squawbush . . . CONDALIA, KNIFELEAF: **Condalia spathulata;** DOGWOOD, RED-OSIER: **Cornus stolonifera;** SUMAC, SKUNKBUSH: **Rhus trilobata;** WOLFBERRY: **Lycium**

SQUILL . . . . **Scilla**
AUTUMN S. . . . . . **S. autumnalis**
AZURE PERUVIAN S. **S. peruviana caerulea**
CHINESE S. . . . . . . **S. chinensis**
COBALT TWINLEAF S. **S. bifolia splendens**
COMMON BLUE S. . . . . **S. nonscripta**
HYACINTH S. . . . . **S. hyacinthoides**
ITALIAN S. . . . . **S. italica**
MEADOW S. . . . . **S. pratensis**
NATAL S. . . . . **S. natalensis**
PERUVIAN S. . . . . . . **S. peruviana**
PINK TWINLEAF S. . . **S. bifolia rosea**

SQUILL, continued
RED TWINLEAF S. **Scilla bifolia ruberrima**
ROSE SPANISH S. . **S. hispanica rosea**
SIBERIAN S. . . . . **S. sibirica**
SPANISH S. . . . . **S. hispanica**
SPRING S. . . . . **S. verna**
STARHYACINTH S. . . . . . **S. amoena**
TWINLEAF S. . . . . **S. bifolia**
WHITE PERUVIAN S.. **S. peruviana alba**
WHITE SPANISH S. . . **S. hispanica a.**
WHITE TWINLEAF S. . . **S. bifolia a.**

SQUIRRELCORN . . **Dicentra canadensis**

SQUIRRELTAIL . . . . **Sitanion**
BIG S. . . . . **S. jubatum**
BOTTLEBRUSH S. . . . . . **S. hystrix**
HANSEN S. . . . . **S. hanseni**

SQUIRTINGCUCUMBER **Ecballium; E. elaterium**

STACHYOPHOR'BE **CHAMAEDOREA**

STA'CHYS (*BETONICA*) |w . BETONY (*Woundwort*)
agra'ria . . . . SHADE B.
alpi'na . . . . ALPINE B.
an'nua . . . . HEDGENETTLE B.
arven'sis . . . . . . FIELDNETTLE B.
as'pera . . . . . . ROUGHNETTLE B.
bulla'ta . . . . PUFFNETTLE B.
cilia'ta . . . . OREGON B.
coccin'ea . . . . TEXAS B.
cor'sica . . . . CORSICA B.
florida'na . . . . FLORIDA B.
german'ica . . . . MOUSEEAR B.
grandiflo'ra (*S. rosea g.; B. g.*) . BIG B.
—robus'ta . . . . ROSY B.B.
—super'ba (*Betonica s.*) . MAUVE B.B.
lana'ta . . . . WOOLLY B.
lavandulaefo'lia . LAVENDERLEAF B.
officina'lis (*Betonica o.*) COMMON B.
palus'tris |w . . . . MARSH B.
scar'dica . . . . GREEK B.
seric'ea . . . . HIMALAYA B.
sie'boldi . . . ARTICHOKE B. (*Chinese Artichoke; Japanese A.; Chorogi*)
sylvat'ica . . . . . . WHITESPOT B.
tenuifo'lia |w . . . . SLENDERLEAF B.
tmo'lea . . . . MT.TMOLUS B.

STACHYTAR'PHETA (*VALERIANOIDES*) . . . . FALSEVALERIAN
coccin'ea . . . . SCARLET F.
jamaicen'sis (*indica*) . . JAMAICA F.
mutab'ilis . . . . VARIABLE F.

STACHYU'RUS
chinen'sis
prae'cox

STAGHORNFERN . . . . . **Platycerium**
ANGOLA S. . . . . . . **P. angolense**
AUSTRALIAN S. . . . . . . **P. veitchi**
COMMON S. . . . . . . **P. bifurcatum**
DISK S. . . . . **P. coronarium**
GIANT S. . . . . **P. grande**
GREATER GREEN S. . . **P. hilli majus**
GREEN S. . . . . **P. hilli**
INDIA S. . . . . **P. wallichi**
JAVA S. . . . . **P. willincki**
TRIANGLE S. . . . . **P. stemaria**

ST.ANDREWSCROSS **Ascyrum hypericoides**

STANGE'RIA . . . . . FERNCYCAD
See **CYCAD GENERA.**

STANHO'PEA
See **ORCHID GENERA.**

STAN'LEYA . . . . . . PRINCESPLUME
albes'cens . . . . ARIZONA P.
bipinna'ta . . . . ALKALI P.

STANLEYA, continued
ela'ta . . . PANAMINT PRINCESPLUME
pinna'ta (*arcuata; glauca*) . DESERT P.
—integrifo'lia (*S. integrifolia*) WHOLELEAF D.P.

Stanleyel'la wright'i . . **Thelypodium w.**

STAPE'LIA . . . . . CARRIONFLOWER
See **SUCCULENTS.**

STAPHYLE'A . . . . . . BLADDERNUT
boland'eri . . . . SIERRA B.
bumal'da . . . . BUMALDA B.
col'chica . . . . COLCHIS B.
—coulombier'i . . . . . . FRENCH B.
—kochia'na . . . . KOCHS B.
∞ **el'egans** (*colchica* × *pinnata*)
¢HESSE (*hessei*) HV.
emo'di . . . . HIMALAYAN B.
holocar'pa . . . . CHINESE B.
—rose'a . . . . PINK C.B.
pinna'ta . . . . EUROPEAN B.
trifo'lia (*trifoliata*) . . AMERICAN B.
—pauciflo'ra . . . . . . DWARF A.B.

STARAPPLE . . . . **Chrysophyllum**
AFRICAN S. . . . . . . **C. africanum**
CAINITO S. . . . . **C. cainito**
SATINLEAF S. . . . . . . **C. oliviforme**

STARBUR . . . . **Acanthospermum**
PARAGUAY S. . . . . . . **A. australe**

STARBUSH . . . . **Turraea**
BLUNTLEAF S. . . . . **T. obtusifolia**

STARCACTUS . . . . **Astrophytum**
BISHOPSHOOD S. . . **A. myriostigma**
GOATHORN S. . . . . **A. capricorne**
SEAURCHIN S. . . . . . . **A. asterias**

STARCHES (Plant Sources of)
See **ECONOMIC PLANTS, STARCHES.**

STARCLUSTERS . . . . **Pentas**
EGYPTIAN S. . . . . . **P. lanceolata**
SCARLET S. . . . . **P. coccinea**

STARFLOWER . . . . **Trientalis**
AMERICAN S. . . . . **T. borealis**
EUROPEAN S. . . . . . . **T. europaea**
WESTERN S. . . . . **T. latifolia**

STARGLORY . . . . **Quamoclit**
CARDINAL S. . . . . **Q. sloteri**
CRIMSON S. . . . . **Q. lobata**
CYPRESSVINE S. . . . . . **Q. pennata**
IVY S. . . . . **Q. coccinea hederifolia**
SCARLET S. . . . . **Q. coccinea**
WHITE CYPRESSVINE S. **Q. pennata alba**

STARGRASS . . . . **Aletris**
WHITETUBE S. . . . . . . **A. farinosa**

Stargrass . WINDMILLGRASS, CREEPING: **Chloris truncata**

STARJASMINE . . . . **Trachelospermum**
CHINESE S. . . . . . **T. jasminoides**
JAPANESE S. . . . . . . **T. asiaticum**

STARLILY . . . . **Leucocrinum**
COMMON S. . . . . . . **L. montanum**

STAR-OF-BETHLEHEM . . **Ornithogalum**
ARABIAN S. . . . . **O. arabicum**
CAPE CHINKERICHEE . **O. thyrsoides**
COMMON S. . . . . . **O. umbellatum**
GLOWING S. . . . . **O. splendens**
GOLDEN CAPE CHINKERICHEE **O. thyrsoides aureum**
GRASSY S. . . . . . **O. graminifolium**
KEW CHINKERICHEE . ×**O. kewense**
MILK S. . . . . **O. lacteum**
NARBONNE S. . . . . **O. narbonense**
NODDING S. . . . . **O. nutans**
PYRAMID S. . . . . . . **O. pyramidale**
SHOWY S. . . . . **O. speciosum**

STAR-OF-BETHLEHEM, continued
- SWEET S. . Ornithogalum suaveolens
- THUNBERG S. . . O. thunbergianum
- WHIPLASH S. . . . . . O. caudatum

STAR-OF-TEXAS . . **Xanthisma texanum**

STARPINK . . . . **Chironia**
- CHIRONIA S. . . . . . . **C. ixifera**

STARTHORN . . . . **Hygrophila spinosa**

STARTREE . . . . **Astronium**
- ASHLEAF S. . . . . **A. fraxinifolium**
- FETID S. . . . . **A. graveolens**

Startulip
- *Douglas S.* . . . . MARIPOSA, DOUGLAS: **Calochortus douglasianus**
- *Least S.* . . . LEAST M.: **C. minimus**
- *Longhair S.* . . . . . . LONGHAIR M.: **C. longebarbatus**
- *Lyall S.* . . . . . LYALL M.: **C. lyalli**
- *Monterey S.* MONTEREY M.: **C. uniflorus**
- *Oakland S.* OAKLAND M.: **C. umbellatus**
- *Persistent S.* . . . . PERSISTENT M.: **C. persistens**

Startulip, continued
- *Sierra S.* . . . SIERRA M.: **C. nudus**

STARWORT . . . . **Stellaria**
- BOG S. . . . . **S. uliginosa**
- CHICKWEED . . . . **S. media**
- EASTERBELL S. . . . . . **S. holostea**
- GREAT S. . . . . **S. pubera**
- LITTLE S. . . . . **S. graminea**
- LONGSTALK S. . . . . . **S. longipes**
- LOW S. . . . . **S. humifusa**
- NORTHERN S. . . . . . **S. borealis**
- TUBER S. . . . . . . **S. jamesiana**

STATE FLOWERS AND TREES

STATE	STATE FLOWER Year of Adoption	STATE TREE Year of Adoption	SOURCE OF INFORMATION
Alabama	GOLDENROD **Solidago** spp.	None	B. P. Livingston, Chf., Div. Plant Ind., St. Dept. Agr., Montgomery, Ala.
Alaska	FORGETMENOT (1917) **Myosotis alpestris**	None	J. P. Anderson, Bot., Juneau, Alaska.
Arizona	SAGUARO (1933) **Cereus giganteus**	None	Harriet Jean Oliver, Sec., Comm. Agr. & Hort., Phoenix, Ariz.
Arkansas	"APPLE BLOSSOM" **Malus**	PINE (1939) **Pinus** spp.	H. E. Thompson, Asst. Dir., Coop. Extension Work in Agr. & Home Econ., Little Rock, Ark.
California	GOLDENPOPPY (1903) Californiapoppy-SPN **Eschscholtzia californica**	"CALIFORNIA REDWOOD" (1937) Redwood-SPN **Sequoia sempervirens**	W. B. Parker, Dir., St. Dept. Agr., Sacramento, Calif.
Colorado	COLORADO COLUMBINE **Aquilegia coerulea**	BLUE COLORADO SPRUCE **Picea pungens glauca**	F. Herbert Gates, St. Entom., Bur. Pl. & Insect Control, Denver, Colo.
Connecticut	"MOUNTAINLAUREL" (1907) Mountainlaurel Kalmia-SPN **Kalmia latifolia**	None	Olcott F. King, Comm., St. Dept. Agr., Hartford, Conn.
Delaware	PEACH BLOSSOM (1895?) **Prunus persica**	"HOLLY" (1939) American Holly-SPN **Ilex opaca**	V. J. Carmine, Sec., St. Bd. Agr., Dover, Del.
Florida	ORANGE BLOSSOM (1909) **Citrus** spp.	"CABBAGEPALM" (*Not official*) Cabbage Palmetto-SPN **Sabal palmetto**	R. A. Gray, Sec. of St., Tallahassee, Fla.
Georgia	CHEROKEE ROSE (1916) **Rosa laevigata**	LIVE OAK (1937) **Quercus virginiana**	Stiles A. Martin, Statis., St. Dept. Agr., Atlanta, Ga.
Hawaii	"PUA ALOALO" (1923) Hibiscus-SPN **Hibiscus** spp.	"COCOANUT PALM" Coconut-SPN **Cocos nucifera**	J. L. Dwight, Exec. Sec., Bd. of Comm. Agr. & For., Honolulu, T. H.
Idaho	LEWIS MOCKORANGE (1931) **Philadelphus lewisi**	None	George H. Curtis, Sec. of St., Boise, Idaho.
Illinois	"NATIVE VIOLET" (1908) **Viola** spp.	"NATIVE OAK" (1937) **Quercus** spp.	Milburn P. Akers, Supt., St. Dept. Finance, Springfield, Ill.
Indiana	COMMON ZINNIA (1931) **Zinnia elegans**	TULIPTREE (1931) **Liriodendron tulipifera**	H. C. Gray, Sec., Indiana Historical Bur., Indianapolis, Ind.
Iowa	"WILD ROSE" (1897) **Rosa** spp.	None	Mark G. Thornburg, Sec., St. Dept. Agr., Des Moines, Ia.
Kansas	COMMON SUNFLOWER (1903) **Helianthus annuus**	COTTONWOOD (1937) **Populus** spp.	J. C. Mohler, Sec., Kans. St. Bd. Agr., Topeka, Kans., & H. C. Gates, Kans. St. Coll. Agr. & Appl. Sc., Manhattan, Kans.
Kentucky	GOLDENROD (1926) **Solidago** spp.	TULIPTREE (*Unofficial*) **Liriodendron tulipifera**	Garth K. Ferguson, Comm. Agr., Frankfort, Ky.
Louisiana	"MAGNOLIA" (1900) Southern Magnolia-SPN **Magnolia grandiflora**	None	Harry D. Wilson, Comm., St. Dept. Agr. & Immig., Baton Rouge, La.
Maine	"PINE CONE & TASSEL"? (1895?) **Pinus strobus?**	"Pine" Eastern White Pine-SPN **Pinus strobus**	Frank P. Washburn, Comm., St. Dept. Agr., Augusta, Me.; & C. W. Johnson, Springfield, Mass.
Maryland	BLACKEYEDSUSAN (1918) **Rudbeckia hirta**	None	J. E. Metzger, Dir., Agr. Expt. Sta., College Park, Md.
Massachusetts	TRAILING-ARBUTUS **Epigaea repens**	None	R. B. Allen, Dir., Div. Pl. Pest Cont., St. Dept. Agr., Boston, Mass.
Michigan	"APPLE BLOSSOM" **Malus**	None	H. D. Hootman, Ext. Spec. Hort., St. Coll. Agr., E. Lansing, Mich.
Minnesota	SHOWY LADYSLIPPER (1902) **Cypripedium reginae**	None	C. P. Bull, Dir., Div. Weed & Seed Cont., St. Dept. Agr., St. Paul, Minn.

State	State Flower Year of Adoption	State Tree Year of Adoption	Source of Information
Mississippi	"Magnolia" (1900) Southern Magnolia-SPN **Magnolia grandiflora**	"Magnolia" (1938) Southern Magnolia-SPN **Magnolia grandiflora**	Mrs. G. H. Reeves, Educ. Dir., Forest & Park Svc., Jackson, Miss.
Missouri	"Hawthorn" **Crataegus** spp.	None	Jewell Mayes, Comm., St. Dept. Agr., Jefferson City, Mo.
Montana	Bitterroot (1895) Bitterroot Lewisia-SPN **Lewisia rediviva**	None	Lois Fladeger, Sec. to James T. Sparling, Comm., St. Dept. Agr., Labor & Industry, Helena, Mont.
Nebraska	Goldenrod (1895) November Goldenrod-SPN **Solidago serotina**	None	R. C. Kinch, St. Dept. Agr., Lincoln, Nebr.
Nevada	"Sagebrush" Big Sagebrush-SPN **Artemisia tridentata**	None	Geo. G. Schweis, Dir., Div. Pl. Ind., St. Dept. Agr., Reno, Nev.
New Hampshire	Purple Lilac Common Lilac-SPN **Syringa vulgaris**	None	Enoch D. Fuller, Sec. of St., Concord, N. H.
New Jersey	Violet (1913) **Viola** spp.	None	Kathryn B. Greywacz, Curator, N. J. St. Museum, Trenton, N. J.
New Mexico	Yucca **Yucca** spp.	None	F. F. Whitley, Ext. Hort., Ext. Svc., State College, N. M.
New York	Rose (*Unofficial*) **Rosa** spp.	None	H. D. House, St. Bot., N. Y. St. Museum, Albany, N. Y.
North Carolina	None	None	Harry T. Davis, St. Dept. Agr., Raleigh, N. C.
North Dakota	"Wild Prairie Rose" (1907) Arkansas Rose-SPN **Rosa arkansana**	Green Ash (*Unofficial*) **Fraxinus pennsylvanica lanceolata**	M. Quinnell, Dept. Agr. & Labor, Bismarck; O. A. Stevens, N. D. Agr. College, Fargo, N. D.
Ohio	"Scarlet Carnation" (1904) **Dianthus caryophyllus**	"Buckeye" (*Unofficial*) Ohio Buckeye-SPN **Aesculus glabra**	John T. Brown, St. Dir. Agr., Columbus, Ohio.
Oklahoma	American Mistletoe Christmas Am.-mistletoe-SPN **Phoradendron flavescens**	"Redbud Tree" Eastern Redbud-SPN **Cercis canadensis**	Joe C. Scott, Pres., St. Bd. of Agr., Oklahoma City, Okla.
Oregon	Oregongrape (1899) **Mahonia aquifolium**	Douglasfir (1939) Common Douglasfir-SPN **Pseudotsuga taxifolia**	Frank McKennon, Div. Chf., St. Dept. Agr., Salem, Ore.
Pennsylvania	"Mountainlaurel" (1933) Mountainlaurel Kalmia-SPN **Kalmia latifolia**	Hemlock (1931) Canada Hemlock-SPN **Tsuga canadensis**	John S. Light, Sec., St. Dept. Agr., Harrisburg, Penna.
Puerto Rico	None	None	F. A. Lopez Dominguez, Dept. Agr. & Comm., San Juan, P. R.
Rhode Island	Violet (1897) **Viola** spp.	Maple (1894) **Acer** spp.	A. E. Stone, St. Entom., St. Dept. Agr. & Cons., Providence, R. I.
South Carolina	"Yellow Jessamine" Carolinajessamine-SPN **Gelsemium sempervirens**	Palmetto (1939) Cabbage Palmetto-SPN **Sabal palmetto**	A. S. Salley, Sec., Hist. Comm. of S. C., Columbia, S. C.
South Dakota	American Pasqueflower **Anemone ludoviciana**	Cottonwood (*Unofficial*) **Populus** spp.	E. H. Everson, Sec., St. Dept. Agr., Pierre, S. D.
Tennessee	Iris **Iris** spp.	None	C. C. Flanery, Comm., St. Dept Agr., Nashville, Tenn.
Texas	"Texas Bluebonnet" Texas Lupine-SPN **Lupinus subcarnosus**	"Pecan Tree" Pecan-SPN **Carya illinoensis** (*pecan* Auth.)	B. C. Tharp, Univ. Tex., Austin, Tex.
Utah	Segolily (1911) Segolily Mariposa-SPN **Calochortus nuttalli**	"Blue Spruce" (1933) Blue Colorado Spruce-SPN **Picea pungens glauca**	E. E. Monson, Sec. of St., Salt Lake City, Utah.
Vermont	Red Clover (1894) **Trifolium pratense**	Sugar Maple (*Unofficial*) **Acer saccharum**	E. H. Jones, Comm., St. Dept. Agr., Montpelier, Vt.
Virginia	"American Dogwood" (1918) Flowering Dogwood-SPN **Cornus florida**	"American Dogwood" (1918) Flowering Dogwood-SPN **Cornus florida**	Margaret A. Young, Sec., Dept. Agr. & Immig., Richmond, Va.
Washington	Rhododendron Coast Rhododendron-SPN **Rhododendron macrophyllum**	None	Walter J. Robinson, Dir., St. Dept. Agr., Olympia, Wash.
West Virginia	"Big Laurel or Rhododendron" (1903) Rosebay Rhododendron-SPN **Rhododendron maximum**	None	J. B. McLaughlin, Comm., St. Dept. Agr., Charleston, W. Va.
Wisconsin	Violet (*Unofficial*) **Viola** spp.	None	Bronte H. Leicht, Editor, St. Dept. Agr., Madison, Wis.
Wyoming	Indian Paintbrush (1917) Wyoming Paintedcup-SPN **Castilleja linariaefolia**	None	George O. Houser, Exec. Mgr., St. Dept. Comm. & Indus., Cheyenne, Wyo.

STAT'ICE . **ARMERIA; LIMONIUM**
arme'ria . . . . . **Armeria maritima**
auriculaefo'lia **Limonium binervosum**
bonduel'li . . . . **Limonium b.**
brasilien'sis . . **Limonium brasiliense**
brassicaefo'lia
Limonium brassicaefolium
bupleuroi'des . . . . . . **Armeria b.**
×*caesalpi'na* . . . . ∞**Armeria c.**
caespito'sa . . . . **Armeria c.**
canes'cens . . . . **Armeria c.**
carolinia'na . **Limonium carolinianum**
cas'pia . . **Limonium reticulatum**
dianthoi'des . . **Armeria plantaginea**
elonga'ta . . . . **Armeria e.**
exim'ia . . . . **Limonium eximium**
formo'sa Hort. **Armeria pseudoarmeria**
gmeli'ni . . . . **Limonium g.**
hal'leri . . . . **Armeria h.**
imbrica'ta . . **Limonium imbricatum**
inca'na
Limonium tataricum angustifolium
—al'ba . . **Limonium t. angustifolium**
—na'na . . . . **Limonium t. nanum**
jun'cea . . . . . . **Armeria setacea**
latifo'lia . . . **Armeria pseudoarmeria**
lauchea'na . . . **Armeria maritima l.**
leucoceph'ala . . . . **Armeria l.**
limo'nium califor'nica
Limonium californicum
macrophyl'la **Limonium macrophyllum**
mauritan'ica . . . . . . **Armeria m.**
monta'na . . . . **Armeria m.**
pectina'ta . . . **Limonium pectinatum**
perez'i . . . . **Limonium p.**
plantagin'ea . . . . . . **Armeria p.**
pseudoarme'ria . . . . . **Armeria p.**
—cephalo'tes . . . . **Armeria p. rubra**
pun'gens . . . . **Armeria p.**
purpu'rea . . . . **Armeria p.**
sinua'ta . . . . **Limonium sinuatum**
suworo'wi . . . . . . **Limonium s.**
tatar'ica . . . . **Limonium tataricum**
vulga'ris . . . . . **Armeria maritima**

St. Augustinegrass
Stenotaphrum secundatum

STAUNTO'NIA . . . . Stauntonvine
hexaphyl'la . . . . Japanese S.
latifo'lia . . . . **Holboellia l.**

Stauntonvine . . . . **Stauntonia**
Japanese S. . . . . . . **S. hexaphylla**

St.Bernardlily . . **Anthericum liliago**

St.Brunolily . **Paradisea; P. liliastrum**
Great S. . . . . **P. l. major**

STEGNOSPER'MA
halimifo'lium

STEIRONE'MA |w . . . . Steironema
cilia'tum (*Lysimachia ciliata*) |w
Fringed S.
lanceola'tum . . . . . Lanceleaf S.
pu'milum . . . . Low S.
quadriflo'rum . . . . Prairie S.

STELECHOCAR'PUS
bura'hol

STELLA'RIA (*ALSINE*) |w . Starwort
borea'lis |w . . . . . . Northern S.
gramin'ea (*Alsine g.*) . . . Little S.
holos'tea (*Alsine h.*) . Easterbell S.
humifu'sa . . . . Low S.
jamesia'na (*Alsine j.*) . . Tuber S.
lon'gipes . . . . Longstalk S.
me'dia |w . . . . Chickweed
pu'bera (*Alsine p.*) |w . . . Great S.
uligino'sa . . . . Bog S.

STENAC'TIS . . . . . . **ERIGERON**

STENAN'DRIUM
lin'deni

STENAN'THIUM . . . Stenanthium
gramin'eum (*angustifolium*)
Grassleaf S.
occidenta'le . . . . . . Western S.
robus'tum . . . . Featherfleece S.

STENOCAC'TUS (*ECHINOFOSSULOCACTUS*)
See **CACTUS GENERA.**

STENOCA'LYX . . . . . **EUGENIA**
michel'i . . . . **E. uniflora**

STENOCAR'PUS . . Firewheeltree
cunningham'i . . . Cunningham F.
This name is often misapplied to S. sinuatus.
salig'nus . . . . Willow F.
sinua'tus . . . . Tall F.

STENOCHLAE'NA . . . Stenochlaena
See **FERN GENERA.**

STENOGLOT'TIS
See **ORCHID GENERA.**

STENOLO'BIUM . . Yellowtrumpet
garro'cha (*Tecoma g.*) . Argentine Y.
stans' (*Bignonia s.; Tecoma s.*)
Florida Y.
—angusta'tum (*Tecoma stans angustata*)
Hardy Y.
—veluti'num (*S. velutinum; Tecoma mollis; T. s. velutina; T. velutina*)
Velvety F.Y.

STENOMES'SON . . . Stenomesson
auranti'acum . . . . . . Orange S.
coccin'eum . . . . Scarlet S.
cro'ceum . . . . Yellow S.
fla'vum . . . . Golden S.
incarna'tum . . . . . . Crimson S.
ru'brum . . . . Red S.

STENOPHRAG'MA. . **SISYMBRIUM**

STENOPHYL'LUS. . **BULBOSTYLIS**

STENOSPERMA'TION
multiovula'tum
popayanen'se

STENOTA'PHRUM
See **GRASS GENERA.**

STENOTOP'SIS . . **APLOPAPPUS**

STENO'TUS . . . . **APLOPAPPUS**
caespito'sus . . . . . . **A. falcatus**

STEPHANAN'DRA . Stephanandra
chinen'sis . . . . Chinese S.
inci'sa (*flexuosa; Spiraea i.*)
Cutleaf S.
tana'kae . . . . Tanaka S.

STEPHANOCE'REUS
CEPHALOCEREUS
See **CACTUS GENERA.**

STEPHANOME'RIA (*PTILORIA*) |w
Wirelettuce
cichoria'cea . . . . Tejon W.
runcina'ta . . . . Desert W.

STEPHANOPHY'SUM . . **RUELLIA**
longifo'lium . . . . . . **R. amoena**

STEPHANOSTA'CHYS
CHAMAEDOREA
See **PALM GENERA.**

STEPHANO'TIS . . . . Stephanotis
floribun'da . . . . Madagascar S.
(*Madagascar-jasmine*)

STERCU'LIA . . . . . . Sterculia
acerifo'lia . . **Brachychiton acerifolius**
ala'ta . . . . **Pterygota a.**
apet'ala (*carthaginensis*) . . Coolie S.
bid'willi . . . . **Brachychiton b.**
caribae'a . . . . Carib S.
dis'color . . . . **Brachychiton d.**
diversifo'lia . **Brachychiton populneus**
foe'tida . . . . Hazel S.
ful'gens
lanceola'ta
lur'ida . . . . **Brachychiton luridus**
platanifo'lia . . . **Firmiana simplex**
—variega'ta . . . . **Firmiana s. v.**
rupes'tris . . . . . **Brachychiton r.**
u'rens . . . . Kuteeragum S.
¢Sexton (*sextoni*) hv. Sterculia

STEREOSPER'MUM . . Padritree
fimbria'tum (*Bignonia fimbriata*)
Fringed P.
si'nicum . . . . . **Radermachia sinica**
suave'olens

STE'REUM . . . . Stereum
frustulo'sum . . . Honeycombrot S.

STERIPHO'MA . . . . . Steriphoma
ellip'ticum . . . . Trinidad S.
paradox'um . . . . . Venezuela S.

STERNBERG'IA . . . . Sternbergia
colchiciflo'ra . . . . . Colchicum S.
lute'a (*Amaryllis l.*) . . Falldaffodil

STETSO'NIA . . . . **CEREUS**
See **CACTUS GENERA.**

STEVENSO'NIA (*PHOENICOPHORIUM; STEPHENSONIA*)
Stevensonpalm
See **PALM GENERA.**

Stevensonpalm . . . . . **Stevensonia**
Feather S. . . . . . . **S. borsigiana**

STE'VIA . . . . Stevia
ivaefo'lia . . . . Ivaleaf S.
purpu'rea . . . . Purple S.
salicifo'lia . . . . . . Willowleaf S.
serra'ta . . . . Sawtooth S.
serra'ta Hort., *not* Cav.
Piqueria trinervia

STEWART'IA (*STUARTIA*) Stewartia
grandiflo'ra . . . **S. pseudocamellia**
korea'na . . . . Korean S.
malacoden'dron (*virginica*) Virginia S.
monadel'pha . . . . Tall S.
ova'ta (*pentagyna*) . . Mountain S.
—grandiflo'ra (*S. pentagyna g.*)
Showy M.S.
pseudocamel'lia (*grandiflora*)
Japanese S.
serra'ta
sinen'sis . . . . Chinese S.
virgin'ica . . . . . . **S. malacodendron**

Stickseed . . . . **Lappula**
European S. . . . . **L. echinata**

STIC'TA . . . . Sticta
croca'ta . . . . Yellow S.
pulmona'ria (*Lobaria p.*) Lungwort S.
scrobicula'ta . . . . Pitted S.

Stiffgrass . . . **Scleropoa; S. rigida**

STIFF'TIA . . . . Stifftia
chrysan'tha . . . . Brazil S.

STIGMAPHYL'LON . . . Amazonvine
bogoten'se . . . Bogota A.
cilia'tum . . . Fringed A.
ful'gens
ledifo'lium . . . Ledumleaf A.
lingula'tum
littora'le . . . Argentine A.
sagraea'num

STILBOCAR'PA
ly'alli
pola'ris

STILLIN'GIA |w . . . Stillingia
aquat'ica |w . . . Corkwood S.
denta'ta |w
linearifo'lia . . . Desert S.
sebif'era . . . **Sapium sebiferum**
sylvat'ica |w . . . Queensdelight S.

Stingbush . . . **Eucnide urens**

Stinglily . . . **Blumenbachia**
Redspot S. . . . **B. insignis**

Stinkbush, Mediterranean
Anagyris foetida

Stinkdragon . . . **Dracunculus**
Canary S. . . . **D. canariensis**
Common S. . . . **D. vulgaris**

Stinkgrass . . . **Eragrostis cilianensis**

Stinkingcedar . . . Torreya, Florida: **Torreya taxifolia**

STI'PA . Needlegrass; Feathergrass
See **GRASS GENERA.**

STIZOLO'BIUM |w . . . Velvetbean
Mucuna is conserved under International Rules as against Stizolobium, but L. H. Bailey recognizes Stizolobium as valid, distinct from Mucuna.
ater'rimum . . . Bengal V.
deeringia'num (*Mucuna deeringiana*) Deering V.
Known in the trade as Florida V.
hass'joo . . . Yokohama V.
niv'eum . . . Chinese V. (*Lyon Bean*)
pachylo'bium
pruri'tum (*pruriens; Mucuna p.*) Cowage V.
rostra'tum . . . Beaked V.
sloan'ei . . . Sloane V.
u'rens . . . **Mucuna u.**
u'tile (*Mucuna utilis*)

St.Jameslily . . . Azteclily: **Sprekelia**

St.Johnsbread . Carob: **Ceratonia siliqua**

St.Johnswort . . . **Hypericum**
Aaronsbeard S. . . . **H. calycinum**
∞ Arnold S. . . . ∞ **H. arnoldianum**
Balearic S. . . . **H. balearicum**
Bedstraw S. . . . **H. galioides**
Blueridge S. . . . **H. buckleyi**
California S. . . . **H. concinnum**
Canada S. . . . **H. canadense**
CanaryIslands S. . . . **H. canariense**
Chinese S. . . . **H. chinense**
Cluster S. . . . **H. glomeratum**
Common S. . . . **H. perforatum**
Creeping S. . . . **H. repens**
∞ Dawson S. . . . ∞ **H. dawsonianum**
Dense S. . . . **H. densiflorum**
Egyptian S. . . . **H. aegypticum**
Giant S. . . . **H. ascyron**
Goat S. . . . **H. hircinum**
Goldencup S. . . . **H. patulum**
Golden S. . . . **H. frondosum**
Greek S. . . . **H. fragile**
Henry S. . . . **H. patulum henryi**
Hookers S. . . . **H. hookerianum**

St.Johnswort, continued
Japanese S. . . **Hypericum japonicum**
Kalm S. . . . **H. kalmianum**
Marsh S. . . . **H. virginicum**
Mediterranean S. . . . **H. australe**
Northern S. **H. canadense boreale**
Olympic S. . . . **H. olympicum**
Pale S. . . . **H. ellipticum**
Pineweed S. . . . **H. gentianoides**
Pyrenees S. . . . **H. nummularium**
Rhodope S. . . . **H. rhodopeum**
Sandbush S. . . . **H. fasciculatum**
Scouler S. . . . **H. scouleri**
Shore S. . . . **H. adpressum**
Shrubby S. . . . **H. prolificum**
Siberian S. . . . **H. elegans**
Southwestern S. . . **H. formosum**
Spotted S. . . . **H. punctatum**
Syrian S. . . . **H. orientale**
Trailing S. . . . **H. anagalloides**
Tutsan S. . . . **H. androsaemum**
Ural S. . . . **H. patulum uralum**
VanFleet S. . . . ×**H. vanfleeti**
Woolly S. . . . **H. tomentosum**

Stock . . . **Mathiola**
Annual S. . . . **M. incana annua**
Common S. . . . **M. incana**
Grecian S. . . . **M. bicornis**

STOKE'SIA . . . Stokesia
lae'vis (*cyanea*) . . . Stokesia
₵Azure (*caerulea*) hv.
₵Big Lilac (*lilacina grandiflora*)
₵Cream (*lutea*)
₵Early Lavender (*praecox*)
₵Pink (*rosea*)
₵Purple (*purpurea*)
₵White (*alba*)

STOMA'TIUM **MESEMBRYANTHEMUM**
See **SUCCULENTS.**

Stonecress . . . **Aethionema**
Alpine S. . . . **A. alpinum**
Armenian S. . . . **A. armenum**
Buxbaum S. . . . **A. buxbaumi**
Cliff S. . . . **A. saxatile**
Crete S. . . . **A. creticum**
Greek S. . . . **A. oppositifolium**
Kotschy S. . . . **A. kotschyi**
Lebanon S. . . . **A. coridifolium**
Persian S. . . . **A. grandiflorum**
Purple S. . . . **A. purpureum**
Pyrenees S. . . . **A. pyrenaicum**
Showy S. . . . **A. amoenum**
Slender S. . . . **A. gracile**
Spanish S. . . . **A. iberideum**
Warley S. . . . **A. warleyense**

Stonecrop . . . **Sedum**
Adolph S. . . . **S. adolphi**
Aizoon S. . . . **S. aizoon**
Albert S. . . . **S. alberti**
Allegany S. . . . **S. telephioides**
Annual S. . . . **S. annuum**
Big Goldmoss S. . . . **S. acre majus**
Blue S. . . . **S. caeruleum**
Blush S. . . . **S. alboroseum**
Copper S. . . . **S. cupreum**
Cream Jenny S. **S. reflexum albescens**
Cypress S. . . . **S. cupressoides**
Ditch S. . . . Penthorum, Virginia: **Penthorum sedoides**
English S. . . . **S. anglicum**
Evergreen S. . . . **S. hybridum**
Ewers S. . . . **S. ewersi**
Falsehouseleek . **S. sempervivoides**
Goldmoss S. . . . **S. acre**
Great S. . . . **S. maximum**

Stonecrop, continued
Guatemala S. . **Sedum guatemalense**
Gypsum S. . . . **S. gypsicola**
Hairy S. . . . **S. hirsutum**
Hexagon S. . . . **S. sexangulare**
Jenny S. . . . **S. reflexum**
Lanzarote S. . . . **S. lancerottense**
Leafy S. . . . **S. dasyphyllum**
Liebmann S. . . . **S. liebmannianum**
Little English S. **S. anglicum minus**
Littleflower S. **S. album chloroticum**
Little Goldmoss S. . **S. acre minus**
Liveforever S. . . . **S. telephium**
Lydian S. . . . **S. lydium**
Middendorf S. . **S. middendorffianum**
Moran S. . . . **S. moranense**
Moroccan S. . . . **S. atlanticum**
Mountain S. . . . **S. ternatum**
Nuttall S. . . . **S. nuttallianum**
Oaxaca S. . . . **S. oaxacanum**
Oneflower S. . . . **S. uniflorum**
Orange S. . . . **S. kamtschaticum**
Oregon S. . . . **S. oreganum**
Palmer S. . . . **S. palmeri**
Plume S. . . . **S. pallidum**
Poplar S. . . . **S. populifolium**
Purdy S. . . . **S. purdyi**
Purple Showy S.
S. spectabile atropurpureum
Redpod S. . . . **S. rhodocarpum**
Red S. . . . **S. rubens**
Redtip Great S.
S. maximum haematodes
Roseroot S. . . . **S. rosea**
Running S. . . . **S. stoloniferum**
Sanluispotosi S. . . . **S. potosinum**
Scarlet Running S.
S. stoloniferum coccineum
Schotts S. . . . **S. schotti**
Shortleaf S. . . . **S. brevifolium**
Showy S. . . . **S. spectabile**
Shy S. . . . **S. anacampseros**
Siebold S. . . . **S. sieboldi**
Spanish S. . . . **S. hispanicum**
Stahl S. . . . **S. stahli**
Star S. . . . **S. stellatum**
Stribrny S. . . . **S. stribrnyi**
Stringy S. . . . **S. sarmentosum**
Tailors S. . . . **S. sartorianum**
Texas S. . . . **S. pulchellum**
Trelease S. . . . **S. treleasei**
Tworow S. . . . **S. spurium**
Variegated S.
S. kamtschaticum variegatum
Watson S. . . . **S. watsoni**
White Goldmoss S. . **S. acre album**
White S. . . . **S. album**
White Showy S. . . **S. spectabile a.**
Winkler S. . . . **S. winkleri**
Woods S. . . . **S. woodi**
Wormleaf S. . . . **S. stenopetalum**
Yellowleaf Goldmoss S.
S. acre aureum
Yosemite S. . . . **S. yosemitense**

Stonemint . . . **Cunila**
Maryland S. . . . **C. origanoides**

Stonewood . . . **Tarrietia**
Dungon S. . . . **T. sylvatica**
Java S. . . . **T. javanica**
Silver S. . . . **T. argyrodendron**

Stonewort . . . **Chara**
Brittle S. . . . **C. fragilis**
Crown S. . . . **C. coronata**
Female S. . . . **C. crinita**

St.Paulswort . . . **Siegesbeckia**
Common S. . . . **S. orientalis**

St.Petersworт, Atlantic **Ascyrum stans**

STRANVAE'SIA . . . . . Stranvaesia
davidia'na . . . . Chinese S.
—**salicifo'lia** . . . . Willowleaf S.
—**undula'ta** (*S. undulata*) . . Low S.
¢Yellowberry (*fructu-luteo*) hv. S. davidiana
nus'sia (*glaucescens*) . Himalayan S.

STRATIO'TES . . . . . Watersoldier
aloi'des . . . . Watersoldier

Strawberry . . . . **Fragaria**
Alpine S. . . . . . . **F. semperflorens**
American S. . . . **F. vesca americana**
Blueleaf S. . . . . . . **F. glauca**
Bracted S. . . . . . . **F. bracteata**
Broadpetal S. . . . . **F. platypetala**
California S. . . . . **F. californica**
Chiloe S. . . . . . . **F. chiloensis**
European S. . . . . **F. vesca**
Hautbois S. . . . . . **F. moschata**
Illinois S. . **F. virginiana illinoensis**
Mexican S. . . . . . . **F. mexicana**
Pine S. . . . . **F. ananassa**
Virginia S. . . . . . **F. virginiana**

Strawberryfern . **Hemionitis palmata**

Strawflower. **Helichrysum bracteatum**

Strawmushroom . . . . Volvaria, Padi: **Volvaria volvacea**

STRELITZ'IA Bird-of-paradise-flower
augus'ta
nicola'i
parvifo'lia (*angustifolia*) . . Lance B.
regi'nae . . . . Queens B.

STREPTAN'THERA
cu'prea

STREPTAN'THUS . . . Twistflower
corda'tus . . . . . . Heartleaf T.
infla'tus (*Caulanthus i.*) Desertcabbage T.

STREPTOCAR'PUS . Cape-primrose
dunn'i . . . . Dunns C.
∞**kewen'sis** (*dunni* × *rexi*) . ∞Kew C.
rex'i
wend'landi . . . . . Wendland C.

STREP'TOPUS . . . . Twistedstalk
amplexifo'lius . . . . Claspleaf T.
rose'us . . . . Rosy T.

STREPTOSO'LEN . . . Streptosolen
jameso'ni (*Browallia j.*) . . Orange S.

STROBILAN'THES . . . . Conehead
anisophyl'lus . . . . . . Zigzag C.
dyeria'nus . . . . Burma C.
isophyl'lus . . . . Bedding C.

STROBILOMY'CES . Strobilomyces
strobila'ceus . . . . . Porecone S.

STROMAN'THE
portea'na

STROMBOCAC'TUS
See **CACTUS GENERA.**

STROMBOCAR'PA |w . . Screwbean
cineras'cens (*Prosopis c.*) . Dwarf S.
odora'ta (*pubescens; Prosopis o.; P. pubescens*) |w . . . . Fremont S.

Strongbark . . . . **Bourreria**
Ovalleaf B . . . . **B. ovata**

STROPHAN'THUS . . Strophanthus
gla'ber (*gratus*)
his'pidus . . . . . . Transvaal S.
kom'be . . . . Kombe S.
sarmento'sus . . . Arrowpoison S.
specio'sus

STROPHA'RIA . . . . . Stropharia
semigloba'ta . . . . Poison S.

STROPHOCAC'TUS
See **CACTUS GENERA.**

STROPHOLIR'ION . . . **BRODIAEA**
califor'nicum Torr., *not B. californica* Lindl. . . . . **B. volubilis**

STROPHOSTY'LES |w . . . Wildbean
helvo'la |w . . . . . . Trailing W.
pauciflo'ra |w . . . . . . Small W.
umbella'ta |w . . . . Pink W.

STRUTHIOP'TERIS Willd., *not* Weis. **PTERETIS**
See **FERN GENERA.**

STRYCH'NOS (*IGNATIA*). Poisonnut
castelnae'i . . . . Amazon P.
hu'milis
ica'ja . . . . Icaya P.
igna'ti (*Ignatia amara*). St.Ignatius P.
malaccen'sis (*gautheriana*) Malacca P.
nuxvom'ica . . . . . Nuxvomica P.
potato'rum . . . . Clearing P.
spino'sa . . . . . . Kafirorange P.
toxif'era . . . . Curare P.

STRYPHNODEN'DRON Alumbarktree
barba'timam . . . . . Barbatimao A.
guianen'se

The botanical identity of this valuable timber tree of French Guiana, known as "Bois Serpent," is uncertain. Some botanists refer it to Pithecellobium or Mimosa.

polyphyl'lum . . . . Leafy A.
rotundifo'lium . . . . Roundleaf A.

STUART'IA . . . . . **STEWARTIA**

Stylewort . . . . **Stylidium**
Folded S. . . . . . . **S. reduplicatum**
Trigger S. . . . . **S. graminifolium**

STYLID'IUM . . . . . . Stylewort
graminifo'lium . . . . . . Trigger S.
reduplica'tum . . . . . . Folded S.

STYLO'MA . . . **EUPRITCHARDIA**
See **PALM GENERA.**

STYLOPH'ORUM
diphyl'lum . . . . Celandine-poppy

STYLOPHYL'LUM . . **ECHEVERIA**
See **SUCCULENTS.**

STYLOSAN'THES |w . Pencilflower
biflo'ra |w

STYPAN'DRA
glau'ca

STY'RAX |w . . . . Snowbell
america'na |w . . . . American S.
—**pulverulen'ta**
benzoi'des . . . . Siam S.
ben'zoin . . . . Sumatra S.
califor'nica (*S. officinalis c.*) California S.
—**fulves'cens** (*S. officinalis f.*) Southern C.S.
calves'cens
dasyan'tha
grandifo'lia |w . . . . . . Bigleaf S.
hemsleya'na . . . . Hemsley S.
japon'ica . . . . Japanese S.
—**far'gesi** . . . . Farges J.S.
langkongen'sis . . . . Langkong S.
obas'sia . . . . Fragrant S.

STYRAX, continued
officina'lis . . . . . Drug Snowbell
—*califor'nica* . . . . . **S. californica**
—*fulves'cens* . . . . **S. californica f.**
philadelphoi'des . . Philadelphia S.
platanifo'lia . . . Sycamoreleaf S.
pulverulen'ta |w . . . . . Downy S.
shiraia'na . . . . Strigila S.
shwelien'sis
suberifo'lia . . . . . . Corkleaf S.
tonkinen'sis . . . . Tonkin S.
veitchio'rum . . . . Veitch S.
wilso'ni . . . . Chinese S.

SUAE'DA (*DONDIA*) |w . . Seepweed
america'na |w . . . . American S.
califor'nica . . . . . California S.
depres'sa |w . . . . Pursh S.
frutico'sa (*moquini; Dondia f.*) Alkali S.
marit'ima |w . . . . Sea S.
occidenta'lis |w . . . . . Western S.
ramosis'sima . . . . Bush S.
rich'i |w
suffrutes'cens . . . . . . Desert S.
torreya'na |w . . . . Torrey S.

SUBULA'RIA |w . . . . . . Awlwort
aquat'ica |w . . . . Water A.

SUCCI'SA . . . . Succisa
austra'lis (*Scabiosa a.*) . Southern S.
praten'sis (*Scabiosa succisa*) Meadow S.

SUCCULENTS
See also **CACTUS GENERA.**

The interest in Succulents and Cacti is increasing tremendously in America. Taxonomically they are among the difficult groups in the plant world to classify, while certain genera are quite subject to natural species (if not generic) hybridization, as Sempervivum and Sedum.

Hybridizers producing known either generic or species polybrids would confer a lasting benefit to science and to horticulture by indicating the definite parentage, particularly in the case of intergeneric hybrids. For such polybrids a suitable "fancy" or coined vernacular name is far preferable to a Latin name.

In editing this list the Committee consulted a great many works of reference. Among these the more important are the following: Alwin Berger's "Sukkulente Euphorbien" (Stuttgart, 1907), and "Stapelieen und Kleinen" (Stuttgart, 1910); F. Vaupel's "Zeitschrift fur Sukkulentenkunde," Vol. 1, Berlin-Dahlem Bot. Mus., 1923–4; A. Engler's "Saxifragaceae," in Engler & Prantl's "Die Naturlichen Pflanzenfamilien," Vol. 18a (Leipzig, 1930); N. E. Brown, A. Tischer & M. C. Karsten's "Mesembryanthema" (Ashford, England, 1931); J. A. Huber's "Zur Systematik der Gattung Sedum L." (Germany, 1931); R. Lloyd Praeger's "Sempervivums," The Royal Horticultural Soc. (London, 1932); F. Pax & K. Hoffmann's "Aizoaceae" and "Portulacaceae" in Engler & Prantl's "Die Naturlichen Pflanzenfamilien," Vol. 16c (Leipzig, 1934); H. Jacobsen's "Succulent Plants," translated by Vera Higgins (London, 1935); and Bailey's "Hortus Second."

Warm thanks are extended to Robert T. Clausen, Bailey Hortorium, Ithaca, N. Y., an outstanding authority on the family Crassulaceae, for aid with those genera especially Sedum and Sempervivum.

Louis C. Wheeler, now with the National Park Service, who has specialized in Euphorbiaceae, reviewed the galley proof of Euphorbia and made important corrections and suggestions.

SUCCULENTS, continued
AC'RODON **MESEMBRYANTHEMUM**

ADROMIS'CHUS . ADROMISCHUS
clavifo'lius (*vanderheydeni* Hort.; *Cotyledon clavifolia*)
coo'peri (*Cotyledon c.; Echeveria c.*) COOPER A.
crista'tus (*Cotyledon cristata*) CRESTED A.

AEO'NIUM . . . . . . AEONIUM
arbo'reum (*Sedum a.* Hegi; *Sempervivum a.* L., *not* (Bory) Ktze.)
balsamif'erum (*Sempervivum b.*) BALSAM A.
burch'ardi (*Sempervivum b.*) BURCHARD A.
caespito'sum (*floribundum; Sempervivum c.*)
canarien'se (*giganticum; Sempervivum c.*) . . . . CANARY A.
castello-pai'viae (*Sempervivum c.*)
cilia'tum (*Sempervivum c.* Willd., *not* Auth. *nor* Hort.)
cruen'tum . . . . **A. spathulatum c.**
cunea'tum (*Sempervivum c.*)
deco'rum (*Sempervivum d.*)
domes'ticum . . . . . . **Aichryson d.**
dora'mae . . . . **A. manriqueorum**
floribun'dum . . . . . **A. caespitosum**
gigan'ticum . . . . . . **A. canariense**
glutino'sum (*Sempervivum g.*) GUMMY A.
gooch'iae (*Sempervivum g.*). GOOCH A.
ha'worthi (*Sempervivum h.* Hort.) HAWORTH A.
hierren'se (*Sempervivum h.*)
holochry'sum (*Sempervivum arboreum* (Bory) Ktze., *not* L.; *S. holochrysum; S. urbicum* Lindl., *not* C. Smith *nor* Hook. f.)
lind'leyi (*tortuosum* Pit. & Proust, *not* Berg.; *Sempervivum l.; S. tortuosum* Link) . . . . LINDLEY A.
manriqueo'rum (*doramae; Sempervivum m.*)
no'bile (*Sempervivum n.*)
percar'neum (*Sempervivum p.*)
sedifo'lium (*Aichryson s.; Greenovia s.; Sempervivum s.*)
spathula'tum (*strepsicladum; tournefortі; Sempervivum s.; S. villosum* Lindl., *not* Ait., Haw. *nor* Lamotte)
—cruen'tum (*A. cruentum; Aichryson pulchellum; Sempervivum cruentum; S. pulchellum*)
tabulaefor'me (*Sempervivum t.*)
tortuo'sum Berg., *not* Pit. & Proust **Aichryson t.**
tortuo'sum Pit. & Proust, *not* Berg. **A. lindleyi**
tournefort'i . . . . . **A. spathulatum**
undula'tum (*Sempervivum u.; S. urbicum* Hook. f., *not* C. Smith *nor* Haw., Lindl.)
urb'icum (*Sempervivum u.* C. Smith, *not* Haw., Lindl. *nor* Hook. f.)

AGA'VE W . . . . AGAVE
affi'nis
al'bicans
america'na (*altissima*) CENTURYPLANT A.
MARGINATA. HV.
MEDIO-PICTA
STRIATA
VARIEGATA
angustifo'lia (*cantula; ixtlioides* Hook., *not* Lem.)

SUCCULENTS (AGAVE), continued
antilla'rum
applana'ta
atrovi'rens . . . . . PULQUE AGAVE
attenua'ta (*glaucescens*)
ber'geri . . . . BERGER A.
brachysta'chys . . . . . **Manfreda b.**
caerules'cens . . . . . **A. lophantha c.**
can'tula . . . . **A. angustifolia**
carchariodon'ta
cerula'ta
chiapen'sis . . . . . . **A. polyacantha**
consideran'ti . . **A. victoriae-reginae**
daty'lio
decip'iens (*spiralis*)
des'erti
eich'lami
el'egans . . . . **A. potatorum**
eva'dens
ferdinandi-re'gis
fe'rox
filif'era
—compac'ta
fourcroy'des (*ixtli; longifolia; rigida*) HENEQUEN A.
franceschia'na
franzosi'ni
funkia'na . . JAUMAVE LECHUGUILLA
geminiflo'ra
ghiesbreght'i (*ghiesbrechti*)
glauces'cens . . . . . . **A. attenuata**
hart'manni
haseloff'i
hor'rida (*splendens*)
hor'rida Hort., *not* Lem. **A. nolitangere**
houllet'i; houlletia'na . . **A. sisalana**
huachucen'sis . . . . HUACHUCA A.
hys'trix . . . . **A. stricta**
in'gens
—pic'ta
ix'tli . . . . **A. fourcroydes**
ixtlioi'des Hook., *not* Lem. **A. angustifolia**
kercho'vei
lae'vis . . . . **A. sisalana**
latifo'lia . . . . **A. potatorum**
lecheguil'la . . **A. lophantha poselgeri**
leh'manni
leto'nae . . . . LETONA A.
longifo'lia . . . . . . **A. fourcroydes**
lophan'tha . . . . CRESTED A.
—caerules'cens (*A. caerulescens*)
—posel'geri (*A. lecheguilla*) LECHUGUILLA A.
lu'rida (*mexicana*)
macran'tha
maculo'sa . . . . . . **Manfreda m.**
margari'tae
marmora'ta (*todaroi*)
mesotil'lo
mexica'na . . . . **A. lurida**
micracan'tha
miradoren'sis . . . . . . DWARF A.
mi'tis
mitraefor'mis
neglec'ta . . . . BLUE A.
nelso'ni
nick'elsi

Perhaps a var. or form of A. ferdinandi-regis.

nolitan'gere (*horrida* Hort., *not* Lem.)
oblonga'ta
orcuttia'na . . . . ORCUTT A.
pal'meri . . . . PALMER A.
par'ryi . . . . PARRY A.
parviflo'ra
pic'ta
polyacan'tha (*chiapensis*)

SUCCULENTS (AGAVE), continued
potato'rum (*elegans; latifolia; pulchra*)
pseudotequila'na MESCALFIBER AGAVE
rig'ida . . . . **A. fourcroydes**
rigidis'sima
roezlia'na
—ing'hami
rosea'na
salmia'na
sca'bra (*wislizeni*)
schidig'era
schott'i
sebastia'na
shaw'i
sisala'na (*houlleti; houlletiana; laevis; sisala*) . . . . SISAL A.
spira'lis . . . . **A. decipiens**
splen'dens . . . . **A. horrida**
stria'ta
stric'ta (*hystrix*) . . . HEDGEHOG A.
—glau'ca . . . . BLUE H.A.
tequila'na . . . . TEQUILA A.
todaro'i . . . . **A. marmorata**
treleas'i
utahen'sis . . . . UTAH A.
variega'ta . . . . **Manfreda v.**
verschaf'felti
vesti'ta
victoriae-regi'nae (*consideranti*)
virgin'ica . . . . **Manfreda v.**
web'eri
wein'garti
wislize'ni . . . . **A. scabra**
xylonacan'tha
zapu'pe

AGNIRIC'TUS **MESEMBRYANTHEMUM**

AICHRY'SON . . . . AICHRYSON
dichot'omum (*Sempervivum annuum; S. dichotomum* DC., *not* Hort.)
domes'ticum (*Aeonium d.; Sempervivum d.; S. tortuosum* DC. & Auth., *not* Ait.)
pulchel'lum **Aeonium spathulatum cruentum**
pyg'maeum . . . . . **A. tortuosum**
sedifo'lium . . . . **Aeonium s.**
tortuo'sum (*pygmaeum; Aeonium t.* Berg., *not* Pit. & Proust.; *Sempervivum pygmaeum; S. tortuosum*, Ait., *not* DC. & Auth.; *S. villosum* Haw., *not* Ait. *nor* Lamotte *nor* Lindl.)
villo'sum (*Sempervivum v.* Ait.)

A'LOE . . . . ALOE

Dr. L. H. Bailey calls attention to the fact that the word Aloe, in Latin, has three syllables and in English two.

The Latin name is pronounced A-lo-ee; the English name, Al-oh.

abyssin'ica . . . . . ETHIOPIAN A.
affi'nis
africa'na
arbores'cens (*arborea*)
—frutes'cens (*A. frutescens*)
—natalen'sis
—pachythyr'sa
arista'ta
ausa'na Hort.

Botanical identity is uncertain.

barbaden'sis (*A. petiolata vera; vera* Auth., *not* Mill.; *vulgaris*) MEDITERRANEAN A.

Albert F. Hill, of Harvard University, points out that **A. barbadensis** Mill. (1768) is the oldest tenable name for this plant, and that "*A. vera*" of authors is preempted by **A. vera** Mill., "a different plant."

SUCCULENTS (ALOE), continued
brevifo'lia
cae'sia
candela'brum
cilia'ris . . . . . . CLIMBING ALOE
commuta'ta
coop'eri . . . . **A. johnstoni**
davya'na
dichot'oma . . . . QUIVERTREE A.
dis'tans
dy'eri
echina'ta . . . . **A. humilis e.**
e'ru
—cornu'ta Hort.
—macula'ta
fe'rox . . . . CAPE A.
frutes'cens . . . . . **A. arborescens f.**
green'i
hanburia'na . . **A. striata rhodocincta**
hele'niae
hereroen'sis
heteracan'tha
hu'milis . . . . HEDGEHOG A.
—echina'ta (*A. echinata*)
—incur'va
john'stoni (*cooperi*)
jut'tiae
krapohlia'na
latifo'lia
linea'ta
longis'tyla
macrocar'pa
mar'lothi
microdon'ta
microstig'ma
mitrifor'mis
no'bilis
obscu'ra (*picta*) . . . . SOAP A.
parvibractea'ta
parvispi'na
pax'i
Perhaps a hybrid between A. commutata and A. striata.

peg'leri
percras'sa
per'ryi . . . . PERRY A.
petiola'ta ve'ra . . . . **A. barbadensis**
pic'ta . . . . **A. obscura**
pienaar'i
pillans'i
plicat'ilis . . . . FAN A.
plur'idens
praten'sis
pretorien'sis
rubrolute'a
runcina'ta
salmdyckia'na
sapona'ria (*umbellata*)
schim'peri
schlech'teri
socotri'na . . . . **A. succotrina**
specio'sa
×**spinosis'sima** Hort.
spu'ria
Probably a hybrid.

strauss'i
stria'ta
—rhodocinc'ta (*A. hanburiana*)
striat'ula
succotri'na (*socotrina*)
supralae'vis
thorn'crofti
thrask'i
umbella'ta . . . . **A. saponaria**
variega'ta . . . . KANNIEDOOD A.
ve'ra . . . . TRUE A.
ve'ra Auth., *not* Mill. . **A. barbadensis**

SUCCULENTS (ALOE), continued
vi'rens
vulga'ris . . . . **A. barbadensis**
wick'ensi
zebri'na

ALTAMIRANO'A . . **VILLADIA**

ANACAMP'SEROS
albis'sima
al'ta
arachnoi'des
—grandiflo'ra (*A. filamentosa* De Willd., *not* Sims; *A. rufescens*)
filamento'sa
filamento'sa De Willd., *not* Sims **A. arachnoides grandiflora**
lanceola'ta
mey'eri
papyra'cea
parviflo'ra
rufes'cens . **A. arachnoides grandiflora**
telephias'trum
tomento'sum

ANACAMP'SEROS Haw., *not* L. **SEDUM**

API'CRA
as'pera
pentag'ona (*Haworthia p.*)

APTE'NIA; ARGE'TA; ARGYRODER'MA; ARIDA'RIA; ASTRID'IA; BERGERAN'THUS **MESEMBRYANTHEMUM**

BRYOPHYL'LUM **KALANCHOE**
calyci'num . . . . **K. pinnata**
crena'tum . . . . **K. laxiflora**
tubiflo'rum . . . . . . **K. verticillata**

BULBI'NE
alooi'des
an'nua
bulbo'sa
caules'cens
semibarba'ta

BYRNES'IA **GRAPTOPETALUM**
wein'bergi . . . . . **G. paraguayense**

CARALLU'MA
bur'chardi
cauda'ta
europae'a
lute'a
melanan'tha
nebrown'i
pseudo-nebrown'i
ramo'sa
spreng'eri

CARPAN'THEA; CARPOBRO'TUS; CEPHALOPHYL'LUM; CEROCHLA'MYS **MESEMBRYANTHEMUM**

CEROPE'GIA . . . . CEROPEGIA
bark'lyi . . . . BARKLY C.
bulbo'sa
caffro'rum . . . . KAFIR C.
deb'ilis
fus'ca
hasta'ta
mey'eri . . . . MEYER C.
rad'icans
sanderso'ni . . . . . SANDERSON C.
stapeliaefor'mis
thorn'crofti . . . . THORNCROFT C.
wood'i . . . . WOODS C.

CHAMAESY'CE . . **EUPHORBIA**

SUCCULENTS, continued
CHASMATOPHYL'LUM; CHEIRIDOP'SIS **MESEMBRYANTHEMUM**

CHIASTOPHYL'LUM **COTYLEDON**

CLEMENT'SIA . . . **SEDUM**

CONICO'SIA; CONOPHYL'LUM; CONOPHY'TUM; CORPUSCULA'RIA **MESEMBRYANTHEMUM**

COTYLE'DON (*CHIASTOPHYLLUM*) COTYLEDON
adun'ca . . . . **Pachyphytum hookeri**
agavoi'des . . . . **Echeveria a.**
arbores'cens . . . . **Crassula a.**
attenua'ta . . . . **Echeveria a.**
ausa'na . . . . **C. orbiculata**
bar'beyi . . . . BARBEY C.
caespito'sa . . . . . . **Echeveria c.**
califor'nica . . . . . . **Echeveria c.**
carnic'olor . . . . **Echeveria c.**
chrysan'tha . . **Sedum chrysanthum**
clavifo'lia . . **Adromischus clavifolius**
coccin'ea . . . . **Echeveria c.**
compac'ta . . . . **Echeveria c.**
coop'eri . . . . **Adromischus c.**
crista'ta . . . **Adromischus cristatus**
cymo'sa . . . . **Echeveria c.**
decussa'ta
densiflo'ra . . . . **Echeveria d.**
ed'ule . . . . **Echeveria edulis**
el'egans . . . . **Echeveria e.**
farino'sa . . . . **Echeveria f.**
fimbria'ta . . . . . **Sedum fimbriatum**
gibbiflo'ra . . . . **Echeveria g.**
hov'eyi . . . . **Echeveria h.**
lanceola'ta . . . . **Echeveria l.**
lax'a . . . . **Echeveria l.**
lu'rida . . . **Echeveria lanceolata l.**
macran'tha
nevaden'sis . . . . **Echeveria n.**
nudicau'lis Abrams, *not* Lam. **Echeveria densiflora**
oppositifo'lia (*Chiastophyllum oppositifolium*)
orbicula'ta (*ausana*)
—compac'ta
—ma'jor
—mi'nor
pachyphy'tum **Pachyphytum bracteosum**
papilla'ris
papillo'sa . . . . AFGHAN C.
paraguayen'sis **Graptopetalum paraguayense**
penduli'na . . . **Umbilicus pendulinus**
pinna'ta . . . . . . **Kalanchoe pinnata**
plattia'na . . . . **Echeveria p.**
platyphyl'la . **Sedum sempervivoides**
pulverulen'ta . . . . . . **Echeveria p.**
purpus'i . . . . **Echeveria p.**
secun'da . . . . **Echeveria s.**
semeno'vi . . . . **Sedum s.**
septentriona'lis . . . . **Echeveria s.**
simplicifo'lia
spino'sa . . . . **Sedum spinosum**
teretifo'lia
umbil'icus . . . **Umbilicus pendulinus**
undula'ta
wick'ensi
wink'leri . . . . **Sedum w.**

COURAN'TIA . . **ECHEVERIA**

SUCCULENTS, continued

CRAS'SULA . . . . . . CRASSULA
acutifo'lia (*densifolia*)
albiflo'ra (*obvallata* Thunb., *not* Linn.; *Rochea a.*)
al'stoni . . . . ALSTON C.
aquat'ica . . . . **Tillaea a.**
arbores'cens (*C. cotyledon* Jacq., *not* Haw.; *Cotyledon a.*)
argen'tea (*portulacea*) . . . SILVER C.
ar'ta (*deltoidea* Harv., *not* Thunb.)
barba'ta
bo'lusi . . . . **C. cooperi**
centauroi'des Hort. . . . **C. lineolata; C. marginalis; C. pellucida**
clavifo'lia . . . . KEYLEAF C.
coccin'ea . . . . **Rochea c.**
columna'ris . . . . . COLUMNAR C.
conges'ta (*laticephala; pachyphylla*)
coop'eri (*bolusi*) . . . . COOPER C.
coralli'na . . . . CORAL C.
corda'ta
corda'ta Lodd., *not* Thunb. **C. spathulata**
cornu'ta . . . . HORNED C.
corymbulo'sa
cotyle'don Jacq., *not* Haw. **C. arborescens**
cultra'ta
decep'trix
decip'iens . . . . **C. tecta**
deltoi'dea (*rhomboidea*)
deltoi'dea Harv., *not* Thunb. . **C. arta**
densifo'lia . . . . **C. acutifolia**
denta'ta (*minima*)
dichot'oma . . . . . . **Vauanthes d.**
dregea'na
ela'ta
falca'ta (*Rochea f.*)
grac'ilis Hort. . . . . . **C. schmidti**
hemisphae'rica
hook'eri Hort.; *impres'sa* **C. schmidti**
lac'tea . . . . MILKY C.
laticeph'ala . . . . . . **C. congesta**
lineola'ta (*centauroides* Hort. in part)
lu'cida . . . . **C. spathulata**
lycopodioi'des (*Sedum l.*) CLUBMOSS C.
margina'lis (*centauroides* Hort. in part; *profusa*)
min'ima . . . . **C. dentata**
montic'ola . . . . **C. rupestris**
multica'va (*quadrifida*)
namaquen'sis
—brevifo'lia
nudicau'lis
obova'ta
Hardly more than a var. or form of C. ramuliflora.
obvalla'ta
obvalla'ta Thunb., *not* Linn. **C. albiflora**
orbicula'ris
pachyphyl'la . . . . . . **C. congesta**
peg'lerae
pellu'cida (*centauroides* Hort. in part)
perfolia'ta . . . . . THOROWORT C.
perfora'ta (*perfossa* DC., *not* Lam.)
perfos'sa Lam., *not* DC. . **C. rupestris**
portula'cea . . . . **C. argentea**
profu'sa . . . . **C. marginalis**
pseudolycopodioi'des
puncta'ta Hort.
A name misapplied to C. arborescens, C. ramuliflora, and C. rupestris.
pyramida'lis
quadrif'ida . . . . **C. multicava**
rad'icans
ramuliflo'ra
rhomboi'dea . . . . . **C. deltoidea**
rosula'ris

SUCCULENTS (CRASSULA), continued

ru'bens . . . . **Sedum r.**
rupes'tris (*monticola; perfossa* Lam., *not* DC.)
sarcocau'lis
schmidt'i (*gracilis* Hort.; *hookeri* Hort.; *impressa*) . . . SCHMIDT CRASSULA
sedifo'lia
spathula'ta (*cordata* Lodd., *not* Thunb.; *lucida*)
tec'ta (*decipiens*)
te'res
tetrag'ona
tomento'sa . . . . WOOLLY C.
trachysan'tha
tur'rita

CRYOPHY'TUM . **MESEMBRYANTHEMUM**
Cylindrophyl'lum calamifor'me **Mesembryanthemum c.**
DACTYLOP'SIS; DELOSPER'MA . **MESEMBRYANTHEMUM**
DICHROPHYL'LUM **EUPHORBIA**
DISPHY'MA; DOROTHEAN'THUS; DROSAN'THEMUM **MESEMBRYANTHEMUM**
DUD'LEYA . . . **ECHEVERIA**
grandiflo'ra . . **E. lanceolata aloides**
lax'a cymo'sa . . . . **E. cymosa**
lu'rida . . . . **E. lanceolata l.**

ECHEVE'RIA (*COURANTIA; DUDLEYA; OLIVERANTHUS; STYLOPHYLLUM; URBINIA*) ECHEVERIA
a'bramsi (*Dudleya a.*) . . ABRAMS E.
acutifo'lia
adun'ca . . . . **Pachyphytum hookeri**
agavoi'des (*Cotyledon a.; Urbinia a.*) CARPET E.
albiflo'ra (*Dudleya a.*)
amethysti'na **Graptopetalum amethystinum**
amoe'na (*pusilla*)
arizo'nica Hort. **Graptopetalum paraguayense**
atropurpu'rea (*sanguinea*)
attenua'ta (*Cotyledon a.; Stylophyllum attenuatum; S. orcutti*)
austra'lis . . . . . . SOUTHERN E.
bifurca'ta
caespito'sa (*Cotyledon c.; Dudleya c.*) SANFRANCISCO E.
califor'nica (*Cotyledon c.*)
carnic'olor (*Cotyledon c.*)
coccin'ea (*Cotyledon c.*) . SCARLET E.
compac'ta (*Cotyledon c.; Dudleya c.*) TIGHTTUFT E.
coop'eri . . . . **Adromischus c.**
corderoy'i (*Urbinia c.*)
cotyle'don (*Sedum c.*)
cuspida'ta
cymo'sa (*E. laxa c.; Cotyledon c.; Dudleya l. c.*)
densiflo'ra (*nudicaulis; Cotyledon d.; C. nudicaulis* Abrams, *not* Lam.; *Dudleya d.; Stylophyllum densiflorum; S. nudicaule*)
derenberg'i
desmetia'na . . . . **E. peacocki**
ed'ulis (*Cotyledon edule; Stylophyllum e.*)
el'egans (*Cotyledon e.; Oliveranthus e.*)
expatria'ta
farino'sa (*Cotyledon f.; Dudleya f.*) CHALKY E.

SUCCULENTS (ECHEVERIA), continued

fimbria'ta . . . FRINGED ECHEVERIA
gibbiflo'ra (*grandifolia; Cotyledon g.*)
—metal'lica (*E. metallica*) . BRONZE E.
gigan'tea
glau'ca (*E. secunda g.*)
globo'sa
gold'mani
gorma'nia . . . . . . **Sedum laxum**
grac'ilis
grandiflo'ra . . **E. lanceolata aloides**
grandifo'lia . . . . . . **E. gibbiflora**
harms'i
hook'eri . . . . . . **Pachyphytum h.**
hov'eyi (*Cotyledon h.*)
in'gens (*Dudleya i.*)
lanceola'ta (*Cotyledon l.; Dudleya l.*) LANCELEAF E.
—aloi'des (*E. grandiflora; Dudleya g.*) GREEN L.E.
—lu'rida (*E. lurida; Cotyledon l.; Dudleya l.*) . . . . LURID L.E.
lax'a (*Cotyledon l.; Dudleya l.*)
—cymo'sa . . . . **E. cymosa**
leucot'richa
linguaefo'lia (*Pachyphytum lingua* Hort.) . . . . . TONGUELEAF E.
lozan'i . . . . LOZAN E.
lu'rida . . . . **E. lanceolata l.**
macula'ta . . . . SPOTTED E.
max'oni . . . . MAXON E.
metal'lica . . . . . . **E. gibbiflora m.**
micro'calyx (*purpusi* Britt., *not* K. Schum.)
monta'na . . . . . . MOUNTAIN E.
multicau'lis
nevaden'sis (*Cotyledon n.; Dudleya n.*) NEVADA E.
nudicau'lis . . . . . . **E. densiflora**
obtusa'ta . . . . . **Sedum obtusatum**
orega'na . . . . . **Sedum oreganum**
pal'meri (*rosei*) . . . . . PALMER E.
pea'cocki (*desmetiana*) . . PEACOCK E.
pineto'rum . . . . . . PINEWOODS E.
pittier'i . . . . PITTIER E.
plattia'na (*Cotyledon p.; Dudleya p.*) PLATT E.
prin'glei . . . . PRINGLE E.
pubes'cens
pulverulen'ta (*Cotyledon p.; Dudleya p.*) POWDERED E.
pu'mila
purpus'i (*Cotyledon p.; Dudleya p.*) PURPUS E.
purpus'i Britt., *not* K. Schum. **E. microcalyx**
purpuso'rum (*Urbinia purpusi*)
pusil'la . . . . **E. amoena**
racemo'sa
retu'sa
rose'a (*Courantia r.*)
rose'i . . . . **E. palmeri**
rubromargina'ta . . . . REDRIM E.
run'yoni . . . . RUNYON E.
sanguin'ea . . . . . **E. atropurpurea**
saxo'sa (*Dudleya s.*)
∞ **scaphyl'la** Hort. (*agavoides* × *linguaefolia;* ∞ *scaphophylla* Hort.)
∞ *scheideck'eri* Hort. . ∞ **Pachyveria s.**
scopulo'rum
secun'da (*Cotyledon s.*)
—glau'ca . . . . **E. glauca**
septentriona'lis (*Cotyledon s.; Dudleya s.*) . . . . NORTHERN E.
set'chelli (*Dudleya s.*) . . SETCHELL E.
Hardly more than a var. of E. laxa.
seto'sa

SUCCULENTS (ECHEVERIA), continued
shel'doni (*Dudleya s.*)
Sheldon Echeveria
sim'ulans
spruc'ei . . . . Spruces E.
stolonif'era
strictiflo'ra
subrig'ida
subses'silis
tolucen'sis . . . . Toluca E.
tur'gida
venezuelen'sis . . . . Venezuela E.
vi'rens (*Stylophyllum v.*)
walpolea'na . . . . Walpole E.
watso'ni . . . . **Sedum w.**
wein'bergi **Graptopetalum paraguayense**
wein'garti
A hybrid of some sort.
whit'ei . . . . Whites E.
xan'ti (*Dudleya x.*) . . . Xantus E.

ECHIDNOP'SIS
cereifor'mis
dammannia'na

EREP'SIA
MESEMBRYANTHEMUM

EUPHOR'BIA (*Chamaesyce; Dichrophyllum; Poinsettia; Tithymalopsis; Tithymalus; Trichosterigma; Zygophyllidium*) |w . Euphorbia
To avoid unnecessary repetition, the entire S.P.N. list of this genus is included here. Only a comparatively few of the species named below are not succulent.

abyssin'ica . . . . . Ethiopian E.
acruren'sis
aggrega'ta
albomargina'ta (*Chamaesyce a.*) |w
Whitemargin E.
alcicor'nis . . . . Elkhorn E.
am'mak . . . . Ammak E.
angula'ris (*lemaireana*)
antiquo'rum . . . . . . Ancients E.
antisyphilit'ica (*Trichosterigma a.*)
Wax E.
aphyl'la . . . . Leafless E.
atropurpu'rea . . . . Teneriffe E.
austra'lis . . . . . . Australian E.
avasmonta'na
balsamif'era . . . . . . Balsam E.
barnhart'i . . . . Barnhart E.
bo'jeri . . . . **E. mili**
brasilien'sis |w . . . . . . Brazil E.
bubali'na
bupleurifo'lia
caducifo'lia
califor'nica . . . . . California E.
canarien'sis . . . . . . Canary E.
candela'brum . . . . Candelabra E.
capitella'ta (*Chamaesyce c.*) |w Head E.
caput-medu'sae (*E. c. major; E. c. minor*) . . . . . Medusahead E.
cereifor'mis (*polygonata*) . Cereus E.
chamaesy'ce
clandes'tina
cla'va
coerules'cens
coop'eri . . . . Cooper E.
corolla'ta (*Tithymalopsis c.*) |w
Floweringspurge E.
cotinifo'lia
crenula'ta (*Tithymalus crenulatus*)
Beetle E.
cyparis'sias (*Tithymalus c.*) |w
Cypress E.
denta'ta (*Poinsettia d.*) |w Toothed E.

SUCCULENTS (EUPHORBIA), continued
din'teri . . . . . Dinter Euphorbia
dracunculoi'des . . . Jychee-oil E.
echi'nus . . . . Hedgehog E.
eno'pla
epithymoi'des (*polychroma*) Cushion E.
esculen'ta . . . . Edible E.
e'sula (*virgata*) . . . . . . Leafy E.
eusta'cei (*?hystrix*)
exig'ua
exstipula'ta |w
falca'ta . . . . Sickle E.
fascicula'ta
fend'leri (*Chamaesyce f.*) |w
Fendler E.
fimbria'ta . . . . Fringed E.
flor'ida |w
fournier'i . . . . **E. lophogona**
franckia'na . . . . . . Francks E.
frickia'na Hort.
Perhaps a typographical error for the preceding species.
frutico'sa
ful'gens . . . . . Scarletplume E.
genicula'ta
gey'eri |w . . . . Geyer E.
globo'sa . . . . Globe E.
glyptosper'ma (*Chamaesyce g.*) |w
Ridgeseed E.
gorgo'nis . . . . Gorgo E.
grandicor'nis . . . . . . Bighorn E.
gran'didens . . . . . . Bigtooth E.
grant'i . . . . Grants E.
handien'sis
heliosco'pia (*Tithymalus h.*) . Sun E.
heptag'ona . . . . . Sevenridge E.
hermentia'na
heterophyl'la (*Poinsettia h.*) |w
Painted E.
hexag'ona (*Zygophyllidium hexagonum*)
Sixangle E.
hirsu'ta . . . . **E. vermiculata**
hor'rida . . . . Allthorn E.
hottentot'ae . . . . . Hottentot E.
hys'trix
The botanical identity of this species is uncertain; it may be E. eustacei or E. loricata.
indivi'sa (*Chamaesyce i.*) |w
iner'mis (*viperina*)
in'gens
in'tisy . . . . Intisy E.
ipecacuan'hae . . . . . . Ipecac E.
lac'tea . . . . Milkstripe E.
—crista'ta . . . . . . Crested M.E.
la'ta |w . . . . Hoary E.
la'thyrus . . . . Caper E.
(*Moleplant; Moleweed*)
ledien'i . . . . Ledien E.
lemairea'na . . . . . . **E. angularis**
ligno'sa
ligula'ria . . . . **E. neriifolia**
lophog'ona (*fournieri*)
lorica'ta (*?hystrix*)
lu'cida . . . . Shining E.
lyttonia'na . . . . Lytton E.
macula'ta (*nutans; presli; Chamaesyce m.*) |w . . . . Spotted E.
mammilla'ris
margina'ta (*variegata; Dichrophyllum marginatum*)
Snow-on-the-mountain E.
mar'lothi . . . . **E. montieri**
maurita'nica . . . . . Mauritania E.
melofor'mis . . . . Melon E.
mexica'na (*Tithymalus mexicanus*) |w
Mexican E.

SUCCULENTS (EUPHORBIA), continued
mil'i (*bojeri; splendens*)
Crownofthorns Euphorbia
mis'era
montier'i (*marlothi*)
mo'rini . . . . Morin E.
muir'i . . . . Muir E.
myrsini'tes . . . . Myrtle E.
natalen'sis . . . . Natal E.
neglec'ta
neomexica'na . . . . . . **E. serpyllifolia**
neriifo'lia (*ligularia*) . . . Hedge E.
neu'tra
nicaeen'sis . . . . Nicene E.
nu'bica . . . . Nubian E.
nu'tans . . . . **E. maculata**
nyi'kae
obe'sa
officina'rum . . . . Apothecaries E.
orni'thopus . . . . . . Birdsfoot E.
pal'meri (*Tithymalus p.*) . Palmer E.
pedicul if'era |w
pen'dula
pentag'ona . . . . Fiveridge E.
pep'lus (*Tithymalus p.*) . . Petty E.
pilo'sa
Golden (*major*) hv.
pilulif'era . . . . Pillpod E.
piscato'ria . . . . . . Fishermens E.
polyacan'tha
polycar'pa |w
polychro'ma . . . . . **E. epithymoides**
polyg'ona . . . . Polygon E.
polygona'ta . . . . . . **E. cereiformis**
pres'li . . . . **E. maculata**
procum'bens . . . . . . Trailing E.
pseudocac'tus . . . . . Yellow-U E.
pseudohypogae'a
pteroneu'ra . . . . Wingrib E.
pulcher'rima (*Poinsettia p.*)
Common Poinsettia
Christmas Pink. hv.
Christmas Red
Henrietta Ecke
Mrs. Paul Ecke
Oakleaf
Rosy (*rosea*)
Ruth Ecke
White (*alba*)
pulvina'ta
quadrangula'ris . . . Fourangle E.
regis-ju'bae . . . . . King-Juba E.
reinhardt'i . . . . . Reinhardt E.
resinif'era . . . . Gum E.
revolu'ta |w
rhipsalioi'des
robus'ta (*Tithymalus robustus*)
Robust E.
roylea'na . . . . Royles E.
schim'peri
The botanical identity of this species is uncertain; it may be E. nubica or E. scoparia.
schinz'i . . . . Schinz E.
scopa'ria
scota'num (*venenata*)
segeta'lis
ser'pens |w . . . . Serpent E.
serpyllifo'lia (*neomexicana; Chamaesyce s.*) |w . . . . Thymeleaf E.
ser'rula |w
setilo'ba |w . . . . Yuma E.
sikkimen'sis . . . . Sikkim E.
silicic'ola
sim'ilis
sipolis'i . . . . Sipolis E.
splen'dens . . . . **E. mili**
squarro'sa

SUCCULENTS (EUPHORBIA), continued
stellaespi'na . STARSPINE EUPHORBIA
stella'ta (*uncinata*)
stictos'pora(*Chamaesyce s.*) |w
stolonif'era
stric'ta
submammilla'ris . . . . CORNCOB E.
susan'niae
tenuira'ma . . . . . SLIMBRANCH E.
tetrag'ona . . . . . FOURRIDGE E.
tirucal'li . . . . . MALABARTREE E.
triangula'ris
tridenta'ta
trigo'na . . . . THREERIB E.
tubercula'ta
tu'biglans
uncina'ta . . . . E. stellata
variega'ta . . . . . . E. marginata
va'seyi . . . . Adelia v.
venena'ta . . . . E. scotanum
vermicula'ta (*hirsuta*)
viperi'na . . . . E. inermis
virga'ta . . . . E. esula
viro'sa
wul'feni
xylophylloi'des . . . . FLATSTEM E.

FAUCA'RIA MESEMBRYANTHEMUM
haag'ei . . . . M. bosscheanum

FENESTRA'RIA MESEMBRYANTHEMUM

FOUQUIE'RIA |w
splen'dens |w . . . . . . OCOTILLO

FURCRAE'A . . . . . . FURCREA
altis'sima . . . . F. inermis
andi'na . . . . CHUCHAO F.
bedinghaus'i
cabu'ya . . . . CABUYA F.
gigan'tea . . . . PITEIRA F.
—mediopic'ta (*F. watsoniana*)
hexapet'ala (*cubensis*) . . . PITRE F.
humboldtia'na . . . . HUMBOLDT F. (*Cocuiza Brava*)
iner'mis (*altissima*)
lin'deni . . . . . F. selloa marginata
macrophyl'la . . . . FIQUE F.
pubes'cens
roez'li
sello'a
—margina'ta (*F. lindeni*)
watsonia'na . F. gigantea mediopicta

GASTE'RIA . . . . . . GASTERIA
acinacifo'lia
bowiea'na . . . . G. picta
carina'ta
cheilophyl'la
colubri'na
dic'ta
excava'ta
gla'bra
lin'gua (*disticha*)
macula'ta
ni'gricans
pic'ta (*bowieana*)
planifo'lia
pul'chra
spira'lis
subcarina'ta
sulca'ta
verruco'sa . . . . . . OXTONGUE G.
zey'heri

GIBBAE'UM; GLOTTIPHYL'LUM MESEMBRYANTHEMUM

GORMA'NIA . . . . . SEDUM

SUCCULENTS, continued

GRAMMAN'THES VAUANTHES
chloraeflo'ra; gentianoi'des V. dichotoma

GRAPTOPET'ALUM (*BYRNESIA*) . . . . . . LETTERPETAL
amethysti'num (*Echeveria amethystina; Pachyphytum amethystinum*) AMETHYSTINE L.
bar'trami . . . . BARTRAM L.
or'peti . . . . ORPET L.
pachyphyl'lum (*Sedum atypicum*)
paraguayen'se (*weinbergi; Byrnesia w.; Cotyledon paraguayensis; Echeveria arizonica* Hort.; *Echeveria w.; Sedum w.*) . . . . PARAGUAY L.

GREENO'VIA
diptocy'cla (*Sempervivum diplocyclum*)
dodrenta'lis (*gracilis; Sempervivum dodrentale; S. gracile*)
sedifo'lium . . . . Aeonium s.

HAWORTH'IA
al'bicans
arachnoi'des
atrovi'rens
attenua'ta
—clariper'la
cassy'tha
chal'wini
coarcta'ta
coop'eri
cuspida'ta
cymbifor'mis
—planifo'lia
denticula'ta
en'gleri
fascia'ta
glabra'ta
—pervir'idis
laetevi'rens
margaritif'era
—coralli'na
—erec'ta
—grana'ta
papillo'sa
pea'cocki
pentag'ona . . . . Apicra p.
pilif'era
rad'ula
reinwardt'i
retu'sa
schmidtia'na
semiglabra'ta
tessella'ta
—incur'va
—par'va
tortuo'sa
translu'cens
trunca'ta
tur'gida
visco'sa
vitta'ta

HERERO'A MESEMBRYANTHEMUM

HEUR'NIA (*HUERNIA*)

"The genus is named after Justus Heurnius; unfortunately, the name was originally misspelled Huernia and, by the Rules of Botanical Nomenclature, this is the spelling which should be adhered to; on the Continent the spelling given above is more commonly used." Jacobsen, H.,-Transl. by Vera Higgins, "Succulent Plants." (London, 1935.) It seems permissible, however, to regard Huernia as a typographical error, under Article 70 of the Rules, and follow the common-sense spelling of majority European usage.

SUCCULENTS (HEURNIA), continued
as'pera
barba'ta
breviros'tris
clavig'era
hys'trix
kirk'i
loeseneria'na
longitu'ba
nouhuy'zi
pen'zigi
pil'lansi
primuli'na
reticula'ta
schneideria'na
thure'ti
transvaalen'sis
zebri'na

HEURNIOP'SIS (*HUERNIOPSIS*)
decip'iens

HOOD'IA
bain'i
dre'gei
gor'doni
jut'tiae
lugard'i
macran'tha

HUER'NIA . . . . . HEURNIA

HUERNIOP'SIS . HEURNIOPSIS

HYMENOCY'CLUS MESEMBRYANTHEMUM

ID'RIA
columna'ris . . BOOJAMTREE (*Cirio*)

KALANCHO'E (*BRYOPHYLLUM; KITCHINGIA*) KALANCHOE
alic'iae . . . . ALICIA K.
beharen'sis
bent'i . . . . K. teretifolia
blossfeldia'na (*K. globulifera coccinea*)
carne'a; coccin'ea . . . . K. laciniata
crena'ta . . . . SCALLOPED K.
daigremontia'na (*Bryophyllum daigremontianum*)
farina'cea . . . . K. scapigera
fedtschen'koi . . . FEDTSCHENKO K.
flam'mea . . . . FLAME K.
glauces'cens . . . . . . K. laciniata
globulif'era
—*coccin'ea* . . . . . . K. blossfeldiana
grandiflo'ra
grandiflo'ra A. Rich., *not* Wight & Arn. K. marmorata
∞kewen'sis (*flammea* × *teretifolia*) ∞KEW K.
kirk'i . . . . K. velutina
lacinia'ta (*carnea; coccinea; glaucescens; spathulata; welwitschi*)
laxiflo'ra (*Bryophyllum crenatum*)
marmora'ta (*grandiflora* A. Rich., *not* Wight & Arn.)
pelta'ta (*Kitchingia p.*)
pinna'ta (*Bryophyllum calycinum; B. pinnatum; Cotyledon pinnata*) AIRPLANT K.
scapig'era (*farinacea*)
somalien'sis . . . . SOMALI K.
spathula'ta . . . . K. laciniata
synsep'ala . . . . . MADAGASCAR K.
teretifo'lia (*benti*)
thyrsiflo'ra
uniflo'ra (*Bryophyllum uniflorum; Kitchingia uniflora*)
veluti'na (*kirki*)

SUCCULENTS (KALANCHOE), continued

verticilla'ta (*tubiflora; Bryophyllum tubiflorum*)

welwit'schi . . . . **K. laciniata**

KITCHING'IA . . **KALANCHOE**

KLEIN'IA . . . . KLEINIA

A largely African group botanically very close to Senecio, and not distinguished therefrom by some botanists.

acau'lis

amanien'sis . . . . **Notonia a.**

anteuphor'bium (*Senecio a.*)

articula'ta (*Senecio articulatus*)

CANDLEPLANT

cineras'cens . . . . Senecio c.

ficoi'des (*Senecio f.*) . . . . . FIG K.

ful'gens (*Senecio f.*)

gomphophyl'la

grant'i . . . . **Notonia g.**

ha'worthi . . . **Senecio cinerascens**

longiflo'ra

lon'gipes . . . . **Notonia granti**

mandralis'cae

neriifo'lia

odo'ra (*Senecio odorus*)

pen'dula . . . . **Notonia p.**

pugionifor'mis

rad'icans

re'pens (*Senecio succulentus*)

scapo'sa (*Senecio scaposus*)

stapeliaefor'mis (*Senecio s.*)

tomento'sa Hort. . **Senecio cinerascens**

tropaeolifo'lia . . . **S. tropaeolifolius**

LAMPRAN'THUS **MESEMBRYANTHEMUM**

LI'THOPS **MESEMBRYANTHEMUM**

MALEPH'ORA **MESEMBRYANTHEMUM**

MANFRE'DA

brachysta'chys (*Agave b.*)

maculo'sa (*Agave m.*)

variega'ta (*Agave v.*)

¢GIANT (*gigantea*) HV.

virgin'ica (*Agave v.*)

MESEMBRYAN'THEMUM (*Acrodon; Agnirictus; Aptenia; Argeta; Argyroderma; Aridaria; Astridia; Bergeranthus; Carpanthea; Carpobrotus; Cephalophyllum; Cerochlamys; Chasmatophyllum; Cheiridopsis; Conicosia; Conophytum; Corpuscularia; Cryophytum; Dactylopsis; Delosperma; Disphyma; Dorotheanthus; Drosanthemum; Erepsia; Faucaria; Fenestraria; Gibbaeum; Glottiphyllum; Hereroa; Hymenocyclus; Lampranthus; Lithops; Malephora; Mesembryanthemum; Nananthus; Odontophorus; Oophytum; Oscularia; Pleiospilos; Punctillaria; Rabiea; Rhombophyllum; Rimaria; Ruschia; Sceletium; Semmanthe; Stomatium; Titanopsis; Trichodiadema; Verrucifera*)

MESEMBRYANTHEMUM (*Figmarigold*)

The maritime species are often called Seafigs.

At the suggestion of its consulting experts in the Bureau of Plant Industry, the Editorial Committee maintains this extraordinarily diversified, difficult and imperfectly known group of plants, for the present at least, in the single genus Mesembryanthemum.

SUCCULENTS (MESEMBRYANTHEMUM), continued

aberdeenen'se (*Delosperma a.*)

acinacifor'me (*Carpobrotus acinaciformis*)

acu'tum . . . . . . **M. subulatoides**

aequilatera'le Auth., *not* Haw. **M. chilense**

aequilatera'le Haw. . **M. aequilaterum**

aequilat'erum (*aequilaterale* Haw., *not* Auth.; *Carpobrotus aequilaterus*)

KARKALLA MESEMBRYANTHEMUM

agni'num (*Agnirictus agninus; Stomatium agninum*)

aito'nis (*Cryophytum a.*)

albes'cens (*Conophytum a.*)

albiflo'rum (*Ruschia albiflora*)

albino'tum (*Rabiea albinota*)

albipunc'tum (*Rabiea albipuncta*)

al'bum (*Gibbaeum a.*)

aloi'des (*Nananthus a.*)

al'stoni (*Cephalophyllum a.*)

auranti'acum (*Lampranthus aurantiacus*)

au'reum (*Lampranthus aureus*)

austra'le (*Disphyma a.*)

barba'tum (*Trichodiadema b.*)

bellidiflo'rum (*Acrodon bellidiflorus*)

bellidifor'me (*criniflorum; Dorotheanus bellidiformis; D. criniflorus*)

bel'lum (*Cheiridopsis bella; Lithops bella*)

bijl'iae (*Ruschia b.*)

blan'dum

—curviflo'rum

bo'lusi (*Pleiospilos b.*) . . . BOLUS M.

bosschea'num (*Faucaria bosscheana; F. haagei*)

brown'i (*Lampranthus b.*)

brunntha'leri (*Delosperma b.*)

BRUNNTHALER M.

bulbo'sum (*Trichodiadema b.*)

calamifor'me (*Cylindrophyllum c.*)

calca'reum (*Titanopsis calcarea*)

cal'culus (*Conophytum c.*)

can'dens (*Drosanthemum c.*)

caroli-schmidt'i (*Cheiridopsis c.*)

caules'cens (*Oscularia c.*)

chilen'se (*aequilaterale* Auth., *not* Haw.; *Carpobrotus chilensis*) . CHILEAN M.

This is one of the Seafigs.

cigarettif'erum (*Cheiridopsis cigarettifera*)

coccin'eum (*Lampranthus coccineus*)

conspic'uum (*Lampranthus coccineus*)

cordifo'lium (*Aptenia cordifolia*)

HEARTLEAF M.

—variega'tum Hort. (*A. cordifolia variegata* Hort.)

crassifo'lium (*Disphyma c.*)

cras'sum (*Ruschia crassa*)

criniflo'rum . . . . **M. bellidiforme**

cro'ceum (*Hymenocyclus croceus*)

crystalli'num (*Cryophytum c.*)

ICEPLANT M.

dekena'hi (*Pleiospilos d.; Punctillaria d.*)

deltoi'des (*Oscularia d.*)

den'sum (*Trichodiadema d.*)

digita'tum (*Dactylopsis digitata*)

dolabrifor'me (*Hereroa dolabriformis; Rhombophyllum d.*)

echina'tum (*Delosperma e.*)

PICKLEPLANT

ecklo'nis (*Delosperma e.*)

ed'ule (*Carpobrotus edulis*)

HOTTENTOTFIG

elonga'tum (*Conicosia elongata*)

SUCCULENTS (MESEMBRYANTHEMUM), continued

emargina'tum (*violaceum; Lampranthus emarginatus*)

falca'tum

falcifor'me (*Lampranthus falciformis*)

feli'num (*Faucaria felina*)

filicau'le (*Lampranthus filicaulis*)

floribun'dum (*Drosanthemum f.*)

frames'i (*Drosanthemum f.*)

frutes'cens (*Conophytum f.*)

ful'leri (*Lithops f.; Stomatium f.*)

gem'inum (*Gibbaeum g.*)

glauces'cens (*Carpobrotus g.*)

glau'cum (*Lampranthus glaucus*)

glomera'tum (*Lampranthus glomeratus*)

gramin'eum (*pyropaeum; tricolor; Dorotheanthus gramineus*)

TRICOLOR MESEMBRYANTHEMUM

ha'worthi (*Erepsia h.; Lampranthus h.*)

heath'i (*Gibbaeum h.; Rimaria h.*)

her'rei (*Ruschia h.*) . . . . HERRE M.

hesperan'thum (*Hereroa hesperantha*)

heteropet'alum (*Erepsia heteropetala*)

his'pidum (*Drosanthemum h.*)

inaequa'le (*Cheiridopsis inaequalis*)

inclau'dens (*Erepsia i.*)

inton'sum (*Trichodiadema i.*)

lac'erum (*Semmanthe lacera*)

leh'manni (*Corpuscularia l.*)

les'liei (*Lithops l.*) . . . . LESLIE M.

linguifor'me (*Glottiphyllum l.*)

lon'gum (*Glottiphyllum l.*)

luederitz'i (*Drosanthemum l.*)

lupi'num (*Faucaria lupina*)

lute'um (*Hymenocyclus luteus*)

magnipuncta'tum (*Pleiospilos magnipunctatus; Punctillaria magnipunctata*)

mar'lothi (*Odontophorus m.*)

max'imum (*Astridia maxima*)

mey'eri (*Conophytum m.*)

minu'tum (*Conophytum m.*)

mirab'ile (*Trichodiadema m.*)

mul'ticeps (*Bergeranthus m.*)

multiflo'rum (*Ruschia multiflora*)

multiseria'tum (*Cheiridopsis multiseriata*)

muri'num (*Stomatium m.*)

musculi'num (*Chasmatophyllum m.*)

na'num (*Odontophorus nanus; Oophytum n.*)

nevil'lei (*Conophytum n.*)

no'bile (*Pleiospilos nobilis; Punctillaria n.*)

nodiflo'rum (*Cryophytum n.*)

obtu'sum (*Gibbaeum neli*)

octophyl'lum (*Argyroderma o.*)

EIGHTLEAF M.

odora'tum (*Conophytum odorata*)

pervir'ide (*Gibbaeum p.*)

pillans'i (*Cheiridopsis p.*)

pomeridia'num (*Carpanthea pomeridiana*)

praepin'gue (*Glottiphyllum p.*)

prismat'icum (*roodiae; Pleiospilos prismaticus; Rimaria r.*)

pseudotruncatel'lum (*Lithops pseudotruncatella*)

pubes'cens (*Gibbaeum p.*)

pugionifor'me (*Conicosia pugioniformis*)

pyg'maeum (*Ruschia pygmaea*)

pyropae'um . . . . **M. gramineum**

rhomboi'deum (*Rhombophyllum r.*)

rhopalophyl'lum (*Fenestraria rhopalophylla*)

rig'idum (*Ruschia rigida*)

robus'tum (*Delosperma r.*)

SUCCULENTS (MESEMBRYANTHEMUM), continued

rood'iae . . . . . . **M. prismaticum**
rose'um (*Lampranthus roseus*) ROSE MESEMBRYANTHEMUM
rubricau'le
rubrolinea'tum (*Nananthus rubrolineatus*)
rupic'ola (*Ruschia r.*)
scapig'erum (*Bergeranthus scapiger*)
schoenlandia'num (*Drosanthemum s.*) SCHOENLAND M.
schwant'esi (*Titanopsis s.; Verrucifera s.*)
serra'tum (*Erepsia serrata*)
serrula'tum (*Cheiridopsis serrulata; Ruschia s.*)
sim'ulans (*Pleiospilos s.*)
specio'sum (*Drosanthemum s.*)
spectab'ile (*Lampranthus spectabilis*)
splen'dens (*Aridaria s.*)
stan'leyi (*Hereroa s.*)
steingroe'veri (*Ruschia s.*)
stella'tum (*Trichodiadema s.*)
ste'num (*Lampranthus stenus*)
subcompres'sum (*Drosanthemum s.*)
subinca'num (*Delosperma subincana*)
subulatoi'des (*acutum; Cephalophyllum a.; C. subulatoides*)
tenuifo'lium (*Lampranthus tenuifolius*)
testa'ceum (*Delosperma t.*)
testicula're (*Argyroderma t.*)
The plants in cultivation under this name are frequently octophyllum.
thun'bergi (*Hymenocyclus t.; Malephora t.*)
tigri'num (*Faucaria tigrina*) TIGERSCLAW M.
tortuo'sum (*Sceletium t.*)
tri'color . . . . . . **M. gramineum**
tricolo'rum (*Cephalophyllum t.*)
trig'onum (*Cerochlamys trigona*)
truncatel'lum (*Conophytum t.*)
tubercula'tum (*Cheiridopsis tuberculata*)
tuberculo'sum (*Faucaria tuberculosa*)
uncina'tum (*Ruschia uncinata*)
veluti'num (*Astridia velutina; Gibbaeum velutinum*)
vesperti'num (*Bergeranthus vespertinus*)
viola'ceum . . . . . **M. emarginatum**
vitta'tum (*Nananthus vittatus*)
zey'heri (*Lampranthus z.*)

MONADE'NIUM
lugar'dae

MONAN'THES (*PETROPHYES*) MONANTHES
atlan'tica . . . . **Sedum atlanticum**
brachycau'lon (*Sempervivum lowei*) CANARIES M.
laxiflo'ra . . . . EGGLEAF M.

NANAN'THUS **MESEMBRYANTHEMUM**

NOTO'NIA . . . . . . NOTONIA
Genus somewhat doubtfully distinct from Kleinia and Senecio.
amanien'sis (*Kleinia a.*)
glau'ca . . . . ANGOLA N.
grant'i (*Kleinia g.; K. longipes; Senecio l.*) . . . . GRANTS N.
madagascarien'sis . MADAGASCAR N.
pen'dula (*Kleinia p.; Senecio pendulus*) ARABIAN N.

ODONTOPH'ORUS **MESEMBRYANTHEMUM**

SUCCULENTS, continued

OLIVERAN'THUS . **ECHEVERIA**

OOPHY'TUM **MESEMBRYANTHEMUM**

OROSTACH'YS . . . . **SEDUM**

OSCULA'RIA **MESEMBRYANTHEMUM**

OTHON'NA . . . . . . OTHONNA
carno'sa . . . . SHRUBBY O.
crassifo'lia (*capensis*) LITTLEPICKLE O.

PACHYPHY'TUM
amethyst'inum . . . **Graptopetalum a.**
bracteo'sum (*Cotyledon pachyphytum*)
brevifo'lium
compac'tum
hook'eri (*aduncum; roseum* Hort.; *Cotyledon adunca; Echeveria a.; E. hookeri*)
lin'gua Hort. . **Echeveria linguaefolia**
longifo'lium
ovif'erum
×**pachyphytoi'des** (*bracteosum × Echeveria gibbiflora metallica*)
uniflo'rum

∞**PACHYVE'RIA** (*ECHEVERIA × PACHYPHYTUM*) ∞PACHYVERIA
∞**clava'ta** (*Echeveria* sp. ? ×*P. bracteosum*)
∞*cleve'landi* (*E. secunda* × *P. bracteosum*)
This name for this intergeneric specific cross apparently should be superseded by the older ∞P. scheideckeri, with CLEVELAND as a clon of the latter.
∞**glau'ca** (*Echeveria* sp.? × *P. hookeri*)
∞**or'peti** Hort. (*Echeveria* sp.? × *P. bracteosum*)
∞**scheideck'eri** (*E. secunda × P. bracteosum;* ∞ *Echeveria s.* Hort.)
See note under ∞P. clevelandi.
∞**sobri'na** (*Echeveria* sp. × *P. bracteosum*)

PEDILAN'THUS . SLIPPERFLOWER
aphyl'lus
macrocar'pus
pavo'nis . . . . WAX S.
retu'sus
tithymaloi'des . . . . . REDBIRD S. (*Jewbush; Niggermouth*)
—**cuculla'tus**
—**variega'tus**

PELARGO'NIUM. . PELARGONIUM
echina'tum . . . . SPINY P.

PEN'THORUM . . . PENTHORUM
sedoi'des (*chinense*) . . . VIRGINIA P. (*Ditch Stonecrop*)

PETROPHY'ES . **MONANTHES**

PIARAN'THUS
cornu'tus
foe'tidus

PLEIOSPI'LOS **MESEMBRYANTHEMUM**

POINSET'TIA . . **EUPHORBIA**

PORTULACA'RIA
af'ra

PUNCTILLA'RIA; RABIE'A **MESEMBRYANTHEMUM**

RHODIO'LA . . . . . **SEDUM**
integrifo'lia . . . . **S. integrifolium; S. rosea integrifolium**
odora'ta . . . . **S. rosea**
roanen'sis . . . . **S. rosea roanense**

SUCCULENTS, continued

RHOMBOPHYL'LUM; RIMA'RIA **MESEMBRYANTHEMUM**

RO'CHEA . . . . ROCHEA
albiflo'ra . . . . **Crassula a.**
coccin'ea (*Crassula c.*) . . SCARLET R.
falca'ta . . . . **Crassula f.**
perfolia'ta . . . . **Crassula p.**
versic'olor

ROSULA'RIA . . . . **SEDUM; UMBILICUS**
platyphyl'la . . . **S. sempervivoides**

RUSCH'IA; SCELE'TIUM **MESEMBRYANTHEMUM**

SEDAS'TRUM . . . . **SEDUM**

SE'DUM (*ANACAMPSEROS* Haw., *not* L.; *CLEMENTSIA; GORMANIA; OROSTACHYS; RHODIOLA; ROSULARIA* in part; *SEDASTRUM*) |w STONECROP
a'cre . . . . GOLDMOSS S.
—**al'bum** . . . . WHITE G.S.
—**au'reum** . . . . YELLOWLEAF G.S.
—**el'egans**
—**ma'jus** . . . . BIG G.S.
—**mi'nus** . . . . LITTLE G.S.
—**robus'tum** (*S. robustum* Domin., *not* Praeq.)
acumina'tum (*Sempervivum a.,* Dcne., *not* Schott)
—**mucrona'tum** (*Sempervivum fimbriatum* Klotzsch)
acutifo'lium . . . . . . **S. subulatum**
adol'phi . . . . ADOLPH S.
ai'zoon (*laggeri* Hort.; *maximowiczi*) AIZOON S.
—**auranti'acum**
—**floribun'dum**
al'berti (*Sempervivum a.*) . ALBERT S.
al'berti Praeg., *not* Reg. . . **S. gracile**
alborose'um (*japonicum; macrophyllum* Hort. in part) . . . . . BLUSH S.
The forms medio-variegatis and margine-variegatis are recognized.
al'bum (*balticum; turgidum*). WHITE S.
—**atho'um** (*S. athoum*)
—**brevifo'lium**
—**chlorot'icum** . . . LITTLEFLOWER S.
—**micran'thum**
—**mura'le** (*S. murale*)
—**purpu'reum** Hort.
allantoi'des
altis'simum . . . . **S. sediforme**
amecameca'num (*amaramacanthum* Hort.)
amplexicau'le. . . . . **S. tenuifolium**
anacamp'seros (*rotundifolium*) . SHY S.
an'glicum . . . . ENGLISH S.
—**mi'nus** . . . . LITTLE E.S.
an'nuum . . . . ANNUAL S.
anom'alum
anopet'alum
arbo'reum Hegi . . . . . **Aeonium a.**
arbo'reum Hort.
Various species are offered in the trade under this untenable name, including Crassula argentea, Sedum moranense, and S. sediforme.
asiat'icum . . . . **S. crassipes**
atho'um . . . . **S. album a.**
atlan'ticum (*Monanthes atlantica*) MOROCCAN S.
atra'tum

SUCCULENTS (SEDUM), continued
atropurpu'reum Hort.. **S. maximum a.; S. spectabile a.**
atyp'icum **Graptopetalum pachyphyllum**
au'reum Hort. . . . . **S. mexicanum**
bal'ticum . . . . **S. album**
bolonien'se . . . . . . **S. sexangulare**
bor'deri . . . . . . **S. telephium b.**
bornmuel'leri (*rhodanthum* Bornm., *not* A. Gray)
braun'i Hort.
A name applied to S. kamtschaticum and to S. spurium.
brevifo'lium (*pittoni*) SHORTLEAF STONECROP
brown'i Hort.
A name of no botanical standing applied to various species, particularly to a var. of S. aizoon. Apparently a variation of *S. brauni* Hort.
caeru'leum . . . . BLUE S.
candol'lei (*Umbilicus sedoides*)
car'neum Hort. . **S. lineare variegatum**
—*variega'tum* Hort. . . . **S. lineare v.**
carpa'ticum . . **S. telephium borderi**
chrysan'thum (*Cotyledon chrysantha; Umbilicus chrysanthus*)
coccin'eum Hort., *not* Royle **S. spurium**
coccin'eum Royle, *not* Hort. **S. quadrifidum**
compres'sum
confu'sum
cor'sicum **S. dasyphyllum glanduliferum**
cras'sipes (*asiaticum; wallichianum*)
crassula'ria (*sediforme* Hamet, *not* Jacq.)
crista'tum . . . . **S. rupestre**
crucia'tum . . . . . **S. monregalense**
cruen'tum Hort.
cupressoi'des . . . . . CYPRESS S.
cu'preum Hort. . . . . . COPPER S.
dasyphyl'lum (*glaucum* Lam., *not* Waldst. & Kit.) . . . . LEAFY S.
—**glandulif'erum** (*S. corsicum*)
—**glau'cum** Hort.
—**macrophyl'lum**
dendroi'deum
This name is sometimes misapplied to Crassula argentea (*portulacea*).
diffu'sum
This name is sometimes misapplied to S. potosinum.
diver'gens
doug'lasi
ebractea'tum (*Sedastrum e.*)
el'egans . . . . **S. rupestre**
ellacombia'num
ew'ersi . . . . EWERS S.
—**homophyl'lum**
faba'ria Hort., *not* Koch. . **S. spectabile**
faba'ria Koch., *not* Hort. **S. telephium f.**
fimbria'tum (*Cotyledon fimbriata*)
—**chan'eti** (*Orostachys c.*)
florif'erum
Hardly more than a var. or form of S. kamtschaticum.
forsteria'num . . . . . **S. rupestre f.**
frig'idum . . . . . **S. integrifolium**
fusifor'me
glau'cum Lam. . . . **S. dasyphyllum**
glau'cum Waldst. & Kit. **S. hispanicum bithynicum**
—*pal'lidum* . . . . . . **S. pallidum**
grac'ile (*alberti* Praeg., *not* Reg.)
gregg'i
guatemalen'se . . . . GUATEMALA S.
gypsic'ola . . . . GYPSUM S.

SUCCULENTS (SEDUM), continued
hirsu'tum . . . . HAIRY STONECROP
hispan'icum . . . . SPANISH S.
—**bithyn'icum** (*S. glaucum* Waldst. & Kit., *not* Lam.; *S. h. minus; S. lydium g.* Hort.)
hy'bridum (*sibiricum*) . EVERGREEN S.
ibe'ricum . . . . . **S. stoloniferum**
integrifo'lium (*frigidum; rhodioloides; Rhodiola integrifolia*)
japon'icum . . . . . . **S. alboroseum**
kamtschat'icum . . . . ORANGE S.
—**variega'tum** . . . . VARIEGATED S.
lag'geri Hort. . . . . . . **S. aizoon**
lancerotten'se . . . . LANZAROTE S.
lax'um (*Echeveria gormania; Gormania laxa*)
liebmannia'num . . . LIEBMANN S.
linea're
—**robus'tum**
—**variega'tum** (*S. carneum* Hort.; *S. carneum v.* Hort.; *S. sarmentosum v.* Hort.)
lon'gipes
lycopodioi'des . . . . . **Crassula l.**
ly'dium . . . . LYDIAN S.
—*glau'cum* Hort. **S. hispanicum bithynicum**
macrophyl'lum Hort. **S. alboroseum; S. maximum**
magellen'se
—**olym'picum** (*S. olympicum*)
maximowicz'i . . . . **S. aizoon**
max'imum (*S. telephium m.*). GREAT S.
—**atropurpu'reum** (*S. atropurpureum* Hort.)
—**haemato'des** . . . . . REDTIP G.S.
—**variega'tum**
mexica'num (*aureum* Hort.; *sarmentosum* Mast., *not* Bunge)
middendorffia'num . MIDDENDORF S.
—**diffu'sum**
monregalen'se (*cruciatum*)
moranen'se . . . . MORAN S.
This name is sometimes misapplied to S. greggi and S. liebmannianum.
mul'ticeps
mura'le . . . . **S. album m.**
nevaden'se
nev'i
—**beyrichia'num**
nicaeen'se . . . . **S. sediforme**
nuttallia'num (*torreyi*) . . NUTTALL S.
oaxaca'num . . . . OAXACA S.
obtusa'tum (*Echeveria obtusata; Gormania o.*)
obtusa'tum Hort., *not* A. Gray **S. oreganum**
obtusifo'lium
olym'picum . . . . **S. magellense o.**
oppositifo'lium . . . . . **S. spurium**
orega'num (*obtusatum* Hort., *not* A. Gray; *Echeveria oregana; Gormania o.*) . . . . OREGON S.
oxypet'alum
pachyphyl'lum
pal'lidum (*S. glaucum p.*) . PLUME S.
pal'meri . . . . PALMER S.
pilo'sum (*regeli* Hort.; *Umbilicus pubescens*)
pit'toni . . . . **S. brevifolium**
populifo'lium . . . . POPLAR S.
portulaccoi'des Hort. . . **S. spurium**
potosi'num . . . . SANLUISPOTOSI S.
praeal'tum
pruina'tum
pruina'tum Auth., *not* Brot. **S. rupestre**
—*forsteria'num* . . . . **S. rupestre f.**

SUCCULENTS (SEDUM), continued
pruinoi'des Hort.
Botanical identity uncertain.
pruino'sum
Possibly a form of or even synonymous with S. spathulifolium.
pulchel'lum . . . TEXAS STONECROP
This name is often misapplied to S. mite.
pur'dyi . . . . PURDY S.
This name is sometimes misapplied to other species.
purpuras'cens Hort.
This name appears to be a synonym of Aeonium arboreum and possibly other members of the Crassulaceae.
purpuras'cens Koch. **S. telephium purpureum**
purpu'reum Hort.
An indefinite trade name used for purple-flowered varieties of miscellaneous species.
quadrif'idum (*coccineum* Royle, *not* Hort.)
radia'tum
reflex'um (*rupestre* Auth., *not* L.) JENNY S.
—**albes'cens** . . . . . . CREAM J.S.
—**crista'tum**
—**mi'nus**
re'geli Hort. . . . . **S. pilosum**
replesia'num Hort.
Botanical identity uncertain.
rhodan'thum (*Clementsia rhodantha*)
rhodan'thum Bornm., *not* A. Gray **S. bornmuelleri**
rhodio'la . . . . **S. rosea**
rhodioloi'des . . . . **S. integrifolium**
rhodocar'pum . . . . . . REDPOD S.
roanen'se . . . . **S. rosea r.**
robus'tum
robus'tum Domin., *not* Praeq. **S. acre r.**
rose'a (*rhodiola; roseum; Rhodiola odorata; R. roseum*) . . ROSEROOT S.
—**integrifo'lium** (*Rhodiola integrifolia*)
—**roanen'se** (*S. roanense; Rhodiola roanensis*)
rotundifo'lium . . . **S. anacampseros**
ru'bens (*Crassula r.*) . . . . RED S.
rupes'tre (*cristatum; elegans; pruinatum* Auth., *not* Brot.)
—**forsteria'num** (*S. forsterianum; S. pruinatum f.*)
—**mi'nus**
rupes'tre Auth., *not* L. . . **S. reflexum**
sarmento'sum . . . . . STRINGY S.
—*variega'tum* Hort. . . . **S. lineare v.**
sarmento'sum Mast., *not* Bunge **S. mexicanum**
sartoria'num . . . . . . TAILORS S.
This name is frequently misapplied to S. stribrnyi.
schott'i Hort. . . . . . SCHOTTS S.
sedifor'me (*altissimum; nicaeense; Sempervivum s.*)
sedifor'me Hamet, *not* Jacq. **S. crassularia**
selskia'num
semeno'vi (*Cotyledon s.; Umbilicus s.*)
sempervivoi'des (*sempervivum; Cotyledon platyphylla* Schrenk., *not* Boiss.; *Rosularia p.; Umbilicus platyphyllus*) FALSEHOUSELEEK
sexangula're (*boloniense*) . HEXAGON S.
sibir'icum . . . . **S. hybridum**
siebold'i . . . . SIEBOLD S.

SUCCULENTS (SEDUM), continued

spathulifo'lium
This name is sometimes misapplied to S. confusum.

—purpu'reum
—*ru'brum* Hort.
This name appears to be a synonym of S. spathulifolium purpureum.

specio'sum Hort.
spectab'ile (*fabaria* Hort., *not* Koch; *Anacampseros s.*) SHOWY STONECROP
—al'bum . . . . . . WHITE S.S.
—atropurpu'reum . . . PURPLE S.S.
spino'sum (*Cotyledon spinosa; Orostachys s.; Umbilicus spinosus*)
spu'rium (*coccineum* Hort., *not* Royle; *oppositifolium; portulaccoides* Hort.; *splendens* Hort.; *stoloniferum* Hort., *not* Gmel.) . . . . . . TWOROW S.
White-flowered (S. oppositifolium), scarlet-red (S. coccineum Hort.), and a carmine-red (S. splendens Hort.) form are recognized.

stahl'i . . . . STAHL S.
stella'tum . . . . STAR S.
stenopet'alum (*S. s. subalpinum*) WORMLEAF S.
stolonif'erum (*ibericum*) . RUNNING S.
—coccin'eum . . . . SCARLET R.S.
stolonif'erum Hort., *not* Gmel. **S. spurium**
strib'rnyi . . . . STRIBRNY S.
subula'tum (*acutifolium*)
telephioi'des . . . . . . ALLEGANY S.
tele'phium . . . . LIVEFOREVER S. (*Liveforever*)
—bor'deri (*S. carpaticum; S. borderi*)
—faba'ria (*S. fabaria* Koch, *not* Hort.)
—*max'imum* . . . . . . **S. maximum**
—purpu'reum (*S. purpurascens* Koch, *not* Hort.; *S. triphyllum*)
tenel'lum
tenuifo'lium (*amplexicaule; Sempervivum anomalum* Lag., *not* Hort.; *S. tenuifolium*)
terna'tum . . . . . . MOUNTAIN S.
tor'reyi . . . . . . **S. nuttallianum**
tortuo'sum
tournefort'i Hort.
Botanical identity uncertain.

treleas'ei . . . . TRELEASE S.
triphyl'lum . **S. telephium purpureum**
tur'gidum . . . . **S. album**
uniflo'rum . . . . . . ONEFLOWER S.
villo'sum
wallichia'num . . . . . **S. crassipes**
wat'soni (*Echeveria w.; Gormania w.*) WATSON S.
wein'bergi **Graptopetalum paraguayense**
wink'leri (*Cotyledon w.; Umbilicus w.*) WINKLER S.
wood'i . . . . WOODS S.
yosemiten'se . . . . . . YOSEMITE S.
Hardly more than a var. of S. spathulifolium.

SEMMAN'THE **MESEMBRYANTHEMUM**

SEMPERVI'VUM . . HOUSELEEK
acumina'tum Dcne., *not* Schott. **Sedum a.**
acumina'tum Schott., *not* Dcne. **S. tectorum glaucum**
admonten'se Hort.
al'berti . . . . **Sedum a.**
al'bidum . . . . . . **S. tectorum** form

SUCCULENTS (SEMPERVIVUM), con.

allio'ni (*arenarium* Schott, *not* Koch *nor* Stev.; *austriacum; hirsutum; hirtum* Auth., *not* Sibth. & Sm. *nor* L.)
alpes'tre . . . . **S. montanum**
alpi'num . . . . . . **S. tectorum a.**
∞ *angustifo'lium*
See note on ∞S. schnittspahni, of which this is presumably a clon or other variation.

an'nuum . . **Aichryson dichotomum**
anom'alum Hort., *not* Lag. **S. montanum**
This name is also misapplied to forms of S. tectorum.

anom'alum Lag., *not* Hort. **Sedum tenuifolium**
arachnoi'deum (*sanguineum*) SPIDERWEB HOUSELEEK
—glabres'cens (*S. doellianum; S. heterotrichum; ?S. moggridgei*)
—lag'geri (*S. laggeri*)
—pilif'erum (*S. piliferum*)
It is suspected that S. piliferum may actually be a hybrid between S. arachnoideum and S. tectorum.

—tomento'sum (*S. tomentosum; S. webbianum*)
arbo'reum (Bory) Ktze., *not* L. **Aeonium holochrysum**
arbo'reum L., *not* (Bory) Ktze. **Aeonium a.**
arena'rium (*cornutum* Hort.; *kochi*) SAND H.
arena'rium Schott, *not* Koch. **S. allioni**
arena'rium Stev., *not* Koch **S. ruthenicum**
arvernen'se . . . . . . **S. tectorum a.**
assim'ile . . . . **S. schlehani**
This name is also sometimes misapplied to S. tectorum in the American trade.

atlan'ticum . . . . . . ATLANTIC H.
Hardly more than a var. of S. tectorum.

austri'acum . . . . **S. allioni**
balsamif'erum . . . . . **Aeonium b.**
∞ **barbula'tum** (*arachnoideum* × *montanum*)
At least six names are used for polybrids of the cross between S. arachnoideum and S. montanum, including ∞S. barbatulum; barbulatum; dolomiticum Huter, *not* Faech.; elegans; fimbriatum Schnitt. & Lehm. (*not* Schott.); and funcki Auth. (*not* F. Braun *nor* Jord. & Fourr.). Of these, ∞**S. barbulatum** Schott. (1853) would appear to have priority. The other names presumably should be reduced to varietal, clonal or other status under ∞S. barbulatum.

blan'dum . . . . **S. schlehani**
boissier'i Hort. . . . . . **S. tectorum**
bo'risi . . . . **S. ciliosum**
braun'i (*browni*) Hort. . . BRAUNS H.
A pale-flowered Tyrolese form, perhaps better referable to forms of S. montanum or S. tectorum.

burch'ardi . . . . **Aeonium b.**
caespito'sum . . . . . . **Aeonium c.**
calca'reum . . . . . . **S. tectorum c.**
califor'nicum Hort. **S. tectorum calcareum**
canarien'se . . . . **Aeonium c.**
canta'licum . . . . . . **S. tectorum**
castello-pai'viae . . . . . **Aeonium c.**
cilia'tum Auth., *not* Willd. . **S. ciliosum** and **S. tectorum**, mainly
cilia'tum Willd., *not* Auth. **Aeonium c.**
cilio'sum (*borisi; ciliatum* Auth., *not* Willd. in part; *wulfeni* Velenov., *not* Hoppe *nor* Bert.)

SUCCULENTS (SEMPERVIVUM), con.

cineras'cens . . . . . **S. erythraeum**
comol'li Rota
Probably a hybrid between S. tectorum and S. wulfeni.

compac'tum . . . . **S. tectorum**
cornu'tum Hort. . . . **S. arenarium**
cruen'tum . . **Aeonium spathulatum c.**
cunea'tum . . . . **Aeonium c.**
deb'ile . . . . **S. montanum**
deco'rum . . . . **Aeonium d.**
dichot'omum DC. . . . . **Aichryson d.**
diplocy'clum . . **Greenovia diplocycla**
dodrenta'le . . **Greenovia dodrentalis**
doellia'num **S. arachnoideum glabrescens**
dolomit'icum . DOLOMITE HOUSELEEK
∞ *dolomit'icum* Huter, *not* Faech.
See note on ∞S. barbulatum, of which this is presumably a clon or other variation.

domes'ticum . . . . . . **Aichryson d.**
∞ *el'egans*
See note on ∞S. barbulatum, of which this is presumably a clon or other variation.

erythrae'um (*cinerascens*)
fauconnet'ti (*flavipilum*)
S. fauconnetti is possibly a hybrid between S. arachnoideum and S. montanum. If so, it is probably the oldest name for that polybrid.

∞ **fimbria'tum** Schnitt. & Lehm.
See note on ∞S. barbulatum, of which this is presumably a clon or other variation.

∞ **fimbria'tum** Schott (*arachnoideum* × *wulfeni*)
This polybrid may have to be renamed, if S. fimbriatum proves to be a homonym.

fimbria'tum Klotzsch, *not* Schnitt. & Lehm. **Sedum acuminatum mucronatum**
flavip'ilum . . . . . . **S. fauconnetti**
∞ *funck'i* Auth., *not* F. Braun *nor* Jourd. & Fourr.
See note on ∞S. barbulatum, of which this is presumably a clon or other variation.

×**funck'i** F. Braun.
A multiple hybrid.

∞ *funck'i* Jord. & Fourr.
See note on ∞S. schotti, of which this is presumably a clon or other variation.

gaudi'ni . . . . . . **S. grandiflorum**
glau'cum . . . . . . **S. tectorum g.**
globif'erum Hort.
The plant ordinarily in the trade under this name appears to be a form or hybrid of S. montanum. Botanically, the species named globiferum by various authors refer to at least five different species, as listed below.

globif'erum Curt. . . **S. grandiflorum**
globif'erum Jacq. . . . . . **S. hirtum**
globif'erum L. in part . **S. ruthenicum**
globif'erum Reichb. . . **S. soboliferum**
globif'erum Wulf. . . . . **S. wulfeni**
glutino'sum . . . . . . **Aeonium g.**
gooch'iae . . . . **Aeonium g.**
grac'ile . . . **Greenovia dodrentalis**
grandiflo'rum (*gaudini; globiferum* Curt., *not* L.)
green'i . . . **?S. tectorum calcareum**
guillemo'ti . . . . **S. tectorum**
haus'manni
Thought to be a hybrid between S. arachnoideum and S. montanum.

ha'worthi Hort. . . . . **Aeonium h.**
heterot'richum **S. arachnoideum glabrescens**

SUCCULENTS (SEMPERVIVUM), con.
heuf'feli (*hirtum* Sibth. & Sm., *not* L. *nor* Auth.; *patens; reginae-amaliae* Baker, *not* Heldr. & Sarnt.)
hierren'se . . . . **Aeonium h.**
hillebrandt'i . . . Form of **S. hirtum**
hirsu'tum . . . . **S. allioni**
hir'tum (*globiferum* Jacq.)
ITALIAN HOUSELEEK
The forms hillebrandti and neilreichi are recognized.
hir'tum Auth., *not* L. . . . **S. allioni**
The name is also misapplied to a number of other species.
hir'tum Sibth. & Sm., *not* L.
S. heuffeli
holochry'sum . . . . . . **Aeonium h.**
juraten'se . . . . **S. tectorum**
kingding'eri
koch'i . . . . **S. arenarium**
lag'geri . . . . . **S. arachnoideum l.**
laharp'ei Hort. . . . . . LAHARPE H.
lamot'tei Hort. . . . . . LAMOTTE H.
A form of S. tectorum or a hybrid from it.
lesuri'num . . . . **S. tectorum**
lind'leyi . . . . **Aeonium l.**
low'ei . . . **Monanthes brachycaulon**
manriqueo'rum . . . . . **Aeonium m.**
∞ **mettenia'num** Hausm.
See note on ∞S. schnittspahni, of which this is presumably a clon or other variation.
mettenia'num Schnitt. & Lehm., *not* Hausm. . . . Form of **S. tectorum**
minu'tum . . . . **S. tectorum**
∞ *modes'tum*
See note on ∞S. schotti, of which this is presumably a clon or other variation.
mog'gridgei
?S. arachnoideum glabrescens
monta'num (*alpestre; anomalum* Hort., *not* Lag.; *debile*)
neilreich'i . . . . Form of **S. hirtum**
no'bile . . . . **Aeonium n.**
pal'lidum . . . . **S. tectorum**
∞ *par'vulum*
See note on ∞S. schotti, of which this is presumably a clon or other variation.
pa'tens . . . . **S. heuffeli**
∞ *penicilla'tum*
See note on ∞S. schnittspahni, of which this is presumably a clon or other variation.
percar'neum . . . . . . **Aeonium p.**
pilif'erum . . . . **S. arachnoideum p.**
∞ *pilosel'la*
See note on ∞S. schnittspahni, of which this is presumably a clon or other variation.
pitto'ni . . . . PITTON H.
∞ *po'meli*
One of the numerous specific names given to a hybrid of S. arachnoideum × tectorum. See note on ∞S. schnittspahni.
pulchel'lum
Aeonium spathulatum cruentum
pu'milum
pyg'maeum . . **Aichryson tortuosum**
pyrena'icum . . . . **S. tectorum** form
reginae-ama'liae Baker . . **S. heuffeli**
reginae-ama'liae Heldr. & Sarnt.
S. schlehani
∞ *rhae'ticum*
See note on ∞S. schotti, of which this is presumably a clon or other variation.
rhoda'nicum . . . . . . **S. tectorum**
robus'tum . . . . . . **S. tectorum r.**

SUCCULENTS (SEMPERVIVUM), con.
robus'tum; roya'num **S. tectorum** forms
rubicun'dum . . . . **S. schlehani**
∞ **rupic'ola** (*montanum* × *wulfeni*)
ruthe'nicum (*arenarium* Stev., *not* Koch *nor* Schott; *globiferum* L. in part; *zelebori*)
sanguin'eum . . . . **S. arachnoideum**
schle'hani (*assimile; blandum; reginae-amaliae* Heldr. & Sarnt., *not* Baker; *rubicundum*)
—brunneifo'lium
∞ **schnittspahn'i** (*arachnoideum* × *tectorum*)
At least five other names are in use for polybrids of the cross between S. arachnoideum and S. tectorum, including S. angustifolium, mettenianum Hausm., *not* Schnitt. & Lehm.; penicillatum, pilosella, and pomeli. See also S. fauconnetti and S. piliferum (see note under S. arachnoideum p.), both older names than S. schnittspahni. If S. fauconnetti should be definitely proved to be a cross between the parents above mentioned, that name, being the oldest, should stand for the group. Meanwhile S. schnittspahni Lagg. (1858) appears to have priority for those of known parentage.
∞ **schott'i** (*montanum* × *tectorum*)
∞ SCHOTT HOUSELEEK
At least six other names are in use for polybrids of the cross between S. montanum and S. tectorum, including S. funcki Jord. & Fourr., *not* F. Braun; modestum; parviflorum; parvulum; rhaeticum, and verloti. S. schotti Lehm. & Schnitt. (1860) appears to have priority. The other names presumably should be reduced to varietal, clonal or other status under S. schotti.
schott'i Baker (1874), *not* Lehm. & Schnitt. (1860) **S. tectorum glaucum**
sedifo'lium . . . . **Aeonium s.**
sedifor'me . . . . **Sedum s.**
sobolif'erum (*globiferum* Reichb.)
This name is sometimes misapplied to S. montanum and S. tectorum.
spathula'tum . . . . . . **Aeonium s.**
tabulaefor'me . . . . . . **Aeonium t.**
tecto'rum (*albidum; arvernense; boissieri* Hort.; *cantalicum; ciliatum* Auth., *not* Willd., in part.; *compactum; guillemoti; juratense; lesurinum; mettenianum* Schnitt. & Lehm., *not* Hausm.; *minutum; pallidum; pyrenaicum; rhodanicum; triste* Hort.; *violascens*) . . . HEN-AND-CHICKENS (*Roof Houseleek*)
—alpi'num (*S. alpinum*)
—calca'reum (*S. calcareum; S. californicum* Hort.; *?S. greeni*)
—glau'cum (*S. acuminatum* Schott, *not* Dcne.; *S. glaucum; S. schotti* Baker, *not* Lehm. & Schnitt.)
—robus'tum (*S. robustum*)
tenuifo'lium . . . . **Sedum t.**
thomay'eri
Usually thought to be a hybrid of S. arachnoideum × tectorum, but some botanists consider it to be a natural species.
tomento'sum . . . **S. arachnoideum t.**
tortuo'sum Ait., *not* DC. & Auth.
Aichryson t.
tortuo'sum DC. & Auth., *not* Ait.
×Aichryson domesticum
tortuo'sum Link, *not* Ait. *nor* DC. & Auth. . . . . . . **Aeonium lindleyi**
tris'te Hort. . . . . **S. tectorum** form

SUCCULENTS (SEMPERVIVUM), con.
undula'tum . . . . . . **Aeonium u.**
urb'icum C. Smith. . . . **Aeonium u.**
urb'icum Hook. f. **Aeonium undulatum**
urb'icum Lindl. **Aeonium holochrysum**
∞ *verlo'ti*
See note on ∞S. schotti, of which this is presumably a clon or other variation.
villo'sum
villo'sum Ait., *not* Lamotte
Aichryson v.
villo'sum Haw., *not* Lamotte
Aichryson tortuosum
villo'sum Lindl., *not* Lamotte
Aeonium spathulatum
viola'ceum Hort.
violas'cens . . . . **S. tectorum**
webbia'num
S. arachnoideum tomentosum
wul'feni (*globiferum* Wulf.)
wul'feni Velenov., *not* Hoppe
S. ciliosum
zelebo'ri . . . . . . **S. ruthenicum**

SESU'VIUM . . . . . . SESUVIUM
portulacas'trum (*sessile*) . PURSLANE S.

STAPE'LIA . . . CARRIONFLOWER
albo-casta'nea (*caroli-schmidti*)
ar'noti
aste'rias . . . . STARFISH C.
bay'fieldi
Perhaps a hybrid.
bi'color Hort.
caroli-schmidt'i . . . **S. albo-castanea**
deflex'a
desmetia'na
din'teri
∞ **dis'color** (*Stapelia* sp.? × *variegata*)
flaviros'tris
gettleff'i
gigan'tea
glabricau'lis
glabriflo'ra
grandiflo'ra
×**hanburya'na**
Parentage uncertain.
hirsu'ta
—depres'sa
kweben'sis
maccabe'ana
maculo'sa
margari'ta
mutab'ilis
no'bilis
pachyrrhi'za
peg'lerae
pulchel'la
∞ **purpu'rea** Hort. (*Stapelia* sp.? × *variegata*)
∞ **radia'ta** (*Stapelia* sp.? × *variegata; Duvalia elegans*)
∞ **salmia'na** Hort. (*Stapelia* sp.? × *variegata*)
schinz'i
scutella'ta
tsomoen'sis (*tomentosa*)
∞ **ura'nus** (*Stapelia* sp.? × *mutabilis*)
variega'ta
—atra'ta
—atropurpu'rea
—clypea'ta
—conspurca'ta
—pic'ta
—rugo'sa
—trisul'ca
verruco'sa
vet'ula

SUCCULENTS, continued
STOMA'TIUM **MESEMBRYANTHEMUM**

STYLOPHYL'LUM **ECHEVERIA**
nudicau'le . . . . **E. densiflora**
orcut'ti . . . . **E. attenuata**

SYNADE'NIUM . . . . MILKBUSH
arbores'cens . . . . ZEBRAPOISON M.
grant'i . . . . GRANTS M.

TILLAE'A . . . . . . PYGMYWEED
aquat'ica (*Crassula a.*) . COMMON P.

TITANOP'SIS **MESEMBRYANTHEMUM**

TITHYMALOP'SIS; TITHYMA'LUS . . . . **EUPHORBIA**

TRICHODIADE'MA **MESEMBRYANTHEMUM**

TRICHOSTERIG'MA **EUPHORBIA**

UMBIL'ICUS (*ROSULARIA* in part) . . . . NAVELWORT
chrysan'thus . . **Sedum chrysanthum**
horizonta'lis
panicula'tus (*platyphyllus* Boiss., *not* Schrenk; *Rosularia paniculata*)
penduli'nus (*Cotyledon pendulina; C. umbilicus*) . . . . . . NODDING N.
platyphyl'lus . **Sedum sempervivoides**
pubes'cens . . . . . **Sedum pilosum**
sedoi'des . . . . . **Sedum candollei**
semeno'vi . . . . **Sedum s.**
spino'sus . . . . . **Sedum spinosum**
wink'leri . . . . **Sedum w.**

URBIN'IA . . . . **ECHEVERIA**
purpus'i . . . . **E. purpusorum**

VAUAN'THES (*GRAMMANTHES*) . . . . LETTERFLOWER
dichot'oma (*chloraeflora; Crassula d.; Grammanthes chloraeflora; G. dichotoma; G. gentianoides*)

VERRUCIF'ERA **MESEMBRYANTHEMUM**

VILLA'DIA (*ALTAMIRANOA*) VILLADIA
elonga'ta (*Altamiranoa e.*)
ramosis'sima

ZYGOPHYLLID'IUM **EUPHORBIA**

SUCK'LEYA . . . . SUCKLEYA
suckleya'na (*petiolaris; Atriplex s.; Obione s.*) . . . . . POISON S.

SUDANGRASS **Sorghum vulgare sudanense**

SUGARAPPLE . . . . **Annona squamosa**

SUGARCANE . . **Saccharum officinarum**

Sugargum . . . . EUCALYPTUS, SUGAR: **Eucalyptus cladocalyx**

SUGARPALM . . . . **Arenga**
BORNEO S. . . . . . **A. undulatifolia**
CURRY S. . . . . . **A. westerhouti**
FORMOSA S. . . . . **A. engleri**
GOMUTI S. . . . . **A. pinnata**
PHILIPPINE S. . . . . . **A. ambong**
SUMATRA S. . . . . **A. obtusifolia**
WIGHT S. . . . . **A. wighti**

SUGARPLUMTREE . . . . . . **Lagunaria**
PATERSON S. . . . . . . **L. patersoni**

SUGARS (Plant Sources of)
See **ECONOMIC PLANTS, SUGARS.**

SUKSDORF'IA . . . . . SUKSDORFIA
viola'cea . . . . VIOLET S.

SULFURROOT . . . . **Anethum officinale**

Sulla . . . . . . SWEETVETCH, SULLA: **Hedysarum coronarium**

SUMAC . . . . **Rhus**
CHINESE S. . . . . . . **R. chinensis**
CUTLEAF SMOOTH S. **R. glabra laciniata**
CUTLEAF STAGHORN S. . . **R. typhina l.**
DESERT LEMONADE S. **R. trilobata anisophylla**
EMORY S. . . . . **R. emoryi**
EVERGREEN S. . . . **R. sempervirens**
FIVELEAF S. . . . . . **R. pentaphylla**
FLAMELEAF S. . . . . . **R. copallina**
FRAGRANT S. . . . . **R. aromatica**
GREEN SHREDLEAF S. **R. typhina viridiflora**
ILLINOIS FRAGRANT S. **R. aromatica illinoensis**
LATE F. S. . . . . . **R. a. serotina**
LAUREL S . . . . **R. laurina**
LEMONADE S. . . . . . **R. integrifolia**
LITTLELEAF S. . . . . **R. microphylla**
MAHOGANY S. . . . . . **R. integrifolia**
MICHAUX S. . . . . . . **R. michauxi**
POTANIN S. . . . . **R. potanini**
PRAIRIE FLAMELEAF S. **R. copallina lanceolata**
PUNJAB S . . . . **R. punjabensis**
ROCKYMOUNTAIN SMOOTH S. **R. glabra cismontana**
ROXBURGH S. **R. chinensis roxburghi**
SANDBIND S. . . . . **R. albida**
SHREDLEAF S. . . . **R. typhina dissecta**
SICILIAN S. . . . . **R. coriaria**
SKUNKBUSH S. . . . . . . **R. trilobata**
SMOOTH S. . . . . **R. glabra**
SOUTHAFRICAN S. . . . . . **R. lancea**
STAGHORN S. . . . . **R. typhina**
SUGAR S. . . . . **R. ovata**
TEREBINTH S. . . . **R. terebinthifolia**
TOOTHED LEMONADE S. **R. integrifolia serrata**
UTAH S. . . . . **R. utahensis**
WHITE FLAMELEAF S. **R. copallina leucantha**
YELLOWFRUIT SMOOTH S. **R. glabra flavescens**

SUMATRA-DRAGONSBLOOD **Daemonorops draco**

SUMBUL . . . . **Dorema**
BOMBAY S. . . . . . . **D. ammoniacum**

SUMMERCYPRESS . . . . **Kochia**
BELVEDERE S. . . . . . . **K. scoparia**
CALIFORNIA S. . . . . . **K. californica**
CHILDS S. . . . . **K. childsi**
GRAY S. . . . . **K. vestita**
GREENMOLLY S. . . . . . **K. americana**
PROSTRATE S. . . . . . . **K. prostrata**

SUMMERHYACINTH . . . . . . **Galtonia**
GIANT S. . . . . **G. candicans**

SUMPWEED . . . . **Iva**
BIGLEAF S. . . . . . . **I. frutescens**
HAYES S. . . . . **I. hayesiana**
NARROWLEAF S. . . . **I. angustifolia**
NORTHERN S. . . . . **I. oraria**
POVERTY S. . . . . **I. axillaris**
RAG S. . . . . **I. xanthifolia**
SEACOAST S. . . . . **I. ciliata**

SUNBUSH . . . . **Bossiaea**
BOXLEAF S. . . . . . . **B. buxifolia**
HOLLY S. . . . . . . **B. aquifolium**
SHOWY S. . . . . **B. ornata**
TWOLOBE S. . . . . **B. biloba**
WOOLLEAF S. . . . . . . **B. eriocarpa**

SUNDEW . . . . **Drosera**
ENGLISH S. . . . . **D. anglica**
NARROWLEAF S. . . . . **D. longifolia**
ROUNDLEAF S. . . . . **D. rotundifolia**
THREADLEAF S. . . . . . **D. filiformis**

SUNDROPS . . . . **Oenothera**
See also EVENINGPRIMROSE.
ANDEAN S. . . . . **O. andina**
BLUELEAF S. . . . . **O. glauca**
BROADLEAF OZARK S. **O. missouriensis latifolia**
COMMON S. . . . . . . **O. fruticosa**
DANDELION S. . . . . **O. acaulis**
FRASER BLUELEAF S. **O. glauca fraseri**
GOLDENEGGS S. . . . . **O. ovata**
MEADOW S. . . . . **O. pratensis**
OZARK S. . . . . . **O. missouriensis**
PERENNIAL S. . . . . . . **O. perennis**
PILGRIM P. S. . . . . . **O. p. pilgrimi**
ROSE S. . . . . **O. rosea**
STREAM S. . . . . **O. riparia**
TWISTED S. . . . . **O. bistorta**
VEITCH T. S. . . . . **O. b. veitchiana**

SUNFLOWER . . . . **Helianthus**
ASHY S. . . . . **H. mollis**
BIGLEAF WOODLAND S. **H. strumosus macrophyllus**
BLACKHEAD S. . . . **H. scaberrimus**
CALIFORNIA S. . . . . **H. californicus**
COMMON S. . . . . **H. annuus**
CUCUMBERLEAF S. . . . . **H. debilis**
DARKEYE S. . . . . . **H. atrorubens**
DIVARICATE S. . . . **H. divaricatus**
DOWELL S. . . . . . **H. dowellianus**
FEWLEAF S. . . . . . **H. occidentalis**
GIANT S. . . . . **H. giganteus**
JERUSALEMARTICHOKE S. **H. tuberosus**
MAXIMILIAN S. . . . . **H. maximiliani**
OBLONGLEAF S. . . . **H. doronicoides**
PRAIRIE S. . . . . . . **H. petiolaris**
RHOMBICLEAF S.. **H. subrhomboideus**
SAWTOOTH S. . . **H. grosseserratus**
SHOWY S. . . . . **H. laetiflorus**
SILVERLEAF S. . . . . **H. argophyllus**
SLENDER S. . . . . . . **H. gracilentus**
SMALLHEAD S. . . **H. microcephalus**
STIFF S. . . . . **H. rigidus**
SWAMP S. . . . . . **H. angustifolius**
THINLEAF S. . . . . . **H. decapetalus**
THROATWORT S. . . **H. trachelifolius**
WILLOWLEAF S. . . . . **H. salicifolius**
WOODLAND S. . . . . . . **H. strumosus**
WOOLLY S. . . . . . . **H. tomentosus**

SUNPITCHER . . . . . . **Heliamphora**
NODDING S. . . . . **H. nutans**

SUNRAY . . . . **Helipterum**
CLUSTER S. . . . **H. corymbiflorum**
HUMBOLDT S. . . **H. humboldtianum**
MANGLES S. . . . . . . **H. manglesi**
ROSE S. . . . . **H. roseum**
SPOTTED MANGLES S. **H. manglesi maculatum**

SUNROSE . . . . **Helianthemum**
ALPINE S. . . . . **H. alpestre**
APENNINE S. . . . . . . **H. apenninum**
FROSTWEED S. . . . . **H. majus**
HOARY S. . . . . **H. canum**
SMOOTH S. . . . . **H. glaucum**

SUPPLEJACK . . . . **Berchemia**
ALABAMA S. . . . . . . **B. scandens**
GIRALD S. . . . . . . **B. giraldiana**
JAPANESE S. . . . . . . **B. racemosa**
LITTLELEAF S. . . . . **B. polyphylla**
STRIPED S. . . . . **B. lineata**
UNDERGOLD S. . . . . **B. hypochrysa**

Supplejack . . . . . SERJANIA: **Serjania**

SURFGRASS . . . . **Phyllospadix**
SCOULER S. . . . . . . **P. scouleri**
TORREY S. . . . . **P. torreyi**

SURIA'NA . . . . BAYCEDAR
marit'ima . . . . BAYCEDAR

Surinamcherry PITANGA: **Eugenia uniflora**

SU'TERA . . . . **CHAENOSTOMA**
brachia'ta . . . . **C. hispidum**
cephalo'tes . . . . . . **C. fastigiatum**

SUTHERLAND'IA . . . . BALLOONPEA
frutes'cens . . . . CAPE B.
—**commu'nis** . . . . SMOOTH C.B.
—**tomento'sa** . . . . WOOLLY C.B.
₵BIGBLOOM (*grandiflora*) HV. S. frutescens
₵WHITE (*alba*)

SUTTO'NIA . . . . SUTTONIA
United by some botanists with Myrsine.
austra'lis . . . . BLACKBERRY S.
salic'ina . . . . . WILLOWLEAF S.

SVI'DA . . . . **CORNUS**

SWAINSO'NA . . . . . SWAINSONPEA
galegifo'lia . . . . . GOATSRUE S.
COOPER (*cooperi*) HV.
CORONILLA (*coronillaefolia*)
LILAC (*pallida*)
LITTLELEAF (*microphylla*)
OSBORN (*osborni*)
PINK (*rosea*)
ROBUST (*robusta*)
VIOLET (*violacea*)
WINTER (*albiflora*)
greya'na (*grandiflora*). HORSEPOISON S.
lessertifo'lia . . . . POISONVETCH S.
macullochia'na . . MINILYA-GLORY S.
sal'sula

SWAINSONPEA . . . . . . **Swainsona**
GOATSRUE S. . . . . . **S. galegifolia**
HORSEPOISON S. . . . . **S. greyana**
MINILYA-GLORY S. . **S. macullochiana**
POISONVETCH S. . . . **S. lessertifolia**

SWALLOWWORT . . . . . . **Cynanchum**
BLACK S. . . . . **C. nigrum**
MOSQUITOTRAP S. . **C. acuminatifolium**
WHITE S. . . . . . . **C. vincetoxicum**

Swampmahogany. EUCALYPTUS, BEAKPOD: **Eucalyptus multiflora**

SWAMPORANGE . . . . . . **Limnocitrus**

SWAMPPINK . . . **Helonias; H. bullata**

SWAMPTIMOTHY. **Heleochloa schoenoides**

SWANORCHID . . . . **Cycnoches**
COMMON S. . . . . **C. chlorochilon**
EGERTON S. . . . . **C. egertonianum**

SWANRIVERDAISY **Brachycome iberidifolia**

SWARTZ'IA . . . . SWARTZPEA
Swartzia Schreb. (1791) is conserved under International Rules.
tomento'sa . . . . . . WAMARA S.

SWARTZ'IA J. F. Gmel., *not* Schreb. **SOLANDRA**

SWARTZPEA . . . . **Swartzia**
WAMARA S. . . . . . **S. tomentosa**

SWEETALYSSUM . . . . . . **Lobularia**

SWEETANISE . . **Osmorhiza occidentalis**

SWEETCANE . . . . **Saccharum**
MUNJ S. . . . . **S. sarc**

SWEETCICELY . . **Myrrhis; M. odorata**

SWEETCLOVER . . . . **Melilotus**
ANNUAL YELLOW S. . . . . **M. indica**
DAGHESTAN S. . . . . **M. suaveolens**
HUBAM S. . . . . . **M. alba annua**
WHITE S. . . . . **M. alba**
YELLOW S. . . . . . **M. officinalis**

SWEETFERN . **Comptonia; C. peregrina**
LITTLELEAF S. . . . **C. p. asplenifolia**

SWEETFLAG . . . . **Acorus**
DRUG S. . . . . **A. calamus**
JAPANESE S. . . . . . **A. gramineus**
WHITESTRIPE J. S. . **A. g. variegatus**
YELLOWSTRIPE S. . . . **A. calamus v.**

SWEETGALE . . . . **Myrica gale**

SWEETGRASS . . **Hierochloe; H. odorata**
ALPINE S. . . . . **H. alpina**
CALIFORNIA S. . . . . **H. occidentalis**

SWEETGUM . . . . **Liquidambar**
AMERICAN S. . . . . . **L. styraciflua**
FORMOSA S. . . . . . **L. formosana**
ORIENTAL S. . . . . . . **L. orientalis**

SWEET'IA . . . . SWEETIA
panamen'sis . . . . . BILLYWEBB S.

SWEETLEAF . . . . **Symplocos**
CHINESE S. . . . . **S. chinensis**
COLOMBIA-TEA S. . . . . . **S. alstonia**
COMMON S. . . . . **S. tinctoria**
LODEBARK S. . . . . . **S. racemosa**
MARTINIQUE S. . . . **S. martinicensis**
SAPPHIREBERRY S. . . **S. paniculata**

SWEETPEA . . . . . **Lathyrus odoratus**
For hort. var. of Sweetpea, see **LATHYRUS.**
DWARF S. . . . . **L. o. nanellus**

SWEETPOTATO . . . . **Ipomoea batatas**

SWEETROOT . . . . **Osmorhiza**
BLUNTSEED S. . . . . . . **O. obtusa**
CLAYTON S. . . . . . . **O. claytoni**
LONGSTYLE S. . . . . **O. longistylis**
SPREADING S. . . . . **O. divaricata**
SWEETANISE . . . . **O. occidentalis**

SWEETSHADE **Hymenosporum; H. flavum**

SWEETSHRUB . . . . **Calycanthus**
BROADLEAF COMMON S. **C. floridus ovatus**
CALIFORNIA S. . . . . **C. occidentalis**
CAROLINA S. . . . . **C. fertilis nanus**
COMMON S. . . . . **C. floridus**
PALE S. . . . . **C. fertilis**
SMOOTH P. S. . . . . . . **C. f. ferax**

Sweetsop SUGARAPPLE: **Annona squamosa**

SWEETSPIRE . . . . **Itea**
CHINESE S. . . . . **I. chinensis**
HOLLYLEAF S. . . . . . . **I. ilicifolia**
VIRGINIA S. . . . . . . **I. virginica**
YUNNAN S. . . . . . **I. yunnanensis**

SWEETSULTAN . . **Centaurea moschata**

SWEETVETCH . . . . **Hedysarum**
MONGOLIAN S. . . . . **H. multijugum**
NORTHERN S. . . . . . . **H. boreale**
SULFUR S. . . . . . **H. sulphurescens**
SULLA S. . . . . . . **H. coronarium**
UTAH S. . . . . **H. utahense**
WESTERN S. . . . . . **H. occidentale**

SWEETWILLIAM. . . **Dianthus barbatus**
ALPINE S. . . . . **D. b. alpinus**
DUNNETT S. . . . . . . **D. b. dunnetti**
EYED S. . . . . **D. b. oculatus**
ROSY S. . . . . **D. b. roseus**
SOLOMON S. . . . . . **D. b. salamoni**

SWERT'IA . . . . SWERTIA
bimacula'ta . . . . TWOSPOT S.
chiray'ita (*chirata*) . . . CHIRETTA S.
dilata'ta
peren'nis . . . . . . ALPINEBOG S.
purpuras'cens . . . . . . PURPLE S.
scopuli'na (*palustris*) ROCKYMOUNTAIN S.
Some botanists maintain that this is identical with the Old World S. perennis.

SWIETE'NIA . . . . MAHOGANY
The South American S. krukovi and S. tessmanni require further field study.
candol'lei . . . . . . VENEZUELA M.
febrif'uga . . . . **Soymida f.**
hu'milis (*cirrhata*) . . MEXICAN M.
macrophyl'la . . . . . HONDURAS M.
mahag'oni . . . . . WESTINDIES M.

SWINGLE'A . . . . TABOG
glutino'sa . . . . TABOG

SWITCHGRASS . . **Panicum virgatum**

Swordbean . . . . HORSEBEAN, SWORD: **Canavalia gladiata**

SWORDFERN . . . . **Nephrolepis**
COMMON S. . . . . . . **N. exaltata**
DUFFS S. . . . . **N. cordifolia duffi**
JAVA S. . . . . **N. acuminata**
PURPLESTALK S. . . . . **N. biserrata**
SCURFY S. . . . . **N. hirsutula**
TUBER S. . . . . **N. cordifolia**
WESTERN S. . **Polystichum munitum**

Swordgrass. . SILVERGRASS: **Miscanthus**

SYA'GRUS (*COCOS* in part; *GLAZIOVA*) . . . . SYAGRUSPALM
See **PALM GENERA.**

SYCAMORE (Forestry) . . . . **Platanus**
See PLANETREE. Sycamore is the forestry name for this genus and is also, unfortunately, strongly entrenched in American usage. Sycamore (meaning "Fig Mulberry" or rather "Mulberry Fig") is a patent misnomer for the genus Platanus, and has arisen from a similarity in leaf shape to the "Sycamore" of the Bible.
AMERICAN S. (Forestry) **P. occidentalis**
ARIZONA S. (Forestry) . . . **P. wrighti**
CALIFORNIA S. (Forestry) . **P. racemosa**
SMOOTH AMERICAN S. (Forestry) **P. occidentalis glabrata**

Sycomore (*Sycamore*) . FIG, SYCOMORE: **Ficus sycomorus**
Sycomore is a more exact spelling.

SYCOP'SIS . . . . FIGHAZEL
sinen'sis . . . . CHINESE F.

SYL'VIA (*SILVIA* Benth., *not* Allem. *nor* Vell.) . . . . SYLVIA
prostra'ta . . . . TRAILING S.
serpyllifo'lia . . . . THYMELEAF S.

SYMPHO'NIA . . . . SYMPHONIA
gabonen'sis . . . . GABON S.
globulif'era . . . . GUIANA S.
Known also as Hog-gum and Mawnatree.

SYMPHORICAR'POS |w . SNOWBERRY
The generic name sometimes appears in literature as Symphoricarpus. The red-fruited species are known as Coralberry.
acu'tus (*S. mollis a.*) . SHARPLEAF S.
al'bus (*racemosus*) |w . . COMMON S.
—**laeviga'tus** (*S. racemosus l ; S. rivularis*) . . . . GARDEN C.S.
—**ova'tus** . . . . . BROADLEAF C.S.
—**pauciflo'rus** . . . . . DWARF C.S.
This varietal name is commonly misapplied to typical S. albus.

SYMPHORICARPOS, continued
∞**chenault'i** (*microphyllus* × *orbiculatus*) ∞ Chenault Coralberry
glomera'tus . . . . . . **S. orbiculatus**
hespe'rius . Washington Snowberry
hey'eri . . . . . . **S. occidentalis h.**
longiflo'rus . . . . Longflower S.
microphyl'lus (*montanus*) . . Pink S.
mol'lis |w . . . . . . Spreading S.
—*acu'tus* . . . . **S. acutus**
occidenta'lis |w . . . . . Western S.
—**hey'eri** (*S. heyeri*) Thinleaf W.S.
orbicula'tus (*glomeratus; parviflorus; vulgaris*) |w Indiancurrant Coralberry
¢Elongatus. hv.
¢Goldnet (*aureo-reticulatus; variegatus*)
¢White (*leucocarpus*)
oreoph'ilus . . . . . Mountain S.
parviflo'rus . . . . . **S. orbiculatus**
racemo'sus . . . . **S. albus**
—*laeviga'tus* . . . . **S. albus l.**
rivula'ris . . . . . **S. a. laevigatus**
rotundifo'lius |w . . . Roundleaf S.
sinen'sis . . . Chinese Coralberry
utahen'sis . . . . Utah S.
vaccinioi'des . . . . Whortleleaf S.
vulga'ris . . . . **S. orbiculatus**

SYMPHYAN'DRA
hof'manni
pen'dula
wan'neri

SYM'PHYTUM . . . . . . Comfrey
as'perum (*asperrimum*) . Prickly C.
¢Goldspot (*aureo-variegatum*) hv.
¢Variegated (*variegatum*)
caucas'icum . . . . . Caucasian C.
officina'le . Common C. (*Woundwort*)
¢Whiterim (*variegatum*) hv.
tubero'sum . Tuber C. (*Knitbone C.*)

SYMPLOCAR'PUS (*SPATHYEMA*) |w Skunkcabbage
foe'tidus (*Spathyema foetida*) |w Skunkcabbage

SYMPLO'COS |w . . . . Sweetleaf
alsto'nia . . . . . . Colombia-tea S.
chinen'sis . . . . Chinese S.
glomera'ta
martinicen'sis . . . Martinique S.
panicula'ta (*crataegoides*) Sapphireberry S.
racemo'sa . . . . Lodebark S.
tincto'ria |w . . . . . . Common S.

SYNADE'NIUM . . . . Milkbush
See **SUCCULENTS.**

SYNCAR'PIA . . Turpentine-myrtle
glomulif'era (*laurifolia*) Burramurra T.
hill'i . . . . Hills T.
leptopet'ala . . . . Brush T.

SYNDES'MON . . . **ANEMONELLA**

SYNECAN'THUS
See **PALM GENERA.**

SYNE'DRA |w
pulchel'la |w

SYNNO'TIA
bi'color

SYNSEP'ALUM
dulcif'icum

SYNTHERIS'MA . . . . **DIGITARIA**
See **GRASS GENERA.**

SYN'THYRIS (*BESSEYA*) Kittentails
alpi'na . . . . Alpine K.
corda'ta . . . . Heartleaf K.
dissec'ta . . . . Cutleaf K.
ma'jor (*S. reniformis m.*) . Major K.
pinnatif'ida . . . . Featherleaf K.
—**lanugino'sa** . . . . Woolly F.K.
plantagine'a . . . Plantainleaf K.
renifor'mis . . . . Kidneyleaf K.
ritteria'na . . . . Ritter K.
rotundifo'lia . . . . . Roundleaf K.
—**sweet'zeri** . . . . Sweetzer R.K.
ru'bra . . . . Red K.
schizan'tha . . . . Fringepetal K.
wyomingen'sis . . . . . Wyoming K.

SYRIN'GA |w . . . . Lilac
adamia'na . . . . . . **S. tomentella**
affi'nis . . . . **S. oblata alba**
—*gir'aldi* . . . . **S. oblata g.**
amuren'sis (*ligustrina; rotundifolia; sibirica* Hort. in part) . . Amur L.
—**japon'ica** (*S. japonica*) Japanese Tree L.
—*pekinen'sis* . . . . . **S. pekinensis**
bretschnei'deri . . . . **S. villosa** hv. Dr. Bretschneider
∞**chinen'sis** (*persica* × *vulgaris; dubia; rothomagensis*) . . . ∞ Chinese L.
—*saugea'na* . . . . . ∞ **S. chinensis** hv. Saugeana
coeru'lea . . . . **S. vulgaris c.**
dilata'ta . . . . **S. oblata d.**
∞**diversifo'lia** (*oblata giraldi* × *pinnatifolia*) . . . . ∞ Varileaf L.
du'bia . . . . ∞ **S. chinensis**
—*ru'bra* . ∞ **S. chinensis** hv. Saugeana
em'odi (*S. villosa e.*) . Himalayan L.
—*au'rea* . . **S. emodi** hv. Yellowleaf
—*aureo-variega'ta* **S. emodi** hv. Yellowspot
—*hy'brida* . . . . ∞ **S. henryi**
—*rose'a* . . . . **S. villosa**
faurie'i . . . . Faurie L.
filicifo'lia Hort. . **S. persica laciniata**
formosis'sima . . . . **S. wolfi**
—*hirsu'ta* . . . . **S. wolfi h.**
gir'aldi . . . . **S. oblata g.**
∞**hen'ryi** (*josikaea* × *villosa; S. emodi hybrida*) . . . . . . ∞ Henry L.
∞**hyacinthiflo'ra** (*oblata* × *vulgaris*) ∞ Hyacinth L.
japon'ica . . . . . **S. amurensis j.**
∞**josiflex'a** (*josikaea* × *reflexa*)
josikae'a . . . . Hungarian L.
julia'nae (*verrucosa*) . . . Juliana L.
kamibayash'i; koehnea'na **S. velutina**
komarow'i (*sargentiana*) . Komarof L.
ligustri'na . . . . . . **S. amurensis**
mey'eri . . . . Meyer L.
microphyl'la . . . . . Littleleaf L.
∞**nanceia'na** (∞ *henryi* × *sweginzowi*) ∞ Nanceiana L.
obla'ta (*S. vulgaris o.*) . . . Early L.
—**al'ba** (*S. affinis; S. o. affinis*) White E.L.
—**dilata'ta** (*S. dilatata*). Korean E.L.
—**gir'aldi** (*S. affinis g.; S. giraldi*) Purple E.L.
palibinia'na . . . . . . **S. velutina**
pekinen'sis (*S. amurensis p.*) Pekin L.
—*pen'dula* **S. pekinensis** hv. Weeping
per'sica . . . . Persian L.
—**integrifo'lia**
The botanical name for the typical form of Persian Lilac. It is not known in the wild state.

SYRINGA, continued
per'sica lacinia'ta (*filicifolia* Hort.; *pinnata; pteridifolia* Hort.) Cutleaf Persian Lilac
The only var. of the species known in the wild state.
¢Alba (*S. steencruysi* Hort.) hv. S. persica
pineto'rum . . . . . . Pinewoods L.
pinnatifo'lia . . . . . . Pinnate L.
potani'ni . . . . Potanin L.
∞**pres'toniae** (*reflexa* × *villosa*) ∞ Preston L.
pteridifo'lia Hort. . **S. persica laciniata**
pubes'cens (*villosa* Dec., *not* Turcz. *nor* Vahl) . . . . Hairy L.
reflex'a . . . . Nodding L.
—**al'ba** . . . . White N.L.
—**pal'lens** . . . . Pale N.L.
rhodo'pea . . . . . . Bulgarian L.
robus'ta . . . . **S. wolfi**
rothomagen'sis . . . . ∞ **S. chinensis**
—*saugea'na* . . . . . ∞ **S. chinensis** hv. Saugeana
rotundifo'lia . . . . . . **S. amurensis**
sargentia'na . . . . **S. komarowi**
saugea'na Hort. **S. chinensis** ¢Sauge
sibir'ica Hort. **S. amurensis** (in part)
steencruys'i Hort. . **S. persica** ¢Alba
∞**swegiflex'a** (*reflexa* × *sweginzowi*) ∞ Swegiflexa L.
sweginzow'i . . . . . . Chengtu L.
—*al'bida; densiflo'ra; super'ba* **S. sweginzowi** hv.
tomentel'la (*adamiana; wilsoni*) Felty L.
veluti'na (*kamibayashi; koehneana; palibiniana*) . . . . Manchurian L.
verruco'sa . . . . **S. julianae**
villo'sa (*S. emodi rosea*) . . . Late L.
—*em'odi* . . . . **S. emodi**
—*rose'a* . . . . **S. villosa**
villo'sa Dec., *not* Turcz. *nor* Vahl **S. pubescens**
vulga'ris |w . . . . . . Common L.
—**al'ba** . . . . White C.L.
—**coeru'lea** (*S. coerulea*)
The botanical name for the typical (blue-flowered) form of Common Lilac.
—*obla'ta* . . . . **S. oblata**
—*ple'na* . . . . **S. vulgaris** hv. Double Common
—**purpu'rea** . . . . . . Purple C.L.
—**viola'cea** . . . . . . Violet C.L.
wil'soni . . . . **S. tomentella**
wolf'i (*formosissima; robusta*) Wolfs L.
—**hirsu'ta** (*S. formosissima h.*) Hairy W.L.
yunnanen'sis . . . . . . Yunnan L.

Hort. var. of **Syringa,** Lilac:

Because of the large number of varieties of Lilac, the horticultural varieties and the hybrids have been combined in the special list below. For Lilac common names, see Lilac, p. 332.

Abbreviations indicate the species to which a horticultural variety is supposed to belong, in whole or in part. Those horticultural varieties with no species indicated after the name are S. vulgaris varieties. Abbreviations of the names of the originators are also given. In many cases the dates refer to the year the original plant was produced, though in the majority of cases the date refers to the year the plant was first reported to have been introduced into the trade. The Editorial Committee acknowledges its indebtedness to John C. Wister, Chairman

SYRINGA, continued

of the Subcommittee on Lilacs, American Association of Botanical Gardens and Arboretums, for the following list.

C. S. chinensis var.
Em. S. emodi var.
Hen. S. henryi var.
Hy. S. hyacinthiflora var.
Josif. S. josiflexa var.
Josik. S. josikaea var.
L. Late hybrid.
Nan. S. nanceiana var.
Pek. S. pekinensis var.
Per. S. persica var.
Pre. S. prestoniae var.
Swe. S. sweginzowi var.
Tom. S. tomentella var.
Vil. S. villosa var.
Vul. S. vulgaris var.

ABBREVIATIONS OF TYPES

D. Double. S. Single.

ABBREVIATIONS OF NAMES OF ORIGINATORS

Arn. Arnold Arboretum, Jamaica Plain, Mass.
Balt. Baltet Nursery, Troyes, France.
Barn. Mrs. A. C. Barnes, Merion, Pa.
Baud. Baudriller, probably French nurseryman.
Bensch Bensch, probably German nurseryman.
Berm. Bermiau Nursery, Orleans, France.
Bill. M. Ch. Billiard, Fontenay-aux-Roses, France.
Brand A. M. Brand, Faribault, Minn.
Briot Briot, Government Nursery, Versailles, France.
Bruch. Bruchet, St. Rambery, s/Loire, Loire, France.
Chen. Leon Chenault, Orleans, France.
Coch. Cochet Nursery, Grisy Suisnes, S. & M., France.
Cray. F. M. Crayton & Sons, Biltmore, N. C.
deM. Stepman de Messemaeker, 61 Rue des Quatre Vents, Brussels, Belgium.
Doug. James Dougal, Windsor, Canada.
Dub. Dubois.
Dunb. John Dunbar, Rochester, N. Y.
E.&B. Ellwanger & Barry, Rochester, N. Y.
Eich. Moritz Eichler, Chemnitz, Germany.
Eken. Brahy Ekenholm, Herstal, near Liege, Belgium.
F.&D. Felix & Dykuis, Boskoop, Netherlands.
Frank. A. B. Franklin, Minneapolis, Minn.
Froeb. Otto Froebel, Zurich, Switzerland.
Gouch. Auguste Gouchault, Orleans, France.
G.R. Grandes Roseraies du Val et de la Loire, Orleans, France.
Grun. Friederich Grunewald, Zossen, Bradenburg, Germany.
Hav. T. A. Havemeyer, Glen Head, L. I., N. Y. (The Havemeyer seedlings, with the exception of MRS. W. E. MARSHALL, are not in commerce and the dates shown, therefore, do not indicate introduction to trade.)
Henry Prof. Louis Henry, Museum of Natural History, Paris, France.
Henry, J.N. Mrs. J. Norman Henry, Gladwyne, Pa.
Hesse Herman A. Hesse, Weemer, Germany.
Kees. K. Keessen, Jr., Aalsmeer, Netherlands.
Kett. Fred Kettler Nursery, Plattville, Wis.
Klag. Mrs. Hulda Klager, Woodland, Wash.
Kost. M. Koster & Sons, Boskoop, Netherlands.
Lamb. Peter Lambert, Trier, Germany.
Lec. Lecointe Nursery, Louveciennes, France.
Led. A. C. Lederman, Wheaton, Ill.
Lem. V. Lemoine & Fils, Nancy, France.
Lib. Libert-Darimont, Thiers-a-Liege, Belgium.
Makoy Jacob Makoy & Co. Nursery, Liege, Belgium.
Math. Mathieu, probably French nurseryman.
Mord. Experiment Station, Morden, Manitoba, Canada.
Morel Morel Nursery, France.
Oliv. A. A. Oliver, Mt. Eden, Calif.
Oud. Ouden.
Pfitz. Pfitzer Nursery, Stuttgart, Germany.
Pill. James Pillow, Cold Spring on Hudson, N. Y.
Prest. Miss Isabella Preston, Central Experimental Farm, Ottawa, Canada.
Rul. Raymond J. Ruliffson, Rochester, N. Y.
Scott Mrs. Arthur H. Scott, Media, Pa.
Seab. Alton Seabury, Little Compton, R. I.
Sim.-L. Simon-Louis Nursery, Metz, Alsace, France.
Simon Francisque Simon Nursery, Cherbonnieres, Rhone, France.
Skin. F. L. Skinner, Dropmore, Manitoba, Canada.
Spae. Ludwig Spaeth, Berlin, Germany.
Tows. Towson Nursery, Towson, Md.
VN. C. B. Van Nes & Sons, Nursery, Boskoop Netherlands.
VT. Jan Van Tol, Hzn. Boskoop, Netherlands.
Wilke Rudolph Wilke, Horstensteiner Nurseries, Berlin, Germany.

Presumably most of the hort. var. listed below are clons.

ABEL CARRIERE. D. (Lem. 1896.)
A. B. LAMBERTON. D. (Dunb. 1917.)
Abundant Bloomer. CITY OF KELSO.
ADELAIDE DUNBAR. D. (Dunb. 1916.)
ADMIRAL FARRAGUT. S. (Dunb.)
ADRIANA. Pre. L. (Prest. 1941?)
A. J. KLETTENBERG. D. (GR. 1933.)
Alba. (Cult. before 1600.) **S. vulgaris alba** (White Common L.)
ALBA GRANDIFLORA. S. Vul. (Before 1832.)
ALBA SANGUINEA. S.
Doubtful name.
ALBA VIRGINALIS. S. (Oud. 1841.) *Virginalis.*
ALBERT, THE GOOD. S. (Doug. 1886.)
ALBIDA. Swe.
Alexander de Humboldt. DE HUMBOLDT.
ALEXANDER HAMILTON. D. (Dunb. 1923.)
ALICE. S. (Klag. 1928.)
Alice. Pre. L. (Prest. & Brand 1941.)
ALINE MOCQUERIS. S. (Before 1872.)
ALLISON GREY. S. (Hav.)
ALMA. S. (Klag. 1932.)
ALPHONSE LAVALLEE. D. (Lem. 1885.)
AMBASSADEUR. S. (Lem. 1930.)
A. M. BRAND. S. (Brand.)
AMBROSE VERSCHAFFELT. S. (Eken. 1863.)
AMETHYST. S. (Spae. 1887.)
AMI SCHOTT. D. (Lem. 1933.)
AMOENA. S. (Before 1846.)
Andenken an Ludwig Spaeth. LUDWIG SPAETH.
ANNA. S. (Klag.)
ANNA ELIZABETH JACQUET. S. (Before 1924.)
ANNE SHIACH. S. (Hav.)
Antoine Buchner. MME. ANTOINE BUCHNER.
ARCHEVEQUE. D. (Lem. 1923.)
ARCHIDUCHESSE CHARLOTTE. S. (Eken. 1861.)
ARGENTEA.
Doubtful name.
ARIEL. Pre. L. (Prest. 1941?)
ARTHUR WILLIAM PAUL. D. (Lem. 1898.)
ASHES OF ROSES. S. (Klag. 1930.)
ASSESSIPPI. Hy.; S. (Skin. 1935.)
AUCUBAEFOLIA. D. (Gouch. before 1919.)
AUDREY. Pre. L. (Prest. 1941?)
AUREA. S. (About 1880.)
AVON. S. (Led. 1930.)
AZUREA PLENA. D. (1854.) *Double Azure.*
BANQUISE. D. (Lem. 1905.)
BEATRICE. Pre. L. (Prest. 1941?)
Beauty of Frankfort. HERMAN EILERS.
BELLE DE NANCY. D. (Lem. 1891.)
BELLICENT. Josif. (Prest.)
BERANGER. S. (Sim.-L. before 1867.)
BERRYER. Hy.; D. (Lem. 1913.)
BEST BLUE.
Doubtful name.
BETTY LOUISE. S. (Klag.)
BIANCA. Pre. L. (Prest. 1941?)
BICOLOR. C. (Lem. before 1853.) *Flore Bicolor.*
Billy Mills. W. K. MILLS.
BLANCH. Pre. L. (Prest. 1941?)
BLEUATRE. S. (Balt. before 1897.)
BLUE HYACINTH. (Clarke 1941.)
BOULE AZUREE. S. (Lem. 1919.)
BOUSSINGAULT. D. (Lem. 1897.)
BUFFON. Hy.; S. (Lem. 1921.)
CALIBAN. Pre. L. (Prest.)
CALPHURNIA. Pre. L. (Prest.)
CALVIN C. LANEY. S. (Dunb.)
Camille de Rohan. PRINCESSE CAMILLE DE ROHAN.
CANDEUR. S. (Lem. 1931.)
CAPITAINE BALTET. S. (Lem. 1919.)
CAPITAINE PERRAULT. D. (Lem. 1925.)
CARLEY. S. (Hav.)
CARMEN. D. (Lem. 1918.)
CARMINE. S. (Klag. 1928.) *Mrs. R. W. Mills.*
Caroli. CHARLES X.
CAROLYN MAE. S. (Sass.)
CASSANDRA. Pre. L. (Prest. 1941?)
CATINAT. Hy.; S. (Lem. 1922.)
CAVOUR. S. (Lem. 1910.)
C. B. VAN NES. S. (VN. 1904.)
CELESTIAL BLUE. S. (Klag. 1930.)
CELIA. Pre. L. (Prest. 1941?)
CHAMPLAIN. D. (Lem. 1930.)
CHARLEMAGNE. S. (Eken. before 1854.)
CHARLES BALTET. D. (Lem. 1893.)
CHARLES JOLY. D. (Lem. 1896.)
CHARLES SARGENT. D. (Lem. 1905.)
CHARLES X. S. (Before 1830.) *Caroli; Rubra Major.*
CHARLOTTE MORGAN. D. (Seab.)
May be the same as Mrs. Morgan.
CHARM. S. (Hav.)
CHARMIAN. Pre. L. (Prest. 1941?)
CHEERBENBURG.
CHENBOLT.
Doubtful name.

SYRINGA, continued

Christophe Colomb. S. (Lem. 1905.)
City of Gresham. S. (Klag. 1915.)
City of Kalama. S. (Klag. 1915.) *Kalama.*
City of Kelso. D. (Klag. 1928.) *Abundant Bloomer.*
City of Longview. S. (Klag. 1930.) *Longview.*
City of Olympia. S. (Klag. 1934.) *Olympia.*
City of Vancouver. S. (Klag. 1930.)
City of Woodland. S. (Klag. 1930.) *Woodland.*
Clara. S. (Klag. 1928.)
Clara Cochet. S. (Coch. before 1885.)
Clarence D. Van Zandt. S. (Dunb.)
Claude Bernard. Hy.; D. (Lem. 1915.)
Claude de Lorrain. S. (Lem. 1889.)
Cleopatra. Pre. L. (Prest.)
Coerulea Superba. S. (E. & B. before 1868.)
Colbert. D. (Lem. 1899.)
Colmariensis. S. (About 1840.)
Col. Wm. R. Plum. S. (Brand.)
Comte Adrien de Montebello. D. (Lem. 1910.)
Comte de Kerchove. D. (Lem. 1899.)
Comte Horace de Choiseul. D. (Lem. 1887.)
Comtesse Horace de Choiseul. D. (Lem. 1891.)
Condorcet. D. (Lem. 1888.)
Congo. S. (Lem. 1896.)
Constance. Pre. L. (Prest.)
Coral. Pre. L. (Mord. before 1937.)
Cora McCormack. S. (Klag.)
Cordelia. Pre. L. (Prest.)
Corinne. S. (Before 1900.)
Crampel. S. (Lem. 1899.)
Crayton. C.
Crepuscule. S. (Lem. 1928.)
Cressida. Pre. L. (Prest.)
Croix de Brahy. S. (Eken. 1850.)
Dame Blanche. D. (Lem. 1903.)
Danton. S. (Lem. 1911.)
Dawn. S. (Hav.)
Dawn. S. (Klag.)
Dawn. Pre. L. (Mord.)
Decaisne. S. (Lem. 1910.)
De Croncels. S. (Balt. or Baud. before 1876.) *Gloire de Croncels.*
De Humboldt. D. (Lem. 1892.) *Alexander de Humboldt.*
De Jussieu. D. (Lem. 1891.)
De Louvain. S. (Before 1859.)
De Miribel. S. (Lem. 1903.)
Densiflora. Swe.
De Saussure. D. (Lem. 1903.)
Descartes. Hy.; S. (Lem. 1916.)
Desdemona. Pre. L. (Prest.)
Desfontaines. D. (Lem. 1906.)
Deuil d'Emile Galle. D. (Lem. 1904.)
Diana. Pre. L. (Prest.)
Diderot. S. (Lem. 1915.)
Dillia. (Klag. 1915.)
Diplomate. S. (Lem. 1930.)
Dorcas. Pre. L. (Prest.)
Double Azure. Azurea Plena.
Double Common. Vul.
Double Hyacinth. Hy. (Lem. 1878.)
Downfield. D. (Hav.)
Doyen Keteleer. D. (Lem. 1895.)
Dr. Bretschneider. Vil.
Dr. Charles Jacobs. S. (deM. 1908.)

SYRINGA, continued

Dr. Gaspard Callot. Souv. de Gaspard Callot.
Dr. Lindley. S. (Before 1861.)
Dr. Maillot. D. (Lem. 1895.)
Dr. Masters. D. (Lem. 1898.)
Dr. Nobbe. S. (1875.)
Dr. Noble. S. (1872.)
Probably same as Dr. Nobbe.
Dr. Troyanowsky. D. (Lem. 1901.)
Dr. Von Regel. S. (Spae. 1883.)
Duc de Massa. D. (Lem. 1905.)
Duchesse de Brabant. S. (Eken. 1861.)
Duchesse d'Orleans. S. (Before 1846.)
Duplex. C. (Lem. 1904.)
Dusk. S. (Hav.)
Eden. S. (Oliver 1939.)
Edith Cavell. D. (Lem. 1916.)
Edmond About. D. (Lem. 1908.)
Edmond Bossier. S. (Lem. 1906.)
Edouard Andre. D. (Lem. 1900.)
Edward A. Schmidt. D. (Rul. 1940.)
Ekenholm. S. (Eken. before 1854.)
Elihu Root. D. (Dunb.)
Elinor. Pre. L. (Prest.)
Elizabeth Mills. S. (Klag. 1930.)
Ellen Willmott. D. (Lem. 1903.) *Miss Ellen Willmott.*
Emile Gentil. D. (Lem. 1915.)
Emile Lemoine. D. (Lem. 1889.)
Emilia. Pre. L. (Prest.)
Emil Liebig. D. (Spae. 1887.)
Enid. Josif. (Prest.)
Erzherzog Johann. S. (Before 1864.)
Ethel duPont. S. (Hav.)
Etna. S. (Lem. 1927.)
Etoile de Mai. D. (Lem. 1905.)
Evangeline. Pre. L. (Prest.)
Evangeline. Hy.; D. (Skin. 1935.)
Excel. Hy.; S. (Skin. 1935.)
Eximia. Josik.
Farrionensis. S. (1905.)
Fellemburg. S.
Fenelon. Hy.; S. (Lem. 1937.)
Firmament. S. (Lem. 1932.)
Floreal. Nan. (Lem. 1925.)
Flore Bicolor. Bicolor.
Flore Pleno. **S. vulgaris plena.**
Fluffy Ruffles. S. (Klag.)
Francisca. Pre. L. (Prest.)
Francisque Morel. D. (Lem. 1896.)
Frank Klager. S. (Klag. 1928.)
Frau (*Bertha*) Dammann. S. (Spae. 1883.)
Frau (*Wilhelm*) Pfitzer. S. (Pfitz. 1910.) *Gen. Haig.*
Fred C. Wilke. S. (Klag. 1934.)
Fred L. Klager. S. (Klag. 1930.)
Fred. Payne. S. (Hav.)
French Giant. S. (1900.)
Fritz. D. (Klag. 1928.)
Fuerst Bulow. S. (Spae. 1920.)
Fuerst Lichtenstein. S. (Spae. 1887.)
Gaspard Callot. *Souvenir de Gaspard Callot.*
Gaudichaud. D. (Lem. 1903.)
Gautois. Le Gaulois.
Geant des Batailles. S. (Before 1867.)
Geheimrat Heyder. S. (Spae. 1883.)
Geheimrat Singelmann. S. (Spae. 1887.)
General Drouot. S. (Lem. 1890.)
General Elwell S. Otis. D. (Dunb.)
General Grant. S. (Dunb. 1917.)
General Haig. Frau Wilhelm Pfitzer.

SYRINGA, continued

General (*John*) Pershing. D. (Dunb. before 1928.)
General Kitchener. D. (Dunb. before 1928.)
General Pershing. D. (Lem. 1924.)
General Sheridan. D. (Dunb. 1917.)
General Sherman. S. (Duab. 1917.)
Georges Bellair. D. (Lem. 1900.)
Georges Claude. D. (Lem. 1935.)
George W. Aldridge. S. (Dunb. 1923.)
Germinal. Hen. × Wil. (Lem. 1939.)
Gertrude. Pre. L. (Prest.)
Gigantea. (E. & B. 1867.)
Gilbert. S. (Lem. 1911.)
Gismonda. S. (Lem. 1939.)
Gloire de Croncels. De Croncels.
Gloire de La Rochelle. S. (Before 1865.)
Gloire de Lorraine. S. (Lem. 1876.)
Gloire de Moulins. S. (Before 1867.)
Glory. S. (Hav.)
Glory of Mt. Hope. S. (E. & B. 1868.)
Godfrey. D.
Godron. D. (Lem. 1908.)
Goliath. S. (Before 1870.)
Grace. Pre. L.; S. (Prest.)
Grace Mackenzie. Hy. (Skin. 1942.)
Grace Orthwaite. S. (Brand 1937.)
Grand-Duc Constantin. D. (Lem. 1895.)
Guinevere. Josif. (Prest.)
Guizot. D. (Lem. 1897.)
Handel. Pre. L. (Skin. 1932.)
Heather. S. (Hav.)
Hecla. Pre. L. (Skin. 1932.)
Hedin. Swe. × Vil. (Skin. 1936.)
Helena. Pre. L. (Prest.)
Henri Martin. D. (Lem. 1912.)
Henri Robert. D. (Lem. 1936.)
Henry Clay. S. (Dunb. 1923.)
Henryi Alba. Hen. (Lem. 1934.)
Henryi Lubet.
Henryi Subjosikae.
Henry (*Wadsworth*) Longfellow. D. (Dunb. 1920.)
Henry (*Ward*) Beecher. D. (Dunb. 1923.)
Hera. Pre. L. (Prest.)
Herman Eilers. (deM. 1923.) *Beauty of Frankfort; Pink Beauty of Frankfort; Sinai.*
Hermia. Pre. L. (Prest.)
Hermione. Pre. L. (Prest.)
Hiawatha. Pre. L. (Skin. 1932.)
Hippolyte Maringer. D. (Lem. 1909.)
Hiram H. Edgerton. S. (Dunb. 1919.)
Holly Ann. S. (Klag.)
Horace. Pre. L. (Skin. 1932.)
Hugo de Vries. S. (Kees. 1927.)
Hugo Koster. S. (Kost. or VT. 1914.)
Hyacinthiflora. D. (Lem. 1875.) *Hyacinthiflora Plena.*
Hyazinthenflieder. S. (Spae. 1906.)
Hybrida. S. (Before 1841.)
H. Zabel. Josif. (Frosb. 1899.)
Imogen. Pre. L. (Prest.)
Irvina. S. (Klag. 1920.)
Isabella. Pre. L. (Prest. 1927.)
Jacquenetta. Pre. L. (Prest.)
Jacques Callot. S. (Lem. 1876.)
James Booth. S. (Eich. 1862.)
James Stuart. S. (Hav.)
Jane Day. S. (Hav.)
Jan Van Tol. S. (VT. about 1916.)
J. de Messemaeker. (deM. 1908.)
Jean Bart. D. (Lem. 1889.)

SYRINGA, continued
Jean Mace. D. (Lem. 1915.)
Jeanne d'Arc. D. (Lem. 1902.)
Jeanne Saint-Didier. S. (1907.)
Jessica. Pre. L. (Prest.)
Joan Dunbar. D. (Dunb. 1923.)
Joyce. S. (Klag.)
Jules Ferry. D. (Lem. 1907.)
Jules Simon. D. (Lem. 1908.) *Mme. Jules Simon.*
Julia. Pre. L. (Prest.)
Julien Gerardin. D. (Lem. 1916.)
Juliet. Pre. L. (Prest.)
June Day. (Hav.)
Justi. S. (Before 1865.)
Kalama. City of Kalama.
Kate Harlin. S. (Pfitz. before 1910.)
Kate Sessions. (Clarke 1941.)
Katharine Havemeyer. D. (Lem. 1922.)
Katherina. Pre. L. (Prest.)
Katherine. S. (Klag. 1939.)
Kim. (Prest.)
Koenigin Luise. S. (Pfitz. 1921.)
Lady Lindsay. S. (Hav.)
La Lorraine. C. (Lem. 1899.)
Lamarck. D. (Lem. 1886.)
Lamartine. Hy.; S. (Lem. 1911.)
LaMauve. D. (Lem. 1893.)
Lambouline. S. (1926.)
Doubtful name.
Languis. S. (Makoy before 1872.)
Laplace. S. (Lem. 1913.)
La Tour d'Auvergne. D. (Lem. 1888.)
Laura Cox. S. (Pfitz. 1907.)
Laura L. Barnes. D. (Barn.)
Lavaliensis. S. (1865.)
Lavender Pearl. D. (Klag. 1915.)
Lavinia. Pre. L. (Prest.)
Lavoisier. S. (Lem. 1913.)
Le Gaulois. D. (Lem. 1884.) *Gautois.*
Lemoinei. D. (Lem. 1878.)
Le Notre. D. (Lem. 1922.)
Leon Gambetta. D. (Lem. 1907.)
Leonie Lambert. S. (Lamb. 1909.)
Leon Mathieu. S. (deM. 1908.)
Leon Portier. S. (Bruch.)
Leon Simon. D. (Lem. 1888.)
Leopold II. S. (deM. 1908.)
Le Printemps. D. (Lem. 1901.)
Le Progres. C. (Lem. 1903.)
LeTroyes. C.
Liberti. D. (Lib. 1843.)
Lilarosa. S. (Before 1887.)
Lillian Lee. S. (Klag. 1935.)
Linne. D. (Lem. 1890.)
L'Oncle Tom. S. (Lem. 1903.)
Longview. City of Longview.
Louise. D. (Klag.)
Louise-Marie. S. (Eken. 1861.)
Louis Henry. D. (Lem. 1894.)
Louis van Houtte. S. (1877.)
Louvois. Hy.; S. (Lem. 1921.)
Lucetta. Pre. L. (Prest. & Brand 1941.)
Lucie Baltet. S. (Balt. before 1888.)
Lucienne Bruchet. S. (Bruch. before 1918.)
Lucinia. Pre. L. (Prest.)
Ludwig Spaeth. S. (Spae. 1883.) *Andenken an Ludwig Spaeth; Souv. de Ludwig Spaeth.*
Lutece. Hen. (Henry 1900.)
Lychorida. Pre. L. (Prest.)
Lynette. Josif. (Prest. 1930?)
Ma Bennet. S. (Klag.)
Macrostachya. S. (Before 1844.)

SYRINGA, continued
Madeleine Lemaire. D. (Lem. 1928.)
Magellan. D. (Lem. 1915.)
Major. (Before 1872.)
Marceau. S. (Lem. 1913.)
Marc Micheli. D. (Lem. 1898.)
Marechal de Bassompierre. D. (Lem. 1897.)
Marechal Foch. S. (Lem. 1924.)
Marechal Lannes. D. (Lem. 1910.)
Marengo. S. (Lem. 1923.)
Margaret. Pre. L. (Prest.)
Marguerite. S. (Klag. 1928.)
Mariana. Pre. L. (Prest.)
Marie Finon. S. (Lem. 1923.)
Marie Guille. S. (Bruch. before 1918.)
Marie Legraye. S. (Before 1879.)
Marleyensis. S. (Before 1839.) *Rouge de Marly; Rubra de Marly.*
Marleyensis Pallida. S. (Before 1864.)
Martha. S. (Klag. 1930.)
Massena. S. (Lem. 1923.)
Mathieu de Dombasle. D. (Lem. 1882.)
Maureen. Hy.; S. (Prest.)
Maurice Barres. S. (Lem. 1917.)
Maurice de Vilmorin. D. (Lem. 1900.) *Mme. Vilmorin.*
Maxima Colbert. D.
Probably same as Colbert.
Maxime Cornu. D. (Lem. 1886.)
Maximowicz. D. (Lem. 1906.)
Metensis. C. (Sim.-L. before 1871.)
Michel Buchner. D. (Lem. 1885.)
Milton. S. (Lem. 1910.)
Minnehaha. Hy.; S. (Skin. 1935.)
Minnehaha. Pre. L. (Prest.)
Mirabeau. Hy.; D. (Lem. 1911.)
Miranda. Pre. L. (Prest.)
Mireille. D. (Lem. 1904.)
Miss Ellen Willmott. Ellen Willmott.
M. LePage. S. (Lem. 1889.)
Mlle. Fernande Viger. S. (Lec. 1894.)
Mlle. Melide Laurent. S. (1898.)
Mme. Abel Chatenay. D. (Lem. 1892.)
Mme. Amelie Duprat. D. (Barbier 1900.)
Mme. Antoine Buchner. D. (Lem. 1909.) *Antoine Buchner.*
Mme. Auguste Gouchault. D. (Gouch. 1915.)
Mme. Briot. S. (Briot 1877.)
Mme. Casimir Perier. D. (Lem. 1894.)
Mme. Catherine Bruchet. D. (Bruch. before 1908.)
Mme. de Miller. D. (Lem. 1901.)
Mme. Fallieres. S. (Bruch. 1908.)
Mme. Felix. S. (F. & D. 1924.)
Mme. Florent Stepman. S. (deM. 1908.)
Mme. F. Morel. S. (Morel 1892.)
Mme. Henri Guillaud. D. (Bruch.)
Mme. Jeanne Cornu. C. (Henry before 1910.)
Mme. Jules Finger. D. (Lem. 1887.)
Mme. Jules Simon. Jules Simon.
Mme. Kreuter. S. (1880.)
Mme. Lemoine. D. (Lem. 1890.)
Mme. Leon Simon. D. (Lem. 1897.)
Mme. Louis Henry. C. (Chen. before 1912.)
Mme. Moser. S. (Briot 1877.)
Mme. R. Goyer. S. (Before 1924.)

SYRINGA, continued
Mme. Vilmorin. Maurice de Vilmorin.
Monge. S. (Lem. 1913.)
Monique Lemoine. D. (Lem. 1939.)
Montaigne. D. (Lem. 1907.)
Mont Blanc. S. (Lem. 1915.)
Montesquieu. Hy.; S. (Lem. 1926.)
Montgolfier. S. (Lem. 1905.)
Monument. S. (Lem. 1934.)
Monument Carnot. D. (Lem. 1895.)
Moonlight. S. (Hav.)
Moritz Eichler. S. (Eich. 1862.)
Mrs. A. Belmont. S. (Hav.)
Mrs. B. S. Williams. S. (Hav.)
Mrs. Calvin Coolidge. S. (Frank about 1935.)
Mrs. Edward Harding. D. (Lem. 1922.)
Mrs. E. Van Nes. S.
May be same as C. B. Van Nes.
Mrs. Flanders. S. (Hav.)
Mrs. John W. Davis. D. (Hav.)
Mrs. Morgan. D. (Klag. 1928.)
Mrs. R. W. Mills. Carmine.
Mrs. Trapman. S. (Hav.)
Mrs. Watson Webb. S. (Hav.)
Mrs. W. E. Marshall. S. (Hav. 1924.)
Muriel. Hy. (Prest.)
Murillo. D. (Lem. 1901.)
M. van Aerschot. (Before 1923.)
My Favorite. D. (Klag. 1928.)
Nana. (Before 1884.)
Nancy Frick. S. (Hav.)
Naomi. S. (Klag. 1934.)
Naudin. D. (Lem. 1913.)
Necker. Hy.; S. (Lem. 1920.)
Negro. S. (Lem. 1899.)
Nerissa. Pre. L. (Prest.)
Night. S. (Hav.)
Nigricans. S. (Before 1872.)
Nocturne. Pre. L. (Mord. before 1937.)
Noisetiana Alba. S. (Before 1889.)
Nokomis. Hy.; S. (Skin. 1935.)
Nokomis. Pre. L. (Prest.)
Norah. Hy. (Prest.)
Obelisque. G. (Lem. 1894.)
Oberon. Pre. L. (Prest. 1930?)
Octavia. Pre. L. (Prest.)
Oeil de Paupre. S.
Old Rose. S. (Klag. 1928.)
Olivia. Pre. L. (Prest.)
Olivier de Serres. D. (Lem. 1909.)
Olympia. City of Olympia.
Ophelia. Pre. L. (Prest.)
Ostrander. D. (Klag. 1928.)
Othello. S. (Lem. 1900.)
Paradise. S. (Kett. 1941.)
Pascal. Hy.; S. (Lem. 1916.)
Pasteur. S. (Lem. 1903.)
Patience. Pre. L. (Prest.)
Patricia. Hy. (Prest.)
Patrick Henry. D. (Dunb. 1923.)
Paul Deschanel. D. (Lem. 1924.)
Paul Hariot. D. (Lem. 1902.)
Paulina. Pre. L. (Prest.)
Paul Thirion. D. (Lem. 1915.)
Peau de Chamois. S. (Clarke 1936.)
Peggy. Hy; S. (Prest.)
Perdita. Pre. L. (Prest.)
Perle von Stuttgart. D. (Pfitz. 1910.)
Perle von Teltow. S. (Grun. before 1914.)
Phebe. Pre. L. (Prest.)
Philemon. S. (Coch. before 1846.)
Pierre Joigneaux. D. (Lem. 1892.)

SYRINGA, continued
Pink Beauty of Frankfort. HERMAN EILERS.
PLANCHON. D. (Lem. 1908.)
POCAHONTAS. Hy.; S. (Skin. 1935.)
PORTIA. Pre. L. (Prest.)
PRAIRIAL. Hen. × Wil. (Lem. 1933?)
PRESIDENT ALIX. S. (1925.)
PRESIDENT CARNOT. D. (Lem. 1890.)
PRESIDENT CHAUVET. D. (Bruch. before 1918.)
PRESIDENT FALLIERES. D. (Lem. 1911.)
PRESIDENT GREVY. D. (Lem. 1886.)
PRESIDENT HARDING. S. (Dunb. before 1928.)
President Harjes. PRESIDENT HAYES.
PRESIDENT HAYES. C. (Lem. 1889.) *President Harjes*.
PRESIDENT JOHN ADAMS. D. (Dunb. 1923.)
PRESIDENT LAMBEAU. S. (deM. 1908.)
PRESIDENT LEBRUN. S. (GR. 1933.)
PRESIDENT LINCOLN. S. (Dunb. 1916.)
PRESIDENT LOUBET. D. (Lem. 1901.)
PRESIDENT MASSART. S. (Eken. 1863.)
PRESIDENT MONROE. D. (Dunb. 1923.)
PRESIDENT POINCARE. D. (Lem. 1913.)
PRESIDENT ROOSEVELT. S. (Dunb. before 1928.)
PRESIDENT VIGER. D. (Lem. 1900.)
PRINCE DE BEAUVAU. D. (Lem. 1897.)
PRINCE IMPERIAL. S. (Dab. 1861.)
PRINCE LEOPOLD. S.
Probably same as Leopold II.

PRINCE NOTGER. S. (Before 1841.)
PRINCE OF WALES. S. (Doug. 1889.)
PRINCESS ALEXANDRA. S. (Doug. 1886.)
PRINCESSE CAMILLE DE ROHAN. S. (Eken. before 1856.) *Camille de Rohan*.
PRINCESSE CLEMENTINE. D. (Math. before 1708.)
PRINCESSE MARIE. S. (Before 1846.)
PRINCESS PINK. S. (Klag. 1938.)
PRISCILLA. S. (Hav. 1937.)
PRODIGE. S. (Lem. 1928.)
PROFESSOR E. H. WILSON. D. (Hav.)
PROFESSOR E. STOEKHARDT. D. (Eich. 1862.)
PROFESSOR SARGENT. S. (Spae. 1889.)
PUCK. Pre. L. (Prest.)
PULVERULENTA TRICOLOR. (Baud. before 1890.)
PYRAMIDAL. D. (Lem. 1866.)
PYRAMIDALIS ALBA. S. (1845.)
QUADRICOLOR. S. (Bensch before 1890.)
QUEEN ANNE. S. (Pill. 1926.)
RABELAIS. D. (Lem. 1896.)
REAUMUR. S. (Lem. 1904.)
REDWINE. Pre. (Mord. before 1937.)
REGAN. Pre. L. (Prest. 1940.)
REINE DE PAYS-BAS. S. (1874.)
REINE ELISABETH. S. (deM. 1908.)
REINE MARGUERITE. D. (Before 1897.)
RENE JARRY-DESLOGES. D. (Lem. 1905.)
RENONCULE. D. (Lem. 1881.)
ROCHAMBEAU. S. (Lem. 1919.)
ROI ALBERT. S. (deM. 1908.)
ROLAND MILLS. S. (Klag. 1930.)
ROMEO. Pre. L. (Prest. 1930?)
RONSARD. S. (Lem. 1912.)
ROSACE. D. (Lem. 1932.)
ROSALIND. Pre. L. (Prest.)
ROSEA GRANDIFLORA. D. (Before 1851.)
Rouge de Marley. MARLEYENSIS.

SYRINGA, continued
ROUGE DE TRIANON. S. (Briot before 1868.)
ROYALTY. Josif. (Prest.)
RUBELLA PLENA. D. (Lem. 1881.)
Rubra de Marley. MARLEYENSIS.
RUBRA INSIGNIS. S. (Before 1876.)
RUBRA JOSIKAEA. Josik.
Rubra Major. CHARLES X.
RUBY. S. (Klag. 1920.)
RUHM VON HORSTENSTEIN. S. (Wilke 1921.)
RUTILANT. Nan. (Lem. 1931.)
R. W. MILLS. D. (Klag. 1928.)
SARAH SANDS. S. (Hav.)
SATURNALE. S. (Lem. 1916.)
SAUERBREY. D. (Tows. about 1936.)
SAUGEANA. C. (Rehder before 1885.)
SAVANAROLE. D. (Lem. 1935.)
SCHERMERHORN. S. (Before 1889.)
SCHNEELAVINE. S. (Before 1875.)
SCIPION COCHET. S. (Coch. before 1876.)
SCOTIA. Hy.; S. (Scott.)
SENATEUR VOLLAND. D. (Lem. 1887.)
SIBIRICA. S. (Before 1836.)
SIEBOLD. D. (Lem. 1906.)
SILVIA. Pre. L. (Prest.)
Sinai. HERMAN EILERS.
SONIA COLFAX. S. (Hav.)
SOUV. D'ALICE HARDING. D. (Lem. 1938.)
SOUV. DE BILLIARD. (Bill. 1875.)
SOUV. DE CLAUDIUS GRAINDORGE. S.
(Souv. de) GASPARD CALLOT. D. *Dr. Gaspard Callot*.
SOUV. DE GUSTAVE GRAINDORGE. S.
SOUV. DE HENRI SIMON. S. (Simon before 1920.)
SOUV. DE L. THIBAUT. D. (Lem. 1893.)
Souv. de Ludwig Spaeth. LUDWIG SPAETH.
SOUV. DE SIMONE. D. (Bruch. before 1923.)
SPECIOSA. S. (Before 1857.)
SPECTABILIS. S. (Before 1846.)
STADTGARTNER ROTHPLETZ. D. (Froeb. 1905.)
SUNOL. D. (Clarke 1936.)
SUPERBA. Swe.
SUSAN B. ANTHONY. S. (Dunb. 1923.)
SUSANNA. S. (Klag. 1928.)
SWANEE. Pre. L. (Mord. 1937.)
SWEGIFLEXA.
TAGLIONI. D. (Lem. 1905.)
TAMORA. Pre. L. (Prest.)
THOMAS A. EDISON. S. (Dunb. 1922.)
THOMAS JEFFERSON. S. (Dunb. 1922.)
THUNBERG. D. (Lem. 1913.)
TIMANDRA. Pre. L. (Prest.)
TITANIA. Pre. L. (Prest.)
TOMBOUCTOU. S. (Lem. 1910.)
TOURNEFORT. D. (Lem. 1887.)
TOUSSAINT-LOUVERTURE. S. (Lem. 1898.)
TOWSON BEAUTY. D. (Tows. 1938.)
TRIOMPHE DE MOULINS. S. (Before 1880.)
TRIOMPHE D'ORLEANS. S. (Berm. 1854.)
TRUE BLUE. S. (Hav.)
TURENNE. S. (Lem. 1916.)
TURGOT. Hy.; S. (Lem. 1920.)
URSULA. Pre. L. (Prest.)
VALERIA. Pre. L. (Prest.)
VALETTEANA. D. (Before 1846.)
VAN AERSCHOTT. S. (deM. before 1923.)
VAUBAN. Hy.; D. (Lem. 1913.)
VERGISSMEINNICHT. S. (Spae. 1887.)

SYRINGA, continued
VERSALIENSIS. S. (Before 1857.)
VERSCHAFFELTI. S. (Before 1865.)
VESTALE. S. (Lem. 1910.)
VESUVE. S. (Lem. 1916.)
VICTOR LEMOINE. D. (Lem. 1906.)
VILLARS. Hy.; S. (Lem. 1920.)
VILLE DE LIMOGES. S. (Before 1923.)
VILLE DE TROYES. S. (Balt. before 1868.)
VIOLA. Pre. L. (Prest.)
VIOLETTA. D. (Lem. 1916.)
VIRGILIA. Pre. L. (Prest.)
Virginalis. ALBA VIRGINALIS.
VIRGINITE. D. (Lem. 1888.)
VIVIAND-MOREL. D. (Lem. 1902.)
V. L. WING. S. (Klag.)
VOLCAN. S. (Lem. 1899.)
WALDECK-ROUSSEAU. D. (Lem. 1904.)
WEDDLE. D. (Klag. 1928.)
WEEPING. Pek.
WHITE SWAN. S. (Hav.)
WILLIAM C. BARRY. S. (Dunb. before 1928.)
WILLIAM ROBINSON. D. (Lem. 1899.)
WILLIAM S. RILEY. S. (Dunb. 1922.)
WILL ROGERS. S. (Klag.)
W. K. MILLS. S. (Klag. 1930.) *Billy Mills*.
Woodland. CITY OF WOODLAND.
W. T. MACOUN. Pre. L. (Prest. 1927.)
YELLOWLEAF. Em.
YELLOWSPOT. Em.
ZULU. S. (Hav.)

SYZY'GIUM (*CLEISTOCALYX* Blume; *EUGENIA* in part; *JAMBOSA*)
This genus is united by some botanists with Eugenia.

aque'um (*Eugenia aquea*)
aromat'icum (*Caryophyllus aromaticus; Eugenia aromatica; E. caryophyllata*) CLOVETREE
The correct Latin name of the source plant of commercial cloves is controversial. Even some botanists who maintain Syzygium as a valid genus, distinct from Eugenia, prefer to keep this species in Eugenia.

cum'ini (*jambolanum; Eugenia c.; E. jambolana*) . . . . JAMBOLAN (*Duhat; Jambolanplum*)
jam'bos (*Caryophyllus j.; Eugenia j.*) ROSEAPPLE
linea'tum (*Eugenia lineata*)
malaccen'se (*Caryophyllus malaccensis; Eugenia m.; Jambosa m.*) . . OHIA (*Malayapple; Otaheiteapple* in part)
opercula'tum (*Eugenia operculata*)
owarien'se (*Eugenia owariensis*)

TABEBUI'A . . . . . . TRUMPETTREE
See also **TECOMA**.

argen'tea (*Tecoma a.*) . . . SILVER T.
donnell-smith'i . . . . . **Cybistax d.**
pal'lida (*leucoxyla; Bignonia l.* Vell., *not B. leucoxylon* L.; *B. pallida*) WHITEWOOD T.
pal'meri . . . . PALMER T.
pentaphyl'la (*Bignonia leucoxylon* L., *not B. leucoxyla* Vell.; *B. pentaphylla; Tecoma leucoxylon; T. pentaphylla*)
serratifo'lia (*Tecoma s.*) YELLOWPOUI T.

TABERNAEMONTA'NA TABERNAEMONTANA
amblyocar'pa
arbo'rea . . . . PANAMA T.

TABERNAEMONTANA, continued
austra'lis
PALOVIVORA TABERNAEMONTANA
borbon'ica . . . . BOURBON T.
citrifo'lia . . . . . ORANGELEAF T.
corona'ria . . . . CRAPEJASMINE T.
₵DOUBLE (*florepleno*) HV.
dichot'oma . . . FORBIDDENFRUIT T.
grandiflo'ra . . . YELLOWSWEET T.
mauritia'na . . . . MAURITIUS T.
u'tilis . . . . COWTREE T.

TABOG . . . . **Swinglea; S. glutinosa**

TAC'CA . . . . TACCA
chantrie'ri . . . . . . CHANTRIER T.
crista'ta . . . . CRESTED T.
pinnatif'ida . . . FIJI-ARROWROOT T.

TACH'IA . . . . TACHIA
guianen'sis . . . . GUIANA T.

TACIN'GA
See **CACTUS GENERA.**

TACSO'NIA . . . . . **PASSIFLORA**
vanvolx'emi . . . . **P. antioquiensis**

TAENID'IA . . . . TAENIDIA
integer'rima . . . . YELLOW T.

TAGE'TES . . . . MARIGOLD
apet'ala . . . . RAYLESS M.
erec'ta . . . . AZTEC M.
This species often bears the inappropriate name African Marigold.
lu'cida . . . . SWEET M.
micran'tha . . . . LITTLE M.
pat'ula . . . . FRENCH M.
tenuifo'lia (*signata*) . . . STRIPED M.
₵DWARF (*pumila*) HV.

Taguanut . . . . IVORYPALM, COMMON: **Phytelephas macrocarpa**

TAHITI-CHESTNUT. . **Inocarpus fagiferus**

Tahitinut . IVORYNUTPALM, POLYNESIAN: **Metroxylon amicarum**

TAILGRAPE . . . . **Artabotrys**
FRAGRANT T. . . . . . . **A. uncinatus**

TAI'NIA (*ASCOTAINIA*)
See **ORCHID GENERA.**

TAIWA'NIA . . . . TAIWANIA
cryptomerioi'des . . . . . TAIWANIA

TALAU'MA . . . . TALAUMA
hodgso'ni . . . . HODGSON T.

TALI'NUM |w . . . . . FAMEFLOWER
auranti'acum |w . . . . . ORANGE F.
calyc'inum . . . . . . ROCKPINK F.
crena'tum . . . . . COWSTONGUE F.
panicula'tum (*patens*) |w. PANICLED F.
₵WHITERIM. HV.
parviflo'rum . . . . . . PRAIRIE F.
rugosper'mum . . . WRINKLESEED F.
spines'cens . . . . SPINY F.
teretifo'lium . . . . QUILL F.
triangula're . . . . . . POTHERB F.

TALIPOTPALM . . **Corypha umbraculifera**

TALI'SIA . . . . TALISIA
pedicella'ris . . . . . . FLORIDA T.

TALLOWTREE, CHINESE
Sapium sebiferum

TALLOWWOOD . . . **Ximenia americana**

TALQUEZAL . . . . **Paspalum virgatum**

TAMARIN'DUS . . . . . . TAMARIND
in'dica . . . . TAMARIND

TAMARISK . . . . **Tamarix**
AFRICAN T. . . . . **T. africana**
ALGERIAN T. . . . . *T. algerica*
ATHEL T. . . . . **T. aphylla**
CHINESE T. . . . . **T. chinensis**
ENGLISH T. . . . . **T. anglica**
FIVESTAMEN T. . . . . . . **T. pentandra**
FOURSTAMEN T. . . . . . . **T. tetrandra**
FRENCH T. . . . . **T. gallica**
INDIA T. . . . . **T. g. indica**
JUNIPER T. . . . . **T. juniperina**
KARELIN T. . . . . **T. karelini**
KASHGAR T. . . . . **T. hispida**
ODESSA T. . . . . **T. odessana**
SMALLFLOWER T. . . . . . . **T. parviflora**

TAM'ARIX |w . . . . TAMARISK
aestiva'lis . . . . **T. pentandra**
africa'na . . . . AFRICAN T.
The name T. africana is often misapplied to T. gallica and T. parviflora.
alge'rica . . . . ALGERIAN T.
This form is in dispute. Some botanists regard it as probably synonymous with T. gallica; others, with T. parviflora.
amuren'sis Hort. . . . . **T. pentandra**
an'glica . . . . ENGLISH T.
aphyl'la (*articulata*) . . . . ATHEL T.
chinen'sis . . . . CHINESE T.
gal'lica |w . . . . FRENCH T.
—in'dica (*T. indica*) . . . . INDIA T.
₵SLENDER (*elegans*) HV. T. gallica
german'ica . . . . **Myricaria g.**
his'pida . . . . KASHGAR T.
—aestiva'lis . . . . **T. pentandra**
₵COOLIDGE (*coolidgei*) HV. T. hispida
in'dica . . . . **T. gallica i.**
juniperi'na (*japonica; plumosa*)
JUNIPER T.
kareli'ni . . . . KARELIN T.
odessa'na . . . . ODESSA T.
parviflo'ra (*algerica* Hort.?)
SMALLFLOWER T.
₵PURPLE (*purpurea*) HV.
pentan'dra (*aestivalis; amurensis* Hort.; *T. hispida a.*) . . FIVESTAMEN T.
plumo'sa . . . . **T. juniperina**
specio'sa
tetran'dra . . . . FOURSTAMEN T.

TA'MUS . . . . BLACKBRYONY
The generic name sometimes appears in literature spelled Tamnus.
commu'nis . . . . COMMON B.

TANACE'TUM . . . . TANSY
balsami'ta . . **Chrysanthemum majus**
borea'le . . . . ARCTIC T.
camphora'tum . . . . DUNE T.
capita'tum . . . . ROCK T.
huronen'se . . . . HURON T.
macrophyl'lum . **Chrysanthemum m.**
umbellif'erum . . . . UMBEL T.
vulga're (*Chrysanthemum v.*)
COMMON T.
₵CURLYLEAF (*crispum*) HV.

TANAE'CIUM . . . . ROPEVINE
jaro'ba . . . . TRINIDAD R.

TANAKAE'A
rad'icans

∞TANGELO . . . . **Citrus paradisi × C. reticulata**
For hort. var. see **FRUIT AND EDIBLE NUT NAMES.**

∞TANGERINE . . **Citrus reticulata** HV.

TANGHIN'IA . . . . TANGHIN
venenif'era . . . . . MADAGASCAR T.

TANGLEHEAD . . **Heteropogon contortus**
SWEET T. . . . . . . **H. melanocarpus**

∞TANGOR . . . . **Citrus reticulata × C. sinensis**

TANNING MATERIALS (Plant Sources of)
See **ECONOMIC PLANTS, TANNING MATERIALS.**

TANOAK . . **Lithocarpus; L. densiflorus**
HENRY T. . . . . **L. henryi**
JAPANESE T. . . . . **L. edulis**
SCRUB T. . . **L. densiflorus montanus**

TANSY . . . . **Tanacetum**
ARCTIC T. . . . . **T. boreale**
COMMON T. . . . . **T. vulgare**
DUNE T. . . . . **T. camphoratum**
HURON T. . . . . **T. huronense**
ROCK T. . . . . **T. capitatum**
UMBEL T. . . . . **T. umbelliferum**

TANSYBUSH. **Chamaebatiaria millefolium**

TANSYMUSTARD . . . . **Descurainia**
CREAMY MENZIES T.
D. menziesi ochroleuca
FLIXWEED T. . . . . **D. sophia**
MENZIES T. . . . . **D. menziesi**
PINNATE T. . . . . **D. pinnata**
RICHARDSON T. . . . . . **D. richardsoni**
SLIMSTEM T. . . . **D. longipedicellata**
TOOTHED T. . . . . **D. serrata**
WESTERN T. . . . . **D. incisa**

TAPIS'CIA . . . . . FALSEPISTACHE
sinen'sis . . . . CHINESE F.

TARAKTOG'ENOS
kurz'i (*Hydnocarpus k.*)

Tara Vine . . . . . ACTINIDIA, BOWER: **Actinidia arguta**

TARAX'ACUM |w . . . . . DANDELION
This genus is frequently confused with Leontodon in literature.
ceratoph'orum . . . . . . ROUGH D.
laeviga'tum (*erythrospermum*)
SMOOTH D.
officina'le (*vulgare; Leontodon taraxacum*) |w . . . . COMMON D.

TARAX'IA . . . . . . **OENOTHERA**
heteran'tha . . . . **O. subacaulis**

TARBUSH . . . . **Flourensia**
AMERICAN T. . . . . **F. cernua**

TARCHONAN'THUS
camphora'tus . HOTTENTOT-TOBACCO

TARO . . . . . . **Colocasia antiquorum**
DESFONTAINES T. . . . **C. a. fontanesi**
GREEN T. . . . . **C. indica**
IMPERIAL T. . **C. antiquorum illustris**

TARRAGON . . . **Artemisia dracunculus**

TARRIET'IA . . . . . . STONEWOOD
argyroden'dron . . . . . . SILVER S.
javan'ica . . . . JAVA S.
sylvat'ica . . . . DUNGON S.
u'tilis

TARWEED . . . . **Madia**
CHILEAN T. . . . . **M. sativa**
CLUSTER T. . . . . **M. glomerata**

TASSELFLOWER . . . . **Emilia**
EARLEAF T. . . . . **E. sagittata**
SOWTHISTLE T. . . . . . **E. sonchifolia**

TAVARE'SIA
grandiflo'ra

TAWHERO . . . **Weinmannia sylvicola**

TAXO'DIUM |w . . . . Baldcypress
ascen'dens (*T. distichum imbricarium*) |w . . . . Pond B. (*Pondcypress*)
¢Weeping (*nutans*) hv.
dis'tichum |w . . . . . Common B.
¢Columnar (*fastigiatum*) hv.
¢Dwarf (*nanum*)
¢Pyramidal (*pyramidale*)
¢Weeping (*pendens*)
mucrona'tum (*T. distichum m.*) Montezuma B.

TAX'US |w . . . . Yew
bacca'ta . . . . English Y.
—*brevifo'lia* . . . . . . **T. brevifolia**
—*canaden'sis* . . . . **T. canadensis**
¢Barrons (*barroni*) hv. T. baccata
¢Broom (*erecta; pyramidalis*)
¢Cheshunt (*cheshuntensis*)
¢Compact (*compacta*)
¢Dovaston (*dovastoni*)
¢Dwarf (*pygmaea*)
¢Elegant (*elegantissima*)
¢Evergold (*semperaurea*)
¢Golden (*aurea; variegata*)
¢Golden Irish (*fastigiata aurea*)
¢Heath (*ericoides*)
¢Horizontal (*horizontalis*)
¢Irish (*fastigiata; hibernica; stricta*)
¢Jackson (*jacksoni*)
¢Michel (*micheli*)
¢Neidpath Castle (*nidpathensis*)
¢Prostrate (*procumbens*)
¢Roundtop (*expansa*)
¢Shortleaf (*adpressa; tardiva*)
¢Shortleaf Upright (*adpressa stricta*)
¢Shortleaf Yellow (*adpressa aurea*)
¢Slimleaf (*linearis*)
¢Spreading (*repanda; repandens*)
¢Variegated (*argentea; variegata*)
¢Variegated Irish (*fastigiata variegata*)
¢Washington (*washingtoni*)
¢Weeping (*pendula*)
¢Yellowberry (*cavendishi; fructuluteo; lutea; luteobaccata*)
¢Yellow Broom (*erecta aurea*)
¢Yellow Dovaston (*dovastoni aureovariegata*)
brevifo'lia (*T. baccata b.*) . Pacific Y.
canaden'sis (*minor; T. baccata c.*) |w Canada Y.
¢Dwarf Hedge (*stricta*) hv.
chinen'sis (*T. cuspidata c.*) Chinese Y.
cuspida'ta . . . . . . Japanese Y.
—*capita'ta* Hort. . . . . **T. cuspidata**
This name is sometimes applied to the typical, upright tree form of this species, which is said to attain a height of 50 feet in its native habitat. When this species is grown from seed many variations occur. Some are low and vase-shaped; others are upright and treelike in growth habit.
—*chinen'sis* . . . . . . **T. chinensis**
—**expan'sa**
¢Columnar (*columnaris*) hv. T. cuspidata
¢Cushion (*densa*)
¢Dwarf (*nana*)
¢Dwarf Golden (*nana aurea*)
¢Erect (*erecta*)
¢Goldtip (*aurea; aurescens; T. tardiva aurea*)
¢Pygmy (*minima*). *Slavin.*
¢Thayer (*thayerae*)
¢Vermeulen
¢Yellowberry (*luteo-baccata*)
florida'na . . . . . . Florida Y.

TAXUS, continued
∞**hunnewellia'na** (*canadensis* × *cuspidata*) . . . . ∞Hunnewell Yew
∞**me'dia** (*baccata* × *cuspidata*) ∞Anglojap Y.
¢Anderson (*andersoni; T. cuspidata a.*) hv.
¢Browns (*browni; T. cuspidata b.*)
¢Hatfield (*hatfieldi*)
¢Hicks (*hicksi; T. cuspidata h.*)
¢Kelsey (*kelseyi*)
¢Wellesley (*wellesleyana*)
mi'nor . . . . **T. canadensis**

Tea . . . . **Camellia**
Botanists have decreed that Teas are Camellias, although a few regard them as distinct but *closely allied* genera. Horticulturally and economically, however, a wide gulf separates these two groups. The Camellia, whose beauty and fragrance is a chief charm of Southern gardens and of Northern hothouses and floral establishments, is grown for ornament. Teas, on the other hand, and especially Common Tea (**Camellia sinensis,** synonym *Thea sinensis*), are for use, providing a beverage of worldwide popularity which has given its name to an evening meal and made these plants an outstanding agricultural crop of the Orient.
Botanically the differences between Camellias and Teas are minor.
Assam T. . . . **C. sinensis assamica**
Bohea T. . . . . **C. s. bohea**
Canton T.. . . . **C. s. cantoniensis**
Common T. . . . . . . **C. sinensis**
Green T. . . . . **C. s. viridis**
Taperleaf T. . . . . . **C. cuspidata**

Teak . . . . **Tectona**
Common T. . . . . **T. grandis**

Tealgrass . . . . Lovegrass, Teal: **Eragrostis hypnoides;** Lovegrass, Creeping: **E. reptans**

Tearthumb . . . . **Tracaulon**
Arrowleaf T. . . . . . **T. sagittatum**
Halberdleaf T. . . . . **T. arifolium**

Teasel . . . . **Dipsacus**
China T. . . . . **D. chinensis**
Cutleaf T. . . . . . . **D. laciniatus**
Fullers T. . . . . . . **D. fullonum**
Hairy T. . . . . **D. pilosus**
Himalaya T . . . . **D. asper**
Spineless T. . . . . . . **D. inermis**
Venuscup T. . . . . . **D. sylvestris**

Teaselgourd . . . **Cucumis dipsaceus**

Teaselmallow . . . . . . **Wercklea**
CostaRica T. . . . . . . **W. insignis**

Teatree . . . . **Leptospermum**
Broom T. . . . . **L. scoparium**
Heath T. . . . . **L. ericoides**
Slender T. . . . . . . **L. ellipticum**
Spiny T. . . . . **L. spinescens**
Victoria T. . . . . . **L. laevigatum**
Yellow T. . . . . **L. flavescens**

TECO'MA . . . . . Trumpetbush
See also **CAMPSIS, STENOLOBIUM, TABEBUIA.**
argen'tea . . . . **Tabebuia a.**
austra'lis . . . **Pandorea pandorana**
capen'sis . . . . **Tecomaria c.**
garro'cha . . . . . **Stenolobium g.**
gaudichau'di
grandiflo'ra . . . . . . **Campsis g.**
interme'dia . . ∞**Campsis tagliabuana**
jasminoi'des . . . . . . **Pandorea j.**
leucox'ylon . . . **Tabebuia pentaphylla**
mack'eni . . . . **Pandorea ricasoliana**

TECOMA, continued
mol'lis . **Stenolobium stans velutinum**
pentaphyl'la . . . . . . **Tabebuia p.**
pero'ba . . . . **Paratecoma p.**
rad'icans . . . . **Campsis r.**
reginae-sa'bae . . . **Pandorea brycei**
ricasolia'na . . . . . . **Pandorea r.**
serratifo'lia . . . . . . **Tabebuia s.**
smith'i (*Bignonia s.*) Australian Trumpetbush
spectab'ilis . . . . . Yellowpoui T.
stans' . . . . **Stenolobium s.**
—*angusta'ta* **Stenolobium s. angustatum**
—*veluti'na* . **Stenolobium s. velutinum**
veluti'na . . **Stenolobium s. velutinum**

TECOMA'RIA . . . . . . Tecomaria
capen'sis (*Tecoma c.*) Cape-honeysuckle
shiren'sis

TECTA'RIA
See **FERN GENERA.**

TEC'TONA . . . . Teak
gran'dis . . . . Common T.

Teff . . . . . . **Eragrostis abyssinica**

TELANTHE'RA **ALTERNANTHERA**

TELE'KIA . . . . **BUPHTHALMUM**

TELE'PHIUM . . . . Orpine
impera'ti . . . . Common O.

Telephonepole, Living **Idria columnaris**

TELFAIR'IA . . . . Oilvine
occidenta'lis Common Oysternuttree
peda'ta . . . . . Zanzibar Oilvine

TEL'LIMA . . . . Fringecup
affi'nis . . . . . . **Lithophragma a.**
grandiflo'ra . . . . Alaska F.
¢Purple (*purpurea*) hv.
¢Redleaf (*rubra*)
odora'ta . . . . Fragrant F.

TELO'PEA . . . . Waratah
orea'des . . . . . . Gippsland W.
speciosis'sima . . . . . Crimson W.
trunca'ta . . . . . . Tasmanian W.

TEMPLETO'NIA . . . . Coralbush
ege'na . . . . Leafless C.
muel'leri . . . . Mueller C.
retu'sa . . . . Red C.
sulca'ta . . . . Yellow C.

Tenio. . . . **Weinmannia trichosperma**

Teosinte . . . . **Euchlaena**
Mexican T. . . . . . . **E. mexicana**
Perennial T. . . . . . . **E. perennis**

TEPHROCAC'TUS . . . **OPUNTIA**
See **CACTUS GENERA.**

TEPHRO'SIA (*CRACCA*) |w Tephrosia
Tephrosia, a later name, is conserved under International Rules.
can'dida . . . . White T.
cine'rea (*Cracca c.*) . . . . Ashen T.
frutes'cens . . . . . Tipsywood T.
grandiflo'ra . . . . Showy T.
leiocar'pa . . . . . Smoothpod T.
leucoseric'ea . . . . Pastel T.
noctiflo'ra (*Cracca n.*) Nightblooming T.
purpu'rea (*Cracca p.*) |w . Purple T.
spica'ta |w . . . . . . Brownhair T.
tenel'la . . . . Red T.
toxica'ria . . . . Fishdeath T.
virginia'na (*Cracca v.*) |w Virginia T.
vo'geli . . . . Vogel T.

Tephrosia . . . **Tephrosia**
Ashen T. . . . **T. cinerea**
Brownhair T. . . . **T. spicata**
Fishdeath T. . . . **T. toxicaria**
Nightblooming T. . . . **T. noctiflora**
Pastel T. . . . **T. leucosericea**
Purple T. . . . **T. purpurea**
Red T. . . . **T. tenella**
Showy T. . . . **T. grandiflora**
Smoothpod T. . . . **T. leiocarpa**
Tipsywood T. . . . **T. frutescens**
Virginia T. . . . **T. virginiana**
Vogel T. . . . **T. vogeli**
White T. . . . **T. candida**

TERAM'NUS
uncina'tus

Terfas . . . **Terfezia**
Liontruffle T. . . . **T. leonis**

TERFEZ'IA . . . Terfas (*Kamea*)
leo'nis . . . Liontruffle T.

TERMINA'LIA (*CHUNCOA*) Terminalia
acumina'ta . . . Guarabu T.
arju'na . . . Arjan T.
austra'lis
belle'rica . . . Belleric T.
biala'ta . . . Two-wing T.
buce'ras . . . **Bucida b.**
catap'pa . . . Tropical-almond T.
(*Myrobalan* in part; *Tropical-almond*)
chebu'la . . . Chebula T.
citri'na . . . Haranut T.
cominta'na . . . Binggas T.
gla'bra . . . Smooth T.
ivoren'sis . . . Ivorycoast T.
januaren'sis . . . RioJaneiro T.
macrop'tera . . . Rebreb T.
ma'ni . . . Mani T.
marsu'pium . . . Bijasal T.
mauritia'na . . . Mauritius T.
muel'leri . . . Mueller T.
myriocar'pa . . . Prolific T.
obova'ta . . . Nargusta T.
pro'cera . . . Bombway T.
saf'fordi . . . Safford T.
super'ba . . . Afara T.
tomento'sa . . . Woolly T.

Terminalia . . . **Terminalia**
Arjan T. . . . **T. arjuna**
Belleric T. . . . **T. bellerica**
Bijasal T. . . . **T. marsupium**
Binggas T. . . . **T. comintana**
Bombway T. . . . **T. procera**
Chebula T. . . . **T. chebula**
Guarabu T. . . . **T. acuminata**
Haranut T. . . . **T. citrina**
Ivorycoast T. . . . **T. ivorensis**
Mani T. . . . **T. mani**
Mauritius T. . . . **T. mauritiana**
Mueller T. . . . **T. muelleri**
Nargusta T. . . . **T. obovata**
Prolific T. . . . **T. myriocarpa**
Rebreb T. . . . **T. macroptera**
RioJaneiro T. . . . **T. januarensis**
Safford T. . . . **T. saffordi**
Smooth T. . . . **T. glabra**
Tropical-almond T. . . . **T. catappa**
Two-wing T. . . . **T. bialata**
Woolly T. . . . **T. tomentosa**

TERNSTROE'MIA
fortun'ei . . . **Cleyera japonica tricolor**
gymnan'thera (*japonica*)

Terrellgrass . . . Wildrye, Virginia: **Elymus virginicus**

Tesajo . . . **Opuntia leptocaulis**
Tesota . . . **Olneya tesota**

TESTUDINA'RIA . . . Tortoiseplant
elephan'tipes . . . Hottentotbread T.
panicula'ta . . . Panicled T.

TETRACEN'TRON
sinen'se

TETRACLE'A |w
coul'teri |w

TETRACLI'NIS . . . Arartree
Some botanists unite this monotypic genus with Callitris.
articula'ta (*Callitris quadrivalvis*) Arartree

TETRACOC'CUS . . . Fourpodspurge
dioi'cus (*engelmanni*) . . . California F.
hall'i (*Securinega fasciculata*) . Hall F.
ilicifo'lius . . . Hollyleaf F.

TETRADYM'IA |w . . . Horsebrush
axilla'ris . . . Longspine H.
canes'cens . . . Gray H.
—iner'mis . . . Spineless G.H.
como'sa . . . Hairy H.
glabra'ta . . . Littleleaf H.
nutt'alli . . . Nuttall H.
spino'sa |w . . . Cottonthorn H.
stenol'epis . . . Mohave H.

TETRAGAS'TRIS
panamen'sis

TETRAGO'NIA
crystalli'na
expan'sa . . . NewZealand-spinach

TETRAGONOLO'BUS . . . **LOTUS**
purpu'reus . . . **L. tetragonolobus**

TETRAME'RIUM |w
his'pidum |w

TETRAMI'CRA . . . **LEPTOTES**
See **ORCHID GENERA.**

TETRANE'MA . . . **ALLOPHYTON**

TETRANEU'RIS . . . **ACTINEA**
stenophyl'la . . . **A. fastigiata**

TETRA'PANAX . . . Ricepaperplant
papyrif'erus (*Aralia papyrifera; Fatsia p.*) . . . Ricepaperplant

TETRAPATHAE'A
tetran'dra

TETRAP'TERIS
dis'color

TETRASTIG'MA
har'mandi . . . Ayo
obtec'tum
—pilo'sum
serrula'tum
voinieria'num (*Vitis voinieriana*)

TETRATHE'CA . . . Tetratheca
cilia'ta . . . Pinkglory T.
—al'ba . . . White P.T.
ericifo'lia . . . Heath T.
hirsu'ta . . . Anglestem T.
jun'cea . . . Rush T.
pilo'sa . . . Hairy T.
thymifo'lia . . . Thymeleaf T.

TETRAZY'GIA . . . Tetrazygia
bi'color . . . Florida T.

TEU'CRIUM |w . . . Germander
ardui'ni
au'reum . . . **T. polium**
campanula'tum
canaden'se |w . . . American G.
chamae'drys . . . Chamaedrys G.
—glabra'tum
₵Dwarf (*prostratum*) hv. T. chamaedrys
fla'vum . . . Yellow G.
fru'ticans . . . Bush G.
ma'rum . . . Cat-thyme G.
massilien'se . . . Rose G.
monta'num . . . Mountain G.
occidenta'le |w . . . Hairy G.
orienta'le . . . Oriental G.
po'lium (*aureum*) . . . Golden G.
pyrena'icum . . . Pyrenees G.
scorodo'nia . . . Wood G.

Texasgrass . **Vaseyochloa multinervosa**
Texasplume . . . **Gilia rubra**

THALAS'SIA |w . . . Turtlegrass
testudi'num |w . . . Turtlegrass

THALES'IA . . . Ghostpipe
uniflo'ra (*Orobanche u.*) . Ghostpipe

THA'LIA |w . . . Thalia
dealba'ta |w . . . Powdered T.
divarica'ta . . . Bananaleaf T.
This native Florida species has been confused with the exotic T. geniculata.
genicula'ta |w

THALIC'TRUM |w . . . Meadowrue
alpi'num . . . Alpine M.
anemonoi'des **Anemonella thalictroides**
angustifo'lium . . . **T. lucidum**
aquilegifo'lium (*rubellum*) Columbine M.
₵Orange (*aurantiacum*) hv.
₵Pink (*roseum*)
₵Purple (*atropurpureum. Purple Cloud*)
₵White (*album*)
baicalen'se . . . Baikal M.
chelido'ni . . . Celandine M.
confi'ne . . . Critical M.
cornu'ti . . . **T. polygamum**
cultra'tum
dasycar'pum . . . Purple M.
delava'yi . . . Delavay M.
dioi'cum . . . Early M.
dipterocar'pum . . . Yunnan M.
—al'bum . . . White Y.M.
fend'leri . . . Fendler M.
fla'vum . . . Yellow M.
₵Blue (*glaucum*) hv.
flexuo'sum
foe'tidum . . . Fetid M.
foliolo'sum
glau'cum . . . Dusty M.
kiusia'num
lu'cidum (*angustifolium*) Narrowleaf M.
macrocar'pum . . . Bigfruit M.
ma'jus . . . Greater M.
mi'nus . . . Low M.
₵Maidenhair (*adiantifolium*) hv.
occidenta'le . . . Western M.
panicula'tum
This "horticultural name of uncertain application" is frequently misapplied to T. flavum and other yellow-flowered species, varieties and forms of this genus.

Hort. var.; hv. = horticultural variety (or varieties); sp. = species (singular); spp. = species (plural).
₵ = clon; × (as a prefix) = hybrid; × (between scientific plant names) = crossed by; ∞ = polybrid; |w = plant useful to wildlife.
See Glossary for definitions of clon, hybrid, and polybrid.

THALICTRUM, continued
petaloi'deum
polycar'pum . . SIERRA MEADOWRUE
polyg'amum (*cornuti*) . . . TALL M.
rhynchocar'pum . . . SNOUTSEED M.
rubel'lum . . . . . **T. aquilegifolium**
sim'plex . . . . SLIMTOP M.
squarro'sum . . . . . . NODDING M.
venulo'sum . . . . . . VEINY M.
₵SULFUR (*sulphureum*) HV. Thalictrum

THAMNOCAL'AMUS
See **BAMBOO GENERA.**

THAMNOS'MA . . . . . DESERTRUE
monta'na . . . . MOHAVE D.
texa'na . . . . TEXAS D.

THAP'SIA . . . . . . DEATHCARROT
gargan'ica . . . . GARGAN D.

THAS'PIUM |W . . . . . . THASPIUM
barbino'de |W

THATCHPALM . . . . **Thrinax**
BRITTLE T. . . . . **T. microcarpa**
JAMAICA T. . . . . **T. parviflora**
LITTLEFRUIT T. . . . . **T. punctulata**
MORRIS T.. . . . . **T. morrisi**

THE'A . . . . **CAMELLIA**

THELESPER'MA (*COSMIDIUM*) GREENTHREAD
ambig'uum . . . . . COLORADO G.
burridgea'num (*hybridum; Cosmidium b.*) . . . . . . BURRIDGE G.
ela'tum (*Cosmidium e.; C. gebanga*) GEBANGA G.

THELOCAC'TUS (*ECHINOMASTUS*)
See **CACTUS GENERA.**

THELYPO'DIUM . . . . THELYPODY
wright'i (*Stanleyella w.*) . WRIGHT T.

THELYPODY . . . . . . **Thelypodium**
WRIGHT T. . . . . **T. wrighti**

THELYP'TERIS . . . **DRYOPTERIS**
See **FERN GENERA.**

THEME'DA
gigan'tea
—vulpi'na

THEOBRO'MA . . . CHOCOLATETREE
angustifo'lia . . . . . . MONKEY C.
bi'color . . . . NICARAGUA C.
caca'o . . . . CACAO

THERMOP'SIS |W . . . . THERMOPSIS
califor'nica . . . . . CALIFORNIA T.
carolinia'na . . . . . . CAROLINA T.
divarica'ta . . . . . . SPREADING T.
faba'cea . . . . BEAN T.
fraxinifo'lia . . . . . . ASHLEAF T.
lanceola'ta . . . . . . LANCELEAF T.
macrophyl'la . . . . . . BIGLEAF T.
mol'lis . . . . SOFT T.
monta'na . . . . MOUNTAIN T.
—veno'sa (*T. gracilis v.; T. venosa*) SHASTA T.
pineto'rum . . . . PINE T.
Regarded by some botanists as synonymous with T. divaricata.
rhombifo'lia . . . . PRAIRIE T.

THESPE'SIA
grandiflo'ra. **Montezuma speciosissima**
popul'nea . . . . PORTIATREE
rog'ersi

THEVE'TIA . . . . THEVETIA
nereifo'lia (*Cerbera thevetia*) LUCKYNUT T. (*Yellow-oleander*)
yccot'li . . . . JOYOTE T.

THIMBLEBERRY
FRAGRANT T.. . . . . **Rubus odoratus**
∞FRASER T. . . . . ∞**R. fraseri**
WESTERN T. . . . . . **R. parviflorus**
WHITE T. . . . . **R. odoratus albidus**

Thingrass . . . . . BENTGRASS, THIN: **Agrostis diegoensis**

THINTAIL . . . . **Lepturus cylindricus**

THISTLE . . . . **Cirsium**
ANDREWS T. . . . . . . **C. andrewsi**
BULL T. . . . . **C. lanceolatum**
CANADA T. . . . . **C. arvense**
COULTER WESTERN T. **C. occidentale coulteri**
CURLY T. . . . . **C. crispum**
DRUMMOND T. . . . . **C. drummondi**
ELK T. . . . . **C. foliosum**
FIELD T. . . . . **C. discolor**
FRAGRANT T.. . . . . . . **C. pumilum**
HILLS T. . . . . **C. hilli**
INDIAN T. . . . . **C. edule**
SCARLET WESTERN T. **C. occidentale venustum**
SILVERLINE T. . . . . . **C. diacanthum**
SNOWWOOL WESTERN T. **C. occidentale candidissimum**
SWAMP T. . . . . **C. muticum**
SYRIAN T. . . . . **C. syriacum**
TALL T. . . . . **C. altissimum**
VELENOVSKY T. . . . **C. velenovskyi**
WAVYLEAF T. . . . . . **C. undulatum**
WESTERN T. . . . . . . **C. occidentale**

THITKA . . . . **Pentace**
BURMA T. . . . . **P. burmanica**
TAVOY T. . . . . **P. griffithi**

THLADIAN'THA . . . TUBERGOURD
du'bia . . . . MANCHU T.
oli'veri . . . . TALL T.

THLAS'PI |W . . . . . . PENNYCRESS
arven'se |W . . . . FIELD P.
bulbo'sum . . . . BULB P.
cilic'icum . . . . CILICIAN P.
glau'cum . . . . BLUE P.
Some botanists regard this as synonymous with the Old World T. alpestre. Other botanists recognize not only T. glaucum as the U. S. analogue of T. alpestre but also consider the western U. S. T. coloradense and T. purpurascens as valid species, allied to T. glaucum.
monta'num . . . . ALPS P.
perfolia'tum . . . . THOROWORT P.
prae'cox (*jankae*) . . . . . EARLY P.
rotundifo'lium . . . . ROUNDLEAF P.
stylo'sum . . . . ITALIAN P.
violas'cens . . . . VIOLET P.

THOMA'SIA . . . . . WRENFLOWER
purpu'rea . . . . PURPLE W.
rugo'sa . . . . . . WRINKLELEAF W.

THOMSO'NIA
nepalen'sis

THORN, CRUCIFIXION **Holacantha emoryi**

THOROWAX . . . . **Bupleurum**
ROUNDLEAF T. . . . **B. rotundifolium**
SHRUB T. . . . . . . **B. fruticosum**

THREEAWN . . . . **Aristida**
ARIZONA T. . . . . **A. arizonica**
ARROWFEATHER T. . **A. purpurascens**
BEACHWOODS T. . . . **A. tuberculosa**

THREEAWN, continued
BIG T. . . . . . **Aristida condensata**
BLUE T. . . . . **A. glauca**
BOTTLEBRUSH T. . . . **A. spiciformis**
CHAPMAN T. . . . . . **A. simpliciflora**
CHURCHMOUSE T. . . . **A. dichotoma**
CORKSCREW T. . . . . **A. gyrans**
CURLY T. . . . . **A. desmantha**
CURTISS T. . . . . **A. curtissi**
FENDLER T. . . . . . . **A. fendleriana**
FLORIDA T. . . . . **A. rhizomophora**
FORKTIP T. . . . . **A. basiramea**
HAVARD T. . . . . **A. barbata**
HILLSBORO T. . . . . . **A. tenuispica**
KEARNEY T. . . . . . . **A. intermedia**
KEYWEST T. . . . . **A. floridana**
LONGLEAF T. . . . . **A. affinis**
MOHAVE T. . . . . . . **A. californica**
MOHRS T. . . . . **A. mohri**
PARISH T. . . . . **A. parishi**
PINELAND T. . . . . **A. stricta**
POVERTY T. . . . . . . **A. divaricata**
PRAIRIE T. . . . . **A. oligantha**
PURPLE T. . . . . **A. purpurea**
RED T. . . . . **A. longiseta**
Reverchon T. . . . . BLUE T.
ROEMER T. . . . . . . **A. roemeriana**
SANTARITA T. . . . . **A. glabrata**
S-CURVE T. . . . . . **A. ramosissima**
SINGLE T. . . . . **A. orcuttiana**
SIXWEEKS T. . . . . **A. adscensionis**
SLIMSPIKE T. . . . . . **A. longespica**
TALL T. . . . . **A. patula**
TRINIUS T. . . . . **A. virgata**
WOOLLYSHEATH T. . . . . . **A. lanosa**
WOOTON T. . . . . **A. pansa**
WRIGHT T. . . . . **A. wrighti**

THREEWINGNUT . . . . **Tripterygium**
FORRESTS T. . . . . **T. forresti**
REGELS T.. . . . . **T. regeli**

THRIFT . . . . **Armeria**
ALGERIAN T.. . . . . **A. mauritanica**
BLOOD COMMON T. **A. maritima rubra**
∞CAESALPINA T. . . . . ∞**A. caesalpina**
CLUMP COMMON T. **A. maritima robusta**
COMMON T. . . . . **A. maritima**
CORSICAN T. . . . . . **A. leucocephala**
GREAT PLANTAIN T. **A. plantaginea gigantea**
HALLER T.. . . . . **A. halleri**
LAUCHE COMMON T. **A. maritima laucheana**
MOUNTAIN T. . . . . **A. montana**
PALE T. . . . . **A. canescens**
PINKBALL T. . . . . **A. pseudoarmeria**
PINKCLUSTER T. . . . . . **A. pungens**
PLANTAIN T. . . . . . . **A. plantaginea**
PURPLEHEAD T. . . . . . **A. purpurea**
PYRENEES T.. . . . . . **A. caespitosa**
ROSEGLOBE COMMON T. **A. maritima splendens**
ROSE PINKBALL T. **A. pseudoarmeria rubra**
RUSHLEAF T. . . . . **A. setacea**
WHITE COMMON T. . **A. maritima alba**
WHITEHEAD T. . . . **A. bupleuroides**
WHITE PINKBALL T. **A. pseudoarmeria alba**

THRI'NAX (*SIMPSONIA*) THATCHPALM
See **PALM GENERA.**

THRINCO'MA . . **COCCOTHRINAX**
See **PALM GENERA.**

THRIN'GIS . . . **COCCOTHRINAX**
See **PALM GENERA.**

Throatwort . . . . . . **Trachelium**
Common T. . . . . . **T. caeruleum**
Rumelian T. . . . . **T. rumelianum**

THRYAL'LIS (*GALPHIMIA*) Thryallis
brasilien'sis . . . . . . Brazil T.
glau'ca (*gracilis*) . . Goldshower T.

THRYPTOME'NE
mitchellia'na

THU'JA (*BIOTA*) |w . . . Arborvitae
dolabra'ta . . . . **Thujopsis d.**
gigan'tea . . . . **T. plicata**
japon'ica . . . . **T. standishi**
koraien'sis . . . . . . Korean A.
lobb'i; menzies'i . . . . . **T. plicata**
occidenta'lis |w . . . . . Eastern A.; Northern White-cedar (Forestry)
¢Batemann (*batemanni*) hv.
¢Bodmer (*bodmeri*)
¢Booth Globe (*boothi*)
¢Buchanan (*buchanani*)
¢Burrows (*burrowi*)
¢Bush (*dumosa*)
¢Bushgold (*aurea*)
¢*Columbia*. Silvertip.
¢*Compact*. Parsons.
¢Cone (*conica*)
¢Crested (*cristata*)
¢Dense (*densiforma*)
¢Douglas (*douglasi; filiformis*)
¢Douglas Golden (*douglasi aurea*)
¢Douglas Pyramidal (*douglasi pyramidalis*)
¢*Dutch Globe*. Tom Thumb.
¢Dwarf Hovey
¢Ellwanger (*ellwangeriana*)
¢*Ellwanger Golden*. Rheingold.
¢Evergold (*semperaurea*)
¢Fernleaf (*filicoides*)
¢George Peabody (*elegantissima; lutea*). *George Peabody Golden.*
¢*Globe*. Tom Thumb.
¢Goldspot (*aurea-maculata; aureovariegata; wareana aurea*)
¢*Green Globe*. Little Gem.
¢Halfhigh (*intermedia*)
¢Heath (*ericoides; Retinospora dubia; R. ericoides*)
¢Hovey (*hoveyi*)
¢Little Gem (*pumila*). *Green Globe.*
¢Little Globe (*nana*)
¢*Masters*. Moss.
¢Meehan
¢Moss (*mastersi; plicata*). *Masters.*
¢Ohlendorf (*spaethi*). *Spaeth.*
¢Parsons (*compacta*). *Compact.*
¢Pygmy (*pygmaea*)
¢Pyramidal Eastern (*pyramidalis*)
¢Queen Victoria (*alba; albo-spicata*)
¢Reeves (*reevesi*)
¢Reid (*reidi*)
¢Rheingold (*ellwangeriana aurea*). *Ellwanger Golden.*
¢Rivers (*riversi*)
¢Rosenthal (*rosenthali*)
¢*Siberian*. Ware.
¢*Siberian Dwarf*. Ware Dwarf.
¢*Siberian Gold*. Ware Gold.
¢Silvertip (*columbia*). *Columbia.*
¢*Spaeth*. Ohlendorf.
¢*Spihlmann*. Tom Thumb.
¢Theodon (*magnifica; theodonensis*)
¢Threadleaf (*filiformis*)
¢Tom Thumb (*froebeli; globosa; spihlmanni*). *Dutch Globe; Globe; Spihlmann.*

THUJA occidentalis, continued
¢Umbrella (*umbraculifera*)
¢Vervaene (*vervaeneana*)
¢Vervaene Gold (*vervaeneana aurea*)
¢Wagner (*wagneriana*)
¢Ware (*T. caucasica; T. tatarica* Hort.; *densa; robusta; sibirica; wareana*)
¢Ware Dwarf (*wareana nana*). *Siberian Dwarf.*
¢Ware Gold (*lutescens; wareana l.*). *Siberian Gold; Yellowleaf.*
¢Weeping (*pendula*)
¢Whitespray (*albo-variegata; argentea; variegata*)
¢Wintergreen Pyramidal (*nigra*)
¢Woodward (*woodwardi*)
¢*Yellowleaf*. Ware Gold.
orienta'lis (*Biota o.*) . . . . Oriental Arborvitae (*Chinese A.*)
¢Baker (*bakeri*) hv.
¢Berckmanns (*aurea nana*)
¢Beverly Hills (*beverleyensis*)
Blue Dwarf (*decussata; Retinospora juniperoides*)
¢Bonita
¢Columnar (*columnaris*)
¢Creamtip (*argenteo-variegata*)
¢Diana (*gracilis*)
¢Drooptwig (*intermedia*)
¢Evergolden (*semperaurescens*)
¢Excelsa
¢Goldbush (*aurea; Biota o. aurea nana*)
¢Goldspire (*aurea conspicua; conspicua*)
¢Goldtwig (*aureo-variegata*)
¢Greiffings Pyramid
¢Hillier (*hillieri*)
¢Howard Bluespire
¢Kallaygold
¢Mayhew Golden
¢*Melden*. Needlespire.
¢Mixleaf (*funiculata*)
Needlespire (*meldensis*). *Melden.*
¢Pompadour (*filiformis stricta*)
¢Pyramidal (*pyramidalis; stricta; Biota p.; T. pyramidalis; T. tatarica*)
¢Rosedale Blue
¢Siebold (*compacta; sieboldi; Biota aurea; B. o. compacta; B. o. sieboldi; B. o. s. japonica*)
¢Silver (*argentea*)
¢Texas Blue
¢Variegated (*variegata*)
¢Weeping (*filiformis; flagelliformis; pendula; B. o. filiformis; T. filiformis*)
¢Yellow Column (*elegantissima*)
plica'ta (*gigantea; lobbi; menziesi*) Giant A.

This enormous conifer of the Pacific Northwest, the main source of wooden shingles in that region and the tree from which Alaskan Indians carved their totem poles, is unfortunately known both popularly and in the lumber trade by the incorrect, and homonymous name Western Redcedar.

Standardized Plant Names definitely objects to this unscientific and misleading practice which only tends to continue plant-name confusion.

¢Columnar (*fastigiata*) hv.
¢Darkgreen (*atrovirens*)
¢Golden (*aurea*)
¢Weeping (*pendula*)
stan'dishi (*japonica; Thujopsis s.*) Japanese A.

THUJOP'SIS . . . Falsearborvitae
dolabra'ta (*Thuja d.*) . . . . Hiba F.
—honda'i . . . . Honda H.F.
¢Dwarf (*laetevirens; nana*) hv. T. dolabrata
¢Whitetip (*variegata*)
stan'dishi . . . . **Thuja s.**

THUNBERG'IA . . . . Clockvine
ala'ta . . . . Blackeyed C.
Baker (*bakeri*) hv.
Orange (*aurantiaca*)
White (*alba*)
coccin'ea . . . . Scarlet C.
erec'ta (*Mayenia e.*) . . . Bush C.
—al'ba . . . . White B.C.
fra'grans . . . . Sweet C.
gib'soni . . . . Orange C.
grandiflo'ra . . . . . . Bengal C.
laurifo'lia (*harrisi*) . . . Laurel C.
mysoren'sis . . . . . . Mysore C.
vogelia'na . . . . Vogel C.
wightia'na . . . . Wight C.

THU'NIA
See **ORCHID GENERA.**

THURBER'IA . . . . **GOSSYPIUM**
thespesioi'des . . . . . . **G. thurberi**

Thyme . . . . **Thymus**
Ashy T. . . . . **T. cinerascens**
Bracted T. . . . . . . **T. bracteosus**
British T. . . . . . . **T. britannicus**
Caraway T. . . . . **T. herba-barona**
Carpet T. . . . . . . **T. przewalski**
Common T. . . . . **T. vulgaris**
Conehead T. . . . . . **T. capitatus**
Epirus T. . . . . **T. epiroticus**
Hairy T. . . . . **T. hirsutus**
Least T. . . . . **T. minimus**
Mastic T. . . . . . . **T. mastichina**
Mother-of-thyme . . . **T. serpyllum**
Paper T. . . . . **T. membranaceus**
Pepper T. . . . . **T. piperella**
Portuguese T. . . . . . **T. carnosus**
Redstem T. . . . . . . **T. cimicinus**
Scandinavian T. . . . . . **T. glaber**
Sicily T. . . . . **T. nitidus**
Spotted T. . . . . . . **T. maculatus**
Upright T. . . . . **T. erectus**
Winter T. . . . . **T. hyemalis**
Woolly Mother-of-thyme **T. serpyllum lanuginosus**
Woollystem T. . . . . . **T. lanicaulis**
Zygis T. . . . . **T. zygis**

THY'MUS . . . . Thyme
alsinoi'des
azor'icus . . . . **T. serpyllum**
bracteo'sus . . . . Bracted T.
britan'nicus . . . . British T.
capita'tus (*Coridothymus c.*) Conehead T.
carno'sus . . . . . Portuguese T.
cephalo'tes
chamae'drys . . . . **T. glaber**
cimici'nus . . . . Redstem T.
cineras'cens . . . . Ashy T.
croa'ticus . . . **Micromeria croatica**
epiro'ticus . . . . Epirus T.
erec'tus . . . . Upright T.
ericaefo'lius . . . . **Micromeria varia**
gla'ber (*chamaedrys; T. serpyllum c.*) Scandinavian T.
herba-baro'na . . . . . . Caraway T.
hirsu'tus . . . . Hairy T.
hyema'lis . . . . Winter T.
lanicau'lis . . . . . Woollystem T.
lanugino'sus . . . . . **T. serpyllum l.**

THYMUS, continued
macula'tus . . . . SPOTTED THYME
mastichi'na . . . . MASTIC T.
membrana'ceus . . . . . PAPER T.
mi'cans . . . . **T. serpyllum**
min'imus . . . . LEAST T.
nit'idus . . . . SICILY T.
pectina'tus (*odoratissimus*)
piperel'la . . . . PEPPER T.
przewal'ski . . . . . . CARPET T.
serpyl'lum (*azoricus; micans*)
MOTHER-OF-THYME
—*chamae'drys* . . . . . . **T. glaber**
—**lanugino'sus** (*T. lanuginosus*)
WOOLLY M.
¢ANNIE HALL. HV. T. serpyllum
¢CRIMSON (*coccineus*)
¢DAINTY (*pulchellus*)
¢DOWNY (*villosus*)
¢DWARF (*minor*)
¢FIREFLY (*splendens*)
¢GOLDEN (*aureus*)
¢LEMON (*citriodorus; vulgaris*)
¢LILAC (*cinereus*)
¢PURPLE (*purpureus*)
¢RED (*ruber*)
¢ROSE (*roseus*)
¢SILVER (*argenteus*)
¢SILVER QUEEN
¢WHITE (*albus*)
¢WHITESPOT (*variegatus*)
vulga'ris . . . . COMMON T.
¢BROADLEAF ENGLISH. HV.
¢FRAGRANTISSIMUS
¢NARROWLEAF FRENCH
¢VARIEGATED (*variegatus*)
zy'gis . . . . ZYGIS T.
¢BALTIC (*balticus*) HV. Thymus
¢GIANT (*maximus*)
¢HEATHLEAF (*ericaefolius*)

THYRSACAN'THUS **ODONTONEMA**
ru'tilans . . . . **O. schomburgkianum**

THYRSOSTA'CHYS
See **BAMBOO GENERA.**

THYSANOLAE'NA . . . . TIGERGRASS
See **GRASS GENERA.**

THYSANO'TUS . . . . . FRINGELILY
bau'eri . . . . BAUERS F.
dichot'omus . . . . . . FORKED F.
jun'ceus . . . . RUSHLEAF F.
multiflo'rus . . . MANYFLOWERED F.
tubero'sus . . . . TUBER F.
—**al'bus** . . . . WHITE T.F.

TIAREL'LA |w . . . . FOAMFLOWER
cordifo'lia |w . . . . ALLEGANY F.
MARBLED (*marmorata*) HV.
PURPLE (*purpurea*)
SALMON (*purpurea major*)
WHITE (*albiflora*)
WINE
polyphyl'la . . . . . . HIMALAYA F.
trifolia'ta . . . . TREFOIL F.
unifolia'ta . . . . . . COOLWORT F.
TIBISEE . . . . **Lasiacis**
FLORIDA T. . . . . **L. divaricata**
Tibisi . . TIBISEE: **Lasiacis**; CARRICILLO: **Olyra latifolia**

TIBOUCHI'NA (*LASIANDRA; PLEROMA*) . . . . . . GLORYBUSH
el'egans (*Pleroma e.*) . BRISTLECUP G.
semidecan'dra (*Lasiandra macrantha*)
BRAZILIAN G.
Tican'to nu'ga . . . . . **Caesalpinia n.**

TICKCLOVER . . . . **Desmodium**
BARESTEM T. . . . . **D. nudiflorum**
BEGGARWEED T. . . . **D. polycarpum**
BIGELOW T. . . . . **D. bigelovi**
CANADA T. . . . . . . **D. canadense**
CHEROKEE T. . . . . **D. tortuosum**
DIAMONDLEAF T. . . **D. rhombifolium**
DILLEN T. . . . . **D. dilleni**
GRAHAM T. . . . . **D. grahami**
HOARY T. . . . . **D. canes ens**
LARGEFLOWER T. . . **D. acuminatum**
LINDENLEAF T. . . . **D. tiliaefolium**
LITTLELEAF T. . . . . . . **D. ciliare**
MARYLAND T. . . . **D. marilandicum**
NARROWLEAF T. . . **D. angustifolium**
NEWMEXICO T. . **D. neo-mexicanum**
PANICLED T. . . . . **D. paniculatum**
ROUNDLEAF T. . . . **D. rotundifolium**
SESSILE T. . . . . . **D. sessilifolium**
SLIMLEAF T. . . . . . **D. tenuifolium**
SMOOTH T. . . . . . . **D. laevigatum**
SPIKE T. . . . . **D. spicatum**
SWEETPEA T. . . . . . **D. formosum**
TELEGRAPH T. . . . . . . **D. gyrans**
VELVETLEAF T. . . . . **D. viridiflorum**
Ticklegrass . . . BENTGRASS, WINTER: **Agrostis hiemalis**
Annual T. . . . . ELLIOTT B. **A. elliottiana**
Arctic T. . . . . ARCTIC WINTER B.: **A. borealis**

TICKSEED . . . . **Corispermum**
HYSSOPLEAF T. . . . **C. hyssopifolium**

TIDESTRO'MIA |w . . TIDESTROMIA
lanugino'sa . . . . WOOLLY T.
oblongifo'lia . . . . HONEYSWEET T.

TIDYTIPS . . . . **Layia**
CHRYSANTHEMUM T.
L. chrysanthemoides
SHOWY T. . . . . **L. elegans**
WHITEDAISY T. . . . . **L. glandulosa**
YELLOWDAISY T. . . . **L. platyglossa**

TIEGHEMOPAN'AX . GINSENGTREE
el'egans (*Panax e.*) . . UMBRELLA G.
mur'rayi (*Panax m.*) PENCILWOOD G.
sambucifo'lius (*Panax sambucifolium*)
ELDERLEAF G.

TIGERFLOWER . . . . **Tigridia**
COMMON T. . . . . **T. pavonia**
TIGERGRASS . . **Thysanolaena maxima**

TIGRID'IA . . . . . . TIGERFLOWER
pavo'nia . . . . COMMON T.
¢BIGSHELL (*grandiflora*) HV.
¢BLUESKY (*coelestina; phalacallis plumbea*)
¢CANARY (*canariensis*)
¢CARMINE (*carminea*)
¢DWARF (*speciosa*)
¢PURE GOLD (*lutea*)
¢RUBY QUEEN
¢SPOTLESS (*immaculata*)
¢SPOTTED LILAC (*lilacea*)
¢YELLOW ROSE (*rosea*)
¢YELLOWSHELL (*conchiflora*)
Tikouka . . . . . . DRACENA, GIANT: **Cordyline australis**

TIL'IA |w LINDEN; BASSWOOD (Forestry)
al'ba Ait. (1789) . . . **T. tomentosa**
al'ba K. Koch (1865) . . **T. petiolaris**
al'ba Michx. (1810)
T. heterophylla michauxi
—*pyramida'lis* Hort. . **T. tomentosa**
—*spectab'ilis* Hort. . . . ∞**T. moltkei**

TILIA, continued
america'na (*glabra; nigra*) |w
AMERICAN LINDEN
—**denta'ta** (*T. a. megalodonta; T. longifolia d.*)
—*pen'dula* Hort. . . . . **T. petiolaris**
¢BIGLEAF (*laxiflora; macrophylla; mississippiensis*) HV. T. americana
¢GRAPELEAF (*ampelophylla; dentata; inciso-dentata*)
¢PYRAMIDAL (*fastigiata*)
amuren'sis (*T. cordata mandshurica; maximowiczi*) . . . . . AMUR L.
argen'tea . . . . **T. tomentosa**
austra'lis . . . . . APPALACHIAN L.; APPALACHIAN BASSWOOD (Forestry)
baronia'na . . . . **T. chinensis**
begonifo'lia . . . . . . **T. dasystyla**
blechia'na Hort. . . . . ∞**T. moltkei**
carlsruhen'sis . . . . . . ∞**T. flaccida**
carolinia'na (*lata*) . . . CAROLINA L.; CAROLINA B. (Forestry)
—**rhooph'ila**
caucas'ica . . . . **T. dasystyla**
chinen'sis (*baroniana*) . . CHINESE L.
cocks'i . . . . LOUISIANA L.; LOUISIANA B. (Forestry)
corda'ta (*europaea* L. in part; *microphylla; parvifolia; silvestris; ulmifolia*) . . . . LITTLELEAF L.
—*japon'ica* . . . . **T. japonica**
—*mandshu'rica* . . . . . **T. amurensis**
¢PYRAMIDAL (*pyramidalis*) HV. T. cordata
dasys'tyla (*begonifolia; caucasica; multiflora; rubra* Stev., *not* DC.)
CAUCASIAN L.
eburne'a (*lasioclada*) . . . HAIRY L.; HAIRY B. (Forestry)
∞**euchlo'ra** (*?cordata* × *dasystyla; T. rubra e.*) . . . . ∞CRIMEAN L.

The name T. dasystyla is often misapplied to this hybrid Linden.

∞**europae'a** (*cordata* × *platyphyllos; intermedia; vulgaris*) . ∞EUROPEAN L.

The name T. europaea is often misapplied to T. cordata and T. platyphyllos.

¢PALELEAF (*pallida*) HV.
¢WEEPING (*pendula; beaumontia p.*)
∞**flac'cida** (*americana* × *platyphyllos; carlsruhensis; praecox* A.Br., *not* Host.)
∞**flaves'cens** (*americana* × *cordata*)
∞YELLOW L.
×*floribun'da* . . . . . . FLORIBUNDA L.

This form was published as a species but is a hybrid of cordata × dasystyla or, according to some, a clon of ∞T. flavescens (*americana* × *cordata*).

florida'na . . . . FLORIDA L.
—**alabamen'sis** . . . . . ALABAMA L.; ALABAMA B. (Forestry)
—**hypoleu'ca**
georgia'na . . . . GEORGIA L.; GEORGIA B. (Forestry)
—**crini'ta**
gla'bra . . . . **T. americana**
grandifo'lia . . . . . **T. platyphyllos**
henrya'na . . . . HENRY L.
—**subgla'bra** . . . . . . SMOOTH H.L.
heterophyl'la . . . . . BEETREE L.
—**michaux'i** (*T. alba* Michx., *not* Ait. *nor* K. Koch; *T. michauxi*)
MICHAUX L.
heterophyl'la Sarg. in part, *not* Vent.
T. monticola
insula'ris . . . . KOREAN L.

TILIA, continued
interme'dia . . . . . . ∞**T. europaea**
inton'sa (*tonsura*)
japon'ica (*T. cordata j.*) JAPANESE LINDEN
∞**juranya'na** (*cordata* × *tomentosa*) ∞HUNGARIAN L.
kiusia'na . . . . KYUSHU L.
lasioc'lada . . . . **T. eburnea**
la'ta . . . . **T. caroliniana**
leucocar'pa . . . . GULF L.; GULF BASSWOOD (Forestry)
—glauces'cens
littora'lis . . . COLONELSISLAND L.; COLONELSISLAND B. (Forestry)
—denta'ta . . . . . **T. americana d.**
—dis'color
mandshu'rica . . . MANCHURIAN L.
maximowicz'i . . . . . **T. amurensis**
maximowiczia'na (*miyabei*) MAXIMOWICZ L.
michaux'i . . . . **T. heterophylla m.**
michaux'i Sarg., *not* Nutt. **T. neglecta**
microphyl'la . . . . **T. cordata**
miquelia'na
This name is sometimes misapplied to T. maximowicziana.
miya'bei . . . . . **T. maximowicziana**
∞**molt'kei** (*americana* × *?petiolaris; T. alba spectabilis* Hort.; *blechiana* Hort.; *spectabilis* Dipp., *not* Host.) ∞MOLTKE L.
mongol'ica . . . . . . MONGOLIAN L.
montic'ola (*heterophylla* Sarg. in part, *not* Vent.) . . . . . HIGHLANDS L.
multiflo'ra . . . . **T. dasystyla**
neglec'ta (*michauxi* Sarg., *not* Nutt.; *T. nigra vestita; pubescens* Hort., *not* Vent.) . . . . . . QUEBEC L.
ni'gra . . . . **T. americana**
—vesti'ta . . . . . . **T. neglecta**
officina'rum . . . . . **T. platyphyllos**
oli'veri (*pendula*) . . . . . OLIVER L.
∞**orbicula'ris** (∞*euchlora* × *petiolaris*) ∞ROUNDLEAF L.
parvifo'lia . . . . **T. cordata**
paucicosta'ta
pen'dula . . . . **T. oliveri**
petiola'ris (*alba* K. Koch, *not* Ait. *nor* Michx.; *T. americana pendula* Hort.; *T. tomentosa petiolaris*) SILVERPENDENT L.
phane'ra . . . KENDALLCOUNTY L.; KENDALLCOUNTY B. (Forestry)
—sca'brida
platyphyl'los (*europaea* in part; *grandifolia; officinarum* in part) BIGLEAF L.
¢CUTLEAF (*aspleniifolia; filicifolia; laciniata*) HV.
¢GOLDTWIG (*aurantia; aurea*)
¢PYRAMIDAL (*fastigiata; pyramidalis*)
¢REDTWIG (*corallina; rubra*)
¢VINELEAF (*vitifolia*)
porra'cea . . . . . . OKALOOSA L.; OKALOOSA B. (Forestry)
prae'cox A.Br., *not* Host. ∞**T. flaccida**
pubes'cens Hort., *not* Vent. **T. neglecta**
ru'bra Stev., *not* DC. . . **T. dasystyla**
—euchlo'ra . . . . ∞**T. euchlora**
silves'tris . . . . **T. cordata**
×*spaeth'i* . . . . SPAETH L.
This form was published as a species but is a hybrid of cordata × dasystyla or, according to some, a clon of ∞T. flavescens (*americana* × *cordata*).
spectab'ilis Dipp., *not* Host. ∞**T. moltkei**

TILIA, continued
texa'na . . . . . . TEXAS LINDEN; TEXAS BASSWOOD (Forestry)
tomento'sa (*alba* Ait., *not* K. Koch *nor* Michx.; *T. a. pyramidalis* Hort.; *argentea*) . . . . SILVER L.
—petiola'ris . . . . . . **T. petiolaris**
ton'sura . . . . **T. intonsa**
tu'an . . . . TUAN L.
—chinen'sis . . . WOOLLYTWIG T.L.
ulmifo'lia . . . . **T. cordata**
venulo'sa . . . . . . BLUERIDGE L.; BLUERIDGE B. (Forestry)
—multiner'vis
vulga'ris . . . . ∞**T. europaea**

TILLAE'A |w . . . . . . PYGMYWEED
aquat'ica (*Crassula a.*) |w COMMON P.
drum'mondi |w . . . . DRUMMOND P.

TILLAND'SIA (*DENDROPOGON*) |w TILLANDSIA
duvalia'na . . . . **Vriesia d.**
fascicula'ta . . . . . QUILL-LEAF T.
lindenia'na . . . . . . LINDENS T.
nigres'cens . . . . BLACK T.
stric'ta
usneoi'des (*Dendropogon u.*) |w TREEBEARD T. (*Spanishmoss*)

TIL'MIA . . . . **AIPHANES**
See **PALM GENERA.**

TIM'LIS . . . . **MANICARIA**
See **PALM GENERA.**

TIMOTHY . . . . **Phleum; P. pratense**
ALPINE T. . . . . **P. alpinum**
BRITISH T. . . . . . **P. paniculatum**
ITALIAN T. . . . . . . **P. subulatum**
SAND T. . . . . **P. arenarium**

TINAN'TIA
fu'gax (*erecta; Tradescantia e.*)

Tindalo . . . . . PAHUDIA, PHILIPPINE: **Pahudia rhomboides**

TINGLELILY . . . . **Cajophora**
TWINING T. . . . . . . **C. lateritia**

Tinia'ria scan'dens . . . **Polygonum s.**

TINNE'A . . . . TINNEA
aethio'pica . . . . . . ETHIOPIAN T.
sacleux'i

TINOS'PORA . . . . . . TINOSPORA
cordifo'lia . . . . . . GULANCHA T.

Tiotamal. DIOON, CHESTNUT: **Dioon edule**

TIPUA'NA . . . . TIPUTREE
ti'pu (*speciosa; Machaerium t.*) COMMON T.

TIPULA'RIA . . . . CRANEFLYORCHID
See **ORCHID GENERA, HARDY TERRESTRIAL GROUP.**

TIPUTREE . . . . **Tipuana**
COMMON T. . . . . **T. tipu**

TIRITE . . . . **Ischnosiphon**
BASKET T. . . . . **I. arouma**

TIS'SA . . . . **SPERGULARIA**

TITANOP'SIS **MESEMBRYANTHEMUM**
See **SUCCULENTS.**

TITHO'NIA . . . . TITHONIA
diversifo'lia . . . . . . YUCATAN T.
rotundifo'lia (*speciosa; tagetiflora*) SCARLET T.

TITHYMALOP'SIS; TITHYMA'LUS . . . . **EUPHORBIA**
See **SUCCULENTS.**

TI'UM . . . . **ASTRAGALUS**

TOADFLAX . . . . **Linaria**
ALPINE T. . . . . **L. alpina**
AMETHYST T. . . . . **L. amethystea**
BITTER T. . . . . **L. tristis**
BROOMLEAF T. . . . . **L. genistifolia**
BUTTER-AND-EGGS T. . . **L. vulgaris**
CLOVENLIP T. . . . . . . **L. bipartita**
DALMATIAN T. . . . . . **L. dalmatica**
GOLDDOLLAR T. . . . . . . **L. pancici**
HYBRID T. . . . . ×**L. alpina hybrida**
INFLATED T. . . . . . . **L. ventri osa**
ITALIAN T. . . . . **L. italica**
MACEDONIAN T. . . . **L. macedonica**
MOROCCO T. . . . . . . **L. maroccana**
OLDFIELD T. . . . . . . **L. canadensis**
PALEBLUET T. . . . . **L. repens**
PURPLENET T. . . . . . **L. reticulata**
PURPLE T. . . . . **L. purpurea**
ROYAL CLOVENLIP T. **L. bipartita splendida**
SAPPHIRE T. . . . . . **L. sapphirina**
SHOWY MACEDONIAN T. **L. macedonica speciosa**
SMALL T. . . . . **L. minor**
THREELEAF T. . . . . . . **L. triphylla**
TOURNEFORT T. . . . . **L. tourneforti**
WHITE CLOVENLIP T. **L. bipartita alba**

TOADLILY . . . . **Tricyrtis**
BROADLEAF T. . . . . . . **T. latifolia**
FORMOSA T. . . . . . . **T. formosana**
HAIRY T. . . . . **T. hirta**
SPECKLED T. . . . . . **T. macropoda**
TRAILING T. . . . . . **T. stolonifera**
YELLOW T. . . . . **T. flava**

TOBACCO . . . . **Nicotiana**
AZTEC T. . . . . **N. rustica**
BIGLEAF COMMON T. **N. tabacum macrophylla**
COMMON T. . . . . **N. tabacum**
COYOTE T. . . . . **N. attenuata**
DESERT T. . . . . . **N. trigonophylla**
GIANT T. . . . . **N. tomentosa**
INDIAN T. . . . . **N. bigelovi**
NARROWLEAF COMMON T. **N. tabacum angustifolia**
∞SANDER T. . . . . . . ∞**N. sanderae**
TREE T. . . . . **N. glauca**
WINGED T. . . . . **N. alata**

TOBOSA . . . . **Hilaria mutica**

TOCO'CA . . . . TOCOCABUSH
guianen'sis . . . . GUIANA T.
imperia'lis . . . . ROYAL T.
platyphyl'la (*Sphaerogyne latifolia*) BROADLEAF T.

TOCOCABUSH . . . . **Tococa**
BROADLEAF T. . . . . **T. platyphylla**
GUIANA T. . . . . . . **T. guianensis**
ROYAL T. . . . . **T. imperialis**

TODDA'LIA . . . . TODDALIA
asiat'ica (*aculeata*) . . . . ASIAN T.
lanceola'ta . . . . **Vepris l.**

TOFIELD'IA . . . . TOFIELDIA
gla'bra . . . . SMOOTH T.
occidenta'lis (*intermedia*) . . TALL T.
racemo'sa . . . . STICKY T.

Tokopat . . . . . . FANPALM, ASSAM: **Livistona jenkinsiana**

TOLMIE'A . . . . TOLMIEA
menzies'i . . . . MENZIES T.

TOL'PIS
barba'ta (*Crepis b.*)

TOLUIF'ERA . . . **MYROXYLON**

TOLYPEL'LA |w . . . . . TOLYPELLA
fimbria'ta |w
prolif'era |w

TOMATO . . . . **Lycopersicon**
BIGLEAF T. **L. esculentum grandifolium**
CHERRY T. . . . . . **L. e. cerasiforme**
COMMON T. . . . . . **L. esculentum**
CURRANT T. . . . **L. pimpinellifolium**
PEAR T. . . **L. esculentum pyriforme**
UPRIGHT T. . . . . . **L. e. validum**

TONEL'LA . . . . . **COLLINSIA**

TONES'TUS . . . . **APLOPAPPUS**

TONGAVINE, CENTIPEDE
Epipremnum pinnatum

Tongusa . . . . AGAR: **Gelidium**

TONKABEAN . . . . **Dipteryx**
BRITISH T. . . . . . **D. oppositifolia**
DUTCH T. . . . . **D. odorata**
PANAMA T. . . . . . **D. panamensis**

Tooart . . . . . EUCALYPTUS, TUART:
Eucalyptus gomphocephala

TOO'NA . . . . TOON

This Old World genus, the analogue of the New World Cedrela, is united with it by some botanists.

austra'lis (*Cedrela a.*) . AUSTRALIAN T.
calan'tas . . . . PHILIPPINE T.
cilia'ta (*Cedrela toona*) . . . BURMA T.
serra'ta (*Cedrela s.*) . . HIMALAYA T.
sinen'sis (*Cedrela s.*) . . CHINESE T.

TOOTHACHEGRASS . **Ctenium aromaticum**

TOOTHWORT . . . . **Dentaria**
CALIFORNIA T. . . . . **D. californica**
CASCADE T. . . . . **D. macrocarpa**
CRINKLEROOT T. . . . . **D. diphylla**
CUTLEAF T. . . . . . . **D. laciniata**
LARGE T. . . . . **D. maxima**
OREGON T. . . . . **D. tenella**

Topee Tambo . . . CALATHEA, EDIBLE:
Calathea allouia

TORCHLILY. . . . . **Kniphofia**
COMMON T. . . . . **K. uvaria**
CORALQUEEN T. . . . . . **K. gracilis**
∞ CORAL T. . . . . . . ∞ **K. corallina**
EARLY T. . . . . **K. rufa**
GALPIN T. . . . . **K. galpini**
HOTPOKER T. . . . . . . **K. elegans**
MACOWAN T. . . . . . . **K. macowani**
NELSON T. . . . . **K. nelsoni**
NORTHS T. . . . . **K. northiae**
SULFUR T. . . . . **K. sulphurea**
SWORDLEAF T. . . . . . **K. ensifolia**
SWORD T. . . . . **K. foliosa**
TRAVELING T. . . . . **K. sarmentosa**
TUCK T. . . . . **K. tucki**

TORE'NIA . . . . TORENIA
asiat'ica . . . . PANSY T.
fla'va (*bailloni*) . . . . . YELLOW T.
fournier'i . . . . BLUE T.
₵BIGBLOOM (*grandiflora*) HV.
₵SHOWY (*speciosa*)
peduncula'ris . . . . . . MALAY T.

TO'RILIS . . . . HEDGEPARSLEY
nodo'sa (*Caucalis n.*) . . KNOTTED H.

Tormina'ria tormina'lis . . . **Sorbus t.**

Torpedograss . . . PANICUM, TORPEDO:
Panicum repens

TORRE'SIA . . . . . **HIEROCHLOE**
See **GRASS GENERA**.

TOR'REYA (*TUMION*) . . TORREYA
califor'nica (*Tumion californicum*)
CALIFORNIA T. (*California-nutmeg*)
farge'si . . . . FARGES T.
gran'dis (*Tumion nuciferum grande*)
CHINESE T.
nucif'era (*Tumion nuciferum*)
JAPANESE T.
taxifo'lia (*Tumion taxifolium*)
FLORIDA T. (*Stinkingcedar*)

TORRU'BIA . . . . BLOLLY
longifo'lia (*Pisonia obtusata* U. S. Auth., *not* Jacq.) . . LONGLEAF B.
obtusa'ta (*Pisonia o.* Jacq., *not* U. S. Auth.)

TORTOISEPLANT. . . . . . **Testudinaria**
HOTTENTOTBREAD T. . **T. elephantipes**
PANICLED T. . . . . . . **T. paniculata**

TORUSHERB . . . . **Dorstenia**
CONTRAYERVA T. . . . **D. contrajerva**

TOTAIPALM . . . . . **Acrocomia totai**

TOTEMPOLE-CACTUS
Lophocereus schotti monstrosus

TOUCHAR'DIA
latifo'lia . . . . OLONA

TOU'MEYA
See **CACTUS GENERA**.

TOURNEFORT'IA . . . TOURNEFORTIA
acumina'ta . . . . . . MASCARA T.
argen'tea . . . . . . VELVETLEAF T.
hirsutis'sima . . . . . . TRINIDAD T.
sca'bra . . . . ROUGH T.
sibir'ica . . . . SIBERIAN T.

TOVA'RA |w . . . . TOVARA
virginia'na (*Polygonum virginianum*) |w
VIRGINIA T.
—**filifor'mis** (*Polygonum filiforme*)
MARBLED (*variegata*) HV.

TOWELGOURD . . . . **Luffa**
SINGKWA T. . . . . . **L. acutangula**
SUAKWA VEGETABLESPONGE
L. cylindrica

TOWER-OF-JEWELS . . **Echium roseum**

TOWER-OF-PISATREE
Platylophus trifoliatus

TOWNSEND'IA . . . . TOWNSENDIA
exsca'pa (*sericea; wilcoxiana*)
STEMLESS T.
flo'rifer
grandiflo'ra
inca'na . . . . HOARY T.
par'ryi . . . . PARRY T.
scapig'era . . . . TUFTED T.
seric'ea; wilcoxia'na . . . **T. exscapa**

TOWRI . . . . . . **Caesalpinia digyna**

TOXICODEN'DRON |w

This genus is regarded by some of the more conservative botanists as a synonym of Rhus. The group, however, is everywhere recognized by people as distinct from true Sumacs (Rhus); economically it is quite different, its peculiar poisonous and chemical properties setting it apart. Furthermore it has good morphological characters (including loose, delicate, axillary inflorescence; solitary terminal style, rounded, mostly whitish and smooth fruit; and striate stone). Prof. Rehder writes "There can be no strong objection to separating Toxicodendron from Rhus as a distinct genus" and, from the practical and nomenclatural standpoints, there are distinct advantages in making such a separation.

TOXICODENDRON, continued

capen'se . . . . **Hyaenanche capensis**
delavay'i (*Rhus d.*)
DELAVAY POISONSUMAC
diversilo'bum (*Rhus diversiloba*) |w
PACIFIC POISONOAK
orienta'le (*Rhus orientalis*)
ORIENTAL POISONOAK
quercifo'lium (*Rhus quercifolia; R. toxicodendron* L., *not* Auth.) POISONOAK
rad'icans (*Rhus r.; R. toxicodendron* Auth., *not* L.) |w COMMON POISONIVY
—**rydberg'i** (*T. rydbergi; Rhus r. r.; R. rydbergi*) . WESTERN POISONIVY
succeda'neum (*Rhus succedanea*)
WAXTREE
sylves'tre (*Rhus sylvestris*)
ORIENTAL POISONSUMAC
trichocar'pum (*Rhus trichocarpa*)
PEELBERRY POISONSUMAC
verniciflu'um (*Rhus vernicifera; R. verniciflua*) JAPANESE LACQUERTREE
ver'nix (*Rhus venenata; R. vernix*) |w
POISONSUMAC

TOXICOPHLOE'A . **ACOKANTHERA**

TOXICOSCOR'DION . **ZIGADENUS**
interme'dium . . . . . **Z. gramineus**

TOX'YLON . . . . **MACLURA**

Toyon . . . . CHRISTMASBERRY:
Photinia arbutifolia

TRACAU'LON |w . . . . TEARTHUMB

This genus is united by some botanists with Polygonum.

arifo'lium (*Polygonum a.*) |w
HALBERDLEAF T.
sagitta'tum (*Polygonum s.*) |w
ARROWLEAF T.

TRACHE'LIUM . . . . THROATWORT
caeru'leum . . . . COMMON T.
rumelia'num . . . . . RUMELIAN T.

TRACHELOSPER'MUM (*RHYNCHOSPERMUM*) . STARJASMINE
asiat'icum (*crocostemon; divaricatum*)
JAPANESE S.
diffor'me
jasminoi'des (*Rhynchospermum j.*)
CHINESE S. (*Confederate-jasmine*)
₵MANDAI (*mandaianum*) HV.
₵VARIEGATED (*variegatum*)

TRACHYCAR'PUS (*CHAMAEROPS* in part) . . . . . . WINDMILLPALM
See **PALM GENERA**.

TRACHYLO'BIUM . . . . RASPPOD
hornemannia'num . . . ZANZIBAR R.
verruco'sum

These species have been confused with each other.

TRACHYME'NE (*DIDISCUS*)
LACEFLOWER
austra'lis . . . . . . AUSTRALIAN L.
coeru'lea (*Didiscus c.*) . SKYBLUE L.
glaucifo'lia. . . . . . BLUELEAF L.
pilo'sa . . . . HAIRY L.

TRACHYPO'GON
See **GRASS GENERA**.

TRACHYSPER'MUM
am'mi (*Carum copticum*)
AJOWAN-CARAWAY

TRACHYSTE'MON (*PSILOSTEMON*)
orienta'lis (*Borago o.*)

Tracyan'thus angustifo'lius . **Zigadenus a.**

TRADESCAN'TIA |w . . . Spiderwort
bractea'ta . . . . Bracted S.
brevicau'lis . . . . . Shortstem S.
dis'color . . . . **Rhoeo d.**
dracaenoi'des . . . . . Dracena S.
fluminen'sis (*repens; striata*) Wanderingjew
fusca'ta
genicula'ta
hu'milis . . . . Texas S.
micran'tha . . . . . Littleflower S.
monta'na . . . . **T. virginiana**
multicol'or **Zebrina pendula quadricolor**
multiflo'ra . . . . Jamaica S.
occidenta'lis . . . . Prairie S.
₵Red (*rubra*) hv.
pilo'sa . . . . Zigzag S.
quadricol'or . . . **Zebrina pendula q.**
reflex'a
regi'nae . . . . Queens S.
re'pens; stria'ta . . . . **T. fluminensis**
virginia'na (*montana*) |w . Virginia S.
₵Bartram. hv.
₵Crimson (*coccinea*)
₵Double (*major*)
₵Dwarf Blue (*nana*)
₵Leonora
₵Lilac (*lilacina*)
₵Pink (*rosea*)
₵Purple (*purpurea*)
₵Red (*rubra*)
₵Skyblue (*caerulea*)
₵Violet (*violacea*)
₵White (*alba*)
zebri'na . . . . . . **Zebrina pendula**
₵Bengal (*bengalensis*) hv. Tradescantia
₵Laeken (*laekenensis*)
₵Lanceleaf (*lanceolata*)
₵Thuringia
₵Yellowstripe (*aureostriata*)

TRA'GIA |w . . . . Noseburn
ramo'sa
u'rens |w

TRAGOPO'GON |w . . . . . Salsify
porrifo'lius |w . Vegetable-oyster S. (*Oysterplant*)
praten'sis . . . . Meadow S.

TRAGOPY'RUM . . **ATRAPHAXIS**
lanceola'tum latifo'lium **A. muschketowi**

TRA'GUS (*NAZIA*) . . . . Burgrass
See **GRASS GENERA.**

Trailing-arbutus . **Epigaea; E. repens**
Asiatic T. . . . . **E. asiatica**
Double T. . . . . **E. repens plena**
Smoothleaf T. . . . . **E. r. glabrifolia**

Trajanscolumn **Pachycereus columna-trajani**

TRA'PA |w
bispino'sa . . . . . . Singharanut
na'tans |w . . . . . Waterchestnut

TRAPEL'LA . . . . Trapella
sinen'sis . . . . Chinese T.

TRAUTVETTE'RIA
carolinen'sis (*palmata*)
gran'dis

Travelersjoy . . . . **Clematis vitalba**

Travelerstree . . . . . . **Ravenala**
Madagascar T. **R. madagascariensis**

Treadsoftly . . . . . . **Cnidoscolus**
Drug T. . . . . **C. urens**
Risky T. . . . . . . **C. stimulosus**
Texas T. . . . . **C. texanus**

Treebine . . . . **Cissus**
Acid T. . . . . **C. acida**
Begonia T. . . . . . . **C. discolor**
Evergreen T. . . . . . **C. capensis**
Ivy T. . . . . **C. incisa**
Kangaroo T. . . . . . **C. antarctica**
Marble T. . . . . . **C. gongylodes**
Queensland T. . . . . **C. oblonga**
Striped T. . . . . **C. striata**
Venezuela T. . . . . **C. rhombifolia**
Waterwithe T. . . . . **C. sicyoides**
Winged T. . . . **C. quadrangularis**

Treebuckthorn . **Alphitonia; A. excelsa**

Treefern . . . . . **Alsophila; Cyathea**
Australian T. . . . . . **A. australis**
Cooper T. . . . . **A. cooperi**

Treemallow . . . . **Lavatera**
Bush T. . . . . . . **L. malopetrifida**
California T. . . **L. assurgentiflora**
Crete T. . . . . **L. cretica**
Herb T. . . . . **L. trimestris**
Island T. . . . . **L. insularis**
Mauritius T. . . . . **L. mauritanica**
Portugal T. . . . . **L. davaei**
Velvet T. . . . . **L. arborea**

Treetomato . . **Cyphomandra betacea**

TRE'MA . . . . Trema
as'pera . . . . Poisonbush T.
bracteola'ta . . . . . Blackpod T.
lamarckia'na . . . . WestIndies T.
mol'lis (*floridana*) . . . Florida T.
orienta'lis . . . . India-charcoal T.

TREVE'SIA . . . . Trevesia
palma'ta (*Gastonia p.*) . Himalayan T.
₵Sundai (*sundaica* Regel, *not* Miq.) hv.
san'deri Hort. . . . . Annamese T.
sunda'ica . . . . Sumatra T.

TREVO'A . . . . Trevoa
triner'vis . . . . Chilean T.

TRIAN'THEMA |w . . Horse-purslane
portulacas'trum |w . . . Desert H.

TRIB'ULUS |w
cistoi'des . . . Jamaica Feverplant
terres'tris |w . . . . Puncturevine

TRICALY'SIA (*KRAUSSIA*)
kraussia'na (*floribunda; Kraussia f.*)

TRICHACH'NE (*VALOTA*) Cottontop
See **GRASS GENERA.**

TRICHEROSTIG'MA . **EUPHORBIA**

TRICHIL'IA . . . . Bitterwood
al'ta . . . . Pimenteira B.
catigua' . . . . Catigua B.
cruegeria'na . . . . . Trinidad B.
emet'ica . . . . Mafura B.
moscha'ta . . . . Musk B.
oblanceola'ta . . . . . . Acurel B.
spondioi'des . . . . White B.
triphyl'la . . . . Bagre B.

TRICHIN'IUM . . . . . **PTILOTUS**

TRICHLO'RIS . . . . . . Trichloris
See **GRASS GENERA.**

TRICHOCAU'LON
delaetia'num
melofor'me

TRICHOCE'REUS (*ARTHROCEREUS; ERIOSYCE*)
See **CACTUS GENERA.**

TRICHODIADE'MA **MESEMBRYANTHEMUM**
See **SUCCULENTS.**

TRICHOLAE'NA
See **GRASS GENERA.**

TRICHOLO'MA . . . . . Tricholoma
eques'tre . . . . Equestrian T.
nu'dum
persona'tum . . . . Blewits T.
rus'sula . . . . Red T.
ter'reum

TRICHOM'ANES . . . . . Filmfern
See **FERN GENERA.**

TRICHONEU'RA
See **GRASS GENERA.**

TRICHOPIL'IA
See **ORCHID GENERA.**

TRICHOSAN'THES . . Snakegourd
angui'na (*colubrina*) . . . . Edible S.
bractea'ta (*palmata* Roxb., *not* Wall.) Redball S.
corda'ta (*palmata* Wall., *not* Roxb.) Heartleaf S.
cucumeroi'des . . . . . Japanese S.
kirilow'i . . . . Mongolian S.
palma'ta Roxb., *not* Wall. **T. bracteata**
palma'ta Wall., *not* Roxb. **T. cordata**

TRICHOS'MA . . . . **ERIA**
See **ORCHID GENERA.**

TRICHOS'PORUM **AESCHYNANTHUS**

TRICHOSTE'MA |w . . . Bluecurls
dichot'omum |w . . . . Forked B.
lana'tum . . . . Woolly B.
lanceola'tum . . . . . . Vinegar B.
par'ishi . . . . Parish B.

TRICHOSTERIG'MA . **EUPHORBIA**
See **SUCCULENTS.**

TRICHOSTIG'MA
peruvia'num

TRICUSPIDA'RIA **CRINODENDRON**
lanceola'ta . . . . **C. patagua**

TRICYR'TIS (*COMPSOA*) . Toadlily
brachycyr'tis . . . . . **T. macrantha**
fla'va (*nana*) . . . . . . Yellow T.
formosa'na . . . . Formosa T.
hir'ta (*japonica; Compsoa h.*) Hairy T.
latifo'lia . . . . Broadleaf T.
macran'tha (*brachycyrtis*)
macrop'oda (*Compsoa m.*) Speckled T.
₵Stippled (*striata*) hv.
na'na . . . . **T. flava**
stolonif'era . . . . . . Trailing T.

TRI'DAX . . . . Tridax
triloba'ta . . . . Trilobe T.

TRI'DENS . . . . **TRIODIA**
See **GRASS GENERA.**

TRIENTA'LIS |w. . . . . Starflower
borea'lis (*americana*) |w . American S.
europae'a . . . . European S.
latifo'lia (*T. europaea l.*) . Western S.

Trifoliate-orange **Poncirus; P. trifoliata**
Flyingdragon T. . . **P. t. monstruosa**

TRIFO'LIUM |w . . . . CLOVER

Clovers, of which about 300 species occur widely distributed in the cooler portions of the earth, play an important role in soil conservation. Being legumes, the nitrogen-fixing bacteria on their roots build up soil fertility. They are unexcelled pasture and hay plants. The present acreage of cultivated Clovers in the United States is nearly five times that of Alfalfa. The native Clovers of our country furnish extensive and nutritious pasturage to domestic livestock and other animals. Dr. Edward H. Graham, Biologist of the Soil Conservation Service, U. S. Department of Agriculture, states that "Trifolium leads all other leguminous genera in its usefulness to wildlife" ("Legumes: Their Erosion-Control and Wildlife Values," 1939). The list below of nearly 100 species and varieties of Trifolium is built upon an initial one of 25 names prepared in 1929 by the late Dr. Frederick V. Coville, Botanist of the Bureau of Plant Industry and U. S. Department of Agriculture representative on the original Editorial Committee of STANDARDIZED PLANT NAMES. With that list of Clovers, prepared with Dr. Coville's inimitable flair for apt vernacular or common plant names, have been merged other names, more especially of western range plant Clovers (from U. S. Forest Service records) and of cultivated species described in Federal and State agricultural publications.

acicula're . . . . . . **T. tridentatum**
agra'rium . . . . HOP C.
albopurpu'reum . . . RANCHERIA C.
alexandri'num |w . . . . EGYPTIAN C. (*Berseem*)
alpes'tre . . . . . . PURPLEGLOBE C.
alpi'num . . . . ALPINE C.
amab'ile . . . . AZTEC C.
ambig'uum . . . . KURA C.
amplec'tens . . . . . BLADDER C.
anderso'ni . . . . . . FIVELEAF C.
anemoph'ilum . . . . WYOMING C.
angula'tum . . . . . . CROOKED C.
angustifo'lium . . . . FINELEAF C.
appendicula'tum . . . . . LOST C.
arcua'tum . . . . . SPINDLEROOT C.
arizo'nicum . . . . . . ARIZONA C.
arven'se |w . . . . . RABBITFOOT C.
beck'withi . . . . . . BECKWITH C.
bi'fidum |w . . . . PINOLE C.
bolan'deri . . . . . . BOLANDER C.
bractea'tum . . . . . . BRACTED C.
bracteola'tum
brandeg'ei . . . . . BRANDEGEE C.
brew'eri . . . . BREWER C.
carolinia'num |w . . . . CAROLINA C.
cer'nuum . . . . NODHEAD C.
ciliola'tum (*ciliatum* Nutt., *not* Clarke) FOOTHILL C.
covil'lei . . . . COVILLE C.
cyathif'erum . . . . CUP C.
dasyphyl'lum . . . WHIPROOT C.
depaupera'tum |w . DEPAUPERATE C.
doug'lasi . . . . DOUGLAS C.
du'bium (*minus*) . . . . SUCKLING C.

The name Shamrock is sometimes applied to this species as well as to other species of Clover and to other plants that have three leaflets.

el'egans . . . . SHOWY C.
el'meri . . . . **T. longipes e.**
erioceph'alum . . . WOOLLYHEAD C.
fend'leri . . . . FENDLER C.
filifor'me . . . . THREAD C.
fimbria'tum . . . . . COLUMBIA C.
fragif'erum . . . . STRAWBERRY C.
fuca'tum . . . . PUFF C.

TRIFOLIUM, continued
fuca'tum gam'beli (*T. gambeli*) GAMBEL CLOVER
glomera'tum . . . . . . CLUSTER C.
gracilen'tum . . . . . PINPOINT C.
gray'i . . . . SONOMA C.
gymnocar'pon . . . . HOLLYLEAF C.
hall'i . . . . HALLS C.
han'seni . . . . HANSEN C.
hay'deni . . . . HAYDEN C.
how'elli . . . . BIGLEAF C.
hy'bridum |w . . . . ALSIKE C.
incarna'tum |w . . . . . CRIMSON C.
involucra'tum Ortega . **T. wormskjoldi**
king'i (*productum*) . . . . KINGS C.
lac'erum . . . . . . CUTCOLLAR C.
lappa'ceum . . . . . . BURDOCK C.
latifo'lium . . . . TWIN C.
lem'moni . . . . LEMMONS C.
lon'gipes . . . . . . LONGSTALK C.
—el'meri (*T. elmeri*) ELMERDREW C.
macilen'tum . . . . UTAH C.
macrae'i . . . . MACRAE C.
macroceph'alum . . . . BIGHEAD C.
me'dium . . . . ZIGZAG C.

The name Trifolium medium is often misapplied to MAMMOTH, a hort. var. of T. pratense.

microceph'alum . . . LITTLEHEAD C.
mi'crodon
mi'nus . . . . **T. dubium**
monan'thum . . . . CARPET C.
monoen'se . . . . MONO C.
montanen'se . . . . . . MONTANA C.
monta'num . . . . . . MOUNTAIN C.
na'num . . . . DWARF C.
obtusiflo'rum CLAMMY C. (*Soursalt C.*)
oligan'thum . . . . LANKY C.
orega'num . . . . OREGON C.
panno'nicum . . . . . HUNGARIAN C.
par'ryi . . . . PARRY C.
parviflo'rum . . . . TEASEL C.
plumo'sum . . . . PUSSY C.
praten'se |w . . . . RED C.
MAMMOTH. HV.
procum'bens |w . . . . LOW HOP C. (*Mignonette C.*)
produc'tum . . . . **T. kingi**
reflex'um . . . . BUFFALO C.
re'pens |w . . . . WHITE C.
—purpu'reum . . . PURPLELEAF W.C.
LADINO (*Lodi; Lodino*) HV. T. repens
resupina'tum (*suaveolens*) PERSIAN C. (*Shaftal C.*)
ru'bens . . . . FOXTAIL C.
rus'byi . . . . RUSBY C.
rydberg'i . . . . RYDBERG C.
salicto'rum . . . . WILLOW C.
sca'brum . . . . ROUGH C.
stella'tum . . . . STELLATE C.
stenolo'bum . . . . THRIFT C.
stria'tum . . . . KNOTTED C.
suave'olens . . . . . **T. resupinatum**
subsali'num |w
subterra'neum . . SUBTERRANEAN C.
suffoca'tum
supi'num . . . . COCKLEBUR C.
tomento'sum . . . . WOOLLY C.
tridenta'tum (*aciculare*) |w TOMCAT C.
uniflo'rum . . . . SOLITARY C.
variega'tum . . . . . . WHITETIP C.
wormskjold'i (*involucratum* Ortega, *not* Lam.) |w . . . . SIERRA C.

TRIGLO'CHIN |w . . . . . . PODGRASS
marit'ima |w . . . . SHORE P.
palus'tris |w . . . . ARROW P.
stria'ta |w . . . . RIDGED P.

TRIGONEL'LA . . . . . TRIGONELLA
caeru'lea (*Melilotus c.*) BLUEWHITE T.
cornicula'ta . . . . HORNED T.
foenum-grae'cum . . FENUGREEK T. (*Fenugreek*)

TRIGONID'IUM
See **ORCHID GENERA.**

TRIL'ISA . . . . TRILISA
odoratis'sima (*Liatris o.*) . VANILLA T. (*Carolina-vanilla*)
panicula'ta (*Liatris p.*) . . HAIRY T.

TRIL'LIUM |w . TRILLIUM (*Wakerobin*)
apet'alon . . . . NOPETAL T.
catesbae'i . . . . CATESBY T.
cer'nuum . . . . NODDING T.
chloropet'alum (*T. sessile californicum*) CALIFORNIA T.
declina'tum . . . . SHY T.
dis'color . . . . MOTTLED T.
erec'tum . . . . PURPLE T.
—al'bum . . . . WAX P.T.
grandiflo'rum . . . . SNOW T.
hu'geri . . . . HUGERS T.
lute'um . . . . **T. sessile l.**
niva'le . . . . DWARF T.
ova'tum . . . . PACIFIC T.
petiola'tum . . . . IDAHO T.
pusil'lum . . . . CAROLINA T.
recurva'tum . . . . PRAIRIE T.
riva'le . . . . OREGON T.
ses'sile . . . . TOAD T.
—califor'nicum . . . **T. chloropetalum**
—lute'um (*T. luteum*) . YELLOW T.T.
—ru'brum . . . . RED T.T.
¢SNOWQUEEN. HV. T. sessile
sim'ile . . . . GEORGIA T.
stylo'sum . . . . ROSE T.
tschono'ski
undula'tum . . . . PAINTED T.
vir'ide . . . . GREEN T.

TRILLIUM . . . . **Trillium**
CALIFORNIA T. . . . **T. chloropetalum**
CAROLINA T. . . . . **T. pusillum**
CATESBY T. . . . . **T. catesbaei**
DWARF T. . . . . **T. nivale**
GEORGIA T. . . . . **T. simile**
GREEN T. . . . . **T. viride**
HUGERS T. . . . . **T. hugeri**
IDAHO T. . . . . **T. petiolatum**
MOTTLED T. . . . . **T. discolor**
NODDING T. . . . . **T. cernuum**
NOPETAL T. . . . . **T. apetalon**
OREGON T. . . . . **T. rivale**
PACIFIC T. . . . . **T. ovatum**
PAINTED T. . . . . **T. undulatum**
PRAIRIE T. . . . . **T. recurvatum**
PURPLE T. . . . . **T. erectum**
RED TOAD T. . . . . **T. sessile rubrum**
ROSE T. . . . . **T. stylosum**
SHY T. . . . . **T. declinatum**
SNOW T. . . . . **T. grandiflorum**
TOAD T. . . . . **T. sessile**
WAX PURPLE T. . . **T. erectum album**
YELLOW TOAD T. . . **T. sessile luteum**

TRIME'ZA (*TRIMEZIA*) . TRIMEZA
lu'rida . . . . MEXICAN T.
martinicen'sis (*Cipura m.*) MARTINIQUE T.

TRINCOMALIWOOD . . . **Berrya cordifolia**

TRIO'DIA (*TRIDENS*) . . . TRIODIA
See **GRASS GENERA.**

TRIOP'TERIS
jamaicen'sis

TRIOS'TEUM |w . . . Horsegentian
angustifo'lium |w . . Narrowleaf H.
auranti'acum . . . . . . Orange H.
perfolia'tum |w Common H. (*Feverwort*)

TRIPETALEI'A (*BOTRYOSTEGE*)
bractea'ta (*Botryostege b.*)
panicula'ta

TRIPHA'SIA . . . . . . Limeberry
buxifo'lia; monophyl'la **Severinia b.**
trifo'lia (*aurantiola; trifoliata*) Limeberry

TRI'PHORA . . . . **POGONIA**
See **ORCHID GENERA, HARDY TERRESTRIAL GROUP.**

TRIPLA'RIS . . . . Anttree
america'na . . . . . . Longjohn A.
bonplandia'na . . . . . . Peru A.
caracasa'na . . . . . . Caracas A.
felipen'sis
surinamen'sis . . . . . Surinam A.

TRIP'LASIS . . . . . . Sandgrass
See **GRASS GENERA.**

TRIPLOCHI'TON
sclerox'ylon

TRIPO'GON . . . . Tripogon
See **GRASS GENERA.**

TRIP'SACUM . . . . . . Gamagrass
See **GRASS GENERA.**

TRIP'TERIS
vaillan'ti

TRIPTERYG'IUM . . Threewingnut
for'resti . . . . Forrests T.
re'geli (*wilfordi* Regel, *not* Hook. f.) Regels T.

TRIRA'PHIS
See **GRASS GENERA.**

TRISE'TUM . . . . Trisetum
See **GRASS GENERA.**

TRISTA'NIA . . . . Tristania
confer'ta . . . . . Brisbanebox T.
lauri'na . . . . Kanooka T.

TRITELEI'A . . . . . . **BRODIAEA**
grandiflo'ra . . . . . . **B. douglasi**

TRITHRI'NAX . . . Trithrinaxpalm
See **PALM GENERA.**

TRIT'ICUM . . . . Wheat
See **CEREALS** and **GRASS GENERA.**

TRIT'OMA . . . . . **KNIPHOFIA**
no'bilis . . . . **K. uvaria n.**

TRITO'NIA (*MONTBRETIA*) Tritonia
croca'ta . . . . Saffron T.
—minia'ta
₵Crimson (*coccinea*) hv. **T. crocata**
₵Orange (*aurantiaca*)
₵Purple (*purpurea*)
∞**crocosmaeflo'ra** (*Crocosma aurea* × *Tritonia pottsi*) . . . ∞Crocus T.
₵Orange (*aurantiaca*) hv.
deus'ta
hyali'na . . . . Thinrim T.
linea'ta
potts'i . . . . Potts T.
rose'a . . . . Cape T.
securig'era
squal'ida
undula'ta
Etoile de Feu. hv. Tritonia
Fiery Cross
Fire King

TRITONIA, continued
George Davison
Germania
Golden West
Hereward
His Majesty
King Edmund
Lady Hamilton
Lord Nelson
Martagon
Princess Mary
Prometheus
Queen Alexandra
Queen of Spain
Rayon d'Or
Reingold
Rosea
Star of East
Transcendent
Una
Vesuve

TRIX'IS . . . . Trixis
califor'nica . . . . . American T.

TROCHOCAR'PA . Wheelfruitbush
lauri'na . . . . . . Laurelleaf W.
thymifo'lia . . . . . Tasmanian W.

TROCHODEN'DRON Wheelstamentree
aralioi'des . . . Wheelstamentree

TROL'LIUS . . . . . . Globeflower
acau'lis . . . . Himalaya G.
albiflo'rus . . . . White G.
alta'icus (*T. caucasicus a.*) . Altai G.
asiat'icus . . . . Siberian G.
Giant (*giganteus*) hv.
caucas'icus . . . . . Caucasian G.
chinen'sis (*sinensis*) . . Chinese G.
dshunga'ricus . . . . Turkestan G.
europae'us . . . . Common G.
Goldenball (*loddigesi*) hv.
Napelliform (*napelliformis*)
Showy (*grandiflorus*)
Superb (*superbus*)
japon'icus . . . . Japanese G.
Double (*flore-pleno*) hv.
lax'us . . . . American G.
ledebour'i . . . . Ledebour G.
pat'ulus . . . . Persian G.
pu'milus . . . . Dwarf G.
—yunnanen'sis . . . . . . Yunnan G.
sinen'sis . . . . **T. chinensis**
Canary Bird. hv. Trollius
Earliest of All
Eleanor
Empire Day
Excelsior
First Lancers
Fortune (*fortunei*)
Giant (*giganteus*)
Goldenball (*loddigesi*)
Golden Gleam
Golden Queen
Gold Quelle
Goliath
Herbert Asquith
His Majesty
Lichtball
Loddigesi. Goldenball
Meteor
Orange Globe
Orange Princess
Salamander
Shelburne Beauty
Showy (*grandiflorus*)
Superb (*superbus*)
Thora Perry

TROPAE'OLUM . . . . . Nasturtium
azu'reum . . . . Azure N.
brachyc'eras . . . . . . Slender N.
canarien'se . . . . . . **T. peregrinum**
digita'tum . . . . . Venezuela N.
leptophyl'lum . . . . Thinleaf N.
lin'deni . . . . Whitevein N.
lobbia'num . . . . . **T. peltophorum**
ma'jus . . . . Common N.
—na'num . . . . Tomthumb N.
mi'nus . . . . Bush N.
peltoph'orum (*lobbianum*) Shield N.
—fimbria'tum
—hederifo'lium
—minia'tum
—regi'na
pentaphyl'lum . . . Fivefinger N.
peregri'num (*canariense*). Canary N.
pinna'tum . . . Featherflower N.
polyphyl'lum . . . . . . Wreath N.
specio'sum . . . . . Vermilion N.
tri'color . . . . . . Cornucopia N.
tubero'sum . . . . Tuber N.

Hort. var. of **Tropaeolum,** Nasturtium:

To Elizabeth M. Bodger, who compiled this list, the Editorial Committee wishes to express its indebtedness and thanks.

Abbreviations of Classification

Azu.	T. azureum.
D.	Double.
Maj.	T. majus.
Maj.n.	T. majus nanum.
Pel.	T. peltophorum.
Pin.	T. pinnatum.
SD.	Single Dwarf.
SDSD.	Semidouble Sweetscented Dwarf.
SDSG.	Semidouble Sweetscented Gleam.
ST.	Single Tall.
Tri.	T. tricolor.

Abbreviations of Names of Originators

Bod.	Bodger Seeds, Ltd., El Monte, Calif.
Bur.	W. Atlee Burpee Co., Philadelphia, Pa.
Hurst	Hurst & Son, London, England.
Mac.	Wm. MacDonald Seed Co., Santa Maria, Calif.
Vis	Vis Brothers, Ltd., Enkhuizen, Netherlands.

Amberglow. SDSG. (Mac.)
Apricot. SDSG. (Bur.)
Atropurpureum.
See Common Atropurpureum, Tomthumb A., Shield A.
Atrosanguineum. Maj.n.
Aureum. Pel.
Aurora. SD.
Azure Grandiflorum. Azu.
Beauty. SD.
Bimaculatum. Pin.
Brilliant. ST.
Butterfly. ST.
Caeruleorosea. Maj.n.
Caprice. SDSG. (Bur.)
Chaixianum. Pel.
Coccineum.
See Common C., Tomthumb C.
Common Atropurpureum. Maj.
Common Coccineum. Maj.
Common Luteum. Maj.
Common Regelianum. Maj.
Cornucopia Grandiflorum. Tri.
Crimson Dwarf. SD.
Crimson Glow. SDSG. (Mac.)
Crimson Tall. ST.
Crystal Palace. SD. (Bur.) *Gem.*

TROPAEOLUM, continued
DELIGHTFUL. SDSD. (Bur.)
(*Double and*) SUPER DOUBLE MIXED. D. (Bur.)
DUNNETS ORANGE. ST.
EMPRESS OF INDIA. SD.
FEATHERFLOWER LUTEUM. Pin.
FIESTA. SDSG. (Bur.)
FIREBRAND. SDSD.
FIREFLY. ST.
FIREGLEAM. SDSG.
FIREGLOBE. SDSD. (Vis.)
FLAME EMPEROR. SDSD. (Mac.)
FULGENS. Pel.
GARNET GEM. SDSD. (Bur.)
Gem. CRYSTAL PALACE.
GEM MIXTURE. SDSD. (Bod.)
GLORIOUS GLEAM Hybrids. SDSG. (Bod.)
GOLDEN GLEAM. SDSG. (Bod.)
GOLDEN GLOBE. SDSD. (Vis.)
GOLDEN KING. SD.
GOLDEN ORANGEGLOW. SDSG. (Mac.)
GOLDEN QUEEN. SD.
GOLDENROSE EMPEROR. SDSD. (Mac.)
GOLD GARNET. ST.
GOLDLEAF. Maj.n.
Grandiflorum.
See Azure Grandiflorum, Cornucopia G.
HARMONY. SDSG. (Bur.)
HEINEMANNI. Maj.
HEMISPHERICUM. Maj.
INDIAN CHIEF. SDSG.
INDIAN SUMMER. SDSG.
JUPITER. ST.
KING OF BLACKS. ST.
KING OF TOMTHUMBS. SD.
KING THEODORE DWARF. SD.
KING THEODORE TALL. ST.
Luteum.
See Common Luteum, Tomthumb L., and Featherflower L.
MAHOGANY. SDSG. (Bur.)
MAHOGANY GEM. SDSD. (Bur.)
MOONBEAM. SDSG. (Bur.)
MOONGLEAM. SDSG. (Bod.)
ORANGE GEM. SDSD. (Bod.)
ORANGE GLEAM. SDSG. (Bod.)
ORANGE GLORY. SDSD. (Bur.)
PEARL DWARF. SD. *Moonlight.*
PEARL TALL. ST. *Moonlight.*
PRIMROSE GEM. SDSD. (Bur.)
PRIMROSE GLEAM. SDSG. (Hurst)
PRIMROSE GLOW. SDSG. (Mac.)
PRINCE HENRY. SD.
Regelianum.
See Common R.; Tomthumb R.
REGELIANUM DWARF. SD.
REGELIANUM TALL. ST.
ROSE. ST.
ROSEGLOW. SDSG. (Mac.)
ROSEUM COERULEUM. SD.
RUBY. ST.
RUBY GEM. SDSD. (Bur.)
RUBY KING. SD.
SALMON BEAUTY. SDSG. (Bur.)
SALMON GEM. SDSD. (Bod.)
SALMON GLEAM. SDSG. (Bod.)
SALMON GLOW. SDSG. (Mac.)
SALMON QUEEN DWARF. SD.
SALMON QUEEN TALL. ST.
SCARLET EMPEROR. SDSD. (Mac.)
SCARLET EMPRESS. SDSD.
SCARLET GEM. SDSD. (Bod.)
SCARLET GLEAM. SDSG. (Bod.)
SCARLET GLEAM FUSILIER (*Stock*). SDSG. (Hurst)

TROPAEOLUM, continued
SCARLET GLOBE. SDSD. (Bur.)
SCHEUERIANUM. Maj.
SCHILLINGI. Maj.
Schillingi. ST.
SCHULZI MAJUS. Maj.
SCHULZI SINGLE TALL. ST.
SHIELD ATROPURPUREUM. Pel.
SPOTTED KING. SD.
SUNBALL. SDSD. (Bur.)
SUN EMPEROR. SDSD. (Mac.)
SUNGLEAM. SDSG. (Bur.)
SUNSETGLOW. SDSG. (Mac.)
SUPREME. SDSG. (Bur.)
TOMTHUMB ATROPURPUREUM. Maj.n.
TOMTHUMB COCCINEUM. Maj.n.
TOMTHUMB LUTEUM. Maj.n.
TOMTHUMB REGELIANUM. Maj.n.
TWILIGHT. ST.
VERMILLION GLOW. SDSG. (Mac.)
VESUVIUS DWARF. SD.
VESUVIUS TALL. ST.

Tropical-almond TERMINALIA, TROPICAL-ALMOND: **Terminalia catappa**

Troutlily . . FAWNLILY: **Erythronium**

TROX'IMON . . . . . . **AGOSERIS**

TRUFFLE, PERIGORD **Tuber melanosporum**

TRUMPETBUSH . . . . **Tecoma**
AUSTRALIAN T. . . . . **T. smithi**
YELLOWPOUI T. . . . . **T. spectabilis**

TRUMPETCREEPER . . . . . **Campsis**
CHINESE T. . . . . . . **C. grandiflora**
COMMON T. . . . . . . **C. radicans**
∞HYBRID T. . . . . . ∞**C. tagliabuana**

TRUMPETFLOWER, INDIA **Oroxylum; O. indicum**

TRUMPETTREE . . . . **Tabebuia**
PALMER T. . . . . **T. palmeri**
SILVER T. . . . . **T. argentea**
WHITEWOOD T. . . . . . **T. pallida**
YELLOWPOUI T. . . . **T. serratifolia**

Trumpettree . . . PUMPWOOD: **Cecropia**

TRUMPETVINE . . . . . . **Clytostoma**
ARGENTINE T. . . . **C. callistegioides**
URUGUAY T. . . . . . **C. purpureum**

Trumpetvine . . . . TRUMPETCREEPER, COMMON: **Campsis radicans**

TSU'GA |w . . . . HEMLOCK
albertia'na . . . . . **T. heterophylla**
brunonia'na . . . . **T. dumosa**
canaden'sis |w . . . . . CANADA H.; EASTERN H. (Forestry)
See hort. var. list below.
carolinia'na . . . . . . CAROLINA H.
—compac'ta . . . . . LOWDENSE C.H.
chinen'sis . . . . CHINESE H.
diversifo'lia . . . . . . JAPANESE H.
dumo'sa (*brunoniana*) . HIMALAYAN H.
formosa'na . . . . FORMOSA H.
heterophyl'la (*albertiana*) |w PACIFIC H.; WESTERN H. (Forestry)
—flac'cida . . . . . . WEEPING P.H.
hookeria'na . . . . **T. mertensiana**
×**jef'freyi** (*heterophylla* × *mertensiana*) JEFFREY H.
mertensia'na (*hookeriana*) |w MOUNTAIN H.
—argen'tea . . . . . SILVER M.H.
sie'boldi . . . . SIEBOLD H.
yunnanen'sis . . . . . . YUNNAN H.

Seed Variation Clons of **Tsuga canadensis**, CANADA HEMLOCK:

This presentation of Canada Hemlock types and clons is adapted from "Canada Hemlock and Its Variations," a thesis from Cornell University by John C. Swartley. It was the explicit policy of the author to include a sufficient number of *botanical* varieties to cover all the different types of variations found in this species. This treatment, however, of giving Latin or botanical names to natural seed variation types or to clons is against the adopted principle of STANDARDIZED PLANT NAMES as stated in the Preface and many other places in this book, and which is based on the grounds of correct scientific procedure and the elimination of confusion and inaccuracy which otherwise is quite inevitable. In the present list, therefore, the individual variants or clons are listed under vernacular or common names with references to the particular *types* to which they belong.

Most of the clons here listed have been mentioned and described in Mr. Swartley's thesis. But the clons appear there by number rather than by name, therefore these numbers have been included in the following list to insure so far as possible the correct identity of the respective clons.

ABBREVIATIONS OF NATURAL SEED VARIATION TYPES OF CANADA HEMLOCK

B.G.	Bushy Globe
Bro.	Broadleaf
Cin.	Cinnamon
Dense	Dense
DL.	Denseleaf
Fas.	Fastigiate (*fastigiata*)
Globe	Globe (*globosa*)
Gold.	Golden (*aurea*)
Lar.	Largeleaf (*macrophylla*)
Lit.	Littleleaf (*microphylla; parvifolia*)
Pros.	Prostrate
Pyg.	Pygmy (*nana*)
Pyr.	Pyramidal
Pyr.D.	Dwarf Pyramidal
Slen.	Slender (*gracilis*)
Spar.	Sparseleaf
Spr.	Spreading
Twig.	Twiggy
Weep.	Weeping
WT.	Whitetip (*albospica*)
Yew	Yewlike

The varietal names which follow are all clons.

ABBOTT PYGMY. Pyg. (1349)
ABBOTT WEEPING. Weep. (1401a)
AMAWALK WEEPING. Weep. (1273)
ATHENS CINNAMON. Cin. (1348)
ATHENS HEDGE. DL. (1401)
ATHENS YEWLIKE. Yew. (1369)
BENNETT SPREADING. Spr. (1376)
BRANDLEY. Pyr.D. (1458)
CALLICOON DENSE. Dense.
CALLICOON LACY. Spar. (J70)
CHARLOTTE PYGMY. Pyg. (1529)
COLE PROSTRATE. Pros. (1391)
COPLEN PYRAMIDAL. Pyr. (1418)
CURTIS IDEAL. Globe. (1317)
CURTIS PYGMY. Pyg.
CURTIS SPREADING Spr. (J90)
DANBY. Dense. (1526)
DAUBER CINNAMON. Cin. (1433)
DAWSON (*dawsoniana*).
DEEPGREEN (*atrovirens*). Lar.
DROOPTIP (*gracilis*).
DWARF WHITETIP. WT. (1238)
EVERITT GOLDEN. Gold. (1224)
FOLLANSBEE. Dense. (1387)
FREMD (*fremdi*). Dense.
GARDENCITY. Fas. (1296a.)
GENEVA. Globe.

TSUGA, continued
Greenwood Lake. Pyg.
Heistad. Dense.
Holliston. Dense. (1458)
Hunnewell. Lar. (1483)
Huss Twiggy (*hussi*). Twig. (1377)
Jenkins (*jenkinsi*). Lit.
Jennings Lacy. Spar. (1375)
Kelsey Weeping. Weep. (1484)
Labar Gem. DL. (1437)
Largeleaf (*macrophylla*). Lav.
Laurie. B.G. (1445)
Liberty. Pyr.D. (1323)
Matthews. Spr. (1210)
Meneilly. Twig. (1528)
Moon. Dense. (1207)
Narrowleaf (*angustifolia*).
Outpost Weeping. Weep. (1267a)
Parsons Littleleaf. Lit. (1389)
Perth Prostrate. Pros.
Pomfret. Dense. (1219)
Princeton Littleleaf. Lit. (1374)
Redding. DL. (1482)
Rockcreek. Dense. (1417)
Rush Golden.
Saratoga Broom (*beaujeani*). Spr. (1233).
Sargent Weeping (*pendula; sargentiana; sargenti p.*). Weep.
Stranger. Dense. (1456)
Swayne Denseleaf. DL.
Towson. Lar. (1432)
Vonheiningen. Bro. (1277)
Vonhelms Dwarf. DL. (1227)
Wilton Bushy. B.G. (1232a)
Wilton Weeping. Weep. (1281)
Wilton Whitetip. WT. (1460a)
York, Semiweeping. Weep. (1430)

TSUSIOPHYL'LUM
tana'kae

Tubeflower . . . . . . **Siphonanthus**
India T. . . . . **S. indicus**

TU'BER
melanos'porum . . Perigord Truffle

TUBERA'RIA
vulga'ris (*Helianthemum tuberaria*)

Tubergourd . . . . **Thladiantha**
Manchu T. . . . . **T. dubia**
Tall T. . . . . **T. oliveri**

Tuberose . . . **Polianthes; P. tuberosa**

Tubervine . . . . **Rajania**
Cockscombyam T. . . . . **R. cordata**

Tuftroot . . . . **Dieffenbachia**
∞ Bause T. . . . . **∞ D. bausei**
Bowmann T. . . . . . **D. bowmanni**
Imperial T. . . . . . . **D. imperialis**
Seguin T. . . . . **D. seguine**
Variable T. . . . . **D. picta**
∞ Whitespot T. . . . . **∞ D. splendens**

TULBAGH'IA . . . . . . Tulbaghia
capen'sis (*pulchella*) . Goodhope T.
—al'ba . . . . White G.T.
fra'grans . . . . Fragrant T.
simm'leri . . . . Transvaal T.
viola'cea . . . . Violet T.

TU'LIPA . . . . Tulip
abatino'i . . . . Tripoli T.
acrocar'pa . . . . **T. gallica**
acumina'ta (*chinensis; cornuta; media; stenopetala; turcica* Kunth) Turkish T.
acutiflo'ra DC. . . . . **T. didieri**
acutiflo'ra Poir.; *agenen'sis* **T. oculussolis**

TULIPA, continued
aitchiso'ni . . . . . Aitchison Tulip
—cashmeria'na . . . . . Kashmir T.
al'berti . . . . Albert T.
aleppen'sis; alep'pica . . **T. oculussolis**
alpes'tris . . . . **T. australis**
alpi'na . . . . **T. pulchella**
alta'ica Pall. (*sylvestris* Falk) Altai T.
alta'ica Geb. . . . . **T. uniflora**
amab'ilis . . . . Lovely T.
androssow'i . . . . . Androssow T.
anisophyl'la
ap'ula . . . . **T. praecox**
arista'ta . . . . Bearded T.
arme'na . . . . **T. gesneriana**
athenien'sis . . . . . . **T. orphanidea**
aucheria'na . . . . Aucher T.
austra'lis (*alpestris; breyniana* Ker.-Gawl.; *caucasica* Orsin.; *celsiana* DC.; *maculata* Roth; *silvestris; sylvestris* Gouan; *transtagana*) Southern T.
—arvo'rum . . . . . . Glebe S.T.
aximen'sis . Hort. var. of **T. didieri a.**
ba'keri . . . . Baker T.
balcan'ica . . . . Balkan T.
baldac'ci . . . . Baldacci T.
batali'ni . . . . Batalin T.
beccaria'na . . . . Beccari T.
behmia'na . . . . Behm T.
bessarab'ica . . . . . Bessarabian T.
bi'color . . . . Bicolor T.
—afghan'ica . . . . . . Afghan B.T.
biebersteinia'na (*biflora* Beck.; *celsiana* Hen.; *microgyna; pumila* Tausch; *sylvestris* Bieb.; *thirkeana; tricolor* Beck.; *tricolor* C. Koch) Bieberstein T.
biflo'ra Pall. . . . . Twoflower T.
biflo'ra Beck. . . . . **T. biebersteiniana**
biflo'ra Donn. . . . . **T. clusiana**
biflo'ra Hort. Lund. . . . . **T. patens**
biflorifor'mis
billietia'na . . . . Savoy T.
bithyn'ica (*turcica* Griseb.) Bithynian T.
boelt'geri . . . . Boeltger T.
boeot'ica (*eunanthiae; oculussolis* Heldr.; *strangulata* Heldr.) . . Boeotian T.
boissier'i . . . . **T. montana**
bonarotia'na . . . . . . **T. strangulata**
borszczow'i Reg. (*glaucophylla*) Aralsea T.
borszczow'i Bak. . **T. kolpakowskiana**
brachyan'thera
brachyste'mon
breynia'na Ker.-Gawl. . . . **T. australis**
breynia'na L. . **Baeometra columellaris**
brownea'na . . . . **T. patens**
buchar'ica . . . . **T. sogdiana**
buhsea'na . . . . **T. humilis**
callier'i . . . . Callier T.
campsopet'ala
carina'ta . . . . Keeled T.
caucas'ica Otto. . . . . . Caucasian T.
caucas'ica Orsin.; *celsia'na* DC. **T. australis**
celsia'na Hen. . . . **T. biebersteiniana**
celsia'na Kotschy . . . . . **T. humilis**
chinen'sis . . . . **T. acuminata**
chrysan'tha (*lehmanniana; undulata*) Golden T.
chrysoba'sis . . . . . Goldheart T.
ciliat'ula . . . . Fringed T.
clusia'na DC. (*biflora* Donn; *cypriani; hispanica; maculata* Dulac.; *praecox* Cav.; *rubroalba*) . . . Clusius T.
clusia'na Orph. . . . . **T. orphanidea**

TULIPA, continued
clusia'na Shep. . . . . **T. stellata**
concin'na . . . . Prim Tulip
conniv'ens (*gesneriana* Reboul) Italian T.
cornu'ta . . . . **T. acuminata**
corona'ria . . . . **T. gesneriana**
cret'ica . . . . Cretan T.
crispat'ula
croca'ta . . . . **T. orphanidea**
cuspida'ta Reg. (*elwesi*) . . Elwes T.
cuspida'ta Stapf . . . . **T. stapfi**
cyp'ria . . . . Cyprus T.
cypria'ni . . . . **T. clusiana**
dammann'i . . . . . . Dammann T.
dasyste'mon Reg. . . . Kuenlun T.
dasyste'mon Hort. . . . . . . **T. tarda**
dasystemonoi'des
didier'i Jord. (*acutiflora* DC.; *fransoniana; gesneriana* Bell; *mauritiana; oculussolis* Koch) . . . . Didier T.
—aximen'sis
—mauria'na (*T. mauriana*) Yellowblotch D.T.
—planifo'lia (*T. planifolia*) Narrowleaf D.T.
didier'i Passer . . . **T. passeriniana**
doerf'leri . . . . Doerfler T.
du'bia
dykesia'na (*hoeltzeri*) . . . Dykes T.
ed'ulis (*graminifolia*) . . . Edible T.
—latifo'lia (*T. latifolia*) Broadleaf E.T.
eich'leri . . . . Eichler T.
el'egans
el'wesi . . . . **T. cuspidata**
erythronioi'des . . . . Troutlily T.
etrus'ca . . . . Etruscan T.
eunan'thiae . . . . **T. boeotica**
fergan'ica . . . . Ferghana T.
fernan'dezi . . . . . . Fernandez T.
floren'skyi . . . . . . Florensky T.
florenti'na . . . . **T. sylvestris**
folio'sa . . . . Leafy T.
fosteria'na . . . . Foster T.
foxia'na . . . . **T. praecox**
fra'grans . . . . Fragrant T.
fransonia'na . . . . **T. didieri**
ful'gens . . . . Shiny T.
galat'ica . . . . Galatian T.
gal'lica (*acrocarpa*) . . . . French T.
gesneria'na L. (*armena; coronaria; hortensis; laciniata* Fisch.; *schrenki; spathulata; stricta*) . . Common T.
—lute'a . . . . Yellow C.T.
—spathula'ta (*T. g. major*)
—strangways'i . . . Strangways T.
gesneria'na Bell . . . . . . **T. didieri**
gesneria'na Ker.-Gawl. . . **T. praecox**
gesneria'na Reboul . . . **T. connivens**
glaucophyl'la . . . . . **T. borszczowi**
graminifo'lia . . . . **T. edulis**
greig'i . . . . Greig T.
—au'rea . . . . Yellow G.T.
grisebach'i . . . . **T. praecox**
grisebachia'na . . . . . **T. orphanidea**
ha'geri . . . . Hager T.
—ni'tens . . . . Shiny H.T.
harmo'nia . . . . . . **T. undulatifolia**
haya'ti . . . . Hayati T.
heliophthal'ma . . . . . **T. oculussolis**
hellespon'tica . . . . Hellespont T.
heterochro'a
heteropet'ala . . . . **T. uniflora**
heterophyl'la
hexagona'ta . . . . **T. praecox**
hispan'ica . . . . **T. clusiana**
hissar'ica . . . . Hissar T.

TULIPA, continued

hoeltz'eri . . . . **T. dykesiana**
hoogia'na . . . . Hoog Tulip
horten'sis . . . . . . **T. gesneriana**
hortulano'rum . . . . **T. suaveolens**
hu'milis (*buhseana; celsiana* Kotschy) Ground T.
hungar'ica (*neilreichi; rocheliana*) Hungarian T.
ilien'sis . . . . . . Ili-Mountain T.
in'gens . . . . Bokhara T.
jul'ia . . . . **T. montana**
kaghyzman'ica . . . Kaghyzman T.
kaufmannia'na . . . Waterlily T.
—au'rea . . . . Yellow W.T.
—coccin'ea . . . . . Scarlet W.T.
kesselring'i . . . . Kesselring T.
koktebel'ica . . . . . Crimean T.
kolpakowskia'na Reg. (*borszczowi* Bak.) Kolpak T.
—coccin'ea . . . . . Scarlet K.T.
—splen'dens . . . . . . Great K.T.
kolpakowskia'na Bak. **T. ostrowskiana**
kopetdaghen'sis . . . . Caspian T.
korolkow'i . . . . . . Korolkow T.
—bi'color . . . . . . Bicolor K.T.
—con'color . . . . . Concolor K.T.
korshin'skyi . . . . Korshinsky T.
krausea'na . . . . Krause T.
kuschken'sis . . . . . . Kuschk T.
lacinia'ta Fisch. . . . **T. gesneriana**
lacinia'ta Raf. . . . . . . **T. praecox**
lana'ta . . . . Woolly T.
latifo'lia . . . . **T. edulis l.**
lehmannia'na . . . . . **T. chrysantha**
leicht'lini . . . . . . Leichtlin T.
levier'i . . . . Levier T.
libanot'ica . . . . Lebanon T.
linifo'lia . . . . Slimleaf T.
lip'skyi . . . . Lipsky T.
lortet'i . . . . **T. oculussolis**
lown'ei . . . . Lowne T.
lur'ida . . . . Lurid T.
lute'a . . . . Topaz T.
macedon'ica . . . . Macedonian T.
macula'ta Hort. . . . . Spotted T.
macula'ta Dulac. . . . . **T. clusiana**
macula'ta Roth. . . . . **T. australis**
male'olens
marjolet'ti . . . . . Marjolett T.
marshallia'na . . . . . **T. sylvestris**
martellia'na . . . . . . Martell T.
mauria'na . . . . . . **T. didieri m.**
mauritia'na . . . . **T. didieri**
maximowicz'i . . . Maximowicz T.
me'dia . . . . **T. acuminata**
michelia'na . . . . Michel T.
microg'yna . . . . **T. biebersteiniana**
miner'vae . . . . **T. orphanidea**
mogoltav'ica
monta'na (*boissieri; julia; pulchella* Boiss.) . . . . Cilician T.
montic'ola . . . . . . Mountain T.
mucrona'ta
neglec'ta . . . . **T. strangulata**
neilreich'i . . . . **T. hungarica**
nit'ida . . . . . . Bellflower T.
nu'tans . . . . Nodding T.
oculusso'lis St. Amans (*acutiflora* Poir.; *agenensis; aleppensis; aleppica; heliophthalma; lorteti*) . . . Daystar T.
—merven'sis
oculusso'lis Heldr. . . . **T. boeotica**
oculusso'lis Ker.-Gawl. . **T. praecox**
oculusso'lis Koch . . . . **T. didieri**
odoratis'sima . . . . . **T. suaveolens**
orienta'lis . . . . Oriental T.
orithyioi'des . . . . . Orithyia T.

TULIPA, continued

orphanid'ea (*atheniensis; clusiana* Orph.; *crocata; grisebachiana; minervae*) . . . . Spartan Tulip
—whittall'i (*T. whittalli*) Whittall S.T.
orphanid'esi . . . . . . **T. praecox**
ostrowskia'na (*kolpakowskiana* Bak.) Ostrowsky T.
oxypet'ala . . . . . Sharppetal T.
paradasyste'mon
pas'chalis . . . . Easter T.
passerinia'na (*didieri* Passer) Sparrow T.
pa'tens (*biflora* Hort. Lund; *browneana; persica; sibirica; sylvestris* Laxm.; *tricolor* Ledeb.) . . . . Persian T.
per'sica . . . . **T. patens**
planifo'lia . . . . **T. didieri p.**
platyste'mon
platystig'ma
polychro'ma . . . . Josephscoat T.
porphyreo-chrysan'tha Purplegold T.
prae'cox Ten. (*apula; foxiana; gesneriana* Ker.-Gawl.; *grisebachi; hexagonata; laciniata* Raf.; *oculussolis* Ker.-Gawl.; *orphanidesi; raddi; strangwaysiana*) . . . . Olden T.
prae'cox Cav. . . . . . . **T. clusiana**
prae'stans . . . . . Leatherbulb T.
primuli'na . . . . Primrose T.
pubes'cens . . . . Downy T.
pulchel'la Fenzl (*alpina*) Dwarf Taurus T.
pulchel'la Boiss. . . . . **T. montana**
pu'mila Moench . . . . **T. sylvestris**
pu'mila Tausch . **T. biebersteiniana**
rad'di . . . . **T. praecox**
regel'i . . . . Regel T.
re'pens . . . . **T. sylvestris**
rhodope'a . . . . Redface T.
rochelia'na . . . . **T. hungarica**
rose'a . . . . Rosy T.
rubroal'ba . . . . **T. clusiana**
saracen'ica . . . . Saracen T.
saxat'ilis . . . . Cliff T.
scabrisca'pa . . . . Roughstalk T.
scar'dica . . . . Scardic T.
schmidt'i . . . . Schmidt T.
schrenk'i . . . . **T. gesneriana**
segusia'na
serot'ina . . . . Late T.
sharonen'sis . . . . Sharon T.
sibir'ica . . . . **T. patens**
silves'tris . . . . **T. australis**
sintenes'i . . . . Sintenes T.
sogdia'na (*bucharica*)
sommier'i . . . . Sommier T.
spathula'ta . . . . **T. gesneriana**
spreng'eri . . . . Sprenger T.
stapf'i (*cuspidata* Stapf) . . Stapf T.
stella'ta (*clusiana* Shep.) . . Starry T.
stenopet'ala . . . . . . **T. acuminata**
stolonif'era . . . . . . Creeping T.
strangula'ta Reboul (*bonarotiana; neglecta; variopicta*) . Blackblotch T.
—macula'ta . . . . . Yellow B.T.
—pic'ta . . . . Painted B.T.
—primuli'na . . . . Primrose B.T.
strangula'ta Heldr. . . . . **T. boeotica**
strangwaysia'na . . . . . . **T. praecox**
strauss'i . . . . Strauss T.
stric'ta . . . . **T. gesneriana**
stylo'sa . . . . **T. uniflora**
suave'olens (*hortulanorum; odoratissima; turcarum; volgensis*) Ducvanthol T.
subprae'stans

TULIPA, continued

sultanabaden'sis . Sultanabad Tulip
sylves'tris L. (*florentina; marshalliana; pumila* Moench; *T. repens; turcica* Roth) . . . . . Florentine T.
sylves'tris Bieb. . . **T. biebersteiniana**
sylves'tris Falk . . . . **T. altaica**
sylves'tris Gouan. . . . . . **T. australis**
sylves'tris Laxm. . . . . . . **T. patens**
sys'tola
tar'da (*dasystemon* Hort.)
tchitoun'yi . . . . Tchitouny T.
tetraphyl'la . . . . . . Fourleaf T.
theophrast'i . . . Theophrastus T.
thianschan'ica . . . Thianschan T.
thirkea'na . . . . **T. biebersteiniana**
thrac'ica . . . . Thracian T.
transtaga'na . . . . **T. australis**
tri'color C. Koch . **T. biebersteiniana**
tri'color Ledeb. . . . . **T. patens**
triphyl'la . . . . . . Threeleaf T.
tubergenia'na . . . . . Tubergen T.
turca'rum . . . . **T. suaveolens**
turc'ica Griseb. . . . . . **T. bithynica**
turc'ica Kunth . . . . . **T. acuminata**
turc'ica Roth . . . . **T. sylvestris**
turcoman'ica . . . . . Turcoman T.
turkestan'ica . . . . . Turkestan T.
undula'ta . . . . **T. chrysantha**
undulatifo'lia (*harmonia*) Wavyleaf T.
—boissier'i . . . . . . Boissiers W.T.
uniflo'ra (*altaica* Geb.; *heteropetala; stylosa*) . . . . Singleflower T.
urumien'sis . . . . Urumiya T.
urumof'fi . . . . Urumoff T.
variopic'ta . . . . . . **T. strangulata**
ven'eris . . . . Venus T.
viola'cea . . . . Violet T.
—pal'lida . . . . Pale V.T.
volgen'sis . . . . **T. suaveolens**
watsonia'na . . . . **T. wilsoniana**
whittall'i . . . . . . **T. orphanidea w.**
willmot'tae . . . . . . Willmott T.
wilsonia'na (*watsoniana*) . . Wilson T.
zena'idae . . . . Zenaida T.

Hort. var. of **Tulipa**, Tulip:

The following abridged list of horticultural varieties of Tulips is adapted from "A Classified List of Tulip Names," published by the Royal Horticultural Society in London in 1939, to the fuller list of which attention is invited. The book referred to has numerous names of "surpassed and obsolete varieties," printed in small type, which are omitted in the following list for lack of space.

Some of the names in this list which appear as botanical species are probably of horticultural origin, and it is possible that some of them may not be validly published under International Rules.

Attention is invited to the list of Tulip varieties which appeared in the original edition of Standardized Plant Names, prepared by O. M. Freeman, Bureau of Plant Industry, Department of Agriculture, Washington, D. C., and which was probably the first attempt in America to make available for general horticultural use a carefully compiled authentic grouping, with verified names, of this important bulb.

In order that all the Tulip names in this catalogue may be found in one alphabetical sequence, the common names and the Latin names of the wild species and subspecies have been repeated, in their proper alphabetical position, in this list of horticultural varieties.

The Committee feels that the Royal Horticultural Society list, despite its acceptance of duplicated names, which we

TULIPA, continued

cannot condone, is probably the best Tulip list available at the present time and, therefore, substitutes it for the one it formerly published.

Italicized hort. var. names prefixed by an asterisk (*) indicate homonyms. In each of these cases, recognized Tulip authority should endeavor to determine the oldest name, accepting that and rejecting the later names.

American Joint Committee on Horticultural Nomenclature
Harlan P. Kelsey, *Chairman, Editorial Committee*

Abbreviations and Explanations
Tulip Type Divisions

A. Early-Flowering.
1. Ducvanthol Tulips. Very early tulips, rarely exceeding six inches in height.
2. Single Early Tulips.
3. Double Early Tulips.
4. Mendel Tulips. Midseason, single tall tulips of medium build.
5. Triumph Tulips. Midseason, single tall tulips of stouter build than Mendel tulips and not so tall as Darwin tulips.

B. May-Flowering.
6. Cottage Tulips. All tulips, including lily-flowered, which do not fall within the other classes.
7. Dutch Breeders. Flower oval or cupped, brown, purple or red, but sometimes bronze; base white or yellow, but generally stained blue or green to blue-black.
8. English Breeders. Flowers forming one-third to a half of a hollow ball when fully expanded; base always white or yellow, without trace of other color.
9. Darwin Tulips. Lower portion of flower usually rectangular in outline; segments of good substance; stems tall and strong.
10. Broken Dutch Breeders.
11. Broken English Breeders.
12. Rembrandt Tulips. Broken Darwin tulips.
13. Broken Cottage Tulips.
14. Parrot Tulips. Varieties with laciniate segments.
15. Late Double Tulips.
16. Species and First Crosses Between Species.

Abbreviations of Names of Originators

AA C. Alkemade Azn., Noordwijk, Holland. (1870–.)
Ash. Luke Ashmole, Middleton. About 1860.
Barr Barr & Sons, Covent Garden, London, W.C.2. (1883–.)
Bath R. H. Bath, Ltd., Wisbech, Cambs. (1894–.)
Batt. J. Battersby, Mansfield.
Birt. R. Birtwistle, Blackburn. About 1850.
Bout. —Boutaux, Lille, France.
Br. Miss Brown, Coulsdon. Died 1885.
Bur. H. Burger Mzn., Beverwijk, Holland. (1860–1932.)
Camp —Camp, Schwarkestone, Derbyshire.
Carl. H. Carlee, Ltd., Haarlem, Holland. (1902–.)
Chap. F. Herbert Chapman, Peasmarsh, Sussex. (1868–.)
Col. W. A. Collier, Redbourne. About 1840.
Da. Nicolaas Dames, Lisse, Holland. (1863–1920.)
Deh. —Dehove, Tournai, Belgium. Died 1875.
deR. J. de Ruyter, Rijnsburg, Holland. Died 1900.
deW. J. J.C.D. de Wilde, Heemskerk, Holland. (1865–1937.)
dGra. de Graaff Bros., Ltd. (de Graaff Bros. and S. A. van Konijnenburg & Co.), Noordwijk, Holland. (1919–.)
dGro. de Groot & Co., N.V., Hillegom, Holland. (1923–.)
Dym. William Dymock, Stockport. About 1880.
EldC. James G. Eldering & Co., Ltd., Overveen, Holland. (1896–.)
EldS. W. J. Eldering & Son, Ltd., Sassenheim, Holland. (1896–.)
Gal. —Galler.
Goe. Jasper Goemans, Hillegom, Holland. (1856–1928.)
Gre. T. Greasley, Sandiacre, Noots. About 1847.
Gro. Groeneveld & Lindhout, Noordwijk, Holland. (1890–.)
Gru. J. J. Grullemans & Sons, N.V., Lisse, Holland. (1900–.)
Hall Sir (Alfred) Daniel Hall, Merton.
Hard. Dr. G. W. Hardy, Warrington. About 1840–1860.
Hardw. G. Hardwick.
Hart. William Baylor Hartland, Cork. (1836–1912.)
Hay. The Rev. George Philip Haydon, Hatfield, Yorks. (1846–1913.)
Head. Richard Headley, Stapleford, Cambridge.
Heem. Heemskerk, Rijnsburg, Holland.
Hep. John Hepworth, Wakefield. About 1847.
Hoek L. A. Hoek, 's-Gravenhage, Holland. (1931–.)
Hogg Hogg & Robertson, Dublin.
Hoog. H. Hoogervoorst, Hillegom. Died.
Jack. —Jackson.
Jaco. The Rev. Joseph Jacob, Whitchurch. (1859–1926.)
Kerb. J. J. Kerbert, formerly Kerbert & van Waveren, now N.V. Hybrida, Heiloo, Holland.
Kers. J. H. Kersten & Co., Haarlem, later Heemstede, Holland. (1853–1908.)
Kre. E. H. Krelage & Son, Haarlem, Holland. (1811–1931.)
Law. R. J. Lawrence, Hampton, Middlesex. About 1830.
Leem. G. Leembruggen, Veenenburg, Lisse, Holland. (1801–1865.)
Lef. D. W. Lefeber & Co., N.V., Lisse, Holland. (1923–.)
Len. J. C. Lenglart, Lille, France. (1827–1901.)
Li. —Lightbody, Falkirk.
Ll. Miss Lloyd, Petersfield, Hants.
LlA. Alfred Lloyd, Sheet, nr. Petersfield, Hants. Died 1893.
Mal. —Mallez, Wasquehal, nr. Lille, France.
Mar. R. Martin, Whalley. About 1850.
Mooy Polman Mooy, Haarlem, Holland. (1811–1914.)
Nijs. A. and P. Nijssen Bros., N.V., Santpoort, Holland. (1920–.)
Old. T. Oldfield, Bollington, Cheshire. About 1860.
Pij. J. Pijnacker & Sons, N.V., Lisse, Holland. (1882–.)
Pri. H. Prins, Lisse, Holland. (1866–1933.)
Rijn. F. Rijnveld & Sons, N.V., Hillegom, Holland. (1890–.)
Roes Jan Roes, Heemstede, Holland, now Huis ter Heide, Holland. (1907–1936.)
RooF. Frans Roozen Lzn., Vogelenzang, Holland. (1932–.)
RooL. Leo Roozen Fzn., Heemstede, Holland. (Formerly F. A. Roozen.) (1887–1932.)
RooM. M. J. Roozen, Hillegom, Holland. Died.
RooN. N. L. A. Roozen, Heemstede, Holland. (1907–.)
Sab. A. Sabelis, Heemstede, Holland. (1936–.)
Sch. E. H. Schofield. About 1880.
Seg. Segers Bros., N.V., Lisse, Holland. (1869–.)
Sla. John Slater, Manchester. About 1850.
Sleg. H. Slegtkamp & Co., Lisse, Holland. (1882–.)
Spu. Miss Katherine Spurrell, Norwich. Died 1912.
Sto. T. Storer, Derby. About 1880.
Str. —Strong.
vaZ. van Zanten Bros., N.V., Hillegom, Holland. (1862–.)
vBG. A. van den Berg Gzn., Anna-Paulowna, Holland. (1873–.)
vBJ. Jan F. van den Berg, Anna-Paulowna, Holland. Born 1896.
vBQ. Quirinus van den Berg, Heemstede, Holland. (1850–1920.)
vBS. Q. van den Berg & Sons, N.V., Heemstede, Holland. (1850–.)
vdM. J. C. van der Meer, Noordwijk, Holland. (1880–.)
vdMS. G. van der Mey's Sons, Lisse, Holland. (1850–.)
Ver. —Verweylen, Louvain, Belgium.
Vi. Vincent van der Vinne, Haarlem, Holland. (1799–1879.) In business 1823–1863.
Vink P. Vink, Noordwijk, Holland.
Vlu. Arie van der Vlugt, A. van der Vlugt & Sons, Lisse, Holland. (1870–.)
Voet P. W. Voet, Haarlem, later Overveen, Holland. (1865–1915.) In business 1887–1915.
Voor. Voorhelm & Schneevoogt, Haarlem, Holland. (1768–1837.)
Vre. A. H. Vreugdenhil, Naaldwijk, Holland. (1860–1937.)
vTL. C. G. van Tubergen, Ltd., Zwanenburg Nurseries, Haarlem, Holland. (1868–.)
vWK. Gt. van Waveren & Kruyff, Sassenheim, Holland. (1865–1921.)
Walk. J. Walker, Winton, Manchester. About 1860.
Walm. J. Walmsley. About 1847.
Ware Walter T. Ware, Ltd., Inglescombe, Bath.
Warn. Warnaar & Co., N.V., Sassenheim, Holland. (1898–.)
Wav. —Wavrin, Beuvry, nr. Lille, France.
Wil. W. Willison, Whitby. About 1840.
Wit. J. Witteman, Hillegom, Holland. (1850–1910.)
Zoch. Zocher & Co., Haarlem, Holland. (1869–1930.)

Abdelkader. 7. (Vi.)
Abercorn. 6. (vTL.)
Absalom. 10. (1780.)
Abundance. 7. (vTL.)
Ace of Diamonds. 12.
Actaea. 6. (Kre.)
Acushla. 6. (dGra.)
Ada. 3.
Ada Finch. 6. (dGra.)
Addison. 9. (Kre.)
Adelaar. 2.
Adelgar. 6. (dGra.)
Adinda. 4. (Kre.)
Admiral Tromp. 7. (vTL.)
Admiral Vankinsbergen. 10.
Adolphe Vandenheede. 9. (Kre.)
**Adonis*. 6. (Kre.)
**Adonis*. 8. (Head.)
Adonis (broken). 11. (Head.)
Adoration. 4. (Kre.)
Adria. 12. (Bath)

TULIPA, continued
Adriani. 6. (dGra.)
Advance. 6. (vTL.)
Aegir. 6. (Kre.)
Afghan Bicolor T. **T. bicolor afghanica.**
Afterglow. 9.
Agatha. 6. (vTL.)
Aglaia. 6. (vTL.)
Agneta. 9. (Kre.)
Aida. 4. (Kre.)
Aitchison T. **T. aitchisoni.**
Akhissar. 5. (Zoch.)
Alaraph. 5. (Zoch.)
Alaska. 6. (Kre.)
Alberio. 5. (Zoch.)
Albertine. 6. (vTL.)
Albert Moore. 12. (Bath)
Albert T. **T. alberti.**
Albertus Magnus. 4. (Kre.)
Albino. 6. (Kre.)
Alblas. 9. (vTL.)
Alcmene. 6. (Kre.)
Alcyone. 4. (Kre.)
Aldib. 5. (Zoch.)
Aletta. 2. (Da.)
Algiba. 5. (Zoch.)
Alhena. 5. (Zoch.)
Alice. 3. (vBG.)
Alice Keith. 7. (Kre.)
Alice Roosevelt. 2.
Aljechin. 5.
Allard Pierson. 9. (Kre.)
Allbright. 9.
Allegro. 15. (Zoch.)
**Almirante.* 2.
**Almirante.* 6. (vTL.)
Alphons Diepenbrock. 4. (Kre.)
Alphonse Kerr. 9. (vTL.)
Alsace. 4. (Kre.)
Altai T. **T. altaica.**
Aludra. 5. (Zoch.)
Amanda. 4. (Kre.)
Amaranthe. 6. (Kre.)
Ambassadeur Dehollande. 10.
Amber. 6. (Kre.)
Ambercrown. 6. (Barr.)
Ambition. 9. (Seg.)
Ambrosia. 6. (Kre.)
Amelia Miller. 5. (vBJ.)
American Flag. 12.
Amethyst. 6. (Da.)
Amidonette. 4. (Kre.)
Amiral Deconstantinople. 14.
Amphion. 9.
Amsterdam. 4. (Kre.)
Amunra. 7. (dGra.)
Anacreon. 6. (vTL.)
Anatole France. 6. (vTL.)
Andante. 4. (Kre.)
Androcles. 12. (Bath)
Androssow T. **T. androssowi.**
Angelina. 9.
Anitra. 5. (vBG.)
Anna Pavlova. 6. (vTL.)
Anna Roose. 3.
Anne Boleyn. 9. (vTL.)
Anne Marie. 12. (Len.)
Annette. 6. (vTL.)
**Annie.* 3.
**Annie.* 6. (Barr)
Annie Laurie. 9. (Kre.)
Annie McGregor. 8. (Mar.)
Annie McGregor (broken). 11. (Mar.)
Annie Speelman. 9. (Gru.)
Annie Vanees. 9. (Gru.)
Antique. 12. (Barr)

TULIPA, continued
Anton Coolen. 5. (Goe.)
Antonio. 6. (vTL.)
Anton Mauve. 9. (Kre.)
Anton Thoolen. 4. (Kre.)
Antony Roozen. 9. (Kre.)
Aphrodite. 9. (Kre.)
Appleblossom. 3.
Apricot. 7. (Barr)
Apricot Yellow. 2.
Aprilqueen. 4. (Kre.)
Ara. 3.
Aralsea T. **T. borszczowi.**
Arethusa. 6. (vTL.)
Argo. 6. (Kre.)
Argolus. 4. (Kre.)
Ariadne. 9. (Kre.)
Aristocrat. 9. (Seg.)
Arkadia. 6. (vTL.)
Armada. 9. (vTL.)
Arta. 6. (Roes)
Artemis. 6. (Kre.)
Artus. 2. (Voor.)
Asaph. 6. (vTL.)
Askelon. 12. (Bath)
Assouan. 9. (vTL.)
Astarte. 7. (vTL.)
Astor. 6. (vTL.)
Astra. 9. (Seg.)
Athalia. 10.
Athene. 4. (Kre.)
Athos. 8. (Hall)
Athos (broken). 11. (Hall)
**Attraction.* 2. (Da.)
**Attraction.* 11. (Hardw.)
Aucher T. **T. aucheriana.**
Augusta. 2.
Augustina Rosa. 5. (Zoch.)
Augustus. 7. (vTL.)
Aurola. 9. (Seg.)
Austrinus. 5. (Zoch.)
Avalanche. 9. (vTL.)
Avalon. 9. (Gru.)
Avanti. 9. (Seg.)
Averkamp. 9. (vTL.)
Aviator. 5. (Zoch.)
Aviator Hawkes. 9. (vTL.)
Aviatrice. 5. (vBJ.)
Avignon. 9. (vTL.)
Avis Kennicott. 6.
Aviso. 6. (Kre.)
Avondzon. 3. (Zoch.)
Azalea. 3.
Azellus. 5. (Zoch.)
Babylon. 9. (vTL.)
Bacchus. 7.
Bacchus (broken). 10. (1780)
Bach. 5.
Backhouse. 4. (Kre.)
Baguette Derigaut. 10.
Baker T. **T. bakeri.**
Baldacci T. **T. baldacci.**
Baldwin. 6. (Da.)
Balkan T. **T. balcanica.**
Baltimore. 15. (Zoch.)
Bandoeng. 5. (vBJ.)
Barbara Pratt. 6. (dGra.)
Barcarolle. 7. (dGra.)
Barnby Rudge. 6. (Gru.)
Baroda. 7. (vTL.)
Baronne Delatonnaye. 9. (Kre.)
Baron Vangoltstein. 9. (Kre.)
Bartigon. 9. (Kre.)
Bartigon Maxima. 9.
Bartlett. 12. (Bath)
Batalini Sunrise. 16.
Batalin T. **T. batalini.**
Batavus. 6. (vTL.)

TULIPA, continued
Baucis. 6. (vTL.)
Bearded T. **T. aristata.**
Beauty of Bath. 6. (Ware)
Beccari T. **T. beccariana.**
Beethoven. 4. (Kre.)
Behm T. **T. behmiana.**
Belinda. 4. (Kre.)
Belladonna. 6. (Da.)
Bellagio. 9. (vTL.)
Belle Esther. 6. (vTL.)
Belle Forme. 10.
Belle Jaune. 6. (vTL.)
Belle Mauve. 9. (vTL.)
Bellflower T. **T. nitida.**
Benedictine. 7. (dGra.)
Bene Est. 9. (Da.)
Bene Habet. 5. (Goe.)
Benjamin Franklin. 9. (Gru.)
Beppie. 6. (Da.)
Beranger. 6. (vTL.)
Berengaria. 12. (EldC.)
Berenice. 5. (Zoch.)
Berlin. 9.
Berna. 5. (Lef.)
Beryl. 3.
Bessarabian T. **T. bessarabica.**
Betsy. 9. (Da.)
Betsy Ross. 9. (Kre.)
Beverley. 6. (vTL.)
Bicolor Korolkow T. **T. korolkowi bicolor.**
Bicolor T. **T. bicolor.**
Bieberstein T. **T. biebersteiniana.**
Biscay. 7. (vTL.)
Bithynian T. **T. bithynica.**
Bixlo. 5.
Blackblotch T. **T. strangulata.**
Blackboy. 10.
Blackburne. 6. (Da.)
Blackeagle. 9. (Da.)
Blackgirl. 9. (Goe.)
Blameless. 2.
Blanca. 6. (vTL.)
Bleu Aimable. 9. (Kre.)
Bleu Celeste. 9. (Kre.)
Blucher. 7. (vTL.)
Bluebird. 9. (Kre.)
Bluedanube. 9. (Gru.)
Blueflag. 15.
Bluegem. 9. (Seg.)
Blueparrot. 14.
Bluepearl. 9. (Seg.)
Blueperfection. 9. (dGra.)
Blueribbon. 9. (Seg.)
Bluestar. 6.
Boadicea. 6.
Boeltger T. **T. boeltgeri.**
Boeotian T. **T. boeotica.**
Bohemienne. 10.
Boissiers Wavyleaf T. **T. undulatifolia boissieri.**
Bokhara T. **T. ingens.**
Boma. 4. (Kre.)
Bonaparte. 10.
Bonfire. 4. (Kre.)
Bootes. 5.
Bordeaux. 4. (Kre.)
Borneo. 6. (dGra.)
Boston. 5. (Zoch.)
Bouledeneige. 3.
Bourgogne. 9. (Gru.)
Bouton d'Or. 6.
Bowmont. 12.
Brahms. 4. (Kre.)
**Brandenburg.* 2. (vBJ.)
**Brandenburg.* 7. (vTL.)
Brederode. 6. (vTL.)

TULIPA, continued
Breitner. 9. (Lef.)
Brenda. 6. (Ware)
Bretagne. 9. (vTL.)
Bretano. 12. (EldC.)
Briand. 4. (Kre.)
Brigadier. 7. (vTL.)
Brightling. 4. (Kre.)
Brightness. 6. (vTL.)
Brilliancy. 6. (Bath)
Brilliant Star. 2.
Bristol. 9.
Broadleaf Edible T. **T. edulis latifolia.**
Brocade. 7. (Kre.)
Bronzechief. 7. (Bath)
Bronzeknight. 7. (Bath)
Bronzequeen. 7.
Brooklyn. 10.
Brunhilde. 2.
Bruno Walter. 5. (Kre.)
Buddha. 7. (vTL.)
Buffalo. 5. (Zoch.)
Buff Beauty. 6. (Kre.)
Bunkerhill. 4. (Kre.)
Burgomaster Devlugt. 9. (RooL.)
Burgomaster Sandberg. 9. (vTL.)
Cabiria. 4. (Kre.)
Cafe Brun. 14.
Cafe Pourpre. 14.
Calderon. 6.
Caledonia. 6.
California. 5. (Zoch.)
Callier T. **T. callieri.**
Calypso. 2.
Cambrinus. 5.
Campfire. 9.
Canada. 5. (Zoch.)
Canarybird. 9.
Canaryking. 2. (Mooy)
Canaryqueen. 2. (Mooy)
Canberra. 7. (vTL.)
Capablanca. 6. (Da.)
Cappriccio. 14.
Capri. 6. (vTL.)
Captain Fryatt. 6. (vTL.)
Captain Lehmann. 4. (Kre.)
Captain of Violets. 2. (vBQ.)
Captain Smoolenaars. 4. (Kre.)
Caracalla. 12.
Cardinal Manning. 7.
Cardinal Rampollo. 2.
Carmen. 9. (Kre.)
Carmencita. 7. (dGra.)
Carminata. 10.
Caroline Testout. 9. (Gru.)
Carolus Duran. 12. (Len.)
Carrara. 6. (Kre.)
Caruso. 5. (Zoch.)
Casanova. 7. (Roes)
Caserta. 7. (vTL.)
Caspian T. **T. kopetdaghensis.**
Cassandra. 6. (Barr)
Cassiope. 6. (vTL.)
Castor. 5. (Zoch.)
Catharina. 6. (vTL.)
Catherine. 6. (Ware)
Cattleya. 4. (Kre.)
Caucasian T. **T. caucasica.**
Cecil Dolling. 8. (Hall)
Cecil Dolling (broken). 11. (Hall)
Cecile. 6. (Kre.)
Cecilia. 11. (Hall)
Cellini. 4. (Kre.)
Centaur. 6.
Centenaire. 9. (Kre.)
Centenaire (broken). 12. (Kre.)
Cerise. 4. (Kre.)

TULIPA, continued
Cerise a Belle Forme. 10. (1780)
Cerise Beauty. 5. (Goe.)
Cerise Gris-de-lin. 2. (Voor.)
Chameleon. 13.
Champion. 9.
Changeant. 5. (vBJ.)
Chant Ducygne. 9. (Kre.)
Chanteclair. 4. (Kre.)
Charles Debosschere. 9. (Da.)
Charles Needham. 9. (vTL.)
Charles X. 11. (Str.)
Charming. 14.
Cheerful. 7. (Goe.)
Cheerio. 4. (Kre.)
Cherbourg. 7.
Cherbourg (broken). 10.
Cheron. 2. (Zoch.)
Cherryblossom. 9.
Cherrypink. 9. (Gru.)
Cherubini. 6. (vTL.)
Chesterfield. 5.
Chester (*Jay*) Hunt. 7.
Chestnut. 7.
Chic. 9. (Lef.)
Chicago. 5. (Zoch.)
Chilton. 2. (Lef.)
Christina Vetter. 6. (Da.)
Christmas Fire. 4. (Kre.)
Christmas Star. 2. (Da.)
Christmas Surprise. 4. (Kre.)
Chrysolora. 2. (Voor.)
Cicero. 7. (Roes)
Cicilie. 6. (Zoch.)
Cilician T. **T. montana.**
Citronella. 9. (Da.)
City of Haarlem. 9. (Kre.)
Clara. 12. (Bath)
Clara Butt. 9. (Kre.)
Clemens. 9. (Goe.)
Clementia. 7. (vTL.)
Cleopatra. 6.
Clifford. 4. (Kre.)
Cliff T. **T. saxatilis.**
Clingendaal. 15. (Hoek)
Clos Devougeot. 6. (Hall)
Clusius T. **T. clusiana.**
Cocade. 12. (Bath)
Cocarde. 6. (dGra.)
Colonel Astor. 7.
Colonel Cuney. 9. (dGra.)
Colorado. 6. (Zoch.)
Columbia Beauty. 13.
Columbine. 8. (Hall)
Columbine (broken). 11. (Hall)
Coma. 15.
Comedy. 6. (Ware)
Common T. **T. gesneriana.**
Competitor. 2. (vBQ.)
Comte Decambridge. 10.
Con Amore. 2.
Concolor Korolkow T. **T. korolkowi concolor.**
Condor. 4. (Kre.)
Constance. 9. (vTL.)
Copernicus. 5.
Copper Beauty. 7. (Bath)
Cordell Hull. 12.
Cordova. 9. (vTL.)
Corelli. 2. (Kre.)
Coridion. 7.
Corinna. 7. (vTL.)
Corinthe. 4. (Kre.)
Coronation Scarlet. 6.
Coronelly. 2. (Mooy)
Cosette. 12. (Len.)
Cosmos. 9.
Cote d'Azur. 9. (Gru.)

TULIPA, continued
Cottage Boy. 2.
Cottage Maid. 2.
Couleur Cardinal. 2. (1815)
Countess. 9. (Ware)
Couronne d'Or. 3. (1770)
Couronne d'Orange. 3.
Coxa. 15. (Zoch.)
Cramoisi Brillant. 2. (1785)
Cramoisi Royal. 2.
Crater. 5. (Zoch.)
Creation. 7. (Kre.)
Creeping T. **T. stolonifera.**
Crepuscule. 9. (Kre.)
Cretan T. **T. cretica.**
Crimean T. **T. koktebelica.**
Crimsonbeauty. 14.
Crimsoncrusader. 7. (Ware)
Crimsonqueen. 2.
Crown Imperial. 2. (Zoch.)
Crown Princess. 6. (vTL.)
Crusader. 7. (vTL.)
Cullinan. 2.
Cunera. 7. (vTL.)
Cupid. 12. (Bath)
Cymbola. 9. (Lef.)
Cynthia. 6. (Ware)
Cypria. 6. (vTL.)
Cyprus T. **T. cypria.**
Cyrano. 8. (Hall)
Cyrano (broken). 11. (Hall)
Daintymaid. 10.
Daisy Schaffer. 6. (dGra.)
Dal Ongaro. 9. (Kre.)
Dalton. 6. (vTL.)
Damiate. 9. (vTL.)
Dammann T. **T. dammanni.**
Dandy. 5. (Kre.)
Dante. 3. (vBJ.)
Daphne. 6. (Kre.)
Darling. 4. (Kre.)
Darlington. 9. (Seg.)
Dave Scott. 6. (Da.)
Dawson City. 9. (Da.)
Daystar T. **T. oculussolis.**
Debutante. 5. (vBJ.)
Decandolle. 4. (Kre.)
Decorator. 4. (Kre.)
Decorum. 5. (vBJ.)
Defender. 6. (Da.)
Deladier. 15.
Delden. 5. (Pij.)
Delicate. 4. (Kre.)
Delice. 4. (Kre.)
Delicious. 6. (vTL.)
Delion. 6. (Roes)
Delos. 6. (Roes)
Delphi. 9. (Kre.)
Delphin. 9. (Lef.)
Delphinus. 5. (Zoch.)
Demeter. 9. (vTL.)
Demetrius. 7. (vTL.)
Denbola. 5. (Zoch.)
Deneb. 5. (Zoch.)
Detroit. 4. (Kre.)
Diadem. 2. (vBS.)
Diana. 2. (vBG.)
Didier T. **T. didieri.**
Dido. 6. (Kre.)
Dillenburg. 7. (vTL.)
Dina. 5. (Zoch.)
Dinant. 7. (vTL.)
Director Hoog. 7. (vTL.)
Discovery. 14.
Display. 9. (Seg.)
Distinction. 3.
Divera. 12. (EldC.)
Dodonaeus. 4. (Kre.)

TULIPA, continued
Doerfler T. **T. doerfleri.**
Dollfuss. 6. (Da.)
Dolora. 7. (Roes)
Dompedro. 7.
Donizetti. 4. (Kre.)
Donjose. 6. (vTL.)
Dorado. 5. (Zoch.)
Doris. 6. (Barr)
Doro. 12. (Bath)
Dorothy Ann. 8. (Hall)
Dorus Rijkers. 5. (Zoch.)
Dosia. 6. (Gru.)
Douglas Fairbanks. 4. (Kre.)
Downy T. **T. pubescens.**
Dr. Bruning. 5. (Zoch.)
Dream. 9. (Kre.)
Dreaming Maid. 4. (Kerb.)
Dreamland. 12.
Dresden China. 9. (vTL.)
Dr. Euwe. 6. (Da.)
Dr. Hardy. 11. (Sto.)
Dr. Lovink. 5. (Zoch.)
Dr. Sinclair. 6. (Bath)
Dr. Verhage. 7. (Lef.)
Duc de Berlin. 2.
Duchesse deParme. 2. (Voor.)
Duchess of Bedford. 7. (Goe.)
Duchess of York. 6. (vTL.)
Ducvanthol T. **T. suaveolens.**
Duc Vanthol Cochineal. 1. Cochineal Thol.
Duc Vanthol Excelsior. 1. Excelsior Thol.
Duc Vanthol Orange Maxima. 1. Great Orange Thol.
Duc Vanthol Orange, Scarlet-Striped. 1. Striped Orange Thol.
Duc Vanthol Primrose. (Sleg.) Primrose Orange Thol.
Duc Vanthol Red and Yellow. 1. (1620.) Red-Yellow Thol.
Duc Vanthol Red and Yellow Maxima. 1. Great Red-Yellow Thol.
Duc Vanthol Red Maxima. 1. (Sleg.) Great Red Thol.
Duc Vanthol Rose. 1. Rose Thol.
Duc Vanthol Scarlet. 1. (EldS.) Scarlet King.
Duc Vanthol White Maxima. 1. Great White Thol.
Duc Vanthol Yellow Maxima. 1. Great Yellow Thol.
Duc Vanthol Yellow and White Maxima. 1. Yellow-White Thol.

The repetition of the name Duc Vanthol is perhaps the most striking example of needless duplication to be found in Tulip. The fact that Duc Vanthol Scarlet was changed to Scarlet King shows the ease with which all the duplications could have been avoided.

Duke of Cambridge. 10.
Duke of Edinburgh. 7.
Duke of Portland. 9. (Kre.)
Duke of Wellington. 9. (Gru.)
Dulcinea. 6. (Kre.)
Dusart. 2. (Leem.)
Dutch Olympiade. 2. (Vink.)
Dutch Prince. 12. (Bath)
Dwarf Taurus T. **T. pulchella.**
Dykes T. **T. dykesiana.**
Eagle. 4. (Kre.)
Early Beauty. 4. (Kre.)
Early Express. 2. (Kre.)
Early Orange. 3. (vBJ.)
Early Queen. 4. (Kre.)
Early Sensation. 4. (Kre.)

TULIPA, continued
Early Wonder. 4. (Kre.)
Early Yellow. 2. (vBS.)
Easter T. **T. paschalis.**
E. Aug. Bowles. 9. (vTL.)
Eclair. 4. (Kerb.)
Eclatant. 6. (Kre.)
**Eclipse.* 6. (Kre.)
**Eclipse.* 9. (Kre.)
Edible T. **T. edulis.**
Edith. 6. (Ware)
Edith Carter. 7. (Kre.)
Edith Eddy. 5. (Zoch.)
Edmee. 9. (Kre.)
Edmond Rostand. 9. (vTL.)
Edna. 12. (Bath)
Edward Elgar. 4. (Kre.)
Effect. 6. (dGra.)
Eggink Senior. 5. (Kre.)
Egginks Favourite. 9. (Lef.)
Egginks Ideal. 9. (Lef.)
Eichler T. **T. eichleri.**
Eifel. 6. (Kre.)
Eileen Donovan. 5. (Zoch.)
Eldorado. 6. (Da.)
Eleanor Roosevelt. 9. (Seg.)
Electra. 3.
Electric. 12. (Bath)
Elegansalba. 6.
Eleonora Pratt. 6. (dGra.)
Elisabeth Evers. 5. (Zoch.)
Elizabeth Pegg. 8. (Camp)
Elizabeth Pegg (broken). 8.
Ellen Key. 15.
Ellen Moore. 2.
Ellen Willmott. 6.
Elmus. 5. (vBJ.)
Elsa Hartz. 9.
Elspeth. 9. (Ware)
Eltintoretto. 5.
Eltoreador. 3.
Elvira. 5.
Elwes T. **T. cuspidata.**
Enchanting. 6. (Gru.)
Ensor. 2. (Zoch.)
Epicure. 15. (vBQ.)
Erdal. 9.
Erguste. 9. (Kre.)
Erica Dorst. 9.
Erinna. 7. (vTL.)
Erl Konig. 6. (Da.)
Eros. 15. (Zoch.)
Esmeralda. 4. (Kerb.)
Essen. 5. (Zoch.)
Ethel Roosevelt. 9. (Kre.)
Etruscan T. **T. etrusca.**
Eunice. 9. (vTL.)
Euripides. 12. (Bath)
Europe. 9. (Kre.)
Eurydice. 9. (Da.)
Euterpe. 9. (Kre.)
Excelsior. 4. (Kre.)
Exponent. 4. (Kre.)
Expressione. 6. (Gru.)
Extase. 4. (Kre.)
Extrema. 5. (Kre.)
Fabiola. 4. (Kre.)
Faience. 5.
Fairynymph. 7. (Kre.)
Fairyqueen. 6.
Fancy. 10.
Fantasy. 14.
Farncombe Sanders. 9. (Kre.)
Fascinating. 6. (Gru.)
Fascination. 2. (EldS.)
Faust. 9. (Kre.)
Favourite. 4. (Kre.)
Ferghana T. **T. ferganica.**

TULIPA, continued
Fernandez T. **T. fernandezi.**
Feu Ardent. 7. (Vi.)
Feu Brillant. 9. (Kre.)
Fiery Diamond. 4. (Kre.)
Fieryred. 5. (Lef.)
Fireball. 4. (Kre.)
Firebird. 14.
Firedragon. 13. (Barr)
Fireglow. 4. (Kre.)
Firenze. 6.
Firestone. 4. (Kre.)
First Quarter. 6. (vTL.)
First Rate. 4. (Kre.)
Flag of War. 9. (vTL.)
Flamboyante. 10.
Flame. 6. (Barr)
Flamingo. 2.
Flaming Torch. 2. (Kerb.)
Flava. 6. (Vi.)
Flavius. 5. (Zoch.)
Fleurop. 9.
Fleur Printaniere. 5. (vBJ.)
Flora. 5. (Zoch.)
Floraison. 5. (vBJ.)
Florensky T. **T. florenskyi.**
Florentine T. **T. sylvestris.**
Florestan. 6. (vTL.)
Florida. 5. (Mooy)
Fokker. 5. (Zoch.)
Forbra. 9. (Ware)
Formalhout. 5. (Zoch.)
Formidable. 7. (vTL.)
Formosa. 6. (Mooy)
Fortuna. 2. (EldS.)
Forward. 9. (vTL.)
Fosteriana Agamemnon. 16. **Agamemnon Fosteriana.**
Fosteriana Defiance. 16. (vTL.) **Defiance F.**
Fosteriana Mme. Lefeber. 16. **Mme.** (*Lefeber*) **F.**
Fosteriana Princeps. 16. **Princeps F.**
Foster T. **T. fosteriana.**
Fourleaf T. **T. tetraphylla.**
Fragrant T. **T. fragrans.**
Fram. 4. (Kerb.)
Francois Coppe. 7.
Frans Hals. 9. (Kre.)
Fraulein Amberg. 9. (Kre.)
Fred. Moore. 2.
French T. **T. gallica.**
Fridjof Nansen. 4. (Kre.)
Fridolin. 3.
Fringed Beauty. 3.
Fringed T. **T. ciliatula.**
Fuga. 4. (Kre.)
Fulgurant. 6. (vTL.)
Fullmoon. 6. (vTL.)
Gadelan. 14.
Gala Beauty. 13.
Galatian T. **T. galatica.**
Gallicurci. 4. (Kre.)
**Garibaldi.* 7. (Vi.)
**Garibaldi.* 11. (Ash.)
Gavotte. 9. (vTL.)
Geisha. 6. (vTL.)
Gellert. 10. (Vi.)
Gemma. 14.
Generaal Dewet. 2.
General. 9.
**General French.* 6. (vTL.)
**General French.* 12. (Bath)
General Snijders. 5. (Zoch.)
Geo. (*H.*) Dicks. 9. (Lef.)
George Edward. 11. (Sch.)
George Hayward. 11. (Law.)
Georges Grappe. 7. (vTL.)

TULIPA, continued
George Voorheim. 4. (Kre.)
Geraldine. 6. (vTL.)
Gerontius. 9. (Ware)
Gertrude. 2. (Mooy)
Gertrude Carlee. 4. (Carl.)
Geysendorffer J. A. 2. (Da.)
Giant. 9. (Kre.)
Gil Blas. 7. (vTL.)
Gipsy. 4. (Kre.)
Gladness. 9. (dGro.)
Glare of the Garden. 6.
Glaucus. 9.
Gleam. 8. (Hall)
Gleam (broken). 11. (Hall)
Glebe Southern T. **T. australis arvorum.**
Globe of Fire. 6.
Gloire Dehollande. 10.
Gloriana. 12. (Rijn.)
Gloria Nigrorum. 10. (Voor.)
Gloria Solis. 10.
Gloria Swanson. 9. (Gru.)
Glory. 4. (Kre.)
Glory of Lisse. 2. (Da.)
Glory of Noordwijk. 5. (vBJ.)
Glow. 9. (Kre.)
Goethe. 5. (Zoch.)
Goldenage. 9. (vTL.)
Golden Beauty. 9. (Da.)
Goldenbrilliant. 2.
Goldenbronze. 7.
Goldenbuff. 7.
Goldenchief. 2.
Goldencrown. 6.
Goldendiamond. 5. (Zoch.)
Goldendrop. 4. (Kerb.)
Goldenduchess. 6. (vTL.)
Goldenemblem. 6. (Gru.)
Goldenesonne. 2.
Goldenfleece. 9. (Da.)
Goldengate. 6. (Zoch.)
Goldengiant. 3.
Goldenglory. 2. (dGra.)
Goldenharvest. 6. (Da.)
Goldenking. 3.
Goldenmascot. 2. (dGra.)
Goldennugget. 6. (Gru.)
Goldenophelia. 3. (dGra.)
Goldenpheasant. 2.
Goldenpromise. 6. (vTL.)
Goldenrain. 6. (vTL.)
Goldenspire. 6.
Goldenstatue. 6. (vTL.)
Golden T. **T. chrysantha.**
Goldenwest. 2.
Goldenwonder. 5. (vBJ.)
Goldfinch. 2.
Goldfinder. 8. (Hep.)
Goldheart T. **T. chrysobasis.**
Goldini. 5. (Zoch.)
Goldlake. 9. (Da.)
Goodluck. 2.
Goodmorning. 2. (Kerb.)
Goudvink. 7.
Govert Flink. 5. (Zoch.)
Goya. 3.
Graaf Vanburen. 10.
Grace. 6. (dGra.)
Granados. 12. (EldC.)
Grand Conquerant. 7.
Grand Duke. 12. (Bath)
Grandeur Triomphante. 7.
Grand Lilac. 5. (Zoch.)
Grand Monarque. 7.
Grand Yellow 6. (Da.)
Graziella. 9.
Great City. 2. (vBJ.)

TULIPA, continued
Great Kolpak T. **T. kolpakowskiana splendens.**
Greigi Alba. 16.
¢Bellini
¢Edwin Fisher
¢Fair Lady
¢Gluck
¢Johann Strauss
¢Robert Schumann
¢Rossini
¢Vivaldi
Greigi Primrose. 16.
Greigi Princeps. 16.
Greig T. **T. greigi.**
Grenadier. 6.
Grenat Rouge. 6. (vTL.)
Greta. 6. (vTL.)
Gretchen. 12.
Greuze. 9. (Kre.)
Greydawn. 8. (Hall)
Grisilde. 6. (Gru.)
Grotius. 5. (Zoch.)
Ground T. **T. humilis.**
Grullemans Giant. 9. (Gru.)
Gryphus. 9. (Kre.)
Guinevere. 6. (Ware)
G. W. Leak. 6. (vTL.)
Habana. 7. (vTL.)
Hager T. **T. hageri.**
Hal Kenyon. 9. (Bath)
Hamburg. 5. (vBJ.)
Hamburgia. 9.
Hammer Hales. 6. (dGra.)
Hampton Court. 6. (vTL)
Handel. 4. (Kre.)
Harmony. 9. (Lef.)
Harold. 12. (Barr)
Harry Veitch. 9. (Kre.)
Harvest Moon. 6. (Gru.)
Hautain. 6. (Kre.)
Hawaii. 3.
Hayati T. **T. hayati.**
Haydn. 4. (Kre.)
Heart of Gold. 7. (Kre.)
Hebe. 12.
Hecate. 6. (Gru.)
Hela. 5. (Zoch.)
Helena. 6. (vTL.)
Helen Eakin. 9. (dGra.)
Helen Madison. 9. (RooF.)
Helen Wills. 9. (Gru.)
Helga Jone. 5. (Kre.)
Helicon. 7. (Lef.)
Helios. 2.
Heliotrope. 9. (Gru.)
Hellespont T. **T. hellespontica.**
Heloise. 7. (Vi.)
Henrico. 6. (vTL.)
Henry Correvon. 6. (vTL.)
Henry Witte. 3.
Heraut. 4. (Kre.)
Hercules. 9. (Seg.)
Her Grace. 4. (Kre.)
Hermer. 15.
Hermina. 5.
Herod. 6. (Ware)
Herodiade. 9. (Kre.)
Heroine. 6. (Zoch.)
Herzogin Vonhohenberg. 9. (Kre.)
Hesperos. 5. (Zoch.)
Hiawatha. 4. (Kre.)
Highlander. 5. (Kre.)
Hildebrand. 9.
Hildegarde. 4. (Kre.)
Hindenburg. 5. (Zoch.)
Hirschbrun. 7. (dGra.)
Hissar T. **T. hissarica.**

TULIPA, continued
Hollandia. 5. (vBJ.)
Honeymoon. 6. (vTL.)
Hoog T. **T. hoogiana.**
Hope of Holland. 4. (Kre.)
Horace Virnot. 9. (vTL.)
Hubert. 7. (dGra.)
Huchtenburg. 7. (dGra.)
Hudson. 5. (vBJ.)
Hugo Devries. 5. (Zoch.)
Hugo Stinnes. 5. (Zoch.)
Hungarian T. **T. hungarica.**
Hydra. 5. (Zoch.)
Hyperion. 2. (Zoch.)
Ibis. 2.
Iceberg. 6. (Ware)
Idaho. 5. (Zoch.)
Idyll. 6. (Kre.)
Ilias. 7. (Kre.)
Ili-Mountain T. **T. iliensis.**
Illuminator. 6.
Imperator. 4. (Kre.)
Imperator Rubrorum. 3.
Indian. 4. (Kre.)
Indiana. 7. (Seg.)
Indian Chief. 7. (Vi.)
Indus. 5. (Zoch.)
Inga Hume. 6. (Gru.)
Inglescombe Beauty. 14.
Inglescombe Pink. 6. (Ware)
Inglescombe Primrose. 6. (Ware)
Inglescombe Scarlet. 6. (Ware)
Inglescombe White. 6. (Ware)
Inglescombe Yellow. 6. (Ware)
Ingrid. 6. (Gru.)
Inimitable. 6. (vTL.)
Insulinde. 10. (Kre.)
Insurpassable. 9. (Gru.)
Invicta. 2. (Da.)
Invincible. 10. (vTL.)
Irene. 12. (Kre.)
Iris Origo. 9. (vTL.)
Irma. 7. (Lef.)
Irmen. 5. (vBJ.)
Isabella. 4.
Isis. 9. (Kre.)
Island Poppy. 4. (Kre.)
Isolde. 6. (vTL.)
Italian T. **T. connivens.**
Ithaca. 6. (vTL.)
Ivory. 6. (vTL.)
Ivory King. 6. (Da.)
Ixioides. 6. (Hart.)
Jacob Maris. 9. (Kre.)
Jacqueline. 4. (Kre.)
Jaffa. 2.
James A. Macdonald. 7. (Kre.)
James Watt. 7.
James White. 5. (Kre.)
James Wild. 8. (Walk.)
James Wild (broken). 11.
Jane Cowl. 15. (Zoch.)
Jason. 6. (Ware)
Jaune d'Oeuf. 7. (Vi.)
Jaune Supreme. 2. (vBS.)
Java. 6. (Kre.)
J. B. Ivey. 9. (Seg.)
Jeanne Desor. 6. (vTL.)
Jenny Schneider. 9. (vTL.)
Jeroen Bosch. 7. (vTL.)
Jersey Beauty. 6. (dGra.)
Jessy. 7. (vTL.)
Jewel of Holland. 4. (Kre.)
J. J. Bouwman. 7. (vTL.)
Joan of Arc. 6. (dGra.)
Joffre. 2.
Johanna. 5. (Zoch.)
John Dix. 4. (Kre.)

TULIPA, continued
JOHN D. ROCKEFELLER. 5. (Zoch.)
JOHN GAY. 4. (Sab.)
JOHN HOOG. 6. (vTL.)
JOHN (*M.*) GOOD. 6. (Da.)
JOHN RIDING. 7. (dGra.)
JOHN RUSKIN. 6. (Barr)
JOLIJT. 4. (Kre.)
JOLLY. 4. (Kre.)
JONG EUROPA. 5. (vBJ.)
JONKOPING. 2. (Mooy)
JOOST VANDENVONDEL. 2.
JORDAN. 4. (Kre.)
JOSEPHINE. 6. (vTL.)
JOSEPHSCOAT T. **T. polychroma.**
JOSINE. 4. (Kre.)
JO VANLOON. 5. (Zoch.)
JOYCE. 6. (dGra.)
JOY MCARDEN. 7. (Kre.)
JUBILEE. 9. (Kre.)
JUDITH. 6. (vTL.)
JULIA FARNESE. 11. (Sla.)
JULIANA VANSTOLBERG. 5. (Zoch.)
JULIENNE. 12. (Li.)
JULIUS CAESAR. 4. (Kre.)
JUPITER. 7.
KAGHYZMAN T. **T. kaghyzmanica.**
KALEIDOSCOPE. 13.
KANSAS. 5. (Zoch.)
KANTARA. 5. (vBJ.)
KARINA. 5. (vBJ.)
KASHMIR T. **T. aitchisoni cashmeriana.**
KATHLEEN. 12. (vTL.)
KATHLEEN PARLOW. 9. (vTL.)
Kaufmanniana Brilliant. 16. BRILLIANT KAUFMANNIANA.
Kaufmanniana Elliott. 16. ELLIOTT K.
Kaufmanniana Fritz Kreisler. 16. FRITZ KREISLER K.
Kaufmanniana Gaiety. 16. GAIETY K.
Kaufmanniana Lady Rose. 16. LADY ROSE K.
Kaufmanniana Primrose. 16. PRIMROSE K.
Kaufmanniana Ryensis. 16. RYE K.
KEELED T. **T. carinata.**
KEIZERSKROON. 2.
KERBERT. 5. (Zoch.)
KESSELRING T. **T. kesselringi.**
KIMBERLEY. 2. (Mooy)
KING EDWARD VIII. 3.
KINGFISHER. 10.
KING GEORGE V. 9. (Kre.)
KING HAROLD. 9. (Kre.)
KING LEAR. 7. (dGra.)
KINGMAUVE. 9. (vTL.)
KING OF THE REDS. 4. (Kre.)
KING OF THE YELLOWS. 2.
KINGWHITE. 9. (Gru.)
KISMETH. 5.
KLOPSTOCK. 7. (Vi.)
KOCHAB. 5. (Zoch.)
KOLPAK T. **T. kolpakowskiana.**
KONG HAAKON. 5. (Zoch.)
KORNEFOROS. 5. (Zoch.)
KOROLKOW T. **T. korolkowi.**
KORSHINSKY T. **T. korshinskyi.**
KRAKATEAU. 7. (Lef.)
KRAUSE T. **T. krauseana.**
KRELAGES TRIUMPH. 4. (Kre.)
KRIEMHILDE. 9. (Gru.)
KUENLUN T. **T. dasystemon.**
KUSCHK T. **T. kuschkensis.**
LABARONNE. 4. (Kre.)
LABIZARRE. 7. (Kre.)
LABURNUM. 10.
LACANDEUR. 3.

TULIPA, continued
LACLARTE. 10.
LACONIA. 12. (Bath)
LAC SANS PAREILLE. 10.
LAC VANHAARLEM. 3.
LADDIE. 4. (Kerb.)
LADYBIRD. 7. (vTL.)
LADY BOREEL. 2.
LADY CATHERINE GORDON. 8. (Li.)
LADY CATHERINE GORDON (broken). 11. (Li.)
LADY CHAMBERLAIN. 9. (vTL.)
LADY CURZON. 5. (Zoch.)
LADY DERBY. 14.
LADY ERNLE. 6. (Hall)
LADY GODIVA. 3.
LADY HILLINGDON. 9. (Gru.)
LADY LOVE. 3.
LADY MAY. 5. (vBJ.)
LADY MOORE. 2.
LAEKEN. 5. (vBJ.)
LAETITIA. 14.
LAFIANCEE. 9. (Kre.)
LAFONTAINE. 9. (Ware)
LAFRANCE. 9. (Gru.)
LAGONDA. 7. (Ware)
LAJOYEUSE. 7. (Vi.)
LAKEHURST. 4. (Kre.)
LAKME. 7. (Roes)
LALAITIERE. 2. (Voor.)
LAMERVEILLE. 6.
LAREINE. 2.
LAREINE MAXIMA. 2.
LAREINE ROSE. 2.
LAREMARQUABLE. 2. (Voor.)
LARGO. 9.
LASALLE. 9. (Gru.)
LASINGULIERE. 7. (Vi.)
LATE T. **T. serotina.**
LATRISTESSE. 9. (Kre.)
LATULIPE NOIRE. 9. (Kre.)
LAURA. 9. (vTL.)
LAURENTIA. 9. (Kre.)
LEAFY T. **T. foliosa.**
LEANDER. 5. (Kerb.)
LEATHERBULB T. **T. praestans.**
LEBANON T. **T. libanotica.**
LEDA. 6. (Kre.)
LEDUEL. 10.
LEGHORN BONNET. 6.
LEICHTLIN T. **T. leichtlini.**
LEMATELAS. 2. (Voor.)
LEMOGOL. 7.
LEMON PERFECTION. 6. (Kre.)
LENOTRE. 9. (Kre.)
LEONARD BARRON. 7. (Kre.)
LEONARD SUTTON. 14.
LEONORE. 6. (vTL.)
LEREVE. 2.
LEROI. 10.
LEVIATHAN. 2. (Mooy)
LEVIER T. **T. levieri.**
L'HERMITE. 13.
LIBANON. 5. (vBJ.)
LIBELLE. 6. (Kre.)
LIBERTY. 4. (Kre.)
LIDY. 12. (EldC.)
LIGHTTOWER. 5. (Kre.)
LILAC WONDER. 9. (Gru.)
LILARAN. 4. (Kre.)
LIMNOS. 7. (Roes)
LINDA. 12. (Bath)
LINNAEUS. 2. (vBS.)
L'INNOCENCE. 6. (vTL.)
LIPSKY T. **T. lipskyi.**
LIVIA. 4. (Kerb.)
LIVINGSTONE. 15. (Zoch.)
LIZAMO. 4. (Kre.)

TULIPA, continued
LOCARNO. 4. (Kre.)
LOHENGRIN. 6. (vTL.)
LOLA. 12.
LORD CARNARVON. 5. (Zoch.)
LORD DERBY. 15.
LORD (*Frederick*) CAVENDISH. 11. (Hardw.)
LORD NELSON. 2. (Mooy)
LORD STANLEY. 11. (Sto.)
LORENZO BERNINI. 9. (vTL.)
LORETTE. 6. (Kre.)
LOSANGELES. 6. (dGra.)
LOTHARIO. 6. (vTL.)
LOUIS. 12. (Len.)
LOUISA KING. 6. (vTL.)
LOUIS BOUWMEESTER. 2. (Da.)
LOUISE. 12. (Bath)
LOUISE DELAVALLIERE. 9. (Kre.)
LOUIS PASTEUR. 2. (vBS.)
LOUIS SEIZE. 7.
LOUIS XIV. 7.
LOVEBIRD. 2.
LOVEDREAM. 9. (Gru.)
LOVELY T. **T. amabilis.**
LOWNE T. **T. lownei.**
LUCIA. 12.
LUCIFER. 7.
LUCY. 9. (Lef.)
LUCY LUARD. 8. (Hall)
LUCY LUARD (broken). 11. (Hall)
LUNA. 6. (Kre.)
L'UNION. 10.
LURID T. **T. lurida.**
LUTEAMAJOR. 14. (1680.)
LUXEMBOURG. 9. (vTL.)
LYBRA. 5. (Zoch.)
LYRA. 5. (Zoch.)
MAB. 4. (Kerb.)
MABEL (broken). 11. (Mar.)
MACEDONIAN T. **T. macedonica.**
MACULATA BRILLIANT.
MAGNOLIA. 6. (Gru.)
MAHARAJAH. 7. (Roes)
MAHOGANY. 9. (Gru.)
MAHOGANY KING. 7.
MAIDENHOOD. 12. (Bath)
MAJESTIC. 6. (vTL.)
MALAGA. 6. (dGra.)
MALVERN PATTERSON. 9. (vTL.)
MARATHON. 9. (Lef.)
MARCELLINE. 6. (vTL.)
MARCHIONESS OF LONDONDERRY. 6. (vTL.)
MARCIA. 14. (vTL.)
MARCONI. 9. (Kre.)
MARECHAL NIEL. 3.
MARECHAL VICTOR. 7. (Vi.)
MARGARET. 9. (Kre.)
MARGEAUX. 9. (Gru.)
MARGINATA. 7. (Vi.)
MARGOT. 9. (vTL.)
MARIAGE DEMAFILLE. 15. (1750.)
MARIE LOUISE. 7.
MARIGOLD. 4. (Kre.)
MARION. 7. (vTL.)
MARION CRAN. 9. (vTL.)
MARION VOORHIES. 6. (dGra.)
MARITZA. 9.
MARJOLETT T. **T. marjoletti.**
MARJORIE BOWEN. 6. (vTL.)
MARKETGLORY. 4. (Kre.)
MARKETQUEEN. 9. (Gru.)
MARKGRAAF. 14.
MARKSMAN. 6.
MAROON PRINCE. 9. (vTL.)
MARQUETTE. 3.
MARQUIS. 6. (Da.)

TULIPA, continued
**Mars*. 4. (Kre.)
**Mars*. 8. (Hall)
MARSHALL HAIG. 6. (Da.)
MARTELL T. **T. martelliana.**
MARTHA. 6. (vTL.)
MARUSCHKA. 7. (Lef.)
MARVEL. 6. (Kre.)
MARY PICKFORD. 4. (Kre.)
MARY SENNI. 9. (vTL.)
MARY SWAN. 8. (Hall)
MASCOTTE. 6. (Da.)
MASSACHUSETTS. 9. (Kre.)
MASSENET. 9. (Kre.)
**Masterpiece*. 9. (Gru.)
**Masterpiece*. 11. (Sla.)
MATCHLESS. 6. (vTL.)
MATHILDA. 2. (Mooy)
MAUVE CLAIR. 9. (Kre.)
MAX HAVELAAR. 2.
MAXIMOWICZ T. **T. maximowiczi.**
MAYA. 9. (Kre.)
MAYBLOSSOM. 10.
MAYFLOWER. 6. (vTL.)
MAYKISS. 6. (Kre.)
MAZEPPA. 6. (vTL.)
MCKINLEY. 2.
MEBSUTA. 5. (Zoch.)
MEDEA. 7.
MEKBUDA. 5. (Zoch.)
MELICETTE. 9. (Kre.)
MELODY. 10.
MELVA. 7. (Kre.)
MEMPHIS. 7. (Kre.)
MENDELINA. 4. (Kre.)
MENGELBERG. 4. (Kre.)
MENNY. 6. (Kre.)
MENSA. 5. (Zoch.)
MEPHISTO. 6. (Kre.)
MERAPI. 4.
MERCEDES. 6. (vTL.)
MERCURIUS. 7. (vTL.)
MERLIN. 9. (Ware)
MERMAID. 9. (Gru.)
MERVEILLE DEHAARLEM. 9. (vTL.)
MERVEILLEUSE. 13. (Bath)
MESDAG. 9. (vTL.)
MEVROUW LOVINK. 5. (vBJ.)
MICHAEL ANGELO. 7. (Roes)
MICHEL T. **T. micheliana.**
MICHIGAN. 5. (Zoch.)
MIKADO. 2. (Mooy)
MILLET. 9. (Kre.)
MILTON. 12.
MIMOSA. 6. (Gru.)
MINERVA. 7. (vTL.)
MINISTER KAN. 2.
MINKA. 4. (Kerb.)
MINNESOTA. 5. (Zoch.)
MIRABEAU. 15. (dGra.)
MIREILLE. 5. (Kerb.)
MISS BLANCHE. 6. (Kre.)
MISS CURREY. 9. (Da.)
MISS DEBBY. 4. (Kre.)
MISS (*Ellen*) TERRY. 2 (Vre.)
MISS HOLLAND. 6. (vTL.)
MISSISSIPPI. 5. (Zoch.)
MISS JEKYLL. 6. (Hogg)
MIZAR. 5. (Zoch.)
MME. BARROIS. 9. (Kre.)
MME. BUTTERFLY. 9. (Kre.)
MME. BUYSSENS. 6. (vTL.)
MME. DE COON. 6.
MME. DUBARRY. 10. (vTL.)
MME. GEVERS. 2.
MME. HERRIOT. 2.
MME. KRELAGE. 9. (Kre.)
MME. LETHIERRY. 9. (Kre.)

TULIPA, continued
MME. MELBA. 9. (vTL.)
MME. VANDENBERG. 5. (vBJ.)
MME. VANZANTEN. 3.
MOHICAN. 5. (vBJ.)
MONARCH. 9.
MONGOLIA. 6. (vTL.)
MONICA. 9. (vTL.)
MONSIEUR DEFAESCH. 10.
MONSIEUR (*S.*) MOTTET. 6.
MONTRESOR. 2.
MONTROSA. 9. (Seg.)
MOONGLADE. 6. (dGra.)
MOONLIGHT. 6.
MOORISH KING. 2.
MOREA. 4. (Warn.)
MORENO. 4. (Kre.)
MORNINGGLORY. 2. (Da.)
MORNINGGLOW. 3. (vBQ.)
MOSAIQUE BRUN. 10.
MOTHERS DAY. 6. (Kre.)
MOUNTAIN T. **T. monticola.**
MOUNT EREBUS. 6. (vTL.)
MOUNT EVEREST. 3. (Mooy)
MOUNT RAINIER. 9. (dGra.)
MOUNT TACOMA. 15. (Mooy)
MOZART. 4. (Kre.)
MR. HOOVER. 9. (vTL.)
MRS. (*Beecher*) STOWE. 7. (Vi.)
MRS. BEERHORST. 4. (Kre.)
MRS. (*E. H.*) KRELAGE. 4. (Kre.)
MRS. (*Elizabeth S.*) PRENTISS. 6. (dGra.)
MRS. FARR. 12.
MRS. (*F. E.*) DIXON. 6. (Kre.)
MRS. (*Grace*) COOLIDGE. 9. (vTL.)
MRS. GRULLEMANS. 9. (Gru.)
MRS. (*Harold I.*) PRATT. 9. (Kre.)
MRS. HOOG. 6. (vTL.)
MRS. (*John T.*) SCHEEPERS. 6. (vTL.)
MRS. KEIGHTLEY. 6. (Hart.)
MRS. KERRELL. 6. (Br.)
MRS. MANDEL. 9. (Gru.)
MRS. MOON. 6.
MRS. (*Potter*) PALMER. 9. (Kre.)
MRS. WHITNEY. 6. (Roes)
MR. VANDERHOEF. 3.
MR. VANTUBERGEN. 3.
MR. VANZIJL. 9. (vTL.)
MR. WENTHOLT. 6. (vTL.)
MURIEL. 9. (Gru.)
MURILLO. 3. (Leem.)
MUSIC. 8. (Jack.)
MYSTERY. 9. (Kre.)
MYSTERY OF INDIA. 3. (vBS.)
NANKING. 6. (Nijs.)
NAPOLEON. 4. (Kre.)
NARROWLEAF DIDIER T. **T. didieri planifolia.**
NATAL. 6. (vTL.)
NATHALINE MAY. 6. (dGra.)
NAUSICAA. 6. (Kre.)
NECTAR. 6. (Kre.)
NELL GWYN. 9. (vTL.)
NEREUS. 6. (vTL.)
NETTY. 6. (vTL.)
NEVADA. 7. (Kre.)
NEVILLE CHAMBERLAIN. 5. (vBJ.)
NEW ORLEANS. 9. (dGra.)
NEWTON. 7.
NIOBE. 9. (Da.)
NIPHETOS. 9. (Gru.)
NIRVANA. 7. (Bath)
NIVEA. 5. (vBJ.)
NIZZA. 15. (vBJ.)
NODDING T. **T. nutans.**
NON PLUS ULTRA. 11.
NORHAM BEAUTY. 6. (Spu.)
NORTH DAKOTA. 9. (Kre.)

TULIPA, continued
NORTHERN QUEEN. 6. (vBG.)
NOVA. 5. (Zoch.)
NYMPH. 2. (vdMS.)
NYMPHEA. 15.
OCTAVIA. 4. (Kre.)
OCTAVIUS. 6. (vTL.)
ODETTE. 9. (vTL.)
OLAF. 4. (Kerb.)
OLD CHINA. 12. (Bath)
OLDEN T. **T. praecox.**
OLIPHANT. 9. (Kre.)
OLIVE. 6. (Bath)
OLYMPIADE. 2. (Mooy)
OPHELIA. 2. (Da.)
OPTIMA. 6. (dGro.)
ORANGEADE. 10.
ORANGEBEAUTY. 7.
ORANGEBLOSSOM. 3.
ORANGEBRILLIANT. 2.
ORANGEDELIGHT. 7. (Kre.)
ORANGEDREAM. 2.
ORANGEFAVORITE. 14.
ORANGEFLAME. 6.
ORANGEGEM. 2. (Kerb.)
ORANGEGIANT. 2.
**Orangeglobe*. 3.
**Orangeglobe*. 6.
ORANGEGLOW. 2. (Da.)
ORANGEHAWK. 2.
ORANGEKING. 6.
ORANGEMAN. 7. (Roes)
ORANGEMOON. 6.
ORANGEOPHELIA. 7. (dGra.)
ORANGEPERFECTION. 9. (Kre.)
ORANGEPRINCESS. 6. (vTL.)
ORANGEPROSPECT. 3.
ORANGES AND LEMONS. 6. (Da.)
ORANGESUPERBA. 15.
ORANGEVICTORY. 2. (Kerb.)
ORANGEWONDER. 4. (Sab.)
ORANJA. 4. (Kre.)
ORANJE BOVEN. 6. (vTL.)
ORANJE NASSAU. 3.
ORCHID. 2.
ORIENT. 6. (Kre.)
ORIENTAL T. **T. orientalis.**
ORITHYIA T. **T. orithyioides.**
OSLO. 9. (Seg.)
OSSI OSWALDA. 6. (Gru.)
OSTROWSKY T. **T. ostrowskiana.**
OUIDA. 9. (Kre.)
OVERWINNAAR. 15.
PAINTED BLACKBLOTCH T. **T. strangulata picta.**
PAINTEDLADY. 9. (Kre.)
PALATINE. 6. (Ware)
PALEMON. 6. (vTL.)
PALE VIOLET T. **T. violacea pallida.**
PALISA. 9. (Kre.)
PALLIETER. 6. (Kre.)
PALMYRA. 9. (vTL.)
PANORAMA. 7. (Vi.)
PAOLA. 6. (vTL.)
PAPAVER. 4. (Kre.)
PAREL SCHAAP. 10.
PARISIAN WHITE. 6.
PARISIAN YELLOW. 6.
PARKINSON. 4. (Kre.)
PARKLANE. 9. (Lef.)
PARNASSUS. 7. (Lef.)
PASSE MARATHON. 10.
PASTEUR. 6. (Roes)
PASTORALE. 4. (Kre.)
PATRIA. 5. (Lef.)
PAULA. 4. (Kre.)
PAUL BOUDRY. 9. (Kre.)
PAUL CRAMPEL. 3.

TULIPA, continued
PAVO. 15.
PEACH. 9. (Gru.)
PEACHBLOSSOM. 3.
PEER GYNT. 7. (vTL.)
PEERLESS. 9. (vTL.)
PEERLESS PINK. 4. (Carl.)
PEKING. 9. (Da.)
PELICAN. 2.
PENSEE AMERE. 9. (Kre.)
PENSEE ROSE. 15.
PENSEROSA. 15.
PEREANDER. 5. (Zoch.)
PERFECTA. 14. (1680.)
PERICLES. 7. (vTL.)
PERLE ROYALE. 7. (Vi.)
PERSEUS. 6. (vTL.)
PERSIAN T. **T. patens.**
PERSIMMON. 9. (vTL.)
PETER PAN. 6.
PETER (*R.*) BARR. 9. (vTL.)
PETRUS HONDIUS. 9. (Kre.)
PHENOMEN. 4. (Kre.)
PHILEMON. 6. (vTL.)
PHILIPPE DECOMINES. 9. (Kre.)
PHILIP SNOWDEN. 9.
PICCADILLY. 5. (vBJ.)
PICOTEE. 6.
PICTOR. 5. (Zoch.)
PIERRE MONTEUX. 5. (Kre.)
PIERSON. 14.
PINKBEAUTY. 2.
PINKDELIGHT. 6. (Da.)
PINKFAVOURITE. 4. (Kre.)
PINKGEM. 4. (Kre.)
PINKGIANT. 6. (dGra.)
PINKGLORY. 4. (Kre.)
PINKIE. 4. (Kre.)
PINKPEARL. 7.
PINKPERFECTION. 2. (Mooy)
PINKPICTURE. 4. (Kre.)
PINKSATIN. 4. (Kre.)
PINKSENSATION. 4. (Kre.)
PINKWONDER. 6. (Gru.)
PIQUANTE. 4. (Kre.)
PLUTO. 6.
PLUVIA D'ORO. 2. (Zoch.)
POCAHONTAS. 7. (Kre.)
POINCARE. 3.
**Pola Negri.* 2. (Mooy)
**Pola Negri.* 9. (Gru.)
POLAR ICE. 5. (vBJ.)
POLARIS. 5. (Zoch.)
POLLUX. 5. (Zoch.)
POLLY. 4. (Kerb.)
POLYDORUS. 7. (vTL.)
POLYPHEME. 12. (Kre.)
POMPADOUR. 3.
PORTHOS. 6. (dGra.)
POSEIDON. 7. (vTL.)
POURPRE MAGNIFIQUE. 7.
PRAESTANS FUSILIER. 16.
PRAESTANS ISPAHAN. 16.
PRAESTANS REGEL. 16.
PRAESTANS VANTUBERGEN. 16. (Hoog.)
PRAESTANS ZWANENBURG. 16.
PRECIOSA. 14.
PREMIER. 4. (Kre.)
PREMIER GLADSTONE. 3.
PRESIDENT DOUMER. 5. (Zoch.)
PRESIDENT GARFIELD. 9. (vTL.)
PRESIDENT HARDING. 9. (vTL.)
PRESIDENT HOOVER. 7. (Kre.)
PRESIDENT LEBRUN. 5. (Zoch.)
PRESIDENT LINCOLN. 2.
PRESIDENT TAFT. 9. (Kre.)
PRIAPUS. 13. (EldS.)
PRIDE OF GROENENDAAL. 9. (vTL.)

TULIPA, continued
PRIDE OF HAARLEM. 9. (Kre.)
PRIDE OF INGLESCOMBE. 6. (Ware)
PRIDE OF ZWANENBURG. 9. (vTL.)
PRIMADONNA. 9. (vTL.)
PRIMAVERA. 6. (vTL.)
PRIMROSE BEAUTY. 6. (Barr)
PRIMROSE BLACKBLOTCH T. **T. strangulata primulina.**
PRIMROSE EMPRESS. 2.
PRIMROSE QUEEN. 2.
PRIMROSE T. **T. primulina.**
PRIM T. **T. concinna.**
PRINCE. 6. (Da.)
PRINCE ALBERT. 7. (Vi.)
PRINCE CAROL. 6. (Kre.)
PRINCE DELIGNY. 2.
PRINCE HENRY. 10.
PRINCE OF AUSTRIA. 2.
PRINCE OF NETHERLANDS. 9. (Kre.)
PRINCE OF WALES. 7. (Vi.)
PRINCE OF WALES (broken). 10. (Vi.)
PRINCE ROSE. 4. (Kre.)
PRINCES MARTHA. 6. (dGro.)
PRINCESS BEATRIX. 5.
PRINCESS ELIZABETH. 9. (Kre.)
PRINCESS JULIANA. 2.
PRINCESS MARY. 9. (Kre.)
PRINCESS OF HOLLAND. 6. (vTL.)
PRINS CARNAVAL. 2.
PRINSES MARIANNA. 2.
PRINS HENDRIK. 13.
PRINS MAURITS. 9. (Kre.)
PRIZEWINNER. 4. (Kre.)
PROCLES. 12. (Li.)
PROFESSOR. 12. (Bath)
PROFESSOR BATESON. 4. (Kre.)
PROFESSOR DARWIN. 9. (Kre.) *Professor Francis Darwin.*
PROFESSOR DEBOSSCHERE. 9. (Da.) *Professor Charles Debosschere.*
PROFESSOR FOSTER. 9. (Kre.) *Professor Michael Foster.*
PROFESSOR KEESOM. 4. (Kre.)
PROFESSOR LORENTZ. 5. (Zoch.)
PROFESSOR NOBEL. 5. (Zoch.)
PROFESSOR RAUWENHOF. 9. (Kre.)
PROFESSOR SARGENT. 4. (Kre.)
PROFESSOR SCHOTEL. 7. (Vi.)
PROFESSOR TENDELOO. 5. (Zoch.)
PROFESSOR VANEYSINGA. 2. (Zoch.)
PROFESSOR VANSLOGTEREN. 4. (Kre.)
PROFESSOR ZEEMAN. 4. (Kre.)
PROGRESSION. 2.
PROSERPINE. 2.
PROSPERITY. 2.
PROTECTOR. 5. (vBJ.)
PRUNUS. 9.
PSYCHE. 9. (Kre.)
PULCHELLA HUMILIS. 16.
PULCHELLA ROSEA. 15.
PULCHELLA VIOLACEA (blue base). 16.
PULCHELLA VIOLACEA (yellow base). 16.
PURITY. 10.
PURPLEGIANT. 5. (Goe.)
PURPLEGOLD T. **T. porphyreo-chrysantha.**
PURPLEKING. 1. (Vre.)
PURPLE PERFECTION. 9.
PURPURELLA. 4. (Kre.)
PYRAMUS. 7. (vTL.)
QUAINTNESS. 6.
QUASIMODO. 12. (Bout.)
QUEEN ALEXANDRA. 7. (Barr)
QUEEN AUGUSTA. 4. (Kre.)
QUEEN FLORA. 2.
QUEEN MARY. 9. (Kre.)
QUEEN OF HEARTS. 9.

TULIPA, continued
QUEEN OF NAPLES. 9. (Gru.)
QUEEN OF NIGHT. 9. (Gru.)
QUEEN OF SPAIN. 6. (vTL.)
QUEEN OF THE PINKS. 3.
QUEEN OF TULIPS. 4. (Kre.)
QUEEN OF VIOLETS. 10.
QUELLINUS. 9. (vTL.)
RADIUM. 2.
RADJAH. 4. (Kre.)
RAINBOW. 6. (Da.)
RAMESES. 9. (Ware)
RAPALLO. 7. (vTL.)
RAPHAEL. 9. (Kre.)
RECTOR OF WHITEWELL. 6. (vTL.)
REDADMIRAL. 2.
RED AND SILVER. 13.
REDBEAUTY. 2.
REDCHAMPION. 14.
REDCHIEF. 5. (Lef.)
REDCOAT. 4. (Kerb.)
REDCONQUEROR 5. (Kerb.)
REDDOUGLAS. 6. (Ware)
REDENSIGN. 2. (Da.)
REDFACE T. **T. rhodopea.**
REDFLAG. 4. (Kerb.)
REDFLAME. 6. (Zoch.)
REDGAUNTLET. 9. (vTL.)
REDGEM. 4. (Kerb.)
REDGIANT. 5. (Lef.)
REDGUARD. 5. (Lef.)
REDINDIAN. 6. (vTL.)
REDMONARCH. 7. (Roes)
REDMOORE. 2.
REDPLANET. 5. (Kre.)
REDPOPPY. 4. (Kre.)
REDPRINCE. 12. (Kre.)
REDROSE. 15.
REDROVER. 4. (Kre.)
REDSIGNAL. 5. (Kre.)
REFULGENCE. 6. (vTL.)
REGEL T. **T. regeli.**
REGIDE. 4. (Kre.)
REGINA. 4. (Kre.)
REINE BLANCHE. 9. (vTL.)
REINE DESCERISES. 10.
REINE MARIE. 9. (vTL.)
REINE NATHALIE. 10.
RELIANCE. 9. (Seg.)
REMBRANDT. 7. (Vi.)
REMEMBRANCE. 9. (Kre.)
REMEMBRANCE (broken). 12. (Kre.)
REMUS. 6. (Kre.)
RENATA. 4. (Kre.)
RENSSELAER. 9. (dGra.)
REO. 5. (Kre.)
RETROFLEXA. 6. (Vi.)
REVE D'AMOUR. 9.
REVERIE. 4. (Kre.)
REV. (*H.*) EWBANK. 9. (Kre.)
REV. (*H. H.*) D'OMBRAIN. 9. (Kre.)
REV. (*Joseph*) JACOB. 6. (vTL.)
REV. (*Rollo*) MEYER. 9. (vTL.)
REV. WOLLEY-DOD. 9. (Kre.)
RHAPSODIE. 7. (dGra.)
RHINOCEROS. 15.
RHODES. 6. (vTL.)
RIBERA. 6. (Zoch.)
RICHARD STRAUSS. 5. (Kre.)
RICHARD WAGNER. 9. (vTL.)
RICHMOND. 9.
RIJNLAND. 5. (Zoch.)
RIPPERDA. 9. (Kre.)
RISINGSUN. 2.
RIVIERA. 9. (Lef.)
ROBINETTE. 4. (Kre.)
ROBINIA. 5. (Lef.)
ROBINO. 4. (Kre.)

TULIPA, continued
Roi Cramoisi. 2. (Voor.)
Roi Desbelges. 9. (vTL.)
Roi Desiam. 7.
Roi d'Islande. 9. (Kre.)
Roi Leopold. 7. (vTL.)
Roi Soleil. 7.
Roland. 4. (Kerb.)
Romeo. 12. (Len.)
Romulus. 2. (Kre.)
Ronald Gunn. 9. (Kre.)
Ronnie. 4. (Kre.)
Roos Vandekama. 2. (Kers.)
Rosabella. 6. (vTL.)
Rosa Bonheur. 9. (vTL.)
Rosalie. 4. (Kre.)
Rosamunde. 9. (vTL.)
Rosary. 6. (Ware)
Rosea Superba. 9. (vTL.)
Rosebeauty. 5. (vBJ.)
Rosebud. 6. (Kre.)
Rosecopland. 9.
Roseday. 9. (Seg.)
Rose Gris-de-lin. 2. (Voor.)
Rosehebe. 10.
Rosehelene. 6. (vTL.)
Roselandia. 4. (Kerb.)
Roseluisante. 2. (Voor.)
Roseluisante (variegated). 2. (?)
Rosemarie. 4. (Kre.)
Rose of Sharon. 15.
Roseprecoce. 2.
Rose Sanspareille. 10.
Rosetriumph. 6.
Rosetta. 6. (Barr)
Rosy Cloud. 14.
Rosy T. **T. rosea.**
Rotha. 9. (Seg.)
Rotterdam. 5.
Roughstalk T. **T. scabriscapa.**
Royal Salute. 9. (Ware)
Rubella. 12.
Rubens. 7. (Lef.)
Rubens (broken). 12. (Bath)
Rubin. 5. (Kre.)
Rubis Condor. 10.
Rubra Major. 14. (1680.)
Rubra Maxima. 3.
Rubyqueen. 6. (Kre.)
Rubyray. 4. (Kre.)
Ruhm Vonberlin. 5. (vBJ.)
Ruth. 4. (Kerb.)
Sabaros. 4. (Kerb.)
Sabina. 5.
Sagittarius. 5. (Zoch.)
Sallandia. 4. (Kerb.)
Salmonea. 9. (Kre.)
Salmonetta. 3.
Salmoran. 4. (Kre.)
Salome. 12. (Len.)
Salomon. 7.
Saloniki. 12. (Bath)
Salutate. 6. (Kre.)
Salvator Rosa. 3. (Leem.)
Sam Pierce. 5. (Zoch.)
Samuel Barlow. 8. (Sto.)
Samuel Barlow (broken). 11. (Sto.)
Sandringham. 5. (vBJ.)
Sang Deboeuf. 10.
Sanspareille. 7. (Vi.)
Santarosa. 9.
Santiago. 6. (dGra.)
Sappho. 7. (Vi.)
Saracen T. **T. saracenica.**
Sarah Headley. 11. (Head.)
Sarazen. 9. (Kre.)
Sardonix. 5. (Zoch.)
Saskia. 12.

TULIPA, continued
Sassenheim Amethyst. 6. (Da.)
Saturnus. 2. (Da.)
Savoy T. **T. billietiana.**
Saxonia. 6. (Mooy)
Scardic T. **T. scardica.**
Scarlet Admiral. 4. (Kre.)
Scarlet Beauty. 9. (Kre.)
Scarlet Brilliancy. 2.
Scarlet Cardinal. 3. (deR.)
Scarlet Delight. 4. (Carl.)
Scarlet Emperor. 6.
Scarlet Flame. 6. (dGra.)
Scarlet Glory. 6. (Kre.)
Scarlet Kolpak T. **T. kolpakowskiana coccinea.**
Scarlet Leader. 9. (vBJ.)
Scarlet Perfection. 9. (Kre.)
Scarlet Pimpernel. 4. (Kre.)
Scarlet Prince. 4. (Kre.)
Scarlet Royal. 2. (Wit.)
Scarletta. 6. (Kre.)
Scarlet Waterlily T. **T. kaufmanniana coccinea.**
Scarlet Wonder. 4. (Kre.)
Schmidt T. **T. schmidti.**
Schoonoord. 3.
Schubert. 4. (Kre.)
Scotch Lassie. 9. (Gru.)
Scotia. 13.
Scotland. 3. (vBJ.)
Secretary Voors. 5. (vBJ.)
Sedalia. 5. (Zoch.)
Sedan. 9.
Selma. 6. (dGra.)
Semele. 12. (Len.)
Sensation. 14.
Senta. 6. (Ware)
Sharon T. **T. sharonensis.**
Sharppetal T. **T. oxypetala.**
Shenandoah. 2. (Zoch.)
Shiny Hager T. **T. hageri nitens.**
Sh ny T. **T. fulgens.**
Siegfried. 3.
Sieraad Vanflora. 9. (Kre.)
Silvercity. 6. (dGra.)
Silvermoon. 6. (Da.)
Silverwing. 5. (Zoch.)
Simmerjoun. 3.
Sinbad. 6. (Ware)
Singapore. 7. (Goe.)
Singleflower T. **T. uniflora.**
Sintenes T. **T. sintenesi.**
Sioux. 6. (vTL.)
Siren. 6. (Kre.)
Sir Harry. 6.
Sir (*Joseph*) Paxton (broken). 11. (Wil.)
Sir (*Thomas*) Lipton. 2.
Sir (*Trevor*) Lawrence. 9. (Kre.)
Sithaula. 5. (Zoch.)
Slimleaf T. **T. linifolia.**
Smiling Ann. 6. (Kre.)
Smiling Henny. 4. (Kre.)
Smiling Queen. 6. (RooN.)
Smyrna. 7. (Roes)
Snowdrift. 5. (Zoch.)
Snowqueen. 3. (vBG.)
Socrates. 7. (Vi.)
Soestdijk. 5. (vBJ.)
Solange. 6. (vTL.)
Solita. 2.
Solon. 6. (vTL.)
Sommier T. **T. sommieri.**
Sonate. 7. (Kre.)
Sonia. 4. (Kre.)
Southerncross. 7. (Kre.)
Southern T. **T. australis.**

TULIPA, continued
Southpole. 6. (Kre.)
Souvenir. 6. (vTL.)
Sovereign. 9. (Lef.)
Sparrow T. **T. passeriniana.**
Spartan T. **T. orphanidea.**
Spinoza. 5. (Zoch.)
Splendour. 6. (Bath)
Spotted T. **T. maculata.**
Sprenger T. **T. sprengeri.**
Springdream. 2. (vBJ.)
Springfield. 9. (dGra.)
Springglory. 2.
Springtime. 5. (Zoch.)
Stability. 4. (Sab.)
Stadion. 5. (vBJ.)
Stanislaus. 6. (vTL.)
Stanja. 6. (dGra.)
Stapf T. **T. stapfi.**
Starlight. 9. (Gru.)
Star of the East. 2. (Da.)
Starry T. **T. stellata.**
Statendam. 3.
Stella. 4. (Kerb.)
Stephanie. 7. (vTL.)
Stephanie Ritmeester. 3. (vBJ.)
St. George. 4. (Kre.)
St. James. 7.
St. John. 12. (Bath)
St. Moritz. 5. (vBJ.)
Strangways T. **T. gesneriana strangwaysi.**
Strauss T. **T. straussi.**
Striped Beauty. 13.
Stromboli. 6. (vTL.)
St. Simon. 9. (Kre.)
Subra. 5.
Success. 4. (Kre.)
Sudan. 9. (vTL.)
Sulphur. 8. (Birt.)
Sulphur Ball. 5. (Kerb.)
Sulphureum. 5. (Lef.)
Sulphur Glory. 5. (Kerb.)
Sultanabad T. **T. sultanabadensis.**
Sultane. 4. (Kre.)
Sumatra. 5. (vBJ.)
Sunburst. 2. (Da.)
Sundance. 7. (Kre.)
Sundew. 14.
Sunflower. 2.
Sunglory. 6. (vTL.)
Sunkist. 9. (vTL.)
Sunrise. 9. (Da.)
Sunshine. 14.
Superba. 4. (Kre.)
Suriname. 5. (vBJ.)
Susanne. 6. (vTL.)
Suzanne. 12. (Len.)
Suzette. 4. (Kre.)
Suzon. 9. (Kre.)
Sven Hedin. 2. (Zoch.)
Swastika. 7. (dGra.)
Sweetheart. 12. (Bath)
Sweetmemory. 6. (Ware)
Swinny. 4. (Kerb.)
Sylphide. 5. (Lef.)
Sylvanus. 5. (Zoch.)
Sylvestris Tabris. 16. (vTL.)
Tableau Derubens. 10. (Vi.)
Tak Vanpoortvliet. 9. (Kre.) *Minister Tak Van Poortvliet.*
Talisman. 8. (Hard.)
Talisman (broken). 11. (Hard.)
Tantalus. 7. (Kre.)
Tchitouny T. **T. tchitounyi.**
Telescopium. 5. (Zoch.)
Tenneriza. 12. (EldC.)
Terpander. 7. (vTL.)

TULIPA, continued
Terracotta. 9. (Kre.)
The Admiral. 12. (Bath)
The Baron. 12. (Bath)
The Big Boss. 2. (Da.)
The Bishop. 9. (Kre.)
The Bride. 6. (Kre.)
The Chief. 6. (Da.)
Theeroos. 3.
The Fawn. 6.
The King. 12. (Bath)
Themis. 6. (Kre.)
Theodora. 7. (vTL.)
Theophrastus T. **T. theophrasti.**
The Queen. 10. (Bath)
Therese. 14.
The Rose. 4. (Kre.)
The Sultan. 9. (Kre.)
Thetis. 12. (Len.)
Thianschan T. **T. thianschanica.**
Thomas Edison. 2. (Da.)
Thomas Morus. 2. (1820.)
Thomas Stephenson. 7. (vTL.)
Thracian T. **T. thracica.**
Threeleaf T. **T. triphylla.**
Thuban. 5. (Zoch.)
Tilly Lus. 9. (Gru.)
Tindal. 9.
Titania. 6. (vTL.)
Titanic. 7. (vTL.)
Titian. 3. (Leem.)
Titus. 7. (vTL.)
Tivoli. 9. (Lef.)
Tokay. 9. (Gru.)
Tokio. 9. (Da.)
Tollens. 15.
Tony. 12. (Bath)
Topaz T. **T. lutea.**
Toplight. 9. (Kre.)
Tornax. 5. (Zoch.)
Toronto. 9. (Lef.)
Tosca. 5. (Zoch.)
Toscelli. 5. (vBJ.)
Tournesol Red-Yellow. 3. (1769.)
Trader Horn. 2. (Zoch.)
Trafalgar. 10.
Tregenna. 6. (Ware)
Trianon. 4. (Kerb.)
Tricolor. 9. (Da.)
Triomphe de Paris. 5. (vBJ.)
Tripoli T. **T. abatinoi.**
Tristan. 4. (Kre.)
Triton. 6. (Kre.)
Triumphator. 3.
Triumph of Holland. 2.
Trixy. 15.
Troje. 7. (vTL.)
Troutlily T. **T. erythronioides.**
Trude. 6. (vTL.)
Tschigorin. 6. (Da.)
Tubergen Glory. 9. (vTL.)
Tubergen T. **T. tubergeniana.**
Turcoman T. **T. turcomanica.**
Turenne. 7.
Turkestan T. **T. turkestanica.**
Turkish T. **T. acuminata.**
Turner. 9. (vTL.)
Tutankhamen. 12.
Twilight. 13.
Twoflower T. **T. biflora.**
Umberto. 5.
Uncle Tom. 15.
Undine. 12. (Kre.)
Unicorn. 6. (vTL.)
Unionjack. 13.
Unique. 7. (vTL.)
Ursa Minor. 2. (Zoch.)
Urumiya T. **T. urumiensis.**

TULIPA, continued
Urumoff T. **T. urumoffi.**
U. S. A. 5.
Utopia. 9. (Seg.)
Utrecht. 4. (Kre.)
Valentine. 9. (Kre.)
Valentine Demilan. 10.
Valery. 7. (Lef.)
Valiant. 9. (vTL.)
Vandereerden. 4. (Kre.)
Vanderneer. 2. (Leem.)
Vangogh. 9. (Lef.)
Vanhall. 4. (Kre.)
Vela. 5. (Zoch.)
Veldheer. 13.
Velvet King. 7. (Barr)
Venice. 5. (vBJ.)
Venus. 9. (Kre.)
Venus T. **T. veneris.**
Vera. 4. (Kre.)
Vermeer. 9. (Lef.)
Vermillon Brillant. 2.
Vermillon Brillant Maximus. 2.
Verona. 4. (Kre.)
Veronese. 6. (vTL.)
Vertumnus. 7. (Vi.)
Vesta. 6. (Kre.)
Victoire d'Oliveira. 9. (Kre.)
Victor. 7. (Kre.)
Victor Hugo. 12. (Len.)
Victory. 10.
Victressa. 9. (Lef.)
Viking. 9. (Kre.)
Villafranca. 9. (vTL.)
Vindictive. 7. (vTL.)
Viola. 9. (Kre.)
Violet Favourite. 12. (Gru.)
Violet Queen. 14.
Violet Superbe. 10.
Violet T. **T. violacea.**
Viotta. 5. (vBJ.)
Virgilius. 7. (Vi.)
Virginia. 4. (Kre.)
Virgo. 5. (Zoch.)
Viridiflora. 6.
Viridiflora Praecox. 6.
Vitellina. 6. (Vi.)
Vivid. 9. (Seg.)
Vola. 9. (Lef.)
Vondel. 13.
Von Moltke. 5. (Zoch.)
Vulcain. 7.
Vuurbaak. 3. (AA.)
Vuurland. 3. (vBJ.)
Wagner. 4. (Kre.)
Wagram. 9. (vTL.)
Walewski. 7. (vTL.)
Wallflower. 6. (Da.)
Wallstreet. 6. (Da.)
Wally Moes. 9. (Kre.)
Walter (*T.*) Ware. 6.
Waterlily. 6.
Waterlily T. **T. kaufmanniana.**
Waterloo. 2.
Watson. 6. (Da.)
W. A. Viruly-Verbrugge. 9. (Kre.)
Wavyleaf T. **T. undulatifolia.**
Weber. 4. (Kre.)
Wedding Robe. 12.
Wega. 5. (Zoch.)
Welcome. 9. (Seg.)
Wellwynn. 6. (dGra.)
Wembley. 4. (Kre.)
Westland. 2.
Whistler. 9. (Kre.)
Whitebeauty. 2.
Whitecity. 6. (vTL.)
Whitecross. 6. (Kre.)

TULIPA, continued
Whiteduchess. 6. (Kre.)
Whiteensign. 6. (Kre.)
Whiteexcelsior. 2.
Whitegem. 4. (Kerb.)
Whitegiant. 9. (Gru.)
Whiteknight. 9. (Ware)
Whitepearl. 6. (dGra.)
Whitequeen. 9. (Kre.)
Whitesail. 4. (Kre.)
Whiteswan. 2.
Whitevirgin. 4. (Kre.)
Whittall Spartan T. **T. orphanidea whittalli.**
Whynot. 4. (Kre.)
Widar. 4. (Kerb.)
Wilberforce. 7. (Vi.)
Wildfire. 2. (Da.)
Wildlust. 9. (Gru.)
Willem Dezwijger. 7. (Vi.)
Willemsoord. 3.
Willem Vanderlaan. 2. (Gro.)
Willem Vanorange. 3.
William Copland. 9. (Kre.)
William Hogarth. 9. (vTL.)
William Pitt. 9.
William Wilson. 11. (Hard.)
Willmott T. **T. willmottae.**
Wilson T. **T. wilsoniana.**
Winter. 4. (Kre.)
Winter Gem. 4. (Kerb.)
Wisconsin. 5. (Zoch.)
Wocana. 7. (Lef.)
Wodan. 5. (vBJ.)
Wonderful. 4. (Kre.)
Woolly T. **T. lanata.**
Worlds Fair. 5.
Wouwerman. 2. (Leem.)
Yellowbeauty. 5. (Kerb.)
Yellow Blackblotch T. **T. strangulata maculata.**
Yellowblotch Didier T. **T. didieri mauriana.**
Yellowbrilliant. 2.
Yellowcloud. 6. (dGra.)
Yellow Common T. **T. gesneriana lutea.**
Yellowdiamond. 5. (Mooy)
Yellowemperor. 6. (vTL.)
Yellowfavourite. 2.
Yellowfortune. 6.
Yellowgiant. 9. (Da.)
Yellow Greig T. **T. greigi aurea.**
Yellowknight. 5. (Kerb.)
Yellowmarvel. 6. (vTL.)
Yellowperfection. 7.
Yellowpicotee. 6.
Yellowpoppy. 2. (Kerb.)
Yellowprince. 2. (1780.)
Yellowprince (variegated). 2.
Yellowqueen. 2.
Yellowrose. 15. (1700.)
Yellow Waterlily T. **T. kaufmanniana aurea.**
Yolande. 9. (Kre.)
Yukisan. 5.
Zany. 10. (Jaco.)
Zanzibar. 7.
Zebra. 10.
Zenaida T. **T. zenaidae.**
Zenith. 4. (Kre.)
Zenober. 4. (Kre.)
Zeus. 6. (Kre.)
Zev. 9. (Kre.)
Zibal. 5. (Zoch.)
Zidorion. 4. (Kre.)
Zimmerman. 5. (Zoch.)
Zomerschoon. 13. (1620.)

TULIPA, continued
Zulu. 9. (Kre.)
Zulu King. 7. (vTL.)
Zwanenburg. 9. (vTL.)

Tuliporchid . . . . . **Cattleya citrina**

Tuliptree . **Liriodendron; L. tulipifera**
Chinese T. . . . . **L. chinense**
Roundlobe T. **L. tulipifera obtusilobum**

Tulipwood . . . . **Harpullia pendula**

Tumblegrass
Schedonnardus; S. paniculatus

Tumblemustard **Sisymbrium altissimum**

TUMBO'A . . . . . . **WELWITSCHIA**

TU'MION . . . . **TORREYA**
nucif'erum gran'de . . . **T. grandis**

Tuna . . . . Pricklypear, Tuna: **Opuntia tuna**

The name Tuna is applied to the edible fruits of O. tuna and several other related species.

Tungoiltree . . . . . **Aleurites fordi**

TU'NICA (*PETRORHAGIA*)
Tunicflower
gramin'ea . . . . Grass T.
prolif'era . . . . . Littleleaf T.
saxif'raga (*Petrorhagia s.*)
Saxifrage T.
—al'ba . . . . White S.T.
—floreple'no . . . . . . Double S.T.
—rose'a . . . . Pink S.T.
veluti'na . . . . Hairy T.

Tunicflower . . . . **Tunica**
Double Saxifrage T.
T. saxifraga florepleno
Grass T. . . . . **T. graminea**
Hairy T. . . . . **T. velutina**
Littleleaf T. . . . . . . **T. prolifera**
Pink Saxifrage T. **T. saxifraga rosea**
Saxifrage T. . . . . . . **T. saxifraga**
White S. T. . . . . **T. s. alba**

Tunisgrass . . . . **Sorghum virgatum**

TU'PELO . . . . **NYSSA**

Tupelo . . . . **Nyssa**
Bear T. . . . . **N. ursina**
Black T. . . . . **N. sylvatica**
Chinese T. . . . . **N. sinensis**
Ogeechee T. . . . . **N. ogeche**
Swamp Black T. . **N. sylvatica biflora**
Water T. . . . . **N. aquatica**
Weeping Black T.
N. sylvatica pendula

TUPIDAN'THUS
calyptra'tus

Turfingdaisy . **Matricaria tchihatchewi**

Turkeyfoot . . . . . Bluestem, Sand: **Andropogon halli**
Bluejoint T. . . . Big B.: **A. furcatus**

Turkeymullein
Eremocarpus; E. setigerus

Turksrug . . . **Chorizanthe staticoides**

Turmeric . . . . **Curcuma**
Common T. . . . . **C. longa**
Zedoary T. . . . . **C. zedoaria**

TURN'ERA . . . . Turnera
diffu'sa (*aphrodisiaca; T. d. aphrodisiaca*) . . . Damiana T. (*Damiana*)
ulmifo'lia . . . . Sweet T.

Turnip . . . . **Brassica rapa**

Turpentine-myrtle . . . . **Syncarpia**
Brush T. . . . . **S. leptopetala**
Burramurra T. . . . **S. glomulifera**
Hills T. . . . . **S. hilli**

TURPI'NIA
pomif'era

TURRAE'A . . . . Starbush
obtusifo'lia . . . . . Bluntleaf S.

TURRAEAN'THUS . . . . . . Avodire
africa'na . . . . African A.

Turtlegrass **Thalassia; T. testudinum**

Turtlehead . . . . **Chelone**
Pink T. . . . . **C. lyoni**
Rose T. . . . . **C. obliqua**
White T. . . . . **C. glabra**

TUSSA'CIA . . . . Tussacia
pulchel'la . . . . Salmon T.

TUSSILA'GO . . . . Coltsfoot
far'fara . . . . Common C.
fra'grans . . . . **Petasites f.**

Tutu . . . . Coriaria, NewZealand: **Coriaria ruscifolia**

Twayblade . . . . **Liparis**
Lily T. . . . . **L. liliifolia**
Loesel T. . . . . **L. loeseli**

Twiggygum . Eucalyptus, Angletwig: **Eucalyptus virgata**

Twinbloom, Mexican **Bravoa geminiflora**

Twinebark . . . . **Plagianthus**
Hempbush T. . . . . . **P. pulchellus**
Ribbonwood T. . . . . . **P. betulinus**

Twinflower . . . . **Linnaea**
American T. . . **L. borealis americana**
Longtube T. . . . . . **L. b. longiflora**

Twinleaf . . . . **Jeffersonia**
American T. . . . . **J. diphylla**
Chinese T. . . . . **J. dubia**

Twinpod . . . . **Physaria**
Common T. . . . . . **P. didymocarpa**

Twinspur . . . . **Diascia**
Rose T. . . . . **D. barberae**

Twistarum **Helicodiceros; H. muscivorus**

Twistedstalk . . . . **Streptopus**
Claspleaf T. . . . . . **S. amplexifolius**
Rosy T. . . . . **S. roseus**

Twistflower . . . . **Streptanthus**
Desertcabbage T. . . . . **S. inflatus**
Heartleaf T. . . . . **S. cordatus**

TYLOPH'ORA . . . . Tylophora
in'dica (*asthmatica*) . . . . Ipecac T.

TYLOSTE'MON
crassifo'lius
mann'i

TY'PHA |w . . . . Cattail
angustifo'lia |w . . . Narrowleaf C.
elephanti'na . . . Elephantgrass C.
latifo'lia |w . . . . Common C.

Udo . . . . **Aralia cordata**

UG'NI . . . . Chileguava
moli'nae (*Myrtus m.; M. ugni*)
Chileguava

U'LEX . . . . Gorse (*Furze*)
europae'us . . . . Common G.
¢Double (*florepleno; plenus*) hv.
¢Irish (*pyramidalis; strictus*)
∞ **gal'li** (*europaeus × nanus*)

The plant in cultivation is probably a clon of this polybrid.

ULEX, continued
na'nus . . . . Dwarf Gorse
parviflo'rus . . . Smallflower G.
—provincia'lis . . . . Slender S.G.

ULLU'CUS . . . . Ullucus
tubero'sus . . . . Tuber U.

ULMA'RIA . . . . . **FILIPENDULA**
filipen'dula . . . . . **F. hexapetala**

UL'MUS |w . . . . Elm
ala'ta . . . . Winged E.
america'na |w . . . . . American E.
¢Ascendens. hv.
¢Column (*columnaris*)
¢Golden (*aurea*)
¢Lake City
¢Littleford (*littlefordi*)
¢Moline (*molini*)
¢Princeton
¢Vase (*urni*)
¢Weeping (*pendula*)
∞ **arbus'cula** (*glabra × pumila*)
bergmannia'na . . . . . Bergmann E.
—lasiophyl'la . . . . Hairyleaf B.E.
brandisia'na . . . . Brandis E.
campes'tris . **U. carpinifolia; U. procera**

By Linnaeus all European Elms were classed under U. campestris. Later the name was applied by English authors chiefly to U. procera, and by continental authors to U. carpinifolia.

—japon'ica . . . . **U. japonica**
—stric'ta . **U. carpinifolia cornubiensis**
—wheat'leyi . . . . . **U. c. sarniensis**
carpinifo'lia (*campestris* in part; *foliacea; nitens*) . . . . Smoothleaf E.
—cornubien'sis (*U. campestris stricta; U. stricta*) . . . . . Cornish S.E.
—ital'ica . . . . Italian S.E.
—sarnien'sis (*U. campestris wheatleyi; U. sarniensis*) . . . . . Sarnia S.E.
—subero'sa (*U. suberosa* Moench, *not* Ehrh.) . . . . . Corkbark S.E.
¢Dampier (*dampieri*) hv. U. carpinifolia
¢Globe (*umbraculifera*)
¢Italian (*italica*)
¢Jersey (*sarniensis; wheatleyi*)
¢Koopmann (*koopmanni*)
¢Propendens
¢Slenderbranch (*gracilis*)
¢Variegated (*variegata*)
¢Webb (*webbiana*)
¢Weeping (*pendula*)
¢Wrede (*wredei*)
crassifo'lia . . . . Cedar E.
davidia'na . . . . David E.
dippelia'na . . . . . ∞ **U. hollandica**
ellip'tica . . . . Armenian E.
folia'cea . . . . **U. carpinifolia**
ful'va . . . . Slippery E.
gla'bra (*montana; scabra*) . Scotch E. (*Wych E.*)
¢Bush (*nana*) hv.
¢Camperdown (*camperdowni*)
¢Cornuta
¢Exeter (*exoniensis*)
¢Fernleaf (*crispa*)
¢Monstrosa
¢Purple (*purpurea*)
¢Purpleleaf (*atropurpurea*)
¢Redtwig (*rubra*)
¢Tabletop (*pendula*)
¢Threelobe (*grandidentata*)
¢Variegated (*variegata*)
¢Yellowleaf (*lutescens*)

ULMUS, continued
hill'ieri Hort. . . . . . HILLIER ELM
Introduced by Hillier & Son (1935?). Presumably a hybrid or a clon.
∞**holland'ica** (*?carpinifolia* × *glabra; dippeliana; major*) . . ∞ DUTCH E.
BELGIAN (*belgica*) HV.
This var. is reputed to be native and not a clon.
₵BLANDFORD (*superba*)
₵DAUVESSE (*dauvessei*)
₵DOWNTON (*pendula*)
₵DUMONT (*dumonti*)
₵HUNTINGDON (*vegeta*)
₵KLEMMER
₵PITTEURS (*pitteursi*)
japon'ica (*U. campestris j.*) JAPANESE E.
lacinia'ta . . . . . MANCHURIAN E.
—nikkoen'sis . . . . . NIKKO M.E.
lae'vis (*pedunculata*) . . RUSSIAN E.
macrocar'pa . . . . . . BIGFRUIT E.
ma'jor . . . . ∞**U. hollandica**
mexica'na . . . . MEXICAN E.
mi'nor Henry, *not* Mill. . . . **U. ploti**
monta'na . . . . **U. glabra**
ni'tens . . . . **U. carpinifolia**
parvifo'lia . . . . CHINESE E.
In the United States, especially in the Prairie States where it is being extensively planted in shelterbelts, etc., the Siberian U. pumila is generally called Chinese E. The Editorial Committee believes this misnomer is a source of confusion and adheres here to original S.P.N. usage (hitherto accepted in the U. S. Dept. of Agriculture), which is also the usage of Rehder's Manual and of Bailey's Hortus Second.
peduncula'ta . . . . **U. laevis**
plo'ti (*minor* Henry, *not* Mill.; *sativa* Moss, *not* Mill.) . . . . PLOTS E.
proce'ra (*campestris* in part) ENGLISH E.
This is U. campestris as interpreted by Miller.
—austra'lis . . . . SOUTHERN E.E.
₵BERARD (*berardi*) HV. U. procera
₵MARGINATA
₵MONUMENT (*monumentalis*)
₵MYRTIFOLIA
₵PURPLE (*purpurascens*)
₵PURPLELEAF (*purpurea*)
₵SILVERVARIEGATED (*argenteo-variegata*)
₵VANHOUTTE (*vanhouttei*)
₵WENTWORTH (*wentworthi*)
₵WILLOW (*viminalis*)
₵YELLOWLEAF (*aurea*)
pu'mila . . . . SIBERIAN E.
See note under U. parvifolia.
—arbo'rea . . . . . NARROW S.E.
ANDROSSOW (*androssowi*) HV. U. pumila
Probably a natural botanical form in cultivation, rather than a clon.
₵WEEPING (*pendula*)
racemo'sa Thomas, *not* Borkh. **U. thomasi**
sarnien'sis . . . . . **U. carpinifolia s.**
sati'va Moss., *not* Mill. . . . **U. ploti**
sca'bra . . . . **U. glabra**
serot'ina . . . . . SEPTEMBER E.
stric'ta . **U. carpinifolia cornubiensis**
subero'sa Moench, *not* Ehrh. **U. carpinifolia s.**
thom'asi (*racemosa* Thomas, *not* Borkh.) ROCK E.
wal'lichi (*wallichiana*) . HIMALAYAN E.
wilsonia'na . . . . . . WILSON E.

UL'VA W . . SEALETTUCE (*Greenlaver*)
lactu'ca W . . . . COMMON S.

UMBELLULA'RIA W CALIFORNIALAUREL
califor'nica W . . CALIFORNIALAUREL (*Oregon-myrtle*)
₵WEEPING (*pendula*) HV.

UMBILICA'RIA . . . . . UMBILICARIA
pustula'ta . . . . BLISTER U.
velle'a . . . . FLEECY U.

UMBIL'ICUS (*ROSULARIA* in part) NAVELWORT
See **SUCCULENTS.**

UMBRELLALEAF . . . . **Diphylleia**
AMERICAN U. . . . . **D. cymosa**
JAPAN U. . . . . **D. grayi**
UMBRELLAPALM . . . . . **Hedyscepe**
CANTERBURY U. . **H. canterburyana**
UMBRELLAPINE **Sciadopitys; S. verticillata**
Umkokolo . . KEIAPPLE: **Dovyalis caffra**

UNCA'RIA . . . . . . GAMBIRPLANT
gam'bir (*Ourouparia g.*) . BENGAL G.

UNGNA'DIA . . . MEXICANBUCKEYE
specio'sa . . . . MEXICANBUCKEYE

UNICORNPLANT . . . . **Ibicella**
YELLOW U. . . . . **I. lutea**

UNIFO'LIUM . . **MAIANTHEMUM**

UNI'OLA . . . . UNIOLA
See **GRASS GENERA.**

UPASTREE . . . . . . **Antiaris toxicaria**

URAN'DRA . . . . URANDRA
cornicula'ta . . . . DARU U.

URA'RIA . . . . URARIA
lago'pus

URBIN'IA . . . . . . **ECHEVERIA**
See **SUCCULENTS.**

URCE'OLA
esculen'ta

URCEOLA'RIA . . . . . URCEOLARIA
calca'rea . . . . LIMESTONE U.
cine'rea . . . . ASHY U.
scrupo'sa . . . . JAGGED U.

URCEOLI'NA . . . . . PITCHERLILY
latifo'lia . . . . BROADLEAF P.
minia'ta . . . . SCARLET P.
pen'dula . . . . YELLOW P.

Urd . BEAN, MUNGO: **Phaseolus mungo**

URECHI'TES . . . . VIPERTAIL
lute'a (*Echites andrewsi*) HAMMOCK V.
pineto'rum . . . . . FLATWOODS V.
suberec'ta . . . . . . DOMINICAN V.

URE'NA
loba'ta . . . . CADILLO

URE'RA . . . . SCRATCHBUSH
baccif'era . . . . . . BROADLEAF S.
caracasa'na . . . . FLAMEBERRY S.

URGIN'EA . . . . SEAONION
in'dica . . . . . INDIA DRUGSQUILL
marit'ima (*Scilla m.*) . . . SHORE D.

UROPAP'PUS
linearifo'lius (*Microseris linearifolia*)

URSIN'IA (*SPHENOGYNE*) . URSINIA
anethoi'des (*Sphenogyne a.*) DILL-LEAF U.
anthemoi'des (*Sphenogyne a.*) JEWEL U.
foenicula'cea (*Sphenogyne f.*) FENNELLEAF U.
pul'chra (*Sphenogyne speciosa*) ORANGE U.

URTI'CA W . . . . NETTLE
dioi'ca . . . . BIGSTING N.
grac'ilis . . . . SLIM N.
—holoseric'ea (*U. holosericea*) CALIFORNIA S.N.
ly'alli . . . . LYALL N.
pilulif'era . . . . ROMAN N.
proce'ra . . . . TALL N.
u'rens . . . . DOG N.
u'tilis . . . . **Boehmeria nivea**
Urticas'trum divarica'tum **Laportea canadensis**

URVIL'LEA . . . . URVILLEA
ulma'cea

US'NEA . . . . USNEA
barba'ta . . . . BEARDED U.
flor'ida . . . . FLORIDA U.
plica'ta . . . . PLEATED U.

USTILA'GO
ze'ae (*maydis*) . . . . . CORNSMUT

UTA'HIA
See **CACTUS GENERA.**

UTRICULA'RIA W . . BLADDERWORT
alpi'na . . . **Orchyllium alpinum**
clandesti'na W
cleistog'ama W
cornu'ta W . . . . . . HORNED B.
fibro'sa W . . . . FIBER B.
florida'na W . . . . . FLORIDA B.
folio'sa W
gib'ba W
infla'ta W . . . . FLOATING B.
interme'dia W
jun'cea W . . . . RUSH B.
mi'nor W . . . . LESSER B.
monta'na . . . . . . MARTINIQUE B.
monta'na Jacq., *not* Poir. **Orchyllium alpinum**
pu'mila W
purpu'rea W . . . . . . PURPLE B.
resupina'ta W
subula'ta W . . . . AWN B.
virga'tula W
vulga'ris W . . . . . . COMMON B.

UVAGRASS . . . . **Gynerium sagittatum**

UVULA'RIA (*OAKESIA*) MERRYBELLS
grandiflo'ra . . . . BIG M.
perfolia'ta . . . . WOOD M.
—fla'va . . . . YELLOW W.M.
sessilifo'lia (*Oakesia s.*) . . LITTLE M.

VACCA'RIA . . . . **SAPONARIA**
pyramida'ta; vulga'ris . . . **S. vaccaria**

VACCIN'IUM (*BATODENDRON; OXYCOCCUS; POLYCODIUM*) W BLUEBERRY
For hort. var. of Blueberry see **FRUIT AND EDIBLE NUT NAMES.**
angustifo'lium (*V. pensylvanicum a.*) W LOWBUSH B.
—laevifo'lium (*V. pensylvanicum*) W SMOOTHLEAF L.B.
—leucocar'pum . WHITEBERRY L.B.
—myrtilloi'des . . . . MYRTLE L.B.
—ni'grum

VACCINIUM, continued
arbo'reum (*Batodendron a.*) |w FARKLEBERRY
—glauces'cens . . . . MISSOURI F.
arctosta'phylos CAUCASIAN WHORTLEBERRY
∞**atlan'ticum** (*angustifolium* × *corymbosum*) . . . ∞ATLANTIC BLUEBERRY
A natural, variable species.
atrococ'cum . . . . . . DOWNY B.
—leucocar'pum . . . . WHITEFRUIT D.B.
bractea'tum . . . . . ORIENTAL B.
canaden'se |w . . . . . CANADA B.
cespito'sum . . . . DWARF B.
—arbus'cula . . . . . TALLER D.B.
cilia'tum . . . . **V. oldhami**
corymbo'sum |w . . . HIGHBUSH B.
—albiflo'rum . . WHITEFRUIT H.B.
—caesarien'se . . ENTIRELEAF H.B.
—gla'brum (*V. c. pallidum* A. Gray, *not* **V. pallidum** Ait.) PALELEAF H.B.
crassifo'lium (*Herpothamnus crassifolius*) . . . . CREEPING B.
delava'yi . . . . DELAVAY B.
delicio'sum |w . . . . DELICIOUS B.
dunalia'num . . . . . HIMALAYA B.
erythrocar'pum (*Oxycoccus erythrocarpus*) . . . . DINGLEBERRY
floribun'dum (*mortinia*) COLOMBIAN B.
frag'ile . . . . SZECHWAN B.
hirsu'tum . . HAIRY WHORTLEBERRY (*Hairy Huckleberry*)
hir'tum . . . . REDJAP B.
∞**interme'dium** (*myrtillus* × *vitis-idaea*)
japon'icum . . . . . . JAPANESE B.
korea'num . . . . KOREAN B.
macrocar'pum (*Oxycoccus macrocarpus*) |w . . . . CRANBERRY
mandarino'rum . . . . . **V. sprengeli**
melanocar'pum . . . . . GEORGIA B.
membrana'ceum BIG WHORTLEBERRY
merrillia'num . . . . . FORMOSA B.
morti'nia . . . . . **V. floribundum**
moupinen'se . . . . KANSU B.
myrsini'tes . . . . . . GROUND B.
myrtil'lus . MYRTLE WHORTLEBERRY (*Wineberry*)
—leucocar'pum . WHITEFRUIT M.W.
neglec'tum . SOUTHERN DEERBERRY
nummula'ria . . . . . . THIBET B.
occidenta'le . . . . WESTERNBOG B.
old'hami (*ciliatum*) . . . OLDHAM B.
oreoph'ilum |w ROCKYMOUNTAIN WHORTLEBERRY
ovalifo'lium OVALLEAF WHORTLEBERRY
ova'tum |w . . . . BOX B.
oxycoc'cos (*Oxycoccus palustris*) |w SMALL CRANBERRY
—interme'dium (*Oxycoccus intermedius; O. palustris i.*) . . . WESTERN S.C.
pal'lidum (*vacillans*) . BLUERIDGE B.
parvifo'lium . . RED WHORTLEBERRY
pensylva'nicum **V. angustifolium laevifolium**
—angustifo'lium . . **V. angustifolium**
prae'stans . . . . CHERRY B.
reticula'tum
retu'sum
scopa'rium . GROUSE WHORTLEBERRY
small'i . . . . SMALLS B.
spren'geli (*mandarinorum*) SPRENGEL B.
stamin'eum (*Polycodium s.*) |w COMMON DEERBERRY
uligino'sum |w . . . . BOG BILBERRY
urceola'tum
vac'illans . . . . **V. pallidum**
virga'tum (*tenellum*) |w RABBITEYE B.
—tenel'lum . . SMALLCLUSTER R.B.

VACCINIUM, continued
vitis-idae'a |w . . . . . COWBERRY
The typical form of this species is confined to the Old World.
—ma'jus . . . . SHORE C.
—mi'nus . . . . . . MOUNTAIN C.

VAG'NERA . . . . . **SMILACINA**
lilia'cea . . . . **S. stellata**

VALERIAN . . . . **Valeriana**
ARIZONA V. . . . . **V. arizonica**
AUSTRIAN V. . . . . **V. supina**
BOG V. . . . . **V. uliginosa**
CAUCASIAN V. . . . . **V. phu**
COLUMBIA V. . . . . . . **V. columbiana**
COMMON V. . . . . **V. officinalis**
EDIBLE V. . . . . **V. edulis**
EURASIAN V. . . . . **V. alliariaefolia**
MARSH V. . . . . **V. dioica**
MEXICAN V. . . . . **V. mexicana**
MOUNTAIN V. . . . . **V. montana**
PYRENEES V. . . . . . . **V. pyrenaica**
RED V. . . . . . **V. officinalis rubra**
ROSETTE V. . . . . **V. excelsa**
SCOULER V. . . . . **V. scouleri**
SHARPLEAF V. . . . . . . **V. acutiloba**
SITKA V. . . . . **V. sitchensis**
SMALLFLOWER V. . . . . **V. micrantha**
TOLUCA V. . . . . **V. toluccana**
WESTERN V. . . . . . **V. occidentalis**
WHITE COMMON V. . **V. officinalis alba**
YELLOW CAUCASIAN V. . **V. phu aurea**

VALERIA'NA |w . . . . . . VALERIAN
acutilo'ba . . . . . . SHARPLEAF V.
al'ba
Name misused for white vars. of Jupitersbeard Centranthus (Centranthus ruber) and Common Valerian (V. officinalis).
alliariaefo'lia . . . . . . EURASIAN V.
arizo'nica . . . . ARIZONA V.
ceratophyl'la Piper, *not* H.B.K. **V. edulis**
coccin'ea . . . . **Centranthus ruber**
columbia'na . . . . . COLUMBIA V.
dioi'ca (*palustris*) . . . . . MARSH V.
echina'ta . . . . **Valerianella e.**
ed'ulis (*ceratophylla* Piper, *not* H.B.K.) EDIBLE V.
excel'sa . . . . ROSETTE V.
mexica'na . . . . MEXICAN V.
micran'tha . . . . SMALLFLOWER V.
monta'na . . . . MOUNTAIN V.
occidenta'lis . . . . . . WESTERN V.
officina'lis . . . . COMMON V.
—al'ba . . . . WHITE C.V.
—ru'bra . . . . RED V.
phu' . . . . CAUCASIAN V.
—au'rea . . . . YELLOW C.V.
pyrena'ica . . . . PYRENEES V.
ru'bra . . . . . . **Centranthus ruber**
scou'leri . . . . SCOULER V.
sitchen'sis . . . . SITKA V.
supi'na . . . . AUSTRIAN V.
tolucca'na . . . . TOLUCA V.
trip'teris
uligino'sa . . . . BOG V.

VALERIANEL'LA . . . . CORNSALAD
conges'ta . . . . **Plectritis c.**
denta'ta . . . . TOOTHED C.
echina'ta (*Valeriana e.*) . PRICKLY C.
eriocar'pa . . . . ITALIAN C.
interme'dia
locus'ta
Dr. Sarah Dyal, the monographer of this genus, says there is no type of this "species" in the Linnean Herbarium; apparently Linnaeus used the name merely as "a binding word for his varieties."

VALERIANELLA, continued
locus'ta olito'ria . . . . . **V. olitoria**
longiflo'ra
macro'cera . . . . **Plectritis m.**
nutt'alli . . . . NUTTALL CORNSALAD
olito'ria (*V. locusta o.*) EUROPEAN C.
radia'ta
woodsia'na . . . . WOODS C.

VALERIANOI'DES **STACHYTARPHETA**

VALLA'RIS . . . . VALLARIS
heyn'ei (*dichotoma*) . . . . BURMA V.
solana'cea

VALLISNE'RIA |w . . . . WILDCELERY
america'na . . . . . AMERICAN W.
gigan'tea . . . . GIANT W.
spira'lis |w . . . . SPIRAL W.

VALLO'TA . . . . VALLOTA (*Scarboro(ugh) lily*)
specio'sa (*purpurea*)
₵ALBA. HV.
₵EXIMIA
∞HYBRIDA (*Cyrtanthus sanguineus* × *V. purpurea*)
₵MAGNIFICA
₵MAJOR
₵MINOR

VALO'TA . . . . . **TRICHACHNE**
See **GRASS GENERA.**

VANCOUVE'RIA
chrysan'tha
hexan'dra
parviflo'ra

VAN'DA
See **ORCHID GENERA.**

VANDOP'SIS
See **ORCHID GENERA.**

VANGUE'RIA . . . . . . VANGUERIA
ed'ulis
infaus'ta
madagascaren'sis . . . . . VOAVANGA

VANIE'RIA . . . . . . **CUDRANIA**

VANIL'LA . . . . VANILLA
See **ORCHID GENERA.**

Vanillagrass . . . . SWEETGRASS: **Hierochloe odorata**

VANILLALEAF . . . . **Achlys**
DEERFOOT V. . . . . . . **A. triphylla**

VASEYGRASS . . . . **Paspalum urvillei**

VASEYOCH'LOA
See **GRASS GENERA.**

VATAI'REA
lundell'i

VATAIREOP'SIS . . . . **ANDIRA**
Some botanists regard Vataireopsis as a distinct genus.

VATE'RIA
in'dica

VAUAN'THES (*GRAMMANTHES*) LETTERFLOWER
See **SUCCULENTS.**

VAUCHE'RIA |w . . . . . GREENFELT
gemina'ta . . . . TWINEGG G.
ses'silis
terres'tris . . . . LAND G.

VAUQUELI'NIA . . . . VAUQUELINIA
califor'nica (*torreyi*) . . . TORREY V.

VEGETABLE DYES; VEGETABLE IVORY; VEGETABLES (Plant Sources)
See **ECONOMIC PLANTS, VEGETABLE DYES, VEGETABLE IVORY, VEGETABLES.**

VEGETABLESPONGE, SUAKWA **Luffa cylindrica**

VEITCH'IA . . . . VEITCHIA
See **PALM GENERA.**

Vel'la integrifo'lia; pseudocyt'isus **Pseudocytisus integrifolius**
spino'sa . . . . **P. spinosus**

VELTHEIM'IA
glau'ca
viridifo'lia

VELVETBEAN . . . . **Stizolobium**
BEAKED V. . . . . **S. rostratum**
BENGAL V. . . . . . . **S. aterrimum**
CHINESE V. . . . . . . **S. niveum**
COWAGE V. . . . . . . **S. pruritum**
DEERING V. . . . . **S. deeringianum**
SLOANE V. . . . . . . **S. sloanei**
YOKOHAMA V. . . . . . . **S. hassjoo**

VELVETCACTUS . . **Bergerocactus emoryi**

VELVETGRASS . . . . **Holcus**
COMMON V. . . . . **H. lanatus**
GERMAN V. . . . . **H. mollis**
Korean V. . . . . MASCARENEGRASS: **Zoysia tenuifolia**

VELVETLEAF . . . . **Limnocharis**
YELLOW V. . . . . **L. flava**

VELVETPLANT . . . . **Gynura**
ANGLED V. . . . . **G. angulosa**
JAVA V. . . . . **G. aurantiaca**

VELVETSEED . . . . **Guettarda**
EVERGLADES V. . . . . **G. elliptica**
ROUGHLEAF V. . . . . . . **G. scabra**

VELVET-TAMARIND . **Dialium guineense**

VENEGA'SIA . . CANYON-SUNFLOWER
carpesioi'des . . . . . . COMMON C.

VENID'IUM . . . NAMAQUALAND-DAISY
decur'rens (*calendulaceum*) SUNBURST N.
fastuo'sum . . . . . MONARCH N.

VENUSFLYTRAP . **Dionaea; D. muscipula**

VENUSLOOKINGGLASS . . . . **Specularia**
CLASPING V. . . . . . **S. perfoliata**
SMALL V. . . . . **S. biflora**

VE'PRIS
lanceola'ta (*Boscia undulata; Toddalia l.*)

VERA'TRUM |w . . . FALSEHELLEBORE
al'bum . . . . WHITE F.
califor'nicum (*speciosum*) CALIFORNIA F.
eschscholtz'i . . . . ESCHSCHOLTZ F.
fimbria'tum . . . . . . FRINGED F.
insoli'tum
ni'grum . . . . BLACK F.
specio'sum . . . . . **V. californicum**
tenuipet'alum . . . . COLORADO F.
vir'ide . . . . . . AMERICAN F.

VERBAS'CUM |w . . . . . MULLEIN
baldac'ci
blatta'ria |w . . . . MOTH M.
—**albiflo'rum** (*V. b. album*) WHITE M.M.
chaix'i . . . . CHAIX M.
—**al'bum** . . . . . . WHITE C.M.
crassifo'lium . . . . . PORTUGAL M.
densiflo'rum . . . . **V. thapsiforme**

VERBASCUM, continued
flocco'sum . . . . . **V. pulverulentum**
leian'thum . . YELLOWWAND MULLEIN
liba'ni Hort.
longifo'lium . . . . . LONGLEAF M.
—**panno'sum** (*V. pannosum*) GOLDENGATE L.M.
macedo'nicum . . . MACEDONIAN M.
ni'grum (*vernale*) . . . . . BLACK M.
olym'picum . . . . . . OLYMPIC M.
panno'sum . . . . . **V. longifolium p.**
phlomoi'des . . . . . CLASPING M.
phoenic'eum . . . . . . PURPLE M.
plica'tum
pulverulen'tum (*floccosum*) VIOLETSTAMEN M.
∞ **pyramida'le** (*orientale × speciosum*) ∞ PYRAMID M.
sinua'tum . . . MEDITERRANEAN M.
thapsifor'me (*densiflorum*) . WOOL M.
thap'sus |w . . . . . . FLANNEL M.
verna'le . . . . **V. nigrum**
virga'tum . . . . PURPLESTAMEN M.
wiedemannia'num . WIEDEMANN M.
willmot'tiae . . . . . WILLMOTT M.

VERBE'NA |w . . . . VERBENA
alpi'na
angustifo'lia |w . . . NARROWLEAF V.
bipinnatif'ida |w . . . . DAKOTA V.
bonarien'sis
bractea'ta (*bracteosa*) |w . BIGBRACT V.
canaden'sis (*aubletia; montana*) |w ROSE V.
chamaedryfo'lia
cilia'ta
citriodo'ra . . . . **Lippia c.**
erinoi'des . . . . **V. laciniata**
hasta'ta |w . . . . BLUE V.
his'pida
horten'sis Hort. (*hybrida* Hort.) GARDEN V.

A name loosely and erroneously used by gardeners for the Garden Verbena, a group of hybrids derived from several species.

₵COCCINEA. HV.
₵LUMINOSA
₵VIOLACEA
₵VIOLACEA STELLATA

inci'sa
jun'cea . . . . **Baillonia j.**
lacinia'ta (*erinoides*) . . . MOSS V.
monta'na . . . . . . **V. canadensis**

A name often used erroneously for V. bipinnatifida and V. canadensis.

officina'lis . . . . EUROPEAN V.
peruvia'na
phlogiflo'ra
pulchel'la
rig'ida (*venosa*)
—**lilac'ina** (*V. venosa l.*)
stric'ta |w . . . . WOOLLY V.
ten'era
—**maonet'ti** (*V. t. mahoneti*)
teucrioi'des . . . . . . FRAGRANT V.
tri'dens
urticaefo'lia |w . . . . . . WHITE V.
veno'sa . . . . **V. rigida**
—lilac'ina . . . . **V. rigida l.**
wright'i . . . . WRIGHTS V.

VERBENA . . . . **Verbena**
BIGBRACT V. . . . . . . **V. bracteata**
BLUE V. . . . . **V. hastata**
DAKOTA V. . . . . . **V. bipinnatifida**
EUROPEAN V. . . . . . . **V. officinalis**
FRAGRANT V. . . . . . **V. teucrioides**
GARDEN V. . . . . *V. hortensis*

VERBENA, continued
MOSS V. . . . . . **Verbena laciniata**
NARROWLEAF V. . . . **V. angustifolia**
ROSE V. . . . . **V. canadensis**
WHITE V. . . . . . . **V. urticaefolia**
WOOLLY V. . . . . **V. stricta**
WRIGHTS V. . . . . **V. wrighti**

VERBESI'NA (*XIMENESIA*) |w CROWNBEARD
croca'ta . . . . MEXICAN C.
encelioi'des (*Ximenesia e.*) |w GOLDEN C.
—**exauricula'ta** (*Ximenesia exauriculata*) |w
helianthoi'des . . . GRAVELWEED C.
lin'deni . . . . LINDEN C.
occidenta'lis . . . . . . YELLOW C.
virgin'ica |w . . . . WHITE C.

VERNALGRASS . . . . . . **Anthoxanthum**
ANNUAL V. . . . . **A. aristatum**
ITALIAN V. . . . . **A. gracile**
SWEET V. . . . . **A. odoratum**

VERNO'NIA . . . . IRONWEED
altis'sima (*maxima*) . . . . . . TALL I.
anthelmin'tica . . . . . KINKAOIL I.
bald'wini . . . . BALDWIN I.
crini'ta (*arkansana*) . . . . . BUR I.
fal'lax
fascicula'ta . . . . WESTERN I.
inte'rior
margina'ta
max'ima . . . . **V. altissima**
nigritia'na . . . . NIGERIAN I.
noveboracen'sis . . . NEWYORK I.
scorpioi'des

VERON'ICA |w . . . . . . SPEEDWELL
agres'tis . . . . FIELD S.
al'bicans . . . . **Hebe a.**
allio'ni . . . . ALLIONI S.
alpi'na . . . . ALPINE S.
amab'ilis . . . . **Hebe a.**
—blan'da . . . . **Hebe a. b.**
america'na |w . . . . . AMERICAN S.
amethys'tina . . . . **V. spuria**
amplexicau'lis . . . . **Hebe a.**
anagallis-aquat'ica |w . . . WATER S.
anderso'ni . . . . **Hebe a.**
—variega'ta . . . . **Hebe a. v.**
angustifo'lia . . . . **Hebe a.**
anom'ala . . . . **Hebe a.**
arme'na
arm'strongi
argu'ta
arven'sis |w . . . . . . COMMON S.
austri'aca (*prenja*)
bachofe'ni . . . . BACHOFENS S.
baileya'na . . . . **Hebe b.**
balfouria'na . . . . **Hebe b.**
bar'keri . . . . **Hebe b.**
beccabun'ga |w . . BECCABUNGA S.
bellidioi'des (*townsendi*)
bid'willi . . . . **Hebe b.**
bol'lonsi . . . . **Hebe b.**
bonaro'ta
brachysi'phon
buchan'ani . . . . **Hebe b.**
buxifo'lia . . . . **Hebe b.**
caespito'sa
canes'cens
car'nea . . . . **Hebe c.**
carno'sula . . . . **Hebe c.**
car'sei . . . . **Hebe c.**
catarrac'tae . . . . **Hebe c.**
caucas'ica
chamae'drys . . . . . GERMANDER S.

VERONICA, continued
chatham'ica . . . . **Hebe c.**
—erec'ta . . . . **Hebe c. e.**
cine'rea
colenso'i . . . . **Hebe c.**
conna'ta |w
cookia'na . . . . **Hebe c.**
cupressoi'des . . . . **Hebe c.**
cu'sicki . . . . CUSICK SPEEDWELL
darwinia'na . . . . **Hebe d.**
decum'bens . . . . **Hebe d.**
dieffenbach'i . . . . **Hebe d.**
diosmaefo'lia . . . . **Hebe d.**
diver'gens
dorrien-smith'i . . . . **Hebe d.**
ela'tior . . . . **V. latifolia**
el'egans . . . . **V. spuria e.**
ellip'tica . . . . **Hebe e.**
epacrid'ea . . . . **Hebe e.**
eveno'sa . . . . **Hebe e.**
excel'sa . . . . **V. maritima**
filifo'lia
filifor'mis
formo'sa . . . . **Hebe f.**
fruticulo'sa (*fruticans; saxatilis*)
gentianoi'des (*glabra*) . . GENTIAN S.
gibbs'i
gigan'tea . . . . **Hebe g.**
glandif'era |w
glaucophyl'la . . . . **Hebe g.**
gracil'lima . . . . **Hebe g.**
guthriea'na . . . . **Hebe g.**
haas'ti . . . . **Hebe h.**
hec'tori . . . . **Hebe h.**
hederaefo'lia . . . . . . IVYLEAF S.
himalen'sis
hookeria'na (*nivalis*)
hulkea'na . . . . **Hebe h.**
humifu'sa . . . . . . **V. serpyllifolia**
imperia'lis . . . . . . **Hebe speciosa**
inca'na . . . . WOOLLY S.
insula'ris . . . . **Hebe i.**
kirk'i . . . . **Hebe k.**
lae'vis . . . . **Hebe l.**
latifo'lia (*elatior; teucrium*)
HUNGARIAN S.
—prostra'ta (*V. prostrata; V. teucrium p.*) . . . . HAREBELL H.S.
RUPESTRIS. HV. V. latifolia
latisep'ala . . . . **Hebe macrocarpa l.**
lavaudia'na . . . . **Hebe l.**
leiophyl'la . . . . **Hebe l.**
lew'isi . . . . **Hebe l.**
ligustrifo'lia . . . . **Hebe l.**
linifo'lia . . . . **Hebe l.**
loganioi'des . . . . **Hebe l.**
longifo'lia . . . . **V. maritima**
—elegantis'sima . . . **V. maritima e.**
—rose'a . . . . **V. maritima r.**
—subses'silis . . . . . **V. maritima s.**
ly'alli . . . . **Hebe l.**
macran'tha . . . . **Hebe m.**
macrocar'pa . . . . **Hebe m.**
macrou'ra . . . . **Hebe m.**
marit'ima (*excelsa; longifolia*)
—elegantis'sima (*V. longifolia e.*)
—rose'a (*V. longifolia r.*)
—subses'silis (*V. longifolia s.; V. subsessilis*) . . . . CLUMP S.
matthews'i . . . . **Hebe m.**
michaux'i
multif'ida
niv'alis . . . . **V. hookeriana**
nummula'ria
obova'ta . . . . **Hebe o.**
obtusa'ta . . . . **Hebe o.**
officina'lis |w . . . . DRUG S.
ol'seni . . . . **Hebe o.**

VERONICA, continued
orchid'ea
orienta'lis
parviflo'ra . . . . **Hebe p.**
pectina'ta . . . . . COMB SPEEDWELL
—rose'a . . . . ROSY C.S.
peduncula'ris
peregri'na . . . . PURSLANE S.
per'sica . . . . **V. tourneforti**
pimeleoi'des . . . . **Hebe p.**
pinguifo'lia . . . . **Hebe p.**
pinna'ta
poli'ta . . . . WAYSIDE S.
pren'ja . . . . **V. austriaca**
propin'qua . . . . **Hebe p.**
prostra'ta . . . . **V. latifolia p.**
pubes'cens . . . . **Hebe p.**
pu'mila
re'pens . . . . CREEPING S.
rigid'ula . . . . **Hebe r.**
rose'a Hort.
This garden name is sometimes loosely used for Pinkspike, Rosy, and other HV. of Veronica.
rotunda'ta . . . . **Hebe r.**
rupes'tris Hort. . . . . . . **V. latifolia**
HV. RUPESTRIS
rupic'ola . . . . **Hebe r.**
salicifo'lia . . . . **Hebe s.**
—kirk'i . . . . **Hebe k.**
salicornioi'des . . . . **Hebe s.**
saturejoi'des
saxat'ilis . . . . **V. fruticulosa**
scutella'ta |w . . . . MARSH S.
serpyllifo'lia (*humifusa*) |w
THYMELEAF S.
specio'sa . . . . **Hebe s.**
spica'ta . . . . SPIKE S.
—al'ba . . . . WHITE S.S.
—corymbo'sa
—er'ica . . . . HEATH S.S.
—rose'a . . . . PINK S.S.
spu'ria (*amethystina*) . . BASTARD S.
—el'egans (*V. elegans*)
subalpi'na . . . . **Hebe s.**
subses'silis . . . . . . **V. maritima s.**
teu'crium . . . . **V. latifolia**
—prostra'ta . . . . . . **V. latifolia p.**
—rupes'tris Hort. . . . . . **V. latifolia**
HV. RUPESTRIS
tournefort'i (*persica*) . TOURNEFORT S.
town'sendi . . . . . . **V. bellidioides**
town'soni . . . . **Hebe t.**
tra'versi . . . . **Hebe t.**
triphyl'los
vernico'sa . . . . **Hebe v.**
virgin'ica . **Veronicastrum virginicum**
wormskjold'i

VERONICAS'TRUM
virgin'icum (*Leptandra virginica; Veronica v.*) . . . . CULVERSPHYSIC

VERRUCIF'ERA
MESEMBRYANTHEMUM
See **SUCCULENTS.**

VERSCHAFFELT'IA . VERSCHAFFELTIA
See **PALM GENERA.**

VERTICOR'DIA . . . . HEATHMYRTLE
densiflo'ra . . . . FRINGE H.
fontane'si . . . . FONTANES H.

VESICA'RIA
LESQUERELLA; PHYSARIA

VESSELFERN . . . . **Angiopteris**
ORIENTAL V. . . . . **A. erecta**

VETCH . . . . **Vicia**
AMERICAN V. . . . . . **V. americana**
BARD V. . . . . **V. monantha**
BIGHORN V. . . . . . . **V. vexillaris**
BIGPOD V. . . . . . . **V. macrocarpa**
BIRD V. . . . . **V. cracca**
BITLEAF AMERICAN V.
V. americana truncata
BITTER V. . . . . **V. ervilia**
BRAMBLE V. . . . . **V. tenuifolia**
BROADBEAN . . . . **V. faba**
BROADLEAF V. . . . . **V. amoena**
Bush V. . . . . HEDGE V.
CALIFORNIA V. . . . . . **V. californica**
CAROLINA V. . . . . . . **V. caroliniana**
CLUBLEAF V. . . . . **V. trifida**
COMMON V. . . . . **V. sativa**
Cow V.; Crow V. . . . . BIRD V.
FINELEAF V. . . . . . . **V. perangusta**
FLORIDA V. . . . . **V. floridana**
Fodder V. . . . . COMMON V.
FOURLEAF V. . . . . **V. acutifolia**
FOURSEED V. . . . . . . **V. tetrasperma**
French V. . . . . NARBONNE V.
GERARD V. . . . . . . **V. cracca gerardi**
GERMAN V. . . . . **V. dumetorum**
GIANT V. . . . . **V. gigantea**
GRAY V. . . . Hort. form of **V. sativa**
HAIRY V. . . . . **V. villosa**
HEDGE V. . . . . **V. sepium**
HORSEBEAN . . . . **V. faba equina**
HUGER V. . . . . **V. hugeri**
HUNGARIAN V. . . . . . . **V. pannonica**
JAPANESE V. . . . . **V. japonica**
LEAVENWORTH V. . . **V. leavenworthi**
LOUISIANA V. . . . . . **V. ludoviciana**
MAT V. . . . . **V. caespitosa**
MODOC V. . . . . **V. semicincta**
MOGOLLON V. . . . . . . **V. leucophaea**
NARBONNE V. . . . . . . **V. narbonensis**
NARROWLEAF V. . . . . **V. angustifolia**
NOE V. . . . . **V. noeana**
ONEFLOWER V. . . . . . . **V. articulata**
OREGON AMERICAN V.
V. americana oregana
OROBUS V. . . . . **V. oroboides**
PAIR V. . . . . **V. unijuga**
PEARL V. . . Hort. form of **V. sativa**
PEA V. . . . . **V. pisiformis**
Pigeon V. . . . . TINY V.
PURPLE V. . . . . **V. atropurpurea**
PYRENEES V. . . . . **V. pyrenaica**
Russian V. . . . . HAIRY V.
SARDINIA V. . Hort. form of **V. sativa**
SCARLET V. . . . . **V. fulgens**
SHOWY V. . . . . **V. grandiflora**
SLENDER V. . . . . **V. gracilis**
SLIM V. . . . . **V. exigua**
SMALLFLOWER V. . . . . . **V. micrantha**
SMALL HORSEBEAN . . . . **V. faba minor**
SMOOTH V. . . . **V. villosa glabrescens**
Sparrow V. . . . . FOURSEED V.
SPRING V. . . Hort. form of **V. sativa**
STIFFLEAF V. . . . . **V. sparsifolia**
Summer V. . . . . . . NARROWLEAF V.
SWEETCLOVER V. . . . . . **V. pulchella**
Tare V. . . . . TINY V.
TEXAS V. . . . . **V. texana**
TINY V. . . . . **V. hirsuta**
TRELLISLEAF V. . . . . **V. dissitifolia**
WHITE V. . . . . **V. producta**
WILLAMETTE V. Hort. form of **V. sativa**
WINTER V. . . Hort. form of **V. sativa**
The name Winter Vetch is sometimes applied to V. villosa also.
WOOD V. . . . . **V. sylvatica**
WOOLLYPOD V. . . . . . **V. dasycarpa**
YELLOW V. . . . . **V. lutea**

VETIVE'RIA (*ANATHERUM*) VETIVER
See **GRASS GENERA.**
Viapple. AMBARELLA: **Spondias cytherea**
VIBOR'QUIA . . **EYSENHARDTIA**
VIBUR'NUM |w . . . . . VIBURNUM
acerifo'lium |w . . . . MAPLELEAF V.
—glabres'cens . . . . SMOOTH M.V.
—ova'tum
affi'ne . . . . . **V. rafinesquianum a.**
—hypomal'acum . . **V. rafinesquianum**
alnifo'lium (*lantanoides*) |w
HOBBLEBUSH V.
—prae'cox . . . . EARLY H.V.
america'num Auth., *not* Mill.
V. trilobum
betulifo'lium . . . . . BIRCHLEAF V.
bitchiuen'se . . . . YEDDO V.
bractea'tum . . . . . . BRACTED V.
buddleifo'lium . . . . . WOOLLY V.
bureja'eticum . . . MANCHURIAN V.
∞ **burk'woodi** (*carlesi* × *utile*)
∞ BURKWOOD V.
The trade name Breath of Spring has been selected by one dealer for this hybrid.
cal'vum (*schneiderianum*)
BLUEBLACK V.
carle'si . . . . . KOREANSPICE V.
cassinoi'des |w . . . . WITHEROD V.
ceanothoi'des . . . . . **V. foetidum c.**
cinnamomifo'lium . . CINNAMON V.
cordifo'lium . . . . . HEARTLEAF V.
corylifo'lium . . . . . HAZELLEAF V.
cotinifo'lium (*multratum*) SMOKETREE V.
cylin'dricum (*coriaceum*)
TUBEFLOWER V.
dasyan'thum
da'vidi . . . . DAVID V.
davu'ricum . . . . . . **V. mongolicum**
deam'i . . . . . . **V. pubescens d.**
denta'tum |w . . . ARROWWOOD V.
—longifo'lium . . . **V. pubescens l.**
dilata'tum . . . . LINDEN V.
—xanthocar'pum . YELLOWBERRY L.V.
ellip'ticum |w . . . . . OREGON V.
ero'sum . . . . BEECH V.
—taque'ti . . . . . . LOBELEAF B.V.
erubes'cens
—gracil'ipes
foe'tens . . . . . . **V. grandiflorum**
foe'tidum . . . . FETID V.
—ceanothoi'des (*V. ceanothoides*)
—rectangula'tum (*V. rectangulatum*)
RIGHTANGLE F.V.
—variega'tum
fra'grans . . . . . . FRAGRANT V.
furca'tum . . . . FORKED V.
grandiflo'rum (*foetens*)
harrya'num
hen'ryi . . . . HENRY V.
hupehen'se . . . . HUPEH V.
ichangen'se . . . . ICHANG V.
∞ **jack'i** (*lentago* × *prunifolium*)
∞ JACK V.
japon'icum (*macrophyllum*) JAPANESE V.
∞ **judd'i** (*bitchiuense* × *carlesi*) ∞ JUDD V.
kansuen'se . . . . KANSU V.
lanta'na |w . . . WAYFARINGTREE V.
—dis'color . . . . . WHITELEAF W.V.
—rugo'sum (*V. rugosum*)
WRINKLELEAF W.V.
—variega'tum . YELLOWBLOTCH W.V.
lantanoi'des . . . . . **V. alnifolium**
latifo'lium . . . . **V. rigidum**
lenta'go |w . . . . NANNYBERRY V.
—sphaerocar'pum ROUNDFRUIT N.V.
lobophyl'lum

VIBURNUM, continued
luzon'icum . . . . LUZON VIBURNUM
—formosa'num . . . . . FORMOSA V.
macroceph'alum . . . . CHINESE V.
—keteleer'i . . . . . . WILD C.V.
—ster'ile (*V. sterile* Hort. in part)
SNOWBALL C.V.
macrophyl'lum . . . . **V. japonicum**
mol'le |w . . . . . . KENTUCKY V.
This name is sometimes misapplied to V. canbyi and V. venosum.
—leiophyl'lum . . . . SMOOTH K.V.
mongo'licum (*davuricum*)
MONGOLIAN V.
multra'tum . . . . . . **V. cotinifolium**
nepalen'se . . . . . . **V. pubescens**
nu'dum |w . . . . . . POSSUMHAW V.
—angustifo'lium (*V. n. nitidum*)
SHINING P.V.
obova'tum . . . . WALTERS V.
odoratis'simum . . . . . . SWEET V.
o'pulus |w . . . . EUROPEAN CRANBERRYBUSH V. (*European Cranberrybush; Pincushiontree*)
—america'num . . . . . **V. trilobum**
—na'num
—rose'um (*V. sterile* Hort. in part; *V. o. sterile*) . . SNOWBALL EUROPEAN V.
¢COMMON SNOWBALL (*roseum* in part; *sterile* in part; *V. roseum. Guelderrose*). HV. V. opulus
¢DWARF (*nanum*)
¢VARIEGATED (*variegatum; V. variegatum*)
¢YELLOWFRUIT (*xanthocarpum*)
o'pulus Auth., *not* L. . . **V. trilobum**
orienta'le . . . . URAL V.
ovatifo'lium . . . . . . EGGLEAF V.
oxycoc'cus . . . . **V. trilobum**
pauciflo'rum |w . . . MOOSEBERRY V.
phlebot'richum
propin'quum
prunifo'lium (*pyrifolium*) |w
BLACKHAW V.
pubes'cens (*nepalense; venosum*) |w
DOWNY V.
pubes'cens Auth., *not* Pursh.
V. rafinesquianum
—affi'ne . . . . **V. r. affine**
—can'byi (*V. venosum c.*). CANBY D.V.
—deam'i (*V. deami*) . . DEAMS D.V.
—indianen'se . . . . INDIANA D.V.
—longifo'lium (*V. dentatum l.; V. venosum l.*) . . . LONGLEAF D.V.
pyrifo'lium . . . . . **V. prunifolium**
rafinesquia'num (*V. affine hypomalacum; V. pubescens* Auth., *not* Pursh.)
RAFINESQUE V.
—affi'ne (*V. affine; V. pubescens a.*)
rectangula'tum . . . . **V. foetidum r.**
∞ **rhytidocar'pum** (*buddleifolium* × *rhytidophyllum*) . . ∞ BUDPHYLLUM V.
∞ **rhytidophylloi'des** (*lantana* × *rhytidophyllum*) . ∞ LANTANAPHYLLUM V.
rhytidophyl'lum . . LEATHERLEAF V.
—rose'um
rig'idum (*latifolium*)
rufid'ulum . . . RUSTY BLACKHAW V.
rugo'sum . . . . **V. lantana r.**
sandan'kwa . . . . . **V. suspensum**
sar'genti . SARGENT CRANBERRYBUSH V. (*Sargent Cranberrybush*)
—calves'cens
—fla'vum . . . YELLOWFRUIT S.C.V.
scabrel'lum
schensia'num . . . . SHENSI V.
schneideria'num . . . . . **V. calvum**

VIBURNUM, continued
setig'erum (*theiferum*) . TEA VIBURNUM
—auranti'acum (*V. theiferum setigerum*) . . . . . ORANGEBERRY T.V.
sie'boldi . . . . SIEBOLD V.
—reticula'tum
¢VARIEGATED (*variegatum*) HV. V. sieboldi
stellula'tum
ster'ile Hort. . . **V. macrocephalum s.; V. opulus roseum**
suspen'sum (*sandankwa*)
SANDANKWA V.
sympodia'le
theif'erum . . . . **V. setigerum**
—auranti'acum . . . **V. setigerum a.**
—setig'erum **V. setigerum aurantiacum**
ti'nus . . . . LAURESTINUS V.
—hir'tum . . . . FUZZY L.V.
—lu'cidum . . . . . SHINING L.V.
—robus'tum . . . . ROUNDLEAF L.V.
—stric'tum . . . . SPIRY L.V.
—variega'tum . . . VARIEGATED L.V.
FRENCH WHITE. HV. V. tinus
PURPLE (*purpureum*)
PYRAMIDAL (*pyramidale*)
tomento'sum . . . . DOUBLEFILE V.
—lancea'tum . . . . . . LANCE D.V.
—maries'i . . . . MARIES D.V.
—parvifo'lium . . . . . LITTLE D.V.
—rotundifo'lium . . ROUNDLEAF D.V.
—ster'ile (*V. t. plenum; V. t. plicatum*)
JAPANESE SNOWBALL V.
trilo'bum (*americanum* Auth., *not* Mill.; *opulus* Auth., *not* L.; *V. o. americanum; oxycoccus*) . AMERICAN CRANBERRYBUSH V. (*American Cranberrybush; Squawbush*)
urceola'tum . . . . VASEFLOWER V.
u'tile . . . . SERVICE V.
variega'tum . . . . **V. opulus v.**
veitch'i . . . . VEITCH V.
veno'sum . . . . . . **V. pubescens**
—can'byi . . . . . . **V. pubescens c.**
—longifo'lium . . . **V. pubescens l.**
∞ **vet'teri** (*lentago* × *nudum*). ∞ VETTER V.
wil'soni . . . . WILSON V.
wright'i . . . . WRIGHT V.
—hes'sei . . . . SMALL W.V.
VIBURNUM . . . . **Viburnum**
AMERICAN CRANBERRYBUSH V.
V. trilobum
ARROWWOOD V. . . . . . **V. dentatum**
BEECH V. . . . . **V. erosum**
BIRCHLEAF V. . . . . . **V. betulifolium**
BLACKHAW V. . . . . . **V. prunifolium**
BLUEBLACK V. . . . . **V. calvum**
BRACTED V. . . . . . . **V. bracteatum**
∞ BUDPHYLLUM V. . ∞ **V. rhytidocarpum**
∞ BURKWOOD V. . . . . ∞ **V. burkwoodi**
CANBY DOWNY V. **V. pubescens canbyi**
CHINESE V. . . . **V. macrocephalum**
CINNAMON V. . . **V. cinnamomifolium**
DAVID V. . . . . **V. davidi**
DEAMS DOWNY V. **V. pubescens deami**
DOUBLEFILE V. . . . . **V. tomentosum**
DOWNY V. . . . . **V. pubescens**
EARLY HOBBLEBUSH V.
V. alnifolium praecox
EGGLEAF V. . . . . . . **V. ovatifolium**
EUROPEAN CRANBERRYBUSH V.
V. opulus
FETID V. . . . . **V. foetidum**
FORKED V. . . . . **V. furcatum**
FORMOSA V.. **V. luzonicum formosanum**
FRAGRANT V.. . . . . . . **V. fragrans**
FUZZY LAURESTINUS V. **V. tinus hirtum**

Viburnum, continued

Hazelleaf V. . **Viburnum corylifolium**
Heartleaf V. . . . . **V. cordifolium**
Henry V. . . . . **V. henryi**
Hobblebush V. . . . **V. alnifolium**
Hupeh V. . . . . . . **V. hupehense**
Ichang V. . . . . . . **V. ichangense**
Indiana Downy V.
V. pubescens indianense
∞Jack V. . . . . ∞**V. jacki**
Japanese Snowball V.
V. tomentosum sterile
Japanese V. . . . . . **V. japonicum**
∞Judd V. . . . . ∞**V. juddi**
Kansu V. . . . . . . **V. kansuense**
Kentucky V. . . . . **V. molle**
Koreanspice V. . . . . . **V. carlesi**
Lance Doublefile V.
V. tomentosum lanceatum
∞Lantanaphyllum V.
∞**V. rhytidophylloides**
Laurestinus V. . . . . **V. tinus**
Leatherleaf V. . **V. rhytidophyllum**
Linden V. . . . . **V. dilatatum**
Little Doublefile V.
V. tomentosum parvifolium
Lobeleaf Beech V. **V. erosum taqueti**
Longleaf Downy V.
V. pubescens longifolium
Luzon V. . . . . **V. luzonicum**
Manchurian V. . . **V. burejaeticum**
Mapleleaf V. . . . . **V. acerifolium**
Maries Doublefile V.
V. tomentosum mariesi
Mongolian V. . . . . **V. mongolicum**
Mooseberry V. . . . **V. pauciflorum**
Nannyberry V. . . . . . . **V. lentago**
Orangeberry Tea V.
V. setigerum aurantiacum
Oregon V. . . . . . . **V. ellipticum**
Possumhaw V. . . . . . . **V. nudum**
Rafinesque V. . . **V. rafinesquianum**
Rightangle Fetid V.
V. foetidum rectangulatum
Roundfruit Nannyberry V.
V. lentago sphaerocarpum
Roundleaf Doublefile V.
V. tomentosum rotundifolium
Roundleaf Laurestinus V.
V. tinus robustum
Rusty Blackhaw V. . . **V. rufidulum**
Sandankwa V. . . . . **V. suspensum**
Sargent Cranberrybush V. **V. sargenti**
Service V. . . . . **V. utile**
Shensi V. . . . . . . **V. schensianum**
Shining Laurestinus V.
V. tinus lucidum
Shining Possumhaw V.
V. nudum angustifolium
Siebold V. . . . . **V. sieboldi**
Small Wright V. . **V. wrighti hessei**
Smoketree V. . . . . **V. cotinifolium**
Smooth Kentucky V.
V. molle leiophyllum
Smooth Mapleleaf V.
V. acerifolium glabrescens
Snowball Chinese V.
V. macrocephalum sterile
Snowball European V.
V. opulus roseum
Spiry Laurestinus V.
V. tinus strictum
Sweet V. . . . . **V. odoratissimum**
Tea V. . . . . **V. setigerum**
Tubeflower V. . . . **V. cylindricum**
Ural V. . . . . **V. orientale**
Variegated Laurestinus V.
V. tinus variegatum

Viburnum, continued

Vaseflower V. **Viburnum urceolatum**
Veitch V. . . . . **V. veitchi**
∞Vetter V. . . . . ∞**V. vetteri**
Walters V. . . . . . . **V. obovatum**
Wayfaringtree V. . . . . **V. lantana**
Whiteleaf W. V. . . . **V. l. discolor**
Wild Chinese V.
V. macrocephalum keteleeri
Wilson V. . . . . **V. wilsoni**
Witherod V. . . . . . **V. cassinoides**
Woolly V. . . . . **V. buddleifolium**
Wright V. . . . . **V. wrighti**
Wrinkleleaf Wayfaringtree V.
V. lantana rugosum
Yeddo V. . . . . **V. bitchiuense**
Yellowberry Linden V.
V. dilatatum xanthocarpum
Yellowblotch Wayfaringtree V.
V. lantana variegatum
Yellowfruit Sargent Cranberrybush V. . . . . **V. sargenti flavum**

VIC'IA (*OROBUS* in part) |w . . Vetch

Vetches form one of the most important genera of Legumes and are of interest to the horticulturist, farmer, stockman, wildlife specialist, and the general public. About 150 species of Vetch have been described, chiefly from the northern hemisphere and from southern and western South America. All of them are valuable soil-cover, particularly because of their ability to add nitrogen to the soil, and many of them are used as cover crops. Few, if any, plants are more palatable to domestic livestock. Deer, beaver, doves, quail and many other forms of wildlife seek out the nourishing foliage, pods, and seeds of these plants. A number of the Old World species are commonly cultivated for forage; a few are used as ornamentals; some are grown for human consumption because of their edible seeds. There are about 22 species of Vetch native to the United States and about 4 others are naturalized; many of these are, at least locally, important forage plants. The list below contains the names of over 50 species and varieties and of 5 horticultural varieties of Vetch. It is based on a list of 36 species prepared in 1930 by the late Frederick V. Coville, to whose genius much of the credit for the first edition of Standardized Plant Names is clearly due. To this list have been added the names of native western range Vetches and of Old World species which have recently come into prominence. The Editorial Committee wishes to express its gratitude to the large number of people who have been kind enough to review this list and offer constructive criticism. Especial thanks are due Roland McKee, senior agronomist of the Division of Forage Crops and Diseases, Bureau of Plant Industry, U. S. Department of Agriculture; and H. A. Schoth, agronomist, Division of Forage Crops and Diseases, Bureau of Plant Industry, U. S. Department of Agriculture, both widely known as authorities on the agronomy of Legumes and joint-authors of "Vetch Culture and Uses" (U. S. Dept. Agr. Farmers' Bull. 1740. 1934); also to Atlee L. Hafenrichter and Paul Tabor of the Soil Conservation Service, and to F. J. Hermann, of the Division of Plant Exploration and Introduction, Bureau of Plant Industry.

acutifo'lia . . . . . . Fourleaf V.
america'na . . . . . American V.
—*linea'ris* . . . . . . **V. sparsifolia**
—**orega'na** (*V. oregana*) Oregon A.V.
—**trunca'ta** (*V. truncata*) Bitleaf A.V.
amoe'na . . . . Broadleaf V.

Vicia, continued

angustifo'lia |w . Narrowleaf Vetch (*Summer V.*)
articula'ta (*monanthos* (L.) Desf. (1800), *not* Ucria (1796) *nor* Viv. (1824) *nor* **V. monantha** Retz. (1783)) Oneflower V.
atropurpu'rea . . . . . . Purple V.
caespito'sa . . . . Mat V.
calcara'ta . . . . **V. monantha**
califor'nica . . . . . California V.
carolinia'na |w . . . . . Carolina V.
—*texa'na* . . . . **V. texana**
crac'ca . Bird V. (*Cow V.; Crow V.*)
—**gerard'i** (*V. gerardi*) . . Gerard V.
dasycar'pa . . . . . . Woollypod V.
dissitifo'lia . . . . Trellisleaf V.
dumeto'rum . . . . German V.
ervi'lia . . . . Bitter V.
exig'ua |w . . . . Slim V.
fa'ba . . . . Broadbean
—**equi'na** . . . . Horsebean
—**mi'nor** . . . . Small H.
florida'na . . . . Florida V.
ful'gens . . . . Scarlet V.
gerard'i . . . . **V. cracca g.**
gigan'tea . . . . Giant V.
grac'ilis . . . . Slender V.
grandiflo'ra . . . . Showy V.
hirsu'ta |w . . . . Tiny V. (*Pigeon V.; Tare V.*)
hu'geri . . . . Huger V.
japon'ica . . . . Japanese V.
leavenworth'i . . Leavenworth V.
leucophae'a . . . . . Mogollon V.
linea'ris . . . . **V. sparsifolia**
ludovicia'na . . . . . Louisiana V.
lute'a . . . . Yellow V.
macrocar'pa . . . . Bigpod V.
melilotoi'des . . . . . . **V. pulchella**
micran'tha . . . . . Smallflower V.
monan'tha (*calcarata*) . . . Bard V.
monan'thos (L.) Desf. (1800), *not* Ucria (1796) *nor* Viv. (1824) *nor* **V. monantha** Retz. (1783) . **V. articulata**
narbonen'sis . . . . . Narbonne V. (*French V.*)
noea'na . . . . Noe V.
orega'na . . . . . . **V. americana o.**
oroboi'des (*Orobus lathyroides*) Orobus V.
panno'nica (*purpurascens*) Hungarian V.
perangus'ta . . . . . . Fineleaf V.
pisiform'is . . . . Pea V.
produc'ta . . . . White V.
pulchel'la (*melilotoides*) Sweetclover V.
purpuras'cens . . . . **V. pannonica**
pyrena'ica . . . . . . Pyrenees V.
sati'va |w . . Common V. (*Fodder V.*)
Gray. hv. — Spring
Pearl — Willamette
Sardinia — Winter
semicinc'ta . . . . Modoc V.
se'pium . . . . Hedge V. (*Bush V.*)
sparsifo'lia (*V. americana linearis; linearis*) . . . . Stiffleaf V.
sylvat'ica . . . . Wood V.
tenuifo'lia . . . . Bramble V.
tetrasper'ma Fourseed V. (*Sparrow V.*)
texa'na (*V. caroliniana t.*) . Texas V.
trif'ida . . . . Clubleaf V.
trunca'ta . . . . . . **V. americana t.**
uniju'ga . . . . Pair V.
vexilla'ris . . . . Bighorn V.
villo'sa . . . Hairy V. (*Russian V.*)
—**glabres'cens** . . . . . Smooth V.

VICTO'RIA . . . . . WATERPLATTER
See **WATERLILY GENERA.**

VIG'NA |w . . . . COWPEA
cat'jang . . . . CATJANG C.
mari'na (*lutea*) . . . . . SEASHORE C.
pilo'sa . . . . HAIRY C.
sesquipeda'lis (*Dolichos s.*)
YARDLONG C.
sinen'sis |w . . . . . . COMMON C.

VIGUIE'RA (*GYMNOLOMIA*) |w
GOLDENEYE
an'nua (*Gymnolomia a.*) . ANNUAL G.
brev'ipes
cilia'ta . . . . HAIRY G.
cordifo'lia . . . . . . HEARTLEAF G.
deltoi'dea
—par'ishi (*V. parishi*) . . PARISH G.
denta'ta (*texana*)
—helianthoi'des (*V. helianthoides*)
lacinia'ta . . . . CUTLEAF G.
longifo'lia . . . . . . LONGLEAF G.
multiflo'ra (*Gymnolomia m.*) SHOWY G.
—nevaden'sis (*Gymnolomia linearis; G. nevadensis*) . . . . . NEVADA S.G.
ova'lis . . . . OVALLEAF G.
par'ishi . . . . **V. deltoidea p.**
por'teri . . . . PORTER G.
reticula'ta . . . . . DEATHVALLEY G.
stenolo'ba . . . . SKELETONLEAF G.
tenuifo'lia . . . . SLIMLEAF G.
texa'na . . . . **V. dentata**

VILLA'DIA (*ALTAMIRANOA*)
VILLADIA
See **SUCCULENTS.**

Villano'va dissec'ta . . . . . **Bahia d.**

VILLARE'SIA
mucrona'ta

VIMINA'RIA
denuda'ta

VIN'CA . . . . PERIWINKLE
herba'cea . . . . . . HERBACEOUS P.
ma'jor . . . . BIGLEAF P.
—elegantis'sima . . WHITESPOT B.P.
—variega'ta . . . . . MOTTLED B.P.
mi'nor . . . . COMMON P.
¢AZURE (*azurea*) HV.
¢BOWLES
¢BUTTERFLY
¢GENTIAN (*caerulea*)
¢PURPLE (*atropurpurea; purpurea*)
¢PURPLE DOUBLE (*multiplex; purpurea plena*)
¢SILVERLEAF
¢WHITE (*alba*)
¢WHITEBLOTCH (*argenteo-variegata*)
¢YELLOWBLOTCH (*aurea; aureo-variegata*)
rose'a . . . . **Lochnera r.**

VINCETOX'ICUM . . . . . MILKVINE
acumina'tum
Cynanchum acuminatifolium
gonocar'pos (*Gonolobus macrophyllus*)
ANGLEPOD M.
hirsu'tum . . . . HAIRY M.
japon'icum
Cynanchum acuminatifolium
ni'grum . . . . **Cynanchum n.**
officina'le . **Cynanchum vincetoxicum**
subero'sum . . . . . . CORKPOD M.

VINECLETHRA . . . . **Clematoclethra**
VINELILAC . . . . **Hardenbergia**
COMPTON V. . . . . **H. comptoniana**
SINGLELEAF V. . . . . **H. monophylla**
WHITE COMPTON V.
H. comptoniana alba
VINELIME . . . . **Paramignya**
ONELEAF V. . . . . . . **P. monophylla**
PHILIPPINE V. . . **P. longipedunculata**
VINE-MESQUITE . . **Panicum obtusum**
VINESPINACH . . . . **Basella**
RED V. . . . . **B. rubra**
WHITE V. . . . . **B. alba**

VIO'LA |w . . . . VIOLET
The Editorial Committee acknowledges with thanks and appreciation, valuable help and constructive criticism in the preparation of the Viola list from Maxim Ethan Armbruster, Pittsburgh, Pa.

adun'ca (*drepanophora; monticola* Rydb., *not* Jord.; *oxysepala; subvestita*) . . . . HOOK V.
aeto'lica . . . . AETOLIAN V.
affi'nis . . . . LECONTE V.
alpi'na . . . . ALPINE V.
alta'ica . . . . ALTAI V.
arena'ria . . . . SAND V.
ROSEA. HV.
arizo'nica . . . . . . **V. nephrophylla**
arven'sis . . . . FIELD V.
atriplicifo'lia . . . **V. purpurea venosa**
au'rea . . . . **V. purpurea**
—veno'sa . . . . . . **V. purpurea v.**
beck'withi . . . . . . BECKWITH V.
bellidifo'lia (*demissa*) . DAISYLEAF V.
biflo'ra . . . . TWINFLOWER V.
blan'da (*leconteana*) . SWEET WHITE V.
—maclos'keyi . . . . **V. macloskeyi**
bosnia'ca . . . . **V. elegantula**
brittonia'na . . . . BRITTON V.
calcara'ta . . SWISS V. (*Spurred V.*)
califor'nica Hort. . . . . . **V. odorata**
Unfortunately, V. odorata on the Pacific Coast is frequently miscalled V. californica.
canaden'sis (*geminiflora; muriculata; neo-mexicana*) . . . . CANADA V.
—rydberg'i . . . . **V. rugulosa**
cani'na . . . . DOG V.
caroli'na . . . . **V. villosa**
cenis'ia . . . . MONTCENIS V.
chalcosper'ma . . . JACKSONVILLE V.
chrysan'tha Hook., *not* Schrad.
V. douglasi
cogna'ta . . . . . . **V. nephrophylla**
consper'sa (*muhlenbergi*)
AMERICAN DOG V.
cornu'ta . . . . HORNED V.
Discarded names are Bedding Pansy, Bedding V., Pyrenees V., Spanish V., and Tufted Pansy.
ADMIRATION (*admirabilis; V. cornuta a.*). HV. V. cornuta
Possibly a hybrid.
ALBA
ARKWRIGHT RUBY
ATROPURPUREA
AUREA
BLUE PERFECTION
BUTTERFLY (*papilio*)
GRANDIFLORA
G. WERMIG

VIOLA cornuta, continued
HANSA
JERSEY GEM
MAUVE QUEEN
PURPLE (*purpurea*)
PURPLE QUEEN
SUTTONS PALE PINK
SUTTONS PALE YELLOW
WHITE PERFECTION
YELLOW GOLD (*lutea*)
cuculla'ta . . . . . BOGBICE VIOLET
cunea'ta . . . . WEDGELEAF V.
delphinifo'lia . . . . **V. pedatifida**
demis'sa . . . . **V. bellidifolia**
doug'lasi (*chrysantha* Hook., *not* Schrad.)
DOUGLAS V.
drepanoph'ora . . . . **V. adunca**
egglesto'ni . . . . . . EGGLESTON V.
ela'tior . . . . TALL V.
elegan'tula (*bosniaca*) . . . BOSNIAN V.
emargina'ta . . . TRIANGLELEAF V.
erectifo'lia . . **V. nuttalli linguaefolia**
eriocar'pa . . . . WOOLPOD V.
Hardly more than a smooth, leafy form of V. pubescens.
esculen'ta . . . . SALAD V.
fimbria'tula . . . . FRINGED V.
flavovi'rens . . . YELLOWGREEN V.
flett'i . . . . FLETT V.
×**florarien'sis** (*cornuta* × *V. tricolor* HV. ROTHOMAGENSIS) . . YELLOWLIP V.
florida'na . . . . FLORIDA V.
geminiflo'ra . . . . . . **V. canadensis**
glabel'la . . . . PIONEER V.
grac'ilis . . . . GREEK V.
—al'ba . . . . WHITE G.V.
—lute'a . . . . YELLOW G.V.
LORD NELSON. HV. V. graeilis
TIM CARWAY
hall'i . . . . OREGON V.
hasta'ta . . HALBERDLEAF YELLOW V.
hedera'cea (*Erpetion reniforme*)
AUSTRALIAN V.
hirsu'tula . . . . . . APPALACHIAN V.
hir'ta . . . . HAIRY V.
how'elli . . . . HOWELL V.
incog'nita . . . . BIGLEAF WHITE V.
kitaibelia'na . . . . IBERIAN V.
—rafines'qui (*V. rafinesqui*)
JOHNNYJUMPUP
labrador'ica . . . . . . LABRADOR V.
lanceola'ta . . . . . . LANCELEAF V.
langlois'i . . . . BAYOU V.
langsdorf'i . . . . ALEUTIAN V.
latius'cula . . . . . BEECHWOODS V.
lecontea'na . . . . **V. blanda**
linearifo'lia **Hybanthus linearifolius**
linguaefo'lia . . . . . . **V. nuttalli l.**
loba'ta . . . . MOOSEHORN V.
—integrifo'lia . . . . . UNCUT M.V.
lovellia'na . . . . LOVELL V.
lute'a . . . . EUROPEAN YELLOW V.
SPLENDENS. HV.
maclos'keyi (*V. blanda m.; parnassifolia*) . . . . MACLOSKEY V.
mirab'ilis . . . . WONDER V.
missourien'sis . . . . . MISSOURI V.
montanen'sis (*odontophora*)
Perhaps only a form of V. adunca.
montic'ola Rydb., *not* Jord. . **V. adunca**
muhlenberg'i . . . . . . **V. conspersa**
munbya'na . . . . . ALGERIAN V.

Hort. var.; HV. = horticultural variety (or varieties); sp. = species (singular); spp. = species (plural).
¢ = clon; × (as a prefix) = hybrid; × (between scientific plant names) = crossed by; ∞ = polybrid; |w = plant useful to wildlife.
See Glossary for definitions of clon, hybrid, and polybrid.

VIOLA, continued
muricula'ta; neo-mexica'na . . . **V. canadensis**
nephrophyl'la (*arizonica; cognata*) . . . Wanderer Violet
novae-an'gliae . . . NewEngland V.
nummularifo'lia . . . . Liraleaf V.
nutt'alli (*vallicola*) . . . . Nuttall V.
—**linguaefo'lia** (*V. erectifolia; V. linguaefolia; V. praemorsa l.*) . . . Tongueleaf V.
—*praemor'sa* . . . . . **V. praemorsa**
—*veno'sa* . . . . . . **V. purpurea v.**
occidenta'lis (*V. primulifolia o.*) . . . Siskiyou V.
ocella'ta . . . . Pinto V.
odontoph'ora . . . . **V. montanensis**
odora'ta (*californica* Hort.) . Sweet V.
See note under V. californica.
—**al'ba** . . . . White S.V.
—**sulfu'rea** . . . . . . Sulfur S.V.
Alba. hv. V. odorata
Czar
Double Russian
Marie Louise
Princess of Wales
Rosina
Russian
Semperflorens
Swanley White
White
orbicula'ta . . . . . . Darkwoods V.
oxysep'ala . . . . **V. adunca**
pal'lens . . . . Pallid V.
palma'ta . . . . Palmate V.
palus'tris . . . . Marsh V.
papil'io . . **V. cornuta** hv. Butterfly
papiliona'cea . . . . Butterfly V.
—**pricea'na** (*V. priceana*) . Price V.
A form of this variety, known as Confederate Violet (V. confederata), but apparently without botanical standing, is often grown in the South as an emblem of the Confederacy. It has silvery white, blue-centered flowers. Typical V. p. priceana has pale lilac petals, violet-veined, and purplish near the base.
parnassifo'lia . . . . **V. macloskeyi**
peda'ta . . . . Birdsfoot V.
The typical bicolored form of this species, with the two upper petals dark violet, is sometimes erroneously called V. pedata bicolor.
—**al'ba** . . . . White B.V.
—**linearilo'ba** . . . . Lilac B.V.
Grandiflora. hv. V. pedata
pedatif'ida (*delphinifolia*). Prairie V.
peduncula'ta . . . . . California V.
pineto'rum . . . . . . **V. purpurea p.**
pinna'ta . . . . Feather V.
praemor'sa (*V. nuttalli p.*) Canary V.
—*linguaefo'lia* . . . . . **V. nuttalli l.**
—*veno'sa* . . . . . . **V. purpurea v.**
pricea'na . . . . **V. papilionacea p.**
primulifo'lia . . . . . Primrose V.
—*occidenta'lis* . . . . **V. occidentalis**
prin'glei . . . . **V. reptans**
puber'ula How., *not* Lange . . . **V. retroscabra**
pubes'cens . . . . Downy V.
purpu'rea (*aurea*) . . . Goosefoot V.
—**pineto'rum** (*V. pinetorum*) . . . Piney G.V.
—**veno'sa** (*V. atriplicifolia; V. aurea v.; V. nuttalli v.; V. praemorsa v.; V. venosa*) . . . . . . Veiny G.V.
afines'qui . . . . . **V. kitaibeliana r.**
enifo'lia . . . . . Kidneyleaf V.

VIOLA, continued
rep'tans (*pringlei*) . Creeping Violet
retroscab'ra (*puberula* How., *not* Lange)
Perhaps only a form of V. adunca.
retu'sa . . . . Kansas V.
rivinia'na . . . . Rivini V.
rosa'cea . . . . Biloxi V.
rostra'ta . . . . Longspur V.
rotundifo'lia . . . . . Roundleaf V.
rugulo'sa (*V. canadensis rydbergi; rydbergi*) . . . . . . Cheyenne V.
sagitta'ta . . . . Arrowleaf V.
sarmento'sa Dougl., *not* Bieb. . . . **V. sempervirens**
scopulo'rum . . . . . . Colorado V.
selkirk'i . . . . Wilderness V.
sempervi'rens (*sarmentosa* Dougl., *not* Bieb.) . . . . Redwoods V.
septemlo'ba . . . . . Sevenlobe V.
septentriona'lis . . . . . Ontario V.
shel'toni . . . . Shelton V.
sie'boldi . . . . Siebold V.
sieboldia'na Hort.
Mr. Armbruster informs the Editorial Committee that the silvery-leaved material introduced into this country from Japan under the above name appears to be V. dissecta chaerophylloides, form sieboldiana.
silvat'ica . . . . **V. sylvestris**
soror'ia . . . . Sister V.
stonea'na . . . . Stones V.
stria'ta . . . . Striped V.
subvesti'ta . . . . **V. adunca**
sylves'tris (*silvatica*) . . . Sylvan V.
—**rose'a** . . . . Rosy S.V.
tidestrom'i . . . . . . Tidestrom V.
Perhaps only a form of V. adunca.
tri'color . . . . Wild Pansy
The wild stock, from which the cultivated Garden Pansy (var. hortensis) has been derived.
—**horten'sis** . . . . . . Garden P.
Black Imp (*nigra; Bowles Black*). hv.
Rothomagensis
trilo'ba . . . . Trilobe V.
—**dilata'ta**
trinerva'ta . . . . Rainier V.
triparti'ta . . . . . . Threeleaf V.
vallic'ola . . . . **V. nuttalli**
veno'sa . . . . **V. purpurea v.**
via'rum . . . . Ozark V.
villo'sa (*carolina*) . . . . Carolina V.
vitta'ta . . . . Gulf V.
wal'teri . . . . Walter V.

Violet . . . . Viola
For hort. var. of Violet see **VIOLA.**
Aetolian V. . . . . **V. aetolica**
Aleutian V. . . . . . . **V. langsdorfi**
Algerian V. . . . . . . **V. munbyana**
Alpine V. . . . . **V. alpina**
Altai V. . . . . **V. altaica**
American Dog V. . . . . **V. conspersa**
Appalachian V. . . . . . **V. hirsutula**
Arrowleaf V. . . . . . . **V. sagittata**
Australian V. . . . . . **V. hederacea**
Bayou V. . . . . **V. langloisi**
Beckwith V. . . . . . . **V. beckwithi**
Beechwoods V. . . . . . **V. latiuscula**
Bigleaf White V. . . . . **V. incognita**
Biloxi V. . . . . **V. rosacea**
Birdsfoot V. . . . . **V. pedata**
Bogbice V. . . . . **V. cucullata**
Bosnian V. . . . . **V. elegantula**
Britton V. . . . . **V. brittoniana**
Butterfly V. . . . . . **V. papilionacea**
California V. . . . . **V. pedunculata**

Violet, continued
Canada V. . . . . . . Viola **canadensis**
Canary V. . . . . **V. praemorsa**
Carolina V. . . . . **V. villosa**
Cheyenne V. . . . . **V. rugulosa**
Colorado V. . . . . . . **V. scopulorum**
Confederate V. . . . **V. papilionacea priceana form**
See note under V. papilionacea priceana.
Creeping V. . . . . **V. reptans**
Daisyleaf V. . . . . . . **V. bellidifolia**
Darkwoods V. . . . . . . **V. orbiculata**
Dog V. . . . . **V. canina**
Douglas V. . . . . **V. douglasi**
Downy V. . . . . **V. pubescens**
Eggleston V. . . . . . . **V. egglestoni**
European Yellow V. . . . . **V. lutea**
Feather V. . . . . **V. pinnata**
Field V. . . . . **V. arvensis**
Flett V. . . . . **V. fletti**
Florida V. . . . . **V. floridana**
Fringed V. . . . . **V. fimbriatula**
Garden Pansy . **V. tricolor hortensis**
Goosefoot V. . . . . **V. purpurea**
Greek V. . . . . **V. gracilis**
Gulf V. . . . . **V. vittata**
Hairy V. . . . . **V. hirta**
Halberdleaf Yellow V. . **V. hastata**
Hook V. . . . . **V. adunca**
Horned V. . . . . **V. cornuta**
Howell V. . . . . **V. howelli**
Iberian V. . . . . **V. kitaibeliana**
Jacksonville V. . . . **V. chalcosperma**
Johnnyjumpup . . . **V. kitaibeliana rafinesqui**
Kansas V. . . . . **V. retusa**
Kidneyleaf V. . . . . **V. renifolia**
Labrador V. . . . . . . **V. labradorica**
Lanceleaf V. . . . . **V. lanceolata**
LeConte V. . . . . **V. affinis**
Lilac Birdsfoot V. . . . **V. pedata lineariloba**
Liraleaf V. . . . **V. nummularifolia**
Longspur V. . . . . **V. rostrata**
Lovell V. . . . . **V. lovelliana**
Macloskey V. . . . . . . **V. macloskeyi**
Marsh V. . . . . **V. palustris**
Missouri V. . . . . . **V. missouriensis**
Montcenis V. . . . . **V. cenisia**
Moosehorn V. . . . . **V. lobata**
NewEngland V. . . **V. novae-angliae**
Nuttall V. . . . . **V. nuttalli**
Ontario V. . . . . . **V. septentrionalis**
Oregon V. . . . . **V. halli**
Ozark V. . . . . **V. viarum**
Pallid V. . . . . **V. pallens**
Palmate V. . . . . **V. palmata**
Piney Goosefoot V. . . . **V. purpurea pinetorum**
Pinto V. . . . . **V. ocellata**
Pioneer V. . . . . **V. glabella**
Prairie V. . . . . **V. pedatifida**
Price V. . . **V. papilionacea priceana**
Primrose V. . . . . **V. primulifolia**
Rainier V. . . . . **V. trinervata**
Redwoods V. . . . . . . **V. sempervirens**
Rivini V. . . . . **V. riviniana**
Rosy Sylvan V. . . **V. sylvestris rosea**
Roundleaf V. . . . . . . **V. rotundifolia**
Salad V. . . . . **V. esculenta**
Sand V. . . . . **V. arenaria**
Sevenlobe V. . . . . **V. septemloba**
Shelton V. . . . . **V. sheltoni**
Siebold V. . . . . **V. sieboldi**
Siskiyou V. . . . . **V. occidentalis**
Sister V. . . . . **V. sororia**
Spurred V. . . . . Swiss V.

VIOLET, continued
STONES V. . . . . Viola stoneana
STRIPED V. . . . . V. striata
SULFUR SWEET V. V. odorata sulfurea
SWEET V. . . . . V. odorata
SWEET WHITE V. . . . . . V. blanda
SWISS V. . . . . V. calcarata
SYLVAN V. . . . . V. sylvestris
TALL V. . . . . V. elatior
THREELEAF V. . . . . . V. tripartita
TIDESTROM V. . . . . V. tidestromi
TONGUELEAF V. V. nuttalli linguaefolia
TRIANGLELEAF V. . . . V. emarginata
TRILOBE V. . . . . V. triloba
TWINFLOWER V. . . . . . . V. biflora
UNCUT MOOSEHORN V. V. lobata integrifolia
VEINY GOOSEFOOT V. V. purpurea venosa
WALTER V. . . . . V. walteri
WANDERER V. . . . . V. nephrophylla
WEDGELEAF V. . . . . . . V. cuneata
WHITE BIRDSFOOT V. . V. pedata alba
WHITE GREEK V. . . . . V. gracilis a.
WHITE SWEET V. . . . . V. odorata a.
WILDERNESS V. . . . . . . V. selkirki
WILD PANSY . . . . V. tricolor
WONDER V. . . . . V. mirabilis
WOOLPOD V. . . . . V. eriocarpa
YELLOW GREEK V. . V. gracilis lutea
YELLOWGREEN V. . . V. flavovirens
YELLOWLIP V. . . . ×V. florariensis

VIOLETBUSH . . . . Iochroma
COLOMBIAN V. . . . . . I. tubulosum
ORANGE V. . . . . . . I. fuchsioides
PURPLE TOBACCO V. . ×I. purpureum
PURPLE V. . . . . . . I. lanceolatum
SCARLET V. . . . . . . I. coccineum

VIOR'NA . . . . CLEMATIS

VIPERSBUGLOSS . . . . Echium
COMMON V. . . . . E. vulgare
CRETAN V. . . . . E. creticum
HONEYBELL V. . . . . . E. wildpretti
MADEIRA V. . . . . . . E. candicans
PININANA V. . . . . . . E. pininana
PRIDE-OF-MADEIRA . . E. fastuosum
TENERIFFE V. . . . . E. giganteum
TOWER-OF-JEWELS . . . . E. roseum

VIPERTAIL . . . . Urechites
DOMINICAN V. . . . . U. suberecta
FLATWOODS V. . . . . U. pinetorum
HAMMOCK V. . . . . U. lutea

VIRARU . . . . Ruprechtia
BULLSBLOOD V. . . . . . . R. deami

VIRGIL'IA . . . . VIRGILIA
capen'sis . . . . LILAC V.
lute'a . . . . Cladrastis l.

VIRGINSBOWER . . . Clematis virginiana
CALIFORNIA V. C. ligusticifolia californica
MISSOURI V. C. virginiana missouriensis
WESTERN V. . . . . . C. ligusticifolia

VIRO'LA . . . . VIROLA
merendo'nis . . . . MERENDON V.
panamen'sis . . . . . . PANAMA V.

VISCA'RIA . . . . LYCHNIS

VIS'CUM
al'bum . . . EUROPEAN MISTLETOE

VI'TEX . . . . CHASTETREE
agnuscas'tus . . . . . . LILAC C.
—al'ba (*V. albiflora* Hort.). WHITE C.
—latifo'lia (*V. macrophylla* Hort.) HARDY L.C.

VITEX, continued
divarica'ta . . . GUIANA CHASTETREE
littora'lis (*timoriensis*) . . . TIMOR C.
lu'cens (*littoralis* A. Cunn., *not* Decaisne) . NEWZEALAND C. (*Puriri*)
negun'do . . . . NEGUNDO C.
—inci'sa . . . . CUTLEAF C.
parviflo'ra . . . . MOLAVE C.
quina'ta . . . . FIVELEAF C.
rotundifo'lia (*ovata; V. trifolia simplicifolia*) . . . SIMPLELEAF SHRUB C.
timorien'sis . . . . . . V. littoralis

VI'TIS . . . . GRAPE
ac'ida . . . . Cissus a.
aconitifo'lia . . . . . Ampelopsis a.
aestiva'lis . . . . . . SUMMER G.
—bourquinia'na (*V. bourquiniana*) BOURQUIN G.
amuren'sis . . . . . . AMUR G.
∞ **anderso'ni** (*coignetiae* × *riparia*) ∞ ANDERSON G.

The cultivated plant is presumably a clon of this cross.

antarc'tica . . . . Cissus a.
arbo'rea . . . . Ampelopsis a.
argentifo'lia (*bicolor; leconteana*) BLUELEAF G.
arizo'nica . . . . CANYON G.
arma'ta . . . . V. davidi
baileya'na . . . . POSSUM G.
berlandier'i . . . . . . WINTER G.
betulifo'lia . . . . BIRCH G.
bi'color . . . . V. argentifolia
bipinna'ta . . . . Ampelopsis arborea
bourquinia'na . . . . V. aestivalis b.
brevipeduncula'ta . . . Ampelopsis b.
califor'nica . . . . . CALIFORNIA G.
can'dicans . . . . MUSTANG G.
capen'sis . . . . Cissus c.
cham'pini . . . . CHAMPIN G.
cine'rea . . . . SWEET WINTER G.
coignet'iae . . . . . . GLORYVINE G.

Prof. Rehder reports that the name V. kaempferi has been erroneously applied to V. coignetiae.

corda'ta . . . . Ampelopsis c.
cordifo'lia . . . . V. vulpina
da'vidi (*armata*) . . . . BRIER G.
—cyanocar'pa . . . . . BLUE B.G.
delavaya'na . . . . . Ampelopsis d.
dis'color . . . . Cissus d.
doania'na . . . . DOAN G.
flexuo'sa . . . . ORIENTAL G.
—parvifo'lia . . . . LITTLELEAF O.G.
gi'gas . . . . FLORIDA BLUE G.
girdia'na . . . . VALLEY G.
gongylo'des . . . . Cissus g.
henrya'na . . . . Parthenocissus h.
heterophyl'la . . . . . . Ampelopsis brevipedunculata maximowiczi
—citrulloi'des . . . . A. b. citrulloides
—el'egans . . . . A. b. elegans
himalaya'na . . . Parthenocissus h.
—rubrifo'lia . . . . . P. h. rubrifolia
hypoglau'ca . . . . Cissus h.
inci'sa . . . . Cissus i.
incon'stans Parthenocissus tricuspidata
indivi'sa . . . . Ampelopsis cordata
labrus'ca . . . . FOX G.
—al'ba . . . . WHITE F.G.

The so-called Labruscan Grapes (V. labruscana Bailey) are cultigens derived from V. labrusca and hybrids of it and other species.

lana'ta . . . . DOWNY G.
lecontea'na . . . . V. argentifolia

VITIS, continued
lin'cecumi . . . . PINEWOODS GRAPE

This native southeastern grape, named for Dr. Lincecum, was originally published as V. linsecomi, but later corrected. It is usually spelled linsecomi in literature.

long'i . . . . LONGS G.
megalophyl'la . . . . Ampelopsis m.
mi'cans . . . . A. bodinieri
montic'ola . . . SWEET MOUNTAIN G.
munsonia'na . . . . BIRD G.
novae-an'gliae . . . NEWENGLAND G.
oblon'ga . . . . Cissus o.
orienta'lis . . . . . . Ampelopsis o.
pagnuc'ci . . . . . . V. piasezki p.
palma'ta (*rubra*) . . . . . . CAT G.
penta'gona . . . . . CHINAWOOL G.
—bell'ula . . . . LITTLELEAF C.G.
piasez'ki (*Parthenocissus sinensis*) PIASEZKY G.
—pagnuc'ci (*V. pagnucci*) PAGNUCCI G.
popeno'ei . . . . . . TOTOLOCHE G.
pteroph'ora . . . Cissus gongylodes
pul'chra . . . . . . BRONZELEAF G.
quadrangula'ris . . . . . . Cissus q.
quinquefo'lia . . . Parthenocissus q.
reticula'ta . . . . V. wilsonae
rhombifo'lia . . . . Cissus r.
ripa'ria . . . . RIVERBANK G.

This species is sometimes confused with V. vulpina.

—prae'cox (*V. vulpina p.*) . JUNE R.G.
—syrtic'ola . . . . QUICKSAND R.G.
romanet'i (*rutilans*) . . . ROMANET G.
rotundifo'lia . . . . . MUSCADINE G.
ru'bra . . . . V. palmata
rufotomento'sa . . . . REDSHANK G.
rupes'tris . . . . SAND G.
ru'tilans . . . . V. romaneti
sempervi'rens . . . . . Cissus striata
serjaniaefo'lia . Ampelopsis japonica
shuttleworth'i . . . . . CALLOOSE G.
siebold'i . . . . V. thunbergi
simp'soni . . . . SIMPSON G.
∞ **sla'vini** (*argentifolia* × *riparia*) ∞ SLAVIN G.

The cultivated plant is presumably a clon of this cross.

smallia'na . . . . FIGLEAF G.
so'la . . . . CURTISS G.
stria'ta . . . . Cissus s.
thom'soni . . . . . Parthenocissus t.
thunberg'i (*sieboldi*) . . THUNBERG G.
—sinua'ta . . . . AUTUMNGLOW T.G.
treleas'ei . . . . TRELEASE G.
vinif'era . . . . EUROPEAN G.
—apiifo'lia . . . . PARSLEYLEAF E.G.
—purpu'rea . . . . CLARETLEAF E.G.
—sylves'tris . . . . . WOODLAND E.G.
vita'cea . . . . Parthenocissus inserta
voinieria'na Tetrastigma voinierianum
vulpi'na (*cordifolia*) . . . . FROST G.
—prae'cox . . . . V. riparia p.
wil'sonae (*reticulata*) . . WILSON G.

VITTADI'NIA . . . . . . VITTADINIA
austra'lis (*triloba*) . . AUSTRALIAN V. (*NewHolland Daisy*)

VITTA'RIA
See **FERN GENERA.**

VOANDZEI'A . . GOOBER (*Groundnut*)
subterra'nea . . . . . . CONGO G.

VOAVANGA . Vangueria madagascarensis

VOLUTAREL'LA . . . AMBERBOA

VOLVA'RIA . . . . Volvaria
bombyci'na . . . . Silky V.
volva'cea . Padi V. (*Strawmushroom*)

VONI'TRA . . . . . . Vonitrapalm
See **PALM GENERA.**

VOUACAPOU'A . . . . . **ANDIRA**
america'na . . . . **A. inermis**

VRIES'IA . . . . Vriesia
barille'ti . . . . Barillet V.
×**cardina'lis** . . . . . . Cardinal V.
duvalia'na (*Tillandsia d.*) . Duval V.
∞**erec'ta** (×*poelmani* × ∞*rex*) ∞Poelrex V.
fenestra'lis . . . . Windowpane V.
hieroglyph'ica . . . Hieroglyphic V.
∞**magnisia'na** (*barilleti* × *fenestralis*) ∞Baristralis V.
morre'ni . . . . Morren V.
×**poel'mani** . . . . Poelman V.
Undoubtedly a hybrid, but parentage uncertain.
∞**rex'** (*barilleti* × ×*cardinalis* × *morreni*) ∞King V.
saun'dersi (*Encholirion s.*) Whitedot V.
specio'sa (*picta; splendens; zebrina*) Flaming V.
—ma'jor . . . . Great F.V.

Vriesia . . . . **Vriesia**
Barillet V. . . . . **V. barilleti**
∞Baristralis V. . . . ∞**V. magnisiana**
Cardinal V. . . . . . ×**V. cardinalis**
Duval V. . . . . **V. duvaliana**
Flaming V. . . . . **V. speciosa**
Great F. V. . . . . **V. s. major**
Hieroglyphic V. . . **V. hieroglyphica**
∞King V. . . . . ∞**V. rex**
Morren V. . . . . **V. morreni**
Poelman V. . . . . . ×**V. poelmani**
∞Poelrex V. . . . . . . ∞**V. erecta**
Whitedot V. . . . . . **V. saundersi**
Windowpane V. . . . **V. fenestralis**

WACHENDORF'IA
thyrsiflo'ra . . . . . . Goldwand

WAHLENBERG'IA (*CERVICINA*) Rockbell
capen'sis . . . . Cape R.
conges'ta . . . . . . Creeping R.
dalma'tica . . . . . Dalmatian R.
grac'ilis (*vincaeflora*) . . Gentian R.
grandiflo'ra . . . . . **Platycodon g.**
hedera'cea (*Campanula arvatica*) Ivy R.
matth'ewsi . . . . . . Matthews R.
pen'dula (*lobelioides*) . . Madeira R.
saxic'ola . . . . Tasmania R.
vincaeflo'ra . . . . **W. gracilis**

Wahoo
Eastern W. **Euonymus atropurpureus**
Western W. . . . . . **E. occidentalis**

Waiuatua . . . . . . **Rhabdothamnus**
NewZealand W. . . . . **R. solandri**

Wakerobin . . . . . Trillium: **Trillium**

WALDSTEIN'IA
fragarioi'des . . Barrenstrawberry
sibir'ica

Walkingfern . . . . . **Camptosorus**

Wallabatree . . . . **Eperua**
Bimiti W. . . . . **E. schomburgkiana**
Ituri W. . . . . **E. jenmani**
Soft W. . . . . **E. falcata**

WALLACEODEN'DRON. Wallacetree
celeb'icum . . . . . . Celebes W.

Wallacetree . . . . **Wallaceodendron**
Celebes W. . . . . . . **W. celebicum**

Wallflower . . . . **Cheiranthus**
Alpine W. . . . . **C. alpinus**
Common W. . . . . **C. cheiri**
Greek W. . . . . **C. senoneri**
Kew W. . . . . ×**C. kewensis**
Meyer W. . . . . **C. meyeri**
Morocco W. . . . . **C. semperflorens**

WALLICH'IA . . . . . Wallichpalm
See **PALM GENERA.**

Wallichpalm . . . . **Wallichia**
Fishtail W. . . . . . **W. caryotoides**
Straddleleaf W. . . . . **W. disticha**

Wallrocket . . . . **Diplotaxis**
Garden W. . . . . . . **D. erucoides**
Slimleaf W. . . . . . . **D. tenuifolia**
Stinking W. . . . . **D. muralis**

Walnut . . . . **Juglans**
Argentine Black W. . . **J. australis**
Arizona B. W. . . . . **J. major**
∞Bixby W. . . . . ∞**J. bixbyi**
Bolivian Black W. . . . **J. boliviana**
Butternut . . . . **J. cinerea**
California Black W. . . **J. californica**
Cathay W. . . . . . . **J. cathayensis**
∞Chinese W. . . . . . . ∞**J. sinensis**
Colombian Black W. . **J. columbiensis**
Cuban W. . . . . **J. insularis**
Eastern Black W. . . . . . . **J. nigra**
Ecuador W. . . . . **J. honorei**
Flat Siebold W. **J. sieboldiana cordiformis**
Guatemalan W. . . . . **J. mollis**
Himalayan Persian W. **J. regia kamaonia**
Hinds Black W. . . . . **J. hindsi**
∞Lancaster W. . . . ∞**J. lancastriensis**
The nuts are known as Lancaster Buartnut.
Manchu W. . . . . . . **J. mandshurica**
∞Nigornica W. . . . . . **J. californica** × **J. nigra**
∞Nigroldiana W. . . . . **J. nigra** × **J. sieboldiana**
∞Notha W. . . . . ∞**J. notha**
∞*Perbold W.* . . . . ∞Notha W.
∞Perbut W. . . . . ∞**J. quadrangulata**
Persian W. . . . . **J. regia**
∞Regifornica W. . . . . **J. californica** × **J. regia**
∞Regindsi W. . . . . **J. hindsi** × **J. regia**
∞Reginigra W. . . **J. nigra** × **J. regia**
Siebold W. . . . . . . **J. sieboldiana**
Texas Black W. . . . . . **J. rupestris**
Thickshell Persian W. **J. regia fallax**
Threeleaf California Black W. **J. californica quercina**
Turkestan Persian W. **J. regia turcomanica**

WALTHE'RIA |w . . . . . Waltheria
america'na |w . . . . . Florida W.

Wampee . . . . **Clausena**
Aniseoil W. . . . . . **C. anisum-olens**
Chinese W. . . . . **C. lansium**
India W. . . . . . **C. dentata dulcis**

Wanderingjew **Tradescantia fluminensis**

Wandflower . . . . **Sparaxis**
Big W. . . . . **S. grandiflora**
White B. W. . . . . **S. g. alba**

Waratah . . . . **Telopea**
Crimson W. . . . . . **T. speciosissima**
Gippsland W. . . . . **T. oreades**
Tasmanian W. . . . . . . **T. truncata**

WARIO'NIA
saha'rae . . Sahara Beggarticktree

WARNE'RIA . . . . . . **GARDENIA**

WARSCEWICZEL'LA
See **ORCHID GENERA.**

WARSZEWIC'ZIA . . . . . Chaconia
coccin'ea . . . . . . Orangegold C.

Wartcress . . . . **Coronopus**
Creeping W. . . . . . **C. procumbens**
Swine W. . . . . **C. didymus**

WASHINGTO'NIA (*NEOWASHINGTONIA*) . . . Washingtonpalm
See **PALM GENERA.**

Washingtonpalm . . . **Washingtonia**
California W. . . . . **W. filifera**
Mexican W. . . . . **W. robusta**

Waterbugtrap. . **Aldrovanda vesiculosa**

Waterchestnut . . . . . **Trapa natans**

Waterchinkapin **Nelumbium pentapetalum**

Watercress **Rorippa nasturtium-aquaticum**

Waterdropwort . . . . . . **Oenanthe**
Fennelleaf W. . . . **O. phellandrium**
Hemlock W. . . . . **O. crocata**
Pacific W. . . . . . . **O. sarmentosa**

Waterelm . . . **Planera; P. aquatica**

Waterfern . . . . **Ceratopteris**
American W. . . . . . **C. pteridoides**
Deltoid W. . . . . **C. deltoidea**
Oriental W. . . . . . **C. thalictroides**

Watergrass **Hydrochloa; H. caroliniensis**

Waterhawthorn . . . . . **Aponogeton**
Cape W. . . . . **A. distachyus**
Giant C. W. . . . . . **A. d. giganteus**
Lace W. . . . . **A. fenestralis**

Waterhemlock . . . . **Cicuta**
Bolander W. . . . . . . **C. bolanderi**
Bulb W. . . . . **C. bulbifera**
California W. . . . . . **C. californica**
Curtiss W. . . . . **C. curtissi**
Douglas W. . . . . **C. douglasi**
European W. . . . . **C. virosa**
Spotted W. . . . . **C. maculata**
Tuber W. . . . . **C. vagans**
Western W. . . . . . **C. occidentalis**

Waterhemp . . . . **Acnida**
Florida W. . . . . **A. floridana**
Gulfcoast W. . . . . . **A. alabamensis**
Tall W. . . . . **A. altissima**
Tidemarsh W. . . . . . . **A. cannabina**

Waterhyacinth . . . . . . **Eichhornia**
Common W. . . . . **E. crassipes**
Rosy W. . . . . **E. c. major**
Sawpetal W. . . . . **E. azurea**
Showy W. . . . . **E. speciosa**

Waterhyssop . . . . **Bacopa**
Carolina W. . . . . . . **B. caroliniana**
Coastal W. . . . . **B. monnieria**
Disk W. . . . . **B. rotundifolia**

Waterleaf . . . . **Hydrophyllum**
Ballhead W. . . . . **H. capitatum**
Canada W. . . . . **H. canadense**
Fendler W. . . . . **H. fendleri**
Virginia W. . . . . . . **H. virginianum**
Western W. . . . . . . **H. occidentale**
Whiteface Fendler W. **H. fendleri albifrons**

WATERLEMON . . . **Passiflora laurifolia**
WATERLETTUCE . . **Pistia; P. stratiotes**
WATERLILY . . . . **Nymphaea**
AMAZON W. . . . . . **N. amazonum**
AMERICAN W. . . . . . **N. odorata**
AUSTRALIAN W. . . . . **N. gigantea**
BLUE EGYPTIANLOTUS . . **N. caerulea**
BLUE INDIALOTUS . . . . **N. stellata**
BULBLEAF W. . . . . **N. micrantha**
BURTT W. . . . . **N. burtti**
CAMEROON W. . . . . . **N. zenkeri**
CAPECOD W. . . . **N. odorata rosea**
CAPE W. . . . . . . **N. capensis**
CAPEYORK W. . . . . . **N. violacea**
DISHLEAF W. . . . . **N. lekophylla**
DOTLEAF W. . . . . . . **N. ampla**
EUROPEAN WHITE W. . . . . **N. alba**
HOPATCONG MAGNOLIA W.
N. tuberosa maxima
LARGE EUROPEAN WHITE W.
N. alba candidissima
MAGNOLIA W. . . . . . **N. tuberosa**
PALE CAPE W. . . **N. capensis azurea**
PYGMY W. . . . . . **N. tetragona**
RED INDIA W. . . . . **N. magnifica**
RICEFIELD AMERICAN W.
N. odorata gigantea
ROSY CAPE W. . . **N. capensis rosea**
RUDGE W. . . . . **N. rudgeana**
SENORITA W. . . . . . . **N. elegans**
SIERRALEONE W. . . **N. lotus dentata**
SMALL AMERICAN W. **N. odorata minor**
TABORA W. . . . . . . **N. ovalifolia**
WHITE EGYPTIANLOTUS . . . **N. lotus**
YELLOW MEXICAN W. . . **N. mexicana**
YELLOW PYGMY W.
N. tetragona helvola
ZANZIBAR W. **N. capensis zanzibariensis**

WATERLILY GENERA

In the preparation of this list the Editorial Committee had the benefit of constructive criticism and suggestions from two outstanding authorities on these genera, G. H. Pring, Supt. Missouri Botanical Garden, St. Louis, Mo., and Henry S. Conard, Professor of Botany, Grinnell College, Iowa. To both the Committee extends its appreciation and sincere thanks.

ABBREVIATIONS OF CLASSIFICATIONS
HW. Hardy Waterlilies
TD. Tropical Day-blooming Waterlilies
TN. Tropical Night-blooming Waterlilies

BRASE'NIA . . . . WATERSHIELD
schre'beri (*peltata*) . . SCHREBER W.

CASTA'LIA . . . **NYMPHAEA**

EURY'ALE . . . . . . EURYALE
fe'rox . . . . GORDON E.

NELUM'BIUM (*NELUMBO*) lw
LOTUS
lu'teum . . . . . . **N. pentapetalum**
nelum'bo (*indicum; nuciferum; speciosum*) lw . . . . HINDU L.
—kermesia'num . . . KERMES H.L.
—kinshi'ren . . . KINSHIREN H.L.
₵ALBUM GRANDIFLORUM. HV. N. nelumbo
DAWN (*roseum*)
DOUBLE DAWN (*roseum plenum*)
EMPRESS
₵ERNST LUDWIG
MAGNOLIA (*album grandiflorum*)
₵OSIRIS
₵PEKINENSE PLENUM

WATERLILY GENERA (NELUMBIUM nelumbo), continued
₵PEKINENSE RUBRUM
PEKING
₵PULCHRUM
₵PYGMAEUM
₵SHIROMAN (*album plenum*)
pentapet'alum (*luteum*) lw
AMERICAN LOTUS; WATERCHINKAPIN

NELUM'BO . . . **NELUMBIUM**

NU'PHAR (*NYMPHOZANTHUS*)
lw . . . . COWLILY
adve'na (*bombycinum; chartaceum; fluviatile; macrophyllum; orbiculatum; Nymphozanthus a.*) lw
SPATTERDOCK C.
japon'icum (*Nym. japonicus*)
JAPANESE C.
lu'teum (*Nym. luteus*) EUROPEAN C.
macrophyl'lum . . . . . . **N. advena**
microphyl'lum (*Nym. microphyllus*) lw
LETTUCE C.
min'imum . . . . LEAST C.
orbicula'tum . . . . **N. advena**
polysep'alum (*Nym. polysepalus*) lw
ROCKYMOUNTAIN C.
rubrodis'cum (*Nym. rubrodiscus*) lw
REDDISK C.
sagittifo'lium (*ulvaceum; Nym. sagittifolius*) lw . . . . ARROW C.
variega'tum (*Nym. variegatus*)
PAINTED C.

Perhaps not specifically distinct from N. advena.

NYMPH'AEA (*CASTALIA*) lw
WATERLILY
al'ba (*Castalia a.*) HW.
EUROPEAN WHITE W.
—candidis'sima. HW. LARGE E.W.W.
amazon'um. TN. . . . . AMAZON W.
am'pla (*Castalia a.*) lw. TD.
DOTLEAF W.
—specio'sa (*N. gracilis*)
GERARDIANA. HV. N. ampla
burtt'i. TD. . . . . BURTT W.
caeru'lea (*Castalia c.*). TD.
BLUE EGYPTIANLOTUS
capen'sis. TD. . . . . CAPE W.
—azu'rea. TD. . . . . . PALE C.W.
—rose'a. TD. . . . . . ROSY C.W.
—zanzibarien'sis (*N. zanzibariensis*) TD. . . . . ZANZIBAR W.
citri'na. TD.
colora'ta. TD.
denta'ta . . . . **N. lotus d.**
el'egans (*Castalia e.*) lw. TD.
SENORITA W.
fla'va . . . . **N. mexicana**
flavo-vi'rens. TD.
See note under N. gracilis.
gigan'tea (*Castalia g.*). TD.
AUSTRALIAN W.
grac'ilis . . . . . **N. ampla speciosa**

N. flavo-virens is frequently misnamed N. gracilis in gardens.

lekophyl'la (*Castalia l.*) lw DISHLEAF W.
(*Apple Lotus*)
lo'tus (*Castalia l.*). TN.
WHITE EGYPTIANLOTUS
—denta'ta (*dentata; Castalia d.*). TN.
SIERRALEONE W
magnif'ica (*rubra*). TN. RED INDIA W.
mexica'na (*flava; Castalia m.*) lw. HW.
YELLOW MEXICAN W.
micran'tha. TD. . . . BULBLEAF W.
mi'nor . . . . **N. odorata m.**

WATERLILY GENERA (NYMPHAEA), con.
odora'ta (*Castalia o.*) lw. HW.
AMERICAN WATERLILY
—gigan'tea. HW. . RICEFIELD A.W.
—max'ima . . . . . **N. tuberosa m.**
—mi'nor (*N. minor*). HW.
SMALL A.W.
—rose'a (*N. o. rubra*). HW.
CAPECOD W.
ovalifo'lia. TD. . . . . TABORA W.
pyg'maea . . . . **N. tetragona**
—helvo'la . . . . . **N. tetragona h.**
ru'bra . . . . **N. magnifica**
rudgea'na. TN. . . . . . RUDGE W.
stella'ta (*Castalia s.*). TD.
BLUE INDIALOTUS
tetrag'ona (*pygmaea; Castalia t.*) lw HW. . . . . PYGMY W.
—helvo'la (*N. pygmaea h.*). HW.
YELLOW P.W.
tubero'sa (*Castalia t.*) lw. HW.
MAGNOLIA W.
—max'ima (*N. odorata m.*). HW.
HOPATCONG M.W.
viola'cea. TD. . . . . CAPEYORK W.
ELEONORE. HV.
zanzibarien'sis . . . . **N. capensis z.**
zenk'eri. TN. . . . . CAMEROON W.

Probably most, if not all, of these are clons.

AMABILIS. HW. HV. Nymphaea
ANDRE (*andreana*). HW.
ARETHUSA. HW.
ATROPURPUREA. HW.
ATTRACTION. HW.
AUGUST KOCH. TD.
AURORA. HW.
BAGDAD. TD. (Pring 1941.)
BISSETT (*bissetti*). TN.
BLUEBEAUTY (*pulcherrima*). TD.
BLUEBIRD. TD.
CASTALIIFLORA. TD. (Pring 1913.)
CELESTE. TD. (Pring 1941.)
CHRYSANTHA. HW.
CLEVELAND. TD.
COL. LINDBERGH. TD.
COMANCHE. HW.
CONQUEROR. HW.
DAISY. TD. (Pring 1941.)
DAUBEN (*daubeniana*). TD.
DEAN (*deaniana*). TN.
DEVON (*devoniensis*). TN.
DIRECTOR (*George T.*) MOORE. TD. (Pring 1940.)
EDWARD C. ELIOT. TD. (Pring 1924.)
ELLISIANA (*marliacea*). HW.
EMILY (*Grant*) HUTCHINGS. TN.
ENCHANTRESS. TD.
ERNST LUDWIG (*Grossherzog Ernst Ludwig*). TD.
ESCARBOUCLE. HW.
EUGENIA DELAND. HW.
EXQUISITE (*odorata exquisita*). HW.
FIRECREST. HW.
FIRE MARLIAC (*marliacea ignea*). HW.
FLAME MARLIAC (*marliacea flammea*). HW.
FLESH MARLIAC (*marliacea carnea*). HW.
FORMOSA. HW.
FRANK TRELEASE. TN.
FROEBEL (*froebeli*). HW.
GENERAL PERSHING. TD. (Pring 1917.)
GEORGE HUSTER. TN.

WATERLILY GENERA (NYMPHAEA), con.
GLADSTONE (*gladstoniana*). HW.
GLOIRE DU TEMPLE-SUR-LOT (*marliacea*). HW.
GLORY (*gloriosa*). HW.
GOLDEN WEST. TD.
GONNERE. HW.
GRAZIELLA. HW.
Grossherzog Ernst Ludwig. ERNST LUDWIG.
H. C. HAARSTICK. TN.
HELEN FOWLER. HW.
HELVOLA (*mexicana* × *tetragona*). HW.
HENRY SHAW. TD. (Pring 1919.)
HESSEL (*odorata sulphurea grandiflora*). HW.
HOPATCONG (*tuberosa maxima*). HW.
IMPERIAL. TD.
INDEPENDENCE. TD.
ISABELLE PRING. TD. (Pring 1941.)
JAMES BRYDON. HW.
JAMES GURNEY. TN.
JANICE. TD.
JUBILEE. TN.
JUDGE HITCHCOCK. TD. (Pring 1940.)
JUNO (*dentata superba*). TN.
JUPITER. TD.
KEW (*kewensis*). TN.
LAYDEKER (*laydekeri*). HW.
LILAC LAYDEKER (*laydekeri lilacea*). HW.
LOOSE. HW.
LOTUS JUNO. TN.
LUCIDA. HW.
LUSTROUS. HW.
MARLIAC (*marliacea*). HW.
MASANIELLO. HW.
MIDNIGHT. TD. (Pring 1941.)
MINERVA (*dentata magnifica*). TN.
MISSOURI. TN. (Pring 1932.)
MORNINGGLORY. HW.
MRS. BUSKIRK. TD.
MRS. C. W. WARD. TD.
MRS. (*Edwards*) WHITAKER. TD. (Pring 1917.)
MRS. (*Edwards*) WHITAKER MARMORATA. TD.
MRS. (*George C.*) HITCHCOCK. TN. (Pring 1926.)
MRS. G. H. PRING. TD. (Pring 1922.)
MRS. SAWYER. TD.
MRS. (*Woodrow*) WILSON. TD. (Tricker.)
MRS. (*Woodrow*) WILSON GIGANTEA. TD. (Pring 1918.)
NEPTUNE. HW.
NEWTON. HW.
O'MARA (*omarana*). TN.
PALECAPE. TD.
PANAMA-PACIFIC. TD.
PATRICIA. TD.
PAUL HARIOT. HW.
PEACHBLOW. TD. (Pring 1941.)
Pennsylvania. PULCHERRIMA.
PERSHING LILAC. TD. (Pring 1941.)
PINK OPAL. HW.
PINK PLATTER. TD. (Pring 1941.)
PULCHERRIMA. TD. *Pennsylvania.*
PURPLE LAYDEKER (*laydekeri purpurea*). HW.
RED EUROPEAN (*alba rubra*). HW.
RED LAYDEKER (*laydekeri rosea*). HW.
RED MAGNOLIA (*tuberosa rubra*). HW.
RENE GERARD. HW.

WATERLILY GENERA (NYMPHAEA), con.
RICHARDSON (*tuberosa richardsoni*). HW.
RIO RITA. TD. (Pring 1941.)
ROBINSON (*robinsoni*). HW.
ROSE AREY. HW.
ROSE MAGNOLIA (*tuberosa rosea*). HW.
ROSE MARLIAC (*marliacea rosea*). HW.
ROSYCAPE. TD.
ROYAL PURPLE. TD.
SEIGNORET (*seignoreti*). HW.
SHELL PINK. TD. (Pring 1940.)
SHIRLEY MARIE. TD.
SIOUX. HW
SMALL AMERICAN.
SNOW WHITE. TD.
SOLFATARE. HW.
SPOTTED MARLIAC (*marliacea rubra punctata*). HW.
STELLA GURNEY. TD.
ST. LOUIS. TD. (Pring 1932.)
ST. LOUIS MARMORATA. TD.
STURTEVANT (*sturtevanti*). TN.
SULPHUR (*odorata sulphurea*). HW.
SULTAN. HW.
SUMPTUOSA. HW.
SUNBEAM. TD. (Pring 1941.)
SUNRISE. HW.
TALISMAN. TD. (Pring 1941.)
VESUVE. HW.
W. B. SHAW.
WHITE MARLIAC (*marliacea albida*). HW.
WILDROSE. TD. (Pring 1941.)
WILLIAM BECKER.
WILLIAM DOOGUE.
WILLIAM FALCONER. HW.
WILLIAM STONE. TD.
YELLOW LAYDEKER (*laydekeri fulva*). HW.
YELLOW MARLIAC (*marliacea chromatella*). HW.
YELLOWSTAR. TD. (Pring 1940.)

NYMPHOZAN'THUS . **NUPHAR**

VICTO'RIA . . . WATERPLATTER
cruzia'na . . . . PARANA W.
—mattogrossen'sis . MATTOGROSSO W.
re'gia . . . . ROYAL W.
—rand'i . . . . COMMON R.W.

WATERLOCUST . . . **Gleditsia aquatica**

WATERMEAL . . . **Websteria submersa**

WATERMELON . . . . **Citrullus vulgaris**

WATERMOSS . . . . **Fontinalis**
FEVER W. . . . . . . **F. antipyretica**

WATERNUT . . . . **Eleocharis tuberosa**

WATERPARSNIP . . . . **Sium**
HEMLOCK W. . . . . **S. suave**
SKIRRET W. . . . . **S. sisarum**

WATERPLANTAIN . . . . **Alisma**
AMERICAN W. . . **A. plantago-aquatica**
GEYER W. . . . . **A. geyeri**
GRASS W. . . . . **A. plantago**
SUBCORDATE W. . . **A. subcordatum**

WATERPLATTER . . . . **Victoria**
COMMON ROYAL W. . . **V. regia randi**
MATTOGROSSO W.
V. cruziana mattogrossensis
PARANA W. . . . . **V. cruziana**
ROYAL W. . . . . **V. regia**

WATERPOPPY
Hydrocleis; H. nymphoides

WATERPRIMROSE . . . . . . **Jussiaea**
BRAZILIAN W. . . . . . **J. longifolia**
CALIFORNIA W. . . . . **J. californica**
CREEPING W. . . . . **J. repens**
FLOATING W. . . . . **J. diffusa**
LARGE W. . . . . . . **J. grandiflora**
PERU W. . . . . **J. peruviana**

WATERPURSLANE . . . **Didiplis diandra**

WATERRICE . . . . **Hygroryza**
AWNED W. . . . . **H. aristata**

WATERSHIELD . . . . **Brasenia**
SCHREBER W. . . . . . **B. schreberi**

WATERSOLDIER . . **Stratiotes; S. aloides**

WATERSTARWORT . . . . . . **Callitriche**
AUTUMN W. . . . . . **C. autumnalis**
COMMON W. . . . . . . **C. palustris**
LARGER W. . . . . **C. heterophylla**
POND W. . . . . **C. stagnalis**

WATERWEED . . . . **Anacharis**
CANADA W. . . . . . . **A. canadensis**
NARROWLEAF W. . . . . . **A. linearis**
WESTERN W. . . . . . **A. occidentalis**

WATERWILLOW. **Decodon; D. verticillatus**

WATERWORT . . . . **Elatine**
AMERICAN W. . . . . . **E. americana**
LEAST W. . . . . **E. minima**
SHORTSEED W. . . . **E. brachysperma**
WILLIAMS W. . . . . . **E. williamsi**

WATSO'NIA (*MERIANA*) . BUGLELILY
angus'ta . . . . . . TAPERPETAL B.
bea'tricis . . . . BEATRICE B.
brevifo'lia . . . . . . SHORTLEAF B.
bulbillif'era . . . . BULBIL B.
coccin'ea . . . . SCARLET B.
densiflo'ra . . . . ROSEWAND B.
iridifo'lia . . . . IRISLEAF B.
—meria'na . . . . **W. meriana**
O'BRIEN (*White B.; ardernei; obrieni*) HV. W. iridifolia
longifo'lia . . . . . . LONGLEAF B.
margina'ta . . . . FRAGRANT B.
meria'na (*W. iridifolia m.*) MERIANA B.
pillans'i . . . . BRICKRED B.
rose'a . . . . ROSY B.
versfeld'i . . . . VERSFELD B.
wordsworthia'na . . WORDSWORTH B.

WATTAKA'KA
sinen'sis (*Dregea s.*)

WAXES (Plant Sources of)
See **ECONOMIC PLANTS, WAXES.**

WAXGOURD . . . . **Benincasa**
CHINESE W. . . . . **B. hispida**

WAXMALLOW . . . . **Malvaviscus**
DRUMMOND W. . . . . **M. drummondi**
SOUTHAMERICAN W. . . **M. arboreus**

WAXMYRTLE . . . . **Myrica**
See also BAYBERRY.

CANARYISLANDS W. . . . . . . **M. faya**
∞ MACFARLANE W. . . ∞ **M. macfarlanei**
ODORLESS W. . . . . . . **M. inodora**
PACIFIC W. . . . . . . **M. californica**
SIERRA W. . . . . **M. hartwegi**
SOUTHERN W. . . . . . . **M. cerifera**
SWEETGALE . . . . **M. gale**

WAXPALM . . . . **Ceroxylon**
QUINDIO W. . . . . . **C. quindiuense**
SALENTO W. . . . . **C. ferrugineum**
SANTAMARTA W. . . . . **C. ceriferum**

WAXPLANT . . . . **Hoya**
COMMON W. . . . . **H. carnosa**

WAXTREE . **Toxicodendron succedaneum**

WEAVERSBROOM **Spartium; S. junceum**
DWARF W. . . . . **S. j. nanum**

WEBEROCE'REUS
See **CACTUS GENERA.**

WEBSTE'RIA |w
submer'sa |w . . . . WATERMEAL

WEDE'LIA; WEDELIEL'LA **ALLIONIA**

Wedgegrass. WEDGESCALE: **Sphenopholis**

WEDGESCALE . . . . . . **Sphenopholis**
LONGLEAF W. . . . . . . **S. filiformis**
PALE W. . . . . **S. pallens**
PRAIRIE W. . . . . **S. obtusata**
SHINY W. . . . . **S. nitida**
SLENDER W. . . . . . . **S. intermedia**
TEXAS W. . . . . **S. longiflora**

WEEDS

Weeds are "plants out of place" (see Glossary). Especially is this derogatory term applied to unwanted plants which invade such places as cultivated fields, orchards, gardens, lawns, and golf courses. Largely these plants are immigrants which man has, usually unwittingly, transported from their native lands. Some, however, are true aborigines, steadily increasing their area of occupation. Weeds "can take it"; they are tolerant of drought, of extremes of heat and cold, of fire and high wind, and characteristically possess vigorous reproductive powers. Many have highly developed underground persistent systems of rootstocks, tubers and the like; frequently they produce seeds with spines or other prominences which fasten themselves to passing objects, or else with parachutes of down or other appendages, which greatly facilitate their distribution.

Weeds, as such, have far-reaching economic significance. In Iowa alone the amount of loss by weeds is conservatively placed at about $50,000,000 annually. It is important to remember, however, that "weed" is a relative term. The same species which in one place is an obnoxious weed, may be in another place a plant economically very valuable for ground-cover, soil-builder, food for man and animals, medicine, fiber, and many other purposes. A number of these appear in STANDARDIZED PLANT NAMES under several different categories. In fact, almost any known plant *in the wrong place* might aptly be termed a "weed."

The below list includes about 500 species of the more common and important so-called weeds of the United States. There is a very large literature on weeds in this country, chiefly issuing from the U. S. Department of Agriculture and the State agricultural experiment stations. It is not feasible to list all the works which were consulted in the preparation of this list. Of especial value were Walter C. Muenscher's "Weeds" (New York, 1935); L. H. Pammel and others' "The Weed Flora of Iowa" (Iowa Geol. Survey Bull. 41926); W. J. Beal's "Michigan Weeds" (Mich. Agr. Expt. Sta. Bull. 260. 1912); George H. Clark and James Fletcher's "Farm Weeds of Canada" (Canada Dept. Agr. 1923); Bureau of Plant Industry, U. S. Department of Agriculture, "Service and Regulatory Announcements" (Circ. 9. 1926) and Public Document No. 354, 76th Congress, 1st Sess., the "Federal Seed Act" (1939)—both of which contain weed lists; also the late Frederick V. Coville's "Seed List" (Bureau of Plant Industry, Washington. 1935).

ABU'TILON theophras'ti (*avicennae*) . . . . CHINGMA ABUTILON

WEEDS, continued

ACALY'PHA virgin'ica VIRGINIA COPPERLEAF

ACHILLE'A millefo'lium COMMON YARROW

AGRIMO'NIA species . . AGRIMONY

AGROPY'RON re'pens QUACKGRASS

AGROSTEM'MA githa'go (*Lychnis g.*) . . . COMMON CORNCOCKLE

AGROS'TIS spica-vent'i WIND BENTGRASS

AL'LIUM . . . . ONION
canaden'se . . . . CANADA GARLIC
cer'nuum (*recurvatum*) . NODDING O.
vinea'le . . . . FIELD GARLIC

ALTERNAN'THERA philoxeroi'des ALLIGATOR ALTERNANTHERA

ALYS'SUM . . . . ALYSSUM
alyssoi'des (*calycinum*) . . . PALE A.
inca'num . . . . . **Berteroa incana**

AMARAN'THUS . . . AMARANTH
blitoi'des . . . . . PROSTRATE A.
grae'cizans . . . . TUMBLEWEED A.
hy'bridus . . . . SLIM A.
retroflex'us . . . . . . REDROOT A.
spino'sus . . . . SPINY A.

AMBRO'SIA . . . . . RAGWEED
artemisifo'lia (*elatior*) . . COMMON R.
psilosta'chya . . . . . . WESTERN R.
trif'ida . . . . GIANT R.

ANAGAL'LIS arven'sis SCARLET PIMPERNEL

ANAPH'ALIS margarita'cea COMMON PEARLEVERLASTING

ANDROPO'GON . . BLUESTEM
furca'tus . . . . BIG B.
scopa'rius . . . . LITTLE B.
virgin'icus . . . . . YELLOWSEDGE B.

ANEM'ONE canaden'sis (*pennsylvanica*) . . . MEADOW ANEMONE

ANO'GRA . . . **OENOTHERA**
albicau'lis . . . . **O. pallida**

ANTENNA'RIA plantaginifo'lia PLANTAINLEAF PUSSYTOES

AN'THEMIS . . . . . CAMOMILE
arven'sis . . . . FIELD C.
cot'ula . . . . MAYWEED C.

ANTHRIS'CUS sylves'tris WOODLAND BEAKCHERVIL

ANTHYL'LIS vulnera'ria KIDNEYVETCH ANTHYLLIS

ANTIRRHI'NUM oron'tium CORN SNAPDRAGON

APAR'GIA . . . **LEONTODON**

APOC'YNUM cannab'inum HEMP DOGBANE

AR'ABIS gla'bra TOWERMUSTARD ROCKCRESS

ARC'TIUM . . . . . . BURDOCK
lap'pa (*Lappa edulis; L. major*) GREAT B.
mi'nus (*Lappa minor*) . . SMALLER B.
tomento'sum . . . . COTTON B.

WEEDS, continued

ARENA'RIA serpyllifo'lia THYMELEAF SANDWORT

ARGEMO'NE . . . PRICKLEPOPPY
interme'dia
mexica'na . . . . MEXICAN P.
platyce'ras his'pida (*A. hispida*) HEDGEHOG P.

ARGENTI'NA . . **POTENTILLA**

ARIS'TIDA . . . . . THREEAWN
dichot'oma . . . CHURCHMOUSE T.
oligan'tha . . . . PRAIRIE T.
stric'ta . . . . PINELAND T.

ARNOS'ERIS min'ima SMALL LAMBSUCCORY

ARTEMIS'IA SAGEBRUSH; WORMWOOD
bien'nis . . . . BIENNIAL W.
frig'ida . . . . FRINGED S.
ludovicia'na . . . . . . LOUISIANA S.
tridenta'ta . . . . BIG S.

ASCLE'PIAS . . . . MILKWEED
eriocar'pa . . . . WOOLLYPOD M.
galioi'des . . . . POISON M.
incarna'ta . . . . SWAMP M.
mexica'na . . . . MEXICAN M.
pu'mila . . . . PLAINS M.
syri'aca (*cornuti*) . . . . COMMON M.
tubero'sa . . . . . . BUTTERFLY M.

A'TRIPLEX trunca'ta WEDGESCALE SALTBUSH

AVE'NA fa'tua . . . . . WILD OAT

AX'YRIS amaranthoi'des RUSSIAN PIGWEED

BARBARE'A . . . WINTERCRESS
ver'na . . . . EARLY W.
vulga'ris . . . . BITTER W.

BERTERO'A inca'na (*Alyssum incanum*) . . HOARY FALSEALYSSUM

BI'DENS . . . . . BEGGARTICKS
bipinna'ta . . . . . SPANISHNEEDLES
cer'nua . . . . NODDING B.
como'sa . . . . LEAFYBRACT B.
conna'ta . . . . . . PURPLESTEM B.
frondo'sa . . . . DEVILS B.
vulga'ta . . . . TALL B.

BILDERDY'KIA . **POLYGONUM**

BRAS'SICA (*SINAPIS*)
campes'tris . . . . . . BIRD RAPE
jun'cea (*rugosa; Sinapis j.*) INDIA MUSTARD
ka'ber (*arvensis; Sinapis a.*) CHARLOCK
ni'gra . . . . BLACK MUSTARD

BRO'MUS . . . . BROME
commuta'tus . . . . HAIRY B.
mol'lis . . . . SOFT B.
racemo'sus . . . . BALD B.
rig'idus (*villosus* Forsk., *not* Scop.) RIPGUT B.
ru'bens . . . . FOXTAIL B.
secali'nus . . . . CHESS B.
ster'ilis . . . . POVERTY B.
tecto'rum . . . . . CHEATGRASS B.

BUR'SA . . . . . **CAPSELLA**

CALYSTE'GIA . **CONVOLVULUS**

CAMELI'NA . . . . . FALSEFLAX
denta'ta . . . . FLATSEED F.
microcar'pa . . . . . LITTLEPOD F.
sati'va . . . . BIGSEED F.

WEEDS, continued

CAPSEL'LA bursa-pasto'ris (*Bursa b.*) . . . . . . SHEPHERDSPURSE

CARA'RA . . . . **CORONOPUS**

CARDA'RIA (*HYMENOPHYSA*) WHITETOP
dra'ba (*Lepidium d.*) PEPPERWEED W.
pubes'cens (*Hymenophysa p.*) HAIRY W.
—elonga'ta . . . . LONGSTALK H.W.

CAR'DUUS . . . BRISTLETHISTLE
acanthoi'des . . . . . ACANTHUS B.
arven'sis . . . . . . **Cirsium arvense**
benedic'tus . . . . **Cnicus b.**
cris'pus . . . . CURLY B.
dis'color . . . . **Cirsium d.**
lanceola'tum . . . . . . **Cirsium l.**
nu'tans . . . . MUSK B.
undula'tus . . . . **Cirsium undulatum**

CA'RUM car'vi . . . . CARAWAY

CAS'SIA . . . . SENNA
chamaecris'ta **Chamaecrista fasciculata**
nic'titans. . **Chamaecrista procumbens**
occidenta'lis . . . . COFFEE S.

CATHARTOLI'NUM . . **LINUM**

CEN'CHRUS . . . . . SANDBUR
pauciflo'rus . . . . MAT S.
tribuloi'des . . . . DUNE S.

CENTAU'REA . . . . CENTAUREA
america'na . . . BASKETFLOWER C.
benedic'ta . . . . **Cnicus benedictus**
calcitra'pa
cya'nus . . . . CORNFLOWER
iber'ica . . . . IBERIAN CENTAUREA
ja'cea . . . . BROWNSCALE C.
maculo'sa . . . . SPOTTED C.
meliten'sis. . . . . MALTA C.
ni'gra . . . . BLACK C.
re'pens (*picris*) . . . . . RUSSIAN C.
solstitia'lis. . . . . . . YELLOW C.

CERAS'TIUM . . . . CERASTIUM
arven'se . . . . STARRY C.
visco'sum . . . . STICKY C.
vulga'tum . . . . BIG C.

CHAETOCH'LOA . . . **SETARIA**

CHAMAECRIS'TA . PARTRIDGEPEA
fascicula'ta (*Cassia chamaecrista*) SHOWY P.
procum'bens (*nictitans* Auth.; *Cassia n.*) . . . . SENSITIVE P.

CHAMAENE'RION **EPILOBIUM**

CHAMAESY'CE . **EUPHORBIA**
rafines'qui . . . . **E. hirsuta**

Cheiran'thus allio'ni **Erysimum asperum**

CHEIRIN'IA . . . **ERYSIMUM**

CHENOPO'DIUM . . GOOSEFOOT
al'bum . . . . . LAMBSQUARTERS G.
ambrosioi'des . . . . WORMSEED G.
—anthelmin'ticum (*C. anthelminticum*) DRUG W.G.
bonus-hen'ricus. GOODKINGHENRY G.
bo'trys . . . . . JERUSALEMOAK G.
glau'cum . . . . OAKLEAF G.
hy'bridum . . . . . . MAPLELEAF G.
mura'le . . . . NETTLELEAF G.
paga'num . . . . PIGWEED G.
ur'bicum . . . . CITY G.

WEEDS, continued

CHONDRIL'LA jun'cea RUSH SKELETONWEED

CHRYSAN'THEMUM CHRYSANTHEMUM
inodo'rum . . . . **Matricaria inodora**
leucan'themum (*Leucanthemum vulgare*) . . . . OXEYEDAISY
—pinnatif'idum . . . . . FIELD O.
vulga're . . . . **Tanacetum v.**

CICHO'RIUM in'tybus COMMON CHICORY

CIR'SIUM . . . . . . THISTLE
altis'simum . . . . TALL T.
arven'se (*Carduus arvensis*). CANADA T.
dis'color (*Carduus d.*) . . . FIELD T.
lanceola'tum . . . . BULL T.
pu'milum . . . . FRAGRANT T.
undula'tum (*Carduus undulatus*) WAVYLEAF T.

CLEO'ME serrula'ta (*Peritoma serrulatum*) . . . BEE SPIDERFLOWER

CNI'CUS benedic'tus (*Carduus b.; Centaurea benedicta*) BLESSEDTHISTLE

CNIDOS'COLUS stimulo'sus (*Jatropha stimulosa*) RISKY TREADSOFTLY

COMMELI'NA commu'nis COMMON DAYFLOWER

CONRIN'GIA orienta'lis TREACLE HARESEAR

CONVOL'VULUS (*CALYSTEGIA*) . . . . GLORYBIND
arven'sis . . . . EUROPEAN G.
ma'jor. . . . . . . **Ipomoea purpurea**
se'pium (*Calystegia s.*) . . . HEDGE G.

CORISPER'MUM hyssopifo'lium HYSSOPLEAF TICKSEED

CORONO'PUS did'ymus (*Carara didyma*) . . . SWINE WARTCRESS

CORYD'ALIS au'rea GOLDEN CORYDALIS

CRE'PIS . . . . . HAWKSBEARD
bien'nis . . . . ROUGH H.
capilla'ris (*virens*) . . . . SMOOTH H.
tecto'rum . . . . . NARROWLEAF H.

CRO'TON species . . . . CROTON

CU'PHEA petiola'ta (*Parsonsia p.*) CLAMMY CUPHEA

CUSCU'TA . . . . DODDER
cor'yli . . . . HAZEL D.
epili'num . . . . FLAX D.
epithy'mum . . . . CLOVER D.
grono'vi . . . . GRONOVIUS D.
indeco'ra . . . BIGSEED ALFALFA D.
pentag'ona (*arvensis*)
planiflo'ra . . LITTLESEED ALFALFA D.
suave'olens (*C. racemosa chiliana*) CHILE D.

CYCLOLO'MA atriplicifo'lium TUMBLE RINGWING

CY'NODON dac'tylon BERMUDAGRASS

CYNOGLOS'SUM officina'le COMMON HOUNDSTONGUE

CYP'ERUS (*PAPYRUS*) FLATSEDGE
dian'drus
esculen'tus . . . . CHUFA F.
rotun'dus . . . . . . NUTGRASS F.
strigo'sus

WEEDS, continued

CY'TISUS scopa'rius (*Genista scoparia; Spartium scoparium*) SCOTCH BROOM

DATU'RA stramo'nium (*tatula*) JIMSONWEED DATURA

DAU'CUS caro'ta . . WILD CARROT

DENNSTAED'TIA punctilob'ula HAYSCENTEDFERN

DESCURAI'NIA (*SISYMBRIUM* in part; *SOPHIA*) TANSYMUSTARD
inci'sa (*Sisymbrium incisum; Sophia incisa*) . . . . WESTERN T.
longipedicella'ta (*Sisymbrium incisum filipes*) . . . . SLIMSTEM T.
menzies'i (*Sisymbrium canescens; S. pinnatum*) . . . . . . MENZIES T.
pinna'ta (*Sisymbrium sophia*) PINNATE T.
richardso'ni (*Sisymbrium incisum hartwegianum*) . . . . . RICHARDSON T.

DESMO'DIUM canaden'se CANADA TICKCLOVER

DIGITA'RIA . . . . CRABGRASS
ischae'mum . . . . . . SMOOTH C.
sanguina'lis . . . . HAIRY C.

DIO'DIA te'res ROUGH BUTTONWEED

DIPLOTAX'IS . . . WALLROCKET
mura'lis . . . . STINKING W.
tenuifo'lia . . . . . . SLIMLEAF W.

DIP'SACUS . . . . TEASEL
lacinia'tus . . . . CUTLEAF T.
sylves'tris . . . . . . VENUSCUP T.

DRA'BA . . . . DRABA
carolinia'na . . . . CAROLINA D.
nemoro'sa . . . . WOODS D.
ver'na. . . . . SPRING D.

DRACOCEPH'ALUM parviflo'rum (*Moldavica parviflora*) AMERICAN DRAGONHEAD

DUCHES'NEA in'dica (*Fragaria i.*) INDIA MOCKSTRAWBERRY

DYSSO'DIA pappo'sa PRAIRIE DOGWEED

ECHINOCH'LOA crusgal'li BARNYARDGRASS

ECHINOCYS'TIS loba'ta (*Micrampelis l.*) . WILD MOCKCUCUMBER

E'CHIUM vulga're COMMON VIPERSBUGLOSS

EICHHORN'IA cras'sipes (*Piaropus c.*) . . COMMON WATERHYACINTH

ELEUSI'NE in'dica . . GOOSEGRASS

EPILO'BIUM (*CHAMAENERION*) . . . . . . WILLOWWEED
adenocau'lon . . . . STICKY W.
angustifo'lium (*Chamaenerion a.*) FIREWEED

ERAGROS'TIS . . . LOVEGRASS
abyssin'ica . . . . TEFF
cilianen'sis (*major; megastachya*) STINKGRASS
frank'i . . . . SANDBAR L.
pilo'sa . . . . INDIA L.
poaeoi'des (*eragrostis; minor*) LITTLE L.

ERECHTI'TES hieracifo'lia AMERICAN BURNWEED

WEEDS, continued

ERIG'ERON (*LEPTILON*) FLEABANE
an'nuus . . . . ANNUAL F.
canaden'sis (*Leptilon canadense*) HORSEWEED F.
ramo'sus

ERO'DIUM cicuta'rium . ALFILERIA

ERU'CA sati'va . . ROCKETSALAD

ERUCAS'TRUM gal'licum (*pollichi*) ROCKETWEED

ERYS'IMUM (*CHEIRINIA*) ERYSIMUM
as'perum (*arkansanum; Cheiranthus allioni; Cheirinia aspera*) . PLAINS E.
cheiranthoi'des (*Cheirinia c.*) TREACLE E.
officina'le . . . . . . **Sisymbrium o.**
parviflo'rum (*inconspicuum; Cheirinia inconspicua*) . . . SMALLFLOWER E.
repan'dum . . . . . . SPREADING E.

EUPATO'RIUM . . . EUPATORIUM
capillifo'lium . . . . . DOGFENNEL E.
perfolia'tum . . . . BONESET
purpu'reum . BLUESTEM JOEPYEWEED
rugo'sum . . . . WHITE SNAKEROOT

EUPHOR'BIA (*CHAMAESYCE; POINSETTIA; TITHYMALOPSIS; TITHYMALUS*) EUPHORBIA
corolla'ta (*Tithymalopsis c.*) FLOWERINGSPURGE E.
cyparis'sias (*Tithymalus c.*) CYPRESS E.
denta'ta (*Poinsettia d.*) . TOOTHED E.
e'sula (*virgata*) . . . . . . LEAFY E.
glyptosper'ma (*Chamaesyce g.*) RIDGESEED E.
heliosco'pia (*Tithymalus h.*) . SUN E.
heterophyl'la (*Poinsettia h.*) PAINTED E.
lu'cida . . . . SHINING E.
macula'ta (*nutans; presli; Chamaesyce m.*) . . . . SPOTTED E.
pep'lus (*Tithymalus p.*) . . PETTY E.
vermicula'ta (*hirsuta*)

EUPHRA'SIA arc'tica GLANDULAR EYEBRIGHT

FESTU'CA myu'ros RATTAIL FESCUE

Fraga'ria in'dica . . **Duchesnea i.**

FRANSE'RIA (*GAERTNERIA*) BURSAGE
dis'color (*Gaertneria d.*) SKELETONLEAF B.
tomento'sa . . . . WOOLLYLEAF B.

GAERTNE'RIA . . **FRANSERIA**

GALEOP'SIS tetra'hit BRISTLESTEM HEMPNETTLE

GALINSO'GA . . . . QUICKWEED
cilia'ta . . . . FRINGED Q.
parviflo'ra . . . . LITTLEFLOWER Q.

GA'LIUM . . . . . BEDSTRAW
apari'ne . . . . CATCHWEED B.
asprel'lum . . . . ROUGH B.
borea'le . . . . NORTHERN B.
mollu'go . . . . WHITE B.
ve'rum . . . . YELLOW B.

Genis'ta scopa'ria. **Cytisus scoparius**

WEEDS, continued

GERA'NIUM . . . . GERANIUM
columbi'num . . . . . LONGSTALK G.
dissec'tum . . . . CUTLEAF G.
mol'le . . . . DOVEFOOT G.
pusil'lum . . . . SMALL G.

GLECO'MA hedera'cea (*Nepeta h.*)

GLYCYRRHI'ZA lepido'ta AMERICAN LICORICE

GNAPHA'LIUM . . . . CUDWEED
decur'rens . . . . CLAMMY C.
obtusifo'lium (*polycephalum*) FRAGRANT C.
uligino'sum . . . . LOW C.

GRINDE'LIA squarro'sa CURLYCUP GUMWEED

GUTIERRE'ZIA saro'thrae BROOM SNAKEWEED

HACKE'LIA virginia'na (*Lappula v.*)

HEDEO'MA . . FALSEPENNYROYAL
his'pida . . . . ROUGH F.
pulegioi'des . . . . . . AMERICAN F.

HEDYS'ARUM corona'rium SULLA SWEETVETCH

HELE'NIUM . . . SNEEZEWEED
autumna'le . . . . COMMON S.
nudiflo'rum . . . . PURPLEHEAD S.
tenuifo'lium . . . . BITTER S.

HELIAN'THUS . . . SUNFLOWER
an'nuus . . . . COMMON S.
doronicoi'des . . . . OBLONGLEAF S.
maximilia'ni (*maximilianus*) MAXIMILIAN S.
scaber'rimus . . . . . . BLACKHEAD S.
tubero'sus . JERUSALEMARTICHOKE S.

HELIOTRO'PIUM curassa'vicum SALT HELIOTROPE

HIBIS'CUS trio'num (*africanus*) FLOWEROFANHOUR

HIERA'CIUM . . . . HAWKWEED
auranti'acum . . . . ORANGE H.
cladan'thum . . . . . . BRANCHING H.
florenti'num . . . . . KINGDEVIL H.
floribun'dum . . . . . YELLOWDEVIL H.
pilosel'la . . . . . . MOUSEEAR H.
praeal'tum decip'iens
praten'se . . . . FIELD H.

HIEROCH'LOE odora'ta SWEETGRASS

HOL'CUS (*NOTHOLCUS*) VELVETGRASS
halepen'sis . . . . **Sorghum halepense**
lana'tus (*Notholcus l.*) . . COMMON V.

HOR'DEUM . . . . . . BARLEY
juba'tum . . . . FOXTAIL B.
muri'num . . . . MOUSE B.
nodo'sum . . . . MEADOW B.
pusil'lum . . . . LITTLE B.

HYDROCOT'YLE rotundifo'lia SHINY PENNYWORT

HYMENOPHY'SA . **CARDARIA**

HYOSCY'AMUS ni'ger BLACK HENBANE

HYPER'ICUM . . . ST.JOHNSWORT
as'cyron . . . . GIANT S.
ellip'ticum . . . . PALE S.
perfora'tum . . . . COMMON S.
puncta'tum . . . . SPOTTED S.

WEEDS, continued

HYPOCHOER'IS radica'ta SPOTTED CATSEAR

IN'ULA hele'nium ELECAMPANE INULA

IPOMOE'A . . . MORNINGGLORY
coccin'ea . . . . **Quamoclit c.**
hedera'cea . . . . IVYLEAF M.
pandura'ta . . . . BIGROOT M.
purpu'rea (*Convolvulus major*) COMMON M.

IRESI'NE celo'sia JUBASBUSH BLOODLEAF

ISA'TIS tincto'ria . DYERS WOAD

I'VA . . . . SUMPWEED
axilla'ris . . . . POVERTY S.
cilia'ta . . . . SEACOAST S.
xanthifo'lia . . . . RAG S.

Jat'ropha stimulo'sa **Cnidoscolus stimulosus**

JUN'CUS ten'uis (*dichotomus*) POVERTY RUSH

KICKX'IA . . . . . . FLUVELLIN
elati'ne (*Linaria e.*) . . SHARPPOINT F.
spu'ria (*Linaria s.*) . . ROUNDLEAF F.

Knaut'ia arven'sis . . **Scabiosa a.**

KOCH'IA scopa'ria BELVEDERE SUMMERCYPRESS

KYLLIN'GA pu'mila

LACTU'CA . . . . LETTUCE
canaden'sis . . . . CANADA L.
pulchel'la . . . . CHICORY L.
viro'sa . . . . BITTER L.

LA'MIUM . . . . . DEADNETTLE
amplexicau'le . . . . . . HENBIT D.
macula'tum . . . . SPOTTED D.
purpu'reum . . . . PURPLE D.

LAP'PA . . . . . **ARCTIUM**
ed'ulis; ma'jor . . . . **A. lappa**

LAP'PULA . . . . . STICKSEED
echina'ta . . . . EUROPEAN S.
redow'ski
virginia'na . . . . **Hackelia v.**

LAPSA'NA commu'nis COMMON NIPPLEWORT

Legou'zia perfolia'ta. **Specularia p.**

LEON'TODON (*APARGIA*) HAWKBIT
autumna'lis (*Apargia a.*) . . FALL H.
tarax'acum . . . **Taraxacum officinale**

LEONU'RUS cardi'aca COMMON MOTHERWORT

LEPACH'YS . . . . **RATIBIDA**

LEPID'IUM . . . . PEPPERWEED
campes'tre . . . . FIELD P.
densiflo'rum (*apetalum*) . PRAIRIE P.
dra'ba . . . . **Cardaria d.**
perfolia'tum . . . . CLASPING P.
re'pens . . . . LENS P.
sati'vum . . . . . . GARDENCRESS P.
virgin'icum . . . . VIRGINIA P.

LEP'TILON . . . . **ERIGERON**

LEUCAN'THEMUM **CHRYSANTHEMUM**

LINA'RIA . . . . TOADFLAX
elati'ne . . . . **Kickxia e.**
mi'nor . . . . SMALL T.
spu'ria . . . . **Kickxia s.**
vulga'ris . . . . BUTTER-AND-EGGS T.

WEEDS, continued

LI'NUM sulca'tum (*Cathartolinum s.*) . . . . GROOVED FLAX

LITHOSPER'MUM . GROMWELL
arven'se . . . . CORN G.
officina'le . . . . COMMON G.

LOBE'LIA infla'ta INDIANTOBACCO LOBELIA

LO'LIUM temulen'tum DARNEL RYEGRASS

LONIC'ERA japon'ica JAPANESE HONEYSUCKLE

LO'TUS cornicula'tus BIRDSFOOT DEERVETCH

LYCH'NIS . . . . . CAMPION
al'ba (*vespertina*) . . . . EVENING C.
chalcedo'nica . . MALTESECROSS C.
corona'ria . . . . ROSE C.
dioi'ca (*diurna*) . . . . . RED C.
drum'mondi . . . . . DRUMMOND C.
floscu'culi . . . . . RAGGEDROBIN
githa'go . . . . . . **Agrostemma g.**

LYCOP'SIS arven'sis

LYCO'PUS . . . . . BUGLEWEED
america'nus . . . . . AMERICAN B.
uniflo'rus

LYGODES'MIA jun'cea RUSH SKELETONPLANT

LYSIMACH'IA nummula'ria MONEYWORT

MA'DIA . . . . TARWEED
glomera'ta . . . . CLUSTER T.
sati'va . . . . CHILEAN T.

MAL'VA . . . . MALLOW
moscha'ta . . . . MUSK M.
rotundifo'lia . . . . . RUNNING M.

MARRU'BIUM vulga're COMMON HOARHOUND

MATRICA'RIA . . . . MAYWEED
chamomil'la . . . GERMAN-CAMOMILE
inodo'ra (*Chrysanthemum inodorum*) SCENTLESS M.
matricarioi'des . . . PINEAPPLEWEED

MEDICA'GO . . . . . . MEDIC
arab'ica (*maculata*) . . SPOTTED M.
his'pida denticula'ta (*M. denticulata*) TOOTHED BURCLOVER
lupuli'na . . . . BLACK M.

MICRAM'PELIS **ECHINOCYSTIS**

MOLDA'VICA **DRACOCEPHALUM**

MOLI'NIA caeru'lea . MOORGRASS

MOLLU'GO verticilla'ta CARPETWEED

NEP'ETA . . . . NEPETA
cata'ria . . . . CATNIP
hedera'cea . . . . **Glecoma h.**

NES'LIA panicula'ta. BALLMUSTARD

NOR'TA . . . . **SISYMBRIUM**

NOTHOL'CUS . . . . . **HOLCUS**

ODONTI'TES ru'bra. RED BARTSIA

OENOTHE'RA (*ANOGRA*) EVENINGPRIMROSE
bien'nis (*Anogra b.*) . . COMMON E.
pal'lida (*albicaulis; Anogra a.; A. pallida*) . . . . PALE E.

WEEDS, continued

ONOPOR'DUM acan'thium SCOTCH COTTONTHISTLE

ORNITHOG'ALUM STAR-OF-BETHLEHEM
nu'tans . . . . NODDING S.
umbella'tum . . . . . . COMMON S.

OROBAN'CHE species. BROOMRAPE

OX'ALIS (*XANTHOXALIS*) OXALIS
cornicula'ta (*Xanthoxalis c.*) CREEPING O.
europae'a . . EUROPEAN YELLOW O.
stric'ta (*Xanthoxalis s.*) COMMON YELLOW O.

PAN'ICUM PANICUM; WITCHGRASS
capilla're . . . . COMMON W.
dichotomiflo'rum . . . . . . FALL P. (*Knucklegrass*)
virga'tum . . . . . SWITCHGRASS

PAPA'VER . . . . POPPY
du'bium . . . . LONGPOD P.
rhoe'as . . . . CORN P.

PARSONS'IA . . . . **CUPHEA**

PAS'PALUM . . . . . PASPALUM
lae've . . . . FIELD P.
seta'ceum . . . . THIN P.

PASSIFLO'RA incarna'ta MAYPOP PASSIONFLOWER

PASTINA'CA sati'va GARDEN PARSNIP

Perit'oma serrula'tum **Cleome serrulata**

PERSICA'RIA . **POLYGONUM**

PHAL'ARIS canarien'sis CANARYGRASS

PHYTOLAC'CA america'na (*decandra*) . . . COMMON POKEBERRY

PIARO'PUS . . **EICHHORNIA**

PI'CRIS . . . . OXTONGUE
echioi'des . . . . BRISTLY O.
hieracioi'des . . . . . HAWKWEED O.

PLANTA'GO . . . . . . PLANTAIN
arista'ta . BOTTLEBRUSH INDIANWHEAT
in'dica (*arenaria*) . . . . WHORLED P.
lanceola'ta . . . . . . BUCKHORN P.
ma'jor . . . . RIPPLESEED P.
me'dia . . . . SWEET P.
rhodosper'ma . . . . . REDSEED P.
ru'geli . . . . BLACKSEED P.

PO'A compres'sa CANADA BLUEGRASS

POINSET'TIA . . **EUPHORBIA**

POLANIS'IA grave'olens STINKING CLAMMYWEED

POLYG'ONUM (*BILDERDYKIA; PERSICARIA*). KNOTWEED
avicula're . . . . . . PROSTRATE K.
convol'vulus (*Bilderdykia c.*) DULLSEED CORNBIND
erec'tum . . . . ERECT K.
hydropi'per (*Persicaria h.*) MARSHPEPPER SMARTWEED
hydropiperoi'des (*Persicaria h.*) SWAMP S.
lapathifo'lium (*Persicaria lapathifolia*) CURLTOP LADYSTHUMB
muhlenberg'i . . . . . BIGROOT L.

WEEDS (POLYGONUM), continued
orienta'le (*Persicaria orientalis*) PRINCESPLUME LADYSTHUMB
pennsylva'nicum PENNSYLVANIA SMARTWEED
persica'ria (*Persicaria mitis*) SPOTTED LADYSTHUMB
puncta'tum (*acre; Persicaria punctata*) DOTTED SMARTWEED
sagitta'tum . . . . **Tracaulon s.**
scan'dens (*Bilderdykia s.; Tiniaria s.*) HEDGE CORNBIND

PORTULAC'A olera'cea (*aurea*) COMMON PURSLANE

POTAMOGE'TON species PONDWEED

POTENTIL'LA (*ARGENTINA*) CINQUEFOIL
anseri'na (*Argentina a.*) SILVERWEED C.
argen'tea . . . . SILVER C.
canaden'sis . . . . OLDFIELD C.
monspelien'sis . . . MONTPELIER C.
norveg'ica (*P. monspeliensis n.*) NORWEGIAN C.
pu'mila . . . . PETTY C.
rec'ta . . . . SULFUR C.

PRUNEL'LA vulga'ris COMMON SELFHEAL

PTERID'IUM . . . . . BRACKEN
aquili'num pubes'cens . . WESTERN B.
latius'culum . . . . . . EASTERN B.

QUAM'OCLIT coccin'ea (*Ipomoea c.*) . . . . SCARLET STARGLORY

RADIC'ULA . . . . **RORIPPA**

RANUN'CULUS . . . BUTTERCUP
abort'ivus . . . . . . LITTLELEAF B.
a'cris (*acer*) . . . . TALL B.
arven'sis . . . . CORN B.
bulbo'sus . . . . BULB B.
parviflo'rus . . . . . STICKTIGHT B.
re'pens (*speciosus*) . . CREEPING B.
scelera'tus (*eremogenes*) . BLISTER B.

RAPH'ANUS . . . . . . RADISH
raphanis'trum . . . . . . WILD R.
sati'vus . . . . GARDEN R.

RATIB'IDA pinna'ta (*Lepachys p.*)

RESE'DA lute'a YELLOW MIGNONETTE

RHINAN'THUS crista-gal'li COCKSCOMB RATTLEWEED

Rhus' toxicoden'dron **Toxicodendron radicans**

RORIP'PA (*RADICULA*)
austri'aca (*Radicula a.*) AUSTRIAN FIELDCRESS
palus'tris (*Radicula p.*) BOG MARSHCRESS
sylves'tris . . . YELLOW FIELDCRESS

RU'BUS flagella'ris (*procumbens*) NORTHERN DEWBERRY

RUDBECK'IA . . . CONEFLOWER
hir'ta . . . . BLACKEYEDSUSAN
lacinia'ta . . . . CUTLEAF C.

RU'MEX . . . . DOCK
aceto'sa . . . . . . GARDEN SORREL
acetosel'la . . . . SHEEP S.
conglomera'tus . . . . CLUSTERED D.
cris'pus . . . . CURLY D.
mexica'nus . . . . . . MEXICAN D.

WEEDS (RUMEX), continued
obtusifo'lius . . . . . Bitter Dock
patien'tia . . . . Patience D.
persicarioi'des (*maritimus*). Golden D.
veno'sus . . . . Veiny D.

SAL'SOLA ka'li tenuifo'lia (*S. pestifer*). . Tumbling Russianthistle

SAPONA'RIA (*VACCARIA*) Soapwort
officina'lis . . . . . . Bouncingbet
vacca'ria (*Vaccaria pyramidata; V. vaccaria; V. vulgaris*) . . . Cow S.

SCABIO'SA arven'sis (*Knautia a.*) Field Scabious

SCIR'PUS species . . . Bulrush

SCLERAN'THUS an'nuus Annual Knawel

SE'DUM . . . . . . Stonecrop
a'cre . . . . Goldmoss S.
purpu'reum Hort.
tele'phium purpu'reum (*S. triphyllum*)

SENE'CIO . . . . . Groundsel
jacobae'a . . . . Ragwort G.
visco'sus . . . . Sticky G.
vulga'ris. . . . . Common G.

SETA'RIA. Bristlegrass; Millet
lutes'cens . . . . Yellow B.
verticilla'ta . . . . Hooked B.
vir'idis . . . . Green B.

SHERARD'IA arven'sis Fieldmadder

SIC'YOS angula'tus Wall Burcucumber

SI'DA. . . . . Sida
hedera'cea. . . . . Alkali S.
spino'sa . . . . Prickly S.

SILE'NE . . . . Silene
antirrhi'na . . . . Sleepy S.
arme'ria . . . . Sweetwilliam S.
co'nica . . . . Conical S.
dichot'oma . . . . Forked S.
gal'lica (*anglica*) . . . . . French S.
latifo'lia (*vulgaris*) . . . Cowbell S.
noctiflo'ra . . . Nightflowering S.

SINA'PIS . . . . . **BRASSICA**

SISYM'BRIUM (*NORTA*)
altis'simum (*Norta altissima*) Tumblemustard
canes'cens . . . **Descurainia menziesi**
inci'sum fi'lipes **Descurainia longipedicellata**
—hartwegia'num **Descurainia richardsoni**
officina'le (*Erysimum o.*)
pinna'tum . . . **Descurainia menziesi**
sophi'a . . . **Descurainia pinnata**

SMI'LAX . . . . . . Greenbrier
glau'ca . . . . Cat G.
rotundifo'lia . . . . . . Common G.

SOLA'NUM . . . . . Nightshade
carolinen'se . Carolina Horsenettle
dulcama'ra . . . . Bitter N.
elaeagnifo'lium . . . . Silverleaf N.
ni'grum . . . . Black N.
rostra'tum . . . . . Buffalobur N.
triflo'rum . . . . Cutleaf N.

SOLIDA'GO. . . . . Goldenrod
canaden'sis . . . . Canada G.
gigan'tea leiophyl'la (*S. serotina*) November G.

WEEDS (SOLIDAGO), continued
graminifo'lia . Grassleaf Goldenrod
rugo'sa . . . . Wrinkled G.

SON'CHUS . . . . . Sowthistle
arven'sis . . . . Field S.
as'per . . . . Prickly S.
olera'ceus . . . . Common S.

SOPHI'A . . . . **DESCURAINIA**

SOR'GHUM halepen'se (*Holcus halepensis*) . . . . Johnsongrass

Spar'tium scopa'rium **Cytisus scoparius**

SPECULA'RIA perfolia'ta (*Legouzia p.*) Clasping Venuslookingglass

SPER'GULA arven'sis Corn Spurry

SPIRAE'A. . . . . Spirea
doug'lasi . . . . Douglas S.
latifo'lia (*salicifolia* U. S. Auth., *not* L.) Broadleaf Meadowsweet S.
tomento'sa . . . . . . Hardhack S.

SPORO'BOLUS vaginiflo'rus Poverty Dropseed

STA'CHYS . . . . Betony
an'nua . . . . . . Hedgenettle B.
arven'sis . . . . . . Fieldnettle B.
palus'tris . . . . Marsh B.

STELLA'RIA . . . . . Starwort
gramin'ea . . . . Little S.
me'dia . . . . Chickweed

STI'PA Needlegrass; Feathergrass
coma'ta . . . . . Needleandthread
spar'tea . . . . . . Porcupinegrass

SUCCI'SA austra'lis Southern Succisa

SYM'PHYTUM officina'le Common Comfrey

TANACE'TUM vulga're (*Chrysanthemum v.*) . . . Common Tansy

TARAX'ACUM . . . Dandelion
laeviga'tum . . . . . . Smooth D.
officina'le (*Leontodon taraxacum*) Common D.

THLAS'PI. . . . . . . Pennycress
arven'se. . . . . Field P.
perfolia'tum . . . . . Thorowort P.

THY'MUS serpyl'lum Mother-of-thyme

Tinia'ria scan'dens . **Polygonum s.**

TITHYMALOP'SIS; TITHYMA'LUS . . . . **EUPHORBIA**

TOXICODEN'DRON rad'icans (*Rhus toxicodendron*) Common Poisonivy

TRACAU'LON sagitta'tum (*Polygonum s.*) Arrowleaf Tearthumb

TRAGOPO'GON . . . . . Salsify
porrifo'lius. . . Vegetable-oyster S.
praten'sis . . . . Meadow S.

TRA'PA na'tans . Waterchestnut

TRIB'ULUS terres'tris Puncturevine

TRICHOSTE'MA dichot'omum Forked Bluecurls

TRIFO'LIUM species. . . Clover

WEEDS, continued
TUSSILA'GO far'fara Common Coltsfoot

U'LEX europae'us. Common Gorse

URTI'CA . . . . Nettle
dioi'ca . . . . Bigsting N.
grac'ilis . . . . Slim N.
proce'ra . . . . Tall N.
u'rens. . . . . Dog N.

VACCA'RIA . . . **SAPONARIA**

VALERIANEL'LA species Cornsalad

VERBAS'CUM thap'sus Flannel Mullein

VERBE'NA . . . . Verbena
angustifo'lia . . . . Narrowleaf V.
bractea'ta (*bracteosa*) . Bigbract V.
hasta'ta . . . . Blue V.
officina'lis . . . . . . European V.
stric'ta . . . . Woolly V.
urticaefo'lia . . . . White V.

VERNO'NIA noveboracen'sis NewYork Ironweed

VERON'ICA. . . . . Speedwell
agres'tis . . . . Field S.
arven'sis . . . . Common S.
officina'lis . . . . Drug S.
peregri'na . . . . . . Purslane S.
poli'ta. . . . . Wayside S.
serpyllifo'lia (*humifusa*) Thymeleaf S.
tournefort'i (*persica*) . Tournefort S.

VIC'IA . . . . Vetch
angustifo'lia . . . . Narrowleaf V.
crac'ca . . . . Bird V.
sati'va . . . . Common V.
tetrasper'ma . . . . . Fourseed V.
villo'sa . . . . Hairy V.

XAN'THIUM . . . . Cocklebur
orienta'le (*canadense*) . . Oriental C.
spino'sum . . . . Spiny C.

XANTHOX'ALIS . . . **OXALIS**

ZYGOPHYL'LUM faba'go Syrian Beancaper

WEI'GELA (*CALYPTROSTIGMA; DIERVILLA* in part; *WEIGELASTRUM*) . . . . . Weigela

Some authorities list all species of Weigela under Diervilla; others list all but four species under Weigela. This discrepancy is purely taxonomic. The Editorial Committee is following Rehder and Bailey by separating the Weigelas from the true Diervillas.

amab'ilis Hort., *not Diervilla a.* Carr. **W. florida**
arbo'rea Hort. . . **W. coraeensis alba**

This untenable name appears to be occasionally applied also to forms of W. florida.

arbores'cens Hort. **W. floribunda grandiflora**
coraeen'sis (*Diervilla amabilis* Carr., *not W. amabilis* Hort.; *D. coraeensis; D. grandiflora*) . . . . Korean W.
—al'ba (*W. arborea* Hort.; *W. a. grandiflora* Hort.; *W. grandiflora a.; Diervilla c. arborea*) . . . . White K.W.
dec'ora . . . . . . Greenpink W.
floribun'da (*Diervilla f.; D. multiflora*) Crimson W.
—grandiflo'ra (*W. arborescens* Hort.) Showy C.W.

WEIGELA, continued
floribun'da versic'olor (*Diervilla v.*) VERSICOLOR CRIMSON WEIGELA
flor'ida (*amabilis* Hort., *not Diervilla a.* Carr.; *rosea; Diervilla f.; D. pauciflora*) . . . . . OLDFASHIONED W.
—al'ba (*W. rosea a.*) . . WHITE O.W.
—venus'ta (*W. venusta; Diervilla f. v.; D. venusta*)
¢VARIEGATA. hv. D. florida
grandiflo'ra al'ba . . **W. coraeensis a.**
horten'sis Hort. (*W. japonica h.; Diervilla h.; D. j. h.*) . . GARDENERS W.
—niv'ea Hort. (*W. h. albiflora; Diervilla japonica alba; D. j. nivea*) WHITE G.W.

A name of no standing whatever, in rather wide but loose use for all hybrid Weigelas.

japon'ica (*Diervilla j.*) . JAPANESE W.
—horten'sis . . . . . . **W. hortensis**
—si'nica (*Diervilla j. s.*) . CHINESE W.
maximowicz'i (*Diervilla m.; Weigelastrum m.*) . . . . MAXIMOWICZ W.
middendorfia'na (*Calyptrostigma m.; Diervilla m.*) . . . MIDDENDORFF W.
prae'cox (*Diervilla p.*) . . . EARLY W.
rose'a . . . . **W. florida**
sessilifo'lia . . . . **Diervilla s.**
sua'vis
subses'silis
venus'ta . . . . **W. florida v.**
∞**wag'neri** (*coraeensis × florida*) ∞WAGNER W.

ABEL CARRIERE. hv. Weigela
ANDRE THOUIN
AVALANCHE
AVANTE-GARDE
BIFORMIS
BOUQUET
BOUQUET ROSE
CANDIDA. *Snow.*
CHAMELEON
CONQUERANT
CONGO
CONQUETE
DAME BLANCHE
DAUBENTON
DESBOIS (*desboisi*)
DESCARTES
DR. BAILLON
DR. BULLIARD
DUCHARTRE
DWARF VARIEGATED (*nana variegata*)
EDOUARD ANDRE
ESPERANCE
EVA RATHKE
FEERIE
FLEUR DE MAI
FLOREAL
GIGANTIFLORA
GIRONDIN
GRACIEUX
GRATISSIMA
GROENEWEGENI
GUSTAVE MALLET
HENDERSON (*hendersoni*)
INTERMEDIA
ISOLINE
KOSTER (*kosteriana*)
KOSTER VARIEGATED (*kosteriana variegata*)
LAVALLE (*lavallei*)
LE PRINTEMPS
LOOYMANNI-AUREA
LOWE (*lowei*)
MARC TELLIER

WEIGELA, continued
MESSAGER
MME. COUTOURIER
MME. LEMOINE
MONTBLANC
MONTESQUIEU
OTHELLO
PAVILLON BLANC
PERLE
PRES. DUCHARTRE
PROFUSION
PURPUREA
RED (*incarnata*)
RICHESSE
RUBRA
SEDUCTION
SIEBOLD (*sieboldi*)
SIEBOLD SILVEREDGE (*sieboldi argenteomarginata*)
SIMONDS (*simondsi*)
Snow. CANDIDA
STELZNER (*stelzneri*)
STYRIACA
VANHOUTTE (*vanhouttei*)
VENOSA
VERSCHAFFELT (*verschaffelti*)
VESTALE
YELLOWEDGE (*luteomarginata*)

WEIGELA . . . . **Weigela**
CHINESE W. . . . **W. japonica sinica**
CRIMSON W. . . . . . **W. floribunda**
EARLY W. . . . . **W. praecox**
GARDENERS W. . . . . . **W. hortensis**
GREENPINK W. . . . . . . **W. decora**
JAPANESE W. . . . . . . **W. japonica**
KOREAN W. . . . . . **W. coraeensis**
MAXIMOWICZ W. . . **W. maximowiczi**
MIDDENDORFF W. **W. middendorfiana**
OLDFASHIONED W. . . . . **W. florida**
SHOWY CRIMSON W. **W. floribunda grandiflora**
VERSICOLOR C. W. . **W. f. versicolor**
∞WAGNER W. . . . . . ∞**W. wagneri**
WHITE GARDENERS W. **W. hortensis nivea**
WHITE KOREAN W. **W. coraeensis alba**
WHITE OLDFASHIONED W. **W. florida a.**

WEIGELAS'TRUM . . . **WEIGELA**

WEINGAERTNE'RIA
See **GRASS GENERA.**

WEINGART'IA (*SPEGAZZINIA*)
See **CACTUS GENERA.**

WEINMAN'NIA
racemo'sa . . . . KAMAHI
sylvic'ola . . . . TAWHERO
trichosper'ma . . . . TENIO

WELLINGTO'NIA . . . **SEQUOIA**

WELSHPOPPY . . . **Meconopsis cambrica**

WELWITSCH'IA (*TUMBOA*) WELWITSCHIA
mirab'ilis . . . . . . WELWITSCHIA

Welwitschia Hook. f. (1862), *not* Reichb. (1837) is conserved under International Rules. This extraordinary African desert plant has only two leaves, which last the entire life of the plant (perhaps a century).

WELWITSCH'IA Reichb., *not* Hook. f. **GILIA**

WENZE'LIA . . . . WENZELIA
archboldia'na . . . . ARCHBOLDS W.
brev'ipes . . . . . . PHILIPPINE W.
kamba'rae . . . . FIJI W.

WERCK'LEA . . . . TEASELMALLOW
insig'nis . . . . COSTARICA T.

WERCKLEOCE'REUS
See **CACTUS GENERA.**

WestAfrican-Piassava. . . RAFFIAPALM, WINE: **Raphia vinifera**

WESTRIN'GIA . . . . . WESTRINGIA
rosmarinifor'mis . ROSEMARYBUSH W. (*Australian-Rosemary*)

WHEAT . . . . **Triticum; T. aestivum**
See also **CEREALS.**
ALASKA W. Hort. var. of **T. turgidum**
CLUB W. . . . . **T. compactum**
DURUM W. . . . . **T. durum**
POLISH W. . . . . . . **T. polonicum**
POULARD W. . . . . . . **T. turgidum**
TIMOPHEERI W. . . . **T. timopheeri**
WILD W. . . . . **T. dicoccoides**

WHEATGRASS . . . . **Agropyron**
ALPINE BEARDED W. **A. subsecundum andinum**
ANNUAL W. . . . . **A. triticeum**
ARIZONA W. . . . . . . **A. arizonicum**
BAKER W. . . . . **A. bakeri**
BEARDED BLUEBUNCH W. **A. spicatum**
BEARDED W. . . . . **A. subsecundum**
BEARDLESS BLUEBUNCH W. **A. inerme**
BLUESTEM W. . . . . **A. smithi**
CRESTED W. . . . . . . **A. cristatum**
DROOPING W. . . . **A. semicostatum**
DUNE W. . . . . **A. arenicola**
ELMER W. . . . . **A. elmeri**
FOXTAIL W. . . . . **A. saxicola**
GRIFFITHS W. . . . . . . **A. griffithsi**
HAIRY BLUEBUNCH W. **A. spicatum pubescens**
MONTANA W. . . . . . . **A. albicans**
PARISH W. . . . . **A. parishi**
PRINGLE W. . . . . **A. pringlei**
SAUNDERS W. . . . . . **A. saundersi**
SCRIBNER W. . . . . . . **A. scribneri**
SIBERIAN W. . . . . . . **A. sibiricum**
SLENDER W. . . . . . **A. pauciflorum**
STIFFHAIR W. . . . **A. trichophorum**
STREAMBANK W. . . . . . **A. riparium**
SWALE W. . . . . **A. vulpinum**
TALL W. . . . . **A. elongatum**
THICKSPIKE W. . . **A. dasystachyum**
UGAM W. . . . . **A. ugamicum**
VIOLET W. . . . . **A. violaceum**
Western W. . . . . . . BLUESTEM W.

WHEELFRUITBUSH . . . . **Trochocarpa**
LAURELLEAF W. . . . . . **T. laurina**
TASMANIAN W. . . . . **T. thymifolia**

WHEELSTAMENTREE **Trochodendron; T. aralioides**

WHIP'PLEA . . . . WHIPPLEA
modes'ta . . . . MODEST W.
utahen'sis . . . . . . **Fendlerella u.**

WHIPTREE . . . . **Luehea**
COMMON W. . . . . **L. divaricata**

WHISPERINGBELLS . . . **Emmenanthe**
PINK W. . . . **E. penduliflora rosea**
SAGEBRUSH W. . . . . . **E. parviflora**
YELLOW W. . . . . . . **E. penduliflora**

Whitecedar, PortOrford . FALSECYPRESS, LAWSON: **Chamaecyparis lawsoniana**

WHITEGRASS . . . . . **Leersia virginica**

Whitegum . . . EUCALYPTUS, JOUNAMA: **Eucalyptus de-beuzevillei;** ROSS E.: **E. rossi;** SILVERBARK E.: **E. argophloia**

WHITEQUEBRACHO . . . **Aspidosperma**
COMMON W. . . **A. quebracho-blanco**
WOOLLY W. . . . . **A. tomentosum**

WHITESAPOTE . . . **Casimiroa edulis**
WOOLLYLEAF W. . . . **C. tetrameria**

Whitesilk Cotton . SHELLSEED, COTTON: **Cochlospermum religiosum**

WHITETOP . . . . **Cardaria**
HAIRY W. . . . . . . **C. pubescens**
LONGSTALK H. W. . . **C. p. elongata**
PEPPERWEED W. . . . . **C. draba**
PERSIAN W. . . . . . **C. macrocarpa**
TURKESTAN W. . . . . **C. fenestrata**

WHITETOP-SEDGE . . . . **Dichromena**
EVERGLADES W. . . . **D. floridensis**
SANDSWAMP W.. . . . . **D. latifolia**
STARRUSH W. . . . . . **D. colorata**

WHITLA'VIA . . . **PHACELIA**
gloxinoi'des . . . . . . **P. minor g.**
grandiflo'ra . . . . **P. minor**

WHITLOWWORT . **Illecebrum verticillatum**

Whitlowwort . . . . . . DRABA: **Draba**; NAILWORT: **Paronychia**

WHORTLEBERRY
BIG W. . **Vaccinium membranaceum**
CAUCASIAN W. . . . **V. arctostaphylos**
GROUSE W. . . . . . . **V. scoparium**
HAIRY W. . . . . **V. hirsutum**
MYRTLE W. . . . . . . **V. myrtillus**
OVALLEAF W. . . . . **V. ovalifolium**
RED W. . . . . **V. parvifolium**
ROCKYMOUNTAIN W. . **V. oreophilum**
WHITEFRUIT MYRTLE W. **V. myrtillus leucocarpum**

WIDDRINGTO'NIA . WIDDRINGTONIA
cupressoi'des . . . . . SAPREE W.
juniperoi'des (*Callitris arborea*) CLANWILLIAM W.
schwarz'i . . . . SCHWARZ W.
whyt'ei (*Callitris w.*) . . MLANJI W. (*Mlanjicedar*)

WIDGEONGRASS . . . . **Ruppia maritima**

WIDGEONWEED . . . . **Ruppia**

WIGAND'IA. . . . . WIGANDIA
caracasa'na . . . . . . CARACAS W.
—macrophyl'la (*W. macrophylla*) BIGLEAF C.W.
imperia'lis . . . . . . EMPEROR W.
Perhaps only a var. of W. caracasana.
kunth'i . . . . KUNTH W.
u'rens . . . . PERU W.
vigier'i . . . . SILVER W.
Perhaps only a var. of W. caracasana.

WILCOX'IA. See **CACTUS GENERA.**

WILDBEAN . . . . **Strophostyles**
PINK W. . . . . **S. umbellata**
SMALL W. . . . . **S. pauciflora**
TRAILING W.. . . . . **S. helvola**

WILDCABBAGE, THICKSTEM **Caulanthus crassicaulis**

WILDCELERY . . . . **Vallisneria**
AMERICAN W. . . . . . **V. americana**
GIANT W. . . . . **V. gigantea**
SPIRAL W. . . . . **V. spiralis**

WILDCOFFEE . . . . **Psychotria**
BAHAMA W. . . . . . **P. bahamensis**
CAPE W. . . . . **P. capensis**
COMOROISLANDS W. . **P. bacteriophila**
JASMINE W. . . . . . **P. jasminiflora**
SEMINOLE W. . . . . **P. undata**
SHORTLEAF W. . . . . . **P. tenuifolia**
ST.AUGUSTINE W. **P. nervosa lanceolata**

WILDCOFFEE, continued
ST.JOHNS W. . . **Psychotria nervosa**
SULZNER W. . . . . **P. sulzneri**

WILDGINGER . . . . **Asarum**
ARUM W. . . . . **A. arifolium**
BRITISHCOLUMBIA W. . . **A. caudatum**
CANADA W. . . . . . . **A. canadense**
CURLY W. . . . . **A. reflexum**
EUROPEAN W. . . . . **A. europaeum**
LEMMONS W. . . . . . . **A. lemmoni**
MOTTLED W.. . . . **A. shuttleworthi**
SIERRA W. . . . . **A. hartwegi**
VIRGINIA W. . . . . . **A. virginicum**

WILDINDIGO . . . . **Baptisia**
ATLANTIC W.. . . . . . **B. leucantha**
BLUE W. . . . . **B. australis**
CREAM W. . . . . **B. bracteata**
GEORGIA W. . . . . . . **B. perfoliata**
PLAINS W. . . . . . . **B. leucophaea**
WHITE W. . . . . **B. alba**
YELLOW W. . . . . **B. tinctoria**

WILDIXORA . . . . **Isertia**
TRINIDAD W. . . . . . . **I. parviflora**

Wildlemon . . . RHEEDIA, WILDLEMON: **Rheedia edulis**

WILDLICORICE
LANCELEAF W. . **Galium lanceolatum**
NORTHERN W. . . **G. kamtschaticum**

WILDLIME . . . . **Microcitrus**
See also FINGERLIME.
AUSTRALIA ROUND W. . . **M. australis**
QUEENSLAND W. . . . . **M. inodora**

WILDRICE . . . . **Zizania; Zizaniopsis**
ANNUAL W. . . . . **Zizania aquatica**
NORTHERN W. **Zizania a. angustifolia**
SOUTHERN W. . **Zizaniopsis miliacea**
TEXAS W. . . . . . . **Zizania texana**

WILDRYE . . . . **Elymus**
ALASKA W. . . . . **E. hirsutus**
BEARDLESS VIRGINIA W. **E. virginicus submuticus**
BLUE W. . . . . **E. glaucus**
CANADA W. . . . . . . **E. canadensis**
CHINESE W. . . . . **E. chinensis**
COLORADO W. . . . . . **E. ambiguus**
COMMON DUNE W. . . . . . **E. mollis**
CREEPING W. . . . . . **E. triticoides**
DAHURIAN W. . . . . . **E. dahuricus**
EUROPEAN DUNE W. . . **E. arenarius**
FUZZYSPIKE W. . . . **E. innovatus**
GIANT W. . . . . . . **E. condensatus**
HAIRYLEAF CREEPING W. **E. triticoides pubescens**
HAIRYSCALE COLORADO W. **E. ambiguus strigosus**
HAIRYSCALE VIRGINIA W. **E. virginicus intermedius**
HAIRY W. . . . . **E. villosus**
JEPSON W. . . . . **E. glaucus jepsoni**
LONGAWN VIRGINIA W. **E. virginicus glabriflorus**
LOW CREEPING W. **E. triticoides simplex**
MACOUN W. . . . . **E. macouni**
MAMMOTH W. . . . . . . **E. giganteus**
MEDUSAHEAD W. . . **E. caput-medusae**
PACIFIC GIANT W. **E. condensatus pubens**
PACIFIC W. . . . . **E. virescens**
PRAIRIE W. . **E. virginicus australis**
PURPLE W. . . . . **E. aristatus**
RIVERBANK W.. . . . . . . **E. riparius**
ROBUST CANADA W. **E. canadensis robustus**

WILDRYE, continued
RUSSIAN W. . . . . **Elymus junceus**
SALINA W. . . . . **E. salina**
SALTMARSH VIRGINIA W. **E. virginicus halophilus**
SAND W. . . . . **E. arenicola**
SIBERIAN W. . . . . **E. sibiricus**
Siberian W. . . . . MAMMOTH W.
SMOOTHSCALE CANADA W. **E. canadensis brachystachys**
TEXAS W. . . . . **E. interruptus**
THICKSPIKE W. . . . **E. dasystachys**
VANCOUVER DUNE W. **E. vancouverensis**
VANCOUVER W. . **E. glaucus tenuis**
VIRGINIA W. . . . . . . **E. virginicus**
WYOMING W. . . . . . . **E. hirtiflorus**
YELLOW W. . . . . **E. flavescens**

WILDSARSAPARILLA . . **Aralia nudicaulis**

WILDTOBACCO . . . . **Acnistus**
LITTLEFLOWER W. . . **A. parviflorus**
TREE W. . . . . **A. arborescens**

WILLKOM'MIA . . . . WILLKOMMIA
See **GRASS GENERA.**

WILLOW . . . . **Salix**
ALASKABOG W. . . . . **S. fuscescens**
ALMONDLEAF W. . . . **S. amygdalina**
ALPS W.. . . . . **S. glabra**
ARCTIC W.. . . . . **S. arctica**
ARMENIA W. . . . . **S. medemi**
ARROYO W. . . . . **S. lasiolepis**
ATHABASCA W. . . . **S. athabascensis**
∞ AUSTRIAN W. . . . . . ∞ **S. austriaca**
AUTUMN W. . . . . **S. serissima**
BABYLON WEEPING W. **S. babylonica**
BAKER ARROYO W. **S. lasiolepis bakeri**
BALSAM W. . . . . **S. pyrifolia**
BARCLAY W. . . . . **S. barclayi**
BARRATT W. . . . . . **S. barrattiana**
BARRENGROUND W. . **S. brachycarpa**
BASKET W. . . . . **S. viminalis**
BAYBERRY W. . . . ×**S. myricoides**
BEAKED W. . . . . **S. rostrata**
BEARBERRY W. . . . . . . **S. uva-ursi**
BEAUTIFUL W. . . . . **S. bella**
BEBB W. . . . . **S. bebbiana**
BIGCATKIN W. . . . . **S. gracilistyla**
BIGELOW ARROYO W. **S. lasiolepis bigelovi**
BIGLEAF PACIFIC W. **S. lasiandra macrophylla**
BIGLEAF W. . . . . . . **S. grandifolia**
BLACK W. . . . . **S. nigra**
BLUEBERRY W. . . . . **S. myrtillifolia**
BLUELEAF W. . . **S. glaucophylloides**
BLUESTEM W. . . . . **S. irrorata**
BLUE W. . . . . **S. subcoerulea**
BLUNTLEAF W. . . . . . . **S. obtusata**
BOCK W. . . . . **S. bocki**
BOG W. . . . . **S. pedicellaris**
BONPLAND W. . . . **S. bonplandiana**
BREWER W. . . . . **S. breweri**
BRITTLE W. . . . . **S. fragilis**
∞ BROADLEAF W. . . . . . ∞ **S. latifolia**
BROADLEAF WHITE W. . **S. alba ovalis**
CASCADES W. . . . . . **S. cascadensis**
CATHAY W. . . . . **S. cathayana**
CHAMISSO W. . . . . **S. chamissonis**
∞ CHIAROSCURO W. . . ∞ **S. hankensoni**
CLASPING PURPLEOSIER W. **S. purpurea amplexicaulis**
COASTALPLAIN W. . . . . **S. longipes**
∞ COTTET W. . . . . ∞ **S. cotteti**
COULTER W. . . . . **S. coulteri**
COYOTE W. . . . . **S. exigua**
CREEPING W. . . . . **S. repens**

Willow, continued

Daphne W. . . . . **Salix daphnoides**
Delnorte W. . . . **S. delnortensis**
Desert W. . . . . . **S. desertorum**
Diamond W. . . . . **S. missouriensis**
Dodges W. . . . . . . **S. dodgeana**
∞ Dons W. . . . . . . ∞ **S. doniana**
Drummond W. . . **S. drummondiana**
Dudley W. . . **S. gooddingi vallicola**
Dusky W. . . . . **S. melanopsis**
Dwarf Pussy W. . . . . . **S. tristis**
Eastwood W. . . . **S. eastwoodiae**
∞ Ehrhart W. . . . . ∞ **S. ehrhartiana**
Elaeagnus W. . . . . . **S. elaeagnos**
∞ Erdinger W. . . . . . ∞ **S. erdingeri**
Farges W. . . . . **S. fargesi**
Farr W. . . . . **S. farrae**
Feathervein W. . . . . **S. pennata**
Feltleaf W. . . . . . **S. alaxensis**
Firm Blueleaf W.
S. glaucophylloides glaucophylla
Footcatkin W. . . . . . **S. magnifica**
∞ Fourfootsix W. . . ∞ **S. sesquitertia**
∞ Fries W. . . . . . . ∞ **S. friesiana**
Furry W. . . . . . . **S. adenophylla**
Geyer W. . . . . **S. geyeriana**
Gilg W. . . . . **S. gilgiana**
Gmelin Basket W.
S. viminalis gmelini
∞ Goattea W. . . . . . . ∞ **S. laurina**
Goat W. . . . . **S. caprea**
Goodding W. . . . . . **S. gooddingi**
∞ Graham W. . . . . . . ∞ **S. grahami**
Grayleaf W. . . . . . . **S. glauca**
Gray W. . . . . **S. cinerea**
Greenscale W. . . . **S. chlorolepis**
Greensides W. . . . **S. monochroma**
Green Whitecrack W.
×**S. rubens viridis**
Gulf Black W. . **S. nigra altissima**
Hairy Shining W. . **S. lucida intonsa**
Halberd W. . . . . **S. hastata**
Hankow W. . . . . . **S. matsudana**
Harbison W. . . . . . **S. harbisoni**
Heartleaf W. . . . . . . **S. cordata**
Hinds W. . . . . . . **S. hindsiana**
Hooker W. . . . . . **S. hookeriana**
Humboldt W. . . . **S. humboldtiana**
Icy W. . . . . **S. glacialis**
Idaho Wolfs W. . **S. wolfi idahoensis**
Interocean Bog W.
S. pedicellaris hypoglauca
Jalisco W. . . . . . . **S. jaliscana**
Japanese Purpleosier W.
S. purpurea multinervis
∞ Japanese Pussy W. . ∞ **S. multinervis**
Japanese W. . . . . . . **S. japonica**
Jepson W. . . . . **S. jepsoni**
Korea W. . . . . . . **S. koreensis**
Labrador W. . . . . **S. argyrocarpa**
∞ Laestad W. . . . . . ∞ **S. laestadiana**
Lambert Purpleosier W.
S. purpurea lambertiana
Lanceleaf Pacific W.
S. lasiandra lancifolia
Lapland W. . . . . . . **S. lapponum**
Laurel W. . . . . . . **S. pentandra**
Least W. . . . . . . **S. rotundifolia**
Lemmons W. . . . . . . **S. lemmoni**
Littletree W. . . **S. arbusculoides**
Mackenzie W. . . . **S. mackenziana**
Marsh Whitecrack W.
S. rubens palustris
Medwedeff W. . . . **S. medwedewi**
Mexican W. . . . . . . **S. mexicana**
∞ Meyer W. . . . . . ∞ **S. meyeriana**
MissouriRiver W. . . . Diamond W.
Miyabe W. . . . . **S. miyabeana**

Willow, continued

Mono Planeleaf W.
Salix planifolia monica
Moupin W. . . . . **S. moupinensis**
Mouseleaf W. . . . . **S. niphoclada**
Myrtle W. . . . . . **S. myrsinites**
Nelson Planeleaf W.
S. planifolia nelsoni
Netleaf W. . . . . . . **S. reticulata**
Northland W. . . . . . **S. anglorum**
Notchleaf W. . . . . **S. retusa**
OliveleafGray W. **S. cinerea oleifolia**
Ovalleaf W. . . . . . . **S. ovalifolia**
Oxus W. . . . . **S. oxica**
Pacific W. . . . . . . **S. lasiandra**
Parish W. . . **S. hindsiana parishiana**
Park W. . . . . **S. pseudomonticola**
Peachleaf W. . . . **S. amygdaloides**
Pierot W . . . . **S. pieroti**
Piper W. . . . . **S. piperi**
Planeleaf W. . . . . . **S. planifolia**
Polar W. . . . . **S. polaris**
Polished W . . . . . . **S. laevigata**
Pomeranian Daphne W.
S. daphnoides pomeranica
Prairie W. . . . . **S. humilis**
∞ Purpledaphne W. . . ∞ **S. calliantha**
Purpleosier W. . . . . **S. purpurea**
Pussy W. . . . . **S. discolor**
∞ Puzzle W. . . . . . . ∞ **S. ambigua**
Pygmy W. . . . . **S. herbacea**
Pyramidal White W. . . **S. alba calva**
Redstem W. W. . . **S. a. chermesina**
∞ Red W. . . . . ∞ **S. rubra**
Red W. . . . . Polished W.
Rehder W. . . . . . . **S. rehderiana**
∞ Reuter W. . . . . . . ∞ **S. reuteri**
Richardson W. . . . **S. richardsoni**
River W. . . . . **S. fluviatilis**
Rosemary Creeping W.
S. repens rosmarinifolia
Roundear W. . . . . **S. aurita**
Round Netleaf W.
S. reticulata subrotunda
Rowlee W. . . . . **S. rowleei**
Sage W. . . . . **S. candida**
Sakhalin W. . . . . **S. sachalinensis**
Sandbar W. . . . . **S. interior**
Schaffner W. . . . . . **S. schaffneri**
Scouler W. . . . . . **S. scouleriana**
September W. . . . . **S. bocki**
∞ Seringe W. . . . . . ∞ **S. seringeana**
Setchell W. . . . . . **S. setchelliana**
Sharpleaf W. . . . . . **S. acutifolia**
Shining W. . . . . **S. lucida**
Shinleaf W. . . . . . **S. pyrolaefolia**
Siebold W. . . . . . **S. sieboldiana**
Siegert W. . . . . **S. siegerti**
Sierra W. . . . . **S. orestera**
Silesian W. . . . . **S. silesiaca**
Silky Purpleosier W.
S. purpurea sericea
Silky W. . . . . **S. sericea**
Silky White W. . . . . . . **S. alba s.**
Silver Creeping W. **S. repens nitida**
Silverleaf W. . . . . . **S. argophylla**
Silvery Geyer W.
S. geyeriana argentea
Sitka W. . . . . **S. sitchensis**
Sixstamen W. . . . . . **S. hexandra**
Skyland W. . . . . . . **S. petrophila**
Slender Purpleosier W.
S. purpurea gracilis
SmithRiver W. . . . . . **S. parksiana**
∞ Smith W. . . . . . ∞ **S. smithiana**
Smooth Bebb W.
S. bebbiana perrostrata

Willow, continued

Smoothish Grayleaf W.
Salix glauca glabrescens
Snow W. . . . . **S. nivalis**
∞ Soft W. . . . . . . ∞ **S. mollissima**
∞ Solomon Weeping W. ∞ **S. sepulcralis**
Southern Park W.
S. pseudomonticola padophylla
∞ Sport W. . . . . . . ∞ **S. ludificans**
Sprouting W. . . . . . **S. stolonifera**
Stipule W. . . . . **S. stipularis**
St. Lawrence W. . . **S. lawrentiana**
∞ Streakwood W. . . ∞ **S. holosericea**
∞ Subalpine W. . . . . ∞ **S. subalpina**
Summit W. . . . . **S. saximontana**
Swiss W. . . . . **S. helvetica**
Tealeaf W. . . . . . . **S. phylicifolia**
∞ Tea W. . . . . ∞ **S. tetrapla**
Texas Black W. . **S. nigra lindheimeri**
Texas Sandbar W.
S. interior angustissima
Thurlow Weeping W.
S. elegantissima
Thymeleaf W. . . . . **S. serpyllifolia**
Toumey W. **S. bonplandiana toumeyi**
Tracy W. . . . . **S. tracyi**
Treviranus W. . . . . . **S. trevirani**
Tufted Skyland W.
S. petrophila caespitosa
Tweedy W. . . . . **S. tweedyi**
∞ Twocolor W. . . . . . ∞ **S. dichroa**
Tyrrell W. . . . . **S. tyrrelli**
Underblue W. . . . . . **S. hypoleuca**
Undergreen W. . . . . **S. commutata**
Veiny Coastalplain W.
S. longipes venulosa
Velvet W. . . . . . . **S. sessilifolia**
Wallich W. . . . . . **S. wallichiana**
Walpole W. . . . . **S. walpolei**
Ward Coastalplain W.
S. longipes wardi
∞ Wardiana W. . . . . ∞ **S. wardiana**
Wavyleaf W. . . . . . . **S. undulata**
Whiplash W. . . . . . . **S. caudata**
∞ Whitecrack W. . . . . ∞ **S. rubens**
White W. . . . . **S. alba**
Whortleberry W. . . **S. myrtilloides**
Wilhelms W. . . . **S. wilhelmsiana**
∞ Wimmer W. . . . . ∞ **S. wimmeriana**
∞ Wisconsin Weeping W. . ∞ **S. blanda**
Wolfs W. . . . . **S. wolfi**
Woolly Hooker W.
S. hookeriana tomentosa
Woollytwig W. . . . **S. dasyclados**
Woolly W. . . . . **S. lanata**
Wright Peachleaf W.
S. amygdaloides wrighti
Yakutat W. . . . . . . **S. amplifolia**
Yeddo W. . . . . . . **S. jessoensis**
Yellow Scouler W.
S. scouleriana flavescens
Yellowstem White W.
S. alba vitellina
Yellow W. . . . . **S. lutea**
Yewleaf W. . . . . **S. taxifolia**

Willowweed . . . . . . **Epilobium**
Alpine W. . . . . . . **E. alpinum**
Autumn W. . . . . **E. paniculatum**
Canescent W. . . . . . **E. densum**
Dwarf W. . . . . . . **E. obscurum**
Fireweed . . . . **E. angustifolium**
Fleischer W. . . . . . **E. fleischeri**
Francisco W. . . . **E. franciscanum**
Glandular W. . . . **E. glandulosum**
Hairy W. . . . . **E. hirsutum**
Hector W. . . . . **E. hectori**
Hornemann W. . . . **E. hornemanni**

WILLOWWEED, continued
LAMY W. . . . . . Epilobium lamyi
NORTHERN W. . . . . . . E. boreale
PURPLELEAF W. . . . . E. coloratum
RED W. . . . . E. latifolium
SIERRA W. . . . . . E. brevistylum
STICKY W. . . . . . E. adenocaulon
YELLOW W. . . . . E. luteum

WILMAT'TEA
See **CACTUS GENERA**.

WILSONTREE . . . . Sinowilsonia
HENRY W. . . . . S. henryi

Windgrass . . . . . BENTGRASS, WIND: **Agrostis spica-venti**
Italian W. . . ITALIAN B.: **A. interrupta**

WINDMILLGRASS . . . . **Chloris**
Species with stiff, spreading, radiating spikes.
AUSTRALIAN W. . . . . C. ventricosa
CREEPING W. . . . . . . C. truncata
HOODED W. . . . . C. cucullata
NASH W. . . . . C. latisquamea
SHORTSPIKE W. C. subdolichostachya
SLIMSPIKE W. . C. andropogonoides
TEXAS W. . . . . C. texensis
TUMBLE W. . . . . . . C. verticillata

WINDMILLPALM . . . . . Trachycarpus
BUSH W. . . . . T. caespitosus
DWARF W. . . . . T. nanus
FORTUNES W. . . . . T. fortunei
MARTIUS W. . . . . T. martianus
TAKIL W. . . . . T. takil
WAGNER W. . . . . . T. wagnerianus

WINEBERRY . . . . Aristotelia
CHILEAN W. . . . . A. macqui
COLENSO W. . . . . A. colensoi
MAKOMAKO W. . . . . . . A. racemosa
NewZealand W. . . . . MAKOMAKO W.
SHRUBBY W. . . . . A. fruticosa
VARIEGATED CHILEAN W. A. macqui variegata

Wineberry . . CORIARIA, NEWZEALAND: **Coriaria ruscifolia**; CROWBERRY, BLACK: **Empetrum nigrum**; FEATHERWOOD: **Polyosma cunninghami**; RASPBERRY, WINE: **Rubus phoenicolasius**; WHORTLEBERRY, MYRTLE: **Vaccinium myrtillus**

WINGCACTUS . . . . Pterocactus
FISHER W. . . . . P. fisheri
TUBER W. . . . . P. tuberosus

WINGCELTIS . . . . Pteroceltis
TATAR W. . . . . P. tatarinowi

WING-EVERLASTING . Ammobium alatum
BIG W. . . . . . . A. a. grandiflorum

WINGHEAD . . . . Pterocephalus
TEASEL W. . . . . P. parnassi

WINGKELP . . . . Alaria
BADDERLOCKS W. . . . . A. esculenta

WINGNUT . . . . Pterocarya
CAUCASIAN W. . . . . . P. fraxinifolia
CHINESE W. . . . . . . P. stenoptera
DISKFRUIT W. . . . . P. paliurus
HUPEH W. . . . . P. hupehensis
JAPANESE W. . . . . P. rhoifolia
∞ REHDER W. . . . . . . ∞ P. rehderiana
SHRUBBY CAUCASIAN W. P. fraxinifolia dumosa

WINTERACONITE . Eranthis; E. hyemalis
CILICIAN W. . . . . E. h. cilicica
DWARF W. . . . . E. sibirica
TUBERGEN W. . . . . ×E. tubergeni

WINTERBERRY
COMMON W. . . . . . Ilex verticillata
MOUNTAIN W. . . . . . . I. montana
PLUMLEAF COMMON W. I. verticillata padifolia
SMOOTH W. . . . . I. laevigata

WINTERCRESS . . . . Barbarea
BITTER W. . . . . B. vulgaris
DOUBLE W. . . . . B. plena
EARLY W. . . . . B. verna
ERECTPOD W. . . . . B. orthoceras
PLANTAIN W. . . . . B. plantaginea
SARDINIAN W. . . . . . . B. rupicola

WINTERFAT . . . . Eurotia
BUSH W. . . . . E. subspinosa
COMMON W. . . . . E. lanata
OLDWORLD W. . . . . . E. ceratoides

WINTERGREEN . . . . Gaultheria
CHECKERBERRY W. . G. procumbens
FORRESTS W. . . . . G. forresti
FRAGRANT W. . . . G. fragrantissima
HOOKER W. . . . . G. hookeri
LITTLELEAF W. . . . . G. microphylla
MIQUEL W. . . . . . . G. miqueliana
OPPOSITELEAF W. . . . G. oppositifolia
OREGON W. . . . . G. ovatifolia
ROCK W. . . . . G. rupestris
SALAL . . . . G. shallon
VEITCH W. . . . . G. veitchiana
WARD W. . . . . G. wardi
WESTERN W. . . . . G. humifusa

WINTERHAZEL . . . . Corylopsis
BUTTERCUP W. . . . . . . C. pauciflora
CHINESE W. . . . . C. sinensis
FRAGRANT W. . . . . . C. glabrescens
GRIFFITH W. . . . . C. griffithi
SPIKE W. . . . . C. spicata
VEITCH W. . . . . C. veitchiana
WILLMOTT W. . . . . . C. willmottiae
WILSON W. . . . . C. wilsoni
YUNNAN W. . . . . . C. yunnanensis

WINTERSWEET . Chimonanthus praecox

WIRELETTUCE . . . . . Stephanomeria
DESERT W. . . . . S. runcinata
TEJON W. . . . . S. cichoriacea

WIREVINE . . . . Muehlenbeckia
CHILE W. . . . . M. chilensis
COMMON W. . . . . M. complexa
MATBUSH W. . . . . M. axillaris

WIREWEED . . . . Rigiopappus

WISHBONEPLANT . . Mirabilis retrorsa

WISLIZE'NIA lw
refrac'ta

Wissa'dula loza'ni . . **Pseudabutilon l.**

WISTA'RIA (*KRAUNHIA; WISTERIA*) . . . . WISTARIA
The original spelling of the scientific name, Wisteria, is accepted by most botanists as conforming to International Rules. The genus, however, commemorates Dr. Caspar Wistar (1760–1818), distinguished physician and scientist of Philadelphia. The Editorial Committee of STANDARDIZED PLANT NAMES strongly endorses the spelling Wistaria, for both Latin and common names, now used by some botanists and horticulturists, as well as in Webster's New International Dictionary (1940 ed.), which is standard in the Government Printing Office.

brachybo'trys . . . . . . **W. floribunda**
—al'ba . . . . **W. venusta**

WISTARIA, continued
chinen'sis . . . . **W. sinensis**
floribun'da (*brachybotrys; Glycine f.*) JAPANESE WISTARIA
—al'ba (*W. multijuga a.*) WHITE J.W.
—macrobo'trys (*W. multijuga*) LONGCLUSTER J.W.
CARNEA. HV. W. floribunda
FIVEFOOT. *Naga Noda.*
ISSAI (*praecox*)
KYUSHAKU (*ushyima*)
LONGISSIMA
LONGISSIMA ALBA
MURASAKI NODA
PENNVALLEY LONGCLUSTER
ROSEA (*multijuga rosea*)
ROYAL PURPLE
RUBRA
RUSSELL (*russelliana*)
SHIRONODA
VARIEGATED (*variegata*)
VIOLACEAPLENA
∞ **formo'sa** (*floribunda × sinensis*) ∞ CHINAJAP W.
frutes'cens (*speciosa; Kraunhia f.*) AMERICAN W.
—niv'ea (*W. f. alba*) . . WHITE A.W.
japon'ica (*Kraunhia j.; Millettia j.*) NIPPON W.
macrostach'ya (*W. frutescens magnifica; W. magnifica; Kraunhia macrostachya*) . . . . . . KENTUCKY W.
—albolila'cina . . . . LILACPINK K.W.
YELLOWEYE. HV. M. macrostachya
megasper'ma (*Millettia m.*) EVERGREEN W.
multiju'ga **W. floribunda macrobotrys**
—al'ba . . . . **W. floribunda a.**
reticula'ta . . . . **Millettia r.**
sinen'sis (*chinensis; Glycine s.*) CHINESE W.
The name W. sinensis is often misapplied to W. floribunda.
—al'ba . . . . WHITE C.W.
MINIATURE. HV. W. sinensis
specio'sa . . . . **W. frutescens**
venus'ta (*W. brachybotrys alba*) SILKY W.
—ple'na . . . . DOUBLE S.W.
—viola'cea . . . . WILD S.W.
villo'sa . . . . HAIRY W.

WISTARIA . . . . Wistaria
AMERICAN W. . . . . W. frutescens
∞ CHINAJAP W. . . . . ∞ W. formosa
CHINESE W. . . . . . . W. sinensis
DOUBLE SILKY W. . W. venusta plena
EVERGREEN W. . . . W. megasperma
HAIRY W. . . . . W. villosa
JAPANESE W. . . . . . W. floribunda
KENTUCKY W. . . . W. macrostachya
LILACPINK K. W. . W. m. albolilacina
LONGCLUSTER JAPANESE W. W. floribunda macrobotrys
NIPPON W. . . . . W. japonica
SILKY W. . . . . W. venusta
WHITE AMERICAN W. W. frutescens nivea
WHITE CHINESE W. . W. sinensis alba
WHITE JAPANESE W. W. floribunda a.
WILD SILKY W. . W. venusta violacea

WISTE'RIA . . . . . . **WISTARIA**
See note under **WISTARIA**.

Witches-teeth . . . DEERVETCH, COAST: **Lotus formosissimus**

WITCHGRASS
This term, preferably in combination, is applied to members of the sec. Capillaria of the genus Panicum and to the closely related, and similar Leptoloma cognatum.
ARIZONA W. . . **Panicum pampinosum**
COMMON W. . . . . . . **P. capillare**
CUSHION W. . . . . **P. c. occidentale**
FALL W. . . . **Leptoloma cognatum**
GATTINGER W. . . . . **P. gattingeri**
PHILADELPHIA W. **P. philadelphicum**
ROUGHSTALK W. . . . **P. hirticaule**
SONORA W. . . . . . **P. stramineum**
TUCKERMAN W. . . . **P. tuckermani**
WITCHHAZEL . . . . **Hamamelis**
CHINESE W. . . . . **H. mollis**
COMMON W. . . . . . **H. virginiana**
JAPANESE W.. . . . . . **H. japonica**
LEMON J. W. . . **H. j. zuccariniana**
PINK COMMON W.
H. virginiana rubescens
RED JAPANESE W.
H. japonica flavo-purpurascens
REDPETAL VERNAL W. **H. vernalis carnea**
SOUTHERN W. . . . **H. macrophylla**
TREE JAPANESE W. **H. japonica arborea**
VERNAL W. . . . . . . **H. vernalis**
WOOLLYLEAF V. W. . **H. v. tomentella**

WITHA'NIA . . . . WITHANIA
coag'ulans . . . . AFGHAN W.

WIT'TIA . . . . WITTIA
See **CACTUS GENERA.**

WOAD . . . . **Isatis**
BOISSIERS W. . . . . **I. boissieriana**
DYERS W. . . . . **I. tinctoria**
SMOOTH W. . . . . **I. glauca**
WOADWAXEN . . . . **Genista**
AETNA W. . . . . . . **G. aethnensis**
ALPINE COMMON W.
G. tinctoria alpestris
ASHY W. . . . . **G. cinerea**
BRIDALVEIL W. . . . **G. monosperma**
COMMON W. . . . . . . **G. tinctoria**
CUSHION W. . . . . **G. horrida**
DOWNY COMMON W. **G. tinctoria hirsuta**
GENOA W. . . . . **G. januensis**
GERMAN W. . . . . . . **G. germanica**
NEEDLE W. . . . . **G. anglica**
NISH W. . . . . **G. nyssana**
SILKYLEAF W. . . . . . . **G. pilosa**
SPANISH W. . . . . . . **G. hispanica**
SPINELESS NEEDLE W.
G. anglica subinermis
TALL COMMON W. **G. tinctoria virgata**
WOLFBERRY . . . . **Lycium**
ANDERSON W. . . . . . **L. andersoni**
BARBARY W. . . . . . . **L. barbarum**
CALIFORNIA W. . . . **L. californicum**
CAROLINA W. . . . . **L. carolinianum**
CHINESE W. . . . . **L. chinense**
COOPER W. . . . . **L. cooperi**
EUROPEAN W. . . . . **L. europaeum**
FREMONT W. . . . . . . **L. fremonti**
MATRIMONYVINE . . **L. halimifolium**
PALE W. . . . . **L. pallidum**
PARISH W. . . . . **L. parishi**
TORREY W. . . . . **L. torreyi**

WOLF'FIA |w
columbia'na |w
papulif'era |w
puncta'ta |w

WOLFFIEL'LA |w . . . . MUDMIDGET
florida'na |w
lingula'ta |w
oblon'ga |w

WOLFTAIL . . . . **Lycurus; L. phleoides**
WOODAPPLE . . . . **Feronia; F. limonia**
WOODBALM. . . . . **Sphacele calycina**
Woodbetony . PEDICULARIS: **Pedicularis**
Woodbine . . HONEYSUCKLE, WOODBINE: **Lonicera periclymenum**

WOODFERN. . . . . **Dryopteris**
BOOTT W. . . . . **D. bootti**
CINNAMON W. . . . . . . **D. ampla**
CLINTON W. . . . . . **D. clintoniana**
COAST W. . . . . **D. arguta**
COMMON W. . . . . . **D. intermedia**
CREEPING W. . . . . . . **D. reptans**
CRESTED W. . . . . . . **D. cristata**
DOWNY W. . . . . **D. dentata**
EVERGLADE W. . . . **D. gongylodes**
GLOSSY W.. . . . . **D. viridescens**
GOLDIE W.. . . . . . . **D. goldiana**
LEATHER W. . . . . **D. marginalis**
LOUISIANA W. . . . **D. ludoviciana**
MOUNTAIN W. . . . . . . **D. dilatata**
NORTHERN W. . . . . **D. oreopteris**
OVIEDO W. . . . . . **D. uliginosa**
SHAGGY W. . . . . . . **D. hirtipes**
SIERRA W. . . . . . **D. nevadensis**
TOOTHED W. . . . . . **D. spinulosa**

WOODFORD'IA . . . . . WOODFORDIA
frutico'sa . . . . SHRUBBY W.

WOODLANDSTAR . . . . **Lithophragma**
SLENDER W. . . . . **L. tenella**
SMALLFLOWER W. . . . **L. parviflora**
SOUTHERN W. . . . . . **L. australis**
WOODNETTLE. . . . . **Laportea**
CANADA W. . . . . . . **L. canadensis**
WOODNYMPH . . . . **Moneses uniflora**
WOODOILTREE, JAPAN . **Aleurites cordata**
WOODORCHID, SMALLGREEN
Habenaria clavellata
WOODREED. . . . . **Cinna**
DROOPING W. . . . . . . **C. latifolia**
STOUT W. . . . . . . **C. arundinacea**
WOODRUFF . . . . **Asperula**
BEDSTRAW W. . . . . . . **A. galioides**
DYERS W. . . . . **A. tinctoria**
LONGFLOWER W. . . . . **A. longiflora**
MISTY W. . . . . . . **A. hexaphylla**
ORIENTAL W. . . . . . . **A. orientalis**
SWEET W. . . . . **A. odorata**
YELLOW W. . . . . **A. lutea**
WOODRUSH. . . . . **Luzula**
DONNER W. . . . . . **L. subcongesta**
FIELD W. . . . . **L. campestris**
GROVE W. . . . . **L. nemorosa**
HAIRY W. . . . . **L. comosa**
MILLET W. . . . . **L. parviflora**
SPIKE W. . . . . **L. spicata**
SUDETIC W. . . . . **L. sudetica**
WAHLENBERG W. . . . **L. wahlenbergi**

WOODS'IA . . . . WOODSIA
See **FERN GENERA.**

WOODWARD'IA (*ANCHISTEA; LORINSERIA*) . . . . CHAINFERN
See **FERN GENERA.**

WOOLLYHEADPARSNIP . **Sphenosciadium**
RANGE W. . . . . . **S. capitellatum**
WOOLLYMAT . . . . . . **Myriocephalus**
STUART W. . . . . **M. stuarti**
WOOLLYWEED . . . **Hieracium scouleri**

WORM'IA
burbid'gei

WORMWOOD . . . . **Artemisia**
See also SAGEBRUSH.
ASIAMINOR W. . . . . . **A. splendens**
AUSTRIAN W. . . . . . **A. austriaca**
BAUMGARTEN W. . . **A. baumgarteni**
BEACH W. . . . . . . **A. stelleriana**
BIENNIAL W. . . . . **A. biennis**
CAMPHOR W. . . . . **A. camphorata**
COMMON W. . . . . **A. absinthium**
FRENCH W. . . . . **A. suavis**
GHOSTPLANT W. . . . . **A. lactiflora**
GLACIER W. . . . . **A. glacialis**
LEVANT W. . . . . **A. cina**
MARITIME W. . . . . . **A. maritima**
MIXLEAF MUGWORT W.
A. vulgaris heterophylla
MOUNTAIN W. . . . . **A. spicata**
MOXA W. . . . . **A. moxa**
MUGWORT W. . . . . . . **A. vulgaris**
NORTHERN W. . . . . . . **A. borealis**
OLDMAN W. . . . . . . **A. abrotanum**
ORIENTAL W. . . . . . . **A. scoparia**
PERSIAN W. . . . . **A. persica**
PIEDMONT W. . . . **A. pedemontana**
ROCK W. . . . . **A. rupestris**
ROMAN W. . . . . **A. pontica**
RUSSIAN W. . . . . . . **A. sacrorum**
SAGEWORT W. . . . . **A. campestris**
SANDHILL W. . . . **A. pycnocephala**
SHRUBBY W. . . . **A. arborescens**
SILVERALP W. . . . . . . **A. mutellina**
SILVER W. . . . . **A. argentea**
SUMMERFIR RUSSIAN W.
A. sacrorum viridis
SWEET W. . . . . **A. annua**
Woundwort . ANTHYLLIS, KIDNEYVETCH: **Anthyllis vulneraria**; BETONY: **Stachys** spp.; COMFREY, COMMON: **Symphytum officinale**; GOLDENROD, EUROPEAN: **Solidago virgaurea**; LASERWORT: **Laserpitium** spp.; LIABUM, WOUNDWORT: **Liabum brownei**; OPOPANAX, SURGEONS: **Opopanax chironium**; OXEYEDAISY: **Chrysanthemum leucanthemum**
WRENFLOWER . . . . **Thomasia**
PURPLE W. . . . . **T. purpurea**
WRINKLELEAF W. . . . . . **T. rugosa**

WRIGHT'IA
lani'ti

WULFE'NIA . . . . WULFENIA
carinthi'aca . . . . CARINTHIAN W.

WULF'FIA
stenoglos'sa
WURRUS, LONGLEAF
Flemingia macrophylla

WYE'THIA |w . . . . WYETHIA
amplexicau'lis |w . . MULESEARS W.
angustifo'lia . . . . NARROWLEAF W.
gla'bra . . . . SHINY W.
helenioi'des . . . SNEEZEWEED W.
helianthoi'des . . . WHITEHEAD W.
mol'lis . . . . WOOLLY W.

XANTHIS'MA (*CENTAURIDIUM*)
texa'num (*Centauridium drummondi*)
STAR-OF-TEXAS

XAN'THIUM |w . . . . . COCKLEBUR
cal'vum . . . . PALOALTO C.
echina'tum . . . . BEACH C.
ital'icum . . . . ITALIAN C.
orienta'le (*canadense; commune; pennsylvanicum*) |w . . . . ORIENTAL C.
pun'gens
spino'sum |w . . . . SPINY C.
struma'rium

XANTHO'CERAS . . . Yellowhorn
sorbifo'lium . . . . Shinyleaf Y.

XANTHORHI'ZA (*ZANTHORHIZA*)
Yellowroot

The generic name appears in literature as Xanthorhiza, Xanthorrhiza, and Zanthorhiza. The name originated with Humphrey Marshall (1722–1801), whose book "Arbustrum Americanum" (1785) is said to be the first botanical work published in America. Professor Rehder, in a note to the Editorial Committee dated September 9, 1940, says: "Marshall spells Xanthorhiza with one 'r'; the spelling with two 'r's' is probably intended as a grammatical correction by a later author."

simplicis'sima (*Zanthorhiza apiifolia*)
Yellowroot

Zanthorhiza apiifolia is in general use for this shrub in horticulture, but Marshall's name X. simplicissima (1785) antedates L'Heritier's Zanthorhiza apiifolia (1788) three years.

XANTHORRHOE'A . . . Grasstree
arbo'rea . . . . . . Dackowar G.
austra'lis . . . . . . Australian G.
has'tilis . . . . Spearleaf G.
preiss'i . . . . Preiss G. (*Blackboy*)
quadrangula'ta

XANTHOSO'MA (*PHYLLOTAENIUM*) . . . . Malanga
atrovi'rens . . . . . . Darkleaf M.
batavien'se Hort. . . . Batavian M.
Probably a clon.
lin'deni (*Phyllotaenium l.*) Lindens M.
macula'tum . . . . . Spotted M.
mar'shalli Hort. . . . Marshall M.
Probably a clon.
sagittaefo'lium . . . . Yautia M.
viola'ceum . . . . . . Primrose M.

XANTHOSTE'MON
oppositifo'lius
pubes'cens
verdugonia'nus

XANTHOX'ALIS . . . . . **OXALIS**

XANTHOX'YLUM **ZANTHOXYLUM**

XERAN'THEMUM . . . . Immortelle
an'nuum . . . . Common I.
—ligulo'sum (*X. imperiale*)
Semidouble I.
—perligulo'sum (*X. superbissimum*)
Double I.
cylindra'ceum . . . . . Cylinder I.

XEROPHYL'LUM . . . Beargrass
asphodeloi'des . . . Turkeybeard B.
doug'lasi . . . . Douglas B.
ten'ax . . . . Common B.

XIMENES'IA . . . . **VERBESINA**
exauricula'ta . . . . **V. encelioides e.**

XIME'NIA
america'na . . . . . Tallowwood

XIPHAGROS'TIS . . **MISCANTHUS**
See **GRASS GENERA.**

XOLIS'MA . . . . **LYONIA**

XY'LIA
xylocar'pa (*dolabriformis*)
Burma Pyingado

XYLO'BIUM
See **ORCHID GENERA.**

XYLOCOC'CUS . **ARCTOSTAPHYLOS**

XYLOPHA'COS . . . **ASTRAGALUS**
shortia'nus . . . . **A. utahensis**

XYLOPHYL'LA . **PHYLLANTHUS**

XYLORRHI'ZA . . . . **ASTER**
scopulo'rum; villo'sa . . . **A. xylorrhiza**

XYLOS'MA . . . . Xylosma
heterophyl'la . . . . Holly X.
japon'ica (*congesta; racemosa*)
The name X. senticosa is sometimes misapplied to this species.
sentico'sa . . . . Shiny X.

XYLOS'TEON . . . . . . **LONICERA**

XY'RIS |w . . . . Yelloweyegrass
carolinia'na |w . . . . . Carolina Y.
fimbria'ta |w . . . . . . Fringed Y.
flexuo'sa |w . . . . . . Twisted Y.
iridifo'lia |w . . . . . . Irisleaf Y.
smallia'na |w . . . . . . Smalls Y.
stric'ta |w

Yam . . . . **Dioscorea**
Airpotato Y. . . . . . . **D. bulbifera**
Atlantic Y. . . . . **D. villosa**
Attoto Y. . . . . . . **D. cayenensis**
Chinese Y. . . . . . . **D. esculenta**
Cinnamonvine . . . . . . **D. batatas**
Common Y. . . . . **D. sativa**
Cushcush Y. . . . . **D. trifida**
Guinea Y. . . . . . . **D. rotundata**
Whiteband Y. . . . . . . **D. discolor**
Winged Y. . . . . **D. alata**

Yambean . . . . **Pachyrhizus**
Wayaka Y. . . . . . . **P. angulatus**
WestIndies Y. . . . . . **P. tuberosus**

Yampa . . . . **Perideridia gairdneri**

Yampee . . . . Yam, Cushcush:
Dioscorea trifida

Yaragua . . . . . . Molassesgrass:
Melinis minutiflora

Yaray . . . Palmetto, PuertoRico:
Sabal causiarum

Yarrow . . . . **Achillea**
Aizoon Y. . . . **A. ageratifolia aizoon**
Alpine Y. . . . . **A. alpina**
Brownedge Y. . . . . **A. magna**
Clavenn Y. . . . . . . **A. clavennae**
Common Y. . . . . . **A. millefolium**
Dwarf Y. . . . . **A. nana**
Egyptian Y. . . . . . . **A. aegyptiaca**
Fernleaf Y. . . . . . **A. filipendulina**
Fronmueller Y. . . **×A. fronmuelleri**
Greek Y. . . . . **A. ageratifolia**
Italian Y. . . . . **A. rupestris**
Lovage Y. . . . . **A. ligustica**
Macedonian Y. . . . . **A. macedonica**
Musk Y. . . . . **A. moschata**
Palmer Y. . . . . **A. palmeri**
Pink Common Y. **A. millefolium roseum**
Purple C. Y. . . . **A. m. purpureum**
Red C. Y. . . . . **A. m. rubrum**
Santolin Y. . . . **A. santolinoides**
Serbian Y. . . . . **A. serbica**
Siberian Y. . . . . **A. sibirica**
Silver Y. . . . . **A. argentea**
Sneezewort Y. . . . . . . **A. ptarmica**
Subalpine Y. . . **A. lanulosa alpicola**
Sweet Y. . . . . **A. ageratum**
Umbel Y. . . . . **A. umbellata**
Western Y. . . . . **A. lanulosa**
Woolly Y. . . . . **A. tomentosa**
Yellow W. Y. . . . . **A. t. aurea**

Yatay
Argentine Y. . . . . . **Butia yatay**
Paraguay Y. . . . **B. paraguayensis**

Yaupon . . . . **Ilex vomitoria**

Yeast, Brewers
Saccharomyces cerevisiae

Yebbnut . . . . . **Cordeauxia edulis**

Yellowcress . . . . **Rorippa**
Watercress **R. nasturtium-aquaticum**

Yelloweyegrass . . . . **Xyris**
Carolina Y. . . . . . . **X. caroliniana**
Fringed Y. . . . . **X. fimbriata**
Irisleaf Y. . . . . **X. iridifolia**
Smalls Y. . . . . **X. smalliana**
Twisted Y. . . . . **X. flexuosa**

Yellowflax . . . . . . **Reinwardtia**
Indian Y. . . . . **R. indica**
Serrate Y. . . . . . . **R. tetragyna**

Yellowflowergourd
Cucurbita pepo ovifera

Yellowhorn . . . . **Xanthoceras**
Shinyleaf Y. . . . . . **X. sorbifolium**

Yellow-oleander . Thevetia, Luckynut:
Thevetia nereifolia

Yellowpoplar (Forestry name)
Liriodendron tulipifera

Yellowroot
Xanthorhiza; X. simplicissima

Yellowsapote . . Lucuma, Willowleaf:
Lucuma salicifolia

Yellowskunkcabbage
Lysichitum camtschatcense
American Y. . . . . . **L. americanum**

Yellowtop . . Eucalyptus, Angletwig:
Eucalyptus virgata

Yellowtrumpet . . . . . **Stenolobium**
Argentine Y. . . . . **S. garrocha**
Florida Y. . . . . **S. stans**
Hardy Y. . . . . . **S. s. angustatum**
Velvety Florida Y. . **S. s. velutinum**

Yellowwood . . . . **Cladrastis**
American Y. . . . . **C. lutea**
Chinese Y. . . . . **C. sinensis**
Japanese Y. . . . . . **C. platycarpa**
Wilson Y. . . . . **C. wilsoni**

Yellowwort . . . . **Chlora**
Common Y. . . . . . . **C. perfoliata**

Yerbabuena . **Micromeria chamissonis**

Yerbadelvenado . . Poreleaf, Slender:
Porophyllum gracile

Yerbadetajo . . . . . . **Eclipta alba**

Yerbamansa . . . **Anemopsis californica**

Yerbasanta . . . . **Eriodictyon**
California Y. . . . . **E. californicum**
Hairy Y. . . . . **E. trichocalyx**
Lompoc Y. . . . . **E. capitatum**
Narrowleaf Y. . . **E. angustifolium**
SanDiego Y. . . . . **E. lanatum**
Thickleaf Y. . . . . **E. crassifolium**
Trask Y. . . . . **E. traskiae**
Woolly Y. . . . . . . **E. tomentosum**

Yew . . . . **Taxus**
∞Anglojap Y. . . . . **∞T. media**
Canada Y. . . . . . . **T. canadensis**
Chinese Y. . . . . **T. chinensis**
English Y. . . . . **T. baccata**
Florida Y. . . . . **T. floridana**
∞Hunnewell Y. . . **∞T. hunnewelliana**
Japanese Y. . . . . **T. cuspidata**
Pacific Y. . . . . **T. brevifolia**

Ylangylang . . . . . **Cananga odorata**

Yorkgum . . . . Eucalyptus, York:
Eucalyptus loxophleba

Young'ia na'na . . . . **Crepis n.**

YUC'CA (*CLISTOYUCCA; HESPEROYUCCA*) |w . . . . YUCCA
aloifo'lia . . ALOE Y. (*Spanishdagger*)
—tri'color . . . . . STRIPELEAF A.Y.
angustifo'lia . . . . **Y. glauca**
angustis'sima . . . . . FINELEAF Y.
arkansa'na . . . . . . ARKANSAS Y.
bacca'ta . . . . DATIL Y.
brevifo'lia (*arborescens; Clistoyucca b.*) JOSHUATREE Y.
colo'ma . . . . . . **Y. neomexicana**
conca'va . . . . . . **Y. filamentosa c.**
constric'ta . . . . BUCKLEY Y.
ela'ta (*radiosa*) . . . . . SOAPTREE Y.
elephan'tipes (*gigantea; guatemalensis*) BULBSTEM Y.
faxonia'na . . . . FAXON Y.
filamento'sa . . . . ADAMSNEEDLE Y.
—conca'va (*Y. concava*) SPOONLEAF A.Y.
—variega'ta . . . . STRIPELEAF A.Y.
flac'cida . . . . WEAKLEAF Y.
—in'tegra . . . . . FIBERLESS W.Y.
—linea'ta Hort. (*Y. lineata* Hort.)
—ma'jor (*Y. f. glaucescens*) BLUE W.Y.
—orchioi'des . . . . STIFFER W.Y.
¢STRIPED (*lineata*) HV. Y. flaccida
gigan'tea . . . . . . **Y. elephantipes**
glau'ca (*angustifolia*) SMALL SOAPWEED
—rose'a . . . . PINK S.S.
—stric'ta . . . . . . STEMMED S.S.
glorio'sa . . . . MOUNDLILY Y.
—no'bilis (*Y. g. ellacombei*) BLUE M.Y.
—plica'ta . . . . . . PLEATED M.Y.
—recurvifo'lia . . . . **Y. recurvifolia**
—robus'ta . . . . ROBUST M.Y.
—super'ba . . . . GREEN M.Y.
¢VARIEGATED (*variegata*) HV. Y. gloriosa
guatemalen'sis . . . **Y. elephantipes**
harrima'niae . . . . . HARRIMAN Y.
∞ **karlsruhen'sis** (*filamentosa* × *glauca*) ∞ KARLSRUHE Y.
linea'ta Hort. . . **Y. flaccida l.** Hort.
macrocar'pa Engelm. . . . **Y. schotti**
macrocar'pa (Torr.) Cov., *not* Engelm. **Y. torreyi**
mohaven'sis . . . . . **Y. schidigera**
neomexica'na (*coloma*) NEWMEXICAN Y.
radio'sa . . . . **Y. elata**
recurvifo'lia (*Y. gloriosa r.; Y. pendula*) CURVELEAF Y.
—margina'ta . . . YELLOWRIM C.Y.
—variega'ta . . YELLOWSTRIPE C.Y.
rupic'ola . . . . TEXAS Y.
schidig'era (*mohavensis*) . MOHAVE Y.
schott'i (*macrocarpa* Engelm., *not* (Torr.) Cov.) . . . . . SCHOTTS Y.
tenuis'tyla . . . . . . WHITERIM Y.
tor'reyi (*macrocarpa* (Torr.) Cov., *not* Engelm.) . . . . TORREY Y.
treculea'na TRECUL Y. (*Spanishbayonet*)
whip'plei (*Hesperoyucca w.*) WHIPPLE Y.

YUCCA . . . . **Yucca**
ADAMSNEEDLE Y. . . . **Y. filamentosa**
ALOE Y. . . . . **Y. aloifolia**
ARKANSAS Y. . . . . . . **Y. arkansana**
BLUE MOUNDLILY Y. **Y. gloriosa nobilis**
BLUE WEAKLEAF Y. **Y. flaccida major**
BUCKLEY Y. . . . . . . **Y. constricta**
BULBSTEM Y. . . . . **Y. elephantipes**
CURVELEAF Y. . . . . **Y. recurvifolia**
DATIL Y. . . . . **Y. baccata**

YUCCA, continued
FAXON Y. . . . . . **Yucca faxoniana**
FIBERLESS WEAKLEAF Y. **Y. flaccida integra**
FINELEAF Y. . . . . **Y. angustissima**
GREEN MOUNDLILY Y. **Y. gloriosa superba**
HARRIMAN Y. . . . . **Y. harrimaniae**
JOSHUATREE Y. . . . . . **Y. brevifolia**
∞ KARLSRUHE Y. . . ∞ **Y. karlsruhensis**
MOHAVE Y. . . . . . . **Y. schidigera**
MOUNDLILY Y. . . . . . **Y. gloriosa**
NEWMEXICAN Y. . . **Y. neomexicana**
PINK SMALL SOAPWEED **Y. glauca rosea**
PLEATED MOUNDLILY Y. **Y. gloriosa plicata**
ROBUST M. Y. . . . . . **Y. g. robusta**
SCHOTTS Y. . . . . **Y. schotti**
SMALL SOAPWEED . . . . . **Y. glauca**
SOAPTREE Y. . . . . **Y. elata**
SPOONLEAF ADAMSNEEDLE Y. **Y. filamentosa concava**
STEMMED SMALL SOAPWEED **Y. glauca stricta**
STIFFER WEAKLEAF Y. **Y. flaccida orchioides**
STRIPELEAF ADAMSNEEDLE Y. **Y. filamentosa variegata**
STRIPELEAF ALOE Y. **Y. aloifolia tricolor**
TEXAS Y. . . . . **Y. rupicola**
TORREY Y. . . . . **Y. torreyi**
TRECUL Y. . . . . . . **Y. treculeana**
WEAKLEAF Y. . . . . . . **Y. flaccida**
WHIPPLE Y. . . . . **Y. whipplei**
WHITERIM Y. . . . . . **Y. tenuistyla**
YELLOWRIM CURVELEAF Y. **Y. recurvifolia marginata**
YELLOWSTRIPE C. Y. . **Y. r. variegata**

Zacaton . . . . . MUHLY, WHISKGRASS: **Muhlenbergia macroura**

ZALUZIAN'SKYA (*NYCTERINIA*) NIGHTPHLOX
capen'sis (*Nycterinia c.*) . . CAPE N.
villo'sa (*selaginoides*) . . . HAIRY N.

ZA'MIA . . . . ZAMIA
See **CYCAD GENERA.**

ZAMIA . . . . **Zamia**
BAHAMAS Z. . . . . . **Z. angustifolia**
BROOM Z. . . . . **Z. spartea**
COONTIE . . . . . . **Z. integrifolia**
COSTARICA Z. . . . **Z. costaricensis**
ECUADOR Z. . . . . **Z. lindeni**
HONDURAS Z. . . . . . . **Z. latifolia**
KICKX Z. . . . . **Z. kickxi**
LAWSON Z. . . . . . . **Z. lawsoniana**
LEIBOLD Z. . . . . **Z. leiboldi**
LODDIGES Z. . . . . . . **Z. loddigesi**
MOUNTAIN Z. . . . . . . **Z. monticola**
PANAMA Z. . . . . **Z. skinneri**
PUERTORICO Z. . . . **Z. portoricensis**
PYGMY Z. . . . . **Z. pygmaea**
SAND Z. . . . . **Z. silicea**
SCURFY Z. . . . . . . **Z. furfuracea**
SLIMLEAF Z. . . . . **Z. angustissima**
ST.JOHNS COONTIE . . . . **Z. pumila**
TREETRUNK Z. . . **Z. pseudoparasitica**
UNDERSHRUB Z. . . . . . **Z. umbrosa**

ZANNICHEL'LIA |w . . . . POOLMAT
palus'tris |w . . . . . . COMMON P.

ZANTEDES'CHIA (*RICHARDIA* Kunth, *not* (Houst.) L.). CALLALILY
aethio'pica (*Calla a.; Richardia a.; R. africana*) . . . . . COMMON C.
elliottia'na (*Calla e.; Richardia e.*) GOLDEN C.

ZANTEDESCHIA, continued
melanoleu'ca BLACKTHROAT CALLALILY
reh'manni . . . . ROSE C.
CARMINE (*carminea*) HV.

ZANTHORHI'ZA . **XANTHORHIZA**
apiifo'lia . . . . . **X. simplicissima**

ZANTHOX'YLUM (*XANTHOXYLUM*) |w . . . . . . PRICKLYASH
acanthopo'dium . . . HIMALAYA P.
ailanthoi'des . . . . . AILANTHUS P.
ala'tum . . . . WINGLEAF P.
—planispi'num . . . . CHINESE W.P.
america'num (*fraxineum*) |w COMMON P.
bun'gei . . . . **Z. simulans**
clavaher'culis |w . HERCULESCLUB P. (*Herculesclub*)
—frutico'sum . . . . . TEXAS H.P.
coria'ceum . . . . BISCAYNE P.
daniel'li . . . . **Evodia d.**
faga'ra (*pterota*) . . . . . . LIME P.
fla'vum . . . . . . YELLOWHEART P.
fraxin'eum . . . . . . **Z. americanum**
martinicen'se . . . MARTINIQUE P.
microcar'pum . . . . SMALLFRUIT P.
oxyphyl'lum . . . . . SHARPLEAF P.
piase'zki
piperi'tum . . . . . . JAPANESE P.
ptero'ta . . . . **Z. fagara**
schinifo'lium (*Fagara schinifolia*) PEPPERTREE P.
senegalen'se (*Fagara zanthoxyloides*) SENEGAL P.
sim'ulans (*bungei*) . . FLATSPINE P.
stenophyl'lum (*Fagara stenophylla*) CLIMBING P.

ZAUSCHNE'RIA . . . . FIRECHALICE
arizo'nica . . . . ARIZONA F.
califor'nica . . . . . CALIFORNIA F.
—microphyl'la (*cana*) . . . GRAY C.F.
crassifo'lia . . . . . . THICKLEAF F.
garrett'i . . . . GARRETT F.
latifo'lia . . . . BROADLEAF F.

ZE'A
See **CEREALS** and **GRASS GENERA.**

ZEBRAGRASS **Miscanthus sinensis zebrinus**

ZEBRAWOOD . . . . **Connarus**
GUIANA Z. . . . . **C. guianensis**

ZEBRI'NA . . . . ZEBRINA
leiophyl'la . . . . . SMOOTHLEAF Z.
pen'dula (*Tradescantia zebrina*) WANDERINGJEW Z.
—quadricol'or (*Tradescantia multicolor; T. quadricolor*) FOURCOLOR W.Z.
purpus'i . . . . PURPUS Z.

ZEHNTNEREL'LA
See **CACTUS GENERA.**

ZELKO'VA . . . . ZELKOVA
abelic'ea (*cretica*) . . . . CRETAN Z.
acumina'ta . . . . **Z. serrata**
carpinifo'lia (*crenata; ulmoides; Planera crenata; P. richardi*) . . . ELM Z.
da'vidi . . . . **Hemiptelea d.**
schneideria'na . . . . SCHNEIDER Z.
serra'ta (*acuminata; cuspidata; keaki; Planera japonica*) . . . JAPANESE Z.
si'nica . . . . CHINESE Z.
ulmoi'des . . . . . . **Z. carpinifolia**
verschaffelt'i . . . . VERSCHAFFELT Z.
Perhaps only a var. of Z. carpinifolia.

ZENO'BIA . . . . ZENOBIA
pulverulen'ta (*speciosa; Andromeda s.*) DUSTY Z.
—**nu'da** (*Z. cassinifolia*) . . GREEN Z.
HONEYCUP. HV.

ZEPHYRAN'THES (*ARGYROPSIS; ATAMOSCO*) . . . . ZEPHYRLILY
anderso'ni; andersonia'na **Habranthus andersonianus**
atamas'co (*Amaryllis a.; Atamosco a.*) ATAMASCOLILY
HAYWARD (*haywardi*) HV.
au'rea . . . . . . **Pyrolirion aureum**
can'dida . . . . AUTUMN Z.
MAJOR. HV.
citri'na . . . . CITRON Z.
conzat'ti . . . . CONZATTI Z.
fos'teri . . . . FOSTER Z.
grandiflo'ra (*carinata*) . . ROSEPINK Z.
longifo'lia . . . . COPPER Z.
macrosi'phon . . . . . MEXICAN Z.
mesoch'loa . . . . . ARGENTINE Z.
pal'lida . . . . PALLID Z.
pulchel'la
robus'ta . . . . **Habranthus robustus**
rose'a . . . . CUBAN Z.
ses'silis
simp'soni . . . . SIMPSON Z.
texa'na . . . . **Habranthus texanus**
tubispa'tha . . . . . VENEZUELA Z.
treat'iae . . . . TREATS Z.
verecun'da
AJAX. HV. Zephyranthes

ZEPHYRLILY . . . . **Zephyranthes**
ARGENTINE Z. . . . . . **Z. mesochloa**
ATAMASCOLILY . . . . . **Z. atamasco**
AUTUMN Z. . . . . **Z. candida**
CITRON Z. . . . . **Z. citrina**
CONZATTI Z. . . . . **Z. conzatti**
COPPER Z. . . . . **Z. longifolia**
CUBAN Z. . . . . **Z. rosea**
FOSTER Z. . . . . **Z. fosteri**
MEXICAN Z. . . . . . **Z. macrosiphon**
PALLID Z. . . . . **Z. pallida**
ROSEPINK Z. . . . . . . **Z. grandiflora**
SIMPSON Z. . . . . **Z. simpsoni**
TREATS Z. . . . . **Z. treatiae**
VENEZUELA Z. . . . . . **Z. tubispatha**

ZEXME'NIA . . . . ZEXMENIA
brevifo'lia . . . . . . SHORTHORN Z.
his'pida . . . . ORANGE Z.

ZIGADE'NUS (*AMIANTHIUM; ANTICLEA; TOXICOSCORDION; ZYGADENUS*) |w DEATHCAMAS
The original spelling of the generic name is Zigadenus.

angustifo'lius (*Amianthium angustifolium; Tracyanthus angustifolius*) PINK D.
el'egans (*Anticlea e.*) . MOUNTAIN D.
fre'monti (*douglasi*) . . . FREMONT D.
glaber'rimus . . . . . . ATLANTIC D.
gramin'eus (*intermedius; Toxicoscordion gramineum; T. intermedium*) GRASSY D.
leimanthoi'des (*Oceanorus l.*) PINEBARREN D.
muscaetox'icum . . . **Amianthium m.**
nutt'alli . . . . NUTTALL D.
panicula'tus . . . . . . FOOTHILL D.
veneno'sus . . . . . . MEADOW D.
—**micran'thus** . . . . . SMALL M.D.

ZIN'GIBER . . . . GINGER
cassumunar' . . . . CASSUMUNAR G.
cylin'dricum . . . . . . CATTAIL G.
dar'ceyi Hort. . . . . HARLEQUIN G.
mio'ga . . . . MIOGA G.
officina'le . . . . COMMON G.
spectab'ile . . . . . . REDBRACT G.
zerum'bet . . . . . . ZERUMBET G.

ZIN'NIA (*CRASSINA*) . . . . ZINNIA
angustifo'lia (*mexicana*) OBLONGLEAF Z.
el'egans . . . . COMMON Z.
grandiflo'ra . . ROCKYMOUNTAIN Z.
haagea'na . . . . ORANGE Z.
Perhaps hardly more than a broad-leaved variety of Z. angustifolia.

linea'ris . . . . . . NARROWLEAF Z.
mexica'na . . . . . . **Z. angustifolia**
multiflo'ra (*tenuiflora*) . . REDSTAR Z.
peruvia'na (*pauciflora*) . PERUVIAN Z.
pu'mila (*Crassina p.*) |w
tenuiflo'ra . . . . . . **Z. multiflora**

ZINNIA, continued
verticilla'ta . . . WHORLLEAF ZINNIA
Through lack of cooperation from seedsmen, the Editorial Committee regrets that a list of horticultural varieties of Zinnia cannot be furnished here.

ZIZA'NIA; ZIZANIOP'SIS . WILDRICE
See **GRASS GENERA.**

ZI'ZIA . . . . ZIZIA
au'rea . . . . GOLDEN Z.

ZIZ'YPHUS . . . . JUJUBE
chlorox'ylon . . . . . . COGWOOD J.
juju'ba (*sativa; vulgaris*) . COMMON J. (*Chinese-date*)
—**iner'mis** . . . . . . SPINELESS C.J.
lycioi'des . . . . **Condalia l.**
—*canes'cens* . . . . . **Condalia l. c.**
mauritia'na . . . . INDIA J.
mis'tol . . . . ARGENTINE J.
mucrona'ta
obtusifo'lia . . . . **Condalia o.**
par'ryi . . . . **Condalia p.**
sati'va; vulga'ris . . . . . **Z. jujuba**

ZOM'BIA . . . . ZOMBIPALM
See **PALM GENERA.**

ZOMBIPALM . . **Zombia; Z. antillarum**

ZORN'IA . . . . ZORNIA
bractea'ta . . . . BRACTED Z.

ZOSTE'RA |w . . . . EELGRASS
mari'na |w . . . . COMMON E.

ZOY'SIA (*OSTERDAMIA*)
See **GRASS GENERA.**

ZYGOCAC'TUS . **SCHLUMBERGERA**
See **CACTUS GENERA.**

ZYGOPET'ALUM
See **ORCHID GENERA.**

ZYGOPHYLLID'IUM . **EUPHORBIA**
See **SUCCULENTS.**

ZYGOPHYL'LUM . . . . BEANCAPER
faba'go . . . . SYRIAN B.

GLOSSARY

Horticultural, Botanical and Plant Terms of Special Interest to Users of STANDARDIZED PLANT NAMES

Adventi'tious buds: Buds produced without order or in an unusual place on any part of a plant, as from the stem instead of the leaf-axils.

Aquat'ic: A plant inhabiting water.

Arbores'cent: Treelike in size or form, or both.

Arbore'tum: A collection of living trees, grown especially for scientific or educational purposes. A tree botanical garden. The present tendency of Arboretums, both for good horticultural reasons and for scientific interest and use, is to include various definite wildlife associations in which trees are dominant.

Arboricul'ture: The science and art of growing trees, especially as ornamental or shade trees. Distinguished from silviculture or forestry (the science and art of growing trees as a forest or for lumber) and from tree horticulture or pomology (growing trees for fruit, nuts, etc.).

Ar'borist: One who practices arboriculture. Today as a professional title this also covers the treatment of tree diseases, insect pests, and tree surgery.

Asex'ual: Without sexual conjugation; a grass which propagates by rootstocks is said to exhibit asexual reproduction.

Asex'ual reproduc'tion: Reproduction produced vegetatively without the aid of sexual organs; as budding, grafting, layering, cuttings, etc.

Associa'tion: A biologically stabilized or balanced group of plants, with their accompanying animal life, forming a natural, persistent entity; a "climax" unit of vegetation or animal life, or preferably a combination of both, used especially of major groups. Examples, an Eastern Arborvitae, or Hemlock-Sphagnum bog; an Eastern White Pine forest; a Buffalograss-Blue Grama prairie or savanna.

Bien'nial: Enduring for two years. A herb which germinates (typically in the spring of) one year and flowers, fruits, and dies (typically in the fall or winter of) the succeeding year.

Bino'mial: Literally, consisting of two names; used especially of scientific names of species. The term also applies to common and to horticultural variety names. Examples: **Acer rubrum,** TIGER LILY, ROYAL SOVEREIGN.

Bisex'ual: Having both stamens and pistils.

Botanical Garden: A garden, especially a public or endowed institution of considerable size, devoted to the cultivation of plants from the scientific and educational standpoints.

Breed: Specifically a race of men or animals, allied by nativity and some distinctive qualities in common, which are transmitted by heredity; as, the Chihuahua breed of dog. Sometimes also used of plants; as, the Country Gentleman breed of Maize. Breeds require control by man to prevent loss of their distinctive characteristics, and are also subject to improvement through selection, hybridizing, and other ways. (See **Race, Strain.**)

Browse: Twigs and shoots, with their leaves, cropped by livestock from shrubs, trees, and woody vines. **Browse plants** comprise one of the four commonly recognized classes of plants producing range forage, the others being grasses, grasslike plants, and weeds. In STANDARDIZED PLANT NAMES these are included under Range Plants.

Bud muta'tion; Bud varia'tion: Same as **Budsport.**

Budsport: An abnormal or freakish shoot or branch developed from a bud; a sport developed from a bud; as an awlleaf shoot on an otherwise scaleleaf Juniper tree. A budsport (or bud variation) involving genetic changes is called a **bud mutation;** as a yellowleaf shoot on a normally greenleaf plant.

Bulb: A thickened, usually subterranean and scaly base of a plant stem, from which roots are emitted below. It consists of a modified stem and leaf bud and is not a true root. Example, Lily.

Bur: A prickly or spiny fruit envelope, as a Chestnut or Burdock bur.

Ca'lyx (pl. **-yces**): The outer series of the floral envelope, or perianth; the parts immediately below the corolla; the sepals (calyx parts or lobes) as a unit. Example, the persistent calyx of a strawberry.

Cereal: A grass (such as Barley, Maize, Rice, Rye, Wheat), whose edible seeds or grains are cultivated especially for human consumption.

Chime'ra: A novel growth due to the mixing of tissues of two or more different plants; a graft hybrid exhibiting characters of both stock and cion, caused by the blending of the tissues of both.

Chlo'rophyl: The complex nitrogenous substance responsible for the prevalent green hue of the vegetable kingdom. Chlorophyl is essential in plant nutrition, starch being formed through its agency in the leaves, with the presence of sunlight and air. In algae and certain other plants the green hue is frequently obscured by other pigments.

Chloro'sis: A plant disease characterized by yellowing or blanching of the leaves and other green (chlorophyl-bearing) parts. It is due to chemical and physical soil deficiencies, as well as to pathological conditions, and is distinguished from blanching due to absence of light (*etiolation*).

Ci'on: A slip or shoot used for grafting.

Climat'ic: Of or pertaining to climate, *i.e.*, the weather for a particular area over an extended period of time. Example, Climatic Zones, or belts of the earth's surface having approximately uniform rainfall, temperature, and other weather conditions. Climatic requirements of plants refer to their annual temperature, precipitation, humidity, and other weather requirements irrespective of their soil needs, and have a direct bearing on their hardiness.

Clon (pronounced klone): A clon is a group of plants propagated only by vegetative and asexual means, all members of which have been derived by repeated propagation from a single individual. The original individual so propagated may be a member of a good species or variety, a variation or mutation within a species, such as a budsport, or plant of hybrid origin. It may have a simple or complex origin and constitution, and it may be a polyploid of a single species or of a hybrid. Clons may be propagated by buds, bulbs, cuttings, grafts, runners, tubers, etc. Most so-called hort. var. of cultivated ornamentals, fruits, and edible tubers, such as apples, dahlias, potatoes, roses, and strawberries, are clons. But the breeds, races, and strains of cereals (such as Indian Corn, Oats and Wheat) which reproduce practically true from seed are not clons. Unfortunately polybrid (group hybrid) names have very often been misapplied to clons as: **Malus atrosanguinea** (**M. halliana** × **sieboldi**) as applied to CARMINE CRAB: whereas the name **M. atrosanguinea** is properly the group name covering any cross between the two species named above, Carmine Crab being a single described clon, selected from the polybrid hybridization named atrosanguinea. Polybrids are always hybrids, but clons may or may not be of hybrid origin. The term clon, originally so spelled, was introduced by Webber and Cook. Clons are indicated in S.P.N. by the prefixed symbol ₵ as devised and here published by the American Joint Committee on Horticultural Nomenclature for the first time.

Con'ifer: A plant of the natural plant family Coniferae, to which Cedars, Firs, Hemlocks, Pines, Spruces, and numerous other well-known trees belong. Most of the species have evergreen, needlelike or scalelike leaves, and the fruit in the form of a cone. Ginkgo, Taxus, Cephalotaxus, Juniperus, and a few other non-cone-bearing genera are closely related.

Corm: A swollen or enlarged, rounded, solid, fleshy, mostly subterranean stem base. Like a bulb in shape and appearance, except that it is solid, instead of being composed of fleshy scales. Example: **Arisaema triphyllum,** INDIAN JACKINTHEPULPIT.

Corol'la: The inner series of the floral envelope parts: the petals as a unit. The five petals of a Geranium blossom compose its corolla. A corolla may be composed of separate petals, or have its parts united. A showy, flowerlike part is not necessarily a corolla. The white, petal-like parts of a Flowering Dogwood inflorescence are an *involucre* of modified leaves, the true corollas being small, numerous, greenish, and four-petaled. In a Callalily and other Arums, the conspicuous part of the flower is the showy outer bract, or *spathe*, the floral organs (stamens and pistils) being borne without any true corolla (except sometimes a few scales) on an elongated spike (spadix) as "Jack" in Jackinthepulpit. In the Four-o'clock there is no corolla, the showy part of the flower being the calyx.

Cross: Hybrid of any description, whether natural or artificial.

Cross-fertilization; Cross-pollination: Fertilization secured by pollen from the flower of another plant; transfer of the pollen of one flower to the pistil of another.

Cryp'togam: A non-seed-producing plant of lower rank than the flowering plants. Thus, Fungi, Algae, Lichens, Mosses, and the Ferns are cryptogams, reproducing by spores, instead of seed.

Cul'tigen: A domesticated "species" or other group, whose origin may be unknown or obscure, whose characters are such as to separate it from known natural species (indigens), and which is probably not represented by any type specimen filed in a herbarium or by an exact description. Therefore, it has no clear taxonomic beginning, as, BARLEY (**Hordeum vulgare**), and MAIZE (**Zea mays**). See **Indigen.**

Cul'tivar: So-called "horticultural variety" or "garden variety." Progeny of a clon, chimera, or the result of selective hybridization, which is known only in cultivation and may or may not be reproduced from seed. The name, usually selected by the propagator, appended to either a generic name or a binomial, should be set off by different type or included within quotations to distinguish it from the binomial of a natural species. Examples: **Syringa** ₵CONGO; **Malus** ₵BOBWHITE; **Deutzia scabra** ₵PRIDE OF ROCHESTER.

Cutting: A severed vegetative or asexual part of a plant used in propagation; as a cutting of root, of stem, or of leaf. **Cion** is a cutting used for grafting.

Dioe'cious: Literally, in two houses. One-sexed; male or female only, the staminate (male) and the pistillate (female) flowers borne on different individual plants. The flowers of BUFFALOGRASS (**Buchloe**), for example, and of many Ashes (**Fraxinus** spp.), Maples (**Acer** spp.), and Hollies (**Ilex** spp.) are dioecious.

Drug Plants: Medicinal plants; plants producing products or compounds used in medicine and sold by druggists.

Drupe: A simple, fleshy, or pulpy fruit, the inner portion of the pericarp being hard and stony. A stone fruit, as Peach, Plum, and Cherry.

Em'bryo: The rudimentary, undeveloped plant in a seed, resultant from the union of a staminate (male) and a pistillate (female) cell.

Endem'ic: Indigenous or native in a restricted locality; confined naturally to a certain limited area or region. Opposed to exotic.

En'docarp: The inner layer of a pericarp, or covering of a fruit, as the bony part of the stone of a Cherry or Plum.

Ep'iphyte: An airplant. A plant which grows on another plant but is not nourished by it and hence not a parasite, as many Lichens, Mosses, Ferns, and Orchids.

Espal'ier: A fruit tree trained lattice-fashion in one plane.

Evergreen: Remaining green throughout the year, as Pines and some Rhododendrons. Does not necessarily refer to cone-bearing plants.

Exot'ic: Foreign; not native; introduced from another region. Opposed to indigenous or endemic.

Eye: The marked center of a flower; a bud on a tuber, as on the potato; a single-bud cutting.

Fastig'iate: With close and erect branches, as in the Lombardy Poplar.

Fertiliza'tion: The effect of the deposition of pollen on a stigma of a flower, resulting in the conversion of flower into fruit and of ovule into seed.

Fiber Plants: Plants producing fibers of commercial or other economic use, as Cotton, Flax, etc. A **fiber** is an elongated, threadlike plant cell, capable of being spun, woven or otherwise worked into cloth, rope, or some other fabric.

Form: A subdivision of a botanical variety (see **Variety**), distinguished by some minor character, as: the dwarf "form" with white flowers of Sitka Columbine (**Aquilegia formosa nana alba**). In systematic botany, forms (**formae**) are represented by quadrinomial Latin names. As STANDARDIZED PLANT NAMES does not accept scientific names longer than trinomial, "form" names, when used, are listed with those of hort. var.

Frond: The leaf of a Fern, Palm, or the like.

Fruit: The ripened ovary of a seed plant with its contents and various envelopes. For example, a Pea pod, a grain of Wheat, an Apple, a Hickorynut, and a Rose hip are all, botanically speaking, fruits.

Genet'ics: The science of plant or animal breeding. The branch of biology dealing with heredity and all its phases.

Graft: A shoot (cion) or bud inserted in (or affixed to) another plant or root with the intention that it will grow there.

Graft-hybrid: Same as **Chimera.**

Grove: A group of trees in area smaller than a forest and without underwood. The term is preferably applied to *natural*, parklike growths, as distinguished from plantations or orchards.

Habit: Aspect or manner of growth; as, prostrate, pyramidal, shrubby, trailing, treelike, vase-shaped, etc.

Halfbreed: A cross between botanical varieties of the same species. Thus, a cross between **Rosa rugosa alba** and **R. r. kamtchatica** would be a halfbreed. Crosses between two races are also sometimes called halfbreeds.

Herbgarden: A garden of herbs, especially of old-fashioned herbs and simples, cultivated for culinary purposes and for fragrance, historic, legendary, and other interest, together with the trees, shrubs, and woody vines traditionally associated with such collections.

Het'erogen: A term, apparently newly coined, used by geneticists for a variable group of plants or animals, arising as hybrids, budsports, and other mutations, and the like, among which are several to many forms or types which may or may not breed true. Those interested in a fuller explanation of this term should refer to the admirable paper by Dr. A. B. Stout, "The Nomenclature of Cultivated Plants," referred to in the bibliography at the end of this glossary. See also **Polybrid, Clon, Cultivar, Chimera, Ortet, Ramet.**

Ho'monym: The same name for a different plant; a name untenable because preoccupied. For example, the generic name Pinus would be a homonym, and untenable, if applied to any group of plants other than the Pines.

Hull: The outer covering of a fruit, especially if smooth or relatively so (as differentiated from *husk*), as the hull of a Hickory or a Walnut nut, as distinguished from the shell.

Husk: An outside envelope of a fruit, especially if coarse, harsh or rough, as the husk of a Filbertnut or the husks (glumes) of an ear of Indian Corn.

Hy'brid: A plant resulting from a cross between two or more parents that are more or less unlike.

Hybridiza'tion: The obtaining of hybrids by either artificial or natural crossing.

Hydropon'ics: The science, art or practice of growing plants in aqueous chemical solutions rather than in soil.

Imperfect Flower: Having either stamens or pistils, but not both.

In'digen: An indigenous, or native plant. Opposed to cultigen and exotic.

Indig'enous: Native. Thus, **Achillea lanulosa** is the common indigenous Yarrow of the western United States, while **A. millefolium** is the common Yarrow introduced from the Old World. Opposed to exotic.

Insectiv'orous Plant: A plant which captures and digests insects, as Pitcherplant, Sundew, and Venusflytrap.

Kernel: The inner, often edible portion of a nut; the *endocarp*, as the kernel of a Butternut or of a Peach pit. The kernel is the portion of the seed which contains the plant embryo.

La'tex: A milky, usually white fluid found in certain plant cells. The latex contains various gum resins, waxes, etc. Rubber, guttapercha, and chicle are commercial examples of latex.

Leg'ume: (1) A simple, usually dry pod, splitting along the back into two valves or parts; the fruit of any leguminous plant, *i. e.*, a member of the Pea family (Fabaceae) or families closely related thereto (Caesalpiniaceae, etc.); (2) a plant belonging to these leguminous families or subfamilies.

Lia'na: A high-climbing or long-running vine. In temperate regions lianas are often herbaceous; in the tropics and subtropics, lianas are predominantly woody.

Metab'olism: The life processes of plants as summed up in the chemical and physical changes involved in their growth, reproduction, and decay. Thus, the formation of starch in the plant leaves; its transformation into sugar and transportation to the roots for winter storage; the production of flowers and seed; the bringing in, through the roothairs on the roots, of water and soil solutes from the soil; the withering and dropping off of the leaves in the fall, are all phases of metabolism.

Monoe'cious: Literally, in one house. Having the flowers differentiated as to sex, the staminate (male) and pistillate (female) flowers in separate inflorescences, but borne on the same individual plant.

Muta'tion: A sudden variation shown in the offspring of plants (or animals) which differ from their parents in some well-marked character or characters. Familiar examples of mutation are shown in such groups as the Eveningprimrose genus (**Oenothera**) and the Rose family (Rosaceae). A "sport" is a mutation.

Node: A stem joint. Nodes are a very conspicuous feature of grass stems as, for example, Bamboos and Indian Corn. Nodes usually represent the points on the stem from which the leaves are produced.

No'men conservan'dum: Literally, a conserved name. A name retained in Latin plant nomenclature regardless of priority. Nomina conservanda usually have a history behind them of long usage (possibly pre-Linnaean), or of acceptance by the great botanical figures of the past, better and fuller publication, questions of propriety, etc.

No'men nu'dum (pl. **-ina nuda**): A naked botanical name, printed in a book or other publication without any description or illustration. Nomina nuda are very properly rejected.

Nut: In botany, a nonsplitting 1-seeded fruit, with hard woody shell. In common usage, a hard-shelled fruit or seed containing an edible kernel. In popular parlance, Almonds, Peanuts, and Brazilnuts are nuts, but they are not so botanically; an Almond is a drupe (close akin to a Peach); a Peanut is a legume; while the fruit of the Brazilnut tree (**Bertholletia excelsa**) is a sort of large woody-shelled capsule (pyxis) containing nutlike seeds.

Orchard: A plantation of trees for the production of tree products—such as fruits, nuts, commercial oils, sugars, etc. The term is distinguished from grove, which is preferably applied to a natural growth of trees.

Or'tet: The one original plant from which a *clon* ultimately derives. A term introduced by A. B. Stout, derived from the Latin word *ortus*, origin.

Par'asite: An organism which derives its sustenance from another. Thus, mistletoes are parasites of oaks, pines, and other woody plants.

Peren'nial: Lasting for three or more years; said especially of herbaceous plants that are neither annual nor biennial. A perennial plant.

Photot'ropism: The common phenomenon exhibited by plants or their organs in growing inward or turning to a source of light. Heliotropism (turning toward the sun) is practically synonymous with phototropism, though similar tropisms can be induced by artificial light.

Pol'ybrid: A group name for hybrids from crosses between two particular species, varieties, or genera. The distinction between this term and the term **heterogen** is more fully discussed under that term. It is used for the purpose of clearly distinguishing between the definite individual selection called *clon*, which must be reproduced asexually, and the indefinite and variable forms which result from single or repeated crosses between two particular species, varieties, or genera, and from which a clon may be taken. Thus, all the diverse variations resultant from crossing FLAME AZALEA (**Rhododendron calendulaceum**) and PINXTERBLOOM AZALEA (**R. nudiflorum**) are called by botanists a hybrid species, ∞MORTIER AZALEA (∞**R. mortieri**). It would seem better policy, in future, not to give such crosses a specific scientific name, but to give them a common name (such as MORTIER AZALEA) prefixed by the polybrid symbol (∞). The symbol would warn horticulturists and others of the immense and uncertain variability of such a nexus. The term *polybrid* is here introduced by the editors, Harlan P. Kelsey and W. A. Dayton.

Polyg'amous: Having both perfect and unisexual, or imperfect (*i. e.*, either staminate or pistillate) flowers borne on the same individual, as, for example, in certain species of Maple.

Pome: The fleshy, applelike fruit of a member of the Apple family; also, though less exactly, a Rose hip or similar fruit of the Rose family (Rosaceae).

Race: A group, especially of cultivated plants, that possess certain well-marked differentiating characters, and which propagate true to seed except for simple fluctuating variations. The different groups of Beans, Indian Corn, Cotton, and Wheat, for example, often referred to as "varieties," are, in a more restricted sense, **races.** Golden Bantam, Leaming, and so on, may be recognized as **races** of Indian Corn; Fultz and Turkey, as **races** of Wheat; and Dwarf Erfurt and Snowball as **races** of Cauliflower. See **Breed** and **Strain.**

Ra'met: An individual member of a clon. A term introduced by A. B. Stout, derived from the Latin word *ramus*, branch.

Range Plants: Plants inhabiting natural grazing grounds as in the Far West. In general, range occupies country too high in elevation, too rough, too dry, or too rocky to be suitable for agricultural development, and differs from pasture usually in great extent, as well as in relative freedom from artificial improvement, the vegetation being almost entirely indigenous, and the areas usually unfenced.

Rootstock: (1) In botany, a rootlike stem or branch under or sometimes on the ground; a rhizome, as in Iris and Quackgrass. (2) In horticulture, a root, usually of a seedling, on which a cion, usually of a clon, is grafted.

Runner: A long, slender, tendril-like leafless form of creeping branch, prostrate on the ground. Each runner, after having grown to its full length, strikes root from the tip (it sometimes roots at the joints also), in which case it may merge into a stolon, fixing the tip to the ground, then forms a bud at that point, which later develops into a tuft of leaves and so gives rise to a new plant, as in Strawberry.

Se'pal: A division of the calyx corresponding to a petal in the corolla.

Ses'sile: Without a stem or stalk; a sessile leaf is without a petiole, or leafstalk, sitting directly on the axis or stem of the plant; as, the sessile leaves of St. Johnswort and the sessile cones of Hemlock. In a true spike all the flowers are sessile.

Shell: The hard layer of a nut, as distinguished from its hull (soft, outermost rind) and kernel, as the shell of a Hickorynut which, when cracked open, discloses the edible kernel.

Slip: A softwood or hardwood cutting "slipped," pulled or cut off, for propagating purposes. See **Cutting, Cion.**

Spe'cies (pl. **Species**)**:** The unit of plant (or animal) classification. A group of individuals with so many characteristics in common as to indicate a very high degree of relationship and a common descent. Eastern White Pine (**Pinus strobus**) and Colorado Columbine (**Aquilegia coerulea**) are familiar illustrations of species.

Spore: The 1-celled, powderlike fruiting body (somewhat analogous to a seed in a seed plant) of a cryptogam, produced asexually, and without an embryo. See **Cryptogam.**

Sport: A variation starting from a bud or seed; a mutation. These when propagated are termed **Ramets.**

Sti'on: A plant composed of a stock and cion growing in combination regardless of the method of propagation. (A term proposed by Webber, based on an ellipsis of the combined two terms, stock and cion.)

Stock: (1) In horticulture: (a) The plant stem or root which receives the cion or other graft: as, a COMMON CHOKECHERRY (**Prunus virginiana**) **stock** for some Cherry or Plum hort. var. (also Understock); (b) The original progenitor of a group of closely related plants (as a **race**); (c) The supply of a species or variety or any number of species or varieties of plants or seeds in a nursery, seedhouse or other horticultural establishment; (2) In botany, (a) A plant of the genus Mathiola; (b) A main plant stem (stalk or trunk); (c) A root-producing caudex or rhizome (rootstock); (3) In forestry: (a) Forest nursery seedlings; (b) Logs delivered from stump to mill or railroad; (c) Coppice stumps, expected to produce new sprouts; (d) Specified growth constituting a given forest cover.

Sto'lon: A trailing or reclining branch above ground, which strikes root where it touches the soil, there sending up new shoots which, later, may become separate plants. Many plants multiply vegetatively in this way.

Stool: A clump of roots or rootstocks that may be used in propagation; also an established low plant from which layers are taken.

Strain: A group of cultivated plants derived from a **race,** which do not differ from the original of the race in visible taxonomic characters. When, for example, the breeder, by a careful selection of Pacific Bluestem Wheat, produces a new sort of Pacific Bluestem Wheat that differs from the original race only in the quality of yielding heavily, it would be called a strain of Pacific Bluestem Wheat. If, however, the breeder selects Jones Fife and changes the chaff from hairy to smooth he has produced a new race. The demarcation, however, between **race** and **strain** is none too sharp. Strain is a term which should be far more often used than at present by seedsmen and other horticulturists.

Stratifica'tion: The operation or method of burying seeds to keep them fresh and to soften their integuments, or to expose them without injury to cold temperatures, that they may be more readily germinated.

Subspe'cies: A taxonomic rank immediately below that of species; by some authors regarded as a synonym of **variety,** but if subspecies and varieties are both recognized, then variety (which see) ranks below subspecies.

Sucker: A branch or shoot from a creeping underground stem or root which ascends above ground and tends eventually to become a separate individual plant. Suckers are common on many woody plants, such as Blackberry, Locust, Sassafras; on budded roses when a sucker from the understock is permitted to grow.

Suffrutes'cent; Suffrut'icose: Undershrubby. A term applied to perennial plants, usually smaller than true shrubs, whose stems are partly herbaceous and partly woody, dying down near to (but not entirely to) the ground each year.

Syn'onym: A different name for the same plant; an untenable specific or generic name. For example, *Abies picea* is a synonym of **Picea abies.**

Taxon'omy: The science of classification.

Terminol'ogy: A group name for special terms used in an art, science, craft, or other phases of human study or activity, as horticultural terminology, botanical terminology, fiber plant terminology, etc.

Type: In systematic biology (taxonomy), the specimen or specimens on which a species or other group is based and from which the author of that species or other group described it.

Understock: The presumably more sturdy or favorable plant or root upon which a clon is grafted or budded, in order to give greater vigor to a variety or to more rapidly propagate it. Same as **Stock.**

Vari'ety: In systematic biology, a division of a species. For example, the short-, squared-petal **Aquilegia formosa truncata** is a variety of the typical SITKA COLUMBINE (**A. formosa**). STANDARDIZED PLANT NAMES adopts the principle that *natural* variations only, that hold true to type, should be given Latin names. The term variety in horticulture is therefore lower in the systematic scale than the taxonomic term variety.

Weed: To the farmer, a plant out of place, especially an aggressive and pestiferous, often coarse, mostly herbaceous, usually introduced plant species (such as Crabgrass, Dandelion, Mustard, Plantain, and Wild Carrot) which takes possession of cultivated and fallow fields and pastures. A weed species may possess intrinsic values in horticulture for medicine, soil-improvement, etc. quite apart from its nuisance status as a weed. To the western stockman, a "weed" is a herbaceous, non-grasslike plant occurring on the range. An appreciable number of the weeds of the farmer are good range forage plants of the western stockman, especially on those ranges where under unfavorable growing conditions the same aggressiveness which renders a species a pest in agricultural land clothes it with utility if it possesses palatability to grazing animals.

Xer'ophyte: A plant adapted to arid conditions; a desert plant. Cacti are familiar examples of xerophytes.

Zone: A region or belt of the earth's surface characterized by similar climatic, growth or other conditions or by resemblances in the flora and fauna, as a Tropical or Temperate Zone; a Hudsonian (timberline) or Austral (southern United States) Zone.

BIBLIOGRAPHY

No existing glossary of definitions could be found that seemed adequate properly to fill the requirements of this book.

Many authorities were consulted, definitions revised or entirely rewritten, and a few new ones added. The bibliography below represents those authors on whom we have drawn most freely.

ANONYMOUS. Terms Used in Forestry and Logging. U. S. Dept. Agr., Bur. Forestry Bul. 61. 1905.

BAILEY, L. H. The Indigen and Cultigen. Science, n. s. 47: 306–308. 1918.

———The Standard Cyclopedia of Horticulture. 1935.

CARPENTER, J. R. An Ecological Glossary. 1938.

DAYTON, W. A. Glossary of Botanical Terms Commonly Used in Range Research. U. S. Dept. Agr., Misc. Pub. 110. 1931.

FEDERAL SEED ACT, 1940.

JACKSON, B. D. A Glossary of Botanical Terms. 1900.

KOBUSKI, C. E. A Brief Glossary of the More Common Botanical and Horticultural Terms. Arnold Arboretum Bul. 8, (7–10): 37–56, ser. 4. 1940.

MERRIAM, G. & C. Webster's New International Dictionary of the English Language. 1940.

STOUT, A. B. The Clon in Plant Life. Journ. N. Y. Bot. Garden 30: 25–37. 1929.

———The Nomenclature of Cultivated Plants. Amer. Journ. Bot. 27 (5): 339–347. 1940.

THE CENTURY CO. The Century Dictionary. 1900.

WEBBER, H. J. New Horticultural and Agricultural Terms. Science, n. s. 18: 501–503. 1903.

———Variations in Citrus Seedlings and Their Relation to Rootstock Selection. Hilgardia 7: 1–79. 1932.

INDEX OF SPECIAL LISTS

While all these Special Lists are in alphabetical order, it is deemed best for convenience to index them here separately. It should be noted that all of these Special Lists are the result of investigation and study in the United States Department of Agriculture, or by outside specialists and experts, resulting in information of high economic value. Thus, for example, the Cereals, Drug Plant Names, Fruit and Edible Nut Names, Lumber Trade Names, and the Range Plants lists make accessible information of great importance.

CORRIGENDA

P. 91. Instead of *Carduus lanceolatum*, **Cirsium l.**, substitute *Carduus lanceolatus*, **Cirsium lanceolatum.**

P. 127. Instead of **Cirsium lanceolatum** (*Carduus l.*), substitute **Cirsium lanceolatum** (*Carduus lanceolatus*).

P. 139. Instead of *CORTADERIA*, substitute **CORTADERIA.**

P. 172. Instead of **Dodecatheon meadia alba,** substitute **Dodecatheon meadia album.**

P. 275. Instead of *Globetulip, Obispo*, MARIPOSA, OBISPO: *Calochortus obispoensis*, substitute *Globetulip, Obispo*, MARIPOSA, OBISPO: **Calochortus obispoensis.**

P. 401. Instead of OAK, ALBERMARLE, substitute OAK, ALBEMARLE.
Instead of OAK, SCRUB, **Q. ilicifolia,** substitute OAK, BEAR, **Q. ilicifolia.**

P. 447. Instead of **Cyrtostachys rendah duvivierianum,** substitute **Cyrtostachys rendah duvivieriana.**

P. 450. Instead of *Phoenix sinpifera* Hort., substitute *Phoenix spinifera* Hort.

P. 507. Instead of **Quercus ilicifolia,** SCRUB OAK, substitute **Quercus ilicifolia,** BEAR OAK.

P. 593. Instead of **Spiraea latifolia** (*bethlehemensis* Hort.; *S. carpinifolia salicifolia* U. S. Auth., *not* L.), substitute **Spiraea latifolia** (*bethlehemensis* Hort.; *carpinifolia; salicifolia* U. S. Auth., *not* L.)

STANDARDIZED PLANT NAMES

has been set up, electrotyped, printed and bound within the Mount Pleasant Press of the J. Horace McFarland Company, Harrisburg, Pa.

Preliminary composition (in 10-point No. 8 Monotype Roman) from the assembled cards began in May, 1938. From the resulting 429 galleys 30 proofs were made, and these were sent out at the Editorial Committee's order to various participating authorities. Upon their return the Committee transferred the work again to cards.

The cards of the "A–Z" list came to the Mount Pleasant Press in October, 1940, in 52 boxes. The necessary cross references were edited into these cards by Miss Meikle, of the Mount Pleasant Press, by December 15, 1940. The 62 special lists coming in from time to time from many sources were also edited into the copy, and proofs were mailed from the Press to the various authorities prior to final passing by Mr. Dayton in Washington.

Before final composition was undertaken many experiments were made. The plan of a two-column page, as in 1923, was given up as the special lists came in, and the three-column page agreed upon. Then came study as to the number of pages the work would make. It was expected to have it set in 8-point. This was found impracticable as running the book beyond 800 pages. Composition in 7-point began early in 1941, and was completed in July, 1941. The entire work, including 646 galleys, weighing about 7000 pounds, was in type before page makeup and electrotyping began in October, 1941. Printing was completed December 31, 1941.

The paper used in the book was selected for easy reading and durability. It is Zenith English Finish Book, made to our order by the Fitchburg Paper Company, Fitchburg, Mass. It was obtained and seasoned for many weeks before printing began.

The binding is in Roxite Library Buckram, made by Holliston Mills, Inc., Norwood, Mass., selected for strength and good appearance.